The Omnibus of

MODERN
CRIME
STORIES

The Omnibus of

MODERN CRIME STORIES

EDITED BY
ELEANOUR SULLIVAN
&
ELLERY QUEEN

Robinson Publishing
London

First published 1991 in the UK by
Robinson Publishing
11 Shepherd House
Shepherd Street
London W1Y 7LD

A copy of the CIP Data for this book
is available from the British Library

ISBN 1 85487 101 3

   Printed and bound in Great Britain by
Mackays of Chatham PLC, Chatham, Kent

CONTENTS

The Sixties

The Seventies

The Eighties

ACKNOWLEDGMENTS

Grateful acknowledgment is made to the following for their permission to use their copyrighted material. Every reasonable effort has been made to trace the ownership of all copyrighted material included in this volume. Any errors which may have occurred are inadvertent and will be corrected in subsequent editions, provided proper notification is sent to the publisher.

The Forties: The Phantom Guest by Frederick Irving Anderson, copyright 1941 by American Mercury, Inc.; *Midnight Adventure* by Michael Arlen, copyright 1938 by Michael Arlen, reprinted by permission of Watkins, Loomis Agency, Inc.; *A Study In White* by Nicholas Blake, copyright 1949 by American Mercury, Inc., reprinted by permission of The Peters Fraser & Dunlop Group Ltd.; *The Bloomsbury Wonder* by Thomas Burke, reprinted by permission of John Hawkins & Associates; *Dressing-Up* by W. R. Burnett, copyright 1930 by Harper & Bros., reprinted by permission of Scott Meredith Literary Agency, Inc.; *The Clue of the Red Wig* by John Dickson Carr, copyright 1948 by John Dickson Carr, reprinted by permission of Harold Ober Associates, Inc.; *Lost Star* by C. Daly King, copyright 1944 by C. Daly King, reprinted by permission of Blanche C. Gregory, Inc.; *Malice Domestic* by Philip MacDonald, copyright 1946 by American Mercury, Inc., from SOMETHING TO HIDE, reprinted by permission of Doubleday, a division of Bantam, Doubleday, Dell Publishing Group, Inc.; *I Can Find My Way Out* by Ngaio Marsh, copyright 1946 by American Mercury, Inc., reprinted by permission of Harold

and Tidy Job by George Harmon Coxe, copyright © 1960 by Davis Publications, Inc., renewed © 1988 by Elizabeth Coxe, reprinted by permission of Brandt & Brandt Literary Agents, Inc.; *Change of Climate* by Ursula Curtiss, copyright © 1967 by Ursula Curtiss, reprinted by permission of Brandt & Brandt Literary Agents, Inc.; *Revolver* by Avram Davidson, copyright © 1962 by Davis Publications, Inc., reprinted by permission of Richard D. Grant, Literary Agent; *The Special Gift* by Celia Fremlin, copyright © 1967 by Davis Publications, Inc., reprinted by permission of the author; *Line of Communication* by Andrew Garve, copyright © 1967 by Andrew Garve, reprinted by permission of Curtis Brown Ltd.; *The Eternal Chase* by Anthony Gilbert, copyright © 1965 by Davis Publications, Inc., reprinted by permission of Curtis Brown Ltd.; *Danger at Deerfawn* by Dorothy B. Hughes, copyright © 1964 by Davis Publications, Inc., reprinted by permission of Blanche C. Gregory, Inc.

The Seventies: Three Ways to Rob a Bank by Harold R. Daniels, copyright © 1972 by Davis Publications, Inc.; *Reasons Unknown* by Stanley Ellin, copyright © 1978 by Stanley Ellin, reprinted by permission of Curtis Brown Ltd.; *The Marked Man* by David Ely, copyright © 1979 by Davis Publications, Inc., reprinted by permission of Roberta Pryor, Inc.; *Woodrow Wilson's Necktie* by Patricia Highsmith, copyright © 1972 by Patricia Highsmith, reprinted by permission of Diogenes Verlag Ag.; *When Nothing Matters* by Florence V. Mayberry, copyright © 1979 by Davis Publications, Inc., reprinted by permission of the author; *The Perfect Servant* by Helen Nielsen, copyright © 1971 by Davis Publications, Inc., reprinted by permission of Ann Elmo Agency, Inc.; *Flowers that Bloom in the Spring* by Julian Symons, copyright © 1971 by Davis Publications, Inc., reprinted by permission of Curtis Brown Ltd., London; *A Nice Place to Stay* by Nedra Tyre, copyright © 1970 by Davis Publications, Inc., reprinted by permission of Scott Meredith Literary Agency, Inc.; *Paul Broderick's Man* by Thomas Walsh, copyright © 1979 by Davis Publications, Inc., reprinted by permission of Thomas

INTRODUCTION

Exactly one hundred years after the publication of "The Murders in the Rue Morgue," which along with Edgar Allan Poe's two subsequent tales featuring C. Auguste Dupin set down the general principles of the pure detective story forever, the need for a magazine devoted to short detective fiction was so great that the busily writing Ellery Queen nevertheless took on the formidable commitment of editing, hands on, a mystery magazine under his name.

"This first issue is frankly experimental," he wrote in the Introduction to Issue 1 in 1941. "Our belief that a large public exists which impatiently awaits such publication can only be confirmed by that public. For the present therefore we plan to publish *Ellery Queen's Mystery Magazine* quarterly. Our ultimate purpose is to publish a new volume each month. That, however, depends upon the reception accorded this and future volumes. The more wholehearted and widespread your response, the more quickly regular monthly publications will be scheduled."

By 1946, *EQMM* had achieved monthularity and the 1962 *Reader's Encyclopedia of American Literature* (Crowell), under its lengthy tribute to Ellery Queen, said: "In 1941 they [Frederic Dannay and Manfred B. Lee, who collaborated as Ellery Queen] began to edit *Ellery Queen's Mystery Magazine,* the finest periodical of its kind. They stated, 'Queen has waged unceasing battle on two fronts: to raise the sights of mystery writers generally to the target of a genuine and respected literary form and to encourage good writing among our colleagues by offering a practical market not otherwise available among American magazines, as well as to develop new writers seeking expression in the genre.'

"Queen has achieved victory on both these fronts; he has given the detective story a respectable place in serious writing. Queen's magazine often carries mystery stories by well-known authors both current and past and has made it seem as if every writer of note in history produced at least one such story."

One can be unnerved at the prospect of selecting stories for any anthology, and choosing the fifty best published in *EQMM*'s first fifty years of publication—fifty stories from some eight thousand, only ten from the hundreds published each of the first five decades—was clearly an enormous challenge, given the fact that the editors have tried to provide the very best stories they could find in every single issue of the magazine published over those fifty years.

We took the task by decades and decided to go after—of those stories to which rights were available and had not been well and duly anthologized already—solid and entertaining stories by regular and significant contributors, stories that reflected the time in which they were written and the best work being produced in that decade. There are authors not included here who ought to be—yet all fifty of the authors who are here should be. They and the stories they wrote elicited the wholehearted and widespread response Ellery Queen openly hoped for when he ventured the editorship of *EQMM* and wrote that first Introduction.

Reflecting the times in which they are written, as most fiction does, the detective/crime/suspense story underwent many changes in the hundred years between "The Murders in the Rue Morgue" and the first publication of *EQMM*, and it has undergone many more in the turbulent years since. (In the past year alone, there has been much conjecture about what will happen with the spy story. What to do? Set them back in time, which would dampen their air of immediacy? Transfer the emphasis to industrial espionage?) Both the straight detective and the private-eye story demand the most innovative imitation if they are not to be stale, and a strong sense of reality in concept and character if they are to be acceptable to contemporary readers.

But this is being managed with such alacrity by a host of mystery writers on both sides of the Atlantic *and* the Pacific, north *and* south of the Equator, investing their imagination and talent in the short form as well as the long, that I'm in awe of the task facing the editor asked to choose the best from the next fifty years of *EQMM*.

—Eleanor Sullivan

The Forties

THE CLUE OF THE RED WIG

by *JOHN DICKSON CARR*

They usually put the paper to press at two a.m. MacGrath, the news editor, who was not feeling well after the Christmas celebrations, went home early to his own bed and left things at the office to young Patterson. MacGrath was sleeping a shivering sleep when the telephone at his bedside rang.

MacGrath made unearthly noises, like a ghost roused before midnight. But he answered the phone.

"Hazel Loring?" he repeated. "What about her?"

"She's dead," answered Patterson. "Murdered, it's pretty certain. Do you know Victoria Square?"

"No."

"It's a quiet little residential square in Bayswater. Hazel Loring lived there. In the middle of the square there's a garden reserved for the use of residents. About eleven o'clock a policeman on his rounds found Hazel Loring dead in the garden with practically no clothes on—"

"What?" shouted MacGrath; and the sleep was struck from his eyes.

"Well, only a brassiere and a pair of step-ins. She was sitting on a bench, dead as Cleopatra, with the rest of her clothes folded up on the bench beside her."

"In *this* weather?"

"Yes. The policeman saw her go into the garden an hour before. Cause of death was a fractured skull, from several blows with a walking stick whose handle was loaded with lead. Signs of a struggle behind the bench."

"Right!" said MacGrath. "Splash it on the front page. Every woman in the land will want to know what happened to Hazel Loring!"

Everybody knew the name of Hazel Loring, the face of Hazel Loring, the opinions of Hazel Loring. "Smile and Grow Fit" was the title of her weekly column in the *Daily Banner,* a deadly rival of MacGrath's own *Daily Record.* "Smile and Grow Fit" was also the title of the booklets, sold by the thousand, in which she explained to housewives how they might keep slim without anguish. She was no grim taskmistress of health. She did not sternly order them to eat a dry biscuit, and like it.

"I've devised these exercises on the advice of a doctor," she wrote. "Just three minutes each morning; and don't bother any more about it. If you like chocolates, in heaven's name eat chocolates. Only mind you do my exercises: and then eat what you like."

Her chatty, intimate manner warmed their hearts. She became more than an adviser on health. She counselled them about love and hats and husbands. Everybody had seen pictures of the strong, square, pleasant face, showing fine teeth in a smile, and with a dimple at each corner of the mouth. She was slim, with a good figure, and intensely active. She was well dressed, but not offensively so. Her brown hair was bobbed, her brown eyes grave. Her age might have been thirty-five. Thousands felt that they knew her personally, and wrote to tell her so.

Yet somebody killed her, half-dressed, in a public garden on a bitter December night.

If truth must be told, even in MacGrath, hard-boiled as he was, the first reaction was a twinge of pity. His wife was even more emphatic.

"Poor woman!" said Mrs. MacGrath from the opposite bed. "Poor woman!"

"Ho? Is that how it strikes you?" asked MacGrath, his news-sense instantly on the alert.

"Of course it is. Of all the brutal, senseless—!"

"Then that's how we'll play the story. I think I'm getting an inspiration. But Hazel Loring. Oh Lord!"

The next day he carried his inspiration to Houston, the managing editor.

The offices of the *Daily Record* occupy a huge modernistic building, a sort of chromium-plated goldfish bowl. Fleet Street was buzzing with gossip. The murder of Hazel Loring, though they could not yet call it a murder, was considered so important that they held a conference in the managing editor's office. Here, in a cubist-designed room with bright curtains, the stately Houston sat behind a desk topped with black glass, and drew down the corners of his mouth.

"Impossible," Houston said. "We can't do it. Dignity."

"All right. *Be* dignified," said MacGrath. "But don't pass up a thing like this. Now see here, J. H. This is a woman's crime; it oozes feminine interest. It's good for a daily story. Our-Correspondent-Watches-Police; Developments-Day-By-Day. So, with half the women in England crying for news of their favorite, what do we do? Why, we put a woman to cover it."

Houston passed a hand over his thin, high forehead.

"A woman doing police reporting?"

"Why not? She can be dignified, can't she? Womanly and kind, with a touch of sadness? Man, they'll eat it up!"

Houston hunched up his shoulders. "She'd have to be tough," he pointed out. "Covering a war is one thing; covering a murder is another. I don't know who I could assign to it."

"What about that French girl? Jacqueline Dubois. Only been with us a week. Came over when things there went to blazes. But I'll tell you something, J. H. She had the reputation of being the smartest news-hawk in Paris; Richart of *L'Oeil* recommended her in superlatives, and I think he's right."

"She speaks English?"

"She's half English. Her mother was a Cockney. She speaks English all right."

"And she will be—er—dignified?"

"Absolutely. I guarantee it, J. H."

"Get her," said Houston.

Nevertheless, he was uneasy until he actually set eyes on Jacqueline Dubois. Then he drew a breath of relief, and almost beamed.

MacGrath, on the other hand, was jarred. In recommending this girl MacGrath had been acting on a hunch; he knew little about her beyond Richart's word. And, at his first sight of Jacqueline, he had a panicky feeling that Richart must have been indulging in a deplorable Gallic sense of humour.

Jacqueline entered the office so timidly that Houston rose to draw out a chair for her. She was a golden blonde, small and plump, with one of those fair skins which flush easily, and those dark blue eyes which are either wide open or modestly lowered. Her mouth expressed confusion, but anxiety to please. Her fur coat was good but unobtrusive; from her plain grey dress to her tan stockings and shoes she was trim and yet retiring. She kept her big eyes fixed on Houston except when he looked directly at her. In a soft, sweet voice she hesitantly asked what was wanted.

While MacGrath stood in despair, Houston told her.

"And that's the idea, Miss Dubois. Your purpose is to—"

"To pester the police," groaned MacGrath.

"To print," said Houston sternly, "all desirable news which will be of interest to our public. Would you like the assignment?"

Jacqueline raised her limpid blue eyes.

"Would I like it?" she breathed. "Hot ziggety damn!"

Houston sat back with a start. She was covered in confusion, modesty struggling with gratitude.

"I thank you on my knees," she went on, clasping her hands together. "Miss Loring. The poor lady who has so unfortunately kicked the ghost. I had wished to cover that story, yes; but, blimey, I never thought I should get it. Oh, you are a dear. Would you like me to kiss you?"

"Good heavens, no!" said Houston.

But Jacqueline was not listening. She was utterly absorbed. The toe of her shoe tapped the carpet. Her eyes were turned inwards, a pucker of concentration between the brows; and, as she reflected, she nodded to herself.

"I am handicap," she confessed. "I am new to England and I do not know the ropes yet. If I get you a scoop, I must get it funny-ways. Who is the head of your whole police department?"

"The Assistant Commissioner for the Criminal Investigation Department," said MacGrath.

"Good!" said Jacqueline briskly. "I make love to him."

Houston gave her a long, slow look.

"No, no, no!" he said.

"Yes, yes, yes!" said Jacqueline, continuing to nod briskly.

"But you can't do that, Miss Dubois!"

"I do not understand," complained Jacqueline, breaking off to look at him with shy astonishment. "You do not wish me to do it? Why?"

"To explain that fully, Miss Dubois, might take a long time. I can sum up by saying that it would hardly be in accord with the policy of this newspaper. Besides, there are—er—practical considerations. In the first place, you'd never get near him. In the second place, even if you did you wouldn't get any story."

A twinkle appeared in Jacqueline's limpid eyes.

"Ha, ha, ha," she said. "That is what they tell me when I make eyes at Mornay, the *juge d'instruction*. He has whiskers this long"—her gesture indicated a beard of improbable dimensions—"but I get from him the official photographs of De La Rive shooting at all the gendarmes in the rue Jean Goujoun, and I scoop the town! Still, if you do not wish it?"

"Definitely not."

Jacqueline sighed. "Orright," she conceded. "Then I must find out the name of the policeman in charge of the case, and make love to *him*. Also, please, I should like a newspaper photographer to go with me all the time."

"A photographer? Why?"

"First because it is practical. I have got some fine pictures when I work for *L'Oeil*. Once I get a picture of the Comtesse de la Tour St. Sulpice, which is a kleptomaniac, pinching a necklace out of Paulier's in the rue de la Paix."

"Is that so?"

"Oo la la, what a sensation!" She gurgled delightedly. "Then too it is useful if you can get a picture of a police officer doing something he should not. You tell him you will publish the picture unless he gives you a story."

Houston had been listening under a kind of hypnosis. Jacqueline seemed to be surrounded by a rose-leaf cloud of innocence, like a figure on a valentine. He could not have been more startled if the Mona Lisa had suddenly leaned out of her frame and put out her tongue at him. He found his voice.

"We begin with vamping and pass on to blackmail," he said. "MacGrath, I can't do it. Young woman, you're fired! You'd ruin this paper in a week."

"If she's fired," roared MacGrath, "I resign. Splendor of saints, here's a newspaperman at last!"

"Do you want the Home Office to put us out of business?"

"We've got subeditors to read her copy, haven't we? I tell you, J. H., if—"

"Then there is another thing," pursued Jacqueline timidly. "One of your photographers is called Henry Ashwin. He is a good fellow, though I think he drink too much visky-soda. He is the photographer I want, please."

"Ashwin? Why Ashwin?"

"I find out he is making the goo-goo eyes at Hazel Loring's maidservant. Yes! That is something the others pass up, eh? So I give him visky-soda and I talk to him. Already I get much information, you see."

"Before you were assigned to the story?"

Jacqueline raised her eyebrows.

"But yes, yes, yes! Of course. Listen! This Miss Loring, her age is thirty-five. In private life she is very bad-tempered. Henry Ashwin thinks she is what you call a phony, somehow, but he is not sure about what. Also she is good-goody, what you call a prude. Is she married? No! But she has a fiancé, a lawyer which is called Edward Hoyt; and he hang about her for five years and still it is no soap. Why does she not marry him, eh?"

"Well?"

"I find out," answered Jacqueline simply. "Now I tell you something the police have not told you."

"Go on," muttered Houston, still hypnotized.

"This is what her maid say to Henry Ashwin, and Henry Ashwin say to me. When Miss Loring is found sitting on the bench in that garden, wearing only the brassiere and the step-ins and her shoes, the other clothes are folded up on the bench beside her."

MacGrath was instantly alert. "We know that. It's in all the papers."

"Yes! *But,*" said Jacqueline, "there are other things too. Folded up in the clothes (so) there is a red wig and a pair of dark spectacles."

Houston and MacGrath stared at each other, wondering whether this might be some obscure French metaphor. But Jacqueline left them in no doubt.

"A red wig," she insisted, tapping her golden hair. "And the smoky spectacles you look through." She cupped her hands over her eyes in mimicry. "Why should Miss Loring have them, eh? Blimey, but that is not all! It is certain she undressed herself, and was not undressed by anybody. Her maid tells Henry Ashwin that Miss Loring has a special way of folding stockings, like . . . ah, zut! . . . would you like me to take off mine and show you?"

"No, no!"

"Orright. I only ask. But it is special. Also the way of folding the dress. So she take her own dress off, and she have a wig and spectacles. Please, will you let me find out why?" Her big blue eyes turned reproachfully on Houston. "You say you will fire me, and that is not nice. I know I am a goofy little beasel; that is what they all say in Paris; but if you will please be a nice man and give me a chance I will get you that story, cross my heart. Yes?"

Houston had the darkest misgivings. But he was a journalist.

"Hop to it," he said.

Inspector Adam Bell, Criminal Investigation Department, stood in the prim little front parlor of number 22 Victoria Square. He looked alternately out of the window, towards the garden in the center, and then back to the white-faced man opposite him.

Sedate and dun-colored was Victoria Square, Bayswater, in the bleak winter afternoon. The house fronts were sealed up. In the garden, surrounded by teeth of spiked iron railings, the branches of trees showed black and knotted against a muddy twilight; its gravel paths wound between iron benches and skeleton bushes, on grass hard with frost.

Inspector Bell, in the white, antiseptic front parlor of the dead woman's house, faced Hazel Loring's fiancé. Inspector Bell was a young and very serious-minded product of Hendon, but his sympathetic manner had already done much.

"And you can't tell me anything more, Mr. Hoyt?"

"Nothing!" said Edward Hoyt, and fingered his black tie. "I wanted to take her to a concert last night, but she refused, and I went alone. I —er— don't read the sensational press. So I knew nothing about this business until Hazel's secretary, Miss Alice Farmer, telephoned me this morning."

Inspector Bell shared Hoyt's views about the sensational press: the house was triple-guarded against reporters, though a hundred eyes came to stop and stare in the square.

Edward Hoyt suddenly sat down beside the small fire in the white grate. He was a long, lean, pleasant-faced man of just past forty, with big knuckly hands and a patient manner. He had certainly, Bell reflected, been a patient suitor. His eyes in the firelight were faintly bloodshot, and he turned them often towards a sofa on which lay a neat wig, a pair of dark spectacles, and a heavy blackthorn walking stick.

"It's fantastic and degrading," he went on, "and I still don't believe it. Can't *you* tell me anything, Inspector? Anything at all?"

Bell was noncommittal.

"You've heard the evidence, sir. Miss Farmer, her secretary, testifies that at a few minutes before ten last night Miss Loring left the house, refusing to say where she was going." He paused. "It wasn't the first time Miss Loring had gone out like that: always about ten o'clock, and usually staying out two or three hours."

Hoyt did not comment.

"From here," said Bell, "she must have gone straight across to the garden—"

"But why, in heaven's name," Hoyt burst out, "the *garden?*"

Bell ignored this. "A policeman on his rounds heard someone fumbling at the gate of the garden. He flashed his light, and saw Miss Loring opening the gate with a key. He questioned her, but she explained that she lived in the square and had a right to use the garden, even on a blacked-out December night.

"The constable let her go. But he was worried. About an hour later, his beat brought him round to the garden again. The gate was still open: he heard it creak. He went in, and found Miss Loring sitting on a bench . . . there . . . at the first turn of the gravel path, about fifteen feet from the gate."

Bell paused.

He visualized the scene, sharp in its loneliness. The gate squeaking in a raw wind; the brief, probing light on icy flesh and white silk underclothing; the head hanging down over the back of the bench; and the high-heeled shoes with button-fastenings undone.

"The rest of her clothing—fur coat, dress, suspender-belt, and stockings —lay beside her: folded in such a way that her maid, Henrietta Simms, swears she took off the clothes herself. Her handbag was untouched. The key to the garden gate, with a large cardboard label attached, lay on the path."

Each time Bell made a statement, Edward Hoyt nodded at the fire.

Bell went over to the sofa and picked up the walking stick. It was top-heavy, because its nickel-plated head contained half a pound of lead.

"She'd been killed," Bell went on, "behind that bench. The ground was hard, but there were prints of those high heels of hers all over the place. There'd been a struggle: she wasn't any weakling."

"No," agreed Hoyt.

"Her skull was fractured over the left temple with this stick." Bell weighed it in his hand. "No doubt about this as the weapon. Microscopic traces of blood, and a hair, on the handle: though the wound hardly bled at all outwardly. Our laboratory identifies—"

He broke off apologetically.

"I beg your pardon, sir. I'm not trying to give you the third degree with this. I only brought it along to see whether anybody could identify it."

Hoyt spoke with old-fashioned courtesy.

"And I beg *your* pardon, Inspector. It is a pleasure to deal with a gentleman." He got to his feet, and drew the back of his hand across his mouth. "I'm glad there was no blood," he added. "I'm glad she wasn't—knocked about."

"Yes."

"But is that reasonable, Inspector? A fatal injury, with so little blood?"

"Oh yes. It's the rupture of brain-tissues that counts. A friend of mine got concussion from being struck by the door of a railway carriage and never knew there was anything wrong with him until he collapsed." Bell's tone changed; he spoke sharply. "Now, sir, I've spoken my piece. Have you anything to tell me?"

"Nothing. Except—"

"Well?"

Hoyt hesitated. "I'd been a bit worried about her. She hasn't been looking at all well lately. I'm afraid she had a tendency to overeat." There was the ghost of a smile on his face, contradicted by the bloodshot eyes. "But she said, 'So long as I do my exercises every morning, as thousands of my followers are doing'—she was very proud of her position, Inspector—"

This was hardly what Bell wanted.

"I mean, do you know any reason why anybody should have wanted to kill her?"

"None. I swear!"

"Or why she should have undressed herself in order to get killed?"

Hoyt's mouth tightened. But he was prevented from answering by the entrance of a soft, quiet, but quick-moving woman in horn-rimmed spectacles. Miss Alice Farmer, the perfect secretary, resembled the old-time notion of a schoolmistress. Her face, though not unattractive, was suggestive of a buttered bun; her brown hair was dressed untidily; she wore paper cuffs and flat-heeled shoes.

Miss Farmer had many times shown her devotion to Hazel Loring during six years' service. Now her eyelids looked pink and sanded, and occasionally she reached under the spectacles to dab at them with the tip of a handkerchief.

"Ghouls!" she said, gripping the handkerchief hard. "Ghouls! Inspector, I —I know poor Hazel's body has been taken away. But didn't you give orders that *none* of those horrible reporters was to be admitted to the square over there?"

"Yes, of course. Why?"

"Well," said Miss Farmer, putting out her chin bravely, "they're there now. You can see them from my window upstairs. Two of them. One is a man taking pictures; and the other, if you please, is a *woman*. How any *decent* woman could lower herself to write for the—" She stopped, and her face grew scarlet. "I mean *report,* of course; not write *nice* things; that's altogether different. Oh, dear. You do see what I mean, don't you?"

Inspector Bell saw only that his orders had been disobeyed. He stiffened. "You're sure they're reporters?"

"Just *look* for yourself!"

Bell's pleasant face grew sinister. He drew a deep breath. He picked up his overcoat and his bowler hat from a chair.

"Excuse me just one moment," he said formally. "I'll attend to them."

By the time he left the house, Bell was running. The garden gate, on the west side of the square, was almost opposite Hazel Loring's house. The iron bench—once green, but now of a rust color—itself faced due west, where the gravel path curved in front of it.

Round it prowled a small golden-haired figure in a fur coat, and a large untidy figure with a mackintosh and a camera. Inspector Bell "Oi'd" at them; then he squared himself in front of them and began to talk.

Henry Ashwin, the photographer, took it stolidly. All he did was to pull his hat farther on a pair of large projecting ears, and shrug his shoulders in an apologetic way. But Jacqueline, between indignation and utter astonishment, was struck dumb. She sincerely felt that she was helping in the investigation, and she could not understand what this man was going on about.

"You must not be such a grimy camel!" she cried, reasoning with him kindly. "You do not understand at all. I am Dubois of the *Record.* This is Mr. Ashwin of the *Record."*

"I know Mr. Ashwin," said Bell grimly. "Now, for the last time, madam: will you get out of here, or must you be taken out by main force?"

"But you do not mean that!"

Bell stared at her.

"What makes you think so?"

"And you should not talk so to the Press. It is not nice and you get yourself into trouble. Henry, I do not like this man. Kick him out of here and then we get on with our work."

"Ashwin," said Bell, "is this girl completely off her head?"

Ashwin intervened in a protesting rumble. "Sorry, Inspector; I'll fix it. Look here, Jackie, things aren't the same here as they are in France. That's what I've been trying to tell you. In England, reporters aren't allowed to—"

"You will not do it?"

"I can't, Jackie!"

"Now I am mad," said Jackie, folding her arms with an air of cold grandeur. "Blimey, now I am good and mad; and just for that I do not tell you anything about the clue I have discovered."

"Clue?" said Bell sharply.

"Ha, *now* you are interested, eh?" cried Jacqueline, wagging her head. Her tone changed: it became timid and pleading. "Please, I like to be nice, and I like you to be nice too. I could help you if you would let me. I think I know what happen here last night. As soon as I hear about Miss Loring's shoes being unbuttoned, and hear about the wig and spectacles—"

Bell whirled round on her.

"How do you know her shoes were unbuttoned? And about any wig and spectacles? That wasn't given out to the Press!"

Twilight was deepening over the spiky trees of the garden. Not a gleam showed in Victoria Square except the hooded sidelights of a taxi, which circled the square with its engine clanking noisily. Jacqueline opened her handbag, and drew out a large oblong of glazed paper.

It was a photograph of Hazel Loring's body, taken from in front and some dozen feet away. The shadows were behind it, so that every detail showed with crude realism: the upright posture but limp arms, the head thrown back, the slim muscular legs and shoes whose open fastenings were visible at a glance.

"Where," Bell shouted, "did you get this?"

"*I* got it, Inspector," Ashwin admitted. "I climbed over the fence this morning, before they'd moved anything. If I'd used a flashbulb your men would have spotted me straightaway; but there was a good strong sun up to ten o'clock, so I just took a snap and hared off."

Ashwin's little eyes blinked out of the shadow of his shabby hat. It had grown so dark in the garden that little more could be seen of him except the shift and shine of his eyes, and the fact that he needed a shave. If ordinarily he might have been something of a swaggerer, he was subdued now. He also had found Jacqueline a handful.

"I wasn't even going to use the picture, I swear!" he went on, and stated his real grievance. "This girl pinched it from me, when I wasn't even going to show—"

"Shoes!" insisted Jacqueline.

Bell swung round again. "What about the shoes?"

"They is clues," said Jacqueline simply. "You must not ask me how I get my information. The wig and the spectacles I learn about from Miss Loring's maid, in a way. But I do not mind telling you what will solve your case for you, strike me pink."

Bell hesitated.

"If this is some sort of game," he snapped, "there's going to be a lot of trouble in store for certain people I could mention. Now, I warn you! But if you've got anything to tell me, let's hear it."

Jacqueline was complacent.

"You do not see that the shoes show what has happen here?"

"Frankly, I don't."

"Ah! That is why you need a woman to detect for you when a woman is murdered. Now I show you. You see in the picture that the shoes have very high heels. Yes?"

"Yes."

"And they fasten only with one strap and one button across the . . . the . . . ah, zut!"

"Instep?"

"I am spikking the English very well, thank you," said Jacqueline, drawing herself up coldly. "I do not need your help to be pure. And I have already think to say instep. But you still do not tumble? No?" She sidled closer. Coaxing and honey-sweet, her voice caressed him out of the twilight. "If I tell you, then you do something for me? You will be a nice man and let me print what I like?"

"I most certainly will not."

"Orright. Then I will not tell you."

Adam Bell's wrath boiled clear to the top. Never in his career had he met anyone quite like this. It is true that his career had not been a long one; but then Jacqueline's could not have been so very long either. Now he meant to have no more nonsense. He would put her in her place, and with no uncertain adjectives.

He had opened his mouth to do this, when there was a flicker of a shrouded light across the square. The door of number 22 opened and closed.

Bell had a sharp premonition of disaster as soon as he heard the flat-heeled footsteps rapping and ringing on frosty pavements. A squat little figure, coatless and with wisps of hair flying, hurried across the street into the garden.

When the figure came closer, Bell saw that tears were trickling down Miss Alice Farmer's face.

"It's all your fault," she said accusingly to Bell. "Oh dear, if only you hadn't left! If only you'd stayed with him!"

"Easy now. What is it? Steady, Miss Farmer!"

"Your sergeant's phoned for the ambulance; and he says they may pull him through, but oh dear, if they don't I don't know what I shall do. Oh dear, it's even more dreadful than—"

Then she pulled herself together.

"I'm sorry. It's poor Mr. Hoyt. He's taken poison. You'd better come over to the house at once."

Adam Bell was not able to interview Hoyt until the following day. That morning's edition of the *Daily Record* was in Bell's pocket: he wondered what the Assistant Commissioner would have to say about Jacqueline Dubois's story.

A nurse conducted him to a small private room, where Edward Hoyt lay propped up among the pillows of a white iron bed. Alice Farmer sat in a squeaky rocking chair by the window, looking out at the snowflakes that had begun to thicken over Kensington Gardens.

"Rather a foolish thing to do, wasn't it, sir?" Bell asked quietly.

"I recognize that, Inspector."

"Why did you do it?"

"Can't you guess?"

Hoyt even managed a sour smile. His hands, snake-veined, lay listless on the coverlet; his gaze wandered over the ceiling without curiosity. Yesterday he had seemed in his middle forties: now he looked ten years older.

"The curious thing is," he went on, frowning, "that I had no intention of doing it. That's a fact, Inspector. I hadn't realized—by George, I hadn't! —how terrible and irresistible a mere *impulse* can be."

He paused, as though to get his breath.

"I went upstairs," he said, "to have a look at Hazel's room. That's all. It honestly is all. I glanced into the bathroom. I saw the medicine cabinet open, and a bottle of morphine tablets inside. Before I had any notion of what I meant, I had filled a glass of water, and swallowed seven or eight of the tablets as fast as I could get them down. At that time, I admit, I didn't want to live any longer."

"No, sir?"

"No. But I have changed my mind now. I am sorry: it was, as you say, a very foolish thing to do."

Always the gentleman, thought Inspector Bell.

From the direction of the window came a sharp, almost malignant squeak from the rocking chair. Alice Farmer glanced over her shoulder, and back again quickly. The snow shed shifting lights into the warm, close room.

"Of course I realize," Bell said awkwardly, "that as Miss Loring's fiancé—"

"It is not quite accurate to call me her fiancé," returned Hoyt, with detached calmness.

His tone made Inspector Bell sit up sharply.

"Meaning, sir?"

"Hazel never intended to get married, to me or anybody else."

"How do you know that?"

"She told me so. But I kept on patiently waiting. I have always had a fancy for the senseless role of the *preux chevalier*. God knows I'm cured of that now." Hoyt closed his eyes, and opened them again. "You see that I am being frank."

"You mean she didn't love you?"

Hoyt smiled faintly. "I doubt if Hazel was ever in love with anybody. No: I wasn't referring to that."

"Well?"

"I think she was married already. One moment!" The weak voice sharpened and grew firm. "I have absolutely no evidence for saying that. It's a guess. An impression. A—well, Inspector, I haven't known Hazel Loring for five years without learning something about her beyond those famous eyebrows and dimples. I knew her moods. And her heart. And her mind: which was, after all, a second-rate mind. Lord forgive me, what am I saying?"

He broke off, looking still more ill. There was another squeak from the rocking chair as Alice Farmer got up to pour him a glass of water from the bedside table.

Hoyt thanked her with a grateful nod; and she hardly glanced at him. But to Inspector Bell, watching every turn of lip or hand, that glance meant much. Bell thought to himself, with a rush of realization: if Hazel Loring wasn't in love with Edward Hoyt, I know who else is.

Miss Farmer fluttered back to her chair.

"I tell you that," pursued Hoyt, setting down the glass, "because I want to see this mess cleared up. If Hazel *had* a husband tucked away somewhere in secret, she could hardly divorce him. She had set herself up in too pious a position before the world."

Drawing up the collar of his overcoat, Bell went out of the nursing-home into the falling snow. Jacqueline Dubois, wearing a fur coat and a hat with an outrageous veil, was waiting for him at the foot of the steps.

Inspector Bell took one look at her, and then began to run.

His excuse for this was a bus, which would set him down beside a hotel in a side street only a few yards away from Victoria Square. The bus was already some distance away, and lumbering fast. Bell sprinted hard after it, sprang aboard, and climbed up to a deserted top deck. He had no sooner settled back than Jacqueline, flushed and panting, was beside him.

The girl was almost in tears.

"You are not genteel!" she wailed. "I have twist my ankle. Would you like it that I should hurt myself bad?"

"Candidly," said Bell, "yes."

"You do not like me at *all?*"

"No. Remember, I've read your story in the *Record* this morning."

"You do not like it? But, *chéri,* I wrote it to please you!"

"In the course of that story," said Bell, "you four times described me as 'handsome.' How I'm going to dare show my face back at Scotland Yard again I don't know. What is more important, you headlined—"

"You are not angry?"

"Oh, no. Not at all."

"Besides, I have a clue."

Despite everything, Bell suddenly found himself chuckling. Rules were rules; but still, he reflected, he had been behaving like a good deal of a stuffed shirt. This girl need give him no trouble. And in her way Jacqueline was rather attractive.

"Not again?" he said.

"No, no, no! It is the same clue. You will not let me explain. You will not let me explain how I know that Miss Loring was not killed in the garden at all, but that the assassin kill her somewhere else and carry her to the garden afterwards."

The bus lurched round a snow-rutted curve.

Bell, taking two tickets from the conductor, almost dropped both of them.

"Is this," he demanded, "another stunt?"

"It is the truth! I know it by the shoes. The shoes have very high heels, and their straps are not buttoned."

"Well?"

"She could not have walked in them. Yes, I tell you so! She could not have walked a step in them. It is impossible. Either the shoes fall off, or *she* fall off.

"Listen! You say to yourself, 'Miss Loring has entered the garden; she has started to undress herself.' So? Then why does she take off her stockings and put her shoes back on? You say, 'While she is like this, the assassin catch her; there is a struggle; she is hit; the assassin pick her up and put her on the bench.' I say, no, no, no! She could not have walked in those shoes. It is jolly sure she could not have *fight* in them. They would just fall off, and then there would be marks on her feet. And there were no marks, eh?"

"Go on," said Bell, after a pause.

"It jumps to the eyes that the assassin has put the shoes on Miss Loring after she is dead."

"But—"

"Now I tell you something else. What is it that puzzle you so much, *chéri?* What is the big headache? It is the reason why Miss Loring should have undress herself in the open with the weather freezing zero. Yes? But she did not.

"She has gone first to the garden. Then she has left the garden, and gone somewhere else which is indoors; and there she has undressed herself. There the assassin catch her and kill her. Then he take her back to the garden in the blackout, to make you think she was killed there. He is just starting to dress her fully when he is interrupted, and has to run. Yes?"

Their bus had gone clanking up Gloucester Terrace, and was turning into Hargreaves Street, which led to Victoria Square. Already Bell could see the square ahead. Bell smote his hand against the top of the seat in front of them.

"By all the—" he burst out, and stopped. "I wonder if it could be?"

"I do not wonder," said Jacqueline. "I am sure it is true. For any woman to take off her clothes outdoors in such weather is not practical; and even if I am a goofy little beasel I see that straightaway, gorblimey!"

"Just a minute. What about the heel marks of the struggle in the earth behind the bench?"

"They is phony," returned Jacqueline calmly. "I do not think there be any marks with the ground so hard. The assassin has made them too."

Stopping with a jolt, the bus threw them against the bench ahead. They climbed down to the pavement beside the quiet hotel only a few steps from Victoria Square. Though Jacqueline was dancing round him, Bell would not be hurried either mentally or physically.

"It's nonsense," he decided.

"You are a nasty man and I do not like you. Why is it nonsense?"

"Well, where did the woman go? You say Miss Loring went somewhere and 'undressed.' Where? Apparently she didn't go back home. Where could any woman go at that hour of the night in order to undr—?"

He checked himself, and raised his eyes. A raw wind shouted down Hargreaves Street, whipping the snow to powder. The grimy red-brick building in front of them had two entrances. Across the top of one was blazoned in gilt letters the name of the hotel. On the glass doors of the other were smaller letters in white enamel, but they were letters which made Bell jump. They said:

LADIES' AND GENTLEMEN'S
TURKISH BATHS.
OPEN DAY AND NIGHT.

The woman behind the counter was scandalized. When she first caught a glimpse of them, coming down in the automatic lift into the warm, dim basement-foyer, she threw up the flap of the counter and ran out.

"You, sir!" she cried. "You can't come in here!"

"I am a police officer—," Bell began.

The woman hesitated only a second. "Sorry, sir, but you still aren't allowed here. This is Wednesday. It's Ladies' Day. Didn't you see the notice upstairs?"

"*I* can come in?" cooed Jacqueline.

"Yes, madam, of course."

" 'Ow much?" asked Jacqueline, opening her handbag.

Taking hold of Jacqueline's arm in a grip that made her squeal, Bell drove the other woman before him until she retreated behind the counter.

First he showed his warrant card. Then he drew out a large close up photograph of Hazel Loring's face.

"Did you ever see this lady before?"

"I—I don't know. There are so many people here. What do you want?"

On the counter lay a tray of pens and pencils. With a coloured pencil Bell drew on the photograph a crude representation of an auburn wig. To this he added a pair of dark spectacles.

"Did you ever see *this* lady before?"

"I did and all!" admitted the woman. "Of course I did. She was always coming here at night. If you'd just tell me what you—"

"Was she here on Monday night?"

The attendant, who seemed less frightened than anxious that Bell should not get beyond the doors at the left, admitted this too.

"Yes, she was. She came in about a quarter past ten, a little later than usual. I noticed because she looked awfully groggy; sick like; and her hands were shaky and she didn't leave any valuables here at the desk."

"What time did she leave?"

"I don't know. I—I don't remember." A puzzled look, a kind of spasm, flickered across the attendant's face. "Here's Mrs. Bradford," she added. "She'll give you what-for if you don't get out of here!"

It was very warm and faintly damp in the tiled basement. A dim humming noise throbbed beyond it. Soft lights shone on the counter, on the wall of steel boxes behind it; and, towards the left, on leather-covered swing doors studded with brass nailheads.

One of these doors was pushed open. A stocky, medium-sized woman, with dark hair drawn behind her ears and eyebrows that met over the top of her nose, first jerked back as though for flight, and then stood solidly. Her face was impassive and rather sinister. She wore a white duck coat and skirt; her bare feet were thrust into beach sandals.

"Mrs. Bradford—," the attendant began.

Mrs. Bradford gave the newcomers a long, slow look. Emotion, harsh and pressed to bursting, filled that foyer as thickly as the damp. Voices, faint laughter, made a ghostly background beyond.

"You'd better come in here," she told them. Opening a door which led into a small office, she nodded at them to precede her. When they were inside, she closed and locked the door. Then she flopped down in an office-chair and presently began to cry.

"I knew I couldn't get away with it," she said.

"So that's it," Bell muttered ten minutes later. "Hoyt told me that Miss Loring was fond of overeating."

Mrs. Bradford uttered a contemptuous snort. She was sitting forward, her elbows carelessly on her knees; she seemed to feel better now that she had been given a cigarette.

"Overeating!" she growled. "She'd have been as big as a barrage-balloon if she hadn't nearly killed herself with more Turkish baths than any human being ought to take. Yes, and keeping a medicine cabinet full of slimming drugs that were downright dangerous. I warned her. But, oh, no! She wouldn't listen. She was making too much money out of this slimming campaign of hers."

"You knew her?"

"I've known Hazel Loring for twenty years. We were kids together in the north. She was always the lady. Not like me. And she was clever: I give her that."

Bell was putting many facts together now.

"Then the simple-exercises-and-keep-fit campaign—?"

"It was all," said Mrs. Bradford, wagging her head and blowing out smoke contemptuously, "a fake. Mind, her exercises maybe did do some people good. There's some women could hypnotize themselves into believing anything. And, if they thought it kept 'em slim . . . why, perhaps it did. But not little Hazel. That's why she had to sneak over here in a damn silly disguise, like a film star or something. She was desperately frightened somebody'd spot her."

"And yet," said Bell, "somebody murdered her. It was you, I suppose?"

The cigarette dropped out of Mrs. Bradford's hand.

"Murdered!" she whispered; and missed the cigarette altogether when she tried to stamp it out with her foot. Then her voice rose to a screech. "Man, what's the matter with you? Are you clean daft? Murdered?"

"Sh-h!"

"Murdered?" said Mrs. Bradford. "She fell down and died in the steamroom. I had to get her out of here on the q.t., or the scandal would have ruined us."

"She died from concussion of the brain."

Mrs. Bradford's eyes seemed to turn inwards.

"Ah? So that was it! I noticed she'd got a kind of red mark on her temple, half under the wig. I supposed she had hit her head on the edge of the marble bench when she collapsed—"

"No," said Bell. "She was beaten to death with a lead-loaded walking stick. The laboratory can prove that."

Distant fans whirred and hummed: the air was astir. Mrs. Bradford slid up from her chair, with a lithe motion for a woman so stocky, and began to back away.

"Don't you try to bluff a woman that's always been honest," she said, in a thin unnatural voice. "It was an accident, I tell you! Either heart failure, or hitting her head when she fell. It's happened before, when people can't stand the heat. And now you come and tell me—"

"Just a moment," said Bell quietly.

The tone of his voice made Mrs. Bradford pause, her hand half-lifted as though to take an oath.

"Now tell me," Bell continued, "did you see Miss Loring arrive here on Monday night?"

"Yes."

"How did she look? Ill, for instance?"

"Very ill. Lucy at the desk can tell you that. All shaky and funny. That's why I kept an eye on her."

"What happened then? No, I'm not accusing you of lying! Just tell me what happened."

Mrs. Bradford stared at him.

"Well . . . she went to one of the booths, and took off her clothes, and wrapped herself up in that cotton robe they wear, and went on to the hot rooms. I'm manager here: I don't act as masseuse usually, but I did it for her so that nobody shouldn't discover about the wig. I was nervous because she looked so ill. Afterwards I went up to the steam room, and there she was lying on the floor. Alone. Dead. I thought: Holy mother, I knew something would happen, and now—!"

"Go on."

"Well, what could I do? I couldn't carry her down to where her clothes were, because there were ten or a dozen other women here and they'd know what had happened."

"Go on."

"I had to get rid of her. I *had* to! I ran down and rolled her clothes and handbag up into a bundle and ran back up to the steam room. But I couldn't dress her there, because somebody might have walked in any minute. Don't you see?"

"Go on."

Mrs. Bradford moistened her lips. "Upstairs there's a door that leads out into an alley by the hotel. I slung her over my shoulder, and carried her out into the blackout wrapped in that cotton robe.

"I knew where to put her, too. Beside her handbag there'd been a big key, with a cardboard label saying it was the key to the garden in Victoria Square. I got her into the garden and sat her down on the first bench I came to. Then I started to dress her properly so nobody shouldn't know she'd ever been at the baths. I'd just got the underclothes on, and slipped the shoes on her feet so they'd be handy, when I heard a noise. I slipped back a little; and it's a good thing I did, for there was a great big blazing light—"

"Did I not say it?" murmured Jacqueline softly. "Did I not say the policeman has come in and interrupted her?"

"So I hopped it," concluded Mrs. Bradford, wiping her eyes. "I still had the cotton robe in my hand; but I forgot the wig and spectacles." Her face grew harsh and ugly. "That's what I did. I admit it. But that's all I did. She wasn't murdered in these baths!"

"As a matter of fact," replied Bell calmly, "I don't think she was. For all practical purposes, I think she was dead before she got here."

It was not easy to frighten Jacqueline Dubois. Only her imagination could do this. Her imagination conjured up wild visions of a dead woman in a red wig, the face already bloodless, walking into the foyer and confronting the attendant with blind black spectacles. It unnerved her. Even the humming of the fans unnerved her.

She cried out at Bell, but he silenced her.

"Queer thing," Bell mused. "I was telling Mr. Hoyt yesterday about a friend of mine. He was struck by the door of a railway carriage. He got up, brushed himself, assured everybody he wasn't hurt, went home, and collapsed an hour later with concussion of the brain. Such cases are common enough. You'll find plenty of them in Taylor's *Medical Jurisprudence.* That's what happened to Hazel Loring, in my opinion."

"You mean . . ."

"Mind!" Bell held hard to his caution. "Mind, I don't promise anything. Whether they'll want to hold you as accessory after the fact, Mrs. Bradford, I can't say. But, just between ourselves, I don't think you've got a lot to worry about.

"As I read it, Hazel Loring met the murderer in the garden at ten o'clock. There was a fight. The murderer struck her down and left her for dead. She got to her feet, thought she was all right, and came over here to the baths. In the steam room she collapsed and died. And you, finding the key to the garden, carried her body straight back to the real scene of the crime."

Bell drew a deep breath and his forehead wrinkled in thought.

"Talk about the wheel revolving!" he added. "All we want now is the murderer."

Edward Hoyt, released from the nursing home on Friday morning, took a taxi to Victoria Square under a bright, watery sun which was turning the snow to slush.

The exposure of Hazel Loring's racket, appearing in Thursday's *Daily Record,* was both a revelation and a revolution. It was a real scoop for the paper.

MacGrath, the news editor, danced the saraband. Henry Ashwin, the photographer, swallowed three quick whiskies and went out to find Jacqueline. Sir Claude Champion, owner of the *Daily Banner,* swallowed aspirins and vowed vengeance. All over the country it made wives pause in the very act of the patent exercises. Yet nobody was satisfied. Through the excitement ran a bitter flavor: however much of a fake the dead woman might have been, still she was dead by a brutal attack and her murderer still walked and talked in the town.

Edward Hoyt's face seemed to express this as he went up the steps of number 22. The door was opened for him by Alice Farmer, whose face brightened with joy. And this performance was watched with interest by Jacqueline Dubois and Henry Ashwin, the photographer, lurking behind the railings in the garden opposite.

"The point is," insisted Ashwin, giving her a sideways glance, "what is Bell doing? He now seems to think you're a kind of mascot—"

Jacqueline was not without modest pride.

"He think I am pretty good," she admitted. "I just try to give him ideas, that is all. But between you and me and the pikestaff, I do not know *what* he is doing. He is very mysterious."

"Beaten, eh? Shame on you!"

Jacqueline's color went up like a flag.

"I am not beaten either! But maybe perhaps I am wrong about him. First I think he is only a stupid Englishman, all dumb and polite, and now I think his mind may work funnier than I expect. He keep talking about lights."

"Lights?"

"Big lights. Oi! Look!"

She pointed. There was another visitor for number 22. Mrs. Eunice Bradford, almost unrecognizable in an oversmart outfit and a saucer hat, strode briskly along the street. The morning sun streamed full on the doorway; they saw Mrs. Bradford punching the doorbell with assurance. She was admitted by Miss Farmer.

"Got 'em taped," said the voice of Inspector Bell.

Jacqueline felt a shock. Bell, followed by Sergeant Rankin and a uniformed constable, was coming across the slush-marshy garden with the sun behind him.

"Don't sneak up like that, Inspector!" protested Ashwin. He nodded towards the house across the way. "So it's a gathering of the suspects, eh?"

"It is."

"And you're going to nab somebody over there?"

"I am."

Jacqueline began to shiver, though the air held an almost springlike thaw. Bell's expression was guileless.

"You can come along, if you like," he said to Jacqueline. "In fact, I might say you've got to come along. A good deal of my evidence depends on you, though you may not know it. I'll give you some poetic justice too. You've spent half your time in this business worming things out of people or pinching things from people. I've taken the liberty of pinching something from you."

"You go away!" said Jacqueline. "Please, what is this? I do not understand."

Bell opened the briefcase he was carrying. "You remember," he said, "how you solved your part of the problem by deducing something from the unbuttoned shoes in a photograph taken the morning after the murder?"

"Yes."

Bell drew a large glazed oblong of paper from the briefcase. It was the picture they had all seen: Hazel Loring's body on the bench, every detail sharp-etched with the shadows behind.

"Is this the same photograph?"

"Ah, zut! Of course it is."

Bell glanced inquiringly at Ashwin.

"You confirm that? This is the same photograph you took at about ten o'clock on Tuesday morning?"

Ashwin, with a face of hideous perplexity, merely nodded. Sergeant Rankin suddenly guffawed: a sharp sound which he covered up with a cough.

"Then it's very curious," said Bell. He held up the photograph. "It's the most curious thing we've come across yet. Look at it. Every shadow in this picture, as we see, falls straight behind bench and body. Yet the bench, as we've known from the start, faces due west and has its back to the east.

"Look at the bench now. See how the shadows fall in front of it along the path. In other words, this photograph couldn't possibly have been taken in the morning. It couldn't have been taken at any time during the day, because the sun was gone in the afternoon. That bright light and those dead-black shadows could have been made in only one way. The photograph must have been taken, after dark, by the glare of a flashbulb: which was the 'great big blazing light' Mrs. Bradford saw when she—"

Jacqueline screamed.

One face in the group altered and squeezed up as though it were crumpling like a wet paper mask. A pair of hands flung forward to grab the photograph from Bell and rend it in pieces; but Sergeant Rankin's arm was round the man's throat and the two of them went over backwards in a crashing cartwheel on the path.

Bell's voice remained level.

"Henry Ashwin, I arrest you for the murder of your wife, Hazel Loring. I have to warn you that anything you say will be taken down in writing and may be used as evidence against you at your trial."

To Jacqueline, that night, Bell was a little more communicative.

"There's nothing much to tell," he said off handedly. "Once I got Hoyt's tip, and we put the organization to work, it didn't take long to discover that one Hazel Ann Loring and one Henry Fielding Ashwin had been married at the Hampstead Registry Office in 1933." He grinned. "That's where the official police will always score over you amateurs."

Jacqueline was agog.

"He try the blackmail on her. Yes?"

"Yes, in a small way. A nasty bit of work is Ashwin. In the first place, he was a no-good who would take some explaining; in the second place, she couldn't afford to have the gaff blown about her racket. That was why Ashwin was pretending to make what you call goo-goo eyes at Hazel Loring's maid: he had to have some excuse for hanging round the house so constantly.

"But Hazel was getting fed up with it. She issued an ultimatum, and arranged to meet him in the garden. There was a wild, blind row: both of them, we know, had ugly tempers. Ashwin laid her out, and then ran. It wasn't a planned crime: he just ran.

"After he'd had a couple of drinks, he began to get scared. He'd left that stick behind. He didn't *think* they could trace it to him; but suppose they did? So he went back to the square—and must have thought he was losing his mind. For he saw Eunice Bradford bringing the body back.

"In any case, he thought it was a gift from heaven. If he could frame any evidence against her, Mrs. Bradford would swing for the crime as sure as eggs. He set his flashbulb and fired blindly for a picture. But in the dark his aim was bad; Mrs. Bradford had jumped back; and he didn't get her in the picture at all. He saw that when he developed the picture. Of course he'd never have shown that photograph to anyone. He'd have torn up the pictures and destroyed the negative. Only—"

Jacqueline nodded radiantly.

"I pinch it from him," she declared, with pride. "And then he have to stew up some explanation for it."

"Yes. Of course, I saw that the dim, paper-covered torch of the policeman who discovered the body could never have produced that 'great big blazing light' described by Mrs. Bradford. Then, once you looked closely at the photograph and noticed the fall of the shadows, that tore it. I gathered the obvious suspects in one house to throw Ashwin off his guard; and got him to confirm his previous story before police witnesses. That's all."

He chuckled.

"There's one good result from it, anyway," he added. "Edward Hoyt and Alice Farmer should be extremely comfortable with each other."

But Jacqueline was not listening. Her eyes were shining and absorbed. She put her hand with innocent fervor on his arm.

"If I had not pinch the picture," she said, "and if I had not deduce those things, maybe you would not have solved the case. Eh?"

"Maybe not."

"You do not think I am such a goofy little beasel. No?"

"No."

"In fact, day by day in every way I am becoming indispensable to you. Yes?"

The hair froze on Bell's head. "Hold on! Take it easy! I didn't say that!"

"But *I* say it," declared Jacqueline, with fiery earnestness. "I think we go well together, yes? I pinch things for you; and if you like you can be my Conscience and go gobble-gobble at me, but you do not be too mad when I help you. Then each day I get an exclusive inter—inter—"

"Interview," suggested Bell.

"Okay, if you say so, though my knowledge of English is formidable and you do not have to tell me. If I like you very much and am a good girl, will you let me help with the detecting when I ask to?"

Bell looked down at the flushed, lovely face.

"I will," he said, *"ou je serai l'oncle d'un singe!* My knowledge of French is formidable too."

LOST STAR

by C. DALY KING

Tarrant and I were sitting quietly enough, that evening, in his apartment in the East Thirties. It was only a day or so after the denouement of what he called the City of Evil episode—in fact, the bullet holes in his living-room walls had not yet been treated by the decorators—and I, for one, had had all the excitement I wanted for the moment.

The scene now, however, was as peaceful as anyone could have wished. Brihido, having served his usual excellent dinner, had cleared away; the tightly closed living-room windows reduced the city's clamor to a low drone only occasionally interrupted by the squawk of a distant taxi; the few, well-placed, mellow lights were pleasant to the eye in this luxuriously masculine room. Across from us the dial of the walnut radio cabinet glowed a dull yellow above the modulated music issuing from beneath it.

Tarrant was slowly turning the stem of his brandy pony. "You know, Jerry, knowledge is sometimes more important than money in getting the good things of life. This brandy costs less than some of the widely advertised brands but it comes from people who know what brandy is and are not trying to unload the tag ends of their product onto the gullible American market. Do you like it?"

I did, and said so. "If it's all the same, I'll have another pony. The brandy is fine but that music is too dopey for me. How about getting a dance orchestra?" Tarrant had tuned the instrument to a popular concert being broadcast from the Mall.

He smiled. "You're a Philistine, Jerry. You are listening to one of the most famous conductors in the world. However, I'll agree that I don't care for his program, myself. That's the trouble with these popular concerts; the musical appreciation of the audiences is so low that the selections have to be fairly uninteresting. This one is almost finished, though. Let's see what he will give us next; if it's no better, I'll turn it off."

But he didn't turn it off; we were destined to listen to most of that concert.

Tarrant was tipping the decanter over my empty glass and the music was entering a rather horrible, syrupy passage when it was abruptly cut off and an unexpected voice spoke distinctly from the radio.

"Trans-Radio Flash. Gloria Glammeris has been kidnapped! Her absence was discovered at nine-forty-two by Operative Huggins of the All-American Agency. This is Lou Vincent speaking for the Trans-Radio News Service. We will stand by and bring you further details as we receive them. Station WJEX."

The instrument was silent for a moment, then brought us smoothly the last two notes of the selection on the Mall, followed by a burst of applause.

I sat up in my chair with the brandy glass in my hand. "Good Lord, Tarrant, that *is* going pretty far for a publicity stunt, isn't it?"

He shook his head. "We don't know that it is a publicity stunt. Our friend, Peake, down at Headquarters is convinced it's not. Of course he has contact with the All-American people and they tell him that they view it seriously. After all, they're the biggest private detective agency in the country; they certainly can't be bribed into staging a fake crime, and when they send ten of their best men out to Hollywood, it looks like business. Just the threatening letter—yes, that might be a phony. But it seems that the thing has actually been pulled off, right under their noses."

The music had commenced again but we were paying no attention to it. I said, "Just the same, her new picture is about to open. And she's the biggest star the Kolossal outfit has. People with brass enough to call themselves Kolossal, and misspell it into the bargain, would do anything."

"All I know is what I've been told," was Tarrant's reply. "Peake says that All-American was hired by Ike Bronsky, Kolossal's president, that he flew east to confer personally with their head office and that they believe he would gladly give up half a year's publicity to get to the bottom of the matter and protect his star. It's true there will be plenty of publicity now; she has a tremendous following and she is certainly a lovely girl."

"Ho-ho! I had no idea you went for film stars. How long has this been going on?"

"Blast it, Jerry," declared Tarrant, "I'm no monk. I admire beauty in any form. And a girl with a face, a figure, and a voice like hers combines all the beauties of painting, sculpture, and music simultaneously. I've never met her but I would say she is no pretty Hollywood blank. Judging from her work, that girl has both talent and intelligence. I'll wager several millions of people are being bored with radio programs all over the country while they're waiting to—"

The music from the Mall was fading out and Tarrant interrupted himself to listen.

"Trans-Radio Flash," came the voice. "Further regarding the kidnapping of Gloria Glammeris. The crime was discovered at 6:42 Pacific Time, 9:42 Eastern Time, not by Operative Huggins, as previously announced, but by

Miss Jane Smith, Miss Glammeris's secretary. At that time Miss Smith went to Miss Glammeris's apartments on the second floor of her Beverly Hills home. Huggins had been on duty outside the door ever since a previous visit of Miss Smith two hours earlier and was still on duty. Miss Smith knocked on the door, opened it, and immediately cried out that Miss Glammeris was not there. Operative Huggins entered the room at once and a hurried search showed that the star had vanished.

"For the benefit of listeners who have not followed the case, I will say that two weeks ago Gloria Glammeris received a letter, which has not yet been traced, threatening her with kidnapping during the present week. As she is not now making a picture, she agreed under protest, but at the urgent request of her employers, Kolossal Films, to spend the week in her private apartments in her home. Today is the third day she has been in retirement, up to this evening in perfect safety. Two detectives of the All-American Agency have been constantly on duty within the house and eight others have been patrolling the grounds outside. In addition, two Special Officers of the Los Angeles Police Department have been stationed in the immediate vicinity. It is therefore out of the question that Miss Glammeris could have been removed from her home. A thorough search is now in progress and it is believed that her whereabouts will be discovered at any moment. A Trans-Radio man is now upon the premises and will give you an immediate bulletin of further developments. This is Lou Vincent of Trans-Radio News Service. This flash was brought to you through the facilities of Station WJEX."

Tarrant smiled, as the music welled up again from the cabinet. "I'm afraid it's a false alarm, Jerry. At first I thought it might be something to sharpen our wits on. But my guess is that Miss Glammeris has retired to one of her beautiful bathrooms to take a bath. Or perhaps she has gone downstairs to consult with her cook. I have no doubt we may very shortly expect a final bulletin in which she indignantly denies any intention of upsetting the detectives. . . . How about a highball, Jerry?"

"Yes, thanks. In which case," I went on, "this certainly isn't a stunt, for an anticlimax like that would be mighty poor publicity. The threat against her will remain, of course. Naturally she must be in the house; but keep it turned on, anyhow, and let's see where they found her."

Tarrant mixed himself a drink but had not yet resumed his seat when Mr. Lou Vincent was with us again.

"Trans-Radio Flash. Our last bulletin on the Glammeris kidnapping was delayed and we now have further details for you. The house and grounds have been thoroughly searched and Miss Glammeris has not been found. The circumstances as reported by our Trans-Radio man on the scene are most extraordinary. Here are the details.

"At four-thirty this afternoon, Pacific Time, Miss Glammeris was finish-

ing a short conference with her secretary in her study on the second floor of
her house. This room is not lavishly furnished; it contains a large desk, a
couch, some portable book cases and several chairs. It has no windows but is
ventilated by the air-conditioning system of the house. There are three
doors; one to the main corridor, where Operative Huggins sat; one to a
small lavatory which is little more than a cubbyhole and has no windows or
other means of exit; the third opens into Miss Glammeris's sleeping apartments and has recently been cut through, since by way of the main corridor
it is some distance between her bedroom and the study.

"At four-thirty Miss Glammeris concluded her conference in the study
and Miss Smith came out. Before Miss Smith left, Huggins had distinctly
heard the two women talking, one voice deep, the other high, through the
corridor door left partially open by Miss Smith when she had come to the
study for the conference a few minutes before.

"From that moment until six-forty-two, Pacific Time, Operative Huggins never left the immediate vicinity of the study-corridor door. No one
passed through this door in either direction. At six-forty-two Huggins
entered the study immediately behind Miss Smith and found the room
empty. There is no place within the study or the adjoining small lavatory
where Miss Glammeris could conceal herself, let alone be concealed by a
kidnapper. The lavatory, as we said, is a mere blind alley from which no
egress is possible. And the door from the study to the sleeping quarters was
locked. This door can be locked from either side by means of two bolts
embedded in the construction of the door itself, each bolt operated by
turning a small handle above the doorknob on either side. It also appears
that, although it is an interior door, it is weather-stripped on both sides.
When Huggins and Miss Smith entered the study, this door was secured not
only by one bolt but by both. In other words, it was not only locked from
the side of the bedchamber, which could be done after Miss Glammeris had
been taken through it, but was also locked from the inside, the study side. It
is established that in the case of this particular door, the inner bolt cannot be
operated after one has passed through and closed the door from the other
side. Detective Huggins at once discovered that both bolts were shot by
unlocking the door from the study side and by finding that it was still
secured by the bolt on the bedroom side.

"Although bewildered by the situation, Huggins did not lose his head.
He ran into the corridor, accompanied by Miss Smith, and locked the
study-corridor door from the corridor side, retaining the key. He then ran
downstairs to acquaint the other detective in the house with the disappearance and to draw the outside cordon closely about the walls. Needless to
say, none of the outside guards had reported anything unusual during the
preceding two hours.

"With two of the other detectives Huggins hurried upstairs again, where they found Miss Smith frantically searching her employer's bedroom, a search which disclosed nothing of any significance. The three detectives, followed by the secretary who was now becoming hysterical, hastily searched the whole house, after which they collected the servants together and put them through a severe questioning. All professed complete ignorance of what had occurred and, as Huggins could testify that none had so much as appeared in the upstairs corridor during the crucial time period, they were segregated in the kitchen while a more thorough search of the whole house went forward.

"This time the All-American operatives went through the rooms more slowly and carefully, from cellar to attic. All closets were opened, the refrigerators and furnaces searched, wardrobes if locked were burst apart, even the film star's forty trunks were each examined in turn. It is hard to believe that such a probing yielded no result—but that is the fact. Meantime, the cordon around the house had stood inactive but alert and the All-American man in charge felt he could no longer put off informing the Los Angeles Prosecutor's Office as to the situation. The Prosecutor's Office, called on the phone, insisted that both outside doors of Miss Glammeris's study be sealed at once and that no one should enter until the morning, when the Prosecutor should have flown back from Palm Springs and undertake the investigation personally.

"The secretary, Miss Jane Smith, has suffered a complete breakdown and has been removed to the Los Angeles Hospital. This is Lou Vincent, speaking for Trans-Radio News Service. This bulletin came to you through Station WJEX."

Whereupon the instrument resumed with its miserable music. Tarrant, who after the first few seconds had been rapidly jotting down notes on the back and face of an old envelope, looked up and gave his peculiar whistle. Brihido stood in the doorway.

" 'Hido, bring me some paper and that drafting board of yours. We have a little puzzle. Rather an old and hackneyed one, I fear; the sealed room trick again—it keeps turning up regularly every so often."

The valet brought in the materials and sidled up with a sly expression. "My help, mebbe," he grinned.

"Why, certainly, doctor," Tarrant answered. "Pull up a chair and I will sketch out the problem for you. See if you can solve it." The maneuver caused me no surprise, for I knew that the butler was a servant, not by class but by exigency; he did, in fact, hold a medical degree in the Philippines.

"Now," Tarrant was saying, "this room that I am diagramming won't be correct, for I've never seen it. It holds a desk, a couch, some chairs, some portable bookcases. No windows. We will put the three doors one on each of three different sides. Their exact location isn't as important as their condition . . . there they are. Now this door—call it A—leads to a corridor and is covered by a guard. This door, B, gives access to a small lavatory from which there is no other exit of any kind. Door C, bolted on both sides, opens into a bedroom."

"Door A, corridor," murmured Brihido. "Door B, lavatory; door C, bedroom. Yiss."

Tarrant then explained the other details, referring to the scribbles on his envelope. "We won't bother now about how Miss Glammeris was taken from the house," he concluded. "The question is: how was she removed from this room? Now, doctor, you've got it all; go ahead."

To me it seemed a somewhat difficult assignment but the Filipino tackled it without hesitation. He said, "First, door A: this covered by guard. Guard could be bribed, hit lady on head and take her out of room in two hours easy. Further difficulty to leave house but this not present problem. How about?"

"No good," smiled Tarrant. "This is a problem with the factors given. You can't change them upside down; you cannot assume that the guard is the kidnapper. Actually, there isn't a chance in the world that he is involved; he's an All-American operative, a carefully picked man. A poor solution, I'd say."

The butler agreed. "Not think so much, myself. Then, if guard honest, door A is out. Door B to lavatory also out: might as well be solid wall. Must go through door C to bedroom. And why not? No guard here, only question of locking door again from outside after lady is taken through. Quite possible for expert crime fella to lock doors from outside, I think."

I told him, "No," for this was one point I had got clearly. "These are bolts, not ordinary locks with a key. One on each side of the door and operated by turning a little handle, like the ones usually installed on bathroom doors. The bolts are inside the door itself, not on the outside."

"That's right," Tarrant confirmed. "Both bolts were shot and my conclusion is that neither could be operated from the wrong side of the door, especially since for some weird Hollywood reason the door is doubly weather-stripped, leaving no possible apertures around its circumference. Apart from my own conviction, the bolts were examined by the All-American men and they—"

The cabinet behind us said sharply, "Trans-Radio Flash. The Glammeris kidnapping. In some way not yet discovered Gloria Glammeris was taken from her guarded study and from her house at 6:42 this afternoon, Pacific Time. The house is still under guard, the study sealed for the Prosecutor's visit in the morning. Alarms have been sent to the police of five states. Air fields and docks are under observation at Los Angeles. The Mexican border patrol has been increased, the Canadian border is being closely watched. By morning the police of the whole country will be on the lookout for the kidnappers. Federal agents are cooperating. This bulletin by Trans-Radio News Service, through Station WJEX."

"Hah," observed Brihido. "Method of leaving house mebbe important, too. We go back to study. Door C could be taken off hinges mebbe and bolts not disturbed. Which side of this door, by the way, sit hinges? Study side or bedroom side? You know?"

"I don't know about the hinges, but it doesn't make any difference, doctor. I think it most unlikely that a door with even one bolt shot could be removed that way and fitted back into its place again, in anything but a most dilapidated old house, which Miss Glammeris's home certainly is not. . . . No, if you have selected door C as the means of her exit from the study, you are squarely up against the problem of relocking that door after she had been taken through. It cannot be done from the bedroom side after the door has been closed, and no one could have reentered the study past the guard at door A, to relock it from the inside. . . . So you give it up, doctor?"

Well, that seemed about the end of it to me. With both those doors disposed of, the only two possible exits from the room, the thing was simply insoluble. I was astonished to hear Brihido reply, "Oh, no; certainly not give up. In fact, see quite clearly now how was done. Please repeat all details of movements by guard and secretary. Only one way possible, I think."

After Tarrant had complied with the request, the valet continued, "Must be what you call publicity gag, like I read in paper when kidnap letter first published. At four-twenty-five lady sit in study with secretary. Door C to bedroom then unlocked both sides. At four-thirty she step through into bedroom and speak a few words with secretary still standing in study, so guard at door A can hear. Secretary is accomplice; then secretary close and bolt door C *on study side* and come out through door A. Lady bolt door C *on bedroom side* because that where she sit until discovery of empty study.

"At six-forty-two secretary come back and make believe finding lady gone from study. She yell, guard run in and guard himself *unlock door C from study side.* Secretary grin at this, mebbe, for he doing some of her work. Then they run into corridor, guard locks door A, puts key into pocket and hastens downstairs. So secretary runs to bedroom and tells lady now all right to go back in study; lady unlocks door, goes in study; secretary bolts door C *on bedroom side* and makes much useless search of that room. Meantime lady lies down under couch in study, in case guard should open door A and take another quick glance from corridor doorway. But he not even do that. Now study all nicely sealed up *with lady inside* and she stay there until Prosecutor come tomorrow morning. By then too late to stop headlines in papers all over country. Good trick, mebbe."

"Excellent, doctor!" said Tarrant. "Of course there's *another* theory—

No, I think you have the proper answer. So that's that; we can forget it now and listen to the music again."

Brihido smiled impishly. "For scientific fella necessary some proof before hypothesis become fact. Not any way in which we can check up on my theory?"

"Not without breaking the seals on the study, I'm afraid. And I could never persuade them to do that." Tarrant remained a moment in thought. "Well, perhaps there is a chance of proof. If your theory is correct, the secretary is an accomplice; therefore, she was pretending hysteria. It will be a little expensive but perhaps I can get some proof for you. You deserve it, after solving the problem."

He walked over to the telephone and slid the dial through its single revolution to call the operator. "Long distance, please. . . . Long distance: A person-to-person call. I want to speak either with Miss Jane Smith, a patient in the Los Angeles Hospital, or to the doctor who is attending her. Yes, I'll hold on. Thank you."

Someone must have left a key up in the central office, for Tarrant apparently could hear the call being put through. "St. Louis," he said to us; "ah, there's Kansas City. The hospital doctor won't have been fooled by a fake hysteria. Phoenix is on. . . . Now we're through to Los Angeles; I can hear them ringing the hospital."

He waited for almost a minute, then cut in with, "Hello. Hello, Los Angeles operator. . . . All right, get me the doctor who took care of her. It's important, operator, I must speak with him. This is a New York police call." I have noticed that Tarrant, for a truthful man, has a singular lack of hesitation about lying when he thinks it's necessary. This lie got him the man he wanted.

We heard him say. "Yes. . . . Yes. . . . When? . . . Well, about when? . . . Thanks. Yes, thanks, doctor. Good-bye."

He placed the receiver back in its cradle and turned around to us. "She faked the hysteria without any doubt. No objective symptoms at all when she got to the hospital. But she wasn't discharged; she was booked for the night. Sometime during the past hour she left without notifying anybody. Sneaked out."

Brihido was beaming with pleasure. "My theory correct—"

"Yes," Tarrant interrupted him seriously, "but there is that other possibility. How much of a chance do I dare take? Suppose the second theory *is* the real one! Suppose . . ."

Tarrant's tone, which had risen from sobriety to tenseness, convinced me that the affair had suddenly become vital. He was dialing the telephone now with quick, nervous tension in his fingers.

"Centre Street? Peake, Inspector Peake, I must speak with him immediately. Hurry!"

Tarrant tapped his foot rapidly against the floor beneath the telephone stand. Then, "Peake? This is Tarrant. Do you know the Glammeris kidnap details? . . . Good, good. Peake, the girl is in that sealed study and is probably dying, if not dead! You must get in touch with Los Angeles at once! Make them break in—tell them to take a doctor along with them! . . . What? Oh, blast it, man, of course I know how it was done! I'll tell you later. I can't get action out there but you can. You've *got* to persuade them. . . . Now, listen, Peake, listen to me! You remember that penthouse job? I warned you and you wouldn't believe me; you let a policeman be murdered, didn't you? *This girl is dying right in her own study while you fuss about proprieties!* By God, Peake, I'll have your name and address on the front page of every newspaper in New York City if you let her die while you delay! I mean it. Good-bye."

Tarrant strode over to the cellarette and splashed whiskey into a highball glass. "The hell with their stuffy, official courtesies," he muttered.

"But what the devil?" I demanded. "Why should she be dying? That's no kind of publicity to—"

"This doesn't look like publicity," was the reply. "Miss Glammeris went through door C both ways, just as Brihido said; he was right about her *movements*. But she didn't go by herself; she was dragged out and dragged back in again by the secretary. At four-thirty Miss Glammeris had already been assaulted and was on the bedroom side of door C. What the guard heard didn't amount to anything; a low voice and a higher one mumbling unintelligible words—it's nothing. Jane Smith did that; you don't have to be even a good mimic to get away with it, under the circumstances. If she shot Miss Glammeris or stabbed her, the girl is dead. But I doubt it. A shot would be heard, a knife would have to be disposed of. There are a good many drugs whose action would be as fatal if the victim gets no attention. And there was a bathroom in which to wash out the glass and dispose of any telltale drug remaining. Some of them work slowly, though; there may be a chance if they break in soon enough.

"Motive? How do I know what the motive was? Maybe the secretary has been stealing her employer's money and has to cover up; maybe Glammeris took a lover away from Jane Smith. There are dozens of motives, but motive doesn't enter the problem, because we have no information on it at all. The problem was a purely mechanical one—the question of what happened in and about the study."

"Wait, pliss," cried Brihido. "What you say not possible, pliss. If secretary drag lady into bedroom at four-thirty and return to study for exit through door A, then lady either dead or unconscious, because she raise no alarm. In this case *who lock door C from bedroom side?* Secretary could bolt door C only from study side."

"True," Tarrant admitted. "But where is the contradiction? When Jane

Smith came out of the study at four-thirty this afternoon, she had just
bolted door C on the study side and of course it was then still unbolted on
the bedroom side. I see nothing, however, that would have hindered her
from visiting the bedroom at some time between four-thirty and six-forty-
two and *at this later time* having bolted the door from the bedroom side,
perhaps over the unconscious body of her employer. She would have had to
do that, as indeed we know it *was* done—in order to prevent the guard,
when he finally entered the study, from going through at once to the
bedroom, as he tried to do when the alarm was first given. Miss Glammeris's body had to be quickly accessible for return to the study and may even
have been in full view. But Jane Smith knew that the guard would have to
inform the other detectives before anything else, and those few minutes
were all she needed. The point is that in any event Miss Glammeris *must*
now be in the study; given the present factors, *there is no other possibility in
logic.* But there are two alternatives concerning her presence there; either it
is a stunt with Jane Smith as accomplice or it is a crime with Jane Smith as
criminal . . . and Jane Smith has run away."

Brihido had screwed up his face and was saying, "Yiss. Mebbe," when
the telephone gave a series of quite angry buzzes. My friend lifted it from
its cradle, said, "Tarrant speaking," and immediately a whole series of
staccato barks issued from the instrument.

For a time Tarrant said nothing. He emitted an incredulous whistle and a
moment later made clucking noises indicative of astonishment or chagrin,
or both. Finally he spoke. "Well. . . . Well, I am sorry, old man. I offer
my most sincere apologies. . . . Yes. If there is anything I can do beyond
apologies, of course I'm at your service." He put down the receiver.

"It seems," he told us quietly, "that Peake got through directly to the
house. At his insistence the police have unsealed the doors and entered the
study." Tarrant paused. "There is no body in the study. There is no one
there at all. The study is *empty.*"

"Eh?" I sounded blank, even to myself. After the way it had all been
figured out so neatly, this pretty well stopped me.

'Hido sat back on his haunches and gave a very fair imitation of Tarrant's
previous whistle. Then he started hissing. "But not possible. *Musst* be lady
in study! No? Iss kidnap, then. But how thiss done?"

Tarrant motioned him to silence. He was murmuring, "We have overlooked something. Probably something so obvious that we can't see it." He
took a pull at his highball and stared down at the rug between his feet.
"And why not?" he asked finally. "Why not the very thing we started
with?"

"How you mean?" 'Hido could hold himself in no longer.

"How about our original notion?" Tarrant reminded him. "The publicity stunt, the faked kidnapping?"

'Hido insisted, "No, not possible. Lady can get out of study, like I invent long ago. But not out of house. House been searched; lady not there, nor in study, either. Must be police mistake; you already say only one possibility in logic."

"With the factors given," Tarrant answered. "But with the factors changed, another possibility arises. Since this possibility has actually occurred, we must deduce a change in our assumed factors."

Tarrant paused, deep in thought.

Then, "There's one catch." My friend smiled wryly. He pulled a fat directory from his shelves and flipped the pages over to the G's. "Yes, here it is. 'Secretary: Jane Smith, 3030 St. Clair Street, Rockford, Ill., or c/o Kolossal Studios, Hollywood, Calif.' Hm. Well," he said suddenly, "we'll have one more try. It will be about the longest shot I've ever played—but here goes."

My first speech for some time: "Here goes what?"

"Some more nice person-to-person business for American Tel. and Tel. If Jane Smith *should* be in Rockford, Illinois—I'd better hurry."

And, indeed, five minutes later, when the operator called him back, he could hardly conceal the surprise in his voice.

"This is Miss Smith? . . . Trevis Tarrant speaking —a friend of Miss Glammeris's. You *are* Miss Smith and you have been in Rockford for a week? . . . Oh, you thought this was from Miss Glammeris because it was a long distance call to you personally? Well, young lady, you are going to receive a lot more long distance calls any minute now but they won't be from friends. If you want my advice, don't answer any more calls at all; just leave word that you are *not* there until Miss Glammeris reaches you. . . ."

Brihido gasped and I cried, "What the hell!", as he turned away from the phone.

Tarrant regarded us quizzically. He said, "Surely you see it now? If Jane Smith is in Rockford tonight, she wasn't in Hollywood this afternoon. Why not a vacation during Gloria's 'retirement' and 'kidnapping'? In other words, there never *was* a secretary—in Hollywood this afternoon, I mean. Miss Glammeris played both roles—that of herself earlier in the day and of her secretary from the four-thirty conference on. No trick at all for an actress of her ability. Remember, we were told that the guard, Operative Huggins, never saw the two women together. The part of Gloria in the afternoon was no more than an offstage voice.

"It's simple enough, once you nail down the vital fact. Gloria's movements were those we have been attributing to Jane Smith, because at that time she *was playing* Jane Smith. That's how she got out of the study. Then she faked the secretarial hysteria—*to get out of the house.* She was taken to a hospital; and skipped at the first opportunity. Probably right now she's registered at the Los Angeles Biltmore as Mrs. F. N. Trelawney or something, all done up in a pair of dark glasses and prepared to wait patiently a few days for a phony exchange of half a million dollars' ransom and the best publicity in film history."

"But in that case," I managed, "Peake—"

"—probably won't speak to me for a week. I hope. As to Gloria versus the public, I'm for Gloria. . . . I trust," he added pleasantly, "that she thanks me for it some day. She really *is* lovely, you know."

THE BLOOMSBURY WONDER

by *THOMAS BURKE*

I

As that September morning came to birth in trembling silver and took life in the hue of dusty gold, I swore.

I had risen somewhat early and was standing at the bathroom window of my Bloomsbury flat shaving. I first said something like "Ooch!" and then I said something more intense. The cause of these ejaculations was that I had given myself the peculiarly nasty kind of cut that you can only get from a safety razor, and the cause of the cut was a sudden movement of the right elbow, and the cause of that was something I had seen from my window.

Through that gracious gold, which seemed almost like a living presence blessing the continent of London, moved a man I knew. But a man I knew transformed into a man I did not know. He was not hurrying, which was his usual gait. He wasn't even walking. He was sailing. I never saw such a schoolgirl step in a man. I never saw such rapture in the lift of a head.

He was not tall, but he was so thin, and his clothes fitted so tightly, that he gave an illusion of height. He wore a black double-breasted overcoat, buttoned at the neck, black trousers and nondescript hat. He held his arms behind him, the right hand clasping the elbow of the left arm. His slender trunk was upright, and his head thrown back and lifted.

In the dusty sunlight he made a silhouette. I saw him in the flat only. And I realised then that I always had seen him in the flat; never all round him. The figure he cut in that sunlight made me want to see round him, though what I should find I did not know and could not guess. And to this day I don't know and can't guess.

II

In conventional society, I suppose, he would have been labelled a queer creature, this Stephen Trink; but the inner quarters of London hold so many queer creatures, and I have so wide an acquaintance among them, that Trink

was just one of my crowd. I forget how I came to know him, but for about
two years we had been seeing each other once or twice a week; sometimes
oftener. I liked him almost at once, and the liking grew. Although I was
always aware in his company of a slight unease, I took every opportunity
of meeting him. He charmed me. The charm was not the open, easy charm
of one's intimate friend, for we never reached that full contact. It was more
spell than charm; the attraction of opposites, perhaps. His only marked
characteristic was a deep melancholy, and now that I try to recall him I find
that that is the one clear thing that I can recall. He was one of those men
whom nobody ever really knows.

Stephen Trink would have been passed over in any company, and at my
place always was. Only when I directed my friends' attention to him, did
they recollect having met him and examine their recollection; and then they
were baffled. I once asked five friends in turn what they thought of him,
and I was given pictures of five totally different men, none of whom I had
myself seen in Trink. Each of them, I noted, had to hesitate on my question,
and stroke his hair, and say: " 'M . . . Trink. We-el, he's just an ordinary
sort of chap—I mean—he's a—sort of—" Then, although he had been
with us ten minutes ago, they would go on to draw a picture as from hazy
memory. They seemed to be describing a man whom they weren't sure they
had seen. Their very detail was the fumbling detail of men who are uncertain what they did see, and try to assure themselves by elaboration that they
did at any rate see *something*. It was as though he had stood before the
camera for his photograph, and the developed plate had come out blank.

In appearance, as I say, he was insignificant, and, with his lean, questing
face and frail body, would have passed anywhere as an insipid clerk. He
stressed his insipidity by certain physical habits. He had a trick of standing
in little-girl attitudes—hands behind back, one foot crooked round the
other—and of demurely dropping his eyes if you looked suddenly at him;
and, when speaking to you, looking up at you as though you were his
headmaster. He had, too, a smile that, though it sounds odd when used of a
man, I can only describe as winsome. The mouth was sharp-cut, rather than
firm, and drooped at the corners. The lower jaw was drawn back. His hair
was honey-coloured and plastered down. His voice was thin, touched with
the east wind; and it was strange to hear him saying the warm, generous
things he did say about people in the sleety tone that goes with spite. To
everything he said that tone seemed to add the words: *Isn't it disgusting?* His
eyes, behind spectacles, were mild and pale blue. Only when the spectacles
were removed did one perceive character; then, one could see that the eyes
held curious experience and pain.

Wherever he might be, he never seemed to be wholly *there*. He had an
air of seeming to be listening to some noise outside the room. He would sit
about in attitudes that, since Rodin's Penseur, we have come to accept as

attitudes of thought; but if you looked at his face you'd say it was empty. He was not thinking; he was brooding. Though indoors he was languid and lounge-y, and his movements were the movements of the sleepwalker, in the street his walk was agitated and precipitous. He seemed to be flying from pursuit. One other notable point about him was that, quiet, insignificant, withdrawn as he was, he could be a most disturbing presence. Even when relaxed in an armchair he somehow sent spears and waves of discomfort through the air, sucking and drying the spirit of the room and giving me that edge of unease.

What his trouble was—if his melancholy arose from a trouble —he never told me. Often, when I urged him, flippantly, to Cheer Up, he spoke of This Awful Burden, but I dismissed it as the usual expression of that intellectual weariness of living which we call "modern."

He had private means by which he could have lived in something more than comfort, but he seemed contented with three rooms in the forlorn quarter where Bloomsbury meets Marylebone—well-furnished rooms that one entered with surprise from the dinge of Fitzroy Square. He was a member of two of the more serious clubs, but used them scarcely twice a year. His time he employed in the Bloomsbury and Marylebone fashion— as an aimless intellectual. He occupied himself writing metallic studies for all sorts of hole-and-corner Reviews; and all the time he was doing it he affected to despise himself for doing it and to despise the breed with whom he mixed. He attended all their clique and coterie gatherings—teas, dinners, Bloomsbury salons, private views—and took part in all the frugal follies of the Cheyne Walk Bohemia. You saw him, as they say, everywhere. Yet, at all these affairs, though he looked younger than most of the crowd, he had always the attitude of the amused grownup overlooking the antics of the nursery. I can't think how even their pallid wits didn't perceive that embodied sneer at them and their doings.

Although not physically strong he had immense vitality, which he exhibited in long night walks through London. This was a habit which I shared with him and which, begun in childhood, gave me my peculiar and comprehensive knowledge of the hinterland of this continent of London. I believe that it was on one of these night wanderings that we first really met, though there must have been a perfunctory introduction in somebody's flat. Knowing that I was an early riser, he would sometimes, at the end of one of these rambles, knock me up at half-past seven for breakfast, and then go to sleep on my settee. Glad as I always was to have his company, he was a difficult guest. He had a disorderly mind and Japanese ideas of time. A "look-in" often meant that he would stay for four or five hours, and an arrangement to dine and spend the evening often meant that he would look-in for ten minutes and then abruptly disappear without a word about dinner. He had a habit of using in casual conversation what is called bad language—a certain sign of uneasy minds—and his talk was constantly agitated with purposeless use of "blasted" and "bloody" and "bastard." In all other matters he was gentle and thoughtful. He would not, as they say, do anything for anybody, but for a few people his time and labour and influence were available in full measure. He was so kind of spirit, so generous of affection, that sometimes I thought that his melancholy arose from a yearning to love and be loved. At other times this would be contradicted by his self-sufficiency.

And that, I think, is all I can tell you about him. He eludes me on paper as he eluded me in life. So with this light sketch I pass on to the real matter of this story—to his friends, the Roakes; for it was by his friendship with them that I was brought into contact with horror.

Another of our points in common was a wide range of friendships. Most men find their acquaintance among their own "sort" or their own "set," and never adventure beyond people of like education, like tastes, and like social circumstances. I have never been able to do that, nor Trink. We made our friends wherever we found them, and we found them in queer places. An assembly of all our friends at one meeting in our rooms would have surprised (and dismayed) those of them who knew us only as writers in such-and-such circumstances. I had, of course, a number of close friends among fellow-authors and among musicians, but my most intimate friend at that time, who knew more about me than any other creature, was an old disciple of Madame Blavatsky, who devoted his spare time to original research on the lost Atlantis. Trink's was a shopkeeper; a man who kept what is called a "general" shop at the northern end of Great Talleyrand Street.

Despite my own assorted friendships, I could never quite understand *this* friendship, for the man had no oddities, no character, no corner where he even grazed the amused observation of Trink. It may have been, of course —and this fact explains many ill-assorted friendships—that they liked the same kind of funny story, or walked at the same pace in the streets. I don't know. Friendships *are* bound by slender things like that. Or it may have been—and I think this is what it was—that they were bound by love. I am sure there was more in it than mere liking of each other's talk and company, for Trink, being what he was, could have found no pleasure in the pale copy-book talk of Horace Roake. I thought I could perceive on either side an essence or aura of devotion, and if the devotion were at all stronger on one side, it was on the side of the cultivated man of brains rather than the tired, brainless shopkeeper. I spent many evenings in their company, either at Trink's flat or in the shop parlour, and I noted their content in long silences, when they merely sat together and smoked, and their quick, voiceless greeting when they met. Trink seemed to be happier in Roake's shabby room than anywhere. *Why* was one of his mysteries.

Although the public spoke of Roake's shop as a General Shop, he did not himself recognise that style. There are traditions in these matters. In trade-lists there are no drapers, or milkmen, or greengrocers, or ironmongers. The man we style milkman styles himself dairyman, though he may never have seen a dairy. The greengrocer is a pea and potato salesman. The bookmaker is a commission agent. Drapers and ironmongers are haberdashers and deal-ers in hardware. The butcher is a purveyor of meat, the publican a licensed victualler. So Mr. Roake, who kept no pastas or Chianti, or bolognas or garlic, styled himself an Italian warehouseman. His shop stood, as I say, at the northern end of Great Talleyrand Street, between Woburn Place and Gray's Inn Road.

This is a district of long, meaningless streets and disinherited houses. Once, these houses were the homes of the prosperous; today they have only faded memories. They lie, these streets and houses, in an uneasy coma, oppressed by a miasma of the secondhand and the outmoded—secondhand shops, secondhand goods, secondhand lodgings, filled with secondhand fur-niture, and used by secondhand people breathing secondhand denatured air.

When Roake set up his shop here, he blunderingly chose the apt setting for himself and his family. They belonged there. They were typical of a thousand decent, hardworking, but stagnant families of our cities. For four generations the family had not moved its social level. A faint desire to rise they must have had, but rising means adventure, and they feared adventure. On the wife's side and the husband's side the strain was the same—luke-warm and lackadaisical. There they had stood, these many years, like root-less twigs in the waste patch between the stones and the pastures; and there, since the only alternative was risk and struggle, they were content to stand. Roake himself, if I saw him truly, had the instincts of the aristocrat hidden in the habits of the peasant. One of life's misfits. He had the fine feature and clean eye of that type, but though he looked like what is called a gen-tleman, nobody would have mistaken him for one. His refinement of fea-ture and manner came really, not from the breeding of pure strains, but from undernourishment in childhood. He had a mind of wide, if aimless, interests, and a certain rough culture acquired by miscellaneous reading.

His wife was largely of his sort, but without the culture. Her life had been a life of pain and trial, and it had taught her nothing. Her large, soft face was expressionless. The thousand experiences of life had left not even a fingerprint there, and she still received the disappointments and blows of fortune with indignation and querulous collapse.

There were two boys and a girl. The girl had something of her father's physical refinement. Her head and face were beautiful; so beautiful that people turned to glance at her as she passed in the streets. Her manners and voice were—well, dreadful. She would often respond to those admiring glances by putting out her tongue. She was wholly unconscious of her beauty, not because she was less vain than her sex, but because her beauty was not to her own taste. She admired and envied girls of florid complexion and large blue eyes and masses of hair and dimpled mouths—chocolate-box beauties —and her own beauty was a glorious gift thrown to the dogs. To see that grave dark head and those deep-pool Madonna eyes set against those sprawling manners and graceless talk gave one a shudder.

Of the two boys, one might say that they saw life as nothing but a programme of getting up, going to work, working, eating, going to bed. Only it wouldn't be true. They saw life no more than a three-months' old baby sees life. They were clods.

These were the people Trink had chosen as friends, and by all of them he was, not adored, for they were incapable of that, but liked to the fullest extent of their liking. He was their honoured guest, and on his side he gave them affection and respect. The two boys worked together in a boot and shoe factory, and the shop was run by Mr. and Mrs. Roake and the girl, Olive. Olive knew enough about the business to do her bit without any mental strain, and she had a flow of smiles and empty chatter that in such a shop was useful.

These General Shops—often spoken of as "little gold mines"—are usually set, like this one, in side streets. It is by their isolated setting that they flourish. The main streets are not their territory, and such a shop in a main street would certainly fail, for these streets hold branches of the multiple stores as well as shops devoted singly to this or that household necessity. Your successful General Shop, then, chooses a situation as far from competition as possible, but in the centre of a thicket of houses. In that situation it wins its prosperity from the housewife's slips of memory. She arrives home from her High Street shopping, and finds that she has forgotten salt or custard powder or bacon, and to save a mile walk she sends one of the children to the General Shop. It is for this that it exists; not for regular supply but as convenience in emergency. Unhampered by other shops and encircled by hundreds of forgetful households, the well-conducted General is certain of success, and many of these shops have a weekly turnover, made up of pennyworths of this and ounces of that, near two hundred pounds.

So the Roakes were doing well. Indeed, they were very comfortable and could have been more than comfortable; but they were so inept, and knew so little of the art of useful spending, that their profits showed little result in the home. If they could not be given the positive description of a happy family, at least they lived in that sluggish sympathy which characters only faintly aware of themselves give each other; and that was the feeling of the home—lymphatic and never *quite*. The wireless set worked, but it was never in perfect tone. The sitting-room fire would light, but only after it had been coaxed by those who knew its "ways." The hot water in the bathroom was never more than very warm. The flowers in the back garden were never completely and unmistakably blossoms. The shop door would shut, but only after three sharp pressures—the third a bad-tempered one. They bought expensive and warranted clocks, and the clocks took the note of the family, and were never "right." New and better pieces of furniture were frequently bought for the sitting room, but it never succeeded in looking furnished. If you saw the house, you could imagine the family; if you met the family, you could imagine the house.

Hardly a family, one would think, marked out for tragedy, or even for disaster; yet it was upon these lustreless, half-living people that a blind fury of annihilation rushed from nowhere and fell, whirling them from obscurity and fixing their names and habits in the scarlet immortality of the Talleyrand Street Shop Murder.

It was about the time when those gangs called "The Boys" were getting too cocksure of their invulnerability, and were extending their attentions from rival gangs and publicans to the general public, that the catastrophe came by which Stephen Trink lost his one close friend. Beginning with sub-Post Offices, the gangs passed to the little isolated shops. From all parts of London came reports of raids on these shops. The approach was almost a formula. "Give us a coupler quid. Come on," or "We want a fiver. Quick. Gonna 'and over or gonna 'ave yer place smashed up?" Given that alternative the little shopkeeper could do nothing but pay. He *might* have refused, and have had his place smashed up, and he might have been lucky enough to get the police along in time to catch two or three of the gang and get them six months or twelve months each. But that wouldn't have hurt *them,* since their brutal and perilous ways of life make them utterly fearless; and he would still be left with a smashed shop, pounds'-worth of damaged and unsaleable goods, the loss of three or four days' custom during repairs, and no hope of compensation from anybody. So, as a matter of common sense, he first paid up, and then reported the matter to the police; and serious citizens took up his grievance, and wrote to the papers and asked what we supported a police force for, etc., etc.

Then, sharply on top of a dozen of these shop raids, came the murder of the Roakes.

III

Marvellous and impenetrable is the potency of words. Hear the faint spirit-echo of *Shelley;* the cold Englishness of *Shakespeare;* the homespun strength of *John Bunyan.* And so it is with ideas; and so, particularly, with that idea for which sign and sound is MURDER.

Now, by long association, murder is linked in our minds with midnight, or at least, with dark; and these two conceptions of the cloaked side of nature combine in dreadfulness to make deeper dread. Again, poetic justice.

But harmonious combinations of dreadfulness, though they intensify each other, are dreadfulness only, and are therefore less potent to pluck at the heart than dreadfulness in discord with its setting; for there comes in the monstrous. Rape of womanhood is dreadful but understandable. Rape of childhood goes beyond the dreadful into depths that the mind recoils from sounding. Murder at midnight, though it will shock as it has shocked through centuries of civilisation, is a shock in its apt setting. But murder in sunlight is a thought that freezes and appals. It bares our souls to the satanic shudder of blood on primroses.

One can catch, then, the bitter savour of a certain moment of a sunny afternoon in Great Talleyrand Street. From the few horrified words of a neighbor I am able to reconstruct the whole scene.

IV

It was just after three o'clock of a September afternoon—a September of unusual heat; hotter than the summer had been. The heat made a blanket over the city, and in the side streets life was in arrest, bound in slumber and steam and dust. In Great Talleyrand Street carts and cars stood outside shops and houses as though they would never move again. Even the shops had half-closed their eyes. Errand boys and workless labourers lounged or lay near the shops, sharing jealously every yard of the shade afforded by the shopblinds. The faded Regency houses stewed and threw up a frowst. Through its dun length, from its beginning near Gray's Inn to its nebulous end somewhere in St. Pancras, the heat played in a fetid shimmer and shrouded either end in an illusion of infinity. The gritty odours of vegetable stalls, mixed with the acrid fumes of the cast-off-clothes shops, were drawn up in the sun's path to float in the air and fret the noses of the loungers. The ice-cream cart, zones with the Italian colours, made a cool centre for the idle young. A woman was offering chrysanthemums from a barrow piled high with that flower. Her barrow and her apron made a patch of living gold against the parched brown of the street.

Then, into this purring hour, came a figure and a voice. From the upper end of the street it came, crying one word; and the blunt syllables of that word went through the heat and dust, and struck the ears of those within hearing with the impact of cold iron. The street did not stir into life. It exploded.

Those nearest scrambled up, crying—not saying; such is the power of that word that it will always be answered with a cry—crying: "Where? Where?" "In there—there—three-ninety-two." And the man ran on to Tenterden Street, still crying, "Murder!" and those who had heard the word ran in a trail to number 392.

The shop, with its battling odours of bacon, cheese, paraffin, spice, biscuits, bread, pickles, was empty. The runners looked beyond it. A small door led from the shop to the back parlour. The upper half of the door was of glass, and this half was veiled by a soiled lace curtain. Its purpose was to screen the folk in the parlour—where they sat at intervals between trade rushes —from the eyes of customers, while those in the parlour could, by the greater light of the shop, see all comers. But since the curtain served a purely workaday office—the private sitting room was upstairs—it had been allowed to overserve its time, and frequent washings had left it with so many holes that its purpose was defeated. People in the shop could, by those holes, see straight and clearly into the parlour; could see the little desk with account books and bills, and could often see the cashbox and hear the rattle of accountancy. It was proved by experiment that a man on the threshold of the shop could, without peering, see what was going on in the shop parlour.

The leaders of the crowd looked hastily about the shop and behind the two small counters; then, through those holes, they had the first glimpse of what they had come to see.

The sun was at the back. It shone through the garden window, and made a blurred shaft of dancing motes across the worn carpet and across the bloody body of Horace Roake. He lay beside his desk. The back of his head was cleanly broken. By the door leading to the inner passage lay the body of Mrs. Roake. She lay with hands up, as though praying. Her head was flung violently back, disjointed. Of the two boys, who had been spending the last day of their holidays at home, the younger, Bert, lay in a corner by the window, almost in a sitting posture. His head hung horridly sideways, showing a dark suffusion under the left ear. The leaders looked and saw; then someone said, "The girl!" They pulled open the door leading to passage and kitchen. In the sun-flushed passage lay the twisted body of Olive Roake. Her head, too, was thrown back in contortion. One glance at the dark excoriations on her neck told them how she had met her death. Three glances told them of the dreadful group that must have made entrance here: one to kill with a knife, one with a blow, and one to strangle with the hands.

For some seconds those inside could not speak; but as the crowd from the street pushed into the shop, and those in the shop were pushed into the parlour, those inside turned to push them back; and one of them, finding voice, cried uselessly, as is the way in dark moments: "Why? Why all this —these nice people—just for a pound or two? It's—it's *unnecessary!*"

He was right, and this was felt more strongly when it was found that this thing had not been done for a pound or two. The desk was locked, and the cashbox and the two tills in the shop were intact. Clearly this was not haphazard killing for robbery. There was a grotesquerie about the scene that hinted at more than killing: an afterthought of the devilish. These people, who had led their ignoble but decent lives in ignoble back streets, were made still more ignoble in death. The battered head of Roake, the crumpled bulk of Mrs. Roake, the macabre mutilation of the gracious symmetry of youth and maidenhood, were more than death. Not only were they dead, but the peace that touches the most ugly and malign to dignity, the one moment of majesty that is granted at last to us all, was denied them. The temple of the Holy Ghost was riven and left in the derisive aspect of a dead cat in a gutter.

So they lay in the floating sunshine of that afternoon, and so the crowd stood and stared down at them until the police came. Who had done this thing? How did they do it in an open shop? How did they get away?

Then someone who knew the family cried, "Where's Artie?" And some went upstairs and some went into the little garden. But all that they found was an open bedroom window and signs of a flight. No Artie.

V

It was between three o'clock and half past of the day when I had given myself that nasty cut that Trink made one of his "drop-in" calls. I was accustomed to these calls. He would come in, potter about, turn over any new books or periodicals I had, make a few remarks about nothing, disturb the atmosphere generally, and then slide away. But this afternoon he didn't disturb the atmosphere. He seemed lighter and brighter than usual. Something of that morning mood that I had seen in him seemed to be still with him. Tired and pale he certainly was—the result of his night-walk, I guessed—but there was a serenity about him that was both new and pleasing. For almost the first time I felt fully at ease with him; no longer conscious of the something that I had never been able to name. In that quarter of an hour I seemed to be nearer to him and to know him better than I had ever known him. To put it into a crude colloquialism, he seemed *more human.* He stayed but a short time, not fidgeting, but sitting restfully on the settee in that complete ease that one knows after long physical exercise. I remarked on this. I told him that I had seen him from my window, bouncing through the square, and told him that the bouncing and his present mood proved that plenty of exercise was what he needed, and that he would probably find, as George Borrow found, that it was a potent agent for the conquest of accidie—or, I added, liver. He smiled; dismissed the diagnosis of his trouble, and soon afterwards went, or, rather, faded away, so that when I resumed work I was barely certain that he had been with me at all.

About an hour later I became aware that I was disturbed, and when, half-consciously and still at work, I located it as something coming from the street; a sound that came at first from below the afternoon din, then rose to its level and spilled over it. It was the cry of newspaper boys.

As my flat is three floors up (no lift) I did not send out for a paper, but I rang up a friend on the *Evening Mercury,* and asked what the big story was. He gave me the story so far as it had then come in.

After the first shock, my first thought was of what it would mean to Trink. Terrible as the fate of that family was, they meant little to me, and I could only feel for them the detached and fleeting pity that we feel at any reported disaster. For you will have noted, as a kink of human nature, that nobody ever does feel sympathy for a murdered man. All our interest—yes, and a perverse, half-guilty sympathy—is on the murderer. But for Trink, their friend, it would be a blow, and a keener blow since it came with such ghastly irony on top of his happy, swinging mood of that day. He had just, it seemed, found some respite from his customary gloom, only to be brutally flung back into it, and deeper. I thought at first of going round to him, and then I thought not. He would want no intruders.

Meantime, the papers were publishing rush extras, and as the news had withdrawn me from work, and I could not return to it, I went out and bought the three evening papers, and sat in a teashop reading them.

There was no doubt that the affair, following on the large publicity and discussion given to the shop-raids, had stirred the press and alarmed the public. I saw it on the faces of the home-going crowd and heard it reflected in the casual remarks of stranger to stranger in the teashop and around the buses. All that evening and night the word Murder beat and fluttered about the streets and alleys and suburban avenues, and wherever it brushed it left a smear of disquiet. Accustomed as London is to murder, and lightly, even flippantly as it takes all disturbances, the details of this one moved them, for clearly it was no ordinary murder of anger or revenge, or for the removal of inconvenient people for gain. How could these little people have offended? Who would want them out of the way? If it was the work of "The Boys," it might be anybody's turn next. If it wasn't the work of "The Boys," then, said the press, it must have been the work of wandering lunatics of gorilla's strength and ferocity. And if they were loose, nobody would be safe. Private houses and people in the streets would be wholly at the mercy of such fearless and furious creatures as these appeared to be. In the meantime they *were* loose; even now, perhaps, prowling about and contemplating another stroke; sitting by your side in train or bus, or marking your home or shop for their next visit. They were loose, and while they were loose they spread their dreadful essence as no artist or prophet can hope to spread *his.* Scores of mothers from the streets about Talleyrand Street, hearing the news and seizing on the press conjecture of wandering madmen, ran to schools in the district to meet their children. They were always aware of peril from the filth that hovers about playground gates; today they were made aware of a more material and annihilating peril.

Through all the thousand little streets of the near and far suburbs went the howl of the newsboy, and its virulent accents went tingling through the nerves of happy households. To people sitting late in their gardens, veiled from the world, came at twilight a sudden trembling and sweeping of the veil as the wandering Chorus stained the summer night with: *Shawking Murd' 'n Blooms-bree—' Pur!' London Fam'ly Mur-der—' purr'!* It broke into the bedrooms of wakeful children, and into the study of the scholar, and into the sick room and across quiet supper tables and wherever it fell it left a wound. The press, having given the wound, went on to probe and exacerbate it with the minutiae of horror; ending with the disturbing advice to householders to see to their bolts and fastenings that night. It was the "splash" story of the day, and each paper had a narrative from neighbours and from those who were near the shop at the time of the crime's discovery. At late evening the story was this.

Artie Roake had been quickly found and interviewed. He frankly explained his absence by the regrettable fact that he had run away. Some information he was able to give, but none that in any way helped the search for the murderers.

As that day was the last day of his holidays, he had, he said, been taking things easy, and after the midday dinner had gone upstairs to lie down. He left his brother in the garden. His father and sister were in the shop-parlour, and his mother was in the shop. From two o'clock to five o'clock was a slack time with them. Most of the business came before twelve or from five o'clock to closing time; the afternoon brought mere straggles of custom. He remembered lying down on his bed, with coat and waistcoat off, and remembered nothing more until he suddenly awoke, and found himself, he said, all of a sweat. His head and hands were quite wet. He jumped up from the bed and stood uncertainly for a few moments, thinking he was going to be ill. And well he might have been ill, seeing what foul force was then sweeping through the air of that little house. Out of the sunlight something from the neglected corners of hell had come creeping upon it, to charge its rooms with poison and to fire it with the black lightning of sudden death. At the moment he awoke this creeping corruption must then have been in the house, and in its presence not the thickest and most wooden organism could have slept; for by some old sense of forest forefathers we are made aware of such presences. We can perceive evil in our neighbourhood through every channel of perception; can even *see* it through the skin. The potency of its vapours, then, must have worked upon the skin and the senses of this lad, as the potency of the unseen reptile works upon the nerves of birds, and he awoke because an alien and threatening presence had called him to awake. It must have been that, and not a cry or a blow, that awoke

him, because he said that, during the few seconds when he stood half-awake
and sweating, he heard his mother's voice in a conversational murmur. It
was some seconds after *that* that the sweat froze on his face at the sound of
his father's voice in three plodding syllables—"Oh . . . my . . . God!"
—and then of a noise such as a coalman makes when he drops an empty
sack on the pavement. And then, almost simultaneously with the sack
sound, he heard a little squeak that ended in a gurgle; and overriding the
gurgle an "Oh!" of surprise from his brother, and soft, choking tones of
terror saying "No—no—no!" And then silence. And then he heard two
sharp clicks, as of opening and shutting a door; and then a moment's pause;
and then swift feet on the stairs. Had he had the courage to go down on his
father's first cry, his courage, one may guess, would have been wasted.
Hands would have been waiting for him, and he too would have ended on
a gurgle. But if he had had the courage to wait before he fled until the
figure or figures on the stairs had come high enough to give him one
glimpse, he might have had the clue to one of the men that would have
helped the police to the others. But he didn't wait. He bolted. He offered
the reporters no feeble excuse of going to raise the alarm or get help. He
said that those sounds and the sort of feeling in the house so affected him
with their hint of some unseen horror that he didn't think of anybody or
anything; only of getting out. Peering from his door, he said, just as the
sound of the feet came, he could see part of the staircase, and the sunlight
through the glazed door between shop-passage and garden threw a shadow,
or it might have been two shadows, half-way up the stairs. He could hear
heavy panting. In the moment of his looking, the shadow began to swell
and to move. He saw no more. In awkward phrases (so one of the reports
stated) he tried to say that he felt in that shadow something more than
assault ending in killing; he felt something horrible. From later information
I understood this. It *was* horrible; so horrible that even this vegetable soul
had responded to it. So, driven by he knew not what, and made, for the
first time in his life, to hurry, he turned from the house of dusty sunshine
and death to the open world of sky and shops and people. He bolted
through the upper window and over the backyard, and did not stop or call
for help until he was four streets away; at which point the cry of Murder
led to a pursuit and capture of him.

He made his confession sadly but without shame. He *knew,* he said, that
it was all over; that he could be of no use; that they were all dead. But
when they pressed him *how* he knew, he relapsed from that moment of
assertion into his customary cowlike thickness, and they could get no more
from him than a mechanical, "I dunno. I just knew."

He was detained by the police for further questioning, and it appeared
later that the questioning had been severe. But though there was at first an

edge of official and public suspicion of him, he was able to satisfy the police that he knew nothing, and was allowed to go home to an uncle's.

No weapons were found, no fingerprints, no useful footprints. Nor had any suspicious characters been seen hanging about; at least, none markedly suspicious to the district; for in these misty byways queer characters of a sort were a regular feature, and its houses were accustomed at all hours of day and night to receiving furtive strangers. Taking it, at first sight, as gang work, the police, it was said, were pursuing enquiries in that direction, which meant that for the next few days all known members of North London and West End gangs were rounded up and harried out of their wits by detentions, questionings, and shadowings. Already, at that early hour, reports had come in of the detention of unpleasant characters at points on the roads from London—Highgate, Ealing, Tooting. Communications had been made with all lunatic asylums in and near London, but none could report any absentees. All those on the police list who might have been concerned in it—the shop and till specialists—were being visited and questioned, and many, knowing that they would be visited anyway, were voluntarily coming in to give satisfactory accounts of themselves.

One bright "special" had put his mind to the case and lighted the darkness of the police with a possible culprit. He learned that Horace Roake was 55, and from his study of "our medical correspondent" he knew that 55 was the male climacteric, the age when men of formerly sober life — particularly quiet men of Roake's type—go off the rails into all sorts of jungles of unnamable adventure. Was it not worth asking, he said, whether Mr. Roake might not have been doing badly in business, and being at that age had . . . ? But a rival paper, in a later issue, took this torch and extinguished it by bank evidence that Roake was not doing badly in business, and by private police-surgeon information that neither Roake nor any other of the victims could possibly have died by suicide.

There, that evening, it was left. Next morning there were further details, but nothing pointing towards an arrest. From some of these details it was clear that the affair, if planned at all, had been most cunningly planned and timed, and swiftly done; for the people were seen alive a minute and a half before the cry of Murder had been raised. The more likely conjecture, though, was that it was the impulsive act of a wandering gang.

A woman volunteered that she had visited the shop just after three — about ten minutes after—and had been served by Mrs. Roake. Nobody else was in the shop. She left the shop and went a little way down the street to leave a message with a friend, and having left the message she repassed the Roakes' shop, and saw a man whom she did not closely notice standing at the counter rattling some coins and calling "Shop!" Her own home was twelve doors from the shop. She had scarcely opened and closed her door, was, indeed, still on the mat, setting down her shopping basket, when she heard the cry of Murder. In the immediate instant of silence following that cry she heard a church clock strike the quarter past three, which meant that only three minutes had passed from the time of her being served by Mrs. Roake, and one minute from the time of her seeing the man.

Another statement came from a man whose house backed on to the Roakes'. He was on a night shift at the docks, and went on at four o'clock. By daily use he knew exactly how to time himself to get there punctually from his home in Frostick Street; the time was fifty minutes; and he left home regularly at ten minutes past three. He was putting on his boots, he said, when, happening to glance through the window, he saw Mr. and Mrs. Roake in the shop parlour doing —well, as he put it, clearly without any intent of flippancy, carrying-on and canoodling. They must then have re-membered that they were open to curious eyes, for they immediately moved away from the window into the darker part of the room. At half-past four the evening paper came into the docks, and he saw that the family had been discovered dead five minutes after he had seen this little husband-and-wife moment.

One of the morning papers gave me a particular irritation. There was a solemn youth named Osbert Freyne (recently down from Cambridge) who used to come into my place at odd times, though I never made him wel-come. He used to sit and blither—talk one could not call it. I don't know why he continued to come, because I was always as rude to him as I can allow myself to be to anybody; but he did come and he did meet Trink, and he knew of Trink's acquaintance with the Roakes.

Well, one of the papers had an appendix to the Talleyrand "story"—an appendix by this solemn youth. Like most of his unbalanced kind, though he affected to despise modern writing, he wasn't above making money out of it when he could. The fellow had had a talk (or blither) with Trink, and had sold it to the paper as an interview with "an intimate friend of the unfortunate family." The result was that Trink had been visited and ques-tioned by the police on the family's history and habits and their friends, and other journalists had followed the police, and altogether the poor fellow's miserable day had been made additionally miserable.

I knew what he must be feeling about it, for I myself began to be moved by it, though quite unwarrantably. I had scarcely any interest in those people, yet whenever I thought about the affair I suffered a distinct chill, as though I personally were in some way touched by it; an entirely unreason-able chill which I could not shake off because common sense could not reach it.

Among the first to be examined were the witnesses who were in the street at the time the alarm was given. This again brought nothing useful; indeed, the result was only confusion on confusion. Seventeen people who had been near the spot were asked—Who was the man who rushed from the shop crying Murder? None of them knew him. They were then asked —What sort of man was he? Not one could make a clear answer. Eleven were so surprised that they didn't look at him. The other six—who, if they had looked at him, hadn't seen him but wouldn't admit it—gave six different descriptions. One saw a tall firmly built man with a red face. One saw a short man in a mackintosh. One saw a man in shirt and trousers only— obviously a confusion with the fleeing boy, Artie. One saw a fat man in a gray suit and a bowler hat. One saw a medium-sized man in cloth cap and the strapped corduroys of the navy. One saw a black man.

It seemed fairly certain, though, that the man who cried Murder could not have been the murderer, for two witnesses had seen members of the family alive within less than two minutes of the murders; and one man could not have been responsible for that wholesale slaughter in that space of time. The man who ran out must have been the man who had been seen by the woman witness standing there and shouting "Shop!" and as that was only one minute before the alarm, clearly *he* could not have been the murderer. He had not come forward, but then, there might be many innocent explanations of that. He might have been a man of nervous type who had received such a shock from what he had seen that he wished to avoid all association with the matter. Or he might have been a quiet, shy fellow who would hate to be mixed up in any sensational public affair. Having given the alarm, and having no useful information to offer beyond what the crowd saw for themselves, he might have considered that he had done his duty.

Generally, it was felt that it must have been the work of a gang—either a gang of thieves who were disturbed by the alarm before they could get at the cash, or, as suggested, a gang of drunken or drugged Negroes—and the gang must have entered from the back, or someone in the street would have noted them. It was the Negro suggestion that caught the public, chiefly because it seemed obvious and because it afforded a pious opportunity of shaking what they liked to think was an un-English crime on to those who were un-English. In talk around the streets the police were criticized for not concentrating on the Negro quarter. It was all very well to say that all the Negroes questioned had accounted for their movements. If the public were in the police's place, the public would know what to do, and so on.

The evening papers of that day brought more news, but none of it led anywhere. More suspicious characters on the outskirts of London had been detained, and two men—one a soldier at Sheerness, the other a tramp at Gerard's Cross—had given themselves up for the murder, only to be thrown out an hour later. People in the neighborhood now began to remember strange and significant happenings centering on the Roakes, which they hadn't remembered the day before. Queer visitors, letters by every post, sudden outgoings, late home-comings—all the scores of commonplace family happenings which, when isolated and focussed and limelit by tragedy and publicity, assume an air of the sinister and portentous. If Mrs. Roake had gone out in a new hat the day before they would have seen *that* as a possible clue.

Day by day the story mounted, and all fact that was thin was fortified by flagrant conjecture and by "sidelights" and comparison with similar crimes.

The police were following a clue at Bristol. A broken and stained bicycle pump had been found behind the mangle in the scullery and was being examined by the Home Office experts. Three of the leading yard men had left London for a destination unknown. The writer of an anonymous letter, received at Bow Street the day after the murders, was asked to communicate with any police station under a pledge of the fullest protection from all consequences. The Flying Squad had spent a whole day combing the road from Stoke Newington to Waltham Cross. Watch was being kept at Gravesend, Queenboro', Harwich, Grimsby, Hull, and Newcastle for two men, believed to be Norwegians. The police were anxious to get in touch with these men. Blandly and hopefully they invited these two men to visit the Yard. But despite these invitations, despite official rewards and newspaper rewards running into many hundreds of pounds, no outside help was secured, no "splits"—those ever-present helps in baffling crimes—came forward to give their pals away.

Then, at the end of the week, the Sunday papers had a plum. All these minor diversions were cancelled and the men called off. The new story was that the District Inspector, with a detachment of officers in an armoured police car, had left for Nottingham; and the story was given out with such a note of assurance that the thing appeared to be settled. And it was. Press and public waited eagerly on the result of this expedition. And they waited. After two days, as the result of waiting, the press was proudly silent on Nottingham. There was no report on the Nottingham expedition, but in its place a calm ignoring of it, as though it had never been. Nottingham was still on the map of England but it was out of the news. The public heard nothing. Not a word. Somewhere between London and Nottingham the Great Talleyrand Murder Mystery faded away; crept into the valley of undiscovered crimes, and died as mysteriously as the Roake family had died.

Thereafter public and press interest declined. From being a "splash" story it came to an ordinary column; then, from the main page it passed to the secondary news page; then it fell to half a column, and at the end of three weeks it had no space at all. The mystery that had been the subject of talk in offices, shops, trains, restaurants, and homes was forgotten. The best brains had been at work upon it and had failed; and although I, in common with other amateurs, had my theories about it, not one of them bore steady examination.

Today I know the solution, but I did not arrive at it by my own thought or by thought based on the experts' labours. We were all looking for madmen, or, if we dismissed madmen, then for some possible motive; and in looking for motives we were looking for the ordinary human motives that we could appreciate, and that appear again and again in murder. None of us thought of inventing a *new* motive; and that was where the solution lay. It was not the experts, but Stephen Trink, the dabbler, who showed me where to look; who took my eyes off a gang, and showed me how all this death and disaster and stretching of police wits could have been the work of two hands belonging to one man. He even pointed to the man.

VI

It was about a month after the affair had died down that I found among the morning mail on my tea tray a letter from Trink. It was dated from a hotel in the New Forest, and was an unusually long letter from one who scarcely ever addressed more than a postcard. And a queer letter. I read it in bed, and for some long time—an hour, I should think—I could not bring myself to get up and face the day. When at last I did, I found work impossible. All that day and night I was haunted by a spectre of forbidden knowledge, and I went perfunctorily about my occasions with a creeping of the flesh, as when one discovers a baby playing with a boiling kettle, or touches something furry in the dark. I knew then what it was that the boy Artie was trying to say.

But as the letter requires no editing or pointing, I give it *verbatim*.

"Dear T.B.,

"As we haven't met for some time I thought you might like a word from Stephen Trink. I've been down here for a week or so among the pines, seeking a little open-air massage for jangled nerves. You understand. It was a dreadful business, and I didn't want to see anybody, especially friends. I'm here doing nothing and seeing nothing—just breathing and drowsing.

"I suppose they've got no farther with it. Strange that the police, so astonishingly clever in making up really baffling and complicated cases, are so often beaten by a simple case. But you, as an artist, know how often a subtle piece of work which the public imagine to have been achieved by laborious and delicate process, was in fact done with perfect ease; and how often the simple piece of work has meant months of planning and revision. I don't know if you've thought about it at all, but it seems to me that they've been misled all along by the matter of time. They assumed that that little time, for such a business, must imply a gang. No sound reason why it should, though. As Samuel Nicks established an alibi by accomplishing the believed impossible—committing a crime at Gad's Hill, Kent, early one morning and being seen at York at seven o'clock the same evening, so this man deceived public opinion. The public of the seventeenth century held that it was not possible for a man to be in Kent in the morning and at York in the evening; all the horses in the kingdom couldn't carry him that distance in that time. Therefore, it hadn't been done, and Sam Nicks hadn't been in Kent that day. But it *was* done. And so here. Four murders by different means had been accomplished in a few seconds over a minute. Therefore, say the public (the experts, too), arguing from the general, it must have been the work of a gang. They were satisfied that no one man could do it, and if no one man could do it, then no one man *had* done it. But public opinion is always saying It Can't Be Done, and is always eating its words. You and I know that what any one man can *conceive,* some other man can *do.* I can imagine that this could be the work of one man, and I'm satisfied that it *was* the work of one man. It was done by the exception to the rule, and I'll show you how he could have done it, and how he got away. As to getting away, of course he got away by running away. If you say that a running man at such a moment would attract attention, well, we know that he did attract attention. He was clever enough to know that in successfully running away, it depends how you run. He covered his appearance and his running by drawing the whole street's attention to himself. He knew enough about things to know that his cry would blind everybody. They might be looking, but they wouldn't be seeing—as we know they weren't. All their senses would gather to reinforce the sense of hearing. As soon as he was round a corner he could slip his hat in his pocket and put on a cap. Nothing makes a sharper edge on the memory, or more effectually changes a man's appearance, than the hat. Then he could fling his coat over his arm, and go back and join the crowd.

"The affair had to the public, as we know, the air of being the work of a brilliant and invincible gang of schemers, who weren't playing by any means their first stroke: or else of a gang of crafty madmen. It was this that increased its horror. But it was no planned affair, and no gang affair. It was the work of a man momentarily careless of results. Being careless, he made no mistakes. As often happens, he, the inexpert, achieved casually what trained minds arrive at step by step.

"Now as to how. Really very simple. The core of the mystery is this: he was a man of unbelievable swiftness of act and motion. That's all.

"People don't seem to realise that taking human life is a very simple matter. They seem to think that it involves thought, planning, struggle, and mess. Nothing of the kind. It can be done as easily as the slaughter of a rabbit—more easily than the slaughter of a hen. A pressure with two fingers on a certain spot, or one sharp flick on a point at the back of the neck, and the business is done. It's part of the irony that plays about the creature, Man, that the neck, which supports his noblest part, should be his weakest part. You could do it without fuss in the club, on top of the bus, at

Lord's, or at the theatre, or in your own home or your victim's. You remember that morning when you were showing me your collection of Eastern weapons? Among them you had a case of Burmese poison darts. You took these out of their cylinder and showed them to me. I was leaning forward with my hands on your desk, and you were turning them about between finger and thumb. One minute movement of a minute muscle of your forefinger, and the point would have touched my hand, and Trink would have been out. Supposing you'd been not feeling very well—liverish—and my face or my voice had irritated you to the point of blind exasperation. A wonderful chance. Accidents often happen when things like that are being shown round. You may have seen the chance. If you did, only common good nature can have restrained you—supposing that you were irritated by me—as nothing but good nature restrains me from slapping a bald head in front of me at the theatre. One second would have done it, where shooting and throat-cutting not only take time but often cause disorder and fuss, besides involving extravagant use of means. One stroke of a finger directed by a firm wrist achieves the result without any stress or display. Many people are killed by four or five stabs of a knife, or by a piece of lead shot from an instrument that has to be loaded, and in which a lever has to be released, causing a loud bang. Unnecessary, and possibly wasted. Because no result can be achieved unless that piece of lead goes to a certain spot. And there's nothing that that piece of lead can do that four fingers can't do. You could have six friends in your room looking over your curios, and with merely the movement of the arm that an orchestral conductor makes in directing a three-four bar, you could, holding one of those Burmese darts, touch the hands of those friends. In five minutes you would have changed your warm gossipy room into a sepulchre. And yet people still think of murder as implying revolvers, knives, arsenic; and murderers still take five minutes over throttling from the front with both hands, when two seconds with the side of one hand will do it from the back. It is because of this that the unintelligent conceive murder as terrific, demanding time and energy; and still think that all murder must leave obvious traces of murder. Not at all. For every one murder that is known to be a murder, I am certain that six other people, who meet Accidental Death or are Found Drowned lose their lives by murder.

"This man, as I say, was swifter than most of us. He strolled into the shop. Calling 'Shop!' he went to the parlour door. There he met Roake. One movement. Mrs. Roake would turn. Another movement. The girl was coming through the door leading to the passage. Two steps and another movement. The boy comes through the garden to the shop. A fourth movement. One movement with a knife on the back of Roake's head. One pressure with the thumb to Mrs. Roake. One movement with both hands to the girl. One sharp touch on the boy's neck. And the foul thing was done in a matter of seconds. A movement overhead. The other boy stirring. He waits for him to come down. The boy doesn't come. He hears the noise of his flight. Then he makes his own by running full tilt into the faces of a score of people and crying his crime.

"That's all.

"Looking over this, I'm afraid it reads as though I'm writing with levity. But I'm not. I'm just analysing the situation and the probable attitude of the man. The whole thing is too frightful for me to treat it as seriously as I naturally feel about it; or, rather, in trying to treat it as a problem, I've forgotten that these poor people were my friends.

"Now as to why any man not a natural criminal or lunatic should have created this horror of destruction—this isn't going to be so easy. Here I'm on dangerous and delicate ground, and before I can present what looks to me like a reasonable explanation I must ask you to empty your mind of your reason and of all that knowledge of human nature on which people base their judgment of human motive and human behaviour. It should never be said that 'people don't do these things' or that such and such a thing is contrary to human nature; because people do anything and are always going contrary to our accepted notions of human nature. You must see it as clearly as one sees a new scientific idea—without reference to past knowledge or belief. It means trespassing into the forbidden, though I think you've peeped into more secret corners of the mind than the ordinary man. Or not peeped, perhaps. I think you've always known without peeping.

"It's difficult to put the presentation of it into assured and assuring phrasing. But I'll try.

"What I offer is this. This man had a motive for this wanton slaughter. But not a motive that would pass with common understanding. Neither hate nor lust nor the morbid vanity that sometimes leads stupid people to the committal of enormous crimes. Nothing of that sort. And he wasn't a madman without responsibility for his actions. He knew fully what he was doing and he did it deliberately. He committed more than a crime; he committed a sin. And meant to. Most men think that sin is the ultimate depth to which man can sink from his gods; but this man didn't sink. He rose, by sin, out of something fouler than sin. That something is the spirit of unexpressed, potential evil; something that corrodes not only the soul of man in whom it dwells, but the souls of men near him and the beautiful world about him. This evil doesn't always—indeed, seldom does—live in what we call wicked people. Almost always in the good. In comparison with such people the wicked are healthy. For these people, the germ-carriers, are more dangerous to the soul of the man than a million criminals or a thousand sinners. They can penetrate everywhere. We have no armour against their miasma. They do no evil, but they're little hives of evil. Just as some people can spread an infection without themselves taking the disease, so these good people can, without sinning, spread among the innocent the infection of sin. They lead stainless lives. Their talk is pure. Yet wherever they go they leave a grey trail that pollutes all that is noble and honest. They diffuse evil as some lonely places—themselves beautiful—diffuse evil. You must have met people of this sort—good people—and have been faintly conscious, after an hour of their company, of some emanation that makes you want to open spiritual windows. Happy for them, poor creatures, if they can discover and prove themselves before death for what they are. Some do. For those who don't, who only discover the foulness of their souls after death, God knows what awaits them.

"There's something in these people. Some awful essence of the world's beginnings. Some possession that can only be cast out in one way—a dreadful way. Where it began one cannot say. Perhaps strange sins, projected in the cold hearts of creatures centuries dead, projected but never given substance, take on a ghost-essence and wander through the hearts of men as cells of evil. And wander from heart to heart, poisoning as they go, until at last they come to life in a positive sin, and, having lived, can die. Nobody knows. But that's my explanation of these people—they're possessed. Possessed by some radioactive essence of evil, and before they can be saved they must sin. Just as poison is necessary to some physical natures and, denied it, they die, so sin may be necessary to these spiritual natures. They must express and release that clotted evil, and they can no more be cleansed of it before it's expressed than a man can be cleansed of a fever before it's reached its climacteric. Once expressed, it can be met and punished and pardoned; but abstract evil can't be met. Even God can't conquer Satan. There's nothing to conquer. Satan lives in these million wandering fragments of potential evil, and until that evil is crystallised in an act, all the powers of good are powerless.

"Let's suppose that this man was one of these, consciously possessed of this intangible essence of evil, conscious of it as a blight upon him and upon those about him; tortured by it like a man with a snake in his bosom, and for many years fighting its desire for expression and release until the fight became unbearable. There's only one way of escape for him—to sin and to sin deeply. Always he's haunted by the temptation to sin. His whole life's been clouded by visions and lures of unnamable sins, and by agonising combats to escape them. Always he fights this temptation, and so, continuing to shelter the evil, he gives it time to grow and to make his own emanations stronger. When his only real hope of conquering it lies in giving it life.

"And then at last he yields. There comes, one day, the eruptive, whirlwind moment of temptation, stronger than any he has known. All his powers of resistance go down in an avalanche. With a sigh of relief he yields. And suddenly, with the disappearance of resistance, and with the resolve to sin, he would find, I think, the serenity of resignation filling his whole being, and setting his pulse in tune with erring humanity. He would walk the streets with a lighter step than he has known since childhood. All his temptations would have been towards the foulest sin he could conceive, the lowest depth; and at last, driven by the importunate fiend, it's this sin that he commits. It may be that he was led farther than he meant to go. He may have intended to murder only one, but in committing the one murder, his fiend broke out in full power, and led him deeper and deeper into maniac slaughter. That's how it looks. But the thing was done, the sin committed, and in the satanic moment he frees himself forever from his fiend, not by binding it, but by releasing it. Like a long-embalmed body exposed to the air, it has one minute of life, and the next it crumbles into dust, and he is free.

"That's my theory. This man, without sin, would have died here and hereafter, for his soul didn't belong to him at all. Indeed, he was a man without a soul. Now he's a man with a stained soul which can be purified. He has seen himself as he is, on this earth, in time to prepare himself for his next stage. By that sin he can now, as a fulfilled and erring soul, work out his penance and his redemption.

"I guess I've said enough. You may dismiss this as a far-fetched and ludicrous fancy. But it isn't a fancy; it's a statement. You may say that no man could, under the most overwhelming temptation, do this appalling act of murdering, not an enemy, but a friend; or, having done it, could live under its burden. I can't argue with you as to what man can and can't do. I only see what is done. It's useless to tell me that this couldn't have happened. I can only say that it did.

"Whatever you may know as to the reactions of humanity to this or that situation, I know that, after years of torment, I'm now, for the first time, at peace.

"Yours,

"S.T."

DRESSING-UP

by W. R. BURNETT

When the store manager saw Blue and his girl, Birdy, coming in the front door, he turned to Al, one of the clerks, and said:

"Look at this, Al. The stockyards're moving downtown."

Al laughed, then he put on his best professional manner, clasped his hands in front of his stomach, inclined his head slightly, and walked up to Blue.

"What can I do for you, sir?"

Blue was short and stocky. His legs were thin, his waist small, but his shoulders were wide enough for a man six feet tall. His face was red and beefy, and his cheekbones were so prominent that they stuck out of his face. He looked up at Al.

"I'm buying an outfit, see," he said. "I'm gonna shed these rags and climb into something slick."

"Yes, sir," said Al. "How about one of our new spring models?"

"He wants a gray suit," said Birdy, adjusting her new fur neckpiece.

"Double-breasted," said Blue.

"Yes, sir," said Al.

"But first I want some silk underwear," said Blue. "I'm dressing from the hide out."

The store manager came over and smiled.

"Take good care of this young man, won't you, Mr. Johnson?"

"Yes, sir," said Al.

"Warm, isn't it?" the store manager said to Birdy.

"Yeah, ain't it?" said Birdy, taking off her neckpiece and dangling it over her arm like the women in the advertisements.

The store manager walked to the back of the shop and talked to the cashier:

"There's a boy that's got a big hunk of money all of a sudden," he said, "and he's gonna lose it the same way."

"Yeah?" said the cashier. "Well, I wish my rich uncle that I haven't got would die. Take a look at that neckpiece his girl's wearing. He didn't get that for five dollars."

Al spread out the silk underwear on the counter, and Blue looked through it. Birdy held up a lavender shirt.

"Here you are, Blue. Here's what you ought to get."

"Say . . . !" said Blue.

"Yes, sir," said Al; "we're selling lots of that. Just had an order for a dozen suits from Mr. Hibschmann out in Lake Forest."

"That's where the swells come from," said Birdy.

Blue looked at the lavender shirt and the lavender shorts and said:

"All right. I'll take a dozen."

Al glanced up from his order book, caught the manager's eye, and winked. The manager came up to Blue, put his hand on his shoulder and said:

"My dear sir, since you seem to know real stuff when you see it, I'll let you in on something. We got a new shipment of cravats that we have only just begun to unpack. But if you'd like to look at them, I'll send down to the stockroom for them."

"Sure," said Blue.

"Thanks awfully," said Birdy.

"It's our very best stock. Handmade cravats of the best material obtainable."

"We want the best, don't we, Blue?" said Birdy.

"Sure," said Blue.

While the manager sent for the cravats, Blue bought a dozen silk shirts, some collars, a solid gold collar pin, some onyx cuff links, a set of military brushes, and two dozen pairs of socks. Al bent over his order book and wrote in the items swiftly, computing the possible amount of this windfall. In a few minutes a stock boy brought up the neckties and stood with his mouth open while Blue selected a dozen of the most expensive ties. The manager noticed him.

"Just leave the rest of the stock, please," he said, then he turned his back to Blue and whispered, "Get out of here!"

The stock boy went back to the basement, and the manager turned back to Blue, smiling.

"Those cravats retail at four dollars apiece," he said, "but because you're giving us such a nice order, I'll let you have them for three fifty."

"O.K.," said Blue.

"Them sure are swell ties, Blue," said Birdy, putting her arm through his. "Won't we be lit up though?"

"Sure," said Blue.

When the accessories had been selected, Blue began to try on the suits Al brought him. Blue strode up and down in front of the big triple mirror, puffed out his chest, struck attitudes, and studied his profile, which he had never seen before except in one Bertillon picture. Al stayed at his elbow, offering suggestions, helping him with the set of a coat, telling him how wonderful he looked; and the manager stayed in the background occasionally making a remark to Birdy whom he addressed as "Madam."

Blue, after a long consultation with Birdy, selected two of the most expensive suits: a blue serge single-breasted and a gray double-breasted. Then he bought a gray felt hat at twelve dollars, a small sailor at eight, and a panama at eighteen.

"Well," said Blue, "I guess you guys got about as much of my jack as you're gonna get."

"How about shoes?" Al put in.

"By God, I forgot," said Blue. "Hey, Birdy, I forgot shoes. Ain't that good? Look at this suitcase!"

He held up his foot. He was wearing big tan brogans, and there was a hole in the sole which went clear through the sock to the skin.

"Put your foot down, Blue," said Birdy. "Where you think you're at?"

Blue bought a pair of tan oxfords, a pair of black oxfords, and a pair of white and tan sport shoes.

"Now we're done," said Blue. "I guess I ought to look pretty Boul' Mich' now."

Al totaled up the bill. Birdy and the manager had a long conversation about the weather; and Blue stood before the triple mirror studying his profile.

Al hesitated before he told Blue the amount of the bill. He called for the manager to O.K. it, then he said:

"Cash or charge, sir?"

Blue took out his billfold which was stuffed with big bills.

"Cash," he said, "how much?"

"Four hundred and sixty-five dollars," said Al.

Blue gave him five one-hundred-dollar bills.

"Now," said Blue, "I want you to get that gray suit fixed up right away so's I can put it on. I'm gonna dress from the hide out, and you guys can throw my old duds in the sewer."

"Yes, sir," said Al. "I'll get our tailor right away. We got a dressing room on the second floor."

The cashier rang up the sale and gave the change to the manager.

"Are you going away for the summer?" asked the manager as he handed Blue his change.

"Yeah," said Blue; "me and the girlfriend are gonna see New York. It'll be our first trip."

"That'll be nice," said the manager. "Are you in business for yourself?"

Blue glanced at Birdy, and she shook her head slightly.

"I'm in the oil business," said Blue. "I got some wells. I'm from Oklahoma."

"That's interesting," said the manager.

When they were leaving the café Blue took out his billfold and gave the doorman a five-dollar bill. The doorman's eyes popped but he managed to bow and smile.

"Yes, sir, yes, sir," he said. "Do you want a cab?"

"Yeah," said Blue, hanging on to Birdy who was drunker than he was.

"Yeah, you're damn right we want a cab," said Birdy. "Do we look like the kind of people that walk?"

"That's right," said Blue.

"Yes, sir," said the doorman, and he went out into the middle of the street and blew his whistle.

Before the taxi came a small sedan drew up at the curb across the street, and two men got out.

"There he is," said one of them, pointing at Blue.

"Hello, Guido," shouted Blue. "Look at me. Ain't I Boul' Mich'?"

Guido ran across the street, took Blue by the arm, shook him several times, and said:

"You got to sober up, keed! Get it! You got to sober up. Somebody spilled something, see? Me and Bud's taking it on the lam. Saint Louie won't look bad to us."

"Yellow," said Blue.

"Sure," said Guido; "but I got a stake and I'm gonna spend some of it before I get bumped. Somebody wised Mike's boys up. They're looking for Pascal right now."

"What the hell!" said Blue, laughing. "Look at me, Guido. Ain't I Boul' Mich'? I got silk underwear under this suit. Look at Birdy."

"Look at me," said Birdy; "ain't I Boul' Mich'?"

"Say," said Guido, "you better ditch that tommy and put in with us. We got room in the heap."

"Not me," said Blue. "I ain't scairt of Mike Bova. I'll bump him next."

"All right," said Guido; "you'll have a swell funeral."

"Guido," called the other man, "let that bum go."

"So long, Blue," said Guido.

"So long," said Blue.

"Bye-bye, Guido," said Birdy.

Guido crossed the street, got into the driver's seat, slammed the door, and the sedan moved off. The taxi was waiting, and the doorman helped Birdy and Blue into it.

"Good night, sir," said the doorman.

Birdy was lying on the lounge flat on her back with her hands under her head and an empty drinking glass sitting upright on her stomach. Blue, in his shirtsleeves, his collar wilted and his tie untied, was sitting at the table reading a crumpled newspaper. There were three-inch headlines.

BOVA'S LIEUTENANT KILLED

SHOT DOWN AS HE LEFT

HIS OFFICE BY GUNMEN

"You hear me!" said Blue. "Funniest thing ever pulled. There I was waiting in a room across the street trying to read a magazine, and Pascal was sitting with his head against the wall sleeping. 'Christ,' I says, 'there's Pete now.' He was coming out of his office. We wasn't looking for him for two hours yet. So I jist set there. Hell, I couldn't move, see, 'cause he come sudden, see, and I was figuring he wouldn't be out for two hours yet. 'Pascal,' I says, 'there's Pete now.' But Pascal he jist opens his eyes like a fish and don't say nothing. Pete he stops and looks right up at the window where I'm sitting, see, and I wonder does this guy know something. Hell, I couldn't move. I wasn't ready, see? Well, so Pascal he slips and falls over and hits his head. This makes me laugh but still I couldn't move my trigger finger. Pete he holds out his hand like he's looking for rain, then I let him have it. I don't know. It was funny. I jist let him have it without knowing it, see, and before, I couldn't pull that trigger when I wanted to. When the old Thompson starts to bark, Pascal gets up and yells, 'What you smoking for, you bum? It ain't time yet.' Then he looks out the window and there's Pete on the sidewalk dead as yesterday's newspaper and an old woman is pointing up at us. We ditch the gun and beat it down the back stairs. That's all there was to it. There wasn't nobody in the alley, see, so we jist walked along slow, and pretty soon we come to a drugstore and went in to get some cigs 'cause we smoked all ours waiting for that guy to come out."

"Pour me a little drink, honey," said Birdy.

Blue got up, took a big flask out of his hip pocket, and poured Birdy another drink. Then he sat down, took out his billfold and extracted a couple of railroad tickets.

"Look at them, old kid," he said. "When we ride, we ride. Twentieth Century to New York. That's us, kid; and won't we give 'em a treat over in Brooklyn! Say, them Easterners think we're still shooting Indians. Hell, Chi makes that place look like a Y. M. C. A. Yeah, I used to know Ruby Welch, and he was big stuff from Brooklyn; but what did he do when Guido started gunning for him? He got himself put in the can as a vag. Yeah, we ought to go over big in New York, kid. What they need over there is guts. We can give 'em that, kid. When somebody needs somebody for the No. 1 caper, Blue's the guy for the job. I was born with a rod in my cradle and I'm the best there is. Yeah, when the Big Boy wanted Pete bumped who did he call on first? Old Blue, yes, sir, old Blue."

Blue got up, turned on the gramophone, and started to dance with a chair.

"Hey," he said, "come on, let's dance, Birdy. We're big shots now, Birdy; let's dance. Look at me! If I had my coat on I'd look like the Prince of Wales. Boul' Mich', kid; that's us; Boul' Mich'. We'll knock their eyes out on Fifth Avenue, kid; yes, sir. Let's dance."

"I'm getting sick," said Birdy.

Blue went over and looked down at her. Her face was pale and drawn; there were blue circles under her eyes.

"Getting sick, Birdy?"

"Yeah. I can't stand it like I used to when I was with The Madam. Put me to bed, honey."

Blue picked Birdy up and carried her into the bedroom. Birdy began to hiccup.

"Gimme glass of water," she said.

"You don't want water," Blue said; "you want a nice big slug."

"No, gimme glass of water."

She lay down on the bed and, before Blue could bring her a glass of water, she was asleep. He stood looking down at her, then he went back into the living room, took a long pull at his flask, and picked up the crumpled newspaper. But he had read the account of the killing of Big Pete so many times that he knew it by heart. He sat staring at the paper, then he threw it on the floor and sat rolling a cigarette between his palms.

It had begun to get light. He heard a milk wagon passing the house. He got up and went over to the window. The houses were still dark, and far off down the street a string of lighted elevated cars ran along the horizon, but the sky was gray and in the east some of the clouds were turning yellow. It was quiet. Blue began to notice how quiet it was.

"Birdy," he called.

But he heard her snoring, and turned back to the table.

The telephone rang, but when he answered it there was nobody on the line.

"What's the idea?" he said.

He sat down at the table, took out his billfold and counted his money; then he took out the railroad tickets and read everything printed on them. Again he noticed how quiet it was. He got up, put away his billfold, and went into the bedroom. Birdy was sleeping with her mouth open, flat on her back, with her arms spread out. Blue lay down beside her and tried to sleep, but he turned from side to side, and finally gave it up.

"I don't feel like sleeping," he thought. "I'm all het up about going East on The Century. Here I am, old Blue, riding The Century dressed up like John Barrymore and with a swell frail. Yeah, that's me. Boul' Mich' Blue."

He got up, put on his coat, and began to pose in front of the living-room mirror.

"Boul' Mich' Blue," he said.

Finally he sat down at the table and laid out a game of solitaire; but he had so many bad breaks with the cards that he began to cheat and then lost interest in the game.

"I know," he said, "what I need is food."

He got up and went to the refrigerator, but there wasn't anything in it except a few pieces of cold meat.

"Hell!" he said, "I guess I'll have to go down to Charley's."

He put on his new soft hat, but hesitated. If they was looking for Pascal, they was looking for him, too. Right now there wasn't nobody on the streets and it was a good time to bump a guy.

"Hell!" he said, buttoning his coat, "I got a streak of luck. It'll hold. Boul' Mich' Blue'll be on The Century tomorrow. Yeah bo! I ain't scairt of no Mike Bova."

When Blue came out of the apartment house the sun was just coming up. The alleys and areaways were still dark, but there was a pale yellow radiance in the streets. There was no one about; no sign of life. Not even a parked car.

"Hell!" said Blue; "safe as a tank-town."

A window across the street was raised, and Blue ducked without meaning to; but a fat woman put her head out of the window and stared into the street.

There was nobody in Charley's, not even a waiter. Behind the counter the big nickel coffee urns were sending up steam. Blue took out a fifty-cent piece and flung it on the counter. Wing, the counterman, looked in from the kitchen.

"Come on, Wing," said Blue, "snap it up."

"Didn't know you, kid," said Wing. "Ain't you dressed up, though? Must've struck it."

"I sure did," said Blue. "Give me a combination and some of that muddy water."

"Muddy water, hell," said Wing. "I jist made that Java."

Blue leaned on the counter and stared at himself in the mirror, while Wing went back to make his sandwich.

"Hey, Wing," Blue shouted, "did you know I was going East on The Century?"

"Are, hunh?" Wing shouted back. "You're on the big time now, ain't you, kid?"

"That's the word," said Blue.

Blue turned to look out into the street. He saw a man passing, and stared at him. The man was small and had a slouch hat pulled down over his face. Blue thought he recognized him and slid his gun out of the holster under his armpit and put it in his coat pocket. The man passed without looking in.

"I got the jumps," said Blue. "It's that rotten gin."

Wing came in with the sandwich, drew Blue a cup of coffee, then leaned his elbows on the counter and watched Blue eat.

"Well," said Wing, "I see where they got Big Pete."

"Yeah," said Blue.

"I knew they was gonna," said Wing. "I got inside dope."

"Yeah?" said Blue.

"It was coming to him."

"Yeah."

Blue finished his sandwich, lighted a cigarette, and sipped his coffee. It was broad daylight now, and trucks had begun to pass the restaurant.

"Going East, are you, kid?" said Wing.

"Yeah," said Blue. "I got in on a big cut and I don't have to worry none for some time. I jist took my dame down and dressed her up this afternoon. Is she hot? Me, I got silk underwear on."

He unbuttoned his shirt and showed Wing his lavender underwear.

"You're sure a dressed-up boy," said Wing. "I bet you paid ten bucks for that hat you got on."

"Twelve," said Blue. "It was the best they had. I paid eighteen for a panama. You like this suit?"

"It's red hot," said Wing; then with a twinge of envy, "If I wasn't going straight maybe I could wear rags like that."

"How long's your parole got to run?"

"Plenty long. And I got the dicks down on me. They thought I'd stool for 'em in this ward. But that ain't my way."

"Why don't you make a break for Canada?"

"Yeah," said Wing, "and get jerked back to stir."

Blue finished his coffee, paid his check, and gave Wing a dollar bill. Wing turned the bill over and over.

"Say," he said, "give me another buck and I'll put you onto something hot at Arlington."

Blue laughed and tossed Wing a silver dollar.

"Never mind the tip," he said. "I know lots of better ways to lose my dough. Why don't you lay off the ponies, Wing? You can't beat that racket."

"I got the itch," said Wing.

Blue looked into the mirror and adjusted his hat to the proper angle.

"Well," he said, "I'm leaving you. I'll send you a postcard from the Big Burg, Wing."

But Blue noticed that Wing had begun to get nervous; his face was twitching.

"Blue," said Wing, "for Christ's sake watch your step. I'm telling you straight, kid. One of Mike's boys was in here buzzing me about you jist 'fore she began to get light. I'm telling you straight, kid. It ain't my fight and I wasn't gonna peep. But you're a right guy, Blue."

Blue rubbed his hand over his face, then he said:

"It was The Wolf. I seen him go past."

"Yeah," said Wing.

"Jesus!" said Blue, "which way'd I better go?"

"I'd put you upstairs . . ." Wing began.

"No use," said Blue. "The Wolf seen me."

Wing drew himself a cup of coffee and drank it at a gulp.

"If they knew I'd peeped they'd bump me sure," said Wing.

Blue stood staring at the counter, then he pulled his hat down over his eyes, and slipped his right hand into the pocket where the gun was.

"Well," he said, "the alley's no good. It's blind my way. The side street won't get me no place. So all I got's the front way. Hell!" he went on, puffing out his chest, "I got a streak of luck, Wing. It'll hold."

Wing drew himself another coffee.

"Here's hoping," he said.

Blue went to the door and, putting his head out a little way, looked up and down. The street was deserted except for a truck which was coming toward him slowly. It was a Standard Oil truck.

"Wing," he said, "has any of Mike's boys got a hide-out anywhere around here?"

"Don't know of none."

"Well," said Blue, "here I go."

"So long," said Wing.

Blue stepped out of the restaurant, threw his shoulders back, and began to walk slowly toward Birdy's apartment. The Standard Oil truck passed him and went on. The street was quiet. At the end of the street he saw an elevated on its way toward the Loop.

"I wish I was on that baby," he said.

But the nearer he got to the apartment the surer he became that his luck would hold. Hell! it was the first break he'd had since he and Guido hijacked that big Detroit shipment. He had tickets on The Century. When a guy has tickets on The Century he uses them. And that wasn't all. He was a big shot now; the Big Boy had promised him a bonus; he had on silk underwear.

"Hell!" said Blue, "it ain't in the cards."

Across from Birdy's apartment he saw the same fat woman leaning out of the window. When he looked up she drew her head in hastily. Blue made a dash for the door, but across the street a Thompson gun began to spit. Blue stumbled, dropped his gun, and ran blindly out into the middle of the street; then he turned and ran blindly back toward the house. An iron fence caught him just below the belt and he doubled over it. Across the street a window was slammed.

MALICE DOMESTIC
by PHILIP MacDONALD

Carl Borden came out of Seaman's bookstore into the sundrenched, twisting little main street of El Morro Beach. He looked around to see if his wife were in view, and then, as she wasn't, walked to the bar entrance of Eagles' and went in. He was a big, loosely built, rambling sort of a man, with untidy blond hair and a small, somehow featureless face which was redeemed from indistinction by his eyes, which were unexpectedly large, vividly blue and always remarkably alive. He was a writer of some merit, mediocre sales, and—at least among the wordier critics—considerable reputation.

He sat on the first stool at the bar and nodded to the Real Estate man, Dockweiler, who had once been a Hollywood actor; to Dariev, the Russian who did the murals; then—vaguely—to some people in booths. He didn't smile at all, not even at the barman when he ordered his beer—and Dockweiler said to old Parry beside him, "Catch that Borden, will you! Wonder whatsa matter. . . ."

The barman, who was always called Hiho for some reason everyone had forgotten, brought Carl's drink and set it down before him and glanced at him and said, "Well, Mr. Borden—and how've you been keeping?"

Carl said, "Thanks, Hiho—oh, all right, I guess. . . ." He took a long swallow from the cold glass.

Hiho said, "And how's Mrs. Borden? Okay?"

"Fine!" Carl said, and then again, "Fine!" He put a dollar bill on the bar and Hiho picked it up and went back to the cash register.

Carl put his elbows on the bar and dropped his face into his hands; then sat quickly upright as Hiho returned with his change. He pocketed it and swallowed the rest of his beer and stood up. He nodded to Hiho without speaking and walked out into the street again.

His wife was standing by the car with her arms full of packages. He said, "Hey, Annette—hold it!" and quickened his pace to a lumbering trot.

She smiled at him. A brief, wide smile which was just a little on the toothy side. She looked slim and straight and cool and soignée, as she always did. She was a blond Norman woman of thirty-odd, and she had been married to Carl for nine years. They were regarded, by everyone who did not know them well, as an "ideal couple." But their few intimates, of late, had been vaguely unsure of this.

Carl opened the door of the car and took the parcels from Annette's arms and stowed them away in the back. She said, "Thank you, Carlo," and got into the seat beside him as he settled himself at the wheel. She said, "Please —go around by Beatons. I have a *big* package there."

He drove down to Las Ondas Road and parked, on the wrong side of the street, outside a white-fenced little building over which a sign announced, BEATON AND SON—NURSERIES.

He went into the shop, and the girl gave him a giant paper sack, stuffed overfull with a gallimaufry of purchases. He picked it up—and the bottom tore open and a shower of the miscellany sprayed to the floor.

Carl swore beneath his breath, and the girl said "Oh, drat!" and whipped around to help him. He put the things he had saved on the counter, then, stooping, retrieved a thick pamphlet called *The Rose-Grower's Handbook* and a carton labeled KILLWEED in white lettering above a red skull-and-crossbones design.

The girl had everything else. Apologizing profusely, she put the whole order into two fresh sacks. Carl put one under each arm and went out into the sunny street again, and saw Dr. Wingate walking along it, approaching the car. Carl called out, "Hi, Tom!" and smiled his first smile of the morning as the other turned and saw him.

"Hi yourself!" Wingate said. He was a man in the middle forties, a little dandiacal as to dress, and he wore—unusual in a medico—a small, neatly trimmed imperial which some people thought distinguished, others merely caprine. He turned to the car and raised his hat to Annette, wishing her good-morning a trifle formally. He opened the rear door for Carl and helped him put the two packages in with the others. He looked at Carl, and for a moment his gaze became sharply professional. He said, "How's the book going?" and Carl hesitated before he answered, "Fine! Tough sledding, of course—but it'll be all right, I think."

"Well—" said Wingate, "don't go cold on it. It's too good."

Carl shrugged. Annette said, impatiently, "We must get back, Carlo," and he got into the car and started the engine and waved to his friend.

He drove back through the town and then branched inland up into the hills and came in five minutes to the narrow, precipitous road which led up to his house, standing alone on its little bluff. It was a sprawling, gray-shingled building, with tall trees behind it and, in front, a lawn which surrounded a rose bed. Beside the lawn a graveled driveway, with traces of devil-grass and other weeds showing through its surface, ran down to the garage.

As he stopped the car, an enormous dog appeared around the corner of the house and bounded towards them. Annette got out first, and looked at the animal and said, "Hello," and put out her hand as if to fondle it.

The dog backed away. It stood with its head up and stared at her. It was a Giant Schnauser, as big as a Great Dane, and it was called G.B. because something about its bearded face and sardonic eye had always made Carl think of Shaw.

Annette looked at it; then, with a quick little movement of her head, at her husband. She said sharply, "The dog! Why does he look at me like that?"

Carl was getting out of the car. "Like what?" he said—and then it was upon him, its tail-stump wagging madly, its vast mouth open in a wet, white-and-scarlet smile.

"Hi there, G.B!" Carl said—and the creature rose up on its hind legs and put its forepaws on his shoulders and tried to lick his face. Its head was almost on a level with Carl's.

Annette said, "It is—peculiar. He does not like me lately." She was frowning.

Carl said, "Oh, that's your imagination," and the dog dropped upon all fours again and stood away while the packages were taken out of the car.

Carl carried most of them, Annette the rest. They stood in the kitchen, and Annette began to put her purchases away. Carl stood and watched her. His blue eyes were dark and troubled, and he looked like a Brobdingnagian and bewildered little boy who has found himself in trouble for some reason he cannot understand.

Annette wanted to get to the icebox, and he was in her way. She pushed at his arm, and said sharply, "Move! You are too big for this kitchen!"

But he put his long arms around her and pulled her close to him. He said, "Annette! What's the matter, darling? What is it? What have I done?"

She strained back against his arms —but he tightened their pressure and drew her closer still and buried his face in the cool, firm flesh of her throat.

"Carl!" she said. She sounded amazed.

He went on talking, against her neck. His voice sounded almost as if there were tears in it. He said, "Don't tell me there isn't something wrong! Just tell me what it *is!* Tell me what I've *done!* It's been going on for weeks now—maybe months. Ever since you came back from that trip. You've been—different. . . ."

His wife stood motionless. She said, slowly, "But, Carlo—that is what I have been feeling about you."

He raised his head and looked at her. He said, "It's almost as if you were —suspicious of me. And I don't know what it's about!"

She frowned. "I—," she said, "I—" and then stopped for a long moment.

She said, "Do you know what I think? I think we are two very stupid people." The lines were leaving her face, the color coming back to it.

"Two stupid people!" she said again. "People who are not so young as they were. People who do not see enough other people—and begin to imagine things. . . ."

She broke off as there drifted through the open window the sound of a car, old and laboring, coming up the hill. She said, "Ah!" and put her hands on Carl's shoulders and kissed him at the corner of his mouth. She said, "The mail—I will get it," and went quickly out of the side door.

He made no attempt to follow her, no suggestion that he should do the errand. Annette had always been very jealous about her letters, and seemed to be growing even more so.

He stood where he was, his big shoulders sagging, the smile with which he had met her smile slowly fading from his face. He shook his head. He drew in a deep breath. He shambled away, through the big living room and through that again into his study. He sat down in front of his typewriter and stared at it for a long time.

He began to work—at first slowly, but finally with a true and page-devouring frenzy. . . .

It was dusk, and he had already switched on his desk light, when there came a gentle sound behind him. He dragged himself back to the world which he did not control and turned in his chair and saw his wife just inside the door. She was very slim, almost boyish, in her gardening overalls. She said, "I do not want to interrupt, Carlo—just to know about dinner." Her face was in shadow, and she might have been smiling.

He stood up and threw his arms wide and stretched. "Any time you like," he said, and then, as she moved to leave the room, "Wait a minute!"

He crossed to her and took her by the shoulders and looked down at her. For a moment she was rigid; then suddenly she put her arms around his neck and moulded her slim strong softness against him and tilted her face up to his.

It was a long and passionate kiss—and it was only broken by the sound of a jarring, persistent thudding at the French windows.

Annette pulled abruptly away from her husband's clasp. She muttered something which sounded like, *"Sacré chien! . . ."* and went quickly out through the door behind her.

Except for the pool of light upon the desk, the room was very dark now, and after a moment Carl reached out and snapped on the switch of the overhead light. Slowly, he walked over to the windows and opened them and let in the big dog.

It stood close to him, its head more than level with his waist, and he stroked it and pulled gently at its ears. He shut the window then, and went out of the study and upstairs to his own room, the animal padding heavily beside him. He took a shower and changed his clothes, and when he had finished, could still hear his wife in her own room. He said, "Come on, G.B." and went downstairs again and out of the house.

He put the car away and shut the garage—and was still outside when Annette called him in to dinner.

This was, like all Annette's dinners, a complete and rounded work of art —and it was made all the more pleasant because, during it, she seemed almost her old self. She was bright, talkative, smiling—and although the dog lay directly in the way of her path to the kitchen and would not move for her, she made no complaint but walked around him.

As usual, they had coffee in the living room. After his second cup, Carl got up, and stretched. He snapped his fingers at G.B., who went and stood expectantly by the door. Carl stood over his wife, smiling down at her. He started to speak—but she was first, looking up at him in sudden concern.

She said, "Carlo—you do not look well! . . . You work, I think, too hard! . . . You should not go out, perhaps."

But Carl pooh-poohed her. "Feel fine!" he said and bent over and kissed her on the forehead and crossed to the door and was gone.

Whistling, and with G.B. bounding ahead of him, he walked down the steep slant of their own road and onto the gentler slopes of Paseo Street.

He had gone less than quarter of a mile when his long, measured stride faltered. He took a few uneven steps, then stopped altogether. He swayed. He put a hand up to his forehead and found it covered with clammy sweat. He wobbled to the edge of the road and sat down upon a grass bank. He dropped his face into both his hands. A vast, black bulk appeared out of the darkness and thrust a damp nose at him. He mumbled something and took his hands away from his face and clapped them to his stomach and bent his head lower, down between his knees, and began to vomit. . . .

Old Parry was sitting in his living room, a book on his knee, a glass on the table beside him. He heard a scratching at the porch door; then a series of short, deep, demanding barks. He stood up creakily and went to the door and pulled it open. He bowed and said, "I am honored, Mr. Shaw!"—and then had his high-pitched giggle cut off short as the enormous dog seized the edge of his jacket between its teeth and began to tug at it with gentle but imperious sharpness.

"Something the matter, boy?" said Parry—and went the way he was being told and in a moment found the sick man by the roadside.

Carl had stopped vomiting now, and was sitting straighter. But he was badly shaken and weak as a kitten. In answer to Parry's shocked inquiries he mumbled, ". . . all right now . . . sorry . . . just my stomach up-set . . ." He tried to laugh—a ghastly little sound. "I'm not drunk," he said. "Be all right in a minute—don't bother yourself . . ."

But Parry did bother himself: he had seen Carl's face—pinched and drawn and of a strange, greenish pallor shining with an oily film. Somehow, he got the big man to his feet; somehow, under the watchful yellow eye of the Schnauser, managed to pilot him into the house and settle him, half-seated, half-sprawling upon a sofa.

"Thanks," Carl muttered. "Thanks . . . that's fine . . ." He sank back on the cushions and closed his eyes.

"Just a minute now—" said old Parry—and went out into his little hallway and busied himself at the telephone to such effect that in less than fifteen minutes, a car pulled up outside and Dr. Thomas Wingate, bag in hand, walked in upon them.

Carl protested. He was much better already, and his face was pale with a more normal pallor. He was embarrassed and shy. He was grateful to old Parry, and yet plainly annoyed by all this fuss. He sat up very straight, G.B. at his feet, and said firmly, "Look, I'm all right now! Just a touch of ptomaine or something." He looked from his host to the doctor. "Awfully good of you to take so much trouble, Parry. And thanks for turning out, Tom. But—"

"But nothing!" Wingate said, and sat down beside him and took hold of his wrist and felt the pulse. "What you been eating?"

Carl managed a grin. "Better dinner than you'll ever get," he said—and then, "Oh—I had lunch out, maybe *that* was it! Annette and I went to The Hickory Nut, and I had fried shrimps—a double order! Tom, I bet that's what it was!"

Wingate let go of his wrist. "Could be," he said. He looked at Carl's face again and stood up. "That's a trick tummy of yours anyway." He turned to Parry. "I'll just run him home," he said.

Carl got up too. He thanked Parry all over again, and followed Wingate to his car. They put G.B. in the back and he sat immediately behind Carl, breathing protectively down his neck.

Wingate slowed down almost to a crawl as they reached Carl's driveway. He said, with the abruptness of discomfort, "Look now, I know you pretty well, both as a patient and a fellow human being: this—call it 'attack'—may not have been caused by bad food at all. Or bad food may have been only a contributing factor. In other words, my friend, what everyone insists on calling 'nerves' may be at the bottom of it." They were in the driveway now, and he stopped the car. But he made no move to get out. He looked at Carl's face in the dimness and said, "Speaking purely as a doctor, Carl, have you been—worried at all lately?" He paused, but Carl said nothing. "You haven't seemed like yourself the past few weeks. . . ."

Carl opened the door on his side. "I don't know what the hell you're talking about," he said curtly.

As he stepped out of the car the front door of the house opened and Annette came out onto the porch. She peered through the darkness at the car. She called, "Who is there? Who is it?" Her voice was high-pitched, sharp.

"Only me, dear," Carl said. "Tom Wingate drove me home." He opened the rear door and G.B. jumped out, then followed his master and Wingate up the steps to the house.

Annette stood just inside the door as they entered. Her face was in shadow, but she seemed pale. She acknowledged Wingate's formal greeting with a stiff little bow, and Carl looked harassed and uncomfortable. He tried to stop Wingate from saying what had happened, but to no purpose. Annette was told the whole story, firmly, politely and incisively—and Annette was given instructions.

She was most distressed. She said that Carl had not looked well after dinner, and she had not wanted him to go out. She was extremely polite to Dr. Wingate, and repeated his instructions carefully and asked for reassurance that the attack had been nothing serious. But all the time she was rigid and unbending, with frost in her manner. Only when Wingate had gone—and that was very soon—did she thaw. It was a most complete thaw, however. She rushed at Carl and fussed over him and got him upstairs and nursed him and mothered him. And when he was comfortably in bed, she kissed him with all the old tenderness.

"Carlo, *mon pauvre!*" she said softly, and then, "I am sorry I was not nice to your doctor, *cheri*. But—but—*eh bien,* you know that I do not like him."

He patted her shoulder, and she kissed him again—and he was very soon asleep. . . .

It was ten days after this that he had the pains again. They struck late at night. He was in his study, working. It was after one, and Annette had been in bed since before midnight.

They were much worse this time. They were agonizing. They started with painful cramps in his thighs—and when he stood up to ease this there was a terrible burning in the pit of his stomach. And then a faintness came over him and he dropped back into his chair. He doubled up, his hands clutching desperately at his belly. Great beads of cold sweat burst out all over his head and neck. He began to retch. Desperately, he swung his chair around until his hanging head was over the big metal wastebasket. He vomited hideously, and for what seemed an eternity. . . .

At last, momentarily, the convulsions ceased. He tried to raise his head—and everything in the room swam before his eyes. Outside, G.B. scratched on the French windows, and a troubled whining came from his throat. Carl pulled a weak hand across his mouth and his fingers came away streaked with blood. He rested his forehead upon the table top and with tremendous effort reached out for the telephone and managed to pull it towards him. . . .

In exactly ten minutes, a car came to a squealing halt in the driveway—and Wingate jumped out of it and raced up the steps. The front door was unlocked, and he was halfway across the living room when Annette appeared at the top of the stairs. She was in a night gown and was fumbling to get her arms into a robe. She said, wildly, "What is it? What is the matter?"

Wingate snapped, "Where's Carl?"—and then heard a sound from the study and crossed to it in three strides and burst in.

Carl was on his hands and knees, near the door of the toilet. He raised a ghastly face to Wingate and tried to speak. The room was a shambles—and beside his master, near the leaf of the French window he had broken open, stood G.B.

Carl tried to stand and could not. "Steady now!" Wingate said. "Take it easy. . . ." He crossed quickly to the sick man and half-dragged, half-lifted him to a couch and began to work over him. G.B. stopped whining and lay down. Annette came into the room and stood at Wingate's shoulder. Her hair was in tight braids and her pallid face shone beneath a layer of cream. Her eyes were wide, their pupils dilated. A curious sound—perhaps a scream strangled at birth—had come from her as she entered, but now she seemed in control of herself, though her hands were shaking. She started to speak but Wingate cut her short, almost savagely.

"Hot water," he snapped. "Towels. Glass."

She ran out of the room—and was quickly back with the things he wanted; then stayed with him, an efficient and self-effacing helper, while for an hour and more he labored.

By three o'clock, though weak and languid and gaunt in the face, Carl was himself again and comfortable in his own bed. He smiled at Wingate, who closed his bag with a snap.

"Thanks, Tom . . ." he said—and then, "Sorry to be such a nuisance."

"You're okay." Wingate smiled back at him with tired eyes—and turned to Annette.

"You go to bed, Mrs. Borden," he said. "He'll sleep—he's exhausted." He turned towards the door, stopped with his fingers on the handle. "I'll call by at eight-thirty. If he wants anything—don't give it to him."

Annette moved towards him but he checked her. "Don't bother—I'll let myself out," he said—and was gone.

Very slowly, Annette moved back to the bed and stood beside it, looking down at her husband. The mask of cold cream over her face had broken into glistening patches which alternated with islands of dryness which showed the skin tight and drawn, its color a leaden gray.

Carl reached out and took her hand. He said, "Did I scare you, darling? . . . I'm awfully sorry!"

Stiffly, she bent over him. She kissed him. "Go to sleep," she said. "You will be all well in the morning. . . ."

And indeed he was, save for a great lassitude and a painful tenderness all around his stomach. He barely waked when Wingate came at eight-thirty, and was asleep again the instant he left five minutes later.

At twelve—like a child about to surprise a household—he got up and washed himself and dressed. He was a little tired when he finished—but less so than he had expected. He opened his door quietly, and quietly went downstairs. As he reached the study door, Annette came out of it. She was in her usual houseworking clothes, and carried a dustpan and broom. Under the gay bandanna which was tied around her head, her face seemed oddly thin and angular.

She gave a little exclamation at the sight of him. "Carlo!" she said. "You should not be up! You should have called me!"

He laughed at her tenderly. He pinched her cheek and then kissed it. "I'm fine," he said. "Sort of sore around the midsection—but that's nothing." He slid his arm around her waist and they went into the study together. She fussed over him, and was settling him in the big chair beside the desk when the telephone rang.

Carl reached out and picked it up and spoke into it. He said, "Hello? . . . Oh, hello, Tom. . . ."

"So you're up, huh?" said Wingate's voice over the wire. "How d'you feel?"

"Fine," said Carl. "Hungry, though. . . ."

"Eaten yet?" The voice on the telephone was suddenly sharp.

"No. But I—"

"Good. Don't. Not until you've seen me. I want to examine you—run a test or two—while that stomach's empty. Can you get down here to the office? That'd be better. Or do you want me to come up?" Wingate's voice wasn't sharp any more: it seemed even more casual than it normally was.

Carl said, "Sure I can come down. When?"

"Right away," said the telephone. "I'll fit you in. G'bye."

Carl hung up. He looked at his wife and smiled ruefully. "Can't eat yet," he said. "Tom Wingate wants to examine me first." He put his hands on the arms of the chair and levered himself to his feet.

Annette stood stock still. "I am coming too," she announced. "I will drive you."

"Oh, phooey!" Carl said. "You know you hate breaking off halfway through the chores." He patted her on the shoulder. "And I'm perfectly all right, darling. Really! Don't you think I've caused enough trouble already?"

"Oh, Carlo—you are foolish!" Her face was very white—and something about the way her mouth moved made it seem as if she were about to cry.

Carl put an arm around her shoulders. "You must be played out, sweet," he said.

"I am very well," she snapped. "I am not tired at all." And then, with effort, she managed to smile. "But perhaps I am," she said. "Do not mind because I am cross. Go and see your Doctor Wingate. . . ."

She hooked her arm in his and walked through the living room with him, and at the front door she kissed him.

"Take care of yourself, Carlo," she said. "And come back quickly." She shut the door behind him.

As he entered the garage, G.B. came racing up—and the moment Carl opened the car door, leapt neatly in to sit enormous in the seat beside the driver's. His tongue was hanging out and he was smiling all around it.

Carl laughed at him; then winced as the laughter hurt his sore stomach-muscles. He said, "All right, you bum," and got in behind the wheel and started the car and backed out.

He drove slowly, but in a very few minutes was parking outside Wingate's office. He left G.B. in charge of the car and walked around to the back door—entrance for the favored few.

Wingate was standing by his desk. The light was behind him and Carl couldn't see his face very well, but he seemed older than usual, and tired. Even the little beard looked grayer. He waved Carl to a chair and then came and stood over him, feeling his pulse and making him thrust out his tongue to be looked at.

Carl grinned at him. "Goddam professional this morning," he said.

But Wingate didn't answer the smile, or the gibe. He sat down in his swivel chair and stared at Carl and said, "You were pretty sick last night, my friend," and then, after Carl had thrown in a "You're telling me!", added sharply, "You're lucky not to be dead."

Carl's grin faded slowly—and he gave a startled "Huh?"

"You heard what I said." Wingate had taken a pencil from the desk and was rolling it around in his fingers. He was looking at the pencil and not at Carl.

He said, "By the way, there's some property of yours there," and pointed with the pencil to a bulky, cylindrical package, roughly wrapped in brown paper, which stood upon a side table. "Want to take it with you?"

Carl looked bewildered. "What? . . ." He stared uncomprehendingly. "What you talking about?"

"That's your wastebasket." Wingate still kept his eyes on the twirling pencil. "From your study. I took it with me last night. . . ."

"Why? . . . Oh—you mean to get it cleaned. . . ." Carl was floundering. He burst out, "What the hell *is* all this? What're you driving at, Tom?"

Wingate looked at him, and drew in a deep breath. He said, in a monotone, "You'll find out very soon. Where did you eat yesterday?"

"At home, of course. What's—"

"Be quiet a minute. So you ate at home. What was the last thing you had? Probably around midnight."

"Nothing. . . . Wait a second, though—I'd forgotten. I had a bowl of soup—Annette's onion soup. She brought it to me before she went to bed. But that couldn't—"

"Wait! So you had this soup, at about twelve. And around an hour later, you have cramps in the legs and stomach, faintness, nausea, acute pain in the intestines. And you vomit, copiously. A lot of it, but by no means all, was in that metal wastebasket. And the contents of the basket, analyzed, show you must have swallowed at least a grain and a half of arsenic. . . ."

He let his voice fade into silence, then stood up to face Carl, who had jumped to his feet. He put his hand on Carl's arm and pushed him back into his chair. He unconsciously repeated the very words he had used the night before. "Steady now!" he said. "Take it easy!"

Carl sat down. His pallor had increased. He pulled a shaking hand across his forehead and then tried to smile.

"Narrow squeak," he said—and after that, "Grain and a half, huh? That's quite a dose, isn't it?"

"Could be fatal," Wingate said. "And you had more, maybe."

Carl said, "How in hell d'you suppose I picked it up?" He wasn't looking at Wingate, but past him. "Vegetables or something? They spray 'em, don't they?"

"Not in that strength." Wingate went back to his own chair and sat in it. "And you had that other attack ten days ago. Same thing—but not so much." His voice was absolutely flat. "And you ate at home, both times."

Carl shot out of his chair again. His face was distorted, his blue eyes blazing.

"For God's sake!" he shouted. "Have you gone out of your mind! What are you hinting at?"

"I'm not hinting anything." Wingate's voice was still toneless. "I'm stating something. You have twice been poisoned with arsenic during the last ten days. The second time provably."

Carl flung his big body back into the chair again. He started to speak, but all that came from him was a muffled groan.

Wingate said, "You don't imagine I like doing this, do you? But you have to face it, man! Someone is feeding you arsenic. The odds against accident are two million to one."

Carl's hands gripped the arms of his chair until his knuckles shone white.

He said, hoarsely, "If I didn't know you so well, I'd break your neck!" His voice began to rise. "Can't you see the whole thing must have been some weird, terrible accident! Don't you *know* that what's in your mind is completely, utterly impossible!" He stopped abruptly. He was panting, as if he had been running.

Wingate sat motionless. His face was shaded by the hands which propped it. He spoke as if Carl had been silent.

"Arsenic's easy to get," he said. "Especially for gardeners—ant paste, Paris green, rose-spray, weed-killer—"

"God blast you!" Carl crashed his fist down upon the chair arm. "There *is* weed-killer in the house—but *I* told her to get it!"

He got to his feet and towered over Wingate. He said, "I'm going. And I'm not coming back. I don't think you're lying about the arsenic, but I know you're making a monstrous, evil mistake about how I got it—a mistake which oughtn't to be possible to a man of your intelligence!"

He started for the door, turned back. "And another thing," he said. "I can't stop you from thinking your foul thoughts—" his voice was shaking with suppressed passion—"but I *can* stop you from voicing them—and I will! If you so much as breathe a word of this to anyone—I'll half kill you, and then I'll ruin you! And don't forget that—because I mean it!"

He stood over the other man for a long moment—but Wingate did not move, did not so much as look at him—and at last Carl went back to the door and opened it and passed out of the room. He got out into the air again and made his way to the car. He was very white. He opened the car and slumped into the driving seat. He put his arms down on the wheel and rested his head upon them. He was breathing in long shuddering gasps. G.B. made a little whimpering sound and licked at his master's ear—and two women passing by looked at the tableau with curiosity.

Perhaps Carl felt their gaze, for he raised his head and saw them. He straightened in his seat, and pushed the dog's great head aside with a gentle hand.

He drove home very slowly. Annette heard the car and opened the front door as he climbed up the steps. She said at once, "What did he say, Carlo? Did he know what is the matter with you?" Her haggard, worn look seemed to have intensified.

Carl looked at her—and then he shook his head. He stepped through the door and sank into the nearest chair. He said, slowly, "No . . . No, he didn't. I don't think he knows much about it. . . ."

He said, "God, I'm tired! . . . Come and give me a kiss, darling."

She came and sat upon the arm of his chair and kissed him. She pulled his head against her breast and stroked his hair. He could not see her face as she spoke.

"But, *chéri,*" she said, "he must know *something.*"

Carl sighed. "Oh, he used a lot of medical jargon—all beginning with *gastro* . . . But I don't think he really knows any more than I do—which is that I happen to have a nervous stomach." He leaned back in the chair and looked up at her. "I tell you—maybe you're right about Tom Wingate. I don't mean as a man—but as a doctor. I think another time—well, I might go to that new man . . ."

Annette jumped up. "That is quite enough talk about doctors," she said. "And I, I am very bad! Here is my poor man here, white and weak because he has no food! Wait one little moment, Carlo. . . ."

She hurried off to the kitchen. She seemed to have shed her fatigue, her tenseness.

Carl sat where he was. He stared straight ahead with eyes which did not look as if they saw what was in front of them.

In a very little while Annette came back. She was carrying a small tray upon which were a spoon, a napkin and a bowl which steamed, gently and fragrantly.

She said, *"Voilà!—"* and set the tray on his knees and put the spoon in his hand and stood back to watch him.

He looked at her for a long unwavering moment—and when she said, "Hurry now and drink your soup!" he did not seem to hear.

He said, very suddenly, "Annette: do you love me?"—and kept on looking at her.

She stared. She said, after an instant, "But yes—but of *course,* Carlo!"

And then she laughed and said, "Do not be a baby! Take your soup—it is not very hot."

He looked at the spoon in his hand and seemed surprised to find it there. He set it down upon the tray and picked up the bowl and looked at his wife over the edge of it.

"Santé!" he said—and put the china to his lips and began to drink in great gulps. . . .

He did not have the pains that night.

A week went by and he did not have them—a week in which he had not spoken to, nor seen, nor heard any word of Dr. Thomas Wingate.

It was past eleven at night, and he was walking with G.B. up the last slope of Pasco Street. Behind him, old Parry called a last good-night, and he half-turned and waved a valedictory hand. He had been returning from a longer walk than usual and had met Parry at the mailbox; a meeting which had somehow led to drinks in Parry's house and a long talk upon Parry's favorite topic, which was that of the world's declining sanity.

He reached his own steep little road and shortened his stride for the climb and whistled for G.B., who came at once and padded beside him.

He was humming as he strode down the drive and up the steps. He opened the front door and let the dog ahead of him and then went in himself.

He said, *"Oh, my God!"*

He stood motionless for an instant which might have been a century.

Annette was lying on the floor, twisted into a strange and ugly shape—and all around her prostrate and distorted body the room was dreadfully befouled.

G.B. stared, then pushed through the half-open door to the kitchen. There was a thump as he lay down.

Carl dropped to his knees beside the prostrate woman. He raised her head and it lolled against his arm. Her eyes were closed and her stained and swollen mouth hung open. She was breathing, but lightly, weakly—and when he felt for her heart its beat was barely perceptible. . . .

Somehow, he was in the study, at the telephone . . . As if automatically, his shaking fingers dialed a number . . .

He was speaking to Wingate. "Tom!" he said, on a harsh high note. "Tom! This is Carl. Come at once! *Hurry!*"

His hand put back the phone. His feet took him out into the living room again. His knees bent themselves once more and once more he held his wife in his arms. . . .

He was still holding her when Wingate came.

Wingate examined her and shook his head. He made Carl get up—and took him into the study. He said, "You've got to face it, Carl . . . She's dead."

Carl was shaking all over—his hands, his body, his head, all of him.

Wingate said, "Sit there—and don't move!" and went out into the living room again.

He looked at the dead woman; at the foulness around her; at everything in the room. He was staring at the two coffee cups which stood on the top of the piano when G.B. came in from the kitchen, paced over to the study and disappeared.

Wingate picked up the cups, one after the other. They were small cups, and each held the heavy, pasty remains of Turkish coffee. He dipped a dampened fingertip into each cup in turn, each time touching the finger to his tongue. The second test gave him the reaction he wanted—and, his face clearing, he strode back to the study.

Carl had not moved, but his trembling had increased. The dog sat beside him, looking into his face.

Wingate put a hand on the shaking shoulder. Carl tried to speak—but his teeth started to chatter and no words came out of him.

Wingate said: "You know, don't you? She tried again . . . You wouldn't let *me* look after you—but the Fates did!"

Carl mumbled, "I—I—I d-don't understand . . ."

Wingate said, "She was overconfident. And something went wrong—some little thing to distract her attention." He lifted his shoulders. "And—well, she took the wrong cup."

Carl said, *"God! . . ."* He covered his face with his hands, the fingers digging into his temples. He said: "Tom—I almost wish it *had* been me!"

"Come on, now!" Wingate took him by the arm. "Stop thinking—just do what I tell you!"

He hauled Carl to his feet and led him out of the study and up the stairs and into his own room. G.B. came close behind them, and lay watchful while Wingate got Carl out of his clothes and into bed and finally slid a hypodermic needle into his arm.

"There!" he said. "You'll be asleep in five minutes. . . ."

He was turning away when Carl reached out and caught his hand and held it.

Carl said, "Don't go . . ." And then he said, "About what I said in your office—I'm sorry, Tom. . . ."

Wingate did not try to release his hand. "Forget it," he said. "I have."

And then he started talking—slowly, quietly, his casual voice a soothing monotone. He said, "All you have to do now is go to sleep . . . I'll see to everything else . . . In a little while, all this will just be a nightmare you've half-forgotten . . . And don't go worrying yourself about publicity and scandal and things like that, Carl . . . There won't be any . . . You see, I was *sure*— and in spite of what you said I told Chief Nichols . . . He and I will explain it all to the coroner . . ."

He let his voice trail off into silence—Carl Borden was asleep.

It was three weeks before Carl permitted himself to smile—and then he was not in El Morro Beach. He was in San Francisco—and Lorna was waiting for him.

When he smiled, he was driving up Market Street, G.B. erect beside him.

"Tell you something, boy," he murmured. "I nearly took too much that second time!"

The smile became a chuckle.

I CAN FIND MY WAY OUT

by NGAIO MARSH

At half-past six on the night in question, Anthony Gill, unable to eat, keep still, think, speak, or act coherently, walked from his rooms to the Jupiter Theatre. He knew that there would be nobody backstage, that there was nothing for him to do in the theatre, that he ought to stay quietly in his rooms and presently dress, dine, and arrive at, say, a quarter to eight. But it was as if something shoved him into his clothes, thrust him into the street and compelled him to hurry through the West End to the Jupiter. His mind was overlaid with a thin film of inertia. Odd lines from the play occurred to him, but without any particular significance. He found himself busily reiterating a completely irrelevant sentence: "She has a way of laughing that would make a man's heart turn over."

Piccadilly, Shaftesbury Avenue. "Here I go," he thought, turning into Hawke Street, "towards my play. It's one hour and twenty-nine minutes away. A step a second. It's rushing towards me. Tony's first play. Poor young Tony Gill. Never mind. Try again."

The Jupiter. Neon lights: I CAN FIND MY WAY OUT—*by Anthony Gill.* And in the entrance the bills and photographs. *Coralie Bourne with H. J. Bannington, Barry George and Canning Cumberland.*

Canning Cumberland. The film across his mind split and there was the Thing itself and he would have to think about it. How bad would Canning Cumberland be if he came down drunk? Brilliantly bad, they said. He would bring out all the tricks. Clever actor stuff, scoring off everybody, making a fool of the dramatic balance. "In Mr. Canning Cumberland's hands indifferent dialogue and unconvincing situations seemed almost real." What can you do with a drunken actor?

He stood in the entrance feeling his heart pound and his inside deflate and sicken.

Because, of course, it was a bad play. He was at this moment and for the first time really convinced of it. It was terrible. Only one virtue in it and that was not his doing. It had been suggested to him by Coralie Bourne: "I don't think the play you have sent me will do as it is but it has occurred to me—" It was a brilliant idea. He had rewritten the play round it and almost immediately and quite innocently he had begun to think of it as his own although he had said shyly to Coralie Bourne: "You should appear as joint author." She had quickly, overemphatically, refused. "It was nothing at all," she said. "If you're to become a dramatist you will learn to get ideas from everywhere. A single situation is nothing. Think of Shakespeare," she added lightly. "Entire plots! Don't be silly." She had said later, and still with the same hurried, nervous air: "Don't go talking to everyone about it. They will think there is more, instead of less, than meets the eye in my small suggestion. Please promise." He promised, thinking he'd made an error in taste when he suggested that Coralie Bourne, so famous an actress, should appear as joint author with an unknown youth. And how right she was, he thought, because, of course, it's going to be a ghastly flop. She'll be sorry she consented to play in it.

Standing in front of the theatre he contemplated nightmare possibilities. What did audiences do when a first play flopped? Did they clap a little, enough to let the curtain rise and quickly fall again on a discomforted group of players? How scanty must the applause be for them to let him off his own appearance? And they were to go on to the Chelsea Arts Ball. A hideous prospect. Thinking he would give anything in the world if he could stop his play, he turned into the foyer. There were lights in the offices and he paused, irresolute, before a board of photographs. Among them, much smaller than the leading players, was Dendra Gay with the eyes looking straight into his. *She had a way of laughing that would make a man's heart turn over.* "Well," he thought, "so I'm in love with her." He turned away from the photograph. A man came out of the office. "Mr. Gill? Telegrams for you."

Anthony took them and as he went out he heard the man call after him: "Very good luck for tonight, sir."

There were queues of people waiting in the side street for the early doors.

At six-thirty Coralie Bourne dialled Canning Cumberland's number and waited.

She heard his voice. "It's me," she said.

"O, God! darling, I've been thinking about you." He spoke rapidly, too loudly. "Coral, I've been thinking about Ben. You oughtn't to have given that situation to the boy."

"We've been over it a dozen times, Cann. Why not give it to Tony? Ben will never know." She waited and then said nervously, "Ben's gone, Cann. We'll never see him again."

"I've got a 'Thing' about it. After all, he's your husband."

"No, Cann, no."

"Suppose he turns up. It'd be like him to turn up."

"He won't turn up."

She heard him laugh. "I'm sick of all this," she thought suddenly. "I've had it once too often. I can't stand any more. . . . Cann," she said into the telephone. But he had hung up.

At twenty to seven, Barry George looked at himself in his bathroom mirror. "I've got a better appearance," he thought, "than Cann Cumberland. My head's a good shape, my eyes are bigger, and my jaw line's cleaner. I never let a show down. I don't drink. I'm a better actor." He turned his head a little, slewing his eyes to watch the effect. "In the big scene," he thought, "I'm the star. He's the feed. That's the way it's been produced and that's what the author wants. I ought to get the notices."

Past notices came up in his memory. He saw the print, the size of the paragraphs; a long paragraph about Canning Cumberland, a line tacked on the end of it. "Is it unkind to add that Mr. Barry George trotted in the wake of Mr. Cumberland's virtuosity with an air of breathless dependability?" And again: "It is a little hard on Mr. Barry George that he should be obliged to act as foil to this brilliant performance." Worst of all: "Mr. Barry George succeeded in looking tolerably unlike a stooge, an achievement that evidently exhausted his resources."

"Monstrous!" he said loudly to his own image, watching the fine glow of indignation in the eyes. Alcohol, he told himself, did two things to Cann Cumberland. He raised his finger. Nice, expressive hand. An actor's hand. Alcohol destroyed Cumberland's artistic integrity. It also invested him with devilish cunning. Drunk, he would burst the seams of a play, destroy its balance, ruin its form, and himself emerge blazing with a showmanship that the audience mistook for genius. "While I," he said aloud, "merely pay my author the compliment of faithful interpretation. Psha!"

He returned to his bedroom, completed his dressing and pulled his hat to the right angle. Once more he thrust his face close to the mirror and looked searchingly at its image. "By God!" he told himself, "he's done it once too often, old boy. Tonight we'll even the score, won't we? By God, we will."

Partly satisfied, and partly ashamed, for the scene, after all, had smacked a little of ham, he took his stick in one hand and a case holding his costume for the Arts Ball in the other, and went down to the theatre.

At ten minutes to seven, H. J. Bannington passed through the gallery queue on his way to the stage door alley, raising his hat and saying: "Thanks so much," to the gratified ladies who let him through. He heard them murmur his name. He walked briskly along the alley, greeted the stage-doorkeeper, passed under a dingy lamp, through an entry and so to the stage. Only working lights were up. The walls of an interior set rose dimly into shadow. Bob Reynolds, the stage manager, came out through the prompt-entrance. "Hello, old boy," he said, "I've changed the dressing rooms. You're third on the right: they've moved your things in. Suit you?"

"Better, at least, than a black hole the size of a W.C. but without its appointments," H.J. said acidly. "I suppose the great Mr. Cumberland still has the star-room?"

"Well, yes, old boy."

"And who pray, is next to him? In the room with the other gas fire?"

"We've put Barry George there, old boy. You know what he's like."

"Only too well, old boy, and the public, I fear, is beginning to find out." H.J. turned into the dressing-room passage. The stage manager returned to the set where he encountered his assistant. "What's biting *him?*" asked the assistant. "He wanted a dressing room with a fire." "Only natural," said the A.S.M. nastily. "He started life reading gas meters."

On the right and left of the passage, nearest the stage end, were two doors, each with its star in tarnished paint. The door on the left was open. H.J. looked in and was greeted with the smell of greasepaint, powder, wet-white, and flowers. A gas fire droned comfortably. Coralie Bourne's dresser was spreading out towels. "Good evening, Katie, my jewel," said H.J. "La Belle not down yet?" "We're on our way," she said.

H.J. hummed stylishly: *"Bella filia del amore,"* and returned to the passage. The star-room on the right was closed but he could hear Cumberland's dresser moving about inside. He went on to the next door, paused, read the card, "Mr. Barry George," warbled a high derisive note, turned in at the third door and switched on the light.

Definitely not a second lead's room. No fire. A wash basin, however, and opposite mirrors. A stack of telegrams had been placed on the dressing table. Still singing he reached for them, disclosing a number of bills that had been tactfully laid underneath and a letter, addressed in a flamboyant script.

His voice might have been mechanically produced and arbitrarily switched off, so abruptly did his song end in the middle of a roulade. He let the telegrams fall on the table, took up the letter and tore it open. His face, wretchedly pale, was reflected and endlessly rereflected in the mirrors.

At nine o'clock the telephone rang. Roderick Alleyn answered it. "This is Sloane 84405. No, you're on the wrong number. *No.*" He hung up and returned to his wife and guest. "That's the fifth time in two hours."

"Do let's ask for a new number."

"We might get next door to something worse."

The telephone rang again. "This is not 84406," Alleyn warned it. "No, I cannot take three large trunks to Victoria Station. No, I am not the Instant All Night Delivery. No."

"They're 84406," Mrs. Alleyn explained to Lord Michael Lamprey. "I suppose it's just faulty dialing, but you can't imagine how angry everyone gets. Why do you want to be a policeman?"

"It's a dull hard job, you know—" Alleyn began.

"Oh," Lord Mike said, stretching his legs and looking critically at his shoes, "I don't for a moment imagine I'll leap immediately into false whiskers and plainclothes. No, no. But I'm revoltingly healthy, sir. Strong as a horse. And I don't think I'm as stupid as you might feel inclined to imagine—"

The telephone rang.

"I say, do let me answer it," Mike suggested and did so.

"Hullo?" he said winningly. He listened, smiling at his hostess. "I'm afraid—," he began. "Here, wait a bit—Yes, but—" His expression became blank and complacent. "May I," he said presently, "repeat your order, sir? Can't be too sure, can we? Call at 11 Harrow Gardens, Sloane Square, for one suitcase to be delivered immediately at the Jupiter Theatre to Mr. Anthony Gill. Very good, sir. Thank you, sir. Collect. Quite."

He replaced the receiver and beamed at the Alleyns.

"What the devil have you been up to?" Alleyn said.

"He just simply wouldn't listen to reason. I tried to tell him."

"But it may be urgent," Mrs. Alleyn ejaculated.

"It couldn't be more urgent, really. It's a suitcase for Tony Gill at the Jupiter."

"Well, then—"

"I was at Eton with the chap," said Mike reminiscently. "He's four years older than I am so of course he was madly important while I was less than the dust. This'll larn him."

"I think you'd better put that order through at once," said Alleyn firmly.

"I rather thought of executing it myself, do you know, sir. It'd be a frightfully neat way of gate-crashing the show, wouldn't it? I did try to get a ticket but the house was sold out."

"If you're going to deliver this case you'd better get a bend on."

"It's clearly an occasion for dressing up though, isn't it? I say," said Mike modestly, "would you think it most frightful cheek if I—well I'd promise to come back and return everything. I mean—"

"Are you suggesting that my clothes look more like a vanman's than yours?"

"I thought you'd have things—"

"For Heaven's sake, Rory," said Mrs. Alleyn, "dress him up and let him go. The great thing is to get that wretched man's suitcase to him."

"I know," said Mike earnestly. "It's most frightfully sweet of you. That's how I feel about it."

Alleyn took him away and shoved him into an old and begrimed raincoat, a cloth cap and a muffler. "You wouldn't deceive a village idiot in a total eclipse," he said, "but out you go."

He watched Mike drive away and returned to his wife.

"What'll happen?" she asked.

"Knowing Mike, I should say he will end up in the front stalls and go on to supper with the leading lady. She, by the way, is Coralie Bourne. Very lovely and twenty years his senior so he'll probably fall in love with her." Alleyn reached for his tobacco jar and paused. "I wonder what's happened to her husband," he said.

"Who was he?"

"An extraordinary chap. Benjamin Vlasnoff. Violent temper. Looked like a bandit. Wrote two very good plays and got run in three times for common assault. She tried to divorce him but it didn't go through. I think he afterwards lit off to Russia." Alleyn yawned. "I believe she had a hell of a time with him," he said.

"All Night Delivery," said Mike in a hoarse voice, touching his cap. "Suitcase. One." "Here you are," said the woman who had answered the door. "Carry it carefully, now, it's not locked and the catch springs out."

"Fanks," said Mike. "Much obliged. Chilly, ain't it?"

He took the suitcase out to the car.

It was a fresh spring night. Sloane Square was threaded with mist and all the lamps had halos round them. It was the kind of night when individual sounds separate themselves from the conglomerate voice of London; hollow sirens spoke imperatively down on the river and a bugle rang out over in Chelsea Barracks; a night, Mike thought, for adventure.

He opened the rear door of the car and heaved the case in. The catch flew open, the lid dropped back and the contents fell out. "Damn!" said Mike and switched on the inside light.

Lying on the floor of the car was a false beard.

It was flaming red and bushy and was mounted on a chin-piece. With it was incorporated a stiffened mustache. There were wire hooks to attach the whole thing behind the ears. Mike laid it carefully on the seat. Next he picked up a wide black hat, then a vast overcoat with a fur collar, finally a pair of black gloves.

Mike whistled meditatively and thrust his hands into the pockets of Alleyn's mackintosh. His right-hand fingers closed on a card. He pulled it out. "Chief Detective-Inspector Alleyn," he read, "C.I.D. New Scotland Yard."

"Honestly," thought Mike exultantly, "this is a gift."

Ten minutes later a car pulled into the curb at the nearest parking place to the Jupiter Theatre. From it emerged a figure carrying a suitcase. It strode rapidly along Hawke Street and turned into the stage-door alley. As it passed under the dirty lamp it paused, and thus murkily lit, resembled an illustration from some Edwardian spy story. The face was completely shadowed, a black cavern from which there projected a square of scarlet beard, which was the only note of color.

The doorkeeper who was taking the air with a member of stage staff, moved forward, peering at the stranger.

"Was you wanting something?"

"I'm taking this case in for Mr. Gill."

"He's in front. You can leave it with me."

"I'm so sorry," said the voice behind the beard, "but I promised I'd leave it backstage myself."

"So you will be leaving it. Sorry, sir, but no one's admitted be'ind without a card."

"A card? Very well. Here is a card."

He held it out in his black-gloved hand. The stage-doorkeeper, unwillingly removing his gaze from the beard, took the card and examined it under the light. "Coo!" he said, "what's up, governor?"

"No matter. Say nothing of this."

The figure waved its hand and passed through the door. " 'Ere!" said the doorkeeper excitedly to the stagehand, "take a slant at this. That's a plainclothes flattie, that was."

"*Plain*clothes!" said the stagehand. "Them!"

" 'E's disguised," said the doorkeeper. "That's what it is. 'E's disguised 'isself."

" 'E's bloody well lorst 'isself be'ind them whiskers if you arst me."

Out on the stage someone was saying in a pitched and beautifully articulate voice: *"I've always loathed the view from these windows. However if that's the sort of thing you admire. Turn off the lights, damn you. Look at it."*

"Watch it, now, watch it," whispered a voice so close to Mike that he jumped. "O.K.," said a second voice somewhere above his head. The lights on the set turned blue. "Kill that working light." "Working light gone."

Curtains in the set were wrenched aside and a window flung open. An actor appeared, leaning out quite close to Mike, seeming to look into his face and saying very distinctly: "God: it's frightful!" Mike backed away towards a passage, lit only from an open door. A great volume of sound broke out beyond the stage. "House lights," said the sharp voice. Mike turned into the passage. As he did so, someone came through the door. He found himself face to face with Coralie Bourne, beautifully dressed and heavily painted.

For a moment she stood quite still; then she made a curious gesture with her right hand, gave a small breathy sound and fell forward at his feet.

*   *   *

Anthony was tearing his program into long strips and dropping them on the floor of the O.P. box. On his right hand, above and below, was the audience; sometimes laughing, sometimes still, sometimes as one corporate being, raising its hands and striking them together. As now; when down on the stage, Canning Cumberland, using a strange voice, and inspired by some inward devil, flung back the window and said: "God: it's frightful!"

"Wrong! Wrong!" Anthony cried inwardly, hating Cumberland, hating Barry George because he let one speech of three words override him, hating the audience because they liked it. The curtain descended with a long sigh on the second act and a sound like heavy rain filled the theatre, swelled prodigiously and continued after the house lights welled up.

"They seem," said a voice behind him, "to be liking your play."

It was Gosset, who owned the Jupiter and had backed the show. Anthony turned on him stammering: "He's destroying it. It should be the other man's scene. He's stealing."

"My boy," said Gosset, "he's an actor."

"He's drunk. It's intolerable."

He felt Gosset's hand on his shoulder.

"People are watching us. You're on show. This is a big thing for you; a first play, and going enormously. Come and have a drink, old boy. I want to introduce you—"

Anthony got up and Gosset, with his arm across his shoulders, flashing smiles, patting him, led him to the back of the box.

"I'm sorry," Anthony said, "I can't. Please let me off. I'm going backstage."

"Much better not, old son." The hand tightened on his shoulder. "Listen, old son—" But Anthony had freed himself and slipped through the passdoor from the box to the stage.

At the foot of the breakneck stairs Dendra Gay stood waiting. "I thought you'd come," she said.

Anthony said: "He's drunk. He's murdering the play."

"It's only one scene, Tony. He finishes early in the next act. It's going colossally."

"But don't you understand—"

"I do. You *know* I do. But you're a success, Tony darling! You can hear it and smell it and feel it in your bones."

"Dendra—," he said uncertainly.

Someone came up and shook his hand and went on shaking it. Flats were being laced together with a slap of rope on canvas. A chandelier ascended into darkness. "Lights," said the stage manager, and the set was flooded with them. A distant voice began chanting. "Last act, please. Last act."

"Miss Bourne all right?" the stage manager suddenly demanded.

"She'll be all right. She's not on for ten minutes," said a woman's voice.

"What's the matter with Miss Bourne?" Anthony asked.

"Tony, I must go and so must you. Tony, it's going to be grand. *Please* think so. *Please.*"

"Dendra—," Tony began, but she had gone.

Beyond the curtain, horns and flutes announced the last act.

"Clear please."

The stagehands came off.

"House lights."

"House lights gone."

"Stand by."

And while Anthony still hesitated in the O.P. corner, the curtain rose. Canning Cumberland and H. J. Bannington opened the last act.

As Mike knelt by Coralie Bourne he heard someone enter the passage behind him. He turned and saw, silhouetted against the lighted stage, the actor who had looked at him through a window in the set. The silhouette seemed to repeat the gesture Coralie Bourne had used, and to flatten itself against the wall.

A woman in an apron came out of the open door.

"I say—here!" Mike said.

Three things happened almost simultaneously. The woman cried out and knelt beside him. The man disappeared through a door on the right.

The woman, holding Coralie Bourne in her arms, said violently: "Why have you come back?" Then the passage lights came on. Mike said: "Look here, I'm most frightfully sorry," and took off the broad black hat. The dresser gaped at him, Coralie Bourne made a crescendo sound in her throat and opened her eyes. "Katie?" she said.

"It's all right, my lamb. It's not him, dear. You're all right." The dresser jerked her head at Mike: "Get out of it," she said.

"Yes, of course, I'm most frightfully—" He backed out of the passage, colliding with a youth who said: "Five minutes, please." The dresser called out: "Tell them she's not well. Tell them to hold the curtain."

"No," said Coralie Bourne strongly. "I'm all right, Katie. Don't say anything. Katie, what was it?"

They disappeared into the room on the left.

Mike stood in the shadow of a stack of scenic flats by the entry into the passage. There was great activity on the stage. He caught a glimpse of Anthony Gill on the far side talking to a girl. The call-boy was speaking to the stage manager who now shouted into space: "Miss Bourne all right?" The dresser came into the passage and called: "She'll be all right. She's not on for ten minutes." The youth began chanting: "Last act, please." The stage manager gave a series of orders. A man with an eyeglass and a florid beard came from further down the passage and stood outside the set, bracing his figure and giving little tweaks to his clothes. There was a sound of horns and flutes. Canning Cumberland emerged from the room on the right and on his way to the stage, passed close to Mike, leaving a strong smell of alcohol behind him. The curtain rose.

Behind his shelter, Mike stealthily removed his beard and stuffed it into the pocket of his overcoat.

A group of stagehands stood nearby. One of them said in a hoarse whisper: " 'E's squiffy." "Garn, 'e's going good." "So 'e may be going good. And for why? *Becos* 'e's squiffy."

Ten minutes passed. Mike thought: "This affair has definitely not gone according to plan." He listened. Some kind of tension seemed to be building up on the stage. Canning Cumberland's voice rose on a loud but blurred note. A door in the set opened. "Don't bother to come," Cumberland said. "Good-bye. I can find my way out." The door slammed. Cumberland was standing near Mike. Then, very close, there was a loud explosion. The scenic flats vibrated, Mike's flesh leapt on his bones and Cumberland went into his dressing rooms. Mike heard the key turn in the door. The smell of alcohol mingled with the smell of gunpowder. A stagehand moved to a trestle table and laid a pistol on it. The actor with the eyeglass made an exit. He spoke for a moment to the stage manager, passed Mike, and disappeared in the passage.

Smells. There were all sorts of smells. Subconsciously, still listening to the play, he began to sort them out. Glue. Canvas. Greasepaint. The call-boy tapped on doors. "Mr. George, please." "Miss Bourne, please." They came out, Coralie Bourne with her dresser. Mike heard her turn a door handle and say something. An indistinguishable voice answered her. Then she and her dresser passed him. The others spoke to her and she nodded and then seemed to withdraw into herself, waiting with her head bent, ready to make her entrance. Presently she drew back, walked swiftly to the door in the set, flung it open and swept on, followed a minute later by Barry George.

Smells. Dust, stale paint, cloth. Gas. Increasingly, the smell of gas.

The group of stagehands moved away behind the set to the side of the stage. Mike edged out of cover. He could see the prompt-corner. The stage manager stood there with folded arms, watching the action. Behind him were grouped the players who were not on. Two dressers stood apart, watching. The light from the set caught their faces. Coralie Bourne's voice sent phrases flying like birds into the auditorium.

Mike began peering at the floor. Had he kicked some gas fitting adrift? The call-boy passed him, stared at him over his shoulder and went down the passage, tapping. "Five minutes to the curtain, please. Five minutes." The actor with the elderly makeup followed the call-boy out. "God, what a stink of gas," he whispered. "Chronic, ain't it?" said the call-boy. They stared at Mike and then crossed to the waiting group. The man said something to the stage manager who tipped his head up, sniffing. He made an impatient gesture and turned back to the prompt-box, reaching over the prompter's head. A bell rang somewhere up in the flies and Mike saw a stagehand climb to the curtain platform.

The little group near the prompt corner was agitated. They looked back towards the passage entrance. The call-boy nodded and came running back. He knocked on the first door on the right. *"Mr. Cumberland! Mr. Cumberland!* You're on for the call." He rattled the door handle. *"Mr. Cumberland! You're on."*

Mike ran into the passage. The call-boy coughed retchingly and jerked his hand at the door. "Gas!" he said. "Gas!"

"Break it in."

"I'll get Mr. Reynolds."

He was gone. It was a narrow passage. From halfway across the opposite room Mike took a run, head down, shoulder forward, at the door. It gave a little and a sickening increase in the smell caught him in the lungs. A vast storm of noise had broken out and as he took another run he thought: "It's hailing outside."

"Just a minute if *you* please, sir."

It was a stagehand. He'd got a hammer and screwdriver. He wedged the point of the screwdriver between the lock and the doorpost, drove it home and wrenched. The screws squeaked, the wood splintered and gas poured into the passage. "No winders," coughed the stagehand.

Mike wound Alleyn's scarf over his mouth and nose. Half-forgotten instructions from antigas drill occurred to him. The room looked queer but he could see the man slumped down in the chair quite clearly. He stooped low and ran in.

He was knocking against things as he backed out, lugging the dead weight. His arms tingled. A high insistent voice hummed in his brain. He floated a short distance and came to earth on a concrete floor among several pairs of legs. A long way off, someone said loudly: "I can only thank you for being so kind to what I know, too well, is a very imperfect play." Then the sound of hail began again. There was a heavenly stream of clear air flowing into his mouth and nostrils. "I could eat it," he thought and sat up.

The telephone rang. "Suppose," Mrs. Alleyn suggested, "that this time you ignore it."

"It might be the Yard," Alleyn said, and answered it.

"Is that Chief Detective-Inspector Alleyn's flat? I'm speaking from the Jupiter Theatre. I've rung up to say that the Chief Inspector is here and that he's had a slight mishap. He's all right, but I think it might be as well for someone to drive him home. No need to worry."

"What sort of mishap?" Alleyn asked.

"Er—well—er, he's been a bit gassed."

"*Gassed!* All right. Thanks, I'll come."

"*What* a bore for you, darling," said Mrs. Alleyn. "What sort of case is it? Suicide?"

"Masquerading within the meaning of the act, by the sound of it. Mike's in trouble."

"What trouble, for Heaven's sake?"

"Got himself gassed. He's all right. Good-night, darling. Don't wait up."

When he reached the theatre, the front of the house was in darkness. He made his way down the side alley to the stage-door where he was held up.

"Yard," he said, and produced his official card.

" 'Ere," said the stage-doorkeeper. " 'ow many more of you?"

"The man inside was working for me," said Alleyn and walked in. The doorkeeper followed, protesting.

To the right of the entrance was a large scenic dock from which the double doors had been rolled back. Here Mike was sitting in an armchair, very white about the lips. Three men and two women, all with painted faces, stood near him and behind them a group of stagehands with Reynolds, the stage manager, and, apart from these, three men in evening dress. The men looked woodenly shocked. The women had been weeping.

"I'm most frightfully sorry, sir," Mike said. "I've tried to explain. This," he added generally, "is Inspector Alleyn."

"I can't understand all this," said the oldest of the men in evening dress irritably. He turned on the doorkeeper. "You said—"

"I seen 'is card—"

"I know," said Mike, "but you see—"

"This is Lord Michael Lamprey," Alleyn said. "A recruit to the Police Department. What's happened here?"

"Doctor Rankin, would you—?"

The second of the men in evening dress came forward. "All right, Gosset. It's a bad business, Inspector. I've just been saying the police would have to be informed. If you'll come with me—"

Alleyn followed him through a door onto the stage proper. It was dimly lit. A trestle table had been set up in the centre and on it, covered with a sheet, was an unmistakable shape. The smell of gas, strong everywhere, hung heavily about the table.

"Who is it?"

"Canning Cumberland. He'd locked the door of his dressing room. There's a gas fire. Your young friend dragged him out, very pluckily, but it was no go. I was in front. Gosset, the manager, had asked me to supper. It's a perfectly clear case of suicide as you'll see."

"I'd better look at the room. Anybody been in?"

"God, no. It was a job to clear it. They turned the gas off at the main. There's no window. They had to open the double doors at the back of the stage and a small outside door at the end of the passage. It may be possible to get in now."

He led the way to the dressing-room passage. "Pretty thick, still," he said. "It's the first room on the right. They burst the lock. You'd better keep down near the floor."

The powerful lights over the mirror were on and the room still had its look of occupation. The gas fire was against the left hand wall. Alleyn squatted down by it. The tap was still turned on, its face lying parallel with the floor. The top of the heater, the tap itself, and the carpet near it, were covered with a creamish powder. On the end of the dressing-table shelf nearest to the stove was a box of this powder. Further along the shelf, greasepaints were set out in a row beneath the mirror. Then came a wash basin and in front of this an over-turned chair. Alleyn could see the track of heels, across the pile of the carpet, to the door immediately opposite. Beside the wash basin was a quart bottle of whiskey, three parts empty, and a tumbler. Alleyn had had about enough and returned to the passage.

"Perfectly clear," the hovering doctor said again, "isn't it?"

"I'll see the other rooms, I think."

The one next to Cumberland's was like his in reverse, but smaller. The heater was back to back with Cumberland's. The dressing-shelf was set out with much the same assortment of greasepaints. The tap of this heater, too, was turned on. It was of precisely the same make as the other and Alleyn, less embarrassed here by fumes, was able to make a longer examination. It was a common enough type of gas fire. The lead-in was from a pipe through a flexible metallic tube with a rubber connection. There were two taps, one in the pipe and one at the junction of the tube with the heater itself. Alleyn disconnected the tube and examined the connection. It was perfectly sound, a close fit and stained red at the end. Alleyn noticed a wiry thread of some reddish stuff resembling packing that still clung to it. The nozzle and tap were brass, the tap pulling over when it was turned on, to lie in a parallel plane with the floor. No powder had been scattered about here.

He glanced round the room, returned to the door and read the card: "Mr. Barry George."

The doctor followed him into the rooms opposite these, on the left-hand side of the passage. They were a repetition in design of the two he had already seen but were hung with women's clothes and had a more elaborate assortment of grease paint and cosmetics.

There was a mass of flowers in the star-room. Alleyn read the cards. One in particular caught his eye: "From Anthony Gill to say a most inadequate 'thank you' for the great idea." A vase of red roses stood before the mirror: "To your greatest triumph, Coralie darling. C.C." In Miss Gay's room there were only two bouquets, one from the management and one "from Anthony, with love."

Again in each room he pulled off the lead-in to the heater and looked at the connection.

"All right, aren't they?" said the doctor.

"Quite all right. Tight fit. Good solid grey rubber."

"Well, then—"

Next on the left was an unused room, and opposite it, "Mr. H. J. Bannington." Neither of these rooms had gas fires. Mr. Bannington's dressing-table was littered with the usual array of greasepaint, the materials for his beard, a number of telegrams and letters, and several bills.

"About the body," the doctor began.

"We'll get a mortuary van from the Yard."

"But— Surely in a case of suicide—"

"I don't think this is suicide."

"But, good God!— D'you mean there's been an accident?"

"No accident," said Alleyn.

At midnight, the dressing-room lights in the Jupiter Theatre were brilliant, and men were busy there with the tools of their trade. A constable stood at the stage-door and a van waited in the yard. The front of the house was dimly lit and there, among the shrouded stalls, sat Coralie Bourne, Basil Gosset, H. J. Bannington, Dendra Gay, Anthony Gill, Reynolds, Katie the dresser, and the call-boy. A constable sat behind them and another stood by the doors into the foyer. They stared across the backs of seats at the fire curtain. Spirals of smoke rose from their cigarettes and about their feet were discarded programs. "Basil Gosset presents I CAN FIND MY WAY OUT by Anthony Gill."

In the manager's office Alleyn said: "You're sure of your facts, Mike?"

"Yes, sir. Honestly. I was right up against the entrance into the passage. They didn't see me because I was in the shadow. It was very dark off-stage."

"You'll have to swear to it."

"I know."

"Good. All right, Thompson. Miss Gay and Mr. Gosset may go home. Ask Miss Bourne to come in."

When Sergeant Thompson had gone Mike said: "I haven't had a chance to say I know I've made a perfect fool of myself. Using your card and everything."

"Irresponsible gaiety doesn't go down very well in the service, Mike. You behaved like a clown."

"I *am* a fool," said Mike wretchedly.

The red beard was lying in front of Alleyn on Gosset's desk. He picked it up and held it out. "Put it on," he said.

"She might do another faint."

"I think not. Now the hat: yes—yes, I see. Come in."

Sergeant Thompson showed Coralie Bourne in and then sat at the end of the desk with his notebook.

Tears had traced their course through the powder on her face, carrying black cosmetic with them and leaving the greasepaint shining like snail-tracks. She stood near the doorway looking dully at Michael. "Is he back in England?" she said. "Did he tell you to do this?" She made an impatient movement. "Do take it off," she said, "it's a very bad beard. If Cann had only looked—" Her lips trembled. "Who told you to do it?"

"Nobody," Mike stammered, pocketing the beard. "I mean—As a matter of fact, Tony Gill—"

"*Tony?* But *he* didn't know. Tony wouldn't do it. Unless—"

"Unless?" Alleyn said.

She said frowning: "Tony didn't want Cann to play the part that way. He was furious."

"He says it was his dress for the Chelsea Arts Ball," Mike mumbled. "I brought it here. I just thought I'd put it on—it was idiotic, I know—for fun. I'd no idea you and Mr. Cumberland would mind."

"Ask Mr. Gill to come in," Alleyn said.

Anthony was white and seemed bewildered and helpless. "I've told Mike," he said. "It was my dress for the ball. They sent it round from the costume-hiring place this afternoon but I forgot it. Dendra reminded me and rang up the Delivery people—or Mike, as it turns out—in the interval."

"Why," Alleyn asked, "did you choose that particular disguise?"

"I didn't. I didn't know what to wear and I was too rattled to think. They said they were hiring things for themselves and would get something for me. They said we'd all be characters out of a Russian melodrama."

"Who said this?"

"Well—well, it was Barry George, actually."

"*Barry,*" Coralie Bourne said. "*It was Barry.*"

"I don't understand," Anthony said. "Why should a fancy dress upset everybody?"

"It happened," Alleyn said, "to be a replica of the dress usually worn by Miss Bourne's husband who also had a red beard. That was it, wasn't it, Miss Bourne? I remember seeing him—"

"Oh, yes," she said, "you would. He was known to the police." Suddenly she broke down completely. She was in an armchair near the desk but out of the range of its shaded lamp. She twisted and writhed, beating her hand against the padded arm of the chair. Sergeant Thompson sat with his head bent and his hand over his notes. Mike, after an agonized glance at Alleyn, turned his back. Anthony Gill leant over her: "Don't," he said violently. "Don't! For God's sake, stop."

She twisted away from him and gripping the edge of the desk, began to speak to Alleyn; little by little gaining mastery of herself. "I want to tell you. I want you to understand. Listen." Her husband had been fantastically cruel, she said. "It was a kind of slavery." But when she sued for divorce he brought evidence of adultery with Cumberland. They had thought he knew nothing. "There was an abominable scene. He told us he was going away. He said he'd keep track of us and if I tried again for divorce, he'd come home. He was very friendly with Barry in those days." He had left behind him the first draft of a play he had meant to write for her and Cumberland. It had a wonderful scene for them. "And now you will never have it," he had said, "because there is no other playwright who could make this play for you but I." He was, she said, a melodramatic man but he was never ridiculous. He returned to the Ukraine where he was born and they had heard no more of him. In a little while she would have been able to presume death. But years of waiting did not agree with Canning Cumberland. He drank consistently and at his worst used to imagine her husband was about to return. "He was really terrified of Ben," she said. "He seemed like a creature in a nightmare."

Anthony Gill said: "This play—was it—?"

"Yes. There was an extraordinary similarity between your play and his. I saw at once that Ben's central scene would enormously strengthen your piece. Cann didn't want me to give it to you. Barry knew. He said: 'Why not?' He wanted Cann's part and was furious when he didn't get it. So you see, when he suggested you should dress and make-up like Ben—" She turned to Alleyn. "You see?"

"What did Cumberland do when he saw you?" Alleyn asked Mike.

"He made a queer movement with his hands as if—well, as if he expected me to go for him. Then he just bolted into his room."

"He thought Ben had come back," she said.

"Were you alone at any time after you fainted?" Alleyn asked.

"I? No. No, I wasn't. Katie took me into my dressing room and stayed with me until I went on for the last scene."

"One other question. Can you, by any chance, remember if the heater in your room behaved at all oddly?"

She looked wearily at him. "Yes, it did give a sort of plop, I think. It made me jump. I was nervy."

"You went straight from your room to the stage?"

"Yes. With Katie. I wanted to go to Cann. I tried the door when we came out. It was locked. He said: 'Don't come in.' I said: 'It's all right. It wasn't Ben,' and went on to the stage."

"I heard Miss Bourne," Mike said.

"He must have made up his mind by then. He was terribly drunk when he played his last scene." She pushed her hair back from her forehead. "May I go?" she asked Alleyn.

"I've sent for a taxi. Mr. Gill, will you see if it's there? In the meantime, Miss Bourne, would you like to wait in the foyer?"

"May I take Katie home with me?"

"Certainly. Thompson will find her. Is there anyone else we can get?"

"No, thank you. Just old Katie."

Alleyn opened the door for her and watched her walk into the foyer. "Check up with the dresser, Thompson," he murmured, "and get Mr. H. J. Bannington."

He saw Coralie Bourne sit on the lower step of the dress–circle stairway and lean her head against the wall. Nearby, on a gilt easel, a huge photograph of Canning Cumberland smiled handsomely at her.

H. J. Bannington looked pretty ghastly. He had rubbed his hand across his face and smeared his makeup. Florid red paint from his lips had stained the crêpe hair that had been gummed on and shaped into a beard. His monocle was still in his left eye and gave him an extraordinarily rakish look. "See here," he complained, "I've about *had* this party. When do we go home?"

Alleyn uttered placatory phrases and got him to sit down. He checked over H.J.'s movements after Cumberland left the stage and found that his account tallied with Mike's. He asked if H.J. had visited any of the other dressing rooms and was told acidly that H.J. knew his place in the company. "I remained in my unheated and squalid kennel, thank you very much."

"Do you know if Mr. Barry George followed your example?"

"Couldn't say, old boy. He didn't come near *me.*"

"Have you any theories at all about this unhappy business, Mr. Bannington?"

"Do you mean, why did Cann do it? Well, speak no ill of the dead, but I'd have thought it was pretty obvious he was morbid–drunk. Tight as an owl when we finished the second act. Ask the great Mr. Barry George. Cann took the big scene away from Barry with both hands and left him looking pathetic. All wrong artistically, but that's how Cann was in his cups." H.J.'s wicked little eyes narrowed. "The great Mr. George," he said, "must be feeling very unpleasant by now. You might say he'd got a suicide on his mind, mightn't you? Or don't you know about that?"

"It was not suicide."

The glass dropped from H.J.'s eye. "God!" he said. "God, I told Bob Reynolds! I told him the whole plant wanted overhauling."

"The gas plant, you mean?"

"Certainly. I was in the gas business years ago. Might say I'm in it still with a difference, ha-ha!"

"Ha-ha!" Alleyn agreed politely. He leaned forward. "Look here," he said: "We can't dig up a gas man at this time of night and may very likely need an expert opinion. You can help us."

"Well, old boy, I was rather pining for a spot of shut-eye. But, of course—"

"I shan't keep you very long."

"God, I hope not!" said H.J. earnestly.

Barry George had been made up pale for the last act. Colorless lips and shadows under his cheek bones and eyes had skilfully underlined his character as a repatriated but broken prisoner-of-war. Now, in the glare of the office lamp, he looked like a grossly exaggerated figure of mourning. He began at once to tell Alleyn how grieved and horrified he was. Everybody, he said, had their faults, and poor old Cann was no exception but wasn't it terrible to think what could happen to a man who let himself go downhill? He, Barry George, was abnormally sensitive and he didn't think he'd ever really get over the awful shock this had been to him. What, he wondered, could be at the bottom of it? Why had poor old Cann decided to end it all?

"Miss Bourne's theory," Alleyn began. Mr. George laughed. "Coralie?" he said. "So she's got a theory! Oh, well. Never mind."

"Her theory is this. Cumberland saw a man whom he mistook for her husband and, having a morbid dread of his return, drank the greater part of a bottle of whiskey and gassed himself. The clothes and beard that deceived him had, I understand, been ordered by you for Mr. Anthony Gill."

This statement produced startling results. Barry George broke into a spate of expostulation and apology. There had been no thought in his mind of resurrecting poor old Ben, who was no doubt dead but had been, mind you, in many ways one of the best. They were all to go to the Ball as exaggerated characters from melodrama. Not for the world— He gesticulated and protested. A line of sweat broke out along the margin of his hair. "I don't know what you're getting at," he shouted. "What are you suggesting?"

"I'm suggesting, among other things, that Cumberland was murdered."

"You're mad! He'd locked himself in. They had to break down the door. There's no window. You're crazy!"

"Don't," Alleyn said wearily, "let us have any nonsense about sealed rooms. Now, Mr. George, you knew Benjamin Vlasnoff pretty well. Are you going to tell us that when you suggested Mr. Gill should wear a coat with a fur collar, a black sombrero, black gloves and a red beard, it never occurred to you that his appearance might be a shock to Miss Bourne and to Cumberland?"

"I wasn't the only one," he blustered. "H.J. knew. And if it had scared him off, *she* wouldn't have been so sorry. She'd had about enough of him. Anyway if this is murder, the costume's got nothing to do with it."

"That," Alleyn said, getting up, "is what we hope to find out."

In Barry George's room, Detective-Sergeant Bailey, a fingerprint expert, stood by the gas heater. Sergeant Gibson, a police photographer, and a uniformed constable were near the door. In the centre of the room stood Barry George, looking from one man to another and picking at his lips.

"I don't know why he wants me to watch all this," he said. "I'm exhausted. I'm emotionally used up. What's he doing? Where is he?"

Alleyn was next door in Cumberland's dressing-room, with H.J., Mike and Sergeant Thompson. It was pretty clear now of fumes and the gas fire was burning comfortably. Sergeant Thompson sprawled in the armchair near the heater, his head sunk and his eyes shut.

"This is the theory, Mr. Bannington," Alleyn said. "You and Cumberland have made your final exits; Miss Bourne and Mr. George and Miss Gay are all on the stage. Lord Michael is standing just outside the entrance to the passage. The dressers and stage-staff are watching the play from the side. Cumberland has locked himself in this room. There he is, dead drunk and sound asleep. The gas fire is burning, full pressure. Earlier in the evening he powdered himself and a thick layer of the powder lies undisturbed on the tap. Now."

He tapped on the wall.

The fire blew out with a sharp explosion. This was followed by the hiss of escaping gas. Alleyn turned the taps off. "You see," he said, "I've left an excellent print on the powdered surface. Now, come next door."

Next door, Barry George appealed to him stammering: "But I didn't know. I don't know anything about it. I don't *know.*"

"Just show Mr. Bannington, will you, Bailey?"

Bailey knelt down. The lead-in was disconnected from the tap on the heater. He turned on the tap in the pipe and blew down the tube.

"An air lock, you see. It works perfectly."

H.J. was staring at Barry George. "But I don't know about gas, H.J. H.J., tell them—"

"One moment." Alleyn removed the towels that had been spread over the dressing-shelf, revealing a sheet of clean paper on which lay the rubber push-on connection.

"Will you take this lens, Bannington, and look at it. You'll see that it's stained a florid red. It's a very slight stain but it's unmistakably grease-paint.

And just above the stain you'll see a wiry hair. Rather like some sort of packing material, but it's not that. It's crêpe hair, isn't it?"

The lens wavered above the paper.

"Let me hold it for you," Alleyn said. He put his hand over H.J.'s shoulder and, with a swift movement, plucked a tuft from his false moustache and dropped it on the paper. "Identical, you see. Ginger. It seems to be stuck to the connection with spirit gum."

The lens fell. H.J. twisted round, faced Alleyn for a second, and then struck him full in the face. He was a small man but it took three of them to hold him.

"In a way, sir, it's handy when they have a smack at you," said Detective-Sergeant Thompson half an hour later. "You can pull them in nice and straightforward without any 'will you come to the station and make a statement' business."

"Quite," said Alleyn, nursing his jaw.

Mike said: "He must have gone to the room after Barry George and Miss Bourne were called."

"That's it. He had to be quick. The call-boy would be round in a minute and he had to be back in his own room."

"But look here—what about motive?"

"That, my good Mike, is precisely why, at half-past one in the morning, we're still in this miserable theatre. You're getting a view of the duller aspect of homicide. Want to go home?"

"No. Give me another job."

"Very well. About ten feet from the prompt-entrance, there's a sort of garbage tin. Go through it."

At seventeen minutes to two, when the dressing rooms and passage had been combed clean and Alleyn had called a spell, Mike came to him with filthy hands. *"Eureka,"* he said, "I hope."

They all went into Bannington's room. Alleyn spread out on the dressing-table the fragments of paper that Mike had given him.

"They'd been pushed down to the bottom of the tin," Mike said.

Alleyn moved the fragments about. Thompson whistled through his teeth. Bailey and Gibson mumbled together.

"There you are," Alleyn said at last.

They collected round him. The letter that H. J. Bannington had opened at this same table six hours and forty-five minutes earlier, was pieced together like a jigsaw puzzle.

"Dear H.J.

Having seen the monthly statement of my account, I called at my bank this morning and was shown a check that is undoubtedly a forgery.

Your histrionic versatility, my dear H.J., is only equalled by your audacity as a calligraphist. But fame has its disadvantages. The teller recognized you. I propose to take action."

"Unsigned," said Bailey.

"Look at the card on the red roses in Miss Bourne's room, signed C.C. It's a very distinctive hand." Alleyn turned to Mike. "Do you still want to be a policeman?"

"Yes."

"Lord help you. Come and talk to me at the office tomorrow."

"Thank you, sir."

They went out, leaving a constable on duty. It was a cold morning. Mike looked up at the facade of the Jupiter. He could just make out the shape of the neon sign: I CAN FIND MY WAY OUT *by Anthony Gill.*

THE FOURTH DEGREE

by HUGH PENTECOST

"I would stand over the crib and look down at him," Harvey said, "and I would think how easy it would be to turn him over on his stomach and press his tiny face into the pillow until—until he was dead."

The room was dark except for the faint reflection from a street lamp outside. The reflection showed the outline of Paul Harvey sitting on the edge of a couch, his head buried in his hands.

"Go on, Mr. Harvey." It was a colorless voice that came from some invisible recess of the room. Harvey had spoken of an impulse to murder, but the voice reacted to it as unemotionally as if Harvey had been reading a want-ad in the newspaper.

Harvey turned his head from side to side. "I can't make it come together in the right order," he said. "It—it's all jumbled up."

"That doesn't matter," the voice said. "It's my job to put it together. Just go on, Mr. Harvey. You were talking about the impulse to smother your infant son."

"It was when that got bad that I left Ellen," Harvey said.

"Ellen?"

"My wife," Harvey said. "I haven't told you about her yet, have I? I left her and turned to Ruby. It was the only place I had to turn." He twisted his body as though he were suffering from some physical agony. "Ruby was my secretary at Verne Steiger's. She's a strange girl—not like Ellen, or Lilli. Not like anyone I ever cared for before. We don't have the same tastes, but —well, I knew it would never happen with her. I was positive of that."

" 'It' would never happen?" the voice asked.

"The same old thing," Harvey said. "Just the way it happened at Steiger's. I was head of the packaging department there. Do you know about Verne Steiger? She's the outstanding woman industrial designer in America. Very smart, very high-pressure. We were doing a tremendous business in my department—packages and labels for liquor, for perfumes, for drugs of all kinds, for foods and jewelry. I had twenty designers working under me. Then—it happened. Just as it's always happened."

The distant wail of an ambulance siren crept in and out of the dark room.

"Verne called me into her office one day. There was a man there. He was tall and sleek in a pin-stripe suit with padded shoulders. He looked like the vice-president of an advertising agency. Verne introduced me. She said the work was piling up. That I was doing a fine job, but the work was piling up. So, she said, she had decided to hire an assistant for me. Oh, it sounded plausible enough. But I knew. She had heard that I'd left Ellen. She'd heard about Ruby. This was her way of kissing me off. In a few weeks or a few months this 'vice-president' would have my job. I wasn't going to wait for that, you understand. I wasn't going to let it happen again. So—so I resigned." He was silent, except for his labored breathing.

"Didn't Verne Steiger try to persuade you to stay?" the voice asked.

"Oh, yes, she tried," Harvey said, bitterly. "She pretended that I was indispensable. But I knew. I knew this 'vice-president' was going to destroy my position, just as someone has always destroyed my position. Just as David destroyed it."

"David is the boy—your son?" the voice asked.

Harvey nodded. "I met Ellen in my senior year in college. She was—she was wonderful. The minute I saw her, I knew there'd never be anyone else for me. She had yellow hair—a little like Lilli's—and a lovely warm smile. Even the first time I talked to her I knew she understood me—that she understood how much I needed her. I'd decided to go into industrial designing even then. Ellen studied art. We both liked music—the same kind of music. We didn't have to amuse each other. We didn't even have to talk. We just knew about each other, that's all—and gave to each other.

"We were married, as soon as I'd graduated. There was some money— from Lilli, you understand. I got a job with Verne Steiger almost at once. We took a little house in the suburbs and I commuted to town. We were happy—so damned happy!" Harvey's voice broke. Then he drew a deep breath and went on.

"Very soon Ellen told me we were going to have a child. I could see how happy she was. She seemed to shine with it. I could feel the love pouring out of her to me. It was a wonderful period. I did so well at my job I was made head of the department. I had an office and a secretary of my own—Ruby!" He stopped again, and when he went on, the quality of his voice was dead.

"The child was born," he said. He suddenly beat one fist into the palm of his other hand. "It was a boy. We called him David. That day, *that very day,* I knew it had happened again. I'd lost Ellen. It was not *us* any more. She talked endlessly about David. She took care of him. It seemed as though we were never alone. At night she slept lightly, always listening for some sound from David in the next room. David was her life now. David!

David!—Well, I began drinking. I couldn't stand it. I began missing my regular train. I didn't want to get home till David was asleep. But when I *did* get home she'd make me go in and look at him. I'd stand there, looking down at the crib, and thinking how easy it would be to steal in there during the night and turn him over and hold his face down against the pillow so he couldn't cry—so he couldn't make a sound. Hold him there until—" There was a long silence. "So I left Ellen. It had happened again. Just as it always happened. Just as it happened with Lilli."

"Who was Lilli?" the voice asked, casually, out of the darkness.

"Lilli? Why, Lilli was my mother," Harvey said, as though everyone should have known that.

"Ah, yes. Go on, Mr. Harvey."

"I never knew my father," Harvey said. "He was killed in the First World War. Lilli brought me up. We lived in the country. It's funny, but I can only remember her now in a long white evening dress, bending over my bed—close to me, her warmth near my face—the special fragrance that was hers. We did everything together. She used to read to me. We used to walk in the woods. We were never separated. I loved her—*so much!* Then —then *he* came." The last sentence was spoken with explosive violence.

"Go on," the voice said, calmly.

"His name was Daniel Steele. He was a lawyer connected with a firm that handled the small estate my father'd left Lilli. He'd known my father overseas. He was a big man, with a homely face and a kind smile. I—I actually liked him at first. But he began coming often and I knew from his attitude toward Lilli that it wasn't business. Suddenly he was taking a lot of her time. Well, he came to spend the Labor Day weekend with us. I remember Lilli coming upstairs to kiss me good-night. Oh, she was very affectionate, very loving, but she seemed far away. She seemed nervous and excited. And she went downstairs where *he* was waiting for her. I could hear their voices downstairs, but I couldn't hear what they were saying. I was shut out—shut out as though I didn't belong at all!

"Suddenly it seemed to me I had to know what they were saying. I had to! I crept out of bed to the head of the stairs. I sat there, hugging the newel post, listening. *He* was talking! He was telling her that she should send me away to school. He was telling her that she was spoiling me, that I had to learn to stand on my own feet. He said boarding school would be good for me—that I should be separated from her so that I could learn to be an individual. Lilli sounded unhappy. She told him it would break my heart to be sent away. She knew! But he said I'd thank her for it later. And then—then she agreed." Harvey's voice sank so low it was almost inaudible. "I couldn't stand any more. I slipped back to my room—into bed. My world had come to an end. I rolled over on my stomach and sank my teeth into the pillow. I didn't want them to hear me crying."

"And did you go to boarding school?" the voice asked.

"Oh, yes, I went," Harvey said. "Lilli and Daniel Steele took me there. They were going to be married the next day and go on a honeymoon in the Caribbean. I hated it at school. I couldn't seem to get adjusted. All I could think of was *them*—together. Then—when I'd been there about three weeks, the headmaster sent for me. I knew I hadn't been doing well. But—but he didn't scold me. He—he seemed very upset. Finally, he showed me a newspaper that was lying on his desk. I read the headlines. AIRLINER CRASHES. PLANE STRIKES ALLEGHENY MOUNTAIN TOP. NO SURVIVORS. Right under the headlines was a little box containing a list of the known dead. The names seemed to jump out of the page at me. 'Mr. and Mrs. Daniel Steele.' " Suddenly Harvey's voice rose, harshly. "He had taken Lilli away from me. Taken her away forever!"

The voice was silent, waiting.

"So you see," Harvey said, after a while, "it's always happened. First *he* took Lilli away from me. Then David separated me from Ellen. Then the man at Verne Steiger's. And now—and now—"

"Did you murder Edgar Fremont?" the voice asked, as offhandedly as if he were inquiring about the correct time.

"No! *No!*" Harvey cried. Then his voice broke. "I—I don't think so."

"Tell me about Fremont."

"He—he was an egghead," Harvey said.

"A what?"

"An egghead. That—that's a phrase of Ruby's. She always says she's not interested in Arrow-collar men. Interesting-looking men, queer-looking men are her dish. She calls them eggheads. It's just a phrase."

"I see."

"When—when I left Verne Steiger's I decided to free-lance. I—I came here to live with Ruby in this apartment. It's her apartment, you understand. We—we don't have much in common in the way of pleasures, but we both like to drink in odd places—little bars along Third Avenue. One night, in one of those places, Fremont came in and sat down near us. He was short, with almost no neck, and very broad shoulders. It made his head look large for the rest of him. He looked kind of lonely and depressed. Ruby always likes to talk to strangers and we struck up a conversation. Fremont was shy at first, but finally he got talking. He was a writer, he said. He was writing a novel, and doing odd jobs to eat on while he worked at it. He didn't know many people. He didn't have any friends. Ruby and I felt sorry for him. We asked him to come around to see us—any time, we said.

"Well, he came—often. I liked him. He talked my language about books and art and music. We used to argue about things until Ruby got bored. She—she didn't have a feeling for things like that. So, Fremont used to eat with us often—and drop in to see us without waiting for an invitation. Then—then I began to notice. It—it was happening again. I could see that Ruby was falling for him. I had a quarrel with her about it—and others followed. I started to drink pretty heavily. Today was the pay-off. We had a terrible brawl. She—she told me to get out of here and not come back! I —I wasn't surprised, in a way. As I've told you, it always happens."

"But you did come back," the voice said. "You did come back here tonight."

"Not to the apartment," Harvey said. "Not till the police brought me up. You see—I was very drunk. I'd been drinking in a place down the street for hours. I was sitting in a little booth all by myself when, suddenly, Fremont was there. He slid into the seat opposite me. Things were all kind of blurred. He looked like a—like a monstrous little gargoyle sitting there.

" 'I've been looking for you everywhere,' he said to me.

" 'Go away,' I said.

" 'You've got to snap out of this,' he said. 'You're killing yourself, Paul. Ruby isn't worth it.'

" 'That's a funny thing for you to say,' I said.

" 'What do you mean, Paul?' he asked.

" 'I mean *you're* the reason Ruby and I have quarreled. There's no use pretending, Fremont. You're in love with her and you've taken her away from me.'

" 'In love with her!' I remember he started laughing. It sounded crazy. 'Ruby has nothing for me, Paul. Nothing! She has nothing for you, only you won't recognize it. You're killing yourself over a cheap little tart who'll leave you the minute she's bled you dry.'

" 'You can't talk that way about Ruby,' I said. But I wanted to believe he felt that way, do you understand? I wanted to believe it, because then— well, then it might not happen again, the way it always had.

"He stayed with me quite a while, telling me that I'd be better off without Ruby. It—it sounded just like Daniel Steele telling Lilli I'd be better off at school. Better off—with separation and death to follow. Finally, he left me. Then—then I got to thinking. Maybe he just wanted to make sure I wasn't seeing Ruby. Maybe he was going to see Ruby now, being certain I wasn't there. I had to know. I *had* to know. So I got out of there. I—I was drunker than I realized."

Again he paused to take a deep breath. "So—so I came over here to see. This—this old brownstone has a fire-escape leading down into a backyard. I guess you know that. I—I thought I'd go into the backyard and up the fire escape. So I went around the back way and into the yard. I—I was stumbling around there in the dark when suddenly there were lights everywhere, and policemen, and they dragged me up here and—and Fremont was lying there on the floor with—with his face shot off. And they showed me my gun. *My* gun!"

"Your gun," the voice said. "And mud on the fire escape from the backyard. And mud on your shoes from the backyard. Are you sure you didn't come up here?"

"I *was* sure," Harvey said, "before the police worked on me. I was sure. But I was very drunk. And—and maybe I forgot. I know about those things, doctor. I know sometimes, in a situation like this, you draw a blank. Maybe I drew a blank. Is—is that what you think?"

"No," the voice said.

There was the sound of a clicking light switch and the room was flooded with light. It revealed Paul Harvey, slender, dark, his wavy hair damp with perspiration, his brown eyes hollow, haunted. The voice also took shape. The shape was that of a small gray man, an anonymous-looking gray man. No one would ever have turned to look at him on the street. There was nothing about him to arouse interest. He was just small, and gray, and neutral.

The gray man looked around the room, his eyes mild and thoughtful. It was a room that would have had no charm for a man of taste, a man such as Paul Harvey appeared to be. There was a daybed on one side of the room, stacked high with pale pink and green satin cushions. There was a goldfish bowl on a stand by the window with a waving green plant that grew under the water, and two sullen fish. There was a whatnot in one corner laden with souvenirs—souvenirs from Coney Island and Broadway shooting galleries and Third Avenue junk shops. On the wall there were cheaply framed photographs of vacation incidents, intimate yet meaningless to a stranger. There was a reproduction of that tired Maxfield Parrish of the nude boy in a swing against the background of an unreal sky. On the mantelpiece was a stuffed toy panda, ten-cent-store variety, staring out at the room with shoe-button eyes.

The rug was a faded pink broadloom, except in the corner by the front door where there was a dark, irregular stain where Edgar Fremont had bled and died.

The gray man walked over to an inner door which led to the kitchen and bedroom. He opened the door.

"All right, Lieutenant," he said.

Three men came out of the bedroom: Lieutenant Mason of Homicide and two uniformed policemen. Mason was one of the department's bright young men—college degree, good clothes. He looked like a business executive.

"All right, boys, you can take him downtown," Mason said.

The two policemen moved in on either side of Paul Harvey and helped him to his feet.

"Just a minute," Harvey said. "Can I see her for a moment, Lieutenant?"

"Not now," Mason said.

"But I—"

"Not now!"

The policemen led Harvey out of the room. The sound of their feet on the stairs was plainly audible. The little gray man was standing by the window, looking down at the street.

"Well, Dr. Smith?" Mason asked, when they were alone.

Dr. Smith sighed. "God, what children suffer without their parents ever knowing!" he said.

Mason smiled to himself. He'd worked with Dr. John Smith before. He knew you didn't come at things directly with him. Mason remembered his first reaction to the little gray man; that he was the only person who could sign a hotel register 'John Smith' and be believed! Mason also knew how deceptive Dr. Smith's appearance was. Let the police give a crook a thorough going-over with all the approved third-degree methods and fail, and then Dr. Smith would be called in. The motives for murder, he claimed, were to be found, not in bank balances or vaults, not in apparent jealousies or greed, but in the dark and inaccessible corridors of the mind. Searching those corridors, battling with words and ideas, Dr. Smith called "The Fourth Degree."

"I never get to talk to anyone," Dr. Smith said, turning from the window, "till you and your boys have reduced him to a state of abject terror, Mason. Some day you may wake up to the fact that the psychiatrist should be called in first, not last!"

"I just work here," Mason said, grinning. "What do you think about Harvey, Doctor?"

"What I think isn't evidence," Dr. Smith said. "And evidence is all you're concerned with."

"We've got plenty of evidence," Mason said. "We have the note Ruby Lewis left for Harvey before she went out to the Island for the weekend. Here, you haven't actually seen it." Mason took a letter from his pocket and handed it to Smith. The doctor slid on a pair of heavy, bone-rimmed spectacles.

"Paul:" the note began,

I have had enough of your accusations and crazy jealousy of Edgar. I am going away for the weekend to the Island—The Lambert House. I expect you to have all your things moved out when I get back. This is final. Ruby

"The motive is clear," Mason said. "Harvey was crazy-jealous of Edgar Fremont. Fremont came up here and as he walked in the front door Harvey let him have it. Then he went down the fire escape to the backyard where we found him—*and* the gun. His gun! Motive, opportunity, weapon."

"I understand there were no fingerprints on the gun?" Dr. Smith said.

"Naturally—he wiped them off," Mason said.

"Unnaturally," the doctor muttered to himself. "He wiped his fingerprints off the gun, so he wouldn't be caught—and then he waited in the backyard for fifteen minutes while neighbors called the police and they came here with sirens screaming, went upstairs, found the body, and finally —God knows how long afterwards—went down in the yard and found Harvey still waiting for them."

"He was drunk," Mason said. "He didn't know what he was doing."

"But he knew enough to wipe his fingerprints off the gun?"

Mason shrugged. "Everybody knows enough to do that."

The doctor shrugged. "Physical evidence is your department, Mason," he said. "You wouldn't have called me in unless there were some doubts in your mind."

Mason gave the little gray man a wry smile. "I felt sorry for Harvey," he said. "Can you beat that? I felt sorry for him."

"There's no reason to be ashamed of a decent human emotion," Dr. Smith said.

"All the evidence indicates that Harvey set a deliberate trap for Fremont. That he invited him here, laid in wait for him, and shot him when he arrived. That's first-degree murder and it means the chair. But somehow— well, of course if he were a mental case—"

"He isn't—in the legal sense," Dr. Smith said:

"Then that's that," Mason said, and sighed.

"Harvey's a man who has been living under the terrific pressures produced by a childhood trauma," Dr. Smith said. "It has influenced every relationship and every major crisis of his life."

"And finally drove him to murder," Mason said.

"I'm not sure at all. Mason, you look for patterns on the surface—clues, fingerprints, alibis. I look for internal patterns. Harvey's is clear. Every time he's been confronted with a certain kind of situation—one in which it seemed that some woman who was close and dear to him was about to be stolen away by someone else—he reacted in exactly the same way. He ran! Now, if Harvey killed Fremont it means that pattern, which he has followed all his life, was suddenly altered. From all we know about him he should have run this time. But if he killed Fremont, he upset his whole behavior pattern. Why? *Why?*"

"I suppose there came a point when he just blew his top," Mason said.

"We have no right to suppose," Dr. Smith said. "At least, I have to know to be satisfied. Tell me something about the girl, Ruby Lewis."

"Not much to tell," Mason said. "She isn't your type—or mine! Or

Harvey's for that matter. She's like this room—a sort of brightly tinted Easter egg in a ten-cent store. But she's in the clear. She was at the Lambert Inn all evening—thirty miles from here."

"I'd like to talk to her," Dr. Smith said. "Maybe she can tell us something about Harvey that will explain what we don't quite understand at the moment."

"No reason why you shouldn't," Mason said. "She's in the bedroom. Perhaps you'd better see her there. She has a natural reluctance to come in here. We showed her Fremont before we cleaned up the place. It was pretty rough."

"Let's get it over with," Dr. Smith said.

Mason started toward the door of the bedroom. "She's got a friend with her. Fellow named George Lambert who owns the hotel where she was staying. He drove her into town."

The bedroom was almost dark. The only light came from a dim, shaded lamp on the bedside table. It showed Ruby Lewis stretched out on the bed, dabbing at her eyes with a lace-edged handkerchief. There was an almost overpowering scent of perfume in the room. Ruby had flaxen-colored hair done in a feather cut that gave it the look of a curly halo—an artificial halo. Her complexion was peach ice cream. Her figure made it quite understandable why men should be instantly interested.

A man came over to stand in the circle of light from the lamp. He was tall and handsome in a sleek way. His clothes were a little too sharp, and he wore a checkered vest such as horsemen sometimes wear in the field.

Mason introduced Dr. Smith to Ruby and George Lambert.

"I've heard about you, Doc," Lambert said. "The Madden case. I knew Senator Madden's son. You pulled him out of quite a hole."

"You own the Lambert House where Miss Lewis was staying tonight?" asked Dr. Smith.

"That's right, Doc. And that's only the beginning. I'm planning a chain of hotels."

"Dr. Smith wants to ask a few questions," Mason said. Obviously he was annoyed by Lambert's breezy manner toward the doctor.

"Sure, sure," Lambert said. "Ruby and I got nothing to hide. Our alibis stand up, don't they, Inspector?"

"Lieutenant," Mason said, sharply. "Yes, they stand up, Mr. Lambert."

With a cheerful smile which indicated he was ready for anything, Lambert turned to where Dr. Smith had been standing. Dr. Smith wasn't there. He had melted somewhere into the shadows of the room.

"I think Dr. Smith wants to hear your story, Miss Lewis," Mason said.

Ruby lifted the lace handkerchief to her eyes. "It's awful," she said. "To think that if I'd called a doctor for Paul long ago this might not have happened."

Her voice was disillusioning. It sent the curve of her charm dipping sharply downward. It was flat, complaining.

"There's no doubt in your mind that Harvey killed Fremont?" Dr. Smith's voice came from a dark corner of the room.

"He was insanely jealous," Ruby said. "He was jealous of all men but he was insanely jealous of Edgar."

"You wouldn't believe it, just meeting him," George Lambert said. "He seemed like such a quiet guy."

"You broke off with Harvey today, didn't you, Miss Lewis?"

"It was final today," she said. "But it's been coming for a long time. We had a stinker of a quarrel last night about Edgar. This morning, after Paul went to his studio to work, I thought it all over. I decided that was that."

"So you left the note for him and went down to Mr. Lambert's hotel?"

"I had to get hold of my nerves," Ruby said. "George had told me to come any time I wanted."

"Did anyone else have a key to your apartment besides Harvey?"

Ruby pushed herself up on her elbows and peered into the dark. "What kind of a girl do you think I am?" she demanded, indignantly.

"I have no idea, Miss Lewis," the doctor said. "That's why I asked."

"I was strictly on the level with Paul!" she said. "But he was insanely jealous, just the same."

"So you said. You went out to the Lambert House by train?"

"Do I look like I owned a Rolls Royce?" Ruby said, still angry. She lowered herself to the pillows again. "Will they electrocute him or just put him away somewhere?"

Mason answered that one. "It was clearly a premeditated crime. That means the chair."

"For someone," said the colorless voice from the corner of the room.

Ruby sat bolt upright on the bed. "You mean you don't think it was Paul? Why, they caught him here—it was his gun—he was insanely jealous of Edgar. He—"

"It's just that I have to make the internal facts fit the external facts," Dr. Smith said. "I'd like to know whatever you can tell me about Edgar Fremont, Miss Lewis."

Ruby's voice took on a peculiarly harsh quality. "He was going places," she said. "Everyone said he was going to be a really important writer. He just sold his book to one of those book clubs—and Hollywood. He was going to be rich and famous."

"He didn't like you, did he, Miss Lewis?"

"You wouldn't think that if you heard the way he tried to break things up between me and Paul. He was always trying to break things up between me and Paul."

"He wanted you for himself?"

"Why would he try to break things up between me and Paul if he didn't?"

"There could be other reasons."

"Look, Doc, take it easy," George Lambert said. "Ruby don't have to take that kind of a going-over from no one. What other reasons could the guy have?"

"Maybe he liked Harvey," Dr. Smith said. "Maybe he thought it would be good for Harvey if he went back to his wife and child."

"There wasn't anything stopping Paul, if that was what he wanted," Ruby said. "Paul didn't want anything but me. He said over and over he'd never let me go."

"He threatened you?"

"He acted crazy. He said he couldn't stand it if anything happened between us. He acted like it was a matter of life and death."

"It turned out to be a matter of life and death, didn't it?" the doctor said, quietly. "Were you afraid of him?"

"I tell you, he acted crazy!" Ruby said.

"Of course she was afraid of him," George Lambert broke in. "She told me about it one weekend when they were at my place. I told her she could call on me any time Harvey got out of line."

"If I hadn't known I could call on George I'd have been half out of my mind," Ruby said. She looked up at Lambert who was fingering the edge of his gaudy vest.

"What attracted you to Paul Harvey in the first place?" Dr. Smith asked.

"I was his secretary. Everyone said he was going places. He was one of the best designers in the business. I figured he'd become a partner of Verne Steiger's."

"But you stayed with him after he left Steiger's?"

"Well, I didn't think he was going to just quit and drink himself to death. I figured he'd start a business of his own."

"So you only stayed with him because you thought he had a successful future?"

"Is there anything wrong with that?" Ruby demanded. "A woman has a right to expect something from a man, doesn't she?"

"And if he doesn't produce it?"

"You have to look out for yourself," Ruby said. "That's why I finally broke off with him."

"I thought it was because you were afraid of him."

"That, too. He acted crazy about Fremont, I keep telling you."

"And there was no reason for his acting that way because Fremont didn't want you," Dr. Smith said.

"That stuck-up jerk!" Ruby said. "He didn't think I was good enough for him—or Paul either!"

There was a long silence and then the voice came from the corner of the room once more. "What are your plans now, Miss Lewis?"

"Plans?"

"Your affair with Harvey is over. What now?"

"I don't know that's any of your business!" Ruby said.

"It's nothing to be ashamed of, baby," George Lambert said. He turned toward the direction of the voice. "Ruby and I are going to be married, Doc. It's time she had some of the things out of life she wants."

"It might be rather costly for you, Mr. Lambert."

"Nothing's too good for Ruby," Lambert said.

The doctor came out of the darkness and stood in the circle of light, looking down at Ruby. "A perfect epitaph for Miss Lewis, I should say."

"Now look, Doc—" Lambert's voice was angry.

Dr. Smith ignored him. "I have the feeling Miss Lewis usually gets what she wants. Of course she failed once."

Ruby sat up. "I don't like the way you talk to me," she said. She looked at Mason. "Do I have to stand for these cracks, Lieutenant?"

"She missed out on Hollywood and the glamorous position of being a successful author's wife. You wanted Fremont pretty badly, didn't you, Miss Lewis, and he laughed at you."

George Lambert took a step forward and dropped his big hand on Dr. Smith's shoulder. "That'll be about all from you, Doc," he said.

"Oh, I'm quite through," Dr. Smith said. "But I don't imagine you'll sleep very well at night, Lambert—after you're married."

"What do you mean?"

"Well, if the chain of hotels is a little slow in coming about—"

"What do you mean?"

"Miss Lewis might be disappointed."

"So?"

"She doesn't like to be disappointed, Mr. Lambert. Harvey disappointed her, and he's in a very bad spot. Fremont disappointed her, and he's dead. It seems to be extremely unhealthy to disappoint Miss Lewis."

Ruby's voice rose shrilly. "Make him stop talking that way, Lieutenant! I'll sue him! He's got no right to talk that way. I'll—"

"Alibis are not my province," Dr. Smith said, his gray eyes fixed steadily on George Lambert. "I don't know what's wrong with Miss Lewis's alibi, Lambert. But I do know I wouldn't be in your shoes for a million dollars. As a psychiatrist I know that people are driven by repetitive compulsions they can't control. Harvey was a man who always ran away from disaster— before it happened! He actually made it happen by running away. He ran away from the danger of Fremont by drinking."

"What's all that long-haired talk got to do with me?" Ruby demanded.

"Your pattern is more aggressive, Miss Lewis. You want money and position, and you keep after it—first an important designer, then an important writer, now a chain of hotels. What next, Miss Lewis? And how will you get rid of Lambert when the time comes to move on and up?"

Lambert moistened his lips. "Get *rid* of me?"

"I hope for your sake the chain of hotels is a pretty sure thing," the doctor said, "and that it makes you a great deal of money. Otherwise—"

Ruby sat up on the bed, shrieking. "Get that filthy old jerk out of here! Get him out of here! Get him out!"

"We're going, Miss Lewis," Dr. Smith said. He turned to Lambert once more. "Good luck to you, Mr. Lambert. I have a feeling you're going to need it. Come, Mason."

"Wait!" Lambert said and his voice shook. "You—you think she killed Fremont and—and threw the blame on Harvey?"

"I think it's within the framework of her pattern, Mr. Lambert. I think she is capable of it. But—well, she has an alibi. So, of course—"

Beads of sweat glittered on Lambert's forehead. "Lieutenant," he said to Mason, "I—I think I'd like to alter my original statement."

A torrent of screaming abuse came flooding out of Ruby's twisted red mouth. Lambert backed slowly away from the bed toward the door.

" '. . . it isn't that I lied, you understand,' " Mason read aloud from the typewritten pages of George Lambert's new statement, " 'it's just that I didn't tell you everything. Ruby did arrive in the late afternoon and she went to her room, and she was there when you phoned at midnight. What I didn't tell was that she asked to borrow my car so she could go to the movies in town. I let her take the car and I didn't think anything of it until I was driving her to New York after your call. Then she said, 'George, maybe it would be easier for me if you didn't tell the police I went to the movies.' I asked her why, and she said everyone connected with Harvey would be under suspicion and if I didn't tell about her going to the movies she'd have a perfect alibi, and she wouldn't be bothered by the cops. I didn't see any harm in that because I knew—that is, I *thought* I knew—that she was in the clear. I still think she is, but I thought you ought to have all the facts.' "

Dr. Smith was standing by the windows in Mason's office, looking down at the street where the first early morning traffic was beginning to roll.

"There's not much doubt about it," Mason said. "She still contends she went to the movies—a double feature. But she's got an extraordinary lack of memory about those two pictures. The three hours involved was ample time for her to drive to New York, kill Fremont, and get back to the Lambert House without rousing suspicion. She probably had a date with Fremont . . . and he kept it because he wanted to help Harvey. But there's one thing that bothers me, doctor. Why? She didn't have to kill Fremont to get rid of him. He wasn't in her way."

"I'm bad on quotations, particularly corny ones," the doctor said. "But there's something somewhere about the anger of a woman scorned—Fremont had rejected her. Harvey had failed her and would probably make any new relationship extremely difficult. It was a perfect scheme for paying off the one and getting rid of the other."

Mason nodded. "What made you think Lambert would break?"

Dr. Smith turned away from the window. There was a faint smile on his lips. "That checkered vest," he said. "That vest, Mason, matched Ruby Lewis's living room, with the toy panda and the goldfish. They went together like ham and eggs. It occurred to me, without knowing much about Lambert beyond a surface character reading, that he and Ruby were birds of a feather. I was pretty certain Lambert would be much more interested in himself than in any woman, no matter how attractive. He was the male counterpart of Ruby, selfish, greedy, self-centered."

"What made you think Ruby's alibi was phony?" Mason asked.

"It's just the different points of view from which we work, Mason," Dr. Smith said. "You accept the outward physical facts as unassailable, and you make the internal facts fit them. My approach is just the reverse. I believe the internal facts are unassailable. The internal truth about Harvey made me certain he would run, not kill. That left Ruby or Lambert, both of whom were quite capable of killing. Ruby seemed the most likely to me because she had the most to gain—revenge for a jilting and a failure, a chain of hotels, and a man of her own kind."

"So much for scientific crime investigation," Mason said, dryly.

"You think the study of crippled personalities isn't a science?" Dr. Smith asked.

Mason pushed back his chair and stood up. "God forbid I should make such a claim," he said. He punched out his cigarette in the ashtray on the desk. "I'd like to ask you one more favor, doctor."

"Yes?"

"I'd like you to go with me while I break the news to Paul Harvey that he's free," Mason said. "He's had a pretty rough time. He has a wife and a child and a real talent, and I think there must be some way we could help him to rehabilitate himself."

"Of course I'll go with you," Dr. Smith said. "It's time Harvey stopped being afraid of ghosts."

"And that," Mason said, "holds for most of us."

MIDNIGHT ADVENTURE

by MICHAEL ARLEN

Now it is told in London how on one winter's night not long ago a gentleman who was walking from Grosvenor Square down Carlos Place was accosted by a lady in a peculiar manner and with curious results.

Earlier that same evening two gentlemen of correct appearance might have been observed dining together at a quiet corner table in the restaurant of a London hotel which is famous for the distinction of its guests. Our two friends, one lined and gray-haired, the other younger and lean and uncommonly handsome in a saturnine way, appeared to be absorbed in conversation.

The younger gentleman talked the least and, as was only proper, listened attentively to his gray-haired companion. This was not surprising, since the father was telling his son in the most urgent terms that only a rich marriage could appease the ferocity of their overdraft at the bank.

In days gone by, when the last King of Navarre strode into history as Henri IV, first and finest of the Bourbon Kings of France, the mountainous half of Navarre became, owing to reasons we cannot go into now, the Duchy of Suiza. The Dukes of Suiza were royal in that pathetically half-starved way which is disparagingly known as "minor." For several centuries the Duchy of Suiza was respected, or perhaps overlooked, as an independent kingdom, and eventually forgotten.

The two gentlemen at dinner were Carlos XXVII, Duke of Suiza, and his only son, Prince Rudolf. But, as the worldly father pointed out to his worldly son, high titles like Duke and Prince without the cash to support them added up to so much spinach put before a starving man.

"In short," said Duke Carlos, who liked to speak the English he had picked up from the American visitors who had thronged the Casinos of his duchy before his exile, "we are bust wide open, boy—unless you shake the Christmas tree to some effect."

Rudolf sipped his champagne with an air of saturnine fatality. "Our reputation," said he, "is enough to wither even the stoutest Christmas tree as we approach."

"You must find some sweet young innocent, Rudolf. Or haven't I already heard something about you and the American heiress, Baba Carstairs? I can only hope, my friend, that you are impressing the girl as being a romantic person—for you can *look* extremely romantic, particularly when you are telling lies."

Prince Rudolf finished the champagne in his glass. "Dear father," said he at last, "have you ever been in love?"

Duke Carlos looked at his son with pity.

"Frequently," said he. "Why, did you think you had invented love?"

"Perhaps," said the young man moodily, "I could suggest some badly needed improvements on it."

"So you are going to tell me that you are still crazy about that Follies girl you met last year in Paris?"

"No, not last year, but ten years ago, and not a Follies girl, but a girl. But perhaps it would be better for men like us not even to think about her."

"You look so romantic when you speak of her, Rudolf, that I feel sure you told her many lies. Forget her, boy. Remember our traditions. Remember our name. Remember our overdraft. In short, remember Miss Carstairs."

Now, it is of this Prince Rudolf it is told that, as later that night he walked moodily to his modest lodgings in the sulky shadows behind the clubs of Piccadilly, he was accosted by a lady in a peculiar manner.

He saw a car, long and dark, of sober elegance. It passed close by him, as such cars do, with no more sound than a flick of a cat's whiskers. A few yards ahead, it stopped.

As Rudolf walked past, his moody gaze ahead, he was thinking how much better it would be for that pretty, nice, empty-headed little millionairess Baba Carstairs if a selfish brute like himself left her alone. He liked her very well, of course. But it would not have occurred to him to marry her if she had been poor.

It was at that moment that a corner of his eye was caught by something strange and bright in the cold night. It was a hand and arm alight with jewelry against the black background of the car.

"Can I drop you?" said a low voice.

Rudolf, who had been very well brought up, as regards superficial manners anyway, took off his hat to the brilliant arm, observing at the same time that the hand was slender and young and cool, like the voice.

"You are very kind," said he. "But I have only a short way to go."

"There is nothing to fear," said the cool voice.

The correct and incurious profile of the elderly chauffeur at the wheel betrayed nothing but the propriety of his employer. Rudolf, stepping closer to the open window, caught a glimpse of the lady's face within the shadows

—and was lightly touched by a faint perfume that reminded him so poignantly of a past enchantment that for an instant he walked again in a garden with a slight fair girl.

Telling himself that he was a fool, he swiftly opened the door and climbed within.

"Thank you," said the lady, "for being both brave and polite."

Prince Rudolf smiled. "I fancy it is neither courage nor politeness that inspires men to do what beautiful women ask them."

He found the lady examining him with the utmost gravity.

"Height, five-eleven," he said, "hair, black; eyes, brown; one small mole on left cheek; self-confident manner; no distinctive peculiarities. . . ."

Her faint smile did not touch the gravity of her eyes, of which he had already formed a very favorable opinion. They were direct and blue, of a brilliant darkness, like the blue sea whipped by wind. The lady's hair, too, was maybe as you like it, fair and curly, but without frivolity. Rudolf, experienced in petty encounters, saw at once that only some great urgency had forced this lady to address a stranger, for she could not be corrupted by small desires.

"And I?" she said.

He noticed, but without surprise, that the car was moving. It was agreeable to find that he was not so tired of the world as he had fancied he was.

"And I, sir?" she said. "How would you describe the stranger who has kidnapped you?"

"I like you," said Prince Rudolf.

"Dear me," said the lady, "you *are* quick."

"That's me all over," said Rudolf. "The minute I set eyes on you, I said to myself, there's a woman I like a lot."

"I hadn't any idea," said the lady, "that conversation with a stranger could be made so easy as you make it."

"You are not a stranger. I recognized you right away."

"Me? You recognized me?"

"Of course. You have never heard the old chestnut about the woman whom a man always meets too late?"

"Too late? Dear me, for what?"

"For his peace of mind, since she is usually already married."

"Since I am single, sir, your peace of mind is safe. But thank you for saying nice things about my appearance."

"Not only your appearance, madam. I have also taken a big liking to your character."

"Then you are a clairvoyant?"

"A connoisseur—a student of dreams."

"Dreams? Were we talking of dreams?"

"No, but we are going to. When men dream," said Prince Rudolf, "of that kind of happiness which is too often forbidden them owing to having married in haste, or some other silly reason, their dreams are inspired by thoughts of the perfect companion. It is not necessary to shut my eyes to describe her. She must be exquisite, of course, but without the trivial emphasis that merely smart women lay on the small fashions of the moment. Her beauty should wear a certain gravity, for does she not understand much and forgive everything, particularly the greed and the follies of men? She must be wise, naturally, but not too wise never to make a mistake, never to take a risk, never to sigh for romance, never to hurt herself. She will always do her utmost not to hurt anybody else, and at all difficult times she will take refuge in laughing at herself, for above everything she is gifted with the good manners of the heart."

"Dear me," she said, "I never knew that the dreams of men were so informed by kindness. Your reputation, Prince Rudolf, scarcely prepares a listener for such sentiments."

"Madam, in your company I had permitted myself for one moment to forget all but the little that is best in me. But now that you have reminded me of my ordinary self I must admit that I should like nothing so much as to kiss you and damn the consequences."

"That rebuke," she said, "was well deserved. For no one could have been more polite than you. You have not yet asked me how I knew you, where we are going, or who I am. I recognized you from your photographs. I followed you from the restaurant where you dined. We are going to my house, which is here in Belgrave Square. My name is no matter. And I am going to ask you, sir, to do me a service. You see, I make no excuses. My behavior is too outrageous for excuses to have any value. If you wish, you may say good night now, my car will take you home, and I shall be the richer for having enjoyed an instructive conversation with a man of the world."

Undeterred by her gravity, Rudolf laughed outright. For many months he had not felt so light-hearted.

"Miss X," said he, "it was you who spoke of my reputation. So, if you think you can get rid of me so easily, you're crazy."

Her level eyes searched his face. He was sobered by the profound contempt that seemed to add a dark light to their dark brilliance. He would have noticed this contempt before had he not been so engaged, as was his way, in trying to make an impression on a beautiful woman.

"You are afraid of nothing, Prince Rudolf?"

They were on the pavement now, before the house, and he glanced at the dark imposing building.

"Of a great many things," he said, "but of no possible hurt that could come to me from you."

"Perhaps," she said, "you are wrong there."

An elderly manservant let them in. Rudolf, divesting himself of his overcoat in the large hall, had time to realize the substantial wealth of his surroundings. From above the great fireplace, in which the ashes of a log fire glowed dimly, one of Van Dyck's cavaliers thoughtfully measured the world, while on another wall was the dark and sour visage of a Rembrandt.

Then he was shown into a long paneled library. It was dimly lit, and in front of the fireplace at the far end stood the strange lady and a tall, fair, red-complexioned bull of a man of about his own age.

"This is my brother," said the lady, "Mr. Geraldine. I am Iris Geraldine."

Mr. Geraldine's brick-red complexion sharpened by contrast the paleness of his cold blue eyes. He made no attempt to conceal the hostility with which he measured the faintly smiling face of his guest.

"So now you realize," he said, "why I told my sister not to give you her name, for had you known it you certainly would not have come."

"You misjudge me, Mr. Geraldine. For the sake of a woman like your sister I should willingly risk much more than a disagreeable encounter with a man like her brother. Now what is it you want with me?"

"Surely, Prince Rudolf, you can easily guess what I——"

"Wait," said Rudolf sharply. "Before we go any further you will be so good as to ask me to sit down. I thank you. Then you will invite me to have a drink. Thank you. I prefer brandy."

Mr. Geraldine's handsome brick-red face broke into a fighting grin. You could see at once that he had good hands with a horse, that dogs would come to his whistle, and that he could both give and take a kick in the pants.

"Iris," he turned to his sister, "perhaps you had better leave Prince Rudolf and me together."

Miss Geraldine had not yet glanced at her kidnapped guest. She sat, somewhat stiffly, in a high Queen Anne chair, her eyes lost in the leaping colors of the bright fire.

"I am here," said Prince Rudolf, "at Miss Geraldine's express invitation, and I am enjoying her company very much. I hope you will stay with us, Miss Geraldine. No doubt your brother is a splendid fellow, but he is not half so pretty to look at as you are."

She held her small head very still and erect, and he was conscious that she would much prefer to ignore his presence. She spoke to the fire, in her low cool voice, as though she was thinking out loud.

"I do not like," she said, "to see any man humiliated, no matter how much he may deserve it."

"I'll risk that," said Rudolf. "Go ahead, Mr. Geraldine. As you said, I know you are the chairman of the great and famous private bank of Geraldine Brothers, and that you are the trustee of the estate of Miss Carstairs."

"Not only her trustee, Prince, but also her late father's most intimate friend. She told me no later than this afternoon that she had made up her mind to marry you."

"She ought to have told me first," said Prince Rudolf, "but her decision makes me so happy that I must forgive her. Thank you for your congratulations, Mr. Geraldine."

"Hers is a great fortune," said Mr. Geraldine dryly.

"So my father has told me every day for weeks. He will be very pleased about this, as he has been so hard up lately. How agreeable it is to meet nice young girls like Miss Carstairs who think nothing of bringing a little sunshine into the lives of tired old men like my father. When I tell him tomorrow, he will be very touched."

"He won't," Mr. Geraldine said, "because you won't."

Prince Rudolf's attention appeared at that moment to be engaged in an exhaustive study of Iris Geraldine's profile, and that he thought very highly of it was obvious from his expression.

"I won't . . . what?" he said absently.

"You won't tell your father you are going to marry Miss Carstairs, Prince, because you are not going to."

"All complaints on that head," said Rudolf, "should be addressed to Miss Carstairs in person. It is her life. It is her money. It is to be her marriage. And I am her choice."

"A girl so young," said Mr. Geraldine, "does not always know what is best for her. I cannot forbid Baba to marry you, because she is of age. I can't persuade her not to by telling her that you, in spite of your great name, are a well-known waster and adventurer, that you are notorious both for your affairs with women and for your dexterity in getting your bills paid, because she dismisses all such facts as reflections on a misunderstood, handsome, and romantic prince."

"And quite right too. That ought to teach you, Mr. Geraldine, not to go about putting nasty thoughts into young girls' heads. Just because nobody has ever thought you romantic since you were a little boy in velvet pants, why be jealous of me?"

"I am never jealous," said Mr. Geraldine, "of a crook."

"Am I to understand, Mr. Geraldine, that you have just called me a crook?"

"You are. I have."

"In that case," said Prince Rudolf, rising from his chair, "I must have another brandy. You have interested me greatly, Mr. Geraldine. Won't you please develop your theory?"

"It is not a theory, Prince, but a fact. But I had much rather not elaborate it—and I won't, if you promise not to see Miss Carstairs again."

"But that would never do, Mr. Geraldine. The poor girl would be very upset. My poor father would be very disappointed. And my poor creditors would be very angry."

"Very well," said Mr. Geraldine grimly. "On the formal announcement of your engagement to Miss Carstairs I shall notify the proper authorities that I have in my possession a check drawn in your favor by a Mr. John Anderson and cashed by you, which I have every reason to suspect is a forgery."

"But why suspect?" said Prince Rudolf. "You know it's a forgery."

"So you admit forging Anderson's signature to a check for £1,000?"

Prince Rudolf glanced aside at Iris Geraldine—and instantly found, to his surprise and consternation, that something inside him was beating painfully. He could not immediately put this curious phenomenon down to a disturbance of his heart-action, since he had for some years regarded his heart as a leathery veteran, dingily and immovably fixed within a dark cloud of cigarette smoke. But he was a reasonable man and had to face the fact that here the old veteran was, thumping like a boy's just because a fair young woman with level eyes was regarding him gravely and impersonally, as a scientist might regard a maggot.

"Mr. Geraldine," he said at last, and his voice for the first time was without any mockery at all, "when John Anderson died last week, did you not, as his executor, find any note among his papers referring to me?"

"I did not."

"I think you did. I think you have that note in your possession. John Anderson was a gambler, and like nearly all gamblers he was a very honest man. Do you still say that he left no letter in his handwriting with reference to me?"

"I have already said so, Prince Rudolf."

"Then I should like to put it on record, Mr. Geraldine, that you are a liar. This may be due to the fact that you were badly brought up, but the fact remains that you are a liar. A year ago John Anderson bet me a hundred pounds that I could not forge his signature and get away with it without suspicion. It was to be for a check of a thousand pounds merely so that the signature should be scrutinized carefully at the bank. I succeeded, returned the thousand pounds in cash to Anderson, who gave me the bet I had won and also a receipt for the sum of the forged check. I have that receipt. Among his papers you have already found a letter signed by him telling the circumstances of the forged check."

"Prince Rudolf," said Mr. Geraldine, "of course I am very glad that you have John Anderson's receipt. When you come to be examined by the police on the matter of Anderson's forged signature that receipt will no doubt form the pivot of your defense. It might even win you acquittal, and probably will, but in the absence of any letter from John Anderson among his effects exonerating you of all blame, I am afraid that a great deal of doubt will exist in the public mind as to whether you are, or are not, a common swindler. I have not yet found that letter among Anderson's effects. If and when I do, I shall of course be delighted to let you know."

"Thank you very much, Mr. Geraldine. In return I can only say that if I was a cannibal I should simply have to drown you in Worcester sauce before being able to eat you. So I am to understand that unless I give up Miss Carstairs you will make it very unpleasant indeed for me?"

"I prefer to say, Prince, that unless you agree to give up this misguided girl, I shall have to do my best to show her what sort of a man you really are. As you know, by her father's will she comes into her estate on the day she marries. And she told me today that it was her fixed intention, as she is very rich and you are poor, to settle on you a very considerable sum of money which would ensure you a comfortable income for life."

"I wish," sighed Rudolf, "that my father could hear you say that. His enthusiasm would be quite touching."

"I fear he will be disappointed, Prince. But not to depress you both too much, and since after all you are being forced to give up a considerable fortune, I am prepared here and now to write you a check for £4,000. I shall send it to you on the day that Miss Carstairs tells me that she has decided not to marry you."

"Dear me," said Rudolf, "I see that I must have another brandy. Thank you, Mr. Geraldine. Your brandy is superb. Did you say four thousand pounds?"

"I did—merely, you understand, as a small consolation——"

"Nonsense, my dear fellow—it's a big consolation. After all, are there many men whose charms could be valued at four thousand pounds? I fear you are a flatterer, Mr. Geraldine."

The banker's handsome red face was, for a man making a contemptuous offer, curiously eager, and Rudolf regarded him thoughtfully.

"Then you accept, Prince? You will agree to leave Miss Carstairs alone?"

But Rudolf's attention appeared now to be engaged in yet another careful examination of Miss Geraldine's cold profile.

"I note with regret," he said, "that Miss Geraldine's disapproval of me has increased to such an extent that, were she not a lady, she would express it in such old-fashioned terms as swindler, gigolo, and cad."

"Cad," said Iris Geraldine, "is an unpleasant word. But very descriptive. I should prefer you, Prince, to address yourself only to my brother. I am here merely as a witness to a business arrangement."

"Not at all," said Rudolf, with sudden sharpness. "It is a romantic arrangement."

Astonished, they stared at him. He was smiling in his saturnine way. Mr. Geraldine glanced at his sister, and laughed. It was the kind of laugh for which a small chap would have been knocked down, but he was a bull of a man.

"These fellows," said he, "can make anything seem romantic."

"What fellows, Mr. Geraldine?"

"Romantic fellows, Prince—romantic wasters."

"Well, I can promise you that your sister will find what I am going to say a good deal more romantic than you will. I am going to tell you a story."

"Not to me," said Miss Geraldine with spirit. "I am going to bed."

"This story, Miss Geraldine," said Rudolf slowly, "is about your sister."

They stared at him across an appalled silence. But his dark eyes saw only Iris Geraldine's still white face, at last turned full to his.

"You knew her?" she sighed.

"But for her," said Prince Rudolf, "I should not be here tonight."

"Fantastic nonsense!" said Geraldine harshly. "Diana died more than ten years ago."

"Ten years, three months and five days ago, my friend. I came into your car, Miss Geraldine, only because I recognized the faint scent you are wearing. It is made by an obscure perfumer in Paris, and I gave her first bottle to Diana. Then for sentimental reasons I paid my friend Louvois, the perfumer, enough money to buy the rights of the scent outright—that is, so that no one but Diana Geraldine should ever use it. I was a rich man then, you understand. Louvois, for as long as he was in business, was to send her one bottle every six months at this address.

"A year or so after she was killed in that motor accident near Fontain-bleau, Louvois wrote to me enclosing a letter that he had received from England. The letter was from a girls' school near Ascot, and was written by a schoolgirl to the effect that the duty-paid scent from Paris which had been delivered to Miss Geraldine was obviously for her elder sister, who was dead, but could it please go on being sent to the address in Belgrave Square so that she could use it when she was grown up in memory of her dear sister, and it was signed 'Iris Geraldine.'

"So you will see why I so willingly came with you when you invited me. I told you, didn't I, that you weren't a stranger?"

"Diana," said Iris Geraldine, so dimly that she was scarcely audible, "was the loveliest elder sister a little girl could have. I was fourteen when she died, and as our father and mother had died so long before, she was every-thing in the world—all heroines in one—to me. And so I clung to the sweet dry perfume which, so she once told her little sister, a fairytale prince had given her to use forever and ever."

"Well," said Mr. Geraldine bitterly, "there's damn little of the fairytale about the Prince now."

Rudolf smiled. "That's true enough, dear me. But you must remember I was only twenty-three then—and Diana was twenty. Young people, Mr. Geraldine, are sometimes very serious indeed about such trivialities as being in love."

"Now that you have hurt Iris," said her brother harshly, "by bringing up memories of her sister, may I ask what was your point in doing so?"

"He has not hurt me," said Iris. Her eyes were hidden. Her voice came from behind an invisible curtain. "You didn't intend to, did you, Prince?"

"Indirectly, my dear, I fear I must—that is, through this brother of yours. Mr. Geraldine, I told you about Diana because she used to speak of you, her elder brother and the head of the family. You will no doubt already have remarked that I don't like you. This is not due wholly to your manner, which would make an unfavorable impression even on a drunken sailor. It is because Diana did not like you, as you of course know.

"That you are a bully goes without saying. But being a bully is not a crime—indeed it is sometimes an asset. One moment, Mr. Geraldine. I know also that in spite of your very respectable front as a great banker, you are an unscrupulous speculator. Diana—aged twenty to your twenty-five—guessed your true character.

"Now I am going to make the deduction that as Miss Carstairs's trustee you have gambled with part of her funds and that in the recent Wall Street crash you have lost heavily. Wait. On her marriage you will have to show her accounts to her lawyers, with the result that you will find yourself in the dock. That is why you do not want her to marry until you can regain your losses.

"This is all guesswork, you will say, and no doubt you will tell me I am wrong. But on one point I can ease your mind. I am not going to marry Miss Carstairs.

"That is not because I wish to save you, but because I have fallen in love tonight for the second time in my life, though I fear the lady does not approve of me at all. I can only hope to win her approval in time.

"But that is another story. Tomorrow I shall advise Miss Carstairs to ask her lawyers to look into——"

Mr. Geraldine chewed his cigar. His cold eyes were thoughtful, but there was a grin on his handsome red face. This grin had no doubt been put there by an ancestor who had been caught red-handed while committing robbery under arms and had known that the game was over.

"Iris," he said, "somebody ought to have warned me about the intelligence of princes. I begin to see now how even the shrewdest bankers have been persuaded to lend them money."

"My father, Mr. Geraldine, who has had more than sixty years' experience of owing money to the shrewdest bankers in London and New York, says that times are not what they were."

Mr. Geraldine smiled across at him. His eyes were cold and watchful.

"Prince Rudolf, I shall not like standing in the dock charged with having misappropriated my client's funds."

Rudolf nodded sympathetically. "Nor should I. Taking other people's money is nice work, if you can get away with it. Given a bad character— like yours and my father's—it's all a matter of luck."

"Then I am sorry that you are not your father, Prince. If you were, I should offer you £10,000 at the end of six months merely for keeping your mouth shut during that time. But as you are not, I fear I shall have to do something drastic, like shooting myself. But I don't like the idea at all."

Rudolf nodded sympathetically. "Yes, there is a degree of emphasis about suicide which is always disagreeable to a thoughtful mind. I shouldn't commit suicide, Mr. Geraldine. It will probably embarrass more people than it will please."

"But, my dear Prince, what else can I do? Miss Carstairs has never liked me, anyway. And when tomorrow you tell her of your suspicions, she will be only too eager to consult her lawyers."

Rudolf turned to Miss Geraldine. "What do you think of all this, Iris?"

"I think," she said very gravely, "that my brother has been playing with fire for a long time and that he has at last burned his hands. I think that tonight will mark a change for the better in him."

"Then you don't think he will shoot himself?"

She smiled unsteadily. "You are a pair of cruel babies, aren't you?"

"Mr. Geraldine," said Rudolf, "did you hear that? You are a cruel baby."

"You too," said Mr. Geraldine. "Have another brandy."

"Thank you. Then, Iris, you think I ought not to tell Miss Carstairs?"

"I can promise you," said Geraldine, "that her capital will be intact within six months. Also many innocent people will suffer loss if this comes to a head now. Later on, they won't."

"But I am lunching with the girl tomorrow," said Prince Rudolf, "and I might possibly blurt out something."

"You can put off the lunch," said Iris coldly.

"But I hate lunching alone, Iris. Here is an idea. Will you lunch with me?"

"I am already engaged."

Rudolf turned to Geraldine. "There you are, my friend. I've done my best. She doesn't like me. She won't lunch with me. I fear you will have to commit suicide, after all."

"Nonsense, Iris," said her brother. "Of course you can lunch with him."

"But I don't want to," said Iris.

"She doesn't like me," said Rudolf helplessly. "Give it up, Geraldine."

"I do like you," said Iris stormily. "It's only that you talk such nonsense so plausibly that I daren't trust myself alone with you."

"That's splendid," said Rudolf. "Unfortunately, we shall be lunching in a public place, and I shan't be able to do very much."

"But you can always talk," said Iris.

"I shall. I shall propose marriage."

"I shall refuse."

"Naturally. Then I shall point out that you lack foresight. For if you had foresight you would know that it is sheer waste of time to go on refusing a man whom you are going to accept in the end."

"Very well," said Iris, "I lack foresight."

"Mr. Geraldine," said Prince Rudolf, "we have been forgetting my father. Some time ago you called me a crook——"

"That was politics, Prince. Anderson had told me the real story."

"Politics cost money, Mr. Geraldine. In payment for your politics you will be so good as to earn my father's undying gratitude by sending him tomorrow the sum of £4,000 in notes from an Anonymous Admirer. This gift will give him great pleasure both financially and morally, since he has never had any admirers, anonymous or otherwise. Good night, Mr. Geraldine. Your servant, Iris. I shall call for you at one tomorrow."

The two men shook hands. This was a quiet and thoughtful ceremony, which they appeared to enjoy.

Iris, with a sudden high color, walked to the door and out into the hall. Prince Rudolf found her there, and she walked with him towards the front hall. Very lightly she touched his arm.

"Thank you for not ruining my brother. That was because of Diana?"

"Because of Diana and Iris," he said. "Because of enchantment and gentleness. Because I am a lucky man to have found out tonight that, even in this world, they never die."

He stooped to kiss her hand, and as he did so a flutter of lips just touched his forehead.

"Dear me," she whispered, "who would have thought you were such a darling!"

A STUDY IN WHITE

by *NICHOLAS BLAKE*

"Seasonable weather for the time of year," remarked the Expansive Man in a voice succulent as the breast of a roast goose.

The Deep Chap, sitting next to him in the railway compartment, glanced out at the snow, swarming and swirling past the windowpane. He replied:

"You really like it? Oh, well, it's an ill blizzard that blows nobody no good. Depends what you mean by seasonable, though. Statistics for the last fifty years would show———"

"Name of Joad, sir?" asked the Expansive Man, treating the compartment to a wholesale wink.

"No, Stansfield, Henry Stansfield." The Deep Chap, a ruddy-faced man who sat with hands firmly planted on the knees of his brown tweed suit, might have been a prosperous farmer but for the long, steady, meditative scrutiny which he now bent upon each of his fellow travelers in turn.

What he saw was not particularly rewarding. On the opposite seat, from left to right, were a Forward Piece, who had taken the Expansive Man's wink wholly to herself and contrived to wriggle her tight skirt farther up from her knee; a dessicated, sandy, lawyerish little man who fumed and fussed like an angry kettle, consulting every five minutes his gold watch, then shaking out his *Times* with the crackle of a legal parchment; and a Flash Card, dressed up to the nines of spivdom, with the bold yet uneasy stare of the young delinquent.

"Mine's Percy Dukes," said the Expansive Man. "P.D. to my friends. General Dealer. At your service. Well, we'll be across the border in an hour and a half, and then hey for the bluebells of bonny Scotland!"

"Bluebells in January? You're hopeful," remarked the Forward Piece.

"Are you Scots, master?" asked the Comfortable Body sitting on Stansfield's left.

"English outside"—Percy Dukes patted the front of his gray suit, slid a flask from its hip pocket, and took a swig—"and Scotch within." His loud laugh, or the blizzard, shook the railway carriage. The Forward Piece giggled.

"You'll need that if we run into a drift and get stuck for the night," said Henry Stansfield.

"Name of Jonah, sir?" The compartment reverberated again.

"I do not apprehend such an eventuality," said the Fusspot. "The station-master at Lancaster assured me that the train would get through. We are scandalously late already, though." Once again the gold watch was consulted.

"It's a curious thing," remarked the Deep Chap meditatively, "the way we imagine we can make Time amble withal or gallop withal, just by keeping an eye on the hands of a watch. You travel frequently by this train, Mr.——?"

"Kilmington. Arthur J. Kilmington. No, I've only used it once before." The Fusspot spoke in a dry Edinburgh accent.

"Ah, yes, that would have been on the 17th of last month. I remember seeing you on it."

"No, sir, you are mistaken. It was the 20th." Mr. Kilmington's thin mouth snapped tight again, like a rubber band round a sheaf of legal documents.

"The 20th? Indeed? That was the day of the train robbery. A big haul they got, it seems. Off this very train. It was carrying some of the extra Christmas mail. Bags just disappeared, somewhere between Lancaster and Carlisle."

"Och, deary me," sighed the Comfortable Body. "I don't know what we're coming to, really, nowadays."

"We're coming to the scene of the crime, ma'am," said the expansive Mr. Dukes. The train, almost deadbeat, was panting up the last pitch towards Shap Summit.

"I didn't see anything in the papers about where the robbery took place," Henry Stansfield murmured. Dukes fastened a somewhat bleary eye upon him.

"You read all the newspapers?"

"Yes."

The atmosphere in the compartment had grown suddenly tense. Only the Flash Card, idly examining his fingernails, seemed unaffected by it.

"Which paper did you see it in?" pursued Stansfield.

"I didn't." Dukes tapped Stansfield on the knee. "But I can use my loaf. Stands to reason. You want to tip a mailbag out of a train—get me? Train must be moving slowly, or the bag'll burst when it hits the ground. Only one place between Lancaster and Carlisle where you'd *know* the train would be crawling. Shap Bank. And it goes slowest on the last bit of the bank, just about where we are now. Follow?"

Henry Stansfield nodded.

"O.K. But you'd be balmy to tip it off just anywhere on this Godforsaken moorland," went on Mr. Dukes. "Now, if you'd traveled this line as much as I have, you'd have noticed it goes over a bridge about a mile short of the summit. Under the bridge runs a road: a nice, lonely road, see? The only road hereabouts that touches the railway. You tip out the bag there. Your chums collect it, run down the embankment, dump it in the car they've got waiting by the bridge, and Bob's your uncle!"

"You oughta been a detective, mister," exclaimed the Forward Piece languishingly.

Mr. Dukes inserted his thumbs in his armpits, looking gratified. "Maybe I am," he said with a wheezy laugh. "And maybe I'm just little old P.D., who knows how to use his loaf."

"Och, well now, the things people will do?" said the Comfortable Body. "There's a terrible lot of dishonesty today."

The Flash Card glanced up contemptuously from his fingernails. Mr. Kilmington was heard to mutter that the system of surveillance on railways was disgraceful, and the Guard of the train should have been severely censured.

"The Guard can't be everywhere," said Stansfield. "Presumably he has to patrol the train from time to time, and——"

"Let him do so, then, and not lock himself up in his van and go to sleep," interrupted Mr. Kilmington, somewhat unreasonably.

"Are you speaking from personal experience, sir?" asked Stansfield.

The Flash Card lifted up his voice and said, in a Charing-Cross-Road American accent, "Hey, fellas! If the gang was gonna tip out the mailbags by the bridge, like this guy says—what I mean is, how could they rely on the Guard being out of his van just at that point?" He hitched up the trousers of his loud check suit.

"You've got something there," said Percy Dukes. "What I reckon is, there must have been two accomplices on the train—one to get the Guard out of his van on some pretext, and the other to chuck off the bags." He turned to Mr. Kilmington. "You were saying something about the Guard locking himself up in his van. Now if I was of a suspicious turn of mind, if I was little old Sherlock H. in person"—he bestowed another prodigious wink upon Kilmington's fellow-travelers—"I'd begin to wonder about you, sir. You were traveling on this train when the robbery took place. You went to the Guard's van. You *say* you found him asleep. You didn't by any chance call the Guard out, so as to——?"

"Your suggestion is outrageous! I advise you to be very careful, sir, very careful indeed," enunciated Mr. Kilmington, his precise voice crackling with indignation, "or you may find you have said something actionable. I would have you know that, when I——"

But what he would have them know was to remain undivulged. The train, which for some little time had been running cautiously down from

Shap Summit, suddenly began to chatter and shudder, like a fever patient in high delirium, as the vacuum brakes were applied: then, with the dull impact of a fist driving into a feather pillow, the engine buried itself in a drift which had gathered just beyond the bend of a deep cutting.

It was just five minutes past seven.

"What's this?" asked the Forward Piece, rather shrilly, as a hysterical outburst of huffing and puffing came from the engine.

"Run into a drift, I reckon."

"He's trying to back us out. No good. The wheels are slipping every time. What a lark!" Percy Dukes had his head out of the window on the lee side of the train. "Coom to Coomberland for your winter sports!"

"Guard! Guard, I say!" called Mr. Kilmington. But the blue-clad figure, after one glance into the compartment, hurried on his way up the corridor. "Really! I *shall* report that man."

Henry Stansfield, going out into the corridor, opened a window. Though the coach was theoretically sheltered by the cutting on this windward side, the blizzard stunned his face like a knuckleduster of ice. He joined the herd of passengers who had climbed down and were stumbling towards the engine. As they reached it, the Guard emerged from the cab: no cause for alarm, he said; if they couldn't get through, there'd be a relief engine sent down to take the train back to Penrith; he was just off to set fog-signals on the line behind them.

The driver renewed his attempts to back the train out. But what with its weight, the up-gradient in its rear, the icy rails, and the clinging grip of the drift on the engine, he could not budge her.

"We'll have to dig out the bogeys, mate," he said to his fireman. "Fetch them shovels from the forward van. It'll keep the perishers from freezing, anyhow." He jerked his finger at the knot of passengers who, lit up by the glare of the furnace, were capering and beating their arms like savages amid the swirling snow-wreaths.

Percy Dukes, who had now joined them, quickly established himself as the life and soul of the party, referring to the grimy-faced fireman as "Snowball," adjuring his companions to "Dig for Victory," affecting to spy the approach of a herd of St. Bernards, each with a keg of brandy slung round its neck. But after ten minutes of hard digging, when the leading wheels of the bogey were cleared, it could be seen that they had been derailed by their impact with the drift.

"That's torn it, Charlie. You'll have to walk back to the box and get 'em to telephone through for help," said the driver.

"*If* the wires aren't down already," replied the fireman lugubriously. "It's above a mile to that box, and uphill. Who d'you think I am. Captain Scott?"

"You'll have the wind behind you, mate, anyhow. So long."

A buzz of dismay had risen from the passengers at this. One or two, who began to get querulous, were silenced by the driver's offering to take them anywhere they liked if they would just lift his engine back onto the metals first. When the rest had dispersed to their carriages, Henry Stansfield asked the driver's permission to go up into the cab for a few minutes and dry his coat.

"You're welcome." The driver snorted: "Would you believe it? 'Must get to Glasgow tonight.' Damn ridiculous! Now Bert—that's my Guard— it's different for him: he's entitled to fret a bit. Missus been very poorly. Thought she was going to peg out before Christmas; but he got the best surgeon in Glasgow to operate on her, and she's mending now, he says. He reckons to look in every night at the nursing home, when he goes off work."

Stansfield chatted with the man for five minutes. Then the Guard returned, blowing upon his hands—a smallish, leathery-faced chap, with an anxious look in his eye.

"We'll not get through tonight, Bert. Charlie told you?"

"Aye. I doubt some of the passengers are going to create a rumpus," said the Guard dolefully.

Henry Stansfield went back to his compartment. It was stuffy, but with a sinister hint of chilliness, too: he wondered how long the steam heating would last: depended upon the amount of water in the engine boiler, he supposed. Among the wide variety of fates he had imagined for himself, freezing to death in an English train was not included.

Arthur J. Kilmington fidgeted more than ever. When the Guard came along the corridor, he asked him where the nearest village was, saying he must get a telephone call through to Edinburgh—most urgent appointment —must let his client know, if he was going to miss it. The Guard said there was a village two miles to the northeast; you could see the lights from the top of the cutting; but he warned Mr. Kilmington against trying to get there in the teeth of this blizzard—better wait for the relief engine, which should reach them before 9 p.m.

Silence fell upon the compartment for a while; the incredulous silence of civilized people who find themselves in the predicament of castaways. Then the expansive Mr. Dukes proposed that, since they were to be stuck here for an hour or two, they should get acquainted. The Comfortable Body now introduced herself as Mrs. Grant, the Forward Piece as Inez Blake; the Flash Card, with the overnegligent air of one handing a dud half-crown over a counter, gave his name as Macdonald—I. Macdonald.

The talk reverted to the train robbery and the criminals who had perpetrated it.

"They must be awfu' clever," remarked Mrs. Grant, in her singsong Lowland accent.

"No criminals are clever, ma'am," said Stansfield quietly. His ruminative eye passed, without haste, from Macdonald to Dukes. "Neither the small fry nor the big operators. They're pretty well subhuman, the whole lot of 'em. A dash of cunning, a thick streak of cowardice, and the rest is made up of stupidity and boastfulness. They're too stupid for anything but crime, and so riddled with inferiority that they always give themselves away, sooner or later, by boasting about their crimes. They like to think of themselves as the wide boys, but they're as narrow as starved eels—why, they haven't even the wits to alter their professional methods: that's how the police pick 'em up."

"I entirely agree, sir," Mr. Kilmington snapped. "In my profession I see a good deal of the criminal classes. And I flatter myself none of them has ever got the better of me. They're transparent, sir, transparent."

"No doubt you gentlemen are right," said Percy Dukes comfortably. "But the police haven't picked up the chaps who did this train robbery yet."

"They will. And the Countess of Axminister's emerald bracelet. Bet the gang didn't reckon to find that in the mailbag. Worth all of £25,000."

Percy Dukes' mouth fell open. The Flash Card whistled. Overcome, either by the stuffiness of the carriage or the thought of £25,000-worth of emeralds, Inez Blake gave a little moan and fainted all over Mr. Kilmington's lap.

"Really! Upon my soul! My dear young lady!" exclaimed that worthy. There was a flutter of solicitude, shared by all except the cold-eyed young Macdonald who, after stooping over her a moment, his back to the others, said, "Here you—stop pawing the young lady and let her stretch out on the seat. Yes, I'm talking to you, Kilmington."

"How dare you! This is an outrage!" The little man stood up so abruptly that the girl was almost rolled onto the floor. "I was merely trying to—"

"I know your sort. Nasty old men. Now, keep your hands off her. I'm telling you."

In the shocked silence that ensued, Kilmington gobbled speechlessly at Macdonald for a moment; then, seeing razors in the youth's cold-steel eye, snatched his black hat and briefcase from the rack and bolted out of the compartment. Henry Stansfield made as if to stop him, then changed his mind. Mrs. Grant followed the little man out, returning presently, her handkerchief soaked in water, to dab Miss Blake's forehead. The time was just 8:30.

When things were restored to normal, Mr. Dukes turned to Stansfield. "You were saying this necklace of—who was it?—the Countess of Axminster, it's worth £25,000? Fancy sending a thing of that value through the post! Are you sure of it?"

"The value? Oh, yes." Henry Stansfield spoke out of the corner of his mouth, in the manner of a stupid man imparting a confidence. "Don't let this go any further. But I've a friend who works in the Cosmopolitan—the company where it's insured. That's another thing that didn't get into the papers. Silly woman. She wanted it for some big family-do in Scotland at Christmas, forgot to bring it with her, and wrote home for it to be posted to her in a registered packet."

"£25,000," said Percy Dukes thoughtfully. "Well, stone me down!"

"Yes. Some people don't know when they're lucky, do they?"

Duke's fat face wobbled on his shoulders like a globe of lard. Young Macdonald polished his nails. Inez Blake read her magazine. After a while Percy Dukes remarked that the blizzard was slackening; he'd take an airing and see if there was any sign of the relief engine yet. He left the compartment.

At the window the snowflakes danced in their tens now, not their thousands. The time was 8:55. Shortly afterwards Inez Blake went out; and ten minutes later Mrs. Grant remarked to Stansfield that it had stopped snowing altogether. Neither Inez nor Dukes had returned when, at 9:30, Henry Stansfield decided to ask what had happened about the relief. The Guard was not in his van, which adjoined Stansfield's coach, towards the rear of the train. So he turned back, walked up the corridor to the front coach, clambered out, and hailed the engine cab.

"She must have been held up," said the Guard, leaning out. "Charlie here got through from the box, and they promised her by nine o'clock. But it'll no' be long now, sir."

"Have you seen anything of a Mr. Kilmington—small, sandy chap—black hat and overcoat, blue suit—was in my compartment? I've walked right up the train and he doesn't seem to be on it."

The Guard pondered a moment. "Och aye, you wee fellow? Him that asked me about telephoning from the village. Aye, he's awa' then."

"He did set off to walk there, you mean?"

"Nae doot he did, if he's no' on the train. He spoke to me again—juist on nine, it'd be—and said he was awa' if the relief didna turn up in five minutes."

"You've not seen him since?"

"No, sir. I've been talking to my mates here this half-hour, ever syne the wee fellow spoke to me."

Henry Stansfield walked thoughtfully back down the permanent way. When he had passed out of the glare shed by the carriage lights on the snow, he switched on his electric torch. Just beyond the last coach the eastern wall of the cutting sloped sharply down and merged into moorland level with the track. Although the snow had stopped altogether, an icy wind from the northeast still blew, raking and numbing his face. Twenty yards farther on his torch lit up a track, already half filled in with snow, made by several pairs of feet, pointing away over the moor, towards the northeast. Several passengers, it seemed, had set off for the village, whose lights twinkled like frost in the far distance. Stansfield was about to follow this track when he heard footsteps scrunching the snow farther up the line. He switched off the torch; at once it was as if a sack had been thrown over his head, so close and blinding was the darkness. The steps came nearer. Stansfield switched on his torch, at the last minute, pinpointing the squat figure of Percy Dukes. The man gave a muffled oath.

"What the devil! Here, what's the idea, keeping me waiting half an hour in that blasted——?"

"Have you seen Kilmington?"

"Oh, it's you. No, how the hell should I have seen him? Isn't he on the train? I've just been walking up the line, to look for the relief. No sign yet. Damn parky, it is—I'm moving on."

Presently Stansfield moved on, too, but along the track towards the village. The circle of his torchlight wavered and bounced on the deep snow. The wind, right in his teeth, was killing. No wonder, he thought, as after a few hundred yards he approached the end of the trail, those passengers turned back. Then he realized they had not all turned back. What he had supposed to be a hummock of snow bearing a crude resemblance to a recumbent human figure, he now saw to be a human figure covered with snow. He scraped some of the snow off it, turned it gently over on its back.

Arthur J. Kilmington would fuss no more in this world. His briefcase was buried beneath him: his black hat was lying where it had fallen, lightly covered with snow, near the head. There seemed, to Stansfield's cursory examination, no mark of violence on him. But the eyeballs stared, the face was suffused with a pinkish-blue color. So men look who have been strangled, thought Stansfield, or asphyxiated. Quickly he knelt down again, shining his torch in the dead face. A qualm of horror shook him. Mr. Kilmington's nostrils were caked thick with snow, which had frozen solid in them, and snow had been rammed tight into his mouth also.

And here he would have stayed, reflected Stansfield, in this desolate spot, for days or weeks, perhaps, if the snow lay or deepened. And when the thaw at last came (as it did that year, in fact, only after two months), the snow would thaw out from his mouth and nostrils, too, and there would be no vestige of murder left—only the corpse of an impatient little lawyer who had tried to walk to the village in a blizzard and died for his pains. It might even be that no one would ask how such a precise, pernickety little chap had ventured the two-mile walk in these shoes and without a torch to light his way through the pitchy blackness; for Stansfield, going through the man's pockets, had found the following articles—and nothing more: pocketbook, fountain pen, handkerchief, cigarette case, gold lighter, two letters, and some loose change.

Stansfield started to return for help. But only twenty yards back he noticed another trail of footprints, leading off the main track to the left. This trail seemed a fresher one—the snow lay less thickly in the indentations—and to have been made by one pair of feet only. He followed it up, walking beside it. Whoever made this track had walked in a slight right-handed curve back to the railway line, joining it about one hundred and fifty yards up the line from where the main trail came out. At this point there was a platelayers' shack. Finding the door unlocked, Stansfield entered. There was nothing inside but a coke-brazier, stone cold, and a smell of cigar smoke. . . .

Half an hour later, Stansfield returned to his compartment. In the meanwhile, he had helped the train crew to carry back the body of Kilmington, which was now locked in the Guard's van. He had also made an interesting discovery as to Kilmington's movements. It was to be presumed that, after the altercation with Macdonald, and the brief conversation already reported by the Guard, the lawyer must have gone to sit in another compartment. The last coach, to the rear of the Guard's van, was a first-class one, almost empty. But in one of its compartments Stansfield found a passenger asleep. He woke him up, gave a description of Kilmington, and asked if he had seen him earlier.

The passenger grumpily informed Stansfield that a smallish man, in a dark overcoat, with the trousers of a blue suit showing beneath it, had come to the door and had a word with him. No, the passenger had not noticed his face particularly, because he'd been very drowsy himself, and besides, the chap had politely taken off his black Homburg hat to address him, and the hat screened as much of the head as was not cut off from his view by the top of the door. No, the chap had not come into his compartment: he had just stood outside, inquired the time (the passenger had looked at his watch and told him it was 8:50); then the chap had said that, if the relief didn't turn up by nine, he intended to walk to the nearest village.

Stansfield had then walked along to the engine cab. The Guard, whom he found there, told him that he'd gone up the track about 8:45 to meet the fireman on his way back from the signal-box. He had gone as far as the place where he'd put down his fog-signals earlier; here, just before nine, he and the fireman met, as the latter corroborated. Returning to the train, the Guard had climbed into the last coach, noticed Kilmington sitting alone in a first-class apartment (it was then that the lawyer announced to the Guard his intention of walking if the relief engine had not arrived within five minutes). The Guard then got out of the train again, and proceeded down the track to talk to his mates in the engine cab.

This evidence would seem to point incontrovertibly at Kilmington's having been murdered shortly after 9 p.m., Stansfield reflected as he went back to his own compartment. His fellow passengers were all present now.

"Well, did you find him?" asked Percy Dukes.

"Kilmington? Oh, yes, I found him. In the snow over there. He was dead."

Inez Blake gave a little, affected scream. The permanent sneer was wiped, as if by magic, off young Macdonald's face, which turned a sickly white. Mr. Dukes sucked in his fat lips.

"The puir wee man," said Mrs. Grant. "He tried to walk it then? Died of exposure, was it?"

"No," announced Stansfield flatly, "he was murdered."

This time, Inez Blake screamed in earnest; and, like an echo, a hooting shriek came from far up the line: the relief engine was approaching at last.

"The police will be awaiting us back at Penrith, so we'd better all have our stories ready." Stansfield turned to Percy Dukes. "You, for instance, sir. Where were you between 8:55, when you left the carriage, and 9:35 when I met you returning? Are you sure you didn't see Kilmington?"

Dukes, expansive no longer, his piggy eyes sunk deep in the fat of his face, asked Stansfield who the hell he thought he was.

"I am an inquiry agent, employed by the Cosmopolitan Insurance Company. Before that, I was a Detective Inspector in the C.I.D. Here is my card."

Dukes barely glanced at it. "That's all right, old man. Only wanted to make sure. Can't trust anyone nowadays." His voice had taken on the ingratiating, oleaginous heartiness of the small businessman trying to clinch a deal with a bigger one. "Just went for a stroll, y'know—stretch the old legs. Didn't see a soul."

"Who were you expecting to see? Didn't you wait for someone in the platelayers' shack along there, and smoke a cigar while you were waiting? Who did you mistake me for when you said, 'What's the idea, keeping me waiting half an hour?' "

"Here, draw it mild, old man." Percy Dukes sounded injured. "I certainly looked in at the huts: smoked a cigar for a bit. Then I toddled back to the train, and met up with your good self on the way. I didn't make no appointment to meet—"

"Oo! Well I *must* say," interrupted Miss Blake virtuously. She could hardly wait to tell Stansfield that, on leaving the compartment shortly after Dukes, she'd overheard voices on the track below the lavatory window. "I recognized this gentleman's voice," she went on, tossing her head at Dukes. "He said something like: 'You're going to help us again, chum, so you'd better get used to the idea. You're in it up to the neck—can't back out now.' And another voice, sort of mumbling, might have been Mr. Kilmington's—I dunno—sounded Scotch anyway—said, 'All right. Meet you in five minutes: platelayers' hut a few hundred yards up the line. Talk it over.' "

"And what did you do then, young lady?" asked Stansfield.

"I happened to meet a gentleman friend, farther up the train, and sat with him for a bit."

"Is that so?" remarked Macdonald menacingly. "Why, you four-flushing little—!"

"Shut up!" commanded Stansfield.

"Honest I did," the girl said, ignoring Macdonald. "I'll introduce you to him, if you like. He'll tell you I was with him for, oh, half an hour or more."

"And what about Mr. Macdonald?"

"I'm not talking," said the youth sullenly.

"Mr. Macdonald isn't talking. Mrs. Grant?"

"I've been in this compartment ever since, sir."

"Ever since—?"

"Since I went out to damp my hankie for this young lady, when she'd fainted. Mr. Kilmington was just before me, you'll mind. I saw him go through into the Guard's van."

"Did you hear him say anything about walking to the village?"

"No, sir. He just hurried into the van, and then there was some havers about its no' being lockit this time, and how he was going to report the Guard for it."

"I see. And you've been sitting here with Mr. Macdonald all the time?"

"Yes, sir. Except for ten minutes or so he was out of the compartment, just after you'd left."

"What did you go out for?" Stansfield asked the young man.

"Just taking the air, brother."

"You weren't taking Mr. Kilmington's gold watch, as well as the air, by any chance?" Stansfield's keen eyes were fastened like a hook into Macdonald's, whose insolent expression visibly crumbled beneath them.

"I don't know what you mean," he tried to bluster. "You can't do this to me."

"I mean that a man has been murdered, and when the police search you, they will find his gold watch in your possession. Won't look too healthy for you, my young friend."

"Naow! Give us a chance! It was only a joke, see?" The wretched Macdonald was whining now, in his native cockney. "He got me riled—the stuck-up way he said nobody'd ever got the better of him. So I thought I'd just show him—I'd have given it back, straight I would, only I couldn't find him afterwards. It was just a joke, I tell you. Anyway, it was Inez who lifted the ticker."

"You dirty little rotter!" screeched the girl.

"Shut up, both of you. You can explain your joke to the Penrith police. Let's hope they don't die of laughing."

At this moment the train gave a lurch, and started back up the gradient. It halted at the signal-box, for Stansfield to telephone to Penrith, then clattered south again.

On Penrith platform Stansfield was met by an Inspector and a Sergeant of the County Constabulary, with the Police Surgeon. Then, after a brief pause in the Guard's van, where the Police Surgeon drew aside the Guard's black off-duty overcoat that had been laid over the body, and began his preliminary examination, they marched along to Stansfield's compartment. The Guard who, at his request, had locked this as the train was drawing up at the platform and was keeping an eye on its occupants, now unlocked it. The Inspector entered.

His first action was to search Macdonald. Finding the watch concealed on his person, he then charged Macdonald and Inez Blake with the theft. The Inspector next proceeded to make an arrest on the charge of wilful murder. . . .

Whom did the Inspector arrest for the murder of Arthur J. Kilmington?

You have been given no less than eight clues by the author; these eight clues should tell you, by logical deduction, not only the identity of the murderer but also the motive of the crime and the method by which it was committed.

Thus, Nicholas Blake returns to the great 'tec tradition, the pure, unadulterated detective story—the great 'tec tradition of Poe, Gaboriau, Collins, Doyle, Zangwill, Futrelle, Freeman, Chesterton, Post, Bramah, Crofts, Christie, Bailey, Sayers, MacDonald, Berkeley, Biggers, Van Dine, Allingham, Hammett, Carr, Simenon, Gardner, Stout, and so many others. And thus, his story, in the great tradition of 'tec titles, might have been called: "A Study in White; or, The Sign of Eight."

We urge you to accept the author's challenge before going further, and when you have interpreted the eight clues compare your solution with Mr. Blake's.

Solution to

A STUDY IN WHITE

by NICHOLAS BLAKE

The Inspector arrested the Guard for the wilful murder of Arthur J. Kilmington.

Kilmington's pocket had been picked by Inez Blake, when she pretended to faint at 8:25, and his gold watch was at once passed by her to her accomplice, Macdonald. Now Kilmington was constantly consulting his watch. It is inconceivable, if he was not killed till after 9 p.m., that he should not have missed the watch and made a scene. This point was clinched by the first-class passenger who had said that a man, answering to the description of Kilmington, had asked him the time at 8:50: if it had really been Kilmington, he would certainly, before inquiring the time of anyone else, have first tried to consult his own watch, found it gone, and reported the theft. The fact that Kilmington neither reported the loss to the Guard, nor returned to his original compartment to look for the watch, proves he must have been murdered *before he became aware of the loss*— i.e., shortly after he left the compartment at 8:27. But the Guard claimed to have spoken to Kilmington at 9 p.m. Therefore the Guard was lying. And why should he lie, except to create an alibi for himself? This is Clue Number One.

The Guard claimed to have talked with Kilmington at 9 p.m. Now, at 8:55 the blizzard had diminished to a light snowfall, which soon afterwards ceased. When Stansfield discovered the body, it was buried under snow. Therefore Kilmington must have been murdered *while the blizzard was still raging*—i.e., some time before 9 p.m. Therefore the Guard was lying when he said Kilmington was alive at 9 p.m. This is Clue Number Two.

Henry Stansfield, who was investigating on behalf of the Cosmopolitan Insurance Company the loss of the Countess of Axminster's emeralds, reconstructed the crime as follows:

Motive: The Guard's wife had been gravely ill before Christmas: then, just about the time of the train robbery, he had got her the best surgeon in Glasgow and put her in a nursing home (evidence of engine-driver: Clue

Number Three). A Guard's pay does not usually run to such expensive treatment: it seemed likely, therefore, that the man, driven desperate by his wife's need, had agreed to take part in the robbery in return for a substantial bribe. What part did he play? During the investigation the Guard had stated that he had left his van for five minutes, while the train was climbing the last section of Shap Bank, and on his return found the mailbags missing. But Kilmington, who was traveling on this train, had found the Guard's van locked at this point, and now (evidence of Mrs. Grant: Clue Number Four) declared his intention of reporting the Guard. The latter knew that Kilmington's report would contradict his own evidence and thus convict him of complicity in the crime, since he had locked the van for a few minutes to throw out the mailbags himself, and pretended to Kilmington that he had been asleep (evidence of Kilmington himself) when the latter knocked at the door. So Kilmington had to be silenced.

Stansfield already had Percy Dukes under suspicion as the organizer of the robbery. During the journey Dukes gave himself away three times. First, although it had not been mentioned in the papers, he betrayed knowledge of the point on the line where the bags had been thrown out. Second, though the loss of the emeralds had been also kept out of the press, Dukes knew it was an emerald *necklace* which had been stolen: Stansfield had laid a trap for him by calling it a bracelet, but later in conversation Dukes referred to the "necklace." Third, his great discomposure at the (false) statement by Stansfield that the emeralds were worth £25,000 was the reaction of a criminal who believes he has been badly gypped by the fence to whom he has sold them. Dukes was now planning a second train robbery, and meant to compel the Guard to act as accomplice again. Inez Blake's evidence (Clue Number Five) of hearing him say, "You're going to help us again, chum," etc., clearly pointed to the Guard's complicity in the previous robbery: it was almost certainly the Guard to whom she had heard Dukes say this, for only a railway servant would have known about the existence of a platelayers' hut up the line, and made an appointment to meet Dukes there; moreover, if Dukes had talked about his plans for the next robbery, on the train itself, to anyone *but* a railway servant suspicion would have been incurred should they have been seen talking together.

Method: At 8:27 Kilmington goes into the Guard's van. He threatens to report the Guard, though he is quite unaware of the dire consequences this would entail for the latter. The Guard, probably on the pretext of showing him the route to the village, gets Kilmington out of the train, walks him away from the lighted area, stuns him (the bruise was a light one and did not reveal itself in Stansfield's brief examination of the body), carries him to the spot where Stansfield found the body, packs mouth and nostrils tight with snow. Then, instead of leaving well alone, the Guard decides to create an alibi for himself. He takes his victim's hat, returns to train, puts on his own dark, off-duty overcoat, finds a solitary passenger asleep, masquerades as Kilmington inquiring the time, and strengthens the impression by saying he'd walk to the village if the relief engine did not turn up in five minutes, then returns to the body and throws down the hat beside it (Stansfield found the hat only lightly covered with snow, as compared with the body: Clue Number Six). Moreover, the passenger noticed that the inquirer was wearing blue trousers (Clue Number Seven). The Guard's regulation suit was blue; but Duke's suit was gray, and Macdonald's a loud check—therefore, the masquerader could not have been either of them.

The time is now 8:55. The Guard decides to reinforce his alibi by going to intercept the returning fireman. He takes a short cut from the body to the platelayers' hut. The track he now makes, compared with the beaten trail towards the village, is much more lightly filled in with snow when Stansfield finds it (Clue Number Eight): therefore, it must have been made some time after the murder, and could not incriminate Percy Dukes. The Guard meets the fireman just after 8:55. They walk back to the train. The Guard is taken aside by Dukes, who has gone out for his "airing," and the conversation overheard by Inez Blake takes place. The Guard tells Dukes he will meet him presently in the platelayers' hut: this is aimed to incriminate Dukes, should the murder by any chance be discovered, for Dukes would find it difficult to explain why he should have sat alone in a cold hut for half an hour just around the time when Kilmington was presumably murdered only one hundred and fifty yards away. The Guard now goes along to the engine and stays there chatting with the crew for some forty minutes. His alibi is thus established for the period from 8:55 to 9:40 p.m. His plan might well have succeeded, but for three unlucky factors he could not possibly have taken into account—Stansfield's presence on the train, the blizzard stopping soon after 9 p.m., and the theft of Arthur J. Kilmington's watch.

THE PHANTOM GUEST

by FREDERICK IRVING ANDERSON

At midnight the snowstorm flattened out before the driving wind like a mechanical jack rabbit; the blasts rattled their whips on the fluttering shutters, twitched the rusty old tollgate bell on its frozen gimbals until it gave whimpering tongue, roused groans from the stiff limbs of bare trees. It was what they called a milk storm; it was twenty below zero—too cold to snow! All traffic had ceased; only the caterpillar plow swung back and forth through the white night like a sluggish shuttle—a ghostly crunching behemoth breathing fantastic breaths of snow that swirled against the street lamps and turned them into gaudy sundogs. Inside, the radiators bubbled placidly, and the old cat stretched its seven-toed paws in sleepy content.

It was no night for transients to come ringing the bell of the big front door of the Crossings House; nevertheless Elam, mine host, creature of habit that he was, looked up as the old clock tolled the hour and arose to greet, politely to register and to room several purely imaginary personages who, since landlords first hung up the bush, had been arriving at this witching hour craving hypothetical hospitality. Snow nor sleet nor rain nor wind nor dark deterred them. They were known in the trade as phantom guests. They always registered at the very top of the page; their ethereal presence exorcized the ghosts of emptiness. They were as necessary to the proper conduct of a good hotel, as, say, cyanide for the silver, or—or roach food.

First Elam closed up tight—even the cat hole in the woodshed. He put out the lights and the radio and the night latch. He listened at the stairwell in that last wary pause of a prudent landlord. Under the green-shaded desk lamp he turned the register to a new page, and at the top he wrote in an ornate Spencerian hand (with many curves and flourishes—such a hand as one could procure until quite recently at county fairs and cattle drawings on elegant private calling cards, interspersed with billing doves, smiling cupids and bleeding hearts) the new day, and the new date, Friday, the seventeenth of January. From a secret case he took four pens of different habits, four vials of ink of different hues; and without hesitation he registered and roomed four phantom guests. They were as follows:

Horace Manton, Harwinton, Conn.	E	18
J. H. Boles, Slocum, Mass.	E	27
Enid Wallins, N.Y.C.	E	7
Herbert Huffer, New Haven	E	10

Jim the Penman himself couldn't have done better. Elam carefully put away the tools of his guile; and, for verisimilitude, he left a call for the Wallins woman—she always took the seven o'clock train. Thus, having made oblation to the superstition of his flesh-and-blood patrons, he crept away to his apartment behind the stairs. Without arousing his cherubic wife, who slept in the full glare of a shaded lamp, he took off his shoes and put them away in a dated paper sack. This was his sole extravagance, he had a pair of shoes for every day in the month. He crept into bed, thinking of his son who was away at school, and so pleasant were his thoughts he couldn't have told where thoughts ceased and dreams began.

The front door bell rang at two o'clock. As his perspicacious toes found waiting slippers he wondered with a shiver if this were some suicide coming to claim that last divine unction which landlords have to sell. Wrapping his robe about him he went out, and rubbed the frost from the door pane. No, there were two of them. A car stood rammed into the rampart of snow at the curb. Two men stood over it. It steamed like a huge kettle. The car was freezing to death; rigor mortis would soon set in. The night had turned out ironically fine. Elam pulled the latch, pulled on a light, went back of the desk; he turned the register about, one hand on the hinge of the book— some fools will actually shut the book on registering, little suspecting that thereby someone will die in the house that day. It was precaution to put a toe on the police alarm, and to finger the butt of the .45 under the counter. The two men came in, stamping off the snow, rubbing their hands, shaking themselves like dogs as they got out of their coats. They shivered in the delicious warmth of the interior. One was short and heavy, the other was tall and slender. They wore clothes much too good for them.

"Dicks—body-snatchers," thought Elam. He had owned seventeen saloons in New York and he remembered this breed. They all aspired to a queer sartorial elegance.

"We got to get that car under cover," said the short fat man.

"The snowplow will bury it by morning," said Elam. "That's the best we can do for you."

"Oh, one of those wise hicks, eh?" said the fat man. "Well, maybe you're right. How long you been here waiting for us, old man?"

"One hundred and thirty-five years," said Elam.

"I'm glad you stayed on," said the other. "We sure need succor. What's the chance for a good room? Almost perfect?"

"What's the chance for a long stiff drink?" put in the tall one.

"It's a dry house," said Elam.

Whatever repercussion might have followed on the heels of this sad news was squelched by a truly astounding occurrence. Enid Wallins, one of Elam's most faithful and reliable phantom guests, who had been checking in ethereally for more than six years at the top of the page, chose this moment to come to life. The heavy-set man was registering as Matt Glennon, N.Y.C., when his eyes strayed to the signatures above his, and he gasped hoarsely, "Hey, Tony! Look!" Tony looked, stared with an almost cataleptic rigidity.

"Enid Wallins!" he shrilled, his eyes all but popping out of his head. "Here! Well, I'm damned! There goes our meal ticket!"

They looked at each other stupidly. Glennon was the first to come to. He turned fiercely on Elam.

"Is she in the house now?" he demanded.

"She hasn't checked out yet," said Elam weakly.

"Is she alive?" cried Tony.

Elam stared at him in amazement.

"We'll rout her out and see!" announced Tony.

"You'll rout nobody out!" said Elam.

"You're talking to the law!" snarled Glennon. With a flip he tossed a tiny badge on the counter. District Attorney's Office, New York County. Elam wetted his lips. The straightest way was the easiest. He was about to say:

"Gentlemen, do not needlessly excite yourselves. In the hotel business we have to contend with the silly superstitions of our patrons. One of them is their dislike to stop in an empty house, to register at the top of an empty page. So we always start our clean pages with dummy names. Enid Wallins is one of our dummy names. I've used it again and again. I don't know a person of that name. So far as I know, there is no such person. She is a myth, a fancy, a subterfuge, a—a phantom guest—"

But he never said it. The lean silky Tony suddenly shot out his long thin arms; his crushing fingers choked the words in Elam's throat. With a lunge across the desk, he drove Elam's head against the wall behind with a dull thud. But Elam's ready hand came away with the villainous .45; and the next instant Tony was back on his heels, hands high in air, staring into an unwavering muzzle. Elam twisted his tortured neck, wheezing.

"Getting tough, eh?" he gasped. "Softening me up, huh? Keep your hands up, both of you."

"We're the law," protested Glennon weakly.

"Not on this side of the state line!" muttered Elam, caressing the lump on the back of his head. "One more crack out of either of you and you'll sleep in an igloo. Now what's it all about?"

"It's all right—it's all right," urged Glennon placatingly. "Maybe Tony was a bit rough. But who wouldn't be? Listen. We'll put our cards on the table. Put up that gun. Nobody is going to hurt you."

"You ain't," said Elam. He lowered the gun, but kept his guard. He seethed with rage. He knew this breed. Except for that handy gun, this pair would have given him the works, softened him for questioning. "Now, what's it all about?" he said. "Who is this woman you're looking for? And what do you want her for?"

Tony took down his hands slowly, still eyeing the gun.

"She's the corpus delicti in a big-time murder," he said. "We been looking for the remains for eight months. This is bad news for somebody. Isn't there some way I can get a long drink, old man?"

"Well, this one ain't dead by a long shot," said Elam. "Maybe she comes to life again, huh?" he added sarcastically.

"Maybe she ain't so dead," said Glennon. "All we know is she's gone, without a trace. And now she bobs up and hits us in the face. Can't we get a drink? What does this one look like?"

"It's a dry house," said Elam absently. He was thinking fast. His head ached, the bump was as big as an egg; he was not of a mind to call himself a liar for this pair of strongarm johnnies. "Just a mix-up of names," he said easily.

"No," said Glennon. "Odd name. What does she look like?"

As the years had gone by, Elam had actually invented case histories for several of the older customers among his phantom guests. He had embellished the picture of this Enid Wallins in his mind's eye. He had put the name together from two residential hills in town, Eno and Wallins. He pictured her as an interesting, difficult woman with a past.

"What does she look like?" persisted Glennon.

"Classy!" said Elam. "About thirty. Blonde. Swell dresser—in a sort of horsy way."

"Horsy?" The two dicks spoke in unison.

Elam thrilled at the swift look passed. If it is true as the philosophers say that an idea cannot exist without a mind to exist in, then she surely was now alive, because they believed and were dismayed. He lowered his voice.

"We're talking too loud," he said. "She's sleeping right above here." They stared upwards, rapt, at the floor register giving to the room above. "I think she raises hunters on a farm in Vermont. She breaks her journey here." He was lying easily now, savoring the morsels.

"Oh, she's been here before?" This from Glennon, who was shaking his head and muttering to himself. Elam shivered, he was getting in deep, he was nailing it down harder with every spurt of his imagination. Morning was coming, he'd have to think it over.

"Yes, two-three times a year," he said. "She's been coming—oh, say, five or six years."

Their voices were low now, in conspirators' whispers, which somehow increased their sense of her nearness.

"When was she here last?" asked Glennon.

Elam took down one of the old registers for last fall and turned the pages.

"Here we are," he said. "October 13. Checked in late. Checked out for the seven o'clock train in the morning."

There she was indeed, in the same signature, that fetching two-story handwriting. The two dicks studied it in a daze.

"How's she come?" asked Glennon, eyeing Elam sharply. "By car?"

"That's what she always does," said Elam glibly. "Motors this far—sends the man on with the car—and takes the parlor car to town in the morning." He whistled audibly in relief. He had been wondering how he could account for her presence, without a car in the shed. The two dicks compared the signatures sullenly.

"I'd give a sawbuck for a shot!" sighed Tony. In his momentary elation Elam softened. He held up a warning finger and stealthily opened the grandfather's clock behind the desk. To their surprise, he took off the weight, a very quart of a weight. His clever wife had located every cache about the house but this one. He could afford to celebrate a little. He drew the plug and poured out three ample shots. They toasted the overhead register in silence.

"Go to bed," whispered Elam, as he restored the march of time. "I'll call you in time in the morning."

When he had roomed them on tiptoe, he returned to the office and stood holding his aching head in his hands. He interrupted the march of time several times, resetting the clock slyly after each pause. What a devil of a mess that lump on his head—and their eager gullibility—had lured him into! They'd turn him up a liar at dawn. And Enid—Enid, the interesting, the difficult woman with a history would cease to exist, go out of his life forever.

The habit of mundane things put him into his boots, cap, mittens, put the snow shovel into his hands; and he slipped out into the glistening cold to shovel a path to the curb—before people came to trample it, with the day. The frozen car that had started all this mischief lay under a kopje of snow. The street flowed by, smooth and clean, between high ramparts. The state roads were wide open! She could get away, she could go anywhere! She must flee, escape, before dawn!

"I'll have to think this out," he said hazily. He went in and put out the

lights again, and crawled away to bed, to think. But not to his cherubic
wife. He went up to Number Seven, and crawled into Enid's bed, and lay
there open-eyed. He got up and went to the rummage closet for supplies.
One could start a museum out of the odds and ends hotel guests leave
behind in twenty years. He selected a torn stocking—oh, so thin and fine!
A ball of a kerchief. A glove of unusual pattern—he had always wondered
about the hand that glove fitted. A powder pad, a lipstick, and some note
paper as thick as vellum. He planted these articles in strategic suggestive
points about the room. Then he took Enid's pen, and in her swagger two-
story handwriting, he filled one page:

—acable enemies, like poets—and wasps—sting once, and die, in our
regard; but you, dear friend, are of tomorrow, and tomorrow and tomor—

He tore this fragmentary epistle into small bits and dropped them into
the wastebasket. He crept away to his bed behind the stairs, where his
cherubic wife still slept the sleep of the just under the shaded rays of her
lamp.

II

"I know the house," said Parr, the police deputy, taking his chilly eye off
poor Tony for the moment, and nodding to his privileged friend, Oliver
Armiston, who had just come in. "That's where J. P. Morgan used to go for
blueberry pie. That's where they hid Lefty Linkowitz, the bail-bond tycoon, when he was hot. It isn't far from Three Corners, where a good man
can commit perjury in three states at once, if he's got three legs to stand on.
Now what are you going to do for a meal ticket, Tony?"

The unhappy Tony had been sent over as the bearer of ill tidings from
the Prosecutor's office, and for the last half-hour he had been on the carpet,
and wishing he was under it. Mr. Parr's last question was purely rhetorical.
He continued:

"I suppose this young and beauteous female with a Park Avenue air
walked off among the snow drifts on her high heels without arousing any
undue curiosity in the main street?"

Tony wrung his sleek hands. She was gone, indubitably gone, just as she
had come—without the shadow of a shade of circumstance attending her
departure. She had not left by the morning train as was her invariable
custom. The public taxis were still fast in the grip of that terrible frost.
Matt had stayed behind with the car and would leave no stone unturned.
The roads were all open, she could go, go anywhere.

"On foot?" asked the deputy.

Tony wrung his hands again.

"On wings. On skis? How?" No answer.

"Did you see any mortal manifestation of the lady, except her signature on the register?" pursued Parr. "No, you hit the hay. Was she actually there in the flesh, Tony? Or was it just a ghost?"

Tony crossed himself hurriedly. Oh, she was there! One felt a living presence—he relived the moment when the three of them solemnly raised their glasses and toasted that hot-air hole in the ceiling.

"That one is a tough fellow!" he cried. "Oh, if I have him across the state line some day! He talked up through that hole for her to hear."

"Did anyone in the house besides this obliging landlord with the .45 set eyes on this female?" asked Parr.

Tony said, "No, she come after midnight—she go—phut!—before day, like that!"

"And she'd been there before?"

"Yes, yes, sir! Last night. Last October!" cried Tony. He was on more solid ground now. "Five times, ten times. We go back in the old registers. She come and go. Always in this Number Seven—with the hot-air pipe in the floor."

Tony had the dates of these earthly manifestations of the lady of the two-story handwriting. Her first appearance was April 22, 1932.

"That was a few days after rigor mortis set in," said Parr, studying the schedule. With a curt nod he dismissed Tony. As the sad fellow shut the door with the polite caution of the misunderstood, Parr turned with a wry smile to Armiston, his friend and occasional collaborator in those misty upper reaches of crime where gumshoe work must call in fantasy for help.

"The missing bride," he said sententiously. "She disappeared at the altar six years ago. Her husband took another woman on the honeymoon with him, and has been living with her as his wife ever since. We've been quietly looking for the remains, for the past eight months."

"Murder?"

"That's the idea we were playing with," said the deputy. "And this pair of subpoena servers blunder into her in a blizzard last night—and off she goes hopping across the snow like a scared rabbit."

"Ah, the case of the reanimated corpse," said Oliver. "Are these the mortal remains?"

He turned to the exhibits from Number Seven on the desk. The fragmentary letter had been lovingly pieced together by Tony. Oliver shook his head. The paper was hardly boudoir stationery; it was too ostentatious, as heavy as vellum—of the sort bankers affected in the later days of the lamented New Era. But he nodded approvingly over the script. It had dash, élan, a certain powerful grace. "That is a beautiful pen," he said. "I'd like to own it. Odd," he added, "the impression one gets from a fragment. I knew a woman who could have written that hand. I'm thinking of a society woman of several years ago. Tragic, fascinating creature, with tears in her voice. Perfect poise, always sure of herself—and always losing. Towards the end she went on the stage, in one of Shaw's plays. She made a great hit. Finally she killed herself. She could have used that pen. Let's see what she's got to say."

He read the few lines of the broken sentence. Proust, with a dash of Hugh Walpole. It is a terrible responsibility, being a bestseller. So many weeping women borrow your thoughts to trim their sails. He took up the fragment of the stocking. It was gossamer sheer, of the stuff that spiders spin. Some women would wear such a stocking once, maybe twice. You can buy them for, say, $25 the pair, in those coy little shops in the side streets just off the Avenue, shops that cater to lovers who require something very special. The balled-up handkerchief was an airy figment of lace, so delicately true and wistfully fine that it suggested the patient shuttles of novices in a quiet cloister where time is counted on beads. The glove was from the Rue de la Paix. A lipstick, but no rouge. She probably had big round eyes and affected a dead-pan white, thought Oliver.

"You're in sporting high life, Parr," said Oliver. "Can't you see her?"

"That stuff would go over big with a jury," said the man-hunter, smiling.

"Because it's circumstantial, Parr," said Oliver. "So much more forceful than direct evidence. It flatters us, permits us to show how clever we are. Note how the fragment makes the whole picture. Now, if she had left a hairpin—or a broken corset string—or a cotton stocking—!" Armiston grimaced. "Parr, was this stuff planted for you to find?"

The deputy massaged his chin thoughtfully.

"I haven't taken this thing very seriously," he began. "It's the District Attorney's hunch. He's been nosing around—and he comes over here occasionally for moral support. There is no accuser, no corpse; dozens of people ought to suspect—but apparently there is no suspicion. What's the motive? Why should a man go to the risk of publicly marrying a woman before he murders her? We might admit he plans to get rid of her, or else he wouldn't have had the other woman in readiness to take her place." Parr paused, frowning.

"But now that the corpse turns up alive and well," put in Oliver, "a change comes o'er the spirit of your dreams."

"Yes," said Parr. "Was this stuff planted for us to find? It would make a very pretty case, Oliver, if it was—right down your alley. Let us say that he actually got away with murder, and the substitution of a bride. He goes a step farther. He plants another woman on this hotel register, in the image of the murdered bride. Maybe this is the perfect crime you parlor criminologists talk about, Oliver. Let us say that we were expected to stumble on this lady eventually. Okay, that's fine." Parr shook his head. "But not now. They couldn't have foreseen last night's occurrence. That was pure happenstance."

"I suppose it would be too crude to suggest coincidence of names?"

"Then why should she cut and run like a scared rabbit?" said Parr. Elam would have been pleased to eavesdrop through some convenient ceiling hole on the lucubrations of the great Mr. Parr. His Enid was very very much alive, and deeply involved. "Besides, it was an odd name—improbable."

"There is no such word as improbable, Parr," said Oliver. "Probability thins out, yes, approaches zero—but never actually touches zero. It's mathematical. Let a monkey hit a typewriter at random through eternity, and eventually he will write all the sonnets. That's how some people explain Shakespeare. Does the description tally?"

"We've got a vague description of the bride—a black-haired madonna, with big eyes and white skin," said Parr.

"That's the picture I get," said Oliver.

"So does the landlord," said Parr. "He doesn't know much about her. He thinks she is horsy, doggy—has a horse farm up in Vermont some place."

"What is the name?" asked Oliver.

"Enid Wallins," said the deputy, as softly as a gunman pressing a trigger. He covertly watched for the effect. Oliver exploded.

"Enid Wallins!" he ejaculated.

"Just a minute," said Parr. "You're going to tell me you saw her and her husband dining at Chaffard's last night."

"I did!" cried Armiston. "Gregory Wallins, the gentleman jockey—"

"Friend of yours?" inquired the deputy.

"Well, I— No, you've got to smell of horse liniment to get into that crowd," said Oliver. "But I've known of them for years. Why, Parr," he cried, rising, "I was in Bermuda when they came there honeymooning."

"Was the bride a black-haired madonna?"

"She was a tall willowy blonde," said Oliver.

"There you are," said the man-hunter complacently. "We can prove that three days before he sailed on this honeymoon with your blonde he married a brunette."

"It can't be done!" cried Armiston testily. "This Gregory Wallins—he is a waster and a rotter and a drunk, yes. But he comes of good people. He is Master of the Hounds at Cowdrey's. You can't flaunt an irregular female before them for years and get away with it."

"No," said Parr. "You can't. Would you say they were listed in the Register of the Élite?"

"Undoubtedly. The Wallinses always have been."

Parr shook his head slowly.

"Not Gregory," he said. "They dropped his name six years ago."

This brought Oliver up short.

"The devil you say!" he muttered. He took down the book of the social elect. The Gregory Wallinses were not there! This was unanswerable. Next to being posted at a club, there is no blow so devastating to the socially ambitious as being dropped from this sacred index of who's who in Society. New names are admitted grudgingly. Occasionally an old one is dropped out, with a dull thud. Some mysterious *arbiter elegantiarum* turns down his thumb. Why? One might as well try to tap a confessional. Oliver took to pacing the room, pulling at his single white lock.

"Even so, Parr," he said, coming to a stop, "where does it get you? A white-slave case. You talk hypothetical murder. And in the same breath you tell me she has come back. You're a meddling old woman."

"You can't lay this baby on my doorstep," laughed the deputy. "It's the District Attorney's hunch."

"Where did he get it?"

"That's a funny story, too," said Parr. "If you were Gregory Wallins, and wanted to marry secretly, how would you go about it, in this age of candid cameras and tabloids?"

"Rather difficult. He's in the rotogravures a good deal."

"How would a Gretna Green do?" asked Parr. "One of those cut-rate marrying Squires who camp along the state line—who line up elopers Saturday nights, and put them through the hopper in jig time. No questions asked. Most of the couples are from the Connecticut mill towns. They are not news any more. Ever hear of Squire Markum?"

Who had not heard of the Marrying Squire of Ageton? He had a sign on his little shack reading "Cut-Rate Marriages. Unconditional Guarantee." For years he had been good for a laugh in the news, with the freak biota of Winsted, Conn., and the low-reading thermometer of Owl's Head, N.Y.

"There you are," said the deputy. "Your friend Gregory looks like a stable-boy. He would have passed unnoticed with the run-of-the-mill—but the damned fool had to fee the Squire with a hundred-dollar bill, instead of the usual two-spot. Even then it would have been all right, but a few days later the candid-camera boys caught the bridal pair sailing for Bermuda. A tall willowy blonde, in place of the brunette. The Squire saw the photograph and worried over it. He stands back of his guarantee, and frowns on substitutes."

"The story grows less screwy," admitted Oliver.

"For some mysterious reason, after that the Wallinses dropped out of Society news," said Parr. "Somebody knew something. Well, the Squire forgot about them." Parr smiled over the devious ways of the public prints. "But about a year ago, the Wallinses began to come back," he continued. "He got to be Master of Hounds at Cowdrey's. You know there's nothing like a horse and a five-bar gate to dump a man back into the rotogravures. And Greg broke a collarbone now and then, which was news, with action pictures. Well, the Squire woke up again, and came to town and told about the substitute bride. The District Attorney bit—and he's been nosing around ever since. It was two of his bright young flatfoots who turned up the madonna last night in the snowstorm."

At this fitting juncture the door opened and Morel, Parr's handsome young shadow, ushered in a huge waddling gibbous personage of watery eye and lugubrious mien, dressed for winter in the hills. It, of course, was old Squire Markum himself.

"Well, well!" cried Parr, springing up with outstretched hand. "How's the matrimonial market this morning, Squire?"

"Seasonal," intoned the Squire. He turned a beetling brow on Oliver. "Seasonal," he repeated. "The young man's fancy is a little torpid just now." He sat down heavily, mopping his brow. The steam heat of these parts was working its way with him.

"This is Mr. Armiston, the celebrated parlor criminologist," said Parr. "I took the liberty of calling him in as a consultant. I suppose you have heard that the—ah—the lady of the first instance has come back to life?"

The Squire nodded his head slowly.

"Very unfortunate," he rumbled. There was a pause. He looked from Oliver to Parr. "This gentleman is one of us?" he said cautiously.

"He is two of us," said Parr. "Speak freely. What is so unfortunate?"

"I'm afraid I have annoyed the District Attorney," said the Squire sadly. "Something I did last night, with the purest intentions. He told me to give you this, and confess." He struggled to extricate some bulky object caught in a torn pocket.

"Confess? To what?" said Parr.

"He called it blackmail," intoned the old man lugubriously. He lifted his innocent gaze to Parr. At last the bulky object broke free, and he bent forward and laid it on the desk. It was a lump, almost a sodden lump, of money, bills. The bills were pressed into a fat brick held together by a gridiron of rubber bands.

"One thousand dollars, in fives and tens," rumbled the Squire sepulchrally. "Mr. Gregory Wallins was kind enough to give it to me."

There was a deep silence. Deputy Parr arose thoughtfully and wandered over to his pipe rack, a thing he rarely consulted. He selected a pipe with some circumspection, filled it, lighted it, musingly savored the first puff; then he came back and sat down.

"Are you ready now?" asked the Squire. Parr nodded. "I'm like that," said the Squire. "I can't think unless I smoke." He fished out a pipe and a bag of cigar clippings; when he was loaded Parr held the match.

"I met him last night," said Squire Markum sadly. "Quite unexpectedly —to him. In a restaurant. Grand place! He had a lady with him. Beautiful blonde lady! I've seen her pictures in the Sunday papers." The Squire struck another light. "He didn't know me, I guess. Most of them don't. I told him who I was. I said: 'Sir, I trust you still take pleasure in what I did for you.' "

Parr polished the bowl of his brier on a sleeve; Oliver nervously twiddled his stick.

"He didn't say," said the Squire, shaking his head. "I think maybe he didn't like my clothes. You know we dress for winter where I come from. I said: 'Sir, I am raising funds for a boys' camp. I'm putting you down for one thousand dollars.' Well, he thought it over for some time. I said: 'Sir, if convenient, I'd like it in fives and tens, without any consecutive serial numbers.' " There was a long pause.

"Well," went on the Squire, studying Parr with his sad-dog look, "after a long time, he got up, and excused himself to the lady—she didn't seem to be very well. He led me down the aisle to the front door and took me outside. He said, 'Good night. I'll meet you at the Grand Central at eleven in the morning.' "

"And he met you?" This from Parr.

"Yes!" said the Squire, with a surprised look.

"With the money?"

"Yes, oh yes," said the Squire. "He was nice to me. He bought me a ticket, and put me on my train—and waited till it pulled out. I got off at 125th street and came back."

Parr rang a bell, and when Morel came in he said:

"Put two good men on Wallins and the blonde. You and Pelts follow along behind and see what you can see."

"There's one thing I forgot," said Squire Markum, feeling for a match. "I told him I'd come in again, and let him know how things are going. He said: 'No; I'll come up to see you.' I said: 'That's fine, if you don't wait too long.' "

III

These people are always amply documented, accounted for. That is one of the rules of the game. In the so-called rotogravure section of Society the scrutiny is less strict. But the Wallins family were of Washington Square, where the old Directory began in recounting the glories that were Knickerbocker New York. Oliver knew several of the bright young men concerned with the publication of the current Register, and for a moment he speculated on just what chance he might have of finding out what somebody knew down there. Probably nobody knew anything, excepting the grand panjandrum himself—and nobody would admit knowing who he was. In the few instances Oliver knew of noble names being dropped into the dust bin of social oblivion, the best guess was always a déclassé marriage. You can't have thoroughbreds without registered sires and dams.

"However," mused Armiston, "she's not his wife. She is merely a white slave, operating under the Mann Act."

So he put aside the tall willowy blonde for the time being, as merely a confederate who had turned a little sick when the Squire said he would like it in fives and tens with no consecutive serial numbers.

That brought up the madonna for scrutiny.

That marriage was amply documented. The civil authorities, including the cut-rate Squire, would see to that. The gentleman jockey's license was in order, filled in and signed by himself in all verity. But the lady! She wore a broken collarbone at that altar (so a notation by the town clerk recited); and the clerk courteously filled in her license for her and she signed it—with her mark! That broken collarbone was plausible enough. Those people, the horsy set—if she was horsy—collect broken collarbones as service stripes; they even quote sporty pars for certain jumps. She was set forth there, with a vast air of candor, as Enid Wolfert, 22 years old, of— Shanghai, China.

"You can perjure yourself to your heart's content on a marriage license, but perjury doesn't dissolve the holy bonds of wedlock," said Oliver to himself. Shanghai was certainly far enough away to discourage meddling curiosity, should any arise. Then Oliver happened to think of his friend Facey, who was in town. Facey had been everywhere, on government service, especially in China. He ran him down at the club.

"Facey," he said. "You've been everywhere, you know everybody in China." (It is a fact, China is a very small place indeed among whites.) "Who," he asked, "is, or was, Enid Wolfert?"

"I knew of an Enid Wolfert in Shanghai" replied the gaunt horse-faced intelligence officer promptly. "She was an 'American woman.'"

"Naturally, she was an American woman," said Oliver.

"No," said Facey. "Not naturally. Artificially, yes."

"And so, what?"

"I'm using the term 'American woman' in its Chinese sense," said the paradoxical person. "I believe her real name was Enid Wolfert. But she didn't use it. She was Dewy Plum Blossom—or Swaying Marsh Lily— something like that." He looked at Oliver curiously, and Armiston, for his part, stared startled. "Is she a friend of yours?" asked Facey.

"An 'American woman'? What do you mean?" demanded Oliver.

"It's an old Chinese usage," said Facey. "It's not very complimentary to us. In fact, when Secretary Taft was in Shanghai years ago, on that famous world cruise of his, he heard it used, and he protested so indignantly that I believe some official effort was made to suppress its use—in the delicate significance the Chinese are masters of."

"You mean a dissolute woman—a Shanghai Lil?" cried Armiston.

"Why, yes, in a way," said Facey. "Of a sheltered type. Of a type we don't know over here at all. The consort of a Chinese gentleman. Oh, don't raise your hands in pious horror! If you ever knew a Chinese gentleman, you'd think twice about your own culture. What about her?" he asked abruptly.

Facey was, of course, one of them—indeed, as Parr might have put it, two of them. Oliver told him the story.

"It's quite possible," said Facey. "Gregory Wallins was over there five or six years ago—raising hell, as usual." He told Armiston a good deal about this particular American woman. The story could be epitomized in one phrase—in Chinese it was *Mei Kuo Nu Jen,* pronounced May Gwaw Noo Run—American woman. The usage dated back to the days of Salem clippers.

The usual imperturbable Parr tossed away his stogey and filled a pipe and smoked it, when Oliver recited the fruits of this interview with the intelligence official.

"Wallins has been a mark for women all his life," said the deputy—he knew more about New York's first families than many a society doctor.

Passing over, for the time being, the now somewhat enfeebled hypothetical murder of the American woman, Armiston examined the available evidence of what he called her neo-mundane existence. She seemed amply supplied with funds. He was thinking of that atrociously expensive stocking, the convent kerchief, and the custom glove. She had a horse farm in Vermont, and she was in the habit of sending her man on with the car, and taking the parlor-car train to town in the morning. Parr's minions combed the records. A woman of her type, who raised hunters in Vermont, and kept a man and a car should be amply documented. But she was not. Nothing was found. Parr passed this off as insignificant.

"She may run her farm under a stable name," he said. "And she may have her car and chauffeur on hire—many rich people do, to outwit the fake-accident lawyers."

The Pullman porter who served buffet breakfast on that early train remembered several women who might fit the description, such as it was.

"It is a savory morsel for gossip, Parr," said Oliver, finally. "But, is it cricket?"

"You mean, is it proper police inquiry?" said Parr. "No," he said, flatly. "Nevertheless, I'm looking it over."

"I'll trail along," said Oliver. "Let's try a new tack. Why did the gentleman jockey give up the thousand bucks so easily? Why did the willowy blonde get sick when that old reprobate Squire told them he'd like it in fives and tens?"

"They are living in sin, my boy," said the deputy smiling.

"But they are pretty firmly established in their position," objected Oliver. "It takes more than a cock-and-bull story told by your cut-rate Squire to upset them. You started out with what we parlor criminologists call a perfect crime. The murderer makes his kill. The murderer feels safe—but as an added precaution, he plants a dummy to appear ghostily about the country. If he is ever actually accused, he doesn't have to produce her in person. He can always summon Elam as a witness. All he needs is a reasonable doubt. It's a good set up! Elam!" Oliver paused on the name, in a moment of illogical prescience. (They say logic is only practised 100 percent in lunatic asylums.) "Maybe Elam is a holy liar? Who is Elam?"

"A wise bird," said Parr. "His father ran the Grand Dominion Hotel in Fulton Street in this city for forty years."

"I remember his English mutton chops!" sighed Oliver.

"With pickled walnuts!" muttered Parr hungrily.

"Parr," cried Oliver, "either Gregory Wallins knows of this mysterious hotel guest—or he doesn't."

" 'Doesn't?' " said the man-hunter sharply.

"Maybe he doesn't," said Oliver. "Play with that idea for a minute."

Parr whistled. "Damn!" he said. "That's pretty, eh!"

"How would it be to dump her into his lap, and see how he reacts?" proposed Armiston.

Parr touched a bell. Morel, his handsome shadow, appeared. Morel didn't look like a cop, the underworld didn't know him as a cop. He never made an arrest—but he was always around, in what Parr called his dress-suit cases.

"You are a society reporter, Morel," said Parr. "Pick out some good names on the register of the Crossings House for the past week or so. I want a paragraph in the society columns of the *Tribune* and *Times* reading: 'Among the notables registered at the Crossings House, Greenwood's, for the skiing during the past week were Enid Wallins, so-and-so, so-and-so, and so on. Mix them up."

"Would you hold off a day or two?" suddenly asked Oliver. "I'd like to run up there and try a little shee-ing myself—or maybe shee-joring. I'm not too old for that."

Oliver was for the most part a side-lines sportsman, although he could still do fancy work in a pistol gallery. The dernier cri of the sports shop windows daunted him, and he compromised on an old Norfolk, of his student days, a cap with a feather in it, and woolly golf hose. He passed up the lusty turmoil of the snow train for the peace and plenty of his own air-conditioned coupé; and in the steely blue of a winter twilight he presented himself at the Crossings House.

"I've come for some blueberry pie," he said to Elam. "What are the prospects for a choice room? Not quite perfect, I see." There was a goodly muster of autographs on the day's register, as varied as an awkward squad.

Skis and poles leaned in sociable groups against the walls of the corridor, and hobnailed boots foregathered in dark corners. "Might I see the room?" he asked; and when Elam frowned, he added quickly: "I don't steal towels or electric light bulbs." Elam didn't like to show rooms—some people not only looked under his beds but in them. So he showed Armiston the noisiest room in the house, Number Seven, right over the office and told him to take it or leave it. Oliver was delighted.

"Why, there's an old friend of mine!" cried Oliver, stopping before a framed photograph. "The Baron! That brings back the days in the old Grand Dominion. Oh, for one of his English mutton chops!"

"That's my father," said Elam. He eyed Oliver suspiciously. Many people claimed friendship with that famous old restaurateur. "What did he serve with that mutton chop?" he asked slyly.

"A pickled walnut!" cried Oliver.

Elam thrust out his hand. There was something masonic in the clasp.

"Remember Katie's?" he said, his eyes glowing.

"And White's?" countered Oliver.

"And downtown Delmonico's?"

"And Grandpa Mouquin's?"

The ice was broken, crushed; it was merely a matter of proper credentials —that pickled walnut did the trick. This fellow wouldn't pull his .45 on him, thought Oliver. He and Elam had something to talk about that might lead to anything, anything.

The smoky talk of telemark and Christiania turns, passmark, gelaendesprung, and slaloms in the lounging room tapered off towards midnight, and the woolly yodellers of the ski-fraternity clumped their noisy way to bed. Oliver settled down to a dip into an old copy of *Midshipman Easy;* and Elam mopped up. After a time Elam came out with a basket filled with ancient menus. Here was treasure trove. He and Oliver hungrily read the tale of those gustatory days when a man let out his belt before he summoned his waiter; when snipe and quail and grouse, terrapin, mallard and teal, leg of real mutton and broiled venison-liver awaited all comers in Fulton Street.

Oliver brought down his flask to spice the recollections. They talked of Fatty Bliss, Diamond Jim Brady, Old Man Greenhut; of Larry Jerome, Doctor Parkhurst and Brian G. Hughes; of Joe Vendig, Kid Levine, and Alec Williams. Elam revealed the secret of his grandfather clock.

"We didn't tell those old waiters what we were going to eat," said Oliver. "They told us, and we ate it."

"Our customers used to look in over the swing doors at our free lunch before they'd come in," said Elam.

"What was your first job in the hotel business?"

"First, I was a cash boy in A. T. Stewart's," said Elam. "Only gentlemen's sons need apply. I was promoted to the cashier's office for my handwriting."

He took up a pen and wrote rapidly in the elegant hand of long ago, with fat curves, flourishes, and shadings.

"My first job in the hotel business was to register and room the phantom guests," said Elam.

"Eh? Phantom guests?"

"Sure," said Elam. "The signatures on the few three-four lines of the register. They're always dummies. One of the superstitions of the hotel business is never to start off a day with an empty house. That was the first job my father gave me, registering the dummy names. Let me show you."

This was a trade secret, as inviolable as a magician's clove hitch. But this was the witching hour; the phantom guests themselves were about to arrive; and this fellow knew the Baron and his pickled walnuts. Elam produced his pen case and inks; and he wrote rapidly a dozen signatures—and no two of them seemed to have been written by the same hand or pen.

The amazed Armiston let his eye run down the list:

> Amos Corning
> Horace Manton
> J. H. Boles
> Enid Wallins

Oliver's mouth fell open. He stared, dumbstruck.

"I'm good, eh?" cried Elam, delighted with the very obvious effect his art made on his drinking companion.

"Incredible!" gasped Oliver. "Enid Wallins." Her autograph, with its dash, its élan, its powerful grace—her signature stared him in the face! *She was a phantom guest,* a dummy, a figment of the imagination, a sop to superstition. *Then it was murder.*

IV

The room was huge and sumptuous, its furniture arranged in several coteries. There were sporting prints on the walls, also some rare bronzes, one a Rodin; also other bronzes not so rare, of proud hunters, a huntsman with dogs. Everything suggested horse; you could almost smell saddle leather. Gregory Wallins sat deep in a chair, his morning paper trailing from one hand, the other hand tipping an untasted drink. He had been sitting thus minutes on end. Balzac in one of his old stories had an artist with the power to paint an inanimate object so as to draw all eyes to it, in amazement, horror, loathing. That artist might have drawn this trailing newspaper; no one could have looked in on the scene and seen it without a sense of foreboding. After a time a clock, with a pawing hunter atop, struck the hour. Wallins arose and went down the corridor to his wife's room and entered. She too was seated, with a trailing paper beside her. She did not look up as he entered; but when he sat down, after a time she looked at his paper, and then at him.

A paragraph in the Society notes read, under Greenwood's dateline:

"Among the notables registered at the Crossings House for the ski running this week are Trotter Mason, the Sailing Fosters, Enid Wallins, Foster Stowe—"

Some random noise in the street broke the spell.

"Where is Greenwood's?" she asked, wetting her lips.

"In the Connecticut highlands," he said. "Up under the state line." He drained his glass.

"You'd better go slow with that stuff, now, hadn't you?" she cautioned. She asked quietly: "Do you think it possible?"

He shook his head. "No."

"You mean you are not sure? Think! Think!" she cried. "Be sure of something, now."

"That blackmailer, the Squire, knows something," he muttered. "Maybe he thinks he can bay me out from cover. I'll have to go see."

"What am I to know?" she asked.

"Nothing," he said, rising. "I've gone to the Coast on business."

Five minutes later he was in his car driving north. Two good men followed close behind.

Down in Centre Street Deputy Parr was speaking into his phone to the Greenwood's police. The action would be out of his bailiwick. An affair for the local constabulary. Parr would provide the assisting cast, with guest stars. Pelts, a wry little fellow, one of Parr's prize men, was the bell boy; Morel was the head waiter. Pin Point Annie, whom the deputy had rescued, a brand from the burning, when she was a cigarette girl, was the lay figure.

"You're not coming to the party?" said Parr to Oliver. Armiston shook his head. He liked crime in the abstract, academic; he didn't mind sitting in conference, twiddling his stick and pulling at his single white lock, the while he put forward this and that as a suggestion—like dumping a poor dumb ghost into the lap of its destroyer. But to be in at the kill, to see the illusion torn aside, to hear the trap fall—it wasn't pretty.

When Gregory Wallins registered himself as "Lon Fetty," Elam said: "Front! Show this gentleman to Number Six."

Wallins had himself well in hand. He scanned the register, turned the pages: "Enid Wallins." There it was! He wished he could remember her writing. He couldn't even remember having seen it. But there it was! With a snap he shut the book and turned away. His liquor steeled him.

"You fool!" cried the outraged Elam. "What did you do that for?"

"What?" Wallins leered drunkenly.

"Shut the book."

"Well, what of it?"

"It means a death in the house!" cried Elam nervously. He had known it to happen; even now, with the house full of police, when he was supposed to hold himself in hand, he was white with anger. Wallins moved on, grinning to himself.

"What's this next room?" demanded Wallins, as Pelts, the bell boy, unstrapped the bags. Pelts went over to him and whispered.

"Classy dame! Big eyes, white face, blue-black hair. Too swell to come down to her meals."

"What's her name?"

"I'll find out, sir."

"Anybody else on this corridor?"

"No, sir. It's away from the rest of the house."

"You can fetch my supper up here," said Gregory. "Get me some liquor." He gave Pelts a ten dollar bill; this was his besetting sin, this contemptuous giving to underlings. Pelts was hanging up the things from the bags, feeling for guns, shells. There were none; but in the ulster there was a .25, with a silencer. Pelts deftly extracted the loaded cylinder and palmed it. Passing out, the bell boy went to the rummage closet, where Pin Point Annie looked up, wide-eyed, at his entrance.

"These are for you, sister," said Pelts, extracting the bullets. "They got your name on them."

When he brought up the supper—and the liquor—he set out the things, held Gregory's chair for him, gave him his napkin.

"It's an Enid Wallins, sir," he whispered. "From China, I think—she's got some Chinese junk for jewelry, sir."

A shiver went through Gregory Wallins.

"Damn this ice-box climate!" he snarled. "Get me some more heat, and leave me alone." Pelts opened the radiator. He slyly slipped back the revolver cylinder, now loaded with blanks.

The illusion was perfect. As Oliver had said, when he looked at that lacy stocking, the kerchief, and the glove, it takes only the fragment to make the whole picture, in a mind keyed to imaginings. A woman who wore Chinese junk for jewelry!

Up to this moment it had been touch and go. The signature had been the rub—Parr had cast his all on that. A dozen unseen eyes had watched Gregory as he scanned that phantom autograph on the register, with its two-story handwriting, its dash, its élan, its powerful grace. They had won.

"Well," said Pin Point Annie, when they gave her her cue, "a girl's got to eat. I'll see you in Berlin."

She crept into Enid's bed, drew the clothes up about her, lay there waiting; the moon was high and cast deep shadows. Downstairs the revelry of the skiers gradually died; steps stumbled on stairs, the lights went out one by one; the house slept.

It was two o'clock when that shriek came, a muffled cry trailing off into nothingness; then a pleading, "Gregory! No! No!"

Then a soft *phut*—a muffled report hardly more than the slap of a stave on deep snow.

Morel the head waiter, and Pelts, the bell boy, broke in on the instant.

Gregory Wallins was still staring at the object on the couch across the room in the moonlight, swaying drunkenly as he stared. The two men pinioned him with a skill beyond that of menials. The dishevelled Elam came in as they pushed the limp Gregory out into the hall.

"What the hell's going on here?" Elam cried hoarsely, in keeping with his instructions.

"Did he get her? Look and see," directed Morel quietly.

From the room came Elam's voice: "Y-yes. I—I'm afraid so."

"Call your police quietly," said Morel. Lock-steps stumbled off down the stairs. Pin Point Annie sat up, yawning, stretching. She pushed aside her robe and took off a fireman's asbestos vest. "Just in case of fire," she said, to the empty room.

"I suppose every man justifies himself in his own heart for everything he does," said Deputy Parr, settling himself in his favorite elbow chair by Oliver's desk.

"Does Gregory Wallins?"

"Absolutely," said Parr. "The astonishing fact is, this rounder is helplessly in love, for the first time in his life—with his willowy blonde. She came out of Russia. He's been true to her, after his fashion. But when he was in Shanghai, the other woman, this 'American woman,' begged him to fetch her back to the States with him. He did it. But when he got her here and said 'good-bye' she said 'Oh, no! I'm a white slave now.' He took it to be the usual shake-down, and offered her money. She said, 'Oh, no. Marry me.' He was on the point of marrying the other woman, the blonde."

Parr looked up, spread his hands.

"Well, he married the 'American woman,'" said he grimly. "He lured her back in the woods, to the Squire's cut-rate shack, on some cock-and-bull story or other—then he drowned her in the Beaverkill—or thought he did—and went off on the honeymoon with the substitute bride."

"Wait a minute, Parr," said Oliver. "You say he thought he drowned her. Doesn't he actually know yet that he succeeded?"

Parr shook his head. "No," he said, "he still thinks that she somehow got out of the water and escaped."

"Then what have you got on him?" cried Oliver. "You've established no corpus delicti for that crime. Are you proposing to charge him with assault with intent to kill, with blank cartridges, in that fake scene in your hotel room?"

"We've got his signed confession," said the deputy complacently. "And we've established the corpus delicti."

"What!"

"The Beaverkill police turned up with a story of an unidentified drowning at that time," said Parr, smiling at Oliver's astonishment. "They've got photographs—and her effects. And she had a broken collar bone!"

Oliver stared, dumbstruck. Then that broken collar-bone wasn't a fake.

"It was just one of the little 'ifs' that spoil the 'perfect crime' that you parlor criminologists talk about," said Parr. "There is always an if. If she hadn't broken her collar bone—If Gregory hadn't tipped the Squire with a hundred-dollar bill, instead of a two-spot—If the District Attorney's bright young men hadn't roughed up Elam and made him mad—" he paused, eyeing Oliver. "Wait till the poor devil wakes up and discovers that his crime was perfect in the first place—*if* he had had sense enough to leave it alone!"

The Fifties

AS SIMPLE AS ABC

by ELLERY QUEEN

This is a very old story as Queen stories go. It happened in Ellery's salad days, when he was tossing his talents about like a Sunday chef, and a redheaded girl named Nikki Porter had just attached herself to his typewriter. But it has not staled, this story; it has an unwithering flavor which those who partook of it relish to this day. There are gourmets in America whose taste buds leap at any concoction dated 1861–1865. To such, the mere recitation of ingredients like Bloody Angle, Minié balls, Little Mac, *Tenting Tonight,* the brand of General Grant's whiskey, not to mention Father Abraham, is sufficient to start the passionate flow of juices. These are the misty-hearted to whom the Civil War is "the War" and the blue-gray armies rather more than men. Romantics, if you will; garnishers of history. But it is they who pace the lonely sentrypost by the night Potomac, they who hear the creaking of the ammunition wagons, the snap of campfires, the scream of the thin gray line and the long groan of the battlefield. They personally flee the burning hell of the Wilderness as the dead rise and twist in the flames; under lanterns, in the flickering mud, they stoop compassionately with the surgeons over quivering heaps. It is they who keep the little flags flying and the ivy ever green on the graves of the old men.

Ellery is of this company, and that is why he regards the case of the old men of Jacksburg, Pennsylvania, with particular affection.

Ellery and Nikki came upon the village of Jacksburg as people often come upon the best things, unpropitiously. They had been driving back to New York from Washington, where Ellery had done some sleuthing among the stacks of the Library of Congress. Perhaps the sight of the Potomac, Arlington's eternal geometry, Lincoln frozen in giant sadness, brought its weight to bear upon Ellery's decision to veer towards Gettysburg, where murder had been national. And Nikki had never been there, and May was coming to its end. There was a climate of sentiment.

They crossed the Maryland-Pennsylvania line and spent timeless hours wandering over Culp's Hill and Seminary Ridge and Little Round Top and Spangler's Spring among the watchful monuments. It is a place of everlasting life, where Pickett and Jeb Stuart keep charging to the sight of those with eyes to see, where the blood spills fresh if colorlessly, and the highpitched tones of a tall and ugly man still ring out over the graves. When they left, Ellery and Nikki were in a mood of wonder, unconscious of time or place, oblivious to the darkening sky and the direction in which the nose of the Duesenberg pointed. So in time they were disagreeably awakened by the alarm clock of nature. The sky had opened on their heads, drenching them to the skin instantly. From the horizon behind them Gettysburg was a battlefield again, sending great flashes of fire through the darkness to the din of celestial cannon. Ellery stopped the car and put the top up, but the mood was drowned when he discovered that something ultimate had happened to the ignition system. They were marooned in a faraway land, Nikki moaned.

"We can't go on in these wet clothes, Ellery!"

"Do you suggest that we stay here in them? I'll get this crackerbox started if . . ." But at that moment the watery lights of a house wavered on somewhere ahead, and Ellery became cheerful again.

"At least we'll find out where we are and how far it is to where we ought to be. Who knows? There may even be a garage."

It was a little white house on a little swampy road marked off by a little stone fence covered with rambler rose vines, and the man who opened the door to the dripping wayfarers was little, too, little and weatherskinned and callused, with eyes that seemed to have roots in the stones and springs of the Pennsylvania countryside. They smiled hospitably, but the smile became concern when he saw how wet they were.

"Won't take no for an answer," he said in a remarkably deep voice, and he chuckled. "That's doctor's orders, though I expect you didn't see my shingle—mostly overgrown with ivy. Got a change of clothing?"

"Oh, yes!" said Nikki abjectly.

Ellery, being a man, hesitated. The house looked neat and clean, there was an enticing fire, and the rain at their backs was coming down with a roar. "Well, thank you . . . but if I might use your phone to call a garage—"

"You just give me the keys to your car trunk."

"But we can't turn your home into a tourist house—"

"It's that, too, when the good Lord sends a wanderer my way. Now see here, this storm's going to keep up most of the night and the roads hereabout get mighty soupy." The little man was bustling into waterproofs and overshoes. "I'll get Lew Bagley over at the garage to pick up your car, but for now let's have those keys."

So an hour later, while the elements warred outside, they were toasting safely in a pleasant little parlor, full of Dr. Martin Strong's homemade poppy-seed twists, scrapple, and coffee. The doctor, who lived alone, was his own cook. He was also, he said with a chuckle, mayor of the village of Jacksburg, and its chief of police.

"Lot of us in the village run double harness. Bill Yoder of the hardware store's our undertaker. Lew Bagley's also the fire chief. Ed MacShane—"

"Jacksburger-of-all-trades you may be, Dr. Strong," said Ellery, "but to me you'll always be primarily the Good Samaritan."

"Hallelujah," said Nikki.

"And make it Doc," said their host. "Why, it's just selfishness on my part, Mr. Queen. We're off the beaten track here, and you do get a hankering for a new face. I guess I know every dimple and wen on the five hundred and thirty-four in Jacksburg."

"I don't suppose your police chiefship keeps you very busy."

Doc Strong laughed. "Not any. Though last year—" His eyes puckered and he got up to poke the fire. "Did you say, Miss Porter, that Mr. Queen is sort of a detective?"

"Sort of a!" began Nikki. "Why, Dr. Strong, he's solved some simply unbeliev—"

"My father is an inspector in the New York police department," interrupted Ellery, curbing his new secretary's enthusiasm with an iron glance. "I stick my nose into a case once in a while. What about last year, Doc?"

"What put me in mind of it," said Jacksburg's mayor thoughtfully, "was your saying you'd been to Gettysburg today. And also you being interested in crimes . . ." Dr. Strong said abruptly, "I'm a fool, but I'm worried."

"Worried about what?"

"Well . . . Memorial Day's tomorrow, and for the first time in my life I'm not looking forward to it. Jacksburg makes quite a fuss about Memorial Day. It's not every village can brag about three living veterans of the Civil War."

"Three!" exclaimed Nikki.

"Gives you an idea what the Jacksburg doctoring business is like," grinned Doc Strong. "We run to pioneer-type women and longevity . . . I ought to have said we *had* three Civil War veterans—Caleb Atwell, ninety-seven, of the Atwell family, there are dozens of 'em in the county; Zach Bigelow, ninety-five, who lives with his grandson Andy and Andy's wife and seven kids; and Abner Chase, ninety-four, Cissy Chase's great-grandpa. This year we're down to two. Caleb Atwell died last Memorial Day."

"A,B,C," murmured Ellery.

"What's that?"

"I have a bookkeeper's mind, Doc. Atwell, Bigelow, and Chase. Call it a spur-of-the-moment mnemonic system. A died last Memorial Day. Is that why you're not looking forward to this one? B following A sort of thing?"

"Didn't it always?" said Doc Strong with defiance. "Though I'm afraid it ain't—isn't as simple as all that. Maybe I better tell you how Caleb Atwell died . . . Every year Caleb, Zach, and Abner have been the star perform-ers of our Memorial Day exercises, which are held at the old burying ground on the Hookerstown road. The oldest—"

"That would be A. Caleb Atwell."

"That's right. As the oldest, Caleb always blew taps on a cracked old bugle that came from their volunteer regiment. And Zach Bigelow, as the next oldest to Caleb Atwell, he'd be the standard bearer, and Ab Chase, as the next-next oldest, he'd lay the wreath on the memorial monument in the burying ground.

"Well, last Memorial Day, while Zach was holding the regimental colors and Ab the wreath, Caleb blew taps the way he'd been doing nigh onto twenty times before. All of a sudden, in the middle of a high note, Caleb keeled over. Dropped in his tracks. Deader than church on Monday."

"Strained himself," said Nikki sympathetically. "But what a poetic way for a Civil War veteran to die."

Doc Strong regarded her oddly. "Maybe," he said. "If you like that kind of poetry." He kicked a log, sending red sparks flying.

"But surely, Doc," said Ellery with a smile, for he was young in those days, "surely you can't have been suspicious about the death of a man of ninety-seven?"

"Maybe I was," muttered their host. "Maybe I was because it so hap-pened I'd given old Caleb a thorough physical check-up only the day before he died. I'd have staked my medical license he'd live to break a hundred and then some. Healthiest old copperhead I ever knew. Copper-head! I'm blaspheming the dead. Caleb lost an eye at Second Bull Run . . . I know—I'm senile. That's what I've been telling myself."

"Just what was it you suspected, Doc?" Ellery forbore to smile now, but only because of Dr. Strong's evident distress.

"Didn't know what to suspect," said the country doctor shortly. "Fooled around with the notion of an autopsy, but the Atwells wouldn't hear of it. Said I was a blame jackass to think a man of ninety-seven would die of anything but old age. I found myself agreeing with 'em. The upshot was we buried Caleb whole."

"But, Doc, at that age the human economy can go to pieces without warning like the one-hoss shay. You must have had another reason for uneasiness. A motive you knew about?"

"Well . . . maybe."

"He was a rich man," said Nikki.

"He didn't have a pot he could call his own," said Doc Strong. "But somebody stood to gain by his death just the same. That is, if the old yarn's true . . . You see, there's been kind of a legend in Jacksburg about those three old fellows, Mr. Queen. I first heard it when I was running around barefoot with my tail hanging out. Folks said then, and they're still saying it, that back in '65 Caleb and Zach and Ab, who were in the same company, found some sort of treasure."

"Treasure . . ." Nikki began to cough.

"Treasure," repeated Doc Strong doggedly. "Fetched it home to Jacksburg with them, the story goes, hid it, and swore they'd never tell a living soul where it was buried. Now there's lots of tales like that came out of the War—" he fixed Nikki with a stern and glittering eye "—and most folks either cough or go into hysterics, but there's something about this one I've always half-believed. So I'm senile on two counts. Just the same, I'll breathe a lot easier when tomorrow's ceremonies are over and Zach Bigelow lays Caleb Atwell's bugle away till next year. As the oldest survivor Zach does the tootling tomorrow."

"They hid the treasure and kept it hidden for considerably over half a century?" Ellery was smiling again. "Doesn't strike me as a very sensible thing to do with a treasure, Doc. It's only sensible if the treasure is imaginary. Then you don't have to produce it."

"The story goes," mumbled Jacksburg's mayor, "that they'd sworn an oath—"

"Not to touch any of it until they all died but one," said Ellery, laughing outright now. "Last-survivor-takes-all Department. Doc, that's the way most of these fairy tales go." Ellery rose, yawning. "I think I hear the featherbed in that other guest room calling. Nikki, your eyeballs are hanging out. Take my advice, Doc, and follow suit. You haven't a thing to worry about but keeping the kids quiet tomorrow while you read the Gettysburg Address!"

As it turned out, the night shared prominently in Doc Martin Strong's Memorial Day responsibilities. Ellery and Nikki awakened to a splendid world, risen from its night's ablutions with a shining eye and a scrubbed look; and they went downstairs within seconds of each other to find the mayor of Jacksburg puttering about the kitchen.

"Morning, morning," said Doc Strong, welcoming but abstracted. "Just fixing things for your breakfast before catching an hour's nap."

"You lamb," said Nikki. "But what a shame, Doctor. Didn't you sleep well last night?"

"Didn't sleep at all. Tossed around a bit and just as I was dropping off my phone rings and it's Cissy Chase. Emergency sick call."

"Cissy Chase." Ellery looked at their host. "Wasn't Chase the name you mentioned last night—?"

"Old Abner Chase's great-granddaughter. That's right, Mr. Queen. Cissy's an orphan and Ab's only kin. She's kept house for the old fellow and taken care of him since she was ten." Doc Strong's shoulders sloped.

Ellery said peculiarly: "It was old Abner . . . ?"

"I was up with Ab all night. This morning, at six thirty, he passed away."

"On Memorial Day!" Nikki sounded like a little girl in her first experience with a fact of life.

There was a silence, fretted by the sizzling of Doc Strong's bacon.

Ellery said at last, "What did Abner Chase die of?"

"Apoplexy."

"A stroke?"

Doc Strong looked at him. He seemed angry. But then he shook his head. "I'm no Mayo brother, Mr. Queen, and I suppose there's a lot about the practice of medicine I'll never get to learn, but I do know a cerebral hemorrhage when I see one, and that's what Ab Chase died of. In a man of ninety-four, that's as close to natural death as you can come . . . No, there wasn't any funny business in this one."

"Except," mumbled Ellery, "that—again—it happened on Memorial Day."

"Man's a contrary animal. Tell him lies and he swallows 'em whole. Give him the truth and he gags on it. Maybe the Almighty gets tired of His thankless job every once in an eon and cuts loose with a little joke." But Doc Strong said it as if he were addressing, not them, but himself. "Any special way you like your eggs?"

"Leave the eggs to me, Doctor," Nikki said firmly. "You go on up those stairs and get some sleep."

"Reckon I better if I'm to do my usual dignified job today," said the mayor of Jacksburg with a sigh. "Though Abner Chase's death is going to make the proceedings solemner than ordinary. Bill Yoder says he's not going to be false to an ancient and honorable profession by doing a hurry-up job undertaking Ab, and maybe that's just as well. If we added the Chase funeral to today's program, even old Abe's immortal words would find it hard to compete! By the way, Mr. Queen, I talked to Lew Bagley this morning and he'll have your car ready in an hour. Special service, seeing you're guests of the mayor." Doc Strong chuckled. "When you planning to leave?"

"I *was* intending . . ." Ellery stopped with a frown. Nikki regarded him with a sniffish look. She had already learned to detect the significance of certain signs peculiar to the Queen physiognomy. "I wonder," murmured Ellery, "how Zach Bigelow's going to take the news."

"He's already taken it, Mr. Queen. Stopped in at Andy Bigelow's place on my way home. Kind of a detour, but I figured I'd better break the news to Zach early as possible."

"Poor thing," said Nikki. "I wonder how it feels to learn you're the only one left." She broke an egg.

"Can't say Zach carried on about it," said Doc Strong dryly. "About all he said, as I recall, was: 'Doggone it, now who's goin' to lay the wreath after I toot the bugle!' I guess when you reach the age of ninety-five, death don't mean what it does to young squirts of sixty-three like me. What time'd you say you were leaving, Mr. Queen?"

"Nikki," muttered Ellery, "are we in any particular hurry?"

"I don't know. Are we?"

"Besides, it wouldn't be patriotic. Doc, do you suppose Jacksburg would mind if a couple of New York Yanks invited themselves to your Memorial Day exercises?"

The business district of Jacksburg consisted of a single paved street bounded at one end by the sightless eye of a broken traffic signal and at the other by the twin gas pumps before Lew Bagley's garage. In between, some stores in need of paint sunned themselves, enjoying the holiday. Red, white, and blue streamers crisscrossed the thoroughfare overhead. A few seedy frame houses, each decorated with an American flag, flanked the main street at both ends.

Ellery and Nikki found the Chase house exactly where Doc Strong had said it would be—just around the corner from Bagley's garage, between the ivy-hidden church and the firehouse of the Jacksburg Volunteer Pump and Hose Company No. 1. But the mayor's directions were a superfluity; it was the only house with a crowded porch.

A heavy-shouldered young girl in a black Sunday dress sat in a rocker, the center of the crowd. Her nose was as red as her big hands, but she was trying to smile at the cheerful words of sympathy winged at her from all sides.

"Thanks, Mis' Plumm . . . That's right, Mr. Schmidt, I know . . . But he was such a spry old soul, Emerson, I can't believe . . ."

"Miss Cissy Chase?"

Had the voice been that of a Confederate spy, a deeper silence could not have drowned the noise. Jacksburg eyes examined Ellery and Nikki with cold curiosity, and feet shuffled.

"My name is Queen and this is Miss Porter. We're attending the Jacksburg Memorial Day exercises as guests of Mayor Strong—" a warming murmur, like a zephyr, passed over the porch "—and he asked us to wait here for him. I'm sorry about your great-grandfather."

"You must have been very proud of him," said Nikki.

"Thank you, I was. It was so sudden— Won't you set? I mean—Do come into the house. Great-grandpa's not here . . . he's over at Bill Yoder's . . ."

The girl was flustered and began to cry, and Nikki took her arm and led her into the house. Ellery lingered a moment to exchange appropriate remarks with the neighbors who, while no longer cold, were still curious; and then he followed. It was a dreary little house, with a dark and musty-smelling parlor.

"Now, now, this is no time for fussing—may I call you Cissy?" Nikki was saying soothingly. "Besides, you're better off away from all those folks. Why, Ellery, she's only a child!"

And a very plain child, Ellery thought, with a pinched face and empty eyes.

"I understand the parade to the burying ground is going to form outside your house, Cissy," he said. "By the way, have Andrew Bigelow and his grandfather Zach arrived yet?"

"Oh, I don't know," said Cissy Chase dully. "It's all like such a dream, seems like."

"Of course it does. And you're left alone. Haven't you any family at all, Cissy?"

"No."

"Isn't there some young man—?"

Cissy shook her head bitterly. "Who'd marry me? This is the only decent dress I got, and it's four years old. We lived on great-grandpa's pension and what I could earn hiring out by the day. Which ain't much, nor often. Now . . ."

"I'm sure you'll find something to do," said Nikki, very heartily.

"In Jacksburg?"

Nikki was silent.

"Cissy." Ellery spoke casually, and she did not even look up. "Doc Strong mentioned something about a treasure. Do you know anything about it?"

"Oh, that." Cissy shrugged. "Just what great-grandpa told me, and he hardly ever told the same story twice. But near as I was ever able to make out, one time during the War him and Caleb Atwell and Zach Bigelow got separated from the army—scouting, or foraging, or something. It was down South somewhere, and they spent the night in an old empty mansion that was half-burned down. Next morning they went through the ruins to see what they could pick up, and buried in the cellar they found the treasure. A big fortune in money, great-grandpa said. They were afraid to take it with them, so they buried it in the same place in the cellar and made a map of the location and after the War they went back, the three of 'em, and dug it up again. Then they made the pact."

"Oh, yes," said Ellery. "The pact."

"Swore they'd hold onto the treasure till only one of them remained alive, I don't know why, then the last one was to get it all. Leastways, that's how great-grandpa told it."

"Did he ever say how much of a fortune it was?"

Cissy laughed. "Couple of hundred thousand dollars. I ain't saying great-grandpa was cracked, but you know how an old man gets."

"Did he ever give you a hint as to where he and Caleb and Zach hid the money after they got it back North?"

"No, he'd just slap his knee and wink at me."

"Maybe," said Ellery suddenly, "maybe there's something to that yarn after all."

Nikki stared. "But Ellery, you said—! Cissy, did you hear that?"

But Cissy only drooped. "If there is, it's all Zach Bigelow's now."

Then Doc Strong came in, fresh as a daisy in a pressed blue suit and a stiff collar and a bow tie, and a great many other people came in, too. Ellery and Nikki surrendered Cissy Chase to Jacksburg.

"If there's anything to the story," Nikki whispered to Ellery, "and if Mayor Strong is right, then that old scoundrel Bigelow's been murdering his friends to get the money!"

"After all these years, Nikki? At the age of ninety-five?" Ellery shook his head.

"But then what—?"

"I don't know." And Ellery fell silent. But his glance went to Doc Strong and waited; and when the little mayor happened to look their way, Ellery caught his eye and took him aside and whispered in his ear. . . .

The procession—nearly every car in Jacksburg, Doc Strong announced proudly, over a hundred of them—got under way at exactly two o'clock.

Nikki had been embarrassed but not surprised to find herself being handed into the leading car, an old but brightly polished touring job contributed for the occasion by Lew Bagley; and the moment Nikki spied the ancient, doddering head under the Union army hat in the front seat she detected the fine Italian whisper of her employer. Zach Bigelow held his papery frame fiercely if shakily erect between the driver and a powerful red-necked man with a brutal face who, Nikki surmised, was the old man's grandson, Andy Bigelow. Nikki looked back, peering around the flapping folds of the flag stuck in the corner of the car. Cissy Chase was in the second car in a black veil, weeping on a stout woman's shoulder. So the female Yankee from New York sat back between Ellery and Mayor Strong, against the bank of flowers in which the flag was set, and glared at the necks of the two Bigelows, having long since taken sides in this matter. And when Doc Strong made the introductions, Nikki barely nodded to Jacksburg's sole survivor of the Grand Army of the Republic, and then only in acknowledgment of his historic importance.

Ellery, however, was all deference and cordiality, even to the brute grandson. He leaned forward.

"How do I address your grandfather, Mr. Bigelow?"

"Gramp's a general," said Andy Bigelow loudly. "Ain't you, Gramp?" He beamed at the ancient, but Zach Bigelow was staring proudly ahead, holding fast to something in a rotted musette bag on his lap. "Went through the War a private," the grandson confided, "but he don't like to talk about that."

"General Bigelow—"

"That's his deaf ear," said the grandson. "Try the other one."

"General Bigelow!"

"Hey?" The old man turned his trembling head, glaring. "Speak up, bub. Ye're mumblin'."

"General Bigelow," shouted Ellery, "now that all the money is yours, what will you do with it?"

"Hey? Money?"

"The treasure, Gramp," roared Andy Bigelow. "They've even heard about it in New York. What you goin' to do with it, he wants to know?"

"Does, does he?" Old Zach sounded grimly amused. "Can't talk, Andy. Hurts m' neck."

"How much does it amount to, General?" cried Ellery.

Old Zach eyed him. "Mighty nosy, ain't ye?" Then he cackled. "Last time we counted it—Caleb, Ab, and me—came to nigh on a million dollars. Yes, sir, one million dollars." The old man's left eye, startlingly, drooped. "Goin' to be a big surprise to the smart-alecks and the doubtin' Thomases. You wait an' see."

"According to Cissy," Nikki murmured to Doc Strong, "Abner Chase said it was only two hundred thousand."

"Zach makes it more every time he talks about it," said the mayor.

"I heard ye, Martin Strong!" yelled Zach Bigelow, swiveling his twig of a neck so suddenly that Nikki winced, expecting it to snap. "You wait! I'll show ye, ye durn whippersnapper, who's a lot o' wind!"

"Now, Zach," said Doc Strong pacifyingly. "Save your wind for that bugle."

Zach Bigelow cackled and clutched the musette bag in his lap, glaring ahead in triumph, as if he had scored a great victory.

Ellery said no more. Oddly, he kept staring not at old Zach but at Andy Bigelow, who sat beside his grandfather grinning at invisible audiences along the empty countryside as if he, too, had won—or was on his way to winning—a triumph.

The sun was hot. Men shucked their coats and women fanned themselves with handkerchiefs.

"It is for us the living, rather, to be dedicated . . ."

Children dodged among the graves, pursued by shushing mothers. On most of the graves were fresh flowers.

". . . that from these honored dead . . ."
Little American flags protruded from the graves, too.
". . . gave the last full measure of devotion . . ."
Doc Martin Strong's voice was deep and sure, not at all like the voice of
that tall ugly man, who had spoken the same words apologetically.
". . . that these dead shall not have died in vain . . ."
Doc was standing on the pedestal of the Civil War Monument, which
was decorated with flags and bunting and faced the weathered stone ranks
like a commander in full-dress.
". . . that this nation, under God . . ."
A color guard of the American Legion, Jacksburg Post, stood at attention
between the mayor and the people. A file of Legionnaires carrying old
Sharps rifles faced the graves.
". . . and that government of the people . . ."
Beside the mayor, disdaining the wrestler's shoulder of his simian grand-
son, stood General Zach Bigelow. Straight as the barrel of a Sharps, musette
bag held tightly.
". . . shall not perish from the earth."
The old man nodded impatiently. He began to fumble with the bag.
"Comp'ny! Present—arms!"
"Go ahead, Gramp!" Andy Bigelow bellowed.
The old man muttered. He was having difficulty extricating the bugle
from the bag.
"Here, lemme give ye a hand!"
"Let the old man alone, Andy," said the mayor of Jacksburg quietly.
"We're in no hurry."
Finally the bugle was free. It was an old army bugle, as old as Zach
Bigelow, dented and scarred.
The old man raised it to his lips.
Now his hands were not shaking.
Now even the children were quiet.
And the old man began to play taps.
It could hardly have been called playing. He blew, and out of the bugle's
bell came cracked sounds. And sometimes he blew and no sounds came out
at all. Then the veins of his neck swelled and his face turned to burning
bark. Or he sucked at the mouthpiece, in and out, to clear it of his spittle.
But still he blew, and the trees in the burying ground nodded in the warm
breeze, and the people stood at attention, listening, as if the butchery of
sound were sweet music.
And then, suddenly, the butchery faltered. Old Zach Bigelow stood with
bulging eyes. The bugle fell to the pedestal with a tinny clatter.
For an instant everything seemed to stop—the slight movements of the
children, the breathing of the people.

Then into the vacuum rushed a murmur of horror, and Nikki unbelievingly opened the eyes which she had shut to glimpse the last of Jacksburg's G.A.R. veterans crumpling to the feet of Doc Strong and Andy Bigelow. . . .

"You were right the first time, Doc," Ellery said.

They were in Andy Bigelow's house, where old Zach's body had been taken from the cemetery. The house was full of chittering women and scampering children, but in this room there were only a few, and they talked in low tones. The old man was laid out on a settee with a patchwork quilt over him. Doc Strong sat in a rocker beside the body.

"It's my fault," he mumbled. "I didn't examine Caleb's mouth last year. I didn't examine the mouthpiece of the bugle. It's my fault."

Ellery soothed him. "It's not an easy poison to spot, Doc, as you know. And after all, the whole thing was so ludicrous. You'd have caught it in autopsy, but the Atwells laughed you out of it."

"They're all gone. All three." Doc Strong looked up fiercely. "Who poisoned that bugle?"

"God Almighty, don't look at me," said Andy Bigelow. "Anybody could of, Doc."

"Anybody, Andy?" the mayor cried. "When Caleb Atwell died, Zach took the bugle and it's been in this house for a year!"

"Anybody could of," said Bigelow stubbornly. "The bugle was hangin' over the fireplace and anybody could of snuck in durin' the night . . . Anyway, it wasn't here before old Caleb died; *he* had it up to last Memorial Day. Who poisoned it in *his* house?"

"We won't get anywhere on this tack, Doc," Ellery murmured. "Bigelow. Did your grandfather ever let on where that Civil War treasure is?"

"Suppose he did." The man licked his lips, blinking, as if he had been surprised into the half-admission. "What's it to you?"

"That money is behind the murders, Bigelow."

"Don't know nothin' about that. Anyway, nobody's got no right to that money but me." Andy Bigelow spread his thick chest. "When Ab Chase died, Gramp was the last survivor. That money was Zach Bigelow's. I'm his next o' kin, so now it's mine!"

"You know where it's hid, Andy." Doc was on his feet, eyes glittering.

"I ain't talkin'. Git outen my house!"

"I'm the law in Jacksburg, too, Andy," Doc said softly. "This is a murder case. Where's that money?"

Bigelow laughed.

"You didn't know, Bigelow, did you?" said Ellery.

"Course not." He laughed again. "See, Doc? He's on your side, and he says I don't know, too."

"That is," said Ellery, "until a few minutes ago."

Bigelow's grin faded. "What are ye talkin' about?"

"Zach Bigelow wrote a message this morning, immediately after Doc Strong told him about Abner Chase's death."

Bigelow's face went ashen.

"And your grandfather sealed the message in an envelope—"

"Who told ye that?" yelled Bigelow.

"One of your children. And the first thing you did when we got home from the burying ground with your grandfather's corpse was to sneak up to the old man's bedroom. Hand it over."

Bigelow made two fists. Then he laughed again. "All right, I'll let ye see it. Hell, I'll let ye dig the money up for me! Why not? It's mine by law. Here, read it. See? He wrote my name on the envelope!"

And so he had. And the message in the envelope was also written in ink, in the same wavering hand:

"Dere Andy now that Ab Chase is ded to—if sumthin happins to me you wil find the money we been keepin all these long yeres in a iron box *in the coffin wich we beried Caleb Atwell in.* I leave it all to you my beluved grandson cuz you been sech a good grandson to me. Yours truly Zach Bigelow."

"In Caleb's coffin," choked Doc Strong.

Ellery's face was impassive. "How soon can you get an exhumation order, Doc?"

"Right now," exclaimed Doc. "I'm also deputy coroner of this district!"

And they took some men and they went back to the old burying ground, and in the darkening day they dug up the remains of Caleb Atwell and they opened the casket and found, on the corpse's knees, a flattish box of iron with a hasp but no lock. And while two strong men held Andy Bigelow to keep him from hurling himself at the crumbling coffin, Doctor-Mayor-Chief-of-Police-Deputy-Coroner Martin Strong held his breath and raised the lid of the box.

And it was crammed to the brim with moldy bills.

In Confederate money.

No one said anything for some time, not even Andy Bigelow.

Then Ellery said, "It stood to reason. They found it buried in the cellar of an old Southern mansion—would it be Northern greenbacks? When they dug it up again after the War and brought it up to Jacksburg they probably had some faint hope that it might have some value. When they realized it was worthless, they decided to have some fun with it. This has been a private joke of those three old rascals since, roughly, 1865. When Caleb died last Memorial Day, Abner and Zach probably decided that, as the first of the trio to go, Caleb ought to have the honor of being custodian of their Confederate treasure in perpetuity. So one of them managed to slip the iron box into the coffin before the lid was screwed on. Zach's note bequeathing his 'fortune' to his 'beloved grandson'—in view of what I've seen of his beloved grandson today—was the old fellow's final joke."

Everybody chuckled; but the corpse stared mirthlessly and the silence fell again, to be broken by a weak curse from Andy Bigelow, and Doc Strong's puzzled: "But, Mr. Queen, that doesn't explain the murders."

"Well, now, Doc, it does," said Ellery; and then he said in a very different tone: "Suppose we put old Caleb back the way we found him, for your re-exhumation later for autopsy, Doc—and then we'll close the book on your Memorial Day murders."

Ellery closed the book in town, in the dusk, on the porch of Cissy Chase's house, which was central and convenient for everybody. Ellery and Nikki and Doc Strong and Cissy and Andy Bigelow—still clutching the iron box dazedly—were on the porch, and Lew Bagley and Bill Yoder and everyone else in Jacksburg, it seemed, stood about on the lawn and sidewalk, listening. And there was a touch of sadness to the soft twilight air, for something vital and exciting in the life of the village had come to an end.

"There's no trick to this," began Ellery, "and no joke, either, even though the men who were murdered were so old that death had grown tired waiting for them. The answer is as simple as the initials of their last names. Who knew that the supposed fortune was in Confederate money and therefore worthless? Only the three old men. One or another of the three would hardly have planned the deaths of the other two for possession of some scraps of valueless paper. So the murderer has to be someone who believed the fortune was legitimate and who—since until today there was no clue to the money's hiding place—knew he could claim it legally.

"Now, of course, that last-survivor-take-all business was pure moonshine, invented by Caleb, Zach, and Abner for their own amusement and the mystification of the community. But the would-be murderer didn't know that. The would-be murderer went on the assumption that the *whole* story was true, or he wouldn't have planned murder in the first place.

"Who would be able to claim the fortune legally if the last of the three old men—the survivor who presumably came into possession of the fortune on the deaths of the other two—died in his turn?"

"Last survivor's heir," said Doc Strong, and he rose.

"And who is the last survivor's heir?"

"Zach Bigelow's grandson, Andy." And the little mayor of Jacksburg stared hard at Bigelow, and a grumbling sound came from the people below, and Bigelow shrank against the wall behind Cissy, as if to seek her protection. But Cissy moved away.

"You thought the fortune was real," Cissy said scornfully, "so you killed Caleb Atwell and my great-grandpa so your grandfather'd be the last survivor so you could kill him and get the fortune."

"That's it, Ellery," cried Nikki.

"Unfortunately, Nikki, that's not it at all. You all refer to Zach Bigelow as the last survivor—"

"Well, he was," said Nikki.

"How could he not be?" said Doc Strong. "Caleb and Abner died first—"

"Literally, that's true," said Ellery, "but what you've all forgotten is that Zach Bigelow was the last survivor *only by accident.* When Abner Chase died early this morning, was it through poisoning, or some other violent means? No, Doc, you were absolutely positive he'd died of a simple cerebral hemorrhage—not by violence, but a natural death. Don't you see that if Abner Chase hadn't died a natural death early this morning, *he'd still be alive this evening?* Zach Bigelow would have put that bugle to his lips this afternoon, just as he did, just as Caleb Atwell did a year ago . . . *and at this moment Abner Chase would have been the last survivor.*

"And who was Abner Chase's only living heir, the girl who would have fallen heir to Abner's 'fortune' when, in time, or through her assistance, he joined his cronies in the great bivouac on the other side?

"You lied to me, Cissy," said Ellery to the shrinking girl in his grip, as a horror very like the horror of the burying ground in the afternoon came over the crowd of mesmerized Jacksburgers. "You pretended you didn't believe the story of the fortune. But that was only after your great-grandfather had inconsiderately died of a stroke just a few hours before old Zach would have died of poisoning, and you couldn't inherit that great, great fortune, anyway!"

MONEY TO BURN

by *MARGERY ALLINGHAM*

Did you ever see a man set light to money? Real money: using it as a spill to light a cigarette, just to show off? I have. And that's why, when you used the word "psychologist" just now, a little fish leaped in my stomach and my throat felt suddenly tight. Perhaps you think I'm too squeamish. I wonder.

I was born in this street. When I was a girl I went to school just round the corner and later on, after I'd served my apprenticeship in the big dress houses here and in France, I took over the lease of this old house and turned it into the smart little gown shop you see now. It was when I came back to go into business for myself that I saw the change in Louise.

When we went to school together she was something of a beauty, with streaming yellow hair and the cockney child's ferocious, knowing grin. All the kids used to tease her because she was better-looking than we were. The street was just the same then as it is now. Adelaide Street, Soho: shabby and untidy, and yet romantic, with every other doorway in its straggling length leading to a restaurant of some sort. You can eat in every language of the world here. Some places are as expensive as the Ritz and others are as cheap as Louise's papa's Le Coq au Vin, with its one dining room and its single palm in the white-washed tub outside.

Louise had an infant sister and a father who could hardly speak English but who looked at one with proud foreign eyes from under arched brows. I was hardly aware that she had a mother until a day when that gray woman emerged from the cellar under the restaurant to put her foot down and Louise, instead of coming with me into the enchantment of the workshops, had to go down into the kitchens of Le Coq au Vin.

For a long time we used to exchange birthday cards, and then even that contact dropped; but somehow I never forgot Louise and when I came back to the street I was glad to see the name Frosné still under the sign of Le Coq au Vin. The place looked much brighter than I remembered it and appeared to be doing fair business. Certainly it no longer suffered so much by comparison with the expensive Glass Mountain which Adelbert kept opposite. There is no restaurant bearing that name in this street now, nor is there a restaurateur called Adelbert, but diners-out of a few years ago may remember him—if not for his food, at least for his conceit and the two rolls of white fat which were his eyelids.

I went in to see Louise as soon as I had a moment to spare. It was a shock, for I hardly recognized her; but she knew me at once and came out from behind the cashier's desk to give me a welcome which was pathetic. It was like seeing thin ice cracking all over her face—as if by taking her unawares I'd torn aside a barrier.

I heard all the news in the first ten minutes. Both the old people were dead. The mother had gone first but the old man had not followed her for some years after, and in the meantime Louise had carried everything including his vagaries on her shoulders. But she did not complain. Things were a bit easier now. Violetta, the little sister, had a young man who was proving his worth by working there for a pittance, learning the business.

It was a success story of a sort, but I thought Louise had paid pretty dearly for it. She was a year younger than I was, yet she looked as if life had already burned out over her, leaving her hard and polished like a bone in the sun. The gold had gone out of her hair and even her thick lashes looked bleached and tow-colored. There was something else there, too: something hunted which I did not understand at all.

I soon fell into the habit of going in to have supper with her once a week and at these little meals she used to talk. It was evident that she never opened her lips on any personal matter to anyone else; but for some reason she trusted me. Even so it took me months to find out what was the matter with her. When it came out, it was obvious.

Le Coq au Vin had a debt hanging over it. In Mama Frosné's time the family had never owed a penny, but in the year or so between her death and his own, Papa Frosné had somehow contrived not only to borrow the best part of four thousand pounds from Adelbert of the Glass Mountain but to lose every cent of it in half a dozen senile little schemes.

Louise was paying it back in five-hundred-pound installments. As she first told me about it, I happened to glance into her eyes and in them I saw one sort of hell. It has always seemed to me that there are people who can stand Debt in the same way that some men can stand Drink. It may undermine their constitutions but it does not make them openly shabby. Yet to the others, Debt does something unspeakable. The Devil was certainly having his money's worth out of Louise.

I did not argue with her, of course. It was not my place. I sat there registering sympathy until she surprised me by saying suddenly:

"It's not so much the work and the worry, nor even the skimping, that I really hate so much. It's the awful ceremony when I have to pay him. I dread that."

"You're too sensitive," I told her. "Once you have the money in the bank, you can put a check in an envelope, send it to him, and then forget about it, can't you?"

She glanced at me with an odd expression in her eyes; they were almost lead-colored between the bleached lashes.

"You don't know Adelbert," she said. "He's a queer bit of work. I have to pay him in cash and he likes to make a regular little performance of it. He comes here by appointment, has a drink, and likes to have Violetta as a witness by way of audience. If I don't show I'm a bit upset, he goes right on talking until I do. Calls himself a psychologist—says he knows everything I'm thinking."

"That's not what I'd call him," I said. I was disgusted. I hate that sort of thing.

Louise hesitated. "I have watched him burn most of the money just for the effect," she admitted. "There, in front of me."

I felt my eyebrows rising up into my hair. "You can't mean it!" I exclaimed. "The man's not right in the head."

She sighed and I looked at her sharply.

"Why, he's twenty years older than you are, Louise," I began. "Surely there wasn't ever anything between you? You know . . . anything like *that?*"

"No. No, there wasn't, Ellie, honestly." I believed her—she was quite frank about it and obviously as puzzled as I was. "He did speak to Papa once about me when I was a kid. Asked for me formally, you know, as they still did round here at that time. I never heard what the old man said but he never minced words, did he? All I can remember is that I was kept downstairs out of sight for a bit and after that Mama treated me as if I'd been up to something; but I hadn't even spoken to the man—he wasn't a person a young girl *would* notice, was he? That was years ago, though. I suppose Adelbert could have remembered it all that time—but it's not reasonable, is it?"

"That's the one thing it certainly isn't," I told her. "Next time *I'll* be the witness."

"Adelbert would enjoy that," Louise said grimly. "I don't know that I won't hold you to it. You ought to see him!"

We let the subject drop, but I couldn't get it out of my mind. I could see them both from behind the curtains in my shop window and it seemed that whenever I looked out, there was the tight-lipped silent woman, scraping every farthing, and there was the fat man watching her from his doorway across the street, a secret satisfaction on his sallow face.

In the end it got on my nerves and when that happens I have to talk—I can't help it.

There was no one in the street I dared to gossip with, but I did mention the tale to a customer. She was a woman named Mrs. Marten whom I'd particularly liked ever since she'd come in to inquire after the first dress I ever put in my shop window. I made most of her clothes and she had recommended me to one or two ladies in the district where she lived, which was up at Hampstead, nice and far away from Soho. I was fitting her one day when she happened to say something about men and the things they'll stoop to if their pride has been hurt, and before I'd realized what I was doing I'd come out with the story Louise had told me. I didn't mention names, of course, but I may have conveyed that it was all taking place in this street. Mrs. Marten was a nice, gentle little soul with a sweet face, and she was shocked.

"But how awful," she kept saying, "how perfectly awful! To burn the money in front of her after she's worked so hard for it. He must be quite insane. And dangerous."

"Oh, well," I said hastily, "it's his money by the time he does that, and I don't suppose he destroys much of it. Only enough to upset my friend." I was sorry I'd spoken. I hadn't expected Mrs. Marten to be quite so horrified. "It just shows you how other people live." I finished and hoped she'd drop the subject. She didn't, however. The idea seemed to fascinate her even more than it had me. I couldn't get her to leave it alone and she chattered about it all throughout the fitting. Then, just as she was putting on her hat to leave, she suddenly said, "Miss Kaye, I've just had a thought. My brother-in-law is Assistant Commissioner at Scotland Yard. He might be able to think of some way of stopping that dreadful man from torturing that poor little woman you told me about. Shall I mention it to him?"

"Oh, no! Please don't!" I exclaimed. "She'd never forgive me. There's nothing the police could do to help her. I do hope you'll forgive me for saying so, Madam, but I do hope you won't do anything of the sort."

She seemed rather hurt, but she gave me her word. I had no faith in it, naturally. Once a woman has considered talking about a thing, it's as good as done. I was quite upset for a day or two because the last thing I wanted was to get involved; but nothing happened and I'd just started to breathe easily again when I had to go down to Vaughan's, the big wholesale trimmings house at the back of Regent's Street. I was coming out with my parcels when a man came up to me. I knew he was a detective: he was the type, with a very short haircut, a brown raincoat, and that look of being in a settled job and yet not in anything particular. He asked me to come along to his office and I couldn't refuse. I realized he'd been following me until I was far enough away from Adelaide Street where no one would have noticed him approach me.

He took me to his superior who was quite a nice old boy in his way—on nobody's side but his own, as is the way with the police; but I got the impression that he was on the level, which is more than some people are.

He introduced himself as Detective Inspector Cumberland, made me sit down, and sent out for a cup of tea for me. Then he asked me about Louise.

I got into a panic because when you're in business in Adelaide Street, you're in business, and the last thing you can afford to do is get into trouble with your neighbors. I denied everything, of course, insisting that I hardly knew the woman.

Cumberland wouldn't have that. I must say he knew how to handle me. He kept me going over and over my own affairs until I was thankful to speak about anything else. In the end I gave way because, after all, nobody was doing anything criminal as far as I could see. I told him all I knew, letting him draw it out bit by bit, and when I'd finished he laughed at me, peering at me with little bright eyes under brows which were as thick as silver fox fur.

"Well," he said, "there's nothing so terrible in all that, is there?"

"No," I said sulkily. He made me feel like a fool.

He sighed and leaned back in his chair.

"You run away and forget this little interview," he told me. "But just so that you don't start imagining things, let me point out something to you. The police are in business too, in a way. In their own business, that is, and when an officer in my position gets an inquiry from higher up he's got to investigate it, hasn't he? He may well think that the crime of destroying currency—'defacing the coin of the realm,' we call it—is not very serious compared with some of the things he's got to deal with; but all the same if he's asked about it he's got to make some sort of move and send in some sort of report. Then it can all be . . . er . . . filed and forgotten, can't it?"

"Yes," I agreed, very relieved. "Yes, I suppose it can."

They showed me out and that seemed to be the end of it. I'd had my lesson though, and I never opened my lips again on the subject to anybody. It quite put me off Louise and for a time I avoided her. I made excuses and didn't go in to eat with her. However, I could still see her through the window—see her sitting at the cashier's desk; and I could still see Adelbert peering at her from his doorway.

For a month or two everything went on quietly. Then I heard that Violetta's boy had got tired of the restaurant business and had taken a job up North. He had given the girl the chance of marrying and going with him, and they'd gone almost without saying good-bye. I was sorry for Louise, being left alone that way; so I had to go and see her.

She was taking it very well—actually she was pretty lucky, for she had got a new waiter almost at once and her number one girl in the kitchen had stood by her and they managed very well. Louise was very lonely though, so I drifted back into the habit of going in there for a meal once a week. I paid, of course, but she used to come and have hers with me.

I kept her off the subject of Adelbert, but one day near the midsummer's quarter day she referred to him outright and asked me straight if I remembered my promise to be witness on the next pay day. Since Violetta was gone, she'd mentioned me to Adelbert, and he'd seemed pleased.

Well, I couldn't get out of it without hurting her feelings and since nothing seemed to turn on it I agreed. I don't pretend I wasn't curious: it was a love affair without, so far as I could see, any love at all.

The time for payment was fixed for half an hour after closing time on Midsummer's Day, and when I slipped down the street to the corner the blinds of Le Coq au Vin were closed and the door shut. The new waiter was taking a breath of air on the basement steps and he let me in through the kitchens. I went up the dark service stairs and found the two of them already sitting there, waiting for me.

The dining room was dark except for a single shaded bulb over the alcove table where they sat and I had a good look at them as I came down the room. They made an extraordinary pair.

I don't know if you've seen one of those fat little Chinese gods whom people keep on their mantel shelves to bring them luck? They are all supposed to be laughing but some only pretend and the folds of their china faces are stiff and merciless for all the upward lines. Adelbert reminded me of one of those. He always wore a black dinner jacket for work, but it was very thin and very loose. It came into my mind that when he took it off it must have hung like a gown. He was sitting swathed in it, looking squat and flabby against the white paneling of the wall.

Louise, on the other hand, in her black dress and tight woolen cardigan, was as spare and hard as a withered branch. Just for an instant I realized how furious she must make him. There was nothing yielding or shrinking about her. She wasn't giving any more than she was forced to—not an inch. I never saw anything so unbending in my life. She stood up to him all the time.

There was a bottle of Dubonnet on the table and they each had a small glass. When I appeared, Louise poured one for me.

The whole performance was very formal. Although they'd both lived in London all their lives, the French blood in both of them was very apparent. They each shook hands with me and Adelbert kicked the chair out for me if he only made a pretense of rising.

Louise had the big bank envelope in her black bag which she nursed as if it was a pet, and as soon as I'd taken a sip of my drink she produced the envelope and pushed it across the table to the man.

"Five hundred," she said. "The receipt is in there, already made out. Perhaps you'd sign it, please."

There was not a word out of place, you see, but you could have cut the atmosphere with a knife. She hated him and he was getting his due and nothing else.

He sat looking at her for a moment with a steady, fishy gaze; he seemed to be waiting for something—just a flicker of regret or resentment, I suppose. But he got nothing, and presently he took the envelope between his sausage fingers and thumbed it open. The five crisp green packages fell out on the white tablecloth. I looked at them with interest, as one does at money. It wasn't a fortune, of course; but to people like myself and Louise, who have to earn every cent the hard way, it was a tidy sum that represented hours of toil and scheming and self-privation.

I didn't like the way the man's fingers played over it and the sneaking spark of sympathy I'd begun to feel for him died abruptly. I knew then that if he'd had his way and married her when she was little more than a child all those years ago, he would have treated her abominably. He was a cruel beast; it took him that way.

I glanced at Louise and saw that she was unmoved. She just sat there with her hands folded, waiting for her receipt.

Adelbert began to count the money. I've always admired the way tellers in banks handle notes, but the way Adelbert did it opened my eyes. He went through them the way a gambler goes through a pack of cards—as if each individual note were alive and part of his hand. He loved the stuff, you could see it.

"All correct," he said at last, and put the bundles in his inside pocket. Then he signed the receipt and handed it to her. Louise took it and put it in her bag. I assumed that was the end of it and wondered what all the fuss was about. I raised my glass to Louise, who acknowledged it, and was getting up when Adelbert stopped me.

"Wait," he said. "We must have a cigarette and perhaps another little glass—if Louise can afford it."

He smiled but she didn't. She poured him another glass and sat there stolidly waiting for him to drink it. He was in no hurry. Presently he took the money out again and laid a fat hand over it as he passed his cigarette case round. I took a cigarette, Louise didn't. There was one of those metal match stands on the table and he bent forward. I moved too, expecting him to give me a light; but he laughed and drew back.

"This gives it a better flavor," he said, and, peeling off one note from the top wad, he lit it and offered me the flame. I had guessed what was coming, so I didn't show any surprise. If Louise could keep a poker face, so could I. I watched the banknote burn out, and then he took another and lit that.

Having failed to move us, he started to talk. He spoke quite normally about the restaurant business—how hard times were and what a lot of work it meant getting up at dawn to go to the market with the chef and how customers liked to keep one up late at night, talking and dawdling as if there was never going to be a tomorrow. It was all directed at Louise, rubbing it in, holding her nose down to exactly what he was doing. But she remained perfectly impassive, her eyes dark like lead, her mouth hard.

When that failed, he got more personal. He said he remembered us both when we were girls and how work and worry had changed us. I was nettled, but not too upset, for it soon became quite obvious that he did not remember me at all. With Louise it was different: he remembered her— every detail—and with something added.

"Your hair was like gold," he said, "and your eyes were blue as glass and you had a little soft wide mouth which was so gay. Where is it now, eh? Here." He patted the money, the old brute. "All here, Louise. I am a psychologist, I see these things. And what is it worth to me? Nothing. Exactly nothing."

He was turning me cold. I stared at him fascinated and saw him suddenly take up a whole package of money and fluff it out until it looked like a lettuce. Louise neither blinked nor spoke. She sat looking at him as if he was nothing, a passerby in the street. No one at all. I'd turned my head to glance at her and missed seeing him strike another match—so when he lit the crisp leaves it took me completely off guard.

"Look out!" I said involuntarily. "Mind what you're doing!"

He laughed like a wicked child, triumphant and delighted. "What about you, Louise? What do you say?"

She continued to look bored and they sat there facing one another squarely. Meantime, of course, the money was blazing.

The whole thing meant nothing to me; perhaps that is why it was my control which snapped.

Anyway, I knocked the cash out of his hand. With a sudden movement I sent the whole hundred notes flying out of his grasp. All over the place they went—on the floor, the table, everywhere. The room was alight with blazing banknotes.

He went after them like a lunatic—you wouldn't have thought a man that fat could have moved so fast.

It was the one that laddered my stocking which gave the game away. A spark burned the nylon and as I felt it, I looked down and snatched the charred note, holding it up to the light. We all saw the flaw in it at the same moment. The ink had run and there was a great streak through the middle, like the veining in a marble slab.

There was a long silence and the first sound came not from us but from the service door. It opened and the new waiter, looking quite different now that he'd changed his coat for one with a policeman's badge on it, came down the room followed by Inspector Cumberland.

They went up to Adelbert and the younger, heavier man put a hand on his shoulder. Cumberland ignored everything but the money. He stamped out the smouldering flames and gathered up the remains and the four untouched wads on the table. Then he smiled briefly.

"Got you, Adelbert. With it on you. We've been wondering who was passing slush in this street and when it came to our ears that someone was burning cash we thought we ought to look into it."

I was still only half comprehending and I held out the note we'd been staring at.

"There's something wrong with this one," I said stupidly.

He took it from me and grunted.

"There's something wrong with all these, my dear. Miss Frosné's money is safe in his pocket where you saw him put it. These are some of the gang's failures. Every maker of counterfeit money has them—as a rule they never leave the printing room. This one in particular is a shocker. I wonder he risked it even for burning. You didn't like wasting it, I suppose, Adelbert. What a careful soul you are."

"How did you find out?" Louise looked from them to me.

Cumberland saved me.

"A policeman, too, Madam," he said, laughing, "can be a psychologist."

THE GENTLEST OF
THE BROTHERS
by DAVID ALEXANDER

Kevin McCarty was a lay brother at the seminary, happily pruning rose-bushes in the institution's gardens, when word arrived that his young sister, Rose Kathleen, had died by her own hand with mortal sin upon her soul. The death alone was a tragic thing, but even more terrible were the letter and package that Kevin McCarty received on the first day of the laying-out. The letter and package were addressed by Rose Kathleen's own hand, the same hand that had lifted the deadly poison to her pretty mouth.

Poor Kevin read the letter over many times and it was a long and shocking message his sister had written down and mailed, along with the package, just before she took her life. Kevin had believed that Rose Kathleen, the last relative he had in all the world since his mother's death, was an actress in the theater. He did not quite approve of her occupation, but after all it was honest work and she was young and radiant and a pretty thing to see, and there was no real harm in letting people look at her there behind the footlights, for no one was ever hurt by looking upon radiance and beauty. But Rose Kathleen had not really been an actress, it seemed. She had been a "dancer." The quotation marks were her own. She had appeared in specialty numbers at Rory O'Bannon's night club called The Fig Leaf and her letter said that "dancers" there hardly danced at all but stood with blue light on them and bared their bodies before the drunken customers. Also, after hours, the "dancers" were forced to entertain the customers who had the wherewithal to pay them for their favors. Rose Kathleen had done it all because in some unaccountable way she had fallen in love with Rory O'Bannon.

Kevin McCarty knew Rory O'Bannon all too well. He had grown up on the same twisting street in Greenwich Village with him. Even as a youth Rory had been a bully, an oversized lad with a wild light in his eyes and a tangled mop of red, curly hair. When they were kids, Kevin McCarty would never fight back when Rory O'Bannon attacked him. This was not because Kevin was frail and undersized and often sickly. He had courage enough. But he could not stand violence and it was impossible for him to strike a blow that might hurt a living thing. That is why he had sought the peace and spiritual life that the brotherhood offered.

The crooked bone in Kevin's thin nose was the result of a beating Rory O'Bannon had given him for no reason at all one day when he was walking home from St. Ignatius's Parochial School. Sometimes, when the weather changed, Kevin's left arm pained him. Long ago Rory O'Bannon had twisted the arm behind his back and when Kevin had refused to say his mother was a word that the bully tried to make him say, the arm had snapped.

Kevin McCarty was not so far removed from the world outside the stone walls of the seminary that he did not read the newspapers and occasionally listen to the radio. He knew what Rory O'Bannon had become. The police had arrested Rory many times and crime commissions had questioned him as often, but only once had he been sent to jail. That time they had found a deadly weapon on his person. They said that Rory O'Bannon was a right bower of Martello, who headed the Syndicate, and that he dealt in such unsavory commodities as narcotics and prostitution. But when they questioned him, Rory stood on his constitutional rights and refused to answer, or stated he was a good citizen because he paid his taxes, and all they had against him, really, was that he owned a night club of questionable repute.

The undressing in blue light and the entertaining of Rory's customers after hours were not the worst things Rose Kathleen told of in her letter. She had lived with Rory O'Bannon for a while, it seemed, in the way that only a wife should live with a man. When Rory had grown tired of her, she had taken to the drugs her mobster peddled. Soon she was not even fit to earn her living as a "dancer." She had to have the stuff, she said, so she sold the only thing she had to sell to get it. Finally she could stand the life she led no longer and had drunk the poison, and thus had added another sin to her poor young soul that had so many scars already.

In the package that came with the letter Kevin found a diary written in his little sister's childish scrawl. She had kept it while she lived with Rory O'Bannon and she had listed names and dates and places concerning the sale of narcotics and other illegal transactions. The name of Martello appeared in the diary many times. Rose Kathleen had thought the information in the little book might enable Kevin to see that Rory O'Bannon and his dynasty of corruption were destroyed.

After Rose Kathleen's funeral, Kevin McCarty appeared before Father Francis, the seminary's rector, and told him of the contents of the letter and the diary. Father Francis had known Kevin's family and the neighborhood in which they lived for many years. He said, "You must send the letter and the diary to Danny Meighan, my son. He grew up next door to you and he was your boyhood friend. I think he loved your little sister, too. Danny is a detective now, you know."

Kevin McCarty shook his head. "I will see Danny, Father. That much I intend. But Danny cannot make Rory O'Bannon die for his sins, and die he must. It is I who must see that Rory O'Bannon dies. It is that I have come to tell you, Father. I must renounce my vows and go back into the world."

The old priest gazed unbelievingly at the frail young man whose pale skin never seemed to brown under the sun of the gardens. "Your vows . . ." the old priest said.

"The Jesuit vows of obedience and poverty," Kevin McCarty replied. "I am poor enough in both wealth and resource, Father. And I am obedient in a way you can never understand. I am obedient to the thing within me that says Rory O'Bannon must die."

"The devil's counsel," Father Francis said.

"I freely confess it is the devil and not Our Blessed Saviour that has possessed me," Kevin McCarty answered. "But to see that Rory O'Bannon dies is my mission and I cannot shirk it. I do not wish to blaspheme, Father, but I say that some men are too vile and evil for the Lord in His kindness and forgiveness to contend with. The devil is the only match for the likes of Rory O'Bannon."

"My son," said Father Francis, "your shock and grief are great and your mind is unhinged. Do you realize that you are telling me, in effect, that you plan to murder Rory O'Bannon?"

"Rory O'Bannon must die," Kevin McCarty repeated stubbornly.

The old priest shook his head and smiled. "No, my son," he said. "I do not fear for you. You are the gentlest of all the brothers. You are one of the gentlest men who has walked the earth since our Saviour died upon the Cross. I have no fear for you, I say. This mood will pass. You could not kill. You could not inflict hurt upon any living thing. Go, if you must, but I will make no report to the Father Provincial as yet. I have abiding faith you will return."

"I am going out into the world again, Father," Kevin McCarty said. "Rory O'Bannon must die, and I am the one who must see to it."

Kevin McCarty left the seminary wearing wrinkled, outmoded clothes and carrying as luggage only the letter and the diary.

His most urgent problem was to find a temporary means of earning his food and lodging while he set about his more important business. He was almost completely naïve, so the problem did not worry him at all. When he was a boy he had delivered groceries for his father's friends, the Gilberto brothers, and later he had clerked in their delicatessen store on Bleecker

Street. He would simply go to the Gilbertos and ask for his old job back again. He needed very little in the way of money.

He found the old store the same as it had always been, long and narrow and darkish and redolent of aging cheese and spicy peppers. The Gilbertos —Jacomo, Harry, and Charley—were the same, too, only older. They were garrulous, kindly, devoted to their business. The deer head was still hanging there upon the wall. All the Gilbertos were hunters. Kevin's father had sometimes accompanied them on hunting trips to upstate New York and New Jersey and as far away as Canada. The oldest brother, Jacomo, had shot the deer whose head hung on the wall. It was dusty and mangy-looking now and one of the antlers had been broken somehow. The deer's head with the accusing glass eyes had always sickened Kevin McCarty.

The three Gilberto brothers greeted Kevin effusively. At first they could not believe he had given up the religious life or that he really wanted his old job back. When they were convinced, they gave him a job as clerk readily enough, apologizing for the salary they could afford to pay. "We are growing old, the three of us," said Charley. "The hours are long. We can use a little help."

Kevin found a furnished one-room flat almost directly across the street from the store. The room was on the second-floor, in the front of the house, and he could sit by the window and watch the trucks and cars and pushcarts and the milling Irish and Italians on the street. In the distance he could see the old church where he had made his first communion.

It took him a week or so to orient himself and to formulate his plan for the killing of Rory O'Bannon.

The Gilberto brothers agreed that Kevin should open the store each morning at 8 and they gave him a key. At 10, Jacomo came in to help, then later Harry arrived, and finally Charley, who kept the store open until 10 at night. Kevin left at 5 as a rule, but if there was a rush, he often stayed on until well past dinner time. He ate at neighborhood hash counters and was never entirely conscious of what food he had ordered. Sometimes he forgot to eat at all and would be surprised when he awakened in the middle of the night with hunger pangs in his stomach.

He called the Mercer Street Station and found that Detective Danny Meighan was working the 4 to midnight shift that week. One evening he dropped around to see his friend. Danny took him to a little private office off the detective squad room where they could be alone.

They exchanged reminiscences of their boyhood on the Greenwich Village streets and in the paved playground behind St. Ignatius's School. Finally they spoke of Rose Kathleen, whom Danny Meighan had loved when he was very young, and, inevitably, of Rory O'Bannon.

"I knew she had taken up with him while you were away with the Fathers," Danny said. "I tried to stop her in my blundering, stupid way, but it did no good, no good at all. I thought of writing to you, but I doubted it would help and I was afraid it would only worry you, spoil the quiet and holy life you led. When young girls get like that there's no accounting for it. It's a certain kind of craziness, I guess. I see a lot just like her in my job. The worse the man is, the tighter hold he seems to get over young girls like Rose Kathleen."

Kevin McCarty said, "Suppose, just suppose now, Danny, that a young girl who went with a man like Rory O'Bannon kept a diary. Suppose she named names and listed places where drugs were sold and unlawful things were done. If the police had such a document, could they take action?"

Danny Meighan's eyes narrowed. "Are you trying to tell me, Kevin-boy, that your sister left such a diary?"

"Now, now, Danny," Kevin McCarty answered. "It's a game of just-suppose, like we used to play when we were kids. You were brought up by the Jesuits yourself. You should know their propensity for arguing and speculating upon abstract propositions."

"Abstract, is it?" asked the young detective. "Well, Kevin-boy, if you've got evidence of the sort that's concrete and not abstract, you'd best give it to the police without further argument or speculation about abstractions."

Kevin shook his head. "The man of action," he said. "Tell me, now. If I gave you such a little book, what would happen, Danny?"

"The police would investigate all the persons named and raid all the addresses mentioned. Given sufficient grounds, they would make arrests."

"And what would happen to the men after they were arrested?"

"They would go to trial, of course. The diary you mention might prove valuable as substantiating evidence."

"What would be their punishment?"

Danny Meighan chuckled. "None of your Jesuit tricks," he warned. "If they were guilty and the police case was presented properly, the jury would convict and the judge would sentence them."

"What would be the sentence?" the frail man persisted.

The detective shrugged. "Who knows? Ten years, perhaps. More likely five."

Kevin McCarty said, "It's not enough. Rory O'Bannon is our own age, about. He'd still be young enough when he got out of prison to ruin more young girls, to sell more narcotics to high school kids. A man like Rory O'Bannon should be condemned to die."

Danny Meighan was startled. "You say that?" he asked. "A gentle soul like you who would never hurt a fly? But you're right, of course, and I agree entirely. There have been several bills drawn up to make the sale of narcotics a capital crime carrying the death penalty, but none of them has passed."

Kevin McCarty rose. "It's been good to see you," he said. "I'm sorry to have taken up your time with suppositional matters. But Rory O'Bannon must die. I'm determined that he must."

The detective looked even more amazed.

"Wait, now, my gentle friend," he said. "Are you telling me that you'll take the law in your own two hands and go gunning for O'Bannon your own self? I must warn you, then, that the killing of even a louse-bit rat like Rory would be murder under the law."

Kevin McCarty nodded. His face was very serious. "I know," he answered. "If I stumble across something less—abstract—I may call upon you again, Danny."

"Do that," said Danny Meighan. "And be careful, Kevin-lad. The likes of Rory O'Bannon are a bit too tough for Jesuit brothers who grow flowers and ponder on abstractions."

Kevin McCarty was no detective but he had little trouble in finding Rory O'Bannon's address. During the crime investigations the papers had made much of Rory's fancy penthouse on the park. For two nights after work Kevin watched the apartment entrance from a park bench, feeding crumbs to the pigeons from a bag he had brought along, but he failed to see anyone who resembled Rory in the slightest. On the third night he left the store earlier and took up his post before he ate his dinner. His vigil was rewarded. A bulky man with a brash face and unruly red hair fringing the hatbrim of his homburg swaggered out of the glass and chromium entrance of the apartment building, flanked on each side by blank-faced men whose shoulders were ridiculously padded and whose hats appeared a size too large. The three entered a waiting limousine as black and shiny as a hearse. Kevin had not seen Rory since the young bully had gone away to reform school, but he had no trouble recognizing him. The papers had been filled with O'Bannon's pictures. Rory had grown much taller and his middle had widened to a paunch, but the wild, cruel look on his face was just the same as always. For a solid week of nights Kevin watched and fed the pigeons. Each night Rory and the blank-faced men and the big car that looked like a hearse appeared. Rory's routine seemed as well established as any respectable citizen's. His schedule varied only by minutes from night to night.

Kevin McCarty felt no qualms about ending his evening watch. The pigeons were plump to the point of exploding, for many others fed them, too. Kevin McCarty knew where to find Rory O'Bannon when he wanted him.

On the second Sabbath after his return to the world of noise and haste and evil men, Kevin took a bus to the quiet village on the Hudson where the seminary was located. Priests are ordinary men, and like ordinary men, they have their hobbies. Father Francis's hobby was photography. He had a camera with a variety of lenses and filters and he had fitted out a large closet as a darkroom. He had filled albums with his photographs of the fathers and the seminarians and the brothers at their work and studies and devotions. He had taken a great fancy to the gentle brother, Kevin Mc-Carty, and had taught him the elements of such matters as shutter-speeds and f-stops.

Father Francis was overjoyed on that sunny Sabbath afternoon when Kevin McCarty walked into his study that was filled with bright plaster saints who brooded on dark rows of books. He thought a prodigal brother had returned and although he doubted his ability to find a fatted calf on such short notice, he was fully prepared to open the best tinned delicacies in the seminary kitchen in celebration. When he found that Kevin had not returned to the fold for good, but only came to borrow his camera and use his darkroom, Father Francis's lined face fell.

"And what of your crazy fixation about this O'Bannon?" he asked.

"I've seen him several times but only from a distance," Kevin replied evasively.

The mystified old man granted Kevin permission to use his photographic equipment, although he felt a strange premonition that the camera and developers might be used for Satan's work.

Kevin had brought the diary along with him. He photographed several pages that he had marked in advance. He developed the negatives and hung the prints up on a rack to dry before Father Francis's small electric fan.

While he was waiting for the prints to dry he had a glass of wine with the old man and told him of the Gilberto brothers and their kindness and of Danny Meighan. He avoided mentioning the prints he had made or his dead sister or Rory O'Bannon. Later, when the prints were dry, he put them in an envelope, pocketed the envelope, and bade the old priest farewell.

Father Francis pressed Kevin's arm. "My son," he said, "leave God's work to God. I have made no report of you to the Father Provincial as yet."

"Rory O'Bannon is not God's work, Father," Kevin McCarty answered.

For the next two days, Kevin McCarty did little but tend the counter of the store and eat food when he was hungry and sit by the window in his room and compose a letter in his head. When the letter was finally composed to his satisfaction, he put the words upon a piece of paper.

Dear Rory:

You may remember me from our youth or because of my late sister, Rose Kathleen, God rest her soul. I am writing you because Rose Kathleen kept a diary which is now in my possession. I enclose photostats of certain pages from the little book. You will note that your name and the name of Mr. Martello and others are mentioned frequently.

I have not decided just what should be done with this little book. I suppose it is my duty to give it to the authorities. But before I do so I would like to talk to you. If you wish to discuss this matter before I go to the police you must follow my instructions to the letter.

You will come to the room on the second floor front of the house at the address I write below at exactly 3:15 o'clock next Sunday afternoon. You will come alone. I can watch the street from my window and if there are others with you, they will not be admitted to the house. Nor will you be admitted at any time except 3:15 exactly on Sunday afternoon.

You may fear a trap, of course. I tell you that you will find me quite alone and you may remember that I am neither large nor strong. I don't believe that I need warn you to come unarmed. If you fear a trap it would be foolish to supply the police with evidence against you, wouldn't it?

If you do not arrive at 3:15 exactly next Sunday afternoon, I will go directly to the police and the diary will be in their hands by 3:30. If this occurs, you and Mr. Martello and the others will doubtless be arrested and I will make a point of seeing that Mr. Martello knows you could have prevented his arrest by merely talking to me.

Kevin McCarty

Kevin mailed the letter and the enclosures. He stopped at a small shop on Bleecker Street and had duplicates made of the keys to his front door and his room. Then he walked to Mercer Street and mounted the stairs to the detective squad room.

When he and Danny were closeted in the little office again, Kevin said, "Danny, my boy, I've progressed from the abstract to the concrete. If you do exactly as I say you may be able to arrest Rory O'Bannon, with ample evidence of his guilt, next Sunday afternoon." He handed the duplicate keys to the detective. "At 3:30 next Sunday afternoon come to this address." He wrote the address of his house upon a slip of paper and handed it to Danny Meighan. "Use the thick key to open the front door. Walk up one flight of stairs. Then left to the room at the front. Open that door with the thin key. That's all you have to do. But if you value your badge and maybe a promotion, be there at 3:30 on the dot, not a minute early or a minute late."

Danny Meighan protested loudly. He demanded to know what Kevin McCarty was up to and he warned him that Rory O'Bannon was dangerous as a rattlesnake.

Kevin silenced him. "You play my way," he said, "or I call the whole game off."

The gentle brother's next problem was obtaining a gun. He had little knowledge of such matters, but he thought you had to have some kind of permit to purchase firearms. He could think of no good reason he might give the authorities for wanting a license for a gun. The simplest thing was to use one of the hunting rifles the Gilbertos kept racked in a storage closet in the back room of the delicatessen. Acquiring the rifle posed a moral problem. Kevin McCarty had no difficulty at all, in his simple way, in determining right from wrong. But determining between two sins was a different matter. In the end, he decided that lying might be less grievous than stealing. One morning, before the other Gilbertos arrived at the store, Kevin approached Jacomo, the eldest of the brothers. He believed Jacomo would prove the most credulous of the three.

"Mr. Jacomo," he said, and he realized how false his voice must sound, "a friend has asked me to go hunting in the woods next Sunday. I wonder if you would lend me one of your fine guns."

Jacomo was not so credulous. He glared at Kevin and twirled his fierce mustachio. "You! Go hunting! Why, I remember when your father wanted to teach you to shoot when you were a boy. You'd not do so much as wing a rabbit with a BB shot. I think it's bigger game than squirrels and rabbits you want my rifle for, and I refuse." The old man twirled his mustache indignantly. "Besides," he added, "you have no hunting license."

Later in the day Jacomo took his clerk aside. "I did not mean to be so rude," he said. "Take my advice, for I am old and I knew your father, rest his soul. You are not a man who's made for violence. Leave punishment to God and the police."

So the Gilbertos had known about his sister and Rory O'Bannon, too. Everyone had known, it seemed—everyone but Kevin McCarty. He had been too busy with the flowers at the seminary.

In the end he was forced to commit two sins. He had already lied. Now he must steal.

On Friday of that week, two days after he had mailed the letter, Kevin glanced out the window of the store and saw two men eyeing the house where he lived. The shoulders of the men's suits were padded ridiculously and their hats were a size too large. The limousine that was as big and black as a hearse was not in sight, nor was Rory O'Bannon. The two blank-faced men walked down the street to a corner tavern. Presently they returned and entered Gilberto's delicatessen. They must have talked to the bartender who had grown up with Kevin. They walked straight up to him. Kevin was making a "hero" sandwich—a whole small loaf of Italian bread sliced down the middle and stuffed with spiced meat and cheese—for a neighborhood workman. When the two men saw how small and meek Kevin was, they exchanged glances and almost broke out laughing. Kevin finished the sandwich and looked inquiringly at the two blank-faced men as if he had never seen them before.

"Gimme one of them," the first man said, pointing to the bulky sand-wich.

"Make it two," said the second man.

Kevin made the sandwiches, then said, "Mustard?"

"Yeah, mustard," said one blank-faced man.

"That's right," said the other.

"Bottla pop," said one.

"Make it two," said the other.

None of the Gilbertos was near. Kevin opened pop bottles on the counter. One blank-faced man pulled out a clasp knife, snapped it open, held Kevin with his eyes. He halved the sandwich with his knife, saying, "Your name McCarty?"

"It is that," Kevin answered.

The blank-faced man said, "You're gonna have a visitor Sunday. At 3:15. Be nice to him. Give him what he wants. We'll be right outside."

The blank-faced man laid the knife on the counter with the blade un-sheathed. The two men with padded shoulders ate their sandwiches and drank their pop. They stared at Kevin as they ate and drank. They finished and put a bill upon the counter. One man clasped and pocketed the knife. He pushed a half-dollar tip toward Kevin.

"Be nice," he said again.

The two men with the padded shoulders and the hats a size too large left without looking back.

Kevin McCarty did not see Rory's bodyguards again that day or on Saturday.

The day that Kevin had dedicated to what he called the devil's work was a Sabbath shining with God's bright sun. Bleecker Street was festive with small Italian girls in starched and frilly dresses who clutched bouquets of white and pink rosebuds. They were starry-eyed after their first commu-nion.

At noon Kevin crossed the street to the delicatessen store and opened the big door with his key. He nodded to several loungers in the street. The loungers knew he worked at the store—they would think nothing of his entering at a time the delicatessen was supposed to be closed. Kevin went at once to the back room and turned on a dim bulb. He secured a screwdriver from the Gilbertos' tool chest. The door to the closet where the guns were kept was fastened by a padlock that fitted two rings screwed into the wall and door. In five minutes Kevin had removed one of the rings and the door creaked open. Kevin McCarty had never pulled a trigger but he knew something about firearms. His father, hoping to interest his son in the sport of hunting, had made Kevin clean his rifles. Kevin liked the weight and balance of a Marlin rifle. He removed it from the rack and loaded it with the proper ammunition. He did not feel too guilty about taking the rifle. It would be returned when the thing was done. He could not return the ammunition, of course. Once a bullet is fired it is of no further use. He had taken only one bullet, because that was all he would need.

Kevin took his sister's diary from his pocket and placed it in the space the Marlin had occupied. It was a safe enough hiding place.

He tore a long piece of wide, brown butcher's paper from a roll in the store. He wrapped the rifle into a shapeless package and wound heavy string around it. He screwed back the ring, to which the padlock was still attached, into the wall and returned to his room with the shapeless package tucked under his arm.

Kevin unwrapped the rifle, then stuffed the paper and string into a tin wastebasket that had Easter lilies painted on it. He leaned the loaded rifle against the window, behind the drapes. He took a Bible from the table and sat down in the chair by the window. It was just 12:30.

At ten minutes after 3, Kevin glanced at the loud-ticking alarm clock on the table. He placed the Bible in his lap, shifted slightly in his chair, and gazed out the window. He saw a limousine as big and black as a hearse approaching. The car passed under Kevin's window very slowly. He could see a blurred face pressed against the window of the car.

The car moved on to the corner and was steered into a parking space. Three men got out. One was Rory O'Bannon. The other two wore suits with padded shoulders and hats a size too large. Kevin smiled. Rory was afraid to come alone. "We'll be right outside," one of the men had said. Now the two men seemed to be arguing with Rory. At length one returned to the car. The other walked briskly down the street and took up a post outside Gilberto's Delicatessen. Rory O'Bannon crossed to Kevin's side of the street. When he reached the house, he examined the number on the door. The bell buzzed in Kevin's room. It was exactly 3:15. Kevin placed the Bible on the table, then pressed the plunger that released the front door latch. He glanced out the window to make sure that only Rory entered. He opened the door of his room slightly and left it ajar. He returned to the chair by the window. He could feel the rifle through the drapes. The stairs groaned under Rory's weight.

Then there was a soft tapping on the door.

"Come in, Rory. I'm quite alone."

Rory O'Bannon's big frame filled the doorway. The wild eyes darted suspiciously about the little room. The big man crossed to Kevin's chair in three strides. He grabbed Kevin under the arms and pulled him up roughly. Without saying a word, he tapped Kevin's pockets and armpits. He shoved Kevin back into the chair, jerked open the door of the closet, and peered inside. He even looked under the bed. At last he was satisfied. He looked speculatively at Kevin McCarty, gave a short, unpleasant laugh, seated himself on the edge of a chair, and said, "You got the diary? What's the deal?"

"I don't have the diary here," Kevin answered. "It's hidden in a place known only to myself. There's a way you can prevent me taking it to the police. Let's understand each other, Rory. You once tried beating me to make me say a thing I didn't want to say. That didn't work. I know your men are downstairs. You can't kidnap me, though—Bleecker is a crowded street. You could never get away with dragging me to that big car of yours."

"How much you want?" asked Rory. "Wait. I got something to tell you first. It ain't worth much. It ain't worth much because your little sister was a hophead and a tramp. A judge or jury won't believe much of what a hophead and a tramp writes down. But it might cause a little trouble. Martello don't like trouble. He'll pay a little just to save him trouble."

Kevin McCarty stole a glance at the clock. 3:23. Seven minutes more. Maybe he had timed it wrong. Maybe he should have allowed only ten minutes instead of fifteen. He pretended to think over the sum he should ask. The clock ticked loudly but all too slowly.

Finally, he said, "I don't want money, Rory. I took the Jesuit vow of poverty once. I only want to prove a theory. The Jesuits are great ones for proving theories, Rory."

The clock ticked. 3:25. Five minutes more.

"Quit the double-talk," said Rory angrily. "Whatcha trying to prove?"

"I've always had a theory you were yellow, Rory. I want to prove it."

Rory O'Bannon's face went crimson. He rose from his chair, advanced a step toward the frail, calm man. Kevin McCarty hadn't risen from the chair. But a rifle had suddenly appeared in his hands. The rifle was pointed directly at Rory O'Bannon.

3:26.

"Don't come any closer, Rory," Kevin McCarty warned. "The rifle's loaded. Sit down in the chair."

Rory sat. "You double-crossing rat," he said.

Kevin McCarty said, "No, Rory. You'll get your chance, just as I promised. I think you're yellow. I don't think you have the guts to kill a man. I want to prove you haven't."

3:27.

Kevin McCarty glanced out the window. The big, black car was still parked down the street. The blank-faced man was standing intent, motionless, across the street. Then Kevin saw Danny Meighan approaching. He was walking at a pace that was maddeningly slow.

"In just a minute I'm going to walk out that door, Rory," Kevin McCarty said. "I'm going to get the diary and go straight to the police. There's only one way you can stop me. You can kill me."

"You've flipped your lid," said Rory. "Listen, I'll pay, see? I'll pay plenty. You can give it to the church."

Danny Meighan was in front of the house now. He was consulting a slip of paper to confirm the address. He was mounting the stoop. Kevin McCarty rose. He crossed the room. He stood by the door. Below, he heard steps mounting the stairs. He tossed the rifle into Rory O'Bannon's lap. He said, "It's on safety. Snap back that little knob on the right to take it off. I'm leaving, Rory. This is your last chance." He touched the doorknob. "Shoot me now, Rory, or I go to the cops. Be sure you kill me—or I'll talk and tell them where to find the diary."

Rory raised the rifle, complete amazement on his face.

A man, walking cautiously, was coming down the hall.

"Good-bye, Rory O'Bannon," said Kevin McCarty, turning the knob.

The small room was filled with sudden sound.

Kevin McCarty crumpled to the floor.

The gentlest of the brothers lived for just 60 tickings of the clock. But he lived long enough.

He lived long enough to hear the door fly open and to see Danny Meighan standing there with a revolver in his hand. He lived long enough to hear the futile trigger-click of the now empty rifle, to hear the rifle drop to the floor, and to hear Rory's squeal, "Don't shoot! Don't shoot me, copper!"

He lived just long enough to know that Rory O'Bannon would surely die in the electric chair for the murder of Kevin McCarty.

ONE-WAY STREET

by *ANTHONY ARMSTRONG*

If it hadn't been for little Mr. Harold Bent being apparently oblivious of the fact that the Trafalgar Square traffic went one way round only, the body of James Wellson would have been discovered five minutes later than it was. It would also have been discovered half a mile away from where it was. And even an extra five minutes and an extra half-mile can, of course, be extremely useful to a murderer, particularly in London.

It happened like this:

Released by the traffic lights, George Travers, taxi driver, swung his cab round the southeast corner of Trafalgar Square and, mingling with the Whitehall stream in the usual crisscross, dodge-as-dodge-can, made for the Pall Mall destination of his fare. As was his custom in all such traffic maelstroms, he kept up under his breath a running fire of malediction against vehicles cutting across him, vehicles which objected to his cutting across them, and above all pedestrians who seemed sublimely unconscious of the fact that vehicles even existed.

As a general rule, his widely aimed obloquy was automatic and largely unnecessary, but suddenly it seemed for once justified. For as he reached the next corner a man, the above-mentioned Mr. Harold Bent, stepped off the central pavement and, narrowly missing a couple of cars, started across in front of George's taxi with his head turned the other way.

George immediately and indignantly squeezed his horn bulb to produce the two cracked and protesting squawks which should freeze the other to startled immobility while he rattled past; but for once it did not work. Instead of stopping in his tracks the pedestrian leaped wildly forward.

George swung his wheel with a blistering oath—too late. The taxi's wing caught the other above the left knee. His hat went flying in one direction, while the mackintosh he had been carrying spreadeagled itself in another, frightening the life out of George, who momentarily thought it was the body.

"——! First—accident in eighteen—years!" he ejaculated, scared and furious, as his taxi screeched to a standstill within a few yards. Next minute, however, he realized to his relief that the pedestrian, instead of lying bleeding to death in the road, had already scrambled up from the greasy wood paving and, having received his hat from one bystander and his coat from another, was limping angrily towards him. George's relief, however, was almost at once swallowed up in a vast indignation, for the other's furiously expressed idea seemed to be that it was all George's fault for driving on the wrong side of the road.

"Wrong side of the road!" he spluttered. "In Trafalgar Square there's only one—side of the road. Why, you . . ."

But Mr. Harold Bent was not listening to him. He was now appealing vigorously to bystanders. "Might have killed me! I was looking to my right, wasn't I?"

"Didn't see nothing," cautiously replied a large, stolid man.

"Only saw you on the ground," said a little man with a muffler, also keeping out of the witness-box.

Baffled, the victim opened the taxi door and applied to the fare, ignoring both George's rumbling blasphemies and the petulant honking of a No. 11 bus behind.

"Look, sir!" he began. "You saw it all and . . ." He broke off and turned round. "Here!" he said abruptly to George. "What's up with your passenger? He's ill or something."

The gathering crowd surged forward to peer inside at the hunched figure of a fattish, dark young man, who had fallen forward off the seat and was now collapsed on the floor.

"Thrown forward and stunned 'is-self!" volunteered the large stolid man, knowledgeably inactive.

"Attack o' powmain poisoning?" suggested the man with the muffler hopefully, also doing nothing at all about it.

"Maybe he's only fainted from shock," put in Mr. Harold Bent crisply. "Loosen his collar or something. . . ."

But by then a policeman had plowed through the crowd and taken charge. He gently lifted the inert figure back on to the seat; then turned. "Any one of you people a doctor, please?"

"Any doctor here?" spread outwards like a ripple. A moment later a tall, black-coated figure materialized in the little open space round the door. He knelt in the cab, made a brief examination, then said to the constable in an undertone: "This man is dead!"

"Cor!" said P. C. Robinson, startled out of his stolidity for a moment. "Hrm! I mean, shock o' the accident, sir? Or hit his head on . . ."

"No," replied the doctor, still in the same low, serious tones. "As far as I can see he's been stabbed—there's the hilt of a dagger under the right arm. . . ."

*　　　*　　　*

A week had passed and two men sat in armchairs in a small, neatly furnished suburban parlor. Pipes were going and a quart bottle of beer stood half-empty between them. An air of relaxation and contentment hung over the scene, in spite of the fact that the younger man, Inspector Painton, looked worried.

"I'm not happy about it, Dad," he said, chewing on his pipestem. "Here's this chap, James Wellson, stabbed to death about midday in the busiest part of London, a quarter of a mile from Scotland Yard, and we're still just about where we came in."

Ex-Superintendent Painton, a large man who seemed to be built on the lines of a floating dock, grinned over all his chins. "And though, as old Osborn said, you're one of our most promising young Detective-Inspectors, you nevertheless want to talk it out, as usual, with your old father who's now on the shelf."

"Why you ever retired I . . ."

His father waved him to silence.

"Let's talk it over by all means. It does this so-called clear-thinking brain of mine good to tackle a murder problem again—so get going. I've followed fairly closely all that's got into the papers, of course."

His son's face brightened a little and he took some papers from his pocket. "Good. Now, as I expect you know, the taxi driver's statement—without the blasphemy, which cuts it down by 40 percent—is that he was hailed about noon outside a pub near Oxford Circus by the murdered man. He didn't notice the man's companion particularly at that time—he had his back to him and got in quickly—except that he was short and wore a light raincoat, but no hat. Wellson—that's the murdered man—gave the directions—a destination in Pall Mall—but told the driver that his friend wanted to get off first at the southeast corner of Trafalgar Square. So he drives down Regent Street and Haymarket, and turns left for Trafalgar Square, but just as he gets to the near end of the National Gallery the murderer raps on the glass and wants to get out. He's told that this is the northwest corner, the southeast is at Charing Cross, diagonally opposite. He retorts that this is the corner he meant, and out he gets."

"So this is the first time the taxi driver hears his voice? Don't mind my interrupting, boy: I'm just getting the picture."

"That's O.K. . . . Yes, and he says he had a husky voice, as though he had a very bad throat. It's the first time, too, he sees his face and notices he has a small black mustache. Also he's wearing brown gloves."

"So you found no helpful fingerprints on the door handle, hilt of weapon, or elsewhere?"

"Quite right. Well, he tells the driver to carry on to Pall Mall, calls out 'So long' to his companion inside . . ."

"Who didn't answer, of course?"

"No. For by then obviously he was already dead, but probably propped up in the corner to look natural."

The elder man refilled his glass and then stretched his enormous body out more comfortably, as if to give his mind more scope. "What's your idea, son, about why he got out at that particular place?"

"Because he'd done the job."

Here his father nodded slowly to himself three or four times.

"He didn't want to stick around with the body any longer than he had to. He was right, too; because in point of fact it was only a few minutes afterwards that Wellson's body was prematurely discovered through a quite unforeseen accident. Not that it helps. Our murderer, a small man with a mustache—certainly shaved off by now—and a husky voice, probably a disguised one, is at large in London and we've no clue at all."

"What about the weapon?"

"No help. One of those thin, steel, paper knives, such as might have been bought anywhere, and sharpened to a keen point. Used with skill, of course."

The ex-Superintendent grunted, busied himself with refilling his pipe, then asked: "No clues from the Wellson end of the business?"

"Nope. The taxi's destination was only the corner of Pall Mall and St. James's Street—nothing to pick up there—while at the Oxford Circus pub all we've got is a barman who thinks he remembers him and that he was having a drink with a short man. But the place was very full and he was too busy to notice much. He says, however, that this other fellow, whoever he was, had no mustache, hadn't got a raincoat, and anyway, Wellson left the pub alone."

"What about Wellson's background?"

"Not much to find out. He was unmarried and lived in rooms in Hampstead. Out all day—worked in an engineering firm. Lots of pub friends, but no definite enemies at this time. Unfortunately for us, though, he had too many potential enemies from the past."

"Meaning?"

"Well, he was a nasty bit of work—been reserved all the war on a sort of traveling inspector's job and specialized in playing about with wives in the various towns he visited, generally those whose husbands were away in the Services. Almost any wronged husband, therefore, may have had it in for him—*when* he discovered, which may not have been till he came home, some good while after Wellson's association ceased. Naturally it's almost impossible to check up on all these women—different towns over five years or so—particularly when he no doubt kept his affairs as secret as possible."

"Hmf!" went the elder man, in a baffled sort of way, and drank some beer. "You *have* got something to chew on, Jack, haven't you?"

"And even that motive's only guesswork—though I've checked Wellson's background pretty carefully and can't find another as likely."

"It's probably the right one. As a starting point, let's assume it is. O.K.? . . . Right! The murderer has only recently discovered that Wellson was his wife's seducer at some time or another, and is all out for the biggest sort of revenge. Now what? Did Wellson know who he was?"

"No," said the Inspector definitely. "Or he'd have avoided him for a cert. *Yet* he knew him sufficiently well to give him a lift in his cab some distance out of his direct route to Pall Mall. So it wasn't a chance taxi-sharing."

"Good point," agreed his father.

"So the other must have deliberately scraped up an acquaintance—object: murder. But"—and his face clouded—*"why* is it that we can't pick up any hint of their having been seen together at any time prior to the murder. We know all Wellson's haunts."

"Ah!" Ex-Superintendent Painton swallowed some more beer "This at last is where I think," he announced portentously, and closed his eyes. . . .

After ten minutes he opened them and emptied his glass. "I'm getting something, Jack," he said. "Hrm! You've made two false assumptions. . . ."

"Hey, steady, Dad!" cried the other, nettled. "You make me sound like a dumb flattie, not C.I.D."

"When you've been as long in the game as I have," began his father. "However . . . you assumed, correctly, that the murderer adopted a false voice to deceive the taxi driver. But in the same breath, my boy, you assumed that his appearance—i.e. the mustache—was *real*. Why shouldn't that have been false too? In other words, though most criminals commit a crime and then 'disappear' by altering their appearance, may we not have one here who changed his appearance solely for the crime? In other words, the murderer, as seen by the only witness, not only 'disappeared' after the crime, but never existed before it."

Jack Painton was forced to admit his father had got something there. "Which accounts for our finding no trace of Wellson ever being associated with a man with a mustache. . . . Wait! But surely the murderer wouldn't have suddenly put on a mustache to go in a taxi with a fellow who knew him otherwise?"

The elder man smiled tolerantly. "Oh, he didn't do that till after he'd killed him. In the taxi. Nor did he use his disguised voice till afterwards either. Remember, he got in quickly and the driver never heard him speak or saw his face till he . . ."

"I get it," said his son, with a touch of annoyance. "What you mean is that the man we've got to find is a chap associated with Wellson before his death, who wasn't disguising his voice nor wearing a false mustache. Easy!"

"No need to be sarcastic, Jack. At least we know he's short—he can hardly have cut his legs down for the job—and"—he puffed complacently —"wasn't a short man talking to Wellson in that Oxford Circus pub?"

"Ye-es. But he hadn't a raincoat, and he didn't leave with Wellson."

"Be your age, Jack! We're obviously dealing with a clever man. The pub was crowded and you don't notice everything in a crowd. Why shouldn't he have had his raincoat on a seat where the barman couldn't see it, and then put it on and left quickly when the fellow wasn't looking—but in plenty of time to catch his victim before he got a taxi? It's a hundred to one against his finding one waiting outside."

Inspector Painton considered a moment, then his face brightened. "You know, Dad, I believe that may be about the size of it. That brain of yours is still pretty clear. I'll get round to the pub myself first thing tomorrow, as a further check. . . . By the way, didn't you say I'd made another false assumption?"

"Oh, yes. You assumed that the murderer got out at that corner of Trafalgar Square because he'd just done the job. It doesn't ring true to me."

"Why not? What's on that clear-thinking mind of yours now?"

"I don't know," said the ex-Superintendent simply. "Give me time. And get me another bottle of beer. Don't bother about my mind yet: I've got a big frame to support."

After a long draught and five minutes' silence with closed eyes, he again stirred ponderously to life. "Yes," he said. "Yes."

"Spill it, you old has-been," grinned his son.

"Here's the fallacy. It wouldn't take long to do the job, and the natural thing would have been to ask to be stopped anywhere he fancied on the direct route to Pall Mall. But he wants a corner of Trafalgar Square which is out of the way. Why? And he makes a mistake in the corner. Now! *Was* it a mistake?"

"Why not? Not everyone's certain of north and south and so on in London."

"All the same, supposing he *had* correctly specified the corner he wanted at the start. It's only a quarter of a minute's walk from the bottom of Haymarket. The obvious thing, therefore, would be to drop him there, and the taxi could at once turn right and go along Pall Mall. But, asking for the S.E. corner means it's got to go all round two sides of the Square to drop him and then come back along the third side, because Trafalgar Square is one-way. It looks, in fact, as though he wanted it to go right round and yet wanted to get . . . By God!" He heaved his vast bulk almost upright. "What a stroke of genius!"

"What is? What?" His son jumped to his feet in his excitement. "Do you think you've got it?"

"It's all Scotland Yard to a pick-pocket I have," he rumbled in heavy triumph. "This murderer is a very bold man—killing a chap in a taxi in broad daylight proves it—but, if my theory is right, his next move tops even that for audacity. Listen! He's forseen that we might get on to his disguise and start looking for him as the real person, who existed before and after. So, ignoring what we could find out about him before, he's taken terrific care not to be suspected *after.*"

"How?"

"Who of the persons actually connected with the case do you suspect least?"

Jack Painton thought. "Myself," he said, with a smile, "if that's what you mean?"

"That's right. Go on!"

"Well, the taxi driver, the doctor, P. C. Robinson, who discovered the body, the . . ."

"Did the P. C. discover it?"

"Oh, no. The little bloke—what's his name, Harold Bent, who was run over, of course. . . ."

"And *there* you have him," chuckled his father. "Who *could* suspect the man who, by entire accident, discovered the body in front of a score of witnesses and was nearly killed himself into the bargain?"

"Well, I'm . . . but how?"

"Listen!" He spoke in short, triumphant chuckling bursts. "He was the short bloke in the pub: he nips out, putting his raincoat on, and gets his lift, concealing his face from the driver. Does the job. Then putting his mustache and false voice on, he gets out as soon as he has committed the taxi to going round three sides of Trafalgar Square. As it drives on, raincoat off, gloves off, mustache off, and hat on, taken from raincoat pocket. Then he nips down the fourth side of the square in plenty of time to involve himself in a deliberate accident with the taxi he's just left. He has only 50 yards to go, while the taxi has three sides of the square to do, to say nothing of a probable hold-up at one or other of the traffic lights. He waits; along it comes; he starts to cross the road. Remember, the driver said that, instead of stopping short at the horn, he seemed to jump forward. *He* didn't mind risking a broken leg—all the better proof of innocence. In short, your star witness is also your murderer."

He coughed, finished his beer, and said solemnly: "Very good deduction by one of our most promising young Detective-Inspectors. You'll get full marks for it."

Jack Painton rang his father up next morning. "You're right, Dad, as usual, all along," he said. "Harold Bent's wife lived in a North country town where Wellson was in 1944. He seduced her while Bent was a P.O.W. in Burma, and she later on committed suicide in remorse, leaving a letter for her husband. After getting back, Bent spent a year trying to trace the man and only recently got on to him. Then he worked this dodge."

"Have you pulled him in, poor devil?"

"Er—no. And in a way I'm glad not to have had to do it. . . . You see, Dad, Fate's taken a hand in a queer way. Bent got run over yesterday in— of all places—Trafalgar Square, and died this morning. . . ."

MURDER AT THE DOG SHOW

by *MIGNON G. EBERHART*

The P.A. system warbled, Dr. Marrer—Dr. Marrem—Dr. Richard Marr-rry, through the hospital corridors; I translated it to Dr. Richard Marly and went to the charge desk where I was referred to a telephone. It was Jean calling. "Richard—I was shot at just now in the park."

"That's funny. It sounded as if you said somebody shot at you."

"I did. In the park. But I think he was aiming at Skipper. I had him out for an airing. And you know the finals in the show are tonight—"

"Who shot at you?"

"I don't know. I couldn't see, there was shrubbery. I ran to the avenue, dragging Skipper, and got a taxi. I think somebody is trying to keep Skipper out of the show."

"Call the police—"

"What could I tell them?" she asked reasonably. "Richard, will you come to the show and—well, keep an eye on things? I'll leave a ticket at the box office for you."

There had been a slight coolness between us, owing to the Dog Show and to Jean's kind but firm observations that my own dog, Butch, a Kerry Blue terrier, was not likely ever to take any ribbons.

"You can get somebody else to fault him," she had said mysteriously; but in her opinion Butch's legs were too much or too little like stove pipes and his coat was too black or too blue—in short, he was not a show dog. Jean confidently expected that Skipper, the Kerry Blue she had trained, would walk away with Best in Show.

Right now I swallowed my pride and said I would be there. Jean hung up, and I finished my round of patients as hurriedly as I could and drove home.

Jean was not the type to get the wind up over nothing. On the other hand, a murderous attack on Jean—or on Skipper—seemed very unlikely.

Dogs had brought us together and had very nearly separated us. She had come to me as a patient following a battle between one of the dogs she was training and a beloved old cat; as sometimes happens with a peacemaker,

Jean had received the only wounds. Perhaps I prolonged the treatment; in any event we began to see each other frequently. Her father had died when she was a child and had left Jean and her mother with little money. Jean's only talent, she told me, was a kind of understanding and love for cats, dogs, and all small creatures. As she grew older, this talent turned into a profession: she and her mother started a small kennel at their country cottage. They prospered moderately at first, and more noticeably after Jean had undertaken the training of dogs, as well as their handling in various dog shows. She had the infinite patience required and Skipper was the first dog she had trained and steered successfully through the requisite shows and ribbons to what promised to be a peak of his, and Jean's, career. If he won Best in Show tonight it would be a very bright feather in Jean's little professional cap, for the Heather Dog Show was one of the big, important shows of the year.

Skipper, I knew, belonged to a Mrs. Florrie Carrister who lived in the country near Jean and was in affluent circumstances; she was divorced from her husband Reginald Carrister, a stockbroker in the city, who had inherited a considerable fortune. Beyond that—and the fact that Jean considered Skipper a far finer dog than my own Butch—I knew nothing of Skipper, and certainly nothing that could account for anyone taking a pot shot at Jean—or at Skipper. While I could believe that rivalries in a dog show do become fervent, still I did not believe that any rival dog owner would go to such lengths.

Arriving at my apartment I told Suki, who cooks, valets, and answers the telephone for me, where I was going, patted Butch consolingly, told him he was better than any dog at the show, and departed again, this time for the Armory where the dog show was being held.

The whole vicinity of the Armory was a bedlam—taxis arriving, taxis departing, the flash of photographers' bulbs as jeweled and furred ladies and their escorts (or a dog, groomed to the last hair and led along as carefully as if it were the Bank of England on a leash) passed through the foyer. My ticket was waiting for me at the box office and I entered the Armory which I found jammed, confirming my suspicion that all the world loves a dog.

I bought a program. An usher directed me and I went upstairs and came out in a box. It was an end box, a choice one, and sparsely occupied. Two women sat in the front row talking with remarkable volubility and watching some dogs marching sedately around the ring; a man sat in the front row too but at the other end of the box, next to the wall, and leaned intently over the railing.

One of the women in the front row turned, saw me, broke off her flood of talk, and spoke to me. "Dr. Marly? I'm Mrs. Carrister. Jean asked me to leave a ticket for you." She was a large woman, with heavy shoulders that slumped down shapelessly in her seat. The woman in the aisle seat turned and she introduced us. "Miss Runcewell—Dr. Marly. You know—Jean's friend." Mrs. Carrister turned back to me. "I bought Skipper from Miss Runcewell's kennels when he was only six weeks old."

Miss Runcewell, very doggy in a tweed suit and leather hat and gloves, looked modest and Mrs. Carrister glanced back to the ring. "Oh, there's Jean!"

I sat down two rows behind them and watched Jean. She was worth watching—tall and slim and pretty with her short dark hair and level blue eyes; she was wearing a blue skirt, a neatly tailored white coat, and a red scarf, and was putting a lovely blue merle Collie through his paces deftly and precisely. But I didn't see how I was going to keep an eye on things as Jean had so confidently asked me to do. There was too much and at the same time too little to keep an eye on.

So I shifted to the dogs entering the ring and going through their prescribed routine, and decided that in the full view of so many thousands of people nothing in the way of violence was likely to happen. The two women ahead of me talked steadily—indeed, Mrs. Carrister never stopped. The man at the end of the box also watched the dogs. After the second event Miss Runcewell left the box and came back with two orange drinks, one of which she gave to Mrs. Carrister. And just before the next event a man came down the steps, took a seat in the row below and in front of me, and touched Mrs. Carrister on the shoulder. "Hello, Florrie," he said amiably.

He was handsome, as she certainly was not, in his mid-forties, and very elegantly turned out. She turned and said, "Oh, Reginald." Miss Runcewell turned and said how-do-you-do and Mrs. Carrister introduced me. "This is Dr. Marly—my former husband, Mr. Carrister."

We nodded. Mrs. Carrister said, "The Field Trials are coming up. Everything is right on time tonight because the show is on television." She turned absorbedly back to watch the ring and resume the steady talk to which Miss Runcewell contributed only rarely. Mr. Carrister folded his coat over his knees and I felt a twinge of uneasiness. Field Trials—or as the program more accurately put it, Gun Dogs in Action—that meant guns, didn't it?

Jean, however, would not be showing in the Field Trials. And, really, nothing *could* happen. Corn shocks and brush began to move into the ring. It was like Birnam Wood moving upon high Dunsinane Hill except that the corn shocks and brush were mounted on wood and carried by attendants who placed them at strategic intervals over the green ground-cloth. A brace of setters turned up, straining at a leash held by a man in a hunter's red shirt, a gun was fired, and the so-called "Field Trials" began. The gun shot was obviously a blank.

I leaned back and before I knew it was caught up in the color and drama and magnificent performance of the hunting dogs. Even Mrs. Carrister stopped talking and if Mr. Carrister ahead of me moved at all I was not aware of it. It was indeed so stunning a show that nobody in the box said a word when it ended.

The man at the end of the box rose and avoided Mrs. Carrister's bulk between him and the aisle by neatly stepping back over the rows of seats and out of the box. His face seemed suddenly but vaguely familiar to me, yet something about him seemed wrong and unfamiliar. His clothes? But he wore an ordinary dark coat and hat. He vanished at once, attendants appeared and cleared the ring, and I decided I must have seen him sometime, at the hospital.

The show went smoothly on and all at once I became aware of a kind of tension in the air. Mrs. Carrister seemed to have slumped down even more absorbedly in her seat, Miss Runcewell sat upright even more rigidly, and Mr. Carrister said over his shoulder, "It's coming up now. The Best in Show."

My own pulse quickened. I leaned forward to watch the dogs enter the ring which they shortly did, stepping very proudly, every one of them, and then Jean entered with Skipper. I had to admit that he was a beautiful dog, moving with incredible grace and ease, his square muzzle lifted so he could watch Jean for commands. Mr. Carrister turned briefly to me again. "It's amazing what Jean has done with that dog. A Kerry Blue is not easy to train—unless you use a two-by-four."

"You are quite mistaken," I said. "My own Kerry Blue understands everything."

He gave me an indulgent smile. "Look at Skipper stand like that! What he really wants to do is take on the lot of them and have a rousing good fight."

It is true there was a kind of quivering intensity about the Kerry Blue. It is also true that a magnificent Doberman was eyeing a Chesapeake next to him in a deeply brooding manner. Jean leaned over to make some invisible adjustment to the Kerry Blue's whiskers—and did not so much as count her fingers afterward which, in view of Skipper's extremely adequate teeth, astounded me—and the judging began with a long, slow parade around the ring. It was about then that I became aware of a curious mass murmur rising in the Armory. And then I saw it.

Now I am reliably informed that this cannot happen at any dog show; I can only say that it did happen. Another Kerry Blue, unattended by a handler, had mysteriously joined the parade and was marching jauntily along. He was perhaps darker than Skipper, perhaps not as stylish and certainly a little shaggy, but full of *joie de vivre*. I rose in sudden panic. It was my own dog—Butch!

Did he really understand everything? Was he determined to enter the show and compete with Skipper? In that dazed second it seemed possible.

But then he found Jean and leaped on her with glee. Skipper rightly resented this and leaped on Butch, a liberty not wisely taken. Butch has a generous nature—until he is annoyed. In the fraction of a second wild contagion blazed around the ring. I had a flashing vision of the Doberman's handler, who imprudently clung to the Doberman's leash, being dragged across the floor. The Armory rose like a tidal wave and roared. Handlers and judges ran and shouted, whistles blew, some cops came at the double from the main entrance under the correct impression that a riot had broken out, Miss Runcewell jumped up and made for the stairs, and I ran after her.

She knew the way, so she had the best of it through passages that echoed with a truly Gargantuan dog fight to the runway that led to the ring. It was a photo finish, however, for I was frightened. While Butch is remarkably intelligent he could not have induced a taxi driver to bring him to the Armory. And his entrance at that time was not an accident. Once at the runway Miss Runcewell dove into the ring.

I was blocked by a frenzied attendant who was wielding a broom over a Coonhound's back with no perceptible effect. I felt a sharp nip on my ankle, detached a tiny pug who was merely a victim of the contagion and desisted quite amiably, and was seized by Suki, in a dashing Homburg. He also had a walking stick and a wild gleam in his eyes. "I only did what you told me to do! Somebody phoned and said you wanted me to bring Butch to this runway, at exactly this time, and just let him off the leash and—ahhh—" Then Suki dashed into the fray himself, his Oriental calm completely deserting him. His hat flew off, and with his walking stick he flailed at every moving object around him including one of the judges who forgot himself and flailed back—striking, as it happened, one of the handlers who absently struck back also, but instead got a policeman squarely on the chin. This second chain reaction might have gone on and on had not the policeman collared me but then released me with a sharp cry and turned to disengage himself from a large and determined Chow.

Suddenly, magically, people and dogs began to sort themselves out. I do not say that order was instantly restored but it is a fact that judges and handlers of dogs are made of stern stuff. Dogs began to be pulled out of the melee; a doctor and some girls in Red Cross uniform set up a hasty emergency table at the edge of the ring. Their first customer was the policeman who had collared me and he had some difficulty rolling up his trouser leg but valiantly refused to remove his trousers.

I emerged at what was still the focus of a certain amount of activity just as Suki, Jean, Miss Runcewell, and a number of other people succeeded in separating Butch and Skipper. The dogs, surprisingly, took a long look at each other and while I cannot say they exchanged a mutual wink they did look all at once mightily pleased with themselves. Jean's cheeks were pink but she gave me a reassuring wave. Somebody shouted, "Get that dog out of here," and Suki and I complied—although with some difficulty—since Butch obviously wished to remain. However, we finally got him to the runway, put his leash on him, and I told Suki to take him home. Butch gave me a deeply reproachful look but disappeared in Suki's wake and by that time—incredibly!—every dog in the ring was back at his place and looking extremely and mysteriously smug.

A loudspeaker announced in shocked tones that the judging would be resumed, and I made for Mrs. Carrister's box. Once there I paused, panted, and looked around. Little had changed in the box. Miss Runcewell was perched, also panting, on the arm of a seat in the last row. Mr. Carrister was standing, looking down at the ring. Mrs. Carrister was slumped even further down in the first row. The fourth occupant of the box had not returned. The Armory still seethed with a sort of uninhibited joy, but suddenly became quiet as the judging began once more. Jean looked up to find me and I waved encouragement—and then saw her eyes travel downward.

I moved without knowing it. Jean was still staring, her face white and fixed, when I reached Mrs. Carrister's side and saw what Jean had observed from the ring. Mrs. Carrister was still slumped down—too far down.

She was dead.

Suddenly Mr. Carrister and Miss Runcewell were beside me. We all saw the dreadful blotch of wet redness on Mrs. Carrister's white blouse, under her suit jacket. And in a moment I knew that there was nothing I could do for her. I sent Carrister for the police. Mainly, just then, I was afraid of starting a mass panic. I remember telling Miss Runcewell to shut up and that she gulped and did so. I was dimly aware that the judging was proceeding; I had a glimpse of Jean, white but controlled, taking Skipper through his paces. Then a group of policemen arrived and made a blue wall around the box.

One of them said the lady had been stabbed. They tried to find the knife and couldn't, as applause suddenly roared through the Armory, flashbulbs popped, and there was Jean taking the trophy. So Skipper had won Best in Show, Mrs. Carrister had been murdered—and I knew who had murdered her.

But I didn't know how to prove it.

Some time later the situation remained much the same and Jean and I were permitted to gather up Skipper, who was yawning almost as cavernously as the by then empty Armory, and we took a taxi to my apartment. Jean thought it was all over and told me I was wonderful— which was very nice except that the investigation had barely begun and I knew it. The police were still casting about with antennae in the hope of picking up a lead. And the police have remarkably sensitive antennae.

The knife had not been found and it was the considered opinion of a police matron who had retired briefly with Jean and Miss Runcewell, and of the sergeant who had searched me and Mr. Carrister, that none of us had it. There was some muttered talk about the angle of the knife wound from which I gathered that anyone in the box could have killed Mrs. Carrister.

Nevertheless, a few facts did emerge. No one knew, or admitted knowing, the identity of the fourth occupant of the box and all I could say was that his face had seemed familiar to me, but not his clothing—which quite comprehensibly drew skeptical looks from the police.

Mr. Carrister protested that he was on good terms with his former wife, denied killing her, but admitted frankly that he paid her an extremely large alimony. He admitted with equal frankness that he—and only he—had not left the box at any time.

Jean's story of having been shot at in the park elicited the facts that both Miss Runcewell and Mr. Carrister owned guns and that neither of them had an alibi for the time when Jean had given Skipper his run in the park—but then neither of them had a conceivable motive for taking a pot shot at Jean, or at Skipper.

I brought up the problem of Butch's little frolic in the ring and the mysterious telephone call that had led to it, but the lieutenant in charge merely gave me a long look and said something about practical jokes and that young people would be young people. Since I could not possibly prove anything at all, I repressed a desire to tell him that doctors who wish to rise in their profession do not make a hobby of provoking dog fights. It was shortly after that Jean and I were permitted—I do not say asked—to leave.

Suki had heard the news over the radio and was waiting for us, with hot milk and sandwiches for Jean and a highball which he slid into my thankful hand. There was a moment of tension when the two dogs met but now, strangely enough, they seemed to regard each other as old and tried friends. Suki's fuller report of the telephone message was not illuminating. He could not be sure whether it was a woman, or a man imitating a woman's voice. "But orders are orders, Doctor," he said. "I took Butch to the side-street entrance and then to the runway, at exactly eleven o'clock as I was told to do, and just—well, let him off the leash. Nobody stopped me. When Butch saw all those dogs—" He shrugged fatalistically.

I reflected that anyone who had a program for the show knew that the final event was scheduled for eleven—which would include some thousands of people. I did not know what to do and Jean's eyes were clearly expecting something in the nature of a full-fledged miracle. So I told Suki to get my revolver.

I felt it was rather impressive; Jean's eyes widened. But Suki said with insufferable calm that he thought I might require it and pulled it from his pocket. "Load it," I said, trying to regain lost ground.

"Oh, I've already done that, Doctor," and he put the revolver on the desk beside me.

But Jean's eyes still demanded action of some sort and indeed a few questions seemed indicated. I said, "Jean, did Mrs. Carrister ever talk of her husband?"

"Oh, yes. She talked about everything really. She talked all the time. I got so I didn't really listen. But honestly, there wasn't a thing that could be —evidence. She was on good terms with him. And with Miss Runcewell, too. They drove up to my kennels often to see how Skipper was shaping up. Mrs. Carrister had her heart set on Skipper winning. She was going to start a kennel of her own, if he won."

"Mrs. Carrister? Did her husband or Miss Runcewell know of this?"

"I don't know about her husband. But she often spoke of it to Miss Runcewell. You see, if Skipper won the big championship, he'd be—he is —a very valuable dog. The fees as sire alone would be considerable."

"So she would then be a rival—at least, a competitor—of Miss Runcewell's."

"Oh, Miss Runcewell didn't mind. I heard her say something about Mrs. Carrister taking over her kennels. So I think she intends to go out of business. I suppose she was going to sell out to Mrs. Carrister."

After a moment I said, "Did they ever ask questions about—say, me? Or Butch?"

"Oh, yes. They asked all sorts of questions. I told them about Butch and —well, that he isn't a show dog. But he is sweet." Butch heard his name and put his great head on Jean's knee with infuriating complacence. Butch is many things—but he is not sweet.

The telephone rang and I picked it up. "Doctor," said a voice with a heavy French accent. "This is Henri."

"Henri," I said, and light broke upon me. "Henri! You were in the box tonight!"

A flood of English and French burst upon my ear. "My heart, she is not so good. *Le docteur* say no excitement. *Il faut que je parts toute de suite—*"

"Why did you part—I mean, leave?"

He told me at some length. "Thank you," I said at last. "No, I'm sure the police will understand. Give me your telephone number."

He did and I hung up. Jean's eyes were round with questions. I said, "That was Henri. He is headwaiter at—" and I named a famous restaurant downtown. "Mrs. Carrister gave him a ticket to her box for the show tonight. He left after the Field Trials."

I went to my bedroom for my book of special telephone numbers. It seemed to me that there was now enough evidence on which to proceed, so

I started to dial the number of a former patient of mine who is a high official in the police department when—if I may speak frankly—all hell broke loose in the front hall.

I felt for my gun, remembered that it was still on my desk, and ran for the hall amid an ear-splitting tumult of barks. Mr. Carrister was just disappearing into my study, Suki and Jean were tugging at Butch, and Miss Runcewell was efficiently scooping up Skipper's leash. Since the dogs were merely in high spirits and meant nothing really serious in the way of mayhem, we soon assembled in the study where we found Mr. Carrister crouching on top of my desk looking extremely indignant.

Miss Runcewell said, "I was worried about you, Jean. You were not at your hotel, so we thought you might be here," and she held a firm grip on Skipper's leash.

Mr. Carrister eyed Butch coldly and said, "I'll put it to you frankly, Doctor. You were in the box tonight. If you have any idea at all about the murder I want to know what it is."

"Why, certainly," I said. "I'll call the police at once and ask them to make the arrest."

His eyes bulged, Jean gave me an admiring glance, and I picked up the telephone and dialed.

"Hello—" my official friend said sleepily.

"This is Doctor Marly. You may send the police to my house to arrest the person who murdered Mrs. Carrister . . . Yes, I have proof."

Something moved behind me. The dogs burst out in full cry, I seized my gun, and my friend on the phone cried out, "Where's the dog fight?"

"Hurry," I shouted and dropped the telephone but unfortunately dropped my gun at the same time.

Miss Runcewell was already at the front door. So it was the dogs that backed Miss Runcewell into the coat closet, assisted in a hurly-burly way by the rest of us. Suki then neatly locked the door of the closet. Mr. Carrister glanced at Butch, took to the top of the desk again, and said, "Do you mean *she* murdered Florrie? But why?"

"Because you were going to be in the box tonight and Miss Runcewell knew it. She also knew that you had an excellent reason for killing your wife."

Mr. Carrister said, "Huh?"

"It was a pattern of diversionary tactics," I explained. "Your wife appears to have been an exceedingly talkative woman." Carrister nodded unhappily. "I feel sure that Miss Runcewell was told of your expected presence in the box. Certainly at some time she was told of me and my dog. She shot at Jean—not to hurt Jean or Skipper—but merely to induce Jean to ask me to come to the Armory tonight. Then later, on the excuse of getting orange drinks, she left the box and phoned Suki, telling him to bring my dog to the Armory—"

"But he's the dog that started the fight!"

"That was exactly Miss Runcewell's intention. The police would believe that Mrs. Carrister was murdered while everyone's attention was diverted by the—er—confusion attending Butch's entrance in the ring. She saw to it that she was well away from the box during that time. You remained, as she hoped, in the box and consequently became a choice suspect. But your wife was actually murdered during the Field Trials. That's why the police could not find the knife. It was tossed down into the nearest corn shock and carried off when the attendants cleared the ring."

"But how do you know that?"

"Henri—a friend of mine—was in the box. He left after the Field Trials, stepping over the seats behind him rather than disturb Mrs. Carrister to get to the aisle. As you know, we were in an end box. He told me a short time ago that he saw the knife flung down into the corn shock."

"But *why* did she kill my wife?" said Mr. Carrister.

There was clearly only one explanation. I said, "I think you'll find that Mrs. Carrister has loaned Miss Runcewell enough money to keep her kennels going. Possibly the understanding was supposed to be a friendly one and Miss Runcewell did not, in writing, use her kennels as collateral. But Mrs. Carrister was intending to take over Miss Runcewell's kennels and means of livelihood—and Miss Runcewell knew that. She kept up a pretense of friendliness, until the time came when Mrs. Carrister decided to act. Then Miss Runcewell acted first."

Jean linked her arm in mine. "But, Richard, I know that you knew who killed her even *before* Henri phoned! How did you know?"

"Oh," I said. "That. Well—it was during the Field Trials that *both women stopped talking*—Mrs. Carrister for an obvious reason, Miss Runcewell because she knew Mrs. Carrister was dead."

That night Mr. Carrister, handsomely in one way but regrettably in another, presented Skipper to Jean.

After he had gone Jean looked thoughtfully at the two dogs. "They do seem friendly," she said.

Friendly, yes. But two Kerry Blues in the same household? "Butch," I said finally, "may not be a show dog but—"

"But he's your dog," Jean smiled, "and he *is* sweet."

ALWAYS TRUST A COP

by OCTAVUS ROY COHEN

The voice at the other end of the telephone said, "I'm talking from the Los Angeles airport," but to Johnny Norton it didn't seem that way. The voice was coming to him across six thousand miles of ocean, from a steaming island in the South Pacific. He'd last heard that voice a half-dozen years ago, at night, in a foxhole. It had said:

"What's eatin' on you, Johnny? How come you ain't sayin' nothin'?"

The voice on the telephone said, "What's eatin' on you? How come you ain't sayin' nothin'?"

Johnny pulled himself together. He said, "Tex Graham!" and the voice answered, "Of course it's Tex! Who else would it be?"

"Well, listen, fella. After all this time . . ."

"Didn't I promise you'd see me after we got off that stinkin' island? How are you, you old so-and-so?" Except that Tex didn't say so-and-so. He used good, old-fashioned, affectionate Marine talk.

"I'm fine, Tex. You?"

"Right side up is all. How's tricks? You married or something?"

"Yeh. Been married six months. Living in Hollywood."

"I know. Found your name in the phone book. Solid citizen, huh? Whatcha doin' for a livin'?"

"I got a pretty good job."

"Well knock off. I'm shovin' off at 2 A.M. You got a car?"

"A sort of one."

"Hop in it. Bring the old lady. We'll have dinner together and shoot the breeze. How long it take you to make it here?"

"Forty minutes maybe."

"I'll be waitin' in the American Airlines Building. Jeez! kid, it'll be good to see you. Specially without them Japs gettin' in our hair."

Johnny Norton hung up the telephone. He was a big blond kid, 28 years old, weighing around 180. He stood with his back against the wall, staring at his wife, Mary, who was also blond and whose eyes were the same color blue as his. Johnny said, "That was Tex Graham."

"No!"

"Yeh. He's at the airport. Invited us for dinner: you and me both."

She moved close to him and put one hand on his arm. "Gee! I'm sorry, Johnny," and he said, "I got to do it, honey. I'm a cop."

Yes, he was a cop. She thought he was the handsomest cop in Los Angeles. Funny, the thrill she got out of his blue uniform with the big gold-and-silver badge, the black Sam Browne belt, and the precisely creased blue shirt. She looked him over now and said, "Where's your gun?"

"Left it with Eddie Morgan. He's putting on a new pair of grips for me. He'll have it fixed by roll call tomorrow morning." Then he caught a question in her eyes, and said, "It's not that kind of a deal, honey. Tex doesn't know I'm a cop. I'll put on civilian clothes."

"It's not going to be easy, is it, Johnny?"

"You can say that again."

"You have to go?"

"Sure. It's been set up a long time. It's my job to finger him for the FBI."

"Why?" she asked. "If they have his picture?"

"Because the boys in the local office don't know him. He may have changed since the picture was taken: deliberately or otherwise. But he couldn't be so much changed that I wouldn't recognize him."

She was sorry for Johnny. This was a tough assignment. He'd never told her much about the war, but everything he'd told her—every experience—had featured Tex Graham. She watched him dial a number.

"FBI? . . . Connor there? . . . Hilton? . . . Can you reach either of 'em? . . . Sure, it's important . . . This is Officer Norton, Hollywood Division . . . Somebody they want is in town . . . No, I'll be gone . . . Tell them to call the Lieutenant. I'll tell him the score."

He called the Station, got the Lieutenant:

"Johnny Norton talking, Lieutenant. Remember that Tex Graham deal the FBI was talking to us about?"

"The guy you was in the Marines with? The one they want for murder and robbery in Oklahoma?"

"Yeh. Well, he's here. Just till 2 A.M. Connor and Hilton, the two FBI special agents: I just called them. They're out. They want this pinch in a big way. I left word for them to give you a buzz as soon as they showed up."

"What's the scoop, Johnny?"

"I'm meeting Tex right away at the International airport. American Airlines Building. He invited Mary and me for dinner, so if we ain't in that shack, maybe we'll be eating on the Flight Deck. If anything slips, I'll phone you."

"Want us to send out a couple of detectives?"

"Handle it your own way, Lieutenant. But it's FBI's baby. I'll be in civvies."

"Keep your guard up."

"Hell! Lieutenant, I'm not in on this. Like I said, it's all FBI. All they wanted was for me to let them know if he ever got in touch with me, then to help identify him. What they do when they pick him up is their business. I'm not sticking my chin out."

The Lieutenant said okay, and Johnny hung up. He took off his uniform and arranged it meticulously on a hanger in the closet of the tiny apartment. He put on a sports shirt, a pair of slacks, and a Hollywood coat. He changed from black shoes to brown. He looked at Mary, tried to smile, and gave it up as a bad job.

She understood. She always understood how Johnny felt about things. She said, "That's why I'm going with you."

"You'll do nothing of the kind."

She came close to him and took his hands in hers. "The reason I'm going," she said, "is because when it's all over you're going to be feeling pretty low."

He was grateful and said so. It wasn't as though there would be danger. It was an FBI show exclusively. She said, "Don't let it get you down, Johnny. What you've got to do isn't easy, but it's your job."

"I know. But I still wish the guy had gone somewhere else. The FBI set up deals like this every place in the country where Tex had a pal. What hurts is . . . well, dammit! I love the guy."

"He's a murderer, isn't he?"

"Yeh. Sure. But that ain't how I remember him . . ."

No, it wasn't. He remembered boot camp, and rigorous training in Panama. Then the islands. Good times and bad times. He remembered Tex Graham as the toughest Marine in a tough outfit. He'd been flattered to be Tex's closest friend.

Tex had been a killer, even in the Marines. But you judged things by different standards then. It was your job to kill, provided you yourself wanted to live. In one or two places, it had been a little war. Even on Tarawa it had seemed little because he and Tex had usually been on patrol, isolated from the main show. A guy was on his own then. Just him and his buddy and the few others that made up the patrol. You did what you had to do, and tried not to think about it afterward.

It hadn't taken Tex long to learn his way around. He said he'd always had it tough, he didn't mind a little thing like a war. The jungle—well, he didn't like that so much, but he got used to it. Pretty soon he was teaching Johnny and the other men in the platoon. They made him corporal, and would have busted him except that he was too valuable on patrol. What he went after, he got.

He and Johnny were always close. They did a lot of talking, when they had time. It was funny about that: Johnny knew which side was up, but Tex's slant on things—once in a while that got him. He tried to shrug it off, to sell himself the idea that Tex was kidding. But he knew it was on the level, really. He had reason to know . . .

Driving out to the airport, Johnny briefed his young wife on the situation. He said they'd taken Tex off Tarawa on a stretcher, and that was the last he'd seen of the guy. Hadn't even heard from him until just now. But *about* him: that was different.

Johnny didn't know for sure whether Tex had always had a bad streak . . . you couldn't tell when there was a war on. But he certainly had gone bad since VJ day. Half a dozen deals, winding up with bank robbery and murder in Oklahoma. That was when FBI got into the case. They'd checked Tex up one side and down the other. They had made contact with everybody they heard about who'd ever been buddies with the guy: Johnny included. Some day, somewhere, they figured Tex might get in touch with one of 'em. They had read the cards right, obviously, because that's what Tex had done.

"Just one thing I'm worried about, Johnny," she said. "Are you sure he doesn't know you're a policeman?"

"Yeh. If he'd known, he'd never have called me."

The set-up seemed fantastic to her. That her Johnny and this Tex Graham had been close friends seemed incredible: one innately decent, the other plumb bad; one proud to be a cop, hating crime and criminals, the other snatching whatever he wanted at the point of a gun.

Well, what Johnny had to do was simple enough: Just meet Tex and keep him occupied until FBI showed up. Then point him out. It was a job Johnny hated, but there was nothing he could do about it. When you're a cop you don't debate letting a murderer get away, even if he is your friend. Sure, you hate to snag him, or even to help; you wish it was somebody else doing it. But when there isn't anyone else, you just go ahead and obey orders.

It was after dark when they reached the airport. Johnny voiced one last word of warning. He said, "Play it smooth, honey. Tex is sharp. Don't give him any hint you're expecting something to happen."

"Will there be trouble, Johnny?"

"Not a chance. Tex won't know these guys. They'll close in on him from both sides before he knows what's happening." He took one hand from the steering wheel and closed it reassuringly over hers. "I wouldn't let you be leading with your chin: you know that."

She said, Yes, she knew—but that didn't keep her from being worried. Not the physical danger: she accepted his word that there wasn't any, but she knew he was having a bad time, that he'd give plenty not to be mixed up in it.

There were a lot of lights at the airport. They found a parking place, and started walking. They passed TWA and United and Western and Pan-American and walked into American Airlines. It was a rather small building, with counters and clerks and porters and a newsstand, and speakers that murmured at you from the wall announcing plane departures and arrivals, summoning passengers who hadn't checked their tickets or had their luggage weighed.

They walked inside. A man got up from a leather-cushioned chair and bore down on them. He was about 30 years old, and approximately Johnny's size and build. He had black eyes and hair, and he looked as though he'd be able to handle himself anywhere.

He grabbed Johnny and started pumping his hand. He called him a lot of names and said profane things, affectionately. Then he turned around and looked at Mary, and Johnny said, "This is the old lady, Tex."

Tex stuck out a big, hard hand. He said he was pleased to meet her, and how did she ever come to pick a no-good so-and-so like Johnny Norton. He had a soft Texas drawl, and he was so unsuspecting and so delighted at meeting his wartime buddy again that Mary felt sorry for him.

Tex started telling her things about Johnny. He was a great ribber. He told about dames, and put it on so thick she knew he was kidding. Meanwhile, she saw Johnny glancing at the door, watching for the FBI agents who were to make the pinch.

"How's about some chow?" inquired Johnny. "You hungry?"

"When'd you ever see me when I wasn't?"

"They got a good restaurant right here."

"Hell," said Tex. "I been livin' in restaurants, 'specially airport ones. What about letting the Missus fix me up some home cooking: I ain't pulling out until two in the morning."

That was what Tex said, but Johnny knew that what he meant was something far deeper than that.

Tex had been on the lam for a long time. He was wanted. He never knew where or when they might close in on him, and the prospect of spending several hours in a public place was bound to make him nervous. Of course, Johnny preferred to remain right where he was, and so he tried to stall. He said, "Well gee! Tex—Mary hadn't figured on doing any cooking tonight."

Tex grinned at her. "Not even for an old friend of your husband's?" and Mary said, sure, she'd be glad to fix a dinner for him. Tex was enthusiastic. Like a kid. He said it'd be swell to relax in Johnny's home, to eat Johnny's wife's cooking, to spend a few hours chewing the fat.

Mary saw that her husband didn't like the way things were going. She knew he was mentally bawling out the Lieutenant for not having kept hard after the FBI, that he was sore at the FBI for not being at the airport. She was afraid Johnny would give himself away, and so she took the reins in her own hands. She said they'd drive back together and that she'd stop at a market and buy some beer and stuff. Johnny caught what she had in mind, and he went along with it.

Driving in, she marveled at their man-talk. Funny how the tiniest detail of their service days together seemed important. They laughed about things that didn't seem very funny to her, and she was shrewd enough to realize that what they were laughing about were the parts they both knew but weren't saying.

They approached a market that was still open and she told Johnny to stop there. She said, pointedly, "You and Tex stay in the car. I'll only be a few minutes."

She made sure they weren't following her before going to a telephone booth at the rear of the market. She called the Hollywood Station and got the Lieutenant. She identified herself, and asked what had gone wrong.

The Lieutenant said, "That's what I'm asking you, Mrs. Norton. I just got a call from those FBI boys at the airport wanting to know where you are."

She told him where they were, and explained that they'd had to play things Tex Graham's way to keep him from suspecting that anything was wrong. Besides, Johnny wasn't armed, and undoubtedly Tex was. She said they were headed home, and that she was going to cook dinner, and then they'd spend the evening until it was time for Tex to go back to the airport.

"I'll get right in touch with them Special Agents," promised the Lieutenant. "They'll probably stake your apartment house, after you get home."

"You know which apartment it is?"

"No. We just got the address."

"It's the first floor, north side of the building. We're the rear apartment. There's a front one, and two just like them on the south side. Same arrangement on the second floor." She lowered her voice. "Will there be trouble?"

"Not where you'll be, there won't. We'll probably send a few of our dicks to assist FBI. They'll stake the building on all four sides. Don't you worry: they won't come busting in. They wouldn't take that chance— shooting it out in a small apartment where there's a woman and a policeman."

"How will they get him?"

"When he goes out. And look, Mrs. Norton—there'll be a man in back of the building. How about making an excuse to step outside: you know, empty the garbage or something? You can give him the setup."

She said, "I've got a disposal unit. If I can think of any other excuse I'll . . ."

"Right. But play it cagey. This Graham is bad medicine."

She hung up, bought some beer, a loaf of bread, and a few other things she didn't need, so as to have enough packages to make her long absence look plausible. As she got in the car, taking the window seat, she caught an inquiring glance from her husband, and gave him an almost imperceptible nod in answer. They backed out of the parking space and started for home.

She'd almost told the Lieutenant she was scared. Thinking it over now, she realized that she was more worried than frightened: worried chiefly because she knew something had to happen, but she didn't know when or where or how. She kept reminding herself that this man whose big body was wedged against hers was a killer, and, what was more, the minute he was caught, his own life was forfeit. She was afraid of the unknown, afraid that her husband might make some betraying move. And she had one fear which was greater than either of those: *she was afraid of the detectives who would be watching their apartment.*

Johnny Norton worked in uniform, and he hadn't been at the Hollywood Station long. He knew a lot of the men downstairs, but he'd told her often that he seldom got to meet detectives. They didn't have much contact with each other, the detectives and the uniformed men. The few times he'd had to go upstairs with suspects or reports, it had been to talk to the day commander, and Johnny had always been in uniform.

There was another angle, too. Johnny worked days. The few detectives he knew—and who knew him—also worked that watch. They changed watch at 5 P.M. , and the men that came on after that were strangers to him and he to them.

No, the night-watch detectives wouldn't know him. The FBI men would, because they'd talked to him about this deal. But two Special Agents couldn't be on four sides of the building at the same time. And if trouble started, there was danger that one of the cops might not know which was Tex Graham and which was Johnny Norton.

They got home, left the car parked at the curb, and went inside. Johnny snapped on the light, and Tex said, "Nice apartment. We never had it so good in the Islands, did we, Johnny?" and Johnny said, No, they never had. He motioned Tex to their best easy chair, shoved some cigarettes at him and told him to make himself at home.

Mary took the men's hats and coats and hung them in the hall closet near the bedroom. She went into the kitchen and started fixing dinner. She could hear them talking. It was the same old theme: the war, the experiences they had shared. Tex lighted a fresh cigarette. "What a life that was," he said. "Nobody gave a hoot for nothin' except gettin' outa there. Didn't care whether school kept or not. When I got hit on Tarawa, it was like gettin' a vacation ticket."

"What'd they do with you?"

"Fixed me up fine after they got to me. I had a bad five hours, though, lyin' there expecting the Nips to pick me up. They didn't like Marines."

"I'll say they didn't."

"Anyway, our gang found me. They shot me full of something and I woke up in a field hospital. Next thing I knew, I was at Base. Then on board ship. Then at General in Australia. Was that a soft touch!" Tex grinned at Johnny. "You never got a scratch, did you?"

"Nah. But what was left of the boys sure missed you. The patrol never was the same."

Mary listened with half an ear. She went ahead with dinner: pork chops, baked beans, a can of asparagus, rolls, coffee, a simple salad. She took three apple turnovers out of the freezing compartment and let them sit a while, preparatory to heating them for dessert.

She wanted to go outside, to talk to whoever was stationed there. But she was afraid. Tex was keen. He might think it was funny, might follow to see what was happening. All she could manage was to get to the back window and peep through a corner of the shade over the sink. Half-concealed in the shadows, she saw a man with a shotgun. FBI or cop, she didn't know. But they were there. Front, back, and sides. No chance for Tex to get away. They'd snag him or shoot him. Either way, with the raps he had hanging over him, he was as good as dead. It didn't check with the laughter she heard coming from the other room.

What they were laughing about, she didn't know; but it must have been some intimate experience, because they'd been discussing it in whispers. There was that service side of Johnny's life, chunks of it she'd never know. It occurred to her that this could have been a wonderful evening for Johnny if his friend had been other than what he was.

Dinner was okay. It was ten o'clock before she'd finished with the dishes and joined them in the living room. There hadn't been a sound from outside.

She could see the strain in Johnny's eyes. She didn't know much, but she knew a lot more than Johnny did, and he must be worried plenty. Some of the time, it seemed as though he wasn't listening to what Tex was saying. Occasionally he looked at her, but she didn't dare to flash him any signal, even of reassurance. All she could do was to smile and give the impression that things were under control.

Time was working against them. The hands of the mantel clock were creeping forward, closer and closer to the moment when Tex would say he had to leave. That was what frightened her. It was the minutes beyond that when the play would pass into other hands. She had quit being sorry for Tex. All she could think of now was her worry about Johnny.

Sooner or later there would be fireworks. There had to be. And when they started, Johnny would be just fool enough to move in on Tex, unarmed. Duty. Johnny was too acutely aware of his responsibilities as a policeman. And she knew he'd do whatever he could to protect her when the trouble started. . . .

Tex got up and stepped into the hall. She saw him open the closet door. He fumbled in his topcoat pocket and came back with a fresh pack of cigarettes.

Tex grinned at them and went to the north window. He pulled back the shade a fraction of an inch and looked out. He said, "Nice view you got," and walked back to his chair.

He sat down, opened his pack of cigarettes, and lighted one. Then he reached under his coat and took out an army .45. He looked straight at Johnny and said quietly, "You're a cop, aren't you, kid?"

Johnny pretended surprise and asked him what gave him such an idea.

"When I got my cigarettes just now. Your uniform is in that closet."

Johnny tried to grin. "Is it so bad to be a cop?" he asked.

"Yeh." Tex's voice was flat. "Especially when there's other cops outside. I saw two of them through that window. One has a shotgun. You knew, didn't you, Johnny?"

Johnny said, Yes, he knew, and the best thing Tex could do would be to give himself up. This was a hell of a note Johnny said, putting an old friend on the spot.

Tex said, "A guy plays 'em as he sees 'em, Johnny. It looks kinda lousy to me, but then I ain't at home on your side of the fence."

Johnny choked up. He asked why Tex had been such a fool as to get in touch with him. "They figured you would if you ever came through L.A. They had the deal all set up."

"How many men outside?"

"I don't know."

Mary said, "Too many for you to have a chance, Tex."

He shook his head. "A guy's always got a chance as long as he's breathing. You know what they want me for?"

Johnny said, Yes, robbery and murder.

"So I'm cooked." Tex was silent for quite a while. "If they was figurin' to bust in, they'd have done it long ago. That means I'm safe as long as I stay here."

Johnny said that was the way it was.

"But I can't stick here forever. I gotta make a pitch."

"It won't get you anywhere, Tex."

"Being picked up wouldn't be healthy, either, Johnny. Remember that deal on one of them little islands, the first time we was on patrol together? Wasn't much chance there, it looked like. But we shot our way out, didn't we?"

"Some of us did."

"You know, that was the night I took a liking to you. Hell, we'd had fun training and in Panama and all that stuff, but that night you came through. I'll bet you're one hell of a swell cop."

There wasn't anything Johnny could say to that. After about a half-minute Tex looked Mary's way and asked a question. "You do any telephoning when you was in that market?"

She nodded.

"What'd they tell you?"

"Just that they would stake the apartment."

He said, "Where's your gun, Johnny?"

Johnny explained he didn't have it: he'd left it with a guy to have a new pair of grips put on.

"You're as crazy as I am—tying up with me without a gun."

Johnny explained he hadn't known about that when he left the Station. It wasn't until he got home that the telephone call came in.

"How did you figure to take me?"

"I didn't. Two FBI agents were supposed to be at the airport. I stalled as long as I could, waiting for them to show up. When they didn't . . . hell, Tex, you ain't any dummy. I had to follow your lead or you'd have figured something was wrong."

"I would at that." He did some more thinking. "You got to get me out of here, Johnny."

"That ain't possible."

"It's got to be. I don't know the layout here. You do. There's got to be some sort of an exit they ain't got covered."

"Not a chance, Tex. You know those guys outside wouldn't overlook something like that."

"Keep thinkin', kid. It'd be a lot healthier if you come up with an idea. What I mean is, I ain't gonna take this sittin' down."

"What can you do?"

Tex looked embarrassed. "I hate to get your wife mixed up in this, Johnny, but there's no other way."

"Meaning . . . ?"

"Well, they haven't come in yet because of her. So they wouldn't take any chances of shootin' her no matter what happened. Pretty soon I'm going out. I'm taking her with me. First move anybody makes, I'll shoot her. I ain't kiddin', Johnny."

No, he wasn't kidding. He'd do just that, because it was the only thing he could do. Tex said to Mary, "Look at it from my angle . . ."

She said she was, but did he think he could bring himself to shoot a woman?

"Sure. Why not? If it's my only chance? You got to believe me, Mary."

Johnny told her he believed Tex. He went on, "But, look—what would that give you? A little breather maybe. Sooner or later they'd snag you."

"Later. That's better than now. And look, kid: don't you start something on account you're scared about her. I'd hate to let you have it, but that's the way it would be."

"I know. Only thing is, Tex, I still don't think it would work. Honest, I don't. There's only one thing I can think of."

"What?"

"Let me talk to one of the boys outside. Or send word through the Station. They'd call it off."

"But they'd still tail me, wouldn't they?"

"Yeh, I guess so."

Mary looked from one to the other. Couple of old friends talking quietly, dispassionately. It was difficult to convince herself that her life was in danger; that, in the long run, Tex didn't have a chance; that Johnny was in the middle. It didn't seem any more real than when they'd been kidding about things that had happened on the other side of the world.

She said, with surprising calm: "We're stymied all around, aren't we, Tex? The men outside won't do anything so long as we're together in here. They can stake the place indefinitely. We can't just sit here that long."

"We won't. Like I said, you and I will walk out together. We'll walk real close, and I'll have my gun on you. They won't shoot. They won't even close in on us."

Johnny said, "I've thought of a dozen schemes, Tex—all tricks. But you'd know they were tricks."

Tex nodded. "You got me pegged, all right. You know, it's funny—you getting me into this thing, and me not being sore."

Johnny said he was thinking of Mary, nobody else.

"That's what I figure. You'd take a chance with yourself, but not with her. She's a swell gal, Johnny. Ain't many guys got it so lucky."

The clock was still moving. Time was closing in on them. Tex leaned back in his chair without relaxing his vigilance. Looked like he didn't want to talk, so they both kept quiet, too. Their eyes met and Mary smiled ever so slightly. It wasn't that she felt like smiling, but she wanted Johnny to know that she wasn't afraid.

But she was afraid. Terribly afraid. She'd been afraid all evening, ever since they left the airport, ever since she'd glanced through the window and seen the detective with the shotgun. She'd known then that the chips were down.

Five minutes passed. Tex said softly, "You'll level with me, won't you, Johnny?"

"Sure. On account of Mary."

"Those guys outside are detectives, aren't they?"

"Yes."

"You're uniform. How many detectives do you know?"

"Mighty few."

"How many know you?"

"Even less than that. And none of the boys on the night watch."

"We're going to walk around the apartment, Johnny. You're gonna peek out, real careful. Tell me whether you know the men on this side and in back."

Johnny got up. So did Mary. Tex kept close to them, his gun handy. Johnny did what he was told, and then they were back in the living room. Johnny said, "I don't know any of the three guys I could see."

"Better be sure, Johnny. If what I got in mind goes wrong, Mary's the one who takes it."

"That's straight, Tex. Of course, I don't know who's in front or on the other side. If the FBI men are there, I know 'em, and they know me."

Tex did a lot more thinking. He said, softly, "It could work, Johnny. It sure could."

Johnny waited.

"Remember in the Marines we used to wear each other's clothes once in a while?"

"What about it?"

"What's to say we couldn't do it again?"

Johnny said he didn't see what Tex was driving at.

"This. Suppose I put on your uniform. I take Mary and we slip out the back door. I make believe I'm you, and Mary plays up to me. If the men back there don't know you, they won't know there's been a switch. If you've fooled me, I'll use Mary to protect myself when the shootin' starts. So you'd better be sure."

Johnny said thoughtfully, "Maybe you got something, Tex. But not enough."

"What's wrong with it?"

"You tell the dicks out back that you're me. Why should they fall for it?"

"Because they don't know what's been going on in here. Because they don't know I got wise to your being a cop. It won't look unnatural to them like it does to us. I'll say you're just about to leave by the front door, and that Mary and I got to go back in. They'll believe me, thinking I'm you. They'll move around the house to tip the others off. Mary and I will go on through to the next street."

"And then?"

"I'll snag a car. Any driver will stop if a cop tells him to. I'll make the guy drive where I want. What do you think of it, kid?"

Johnny said that the first part of it sounded reasonable, but that business about the car . . . hell, in a few minutes a wail would go out to follow any car with a civilian driver and a cop and a girl in back.

"They won't see us, once we get in the car," explained Tex. "Mary and I will get down on the floor, keep out of sight. She won't make a move, and neither will the guy driving the car. I'll see to that."

"You won't . . ." Johnny looked beseechingly at Mary.

"Her? Not unless she forces it. Hell, fella, I like her. She's a good kid. Now, what else is wrong with my ideas?"

Johnny said, "You walk out with Mary. You got a gun on her. That wouldn't look so good."

"It won't be on her, kid. I'll have it ready, is all. I'm you, see? We walk right up to the two detectives and start talkin'. I say you went to the bathroom or something, but they better move fast." He shrugged. "So it ain't perfect—I'll give you that. But it's the best I can think of. And I can't just sit here."

Johnny looked miserable. He looked at his wife and said he guessed it had to be that way. He said, "Don't try anything funny, sweetheart. I know Tex. He'll really do what he says."

She said she understood that. But she was worried about Johnny. Tex asked why.

"Because the detectives don't know him," she said sharply. "After we're gone, Johnny will go out. They'll think he's you. They might shoot."

Johnny said, "I'll stay right here, honey. I'll telephone the station and give 'em the score. By the time they get word back here, you'll be on your way."

Tex nodded approvingly. "Give it as long as you can, kid. You got Mary to think of."

Tex changed clothes. The uniform was a pretty good fit, considering. He slipped his service revolver into Johnny's empty holster. He said, "Never thought I'd see myself rigged up like this."

Johnny said, "You'd better let me take another look out the back window, just to be sure."

Tex stood very close to him. Johnny took his time: he had to be sure, and eventually he was. The two dicks out back, he'd seen them around the second floor of the Station, but he didn't even know their names. He told that to Tex.

They looked at each other. Johnny said, "Take care of Mary, will you?"
"Sure."

She smiled at her husband. "Everything will be all right," she said.

Johnny went back into the living room. Tex said something to Mary.

Then he opened the door, and they stepped into the night. The door closed behind them.

Johnny stood motionless: tense, nervous, waiting. The play had been taken away from him now. Nothing for him to do but stand there and worry about his wife.

For what seemed an eternity there was silence. Then he heard harsh voices and the sound of a scuffle. That was what he'd been waiting for. He ran across the kitchen, flung open the back door, and went outside. A flashlight blinded him. A voice he didn't know came from a man he couldn't see. It said, "Hold it, fella." He froze.

Then someone came to him out of the darkness, and Mary's arms were around his neck. She was crying. She said, "Johnny darling . . . Johnny darling . . ." over and over again.

The flashlight went off. He held Mary tight and stroked her head gently. He saw seven or eight men milling around, then three of them took shape and walked over to him. A man said, "Is this Tex Graham?"

Johnny said, Yes, it was Tex Graham. He could see better now. He could see that they had Tex's hands handcuffed behind his back.

Tex said, "I didn't think you'd take that chance with Mary, kid."

Johnny didn't say anything.

"I figured you was telling the truth when you said you didn't know the two guys staked out in back."

"I was," said Johnny.

"Don't give me that. We walked up to this lad here. I started my spiel. So what happens? Before I can move, he's on me. He's got my gun hand and he's saying something to the other guy. They get me all wrapped up. It wouldn't of happened that quick if they hadn't known you."

Johnny said, "I leveled with you, Tex. But still I figured this would happen."

CHALLENGE TO THE READER: *How did Johnny know that the detectives wouldn't be fooled by Tex dressed in Johnny's uniform? Why did Johnny figure Tex would be nabbed and Mary would be safe?*

Tex said he didn't understand.

Johnny said, "When you suggested wearing my uniform, I pretended to oppose it. But from the beginning, I expected this to happen."

"But why, kid? *Why?*"

"Because of something you yourself said, Tex. You said the guys outside wouldn't know what had been happening in this apartment. Right. But what was the most important thing they wouldn't know? That you had found out I'm a cop. So when someone in uniform came through that back door, I figured they'd know right away it wasn't me. *They'd never believe that I changed from civvies to a uniform right in front of a man wanted by the FBI who didn't know I was a policeman!*"

THE WITHERED HEART

by JEAN POTTS

At the sound of the car turning into the driveway, Voss was instantly, thoroughly, awake. Not even a split second of fuzziness. His mind clicked at once into precise, unhurried action, just as it had last night. He sat up on the edge of his bed—Myrtle's, of course, was empty—and reached for his watch. It was only a quarter to eight. Already? he thought, as the car stopped in the driveway. He had not expected anyone quite so soon. Not that it mattered; he was ready any time.

He waited for the next sound, which would be someone knocking on the screen door of the veranda. The bedroom seemed to wait too, breathlessly quiet, except for the whir of the electric fan, tirelessly churning up the sluggish air. The heat—the relentless South American heat—shoved in past the flimsy slats of the window blinds. Even now, in the early morning, there was no escape from its pounding glare. He ought to be used to it; he had been here long enough. More than ten years stagnating in this unspeakable climate, in this forsaken backwater where nothing ever happened except the heat. . . .

There. Someone was knocking. In his pajama pants and scuffs, Voss shuffled out to the veranda. Frank Dallas—good old Frank—was waiting at the screen door, peering in through the swarming purple bougainvillea. He looked fresh and hearty. His white linen suit had not yet had time to wilt; his thinning hair still showed the marks of a damp comb.

"Rise and shine, you lazy bum! Top of the morning to you!"

Was there perhaps a hollow ring in Frank's voice? Voss could detect none. Nor any trace of trouble in Frank's open, beaming face. Relax, he told himself; it's too soon—he's come for some other reason.

"Hi. What's the idea, rousing the citizenry at this hour . . ." Yawning, Voss unhooked the screen door. "What the hell hour is it, anyway?"

"Quarter of eight. Time you were up. Look, Voss—" Frank lowered his voice to a conspiratorial whisper—"Myrtle's gone, isn't she?"

"Sure." He said it automatically, without hesitation. "She's gone up to her sister's for a couple of days. Left early, before six this morning."

"Yeah. She told me she was planning to. That's why I figured it was safe to stop by. I've got this letter that Enid wanted me to give you. She was all upset yesterday, poor kid, resigning the way she did. Well, it kind of threw me too. Anyway, this letter, I promised to see that you got it . . ."

Poor old Frank had never gotten over being nervous about his role as go-between. He was as jittery—and, Voss supposed, as secretly thrilled—today as he had been six months ago, when Voss and Enid started their clandestine affair. Happily married himself, Frank had the romantic, inquisitive disposition of a maiden aunt. Besides, as American consul, he was Enid's boss. Very natural, very convenient for him to get into the act. Fun for everybody. Great fun at first. Lately—well, it was oversimplification to say that Enid was too serious, too impetuous, too intense. Those were the very qualities in her that made this affair different from the others, that made Enid herself such an irresistible magnet to Voss. Only he couldn't respond to them any more. He did not want to be a philanderer; he wanted to be a true, star-crossed lover—and he had lost the power. It was as if Myrtle had withered his heart.

This envelope in his hand, addressed in Enid's headlong writing—her farewell note, or so she must have thought when she wrote it—even this could not penetrate his benumbed and crippled soul. To be losing, through his own inertia, a love like Enid's, and to feel nothing more than a kind of guilty weariness . . .

He had felt something more last night, all right. Sudden and vivid as lightning, Myrtle's face flashed into his mind. Alive with malice, as it had been last night—the vulgar, coarse, knowing face of his wife. "So your girlfriend's leaving," she had said. "I hear she's resigned. My, my, I never thought you'd let this one get away . . ."

Gloating over her own handiwork—because it *was* her doing; the deadly years of being married to Myrtle had very nearly destroyed in him the capacity for feeling anything. Very nearly. But not quite; last night proved that. Hate was left. And if he could hate, he could also love. So Enid need not be lost, after all.

It was going to take time for the numbness to wear off. Voss was still stunned by the impact of release—which, considering everything, was really very fortunate. This morning, if ever in his life, he needed a mind uncluttered by emotion—a mind as cool and accurate as a machine.

"You're all right, aren't you, old man?" Frank was asking anxiously.

"I'll be all right." He paused, conscious of his own pathos as he placed Enid's letter, tenderly, on the wicker table. "It's just that—well, I guess you know how I feel about Enid."

"I know. It's rugged."

Frank was brimming with sympathy. It would be unkind—more than that, it would be indiscreet—to deny him the chance to spill over. "Have a cup of coffee with me," said Voss. "We'll have to make it ourselves. Myrtle always gives the maid time off when she's going to be away. I'd rather eat at the club than up here alone. The maid's a lousy cook, anyway, but we're lucky to get anybody to come this far out." Their house was set off by itself, on the outermost fringe of the American colony. What a break that had turned out to be, last night!

Voss felt a spasm of nervous excitement, rather like stage fright, as he led the way to the kitchen. Here was where it had happened, right here by the sink . . . Another break—the tiles had been a cinch to clean. But might there be some telltale sign?

There was none. Not the smallest. He breathed easy again.

Back on the veranda, with the coffee tray between them, Frank launched into earnest, incoherent speech. The way he looked at it, it was just one of those things. Not that it was any of his business. But look at it one way, and it was the best thing all around—for Enid to pull out, that is. She was really too young for Voss, so she'd get over it. And there was this much about it, a man just couldn't walk out on a wife like Myrtle, not if he had any conscience.

"No," agreed Voss with a wan smile. "I couldn't walk out on Myrtle." But not on account of his conscience, he added to himself. He thought about last night, probing for some tiny qualm, some flicker of remorse. There was none. This extraordinary lack of any kind of feeling . . .

"Myrtle's a good egg, too, you know." Frank took out his handkerchief and mopped his moist red brow. "I've always liked Myrtle."

Oh, sure! Myrtle was more fun than a barrel of monkeys. Everybody said so. The life of every party. Suddenly the memory of the endless chain of parties, monotonous, almost identical, pressed down on Voss like a physical weight. He used to sit and drink steadily, with every nerve stretched rigid in protest against Myrtle's raucous voice, against the flushed, blowzy looseness of her face. For some reason—maybe because it was her lushness and vivacity that had attracted him in the beginning—her antics had a kind of excruciating fascination for Voss. Your wife, he used to tell himself; look at her, listen to her—she's all yours.

"What I say is," Frank floundered on, "when two people have made a go of it like you and Myrtle for this many years, why, they can't just throw it away at the drop of a hat. Myrtle doesn't know, does she?"

Unprepared for this particular question, Voss hesitated. But it took him only a moment to see the danger in assuring Frank—as he would like to have done—that of course Myrtle did not know. Only a romantic innocent like Frank could imagine that the affair had been a secret; in all likelihood Myrtle herself had unloaded to everybody she knew. Much better to play it safe, just in case the question should arise later. "She probably suspects," he said slowly. "But I don't think she has any idea that it's serious. You know how it is in a place like this—flirtations going on all the time."

"Sure. I know," said Frank, very much the man of the world. "Well, one thing, with her away for a couple of days, you'll have a chance to kind of pull yourself together. She couldn't have picked a better time."

"She certainly couldn't," said Voss sincerely. As Frank stood up to leave, he added, once more conscious of his own pathos, "Many thanks for bringing me the letter, Frank. And for the moral support."

Things couldn't have gone more swimmingly, he was thinking. With his mind clicking away in this admirable, mechanical way, there was no reason why he shouldn't breeze through the rest of the morning without turning a hair. All it took was careful planning and a cool head. He had the cool head, all right. And—thanks to Myrtle—the withered heart that would nevertheless come back to life, all in good time.

It was at this self-congratulatory moment that Frank dropped his bomb. Casually; as an afterthought, a final pleasantry that occurred to him when he was halfway out to his car. "I suppose Myrtle took Pepper with her, didn't she?" he called back. "Of course. I never knew her to go half a block without that dog."

Voss himself remained intact. The world around him reeled, and then, with a stately, slow-motion effect, it shattered. Except for Frank, who still waited out there, smiling expectantly.

"Oh, yes." Voss's voice rang, remote and dreamy, in his own ears. "Of course she took Pepper. Myrtle never goes anywhere without Pepper."

"In his traveling case, I suppose? Only dog in the country with his own specially built traveling compartment." Another cheery wave, and Frank was gone.

It was incredible. Only gradually was Voss able to grasp the magnitude of his blunder, the treachery of his own mind, seemingly so faultless in its operation, which had remembered every other detail and had forgotten—of all the ignominious, obvious things—Pepper.

For Pepper and Myrtle were devoted to each other. She referred to herself as his "Muvver." He was a small, beagle-type dog, a cheerful extrovert whose devotion to Myrtle did not prevent him from indulging in an occasional night out, and he had chosen last night for one of these escapades.

Voss closed his eyes. The veranda seemed to echo, as it had last evening, with Myrtle's strident summons: "Here, Peppy, Peppy!" But they had waited in vain for the sound of Pepper tearing through the shrubbery and up the driveway, for his joyful voice proclaiming that he was home. Ordinarily, Myrtle would have kept on calling, at intervals, until Pepper showed up—as he always did, sooner or later—looking ashamed and proud in equal parts. Ordinarily, it wouldn't have mattered that he was still not back.

But there was nothing ordinary about last night and this morning. That was just the point: Voss had to make this extraordinary, deranged, secret stretch of time *seem* ordinary. He had to. And it was impossible, because all his calculations had been made minus Pepper.

A current of panic ran through him. He willed himself to stand still and think. Now was no time to lose his head, or to dissolve in futile self-recrimination. He must think, the way he had thought last night, with that beautiful, unhurried precision. . . .

Pepper at large, perhaps galloping around the neighborhood calling attention to himself, was a shocking hazard. But to call the little beast would only advertise more fatally the fact that he was not where he ought to be, and furthermore that Voss knew it.

There was nothing to do, then, but wait.

He rubbed his clammy hands against his pajama pants. His knees threatened to buckle under him. But it was somehow unthinkable to sit down. He stood in the middle of the veranda, staring at the screen door, where the bougainvillea climbed, trying to get in. It was the personification of Myrtle, that burgeoning vine. Its harsh purplish flowers were her color, and the way it swarmed over everything, its boundless vulgarity—it was Myrtle to the life.

There was nothing to do but wait. . . .

Then all at once Pepper was there. He barked, in an apologetic way, as if he were anxious to make clear that he was only suggesting—but no means demanding—that he be let in. And when Voss tottered to the screen and opened it, the dog swaggered in with an uneasy attempt at bravado.

Trembling all over, Voss collapsed in one of the wicker chairs. He could hear the little dog clicking off in search of a more demonstrative welcome. And in spite of all he could do, memory re-enacted for him last night's whole flawless (almost) project, after— Well, just after. It had seemed to work itself out with such magical accuracy. First of all, the heaven-sent circumstances of Myrtle's visit to her sister, who lived (bless her heart) in an inland town, the road to which was infrequently traveled, curving, and in spots precipitous. Ideal for Voss's purposes. Who was likely to be abroad at three thirty in the morning to see him, either when he left the house—with Myrtle's body and the bicycle bundled in the back seat of her car—or when he returned, alone on the bicycle?

The answer was, no one. He had had the whole moonless, empty world to himself; he had managed the crash—like everything else—with dream-like precision.

And when Myrtle's body and her car were found smashed to bits at the bottom of the gorge, who was going to pry too much? Accidents happened all the time, and Myrtle was a notoriously rash driver.

He had thought of everything, including Myrtle's suitcase which, obligingly enough, she had already packed, and the new hat she had bought for her trip. It had a red veil, not quite the same shade as the flower trimming. Trust Myrtle. He had been very proud of remembering about the hat.

Only he had forgotten Pepper. She never went anywhere without him; she would as soon set out stark naked as without Pepper. She did not trust him to ride on the seat beside her; the possibility that something in the passing scene might prove too much for his inquiring temperament terrified her. So she had had a special traveling case built for him. The case, with Pepper inside, was placed on the floor of the front seat, during even the shortest trips.

When not in use, the case was stored in a corner of the garage. That was where it was now, along with Voss's own car, the one he used to drive back and forth to work. If only, last night, he had happened to glance in that particular corner. . . . He must get rid of it. And he must get rid of Pepper.

At least Pepper was here, under his control, no longer prancing around in public. Perhaps he had already been noticed? Perhaps, Voss answered himself grimly. In which case it would simply be his word against someone else's. All right, his word. But there was no way whatever to account for a hale and hearty Pepper here in the house, or for the telltale case, sitting undamaged in the garage. Voss recalled his own remote voice, replying to Frank: "Oh, yes. Of course she took Pepper." That was his story, and to make it stick, both Pepper and the traveling case ought to be in the car at the bottom of the gorge.

Well, he could get them there. He had his own car. He saw, with a flash of excitement and renewed hope, that there was time, that he still had a chance. A much chancier chance than the one he had taken last night, when no one had been around to notice his coming and going. It was broad daylight now. Even so, he would be safe enough, once he (and Pepper and the case) got on the road that led to the gorge. Getting there was the tricky part; to reach the turn-off he would have to drive through one stretch of the American colony—dark and silent last night, but buzzing with activity now that morning was here. Someone would be sure to see him. Not that that was necessarily fatal. The point was that someone would be sure to hear Pepper, who invariably barked his head off the minute he was put in his case, and kept it up until he reached his destination. No, it was a risk that simply could not be taken. Pepper must be disposed of, silenced forever, before he set off on his final trip.

How to do it? This was the problem, stripped to its basic bones.

As if on cue, Pepper appeared in the doorway between the veranda and the living room. His expression was one of friendly inquiry. If this turned out to be a game of hide-and-seek, his manner seemed to convey, then they could count on him; he was always ready for fun and games; if, on the other hand, his favorite human being had actually gone away and left him—

Well, Pepper was no dog to brood. You would never catch him stretched out on somebody's grave, or refusing to eat and moping himself away to a shadow. Love came easy to this small, sturdy, lively little creature.

Voss eyed him, and Pepper, mistaking speculation for interest, trotted over, all sociability. My God, thought Voss, he'd even get attached to *me*, given time. Which of course was precisely what Pepper was not going to be given. He did not know this, however. He did not know that Voss's heart had all but withered, that he was not yet capable of the tiniest flicker of sympathy for any living thing. In cheerful ignorance, the dog sat down beside Voss's feet—tentatively, with his tail thumping and his spotted head cocked upward. He seemed to be smiling.

"Go away," said Voss coldly.

Pepper could take a hint; still smiling amiably, he ambled over to the living-room door.

A gun would be the easiest way. One neat shot—it would sound like a car back-firing, in case anyone happened to hear it—and a quick, unobtrusive burial. No problem there, with a body as small as Pepper's. But Voss did not own a gun.

Well, there was gas. Except that there wasn't. Everything here was electric.

Where did you stab a dog? That is . . . Voss glanced toward the door, where Pepper sat, alert for the smallest sign of encouragement. His anatomy must be roughly like that of a human being. But somehow his front legs became, in Voss's mind, a hopeless complication. Pepper wasn't large, but he was strong and wiry. And he loved life; he would hang on to it with all his might.

Voss turned away from Pepper's trustful gaze, and, as he turned, his eye fell on the bougainvillea. One strand had thrust its way inside the screen door, probably when he let Pepper in; it swung there, searching for a toehold. He went over, shoved it out savagely, and hooked the screen door against it.

From time to time Pepper left his post to make another fruitless tour of the house. After each trip he looked a little less debonair, a little more anxious. Now he pattered over to Voss's side and uttered a series of barks. Not loud, but insistent.

He would have to be kept quiet until the method of permanent disposal had been decided upon. Food would do it. Voss stood up. Here at least was something he could handle. And anyway, Pepper, being condemned, was entitled to a hearty breakfast. The dog bustled out to the kitchen ahead of Voss, all eagerness and good humor again.

The business of opening a can of dog food and filling Pepper's water bowl was calming. But Voss was startled to see that it was now nine thirty; he should have been at the office an hour ago. He phoned at once, with the first excuse that occurred to him.

His secretary, a flip type, said sure, she understood about his headache, and had he tried tomato juice? Or a hair of the dog?

He had a perilous impulse to laugh and laugh. "I'll see you after lunch," he said icily, and hung up.

Meanwhile Pepper, full of peace and breakfast, had retired to his favorite spot under the dining-room table for a nap. His round stomach rose and fell rhythmically. Now and then his forehead puckered, or his paws flicked busily, in pursuit of a dream-rabbit. Watching him, Voss felt a drowsiness, almost like hypnosis, creeping over him.

The jangling of the telephone jerked him to his feet, wild-eyed and suddenly drenched in cold sweat. After three rings, however, he had collected his wits and was able to answer in a normal, deliberate voice.

"Is that you, Voss? Is something wrong? Why aren't you at the office?" Myrtle's sister sounded flurried. But then she always did.

She always interrupted, too. He had barely begun to explain about his headache when she broke in. "But, Voss, what I called about—what's happened to Myrtle? I thought she was going to get an early start, I've been expecting her for hours."

"You mean she's not there yet?" He paused, just long enough. "But I don't understand it. She left here before six—"

"Before six! But it's ten thirty now, and it's only a three-hour drive—at the very most!"

"I know," he said, aware that the slight edge of irritation in his voice was a convincing touch: worry often made people snappish. "She certainly should be there by now. I don't understand it. I'd better— What had I better do? I can check with—"

"Now keep calm. There must be some simple explanation."

"I don't know what," he said bleakly. "Thank God you called me. I'll get in touch with Frank Dallas right away. He'll know what to do. In the meantime, if you hear anything—"

"I will. Of course I'll call you." Her voice quavered.

This was according to schedule. He had expected the call from Myrtle's sister; the only change was that his next move—to report his problem to good old Frank—must now be delayed until Pepper was dead and at the bottom of the gorge.

Pepper strolled in, pausing at the doorway to yawn luxuriously and stretch each leg in turn. The sight of him chilled Voss; he had a moment's sharp, appalling view not only of his own peril but of his own irresponsibility in the face of it. How could he have let so much of the morning slip by in weak hesitation? What kind of tricks was his mind playing on him, that he could draw an easy breath with Pepper still here to blow his story to smithereens?

It's Pepper or me, he thought. Life or death. Dog eat dog.

In a frenzy now that time was so short, he rushed to the sideboard in the dining room and snatched the carving knife from the drawer. Pepper capered at his heels, making little jumps toward his knee. How easy it would be to grab him by his muzzle, force his head back, and, quickly, with one stroke of the knife . . .

Only not in here. In the kitchen. Tiles, instead of rush matting.

But at that moment it came—the phone call that exploded what was left of his original carefully planned schedule. It was Frank, and his voice was even heartier than usual, in a transparent effort to hide his concern. "Look, Voss, I just had a long-distance call from Myrtle's sister. Seems Myrtle hasn't shown up yet . . ."

Damn the woman, damn her! But damn himself, too, for not foreseeing that she would jump the gun and call Frank herself, instead of leaving it to him. He made a desperate snatch to salvage what little he could. "I know. I've been trying to get you, but your line was busy."

"Now don't get in a sweat, Voss. Like I told her sister, there are any number of simple explanations. Pepper might have gotten car-sick. He does sometimes, you know. I'll get right on it and call you the minute we've found out."

Abandon the idea of getting Pepper and the traveling case out to the gorge. Scrap it—there was no time. There was just time, now, to kill him, hide his body and the case temporarily, and hope that his absence in the wreckage might at first be overlooked. Then later . . .

It came to him then—the best way, the obvious method that he should have thought of right away. He could put Pepper to sleep, the way a veterinary would. Giddy with relief, Voss hurried into the bathroom and flung open the door of the medicine chest. Both he and Myrtle had prescriptions for sleeping pills. A handful of those . . .

There was one lonesome capsule rattling around in his own prescription bottle. Myrtle had evidently packed hers. They were nowhere to be found. It was hopeless, but he could not bring himself to stop searching. Not until the phone rang.

This time Frank's voice, drained of its usual heartiness, was all hushed gravity. "Voss, I'm afraid you've got to prepare yourself for some bad news . . . There's been an accident, a bad one . . . I'll be with you in ten minutes, old man."

Ten minutes, and Pepper still here to give the lie to the whole "accident" story. For his presence would surprise Frank. It would set him to wondering, set him to investigating what wouldn't bear investigating. Pepper stood at Voss's knee, the question—"What can I do for you, sir?"—on the tip of his cordial pink tongue.

"You can die," whispered Voss.

Ten minutes left—probably only nine by now. Voss cast an agonized glance around the room, with its jumble of tawdry color and design, its clutter of Myrtle's gimcracks.

The paperweight was right there on the table beside him. Heavy; a solid, ugly chunk of onyx that fitted suggestively in his hand. One stunning blow aimed at the brown spot between Pepper's ears, and the rest would be easy.

Clasping the paperweight, Voss sat down and patted his lap invitingly. "Here, Peppy," he said.

Pepper leaped up at once; he was used to being held and petted. Snuggling the little dog's head in the crook of his left arm, Voss slowly raised the paperweight, poised it, focusing eye, hand, and will for the one smashing blow.

But he could not bring himself to do it. Now, at this untimely, this fatal, moment, he felt his withered heart stir and come to life—as it should have done for Enid.

His arm sagged; the paperweight thudded to the floor. He grabbed Pepper's warm, sturdy body between his two hands and glared down into the trustful eyes. He did not really like the foolish, friendly creature any more than he ever had. But it was as if he were holding here, in Pepper's compact person, an engine of life. It set up in him a responsive current, melting away the numbness, throbbing all through him in a triumphant flood of warmth.

Yes, triumphant—although he was lost and he knew it, although he could hear the sound of Frank's car already turning into the driveway.

His hands tightened convulsively on Pepper, who had heard too, and was struggling to free himself. Then Voss gave a helpless laugh—or maybe it was a sob—and let go.

Bursting with his tidings of welcome, Pepper rushed out to the veranda. After a moment Voss followed him to the screen door and waited there—waited for Frank.

THE GIRL WHO MARRIED
A MONSTER

by *ANTHONY BOUCHER*

There seemed from the start to be an atmosphere of pressured haste about the whole affair. The wedding date was set even before the formal announcement of the engagement; Doreen was so *very* insistent that Marie must come at once to Hollywood to serve as maid of honor; the engagement party was already getting under way when Marie arrived at the house; and she had barely had time for the fastest of showers and a change of clothes when she was standing beside Cousin Doreen and being introduced to the murderer.

Not that she knew it for certain at that moment. Then—with one of Doreen's friends adlibbing a be bop wedding march on the piano and another trying to fit limerick lyrics to it and all the others saying *"Darling . . . !"* and "But *my* agent says . . ." and "The liquor flows like glue around here" and *"Live TV?* But my dear, how quaintly *historical!"*—then it was only a matter of some forgotten little-girl memory trying to stir at the back of her mind and some very active big-girl instincts stirring in front. Later, with the aid of the man in gray and his strange friend with the invisible fly, it was to be terrifyingly positive. Now, it was vague and indefinable, and perhaps all the more terrifying for being so.

Marie had been prepared to dislike him. Doreen was only a year older than she (which was 27) and looked a year younger; there was something obscene about the idea of her marrying a man in his fifties. Marie was prepared for something out of Peter Arno, and for a moment it was a relief to find him so ordinary-looking—just another man, like the corner grocer . . . or no, more like the druggist, the nice one that was a bishop in the Latter Day Saints. For a moment after that it was a pleasant surprise to find that he was easy, affable, even charming in a way you didn't expect of ordinary elderly men. He was asking all about her family (which was of course Doreen's, too) and about Utah and how was Salt Lake nowadays, and all the time he made you feel that he was asking about these subjects only because they were connected with *you*.

In these first few moments the Hollywood party seemed to vanish and it was almost as if she was still back in Salt Lake and it was perfectly understandable that Doreen should marry him no matter how old he was—and no matter how hard a little-girl memory tried to place the name LUTHER PEABODY (in very black type) and the photograph (much younger) that had gone with it.

At this point Doreen had said, "Luther, be nice to Marie, huh? I have to make like a hostess," and disappeared. Marie was alone with Luther Peabody, the party whirling around them like a montage gone mad. It wasn't quite what he said or where he touched her as he casually steered her toward the bar, though the words were deliberately suggestive and it was not a touch commonly bestowed by a bridegroom upon the maid of honor. It was more that the voice was too soft and the fingers were too soft and the eyes—the eyes that fixed her, and her alone, as if only they were in the room—the eyes were much too hard.

The little-girl memory was still a fragment; but whatever it was, it reinforced this sudden adult recognition of peril. Without conscious thought Marie found that she had evaded Peabody, slipped behind two men arguing about guild jurisdiction in TV, and lost herself in a deep chair in an obscure corner.

Her whole body was trembling, as if it had been, in some curiously public way, outraged. And she was thinking that by contrast, a Peter Arno Lecher-of-Great-Wealth would make a clean and welcome cousin-in-law.

It was in the corner that the man in gray found her.

"You're Doreen's cousin Marie," he stated. "My name's MacDonald. You don't have a drink. Or rather," he added, "you didn't have one." And he passed her one of the two martinis he was holding.

She managed, by an active miracle, not to spill any; but she still needed two sips before she could properly arrange her face into the right smile and say, "Thank you, sir."

"Good," he said. "I wasn't sure about plying you. One never knows with girls from Salt Lake."

"Oh, but I'm not a saint."

"Who is? Thank God."

"I mean" (the smile came more easily now) "I'm not a Mormon. Doreen isn't, either. Our fathers came to Salt Lake when they were both widowers, with us squalling on their hands. They married Utah girls, and all this enormous Mormon family you read about in Doreen's publicity is just step-family."

"Remind Doreen some time," he said dryly. "She's never disbelieved a word of her publicity. Including" (his eyes wandered about the brawling room) "the word 'starlet.' How long does one go on being a starlet? Is it semipermanent, like being a Young Democrat? They're still dunning me for dues when I should be putting the money into a hair-restorer."

"Oh, but *you* are young!" she reacted hastily. She'd never have said so ordinarily—he must be in his late thirties. But she had stopped shaking and he was comfortable and reassuring and not at all like a middle-aged fragment of memory with soft fingers and eyes from hell.

Mac-what'sit seemed almost to read her thoughts. He looked across to the bar, where Luther Peabody was being charming to some columnist's third assistant leg-woman. "You just got in, didn't you?" he asked.

"Yes," Marie said uneasily. "It's all been done in such a rush. . . ."

"And you'd just as soon get out again." It wasn't a question. "I have a car. . . ."

"And that," said MacDonald, "is Catalina."

They were parked on a bluff in Palos Verdes. It was almost sunset.

"There's something so wonderful," Marie said softly, "about being on a high place and looking at something new. The this-is-the-place feeling."

"Kingdoms of the world . . ." MacDonald muttered. "You see, I knew Doreen when she first came here. Met her through a radio–actress friend of mine." His voice hardened oddly.

"Were you . . . ?" But Marie didn't finish the sentence. They had come almost close enough for such a question, but not quite.

". . . in love with Doreen?" MacDonald laughed. "Good Lord, no. No, I was thinking of the girl who introduced us. One of my best friends killed her."

Suddenly the photograph and the black type were very clear, and Marie knew the story that went with them.

MacDonald did not miss her sudden start. He eyed her speculatively. "That's why I recognized you—because I knew Doreen way back when. You don't look anything alike now, but back before she got the starlet treatment . . . And she had the same this-is-the-place look."

"And now . . ." Marie said.

"And now," MacDonald repeated. After a moment of silence he said, "Look. You'd better tell me about it, hadn't you? It's something you can't say to Doreen, and it isn't doing you any good bottled up."

Marie, almost to her own surprise, nodded. "Another martini first."

The seaside bar was small and almost deserted and exactly suited to letting one's hair down. "Not that it isn't as down as it can go, literally," Marie tried to smile.

"And very nice, too. Major difference between you and Doreen-that-was. Hers was always straight."

"I think she won't have it waved because she won't admit she's always been jealous of mine. No, that's catty and I shouldn't; but I think it *is* the only thing in me Doreen's ever envied. And it's your fault. I only said it because you're so easy to talk to."

"Occupational disease," said the man whose occupation she didn't know.

The drinks came and the waiter went and Marie tried to find the words for the thing that frightened her. "You see," she said, "I . . . know what it means to love the wrong man. Not just the wrong man, but a man who's *wrong*. I was a secretary at the radiation lab up at Berkeley and there was this research-worker. . . . You'd know his name; it's been in headlines. He was—it's a melodramatic word, but it's true—he was a traitor, and I was in love with him for months and never dreamed what he was like inside. I even wanted to defend him and stand by him, but then after he was convicted he took the mask off and for the first time . . . Anyway, that's why I went back to Utah. And why I know how Doreen can love this man and yet not know him . . . and why I have to *do* something.

"It isn't just 'woman's intuition,' or the fact that no man would ever see his eyes get like that or feel his fingers go softer than flesh. It's what I've remembered. It must be a long time ago, maybe fifteen years. I think I was in junior high. But there was this big case up in Portland or Seattle or some place. He was a . . . a Bluebeard, and this was the umpteenth wife he'd killed. It was all over the papers; everybody talked about it. And when you said something about a murder, I remembered it all and I could see the papers. It was the same name and the same face."

Now it was out, and she finished her martini in one gulp.

MacDonald showed no surprise. "That isn't," he said levelly, "the one I was thinking of. Maybe because we were obviously in junior high at different times. Funny how murder fascinates kids. I'll never forget Winnie Ruth Judd in 1931, even if I didn't understand half of it. And the one I'm remembering was a little before that, around '29. Right here in L. A. Same name, same face."

"But it can't be the same. Twice? He'd have been gassed the first time."

"Hanged, back then. But he must have been acquitted, both here and in Portland or wherever. Our innocent childish souls remember the grue, but not the trial."

"But they wouldn't acquit him twice, would they?"

"My dear girl, if you want statistics on the acquittal of murderers, even mass repeaters . . . You see, you came to a man in the right business."

Maybe it was the martini. Suddenly she felt that everything was going to be all right. This quiet man in gray would know what to do.

"Formally," he went on, "it's Lieutenant MacDonald, L.A.P.D., Homicide. I don't claim to bat a thousand, but that friend who killed the radio actress is in San Quentin now, doing life. All the information I can find on

Luther Peabody, officially and unofficially, is yours to lay before Doreen. And no matter how much in love she is, it should be hard for her to keep her eyes shut."

"Lieutenant MacDonald, I love you," said Marie. "And you'll check your files right away and let me know?"

"Files?" said MacDonald. "Of course. And," he added with deliberate mystification, "I think I have another source that's even better."

"I'm damned if I see why," Doreen objected petulantly, "you had to run off from the party like that yesterday. It was one wingding of a party and after all as maid of honor you're part of the engagement. Besides, Luther was hurt. He liked you, and you didn't give him any chance to show it."

Marie pulled on a stocking and concentrated on straightening its seam. "Are you really in love with Luther?" she asked.

"I guess so. I like him. He's fun. Even on his feet. Oh—! Want to finish zipping this for me? It always sticks . . . What's the matter? Did I shock ums?"

"Well, I hadn't thought . . . I mean, he's so . . ."

"Old? Listen, darling, there's no substitute for experience. If you knew some of these young Hollywood glamor-boys . . ."

"Doreen . . ." The zipping task over, Marie was concentrating on the other stocking.

"Mmmm?"

"Maybe I shouldn't have as just a house guest, but I asked a friend to drop in for a cocktail."

"Oh? I was kind of hoping you and Luther and I could settle down for the afternoon and make up for yesterday. Who is he?"

"That nice MacDonald man I met at the party."

"Mac? Is that whom you ran away with? He's okay, I guess . . . if you like serious-minded cops. You two can have fun disapproving of me. Doreen Arlen, Girl Failure."

"Oh, Doreen, is it that bad?"

"No, don't mind me. I've got a deal cooking at CBS, and there's one of the independents that— Is that Luther already? How's my face? Quick!"

But it wasn't Luther Peabody. It was Lieutenant Donald MacDonald, and he said, "Hi, Doreen. I hope it isn't an imposition; I brought another guest."

Doreen shrugged. "Why doesn't somebody tell me—?" Then she broke off. She and Marie found themselves involuntarily staring at MacDonald's companion.

He was a small man, almost inhumanly thin. He might have been any age from 40 to 60, and he would probably go on looking much the same until he was 80. The first thing that struck Marie was the dead whiteness of his skin—almost like the skin of a subterranean cave-dweller, or of a corpse. Then she saw the brilliant blue of his eyes, and an odd hint of so much behind the blue that she knew—despite the abnormal pallor, despite the skeletal thinness—this man was, in some way of his own, intensely alive.

"Miss Doreen Arlen," MacDonald said, "Miss Marie Arlen, may I present Mr. Noble?"

"Any friend of Mac's and stuff," said Doreen. "Come on in. Luther isn't here yet; you want to tend bar, Mac?"

And somehow they were all in the living room and MacDonald was mixing drinks and it was a party and MacDonald's Mr. Noble still hadn't said a word. Not until MacDonald was arguing with Doreen about fetching another tray of ice cubes ("The key to a martini is a pitcher *full* of ice"), did Mr. Noble lean toward Marie and say, "Right."

"I beg your pardon?"

"You were." And Mr. Noble was silent again until MacDonald brought around the tray of drinks, when he shook his head and said, "Sherry?"

"Sure," said Doreen. "There's sherry in the kitchen. Nothing special, mostly for cooking, but—"

"Okay," said Mr. Noble.

MacDonald whispered to Doreen as she left, and she returned with a water glass, the sherry bottle, and a puzzled but resolute hostess look. Marie watched Mr. Noble's white hand fill the water glass. *"You were right."* What did he know? Why had MacDonald brought him?

The doorbell rang again, and this time it was Luther. He kissed Doreen, a little less casually than one usually kisses a fiancée before strangers, and then he was moving in on Marie with a cousinly gleam. *If he tries to kiss me . . . ,* she thought in sudden terror.

And Mr. Noble looked up from his water glass of sherry to say flatly, "Peabody."

Luther Peabody looked expectantly at Doreen. He started to say "Introduce me, dar—" and then he looked at Mr. Noble again. Lieutenant Mac-Donald had retired to the bar. He was smiling. Peabody stared at the bony white face as if trying to clothe it with flesh and color.

"Lieutenant Noble," he said suddenly. It was not the voice with which he spoke to women.

"Ex," said Mr. Noble. "Out of the profession now. But not you, eh, Peabody? Still in the same line of work?"

"Doreen!" Luther Peabody's voice had regained its vigor, and a new dignity as well. "What is the meaning of this—this absurd confrontation scene? It's true that many years ago Lieutenant Noble, presumably in order to advance his own police career, chose to hound me as a murderer because of the accidental death of my first wife. It's a matter of public record that I was acquitted. I stand proved innocent by the courts. Why should this tragedy of my youth—?"

Marie could hardly believe it, but she would have sworn that Doreen was on the verge of laughter. Mr. Noble kept looking at Luther, but his bright blue eyes glazed over as though something was going on behind them. "Phoenix," he said. "1932. Same 'accident'—fall from stepladder. Same double-indemnity policy. Not enough evidence. No indictment."

"You see?" Peabody protested. "Another unfortunate—"

"Santa Fe. 1935. Same accident. Same policy. Acquitted. Seattle. 1938." He nodded toward Marie. "Same accident. No policy. Didn't need it; family fortune. Three trials. Three hung juries. State dropped the case. Long gap; Seattle very profitable. Butte. 1945. Same accident. Woman lived. Refused to prosecute, but got divorce. Las Vegas. 1949. Acquitted."

"You left out the funny one, Nick," MacDonald contributed. "Berkeley, 1947. Convicted, served 60 days for molesting. He went and clipped a hunk of hair off a woman he was a-courting, and she didn't like it."

"Fernandez," said Mr. Noble obscurely.

"I trust you appreciate the allusion, Mr. Peabody? Your colleague Raymond Fernandez, New York's 1949 Lonely Hearts killer, who also liked hair. He used it for sympathetic magic, but fetichism may have entered in. Which is it with you, incidentally? Some of the other victims showed signs of amateur barbering."

"Are you comparing *me*, sir, to such a brute as Fernandez?"

"On second thought," MacDonald mused quietly, "I withdraw the fetichism with him; brutes are more direct. Magic was undoubtedly his dominant motive. Now your true fetichist is usually to all appearances a fine plausible citizen. You'll agree, Nick, that we've insulted Mr. Peabody needlessly? He and Fernandez have markedly different attitudes toward hair, if not toward . . ." He left the sentence incomplete.

Marie held her breath, watching Doreen. Her cousin was still looking at Luther Peabody—not with fear and hatred, not with inextinguishable love, but now quite unmistakably with repressed laughter.

"Lieutenant MacDonald!" Luther exploded with seemly rage. "Your ex-colleague may well be irresponsible and I suspect that he is more than a little drunk" (Mr. Noble calmly refilled his water glass) "but you're an officer of the law. You know that the law has no charges to bring against me and that your imputations are slanderous. This is not my house. It's my fiancée's. I'll leave it to her to order you and your sherry-tippling friend from the premises."

Now Doreen's laughter burst out, clear and ringing. *"Dar*ling! You're so cute when you're stuffy."

She was the only unamazed person in the room.

"Look, Mac," she went on. "I've known this all along. I remember the news stories and the pictures. That's why I first went out with Luther. I thought it'd be fun to see what a real, live, unconvicted professional Bluebeard was like. Then I got to know him, and I like him, and he doesn't need to do any explaining to me. He's going to tell me they *were* all accidents and that he's a persecuted victim of fate—and he doesn't need to, because I'm saying it first and I'm saying it to you, Mac, and to you, Mr. Noble. And I'm not ordering anybody out of any doors, but . . . do you really think there's much point in staying?"

"But why, Doreen? For heaven's sake, *why?* "

The girls were going to bed early. Even Luther Peabody had seemed disconcerted by Doreen's reaction and had left soon after. ("I want to be alone, my dear, with this precious trust you have placed in my hands.")

"I told you, darling. I like him. Maybe I even believe him."

"But you *can't!* It can't all be just innocent coincidence. It piles up too much. And that funny thing about the hair . . ."

"That," Doreen admitted, patting her long straight hair, "might give a girl to think. But honest, he hasn't made any passes at my hair. No fetichism about *him.* "

Marie picked up the small book from the night table. It was a WAC textbook on judo for women. "So you believe him?"

"All right, so there's a 5 percent chance I'm wrong. A girl should be able to defend herself, I always say. If she wants to."

"Is that it? You *don't* want to? Are things so bad you're deliberately looking for . . . ?"

Doreen lit a cigarette. "I'm sorry. I don't need your wholesome Utah sympathy, thank you kindly. Doreen can look out for herself. And I'm *not* deliberately plunging to my death. Now will you go to sleep or am I going to have to go out and see what twenty-year-old wonders the TV's offering tonight?"

"May I ask you one question, Doreen?"

"Make it a bargain. One apiece. Something I want to say to you, too . . . You first."

"Has he . . . has he talked to you about insurance?"

"Of course. It's sensible, isn't it? He's better off than you seem to think, you know, and I'm young and healthy so the premiums are low. He's paid the first premium on a policy for me. One hundred grand. And now that your worst fears are confirmed—"

"Oh, Doreen! How *can* you?"

"I've a favor to ask of you. Don't go back to the seagulls and the Tabernacle yet. Stick around a while. We'll find you a job if you want; I've got contacts."

"Then you *do* think you need somebody to—"

"I said I believed him, didn't I? It's just . . . Well . . . Oh, skip it! Go home if you want to. Go marry a Fundamentalist and run off to the Arizona Strip. Luther marries 'em only one at a time—and when he marries me, he's going to stay married."

"I'll stay. Of course I'll stay, Doreen. But oh . . . You're not just my cousin. You've always been my best friend. And now . . . I just don't understand you at all."

"That is news?" Doreen asked, and switched off the light.

It was a small tasteful wedding, held in the Sma' Kirk O' the Braes, and chiefly distinguished by the fact that the maid of honor never met the eyes of the bridegroom.

Throughout the service Marie could not help thinking of what marriage meant to her, or rather what she hoped it might mean. And here were Doreen and Luther . . .

"Why? *Why?* " She was almost in tears as MacDonald helped her into his car after the bridal couple had left for a Palm Springs weekend.

"We're going," MacDonald said, "to see the best man on *Whys* in L.A. You've met him, though it wasn't one of his more brilliant appearances. That's the second time Luther Peabody's bested him, and if I thought Nick was capable of such a human reaction, I'd say it rankles."

"Who *is* he, Mac? That whole scene was so strange . . ."

As they drove to downtown Los Angeles, MacDonald sketched a little of the career of Nicholas Joffe Noble, ex-Lieutenant, L.A.P.D. How the brightest Homicide man in Los Angeles had been framed to take the rap for a crooked Captain under investigation; how the sudden loss of job and reputation at the beginning of the depression had meant no money for an operation for his wife; how her death had broken him until he wound up on Skid Row living on sherry . . . and puzzles.

"Ten years ago," MacDonald said, "on my first case, one of the old-line Homicide boys steered me to him. Called him the Screwball Division, L.A.P.D. If a case makes no sense at all—and Lord knows that one didn't! —feed the facts to Nick Noble. His eyes sort of glaze over and something goes *tick* inside . . . and then the facts make a pattern.

"I've told him a lot about Doreen. He's been looking up some more stuff on Peabody, especially the Seattle case. Way I see it, we've got two problems here: Why is Doreen deliberately marrying a presumable mass murderer, and how in God's name are we going to prevent another 'accident'? And if those questions have an answer, we'll find it in the Chula Negra café, third booth on the left."

The little Mexican café was on North Main Street, near the new Federal Building, and the old Plaza and the medium-new Union Station, and the old Mexican Church and the new freeway which had brought them downtown. It had a new jukebox with some very old records and cheap new sherry in cracked old glasses.

In the third booth on the left the white little man sat, a half-full glass before him. He said "Mac" to MacDonald and "Miss Arlen" to Marie and then he brushed his white hand across his sharp-pointed white nose. "Fly," he said. "Stays there."

There was no fly. Marie looked down, embarrassed, and said, "Lieutenant MacDonald thought maybe you could——"

"Heard Mac's story," Mr. Noble interrupted. "Need yours. Talk."

And while MacDonald beckoned the plump young Mexican waitress and ordered more sherry, Marie talked. When she had finished, she watched the bright blue eyes expectantly. But they didn't glaze. Instead Mr. Noble shook his head, half in annoyance, half perhaps to dislodge the persistent if invisible fly.

"Not enough," he said. "No pattern."

"A whodunit's one thing," said MacDonald. "This is a *why*dunit. Why should a girl deliberately marry a Bluebeard? F. Tennyson Jesse works out quite an elaborate and convincing theory of murderees, people who deliberately invite being murdered."

"But Doreen isn't at all like that!" Marie protested.

"I know. Miss Jesse'd agree; Doreen doesn't fit the type. Some women want morbid sensation and pick out low, often strange kinds of men."

Marie said hesitantly: "You read about people being hypnotized. Luther does have such queer eyes——"

"Tabloid stuff," said Noble. "She knows what she's doing. Not enough. No pattern." He emptied his glass.

"And there's no official action we can take to protect her," said MacDonald. "That's the frustrating part. We can't go spending the taxpayer's money without a complaint. The insurance company's just as helpless. Dan Rafetti from Southwest National was in to see me today. He wanted some notes on Peabody to show Southwest's lawyers, but he wasn't hopeful. They can't dictate the policyholder's choice of beneficiary. All they can do is stop payment—when it's too late."

Slowly Marie rose from the table. "It was very nice of you to bring me here, Mr. MacDonald." She hoped her voice seemed under control. "And it was very silly of me to think you and your friend could pass a miracle. I did think you, at least, as an officer, might protect her."

"Wait a minute, Marie!" MacDonald was on his feet, too.

"It's all right, Mr. MacDonald. I can get home. At least if—*when* Doreen gets back from Palm Springs, I'll be there to——"

"You?" Noble's voice was sharp and dry. "You staying there with them? After marriage?"

"Why, yes. Doreen asked me to."

"Tell," he commanded.

Hesitantly she sat down and told. The blue eyes faded and thought seemed to recede behind them. Suddenly he nodded and said to MacDonald, "Recap M. O."

"Peabody's *modus operandi*? It's stayed the same as in your case. Apparently a mild dose of sleeping pills, then when the woman's unconscious a sharp blow to the base of the skull with the edge of the hand. Defense is always a broken neck by accident while under the influence of a slight self-administered overdose: Almost impossible to disprove."

The eyes glazed again. When their light returned it was almost painfully bright. "Pattern clear," he said. "Obvious *why*. But proof . . . Now listen. Both of you."

The cute plump waitress refilled the water glass uninstructed.

Doreen and Luther had been back from Palm Springs for two days now, and the honeymoon was figuratively as well as literally over.

How could she go on living here? Marie thought. Even to save Doreen. But Mac and Nick Noble said it would be only a matter of days . . . Marie squirmed back into the corner where Mac had first found her and tried to cut herself off from the quarrel that raged.

"But it's only plain damn common horse sense, Luther!" Doreen was screaming. "We have the good luck that Marie's going around with a cop and he lets slip that they're reopening that Seattle case. Are you just going to sit around and wait for them to extradite you?"

Luther Peabody's tone was too imperturbable to be called a shout, but it matched Doreen's in volume. "The Seattle D. A. would be an idiot to reopen the case. I was acquitted—"

"You weren't! They were hung juries. They can try you again and I won't let them!"

"Very well. I wasn't acquitted. But I was released three times. They can't convict me. I'm comfortable here, thank you, and I'm staying."

"I *won't* be the wife of a man on trial for murder! We'll go some place—any place—slip away—use another name for just a little while—just to let it get cold again—"

"My dear Doreen, I am staying."

"And I know why, too! That filthy-rich tin heiress from Bolivia we met at Palm Springs! I see myself getting you out of town while she's here. You'd sooner stay and be indicted or extradited or whatever it is and have all the scandal! What about my career?"

"You won't mind, my dear, if I ask, 'What career?' "

And after that, Marie thought wryly, it began to get nasty. And the plan wasn't working. The Seattle rumor was supposed to make Luther eager to get out, put time-pressure on him. Mac was taking a week's vacation, switching schedules with some other Lieutenant, so that he could act privately. He and a detective he'd hired were taking turns watching the house. And if Marie observed the faintest sign of anything wrong, she was to make a signal . . . What was the signal? She was so sleepy . . .

The newlyweds had stormed off to separate rooms. They had even stopped shouting across the house to each other. She was so sleepy, but it was so much trouble to get to her bed . . .

Marie managed to dig her fingers into her thigh so viciously that her eyes opened. "The faintest sign of anything wrong . . ." Of course. The first thing he'd do would be to drug the watchdog. He'd brought her the cup of cocoa Doreen had fixed. She had to make the signal . . . the signal . . .

She would be black-and-blue for weeks, but she kept digging into her thigh. Doreen insisted on keeping the Venetian blinds throughout the house with their slats slanted *up,* so sunlight couldn't come through to fade the carpeting. If MacDonald saw any window with the slats slanting *down* . . .

She heard the gratifying rattle of the shifting vanes as her hand slipped loosely from the cord and her eyes closed.

"You was supposed to relieve me an hour ago," said the man from the O'Breen Agency reproachfully.

"I know," MacDonald snapped. "I'm on vacation, but that doesn't stop a Homicide Captain from calling me down to Headquarters for more details on a report I filed last month.— What's that!"

"Yeah, I was just gonna tell you, Lieutenant. That blind switched damn near an hour ago. I didn't phone because I figured you was on your way here, and you don't see me risking my license trying to break in—"

But MacDonald was already at the door. He had no more authority to break in than the operative; but he had self-confidence, a marked lack of desire to warn the murderer by ringing a bell, and a lock-gun. The operative followed hesitantly at his heels. They both stopped short at the archway from hall to living room.

With the blinds as Doreen liked them, the room would have been dark, but the moon shone down through the reversed slats of the warning-blind onto the body. It was chicly dressed, as any starlet should be, in a fur-trimmed dressing gown. Its face was painted to starlet-mannequin perfection and the moon gleamed back from a starlet's overpainted fingernails. But one item differed from starlet standards: the coiffure.

The hair was so close-cropped that the head seemed almost bald.

MacDonald had switched the lights on and was bending over the body. "She's breathing!" he yelled. "We got a break! Phone—" And in a moment he was through to Homicide, arranging for official reinforcements, an immediate ambulance, and the nearest patrol car in the meantime.

He set back the phone and looked up at a strange tableau. In the front arch stood the private operative, gun drawn, face questioning. In the other arch, leading to the bedrooms, stood Luther Peabody, staring at the unconscious girl on the floor.

"All right, lover-boy," MacDonald began, not unglad that his position was, at the moment, unofficial. "My man has you covered. You're not trying a thing—not any more. And before the regulars get here, you're going to tell me a few fascinating items—starting with *'Where's Marie?'* "

"I don't understand," Peabody faltered. "I heard all this noise . . ." His eyes never left the body.

MacDonald hesitated. The man worried him. He *did* look as if he had just awakened from a sound sleep. And what was stranger: the gaze he fixed on the body seemed (unless he were the world's leading non-professional actor) to be one of absolute incredulous surprise.

Then a moan came from the floor that sounded almost like words, almost like "Did I . . ." MacDonald knelt and bent closer, still eying Peabody. "Did I . . . did I fix the slats right, Mac?" said the preposterous starlet-lips.

"Marie!" MacDonald gasped. "Then who—" Abruptly he rose as he saw a uniformed patrol-car man looming behind the operative. "MacDonald, Homicide," he said, moving forward with his open wallet extended. "The girl's alive—ambulance on the way."

The patrol-car man said, "We spotted a dame high-tailing it away from here, took a chance on picking her up. Bring her in, Clarence!"

And 200 pounds of Clarence brought in a scratching, biting fury who was unmistakably Doreen Arlen Peabody.

"Didn't mean to be cryptic. Honest," said Nick Noble, brushing away the fly. "Thought you saw pattern. Seattle time-pressure wouldn't pressure Peabody. Be *less* apt to act when under observation. *Would* pressure Doreen. Had to act while she still had him around."

"The hospital says Marie'll be out tomorrow. Nothing serious. Doreen was a failure even at learning judo blows out of handbooks. But if I'm going to shine as Marie's savior, I'd better at least get completely straight what the devil happened. Want to help me sort it out?"

"No sorting. Straight pattern. Clear as soon as I knew Marie was staying on with them. Then all fell into place: Only possible *why*. Failure. Insurance. Family. Judo. Hair. Above all, hair."

"OK. Let *me* try. Doreen's not talking. We're going to have to release her anyway. You can't charge attempted murder when the victim won't make a complaint; and Marie says think what it'd do to the family in Utah."

"Step-family," said Nick Noble.

"Yes, that's a key point. With all Doreen's publicity, you think of this vast Family; but Marie's her only blood relative. That made the whole scheme possible. And the most cold-blooded—But let me try to reconstruct:

"Doreen meets Peabody. She remembers a little, checks up and learns more. Maybe she thinks, 'He can't get away with it forever'—and from that comes the thought: 'If any murder happens with him around, he's *it*.' "

"Why," said Nick Noble.

"Exactly. The only possible *why* for deliberately marrying a mass murderer: to have the perfect scapegoat for the murder you're about to commit. She brings her cousin out here. They used to look a lot alike; really the main differences, speech and action aside, are Doreen's elaborate starlet makeup and Marie's wavy hair. So Doreen insures herself for an enormous amount, or maybe just lets Peabody do it, if that's what *he* has in mind. But Doreen's not worrying— She'll kill Marie, using Peabody's M. O. and putting her own clothes and makeup on the body. There's still the hair. Well, Peabody has a psychopathic quirk about hair. He's clipped tresses from his victims before. This time she'll make it seem he's gone hog-wild and cut off too much . . . too much to tell if it was straight or wavy. Meanwhile she'll scrub her face, use the lightest makeup, wear Marie's clothes, and wave her hair. She'll be the little cousin from Utah. It's her background, too; she was once very like Marie even in actions—it'll be a simple role.

"So Peabody is convicted of the murder of his wife. Maybe even as the Utah cousin she's going to be an eyewitness. It doesn't matter whether he's gassed or found insane. In any case the insurance company won't pay *him*. Policy reverts to the estate, which consists solely of the Utah cousin, who now has a hundred grand in cash and never goes back. Perfect!"

"She thinks."

MacDonald nodded. "She thinks. . . . You know, Nick, unofficial head that you are of the Screwball Division, L.A.P.D., this was the ideally screwball case for you. Exact illustration of the difference between a professional and an amateur. If Peabody had killed Doreen, the motive and what you call the *pattern* would have been completely obvious; and yet he'd probably have executed the details so well that the worst he'd get would be another hung jury. Now Doreen had worked out the damnedest most unlikely pattern conceivable; but if (God forbid!) she'd brought off her murder, I swear she'd have gone straight to the gas chamber. Doreen wasn't really good at anything, from acting to murder. Somewhere along the line, pure ordinary police routine would've caught up with the identification—"

"Radiation Lab," said Nick Noble.

"Of course. Marie's prints would be on file if she'd worked on such a security job. Then the hair: Doreen was giving herself a quicky fingerwave when she heard me rampaging around and panicked. I suppose later she'd have had a pro job done—and that'd be one more witness. Fake identity plus good old *cui bono?* and she's done for. All thought out in advance . . . except what happens next."

"Rouse," Nick Noble agreed.

"Exactly. The English 'blazing car' murderer back around the time of Peabody's debut. Everything brilliantly worked out up through the murder . . . then chaos. Arrested the day after the killing and executed four months later. Doreen would've gone that way too. But thanks to you—"

"What now?" Nick Noble asked as Rosario brought fresh glasses.

"Damned if I know. Maybe your pattern machine can figure it. She says she's going back to Peabody if he'll have her. Says she kind of likes him. Well, Marie didn't! Marie hated him from the start—"

"—and didn't hate you?" It was the first time MacDonald had ever seen a broad grin on that thin white face. "A little like Martha, Mac," said Nick Noble. "A little."

MacDonald remembered Martha Noble's tragic operation. "Luckier," he said. "Thanks to you." He rose, embarrassed. "I'll bring Marie around tomorrow. Want you to see her while she's still all shaven and shorn. She's lovely—it's an experience. Well," he concluded, "it's been a hell of a murder case, hasn't it? The murder case with no murder and no arrest. Files closed with nobody in prison and nobody dead."

"That's bad?" Nick Noble observed to his invisible insect.

BETWEEN EIGHT AND EIGHT

by C. S. FORESTER

At last Manners was keenly interested in his game of chess. He bent forward over the board in an attitude of concentration. He wondered if his opponent would overlook the possibility of the position; that the advance of Manners's Queen's pawn one more square would not only attack a Knight but, by clearing the diagonal, would expose the King and his guard of Pawns to a formidable attack from Bishop as well as Rook and Queen. If his opponent should delay his counter-measure by as much as one single move he would be in a serious position; even if a quick mate did not ensue it would mean the loss of at least one piece.

But the man against whom Manners was playing was not of the type who overlooks things so important. After prolonged consideration he moved his Queen, and he moved her to the one square where she could wreak most destruction.

"Check," he said stolidly.

Manners stared at the board again. He had not paid enough consideration to this possibility. Now that the move was made he could see that it initiated an attack he could not stall off. The game was lost to him, inevitably and speedily. This new guard, who had been found for him by the warden of the prison in answer to his repeated irritated requests for someone who could really play chess, played much too well for him.

And as he stared at the board again, the clock of the parish church outside the prison wall struck once more.

First the four quarters, and then, with unctuous deliberation eight o'clock. Manners's heart throbbed painfully. Where would he be when that clock struck eight again? Manners knew; at least he knew where his limp body would be. He was filled with pettish rage about that clock. Surely the church authorities ought to stop the striking mechanism when they knew that a man lay in the condemned cell within such easy earshot of it.

He rose to his feet and turned away from the chessboard.

"I don't want to play any more," he said, and he knew as he said it that the tone of his voice was that of a spoiled child.

"All right," said the stolid guard. He displayed no annoyance at being thus deprived of a well-earned victory. He spoke indulgently. He could not be exacting with a man who had only twelve hours to live.

"What about a hand of crib?" asked the other guard, the lively one.

"To hell with you and your crib," said Manners, pacing about the cell.

The two guards exchanged glances. They had been expecting this. Manners had stood the strain of the three weeks of waiting well enough up to the present. That it had been a strain was obvious, for Manners's stubbly hair, once chestnut brown, was now white, had turned white in three weeks. But that was the only sign he had shown of the strain until now, until he began pacing round the cell, seven strides up, five across, seven down. Up—across—down—across, with his thoughts racing infinitely faster, but with as little chance of reaching a definite end. Up—across—down—across. The guards were only human after all. That restless pacing began to work on their nerves.

"What about the chaplain?" asked the lively guard. "Would you like to see him now?"

"To hell with the chaplain, too," said Manners, pacing on round the cell. The dreadful throbbing of his heart made his speech blurred and indistinct.

The guards reconciled themselves to the man's caged movements. Guards in a condemned cell, who spend every minute of a man's last three weeks on earth in the closest possible contact with him, must reconcile themselves to much.

But there came a blessed distraction. There was a jingling of keys outside; the door opened to admit the Warden, and then slammed to behind him. He was a man of slight, short figure, like Manners himself, dressed in a finely cut brown suit. Manners hated him; he had a long thin pink nose and a Hapsburg lip like the King of Spain's. Everyone was conscious of a momentary tension on the Warden's entrance, in case, just in case, he bore news of a reprieve. But one glance at his face was sufficient to determine that he did not.

"Well," said the Warden, "how's the chess going this time?"

"Rotten," said Manners, and turned his back. The Warden took the opportunity to ask the guards a question by means of a raised eyebrow; the guards replied in the negative with a shake of the head. Manners had neither offered to confess nor asked for the ministrations of the chaplain.

"Sorry about that," said the Warden to Manners. "What was the matter?"

"Matter?" said Manners, in a cracked hysterical voice. "Matter? Why—why—"

He did not finish his sentence. There is hardly any need for a man who is to be hanged in the morning to explain why he cannot play chess well. The sound of the church clock striking the half-hour came in through the bars of the cell window to accentuate the point.

"Well, what about seeing the chaplain instead?" asked the Warden coaxingly. He spoke as one would to a fretful child, just as the guards had done. Manners eyed the Warden. That coaxing, indulgent tone maddened him. He had heard nothing else for three weeks. And not even to satisfy the consciences of the Warden, and of the hangman, too, for the matter of that, would he be seduced into making a confession.

"I don't want to," he said sullenly.

With all the weight and majesty of the law turned upon him he could still be a rebel.

"Oh, come," said the Warden. "That's hardly fair on us, is it? Just think—"

The thin pink nose fairly quivered with his earnestness as he pleaded for a confession. He mouthed out platitudes that Manners hardly heard; his attention was curiously distracted by that Hapsburg lip. But the Warden went on pleading, and Manners began to feel himself weaken. Three weeks in a condemned cell are bad for a man's strength of will. He felt himself being driven into a confession, and he did not want to confess. Especially he did not want to give any cause for satisfaction to the Warden. And the Warden went on talking, and Manners stared fascinated at that long Hapsburg lip.

"You see what I mean?" said the Warden.

"Oh, shut up," said Manners, and his irritation burst all bounds.

With a single stride forward he brought himself within effective range. As he came forward his right fist came up in an uppercut into which was compressed all the baffled rage which seethed within him. His fist landed on that long chin with a hard, clean smack which echoed sharply round the cell, and the Warden fell to the floor utterly stunned. Not for nothing had Manners been an amateur boxer of repute.

" 'Ere, I say," said the lively guard.

Both he and his stolid partner were on their feet in an instant. They sprang at Manners. The lively guard gripped him round the waist; the stolid guard tried to pinion his arms.

But Manners was too strong for them. Rage and desperation gave him a lunatic's strength. There was plenty of muscle in his slight form. He tore his arms free. One hand gripped the stolid guard by the back of the neck; the other arm held the lively guard pinioned. One fierce mad wrench achieved its object. The head of the stolid guard crashed against the head of the lively guard with a noise like two wooden boxes struck together. That one blow might have been sufficient, but Manners was too insane to check himself. He brought those unresisting heads together again and again, until his strength ebbed from him and he let the two limp forms fall to the ground.

Manners staggered back across the cell and surveyed the wreck he had made. The whole affair had only lasted a few seconds; and perhaps it was not more than two or three more before Manners recovered himself sufficiently to think clearly. Even then his first thought was that he was at last alone, comparatively speaking, for the first time for three weeks; that he could kill himself now and cheat the law if he wanted to—the very thing those two guards had been intended, all those three weeks, to prevent.

A slight movement of the Warden's unconscious body recalled him to action. A man cleanly knocked out, like the Warden, does not take long to recover. For a single split second Manners debated the point; whether he should give himself the not-very-satisfactory satisfaction of cheating the law, or whether he should make a wild attempt to escape.

The chances against escape were still enormous, he knew, but there was a chance, which was more than there had been five minutes ago. With a great effort he steadied himself, although he could not make his hands stop shaking—his heart was beating so fast that he trembled in every joint. But he thought clearly and fast; he was a born plotter and intriguer.

He bent over the Warden, and as the latter's mouth opened to utter the first groan of returning consciousness, he crammed his handkerchief in. Whipping the coarse cover from the long pillow of his bed he wound it round and round the Warden's head. He was about to bind the Warden's arms when he remembered and he tore off the Warden's coat and waistcoat first; it would have been impossible to have done this after tying the man's wrists together, and moreover he was now able to use his suspenders for the purpose.

Now that the Warden was bound, gagged, and helpless, Manners could spare time to attend to the guards; but a moment's examination assured him there was no need.

The two unfortunate men were still unconscious, and likely to remain so. They might even die. Manners neither knew nor cared. He dragged off the Warden's shoes and trousers, and, moving deftly despite his trembling fingers, he dressed himself in the neat brown suit thus put at his disposal. Already the Warden was writhing a little over the floor, but he could make no sound, and it would be some time before he could get to his feet with his arms tied behind him.

In the Warden's pocket he found many things which would be useful. Money—a handful of loose change and a pound or two in notes in the pocketbook. And keys—half a dozen on a ring. The largest, Manners guessed, was the passkey to the cell door. Then there were two Yale keys. For a second Manners stood fingering these, deep in thought. But he had no time to spare. He must do his thinking while in action.

He had to brace himself again to open the cell door; every one of his actions after that must be made without a trace of hesitation. The big key opened the door; of course it would. He stepped out into the corridor with his heart pounding against his ribs. His mind was racing through a long series of mazed recollections. He tried to remember the entrance to the prison; he had seen it several times; when they had taken him out to his trial and when they had brought him back to die.

He had gone more than once to the chapel—he had gone there that very morning (today was Sunday) with a guard at each side of him. Most of all was he trying to remember one certain door in the wall of the long corridor in which he found himself. It was a door rather different from the cell and chapel doors. Once, as he was being led past it, the Warden had come through it, alone, shutting it behind him. It was the door into his private apartments, Manners was sure.

As he walked down the corridor he tried to call up before his mind's eye what he remembered of that door. He could remember the color of it; he could remember the brass knob. With a huge effort he assured himself that he had noticed the tiny brass plate which surrounded the small Yale keyhole. Another huge effort assured him that the keyhole was on the left-hand side of the door—it would never do to hesitate in front of it.

One of the two Yale keys in his pocket would open it; he could not tell which. It would be a frightful risk to fumble, but it was a risk he must take. After all, it was an even chance. He put his hand in his pocket and gripped one of the keys ready. He thought, as he did so, that probably his life depended upon which key of those two chance guided into his fingers.

With such feverish rapidity had his mind worked that he had not taken more than half a dozen strides yet.

He was in the well-remembered long corridor badly lit with a series of electric bulbs at intervals along the wall. It was the ground floor, and the cell from which he had emerged was at the far end, convenient to the execution shed and the yard where he had walked for exercise, a guard on each side of him. But Manners was walking in the opposite direction, towards the entrance hall and the Warden's door.

Far down, at the very end, a guard sat on a chair looking towards him. But he was a long way off; Manners had much the same figure as the Warden's, and he wore the Warden's clothes. And the guard never thought for one moment that the man who was to die tomorrow at eight would be loose in the corridor and walking with a firm step towards him. And the light cast by the unshaded electric bulbs was harsh and deceptive.

Manners walked down towards him, past three empty cells, past the chapel doors. He stopped at the right moment outside the Warden's door. At the same instant he brought the key from his pocket and thrust it into the keyhole. For a heart-rending tenth of a second it would not turn. Then it yielded, and the door opened, and Manners stepped inside and closed the door quietly behind him.

He had never before been where he found himself now. It was a flagged hall with several doors. He flung an agonized glance round the place; his thumping heart leaped more painfully than ever when he caught sight of what was clearly the door into the street at the other end.

Even then he restrained himself sufficiently to look round for a hat and overcoat. But a woman's voice came from behind one of the doors.

"Is that you, George?"

There was no time to lose. He tiptoed across the hall, opened the front door, and passed through it into darkness and freedom, and shut it after him. It was raining terribly, and a cold wind blew, but he must not wait. He ran down the stone steps, and out through the gate to the pavement, where he hurried along, head down, shoulders bent.

There were few people about in such vile weather, and Manners regretted that he had not found a hat and overcoat—his lack of them would call attention to himself. Even as he reached this conclusion, catastrophe ensued. Fate, which had guided him well so far, ordained that it should be beside a street lamp that he should encounter a policeman.

The policeman, his cape glittering with moisture in the lamplight, looked curiously at the coatless figure hurrying by; Manners looked furtively from the corner of his eye at the policeman. He saw the policeman start with incredulous surprise at the first recognition, saw him hesitate, saw him decide, heard his voice calling him back.

Manners broke into a run. Five seconds later he heard the policeman's whistle blow. He ran madly, desperately. Behind him he still heard that remorseless whistle; the policeman, hampered with cape and greatcoat, could not hope to catch him on foot.

The prison entrance stood back from a main road—not so well lighted as usual, this being Sunday—and at the first opportunity Manners turned aside and plunged into a side street; racing down that, he turned corner after corner, his lungs bursting, his heart pounding.

It was a chase like those in a nightmare. Whistles seemed to be blowing everywhere. Once someone tried to seize him, but he tore himself free and pounded on. Luckily there were few people about in those quiet suburban by-streets in that awful weather. Stealing a glance over his shoulder he saw the lights of a motor car in pursuit—the headlights, dazzlingly bright, held him in their beam. He flung himself round another corner, and, with a mad, colossal effort, he leaped in his stride over the hedge and railings of a suburban front garden. Crouching behind the hedge in the pelting rain he saw the car tear past him; then he heard many running feet and voices.

"No 'at," panted someone to someone else as they ran by.

"No 'at? We'll find 'im all right."

Still Manners crouched in the garden; from the lighted, curtained windows behind him came music and laughter. The Sunday evening party in that little suburban house had remained unconscious of the mad pursuit outside.

Long after the last sound of pursuit had died away Manners rose stiffly to his feet. He was shuddering now with cold, and he was drenched with rain and sweat.

But the wait had given him time to plan his next move. He must find shelter and concealment. No hotel, no lodging-house, would offer him those without suspicion, dripping with wet as he was, without luggage, and (he strongly suspected) muddy with crouching in the mould of the front garden.

His wife? She would have gone away for certain, he knew not whither. Nor was he sure she would shelter him; on the contrary, he was nearly sure she would not. And now that the police knew of his escape the first place in which they would seek him would be at his wife's. There he could not go.

He decided almost automatically where he would seek refuge. He would go to Ethel's. The police had no knowledge of any connection between him and Ethel; nothing had come out about her at his trial—although, God knew, enough women had been dragged into that business. Manners, the born intriguer, had seen to it, from long before he was guilty of murder, that no one knew of their friendship, and he could rely upon Ethel not having made public her relationship with Manners, the murderer.

Ethel lived alone in rooms; Ethel had loved him—the first was a subtle result of the second. At Ethel's he would find rest and concealment. Extraordinarily fatigued, he began to walk stiffly through the remorseless rain to where Ethel lived.

He had now only a slight idea of where he was, because the prison was in a suburb with which he had but small acquaintance. But the suburb in which Ethel lived was on the same side of the river. He could probably make his way to it by keeping to the by-streets and steering in a general way eastwards. He was wet through, and excitement and his mad run had made him very tired—the three weeks of agony he had borne since his appeal was dismissed had not helped to keep him fit. But there was no chance of relaxation; not, that is to say, until he reached Ethel's.

Every footstep he heard struck terror into him; every other second he peered anxiously about for the menacing approach of a policeman. Time and time again he turned about in his tracks and made his way round some other corner because he saw people or policemen approaching him. The delays were irritating, but he could not risk passing people in the street, not at this late hour, hatless and coatless and muddy in the pelting rain.

He had to nerve himself to a fierce effort to cross the radial main roads as he encountered them, one after the other. His poor heart flogged away at his ribs; just that was enough to tire anyone, let alone this continual nervous strain and this walking—walking—walking through the dark streets and the pitiless rain. By now he could feel no emotion save that of fear. He felt neither elation nor hope.

He never thought once of the excited headlines which were being drawn up in a thousand newspaper offices, proclaiming his escape, and admitting that he was the first man in England to escape from the condemned cell since Jack Sheppard. All he could do was to tramp onwards, shaken by his pounding heart, peering continually about him.

It was a long, long walk to cross from West to East, but at last he began to reach a neighborhood which was familiar to him, and then he turned another corner and found himself in the suburban street where Ethel had her rooms. He reached the house and turned into the front yard, shutting the gate very, very quietly after him.

There he had to stop for a while, forcing his numbed brain to think clearly. He could not knock at the door. There could be no surer way of attracting attention to himself than by knocking at four in the morning at the door of an apartment house. Besides, it would not be Ethel who opened it.

He crept to the ground-floor front window and stared into the darkness there. Long and anxious peering at the shadowy shapes within assured him at last that the furniture there was familiar to him. Ethel still lived there; this was her sitting-room.

Her bedroom was the corresponding room at the back of the house— Manners knew that well; he knew, too, how the windows opened into the backyard. The house was semi-detached. He tried the side gate—so softly— but it was locked. Once more he nerved himself for an effort.

He stood and listened lest he could detect through the monotonous downpour of the rain the stealthy tread of a policeman's rubber-soled boot. He could hear nothing; bracing himself once more, he stretched his stiff limbs in a wild leap for the top of the gate. His fingers clutched it; then, with an effort which brought the sweat pouring from him in rivers, he dragged himself to the top, sprang over, and lowered himself to the ground on the other side.

He tiptoed down the dark passage to the back of the house. He had reached at last shelter and protection. Turning the corner, he crept into the yard, crept up to the window, and tapped at the pane. He leaned forward in utter exhaustion against the sill.

Ethel was in bed. She might even be said to be dozing. Hour after hour of that dreadful night she had turned back and forward in her bed. She had turned on the light and tried to read; dropping the book restlessly, she had turned off the light and tried to sleep unavailingly. She could not tear her thoughts away from the man who had to die next morning, the man in whose arms she had lain, who had wooed her with honey-sweet words.

Despite the coldness of the night her bed became fever-hot to her. The town-hall clock in the main road, tolling out remorselessly each passing quarter of an hour, sickened her each time she heard it. Not that she loved the man now. The reports of the trial had told her much about him that she had not known—not merely that he was a murderer (that she might have borne with) but that he was a married man and that there were other women in his life, so that she knew him now for the liar and cheat that he was and she hated him for it. But even that did not help her to sleep when she knew that at eight o'clock guards' arms would grasp the waist she had clasped, as they dragged him from the cell, and the hangman's rope would bruise and tear the neck she had kissed.

And yet, towards morning, she fell into a fevered, troubled doze, from which something roused her with a dreadful start. Someone was tapping on the pane of the window. She sat up in panic. Again there came the tapping at the window. Ethel was a brave woman; she flung off the bedclothes, snatched her flashlight, and approached the pane.

A shadowy shape was visible through the glass. Then she pressed the switch and saw the face. For a second she actually did not recognize him, for his hair was white now, and his face was marked with awful anxiety; he was so different from the dapper, self-confident Mr. Manners she had known. She stared dumbly at the vision.

Grimy, bloody hands pressed against the glass. The sagging mouth opened and shut, and the hands made pitiful gestures to her. She understood. She pushed up the sash quietly, and shrank back to the farther end of the room; the beam of the flashlight shone steadily on him.

Slowly, with infinite weariness, Manners hauled himself over the sill and half fell into the room; but he roused himself to close the window behind him before he turned and faced her.

"What do you want?" murmured Ethel; she spoke instinctively in a whisper.

Manners's answer was half a groan.

"Ethel!" he said, staggering blindly towards her.

But Ethel only shrank away.

"Keep back!" she said, and Manners stood still, drooping. Fatigue and anxiety had nearly done their work. But one last effort of the failing consciousness, one last flash of the intriguer's brain, told Manners what he had been fool enough to forget before. The old spell which had bound Ethel to him, which had made her subservient, had lost its power now.

Disappointment and dismay came to help fatigue and anxiety. His heart nearly failed him as he stood there, knees sagging, swaying on his feet.

"So you were married all the time?" said Ethel, bitterly.

Manners could only mumble unintelligibly in reply.

"Then, why don't you go to your wife for help?" asked Ethel. She hated him at that moment, hated him with an intensity which shook her as though in the grip of ague. But her hatred was not great enough to give her the strength to utter the scream which would bring her help and which would result in the arrival of brutal men, who would drag Manners away to the scaffold.

The bitter hostility in her tone completed the work which fatigue and anxiety had begun. Manners uttered a little moan and fell forward on his face, a senseless, motionless lump.

For a long time Ethel could only stand and gaze at him as he lay in the circle of light thrown by the flash. It was the striking of the town-hall clock which roused her. It struck the four quarters and then six o'clock. That reminder of the passage of time called her back to her senses.

She had no notion of how Manners had escaped, but she could picture the fevered search that was happening in the world outside. She could not think what to do; for the matter of that, she grimly realized, she did not know what she wanted to do. She could not bring herself to give Manners up, at the same time she did not want to be the instrument to save him. And her practical sense told her that it would be impossible for her to keep him concealed here in her rooms.

It was not until some time later that she realized that she was shuddering with cold. She dressed herself in the darkness, creeping quietly about the room. The usual early morning noises reached her from the outside.

Then she felt a sudden panic; perhaps the police had traced Manners here; they might already be quietly surrounding the house. She must go and see. She must get into the open to think. And when Manners recovered he would need food. Bread she could buy at the grocer's round the corner, who opened early; tea she would be able to make him over her gas ring here. She realized sadly that however much she hated Manners she could not deny him food. She put on her hat and her coat, and stooped over Manner's prostrate body.

"Dick," she whispered, but Manners did not answer. She shook him, but he made no movement. His clothes were wringing wet—a little pool of water had drained from them onto the floor. But his heart was still beating.

Ethel snatched the blankets from the bed and spread them over him. Then, very quietly, she opened the door, and, as a measure of precaution, she locked it after her. She crept out to the front door, unbolted it, and passed out into the street.

Her voice and her touch had done something towards rousing Manners. Some kind of consciousness began to creep back into his brain as he lay there on the floor. He was in a burning fever; already he was plunged into the semidelirium of pneumonia. And in this delirium all accurate memory of the events of the previous evening was expunged. He had some confused recollection of a fight in his cell, of a wild flight through darkened streets, with remorseless pursuit hard at his heels. What Manners could remember of the night before was no more than he could remember of other nights. And then with a sudden start, with a hideous realization which set the fevered blood pulsing hot under his skin, he remembered that he was to die today. He remembered turning sharply round yesterday afternoon in his cell to see a strange face peering through the grating of the door—the hangman come to look at him, to observe his neck and guess his weight so that he might calculate what drop to allow.

Manners moaned again; the faintest of lights that winter morning was beginning to creep in through the windows. Then he heard the clock strike; four quarters and then—and then—seven o'clock. This was the hour when they would rouse him to make a pretense at breakfast before they dragged him out to the shed in the yard which he had observed when taking exercise. He heard the rattle of a key in the lock; it would be the Warden coming in. For a moment he tried to struggle, but his frantically beating heart could stand the strain no longer.

Ethel, entering, found her problem solved for her.

KNOWING WHAT I KNOW NOW

by BARRY PEROWNE

A porter gave me a hand to lift the trunk into the luggage van. It was an ordinary brown trunk, fibre with wooden battens, like a million others. It was heavy.

"Blimey, what you got in here?" said the porter. "A body?"

I managed a laugh of sorts, and I hoped it sounded all right to him. It had a queer ring in my own ears. But he didn't seem to notice anything.

The trunk bore a label with the name *Frank Venhold,* an address, and the direction *Passenger to London.* Name and address were both fake, and *Passenger to Hell* would have been a truer direction. I had no intention of going all the way to London with that trunk. I never wanted to see it again.

I tipped the porter, and—the luggage van being placed about the middle of the train—walked along the platform toward the rear. The doors of the coaches stood open. There were the usual good-bye groups talking at the doors, the usual station smells, the usual hollow, reverberant station noises. All was as usual, yet all seemed to me subtly different. I felt as though I were walking along the bed of a chasm, with strange echoes beating back at me from soaring rock walls that inclined toward each other. But when, instinctively, I glanced up, there were only spiderwork girders supporting the station roof of dingy glass spattered with rain.

I turned the collar of my trench coat higher, jerked my hatbrim lower over my eyes. I kept a sharp watch on the station entrances. I felt cold to the marrow. My teeth wanted to chatter; my jaws ached from the tension of keeping them clamped. I was poised for a sudden pouring in at any second of burly figures in policeman's blue. I stood outside the door of a coach, my hands clenched hard, deep in my pockets. The station clock looked like a white, enigmatic moon. Its hands seemed painted on it, fixed in an eternal immobility, which it seemed to impose over the whole station. So that, as I looked at the clock face, the people around me, glimpsed out of the corners of my eyes, seemed arrested in mid-stride, held motionless, struck still as headstones. Until the slight, visible jerk of the minute hand broke the spell, loosed the bustle around me, a hiss of released steam, the hollow slam of a door.

Along the platform a guard came walking, whistle between his teeth, holding a green flag furled in one hand, consulting a watch he held in the other. I turned and stepped into the corridor of the train. The compartment before me held three middle-aged women and a small boy with his head in a comic book. I sat down in a corner seat on the corridor side, facing forward, my back to the luggage van with the trunk in it. A jerk and a clanking ran through the train from coach to coach, like a scale played on a cracked xylophone, and the platform sights began to slide away. The dirty glass roof went from overhead, letting in the gray, watery daylight of late afternoon. The train gathered speed and I felt the trunk following me.

I had to force myself to sit there, staring from the window. The gloomy suburbs of the midland town died among green, flat meadows, swollen brown brooks with humped bridges, and lines of leaning willow trees.

We were on our way, the trunk and I. So far, so good. I needed a cigarette badly, but I was afraid to take my hands out of my pockets; I knew they'd shake, and I was afraid the women or the kid would notice.

Then I heard compartment doors being slid open, one after another, all along the coach, and coming closer. It sounded to me as though somebody was being looked for, and I held my breath, strained my ears, trying to hear what was going on above the metallic *tat-tat-tat-too, tat-tat-tat-too* of the train. Suddenly a white-jacketed steward appeared in the corridor. He slid back the door of the compartment, put in his head.

"First dinner now being served," he said. "Take your places for dinner, please."

His call went on along the train, and I breathed again. Two of the women got up and left the compartment, turning to the right along the corridor. I had to have that cigarette. The kid was looking at me unwinkingly over the top of his comic. Kids sense things. I got up, stepped into the corridor, slid the door shut, lighted a cigarette. Twilight mist had quenched meadows and willows. The lights had come on. People squeezed past me along the corridor, going to dinner. It occurred to me that they must have to pass through the luggage van to get to the dining car. If so, I might have a look at the trunk, just make sure it was all right so far. I didn't want anything to happen prematurely.

People had stopped squeezing past me, but I waited till the steward had returned, on his way to the dining car, then I turned and followed him. Three coaches along, I came to the luggage van. I stopped at the edge of the slightly rocking steel footplate connecting the coaches. I peered into the van, but it was dimly lighted and I couldn't spot the trunk right off. I looked back along the corridor. No one was in sight. I stepped into the luggage van. Nobody here, either—just a smell of kippers from a stack of flat wooden crates, and some bicycles, a folding perambulator, an invalid chair, and four trunks. Two of them were exactly alike, and a moment of panic pumped the blood into my head, because I wasn't sure which was mine.

I had to stoop and glance at the label on the nearer one. The label read *G. N. Trevelyan, Passenger to London,* no address given. My trunk was right alongside. They were identical; they were like thousands and thousands of the same make. A thought came to me.

My plan had been to leave the train at Oxford, the first stop, and let the trunk labeled *Frank Venhold* go on to London, be put in the Unclaimed Luggage Office. Only, something had been nagging at the back of my mind —the thought that the porter who had helped me get the trunk into the van might be a luggage porter who traveled with the train, and he might see me leaving it at Oxford, might chase after me, shouting, "Your trunk, sir!"

Now, as I looked at this trunk labeled *G. N. Trevelyan,* I had a better idea. That label was corrugated; the gum on it must have been dry; it looked as if it might peel off easily. I tried it, and it came right off in my hand. A piston thumped in my chest. I glanced around quickly. On a small counter in a corner of the van were various pink and yellow forms, a hurricane lantern with red glass, a stack of labels, and a gluepot with a filthy brush sticking out of it.

I tell you, the thing was set up for me. *Knowing what I know now, I ask myself by what, by whom? By God? By the Devil? By Fate? By mere Chance? What is the riddle of human life? Why are we here?*

It took me thirty seconds to stick the Trevelyan label over the Venhold label, and to write a new Venhold label and stick it on the Trevelyan trunk. Then I walked back along the corridor. I hadn't really had much hope before. Now, I had hope. I was exultant. I didn't want to go back to the compartment where that wretched kid with the knowing eyes was. I looked into the other compartments I passed, but the nearest I found to an empty was one with just a girl in it. Her eyes were closed. Apparently she was asleep. I slid the door back quietly, sat down in the corner seat farthest from her. I was facing the front of the train. *Tat-tat-tat-too, tat-tat-tat-too.* I could feel the two trunks sliding along behind me through the night. But I felt better, easier. I put my hat on the rack. I undid the belt of my trench coat. I could see faintly in the window the reflection of my face against the mist and dark outside. It was a stranger's face to me—the pale, sharpish face of a man of 35, with black hair brushed back with the sheen of enamel from a high, sloping forehead.

I dropped my cigarette, trod on it, and was taking another from my packet when I felt the girl watching me. I met her eyes. They were gray, but looked dark, the pupils were so large. There was something queer about those eyes, though she was an attractive girl, with amber hair done in this short, modern way with a kind of fringe or bang, or whatever they call it. She looked pale, hunched there in her corner, her hands in the pockets of a loose, light, hip-length jacket with a high collar turned up like a frame for her head. She had neat ankles and low-heeled gray suede walking shoes, rather pretty.

I offered her a cigarette. She hesitated, her pupils contracting oddly, making her eyes look light and shallow. Then she leaned forward, took a cigarette from the packet I held out, and I noticed her hands, rather square, with long but strong fingers—imaginative hands—the nails only faintly coral-tinted. I held my lighter for her.

"Thanks," she said, and her eyes came close, looking at me, as she leaned forward to dip her cigarette in the flame.

That continual dilating and contracting of the pupils of the eyes—I had read somewhere that it is called the "hippus" and is supposed to be a sign of nervous and emotional instability. As though in confirmation of my thought, I saw her draw her shoulders together in an odd little movement, as though a kind of shudder had gone through her. I didn't like it.

"What's the matter with you?" I said. "Cold?"

"It's all right." She leaned back in her seat. "Just a goose walked over my grave."

I didn't like her saying that, either. I felt those two trunks pouring along like hounds on my heels through the mist and darkness. I didn't answer her. But she went on watching me with those witch's eyes.

"How do *you* account for that goose-over-your-grave feeling?" she said suddenly. "What's *your* theory about it?"

"I've got none," I said. "I'm not a psychiatrist."

"What are you?" she said.

I didn't like her talk. I felt those trunks sliding up closer to my back.

To shut her up—she sounded like one of these intellectual girls to me—I said, "Me? I'm a medievalist."

I couldn't tell whether she believed it, but again I saw that queer contraction and dilation of her pupils.

"Perhaps they knew more than the psychiatrists do," she said, "more of the—the essential truth, the things of—the things of the spirit—the *mysterious* things."

"Are you a student of—the mysterious things?" I said sardonically.

"I'm a student," she said, "an art student. I've just won a scholarship in London. That's where I'm going now."

An art student, I thought. Maybe that accounted both for the good hands and for the emotional instability hinted at by the curious, quite beautiful eyes. She interested me in spite of the trunks that slid along at my back.

She had a slight accent, and I said, "You aren't English, are you?"

"I grew up in Canada," she said, and again I saw that odd tightening of her shoulders, as though to a fleeting chill. "I remember once—"

She stopped. She drew deeply on her cigarette, watching the smoke drift up to the cluster of light bulbs under the bell-glass. On the rack above her head were a small, soft, green hat and a little overnight bag, faintly vibrant to the monotonous *tat-tat-tat-too* rhythm of the wheels.

"I was thinking, as you came in," she said, "of something that happened to me once in Canada. I was thinking of it because it happened so far away —thousands of miles away—and so long ago. I was thinking of it because I have this scholarship, because I'm going to London, because my real life is just beginning—because," she said, with a flash of vehemence, "I can't forget it, and I wish to heaven I could! But it's always there, following me —waiting." She looked at me with those lovely, disquieting eyes. "Have you ever had that feeling?" she said. "Surely, everyone must have had it— in some form. The feeling that something is waiting for you, something— oh, unimaginable, terrible, whether physical or psychical I don't know, but something inevitable, not to be eluded or escaped, just waiting for you, coldly and very patiently—in an appointed place?"

"Certainly, everyone's had the feeling," I said. I could feel my brow coldly damp. "You're talking of Death, a date we all have—only, we don't harp on it."

"My father called it by a different name," she said. "He called it Failure. But that isn't the answer, either. It's—" She frowned for a moment at her cigarette, then looked at me again. "It was in Canada," she said. "My father and I were living in a fair-sized town, in a rather old house, a red-brick Victorian house, on the outskirts. My father was a widower. He had a poorly paid office job, but he owned the house—on mortgage—and he rented off the upper floors as apartments. We lived below, in a kind of semibasement. He always referred to it as 'the garden apartment.' Poor darling, I loved him dearly, but I have to admit he was—ineffectual, un-lucky—oh, I don't know. Only, I used to wonder, even as a kid, why nothing ever seemed to go right for him—for us. *Little* things! You know? He tried so hard. But if he bought new furniture, for instance, it would seem to get shabby and gloomy quicker than other people's furniture. He would dig and dig in the garden, but where the neighbors' gardens were neat, with lawns and flowers, nothing ever flourished in ours but weeds. Horrible green weeds! Bad luck seemed to follow us. It seemed as though there never could be any escape from it. It was like a quagmire. I used to feel it was something to do with the house, that great, hideous barn of a house. I began to think there never could be any hope for us as long as we stayed there. I *hated* No. 15 George Street."

I wished she would stop. I didn't like this story. The train beat out its monotonous rhythm; the things on the rack vibrated. Our faces were reflected faintly in the windows against the mist and the night. I wished she would stop.

"One rainy afternoon when I was about ten years old," she said, "I walked home from school alone. That afternoon the teacher had been showing us some pictures of desert country, cactus country, dry and wide spaces full of clean, varied colors. Going home, walking home alone with my books, I was wearing rubbers, and a rubber raincoat with a hood. You know how wet rubber feels. Rain, rain, rain! I loathed it. I loathed the puddled lawns, the dripping trees, the dun sky. I loathed all wet, green, slimy things."

She dropped her cigarette, put her neat suede shoe on it. I was trying not to listen. The trunks were following me.

"I always got home before my father," she said. "There was a woman who came in to clean the place for us, leave the kitchen stove burning, everything ready for father and I to cook dinner for ourselves. I had my own key." She was biting her lower lip; her strange, shallow, changing eyes looked through me. "I didn't want to go into the house that afternoon, I hated it so much. I didn't want to set foot in it. I don't know how I made myself walk up the path and unlock that hateful old green-painted front door. It opened into a passage with coats hanging on a row of hooks to the right. On the left was the door of our living room, beyond that the door of father's bedroom. Farther on, stone steps—four stone steps—led down to a kind of flagstoned lobby, off which, on the right, opened a door to a side street. On the left, the wall of the lobby was glasspaned, like a conservatory, with a door opening into the muddy garden. Across the lobby was the kitchen."

Her breathing was quick and shallow; I could scarcely hear her voice.

"I went down the four steps into the lobby," she said, her strange eyes seeing it. "The lobby was full of gray daylight filtering through the filthy panes. I could hear the rain spattering against them. I kicked off my rubbers, as I always did, and hung up my rubber coat on a shelf, meant for flowerpots, which ran the length of the panes. I looked at the water dripping from my coat, making a pool, trickling across the flagstones. I looked out through the panes at tall sunflowers and rank stinging-nettles. The sunflowers were over, their heads hanging heavy and brown and sodden, rocking a little in the rain. The nettles were high and green, like a forest. There never were such nettles anywhere else. Their veined, hairy leaves were pressing up against the glass. They were as tall as I was. I hated to look at them. I turned to go into the kitchen."

She bit at her lips. They were pale pink where her teeth had scraped the lipstick from them. Her pupils were greatly dilated.

"The kitchen door stood open," she said. "It opened inward, to the right. The kitchen was dark except for the red glow of the coal fire through the bars of the old-fashioned stove. There was an old wicker armchair standing obliquely facing the stove, and in the chair—on the worn cushion that always had a wad of old newspapers crammed under it—was our cat. Its forepaws were folded under its chest. I could see the firelight reflected in its eyes. It seemed to be waiting. There was an old alarm clock, with a loud, tinny tick, on the shelf over the stove. I could hear the clock going tick-tick-tick, loudly and questioningly. And I couldn't move. My mouth was dry. I wanted desperately to back away, turn, run. I couldn't move. Only, I felt as though something were drawing me *forward*. But I didn't move at all. I knew that in there, in the shadows behind the open door, there was—something. I don't know. It had no shape. Only, cold came from it. It was waiting. And the clock ticked, the cat watched in the firelight, the rain spattered at the windows, the nettles pressed against the panes, the sunflowers rocked their dead, sodden heads. I don't know—I don't know—"

Suddenly she pressed her hands to her face. She cried as though her heart would break. Never had I seen or imagined such grief. The tragedy of the ages, of the unknown soul of Man and the dim beginnings of life in the swamps of the tree-ferns, was in that brief paroxysm.

"Here," I said roughly, after a minute.

She groped blindly for the handkerchief I held out to her. She wiped her eyes. She blew her nose. I could hear the shudder in her breathing. I looked toward the window, saw the ghost of my own face floating there. I thought of the trunks. I knew, now, that I shouldn't get away. I knew there was no escape for me. Anywhere. I knew they'd get me. I don't know how I knew, but I knew.

The girl spoke.

"When I came to myself," she said, "I was out in the street, in the rain, running, and had run full tilt into a man. I felt his arms go round me, and heard my father's voice, 'Why, Gina, Gina, what's this? What's the matter?' I couldn't tell him, not then. I could only say that I'd never go back into that house—never."

She was silent for a moment.

"He never made me go back," she said. "We went to a hotel for the night. I tried to tell him what had happened. He sat on the edge of my bed, listening. Did I say he was a small man? A small man, with kind eyes. He looked so tragic, so beaten, as he listened. 'Failure,' I heard him murmur— 'Failure was there.' I've thought about that so much, since. He spoke as though of some projection of himself, of some—some abstraction made carnate, waiting in the house. It was almost as though—as though he spoke of some *hump*, not on his own back, but which he feared he had prepared for mine. For me, whom he loved." She shook her head. "But that isn't the answer. I've thought so much. I've dreamed those dreadful seconds, that eternity, so many times, since—the nettles, the sunflowers, the rain, the pool dark on the flagstones, the open door, the fire red between the bars, the watching cat with the shine in its eyes—all the room, waiting for me, unchanged, and the thing waiting in the room, and the clock ticking loudly. My father died within the year. He had relations in England—in the Midlands here—and they sent for me. And I was glad as the miles became hundreds, the hundreds became thousands, between me and the waiting room. *But I know it's still there."*

She looked at me as though asking my opinion, my help; but I had nothing to say to her. The train broke its rhythm, began to clatter over switchpoints. She glanced at my handkerchief, balled in her hand. Then she made a movement—somehow ineffectual, as her father's movements might have been, I imagined—as though to reach down her small grip from the rack, probably to take out a clean handkerchief. I rose and lifted the grip down for her.

I tell you, knowing what I know now—yet, what do I know, or any of us?—I tell you, this whole thing was set up for us. By what design of God or the Devil or Destiny or mere Chance had I chosen this girl's compartment?

As I lifted down the grip for her, I saw for the first time the label on it: *G. N. Trevelyan, Passenger to London.*

The train was slowing. Platform lights slid by, flickering, outside the misted windows. An amplified voice was intoning: "*Oxford— Oxford.* The train now arriving at Platform Four is the train to Paddington."

I muttered, "I'll be back."

But as I stepped out into the corridor, slid shut the door after me, I had no intention of going back. Oxford was where I had planned to leave the train. Yet as it pulled up with a jerk and that cracked xylophone-scale clangor, the girl was in my mind, and the trunks.

It crossed my mind that, though there was not one single Commandment that I had not broken in my futile life, all might yet be forgiven me, at the unknown end of all things, if only I changed those labels back.

I would have done it, too. I would have done it. *But I tell you, this thing was set up.* For when I rubbed the mist from the window, and stooped to peer out, the dimly lighted platform was swarming with police.

I knew who they were after, and I forgot the girl. I panicked. I hurried along the corridor to the end of the coach, where there was a door on the tracks side. The door was locked. I let down the window. There were only two policemen on the opposite platform. Chancing them, I put one foot through the open window, pulled the other foot after it, leaped from the step to the tracks. Under the loom of the train, I walked briskly toward the front, stepping from tie to tie, hoping that, if seen, I might be taken for the man with the hammer who checks on the wheels and couplings. I reached the locomotive, hissing a white cloud of steam from its belly, and glaring red from its cab, when a shout told me I'd been spotted.

I ran for it. I kept to the tracks, leaping from tie to tie. I came to an iron bridge. I knew it was the bridge over the canal. I knew Oxford; I was educated here; I might have made a different life for myself—if I'd been a different man. I'd had chances. If I'd taken them, I might never have known this hour of flight—this insane moment of clawing like an ape over the iron rim of the bridge, hanging by my hands, feeling new tar sticky under my fingers, smelling its strong, asceptic smell close to my nose. I dropped, landing on all fours on a cindered towpath.

I turned and ran.

I was a good distance away, standing—breathing hard, trying to think— between two gasometers of the Gasworks, in its galvanized iron enclosure, when I heard the train whistling. Through the mist and darkness, I saw the smokestack belching a red, pulsing glare with short, quick respirations. I heard the grind of the wheels. I saw the long line of lighted windows go by.

I knew I ought to have changed back those labels.

I kept thinking about them, about the train, about Gina Trevelyan, about what was in the luggage van. I thought Gina somehow an appealing name. I thought about her strange eyes, her good hands, the look of vulnerability about her. She seemed, alone in that compartment with the wheels going *tat-tat-tat-too*, on and on toward London, terribly solitary and defenseless to me. I thought of her as a little girl with braids, wearing rubbers, and a rubber raincoat with a hood—all sleek with rain—coming home alone from school to that great, grim, red-brick house thousands of miles away in Canada. I felt terribly sorry for her. I wanted to sit down, here in the dark, and weep for her.

Somehow, the strength had gone out from me. Guilt about those labels —not about anything I'd done before that—robbed me of the will to fight on, to live.

Knowing what I know now, I can be in two places at once. I can be me on the run and I can be Gina in the train. Take me first . . .

I found I had been walking and walking as I thought about her, and I had come to the gray stone hump of Folly Bridge. The bridge lights glimmered down on the river and on the college barges.

I went on up the lighted slope of St. Aldate's. There was nobody about —just here and there an undergraduate riding a bicycle with his gown wound about his neck like a muffler. Coming on up toward Tom Tower and Carfax, I thought of St. Ebbe's. I thought perhaps I might have a chance in that maze of ancient, squalid alleys. I took to the alleys behind Pembroke College. My mind was with Gina in the train. My own plight had become unreal to me. I knew I ought to have changed back those labels. I was afraid. I had never been so afraid. I was a fugitive in dark and misty alleys, and I was afraid of the dark.

Perhaps I wanted to be caught, rather than be alone in the dark. Anyway, I saw lights and figures and heard trumpets. I went with the figures into a plain, varnished hall, glaringly lighted with naked gasmantels. It was a Salvation Army chapel. I stood at the back of the hall, behind the rows of plain wooden chairs. The people were singing, *Onward, Christian Soldiers*. I wanted to sing with them, but I couldn't. I kept thinking of Gina, and the two trunks, and I was so sorry for her that the tears began to stream down my cheeks.

I felt a hand on my shoulder.

"All right, Caird," a voice said, "better come quietly."

I saw the faces of the congregation turn toward me, in the hard, white glare. I saw the women's faces framed in their bonnets, and the work-worn faces of the men. There was understanding in their eyes, and compassion. They were good, kind people.

I was started on my way to London, handcuffed, under escort, by the next train up. Gina's would not yet have reached Paddington. I realized that these policemen knew nothing about the trunk originally marked *Frank Venhold*, but now marked *G. N. Trevelyan*. I wanted to tell them about the trunk, in case something could be done to warn her. But since they didn't know about the trunk, there might yet be some hope for me, and I couldn't bring myself to speak the words that would hang me.

Instead I asked, "What time is it?"

They told me. I knew her train must be pulling into Paddington . . .

Knowing what I know now—the questions that I've asked and that have been answered for me—I can be with Gina. I can follow her as if she led me by the hand . . .

As her train drew into the great, dingy, echoing London terminus, Gina drew on her small, soft, green hat. Her little overnight bag lay on the seat beside her. She wondered what had happened to the man in the trench coat, the man who had not returned.

She got hold of a porter at Paddington.

"I've a trunk in the luggage van," she said. "The name's Trevelyan."

"Taking a taxi, miss?" said the porter. "All right, you go and get a place in the taxi line an' I'll bring your trunk."

He brought it, wheeling it on a trolley.

"Strike me, miss," he said, as he uptilted the trunk into the small luggage-compartment beside the taxi driver, "what you got in here? The gold reserve?"

"All my worldly belongings," said Gina. "It's my books that weigh so heavy. I'm sorry about that."

"S'all right," said the porter, strapping the trunk, upended, into place.

"Where to, miss?" said the taxi driver.

Gina told him to cruise. She wanted to find a moderate-priced hotel. She gazed from the window as the taxi left the station. The night was very misty; every light had its nimbus; muffled forms passed to and fro before the shop windows. The driver, an elbow resting on the trunk beside him, slowed down before hotel after hotel, looking round at her inquiringly.

"No," she said, shaking her head.

Either they looked too dear or too dirty. But as they passed along a narrow, quiet little street—the only shop in it a small teashop with a steamy window dimly shining through the mist—she caught a glimpse of the word *Vacancies* on a sign on some iron railings. She leaned forward quickly to tap on the glass behind the driver's head.

Gina got out, asked the driver to wait. She ran up the steps and rang the bell. After a minute, the door was opened, and an untidy, thin woman stood outlined against the dim light of a passage.

"I'm looking for lodgings," said Gina. "I wonder if you have a bed-sitting-room among your vacancies?"

The woman stood aside. "Come in. You can see what I've got."

She preceded Gina up four narrow flights of worn-carpeted stairs to a room which was an attic but fairly large and tolerably clean.

"It has a skylight," said Gina. "That's rather an advantage, because I paint. What is the rent, please?"

They arranged terms. Gina paid a week in advance, and they went downstairs.

"I've got a trunk in the taxi," said Gina. "It's rather heavy—"

The woman turned and called down some stairs, "Arthur!"

A youngish, but fat and balding man in his braces and slippers came up the stairs, grinning at Gina inanely. He and the taxi driver lifted the trunk in, dumped it down in the passage. Gina paid the driver and thanked him, and he went away. The landlady shut the front door, turned and looked at the trunk.

"Arthur'll never get that up all them stairs," she said. "You'd better keep it down in our passage and take up what you want bit by bit."

"I'll do that," said Gina.

"My name's Mrs. Coe," said the woman. "Will you be wanting anything further? Me an' Arthur goes across to the local about now."

"There's nothing I need now, thank you," said Gina.

"Then good night to you."

"Good night, Mrs. Coe."

Gina went up to her room, and, soon after, heard the front door slam . . .

Knowing what I know now, I realize that, at about this time, I was stepping

*into the neat, closed, dark-blue van—the Black Maria—which had been sent to
meet the train . . .*

The interior of the Black Maria was brightly lighted. The two policemen sat with their arms folded, watching me, but I was unaware of them. I
kept thinking of Gina and the trunk, and what might have become of her
on her first night alone in the great, grim city of London.

I kept thinking of the story she had told me—of that and of her sudden,
hopeless paroxysm of tears. I kept thinking of my wet handkerchief balled
in her hand, and of when she was a little girl with amber braids, walking
home alone from school, in rubbers and a rubber raincoat with a hood,
carrying her strapped books, on a rainy late afternoon in an unknown town
in faraway Canada. And on this ride from Paddington across London I
couldn't see from my box of a Black Maria, I understood what had happened to me, and why all the strength seemed sucked out of me into those
strange eyes of hers. I knew why I kept thinking, "If only we could have
met before . . ."

For the first time in my life, I knew I was in love—and had been in love
from the moment I had seen her cry. The realization brought me a new
fund of resolve. I knew now what I had to do.

The Black Maria pulled up in New Scotland Yard. I was taken to a room
glaring with light high up in that grim, turreted building overlooking the
Embankment. There was a lean, tight-lipped, gray-haired man sitting beside
the desk.

I stood there, handcuffed to the policeman, before the desk, and said,
"I'm going to confess. I'm doing it for the sake of somebody else. Before I
begin, put out a call for a taxi driver—she'd certainly take a taxi—who
picked up a girl in a small, green hat and a hip-length checked jacket with a
high collar. She got off the earlier train at Paddington."

The man at the desk looked at me steadily. I knew my face was working.
"Any other details, Caird?"

I heard a voice speaking that seemed not to be mine. It sounded like a
voice ringing far off in a chasm of green crystal cliffs.

"Yes," said the voice. "Her name's G. N. Trevelyan and she had a large
brown trunk in the luggage van."

"There's something in the trunk for her to fear, Caird?" said the man at
the desk.

"Yes," I said, "something in the trunk."

I saw the man at the desk reach for the telephone, and I heard a spatter of
rain at the window looking out on the Thames.

*I tell you, this whole thing was designed. It was prepared for us. Knowing
what I know now, I say that every step— Even the rain. Take this rain that
came . . .*

Gina must have been sitting on the bed in her room. She was sitting on the bed, looking round at her first room in London. An uninspiring room, but she imagined it with her canvases hung on the walls, with a studio easel in it, with shelves put up for all her art books. With its skylight, she could make it look something like a studio.

She realized that she was hungry. She hadn't dined on the train. Halfway up this street, she remembered, she had noticed a tea shop. It might still be open. She jumped up. Leaving her hat and grip on the bed, she descended the narrow, dimly lighted stairs. She didn't touch the banisters; she didn't like old houses, didn't like the feel of them.

The house was dead quiet.

She slammed the door behind her. The mist-touch was laid on her brow and lips and hair. She walked fast.

The tea shop, still open, was an arty-crafty little place. She was served coffee and poached eggs by a faded gentlewoman. Gina ate hungrily. She was lighting a cigarette when the gentlewoman apologetically presented the bill.

"We're just closing, madam. I'm sorry."

Gina paid the bill. She opened the door. It had suddenly begun to rain. She hesitated. Her jacket was very light. The tea shop was midway up the street; the lodging-house was near the end, the last house but one, on the left. The rain seemed to have settled in. She couldn't stand in this doorway all night. She thrust her hands into the pockets of her jacket, ducked her head, and walked as fast as she could.

The lights were shining much more clearly now . . .

This was when the police call went out for a taxi driver who had driven from Paddington, to a place unknown, with a girl in a green hat, with a large, brown trunk. In that glaring room in Scotland Yard, I was making a statement, a confession of murder, which was to put the rope round my neck. But as the rain beat across the Thames and ran wet on the window, it was of Gina that I was thinking. . . .

She was drenched when she hurried up the steps, put her key in the lock of the door. She went in, closed the door behind her. She pushed a hand up into her wet hair, gave it a little, quick shake. The light in the narrow passage burned dimly. There was a row of hooks on the right wall, with coats hanging on them. She looked down at herself ruefully. She was soaked to the skin. She had no change of clothes in her overnight bag, up in her room.

She glanced round for the trunk, now, but it was gone; Arthur must have shifted it below. She moved to the head of the short flight of stairs leading to the landlady's quarters.

She called, "Mrs. Coe?"—and listened. "Mrs. Coe?" she called again.

All was still in the house. There was only the sound of the rain.

She could see her trunk, down there in the flagstoned passage. The trunk stood half in light, half in shadow—a very ordinary trunk, hundreds of thousands like it. She took from her pocket the two cheap little keys tied together with a bit of string. She started down the stairs.

The stairs were of stone. There were four of them. Four stairs? She hesitated, looking at the trunk, a pace or two from her. Out of the shadows came the ticking of a clock.

I was thinking of a little girl in rubbers and a rubber coat with a hood, coming home from school through the rain to the enigma of a dark house and a waiting room. But that was in Canada, thousands of miles away . . .

Louder and louder ticked the clock from the darkness, and she could hear the rain spattering on glass somewhere to her left. There was creeping over her a feeling she had known before—in a single memory and many dreams. A feeling of something waiting for her. It had no shape. Only cold came from it. She fought against the feeling. She looked down at the trunk. Rain or something had trickled from it to form a small, dark pool, dimly visible on the flagstones.

In sudden haste, she forced herself to stoop, unlock the trunk.

She threw back the lid, and the cold was released. Wave after wave of cold passed over her. She stared down, backing away, a hand at her mouth. She was backing into the darkness. She wheeled round, as though to run— and there before her, through a door standing half-open, she saw the red glow of a fire between the bars of a kitchen stove. She saw an old wicker chair obliquely facing the stove, and in the chair a cat with its forepaws tucked under its chest, the firelight glinting in its intent eyes. The unseen clock was ticking loudly, questioningly. The rain spattered on glass to her left, and she knew that the wet, hairy leaves of stinging-nettles were there, pressed to the glass, and that the huge, dead, sodden heads of tall sunflowers rocked and nodded in the rain.

All was in waiting . . .

When the call came in, I was signing my statement. I sat with the pen in my hand, listening to the gray-haired, grim man at the desk speaking into the telephone . . .

He finished giving instructions. He was about to hang up when I stopped him. "Wait!"

He glanced at me.

I asked certain questions. He relayed them into the telephone. He repeated the answers to me. I sat with my head in my hands, thinking of Gina, with her strange eyes. Thinking how different things might have been for us— *But I tell you this whole thing was set up for us . . .*

The man at the desk said, "All right, Caird—now, what was the point of those questions you asked? The kitchen, the fire, the cat, the chair, the clock, the garden, the sunflowers, the nettles—these are common to most neglected houses anywhere in England."

"Not only in England," I thought.

I didn't say it. I looked at the keen, rational man, there at his desk, lighting his pipe. What was the good of talking to him of God or the Devil or Destiny or even mere Chance? He only knew the Law—and "facts."

But the address was a fact—the address I had heard him mention on the telephone—that was a fact. What made her go, with that trunk, to that house where she saw the sign saying *Vacancies* in the mist?

"Gina, my poor darling—"

Yet, if I hadn't changed the labels on the trunks—

I don't know. Would it have made any difference? I don't know anything. Did *I* kill her? Or what? She knows, now, the address of the house in the London mist. It was No. 15 George Street.

The Sixties

CHANGE OF CLIMATE

by URSULA CURTISS

"One lam chop," wrote Chloe Carpenter in her diary on an evening in late June—at nine years of age she had, and would have all her life, a natural talent for misspelling—"one baked potatoe, some string beans, a pice of apple pie." She studied the last item and then, because caret marks were still in her future and this was to be a very exact account, she crossed it out and wrote, "a small pice of apple pie."

Hester Carpenter had no idea that her daughter was keeping this meticulous record of Hester's food intake—fortunately; it would have made her self-conscious to the point of being unable to eat at all. But Tom Carpenter knew about it, and was both touched and approving. It seemed to him the day-by-day log of a miracle, although that was the very word he was supposed to avoid.

"Oh, she'll do better in the Southwest, no doubt about it," the doctor had said two months ago in Massachusetts. "In fact, to put it baldly, I doubt very seriously if she'd survive another winter here. But I have to warn you, Tom—after the first dramatic improvement there still may be difficulties. Chances are she'll acquire new allergies, and then there's always the existing damage. You mustn't expect a miracle."

Hester had never been really strong—it was her look of almost luminous fragility which had first caught Tom's eye; but she had not developed asthma until a year after their marriage. Or perhaps it had been there for some time, masquerading as frequent attacks of bronchitis and a faint but noticeable shortness of breath after activities like climbing stairs. In any case, the asthma had become sharply worse after Chloe's birth. At first there were seasons of the year when Hester was entirely free of it; gradually these periods shortened, and pneumonia began to make its appearance.

They saw a parade of specialists—bald and conservative, young and daring, whose advice, with minor differences, came to much the same thing in the end: avoid the known allergens—among them, cat dander; pursue a dust-free routine in the house; and "learn to live with your illness."

Surprisingly enough, until Chloe was seven years old, they managed the last instruction almost as easily as the first two. Hester was determined not to become a professional invalid, or to make a martyr of her husband and a slave of her small daughter; and for a long time she succeeded. She hoarded her strength in unobtrusive ways; on bad days, when the sound of her breathing was like a loud and steady filing, she retired to piled pillows behind her bedroom door.

She had grown up in the small town of Falcon, Massachusetts, and Tom did not have to worry about her being lonely while he was at his office and Chloe at school. Girls she had known since high school dropped in, and neighbors made morning visits for coffee, usually bringing along a sumptuous homemade pastry at which Hester could only nibble. Chloe, arriving home at three o'clock, leaped enthusiastically into her role of "house-woman"—"Housewife, do you suppose she means?" Hester asked Tom, laughing—and polished everything that could possibly be polished: vases, candlesticks, tabletops.

As a result, the little house glowed more than the prescribed dust-free routine demanded; it held a concert of personalities as undivided as a clover. Hale and hearty visitors went away with an illogical feeling of envy; they said, "There's nothing like trouble to bind a family together," but they knew it was more than that.

When Chloe was almost eight, Hester had her first bad attack of pneumonia. Six months later she had another and worse one, shrouded in an oxygen tent while Tom spent two tormented nights at her bedside and the nurses smiled at him with terrifying cheerfulness.

He made the decision then, knowing that it meant giving up the well-paid job which had enabled him to meet the medical bills; giving up their home and their friends. Although it was not really a decision at all in the sense of choosing between alternatives, because it was clear now that there was no alternative. While Hester convalesced, much more slowly than ever before, he quietly organized the move to the Southwest.

June turned and became July. Hester had gained six pounds, and her pearly skin was acquiring a faint tan. The one unfortunate side effect from the change of climate—sinus trouble, which the doctor assured them could be alleviated by drops—seemed a small price to pay.

Chloe had been her mother's anxious companion for too long to let go all at once, but little by little, as Hester grew stronger, Chloe explored a world strange to eastern eyes—a world with fleet little blue lizards, road-runners, and even, in their landlord's back field, an aristocratic but friendly horse that came promptly up to the fence for the carrot or apple she brought. In spite of the wanderings which seemed to her boundless, but were actually contained in less than a half acre, Chloe was always in the driveway to greet Tom when he got home from work.

She was there on a late afternoon in mid-July, wiry, sunburnt, and clearly bursting with something. When Tom asked his ritual, "What did you do today?" she said excitedly, "Oh, Daddy, I helped Mrs. Whitman tear up all her flowers. Look!"

Tom did not merely look; he gaped, appalled. Mrs. Whitman was the other tenant of the duplex apartment, a pleasant gray-haired woman whose chief preoccupation seemed to be the deep brilliant border that edged her little lawn on three sides. The border was now bare drying earth, the flowers themselves a heap of ruffled and shriveling color piled up outside the gate.

To Tom, for just a flash, the child looking up at him seemed to have the wanton triumph of a small boy standing with his slingshot near a shattered greenhouse—and then Chloe was saying defensively, "The flowers, I don't know which ones, made Mother sneeze and her eyes puff up, so Mrs. Whitman *said* to."

Hester was tranquilly regretful. "It's too bad about Mrs. Whitman's garden, isn't it? I felt awful, telling her about the doctor's orders—you know, to sit out in the sun for a little while every day—but she understood perfectly; in fact, she couldn't have been nicer. I came right in and baked her a batch of brownies."

Tom, remembering the weeks of Mrs. Whitman's assiduous weeding, cultivating, watering, sent a look of wonderment at his wife's back. Did Hester possibly think that a confection hastily whipped up in the kitchen—? No, of course she didn't; she had simply made a small token apology in the only way she could on the spur of the moment.

. . . But, he thought later that night while Hester slept, her breath quiet and even, she had been mistaken in thinking that Mrs. Whitman had "understood perfectly." That brutal heap of uprooted flowers, piled there openly by someone who loved them, was a statement of cold anger only emphasized by the invitation to the complainant's child to come and help with the carnage.

It was too bad in every sense, because Tom had hoped that Hester, so used to the daily companionship of other women, would start making friends in the neighborhood. His last waking reflection, still troubled, was that it might not be a bad idea to have Chloe, an avid car washer, surprise Mrs. Whitman tomorrow or the next day by scrubbing her little cherry red Volkswagen . . .

When Tom hinted worriedly to Hester about her possible loneliness, she denied it cheerfully. Her friends back East had been marvelous, and of course she missed them; but it was a positive luxury now to be able to do, unassisted, so many of the domestic things they had helped her with before.

And of course—here she glanced around vaguely—she had Chloe for company.

But this, although it was not borne in on Tom immediately, was less and less the case . . .

The doctor was enormously pleased with Hester's progress, and she apparently took this as carte blanche because, by the time August had arrived, she was seldom still. Wearing Bermuda shorts, a thing she could not have done before because of the sticklike thinness of her legs, Hester took down and washed and rehung the venetian blinds; she carried out the scatter rugs to air. She also washed the windows, inside and out, scoured the oven, and began on the paintwork. If the apartment did not have the warm glow of the little house back East, it was at least very shiny.

Tom did not find it surprising, in view of Hester's steady gain, that Chloe had stopped keeping her diary; the last entry, for July 26th, was: "Steak, asparagis, mashed potatoes, vinila ice cream." He now had a small but annoying problem of his own: his sinuses had evidently become affected by the dry heat and at night, frequently, his forehead felt bound with iron. Hester's wonder-working nose drops, trickling bitterly down the back of his throat no matter how carefully he administered them, did not seem to help.

One night in mid-August, when he was cautiously congratulating himself on feeling fine, the tense pain came creeping back at the dinner table. Maybe a storm approaching, thought Tom; the sky looked thunderous and he had sensed electricity in the air ever since his return home from work. Well, they needed the rain—

"Eat your dinner!" said Hester in a voice that made Tom's fork jump in his hand. He glanced at her astoundedly—she had delivered the words like a cuff; but her attention was on Chloe, fair head bent, hands in her lap although they were having roast chicken, which she loved.

"Eat your dinner," repeated Hester more quietly and perhaps more dangerously. The storm which Tom had thought so innocently to be in the upper elements was closer, and he was so bewildered that he could only stare.

"I'm not hungry," said Chloe, the corners of her mouth beginning to waver helplessly. "I feel sick."

"Very well, then, you're excused," said Hester evenly, and held herself remorselessly still and attentive while the child pushed back her chair, dropped her napkin, bumped her head on the table in the course of retrieving it, and then fled.

The door of her bedroom closed. Hester sprinkled salt and said calmly to Tom, "You look tired—was it a rough day?"

"Not bad," said Tom distractedly, putting down his own napkin and starting to rise. This was like a dream, in which elk went by in Easter bonnets and nobody thought it odd at all. "I'll go see what's the matter with—"

"Chloe is sulking because that foolish horse is gone," said Hester casually, and proceeded to tell him.

Tom had been aware of the affection between Chloe and the horse in the next field, and knew that the landlord let her mount occasionally and go for blissful ambles. As the horse was trained to halt the instant the weight in the saddle began to slip, it had seemed the most innocent of diversions. What Tom hadn't known—"I hate being such a constant nuisance to everybody"—was that Hester reacted badly to close contact with horses, and had begun to wheeze when Chloe came in from her rides.

She had, she said, forbidden Chloe to ride the horse, but at every opportunity the child had slipped over to the fence to caress the whiteblazed face and brush the dark-gold mane dedicatedly. "—which came to pretty much the same thing," said Hester ruefully. "Mr. Lacey saw the problem right away, and said his son would be delighted to keep the horse at his place—it doesn't get enough exercise here anyway. Somehow, I expected Chloe to understand."

Or understand *perfectly,* like Mrs. Whitman with her flowers? Tom was shocked at this disloyal thought—they were here after all for Hester's health, and allergies were not to be played around with; but his forehead now felt sealed with pain. When he had eaten what he could of his dinner he picked up Chloe's untouched plate. "I think I'll bring this in to her now."

Hester's eyebrows rose, but all she said was, "If you think it's wise."

Chloe got over the horse, as Hester had sensibly predicted she would, and settled herself to the serious business of making friends in the neighborhood before the opening of school. This was not the automatic process of a child who had been constantly with other children, but an almost adult approach. As a result, she was home at noontime for a sandwich and milk, usually with a standoffish and staring little girl in tow.

Tom took his headaches to a doctor, was informed that his sinuses were as clear as a bell, and, although he kept it from Hester so that she would not worry, he began to take the tranquilizers the doctor prescribed.

Hester bloomed, even in the scorching heat. Her delicate tan had turned brown, and she was strong and rangy. She was busy making new curtains, busy registering Chloe for school, busy waxing the floors, relining the kitchen shelves, taking down and washing the ceiling light fixtures. She had grown used to, as Tom and Chloe had, her own newly nasal voice, although she would say irritably now and then, "I sound exactly like a duck."

Although it was only the end of August, the annual weather prophets

were out in force. Tom and Hester, who could seldom find any news of
Massachusetts in the local papers, nevertheless learned with guilty pleasure
that an early and very hard winter was predicted for the East.

(But how warm and snug the little house in Massachusetts had been,
with Hester on the couch in a pretty housecoat, Chloe bustling importantly
in the kitchen, Tom peacefully reading the evening paper while the wind
raged outside and the fire simmered and snapped on the hearth. Lamplight
over everything, and a perfect security that had nothing to do with locks or
bolts or storm windows.)

We are all happy, Tom informed himself, swallowing his white pill; the
pity is that we didn't do this sooner.

School was to begin on August 29th. On the 27th, coming home with
the commissioned notebooks and pencils and lunch box, Tom saw that
Chloe had washed Mrs. Whitman's car again; the little red Volkswagen was
dripping and flashing in the sun. And there was, mystifyingly, a cat fight in
progress somewhere close by. Of all the things Hester couldn't have near
her . . . How could a cat have gotten—?

He was alarmedly out of his car and inside the gate when the menacing
shrills became distinguishable words instead of rising and falling howls. "—
so nice of you to be sweet and considerate with the neighbors," shrieked the
cat voice. "Never mind me, *I* don't count. But how many times have I told
you about those filthy sneakers? And look at those shorts. You've been in
the wading pool with those dreadful children, haven't you, Miss? I said,
Haven't you, Miss?"

There was an odd sound then, not a response from Chloe but still a
sound. Tom's stupefied eye caught a lunge past the screen door; his ear
heard a panting, "There you stay!" and then a sharp bang.

The bang seemed to split the frontal bones of his head. Standing paralyzed on the path, at once incredulous and certain, he realized that this
strident plunging creature in Bermuda shorts was his gentle luminous Hester, this contemptible "Miss" his skinny worshipful child.

He made himself go in. Hester was washing lettuce at the sink, her hands
unsteady. There was no sign of Chloe. Tom said with a weariness he did
not know he had accumulated, "What's the matter?" and Hester whirled.

"You'll have to talk to that child, Tom." *That child.* "She's always been
spoiled, but now she's completely out of hand."

Spoiled. The nine-year-old who by now was an expert at doing dishes,
ironing her own clothes, compiling bizarrely spelled shopping lists, and
trudging faithfully around supermarkets . . . "What's she done?"

"Disobeyed me, deliberately. There are some very dubious-looking children up the street who have a wading pool, and I told Chloe that she was
not to go there."

"Hester, this was a hot afternoon—"

"That's not the point. The point is that I told her not to," said Hester, spacing the last five words almost softly. By contrast, pots and their lids leaped into a clattering frenzy under her hands when she turned to the stove, and the glance she flung at Tom was razorish with—was it anger? Or some perverse excitement? Something, at any rate, that changed her into the kind of woman you saw dragging a small sobbing child ruthlessly by the hand, jerking all the harder when the child stumbled.

"I think we'd better get it clear here and now that I won't stand for this kind of behavior," the stranger at the stove was saying in her nasal and driving voice. "If you don't punish her, I will."

There were still a few shafts of late sunlight in Chloe's prim little room. She lay on her bed with her back to the door, not so much crying as shuddering, taking convulsive breaths which she buried fiercely in the pillow. Tom sat down on the bed and turned her gently to face him; he had to glance away quickly for a moment, feeling his own throat prickle at the dull red mark on her cheek.

That was the curious sound he had heard. From outside.

He had meant to tell Chloe quietly and reasonably that she could not disobey her mother, making it—because he realized suddenly that in the past week or so they had understood each other very well indeed—more of a father-to-daughter warning than a parental thunderbolt. But the reasonable words would not come; so he simply sat there, stroking the tumbled hair away from her forehead and talking about small detached things until she was able to heave a very deep breath with only the barest tremor.

She said, "Mother doesn't like being better, does she."

It was neither a question nor an accusation. It was an observation delivered with adult despair, and it encompassed much more than a hard humiliating slap. It took in the last—three weeks, four? Tom could not be sure, in his shock at the nakedness of the words, any more than a man could be sure when, after living with an obscure pain that frightened him, he was asked by the doctor who put an exact finger on the source, "How long have you had this?"

He didn't—at the moment he couldn't—answer his child. He gave her forehead a final pat and walked to the window, where he gazed out blindly into the coming dusk.

Was it possible? Could Hester have acquired the last allergy of all, and be no more able to assimilate health than cat dander? Were there personalities who could not thrive, or thrive sanely, on physical well-being?

It was appalling to think so, but it was less spine-touching than the notion that this personality had dwelt inside Hester all along, and had simply never been well enough to come out before. How, in that case, it must have raged and struggled against the tranquillity and binding love in the little Massachusetts house . . .

Tom's shoulder muscles gave a quick cold ripple as he shook that off and went back to the first possibility. If their past happiness even in the face of illness had been so present in his mind, how much more so must it have been in Hester's? Certainly she had never consciously liked being a semi-invalid, but—the stream of solicitous friends dropping in, the cheerful little gifts of a crocheted bed jacket or a homemade coffee cake, the momentous gaining or losing of half a pound—and, yes, the attention.

Chloe had been her devoted shadow, but now, like any other healthy nine-year-old, Chloe roamed and played. And Hester had flung herself into frenetic activity, perhaps battling unconsciously with this terrible new allergy, before it began to win.

Tom had never asked, but he was coldly sure now that Chloe had admired and helped in Mrs. Whitman's garden. She had worshipped the friendly horse. She had set about making friends, to prepare herself for entering a strange school, and been invited to wade in a back-yard pool. The sacrifices to Hester had not been voluntary, or even appeasing, but they had certainly been made.

And yet . . . Hester will be as upset as I am, said Tom to himself.

Hester was not. Told falsely that Chloe was asleep, she said with an edge, "Funny how easily she falls asleep on nights when we have meat loaf," and attacked her own dinner with zest. It was very good meat loaf, and a few small bites of it settled in Tom's stomach like the best cement; Chloe's vacant place at the table, and the silence from her room, pressed upward against his ribs.

Although Hester said nothing further about punishing Chloe, her face was curiously set, and when she asked Tom after the dishes were done, "Aren't you going to take your usual walk?" he manufactured a yawn and said, "Too tired."

He was, of course, not worried about any small personal action which might be taken in his absence down the long driveway. Certainly not. He was simply—tired.

He lay awake all night—not like someone with merely restless intervals, but literally all night. Once he got up quietly to look in at and cover Chloe; for the rest, he listened to his wife's deep untroubled breathing and studied a number of scenes which unwound like tape against the black ceiling.

In the morning he said cheerfully to Chloe, "Come on, I'll buy you a new dress for school," and to Hester, "They're having some kind of executive session at the office and I don't have to be in until eleven."

Surely Hester did not look somehow impotent as they left?

"Daddy," said Chloe hesitantly in the car—she was pleating the fabric of her skirt incessantly, a new and disturbing habit—"won't Mother be mad because she didn't come too?"

"She's got a million things to do," Tom said airily, and bore her off to the back-to-school department of a downtown store. He found a reliable-looking saleswoman to whom he gave vague suggestions about a dress, and told Chloe firmly to wait for him there.

There were public phone booths on the first floor, and from one of these Tom sent himself an urgent telegram signed with the name of his former employer in Massachusetts; he would be home to open it when it arrived, so that no question would be raised as to its place of origin. To make doubly sure, he instructed the operator to have the message delivered; there would be no one at that telephone all day, he said.

From the phone booth, because it was somehow of immense importance that Chloe should not even uncomprehendingly hear what he was going to say, he proceeded to the railroad station. Judging by a few banners strung about it was "Sunshine Appreciation Week," which was just chasing out "Eat More Cottage Cheese Week." When he asked the pretty clerk at a ticket window for two and a half fares to Falcon, Massachusetts, she said with arch reproachfulness, "Oh, surely that's round trip, sir?"

The buoyancy assumed for Chloe's sake had left him. Perhaps as a result of his sleepless night his ears resounded queerly with the doctor's voice: "To put it baldly, I doubt very seriously . . ." and the prediction of the weather prophets.

There was nothing momentous in the glance he sent through the ticket window. To the pretty clerk, who remembered him for approximately a minute afterward, he was just an ordinary, pleasant-looking man; fair, thirty-fivish, rather tired, with lines around his mouth. There was certainly no special inflection in his voice when he said, as though arousing himself from a dream, "No—that will be one way."

EDITORS' NOTE: *In addition to the killer and the victim, there are three major factors in every murder situation: motive, opportunity, and means. In most cases, real or fictional, the means is "ordinary"—gun, knife, bludgeon, poison, and so on. Now think of Ursula Curtiss' "Change of Climate" from the standpoint of means: to the best of our recollection, Ursula Curtiss has come up with a new means of murder—or, if it is not new, surely one of the most unusual on record . . .*

LIFE IN OUR TIME

by *ROBERT BLOCH*

When Harry's time capsule arrived, Jill made him put it in the guest house.

All it was, it turned out, was a big metal box with a cover that could be sealed tight and soldered so that the air couldn't get at what was inside. Jill was really quite disappointed with it.

But then she was quite disappointed with Harry, too—Professor Harrison Cramer, B.A., B.S., M.A., Ph.D. Half the alphabet wasted on a big nothing. At those flaky faculty cocktail parties, people were always telling her, "It must be wonderful to be married to a brilliant man like your husband." Brother, if they only knew!

It wasn't just that Harry was 15 years older than she was. After all, look at Rex Harrison and Richard Burton and Cary Grant and Lawrence Olivier. But Harry wasn't the movie-star type—definitely not! Not even the mad-scientist type, like Vincent Price in those crazy "campy" pictures. He was nothing—just a big nothing.

Of course, Jill got the message long before she married him. But he did have that imposing house and all that loot he'd inherited from his mother. Jill figured on making a few changes, and she actually did manage to redo the house so that it looked halfway presentable, with the help of that *fagilleh* interior decorator. But she couldn't redo Harry. Maybe *he* needed an interior decorator to work on him, too; *she* certainly couldn't change him.

And outside of what she managed to squeeze out of him for the redecorating, Jill hadn't been able to get her hands on any of the loot, either. Harry wasn't interested in entertaining or going out or taking cruises, and whenever she mentioned a sable jacket he mumbled something under his breath about "conspicuous consumption"—whatever that was! He didn't like modern art or the theater, he didn't drink or smoke—why, he didn't even watch TV. And he wore flannel pajamas in bed. *All* the time.

After a couple of months Jill was ready to climb the walls. Then she began thinking about Reno, and that's where Rick came in. Rick was her attorney—at least, that's the way it started out to be, but Rick had other ideas. Particularly for those long afternoons when Harry was lecturing at seminars or whatever he did over there at the University.

Pretty soon Jill forgot about Reno; Rick was all for of those quickie divorces you can get down in Mexico. He was sure he could make it stick and still see to it that she got her fifty-fifty share under the community property laws, and without any waiting. It could all be done in 24 hours, with no hassle; they'd take off together, just like eloping. Bang, you're divorced; bang, you're remarried; and then, bang, bang, bang—

So all Jill had to worry about was finding the right time. And even that was no problem, after Harry told her about the time capsule.

"I'm to be in full charge of the project," he said. "Complete authority to choose what will be representative of our present culture. Quite a responsibility, my dear—but I welcome the challenge."

"So what's a time capsule?" Jill wanted to know.

Harry went into a long routine and she didn't really listen, just enough to get the general idea. The thing was, Harry had to pick out all kinds of junk to be sealed up in this gizmo so that sometime—10,000 years from now, maybe—somebody would come along and dig it up and open it and be able to tell what kind of civilization we had. Big deal! But from the way Harry went on, you'd think he'd just won the Grand Prix or something.

"We're going to put the capsule in the foundation of the new Humanities Building," he told her.

"What are humanities?" Jill asked, but Harry just gave her one of those *Good-lord-how-can-you-be-so-stupid?* looks that always seemed to start their quarrels; and they would have had a fight then and there, too, only he added something about how the dedication ceremonies for the new building would take place on May 1st, and he'd have to hurry to get everything arranged for the big day. Including writing his dedicatory address.

May 1st was all Jill needed to hear. That was on a Friday, and if Harry was going to be tied up making a speech at the dedication, it would be an A-OK time to make that little flight across the border. So she managed to call Rick and tell him and he said yeah, sure, perfect.

"It's only ten days from now," Jill reminded Rick. "We've got a lot to do."

She didn't know it, but it turned out she wasn't kidding. She had more to do than she thought, because all at once Harry was *interested* in her. *Really* interested.

"You've got to help me," he said that night at dinner. "I want to rely on your taste. Of course, I've got some choices of my own in mind, but I want *you* to suggest items to go into the capsule."

At first Jill thought he was putting her on, but he really meant it. "This project is going to be honest. The usual ploy is pure exhibitionism—

samples of the 'best' of everything, plus descriptive data which is really just a pat on the back for the *status quo ante*. Well, that's not for me. I'd like to include material that's self-explanatory, not self-congratulatory. Not art and facts—but artifacts."

Harry lost her there, until he said, "Everything preserved will be a clue to our contemporary social attitudes. Not what we *pretend* to admire, but what the majority actually *believes in* and *enjoys*. And that's where you come in, my dear. You represent the majority."

Jill began to dig it, then. "You mean like TV and pop records?"

"Exactly. What's that album you like so much? The one with the four hermaphrodites on the liner?"

"Who?"

"Excuse me—it's purportedly a singing group, isn't it?"

"Oh, you're talking about the Poodles!" Jill went and got the album, which was called *The Poodles Bark Again*. The sound really turned her on, but she had always thought Harry hated it. And now he was coming on all smiles.

"Great!" he said. "This definitely goes in."

"But—"

"Don't worry, I'll buy you another." He took the album and put it on his desk. "Now, you mentioned something about television. What's your favorite program?"

When she saw that he was really serious, she began telling him about "Anywhere, U.S.A." What it was, it was about life in a small town, just an ordinary suburb like, but the people were great. There was this couple with the two kids, one boy and one girl, sort of an average family, you might say, only he was kind of playing around with a divorcee who ran a *discothetique* or whatever they call them, and she had a yen for her psychiatrist—he wasn't really *her* psychiatrist, he was analyzing one of the kids, the one who had set fire to the high school gymnasium, not the girl—she was afraid her parents would find out about her affair with the vice-principal who was really an enemy agent only she didn't know it yet, and her real boy friend, the one who had the brain operation, had a "thing" about his mother, so—

It got kind of complicated, but Harry kept asking her to tell him more, and pretty soon he was smiling and nodding. "Wonderful! We'll have to see if we can get films of a typical week's episodes."

"You mean you really want something like that?"

"Of course. Wouldn't you say this show faithfully captured the lives of American citizens today?"

She had to agree he was right. Also about some of the things he was going to put into the capsule to show the way people lived nowadays—like tranquilizers and pep pills and income tax forms and a map of the freeway-expressway-turnpike system. He had a lot of numbers, too, for Zip Code and digit dialing, and Social Security, and the ones the computers punched out on insurance and charge-account and utility bills.

But what he really wanted was ideas for more stuff, and in the next couple of days he kept leaning on her. He got hold of her souvenir from Shady Lawn Cemetery—it was a plastic walnut that opened up, called "Shady Lawn in a Nutshell." Inside were twelve tiny color prints showing all the tourist attractions of the place, and you could mail the whole thing to your friends back home. Harry put this in the time capsule, wrapping it up in something he told her was an actuarial table on the incidence of coronary occlusion among middle-aged, middle-class males. Like heart attacks, that is.

"What's that you're reading?" he asked. And the next thing she knew, he had her copy of the latest Steve Slash paperback—the one where Steve is sent on this top-secret mission to keep peace in Port Said, and right after he kills these five guys with the portable flame thrower concealed in his judo belt, he's getting ready to play beddy-bye with Yasmina, who's really another secret agent with radioactive fingernails—

And that's as far as she'd got when he grabbed the book. It was getting so she couldn't keep anything out of his eager little hands.

"What's that you're cooking?" he wanted to know. And there went the TV dinner—frozen crêpes suzettes and all. To say nothing of the Plain Jane Instant Borscht.

"Where's that photo you had of your brother?" It was a real nothing picture of Stud, just him wearing that beatnik beard of his and standing by his motorcycle on the day he passed his initiation into Hell's Angels. But Harry put *that* in, too. Jill didn't think it was very nice of Harry, seeing as how he clipped it to another photo of some guys taking the Ku Klux Klan oath.

But right now the main thing was to keep Harry happy. That's what Rick said when she clued him in on what was going on.

"Cooperate, baby," he told her. "It's a real kinky kick, but it keeps him out of our hair. We got plans to make, tickets to buy, packing and like that there."

The trouble was, Jill ran out of ideas. She explained this to Rick but he just laughed.

"I'll give you some," he said, "and you can feed 'em to him. He's a real way-out kid, that husband of yours—I know just what he wants."

The funny part of it was that Rick did know. He was really kind of a brain himself, but not in a kooky way like Harry. So she listened to what he suggested and told Harry when she got home.

"How about a sample of the Theater of the Absurd?" she asked. Harry looked at her over the top of his glasses, and for a minute she thought she'd really thrown him, but then he grinned and got excited.

"Perfect!" he said. "Any suggestions?"

"Well, I was reading a review about this new play everybody's talking about—it's about this guy who thinks he's having a baby so he goes to an abortionist, only I guess the abortionist is supposed to be somebody mystical or something, and it all takes place in a greenhouse—"

"Delightful!" Harry was off and running. "I'll pick up a copy of the book. Anything else?"

Thank God that Rick had coached her. So she said what about a recording of one of those concerts where they use a "prepared" piano that makes noises like screeching brakes, or sometimes no sound at all. And Harry liked that. He also liked the idea about a sample of Pop Art—maybe a big blowup of a newspaper ad about "That Tired Feeling" or maybe "Psoriasis."

The next day she suggested a tape of a "Happening" which was the real thing, because it took place in some private sanatorium for disturbed patients, and Harry got really enthusiastic about this idea.

And the next day she came up with that new foreign movie with the long title she couldn't pronounce. Rick gave her the dope on it—some far-out thing by a Yugoslavian director she never heard of, about a man making a movie about a man making a movie, only you never could be quite sure, in the movie, whether the scene was supposed to be a part of the movie or the movie was a part of what was really happening, *if* it did happen.

Harry went for this, too. In a big way.

"You're wonderful," he said. "Truthfully, I never expected this of you."

Jill just gave him her extra-special smile and went on her merry way. It wasn't hard, because he had to go running around town trying to dig up books and films and recordings of all the stuff he had on his list. Which was just how Rick said it would be, leaving everything clear for them to shop and set up their last-minute plans.

"I won't get our tickets until the day before we leave," Rick told her. "We don't want to tip off anything. The way I figure it, Harry'll be moving the capsule over to where they're holding the ceremonies the next morning, so you'll get a chance to pack while he's out of the way." Rick was really something, the way he had it all worked out.

And that's the way it went. The day before the ceremony, Harry was busy in the guesthouse all afternoon, packing his goodies in the time capsule. Just like a dopey squirrel burying nuts. Only even dopey squirrels don't put stuff away for another squirrel to dig up 10,000 years from now.

Harry hadn't even had time to look at her the past two days, but this didn't bother Jill any. Along about suppertime she went out to call him, but he said he wasn't hungry and besides he had to run over and arrange for the trucking company to come and haul the capsule over to the foundation site.

They'd dug a big hole there for tomorrow morning, and he was going to take the capsule to it and stand guard over it until it was time for the dedication ceremonies.

That was even better news than Jill had hoped for, so as soon as Harry left for the trucking company she phoned Rick and gave him the word. He said he'd be right over with the tickets.

So of course Jill had to get dressed. She put on her girdle and the fancy bra and her high heels; then she went in the bathroom and used her depilatory and touched up her hair where the rinse was fading, and put on her eyelashes and brushed her teeth, and attached those new fingernails after she got her makeup on and the perfume.

When she looked at the results in the mirror she was really proud of herself; for the first time in months she felt like her real self again. And from now on it would always be this way—with Rick.

There was a good moment with Rick there in the bedroom after he came in, but of course Harry *would* drive up right then—she heard the car out front and broke the clinch just in time, telling Rick to sneak out the back way. Harry would be busy with the truckers for at least a couple of minutes.

Jill forced herself to wait in the bedroom until she was sure the coast was clear. She kept looking out the window but it was too dark now to see anything. Since there wasn't any noise, she figured Harry must have taken the truckers into the guesthouse.

And that's where she finally went.

Only the truckers weren't there. Just Harry.

"I told them to wait until first thing in the morning," he said. "Changed my mind when I realized how damp it was—no sense my spending the night shivering outside in the cold. Besides, I haven't sealed the capsule yet —remembered a couple of things I wanted to add."

He took a little bottle out of his pocket and carried it over to the time capsule. "This goes in too. Carefully labeled, of course, so they can analyze it."

"The bottle's empty," Jill said.

Harry shook his head. "Not at all. It contains smog. That's right—smog, from the freeway. I want posterity to know everything about us, right down to the poisonous air in which our contemporary culture breathed its last."

He dropped the bottle into the capsule, then picked up something else from the table next to it. Jill noticed he had a soldering outfit there to seal the lid, ready to plug in after he'd used a pump to suck all the air out. He'd explained about the capsule being airtight, soundproof, duralumin-sheathed, but that didn't interest her now. She kept looking at what he held in his hand.

It was one of those electric carving knives, complete with battery.

"Another Twentieth Century artifact," he said. "Another gadget symbol of our decadence. An electric knife—just the thing for Mom when she carves the fast-frozen, precooked Thanksgiving turkey while she and Dad count all their shiny, synthetic, plastic blessings."

He waved the knife.

"They'll understand," he told her. "Those people in the future will understand it all. They'll know what life was like in our time—how we drained Walden Pond and refilled it with blood, sweat, and tears."

Jill moved a little closer, staring at the knife. "The blade's rusty."

Harry shook his head. "That's not rust," he said.

Jill kept it cool. She kept it right up until the moment she looked over the edge of the big metal box, looked down into it, and saw Rick lying there. Rick was stretched out, and the red was oozing down over the books and records and photos and tapes.

"I was waiting for him when he sneaked out the back of the house," Harry said.

"Then you knew—all along—"

"For quite a while," Harry said. "Long enough to figure things out and make my plans."

"What plans?"

Harry just shrugged. And raised the knife.

A moment later the time capsule received the final specimen of life in the Twentieth Century.

THE SPECIAL GIFT

by CELIA FREMLIN

Eileen glanced disconsolately at the little group cowering round the fire in her big, cold sitting room. Only five of them tonight. It was the weather, of course, that was keeping most of the members away; not everyone was willing to battle through wind and sleet just for the pleasure of reading aloud to one another their amateur attempts at writing, and receiving some equally amateur criticism.

Still, thought Eileen, drawing her cardigan more tightly about her, it was a pity; these meetings weren't nearly so much fun with only a few. A crowd might have made it seem a bit warmer, too.

"Well, do you think we ought to begin, Mr. Wilberforce?" she said, sitting down on the big horsehair ottoman next to the secretary.

Mr. Wilberforce, a plump, important-looking man in his fifties, glanced at the clock, rubbing his pink hands together.

"Only twenty past," he said. "Better give them a *few* more minutes. The snow, you know—buses—"

"*I* think we should start," piped up old Mrs. Peterkin, peering out like a little aggrieved mouse from the depths of the fur coat she had refused to take off. "We've got a lot to get through this evening. I've brought one of my little tales of unrequited love, if you'd care to hear it. And I'm sure Miss Williams here"—she indicated a pleasant, vacantly smiling girl on her right —"I'm sure Miss Williams has brought us another chapter of her psychological novel. And Mr. Walters"—the pale young man lowered his eyelashes self-consciously—"we hope Mr. Walters is going to read us another of his Ballads of the Seasons. It'll be summer this time, won't it, Mr. Walters?"

"Yes, it will be summer," agreed Mr. Walters, speaking rapidly and staring at the carpet. "But not summer in the *conventional* sense, you understand. Now, *my* interpretation of summer—"

A sharp, imperative ring at the front door brought Eileen to her feet, and she hurried eagerly out of the room. One more makes six, she was thinking, that's not too bad; all the same, I wish I hadn't made all those cheese sandwiches . . .

A gust of wind and snow swirled into her face as she opened the front door, and the little dark man seemed almost to be blown in by it, so slight and thin in his dark coat.

"You haven't been to these meetings before, have you?" Eileen was beginning—and then stopped, for in the dimness of the hall the stranger seemed to be staring at her with a delighted recognition.

"We—we *haven't* met before, have we?" she went on awkwardly; and the little man seemed to rouse himself.

"Why—er—no," he said hastily, shaking the snow from his boots onto the doormat. "No, indeed, I assure you! I just—well, I had a feeling—"

Again he stared at her with that odd look of recognition in his eyes; and for some reason Eileen began to feel uncomfortable; for some reason she became very eager to escape the piercing gaze of this stranger in the dimly lit hall.

"Come along and meet the others," she said nervously, and led him briskly into the sitting room.

"Fitzroy is my name," the dark man introduced himself. *"Alan* Fitzroy."

He glanced round the company with dark, sparkling eyes, and there was a little stir of interest. Not that anybody had ever heard of him, but something in the way he spoke made them feel that perhaps they *ought* to have heard of him. Perhaps, each of them was thinking, perhaps this at last is the real writer I have always hoped would turn up! The *real* writer who not only gets his own work published, but who will be able to tell me how to get *mine* published; who will recognize it as the fine work it really is . . .

With such thoughts behind them, five pairs of eyes followed the little man as he moved toward the fire; eager hands drew up a comfortable armchair for him; eager voices plied him with questions.

But Alan Fitzroy was not very communicative. No, he didn't know any of the members of this group. No (modestly) he didn't write much—well, not *very* much. No, he hadn't brought anything to read—well, not really—anyway, let everyone else read something first, *please!*

And so the meeting began. Alan Fitzroy sat motionless, his eyes closed. To everyone's disappointment he took no part in the comments and criticisms that followed each reading, and it was only when he was asked for *his* contribution that he roused himself.

"Well," he admitted, "I *have* brought a little thing. Actually, it's part of a larger work. I'm writing my autobiography, you see."

He looked round the room expectantly, and there was an almost audible sigh of disappointment. This, somehow, didn't sound like a real writer; it sounded much more like an ordinary member of the group. However—

"I want you to understand," the stranger continued, "that the whole object of my book is to bring the reader into real contact with my ego—to draw him, or her, into the life of my mind in a way which I believe has never been done before . . ."

As he spoke, he fixed his brilliant eyes on Eileen's face, and again she felt a little flicker of uneasiness—or was it even fear? Quite irrational, anyway, she assured herself; there couldn't possibly be a more harmless little man; and she settled herself to listen as he began to read from a thick, dog-eared manuscript.

"The self-doubt and self-awareness of any repressed, frustrated childhood . . ."

The voice went on and on. At intervals Eileen glanced at the clock. She hoped that Mr. Fitzroy wouldn't be offended if she went out and made the tea before he had finished. She hoped, too, that he hadn't noticed that Mrs. Peterkin was asleep inside her fur coat and might at any moment begin to snore.

Mr. Wilberforce, at Eileen's side, was fiercely making notes on the back of one of his own manuscripts. No doubt he was building up a pungent criticism of the weary verbiage through which this poor little man was plowing.

"Go easy with him!" whispered Eileen softly; somehow it seemed very important to her that nothing should be said to upset the newcomer. "Remember he's new." But Mr. Wilberforce only nodded his head irritably and went on writing.

Wasn't it *ever* coming to an end? But listen! At last! Those, surely, must be the concluding sentences:

"To point the significance of these psychodynamic disturbances to my infantile ego, I must relate a nocturnal hallucination from which I used to suffer. Or, in common parlance, a dream. I dreamed I was walking along a passage, a long stone passage, my feet clanging as I went, as if I were wearing boots of steel or armor or something like that. At the end of the passage I knew I should find my cradle—the cradle I'd had as a baby—and I should have to get into it and lie down. And I knew that as I lay there, I would see a face slowly rising over the side of the cradle, and the face would be mad. I never knew what would happen next, because I always woke up—in fact, I always woke up before I had even reached the end of the passage."

Abruptly the little man laid down his manuscript. He looked round triumphantly, and there was a little embarrassed silence, broken by a snore from Mrs. Peterkin.

"Well," said Eileen at last, wondering how to avoid hurting the little man's feelings. "It's a very *profound* piece of work, of course—"

"But it's too *long!*" exploded Mr. Wilberforce. "And too self-centered, too self-pitying! You've used the word 'I' eighty-seven times in the first six pages! I was counting!"

Alan Fitzroy turned on him indignantly.

"But I *have* to use the word 'I'! The whole book is about myself—I told you! The idea is to get the reader involved with *me*— to bring him right into my very mind, if you understand me—"

"I understand you perfectly," said Mr. Wilberforce heavily, ignoring Eileen's nudges. "The idea is far from being a novel one. But if you will allow me to say so, I think you are deceiving yourself. You speak of bringing the reader right into your mind, and in fact you don't even interest him. The whole thing is too wordy, too abstract. There's nothing in it to grip the attention."

The little man flushed angrily.

"Nothing to grip the attention?" he cried. "What about that dream, eh? Doesn't *that* grip your attention? Doesn't it?"

"Frankly, no," answered Mr. Wilberforce. "It's simply an account of a childish nightmare such as all of us have had at one time or another. I appreciate that it may have frightened you as a child, but believe me, it won't frighten anyone else!"

The little man was trembling with rage now.

"It *will* frighten people!" he almost screamed. "It *will!* I have a special gift for this sort of thing, I *know* I have! Let me tell you, a person once died of fright from hearing that dream!"

There was an awkward little silence. No one knew what to say to that absurd boast. Eileen got hastily to her feet.

"I think we all need a cup of tea!" she said, loudly and brightly, and escaped from the room. As she hurried down the passage to the kitchen, she became aware that Audrey Williams, the young psychological novelist, was following her.

"Thought I might help you, dear," explained Audrey, and added, as she piled cups and saucers onto a tray, "Whoever is that pompous little ass, do you suppose?"

"I can't think," said Eileen. "I felt rather sorry for him, really. He must have worked terribly hard on all that stuff, you know. He had chapters and chapters of it written."

"You're telling me!" giggled Audrey. "I thought at one point that he was proposing to read the whole lot! I nearly died . . ." Her voice trailed away, and both women were aware of Alan Fitzroy standing silently in the doorway.

"Funny you should say that," he said, looking straight at Audrey. "And you?" he went on, turning to Eileen. "Did *you* nearly die, too?"

Eileen flushed. No wonder the poor little chap was bitter! It was shameful of Mr. Wilberforce to have laced into a newcomer like that!

She said gently, "Don't take too much notice of Mr. Wilberforce. He's a very stern critic. He's like that to all of us sometimes, isn't he, Audrey?'

Audrey Williams nodded dumbly; and Alan Fitzroy spoke again, addressing himself to Eileen.

"And what did *you* think of my little effort? I sense a certain sympathy in you. Were you impressed by my dream?"

"Why—yes—" lied Eileen nervously, searching for words. "I thought it was quite—well, quite unusual. If you'd brought it in a bit *sooner,* though, instead of quite so much theory in the beginning—"

"But I *do* bring it in sooner!" exclaimed the little man eagerly—he seemed to have quite recovered his temper. "I bring it in all through the book—just as it has come to me at intervals all through my life. But the reader doesn't know why I keep repeating it until the last episode! Don't you think that's a good idea? Keeping him in suspense, that kind of thing?"

He glanced with pathetic eagerness from one to the other of the two women; and Eileen, anxious to show the poor fellow a little encouragement, paused in fanning biscuits on a plate to say, "Do tell us: what *is* the last episode?"

"Oh, well, you see, it was like this. This dream used to worry me, it really did. I'm not a nervous man—that is to say, my *type* of nerves, as I explain in—"

Hastily Eileen brought him back to the point.

"But the dream?" she said, counting out teaspoons onto the tray, and Alan Fitzroy continued, "Yes, yes. The dream. What worried me, you see, was that each time I dreamed it I got a *little* farther down the passage toward the cradle, where I knew I would have to lie down and see the Face. In the end I was so worried about it that I told my wife. 'If only you could be with me, my dear,' I said—just in fun, you understand—'Then I wouldn't be so scared.'

"Well, that very night I dreamed it again, and, believe it or not, she *was* there! She was walking along in front of me, wearing her old dark dressing gown. She was a big woman, my wife—a big strong woman, and she quite blocked my view of the cradle—the cradle where I knew the madness would begin. So I felt quite safe. I didn't mind the dream a bit. And when I woke up—"

The little man looked eagerly from Eileen to Audrey, like a conjuror bringing off a successful trick. "When I woke up, what do you think my wife told me?"

"Why, that she'd had the dream too, of course!" said Audrey promptly —wasn't that the obvious climax to the tale?

But Alan Fitzroy shook his head. "No," he said. "No, that didn't come till later. No, she told me that as she lay there, her head near to mine, she heard what she thought was my watch ticking under my pillow. But a funny, metallic tick, she said—like a far-off clanging of armor, or of steel boots. And then she knew that it didn't come from under the pillow but from inside my head. It was my boots clanging in my dream, you see, and she'd heard them."

Eileen and Audrey had drawn close together. Eileen's voice trembled a little.

"I think we ought to take the tea in—," she began; but the little man laid his hand on her arm beseechingly.

"Just one moment more!" he begged. "Just a few more words! After that, whenever I dreamed that dream, my wife would hear the clanging in my head, louder each night, until at last *she* had the dream, too! The clanging somehow forced her to go to sleep, she told me, though she tried hard to stay awake—and there she was, she said, right in my dream, walking down the passage in front of me, hearing my boots clanging behind her. What do you think of that?"

Eileen had recovered herself. Of course, this was just a piece of fiction on which he wanted her opinion. Mr. Wilberforce's crushing comments on the autobiography had stung him into trying to enliven it.

"Well," she said consideringly. "I suppose you could work that up into something quite dramatic. But however would you end it?"

"The way it *did* end, of course!" said the little man sharply. "It ended with my wife actually getting into the cradle. Naturally. It was *my* dream, wasn't it, and I *made* it end that way. Though there were one or two terrible struggles first. I told you, my wife was a big strong woman."

"And—and what happens to her in it?" asked Eileen. "Does she see the face? And does she tell you afterwards what it was like?"

"Oh, no!" said the little man, sounding surprised. "Of course not. She couldn't *tell* me any more after she'd got into the cradle. Naturally. She wasn't dead, but she was an imbecile by then. I found her in bed in the morning, all curled up as she would have to be to fit into this little cradle, and she could no longer talk. Naturally. That *would* be the effect of looking at the Face."

Eileen and Audrey glanced at each other. Each noticed that the other had gone rather white; but the little man went cheerfully on, apparently unaware of their dismay.

"They took her away, of course, and put her into some sort of home. But it was all right—I knew I was safe now, because if *she* was in the cradle, then of course *I* couldn't be, could I? Every time I had the dream there she was, filling up the whole cradle in her dark dressing gown so that I couldn't even see it. I felt wonderfully safe for months.

"Until, one night, she wasn't there any more. That was terrible for me. I knew then she must be dead—and sure enough the next day I had word from the Home that this was the case. But come—" he seemed suddenly to rouse himself—"I mustn't keep you ladies from your tea—allow me!" And taking one of the two trays he hurried off to the sitting room.

Eileen and Audrey had only one thought—to get back to their companions. Hastily they loaded the other tray and a few moments later they were in the sitting room.

To their surprise Alan Fitzroy was no longer there.

"Oh, he left as soon as he'd brought the tray in," explained Mr. Wilberforce. "Said he had to catch a train to Guildford, or somewhere. Asked me to apologize to you—why, what's the matter with you?"

Eileen recounted briefly the story that Alan Fitzroy had told them in the kitchen, and Mr. Wilberforce looked grave.

"Fellow must be crazy!" he said. "I *thought* he looked funny. Wouldn't have let him go if I'd known. Should have kept him, and rung the police."

"Oh, I'm only too thankful he *has* gone!" said Eileen. "I don't want a fuss. Besides, he must have meant it as fiction—though even so, he must be a *bit* abnormal to try—"

"Abnormal? Of *course* he was abnormal!" interrupted old Mrs. Peterkin. "I could see *that* the very first moment! 'That's an Egalomaniac!' I said to myself—"

"Egomaniac," corrected Audrey Williams, who was well up in the jargon needed for her novel. "Or do you mean megalomaniac—?"

The chatter went on, and the clink of teacups, and Eileen felt more and more thankful that the strange little man had gone. Suppose he had been the *last* to go instead of the first? She couldn't very well have forced him out—

Eleven o'clock now. One by one the members left, and finally Eileen was alone.

"I must get all this cleared up," she thought, glancing wearily round the untidy room; and she began to move about collecting ashtrays and dirty cups. As she passed the ottoman she noticed that Mr. Wilberforce had left his gloves there; and so she was not surprised when a moment later the front doorbell rang urgently.

But it was not Mr. Wilberforce. The little dark figure had slipped past her into the hall before she had properly taken in what was happening.

She gave a little gasp of horror—and then recovered herself. After all, he seemed a very innocuous little man, standing there under the hall light and asking if he could look at a timetable. He had missed his last train, he said, but maybe—on the other line—perhaps a connection at Croydon—if he might just study the timetable a moment?

Eileen had no alternative but to lead him into the sitting room and hand him the ABC. He settled himself in the armchair with it and was soon thumbing through its pages with apparent concentration. Eileen went on with her tidying, trying to appear quite unperturbed. After all, she was saying to herself, what can he *do?* I'm twice his size, a big strong woman—

Where had she heard that phrase before? The words echoed in her head
—"My wife . . . a big strong woman."

It was then that she noticed how quiet everything was. The rustling of
the pages of the ABC had ceased; and when she looked across at him, Eileen
saw that Alan Fitzroy was asleep. His head was leaning back against the
chair, his mouth was open, and his face was rather white.

"He looks queer!" she thought, stepping closer. "I think perhaps I *will*
ring the police. Luckily the phone's in the kitchen, not in here, so it won't
wake him—"

And then she heard the noise. At first she thought it was a clicking in his
throat, the prelude to a snore. But no, it wasn't a click; it was a tiny
clanking noise—distant—metallic—inside his head.

Eileen did not stop to put down the tray she was carrying. The telephone! The telephone! That was the only idea in her mind as she hurried
through the door and started for the kitchen.

But how loud the clanking sound had grown! It seemed to be following
her out of the room—along the passage—clank—*clank*— CLANK—

And where *was* the kitchen? How had this passage grown so long? And
why were the walls of stone, and the floor too—stone that echoed to the
clanking footsteps behind her—

She could not look behind. She could only hurry on, and on and on,
down the echoing passage, until in front of her she saw the end. The
delicate muslin frills, stirred ever so slightly by an unseen breath. The lacy
pillow, white and waiting. The coverlet, just recently turned back, in readiness, by an unseen hand.

With a strength she never knew she possessed, Eileen made herself stand
still.

"It's a dream, it's a dream!" she told herself. "If I won't go with it, I'll
wake up! I *won't* go with it! I won't! I won't! I *won't!*"

The clanking feet behind came nearer. Hands were pushing—pushing—
fighting with her, and Eileen fought back—with that dim, strengthless
fighting of dreams, which yet somehow takes all a person's strength and
more—I won't! gasped Eileen silently. I won't, I won't, I *won't!*

A crash seemed to split her eardrums, and she found she could open her
eyes. She opened them on her own kitchen, on the tray of crockery lying
smashed at her feet. Sweat was running down her face, and tears of relief
came into her eyes.

A dream, of course! A sleepwalking dream brought on by that awful
little man, and perhaps by overtiredness. Why, it must have been part of the
dream that he ever came back to ask for a timetable at all! Light-hearted in
her relief, Eileen hurried back to the sitting room.

No. That at least hadn't been a dream. But Alan Fitzroy was no longer
sitting upright in his chair. He was sprawled on the floor as if he had been

struck down in a violent fight, and blood was trickling from his head where it had struck the fireplace fender in his fall.

For one insane moment Eileen thought of that dream struggle at the edge of the cradle—*one* of them had had to fall—and then, collecting her wits, she rushed to telephone the doctor . . .

The doctor felt the little man's pulse, his heart; then he shook his head.

"Not a hope, I'm afraid," he said. "You'll have to phone the police, my dear, and get them to find out where he comes from and everything. You go and phone them now, while I attend to the poor fellow."

But why was Eileen still standing there, motionless?

"Go on—phone!" said the doctor irritably. It was bad enough to be called out to a fatal heart attack at this time of night, without a hysterical woman delaying things. "Go on, the telephone!"

As if in a trance, Eileen moved toward the door—along the passage toward the kitchen. After all, perhaps it had been the doctor's watch chain making that tiny clanking noise. Yes, he must still be rattling his watch chain now—louder—*louder*—LOUDER—

A NEAT AND TIDY JOB

by GEORGE HARMON COXE

Her name was Mary Heath and she stood five-foot-three in the medium heels she wore when she was on duty. She weighed one hundred and eight, her hair was shiny black, her eyes were deep blue, and her firmly rounded chin suggested she had been endowed with a full quota of spunk.

Her domain during working hours was the first car in the three-bank elevator system of the Caswell Building; and because she was young—just past nineteen—and friendly, she was a favorite with most of the tenants. They liked her cheerfulness and their kidding was basically well mannered and gentle. The fresh ones saved their more suggestive comments for Ethel and Loretta in the adjoining cars, for though they were not much older than Mary they were married and somewhat more experienced in parrying conversational liberties.

In the months she had been running the first car her passion for neatness had become well-known to the regulars. She could not control the transients but the others avoided spilling ashes on the carpet of her car. If they lit a cigarette they carried the paper match outside before discarding it, and if they forgot and opened a pack in her car they remembered not to drop the cellophane top.

This passion for tidiness was simply a facet of her personality, as much a part of her as her honesty and friendliness. She was fastidious about her appearance and somehow looked a little smarter in her gray-blue uniform than Ethel with her full-blown figure or Loretta with her tinted blond hair. Since Mary always kept her tiny apartment spic and span she saw no reason why this cage, which was actually her business office five days a week, should not be equally neat and tidy. At least, that was how she explained it when Ethel discovered that Mary kept a small whisk broom tucked behind the collapsible seat in her car. If she wanted to stop the empty car between floors on occasion and sweep the carpet, why should anyone object?

Mary's insistence on neatness came up for the umpteenth time at exactly five minutes after three one Friday afternoon in June when Harry Gilmore came into the foyer of the Caswell Building and headed for her empty car.

Harry was a maintenance man and had the title of Assistant Engineer. He wore his customary soiled coveralls and had a handful of tools in his left fist, a cigarette in his mouth.

"How about a ride, baby?" he said. "I've got some plumbing to do on the fourth."

Mary cocked one eye at the wall clock and saw that she had four minutes before she had to go up to the eighth floor and pick up Stan Norton; she cocked the other at the half-inch ash that hung from Gilmore's dangling cigarette.

"Sure, Harry," she said. "Just knock that ash off first, please."

Harry grinned. He removed the cigarette, studied it, then flicked off the ash with an elaborate gesture.

"Okay, Grandma," he said, still grinning. "But what are you going to do when you get married? I mean—if your husband smokes? You going to make him give up the filthy weed?"

"Certainly not. He can smoke as much as he wants to."

"Maybe in a corner of the kitchen with his face to the wall?"

Mary found herself smiling back at him. He had that effect on her and she remembered the speculation he had caused in her when he had come to work one morning about six months ago. For Harry was handsome in a black-browed, curly-headed way; he had a brash and conceited manner but he also had a quick and knowing smile, and his glance was bold, his manner assured.

Mary had felt his appeal, but she kept this to herself until, a few days later, he had had some repair work to do on her elevator. When he finished, there were grease stains on her carpet—pieces of dirt and oily lint had dropped down from the open ceiling hatch and been ground under foot. When she saw the damage she was too upset to control her indignation. She spoke with such spirit that Harry could only stare at her, then retreat fast. It had taken the cleaning woman two nights to get rid of the stains and Mary had even complained to George Allen, the engineer, who, while sympathizing with her complaint, said that elevators were always greasy and that Harry's problem had not been an easy one.

She had almost forgotten the incident when Harry appeared that afternoon just as she was ready to leave the building. When he apologized for dirtying her car and asked if she would let him take her out to dinner to prove he was forgiven, she had no impulse to refuse.

She had gone out with him three times afterward but had not liked his friends, his attitude, or his tactics in a taxi, and when he saw she meant it the invitations stopped. Even so, their relationship had remained friendly. He still joked with her and she knew that he liked her, but by then Stan Norton had become more attentive and she was glad she had sense enough to encourage him—Stan with his slow smile and serious manner, but with a solid dependability that would be more rewarding in the years to come.

But she could still laugh with Harry and she did so now.

"My husband," she said with amiable dignity, "can smoke wherever and whenever he likes. There will be plenty of ashtrays and I'm sure he will be thoughtful enough to use them."

The buxom Ethel, who had just discharged a load of passengers, had overheard the exchange and quickly took advantage of the opportunity.

"Come on, Harry," she said. "I'll give you a ride. You can put your ashes on my carpet any time . . . Besides," she added, "Mary has to carry the mail in a couple of minutes."

Harry accepted without further hesitation. "Right, baby." He waved his cigarette at Mary and grinned again. "And let that be a lesson to you, Grandma."

Ethel's reference to the mail reminded Mary of her weekly task—a task that always made her a little nervous. She let the door close partway and Cliff Forbes, who was the starter when he was not relieving one of the girls at lunch time or for a coffee break, came over to help her.

For the next minute or so he stood beside her in front of the partly open door and directed the incoming traffic to the other two cars. Then they both watched the plate-glass panel which formed one wall of the lobby and looked directly into the City Bank and Trust Company which had its main entrance on the corner.

This weekly routine on the payroll for the Tracy Company had been worked out over a period of time and was as foolproof as it could be made. At ten every Friday morning Stan Norton came down to the bank with a brown-leather valise to collect the currency which had been put up in the proper denominations. Ed Ewald, the bank guard, took a minute from his regular duties to accompany Stan across the lobby to the elevator where Mary made a nonstop run to the eighth floor. There were only two establishments here, one half the space occupied by the Tracy Construction Company and the other half by a girls' secretarial school. During the day the payroll would be made up in individual envelopes and then, shortly after the bank closed, the second half of the operation would begin.

At three o'clock Ed Ewald locked the bank doors from the inside and then changed into street clothes. Now, at ten minutes after three, Mary saw him coming toward the desk in the lobby with his hat and coat on. He nodded to her, picked up the telephone, and dialed the number of the Tracy Company to tell them that he would be ready. When he hung up, he gave a small wave of his hand and Cliff Forbes said, "Okay, Mary," and stepped away from the door.

When it clicked into place, the car started up and the nervousness which had been stirring inside her began to assert itself. She was not worried that anything might happen here—there would be no stops for the elevator, either up or down. As for Ed Ewald, he was a retired policeman who added to his regular income by guarding Stan on his weekly trip. When Stan reached the lobby Ed would fall in beside him, one hand on the gun in his pocket. They would take a taxicab for a ten minute ride to the construction project near the river, deliver the valise, and be back in less than a half-hour.

Stan had assured her many times that there was nothing to fear, but she could not ignore the possibility that something could go wrong. That was why she dreaded Fridays and why she could never feel relaxed until Stan and Ed Ewald were safely back in the Caswell Building.

Mary's car came to a gentle stop. The door slid back—and then she saw him.

He must have been standing close to the door because he was inside before she could move, and in that first terrifying instant she was so shocked that she only knew that he was a man, that he had an ugly short-barreled revolver in his hand, and that his head was covered with a large, brown-paper bag.

She felt the gun jab into her side as he stood beside her. The two eye-holes that had been cut in the bag only added to the grotesqueness of his appearance. She caught a brief glimpse of the eyes but they were in shadow and had no form, color, or shape. The voice that lashed out at her was muffled and distorted.

"Don't move—not a muscle! Make one sound and you're dead."

She could not have moved or cried out had her life depended on it. Her throat was closed, her muscles paralyzed.

"Stick your head out a little," the voice commanded. "Pretend you're watching for him. When you see him, smile."

She did so and now she saw the door down the hall open. Mr. O'Connor, the Tracy office manager, stepped out, glanced up and down. When he moved aside, Stan Norton passed in front of him and then he was walking toward her, the slow smile beginning to work on his angular face.

The gunman had heard the office door and the approaching steps, and the muzzle of the gun dug harder into her side. This time it hurt, but she did not cry out. She saw Stan's smile expand, heard him say, "Hi, sweetheart. Right on the button."

He started to step into the car before he saw the hooded figure, and then it was too late. After that, things happened so fast and were over so quickly that all her mind could retain were fleeting impressions.

She saw the sudden widening of Stan's startled gaze. She saw the color drain from his stricken face. Then he was inside the car and the valise had been snatched from his nerveless fingers. A hand reached out to spin him about so that he faced the elevator door and the gun was withdrawn from her side and jammed against Stan's spine.

"*Seven!* Get moving!"

Somehow she managed to push the correct button. The door closed and they moved down one flight and stopped again. As the door opened, a hand was planted against Stan's back and he was propelled violently into the corridor. She felt herself being jerked away from the controls. Before she could get her balance, she went spinning through the door, her shoes skidding on the waxed composition floor. By the time she could recover her balance and glance round, the elevator door had closed automatically.

The corridor was suddenly quiet and empty and when she glanced at Stan he was already moving. His face was stony, his jaw tight, and he did not stop to ask if she was all right or if she had been hurt.

"Find a phone!" he said. "Quick. Get the police!"

She understood him but in that first instant, not knowing why he should be running toward the fire door, she started after him. When he hit the heavy steel panel at the end of the corridor she realized that he was going to use the stairs and try to head off the gunman in the lobby. She also realized that with his long legs he might be able to do just that. The thought frightened her because she knew the man who had taken the valise still had the gun.

"*No, Stan! Please—*"

They were on the landing between floors when he wheeled on her and grabbed her shoulders. He shook her once, hard, and there was a desperate look in his eyes.

"The phone!" he said harshly. "Hurry!"

He was on his way down then, taking the steps in great leaps that covered three at a time and now the urgency made itself felt and she began running up the stairs. Then, because it seemed the quickest way, she scrambled out on the eighth floor and ran to the door of the Tracy Company.

She was not sure what she said. It exasperated her that she had to repeat her words to make the startled receptionist understand. Then, as the girl began to dial, the door opened at one side and Mr. O'Connor stepped from his office. She turned on him, the words tumbling out, and when Mr. O'Connor understood he wasted no time. He snapped a question at the operator to make sure she had the police on the line, then he took Mary by the arm and hurried her into the hall.

The next few minutes were a hectic period of frustration and confusion for Mary Heath. The first thing she saw when they stepped out on the lobby floor was Stan talking excitedly to Ed Ewald, and an odd sense of relief flowed through her when she realized that he was all right. She noticed next that the door of her elevator was closed and as she glanced at the signal panel on the wall, the light in the first column told her that the car had been stopped at the second floor. She heard Mr. O'Connor tell Ewald to check anyone leaving the building until the police arrived and then he ran into the second car, followed by Stan.

No one asked Mary to go with them, but she did anyway. Ethel, who had been watching mutely, had sense enough not to ask questions and Mr. O'Connor spoke only once.

"Did you bring anyone down from the second floor in the last couple of minutes?"

"No, sir."

When they found Mary's car empty, Stan wheeled and ran toward the fire door. Mr. O'Connor yelled to ask where he was going, and Stan called back over his shoulder.

"The basement. If he didn't come into the lobby he could have gone all the way down."

Mr. O'Connor blew out his breath. He looked at Mary.

"I guess there's nothing more we can do here," he said. "Might as well go back to my office and wait for the police."

Sergeant Cheney, who arrived three or four minutes after the two uniformed men from the radio squad car, took charge of the investigation. He spent most of his time in Mr. O'Connor's office, talking to people and getting reports from the detectives who were doing the legwork. He was still in the office two hours later, and so was Mary.

She was the only one who had not left the room at one time or another, and nothing happened that in any way had changed her first impression of the sergeant—an impression that left her uncomfortable and afraid. In his forties, she thought, with a suggestion of gray in his brown hair, and an impassive, squarish face that never smiled. His voice was level and unaccented but it carried a hint of suspicion, and the shrewd gray eyes seemed not only to take in each physical detail of her appearance, but assess her thoughts as well.

She could not tell whether he believed her story or not, and there was no sign that he recognized Stan Norton until all the details had been brought to light. What he said then filled Mary with a dread she had been unable to shake. She could still see the way he had looked at Stan, could hear the disconcerting effect of his words.

"I know you, don't I, Norton?"

"I guess you do," Stan had said.

"The Lollar job, wasn't it?"

"Yes, sir."

"Sort of looks like history repeating itself."

Mr. O'Connor, who had been listening with a mystified air, asked what the Lollar job was and the sergeant told him. Then, with an odd sense of despair growing in her, Mary was listening to the story of another success-

ful payroll robbery that had happened to Stan and an armed guard three
years ago when he was working for another company. The fact that eventually he had been completely exonerated did not seem now to excuse his
silence about the previous holdup. Mr. O'Connor said so and Stan replied
that he had not thought it important.

"When I came to work for you, sir, I didn't have anything to do with
the payroll."

"But later, when we decided to give you this assignment—"

"I know, sir," Stan said lamely. "I just didn't think such a thing could
happen to me twice."

Mr. O'Connor had made no further comment. He had waited while
Cheney questioned Ed Ewald, and George Allen, the engineer, and Harry
Gilmore. He had listened to reports from the detectives who were searching
the building and had been assured that everyone who had left directly after
the holdup had been given a quick but thorough inspection. When it was
all over Cheney voiced an opinion. He said that in his business he had come
to the conclusion that the obvious solution to any crime was usually the
correct one.

"What did you do with the valise, Norton? Who is in this thing with
you?"

Stan protested, and so did Mary. They had told the truth. It happened
exactly as they said it had and both mentioned that Stan had been empty-
handed when he came out of the fire door on the lobby floor; Ed Ewald
and Cliff Forbes, the starter, could also testify to that.

"Sure," Cheney had said. "But there was a window open on the second-
floor landing of those fire stairs. All you had to do," he added to Stan, "was
toss the bag out that window on your way down. There's a paved court out
there. You can get into it, or out of it, from the back door of the Taylor
Building on the next street. A guy waiting down there at the right time
could pick up the bag, go through the Taylor Building, and be home free."

Mary had waited for Stan to protest again. She had expected a vehement
and indignant denial; instead there was only a hopeless shake of Stan's head
and a barely audible word that sounded like, "No." This attitude dismayed
her but it did not prevent her from turning on Cheney, and she spoke out
in her anger, her blue eyes flashing.

She admitted that whoever took the money had to time the operation
precisely and be familiar with every detail of the routine. But what about
some of the others? What about George Allen, the engineer, who said he
was in the basement all that time, but could not prove it? What about
Harry Gilmore? He was supposed to be fixing some plumbing on the
fourth floor, but was he?

Cheney heard her out and was ready with answers. True, George Allen
had been alone in the basement workshop but there was no money there,

nor any sign of the valise—so what had happened to it? As for Harry Gilmore, he had been seen working in the fourth floor men's room by a clerk employed on that floor.

"The guy couldn't pinpoint the time," Cheney said, "but he'll swear that it was between ten and fifteen minutes after three."

Now with the office quiet and everyone gone except Cheney and his men, the sergeant sat in Mr. O'Connor's desk chair, a dead pipe in his mouth. Mary could tell that the inquisition was about over as she saw him turn to Stan.

"All right, Stanley," he said. "It's time you took a ride down to the precinct house and did some talking."

Mary, watching Stan's bony shoulders move in a faint shrug, sensed that he was deliberately avoiding her glance.

"That's all I've been doing."

"You'll talk some more. The Lieutenant will want to hear your story. He'll have some more questions. So will I. Maybe an assistant district attorney will want to get into the act. I don't know how long it will take —maybe all night. But we've got plenty of time."

Cheney stood up and sighed. "I understand you and Mary want to get married."

Stan nodded.

"You made a nice score this afternoon—nearly ten thousand bucks."

"I've told you," Stan cut in, anger finally showing in his voice.

"I know," Cheney interrupted. "But if you did I promise you'll never enjoy it. We're going to be watching you from now on. You're going to have to account for everything you spend and we'll know about every move you make. It won't be any fun—in fact, it'll be a lousy way to start a marriage . . . Let's go."

He walked to the door with Stan and spoke to one of his men; then he came back, the pipe still in his mouth, and looked at Mary.

"We'll need a statement from you too, but it can wait until morning."

"I told you the truth," Mary said woodenly.

"I'm beginning to believe you."

She wasn't sure she understood him and the faintest of hopes began to stir inside her.

"But if you believe me, you have to believe Stan."

Cheney shook his head.

"So far as *you* know, this thing happened just as you said. But there's another way you haven't thought about. Look." He leaned forward and pointed the pipestem. "Suppose a guy you never heard about—a guy who's been coached on the timing and all the details—walked in downstairs a little after three with a gun in his pocket and a folded paper bag under his coat."

He paused and put the pipe back between his teeth. "The job happens the way you said. You and Stanley get pushed off on the seventh floor. Stanley runs. You run for the telephone. This guy with the bundle rides down to the second, beats it to the fire stairs, and drops the bag out the window. He climbs up a floor or two and rides down again when he can. Who's to stop him? His hands are clean; he's got no package; he gets past the bank guard and the starter even though they search him. He goes around the block, through the Taylor Building, and—"

Mary interrupted him. She didn't like the direction Cheney's reconstruction was taking. "But how could anyone do that without Stan's help?"

"That's what I mean," Cheney said.

He did not finish. He did not have to. The meaning was perfectly clear and as they left the office and went into the hall to wait for the elevator, the thought kept penetrating Mary's consciousness with a terrible persistence. She kept thinking about that earlier robbery, and each time she thrust the thought aside by telling herself that Stan could not have planned such a thing—not the Stan she knew and loved. The sergeant *must* be wrong . . .

The elevator door slid back and when Mary stepped inside and saw the dark smudges on the carpet it was all she could do to keep from bursting into tears. Why, she asked herself, was it always like this whenever she left her car for any length of time? No one seemed to care whether it was clean and tidy and now, with the strain of the past hours working on her, she had to blink back her tears. She kept her face averted until they reached the lobby.

"I have to go back to the second floor," she said; then aware that Cheney did not understand, she added, "To the restroom to change my clothes."

The door closed again and she could not keep her eyes from the floor. The dark spots and smudges looked greasy and she wondered if the cleaning woman would be able to remove them during the night. Only once before had the carpet been so soiled and that time—

She knelt quickly as this new thought overwhelmed her. A touch of her finger told her that the smudges *were* oily, and suddenly her heart gave a little flip and she could feel an odd tension working on the emptiness inside her chest.

Something made her turn and look at a panel in the metal wall of the car. There was an almost invisible door here, its presence indicated by hairline cracks and a tiny keyhole. Its purpose was a means of escape in case the car got caught between floors. When that happened, the adjoining car could move up to the same height and, with both emergency doors open, passengers could move safely from one car to the other. There was still another way out of this car and as her glance moved to the ceiling she felt the tension grow and a new excitement plucked at her nerves.

Unaware that the car had stopped and remembering only the other time when the ceiling hatch was open and the oily pieces of dirt and lint had fallen to the floor, she reached for the round collapsible seat.

When she pulled it down from the side of the car her little whisk broom fell to the floor but this time she did not notice it. Pulling her skirts up, she got one foot on the seat and then the other, straightened up, and placed one hand flat against the metal side panel so that she could keep her balance. A flick of her finger and the little catch on the escape hatch in the ceiling clicked back and she pushed it open; then she was groping above the hatch, her probing fingers sliding over greasy metal surfaces, finally coming to an object which was definitely not metal.

She stood on tiptoe, feeling the strap of her brassiere snap as she strained to get better leverage. Her fingernails helped to draw the object a little closer and then she was pulling it, seeing the edge of the valise now in the opening and pulling still harder until it came too far, slipped from her grasp, and thumped solidly onto the carpet below.

She stepped down carefully and let the seat snap back against the elevator wall. She was still staring at the grease-stained valise when she heard a slight sound behind her. Then, as her muscles froze and she tried to turn, she heard the familiar voice.

"Well, well. So you and old Stan lifted the payroll after all?"

Harry Gilmore stood in the doorway, an odd grin on his handsome face. He looked very sharp in his blue suit with a trench coat thrown over one arm. There was also a narrowed brightness in his gaze.

"We had nothing to do with it," Mary snapped.

"Then how did you know the bag was up there?"

"I didn't." She pointed at the soiled rug. "But I remembered the last time this car was all messed up with grease and dirt was when you were up there working on the machinery with that hatch open. It gave me an idea. I don't know how you did it, Harry—that's for the police to find out—"

She stopped at a movement of his hands and then she was looking at the same revolver she had seen earlier in the afternoon. Before she could fully understand what it meant, Harry had stepped past her and tipped the hatch back into place. He picked up the valise and gestured with the gun.

"Let's go, baby."

"Go? Where?"

"To the girl's room. I'll need a little time to figure things out."

He pulled her into the hall and they walked down the corridor, turned left, and finally came to a door near the end. Mary took the key from her pocket and when the lock clicked they moved into this room which had metal lockers along one wall, a couch, three wicker chairs, a round table, and an electric grill for making coffee.

"Go ahead," Harry said. "Get on with your change."

She saw he meant it. When she realized she had no choice, she stepped over to her locker and worked the combination. She took out her gray dress and cloth coat and put them on the couch. She placed her handbag beside them. She took off her uniform jacket and tossed it aside; then, turning her back to him, she removed her blouse, gave a tug at the zipper on her skirt, and stepped out of it. For a moment only she stood in her slip but there was no room in her mind for embarrassment as she quickly pulled the dress down over her head. She wasted no time on speculation as to what might happen now, but her mind was working and she had to know how Harry had done so much alone.

"After you put Stan and me out on the seventh," she said, "you rode to the second. That gave you time enough to hide the payroll. You went to the fire stairs and made sure they were empty—Stan was probably all the way down to the first floor—and then you went back up to the fourth. When did you change your clothes?"

"There's a vacant office next to the men's john on the fourth floor. I had an old suit on under my coveralls when Ethel took me up. All I had to do in the vacant office was take off the coveralls and leave my tools."

"But that clerk who said he saw you in the men's room—"

"That was a break I hadn't counted on," Harry said. "Nobody saw me get out on the second floor or go in or out of that vacant office on the fourth. The men's room was empty and I tore up the paper bag and flushed it down the toilet. I was still working on that when this character comes in."

"And tonight you were waiting for me to leave the elevator—"

"That's right, baby, and if you hadn't been so nosey it would have been a cinch." He swore softly. "You can't open that damn hatch without some of that oily junk falling into the car, but you were the only one who noticed it."

"But all those pay envelopes?"

"That's why I brought this trench coat. It's got two pockets in it big enough to hold a crate of oranges. Now you can give me a hand."

When she turned she saw that he was inspecting her handbag. It was a large one because she carried her lunch in it every day. Harry had opened the valise and was now tucking some of the pay envelopes inside her bag. The others he distributed in the two pockets of his trench coat. Then, as she hung up her uniform in the locker, he stepped past her and put the valise at the bottom of her locker.

"That's a good place for it," he said. "When the cops find that tomorrow it should make it even tougher for your boyfriend."

"How will it?" Mary said. "I'll simply tell them the truth."

"You'll tell them nothing, baby. I've got other plans for you." He waved the gun. "Right now we're going out together. The night watchman might be down in the lobby and there could be a cop with him, but they're not going to stop us, understand? Because I'm already a two-time loser in Pennsylvania and I've gone too far with this to chicken out now. If I have to use the gun I'll do it, and if I do you're going to get it first. Understand?"

Mary was surprised to find the elevator still there until she realized that they had been gone only a few minutes. Harry Gilmore had draped the trench coat containing most of the pay envelopes over his left arm to hide the gun he was holding. He gave her a final word of caution as the car started down, but it was a phrase he had used earlier that stuck in her mind. She did not know what he meant by having plans for her, but she did understand one thing clearly: if anything did happen to her or if she did not come back, the police would find the valise in her locker and Stan would not only go to prison, he would have on his record another black mark that would remain there as long as he lived.

As they stepped from the car she saw Sergeant Cheney standing by the cigar counter talking to the night watchman and she realized this might be her one and only chance—and her last chance. But she believed what Harry Gilmore had threatened: she knew he would use the gun if he had to. She dared not make a precipitous move, but she was able surreptitiously to twist the catch on her handbag so that it snapped open.

It was the kind of bag which had two straps and when properly held they served to keep the top of it closed. Now, with the catch open, she could only hope that Cheney might catch a glimpse of what was inside. And so she moved up, her young face frozen in a half smile and all too conscious of Harry Gilmore's nearness. As they approached the cigar counter, both Cheney and Charlie Doyle, the night watchman, straightened up from the glass case.

"I thought I might give you a ride home," Cheney said.

"No, thanks, Sergeant," Mary said through stiff lips. "Harry's taking me."

"Yeah," Gilmore said. "It's no trouble."

She came to a stop as they spoke, her handbag turned toward Cheney. When nothing happened, she felt the pressure of Gilmore's arm and trench coat against her back and she started to walk again when she saw something happen to Cheney's eyes. For an instant they flicked to the handbag and seemed to fasten there. When he said, "Just a second, Mary," she made her move.

Having started to step toward the door she spun on her right foot and her arm whipped around, the bag at the end of it. She was aiming at the hand with the gun, feeling a sudden terror as she waited for a shot and finally understanding that the suddenness of her attack had startled Harry into a precious moment of inaction.

Then the bag slammed into the hidden hand and one strap broke. She heard the muffled shot that followed and saw the small pay envelopes begin to spill onto the floor. She knew she had not been hit, but when her momentum carried her against Harry he pushed her violently and she fell. She struck the marble floor on both knees, felt pain, then heard the second shot.

By the time she could get her head up and bring the scene into focus, Harry was on the floor and Cheney and the night watchman were on top of him. Suddenly Cheney had the short-barreled revolver in his hand and Charlie Doyle was jerking Harry to his feet.

Cheney was still too startled to do more than stare at her as she squirmed into a sitting position and pulled her skirt down. She was not really angry with the sergeant but reaction hit her hard and one knee was throbbing painfully. As though in protest against the hours of injustice, she spoke sharply and the words came out high-pitched.

"Now maybe you'll get it through that thick head of yours that Stan had nothing to do with the payroll robbery."

She was ashamed as soon as she said the words. Cheney came over to help her to her feet and ask her if she was all right and then she was telling him what had happened in the elevator and what she knew. It did not take long and Cheney needed no diagram. He had handcuffs on Harry Gilmore and all the pay envelopes were quickly collected and Charlie Doyle was using the telephone.

"I'm going to take this lad with me," Cheney said to her, "but there'll be a car along in a minute for you. You've had a rough day and I think you'll want to go home and maybe put some hot compresses on that knee of yours."

"And where are you taking Harry?" Mary demanded.

"To the precinct house."

"Is that where Stan is?"

"Yes."

"Then I'm going with you. If anybody's going to take me home tonight it's going to be Stan."

"All right, all right," Cheney said, and for the first time he smiled at her. It was a nice smile, genuine and sympathetic, and it changed his whole face. It seemed to Mary that for the first time he really approved of her and, thus comforted, she hitched her coat into place and patted the back of her hair. When she was ready she spoke to Charlie Doyle.

"Will you do something for me, Charlie?"

"Sure, Mary."

"Then *please* tell the cleaning woman to see if she can get those grease spots out of the carpet in my car. Right now it's a mess and I'd like it looking halfway decent in the morning when I come in."

Then, reassured by Charlie's promise, she was ready to ride with Cheney . . . to Stan.

RUN—IF YOU CAN

by CHARLOTTE ARMSTRONG

She was there, of course. She was always there. This was his home, but he never came home without finding her waiting—no matter how late.

There she was. Sitting in the stiff chair under the lamp, wearing a dark blue dress. She was his sister, his whole family, and this was his home, so he had to come here; but he stared at her hands, her splay-fingered, big-knuckled old hands, holding the Book.

"It's midnight," she said.

"I'm a big boy," he answered nastily. "I'm forty-two years old. You know that, Helen?"

He dashed across the sitting room and through the alcove to the kitchen. He found the liquor, poured a drink. The garage was locked—he had remembered to lock it.

He came back with the glass in his hand. "I need this," he whined, because he needed her. She was his sister, she was all he had. "I had a terrible scare just now. I'm pretty much shaken up. I got home all right, though. Nobody saw me."

"Somebody saw you, Walter," she said in that mad and maddening way she had, that way of being so absolutely sure.

"No, no," he said, knowing that his eyes were rolling, that he was sweating again. "Way out in the country. Not a soul around. Listen, I don't know where she came from. All of a sudden there was this little car. How could I stop? It wasn't my fault. I just couldn't stop. I did stop, afterwards." He gulped at the drink. "I don't know who she was. How could I know? I got out of there. Little bitty car, turned right over. They make them too small, too narrow . . . Listen, she was dead. There was nothing I could do for her any more—nothing."

"Alone?" his sister asked.

"Of course, alone," he said angrily. "And I got home all right, didn't I? The car's in the garage. I looked it over, as good as I could. There isn't a mark on it."

"There is a mark," his sister said.

"Quit with that stuff, will you?" he shouted. "It was an accident, I tell you! How can you stop if you're doing seventy? You don't know anything about things like that. I'm telling you, nobody saw, nobody is going to know, and you won't say anything."

"There'll be no need," she said, with the certainty that was like contempt. She had no color in her long narrow face. She never had. Even her lips had no color. Her pale hands lifted the Book. "Nothing shall be hidden," she whispered.

She drove him nuts sometimes. "I couldn't do anything for her, could I? It wasn't really my fault, was it? I'd been driving a long time and my eyes were tired. I couldn't help that, could i? It's too bad. I mean, I'm sorry. I'm upset, believe me I am. Tomorrow I'll change all the tires on the car. I'm not . . ."

Her eyes were set deep, and the eye sockets caught shadows.

"Don't talk about it," he cried, although she was not speaking. "Listen, I'm all in. I had a shock. I got to get some sleep. I had an awful shock and I'm tired. So don't talk about it."

She said nothing. But he went staggering away, off to his bedroom. He'd sleep. He'd take a pill—two of them, to make sure. She wouldn't approve. Helen didn't approve of anything. He ought to get away from her; but he couldn't get away. Curled up in his bed, he could hear her moving around the apartment, making everything neat for the night . . . and somehow he felt safe.

"You're late," she said, when he came home from work the next night and stood, tense and wary, just inside the door.

"Anybody come around? Anybody poking around the garage?"

"No."

"The bus was slower than molasses," he grumbled, and then took a few steps, on tiptoe. Which was absurd. "It's in the evening paper," he told her. "Her name was Mary Lovelace. Lovelace. Some name, eh? She was dead, all right. Some farmer found her, about four in the morning." He moistened his lips. "Hit-and-run, they say in the paper."

"Yes," said his sister, nodding agreement. "Dinner is waiting."

"There was nothing I could do, was there? I didn't see her. I couldn't stop. Didn't mean to do it. Listen, it happens every day—every day. Forget it. Get dinner on, will you?"

"As soon as you wash up, Walter," his sister said.

But at the table he kept talking and talking. "I looked at the car this morning, by daylight, and I couldn't see a thing. Nothing's dented. Didn't scrape the paint, not that I can make out. No glass broken. But I'm not going to drive it, Helen. See, they've got these police laboratories. It's spooky what they can come up with. One speck of dust, maybe, and you're a gone goose. What am I going to do with the car?"

"It doesn't matter what you do with the car," she said.

"Oh, come on," Walter shoved his chair back. "You're nuts, you know that, Helen? *You* ought to know that. I know it. So I'm taking care of this. And you're not going to open your mouth about it—not one word."

He grinned and looked sly, because he was sure. She was all he had, his whole family, and she would not betray him.

"I have prayed for you," she said.

"You'd do better to try and help me figure out how to get rid of it. Of the car, I mean. The *car.*" (Sometimes she looked so stupid!) "Say I buy four new tires. But who knows if they're checking up on sales like that? Say I have a new paint job done. Same thing—they may be checking. What I've got to do, I've got to be a little bit smarter than that, that's all."

She said nothing. She just looked at him in that stupid way.

"Also," he continued, finding some ease in voicing his anxieties, "I know better than to drive it out to the desert, or some place, and just leave it. They'd pick it up and trace it so fast . . . Well, so I can't run it off some cliff into the ocean, either. They'd find it—you can bet on it. They'd want to know how and why. So how am I going to get rid of that car?"

His sister whispered, "How are you going to get rid of your sin?"

"What sin?" he bellowed. "Sure, I broke the law. I know that. Sure, there's a law that says you've got to report a thing like that. Well, I didn't want to report it. I didn't want to be in a mess over just an accident—an unavoidable accident, I tell you! Nobody saw. Nobody knows. Nobody *will* know, if I can only get rid of the car. So that's my problem."

"Why don't you sell it?" she said in a moment.

"What will I do? Trade it in? And the cops find it on a secondhand lot? And there are records kept—damn it, you don't understand."

"I understand better than you," she sighed.

"Oh, shut up, will you? Will you, please? I'm *going* to get rid of the car and the whole mess with it. There must be a way. I'll figure out a way. I can't eat," he said. "I don't want any more dinner." He glowered at her. "Don't you get any nutty idea *you'll* go to the police."

"It won't be necessary," she said.

He flung himself up from the table. "It'll stay in the garage till Saturday. I'll do something about it on Saturday."

"You cannot—"

He interrupted viciously, "You want to bet? You want to put your money where your mouth is, just once in your life? You're getting worse all the time. You know that, Helen? I'm going to buy us a television set too."

He mumbled away into the sitting room. They didn't even have a televi-

sion set. She read one Book—one Book all the time. He had to go watch
television in some bar.

As soon as Walter turned the Saturday sports page, he saw the ad. Carrying the paper, he trotted to where his sister was watering her row of potted
plants in the kitchen window.

"I got it," he told her. "Listen to this swap ad. Talk about perfect! This is
it, Helen.

" 'Exchange: Fine view lot for late model auto. Must be in good condition for long trip. Quick deal. Phone——'

"So?" he cried. "Isn't this it? Isn't it?" She straightened her long flat back,
and her thin neck lengthened. "The perfect way to get rid of the car," he
cried impatiently. "I'll swap it for whatever he's got. A lot, it says here."

"A piece of land?"

"All right! I need a lot like a hole in the head. What's the difference?
Here's a man, he's going on a long trip and he's going quick. So let *him*
drive that car out of the state and that's the way to be rid of it."

"Do you think so?" his sister said tonelessly.

"The deal gets recorded, sure. But so what? License number, engine
number, make and model, and all that. So what about it? They won't tell
anything. The car itself will be gone, far away. So how will the police ever
get the car into their laboratories? This is going to be the way, I tell you,
and it'll work."

"There is another way," she said.

"What way?"

"Confess."

"Oh for . . . ! Listen, I could go to jail! Which I am *not*." Walter
flung himself off to the telephone.

When he hung up, he was sweating a little. But he said to his sister (to
whom else could he say anything?), "Sounds good. Fellow wants me to run
over to his place right away, and we can go take a look at this lot. Well,
from his point of view it makes sense, you know? So I got to take the
chance and drive the car. He's only two, three miles away. Then this lot is
way up in the hills and who's going to be up there? Nobody's been around
here yet, and it's four days. Listen, the best of it is, he wants to take off on a
trip tonight! So this is really it—the way out."

His sister said nothing and he shouted to her silence. "What can happen?
Nothing is going to happen. You're going to keep your mouth shut and
you are the only one who knows."

"I am not the only one who knows," she said.

"God knows, eh?" snarled Walter. "You give me the creeps sometimes.
You know what you are, Helen? You're superstitious, that's what you are.

You're a real nut with this stuff. You don't understand this world at all. I'm going, and I'm going to get rid of the car."

"Go with God," she said sadly.

"With or without, I'm *going*," he shouted, sweating.

But Walter went in terror and he knew it. He backed his car out of the garage for the first time since the accident and walked all around it, convincing himself that there was absolutely no visible sign of any damage. Nothing to betray him.

Then he drove off, carefully. The sight of a prowl car drenched him in sweat, but the policemen didn't even see him.

He was peering at house numbers when a tall thin young man came walking toward him with an air of having been waiting impatiently. He said his name was Anderson. He seemed to have no time to waste and no inclination for small talk. He paid little attention to the appearance of the car, to the paint or the chrome. He did lift the hood. Then he got into the driver's seat and Walter, who kept talking nervously, got in beside him.

"I take care of a car," Walter babbled. "I believe in that. I'm not one of these people who runs a car into the ground. A car's a valuable piece of property. She runs pretty sweet, wouldn't you say?"

Anderson, testing the car's functioning, drove up into the hills along winding streets and then, above the streets, on winding roads. Then he stopped.

"This it?" Walter blinked. Oh, yes, he had better show some interest in the lot.

They got out and Walter blinked again. There was a fine view. The great basin of Los Angeles lay, wide and beautiful in spite of itself, below them. The lot was more level than most. Anderson pointed out the boundary stakes. It wasn't a bad size, either.

"That's it," said the young man with his air of impatient briskness. "I'll take the car if you'll take the lot. Is it a deal?"

Walter licked his lips. "You'll take the car," he said slowly, "and be gone. Right? But this real estate—the title check, the closing? I mean, what guarantee do I have?"

"I've got the deed in my pocket and my lawyer, with a power of attorney, can handle the details. Suppose I have him meet us right away."

"You don't . . . er . . . want to stick around, yourself till Monday?"

"No," said Anderson, and his voice was positive.

Walter glanced around the site once more. "Looks okay," he admitted. "I mean, how can it miss? Unless there's a gimmick. Eh, Mr. Anderson?"

The young man turned his back and started toward the car. "If you don't want it, say so."

"Title clear? No liens?" Walter walked after him.

"That's what I said. You know they'll search it. Well? If not, say so and I'll find another car."

"Well, I'll tell you—" Suddenly Walter recalled his prime motive. "Okay, it's a deal. Say the car is yours, the lot is mine, even swap, as of right now. Okay?"

"Okay."

In the sunlight, on the high hillside, with the wind on them, they shook hands on it.

There remained only the paperwork. Walter said, "Why don't we do this over a cup of coffee? I'll drive. There's a short cut down to my place from here. You can call your lawyer to come over to my place, can't you?" Now he was anxious to get it done with.

"Any way that's quick," Anderson said.

On the way downhill, Walter kept glancing at the face of his silent companion. "This trip," he said, "you taking off tonight?"

"Yes—right away."

"Going far?"

"As far as I can go."

Walter said no more. When they came to the apartment building in which he and Helen lived, he ran the car around the corner and into the garage, pretending that he was doing this absent-mindedly. He apologized and left the garage door open. It was safe enough. He then led his companion up the stairs.

She was there, of course. She was always there.

"This is my sister, Helen, Mr. Anderson. We've got some business," he added quickly, before she could speak. His tone told her that the business was none of hers. "Make us some coffee, will you, Helen?" He showed Anderson to the phone. While Anderson was using it, Walter followed his sister into the kitchen.

"This is it," he said, "So keep still. Swear to me, you'll keep your mouth shut."

Her pale lips parted. Her pale eyes in their deep caverns looked at him with pity. Then they closed, and her lips closed.

The two men sat down at the table in the alcove and began to produce what papers they had. Helen brought in the coffee silently. She left them and sat down in the stiff chair in the other room, and took the Book into her hands.

When there was nothing more to do until the lawyer arrived, there seemed nothing more to say. Anderson glanced at the woman in the chair, glanced at his watch. Walter began to find the silence too hard to bear. "This lawyer *is* coming, isn't he?"

"In a few minutes."

"How do I know—?" Walter began. Then he controlled himself. "Kind of in a hurry, aren't you, Mr. Anderson?" he inquired.

"I'd like to be on my way."

"Well, all we got to do is wait for this . . . er . . . friend of yours."

Walter looked up slyly from under lowered brows. He was nobody's pigeon. How did he know that the man they were waiting for was, in fact, a lawyer?

Anderson looked at his watch again. He glanced through the arch at the silent woman, stiff in the stiff chair.

Walter said, "How come you don't own a car? A young fellow like you. I was kind of wondering."

"I own a car. It's in bad shape."

"No trade-in value?"

"Not worth bothering about."

Walter twitched. After a moment he said, "How long did you say you owned that lot, Mr. Anderson?"

"I didn't say," snapped the young man. He seemed about to jump out of his skin. "A little more than a year," he answered, rather coldly.

"More coffee?" asked Walter, beginning to rise.

"No. No, thanks."

Walter sighed and began to wish that his sister would get up and come over to them and act like—well, like a woman. Chat a little, be pleasant. But she just sat there. He jerked his head to get Anderson's eye and said in a low voice, "My sister's quite a Bible reader. Kind of wrapped up in that stuff, you know?"

"I see." But the man didn't see. He wasn't even listening. He was studying his left hand that clenched and opened and clenched again, in rhythmic tension.

Walter was too nervous to remain silent. "To me," he said, "the times are modern, right? I do my best. I work for a living. I'm a businessman." He went on uncontrollably. "Looks to me, if you'd hang on to that property six months or another year you ought to turn a nice profit. Right now— you know this, don't you?—it's worth more than a second-hand car."

"We have agreed," said Anderson stiffly.

"Oh, sure. Sure, we got a deal. I'm not complaining. No offense, Mr. Anderson. But what would it hurt, for instance, if you'd take your hair down a bit. Eh? Just for the sake of my curiosity, why don't you tell me? What's the gimmick?"

"The what?"

"The hitch? What's wrong with that lot?"

Anderson started to get up.

"No, no," said Walter quickly, holding a protective hand over the papers. "The deal is set. That's what I'm saying. Just looks to me like you're on the short end. I'm wondering why, that's all."

The man stared at him stonily.

"See, it's been my experience," Walter went on, unable to restrain himself, "that people don't ever get something for nothing—not in this world, hah, hah!"

The doorbell rang.

"Get the door, will you, Helen?" Walter called. She rose. He heard a man's voice say politely, "I am looking for a Mr. Robert Anderson."

Helen said nothing.

"Oh, for . . . !" Walter stood up. "Right this way," he called out.

He felt a deep relief, but the aftertaste of his curiosity was still strong. So he looked down and said to the young man softly, "Listen, does *he* know where the body is buried? Maybe?"

Anderson's eyes flashed. He called out the lawyer's name. An older man came toward them, well-dressed, crisp and businesslike in speech and manner. It took only a few minutes more—a few signatures. Then all three rose and Walter held out the car keys.

Anderson snatched the keys and began to cross the sitting room, moving quickly. Walter shuffled fast to keep alongside. He was convinced, now, that this man was running away. But from what?

They almost collided as Anderson stopped and murmured to Helen, still sitting in her chair, "Happy to have met you."

Her pale lips did not open. Oh, she was a nut, *really,* thought her brother.

"Come on," he said crossly, "you can say good-bye to the gentleman, Helen."

"God be with you, gentleman," she said.

This was odd enough to hold Anderson for a moment, as the lawyer, briefcase in hand, joined them.

"Good-bye," he said pleasantly to Helen, and then to Walter, "Good-bye. I'll be seeing you, perhaps. Good luck with your acquisition."

Then Walter was whining at their backs—he just couldn't help it. "Look, gents, excuse me, but that lot is worth five, six thousand, if it's worth a nickel. All right. I'm stuck with it now. And that's okay. But what's the gimmick? Please?"

The lawyer said severely, "No gimmick."

"But there *has* to be a gimmick," cried Walter.

"And you have to know, don't you?" asked Anderson hoarsely.

"Don't, Bob," said the lawyer, touching his client's arm. "We're through here. Let's go."

"Now wait," said Walter frantically. "This is beginning to look pretty funny."

"Funny?" said Anderson. "I bought that lot to put a dream house on it for my bride. There is no bride."

"I see. I see." Walter was deflated so suddenly that he almost fell. "I'm sorry. I didn't realize it was personal. That's okay, then." He was nodding. "Yes, that's all right."

"All right?" said Anderson on a note of rising anger. "All right?"

Walter had begun to sweat. He looked behind him. His sister, with the Book in her hands, had her head high, and on her pale lips was the weird little smile—the smile that was going to drive him nuts one of these days.

"She was driving my sports car last Tuesday night," said Anderson violently, "and somebody flipped her into a ditch. So there'll be no dream house and I never want to see the site of it again. That's what's the matter with the lot."

Now Walter was not only sweating, he was shaking from head to foot.

It was the lawyer who held out his hand in farewell. Walter didn't dare touch it. "Listen. Excuse me. I'm sorry. I didn't mean anything. So long, I mean . . . Go with God," Walter bleated idiotically. A high giggle came out of him.

"Shall we go, Bob?" the lawyer said softly.

But Anderson said, "What's the matter here?"

Walter's jowls were shaking. "No, no," he said. He spread his hands. The palms were wet. "Why should there be a gimmick? Nothing's the matter here—nothing at all."

Anderson's eyes bored into Walter's, then swerved to Helen's.

"What is it?" he said to her, sharply.

But her lips were closed.

For Walter, something cracked. "You're crazy, Helen," he shrieked. "You know that? She's crazy," he sobbed to the two men. "Don't *listen* to her! *Shut your mouth!*" he howled to his silent sister.

The lawyer had dropped any intention of leaving. Anderson spoke, in the stern and quiet voice of doom. "I think you'd better tell me. What's wrong with the car? What's the gimmick?"

LINE OF COMMUNICATION

by ANDREW GARVE

Larry Seton watched the two men come up through the trapdoor. The thin one came first, warily, with the flick knife open and pointing. When he was clear the other followed.

The big man lowered the trapdoor, holding it with his foot while he made a looped twine handle from a spool he'd brought with him. The old rope handle had pulled out, leaving a hole, and the last time they'd come up they'd had trouble raising the trapdoor from above once it was shut.

The thin man crossed to Larry and gave him a piece of paper, a grubby envelope, and a ballpoint pen. "Okay, write," he said.

Larry wrote as instructed:

Dear Father,

I'm sending you this note so you'll know that what the men said on the telephone was true. They're keeping me locked up in a room where no one ever comes. They say they'll kill me if they don't get the £50,000 and I think they mean it. They are going to phone you again at ten o'clock tomorrow evening. Please do as they say about the money and don't try to bring the police in. I'm in good health but rather scared. One of them has a knife. I hope I shall see you again.   Larry

He addressed the envelope and handed it back with the note and the pen. The thin man read the note and gave a satisfied grunt. The big man then raised the trapdoor with the loop he'd improvised and the two of them backed down.

"You'll soon be okay now, mate," the thin man called, as he closed the trapdoor and shot the bolt underneath.

Larry doubted it. Not that he thought his father wouldn't pay the money. The old man was rich, and he'd take the one chance that was offered, however slender it seemed. He'd hope that the kidnappers would keep their word and let Larry go when the money was paid.

But Larry knew they wouldn't. They couldn't afford to—because he knew who they were, and they knew he knew. He'd seen them at his father's factory, where they'd been working as building laborers on a plant extension until a week or two ago. He didn't know their names, but if he ever got free again he'd be able to tell the police enough to make their capture certain.

So he wouldn't be allowed to go free. Once they'd got the money, they'd kill him. Larry had read the intention in the thin man's vicious little eyes.

He gazed desperately around his prison. It was a bare loft, about twelve feet by twenty, poorly lit and black with grime. It had no exit but the trapdoor, and no windows. The sloping raftered sides met in a square of flat roof with a skylight in it that had lost all its glass—but the skylight was at least ten feet up and barred with iron rods. There was no way of escape.

No chance, either, of making a fight of it—not a successful one. Larry was sixteen and well setup—but you couldn't argue with a knife. *He* couldn't, anyway. And the kidnappers always came up together. They never gave him an even chance.

It would have been different if he had a weapon. But there wasn't anything in the loft that he could use. A few bits of glass on the damp boards beneath the skylight—but they were too small to be effective against a knife. A wooden orange crate that they'd brought up to serve as a writing table—too unwieldy to make much of a weapon.

Apart from that, they'd left him with almost nothing. A plastic cup and a plastic water container. A plastic bucket. A plastic plate which still held the remnants of his meager supper. A few candles for use at night. The spool of twine that the big man had chucked into a corner after fixing the trapdoor. And that, literally, was all.

For a moment Larry concentrated on the new object—the spool of twine. It was a big spool, machine-rolled, and the cord was strong. Could he use it? Fantastic ideas chased each other through his head. Rig up a trip line? Weave it into some kind of net? Garotte one of the men with it? Not very promising . . .

If there had been a window he might have dangled something down and tried to attract attention. But there was no window. Or if the skylight had been lower, he might have tried throwing the spool through the bars, with a message on it. He wondered if it was possible.

He put the orange crate under the skylight and climbed onto it. The box was old and frail and gave out ominous cracks. Cautiously he raised his hand. He was still short of the bars by more than two feet. And it would be difficult to throw the spool through the bars, which were only about four inches apart. And even if he got it through, it would only go straight up and fall straight down again onto the flat roof. No good. He'd need a rocket to get it away from the roof. . . .

A rocket! No chance of that, of course—but it started a train of thought. . . .

He climbed down and stood considering. *Could* he? He gazed up through the skylight. Light clouds were moving steadily across the evening sky. Quite fast. There was plenty of wind up there—he could feel the draft through the opening.

He looked around, appraising his resources. The twine, the bits of glass, the wooden crate. The nylon shirt he was wearing. Yes, there was just a chance. Anyway, what did he have to lose?

He examined the bits of glass. There was one piece with a sharp edge. That should do. He examined the crate. The thin strips of wood that formed its sides would probably give him what he needed. It would take time—but he had plenty of that.

He lit a candle in the failing light and stuck it in his cup. Then he peeled off his shirt and spread it on the floorboards. There was more than enough material in the shirt tail, if he was careful and made no mistake. He'd better mark it out first. But with what?

He looked about him. Dirt from the floor mixed with water? Or dirt from the rafters? He ran a finger along one of them. It came away coated with soot. There was so much soot that he could scrape it off into his hand.

He made a little pile of it on the floor, puddled it, and applied some to a bit of the shirt with a sliver of wood from the crate. The mixture wasn't as good as ink, but it left a mark. Yes, it would do.

Cautiously now, using the crate as a straight edge, he sketched his quadrilateral on the nylon shirt. The last time he'd done this sort of thing was five years ago—but he hadn't forgotten the lore his father had taught him. It wasn't the size that mattered, but the proportions—and those he remembered. The two lower sides one and a half times the upper sides. Leave enough material for turning in and sewing. And four flaps for making pockets to hold the struts . . . That should do it.

Cutting out the shape was a long job. The nylon was strong and wouldn't tear easily. The piece of glass wasn't nearly as sharp as a pair of scissors. The final result was ragged at the edges—but it would serve.

Now for the struts. Pull one of the thin battens from the box. Score down it with the glass, half an inch from the edge. Deeper, now. Then the other side. Now a little pressure . . . The wood split and he had his vertical strut.

He worked quietly, methodically, intent on the job. The kidnappers had taken his watch and he could only guess at the time. Occasionally he lit a fresh candle from the stump of the old one.

Sewing the edges, and making the pockets for the struts, was another long job. He used a loose nail from the crate to make the holes, and twine from the spool to thread through them. He tied the struts where they crossed. Finally he stood back and examined his handicraft.

It wasn't much of a kite. All the same, if he could get it through the skylight, it should fly. When it was well up, he'd let go, and it was bound to fall soon, carrying the message he was going to write on it.

It was only when he began to think about the message that he realized he had almost no information to give. He had no idea where he was. He could remember nothing from the time he'd been knocked out till he'd come round in the loft. He thought he was in a city, because of the distant hum of traffic, but he didn't know if he was still in London.

A dirty loft at the top of a building—that was all the description he could give and that wasn't likely to bring rescue. He could say that his kidnappers had worked at the factory—but that wouldn't bring rescue either—certainly not in time. Besides, there wasn't enough room on the kite for a long message. With his improvised ink, the letters would have to be large and thick to be legible.

He pondered. There was no point in letting the kite loose without adequate directions. Better to keep it tethered, and say who had sent it up. When the wind dropped, it would fall, and someone would find it and follow the string. Yes, that was the best bet. . . .

He wrote his message with laborious care. Big letters, well blacked in. FROM LARRY SETON. Every newspaper reader would know his name by now. TELL POLICE. DON'T BREAK STRING. That should do it.

Once more he considered. Assuming the kite flew, how long a line should he give it? In a way, the shorter the better—it would be quicker and easier for the police to follow the string. But suppose it came down on a rooftop—or in a tree? It might not be found at all.

Better to let it fly high and have more than one message. Spaced along the string. Then, wherever it fell, there'd be a good chance that one of the messages would be seen. He cut out some strips of nylon and wrote the same words on each one.

Now he was ready to try the kite. He made the end of the twine fast to it and climbed again onto the orange crate. He could just manage to push the kite through the bars. It lay flat on top of them, stirring a little in the wind but not lifting enough to take off. Somehow he'd have to raise it, give it a start.

He thought for a moment, then broke another batten from the crate and set to work to cut it into strips. Four strips tied to each other with twine made a long rod. He climbed back on the crate and poked the improvised rod through the bars. At the second attempt he found the kite's balancing point and raised it on the rod. In a moment the wind caught it and it was off, straining at the twine, beautifully steady.

Larry could only guess how much twine he was letting out into the darkness above. At what he thought was a couple of hundred feet he tied on one of his strip messages. He let out more twine, then tied on another. Near the end of the string he tied a third.

Now for tethering the kite. The twine had been wound on a stout cardboard cylinder. Placed crosswise under the bars, that would do the trick. Of course, the kidnappers might notice it when they came up in the morning. But they might also notice that the twine on the spool was gone —or that the crate had been partly dismantled. The whole operation was a gamble.

With the end of the twine fast to the cylinder, Larry climbed once more onto the crate. He would have to stretch his arm to the limit to make sure the cylinder got wedged under and across the bars. Balanced on the crate, he reached for the skylight, straining, the cylinder at his fingertips. . . . Then, without warning, with a sudden splintering crash, the crate collapsed under him. As he fell, the cylinder slipped from his grasp. When he looked up from the floor, he saw that it had been drawn through the bars and had disappeared.

He put on the remnants of his shirt, and his jacket, and sank to the floor in despair. With the kite loose, the message he'd written would help no one. FROM LARRY SETON. TELL POLICE. DON'T BREAK STRING. Nobody would find him on that information. It had all been in vain.

Superintendent Grant, in charge of the Seton kidnapping case, was in his office with Larry Seton's father. He had just seen the letter that had arrived from Larry that morning. Now he and Seton were discussing what action to take. Seton, gray with anxiety and sleeplessness, wanted to pay the ransom and keep the police out of it. Grant wanted to set a trap. They were still arguing when Sergeant Ellis entered.

"This has just been brought in, sir. Found in North London—Primrose Hill."

The sergeant put a kite on the table. There was a short length of twine, about twenty feet, attached to it, with a frayed end where the string had snapped.

Grant read the message, fingered the black lettering, examined the fabric. "Could be another hoax," he said doubtfully. He'd already been led off on one false scent.

Seton shook his head. "It's genuine—I'm sure of it." His voice had an edge of excitement. "Larry and I used to make kites like this when he was a lad. We were pretty expert—and he's remembered the model. The proportions are the same, the shape's right. I'm as sure he made it as though he'd put his signature on it."

"I see." Grant grew brisk. "Where exactly was it found, Sergeant?"

"Hanging down over a window at twelve Lucy Street—a boarding house. Chap living there—name of Forbes—found it this morning and dropped it in at his local station."

"We might be able to find the rest of the string and trace it back," Seton said eagerly. "It might lead us to Larry . . ."

Grant nodded. "Let's go."

The Superintendent studied the upper part of 12 Lucy Street through binoculars. Presently he gave a grunt. "I can see it. It's hanging from the gutter—looks as though it goes over the top of the house. Let's try the next street."

They drove round and quickly picked up the trail again. From the house the string crossed the street at rooftop level. With many detours they continued to follow its route. In several places it was broken and they had to cast about for the next piece. Twice they were helped by the sight of scraps of white material attached to it.

They traced it over buildings, over the branches of a tree, across a coal yard, between two coupled coal cars on a rusty railroad track, past a group of men preparing to unload the first car, on over a factory roof. Then, when hope was rising fast, they came upon a cardboard cylinder hanging from a street light, with broken twine attached. Beyond, there was nothing.

"Larry must have let it go," Seton said, with deep dejection.

Grant nodded. "Maybe he was interrupted before he could make it fast. Bad luck. Still, we've got something to work on."

He returned to the police car and radioed urgent instructions.

It took a squad of policemen and a fire-department truck more than two hours to collect all the bits of string they could find. Each one had to be numbered and labeled and its exact position marked on a street map before removal. There were eight breaks, all of them at street crossings—caused, no doubt, by passing traffic.

Back at New Scotland Yard, Grant had the pieces of string put together and measured. Allowing for the street gaps where sections had been carried away, the total length was almost 2000 feet. The recovery data, now plotted on a big wall map, showed that the line had fallen, with much bunching and many twists and turns, in a roughly northerly direction from Lucy Street. To the point where they had found the cardboard cylinder the beeline distance was 1200 feet. Somewhere beyond that, perhaps a long way beyond, was Larry.

*   *   *

Grant said, "You're the expert, Mr. Seton. What would you expect to happen to a kite flying on a two thousand-foot string when the end was released?"

Seton shook his head. "It's hard to say. Every kite behaves differently. The strength and consistency of the wind would clearly be a big factor. The weight of the string would be another. In general, if there was a good wind I'd expect the kite to shoot up rapidly for a short distance, lifting the string with it. Then it would begin to fall, fluttering down, diving and looping, making a good deal of leeway with the wind and carrying the string with it. To find out what this kite did, one would have to fly it experimentally in exactly the same weather conditions—and that's obviously impossible."

"We don't even know when the kite was released," Sergeant Ellis said.

Grant frowned. "What time was it found?"

"One o'clock this morning, sir. That was the time Forbes arrived home from a party. He got into bed and then he heard a tapping on the window. It annoyed him, so he went to see what was causing it, found the kite dangling, and yanked it in. He didn't put on a light, so he didn't see what was written on it till this morning . . . Anyway, he was sure it was one o'clock when he found it."

"Then just before one o'clock is the latest time it could have been released," Grant said. "Now what about the earliest time?"

"Well, Forbes said it wasn't there when he left for work yesterday morning, or he'd have seen it dangling."

"So it was released some time between, say, eight o'clock yesterday morning and one o'clock this morning. Seventeen hours . . . I wonder if the Met people can help us."

Grant was on the phone for some time, making notes as the Met man talked. His expression grew gloomier as he wrote.

"Not much help, I'm afraid," he said, as he hung up. "What you might call typical English weather. The wind yesterday morning was southwesterly, force five. In the afternoon it veered through northwest to north, dropping to force three. At night a narrow ridge of high pressure crossed London and the wind was northeasterly, force two at first, increasing to force three. Then in the early morning it backed again to northwesterly, force two."

"So we're no further forward," Seton said. "The kite was obviously released when the wind was in the northern quadrant—but which bit of the quadrant, and at what force?"

"If only there was some way of narrowing down the time," Grant said. He sat silent for a while. Then a speculative look crept into his face. "Those coal cars that were being unloaded—I wonder . . ."

Once more he reached for the telephone.

*   *   *

This time, when he hung up, his expression was jubilant. "A long shot—
but it worked. Those two coal cars were shunted in just after ten o'clock
last night—and the string fell between them. So now we know the kite was
released between ten o'clock and one. I think I'll have another word with
the Met office."

He made more notes as he repeated the information for the others to
hear. "Ridge of high pressure—yes. Wind northeasterly force three up to
five thousand feet throughout the period . . . Wind steady, not gusty
. . . Now tell me, is there any place nearby where those conditions are
being repeated at this moment? . . . Ridge has moved on—I see . . .
Yorkshire? What part of Yorkshire? . . . Anywhere in the East Riding.
And for how long? . . . About four hours." Grant glanced at his watch.
"Thanks a lot."

He hung up. "Right," he said. "Let's go to Yorkshire and fly a kite."

Just under three hours later, an Army helicopter set down the police
party on a disused airfield a few miles inland from the Yorkshire coast. A
cool but gentle breeze was blowing steadily from the northeast. The sky
was clear.

Grant positioned his men and Seton put the kite up. It rose quickly and
smoothly as the knotted twine was let out. In a few minutes Seton was left
with the bare cylinder. For a moment he held on. The kite was almost
stationary, a mere dot against the blue.

"Right, let her go," Grant said.

Seton released the cardboard cylinder. It shot about fifty feet into the air,
then drifted away out of sight as the kite hesitated, began to dive, turned
and twisted, and slowly fluttered to earth.

A distant watcher signaled where the kite had fallen and the police got to
work, checking the distance from release point to impact point, and the
direction. Grant noted the results in his book. The kite had fallen 2250 feet
from the point of release, on a magnetic bearing of 215 degrees.

Back at the Yard in the early evening Grant drew a circle on the wall
map—2250 feet from 12 Lucy Street, on the reverse compass bearing.

"Well, that should be it," he said. "Somewhere in there. Now what kind
of place are we going to look for?"

"A pretty high building," Seton said. "With some sort of exit to a roof,
I should think, or I can't see how Larry could have got the kite up."

"Probably not a private dwelling," Sergeant Ellis added. "Kidnappers
wouldn't risk keeping anyone shut up where there were other people
around—particularly after all the publicity there's been. These villains usu-

ally hide out in vacant premises—empty warehouses, garages, that sort of thing."

Grant nodded. "I was thinking the same. An industrial building of some sort. I've just had the lab report on the substance used for the message on the kite. It's soot . . . Right, let's go."

The circle, they found, enclosed an area of dingy tenement buildings, a few factories, a scrap-metal dump, and a surprising amount of waste ground. Only the occasional new housing units relieved the squalor.

Grant divided his force into groups, each with a walkie-talkie, and allotted them streets. Every building of the slightest interest was to be reported on and discussed.

Within the circle itself they found nothing. Grant widened the field of search to take in the surrounding streets. It was almost dusk when Sergeant Ellis suddenly exclaimed, "How about that, sir?"

Grant looked ahead at the building. A blackened sign on the wall read: "Oakley Furniture Company. Depository and Repairs." It was a tall building, Victorian Gothic with a kind of tower at one end.

As they drew nearer, Grant saw that it was in fact only the skeleton of a building. Fire had gutted it. Notices above the corrugated iron fence enclosing the site warned: "Danger, keep out." But not everyone had kept out, for two of the corrugated sheets had been forced apart, leaving a two-foot gap.

Cautiously Grant led the way through the gap. He saw at once that not all the building had been destroyed. At the tower end there was a flight of stone steps, intact. They climbed. Soot lay thickly everywhere—soot from the fire.

Through a broken door on the first landing they saw junk, broken furniture, black and abandoned stores. Tensley Grant pointed—to a dirty spool of twine. "Used for furniture repairs," he said softly. "This is it."

They came to a closed door. Voices were audible from inside. Superintendent Grant gently tried the door. It opened a fraction. Sergeant Ellis moved quietly up beside him.

"Right," Grant said, and they burst in. Two men were playing cards on the floor by candlelight. They sprang up.

"Okay," Grant said, "take it easy. We're the police. Where is he?"

The thin man with the vicious little eyes gave an involuntary glance upward. Seton shouted, "Larry!"—and made for the ladder.

DANGER AT DEERFAWN
by DOROTHY B. HUGHES

Dorian said, "Tomorrow we go to Deerfawn Manor."

"Not me," said Jix. Inelegantly when you figure we were in Stratford-upon-Avon, Shakespeare's home town. But then Shakespeare was a great one for the vernacular himself.

"Not me," I echoed also ungrammatically, thankful that Jix at last had taken a stand against his sister's youthful vigor. When I, an assistant-assistant professor of drama from the unsuccessful side of the family, had greedily clutched at the gift horse of a summer in England keeping an eye on my young Hunter cousins, I hadn't considered that Twenty-seven doesn't have the bottomless pit of vitality of Nineteen and Twenty-two.

"And may I ask why not?" Dorian set her elbows on the table, almost but not quite bowling over our mugs of ale. The oaken tables at The Mace and Swan, an old Tudor black-and-white, timber-and-brick pub on Sheep Street, slanted in a Cotswolds downhill.

If Dorian had her way we wouldn't miss one Roman clump of stones, one Saxon antic column, one eroded Norman tympanum, nor one field or hall where the Edwards and Henrys and Charleses might have stopped to rest their horses and yeomen in that order. She'd been mesmerized last term by a fair-haired Briton who was giving a course in English history at Miss Waverly's Finishing School for Young Ladies—now called, in reverse snobbery, Waverly Junior College.

"I'm tired," I said. "My feet hurt. Tomorrow I plan to do nothing more strenuous than recline by the banks by the Avon and commune with the swans."

"And you?" Dorian's gray eyes stoned her brother.

"I'm up to here with manor houses," murmured Jix, his eyes on the touring South Carolina girl several tables away—the one who looked like a strawberry ice-cream cone, not the one who looked like a flute.

"Then I'll go alone." It was all of eight miles to Deerfawn. But Dorian was of an age where for status a girl must have males in tow, if only a big brother and an aging cousin. "And you can forget about the Triumph."

Jix had hire-purchased a snazzy red Triumph convertible in London. The deal was one of those with the privilege of applying the payments on full purchase later. Jix wanted it for keeps. Dorian had a way with their father. But Jix had to toe the line for her support; this tour was Dorian's party, her graduation gift.

Without removing his eyes from South Carolina, Jix agreed, "Okay, okay, I'll go." If he hadn't been wearing that particularly noxious brown-and-mustard hound's-tooth jacket he'd bought in Cambridge, he'd probably have been invited South before now.

Dorian's eyes traveled thoughtfully to Brummel Coombe, two tables away. In The Mace and Swan, two tables removed was close enough for me, in an absent-minded gesture, to have hoisted the young English squire's mug as easily as my own. Ignoring the intervening table, Dorian addressed Brummel, more or less publicly, "Why don't you join us tomorrow?"

He couldn't come out with a final, "No, thank you"—he was too well-bred for that. Brummel was Upper-U, from the crown of his smooth flaxen head to his well-rubbed, handmade London shoes.

What he said was, in that inimitable, gentle British way, "Thank you very much, but I'm afraid you'd be a bit crowded." We had given him a lift from the Theatre last night; we were all stopping at The Oak and Swan, an old Tudor black-and-white, timber-and-brick Inn, likewise on Sheep Street.

"There'll be plenty of room." Dorian tried to keep her voice as quiet and unimpassioned as his but I could detect the victory in it. "Kell isn't going."

"That's right," I said to his questioning expression. "I'm going to take it easy tomorrow."

Brummel smiled on Dorian. You'd think from that smile he'd be as enchanted to go touring with her as vice versa. "If there's room—" He broke off with something like alarm. "Where's Clara?"

The flute answered him. "She said she was going down to the Sweet-potato." Because of the size of The Mace and Swan, anybody's business was everybody's.

Before her words were half piped, Brummel pushed away from his chair, and mumbling something like, "Excuse me one moment," was away.

That Brummel should be smitten with Clara was beyond comprehension. Yet never willingly did he let her out of his sight. Touring German girls we'd previously encountered were scrubbed and polished as by laundry soap and whetstone. Not Clara. Her streaky blond hair hung unwashed and uncombed, now over one shoulder, now another, and her yellow pallor was heightened by smudges of green eye-shadow and a smear of pink lipstick. The only outfit she'd ever been seen wearing was a man's black sweater which hung to her knees, and slacks which might have once been rose colored but were now a gritty red. Even Jix, who had not reached the age of discrimination if a female was under thirty, couldn't stomach careless

Clara. While Brummel, the tweed-and-flannels, best-public-school lamb, followed her as if she were Mary of the children's nursery rhyme.

"Well," Dorian breathed, as the door closed behind him.

I said callously, "Give up, Dorian, it's no good."

"And let her take over?" Sometimes in Dorian, there was resemblance to Medea. "Come on."

"Not me," Jix echoed himself. Strawberry Ice Cream was gazing at him drippingly, I thought, Tom Swiftly.

Dorian didn't wait for more palaver. I caught up with her halfway down the block. "Do you think you're being quite smart?" I asked. "You'll never get anywhere chasing after him. Men don't like it." This hadn't been true since Victorian times but we men kept saying it.

"I am not chasing after him," Dorian retorted loftily. "I merely want to tell him what time we're leaving in the morning. I don't intend to sit up swilling ale all night like you and Jix."

By then we'd reached the Sweetpotato caff, a British version of an American jukebox joint, complete with blaring Elvis Presley records. Definitely non-Tudor, it was enormously popular with Stratford's younger set and with haversack tourists. The size of the Sweetpotato made The Mace and Swan seem spacious, and the saturation point had been reached before our arrival.

Clara's tour was there in numbers, including the bearded wonder she hung on when she could escape Brummel's attention. This was a dour character whose eyeglasses were usually focused on the pen scratches he made in a small black notebook. Neither Clara nor Brummel was present.

We started back to the pub. Halfway along the block, Dorian let out a muted pang. "Look!"

Across the street, just emerging from the close of The Oak and Swan, were the elusive two. Dorian dug her talons into my arm, indicating we were to give the appearance of having sauntered out for a breath of chill, damp night air, but we were counterobserved.

"I say there, Dorian." Brummel didn't yell—English gentlemen don't yell. However, in the hush, his words were quite clear. He came slanting over, leaving Clara in the shadows of the gateway. As he fell in with us, he said, "I'm sorry I had to run out like that. I'd be delighted to go with you tomorrow." Any knucklehead not bemused by Anglophilia would know that he'd checked with Clara.

Because I was annoyed with the way he brushed off either girl at will, I spoke up. "Is Clara going to Deerfawn tomorrow too?"

"No, she's going to Leamington—" He caught his breath. "Did you say Deerfawn?" His face was a study in anxiety, apprehension, and any and all other synonyms for almost fright.

Dorian didn't notice. She was ahead, opening the door—she hadn't learned to wait for men to do the amenities. "Yes, we're doing Deerfawn Manor House in the morning. Is ten o'clock all right? We want to go on to the ruins of St. Orlgwulf's Abbey in the afternoon." Prattling, she led Brummel inside.

I don't know why I looked back toward the close. But I did. The deserted Clara was still there, an incongruously sad little ghost, clutching the shadows. Her dirt was erased by the darkness; only her pale face and hair were visible.

She wasn't my problem; Dorian was. I followed the others into the pub, shutting Clara away in the night. Jix had moved to the southern exposure in our absence. Brummel now had Jix's place and Dorian seemed to have given up the idea of retiring for the night. This made me the happy old fifth wheel. I could now go back to the Inn and get a decent night's sleep.

I was as bright at breakfast next morning as Jix was bleary. Dorian was her normal effervescent self; she didn't need sleep. We'd finished our canned fruit juice and corn flakes, our fried eggs and scarcely cooked bacon with warm tomato, our cold toast and pot of orange marmalade—the traditional English breakfast—and we were dallying over our milk-and-sugar tea when Brummel appeared in the dining room.

We exchanged good mornings and the inevitable weather data before he said shamefacedly, "I'm afraid I can't go with you today after all. Something has come up."

Dorian, after one unbelievably stricken blink, should have been recruited for the Stratford players—her consoling smile was that convincing. "I'm terribly sorry, Brummel. But if you can't, you can't. Maybe some other day."

You could tell he thought it was terribly decent of her to take it so well, and after a few more apologies, he backed away.

"Evidently Clara isn't going to the Spa today." I was sorry as soon as I'd said it. "Long as there's room, I think I'll go Deerfawning with you. I've recovered my youth."

"You can drive," Jix said morosely. He was stuck with the trip because he'd talked Strawberry Ice Cream into meeting him there. Even his cherished jacket failed to uplift him.

It was a blue-sky day, one of the few when we could let down the top of the convertible without bailing. Eight miles is longer in England than in the United States. Who wants to speed through lanes dappled darkly with tall woods, and greened with smooth meadows where the sheep graze in motionless pattern, wearing red badges on their haunches to distinguish them from the pale saffron stones? To augment our leisurely pace, whenever a crumbling rock pile appeared on the horizon we had to stop at the nearest lay-by while Dorian loped back to investigate its import.

It was, therefore, close to eleven when we reached the gatehouse of Deerfawn Manor. The gatekeeper was on hand to collect our two-and-sixes and to present us with pink admission tickets from a wheel such as we used to have in movie houses before automation. We drove on up the cobbled half mile to the courtyard in the rear of the great Georgian house.

Deerfawn was not a National Trust—it wasn't that ancient. But the handbills at the desk of The Oak and Swan had built up a pretty picture of its fine carved staircase, its priceless library, its art masterpieces, and of the marble Folly in its woods, the only remnant of the original manor not destroyed in the Civil War. The English had a Civil War too. There were also peacocks—there were always peacocks—and formal gardens. Although the information had surely been compiled by the Marquis of Deerfawn, who just as surely had opened his house to the public to help pay his taxes, it might turn out to be of more interest than some of the shabby great houses we'd seen. For one thing, there were two authenticated paintings by Rubens and six family portraits by Van Dyck.

There was the usual sign pointing to the west basement where would be found the usual tearoom and curio and postcard counter. This was our first stop—as Jix demanded, to insure his life, coffee with a lacing of aspirin. Dorian chafed and wrote two postcards to her two best friends at home, until Jix could navigate again. She then insisted that we return outdoors and make a proper entrance.

Jix said, "I'll shuck my coat and follow you." From where we'd parked the car we could look down the avenue and see if the coach tour was approaching. I wrote off Jix and his delaying tactics for the rest of the morning.

All in all, Deerfawn Manor House wasn't bad. It wasn't great like Warwick Castle—ah, Warwick! where I'd learned what the Biblical word "covet" truly means—but it wasn't impossibly tawdry like some attractions which shall remain nameless. We went unguided, yet not unobserved. There were guardians of the treasures stationed in each room to make sure filching was out of style.

It was past one o'clock when we again descended the carved staircase to the entrance hall.

"Now we'll do the gardens," Dorian announced.

"Hadn't we better have a bite to eat first?" I'd become as English as the English; despite the breakfast spread, I was ready for another meal.

"Later," Dorian stated.

The English are absolutely mad for gardens. As most of the tours this time of year were overwhelmingly composed of English-speakers, the formal layout surrounding the Manor was already overpopulated with ritual flower-print dresses and flat tweed caps.

One look and Dorian decided, "We'll come back. After we visit the Folly."

She headed for the footpath into the deep woods, just past the handmade wooden sign: *To the Folly*. Almost immediately the path became a narrow aperture leading into far deeper woods, the kind where the sun never penetrates the undergrowth of fern. The trees actually were as tall as cathedrals. Where the bark wasn't twined with ivy, it was deeply coated with lichen.

After a more than sufficient spell of stumbling and edging onward, I ventured, "I think we took the wrong path."

"How could we?" Dorian asked, but not with her usual assurance. "The sign pointed this way. You saw it."

"It could have been turned the wrong way," I suggested half-heartedly.

At that moment a strangled cry rose from somewhere in the density. Dorian bashed up quick against my quaking shoulder. And then I remembered. "Those damn peacocks!"

She managed a shaky grin and was herself again. She crashed on and before long called back to my plodding rearguard, "There's daylight ahead. This must be it."

Hopelessly, I hoped so. I was so hungry I was ready to turn poacher at sight of game. One thing came clear in our meandering: the reason Cromwell hadn't destroyed the Folly. He couldn't find it.

Ahead there was indication of a clearing of some sort. Dorian had disappeared off the path into it. I heard her cry out and I picked up speed. The cry hadn't been of delight but of disaster.

The open space was hardly bigger than a table top. Standing in it, facing each other, were Dorian and Brummel. He wasn't the young aristocrat of The Oak and Swan. He wore the leather apron and the mudsplattered boots of the Manor's outdoor staff.

His face was the color of rain and absolutely vacant of any expression. It took me that long to see what was at his feet. An oversized black sweater, dirty rose-colored pants, and flowing yellow hair. In Brummel's right hand there was a big rock. Its smooth surface was discolored.

"Oh, no," Dorian was whimpering.

My entrance released Brummel from shock. "You, too?"

Dorian also came to life. But she didn't run away. She ran toward him. "Come on. We've got to get you out of here."

He half stumbled as she tugged at him, then stoutly released himself and stood away. "Wait," he said. "I must—"

We all heard the suspicious rustle of leaves. It could have been some Cromwellian spy creeping up on us.

"One moment," Brummel whispered. He actually knelt and with quick fingers explored the crumpled body. He took something from beneath the sweater, palming the object into his apron pocket before we could see what it was. "This way," he said under his breath, absently picking up the weapon before he moved.

He set off into what looked like impenetrable forest but which shortly emerged into a path leading up a hill. Don't ask my why, like a dumb sheep, I followed a red-handed killer. Perhaps at the time it seemed better than being lost in the woods with no chocolate bar. As for Dorian, she doubtless had absolved him from guilt the moment she recognized the victim. Like most women, Dorian has a bloodthirsty streak where rivals are concerned.

When the going was easier, I suggested, "Hadn't you better get rid of that rock?" It was making me nervous.

"What rock?" he said, puzzled, and then realized he was still holding it. "Oh, the rock," he said vaguely. "Yes. Yes, I should, I presume."

He gestured us off the path, then advanced a few yards, pondered, and selected a tree no different from any other of the hundred trees in the forest. Carefully he tucked the rock under the ferns there. It didn't seem my place to point out that his fingerprints might be all over it. Possibly it wouldn't turn up for some three hundred years, and the Dorians of that day would believe the bloodstains were made in the first Danish invasion.

Brummel seemed quite relieved to be rid of it. "Come along now," he said. "We must hurry." He was leading us not back to our hillside path but through and around the woods in what seemed a circular pattern. If Dorian wasn't uneasy, I was ashamed to be. And shortly there lay the enormous Manor House below.

Brummel paused only for a few breaths, looking down on the back court where the cars and coaches were parked. In sight were only a couple of drivers having a gossip over their cigarettes. The red shine of our Triumph was like a beacon.

Brummel said to Dorian, "You and Kell won't have any difficulty getting away. Don't talk to anyone—just go."

"But you're the one who has to get away," Dorian cried out, remembering to keep it a muted cry.

He shook his head. "I can't."

Of course he couldn't: he'd have to hide the body first.

Dorian thought quickly. "We can't either. We can't go off and leave Jix without a ride."

"I'll take care of Jix! Please. Hurry."

I was the practical one. "How do we get to the car? Make like birds or toboggans?"

"I'll lead you down," Brummel said, "but once we're in the court, walk over, get in your car, and take off. Fast." He didn't wait for Dorian to give him further argument. He set off on a transverse, and somehow or other we all managed to get down to the ditch below and start clambering up its slope into the courtyard.

We almost had it made when what can only be described as a hue-and-cry began. There were uniformed attendants legging out of every door and it didn't take someone of normal I.Q. to realize that the body had been discovered.

Under his breath, Brummel muttered, "That's torn it. Come on."

We fled to the Triumph and he squeezed in without the usual preliminary of ladies first. Dorian said, "You drive, Kell," and slid in beside him. The engine caught and we were headed down the drive before anyone could stop us. Not that anyone tried.

"Take off that silly costume," Dorian ordered, "And put on Jix's coat."

Brummel ducked out of the leather apron and stuffed it under the seat while Dorian helped envelop him in Jix's coat of too many colors. As a disguise is wasn't what I'd have chosen.

I kept a nice pace to the gate, not too fast, and returned the gatehouse attendant's friendly salute. The word hadn't reached him yet.

In the lane I picked up speed. "To Stratford?"

"Yes," Brummel said.

By this time we were approaching the turn into the Stratford road—approaching it, I suddenly observed, much too rapidly. I removed my foot entirely from the gas pedal. I didn't want to compound our troubles by crashing into the police car which was blocking the intersection.

Brummel sighed and Dorian, for once, said nothing. I braked, and a young constable strolled over to my side of the car. The bobbies in their helmets and dark formal uniforms somehow look unreal in the country; they belong in London.

"Good afternoon," he said pleasantly. "You've come from Deerfawn Manor?"

There was no other place we could have come from unless we'd been haring across the meadows, and he knew it.

I said meekly, "Yes, sir."

"I'm afraid I'll have to ask you to go back."

"But why?" Dorian asked with outraged innocence.

"There's been a bit of trouble, Miss," he said. "No one is to leave until the Chief Constable arrives."

There was no point to arguing, particularly with Brummel sitting there trying to look unperturbed and, in that dreadful coat, succeeding in looking like some ghastly Teddy boy. Back we crawled to Deerfawn Manor to join the now thronged courtyard.

We didn't need a guide to identify the nationalities of the tourists. The Americans were the indignant ones, the Continentals the wary, and the British the ones who accepted matters as if nothing untoward had hap-

pened. The only exceptions were Jix and his South Carolinian babe—they
didn't mind the delay a bit. I noted that all of Clara's tour were on hand,
including her special boyfriend. He was trying to find the reason for this
procedure in his guide book.

Brummel took off Jix's coat, placed it on the seat, and got out of the car.
A member of the Manor staff was trotting toward him. He tried to cut
away but the man planted himself head on. "I'm terribly sorry, your Lordship. It seems a girl's body has been found in our woods." The words came
out distinctly in spite of the strong country accent.

Your Lordship. Our Brummel was the Marquis of Deerfawn! With my
mouth dropped witlessly, I looked toward Dorian. Her mouth was also
cavernous, but mercifully silent.

Brummel simulated astonishment. "A girl's body?"

"Yes, your Lordship." The servitor volunteered, "It would seem to be
one of the trippers, sir."

"Is Colonel Whitten in charge?"

"He has been notified. He hasn't yet arrived."

Brummel gave some inaudible directions and the man took off at a brisk
pace, away from the stone steps where the constabulary were gathered. Still
ignoring us, Brummel strode toward them.

"Well," I uttered.

"Well what?" Dorian bristled. "Don't just stand there. Come on." She
followed Brummel and I followed her.

By then he was listening with gravity to what the police had to tell him.
Meantime, his eyes were searching frantically, or as near to frantically as a
marquis's eyes could, the sinuous mass in the court. His frenzy changed to
resignation as the police parted the crowd to permit the entrance of a large
black Humber. From it dismounted what had to be Colonel Whitten, Chief
Constable of the shire. His mustaches were as long as a soliloquy. But he
was as deferent to Brummel as the old retainer had been.

An inspection post was being set up and the English, sure enough,
formed the inevitable queue. The foreigners had no choice but to join it.
When in Rome. As Dorian and I were up front, our turn came quickly.
However, before I could give name, address, and passport number to the
officer at the table, Brummel was saying, "These are friends of mine, Colonel Whitten. I can assure you they know nothing about this affair."

"All we know," said Dorian in a sweet, clear voice, "is that Brummel—
his Lordship—couldn't possibly have killed Clara."

If she'd said she was carrying a nuclear warhead in her handbag, she
couldn't have caused more consternation. I wasn't the only one whose
mouth could drop witlessly—every policeman in the vicinity was doing it.
Brummel looked as if he wanted to weep.

"Because," Dorian appeared not to notice any reaction, "she was already dead when he got there."

"You saw the body? You know who this girl was?" It wasn't the speechless Colonel Whitten but an intelligent looking bobby who put the question.

"Of course we knew her. She was the German girl who's been in Stratford all week."

"I can explain," Brummel said without conviction, eyeing the crowd as if trying to find an escape route through it.

"My cousin and I heard her death cry," Dorian orated melodramatically, dragging me into it, "before his Lordship found her."

The Germans who understood some English were falling to pieces. Loudly and tearfully.

"The reason he had that bloody rock—excuse me, but it was bloody—in his hands," Dorian carried on with simple devastation, "was that he knew it must be the murder weapon and he wanted to preserve the evidence for—"

At that moment I heard Jix's voice above all other sounds. A good loud indignant American voice. "What's that guy doing in my coat?"

The queue swayed in the direction of Jix's bellow. We all saw a figure in German shorts and Jix's hound's-tooth jacket racing toward the woods.

"He mustn't get away," Brummel warned as he started after him. The police followed like Keystone Cops. Need I say that I, following Dorian, brought up the usual rear?

But Jix was well ahead in the chase. It was he who brought down the man before the others caught up, and wrestled the jacket off of him.

The thief, shouting and gesticulating in outraged German, was none other than Clara's dour friend, the black-notebook writer. Brummel waited until the German gulped for breath, then said in his most quiet way, "It's no good, Lengel. And it wasn't hidden in that coat."

On the outskirts of our panting group a rather tall man in a gray suit asked calmly, "What's going on here?"

Brummel's expression melted into enormous relief. "What took you so long, Freddie?" He indicated the captive. "This is your man. He gave himself away."

The police recognized Freddie as important. They parted to let him into the inner circle.

Distaste touched Freddie's mouth as he regarded the prisoner. "He didn't get away with anything?"

"With your men on guard? Not half," Brummel assured him. "Besides, he's only an advance man, Freddie. Clara was always sure of that. She nipped the notebook, gave me the nod—" His look saddened. "Evidently he missed it before I could get to her. He got to her first."

Freddie took a step toward the struggling Lengel.

"He doesn't have it," Brummel said. "It seems these Americans—" So much for the earlier friendship he'd protested for us. "—blundered on the meeting place before he had a chance to search the body."

"You have it?" Freddie relaxed.

"I found it." Brummel couldn't resist a gibe at the German. "He thought I'd hidden it in that coat I was wearing."

"You were wearing—" Freddie's calm faltered at sight of the coat on Jix's arm.

"As a disguise," Brummel said quickly. "I wanted to get the notebook to you before it became police property. Colonel Whitten—"

Colonel Whitten hadn't made the run. He could be seen in the distance at stone-step headquarters, puffing nonchalantly on his pipe.

"He does rather talk to reporters," Brummel regretted. "I was hoping we could continue to keep our plans private."

Freddie nodded agreement. "Let me have it."

"It's wedged under the seat of their car." Brummel gave our group the faintest nod. "The little red one."

Freddie took off at a sprint. Brummel loped behind. All strangers, and that included us, were thereupon herded down the hill by the police and pointed to the Manor gates. Dorian was determined not to leave but she had stupidly destroyed whatever influence she might have had with the Marquis of Deerfawn. Without so much as a backward glance, the marquis and Freddie were now moving away from our car, the notebook retrieved.

We drove single file back to Stratford. Even Dorian had no stomach for St. Orlgwulf's Eighth Century disasters after first-hand exposure to Twentieth Century violence. She spent the remainder of the afternoon on the banks of the Avon with me, inventing one far-fetched spy thriller after another to explain what had happened. Jix was again off somewhere with his fancy jacket and southern accent.

Dorian continued to fantasticate at The Mace and Swan that night until unexpectedly Brummel appeared at our table.

"May I sit down with you?" he asked. If he hadn't, Dorian would have yanked him into the empty chair. "I do want to apologize for any inconvenience I may have caused you today."

"They were spies, weren't they?" Dorian burst out.

"Oh, no," Brummel said, for a moment giving her that faintly alarmed glance which Britons reserve for nutty Americans. "They were after the paintings."

This was the summer of increasing thievery of art masterpieces. Dorian was disappointed. The stories she'd dreamed up in her own little head were much wilder and much more exciting.

"Freddie is head of the London branch of Interpol. They had a tip that

Deerfawn was the next target. He asked me to help out. Working with Clara."

"Clara was an operative?" I goggled.

"She was good, wasn't she?" His somber face lighted. "The way she got herself up like a grisette."

"You mean—she wasn't really—," Dorian stammered.

"She was a lovely girl," Brummel said. Defendingly, not romantically. "A very clever girl. She got on the student tour that the gang was using as a cover and attached herself to Lengel." He shook his head. "We don't know if someone informed or if he suddenly realized that she wasn't as stupid as he thought her. But when she found out he was going to Deerfawn after telling her he was going to Leamington Spa, she knew she had to get the notebook as soon as she could. It has the plans for all the robbings in the Midlands. It's my fault she was killed." His emotion was too deep for display. "I didn't arrange carefully enough."

Dorian, possibly therapeutically, broke the silence. "I knew you didn't kill her."

Brummel came out of his shadows. "I'm afraid I panicked a bit when I saw you and Kell there. I'm rather new at this sort of thing. And I had to find that notebook." He turned and looked into Dorian's eyes, not half shy. "And I must say I wanted to get you away from there before you found out my connection with Deerfawn. I was afraid it might spoil things between us."

It didn't. During our last days in the Stratford country, Dorian and Brummel were as inseparable as Jix and South Carolina. This was a happy breather for me. I read Shakespeare by day and watched it by night. I'm as much of a nut on Shakespeare as Dorian is on ancient monuments. Oh, yes, the Folly sign had a habit of veering. Most people had sense enough to take the pebbled path to the right, not wander into untrammeled woods.

I also had plenty of time for thought those days. But I wasn't able to discuss certain peculiar aspects of the Deerfawn day until we were off on the road again, headed toward Shropshire. Without Jix—he would join us after Miss South Carolina moved on.

I asked Dorian flatly, "What were you trying to do to Brummel, hang him? Telling the police all that stuff."

"Of course not!" she replied with indignation. "I knew he wasn't a killer, not even when I first saw him bending over the body with that bloody rock. Before you got there. He isn't the type."

A lecture on criminal types would have made no dent at that moment. She was on her high white horse with banners flying. "But if he was guilty," she proclaimed, "I wasn't going to let him get away with doing Clara in, just because of all that bow-and-scrape-your-Lordship stuff."

For one split second I believed Dorian had recovered from Anglophilia.

And then she was blasting in my ear, "Stop the car! Stop the car!"

I wondered if in the side mirror she'd noted Brummel catching up with us a day early. No, it wasn't that. It was only another ragged clump of rocks rising out of the rolling green.

With a silent sigh I wheeled into the nearest lay-by and stopped the car.

THE MAN WHO UNDERSTOOD WOMEN

by A. H. Z. CARR

We were having lunch together, the four of us, and we started talking about women. Whately, Barker, and I agreed that Dr. Kinsey notwithstanding, women are enigmatic creatures, difficult for the male to comprehend. Whately told a story about his wife to prove it, then Barker and I told stories about our wives to prove it.

Milliken disagreed, as he always does. He is a bachelor, and he writes plays. When we told him that he did not know what he was talking about, he paid no attention.

"The trouble with you husbands," he said, "is that you allow yourselves to be bewildered by what your wives say to you. In my experience—let me finish—if a man listens to what a woman says, he's done for. But he can tell all he has to know about a woman just by looking at her."

He ignored a small crust of bread that Barker threw at him, and continued. "A woman's appearance gives her away every time. It enables you to tell what she has been doing and to predict what she will do. That is, it reveals all this to the discerning."

"Like you," said Whately, frankly sneering.

"Like me," agreed Milliken. "I suppose it's only natural that you fellows should regard women as mysterious. You're all married to wives much smarter than yourselves. But to one who observes carefully, thinks clearly, and has a reasonable amount of intuition, a woman's secret thoughts are exposed before she ever opens her mouth."

Barker said, "It's easy enough to talk."

"It isn't talk. Do you remember Kate Loring, the heroine of my last play?"

"You mean the one that closed the second week?" I said. There is no point in being subtle with Milliken.

"That has nothing to do with it. Everybody who saw the play was sure that I had known a woman like Kate Loring intimately at some time in my life. Because I understood her, felt her, I caught her essence. As a matter of fact, it wasn't the fault of the script that the play flopped. If Hogan, the producer, had only—"

"Stick to the point," said Whately, who is a lawyer.

"All right, then. Now actually, I never even met a woman like Kate Loring. But I saw her once, sitting at a distance of ten feet, in a bar. I studied her for a few minutes, and at the end of that time I knew her past, her future, her whole life, better than she knew it herself."

"Do you dare to say," Barker put in, "that you can look at *any* woman and deduce the facts of her private life just from her appearance?"

"That's what I have been telling you," Milliken said patiently. "I do not say that mine is a unique gift. With application, you could all do it. Even Bob here, if given time and help, might make a stab at it."

"Give us an example," Barker urged. "Take that woman who just came in. At the third table, with that tall man. She looks interesting. What can you tell us about her?"

For some time Milliken stared at the woman indicated. Neither she nor her escort noticed us. They were discussing the menu. Finally Milliken said, "Very well. She is a good subject—an unusual woman. I will take you step by step through the process, leaving out nothing, so you can see exactly how I do it."

He ordered another drink before going on. "That woman is intelligent and purposeful. She is unmarried. Although at one time in her life she was well off, she is now having a hard time making ends meet. A very hard time. Money, or the lack of it, has become almost an obsession with her." He held up his hand to prevent interruption.

"She is in love with that man, and he is with her. He, too, is poor. Now, at the age of thirty-three or thirty-four, she is still highly attractive. But she feels that her chances of the good life are ebbing. And she intends to marry another man, a wealthy man."

"Oh, now, really, Milliken!" exclaimed Barker.

"I've hardly begun," Milliken said. "Within the last few days she has returned from a long stay abroad. She was on the Mediterranean—probably North Africa, Algiers. The chances are that she met the man she intends to marry on that trip."

Whately caught my eye and shrugged. Milliken smiled grimly. "I see that you don't believe me. Let me tell you something else. Her true lover, the man with her now, does not yet know her intention. Soon—perhaps at this very luncheon—she will break the news to him. She will do it even at the expense of her self-respect. For money, as I have said, is now the dominating force of her life. She will sacrifice everything for financial security."

We looked at the woman, and Milliken lowered his voice. "Even now, while she laughs gaily at her companion's remarks, she is considering how best to broach the subject. If we sit here long enough we will witness high drama—the shattering of a sincere love on the shoals of poverty."

He paused for effect and breath. After a short silence Whately said flatly, "Prove it."

"I shall," said Milliken. "Take first the question of intelligence. Observe the broad, high, well-developed forehead and the alert, wide-open eyes— her whole expression, animated yet controlled. These are the universal marks of a good mind. Just as the eyebrows, the set of the mouth, and the resolute chin indicate firmness of character."

This seemed reasonable—or possible—so we said nothing.

"Glance at her hands, feet, ankles, wrists. Slender and shapely, the bones solid but unobtrusive, the limbs rounded. Note the fine texture of her hair. And then her poise, the ease of her manner, her self-assurance, her great natural dignity. These are signs of breeding which even you fellows should be able to recognize."

"There's nothing remarkable about that," Whately said. "I put her down for an intelligent, well-bred woman myself."

"Good. You're coming along," Milliken replied. "How would you deduce that her family was once well-to-do?"

"You're doing this," said Whately, a certain slyness in his tone.

Milliken smiled. "Well, then, observe her clothes. In admirable taste. Expensive. That hat, that dress, those shoes come from Paris."

"How do you know that?" I demanded.

Milliken looked pained. "Surely it is obvious." If he had added, "my dear Watson," I should have kicked him then and there—but he had sense enough to refrain. "The dress is the clue. Fabrics like that are simply not woven in this country. And then, notice the restrained fullness in the upper arm and the subtle molding of the material around the bust. Only Balenciaga or Molyneux gets that effect. As for the hat, it bears the stamp of the Faubourg St. Honoré all over it. Even our smartest shops never quite achieve the quality of excitement that is added by that twist of the crown. The shoes, too, are definitely French. American designers haven't yet adopted that two-way curve of the instep."

None of us felt qualified to argue these points. Whately said, "If her clothes come from Paris, wouldn't that signify she is well off?"

"Ha!" said Milliken. "That's just where the amateur goes wrong. Instead of studying essential details, you jump at conclusions. Of course the clothes are expensive—I said so. But—and mark this—they are far from new. Look carefully, and you can see a slight giving at the seam of the sleeve of her cloth coat. And the shoes, although elegant, are creased by use. The purse is relatively cheap and certainly outmoded. No woman would spoil the whole effect of an ensemble with such a purse if she could afford a finer one. What must we deduce therefore? When she buys clothes, she buys good ones, but she has few. Once she had money enough to indulge expensive tastes. Now, lacking money, she still tries to indulge those tastes."

"You're just guessing," Whately objected. "Her clothes don't necessarily signify her own taste. She may not have selected them herself. Somebody may have given them to her."

"Whately, you're not thinking. Look at that aristocratic, proud face. This is no lady's maid, no poor companion, no impoverished relative, to accept hand-me-downs."

"Well, maybe a man——," Whately began.

"You're suggesting that she is someone's mistress? A kept woman?"

"Why not? There are such women—or haven't you heard?"

"It is your idea that this woman would go into a shop with a man and let *him* pick out her clothes? Good heavens, is this the legal mind in action? Use your head, man! Her refusal to pluck her eyebrows, her subtle use of cosmetics—does that suggest a woman who depends on the fancy of a man for support? The kept woman invariably tries to look feminine and fascinating. She cannot resist the little superficial touches that arrest most masculine eyes—the exaggeration of curves, the vivid color. But not this woman, gentlemen. There can be absolutely no doubt that those clothes were selected by a woman of taste—selected to please herself."

Whately cleared his throat and for a moment looked combative; but he said nothing. I took up the gauntlet. "You still haven't convinced me," I said, "that she is poor. Just because she is wearing an old dress and coat at this moment——"

"There's other evidence. I call your attention to her hair where it shows under her hat. Obviously her natural shade, that brown—and not really flattering. If it were a shade lighter, a dark blond, the effect would be ravishing—and she must know it. Moreover, there's her hairdo. That bun in the back does nothing for her. She certainly would not wear it that way if she could afford a first-class hairdresser."

I had to admit that this did indeed look like drastic economy. "Even so," I contended, "that doesn't mean money is an obsession with her, as you claimed."

"Then you missed the expression on her face when that stout overdressed woman across the room came in. If you had seen our subject's lips tighten when she glanced at that mink coat, you would know what I mean when I speak of an obsession. What was she envying, if not five thousand dollars' worth of mink? Here we have a poised, controlled, proud woman. When she allows such an expression to appear on her face for such a reason, you may be sure that the longing for money has sunk deep into her heart."

"All that may be so," said Barker. "But what I want to know is how you deduced the love affair you spoke of."

Milliken nodded. "Did you get a good look at our lady's escort before he sat down? A fine-looking man. Generous, open features. Not an acquisitive nature. Look at his hands—strong, bony fingers. The hands of an artist —a musician, perhaps, or a painter. But not a 'successful' man. He is close to forty—an age when men who have achieved success wear the stamp of it. But his eyes have a worried look, and his clothes are cheap and ready-made."

"How do you know they're ready-made?" I said, thinking of my own, which were.

"The shoulders are a dead give-away. Those wrinkles at the seams— characteristic of the mass-produced suit, after it has been worn a while. That man is hard up, depend on it."

"Then what's he doing taking her to a restaurant like this?" Whately demanded.

"Ah, there is a good point. Under what conditions does a man strain his purse for a woman? He will do it if he loves her—and especially if it is their first meeting after a long separation. But did you notice that she refused a cocktail? And that he attempted to insist? The inference is clear. She likes a cocktail, he knows it, but she is sparing his pocketbook. And the meal she ordered—ravioli. Substantial and filling, but decidedly inexpensive. Isn't it obvious that he can't really afford an elaborate luncheon?"

"You said she loves him," Barker persisted. "Is that why you thought so —just because she refused a cocktail and ordered ravioli?"

Milliken shook his head. "Her eyes, Barker, her eyes. Surely you have seen love in a woman's face before. The tenderness of her smile tells us all. And he loves her, too. Twice he has surreptitiously touched her hand. He hardly takes his eyes from her face. Lovers, beyond a doubt."

"Maybe you're right," said Barker.

"Of course I'm right."

"But the other man—the rich one," Whately interjected. "Where does he come in? And how do you know she has just been abroad?"

"Start with her complexion," said Milliken. "That deep coat of tan. Where did she get it, in late November?"

"Sun lamp," I suggested.

"Nonsense. People who use sun lamps regularly have pale spots around the eyes, where they put the protective pads. Anyone can see that is no artificial tan."

"Florida?" said Barker.

"At this time of the year? Incredible. Besides, look at her gestures. She is an Anglo-Saxon type, but she uses her hands and shoulders freely. The chances are excellent that she picked up the habit of free gesticulation on the Mediterranean, as so many American women do. But that's not all. You see those two heavy silver bracelets with the exotic design?"

The woman and her companion were so absorbed in their conversation that they never noticed our surreptitious glances. "What about the bracelets?" I said.

"They are the kind of thing you get only in North Africa. The design is absolutely distinctive. And they are not cheap—not the stuff that is provided for the regular tourist trade. Those blue stones in the lower bangle are sapphires, I would swear. I have seen similar things in Marrakesh—there's a shop there that specializes in them."

"Somebody who has recently come back from there may have given them to her," Whately pointed out.

"One, perhaps," Milliken said. "But two? Besides, you will notice that the two bracelets are quite different in detail—and yet both are a perfect match for that dress. Put it all together and what do you have? For this woman to buy two such expensive pieces for herself, when she needs a new handbag, is altogether out of character. For any friend to have bought her two such carefully chosen bracelets, of the same type, is highly unlikely. Add the deep suntan—and can't you see it? She is strolling in Marrakesh, or possibly Algiers, with a friend. She sees the bracelets in a shop window, glinting in the sunlight, and stops to admire them. No woman could resist entering to inquire the price.

"Try to imagine it," Milliken went on, with the air of a visionary. "She looks at some bracelets, is tempted, but disturbed by the price. Finally she succumbs. Very well—she will buy one, the less expensive one. It will mean not buying the new handbag that she needs—but the urge is irresistible and the bracelet goes so perfectly with the dress. It is then that her friend picks up the other bracelet, the one with the sapphires, and insists on presenting her with it."

We all objected at once. "Sheer romancing," Whately growled.

"Not in the least," Milliken replied stoutly. "I admit that I have reconstructed this scene intuitively, rather than from wholly physical evidence. Still, it explains the facts—it explains them better than any other theory you can offer."

"But you're not consistent," I protested. "If this woman is poor, how could she have afforded a trip to Europe and North Africa?"

"My dear fellow," Milliken said, looking at me as if he were wearing a monocle; there are times when he imagines himself to be Lord Peter Wimsey. "Many people of small means manage to get to Europe. They save for it—or they receive a small inheritance—or they win the trip in a contest—or some wealthy aunt puts up the cash. Surely you don't expect me to give you every last detail of her finances. I will tell you, though, that she just got back."

"How do you know that?" I said.

"Again, a combination of things. The weather has been cloudy for weeks, yet her tan has not yet worn off. Even more important, look at her as she talks. The flow of her words, the animation of the man's response, the air of excitement around them. This is plainly their first meeting in a long while. But can you imagine that two people who are in love would let an unnecessary day go by before meeting? She has returned recently, very recently. She may have flown, but my guess is that she came in on the *Liberté*, which docked yesterday. Attractive women usually prefer a boat crossing."

"Still," I said, "I don't get this other man. It seems to me you have just rung him in without reason."

"A lovely woman on a trip abroad, and you do not see a man in the picture? Why, you could not keep men away from her! On a boat especially, a French boat, on her way to Paris, she would have a choice of ardent males within two days. And the man in this case is very likely a Frenchman. Here my reasoning may be a little tenuous, I admit. I judge from the quality of the sentiment in that bracelet, and the fact that it was bought in Algiers. A Frenchman might well have encouraged her to go there. I don't insist on the point, though. All I say is that there was a man, that he is wealthy, and that she has decided to marry him."

"That's all," said Whately, with heavy sarcasm.

"You doubt me? Then I take it that you did not notice the ring she wears on the third finger of her right hand. No, you cannot see it now. She has turned the stone inward. It is a beautiful cabochon emerald, which must have cost thousands. The man with her has been glancing at it curiously, even anxiously, and she has dropped her hand into her lap. She is fidgeting with the ring nervously, now."

Whately frowned. "What of it?"

"Man, man," Milliken sighed. "Don't you see? Her companion is too proud to ask her outright about the ring. But he has never seen it before. What must we conclude? She acquired the ring on the trip from which she has just returned. Where would she get it? She could not afford to buy it for herself. But it is precisely the kind of ring that a wealthy man of excellent taste would give to the woman he loves—and that a woman like her would accept only from the man she intends to marry."

"But she's wearing the ring on her right hand," Barker said.

"Just so, Barker. Ask yourself why."

When Barker looked uncertain, Milliken said, "It's because she does not wish to announce blatantly to her real lover, the man with her now, that she is engaged to marry another. She wants to tell him at the right moment, in the way that will hurt him least. That's the only reasonable explanation of her behavior."

"Then why does she wear the ring at all?" I said.

"Where are your sensibilities? She does not want to deceive this man, or to act a part. This is a fine woman, as you must realize by now. She is letting him draw his own inferences, letting him suspect the truth, so that when the denouement comes it will not be a complete shock to him. See the tenderness in her glance. There is even a little pain in her eyes when she looks away. And now, consider: what would impel her to give up the man she loves for another? We already know the answer. She needs, she craves money. That is the weak spot in an otherwise noble character. To her, happiness without money is inconceivable."

There was tremendous intensity in Milliken's manner as he spoke, and his eyes were somber. He went on, "She will tell him soon—very soon, now. Possibly after the coffee is served. She will not want to prolong the agony of his suspense, or her own self-reproaches. This is going to cost her something of her self-respect, but she cannot help it. Love with her is less important at this moment than security. That is what modern life does to people. And that, you may be sure, is what she is thinking at this moment, behind her mask of gaiety."

None of us spoke. After a moment, Milliken said, "Here we are, four total strangers to this woman. Yet, through a little observation, a little insight, we unravel the mystery of her life. We glimpse her tragedy at the very moment of its climax. We know her past and present. We can guess at her hard, brilliant, regretful future. We understand her motives and her actions; we can predict her behavior. And how have we done all this? Merely, as I maintained in the beginning, by looking at her."

"By George," said Barker. "I've got to admit—that's pretty good."

Whately said grudgingly, "I've got to admit too—you have made out a case."

"There could be something in it," I said.

Milliken glanced at his watch, then rose suddenly. "Great Scott, I've got to run. You take care of my end of the check, will you?" And he dashed off.

We did not mind. It seemed to us that he had earned his lunch. We had all learned something, and we sat silently, thinking how we might apply the lesson Milliken had taught us. If observation and analysis could enable us to penetrate the innermost secrets of our wives' hearts, the power we would gain!

We paid the check and stood up to go. As we passed the table where the couple who had occupied our minds was sitting, we heard a snatch of their conversation.

"Dickie said the cutest thing this morning after you left the house," the woman was saying. "He said, 'Mummy, why does Daddy have to go—' "

We could not hear the rest.

I looked back at the third finger of her left hand, and there was the unmistakable mark of a wedding ring, tight-fitting and long-worn. I suppose she had taken it off for some reason.

The next time Milliken has lunch with us, he pays for it. The charlatan!

REVOLVER

by *AVRAM DAVIDSON*

There was a Mr. Edward Mason who dealt in real estate. His kind of real estate consisted mainly of old brownstone houses into which Mr. Mason crammed a maximum number of tenants by turning each room into a single apartment. Legally this constituted "increasing available residence space" or some similar phrase. As a result of this deed of civic good, Mr. Mason was enabled to get tax rebates, rent increases which were geometrically rather than arithmetically calculated, and a warm glow around his heart.

Mr. Mason's tenants were a select group, hand-picked; one might say— to use a phrase favored in other facets of the real estate profession—that his holdings were "restricted." He didn't care for tenants who had steady employment. You might think this was odd of him, but that would be because you didn't know the philanthropic cast of Mr. Mason's mind. He favored the lame, the halt, and the blind; he preferred the old and the feeble; he had no scruples, far from it, against mothers without marriage licenses.

And his kindheartedness was rewarded. For, after all, employment, no matter how steady, can sometimes be terminated. And then rent cannot be paid. A landlord who can't collect rent is a landlord who can't meet his own expenses—in short, a landlord who is bound to go out of business. In which case it follows that he is a landlord who can no longer practice philanthropy.

Therefore, Mr. Mason would be obliged to evict such a tenant in order to protect his other tenants.

But, owing to his care, foresight, and selectivity, he had no such tenants. Not any more. No, sir. All his tenants at the time our account begins were in receipt of a steady income not derived from employment. Welfare checks come in regularly, and so do old-age assistance checks, state aid checks, and several other variety of checks more or less unknown to the average citizen (and may he never have to know of them from the recipients' point of view—that is our prayer for him), the average citizen whose tax dollar supplies said checks.

Then, too, people who earn their own income are inclined to take a high-handed attitude toward landlords. They seem to think that the real estate investor has nothing better to do with his income than to lavish it on fancy repairs to his property. But a tenant whose soul has been purified by long years as the recipient of public charity is a tenant who is less troublesome, whose tastes are less finicking, who is in no position to carry on about such *rerae natura* as rats, mice, roaches, crumbling plaster, leaky pipes, insufficient heat, dirt, rot, and the like.

Is it not odd, then, that after a term of years of being favored by the philanthropic attentions of Mr. Mason and similarly minded entrepreneurs, the neighborhood was said to have "gone down"? It could not really be, could it, that garbage, for instance, was collected less frequently than in other sections of town? Or that holes in streets and sidewalks were not repaired as quickly as in "better" neighborhoods? Surely it was a mere coincidence that these things were so—if, indeed, they were so at all.

And anyway, didn't the City make up for it by providing more protection? Weren't patrol cars seen on the streets thereabouts more often than elsewhere? Weren't policemen usually seen on the streets in congenial groups of three? To say nothing of plainclothesmen.

This being the case, it was disconcerting for Mr. Mason to acknowledge that crime seemed to be on the increase in the neighborhood where he practiced his multifold benevolences. But no other conclusion seemed possible. Stores were held up, apartments burglarized, cars broken into, purses snatched, people mugged—

It was almost enough to destroy one's faith in human nature.

Finally, there was no other choice but for Mr. Mason to secure a revolver, and a license for same. Being a respectable citizen, a taxpayer, and one with a legitimate reason to go armed—the necessity to protect himself and the collection of his tenants' rents—he had no difficulty in obtaining either . . .

Among Mr. Mason's tenants was a Mrs. Richards. She was quite insistent, whenever the matter was raised (though it was never raised by Mr. Mason, who was totally indifferent to such items), that "Mrs." was no mere courtesy title. She had, indeed, been married to Mr. Richards and she had a snapshot of Mr. Richards to prove it. The wedding may have occurred in North Carolina, or perhaps in South Carolina. Nor did she recall the town or county where the happy event took place: Mr. Richards (she *did* remember that his given name was Charley) had been a traveling man. Also, it was a long time ago.

Mrs. Richards may have been a bit feeble-minded, but she possessed other qualities, such as a warm, loving, and open—very open—heart. She had two children by the evanescent Mr. Richards, and two children by two other gentlemen, with whom she had been scrupulous not to commit bigamy; and was currently awaiting the birth in about six months of her fifth child, the father of whom she thought was most probably a young man named Curtis.

Current social welfare policy held that it would be destructive to the family unit to suggest that Mrs. Richards, now or at any time, place her children in a day nursery and go out and labor for her (and their) bread. Consequently, she was supplied with a monthly check made up with city, state, and federal taxes. It cannot be said that the amount of the check was lavish, but Mrs. Richards did not demand very much and was easily satisfied. She had never been trained in any craft, trade, or profession, and if anyone was crude or unkind enough to suggest that she had enough skill required to manipulate a scrub brush and bucket, she would point out that when she did this her back hurt her.

The state of the floor of her "apartment," on the day when Mr. Mason came to call, at an hour nicely calculated with reference to the mail schedule, indicated that Mrs. Richards had not risked backache lately.

After an exchange of greetings, Mr. Mason said, "If you've cashed your check, I've got the receipt made out."

"I don't believe it's come," she said placidly. This was her routine reply. It was her belief that eventually it might be believed, although it never had been; nor was it now.

"If you spend the rent money on something else," Mr. Mason said, "I'll have to go down to the Welfare and have them close your case." This was his routine reply.

Curtis, in a peremptory tone, said, "Give the man his money." The prospect of approaching fatherhood had raised in him no tender sentiment; in fact, it raised no sentiment at all other than an increasing daily restlessness and a conviction that it was time for him to move on.

Without so much as a sigh Mrs. Richards now produced an envelope from her bosom and examined it closely. "I guess maybe it might be this one," she said. "I haven't opened it."

Curtis, quite tired of every routine gambit of his lady-love, now said, quite testily, "Give the man his money!" He wanted cigarettes and he wanted whiskey and he knew that neither of these could be had until the check was cashed. "If I got to hit you—"

Mrs. Richards endorsed the check with her landlord's pen, and Mr. Mason began to count out her change. A new consideration now entered Curtis's mind—previously occupied only by the desire for cigarettes, whiskey, and moving on; it entered with such extreme suddenness that it gave him no time to reflect on it. He observed that Mr. Mason had a revolver in a shoulder holster inside his coat and he observed that Mr. Mason's wallet was quite engorged with money.

Curtis was not naturally malevolent, but he was naturally impulsive. He whipped Mr. Mason's revolver from its holster, struck Mr. Mason heavily on the side of the head with it, and seized his wallet.

Mr. Mason went down, but he went down slowly. He thought he was shouting for help, but the noise coming out of his mouth was no louder than a mew. He was on his hands and knees by the time Curtis reached the door, and then he slid to one side and lay silent.

Mrs. Richards sat for a moment in her chair. New situations were things she was not well equipped to cope with. After the sound of Curtis's feet on the stairs ceased, she continued to sit for some time, looking at Mr. Mason.

Presently a thought entered her mind. The familiar-looking piece of paper on the dirty table was a receipt for her rent. The money scattered around was the money Mr. Mason had been counting out to cash her check. His practice was to count it out twice and then deduct the amount of the rent.

Mrs. Richards slowly gathered up the money, slowly counted it, moving her lips. It was all there.

And so was the receipt.

Mrs. Richards nodded. She now had the receipt for her rent *and* the money. True, she no longer had Curtis, but, then, she knew he was bound to move along sooner or later. Men always did.

She hid the rent money in one of the holes with which the walls of the "apartment" were plentifully supplied, and then reflected on what she had better do next.

All things considered, she decided it was best to start screaming.

Curtis went down the stairs rapidly, but once in the street he had sense enough to walk at a normal pace. Running men were apt to attract the attention of the police.

Three blocks away was a saloon he favored with his trade. He entered by the back door, causing a buzzer to sound. He tried to slip quickly into the men's room, but wasn't quite quick enough to escape the attention of the bartender-proprietor, an irascible West Indian called Jumby, and no great friend of Curtis's.

"Another customer for the toilet trade," said Jumby, so loudly that he could be heard through the closed door. "I'd make more money if I gave the drinks away free and charged admission to the water closet!"

Curtis ignored this familiar complaint, and emptied the wallet of its money, dropping the empty leather case into the trash container which stood, full of used paper towels, alongside the sink. Then he left.

Police cars sped by him, their sirens screaming.

Vague thoughts of cigarettes and whiskey still floated in Curtis's mind, but the desire to move on was by now uppermost. It was with some relief, therefore, that he saw a young man sitting in an open convertible. The convertible was elegantly fitted out, and so was the young man. His name was William.

"You've been talking about going to California, William," Curtis said.

"I have *also* been talking," William said with precision, "about finding some congenial person with *money* to share the *expenses* of going to California."

Curtis said, "I hit the numbers. I got money enough to take care of all the expenses. Don't that make me congenial?"

"Very *much* so," said William, opening the door. Curtis started to slide in, but William stopped him with a long, impeccably groomed hand, which touched him lightly. "Curtis," he said in low but firm tones, "if you have something *on* you, I really must *insist* that you get *rid* of it first. Suppose I meet you here in an *hour?* That will also enable me to *pack.*"

"One hour," Curtis said.

He went into another bar, obtained cigarettes and whiskey. At the bar was a man generally, if not quite popularly, known as The Rock.

"How you doing, Rock?" Curtis inquired.

The Rock said nothing.

"Got some business to talk over with you," Curtis went on.

The Rock continued to say nothing.

"Like to take in a movie?" Curtis asked.

The Rock finished his drink, set down the glass, looked at Curtis. Curtis put down money, left the bar, The Rock behind him. He bought two tickets at the movie theater and they went in. The house was almost empty.

After a minute or two Curtis whispered, "Fifty dollars buys a gun. I got it on me."

The Rock took out a handkerchief, spread it in his lap, counted money into it, passed it to Curtis. After a moment Curtis passed the handkerchief back. The Rock soon left, but Curtis stayed on. He still had the better part of an hour to kill.

The Rock took a bus and traveled a mile. He walked a few blocks on a side street and entered a house which, like most of its fellows, bore a sign that it has been selected for something euphemistically called "Urban Renewal," and that further renting of rooms was illegal. Most of the windows were already marked with large X signs.

On the second floor The Rock disturbed a teenage boy and girl in close, though wordless, conversation. The boy looked up in some annoyance, but after a quick glance decided to say nothing. The girl clutched his arm until the intruder passed.

The door on the third floor was locked, but The Rock pushed hard, once, and it yielded. The room was ornately furnished, and the dressing

table was crowded with perfumes and cosmetics and a large doll; but seated
on the bed was a man.

"It ain't you," the man said. He was red-eyed drunk.

"It ain't me," The Rock agreed.

"It's Humpty Slade," said the man on the bed. *"He* don't pay for her
rent. *He* don't buy her no clothes. *He* don't feed her. *I* do."

The Rock nodded his massive head.

"Everybody knows that," The Rock said. He took a handkerchief out of
his pocket, laid it on the bed, opened its folds. "Seventy-five dollars," he
said.

A quick turnover and a modest profit—that was The Rock's policy.

The boy and girl, now seated on the stairs, shrank to one side as he came
down. They did not look up. It was not very uncomfortable there in that
all but abandoned house; but it was private—as private as you can get when
you have no place of your own to go.

Upstairs, on the bed, the waiting man stared at the revolver with his red,
red eyes. . . .

After a while the boy and the girl sauntered down into the street and
went separate ways in search of something to eat. But after supper they met
again in the same hallway.

Scarcely had they taken their places when they were disturbed. A man
and woman came up, talking loudly. They paused at the sight of the
younger pair in the dim light of the single bulb, and for a moment the two
couples looked at one another. The older woman was handsome, flamboy-
antly dressed and made up. Her companion was large and on the ugly side,
his looks not improved by a crooked shoulder which jutted back on one
side.

"What are you kids doing here?" he demanded. "Go on, get out—"

"Oh, now, Humphrey," the woman pleaded. "You leave them alone.
They ain't hurting nobody."

"Okay, sugar," the big man said submissively. They continued up the
stairs. The boy and girl listened as they fumbled at the door. Then the
woman's voice went high and shrill with fear, screaming, *"No—no—no—"*

At the loud sound of the revolver the boy and girl leaped to their feet.
Something fell past them, and landed below with a thud.

"You'd point a gun at *me?"* a man's voice growled. Then there was the
noise of a blow.

"My woman—!"

"You'd take a shot at *me?"*

The sound of fist on flesh, again and again. The boy and girl crept down
the stairs.

"No, Humpty, don't hit me any more! I'm sorry, Humpty! I didn't mean it! I was—oh, please, Humpty! *Please?*"

"Don't hit him any more, honey. He was drunk. Honey—"

The boy and girl stopped at the bottom floor for only a moment. Then they were gone. . . .

Curtis paused, uncertain. He was sure that it was dangerous for him to remain on the street, but he didn't know where to go. That little rat, William, had failed to reappear. There were planes flying, and trains and buses running, but even if he decided what to take he would still have to decide *which* airfield, *which* station, *which* terminal. The problems seemed to proliferate each time he thought about them.

He would have a drink to help him consider.

There wasn't really any hurry.

That dirty rat, William!

The Sepoy Lords were holding an informal meeting—a caucus, as it were.

Someone has remarked that the throne of Russia was neither hereditary, nor elective, but occupative. The same might be said of office in the Sepoy Lords.

The scene was a friendly neighborhood rooftop.

"So you think you're going to be Warlord?" a boy named Buzz demanded.

"That's right," said the one called Sonny.

The quorum, including several Sepoy Ladies, listened with interest.

"*I* don't think you're going to be Warlord," said Buzz.

"I *know* I am," said Sonny.

"What makes you so sure?" inquired Buzz.

"*This,*" Sonny said, simply, reaching into his pocket, and taking something out.

Sudden intakes of breath, eyes lighting up, members crowding around, loud comments of admiration. "Sonny got a *piece!*" "*Look* at that piece Sonny's got!"

The President of the Sepoy Lords, one Big Arthur, who had until now remained above the battle, asked, "Where'd you get it, Son'."

Sonny smirked, cocked his head. "*She* knows where I got it," he said. His girl, Myra, smiled knowingly.

Buzz said only one word, but he said it weakly. He now had no case, and he knew it.

The new Warlord sighted wickedly down the revolver. "*First* thing I'm going to do," he announced; "there's one old cat I am going to *burn*. He said something about my old lady, and that is something I don't take from *any*body, let alone from one of those dirty old Ermine Kings."

Diplomatically, no one commented on the personal aspect of his grievance, all being well aware how easy it was to say something about Sonny's old lady, and being equally aware that the old lady's avenging offspring now held a revolver in his hand. But the general aspect of the challenge was something else.

"Those Ermine Kings better watch out, is all!" a Sepoy Lady declared. There was a murmur of assent.

Big Arthur now deemed it time to interpose his authority. "Oh, yeah, sure," he said. " 'They better watch out!'—how come? Because we got one piece?"

Warlord Sonny observed a semantic inconsistency. With eyes narrowed he said, "What do you mean, 'we'? *'We'* haven't got *any*thing. *I'm* the one who's got the piece, and *no*body is going to tell me what to do with my personal property—see?" He addressed this caveat to the exuberant Sepoy Lady, but no one misunderstood him—least of all, Big Arthur.

Allowing time for the message to sink in, Sonny then said, "Big Arthur is right. I mean, one ain't enough. We need money to get more. How? I got a plan. Listen—"

They listened. They agreed. They laughed their satisfaction.

"Now," Sonny concluded, "let's get going."

He watched as most of them filed through the door. He started after them, then stopped. *Was* stopped. Big Arthur seized his wrist with one hand and grabbed the revolver with the other.

Sonny, crying, "Gimme that back!" leaped for it. But Big Arthur, taking hold of Sonny's jacket with his free hand, slapped him—hard—back against the door.

"You got the wrong idea, Son'," Big Arthur said. "You seem to think that *you* are the President around here. That's *wrong*. Now, if you really think you are man enough, you can try to get this piece away from me. You want to try?"

For a while Sonny had been somebody. Now he was nobody again. He knew that he would never in a million years take the revolver away from Big Arthur, never burn that one old cat from the Ermine Kings who had said something about his old lady. Tears of pain and humiliation welled in his eyes.

"Cheer up," Big Arthur said. "We're going to see how your plan works out. And it better work out *good*. Now get down those stairs with the other members, Mr. Sonny Richards."

Head down, Sonny stumbled through the door. Myra started to slip through after him, but Big Arthur detained her. "Not so quick, chick," he said. "Let's move along together. You and me are going to get better acquainted." For just a second Myra hesitated. Then she giggled.

"*Much* better acquainted," Big Arthur said.

Feeling neither strain nor pain, Curtis glided out of the bar. The late afternoon spread invitingly before him. He was supposed to meet somebody and go somewhere . . . William . . .

There, slowly passing by in his fancy convertible, was the man himself. With great good humor Curtis cried, "William!" and started toward him.

William himself saw things from a different angle. Curtis, to be sure, was *rough,* but what had really set William against going to California with him was the fact that he had observed Curtis that way. He, William, wanted nothing to do at any time with people who carried guns. And, anyway, he wasn't quite ready to leave for California—something had come up.

What came up at that moment was Curtis, roaring (so it seemed) with rage, and loping forward with murder in his eye.

William gave a squeak of fright. The convertible leaped ahead, crashing into the car in front. And still Curtis came on—

Screaming, "Keep away from me, Curtis!" William jumped out of the car and started to run. Someone grabbed him. "Don't stop me—he's got a gun—Cur*tis!*" he yelled.

But they wouldn't let go. It was the police, wouldn't you know it, grim-faced men in plain clothes; of all the cars to crash into—

One of them finished frisking Curtis. "Nope, no gun," he said. "This one ain't dangerous. *You.*" He turned to William. "What do you mean by saying he had a gun?"

William lost his head and started to babble, and before he could move, the men were searching *him.* And the *car.* They found his cigarette case stuffed with sticks of tea, and they found the shoebox full of it, too.

"Pot," said one of them, sniffing. "Real Mexican stuff. Convertible, hey? You won't need a convertible for a long time, fellow."

William burst into tears. The mascara ran down his face and he looked so grotesque that even the grim faces of the detectives had to relax into smiles.

"What about this one, Leo," one of them asked, jerking his thumb. "He's clean."

But Leo was dubious. "There must be some connection, or the pretty one wouldn't of been so scared," he said. A thought occurred to him. "What did he call him? What did you say his name was? Curtis?"

The other detective snapped his fingers. "Curtis. Yeah. A question, Curtis: You in the apartment of a Mrs. Selena Richards today?"

"Never heard of her," said Curtis, sobering rapidly. Move on, that's what he should have done—move on.

Mrs. Richards was entertaining company. The baby was awake—had been awake, in fact, since those chest-deep, ear-splitting screams earlier in the afternoon—and the girls had come home from school. She had sent them down to the store for cold cuts and sliced bread; they hadn't eaten more than half of it on the way back, and Mrs. Richards and the neighbors were dining off the other half. There was also some wine they had all chipped in to buy. Excitement didn't come very often, and it was a shame to let it go to waste.

"Didn't that man *bleed!"* a neighbor exclaimed. "All over your floor, Selena!"

"All over *his* floor, you mean—*he* owns this building."

After the whoops of laughter died down, someone thought of asking where Mrs. Richards's oldest child was.

"I don't know where Sonny is," she said, placid as ever. "He takes after his daddy. His daddy always was a traveling sort of man." She felt in her bosom for the money she had placed there—the money she had taken from the hole in the wall after the police and ambulance left. Yes, it was safely there.

All in all, she thought, it had been quite a day. Curtis gone, but he was on the point of becoming troublesome, anyway. Excitement—a *lot* of excitement. Company in, hanging on her every word. The receipt for the rent, *plus* the rent itself. Yes, a lucky day. Later on she would see what the date was, and tomorrow she would play that number.

If luck was coming to you, nothing could keep it away.

They had taken three stitches in Mr. Mason's scalp, and taped and bandaged it.

"You want us to call you a taxi?" the hospital attendant asked.

"No," Mr. Mason said. "I don't have any money to waste on taxis. The bus is still running, isn't it?"

"There's a charge of three dollars," the attendant said.

Mr. Mason snorted. "I don't have three cents. I'll have to borrow bus fare from some storekeeper, I guess. That dirty—he took everything I had. Right in broad daylight. I don't know what we pay taxes for."

"I guess we pay them to reward certain people for turning decent buildings into flophouses," the attendant said. He was old and crusty and due to retire soon, and didn't give a damn for anybody.

Mr. Mason narrowed his eyes and looked at him. "Nobody has the right to tell me what to do with my personal property," he said meanly.

The attendant shrugged. "That's your personal property, too," he said, pointing. "Take it with you; we don't want it."

It was the empty shoulder holster.

On leaving the hospital Mr. Mason headed first for a store, but not to borrow bus fare. He bought a book of blank receipts. He still had most of his rents to collect, and he intended to collect every single one of them. It hardly paid a person to be decent, these days, he reflected irritably. One thing was sure: nobody else had better tangle with him—not today.

He headed for the first house on his round, and it was there, in the hallway, that the Sepoy Lords caught up with him.

THE ETERNAL CHASE

by *ANTHONY GILBERT*

I don't know what to do. I don't know, and there's no one to ask. They say lightning never strikes twice in the same place, but how can you be sure? How can you be *sure?*

When I heard that The Dingle House had been rented by a widow with a little girl I was glad, because I thought now I should have someone to play with. Ours is an old household, just Grandmother and Aunt Agatha, with Uncle Ned coming down from Friday to Monday. And even he's pretty old—about 30. I share a governess with my three sisters, but they're all older and they think I'm silly.

So I waited eagerly for Grandmother to call on Mrs. Craddock. Until she did, of course, I couldn't even ask the little girl to tea. And I expected so much of the meeting.

But that, of course, was before I met Harriet.

In fact, Grandmother never did call at The Dingle House and my first meetings with Harriet were accidental. One afternoon Maryanne—she had been my nurse and had stayed on after I was nine and didn't really need a nurse any more—sent me to the mailbox with a letter she'd forgotten to give to the postman. Coming back, I saw two strangers approaching. In Hilton Abbas you know everyone whether your grandmother calls on them or not, so these had to be the mysterious Mrs. Craddock and her daughter.

It was Harriet I looked at first—and had a shock. She was shorter than I, and as elegant as her mother; they both wore clothes you wouldn't see at The Dower House even on one of Grandmother's "At Home" days; and she was striking enough to hold anyone's attention. Her skin had the soft gold of an apricot, and she had huge brown eyes and long raying lashes.

But at the very first glance I knew she would never be my playmate. Because, though she was two months younger, she wasn't a child. She was like a small adult; even her movements were smooth and controlled. I knew she would never bump into things or break them as I am always doing.

Still, as we drew close I smiled at her—to show that if Grandmother hadn't called it had nothing to do with me.

And she looked straight through me. I actually felt as though I were a ghost. In mortification, I looked at Mrs. Craddock—and got my second shock. I had heard Uncle Ned talk about the Jersey Lily, how people jumped on park benches and crowded the windows just to see her go by. The Immortal Beauty, he called her.

Well, Margaret Craddock was the same. When she caught my eye she smiled, and I just stood and gaped. It was as if someone had switched on the sun.

She didn't speak—she knew the rules of good society as well as I—and the next minute I had gone past, but not so far that I didn't hear Harriet say, "There was no need to take any notice. We don't know her."

And Mrs. Craddock's voice, as lovely as the rest of her, floated back. "I wish we did, Harriet. For your sake, I wish we did."

"I met Mrs. Craddock and her daughter," I told Maryanne when I got back. "Why won't Grandmother call on them?"

"Because!" said Maryanne, as she always did when she didn't know the answer. But later I heard her say to Jessie, the parlormaid, "But who was Mr. C? That's what I'd like to know."

I leaned over the banisters. "He's dead," I called. I supposed he'd been a very wicked man, and it was a case of touching pitch and being defiled. Only no one could really think of Mrs. Craddock as pitch.

Still Grandmother didn't pay the call, and about a month went by before I saw the Craddocks again. Maryanne had taken me to buy a pair of gloves at Robinson's—Mr. Robinson had the only draper's shop in Hilton Abbas. He used to stand in the doorway wearing a morning coat and welcoming important customers; his two daughters, Lucy and Elsie, served in the shop.

We had bought my gloves and Maryanne was whispering with Lucy at the far end of the shop when Mrs. Craddock and Harriet came in. Mrs. Craddock asked for a muff for her little girl. We all wore muffs, mostly of white rabbit fur with little black "tails," strung round our necks with a silk cord.

Elsie said they were out of white muffs, but she showed Mrs. Craddock a very pretty brown one. More serviceable than the white, Elsie said.

Harriet immediately flew into a tantrum. "I won't have a brown one," she screamed. "A horrid dirty color." And she flounced across the shop to where I was looking at some little brooches. There was one shaped like a cat that I thought very pretty.

"They're trash," said Harriet in a scornful voice. In a second she had gone back to her grown-up way of speaking. She picked up a little locket and threw that down, too. "It's not even real," she scoffed.

She was wearing a very pretty locket herself and she began to dangle it before my eyes. She must have accidentally touched a spring in it, because suddenly the chain parted and the locket fell to the ground. I stooped to pick it up. It had a little black band with three pearls in it on one side and initials—*H.W.*— on the other.

"Did it belong to your grandmother?" I said. I had one for Sundays that had been my grandmother's.

"Of course not," said Harriet, bending her head so that I could refasten the chain. "Don't pull my hair. This was given me when I was six years old."

"But it says *H.W.,*" I insisted. "Your initials are *H.C.*"

"That's because my father went away," she said. I knew she meant he had died, but nobody in Hilton Abbas ever died; they passed over or passed on or were gathered by the Grim Reaper, but they all meant the same thing. "Before that I was Harriet Winter and we had a house by the sea and my grandmother had a bigger house than yours and her own carriage. I had an aunt, too," she wound up. "Aunt Grace."

"I will take the brown muff," we heard Mrs. Craddock say.

Harriet looked over her shoulder and laughed. "You will look silly with a muff that small," she said. "If you give it to me I shall never use it. I shall throw it out of the window." And she stamped her little foot.

While Elsie was packaging the muff, Mrs. Craddock turned round and said, "You are the little girl from The Dower House, aren't you?"

Maryanne must have heard her; she was buying a pair of corsets in whispers. Although everyone knew we wore underclothes it was thought more polite to pretend they didn't exist.

"Now, Miss Vicky, I've told you, don't bother people," she said. She put out her hand and I went up reluctantly and took it. Mrs. Craddock took her parcel and went out, followed by Harriet.

"She's nothing but a *baby,*" I heard Harriet say scornfully. "She liked the little cat brooch."

"I know someone who needs a dose of syrup of figs," said Maryanne as we walked home. "The little lady!"

"Maryanne," I asked—I didn't really want to confide in her, but she was the only one I had, "if my father died would I have to change my name?"

"Whyever?" Maryanne exclaimed. "The funny things you say, Vicky. What put that idea into your head?"

"Harriet Craddock used to be Harriet Winter until her father passed on," I said. "She lived in a house by the sea, and she has a grandmother, too, and an aunt called Grace."

There was a minute's silence. Then Maryanne said, in a voice I didn't know, "Is that what she told you? Well, fancy me not thinking of it!"

"Not thinking of what?" I pleaded.

She gave my hand a tug and began to hurry us home. "You know what your grandmother says about repeating gossip," she warned me. "It's vulgar."

There were visitors to lunch, so I had mine in the old nursery that was now the schoolroom. I was never allowed to eat in the kitchen, which I should have liked much better. Afterward, I took my book and went into the garden. The book was dull, and I hoped Uncle Ned would bring me a new one from London, where he worked during the week.

Presently I thought I would try and find a frog in the orchard, but there weren't any, so I decided to ask Gorman, our cook, for a glass of water; even if I couldn't catch a frog I could paint a picture of one.

I skirted round the house, but when I passed the kitchen window I saw Gorman and Maryanne and Jessie and Jessie's sister, Louisa, who was the housemaid, all gathered round the table, with their heads together.

"It's as true as I stand here," said Maryanne. "She couldn't make up a story like that!"

"To think of her coming here and expecting decent people to call on her!" marveled Jessie.

"I think it's lovely," said Louisa. "A real murderer."

"She isn't," said Gorman in her flat Scottish voice. "The court said not. And the poor thing has to live somewhere."

"It's no wonder the little girl's a Tartar," contributed Maryanne. "That's what I can't forgive her, Sarah. (I'd never known Gorman's name was Sarah —I'd never thought of her as having any other name). Letting Harriet be mixed up in it."

"She *was* mixed up in it," asserted Gorman. "Well, it was her father who was poisoned."

I crouched under the sill, shaking with excitement.

"It's a wonder I didn't think of it," Maryanne mused. "Her name being Harriet, I mean—and the pictures in the paper."

Jessie said, "The paper. Let's see, it was four months ago, wasn't it? Has Mr. Coutts called lately, Cook?"

Old newspapers at The Dower House were always stored in the cellar. Every few months Mr. Coutts called for them and bought them by weight for use in his shop, and Gorman gave the money to save little Chinese girl babies who would otherwise be allowed to die.

I heard the cellar door open, so I knew Jessie was going down to look. I raised myself slightly, but I believe if I had sat on the sill none of them would have noticed me. They were too much engrossed.

When Jessie came back I heard the rustle of papers and after a longish time Louisa said, "Here we are! Here's a picture of Harriet Winter in the box."

I couldn't think what box she meant. I wondered if it could be a coffin, only it was Mr. Winter who was dead, not Harriet. They were all so busy they didn't hear Uncle Ned come in. It was earlier than usual for him and he came straight to the kitchen. He was the only member of the household who would have dared appear in the middle of an afternoon, but they would have done anything for him. It wasn't just that he was so goodlooking with his frank, blue eyes and little golden mustache; he was always the same, whatever happened, and hardly anyone is like that.

"Am I interrupting a study group?" I heard him say, and, then, "What a lovely face! I seem to have seen it—of course. But why are you digging up the Winter case? It's closed for good."

It was Maryanne who told him. "It's the new lady at The Dingle House," she said. "Her little girl spoke to Miss Vicky in Robinson's this morning."

When Uncle Ned spoke again I hardly recognized his voice. "So here we go," he said. "The eternal chase. I suppose no one will ever let her forget. Where is she, by the way? Victoria, I mean?"

"In the garden," said Maryanne.

I slipped from under the sill and crawled round the corner of the house. Then I raced down to the orchard and opened my book, waiting for his step on the path.

"Enjoying yourself?" said Uncle Ned. "Since when do you read a book upside down?"

"Did you bring me another?" I asked. "I've read this one."

"How long have you been here?" said Uncle Ned. "Now, Vicky, no lies."

"I didn't mean to listen," I burst out, wondering how Harriet would have coped with the situation. "I went to ask for some water and they were talking, and I heard Harriet's name—"

"And what did you make of it?" my uncle asked.

"That—that Mrs. Craddock poisoned her husband," I faltered.

"No. That Mrs. Craddock was cleared by a jury of poisoning her husband—cleared and sent out to be free."

"If she didn't do it," I said, "why did she have to change her name?"

"Because it's not enough to be innocent—everyone has to believe in your innocence. Do you understand?"

I nodded. "I think so. Last Christmas Aunt Agatha said I had broken the little green vase in the drawing room. And I hadn't. It must have been the wind. But she didn't believe me."

I remembered my dismay at the discovery that you could tell the truth but not be believed because you couldn't prove it. No one but myself knew I hadn't done it—and God, I amended silently. Sometimes I wondered why He didn't speak up for all the people in trouble. But that would mean perfect justice in this world, and what's a heaven for?

"Is it like that for Mrs. Craddock?" I asked.

Uncle Ned nodded. "Yes, Vicky," he said. "It's like that."

When I was crossing the hall that evening, I saw Aunt Agatha pasting long strips of newsprint onto sheets of brown paper. I didn't need to be told it was the story of Mrs. Craddock's trial. Aunt Agatha is like the beasts in the Revelations that had eyes before and behind; she couldn't have seen me, yet she called out, "I've told you before, Victoria (a sign of deep displeasure this) it's vulgar to pry."

I hurried up to bed, resolved that by hook or crook I would get hold of those sheets of brown paper and read the whole story for myself.

I had to wait more than a week. Uncle Ned had gone back to London and I was practically a prisoner in my own house. I wasn't even allowed to go to the mailbox alone.

Then one afternoon the hired carriage came round to take Grandmother and Aunt Agatha calling. I heard her say they might be a little late getting back. I supposed they thought it their duty to tell everyone about Mrs. Craddock.

By good luck (for me) Maryanne had a toothache and had to go to have a tooth pulled, Jessie and Louisa (sisters) had their half day together, and only Gorman was left in the house. I was told not to be a nuisance, but to play quietly in the garden.

As soon as I was sure the coast was clear I crept into the study. I was sure the papers would be in Uncle Ned's Wellington chest. This was locked, but I found the keys in a drawer of his desk, and there they were, pages and pages of small print, with pictures of Mrs. Craddock (whom I must learn to call Mrs. Winter) and Harriet and Mr. Winter, referred to as "the deceased."

I snatched up the bundle and fled to the attic where I knew no one would follow me. Past the roll of oilcloth where I used to hide, and the dressmaker's dummy that used to frighten me out of my wits, I flung myself on the Victorian love seat, with its padding bursting through the fading rose brocade, and started to read.

Some of the wording puzzled me and I had to go back several times to understand certain points; but this was the story I pieced together.

About ten years earlier, Margaret Craddock, then aged 18, married Charles Winter, who was a good deal older; they had one child. Harriet, whom her mother idolized, said Mr. Paull, who was someone called Counsel for the Prosecution, at her husband's expense.

About a month before his death Mr. Winter was offered and accepted a position abroad, where a child could not be taken because of the climate. He proposed to leave Harriet with his mother and his unmarried sister,

Grace. Mrs. Winter said nothing should separate her from her child. Harriet created a scene, as Maryanne would have said, declaring that if her mother went away she would drown herself. It was unfortunate, said Mr. Paull, that so much attention was given to the outbreaks of a spoiled child.

Neither side would yield. Mrs. Winter said that if her husband insisted on going overseas she would remain behind. This was the position when, about a week before his untimely death, Mr. Winter fell ill with a sort of fever. It was not denied, said Mr. Paull, that his wife nursed him with exemplary care and patience, though she refused to allow the little girl to stay with her grandmother and Aunt Grace at the Big House.

There was only one servant in the Winter house, the other having recently given notice and not been replaced, since Mr. Winter intended to close his establishment. Therefore, Mrs. Winter cooked most of the food as well as attended the sick man in the bedroom. The doctor (who also gave evidence) said the fever was running its normal course, and there was no reason to anticipate anything but a happy issue of the illness. Mr. Winter still declared his intention of closing the house and taking up his appointment abroad, and he still insisted that his wife should accompany him.

On the fatal afternoon the servant had gone out to visit her parents and, a fine morning having turned to clouds of rain, the child, Harriet, played on the square landing outside the sickroom. She was giving a doll's tea party, and this fact, irrelevant though it might sound, would be shown to be of the greatest significance.

At about four o'clock Mrs. Winter told Harriet she was going downstairs to prepare tea.

"Sit with your father until I come back," she said. "If he should ask for anything, don't cross him, as he is still very ill."

This was in direct opposition to the doctor's opinion that he was by then well on the road to recovery.

About fifteen minutes later, Mrs. Winter returned with the tea tray, and Harriet went back to her own tea party. Almost immediately, strange sounds were heard from the sickroom, groans and the noise of vomiting. Harriet remained where she was until her mother came to the door to say, "Your father has taken a turn for the worse. We must have Dr. Blair, but who is there to fetch him? Alice has gone out, and I do not like to leave you alone with him when he is so ill."

Harriet said, "I could go for the doctor," and although Mrs. Winter did not like the idea of a little girl going out alone in such weather she felt she had no choice. So she gave Harriet a note, and a little later the child was seen by her Aunt Grace, who was driving home in the family carriage.

The aunt stopped and got out to know why Harriet was wandering about alone. Harriet, who had lost her way, explained about the sudden change, and Miss Winter drove to the doctor's and accompanied both him and the child back to her brother's house.

Mrs. Winter opened the door and said, "Oh, Doctor, come at once, he seems to be sinking fast. I can't think what can have caused the change—it can't be anything he ate, since he's had nothing I haven't prepared myself."

She led the way upstairs, where the door stood open. When Mr. Winter saw his sister he said in a weak voice, "Grace, I have been poisoned."

Miss Winter wanted to stay, but the doctor turned her and Harriet out of the room while he made his examination. It told against Mrs. Winter that she had kept none of the vomited matter. Later, Grace Winter was allowed to come back and she sat by the bedside, holding her brother's hand, and asking him, "Henry, who has done this?" But he was too far gone to speak to her.

Later still, Miss Winter went home with a furious and reluctant Harriet in tow, Mrs. Winter having promised to come and fetch her first thing the next morning. The doctor stayed on at the house, and about 4:00 a.m. Henry Winter died, having drifted into a coma from which he never recovered.

The doctor, in the light of what the dead man had said, declared he could not issue a death certificate until an autopsy had been performed (I wasn't sure what this meant). Mrs. Winter wasn't allowed to go back and get Harriet as she had promised, and she sent the servant Alice with a note. There was no telephone in the house; my grandmother does not have one either, saying she had no intention of being at the beck and call of an "instrument."

Presently the police called at the Big House and asked to see Harriet. She seemed quite composed, asking, "Is he dead? Was it poison? Could it have been something in the milk?"

The police said that so far as they knew he had had no milk and then Harriet told her story. After her mother had gone downstairs her father said, "I am very thirsty. Can you give me something to drink?"

The water carafe had been taken downstairs by Mrs. Winter to be re-filled from the jug of boiled water in the kitchen. There had been a recent typhoid epidemic and all drinking water had to be boiled; so Harriet could not fill a glass from the small sink near the landing. She said she had some milk for her tea party and asked if that would do.

Her father said, "I suppose so." So Harriet poured the milk into a glass and then he said, "Give me my bottle of tablets from the medicine chest." He took one—Harriet was sure it was only one—and it made the milk fizz a little.

He handed back the glass saying, "Do not tell your mother of this—she does not like me to have tablets." And he added half to himself, "Sometimes I think she would be glad if I were dead."

The police asked Harriet, "Why did you say nothing of this before?"
Harriet said, "Because my father told me not to."

"When did you tell your mother?"

"I didn't tell her. I didn't see her again."

"Did you tell anyone?"

"There was no one to tell."

"There was your grandmother and your aunt."

"I should never tell them anything about us," Harriet retorted.

So far as I could understand it, this Mr. Paull wanted to make the jury
believe that the story about the milk was just a fabrication to help Mrs.
Winter, but Harriet clung to it. She had had no chance of concocting it
with her mother, and no one supposed she could have invented it herself.

Since both the glass and the cups from the tea tray had been washed
while Mrs. Winter was waiting for the doctor, there was nothing to show
how the poison had been introduced. In addition to the tea Mr. Winter had
had part of a buttered scone; other scones had been put back on the tray,
but the bitten piece that he had not finished had been disposed of. Mrs.
Winter said she wanted the sickroom to look tidy and she had no reason to
suppose her husband's attack was anything but a natural one.

The autopsy showed that he had had some poison from a tin that had
been bought to kill rats in the garden. The tin was kept on a shelf in the
garden shed. The gardener, a man named Richards, told the court that he
had been given the tin by Mr. Winter, from whom he took his orders. He
only saw Mrs. Winter when she wanted flowers for the house. Mr. Winter
did not care for cut blooms, calling them decaying vegetation. Richards
said he had sometimes heard arguments about this, but about nothing else.
He never came into the house, taking the flowers and vegetables to the
kitchen door; if he wanted a cup of tea it was handed to him through the
kitchen window by one of the servants.

When Mrs. Winter went into the box (I knew what that meant by
now), they seemed to be trying to make out that she liked Richards—who
was about as old as Uncle Ned, though less good-looking—better than she
liked her own husband, which seemed silly, as he was only the gardener and
wouldn't have any money anyway.

Then Harriet was called to the box. The Judge protested, but Mr. Leslie,
the Counsel for the Defense, said she was a vital witness. I could imagine
her, perfectly composed, not stammering or shuddering as I would, saying,
"I don't know," and "I don't remember." She said her mother had not gone
into the garden all that day; she herself had been playing on the lawn until
the rain started. She had been looking out of the window while her mother
got the tea and would have seen her if she had gone to the shed. No trace of
wet shoes or skirt had been found, and the police could not trace any more
of the poison in the house.

There was a great deal more of this—far too much for me to read; but in the end the jury decided that Mrs. Winter had not done it. They said there was insufficient evidence to show how the poison was administered. I supposed they meant he could have taken it himself.

Then there was a clipping to say that Mrs. Winter was taking her child and leaving the neighborhood for some place where she might begin life afresh. That seemed silly to me, too. You can't start life over again when you are quite old, going on 30.

My chief feeling was an overwhelming jealousy of Harriet. To be a heroine before you are even ten years old! There were pictures of her in the paper. I indulged in a daydream in which I stood in the box and gave evidence on Uncle Ned's behalf. He wouldn't be accused of murder, of course, but something nearly as bad; he might perhaps rob a bank, or people would think he had.

I became so lost in this vision that my grandmother almost caught me putting the papers back when she returned from her visits.

"What have you been doing this afternoon?" Aunt Agatha said, and I told her I had been reading. I had Uncle Ned's new book under my arm. I began to wonder if I was getting almost as cunning as Harriet.

Now I longed to meet her again, but she and her mother seemed to have gone to ground like a pair of foxes. I decided I must search her out, so one afternoon I let my ball bounce through the front gate and start running down the hill.

The Dingle House stood at the bottom and one of the reasons it was so often vacant was because it was said to be so damp. As I drew near the gate I could hear Harriet talking and I wondered who was bold enough to visit her.

Deliberately I threw my ball up in the air so that it went into her garden; when I looked over the gate I saw that her companions were imaginary. She was sitting on the lawn and the famous tea set was spread on a white cloth. When she saw me she said imperiously, "What do you want?"

"My ball came over into your garden," I said.

She seemed to think for a minute, then she said, "You'd better come in and fetch it."

I was fascinated by the tea service, which was an exact replica of a real one down to the sugar bowl and tiny spoons. Harriet, who clearly did nothing by halves, had arranged colored pebbles and leaves and bits of twigs to represent biscuits and buns.

"You can stay to tea if you like," she said carelessly. "I set a place for you anyway."

In for a penny, in for a pound, I thought. I was already in trouble just by opening the gate.

"How did you know I was coming?" I asked. "The others are rather late, aren't they?"

She gave me a look brimming with scorn. "They're here," she said. "It's not my fault if you can't see them."

She picked up the teapot and poured out a stream of invisible tea.

"Help yourself to cream," she told me, pointing to the jug.

I poured it carefully. I had never seen cream at home, though I supposed my grandmother gave it to her guests. Then I picked up the sugar bowl and shook some of the sugar into the cup. To my surprise Harriet grasped my arm.

"You're not supposed to help yourself till you're invited to," she said, and again I remembered Grandmother slapping my hand away when I helped myself uninvited to cake.

"But I take sugar," I said.

"That cup isn't for you, it's for your grandmother." Harriet pointed to a place on the grass and meekly I set the cup down.

"Now your aunt." She passed me another cup. "And Mrs. Dixon." That was the Rector's wife. "She doesn't take sugar, either."

"And Uncle Ned?" I urged.

"Oh, we don't ask men," said Harriet. "You can't, if you're ladies living alone. Besides, we don't want them."

"I always want Uncle Ned," I said, and I added cruelly, "Don't you miss your father?"

"Oh, he never played with me—he was always too busy," she replied, in the coolest voice imaginable. "Fathers don't, you know. And they travel all over the world." She fixed me with a furious golden glance. "Where's your father? Did he go away too?"

"He went to India; he has another wife now. I think of The Dower House as my home."

"So he did go away." She sounded triumphant. "I've seen your Aunt Agatha. My mother says she withered on a virgin thorn."

I wasn't sure what that meant, but it sounded unpleasant enough even for Aunt Agatha. Before I could think of a reply someone called my name and there was Uncle Ned standing at the gate.

"Your grandmother is getting anxious about you, Victoria," he said. "You should have left word that you had been invited to tea."

He bowed to Harriet and took off his hat.

"She wanted to stay," said Harriet carelessly.

I began to explain about the ball, then I saw he wasn't looking at me any longer. He was staring at the front door that had just opened. Mrs. Craddock came down the path.

"I will introduce myself if I may," he said. "I am Victoria's uncle, Edward O'Hare. Victoria forgot to tell us where she was going."

"It is a pleasure for Harriet to have a playfellow," Mrs. Craddock said. "There are not many young children here."

Harriet said furiously, "I'm nine, that's not young. And I didn't ask her, she wanted to stay, she threw her ball over the wall on purpose!"

"Then she paid us an unusual compliment," said her mother swiftly. She turned back to Uncle Ned. "I should like to ask her again, but we shall be leaving the neighborhood soon."

"I am sorry," said Uncle Ned. "They say the house—"

"Is damp. Yes. But it's not that. It is just that I never cared for industrial cities—not even Coventry."

"If there is a gate into the city there must also be a gate out of it," said my uncle.

"A secret gate," suggested Mrs. Craddock, and once more I saw that golden, life-giving smile. She should smile more often, I thought; she would light up the world.

"If you can't find the key someone else might find it for you."

"And if it only opens in one direction?"

"One could enter."

They were like two people playing tennis, hitting the ball over the net to each other, indifferent to everyone else. I did not understand what they were saying, but I listened, fascinated.

"It's a solitary place," said Mrs. Craddock.

"Surely that depends on your company. And, you know," Uncle Ned added, "it doesn't do to be swayed by the mob. That is, one doesn't have to believe all one hears."

"You're the first person to tell me that."

This exchange might have gone on endlessly—I could see neither of them remembered we were there—had not Harriet broken in to observe, "If Victoria's grandmother is worried about her, shouldn't she go home?"

"Perhaps you will change your mind, after all," Uncle Ned urged. "I'm sorry to break up your party, Harriet."

"Oh, there are plenty of people left," said Harriet in that grown-up voice she could put on so easily. She looked at me. "I told you we didn't want men. They come and spoil things and then they go away."

"What did Mrs. Craddock mean about Coventry?" I asked Uncle Ned as we went back up the hill.

"It's a place where no one speaks to anyone else."

"Then why go there?"

"You don't go, you're sent. You have no choice."

At the top of the hill Aunt Agatha was waiting. "Where have you been?" she scolded me.

"Her ball ran down the hill, so she had to retrieve it," said Uncle Ned. Not a word about Mrs. Craddock or Harriet. . . .

Suddenly I lost interest in the Craddocks. A family called Weston came to live nearby and their daughter, Cynthia, joined us for lessons. The first day we met I knew she was what I had been waiting for. Like me, she was an only child, and she understood at once my world of Make Believe.

All through those hot summer days we were inseparable. Grandmother called at once, so I was at liberty to invite Cynthia home; even Maryanne liked her. I thought of Harriet, so capricious and domineering. I still caught sight of her occasionally, so I knew they hadn't left The Dingle House yet; but she didn't matter to me anymore—or so I believed.

Then in August the Westons went away to the seashore. We never left the house—Grandmother said there was no better air in the country. I missed Cynthia dreadfully. I used to lie in the long grass in the orchard, making up stories in which I rescued her from plunging horses, charging bulls (though I was terrified of them), and boiling seas.

Aunt Agatha used to scold me. "You will ruin your eyesight and your head will poke forward if you spend all your days with your nose in a book."

Uncle Ned still came on Fridays, but even he had lost some of his glamor. I counted the days until Cynthia's return.

Then came the afternoon when my whole world blew up in my face.

Bored by my book, I looked about me for some distraction and saw a hedgehog squeezing under the fence between the garden and the wild commonland beyond. Grandmother had been asked to grant a right of way there, but she had refused, because of the gypsies who camped in the neighborhood every summer.

I went down to the wild land through the blue wooden gate of the orchard, but the hedgehog had already gone to ground. I thought I would go a little way farther and see if there were any gypsies camped among the furze bushes—they would be a pleasant change from my aunt and Maryanne. But all I saw were two people, a man and woman, walking together; and suddenly he drew her into his arms and they stood like one person.

They were Mrs. Craddock and Uncle Ned.

I don't remember if I cried out—they were too absorbed to hear me anyway; but I knew without being told that this wasn't the first time they had met here. She went to his embrace as readily as a bird to its nest. Cynthia and I had sometimes talked of love and marriage, linking the two like bacon and eggs, or bread and butter. One without the other was unthinkable, yet how could Uncle Ned even consider marrying Mrs. Craddock?

But it seemed that he did. He told Grandmother about it that same night. I had rushed indoors as soon as I could find the strength to plump in Grandmother's arms.

"What has frightened you so?" she asked. She could be surprisingly gentle at times. "You have not got a touch of the sun, I hope?"

She let me come into the drawing room and gave me the Chinese doll that Grandfather had brought back forty years ago. This was an unusual treat. I settled down behind the sofa, glad to escape Grandmother's fierce eyes. She and Aunt Agatha sat at either end of the long sofa, both embroidering an altar cloth. That was how Uncle Ned found us sometime later.

"Have you heard the latest rumor?" Aunt Agatha asked him. "They say Mrs. Craddock is leaving The Dingle House at last. I can't imagine why she stayed so long."

"You get tired of running," said Uncle Ned.

"She will be running somewhere else now," said Aunt Agatha in a satisfied tone.

"But this time she won't be alone. Or unprotected. I shall be going with her."

"You shouldn't joke about things like that," snapped Aunt Agatha. "Even to suggest bringing a low woman into the family, even to suggest it in fun—"

"Margaret is not a low woman," said Uncle Ned. "Soon she will be my wife."

My grandmother asked, "Have you taken leave of your senses? To marry a woman like that would be your ruination. Who do you suppose will bring you his business when it's known?"

"Oh, we don't propose to compromise you," said Uncle Ned. "I am accepting a position in Canada. You know how I have always wished to travel, and in a new country people have better things to do than gossip about someone who has been unfortunate."

"You don't mind that your children's mother was accused of murdering her former husband, and put on trial?"

"She was acquitted," said Uncle Ned.

"For lack of evidence."

"She was found innocent."

"No," said Grandmother. "She was not found guilty. There is a world of difference. Edward, if you do this thing we shall not speak to each other again."

"I refuse to believe you really mean that," said Uncle Ned, "but in any case I cannot give Margaret up. I love her with all my heart."

I must have made some movement then, for suddenly they recalled my presence behind the sofa. Aunt Agatha pounced on me and shook me and told me how wicked it was to eavesdrop.

"Let her alone," said Uncle Ned, as furious as she. "I should be glad to take her with us. In any case, Vicky, I hope one day not too far off you can come and pay us a visit."

But I pushed him away. "You'll belong to them," I cried. "You will forget us. And you don't *know* she didn't do it."

I thrust at him violently, then rushed out of the room.

I met Harriet in the lane some days later. Already the news was all round the village. The Dingle House had the air of a place soon to be deserted.

"Why couldn't you leave him alone?" I burst out. "We were happy until you came."

"It was he who wouldn't leave us alone," she retorted. "We didn't need anyone."

"Your mother doesn't think so. I saw them together."

"She belongs to me," shrilled Harriet.

"Not any more," I said, as cruel as she. "Now he will come first."

Suddenly the fury drained out of her; she seemed miles away, although we were standing face to face.

"He had better watch out," she said. "I told you—didn't I?—that I'm a witch. When I want things to happen they happen."

"You didn't want this to happen," I taunted.

But she only laughed and went away.

That night there was a tremendous thunderstorm. I lay shivering in my bed, hating the roars and the reverberations. I thought of Harriet and her claim: "When I want things to happen they happen." What she wanted was her mother all to herself. Once before someone had tried to separate them, and he had died.

It was like a light going on in a dark room.

In that instant I knew the truth about Mr. Winter's death.

I didn't blame the police for not realizing it—who would suspect a child barely nine years old? But in my imagination I saw her deliberately pouring the milk, adding the poison—she had been playing in the garden that morning and would have seen Richards laying it out for all the rats—and who would notice the movements of a child? She must have taken the poison to use as opportunity offered, not knowing that the chance would come the same day. But intending to use it all the same, because she knew that in the end her mother would leave her—her mother's duty as a wife really gave her little choice.

I had wondered why she didn't go down and fill the glass with water in the kitchen where a supply was always kept handy, but of course the rat powder would show less in milk. And then she washed the glass so that no trace remained.

I knew, I tell you I knew—but I didn't know how to prove it. And no one would listen to me, a jealous child—I might even be whipped for suggesting such a thing.

And then I remembered the day of the tea party in the garden of The

Dingle House. The sugar bowl! That was it. The police might have searched the house for traces of poison, but they wouldn't think of a child being involved. They wouldn't know, as I knew, that Harriet had never been a child.

Now Uncle Ned had to be warned and there was not much time left; but first I must get hold of the sugar bowl. Accusation without proof would be a waste of time.

So the next day I went openly to The Dingle House. Everything had a very desolate air; pictures had been taken from the walls, and there were no carpets on the floor.

Mrs. Craddock came to meet me. Love had made her even more beautiful, though I wouldn't have believed that possible. I knew I was going to wreck that happiness: I didn't think for a moment that she might know what Harriet had done, because surely she wouldn't risk it happening a second time, not to Uncle Ned.

"I came to see Harriet," I told her.

"She has been helping me pack," said Mrs. Craddock. And she called, "Harriet, here is Victoria come to say good-bye. Or perhaps only *au revoir*."

Harriet came slowly out and stopped halfway down the stairs. "Good-bye," she said. Her face was dark and unwelcoming.

"That's no way to say good-bye," Mrs. Craddock told her, laughing. "Come in, Victoria. You don't bring a message from your grandmother? No, I see that was a foolish question. What would you like to do while you are here?"

"I should like to play with the tea set once more," I said. "I never saw one I liked so well."

"Oh, but it's already packed," said Harriet carelessly. "You have come too late."

"We have been washing it," Mrs. Craddock said.

Harriet nodded. "Every single piece."

Her eye held mine, and I understood that she knew what I suspected and was mocking me because now I was helpless. I said, "There was sugar in the bowl," and Harriet said, "It wouldn't be much good if there wasn't."

"Why don't you give it to Victoria?" Mrs. Craddock urged. "Something to remember us by."

"Won't she remember us without that?" asked Harriet, but she went docilely enough to fetch the box in which the tea set was packed. I knew I should never play with it. I hated it; I told myself I would trample it to smithereens, but I was saved the trouble.

Mrs. Craddock was saying, "Harriet would have thought of it herself if she had been used to having a playmate," when there came a tremendous crash. We ran to the foot of the stairs and there lay the tea set, a welter of chipped and broken china, with Harriet bent over the fragments.

"Be careful," Mrs. Craddock warned. "You may cut yourself. What happened?"

"I slipped," said Harriet calmly. "I had to let the box go or I would have hurt myself."

"We will send you another, Vicky," promised her mother. "What is left of this one is only fit for the dustbin."

She fetched a brush and swept up the pieces, wrapping them in paper. I knew then that my last chance had slipped between my fingers. Now there was no proof, no proof at all.

"How about a real cup of tea?" Mrs. Craddock said when she had disposed of the parcel. "Fortunately, we still have some cake. And, Vicky, my dear, do you take sugar?"

I thought, half-dazed, "When I am quite old and write my memoirs I shall be able to say—Once I had tea with a murderer."

That was five days ago. Tomorrow Mrs. Craddock and Harriet leave for London where Uncle Ned will meet them, and Mrs. Craddock and Uncle Ned will be married, and after that it will be too late.

It is three o'clock in the morning—there are still four hours to go. God holds time in the hollow of His hand—a thousand years are but an instant in His sight—there's still time for a miracle, for a thunderstorm to bring The Dingle House crashing to the ground, smothering its occupants . . . for lightning or a fireball to devour all of them.

I sit waiting for the dawn, a pale green sky with the birds calling, then light stealing back to the world, then a sea of pale rose. It's like that poem by Robert Browning:

> *All night long I have not stirred*
> *And still God has not said a word.*

I don't know what to do.
I don't know, and there's no one to ask . . .

The Seventies

REASONS UNKNOWN

by STANLEY ELLIN

This is what happened, starting that Saturday in October.

That morning Morrison's wife needed the station wagon for the kids, so Morrison took the interstate bus into downtown Manhattan. At the terminal there, hating to travel by subway, he got into a cab. When the cabbie turned around and asked, "Where to, mister?" Morrison did a double take. "Slade?" he said. "Bill Slade?"

"You better believe it," said the cabbie. "So it's Larry Morrison. Well, what do you know."

Now, what Morrison knew was that up to two or three years ago, Slade had been—as he himself still was—one of the several thousand comfortably fixed bees hiving in the glass-and-aluminum Majestico complex in Greenbush, New Jersey. There were 80,000 Majestico employees around the world, but the Greenbush complex was the flagship of the works, the executive division. And Slade had been there a long, long time, moving up to an assistant managership on the departmental level.

Then the department was wiped out in a reorganizational crunch, and Slade, along with some others in it, had been handed his severance money and his hat. No word had come back from him after he finally sold his house and pulled out of town with his wife and kid to line up, as he put it, something good elsewhere. It was a shock to Morrison to find that the something good elsewhere meant tooling a cab around Manhattan.

He said in distress, "Jeez, I didn't know, Bill—none of the Hillcrest Road bunch had any idea—"

"That's what I was hoping for," said Slade. "It's all right, man. I always had a feeling I'd sooner or later meet up with one of the old bunch. Now that it happened, I'm just as glad it's you." A horn sounding behind the cab prompted Slade to get it moving. "Where to, Larry?"

"Columbus Circle. The Coliseum."

"Don't tell me, let me guess. The Majestico Trade Exposition. It's that time of the year, right?"

"Right," said Morrison.

"And it's good politics to show up, right? Maybe one of the brass'll take notice."

"You know how it is, Bill."

"I sure do." Slade pulled up at a red light and looked around at Morrison. "Say, you're not in any tearing hurry, are you? You could have time for a cup of coffee?"

There was a day-old stubble on Slade's face. The cap perched on the back of his graying hair was grimy and sweatstained. Morrison felt unsettled by the sight. Besides, Slade hadn't been any real friend, just a casual acquaintance living a few blocks farther up Hillcrest Road. One of the crowd on those occasional weekend hunting trips of the Hillcrest Maybe Gun and Rod Club. The "Maybe" had been inserted in jest to cover those bad hunting and fishing weekends when it temporarily became a poker club.

"Well," Morrison said, "this happens to be one of those heavy Saturdays when—"

"Look, I'll treat you to the best Danish in town. Believe me, Larry, there's some things I'd like to get off my chest."

"Oh, in that case," said Morrison.

There was a line of driverless cabs in front of a cafeteria on Eighth Avenue. Slade pulled up behind them and led the way into the cafeteria which was obviously a cabbies' hangout. They had a little wrestling match about the check at the counter, a match Slade won, and, carrying the tray with the coffee and Danish, he picked out a corner table for them.

The coffee was pretty bad, the Danish, as advertised, pretty good. Slade said through a mouthful of it, "And how is Amy?" Amy was Morrison's wife.

"Fine, fine," Morrison said heartily. "And how is Gertrude?"

"Gretchen."

"That's right. Gretchen. Stupid of me. But it's been so long, Bill—"

"It has. Almost three years. Anyhow, last I heard of her Gretchen's doing all right."

"Last you heard of her?"

"We separated a few months ago. She just couldn't hack it any more." Slade shrugged. "My fault mostly. Getting turned down for one worthwhile job after another didn't sweeten the disposition. And jockeying a cab ten, twelve hours a day doesn't add sugar to it. So she and the kid have their own little flat out in Queens, and she got herself some kind of cockamamie receptionist job with a doctor there. Helps eke out what I can give her. How's your pair, by the way? Scott and Morgan, isn't it? Big fellows now, I'll bet."

"Thirteen and ten," Morrison said. "They're fine. Fine."

"Glad to hear it. And the old neighborhood? Any changes?"

"Not really. Well, we did lose a couple of the old-timers. Mike Costanzo and Gordie McKechnie. Remember them?"

"Who could forget Mike, the world's worst poker player? But McKechnie?"

"That split-level, corner of Hillcrest and Maple. He's the one got himself so smashed that time in the duck blind that he went overboard."

"Now I remember. And that fancy shotgun of his, six feet underwater in the mud. Man, that sobered him up fast. What happened to him and Costanzo?"

"Well," Morrison said uncomfortably, "they were both in Regional Customer Services. Then somebody on the top floor got the idea that Regional and National should be tied together, and some people in both offices had to be let go. I think Mike's in Frisco now, he's got a lot of family there. Nobody's heard from Gordie. I mean—" Morrison cut it short in embarrassment.

"I know what you mean. No reason to get red in the face about it, Larry." Slade eyed Morrison steadily over his coffee cup. "Wondering what happened to me?"

"Well, to be frank—"

"Nothing like being frank. I put in two years making the rounds, lining up employment agencies, sending out enough résumés to make a ten-foot pile of paper. No dice. Ran out of unemployment insurance, cash, and credit. There it is, short and sweet."

"But why? With the record you piled up at Majestico—"

"Middle level. Not top echelon. Not decision-making stuff. Middle level, now and forever. Just like everybody else on Hillcrest Road. That's why we're on Hillcrest Road. Notice how the ones who make it to the top echelon always wind up on Greenbush Heights? And always after only three or four years? But after you're middle level fifteen years the way I was—"

Up to now Morrison had been content with his twelve years in Sales Analysis. Admittedly no ball of fire, he had put in some rough years after graduation from college—mostly as salesman on commission for some product or other—until he had landed the job at Majestico. Now he felt disoriented by what Slade was saying. And he wondered irritably why Slade had to wear that cap while he was eating. Trying to prove he was just another one of these cabbies here? He wasn't. He was a college man, had owned one of the handsomest small properties on Hillcrest Road, had been a respected member of the Majestico executive team.

Morrison said, "I still don't understand. Are you telling me there's no company around needs highly qualified people outside decision-making level? Ninety percent of what goes on anyplace is our kind of job, Bill. You know that."

"I do. But I'm forty-five years old, Larry. And you want to know what I found out? By corporation standards I died five years ago on my fortieth birthday. Died, and didn't even know it. Believe me, it wasn't easy to realize that at first. It got a lot easier after a couple of years' useless job-hunting."

Morrison was 46 and was liking this less and less. "But the spot you're in is only temporary, Bill. There's still—"

"No, no. Don't do that, Larry. None of that somewhere-over-the-rainbow line. I finally looked my situation square in the eye, I accepted it, I made the adjustment. With luck, what's in the cards for me is maybe some day owning my own cab. I buy lottery tickets, too, because after all somebody's got to win that million, right? And the odds there are just as good as my chances of ever getting behind a desk again at the kind of money Majestico was paying me." Again he was looking steadily at Morrison over his coffee cup. "That was the catch, Larry. That money they were paying me."

"They pay well, Bill. Say, is that what happened? You didn't think you were getting your price and made a fuss about it? So when the department went under you were one of the—"

"Hell, no," Slade cut in sharply. "You've got it backwards, man. They do pay well. But did it ever strike you that maybe they pay too well?"

"Too well?"

"For the kind of nine-to-five paperwork I was doing? The donkey work?"

"You were an assistant head of department, Bill."

"One of the smarter donkeys, that's all. Look, what I was delivering to the company had to be worth just so much to them. But when every year —every first week in January—there's an automatic cost-of-living increase handed me I am slowly and steadily becoming a luxury item. Consider that after fourteen-fifteen years of those jumps every year, I am making more than some of those young hotshot executives in the International Division. I am a very expensive proposition for Majestico, Larry. And replaceable by somebody fifteen years younger who'll start for a hell of a lot less."

"Now hold it. Just hold it. With the inflation the way it is, you can't really object to those cost-of-living raises."

Slade smiled thinly. "Not while I was getting them, pal. It would have meant a real scramble without them. But suppose I wanted to turn them down just to protect my job? You know that can't be done. Those raises are right there in the computer for every outfit like Majestico. But nobody in management has to like living with it. And what came to me after I was canned was that they were actually doing something about it."

"Ah, look," Morrison said heatedly. "You weren't terminated because you weren't earning your keep. There was a departmental reorganization. You were just a victim of it."

"I was. The way those Incas or Aztecs or whatever used to lay out the living sacrifice and stick the knife into him. Don't keep shaking your head, Larry. I have thought this out long and hard. There's always a reorganization going on in one of the divisions. Stick a couple of departments together, change their names, dump a few personnel who don't fit into the new table of organization.

"But the funny thing, Larry, is that the ones who usually seem to get dumped are the middle-aged, middle-level characters with a lot of seniority. The ones whose take-home pay put them right up there in the high-income brackets. Like me. My secretary lost out in that reorganization too, after eighteen years on the job. No complaints about her work. But she ran into what I did when I told them I'd be glad to take a transfer to any other department. No dice. After all, they could hire two fresh young secretaries for what they were now paying her."

"And you think this is company policy?" Morrison demanded.

"I think so. I mean, what the hell are they going to do? Come to me and say, 'Well, Slade, after fifteen years on the job you've priced yourself right out of the market, so good-bye, baby?' But those reorganizations? Beautiful. 'Too bad, Slade, but under the new structure we're going to have to lose some good men.' That's the way it was told to me, Larry. And that's what I believed until I woke up to the facts of life."

The piece of Danish in Morrison's mouth was suddenly dry and tasteless. He managed to get it down with an effort. "Bill, I don't want to say it—I hate to say it—but that whole line sounds paranoid."

"Does it? Then think it over, Larry. You still in Sales Analysis?"

"Yes."

"I figured. Now just close your eyes and make a head count of your department. Then tell me how many guys forty-five or over are in it."

Morrison did some unpalatable calculation. "Well, there's six of us. Including me."

"Out of how many?"

"Twenty-four."

"Uh-huh. Funny how the grass manages to stay so green, isn't it?"

It was funny, come to think of it. No, funny wasn't the word. Morrison said weakly, "Well, a couple of the guys wanted to move out to the Coast, and you know there's departmental transfers in and out—"

"Sure there are. But the real weeding comes when there's one of those little reorganizations. You've seen it yourself in your own department more than once. Juggle around some of those room dividers. Move some desks here and there. Change a few descriptions in the company directory. The smokescreen. But behind that smoke there's some high-priced old faithfuls getting called upstairs to be told that, well, somebody's got to go, Jack, now that things are all different, and guess whose turn it is."

Slade's voice had got loud enough to be an embarrassment. Morrison pleaded: "Can't we keep it down, Bill? Anyhow, to make villains out of everybody on the top floor—"

Slade lowered his voice, but the intensity was still there. "Who said they were villains? Hell, in their place I'd be doing the same thing. For that matter, if I was head of personnel for any big outfit, I wouldn't take anybody my age on the payroll either. Not if I wanted to keep my cushy job in personnel, I wouldn't." The wind suddenly seemed to go out of him. "Sorry, Larry. I thought I had everything under control, but when I saw you—when I saw it was one of the old Hillcrest bunch—it was too much to keep corked up. But one thing—"

"Yes?"

"I don't want anybody else back there in on this. Know what I mean?"

"Oh, sure."

"Don't just toss off the 'oh, sure' like that. This is the biggest favor you could do me—not to let anybody else in the old crowd hear about me, not even Amy. No post-mortems up and down Hillcrest for good old Bill Slade. One reason I let myself cut loose right now was because you always were a guy who liked to keep his mouth tight shut. I'm counting on you to do that for me, Larry. I want your solemn word on it."

"You've got it, Bill. You know that."

"I do. And what the hell"—Slade reached across the table and punched Morrison on the upper arm—"any time they call you in to tell you there's a reorganization of Sales Analysis coming, it could turn out you're the guy elected to be department head of the new layout. Right?"

Morrison tried to smile. "No chance of that, Bill."

"Well, always look on the bright side, Larry. As long as there is one."

Outside the Coliseum there was another of those little wrestling matches about paying the tab—Slade refusing to take anything at all for the ride, Morrison wondering, as he eyed the meter, whether sensitivity here called for a standard tip, a huge tip, or none at all—and again Slade won.

Morrison was relieved to get away from him, but, as he soon found, the relief was only temporary. It was a fine Indian summer day, but somehow the weather now seemed bleak and threatening. And doing the Majestico show, looking over the displays, passing the time of day with recognizable co-workers turned out to be a strain. It struck him that it hadn't been that atrocious cap on Slade's head that had thrown him, it had been the gray hair showing under the cap. And there was very little gray hair to be seen on those recognizable ones here at the Majestico show.

Morrison took a long time at the full-length mirror in the men's room, trying to get an objective view of himself against the background of the others thronging the place. The view he got was depressing. As far as he could see, in this company he looked every minute of his 46 years.

Back home he stuck to his word and told Amy nothing about his encounter with Slade. Any temptation to was readily suppressed by his feeling that once he told her that much he'd also find himself exposing his morbid reaction to Slade's line of thinking. And that would only lead to her being terribly understanding and sympathetic while, at the same time, she'd be moved to some heavy humor about his being such a born worrier. He was a born worrier, he was the first to acknowledge it, but he always chafed under that combination of sympathy and teasing she offered him when he confided his worries to her. They really made quite a list, renewable each morning on rising. The family's health, the condition of the house, the car, the lawn, the bank balance—the list started there and seemed to extend to infinity.

Yet, as he was also the first to acknowledge, this was largely a quirk of personality—he was, as his father had been, somewhat sobersided and humorless—and, quirks aside, life was a generally all-right proposition. As it should be when a man can lay claim to a pretty and affectionate wife, and a couple of healthy young sons, and a sound home in a well-tended neighborhood. And a good steady job to provide the wherewithal.

At least, up to now.

Morrison took a long time falling asleep that night, and at three in the morning came bolt awake with a sense of foreboding. The more he lay there trying to get back to sleep, the more oppressive grew the foreboding. At four o'clock he padded into his den and sat down at his desk to work out a precise statement of the family's balance sheet.

No surprises there, just confirmation of the foreboding. For a long time now, he and Amy had been living about one month ahead of income which, he suspected, was true of most families along Hillcrest Road. The few it wasn't true of were most likely at least a year ahead of income and sweating out the kind of indebtedness he had always carefully avoided.

But considering that his assets consisted of a home with ten years of mortgage payments yet due on it and a car with two years of payments still due, everything depended on income. The family savings account was, of course, a joke. And the other two savings accounts—one in trust for each boy to cover the necessary college educations—had become a joke as college tuition skyrocketed. And, unfortunately, neither boy showed any signs of being scholarship material.

In a nutshell, everything depended on income. This month's income. Going by Slade's experience in the job market—and Slade had been the kind of competent, hardworking nine-to-five man any company should have been glad to take on—this meant that everything depended on the job with Majestico. Everything. Morrison had always felt that landing the job in the first place was the best break of his life. Whatever vague ambitions he had in his youth were dissolved very soon after he finished college and learned that out here in the real world he rated just about average in all departments, and that his self-effacing, dogged application to his daily work was not going to have him climbing any ladders to glory.

Sitting there with those pages of arithmetic scattered around the desk, Morrison, his stomach churning, struggled with the idea that the job with Majestico was suddenly no longer a comfortable, predictable way of life but for someone his age, and with his makeup and qualifications, a dire necessity. At five o'clock, exhausted but more wide-awake than ever, he went down to the kitchen for a bottle of beer. Pills were not for him. He had always refused to take even an aspirin tablet except under extreme duress, but beer did make him sleepy, and a bottle of it on an empty stomach, he estimated, was the prescription called for in this case. It turned out that he was right about it.

In the days and weeks that followed, this became a ritual: the abrupt waking in the darkest hours of the morning, the time at his desk auditing his accounts and coming up with the same dismal results, and the bottle of beer which, more often than not, allowed for another couple of hours of troubled sleep before the alarm clock went off.

Amy, the soundest of sleepers, took no notice of this, so that was all right. And by exercising a rigid self-control he managed to keep her unaware of those ragged nerves through the daylight hours as well, although it was sometimes unbearably hard not to confide in her. Out of a strange sense of pity, he found himself more sensitive and affectionate to her than ever. High-spirited, a little scatterbrained, leading a full life of her own what with the boys, the Parent-Teachers Club, and half a dozen community activities, she took this as no less than her due.

Along the way, as an added problem, Morrison developed some physical tics which would show up when least expected. A sudden tremor of the hands, a fluttering of one eyelid which he had to learn to quickly cover up. The most grotesque tic of all, however—it really unnerved him the few times he experienced it—was a violent, uncontrollable chattering of the teeth when he had sunk to a certain point of absolute depression. This only struck him when he was at his desk during the sleepless times considering the future. At such times he had a feeling that those teeth were diabolically possessed by a will of their own, chattering away furiously as if he had just been plunged into icy water.

In the office he took refuge in the lowest of low profiles. Here the temptation was to check on what had become of various colleagues who had over the years departed from the company, but this, Morrison knew, might raise the question of why he had, out of a clear sky, brought up the subject. The subject was not a usual part of the day's conversational currency in the department. The trouble was that Greenbush was, of course, a company town, although in the most modern and pleasant way. Majestico had moved there from New York 20 years before; the town had grown around the company complex. And isolated as it was in the green heartland of New Jersey, it had only Majestico to offer. Anyone leaving the company would therefore have to sell his home, like it or not, and relocate far away. Too far, at least, to maintain old ties. It might have been a comfort, Morrison thought, to drop in on someone in his category who had been terminated by Majestico and who could give him a line on what had followed. Someone other than Slade. But there was no one like this in his book.

The one time he came near bringing his desperation to the surface was at the Thanksgiving entertainment given by the student body of the school his sons attended. The entertainment was a well-deserved success, and after it, at the buffet in the school gym, Morrison was driven to corner Frank Lassman, assistant principal of the school and master of ceremonies at the entertainment, and to come out with a thought that had been encouragingly flickering through his mind during the last few insomniac sessions.

"Great show," he told Lassman. "Fine school altogether. It showed tonight. It must be gratifying doing your kind of work."

"At times like this it is," Lassman said cheerfully. "But there are times—"

"Even so. You know, I once had ideas about going into teaching."

"Financially," said Lassman, "I suspect you did better by not going into it. It has its rewards, but the big money isn't one of them."

"Well," Morrison said very carefully, "suppose I was prepared to settle for the rewards it did offer? A man my age, say. Would there be any possibilities of getting into the school system?"

"What's your particular line? Your subject?"

"Oh, numbers. Call it arithmetic and math."

Lassman shook his head in mock reproach. "And where were you when we really needed you? Four or five years ago we were sending out search parties for anyone who could get math across to these kids. The last couple of years, what with the falling school population, we're firing, not hiring. It's the same everywhere, not that I ever thought I'd live to see the day. Empty school buildings all over the country."

"I see," said Morrison.

So the insomnia, tensions, and tics continued to worsen until suddenly one day—as if having hit bottom, there was no place for him to go but up —Morrison realized that he was coming back to normal. He began to sleep through the night, was increasingly at ease during the day, found himself cautiously looking on the bright side. He still had his job and all that went with it, that was the objective fact. He could only marvel that he had been thrown so far off balance by that chance meeting with Slade.

He had been giving himself his own bad time, letting his imagination take over as it had. The one thing he could be proud of was that where someone else might have broken down under the strain, he had battled it out all by himself and had won. He was not a man to hand himself trophies, but in this case he felt he had certainly earned one.

A few minutes before five on the first Monday in December, just when he was getting ready to pack it in for the day, Pettengill, departmental head of Sales Analysis, stopped at his desk. Pettengill, a transfer from the Cleveland office a couple of years before, was rated as a comer, slated sooner or later for the top floor. A pleasant-mannered, somewhat humorless man, he and Morrison had always got along well.

"Just had a session with the brass upstairs," he confided. "A round table with Cobb presiding." Cobb was the executive vice president in charge of Planning and Structure for the Greenbush complex. "Looks like our department faces a little reorganization. We tie in with Service Analysis and that'll make it Sales and Service Evaluation. What's the matter? Don't you feel well?"

"No, I'm all right," said Morrison.

"Looks like you could stand some fresh air. Anyhow, probably because you're senior man here, Cobb wants to see you in his office first thing tomorrow morning. Nine sharp. You know how he is about punctuality, Larry. Make sure you're on time."

"Yes," said Morrison.

He didn't sleep at all that night. The next morning, a few minutes before nine, still wearing his overcoat and with dark glasses concealing his reddened and swollen eyes, he took the elevator directly to the top floor. There, out of sight on the landing of the emergency staircase, he drew the barrel and stock of his shotgun from beneath the overcoat and assembled the gun. His pockets bulged with 12-gauge shells. He loaded one into each of the gun's twin barrels. Then concealing the assembled gun beneath the coat as well as he could, he walked across the hall into Cobb's office.

Miss Bernstein, Cobb's private secretary, acted out of sheer blind, unthinking instinct when she caught sight of the gun. She half-rose from her desk as if to bar the way to the inner office. She took the first charge square in the chest. Cobb, at his desk, caught the next in the face. Reloading, Morrison exited through the door to the executive suite where Cobb's assistants had been getting ready for the morning's work and were now in a panic at the sound of the shots.

Morrison fired both barrels one after another, hitting one man in the throat and jaw, grazing another. Reloading again, he moved like an automaton out into the corridor where a couple of security men, pistols at the ready, were coming from the staircase on the run. Morrison cut down the first one, but the other, firing wildly, managed to plant one bullet in his forehead. Morrison must have been dead, the medical examiner later reported, before he even hit the floor.

The police, faced with five dead and one wounded, put in two months on the case and could come up with absolutely no answers, no explanations at all. The best they could do in their final report was record that "the perpetrator, for reasons unknown, etc., etc."

Management, however, could and did take action. They learned that the Personnel Department psychologist who had put Morrison through the battery of personality-evaluation tests given every applicant for a job was still there with the company. Since he had transparently failed in those tests to sound out the potentially aberrant behavior of the subject, he was, despite sixteen years of otherwise acceptable service, terminated immediately.

Two weeks later, his place in Personnel was filled by a young fellow named McIntyre who, although the starting pay was a bit low, liked the looks of Greenbush and, with his wife in complete agreement, saw it as just the kind of quiet, pleasant community in which to settle down permanently.

THREE WAYS TO ROB A BANK
by HAROLD R. DANIELS

The manuscript was neatly typed. The cover letter could have been copied almost word for word from one of those "Be an Author" publications, complete with the proforma "Submitted for publication at your usual rates." Miss Edwina Martin, assistant editor of *Tales of Crime and Detection,* read it first. Two things about it caught her attention. One was the title— "Three Ways to Rob a Bank. Method 1." The other was the author's name. Nathan Waite. Miss Martin, who knew nearly every professional writer of crime fiction in the United States and had had dealings with most of them, didn't recognize the name.

The letter lacked the usual verbosity of the fledgling writer, but a paragraph toward the middle caught her eye. "You may want to change the title because what Rawlings did wasn't really robbery. In fact, it's probably legal. I am now working on a story which I will call 'Three Ways to Rob a Bank. Method 2.' I will send this to you when I finish having it retyped. Method 2 is almost certainly legal. If you want to check Method 1, I suggest that you show this to your own banker."

Rawlings, it developed, was the protagonist in the story. The story itself was crude and redundant; it failed to develop its characters and served almost solely as a vehicle to outline Method 1. The method itself had to do with the extension of credit to holders of checking accounts—one of those deals where the bank urges holders of checking accounts to write checks without having funds to back them. The bank would extend credit. No papers. No notes. (The author's distrust of this form of merchandizing emerged clearly in the story.)

Miss Martin's first impulse was to send the story back with a polite letter of rejection. (She never used the heartless printed rejection slip.) But something about the confident presentation of the method bothered her. She clipped a memorandum to the manuscript, scrawled a large question mark on it, and bucked it to the editor. It came back next day with additional scrawling: "This is an awful piece of trash but the plan sounds almost real. Why don't you check it with Frank Wordell?"

Frank Wordell was a vice-president of the bank that served Miss Martin's publisher. She made a luncheon date with him, handed him the letter and the manuscript, and started to proofread some galleys while he looked it over. She glanced up when she heard him suck in his breath. He had turned a delicate shade of greenish white.

"Would it work?" she asked.

"I'm not quite sure," the vice-president said, his voice shaking. "I'd have to get an opinion from some of the people in the Check Credit Department. But I think it would." He hesitated. "Good Lord, this could cost us millions. Listen—you weren't thinking of publishing this, were you? I mean, if it got into the hands of the public—"

Miss Martin, who had no great admiration for the banking mentality, was noncommital. "It needs work," she said. "We haven't made a decision."

The banker pushed his plate away. "And he says he's got another one. His Method Two. If it's anything like this it could ruin the entire banking business." A thought came to him. "He calls this *'Three* Ways to Rob a Bank.' That means there must be a Method Three. This is terrible! No, no, we can't let you publish this and we must see this man at once."

This was an unfortunate approach to use with Edwina Martin who reached out her hand for the letter and manuscript. "That is our decision to make," she told him coldly. It was only after he had pleaded the potential destruction of the country's economy that she let him take the papers back to the bank. He was so upset that he neglected to pay the luncheon check.

He called her several hours later. "We've held an emergency meeting," he told her. "The Check Credit people think that Method One *would* work. It might also be legal but even if it isn't it would cost us millions in lawsuits. Listen, Miss Martin, we want you to buy the story and assign the copyright to us. Would that protect us against him selling the story to someone else?"

"In its present form," she told him. "But there would be nothing to prevent him from writing another story using the same method." Remembering his failure to pay the luncheon check, she was not inclined to be especially cooperative. "And we don't buy material that we don't intend to publish."

But after an emergency confrontation between a committee of the City Banking Association, called into extraordinary session, and the publisher, it was decided to buy Nathan Waite's story and to lock the manuscript in the deepest vault of the biggest bank. In the interest of the national economy.

Economy, Miss Martin decided, was an appropriate word. During the confrontation a saurian old capitalist with a personal worth in the tens of millions brought up the subject of payment to Nathan Waite. "I suppose we must buy it," he grumbled. "What do you pay for stories of this type?"

Miss Martin, knowing the author had never been published and hence had no "name" value, suggested a figure. "Of course," she said, "since it will never be published there is no chance of foreign income or anthology fees, let alone possible movie or TV rights." (The Saurian visibly shuddered.) "So I think it would be only fair to give the author a little more than the usual figure."

The Saurian protested. "No, no. Couldn't think of it. After all, we won't ever get our money back. And we'll have to buy Method Two and Method Three. Think of that. Besides, we've still got to figure out a way to keep him from writing other stories using the same methods. The usual figure will have to do. No extras."

Since there were 30 banks in the Association and since the assessment for each would be less than $10.00 per story, Miss Martin failed to generate any deep concern for the Saurian.

That same day Miss Martin forwarded a check and a letter to Nathan Waite. The letter explained that at this time no publication date could be scheduled but that the editor was very anxious to see the stories explaining the second and third ways to rob a bank. She signed the letter with distaste. To a virgin author, she knew, the check was insignificant compared with the glory of publication. Publication that was never to be.

A week later a letter and the manuscript for "Three Ways to Rob a Bank. Method 2" arrived. The story was a disaster but again the method sounded convincing. This time it involved magnetic ink and data processing. By prearrangement Miss Martin brought it to Frank Wordell's office. He read it rapidly and shivered. "The man's a genius," he muttered. "Of course, he's had a lot of background in the field——"

"What was that? How would you know about his background?" Edwina asked.

He said in an offhand manner, "Oh, we've had him thoroughly checked out, of course. Had one of the best detective agencies in the business investigate him—ever since you showed me that first letter. Couldn't get a thing on him."

Miss Martin's voice was ominously flat. "Do you mean to tell me that you had Mr. Waite *investigated*— a man you only learned of through his correspondence with us?"

"Of course." Wordell sounded faintly surprised. "A man that has dangerous knowledge like he has. Couldn't just trust to luck that he wouldn't do something with it besides write stories. Oh, no, couldn't let it drop. He worked in a bank for years and years, you know. Small town in Connecticut. They let him go a year ago. Had to make room for the president's nephew. Gave him a pension though. Ten percent of his salary."

"Years and years, you said. How many years?"

"Oh, I don't remember. Have to look at the report. Twenty-five, I think."

"Then naturally he wouldn't hold any resentment over being let go," she said drily. She put out her hand. "Let me see his letter again."

The letter that had accompanied the second manuscript had cordially thanked the publisher for accepting the first story and for the check. One paragraph said, "I assume you checked Method 1 with your banker as I suggested. I hope you'll show him Method 2 also, just to be sure it would work. As I said in my first letter, it's almost certainly legal."

Miss Martin asked, "Is it legal?"

"Is what legal?"

"Method Two. The one you just read about."

"Put it this way. It isn't illegal. To make it illegal, every bank using data processing would have to make some major changes in its forms and procedures. It would take months and in the meantime it could cost us even more millions than Method One. This is a terrible thing, Miss Martin—a terrible thing."

Method 2 caused panic in the chambers of the City Banking Association. There was general agreement that the second story must also be bought immediately and sequestered forever. There was also general agreement that since Method 3 might be potentially even more catastrophic, there could be no more waiting for more stories from Mr. Waite. (Miss Martin, who was present, asked if the price of the second story could be raised in view of the fact that Mr. Waite was now, having received one check, a professional author. Saurian pointed out that Waite hadn't actually been published, so the extra expense was not justified.)

A plan was adopted. Miss Martin was to invite Mr. Waite to come up from Connecticut, ostensibly for an author-editor chat. Actually he would be brought before a committee chosen by the City Banking Association. "We'll have our lawyers there," Saurian said. "We'll put the fear of the Lord into him. Make him tell us about that Method Three. Pay him the price of another story if we have to. Then we'll work out some way to shut him up."

With this plan Miss Martin and her fellow editors and her publisher went along most reluctantly. She almost wished that she had simply rejected Nathan Waite's first submission. Most particularly she resented the attitude of the bankers. In their view, Nathan Waite was nothing more than a common criminal.

She called Nathan Waite at his Connecticut home and invited him to come in. The City Banking Association, she resolved to herself, would pay his expenses, whatever devious steps she might have to take to manage it.

His voice on the phone was surprisingly youthful and had only a suggestion of Yankee twang. "Guess I'm pretty lucky selling two stories one right after the other. I'm sure grateful, Miss Martin. And I'll be happy to come in and see you. I suppose you want to talk about the next one."

Her conscience nipped at her. "Well, yes, Mr. Waite. Methods One and Two were so clever that there's a lot of interest in Method Three."

"You just call me Nate, miss. Now, one thing about Method Three: there's no question about it being legal. The fact is, it's downright honest. Compared with One and Two, that is. Speaking about One and Two, did you check them with your banker? I figured you must have shown him Method One before you bought the story. I was just wondering if he was impressed by Method Two."

She said faintly, "Oh, he was impressed all right."

"Then I guess he'll be really interested in Method Three."

They concluded arrangements for his visit in two days and hung up.

He showed up at Miss Martin's office precisely on time—a small man in his fifties with glistening white hair combed in an old-fashioned part on one side. His face was tanned and made an effective backdrop for his sharp blue eyes. He bowed with a charming courtliness that made Miss Martin feel even more of a Judas. She came from behind her desk. "Mr. Waite—," she began.

"Nate."

"All right. Nate. I'm disgusted with this whole arrangement and I don't know how we let ourselves be talked into it. Nate, we didn't buy your stories to publish them. To be honest—and it's about time—the stories are awful. We bought them because the bank—the banks, I should say—asked us to. They're afraid if the stories were published, people would start actually using your methods."

He frowned. "Awful, you say. I'm disappointed to hear that. I thought the one about Method Two wasn't that bad."

She put her hand on his arm in a gesture of sympathy and looked up to see that he was grinning. "Of course they were awful," he said. "I deliberately wrote them that way. I'll bet it was almost as hard as writing good stuff. So the banks felt the methods would work, eh? I'm not surprised. I put a lot of thought into them."

"They're even more interested in Method Three," she told him. "They want to meet you this afternoon and discuss buying your next story. Actually, they want to pay you *not* to write it. Or write anything else," she added.

"It won't be any great loss to the literary world. Who will we be meeting? The City Banking Association? An old fellow who looks like a crocodile?"

Miss Edwina Martin, with the feel for a plot developed after reading thousands of detective stories, stepped back and looked at him. "You know all about this," she accused him.

He shook his head. "Not all about it. But I sort of planned it. And I felt it was working out the way I planned when they put a detective agency to work investigating me."

"They had no business doing that," she said angrily. "I want you to know that we had nothing to do with it. We didn't even know about it until afterwards. And I'm not going to the meeting with you. I wash my hands of the whole business. Let them buy your next story themselves."

"I want you to come," he said. "You just might enjoy it."

She agreed on condition that he hold out for more money than her publisher had ostensibly been paying him. "I sort of planned on charging a bit more," he told her. "I mean, seeing they're that much interested in Method Three."

At lunch he told her something of his banking career and a great deal more about his life in a small Connecticut town. This plain-speaking, simple man, she learned, was an amateur mathematician of considerable reputation. He was an authority on cybernetics and a respected astronomer.

Over coffee some of his personal philosophy emerged. "I wasn't upset when the bank let me go," he said. "Nepotism is always with us. I could have been a tycoon in a big-city bank, I suppose. But I was content to make an adequate living and it gave me time to do the things I really liked to do. I'm basically lazy. My wife died some years after we were married and there wasn't anybody to push me along harder than I wanted to go.

"Besides, there's something special about a small bank in a small town. You know everyone's problems, money and otherwise, and you can break rules now and then to help people out. The banker, in his way, is almost as important as the town doctor." He paused. "It's not like that any more. It's all regimented and computerized and dehumanized. You don't have a banker in the old sense of the word. You have a financial executive who's more and more just a part of a large corporation, answerable to a board of directors. He has to work by a strict set of rules that don't allow for any of the human factors."

Miss Martin, fascinated, signaled for more coffee.

"Like making out a deposit slip," he went on. "Used to be you walked into the bank and filled out the slip with your name and address and the amount you wanted to deposit. It made a man feel good and it was good for him. 'My name is John Doe and I earned this money and here is where I live and I want you to save this amount of money for me.' And you took it up to the cashier and passed the time of day for a minute."

Nate put sugar in his coffee. "Pretty soon there won't be any cashiers. Right now you can't fill out a deposit slip in most banks. They send you computer input cards with your name and number on them. All you fill in is the date and amount. The money they save on clerical work they spend on feeble-minded TV advertising. It was a TV ad for a bank that inspired me to write those stories."

Miss Martin smiled. "Nate, you used us." The smile faded. "But even if you hold them up for the Method Three story, it won't hurt anything but their feelings. The money won't come out of their pockets and even several thousands of dollars wouldn't mean anything to them."

He said softly, "The important thing is to make them realize that any mechanical system that man can devise, man can beat. If I can make them realize that the human element can't be discarded, I'll be satisfied. Now then, I suppose we should be getting along to the meeting."

Miss Martin, who had felt concern for Nathan Waite, felt suddenly confident. Nate could emerge as a match for a dozen Saurians.

A committee of twelve members of the City Banking Association, headed by the Saurian, and flanked by a dozen lawyers, awaited them. Nathan Waite nodded as he entered the committee room. The Saurian said, "You're Waite?"

Nate said quietly, "Mr. Waite."

A young lawyer in an impeccable gray suit spoke out. "Those stories that you wrote and that we paid for. You realize that your so-called methods are illegal?"

"Son, I helped write the banking laws for my state and I do an odd job now and then for the Federal Reserve Board. I'd be happy to talk banking law with you."

An older lawyer said sharply, "Shut up, Andy." He turned to Nate. "Mr. Waite, we don't know if your first two methods are criminal or not. We do know it could cost a great deal of money and trouble to conduct a test case and in the meantime, if either Method One or Two got into the hands of the public it would cause incalculable harm and loss. We'd like some assurance that this won't happen."

"You bought the stories describing the first two methods. I'm generally considered an honorable man. As Miss Martin here might put it, I won't use the same plots again."

Gray Suit said cynically, "Not this week, maybe. How about next week? You think you've got us over a barrel."

The older lawyer said furiously, "I told you to shut up, Andy," and turned to Nate again. "I'm Peter Hart," he said, "I apologize for my colleague. I accept the fact that you are an honorable man, Mr. Waite."

Saurian interrupted. "Never mind all that. What about Method Three— the third way to rob a bank. Is it as sneaky as the first two?"

Nate said mildly, "As I told Miss Martin, 'rob' is a misnomer. Methods One and Two are unethical, perhaps illegal, methods for getting money from a bank. Method Three is legal beyond the shadow of a doubt. You have my word for that."

Twelve bankers and twelve lawyers began talking simultaneously. Saurian quieted the furor with a lifted hand. "And you mean it will work just as well as the first two methods?"

"I'm positive of it."

"Then we'll buy it. Same price as the first two stories and you won't even have to write it. Just tell us what Method Three is. And we'll give you $500 for your promise never to write another story." Saurian sank back, overwhelmed by his own generosity. Peter Hart looked disgusted.

Nathan Waite shook his head. "I've got a piece of paper here," he said. "It was drawn up by the best contract lawyer in my state. Good friend of mine. I'll be glad to let Mr. Hart look it over. What it calls for is that your Association pay me $25,000 a year for the rest of my life and that payments be made thereafter in perpetuity to various charitable organizations to be named in my will."

Bedlam broke loose. Miss Martin felt like cheering and she caught a smile of admiration on Peter Hart's face.

Nate waited patiently for the commotion to die down. When he could be heard he said, "That's too much money to pay for just a story. So, as the contract specifies, I'll serve as consultant to the City Banking Association— call it Consultant in Human Relations. That's a nice-sounding title. Being a consultant, of course, I'll be too busy to write any more stories. That's in the contract too."

Gray Suit was on his feet, yelling for attention. "What about Method Three? Is that explained in the contract? We've got to know about Method Three!"

Nate nodded. "I'll tell you about it as soon as the contract is signed."

Peter Hart held up his hand for quiet. "If you'll wait in the anteroom, Mr. Waite, we'd like to discuss the contract among ourselves."

Nate waited with Miss Martin. "You were tremendous," she said. "Do you think they'll agree?"

"I'm sure they will. They might argue about Clause Seven—gives me the right to approve or disapprove all TV bank commercials." His eyes twinkled. "But they're so scared of Method Three I think they'll agree to even that."

Five minutes later Peter Hart called them back to face a subdued group of committee members. "We have decided that the Association badly needs a Consultant in Human Relations," he said. "Mr. Graves"—he nodded toward a deflated Saurian—"and myself have signed in behalf of the City Banking Association. By the way, the contract is beautifully drafted— there's no possibility of a legal loophole. You have only to sign it yourself."

Gray Suit was on his feet again. "Wait a minute," he shouted. "He still hasn't told us about Method Three."

Nate reached for the contract. "Oh, yes," he murmured, after he had signed it. " 'Three Ways to Rob a Bank.' Method Three. Well, it's really quite simple. *This* is Method Three."

THE PERFECT SERVANT

by HELEN NIELSEN

Lieutenant Brandon was trying to bridge a generation gap when the woman walked into the police station and deposited a wad of currency on the counter. The trio of teenagers he had charged with collecting hubcaps that belonged to irate citizens seemed unimpressed with the idea that they had committed theft, and then the woman, who was in her middle forties, shabbily dressed and wearing a look of quiet despair in her eyes, relinquished a cheap money clip containing the bills and said, "Please, who is the officer I see about this?"

Brandon nodded for a uniformed officer to take away the teenagers, grateful for a release from the pointless conversation, and asked the woman to state her problem.

"I was walking down the street—down Broadway," she stated, "and I saw this on the sidewalk. I picked it up. It is money."

Brandon pulled the bills out of the clip. There were three twenty-dollar bills, three tens, and two fives. "One hundred dollars," he said.

"Yes," the woman agreed. "I counted, too. That's a lot of money for someone to lose."

It was a lot of money, and the woman looked as if she had never had her hands on that much at any one time in all her life. Brandon called the desk sergeant to fill out a report and explained to the woman that the money would be held for 30 days, during which time the real owner could report his loss, describe the bills and the clip, and have the money returned, or, failing a claimant, the money would then become the property of the finder.

"Your name?" asked the sergeant.

She hesitated. "Maria," she said. "Maria Morales."

"Occupation?"

"I have no work now. When I work I am a domestic."

"Address?"

She gave the number of a cheap roominghouse in the Spanish-speaking section of town. She told them she was very poor, unemployed, and without any property of her own. When the report was offered for her signature she placed both hands on the desk. A plain gold band adorned the third finger of her left hand.

"Just sign here, Miss Morales," the sergeant said.

"Mrs. Morales," she corrected. "I am a widow."

Brandon caught the desk sergeant's eye and shook his head in wonder.

"You should get those cocky young kids back in here to see this," the sergeant suggested.

"Waste of time," Brandon answered. "They wouldn't appreciate anything this square. Don't forget now, Mrs. Morales, in thirty days you check back with us. Chances are you'll get the money—or at least a reward."

"Thank you," she said in a very soft voice, "but I would rather have a job."

A young reporter from the Tucson daily came into the station just as Maria Morales was leaving, and Brandon, the bitter taste of the cynical teenagers still in his mouth, related the incident of the honesty of Maria Morales. It was a slow day on the newsfront and when the morning papers came out, the story of the unemployed widow and the $100 was written up in a neat box on the front page.

By noon Lieutenant Brandon was flooded with calls from people who claimed the money, and also with job offers for Maria Morales. Having developed a protective interest in the widow, he took it upon himself to screen the offers and decided that the best prospect was Lyle Waverly, a bachelor and a physician with a lucrative practice among the country-club set.

Waverly needed a housekeeper he could trust. He owned a fine home in one of the better suburbs and entertained a well-heeled social set. He offered Maria a home, a good salary, and free medical care for as long as she remained in his employ.

Brandon approved the credentials and gave Waverly the woman's address, feeling the kind of inner warmth he always got from delivering Christmas parcels to the Neediest Families.

Maria Morales was extremely pleased with young Dr. Waverly. He was easy to work for. The house was large but new, and there was a gardener to help with the heavy work. She was an excellent cook but, aside from breakfast, the doctor seldom dined in. He was a busy man in more ways than one, which was only natural for one so attractive and increasingly affluent.

It soon became apparent that the doctor's love life was divided between two women: Cynthia Reardon, who was 23 and the sole heir of Josiah Reardon of Reardon Savings and Loan, and Shelley Clifford, ten years older, who had an additional handicap of being already married to Ramsey Clifford, the owner of Clifford Construction Company. Clifford was a huge burly man of 50 who had too little time to spend with a lovely wife who liked younger men.

Maria observed these things with professional silence, and long before Dr. Lyle Waverly was aware of his destiny, she knew that Cynthia had the inside track and would eventually get her man.

Life was pleasant in the Waverly house and Maria had no desire to return to the kind of employment she had recently known. She began to plot a campaign of self-preservation. When the doctor gave her an advance on her salary, she purchased fitted uniforms with caps and aprons for the frequent cocktail parties he gave for his wealthy friends and patients.

He soon learned that a caterer was no longer necessary. Maria's canapés became the envy of every hostess, and she herself became a topic of conversation not unwelcome in the tension created whenever Cynthia and Shelley were present on the same occasion. Shelley had the prior claim—a fact made obvious by the way she took over as hostess. She was the "in" woman fighting against the inevitable successor, and only Clifford's preoccupation with business could blind him to what anyone else could see. Of the two women, Maria preferred Shelley, who was no threat to her own position as mistress of the house. Shelley wanted only Lyle Waverly; Cynthia wanted his name, his life, and his home.

"Maria is a miracle," Shelley explained at the second party. "Imagine finding someone with her divine talent who is honest as well. Why, she's a perfect servant!"

"An honest woman?" Cynthia echoed. "Impossible! No woman can be honest and survive! Maria must have a few secrets."

Maria smiled blandly and continued to serve the canapés.

"I refuse to believe it!" Dr. Waverly announced. "All my life I've searched for a pure woman and this is she!"

"Perhaps you'd better marry her, darling," Shelley said. "You could do worse."

That remark was aimed at Cynthia, and Maria didn't wait to hear the reply. She returned to the kitchen and began to clean up the party debris. It was sometime later, after most of the guests had gone home and even Ramsey Clifford had taxied off to catch a late plane for a business appointment, that she heard Shelley berating Dr. Waverly for his interest in Cynthia Reardon. Maria returned to the living room to collect abandoned glasses and saw them alone.

"You needn't think I don't know what you're doing," Shelley was saying. "You needed me when you were beginning your practice—you needed my contacts and influence. Now you want a younger woman."

"Shelley, please," the doctor begged.

"No, I'm going to have my say! You want a younger and a richer woman, don't you, darling? What better catch than Josiah Reardon's sexy daughter? You'll never hold her, Lyle. She'll wear you like a pendant until she's bored with you. She's used up half a dozen handsome young men already."

"I'm not a child!" Waverly protested.

"No. You're a man and vain enough to think you can use Cynthia Reardon. I'm warning you, you'll be the one who gets used!"

"You're jealous," Waverly said.

"Of course I'm jealous. I love you, and I need you, Lyle. Now *I* need *you*—"

Maria retreated quickly to the kitchen before she was noticed. Sometime later the doctor came in carrying the glasses. All the guests were gone. He loosened his tie and drew a deep breath. "The things they don't teach you in medical school!" he sighed. "Maria, you are the only sane person on earth. You must never leave me."

"I'll fix you a hot milk," Maria said.

"Oh, no—"

"A bromide?"

"Brilliant idea. Are you sure you never worked the social route before?"

Maria's face darkened. "I worked for women," she said. "I didn't like it. They talk about you in front of others. 'You just can't trust anyone these days,' she said with savage mockery. 'They'll steal you blind and expect to get paid besides!' "

Waverly laughed. "I think I understand why honesty is so important to you. By the way, the thirty days are up. Did you ever go back to claim that hundred dollars?"

"Tomorrow," Maria said. "Tomorrow I go."

"Good! I hope it's there. If it isn't I'll give you a bonus to make up for losing it."

Maria returned to the police station the next day. Lieutenant Brandon gave her a paper to sign and then handed her the money which was still held in the money clip made of cheap metal with a silver dollar for decoration. None of the claimants could identify the exact denominations of the bills or describe the clip, so the money was now legally hers.

"How's the job?" Brandon asked.

"The best one I ever had," Maria said.

"Now, that's what I like to hear! There's some justice in the world after all."

"Yes," Maria said, and slipped the money into her handbag.

Her position at the Waverly house continued to improve. She had her own room and, with an adequate household budget, was able to buy food less fattening than the starchy diet of the poor. She soon replaced her uniforms with a smaller size and had her hair done once a month. She was beginning to feel and look more like a woman. Waverly soon took notice.

"Maria," he said, "you never told me about your husband. He was one lucky guy. What was his name?"

"Wa—" she began.

"Juan?"

She smiled softly. "Yes," she said, "his name was Juan."

"Handsome?"

"Of course!"

"And a passionate devil, I'll bet! What do you have going for you now? There must be a boyfriend somewhere."

The doctor had been drinking. He slipped a friendly arm about her shoulder.

"No boyfriend," Maria said.

"No? That's a shame! What's the matter? With legs like yours you could still do a fancy fandango. I'll bet you've done many a fancy fandango in your day."

"In my day—yes," Maria admitted.

"Then get back in circulation. Take a night off once in a while. Take tonight off. I'm going out with Miss Reardon."

"In that case, I think I should make you another bromide."

"No, you don't! I'm just a teensy-weensy bit drunk and I need much more fortification tonight. I'm going to ask Miss Reardon to marry me."

"She will accept," Maria said flatly.

"That's what I'm afraid of. You see, Maria, I've never been married. I'm afraid of marriage. I like women but I like my freedom better."

"Then why—?"

"Why marry? Because it's the thing to do. It's stabilizing. It builds character. It's what every rising young doctor should do, Maria, but I'm still scared. I don't like to be dominated."

"Then don't be dominated," Maria said. "Be the boss."

Waverly picked up his glass. "I'll drink to that," he said.

But it was Maria who feared the marriage more than Waverly. No sooner was the engagement announced than Cynthia began to reorganize the household, and Maria began to worry again about her security. Waverly caught her reading the want ads and demanded an explanation.

"What's the matter? Aren't you happy here?" he asked. "Do you want more money?"

"No," Maria said.

"Then what's wrong?"

"Things will change after you marry."

"What things? Don't you like Miss Reardon?"

"It's not what I like. It's what Miss Reardon likes."

"Stop worrying. Nobody's going to treat you the way you were treated before I found you. I like you and that's all that matters. I'll tell you something I was going to keep secret. I've had my lawyer draw up a new will—a man does that when he gets married. I've made a $5000 bequest in your behalf. Now do you feel more secure?"

Maria was reassured, but she had lived long enough to take nothing for granted except money in the bank. Dr. Waverly was impulsive and generous, but Cynthia Reardon was a spoiled, strong-willed girl and Shelley Clifford's description of her character was more accurate than anything a prospective bridegroom was likely to see. What's more, Shelley didn't give up the battle simply because the engagement was announced. The mores of Dr. Waverly's social set, Maria learned, were more liberal than her own.

Shelley immediately developed symptoms requiring the doctor's professional attention at indelicate hours—particularly when her husband was away on business. There were surreptitious calls going both ways. When Waverly finally refused to go to see Shelley again, she came to see him. Traveling over an unpaved, circuitous drive, Shelley's small imported coupe made the trip between the Clifford estate and the doctor's house with increasing frequency.

It was a shameful thing, Maria reflected, for a woman to cling so to a man. As much as she had loved her husband, she would have let him go the minute he no longer wanted her. But no matter how many women Walter might have had before their marriage, he was faithful to his vows. Walter —not Juan. Juan Morales was the name of the father Maria barely remembered. Walter Dwyer was the name of the man she had wed. But when one must work as a domestic for the Anglos, it seemed better not to let it be known that she had once been married to an Anglo, had once lived like a lady.

She had been hardly 20 when Walter married her, but Walter was a gambler and gamblers die broke. After settling with the creditors, there was nothing for the widow Dwyer to do but return to Tucson and again become Maria Morales, domestic.

She had nothing left of the past but what Walter had called her "Irish luck," but her mind was no longer servile. She saw things now with the eyes of Mrs. Walter Dwyer, and what she saw was troubling. When a woman lost at love it was the same as when a man lost at cards. If she cried, she cried alone. What she could never do was cling to anything that was finished.

If Cynthia Reardon knew what was going on, she showed no outward sign. She might even be enjoying Shelley's humiliation. If Ramsey Clifford knew what was going on, he was indifferent. Eventually Dr. Waverly had it out with Shelley in a verbal battle over the telephone. Maria didn't eavesdrop. It was impossible not to hear him shouting in his study.

"No, I won't come over tonight!" he shouted. "There's nothing wrong with you, Shelley, and I won't come over tonight or any other night! I suggest that you get another doctor. I have no time for a chronic neurotic."

It was cruel, but it seemed to work. The telephone calls stopped. Two weeks before the scheduled wedding, Cynthia Reardon moved into the doctor's house and Maria's moral values were again updated. It seemed to be accepted practice in the young doctor's circle and Maria made no comment.

But her worst fears about her future status were soon confirmed. She couldn't please the new mistress who took Maria to task on the slightest provocation. The good days were finished. Cynthia was vicious. She would get whatever she wanted on her own terms either by using her sex or the lure of Josiah Reardon's wealth and prestige. If there was any doubt of who would rule the Waverly manse, it was decided the night of Josiah Reardon's prenuptial dinner party.

Once a week Dr. Waverly spent a day at the local free clinic, and, because Cynthia didn't care about these things, he sometimes talked about this work with Maria. It was the one thing of which he was genuinely proud, and because of it she was proud of him. A twelve-year-old Mexican boy had been under his care for some time. Minor surgery had been performed and confidence carefully built for the major surgery which, if successful, would restore him to a normal life. Half of the battle, Waverly assured her, was in the rapport he had established with the frightened boy. On the evening before the scheduled major surgery Reardon gave his dinner party. Maria heard the doctor try to get Cynthia to change the date.

"I have nine o'clock surgery," he said. "It's imperative that I get my rest."

"You're not the only doctor at the clinic!" Cynthia scoffed.

"But this is a special case!"

"And Daddy's dinner isn't, I suppose! Lyle, you must be mad. You know Daddy doesn't change his plans for anyone, and this is a very special occasion. You see, darling, you're the first man I've ever known that Daddy liked. He thinks you're a stabilizing influence for me. I happen to know what his wedding present is going to be. What would you think of fifteen percent of the Reardon Corporation?"

Dr. Waverly thought through a few moments of absolute silence. "You're dreaming."

"Then I must have dreamed the papers I saw Daddy's lawyer drawing up. That's what the dinner is for tonight—the presentation of the gift. Now I know you can get somebody else to take over for you tomorrow. It's not as if you had a paying patient. It's just one of those clinic cases."

Maria held her breath and said a silent prayer, but she lost. Waverly went to the dinner with Cynthia. It was almost two A.M. when he returned and, minutes later, Cynthia was at the door. Maria heard them laughing in the entry hall.

"You shouldn't have come here," Waverly said. "The old boy doesn't know we've jumped the gun, and he might not like it."

"He would loathe it—but who cares? Darling, isn't it wonderful? You see, I didn't lie to you. We've got something to celebrate."

"It's so late—"

"A little nightcap—please."

Maria, listening from the kitchen, sighed and went back to bed. In the morning she arose, made a pot of coffee, and carried it up to Waverly's room. He was asleep. Cynthia opened one eye and then threw a pillow at her.

"Nobody called you!" she whispered angrily.

"The doctor has a hospital call—"

"Cancel it! Tell them he's sick or something. Can't you see that he's asleep? If you don't call the hospital this minute, I will!"

Maria retreated from the room. She went downstairs and phoned the hospital to inform them that Dr. Waverly couldn't perform the nine o'clock operation. It was noon before the doctor came downstairs and that was just a few minutes after the hospital called to tell him that the boy had died on the operating table. It was a small event in the life of a young doctor who was slated to become the most popular society doctor in the area, but it destroyed Maria's last vision of Camelot.

She remembered that Walter, who was crude and uneducated, had once left a game during a winning streak—and that was the one thing he had taught her a gambler should never do—to donate blood to the black porter who parked his car at the casino each night. The friend who took over Walter's hand had lost everything, but that hadn't mattered because the porter lived and Walter came back as happy as a schoolboy playing hookey. And so Maria was thoroughly disenchanted with her position at the Waverly house even before the night that Shelley Clifford returned.

It was four nights before the wedding. Cynthia, tired from rehearsals of the ceremony, had gone up to bed and taken two sleeping pills. The doctor was preparing a deposit slip for the visit to the bank that he wanted Maria to make for him in the morning. Maria went to the front door when the bell rang and there was no way to keep Shelley out of the house. She had been drinking and was hysterical. One eye was blackened and she had a cut on one cheek. Her husband, she explained when Waverly hurried out of the study, had learned of their relationship and beaten her. Her story might be true or untrue, but the doctor's reaction was firm.

"You can't stay here!" he insisted.

"Just for tonight," she begged. "Ram's been drinking, too. I'm afraid to go home."

"I don't believe you," Waverly said. "Ram Clifford doesn't drink."

"He did tonight. I'm afraid, Lyle. I'm afraid he'll kill me!"

Maria watched the doctor's face. He looked as if he thought that might be a good solution. Firmly he took Shelley by the shoulders and turned her back toward the door.

"Then go to a hotel," he said.

"Why can't I stay here?"

"Because I won't let you."

Waverly was trying to keep his voice down. When Shelley noticed him glance apprehensively toward the stairs, she sensed immediately what he was trying to hide. Her eyes widened. *"She's* here, isn't she? Cynthia's *here!"* And then she laughed and pushed Waverly away from her. "You couldn't even wait for the marriage! Oh, that's beautiful! Now wouldn't old Josiah Reardon love to know about this! His daughter may be a swinger, but the old boy's a stickler for the proprieties! And there's nothing more conservative than a savings and loan corporation, darling. When they hear about this you may not get that partnership and seat on the Board of Directors."

"Get out of the house!" Waverly ordered.

"Oh, I will, I will—just as soon as I've run upstairs to check—"

She lunged past him and started to run up the stairs. Waverly was about two steps behind her when the liquor, the shock, and the injuries caught up with Shelley. She was more than halfway up the stairway when she stumbled and fell against the railing. She shrieked and grabbed at the air and then, as both Waverly and Maria watched in horror, she plummeted over the railing and fell to the marble floor of the entry hall. There was a sickening sound as her head struck the marble. She was dead when Dr. Waverly reached her.

For a few moments he was too stunned to speak. Then he turned to Maria. "You've got to help me," he said.

"What do you mean?" Maria asked.

"You saw what happened. It was an accident—she killed herself. But I can't have her found in my house like this. Can you drive a car, Maria?"

"Yes."

"Good. Cynthia's asleep. The pills I gave her will last until morning. I'll get my car out of the garage and you follow me in it. I'll take Mrs. Clifford's body in her car and leave it out on that short cut she uses."

Maria hesitated.

"Do you understand what I've said?" Waverly asked.

"I understand," Maria said, "but suppose the police come—"

"Out on that unpaved stretch? No chance. Anyway, I'll be the one taking the risk. I'll have the body with me. If you see a police car, just keep going."

"Still, there could be trouble," Maria said.

"Maria, there's no time to argue! I'm not going to hurt Mrs. Clifford—she's already dead. But I can't afford a scandal now. This is a matter of self-preservation!"

"With me, too, it is a matter of self-preservation," Maria said coldly.

It took the doctor a few seconds to understand Maria's words. He had taken her for granted too long a time to make a sudden change without a certain anguish. When he finally did understand, he asked how much self-preservation she had in mind.

"A will is risky," she said. "Wills can be changed. Five thousand dollars in cash is more reliable."

"I don't have that much money in the house," he protested.

"I'll take a check," Maria said.

Minutes later, the doctor's check tucked away in her handbag, Maria drove Waverly's sedan at a safe distance behind Mrs. Clifford's little sports car. There was no traffic at all on the narrow road. When they reached a wide shoulder forming a scenic view over a ravine, Waverly stopped the small car and parked off the roadway. Maria stopped the sedan and watched him carry Shelley Clifford's body to the edge of the shoulder and toss it into the shrubbery.

Waverly then returned to the car and emptied Shelley Clifford's handbag of all cash and credit cards. Leaving the emptied purse on the seat, and pocketing the items that a robber would steal, he then took out his pocket-knife and jammed it between the treads of one rear tire, letting out the air. The scene was set: a flat tire on a seldom-used road; a passing car hailed and a grim harvest of murder and robbery.

Waverly folded his pocketknife and walked to the waiting sedan. He drove the car back to the house himself and then he and Maria scrubbed away the bloodstains on the marble entry floor.

When they had finished, Waverly said, "Nothing happened here tonight."

"Nothing," Maria agreed, "except that there's a bloodstain on your coat sleeve, Doctor. Give me the coat and I'll sponge out the stain before I go to bed."

Waverly pulled off his suit coat and gave it to her without hesitation. "Don't call me in the morning," he said. "I'm going to take a couple of sleeping pills myself."

Maria took the coat to her room but she didn't sponge out the blood. She turned off the light and tried to sleep. When that didn't work, she got up and packed her bag. In the morning, she got the doctor's bank deposit from his study, the suitcase and the stained coat from her room, and then, because the keys were still in the ignition, drove the doctor's car to the bank. Ordinarily she would have taken the bus. Today was urgent. Because she was so well known at the bank, and particularly after having made the doctor's deposit, she had no difficulty cashing the check for $5000.

On the return trip she took the unpaved short cut. No other cars passed and she reached Mrs. Clifford's abandoned coupe unseen. Drawing alongside, she tossed Dr. Waverly's coat into the front seat, and then drove on.

Both Waverly and his fiancé were still asleep when Maria returned the doctor's sedan to the garage. Then, bag in hand, she walked to the bus stop.

Shelley Clifford's body was found early in the afternoon. The story of her death was on the evening television newscasts. An apparent victim of a casual murderer, her death inspired urgent editorial demand for increased police patrols and an end to permissive education. Ramsey Clifford offered a $10,000 reward for the apprehension and conviction of her murderer. It wasn't until the third day after Shelley's body was found that Lieutenant Gannon came to Dr. Waverly's house. He carried a small bundle wrapped in brown paper.

"I've been doing some checking, Doctor," he said. "I understand that you and the late Shelley Clifford were very good friends."

"You've picked up some gossip," Waverly stated.

"I don't think so. We didn't release all the evidence we had in her death when the body was found. We needed a little time to check out something that was found in the seat of her car—" Gannon ripped open the package and held up Waverly's suit coat. "We've traced this to your tailor, Dr. Waverly, and we've matched the bloodstains to Mrs. Clifford's. Now all we want from you is an explanation of what it was doing in her car."

On the fourth day after Shelley Clifford's death a smartly dressed, middle-aged woman checked into a hotel on the Nevada side of Lake Tahoe. She signed the register as Mrs. Walter Dwyer and then took a stroll through the casino because the atmosphere of a gambling town made her feel closer to Walter. Later, upstairs in her room, she studied the Tucson newspaper she had picked up in the lobby and was amused to learn that the police of that area were conducting an intensive search for her body.

Confronted with his blood-stained jacket, Waverly had told the truth— but he wasn't believed. When it developed that his housekeeper had last been seen on the morning of Mrs. Clifford's death cashing a $5000 check at Waverly's bank, Lieutenant Gannon formed the theory that Waverly had used Maria Morales to get him some ready cash in the event the doctor was linked to Mrs. Clifford and had to leave the country, and had then disposed of the woman so she wouldn't talk.

It was all nonsense, of course, and Maria was sure that Gannon could prove nothing. No crime had been committed. The worst that could happen to Dr. Waverly was that his marriage would be called off. That was a little sad since he deserved Cynthia Reardon as much as she deserved him. The other thing that would happen—and this was the reason she had placed the doctor's coat in Mrs. Clifford's car—was that the community would be made aware of Waverly's true character. This was imperative, in Maria's mind, in view of the nature of his profession.

Mrs. Dwyer remained at the hotel for several weeks. By that time the Tucson papers no longer referred to the Shelley Clifford affair, and she could assume that it was in a state of permanent limbo with no need for her reappearance to save Waverly from a murder charge.

Before leaving the resort, Mrs. Dwyer put a down payment on a smartly furnished condominium apartment which, the salesman assured her, would bring a prime weekly rental in high season. Mrs. Dwyer explained that she traveled in her work and would occupy the apartment only a few months of the year, but that it was nice to have roots somewhere and a woman did need a good investment for her retirement years.

A few days later, a shabbily dressed woman, wearing a look of quiet despair in her eyes, entered the Tahoe bus station. She carried a cheap suitcase and a handbag containing $100 in a money clip. The bills were old —in fact, they were the same bills, in the same money clip, that Maria Morales, who was then 19 and the prettiest cocktail waitress on the Strip, saw drop from Walter Dwyer's pocket as he bent over a casino gambling table. Maria had nothing of her own but a $10 advance on her salary, and when she returned the $100 to Dwyer he was so impressed by her honesty, and other attributes, that he took her to dinner. A week later they were married and the marriage was for love—not the cheap bargain that Dr. Lyle Waverly had tried to make with Cynthia Reardon. The money and the clip had been Walter's wedding present.

"Keep it for luck," he said. "Your Irish luck" . . .

In the bus station Maria bought a ticket to Sacramento, the state capital of California. There would be many wealthy people in that area who were so nervous about their own corruption that they would be eager to hire a housekeeper honest enough to go to the police station with $100 found on the street while looking for a job.

Walter had taught her never to walk out on a winning streak.

THE MARKED MAN
by DAVID ELY

It was early evening when he entered the Park. He headed for the darkest part, away from the lamps that lighted the pathways. He didn't see any other strollers, but he hurried all the same, not wanting to take chances.

When he reached the shelter of the first trees, he stopped and looked back toward the drive, even though he knew the car was no longer there. They had driven off as soon as they'd let him out. He'd been clapped on the shoulder—like the jump sign in a plane—and one of them had said, "Good luck, Major," and then he'd stepped out, with the weight of his flying suit dragging on him.

Good luck, Major. If he did have luck, those would be the last words anyone would address to him for four weeks.

He pulled back, startled. Someone had run past him, right past him, no more than a yard away—a man or boy running hard but with light steps in the direction of Fifth Avenue.

The Major squatted; his breath came quick, his pulse beat high. That had shaken him, whatever it had been—some college kid training for track, or some fellow running for the hell of it, or maybe a purse snatcher, and in that case there might be police on the way. The police were the ones he feared the most. The Agency had cleared things with the Commissioner, and the captains of the nearest precincts had been informed, as a safeguard against publicity in the event he got caught, but of course the ordinary officer didn't know. Just one flash of a patrolman's torch could put an end to the project.

He had to avoid the lights. He'd had no idea there would be so many, not only the lamps along the pathways but also the automobile headlights on the drive that crossed the Park, and the big hotels and apartment buildings along its boundaries.

He kept moving through the trees, trying to shore up his confidence by physical activity. This first night would be the hard one. He knew that. If he managed this one, and the day to come, he'd probably be all right. He'd have to pick a hiding place that was far from where people normally went

—away from the zoo, the lake, and the playing fields. He'd rather be caught by a policeman than by kids playing ball. If one of them got a glimpse of him, they'd all come shouting and pointing. He imagined a grotesque chase—a gang of boys pursuing a man made clumsy by the pilot's suit. They'd be yelling: *His head, his head. Look at his head.*

The head—that was the Agency's guarantee of his honesty. He couldn't cheat, not with that head. When they'd told him about it, he hadn't objected. He knew they were right. The project psychologist had talked to him for a long time about it. The object was to measure the psychological stress on a man hiding in the midst of a hostile population. If they could do that, then they could build a rescue program that made sense for the one pilot in twenty who'd been shot down but not captured, and had managed to hide somewhere—in a field, a bomb-blasted ruin, an abandoned apartment, anywhere he could find.

"You'll be that twentieth pilot, Major," the psychologist had told him. "You'll make it to the Park. Then you'll have to hide until you're rescued. But remember, you're a marked man. You're isolated from the people around you by the one thing you can't change—you can't speak the language. Well, for the purposes of this test, we can simulate almost anything but that. Nothing would prevent you from hiding that flying suit and swiping the pants off some Park tramp if you had to. Then you could just stroll over to the nearest bench to spend a quiet day reading the papers with nobody the wiser, and if some policeman came up to you, you could pass the time of day with him just as nicely as you pleased."

"Oh, we know you have no such intention, Major. We know you're determined to play this thing straight. But we also know that when a man is in a stress situation, even if it's a simulated situation, he may do things he wouldn't normally do. So you understand that we've got to protect the project. We've got to give you a handicap that's roughly the equivalent of loss of language. We've got to make you conspicuous in a way that's beyond your control."

And so they'd shaved his head and stained it green, a clear fresh green, green as new-grown grass.

The Major found a crevice between two boulders at the base of a small ridge. It was just wide enough for him to squeeze his body through. He worked for several hours in there with his entrenching tool hollowing out a cavity in the earth. He had stripped off his pilot's suit and laid it on the ground to hold the dirt he dug out. When he had a load, he gathered up the suit in his arms and carried it off, shaking it, so that the dirt was distributed over a wide area. Then from one of his pockets he took a small can—dog-repellent—and sprayed his entrance carefully.

The spring night was chilly, but at least it wasn't raining. On a wet night he'd have left muddy prints and tracks all over. He was lucky, too, that it was midweek, for there'd be fewer people in the Park during the day. It was the weekends that brought the crowds, and by the weekend he'd have his place improved or would have found a better one.

The night was ending. Dawn was on its way. He watched the sky lighten, and the trees and shrubs take shape. The cold mist was drifting where the ground was low. In the distance the skyscrapers blazed with red fire as the sun struck their crowns. He edged out of the crevice to examine the entrance one last time. There were no traces of his work. The grass was flattened where he had laid the flying suit, but it would rise again, and besides, the Park was full of places where kids had played and couples had spread blankets.

Then he saw his entrenching tool lying on open ground ten feet away. He crawled over and grabbed it, scuttled back, wedged himself through and inside, and lay there, breathing hard. That was worse than carelessness, he thought. The psychologist had warned him that he'd be his own worst enemy, that there'd be times when his fear would make traps for him, that there'd be a weakness in him that couldn't take the strain. He cursed himself, and spat in the dirt. Suppose he hadn't seen that tool and had left it there? Typical, he thought bitterly. He'd always forgotten something; he'd always fallen short. He'd tried to qualify for the space program, but he'd been rejected. He hadn't quite been up to the standards.

But the project psychologist hadn't made it either, had he? The psychologist had been nosed out by psychologists who had just a little bit more on the ball. Yes, the Major thought, he and the psychologist were leftovers. They hadn't made the space team. They weren't quite good enough.

And maybe the project wasn't any better than they were. He had wondered about it already. True, it didn't look bad on paper. But suppose a man could survive undetected in the middle of Manhattan for four weeks— would that really produce much useful information for survival-and-rescue planning? Or was it just a flashy stunt dreamed up by some Operations lieutenant bucking for promotion?

Well, it wasn't his job to criticize the project. He was supposed to make it work—and he wasn't starting off very well. He hadn't made that hole long enough. He couldn't stretch out full length. Already his legs were cramping. He began massaging them. Weariness came on him, and hunger. He hadn't eaten since afternoon. He opened a can of rations, and ate with his fingers, then buried the can in the earth beside him, and put the sleeping mask on his face—it covered the mouth to muffle snoring—and settled back to wait out the day.

By nightfall he was in agony. His legs tormented him. He felt stifled by the mask. He kept falling into a dangerous kind of sleep where he twisted like an animal trying to burrow deeper, or maybe to burrow out into the air and sunlight, his traitor hands trying to rip off the mask, his legs threatening at any moment to go into a full screaming cramp.

The entire population of New York came, it seemed, to climb on his boulders and sit on the ridge above him. He heard voices, footsteps, shouts, laughter. At times unseen feet sent dirt sifting down. He cursed those who came. He feared them, he hated them. Yes, it was a definite reaction. He ought to remember to tell the psychologist. He could imagine what these people were from their voices—stupid kids and nagging mothers, and old men full of nastiness, and younger ones who had no business lounging around parks during the day. He was their prisoner. The least of them might find him, and turn him out to sunlight, like a mole. He clasped his knees tighter, and rocked his body to and fro, grinding his teeth to keep from crying out in pain and rage.

When darkness came, he stretched out at last, his head and shoulders thrust out of the hole and into the narrow space between the boulders. He slept until midnight, and woke in panic when the moon sent its light slicing through the crevice to fall on his upturned face. Then he worked, digging to make his burrow longer. After that he crawled about the area outside picking up candy wrappers, cigarette butts, and sandwich bags—why, he didn't know. Perhaps to wipe out every trace of the people who had tormented him all day.

He forced himself to walk off through the trees. He needed to stay away from his refuge until dawn. The psychologist had warned him he'd be tempted to keep too close to it for the safety it offered, until finally he might surrender to a compulsion to remain in it night and day.

He knew he would have to be careful. He was under unusual pressure: a man alone, fearing every hint of human presence—every voice, every movement, every sound—fearing the light of day most of all. True, it was a simulated situation. He could end it any time he chose. But that would be humiliating to his pride, and hurtful to his career. And he was a volunteer. He'd asked for it.

From one of his pockets he took a radio no larger than a pack of cigarettes. He could transmit three simple signals. The first meant: *I am here.* He sat at the base of a tree, holding the radio, studying the shadows that stretched toward the glow of the lamps along the pathways. At five-minute intervals he repeated: *I am here, I am here.* Somewhere someone was listening. He was in contact with another human being. But then he reasoned that the Agency would be unlikely to pay a technician to sit up night after night simply to monitor his signals. They'd have a machine record them. And the machine would answer him—yes, there it was, a return signal, barely audible.

The return signal meant: *We hear you.* He was heard, then, but only by a machine, and it wouldn't be until morning that they'd check to be sure their man in the Park had called in.

He wondered if the green head had been talked about. Probably. It was too ludicrous for the Houston people to keep quiet about. "Remember that gung-ho major who didn't make the space program? Well, guess where he is now. And guess what color his head is . . . That's right, I said his *head*."

He signaled again—*I am here*— just to hear the machine whisper back: *We hear you, we hear you.* Four weeks of this. They said they'd need that much time in a real situation, first to alert the nearest undercover agent that a flyer was down, and then to allow the agent to track down the signal, and finally, to work out a plan of escape.

He sent his second signal, a variation of the first. It meant: *I receive you.* And the machine dutifully replied: *We receive each other.* That was all. A few pulses through the ether, back and forth, meaningless to an enemy monitoring system, and then one day the *we hear you* would become more frequent, indicating that the agent was coming for him.

There was a third signal. *Emergency.* Which would mean he was sick or caught or couldn't stand it any more and was giving up.

I am here.

I receive you.

Emergency.

This was his vocabulary. This was all he had, he thought. He was just a green-headed man in a dirt-caked flying suit, sitting in a city park at night, talking without words to a machine he'd never seen.

As the days went by, he deepened his burrow, made it more comfortable, more secure, better camouflaged. By night he explored the Park, studying each unknown reach of ground with care before venturing onto it. Whenever he passed the zoo, the animals sensed him, and stirred. It occurred to him that he was like them, in a way—a creature caged, and troubled by the scent of man.

Sometimes he saw others at night. He hid from them, drawing back in the deepest shadows. He had known he wouldn't be alone. The Agency people had told him he'd find himself among the scourings of New York— the weird ones, the oddballs, the misfits, the crazy men, all roaming the Park, hunting one another down. Well, he could take care of himself. He could handle two or three of them with judo and the knife. Besides, anybody who got a look at his head would run, for he was weirder than any of them, and more alone. Except that he would have just four weeks of it, and they were trapped for life. That was a difference; quite a difference.

They were frightened; so was he. They were hungry—and he'd be hungry, too. He didn't have enough rations for four weeks. The people at Houston had explained that they wanted him to live off the land—in part, anyway. That meant he would have to rummage through trash baskets looking for apple cores and sandwich leavings. If he had to, he could graze on grass, wild onions, daisies, and chew the bark of saplings. With care he might be able to stretch his rations. He had spent nine days in the Park already. There were nineteen to go, then. He could calculate how much he could allow himself to eat each day.

But of course a downed pilot wouldn't know how long he'd have to hold out. And therefore he, the Major, shouldn't know, either. Surely the Agency people had thought of that. Surely they had planned something to simulate the uncertainties of a real situation.

The Major thought about that. It worried him. He wondered if the Agency people intended to lengthen the test. That must be it. Nobody would come for him on that twenty-eighth night. They'd make him sweat for a few more days, maybe as long as a week.

Or they would trick him in another way. Perhaps they had filled some of the ration cans with water, or sand. It could be that. He would go along half starving himself to maintain food discipline—and then he'd find two or three useless cans.

He hefted each can, and shook it near his ear, but there was no way of telling what was inside. He'd have to wait. He couldn't open the cans early.

They would know that these doubts would occur to him. They would know he'd worry about them. They had planned it that way. It was part of the test. The tension, the strain. On top of the loneliness, on top of the fear. They had lied to him—lied for the good of the project, of course. But it was a dirty business, lying. You told the truth to your friends. That was the rule, wasn't it? It was the enemy you lied to.

The sounding of a siren deep in the city came echoing across the Park. He glanced uneasily around in the darkness, hearing something in that distant mechanical cry that made him want to speak out—to curse, to pray, anything—just to hear his own voice. But he was afraid to speak aloud; he was afraid.

He had premonitions of deep hunger. His limbs and eyes would ache. Sometimes he would drift in the delirium of fatigue. He worried about remembering things. When he filled his canteen at the lake, had he put in the purifier? Fear nagged at his senses, sharpening some, dulling others. He lost the exact count of his days—was it sixteen, seventeen?—but he had a greater awareness of the shape and touch of things.

He lived in the dark. He never saw the sun. By day he lay in his hole, sweating in the thick air, listening drowsily to the voices of people he could not see. He dreamed of capture, of death. When night came, he crept out, his body stiff, his bones aching, to face the dangers of the darkness.

One night he saw an old man shuffling along a path some thirty yards away, and he knew what would happen even before it occurred, as though it had taken place already in his dreams. Two figures rushed out of the dark; the old man fell at once to the ground beneath their blows. They tore at his clothing, searching for something of value. The Major crouched where he was, his knife open in his hand, but he was unable to intervene. He could not jeopardize the project.

Besides, the robbers moved with the swiftness of young men. He might not be equal to them, weakened as he was. They found nothing, and in their fury they kicked their victim, and stamped on his face before they ran off. The old man might be dead or dying, and yet the Major could do nothing, and so he turned away, in a rage that he had been the one to see that attack, impotent as he was, when those who might have helped were sleeping in comfort far away—the ones for whom the Park had been created, for whom it was patrolled and kept clean, and for whose amusement the zoo beasts were caged. The body would be found in the morning, and removed. They would not know about it. The incident was too common to warrant more than a line or two in the newspapers. At noon people would be walking over the very spot.

He saw other things on other nights—a dog stoned to death; a woman raped; a cripple beaten with his own crutch; a tramp sleeping in newspapers set afire and sent dancing, dressed in flames.

His anger left him. He watched as an animal might watch, ready at any moment to retreat and hide. The daytime people had lost the attributes of humankind. They were only voices, and footsteps. He could no longer imagine their faces. The ones who appeared at night were little more than shadows; still, they seemed more real to him. He thought about them often, wondering if any of these miserable, ferocious outcasts inhabited the Park as he did, hiding by day, prowling by night. He wasn't sure; he couldn't tell. But he wanted to believe there were at least a few. It made him feel less alone.

There were heavy rains for several days. His shelter was a morass. He himself was smeared with mud. His hands were blackened now. He thought that perhaps his face, too, had changed color, for the filth and dirt of the Park had been ground into his skin. He could feel his new-grown hair and beard stubble, and he wondered what he might look like, but he could not form a satisfactory picture in his mind.

He thought the full period had elapsed, but he wasn't sure. In any case, he had mastered the test; he had survived. But his achievement wasn't much. He had got through a few weeks. Those others—the night people of the Park—they had survived years. And in all that time no one had come to save them. No one had sought to arrange their escape.

He picked up his radio, and sent the signal. *I am here, I am here.* And the answer came back as always: *We hear you, we hear you.* But now he wondered—did they really hear him, were they listening?

For a time he was ill. He didn't know for how long. He lay in his burrow shivering with fever day and night. He had difficulty remembering why he was there, and pondered the matter, puzzled, until the answer came to him—oh, yes, the project. But it seemed to him that the project was not reason enough for him to be buried this way, alone and suffering and sick. There must be another, more important reason. He could not think what it might be.

His fever slackened, but he remained hidden. He did not care to leave his refuge. The project people might be searching for him, he realized. They would come at night with dogs and flares. But if they couldn't find him? If he'd hidden himself too well? Perhaps this time he had done that absolutely first-rate piece of work he had been struggling to do all his life—and it would be the end of him. How the Agency men would grumble. How annoyed with him they'd be. They might suspect that he had sabotaged the project on purpose, vanishing into the earth like that.

Or maybe they wouldn't come at all. Maybe they wouldn't search. They hadn't looked for the others—the other men who lived underground. They hadn't cared about them. Perhaps he, too, would be abandoned.

He crawled to the lake. He was too weak to stand. At the water's edge he plunged his head down and drank at the reflected lights of the buildings as though by drinking he could extinguish them. He drank the foulness of the water that had already put poison in him, but the lights remained on the surface, and when he roiled the water with his hand, the lights raced back and forth, dancing, shaking, as if quivering with laughter.

The days were hot now, the nights humid. There was the odor of decay everywhere. The rain slid down like grease. There was no grass to eat; it had been trodden away. The bark of the young trees was denied him, for somehow he had lost his knife. He scraped with his fingernails at the saplings, pulled weeds from the earth, leaves from the shrubs.

It was clear to him now that he had misinterpreted the meaning of the test. The object wasn't survival. A man who wants to survive doesn't hide in the earth, doesn't make himself sick with loneliness and fear—no, no, a man who does that has been betrayed into doing it. *Good luck, Major.* They had sent him off to get rid of him. He wasn't quite good enough for their needs, and so they shoved him out with a Judas touch to bury himself among the other outcasts for the sake of the project, which was death.

He was expected to die. He knew that now. They did not really believe, did they, that a man shot out of the sky could be rescued? The risks were too great. No agent—if there were any agents—could be asked to undertake them. Rather, their intention was to prevent a pilot from surrendering by persuading him that all he had to do was find a hiding place and wait for a rescue that had never even been considered. It would be death that came instead.

The radio was the cleverest part of the trick. A desperate man would believe its lies right up to the end, but there was no one listening, not even a machine, for surely it was the radio itself that produced those answering responses, as if they came from far away: *We hear you.* That was the ultimate betrayal, to kill a man with hope.

He was to die, like those others who lived underground, the hopeless ones, too weak to strike out at the enemies who had promised to save them but didn't come, who gave them short rations and told them to eat grass, who'd shorn their heads to humiliate them into hiding. And the poor crippled fools, they had accepted all that, just as he had. They had been eager to make the project work—and if the daytime laughter overhead sometimes drove them to violence, all they were capable of doing was to maim and to kill one another.

The project was death. They were all to die. Very well, he thought, but let them die in the sight of their executioners, let them die in the open air, beneath the sun.

He left his refuge at noon, when the Park was crowded. The sun was blinding. At first he could hardly see the people among whom he staggered, his arms outstretched, feeling his way. He gestured impatiently at trees, bushes, rocks; he shouted for the others to come out of hiding, too. He went tottering about looking for them, commanding them to appear.

The crowds gathered to follow him, warily and at some distance until they saw how weak he was. He fell sometimes, and crawled, rose again to his feet and lurched forward, crying out a summons that went unanswered.

People came nearer; they circled around him. Boys ran up close, hooting. Women held their babies high, so they, too, could see, the young men jogged over from the playing fields, anxious to look at the green-headed man crusted with dried mud, the madman in rags, the zany, the fool howling in their midst—yes, all were eager to have a good look at him before the police arrived to bundle him away.

FLOWERS THAT BLOOM IN THE SPRING

by *JULIAN SYMONS*

The outsider, Bertie Mays was fond of saying, sees most of the game. In the affair of the Purchases and the visiting cousin from South Africa he saw quite literally all of it. And the end was enigmatic and a little frightening, at least as seen through Bertie's eyes. It left him with the question whether there had been a game at all.

Bertie had retired early from his unimportant and uninteresting job in the Ministry of Welfare. He had a private income, he was unmarried, and his only extravagance was a passion for travel, so why go on working? Bertie gave up his London flat and settled down in the cottage in the Sussex countryside which he had bought years earlier as a weekend place. It was quite big enough for a bachelor, and Mrs. Last from the village came in two days a week to clean the place. Bertie himself was an excellent cook.

It was a fine day in June when he called next door to offer Sylvia Purchase a lift to the tea party at the Hall. She was certain to have been asked, and he knew she would need a lift because he had seen her husband Jimmy putting a case into the trunk of their ancient Morris. Jimmy was some sort of freelance journalist, and often went on trips, leaving Sylvia on her own. Bertie, who was flirtatious by nature, had asked if she would like him to keep her company, but she did not seem responsive to the suggestion.

Linton House, which the Purchases had rented furnished a few months earlier, was a rambling old place with oak beams and low ceilings. There was an attractive garden, some of which lay between the house and Bertie's cottage, and by jumping over the fence between them Bertie could walk across this garden. He did so that afternoon, taking a quick peek into the sitting room as he went by. He could never resist such peeks, because he always longed to know what people might be doing when they thought nobody was watching. On this occasion the sitting room was empty. He found Sylvia in the kitchen, washing dishes in a halfhearted way.

"Sylvia, you're not ready." She had on a dirty old cardigan with the buttons done up wrong. Bertie himself was, as always, dressed very suitably for the occasion in a double-breasted blue blazer with brass buttons, fawn trousers, and a neat bow tie. He always wore bow ties, which he felt gave him a touch of distinction.

"Ready for what?"

"Has the Lady of the Manor not asked you to tea?" That was his name for Lady Hussey up at the Hall.

She clapped a hand to her forehead, leaving a slight smudge. "I forgot all about it! Don't think I'll go, can't stand those bun fights."

"But I have called specially to collect you. Let me be your chauffeur. Your carriage awaits." Bertie made a sketch of a bow, and Sylvia laughed. She was a blonde in her early thirties, attractive in a slapdash sort of way.

"Bertie, you are a fool. All right, give me five minutes."

The women may call Bertie Mays a fool, Bertie thought, but how they adore him.

"Oh," Sylvia said. She was looking behind Bertie, and when he turned he saw a man standing in the shadow of the door. At first glance he thought it was Jimmy, for the man was large and square like Jimmy and had the same gingery fair coloring. But the resemblance went no further, for as the man stepped forward he saw that their features were not similar.

"This is my cousin, Alfred Wallington. He's paying us a visit from South Africa. Our next door neighbor, Bertie Mays."

"Pleased to meet you." Bertie's hand was firmly gripped. The two men went into the sitting room, and Bertie asked whether this was Mr. Wallington's first visit.

"By no means. I know England pretty well. The south, anyway."

"Ah, business doesn't take you up north?" Bertie thought of himself as a tactful but expert interrogator, and the question should have brought a response telling him Mr. Wallington's occupation. In fact, however, the other man merely said that was so.

"In the course of my work I used to correspond with several firms in Cape Town," Bertie said untruthfully. Wallington did not comment. "Is your home near there?"

"No."

The negative was so firm that it gave no room for further conversational maneuver. Bertie felt slightly cheated. If the man did not want to say where he lived in South Africa, of course he was free to say nothing, but there was a certain finesse to be observed in such matters, and a crude "no" was not at all the thing. He was able to establish at least that this was the first time Wallington had visited Linton House.

On the way up to the Hall he said to Sylvia that her cousin seemed a dour fellow.

"Alf?" Bertie winced at the abbreviation. "He's all right when you get to know him."

"He said he was often in the south. What's his particular sphere of interest?"

"I don't know. I believe he's got some sort of export business around Durban. By the way, Bertie, how did you know Jimmy was away?"

"I saw him waving good-bye to you." It would hardly do to say that he had been peeping through the curtains.

"Did you now? I was in bed when he went. You're a bit of a fibber, I'm afraid, Bertie."

"Oh, I can't remember *how* I knew." Really, it was too much to be taken up on every little point.

When they drove into the great courtyard and Sylvia got out of the car, however, he reflected that she looked very slenderly elegant, and that he was pleased to be with her. Bertie liked pretty women and they were safe with him, although he would not have thought of it that way. He might have said, rather, that he would never have compromised a lady, with the implication that all sorts of things might be said and done providing they stayed within the limits of discretion.

It occurred to him that Sylvia was hardly staying within those limits when she allowed herself to be alone at Linton House with her South African cousin. Call me old-fashioned, Bertie said to himself, but I don't like it.

The Hall was a nineteenth-century manor house and by no means, as Bertie had often said, an architectural gem, but the lawns at the back where tea was served were undoubtedly fine. Sir Reginald Hussey was a building contractor who had been knighted for some dubious service to the export drive. He was in demand for opening fêtes and fund-raising enterprises, and the Husseys entertained a selection of local people to parties of one kind or another half a dozen times a year. The parties were always done in style, and this afternoon there were maids in white caps and aprons, and a kind of majordomo who wore a frock coat and white gloves. Sir Reginald was not in evidence, but Lady Hussey presided in a regal manner.

Of course Bertie knew that it was all ridiculously vulgar and ostentatious, but still he enjoyed himself. He kissed Lady Hussey's hand and said that the scene was quite entrancing, like a Victorian period picture, and he had an interesting chat with Lucy Broadhinton, who was the widow of an Admiral. Lucy was the president and Bertie the secretary of the local historical society, and they were great friends. She told him now in the strictest secrecy about the outrageous affair Mrs. Monro was having with somebody who must be nameless, although from the details given, Bertie was quite able to guess his identity. There were other tidbits too, like the story of the scandalous misuse of the Church Fund restoration money. It was an enjoyable afternoon, and he fairly chortled about it on the way home.

"They're such snobby affairs," Sylvia said. "I don't know why I went."

"You seemed to be having a good time. I was quite jealous."

Sylvia had been at the center of a very animated circle of three or four young men. Her laughter at their jokes had positively rung out across the lawns, and Bertie had seen Lady Hussey give more than one disapproving glance in the direction of the little group. There was something undeniably attractive about Sylvia's gaiety and about the way in which she threw back her head when laughing, but her activities had a recklessness about them which was not proper for a lady.

Bertie tried to convey something of this as he drove back, but was not sure she understood what he meant. He also broached delicately the impropriety of her being alone in the house with her cousin by asking when Jimmy would be coming back. In a day or two, she said casually. He refused her invitation to come in for a drink. He had no particular wish to see Alf Wallington again.

On the following night at about midnight, when Bertie was in bed reading, he heard a car draw up next door. Doors were closed and there was the sound of voices. Just to confirm that Jimmy was back, Bertie got out of bed and lifted an edge of the curtain. A man and a woman were coming out of the garage. The woman was Sylvia. The man had his arm round her, and as Bertie watched, the man bent down and kissed her neck. Then they moved toward the front door, and the man laughed and said something. From his general build he might, seen in the dim light, have been Jimmy, but the voice had the distinctive South African accent of Wallington.

Bertie drew away from the window as though he had been scalded.

It was a feeling of moral responsibility that took him round to Linton House on the following day. To his surprise Jimmy Purchase opened the door.

"I—ah—thought you were away."

"Got back last night. What can I do for you?"

Bertie said he would like to borrow the electric hedge clippers, which he knew were in the garden shed. Jimmy led the way there and handed them over. Bertie said he had heard the car coming back at about midnight.

"Yeah." Jimmy had a deplorably Cockney voice, not at all out of the top drawer. "That was Sylvia and Alf. He took her to a dance over at Ladersham. I was too fagged out, just wanted to get my head down."

"Her cousin from South Africa?"

"Yeah, right, from the Cape. He's staying here for a bit. Plenty of room."

Was he from the Cape or from Durban? Bertie did not fail to notice the discrepancy.

Bertie's bump of curiosity was even stronger than his sense of propriety. It became important, even vital, that he should know just what was going on next door. When he returned the hedge cutters he asked them all to dinner, together with Lucy Broadhinton to make up the number. He took pains in preparing a delicious cold meal. The salmon was cooked to perfection, and the hollandaise sauce had just the right hint of something tart beneath its blandness.

The evening was not a success. Lucy had on a long dress and Bertie wore a smart velvet jacket, but Sylvia was dressed in sky-blue trousers and a vivid shirt, and the two men wore open-necked shirts and had a distinctly unkempt appearance. They had obviously been drinking before they arrived. Wallington tossed down Bertie's expensive hock as though it were water, and then said that South African wine had more flavor than that German stuff.

"You're from Durban, I believe, Mr. Wallington." Lucy fixed him with her Admiral's-lady glance. "My husband and I were there in the sixties, and thought it delightful. Do you happen to know the Morrows or the Page-Manleys? Mary Page-Manley gave such delightful parties."

Wallington looked at her from under heavy brows. "Don't know them."

"You have an export business in Durban?"

"That's right."

There was an awkward pause. Then Sylvia said, "Alf's trying to persuade us to pay him a visit out there."

"I'd like you to come out. Don't mind about him." Wallington jerked a thumb at Jimmy. "Believe me, we'd have a good time."

"I do believe you, Alf." She gave her head-back laugh, showing the fine column of her neck. "It's something we've forgotten here—how to have a good time."

Jimmy Purchase had been silent during dinner. Now he said, "People here just don't have the money. Like the song says, it's money makes the world go round."

"The trouble in Britain is that too much money has got into the wrong hands." Lucy looked round the table. Nobody seemed inclined to argue the point. "There are too many grubby little people with sticky fingers."

"I wish some of the green stuff would stick to my fingers," Jimmy said, and hiccuped. Bertie realized with horror that he was drunk. "We're broke, Sylvie, old girl."

"Oh, shut up."

"You don't believe me?" And he actually began to empty out his pockets. What appalling creatures the two men were, each as bad as the other. Bertie longed for the evening to end, and was delighted when Lucy rose to make a stately departure. He whispered an apology in the hall, but she told him not to be foolish, it had been fascinating.

When he returned, Wallington said, "What an old battleaxe. *Did you happen to know the Page-Manleys.* Didn't know they were still around, people like that."

Sylvia was looking at Bertie. "Alf, you're shocking our host."

"Sorry, man, but honest, I thought they kept her sort in museums. Stuffed."

"You mustn't say stuffed. That'll shock Bertie too."

Bertie said stiffly, "I am not in the least shocked, but I certainly regard it as the height of bad manners to criticize a guest in such a manner. Lucy is a very dear friend of mine."

Sylvia at least had some understanding of his feelings. She said sorry and smiled, so that he was at once inclined to forgive her. Then she said it was time she took her rough diamonds home.

"Thanks for the grub," Wallington said. Then he leaned across the dining table and shouted, "Wake up, man, it's tomorrow morning already." Jimmy had fallen asleep in his chair. He was hauled to his feet and supported across the garden.

Bertie called up Lucy the next morning and apologized again. She said he should think no more about it. "I didn't take to that South African feller, though. Shouldn't be surprised if he turns out to be a bad hat. And I didn't care too much for your neighbors, if you don't mind my being frank."

Bertie said of course not, although he reflected that there seemed to be a sudden spasm of frankness among his acquaintances. Mrs. Purchase, Lucy said, had a roving eye. She left it at that, and they went on to discuss the agenda for the next meeting of the historical society.

Later in the morning there was a knock on the door. Jimmy was there, hollow-eyed and slightly green. " 'Fraid we rather blotted our copybook last night. Truth is, Alf and I were fairly well loaded before we came round. Can't remember too much about it, but Syl said apologies were in order."

Bertie asked when Sylvia's cousin was leaving. Jimmy Purchase shrugged and said he didn't know. Bertie nearly said that he ought not to leave the man alone with Sylvia, but refrained. He might be inquisitive, but he was also discreet.

A couple of nights later he was doing some weeding in the garden when he heard voices raised in Linton House. One was Jimmy's, the other belonged to Sylvia. They were in the sitting room shouting at each other, not quite loudly enough for the words to be distinguishable. It was maddening not to know what was being said. Bertie moved along the fence separating the gardens, until he was as near as he could get without being seen. He was now able to hear a few phrases.

"Absolutely sick of it . . . drink because it takes my mind off . . . told you we have to wait . . ." That was Jimmy.

Then Sylvia's voice, shrill as he had never heard it, shrill and sneering. "Tell me the old, old story . . . how long do we bloody well wait then . . . you said it would be finished by now." An indistinguishable murmur from Jimmy. "None of your business," she said. More murmuring. "None of your business what I do." Murmur murmur. "You said yourself we're broke." To this there was some reply. Then she said clearly, "I shall do what I like."

"All right," Jimmy said, so loudly that Bertie fairly jumped. There followed a sharp crack, which sounded like hand on flesh.

Sylvia said, "You damn—that's it, then."

Nothing more. No sound, no speech. Bertie waited five minutes and then tiptoed away, fearful of being seen. Once indoors again he felt quite shaky, and had to restore himself by a nip of brandy.

What had the conversation meant? Much of it was plain enough. Sylvia was saying that it was none of her husband's business if she carried on an affair. But what was it they had to wait for, what was it that should have been finished? A deal connected with the odious Alf? And where was Alf, who as Bertie had noticed went out into the village very little?

He slept badly, and was wakened in the middle of the night by a piercing, awful scream. He sat up in bed quivering, but the sound was not repeated. He decided that he must have been having a nightmare.

On the following day the car was not in the garage. Had Jimmy gone off again? He met Sylvia out shopping in the village, and she said that he had been called to an assignment on short notice.

"What sort of assignment?" He had asked before for the name of the paper Jimmy worked on, to be told that he was a freelance.

"A Canadian magazine. He's up in the Midlands, may be away a few days."

Should he say something about the row? But that would have been indiscreet, and in any case Sylvia had such a wild look in her eye that he did not care to ask further questions. It was on that morning that he read about the Small Bank Robbers.

The Small Bank Robbers had been news for some months. They specialized in fast well-organized raids on banks, and had carried out nearly 20 of these in the past year. Several men were involved in each raid. They were armed, and did not hesitate to use coshes or revolvers when necessary. In one bank a screaming woman customer had suffered a fractured skull when hit over the head, and in another a guard who resisted the robbers had been shot and killed.

The diminutive applied to them—small—referred to the banks they robbed, not to their own physical dimensions. A bank clerk who had admitted giving information to the gang had asked why they were interested in his small branch bank, and had been told that they always raided small banks because they were much more vulnerable than large ones. After the arrest of this clerk the robbers seemed to have gone underground. There had been no news of them for the last three weeks.

Bertie had heard about the Small Bank Robbers, but took no particular interest in them. He was a nervous man, and did not care to read about crime. On this morning, however, his eye was caught by the heading: "Small Bank Robbers. The South African Connection." The story was a feature by the paper's crime reporter, Derek Holmes. He said that Scotland Yard knew the identities of some of the robbers, and described his own investigations, which led to the conclusion that three or four of them were in Spain. The article continued:

"But there is another connection, and a sinister one. The men in Spain are small fry. My researches suggest that the heavy men who organized the robberies, and were very ready to use violence, came from South Africa. They provided the funds and the muscle. Several witnesses who heard the men talking to each other or giving orders during the raids have said that they used odd accents. This has been attributed to the sound distortion caused by the stocking masks they wore, but two men I spoke to, both of whom have spent time in South Africa, said that they had *no doubt the accent was South African.*"

The writer suggested that these men were now probably back in South Africa. But supposing that one of them was still in England, that he knew Jimmy and Sylvia and had a hold over them? Supposing, even, that Jimmy and Sylvia were minor members of the gang themselves? The thought made Bertie shiver with fright and excitement. What should or could he do about it? And where had Jimmy Purchase gone?

Again he slept badly, and when he did fall into a doze it was a short one. He dreamed that Wallington was knocking on the door. Once inside the house the South African drew out a huge wad of notes, said that there was enough for everybody, and counted out bundles which he put on the table between them with a small decisive *thwack*. A second bundle, *thwack,* and a third, *thwack*. How many more? He tried to cry out, to protest, but the bundles went on, *thwack, thwack, thwack* . . .

He sat up in bed, crying out something inaudible. The thin gray light of early morning came through the curtains. There was a sound in the garden outside, a sound regularly repeated, the *thwack* of his dream. It took him, in his slightly dazed state, a little while to realize that if he went to the window he might see what was causing the sound. He tiptoed across the room and raised the curtain. He was trembling.

It was still almost dark, and whatever was happening was taking place at the back of Linton House, so that he could not see it. But as he listened to the regularly repeated sound, he had no doubt of its nature. Somebody was digging out there. The sound of the spade digging earth had entered his dream, and there was an occasional clink when it struck a stone. Why would somebody be digging at this time in the morning? He remembered that terrible cry on the previous night, the cry he had thought to be a dream. Supposing it had been real, who had cried out?

The digging stopped and two people spoke, although he could not hear the words or even the tones. One, light and high in pitch, was no doubt Sylvia's, but was the other voice Wallington's? And if it was, had Jimmy Purchase gone away at all?

In the half light a man and woman were briefly visible before they passed into the house. The man carried a spade, but his head was down and Bertie could not see his face, only his square bulky figure. He had little doubt that the man was Wallington.

That morning he went up to London. He had visited the city rarely since his retirement, finding that on each visit he was more worried and confused. The place seemed continually to change, so that what had been a landmark of some interest was now a kebab or hamburger restaurant. The article had appeared in the *Banner,* and their offices had moved from Fleet Street to somewhere off the Gray's Inn Road. He asked for Arnold Grayson, a deputy editor he had known slightly, to be told that Grayson had moved to another paper. He had to wait almost an hour before he was able to talk to Derek Holmes. The crime reporter remained staring at his desk while he listened to Bertie's story. During the telling of it Holmes chewed gum and said "Yup" occasionally.

"Yup," he said again at the end. "Okay, Mr. Mays. Thanks."

"What are you going to do about it?"

Holmes removed his gum and considered the question. "Know how many people been in touch about that piece, saying they've seen the robbers, their landlord's one of them, they heard two South Africans talking in a bus about how the loot should be split, et cetera? One hundred and eleven. Half of 'em are sensationalists, the other half plain crazy."

"But this is different."

"They're all different. I shouldn'ta seen you only you mentioned Arnie, and he was a good friend. But what's it amount to? Husband and wife having a shindig, husband goes off, South African cousin's digging a flowerbed—"

"At that time in the morning?"

The reporter shrugged. "People are funny."

"Have you got pictures of the South Africans you say are involved in the robberies? If I could recognize Wallington—"

Holmes put another piece of gum in his mouth, chewed on it meditatively, then produced half a dozen photographs. None of them resembled

Wallington. Holmes shuffled the pictures together and put them away. "That's it then."

"But aren't you going to come down and look into it? I tell you I believe murder has been done. Wallington is her lover. Together they have killed Purchase."

"If Wallington's lying low with his share of the loot, the last thing he'd do is get involved in this sort of caper. You know your trouble, Mr. Mays? You've got an overheated imagination."

If only he knew somebody at Scotland Yard! But there was no reason to think that they would take him any more seriously than the newspaperman had. He returned feeling both chastened and frustrated. To his surprise Sylvia got out of another carriage on the train. She greeted him cheerfully.

"Hallo, Bertie. I've just been seeing Alf off."

"Seeing Alf off?" he echoed stupidly.

"Back to South Africa. He had a letter saying they needed him back there."

"Back in Durban?"

"That's right."

"Jimmy said he was from the Cape."

"Did he? Jimmy often gets things wrong."

It was not in Bertie's nature to be anything but gallant to a lady, even one he suspected of being a partner in murder. "Now that you are a grass widow again, you must come in and have a dish of tea."

"That would be lovely."

"Tomorrow?"

"It's a date."

They had reached his cottage. She pressed two fingers to her lips, touched his cheek with them. Inside the cottage the telephone was ringing. It was Holmes.

"Mr. Mays? Thought you'd like to know. Your chum Purchase is just what he said, a freelance journalist. One or two of the boys knew him. Not too successful from what I hear."

"So you did pay some attention to what I told you!"

"Always try and check a story out. Nothing to this one, far as I can see."

"Wallington has gone back to South Africa. Suddenly, just like that."

"Has he now? Good luck to him."

Triumph was succeeded by indignation. He put down the telephone without saying good-bye.

Was it all the product of an overheated imagination? He made scones for Sylvia's visit next day and served them with his home-made blackcurrant preserve. Then he put the question that still worried him. He would have liked to introduce it delicately, but somehow didn't manage that.

"What was all that digging in the garden early the other morning?"

Sylvia looked startled, and then exclaimed as a fragment of the scone she was eating dropped onto her dress. When it had been removed she said, "Sorry you were disturbed. It was Timmy."

"Timmy?"

"Our tabby. He must have eaten something poisoned and he died. Poor Timmy. Alf dug a grave and we gave him Christian burial." With hardly a pause she went on, "We're clearing out at the end of the week."

"Leaving?" For a moment he could hardly believe it.

"Right. I'm a London girl at heart, you know, always was. The idea of coming here was that Jimmy would be able to do some writing of his own, but that never seemed to work out—he was always being called away. If I'm in London I can get a job, earn some money. Very necessary at the moment. If Alf hadn't helped out, I don't know what we'd have done. It was a crazy idea coming down here, but then we're crazy people."

And at the end of that week Sylvia went. Since the house had been rented furnished, she had only suitcases to take away. She came to say good-bye. There was no sign of Jimmy, and Bertie asked about him.

"Still up on that job. But anyway he wouldn't have wanted to come down and help, he hates things like that. Good-bye, Bertie, we'll meet again I expect." A quick kiss on the cheek and she was driving off in her rented car.

She departed leaving all sorts of questions unanswered when Bertie came to think about it, mundane ones like an address if anybody should want to get in touch with her or with Jimmy, and things he would have liked to know, such as the reason for digging the cat's grave at such an extraordinary hour. He found himself more and more suspicious of the tale she had told. The row he had overheard could perhaps be explained by lack of money, but it seemed remarkable that Jimmy Purchase had not come back.

Linton House was locked up and empty, but it was easy enough to get into the garden. The area dug up was just inside the boundary fence. It was difficult to see how much had been dug because there was a patch of earth at each side, but it looked like a large area to bury a cat.

On impulse one day, a week after Sylvia had gone, Bertie took a spade into the garden and began to dig. It proved to be quite hard work, and he went down two feet before reaching the body. It was that of a cat, one he vaguely remembered seeing in the house, but Sylvia's story of its death had been untrue. Its head was mangled, shattered by one or two heavy blows.

Bertie looked at the cat with distaste—he did not care for seeing dead things—returned it, and had just finished shoveling back the earth when he was hailed from the road. He turned, and with a sinking heart saw the local constable, P.C. Harris, standing beside his bicycle.

"Ah, it's you, Mr. Mays. I was thinking it might be somebody with burglarious intent. Somebody maybe was going to dig a tunnel to get entrance into the house. But perhaps it was your *own* house you was locked out of." P.C. Harris was well known as a local wag, and nobody laughed more loudly at his own jokes. He laughed heartily now. Bertie joined in feebly.

"But what *was* you doing digging in the next-door garden, may I ask?"

What could he say? I was digging for a man, but only found a cat? Desperately Bertie said, "I'd—ah—lost something and thought it might have got in here. I was just turning the earth."

The constable shook his head. "You was trespassing, Mr. Mays. This is not your property."

"No, of course not. It won't happen again. I'd be glad if you could forget it." He approached the constable, a pound note in his hand.

"No need for that, sir, which might be construed as a bribe and hence an offense in itself. I shall not be reporting the matter on this occasion, nor inquiring further into the whys and wherefores, but would strongly advise you in future to keep within the bounds of your own property."

Pompous old fool, Bertie thought, but said that of course he would do just that. He scrambled back into his own garden, aware that he made a slightly ludicrous figure. P.C. Harris, in a stately manner, mounted his bicycle and rode away.

That was almost, but not quite, the end of the story.

Linton House was empty for a few weeks and then rented again, to a family called Hobson who had two noisy children. Bertie had as little to do with them as possible. He was very conscious of having been made to look a fool, and there was nothing he disliked more than that. He was also aware of a disinclination in himself to enter Linton House again.

In the late spring of the following year he went to Sardinia for a holiday, driving around on his own, looking at the curious nuraghi and the burial places made from gigantic blocks of stone which are called the tombs of the giants. He drove up the western coast in a leisurely way, spending long mornings and afternoons over lunches and dinners in the small towns, and then moving inland to bandit country. He was sitting nursing a drink in a square at Nuoro, which is the capital of the central province, when he heard his name called.

It was Sylvia, so brown that he hardly recognized her. "Bertie, what are you doing here?"

He said that he was on holiday, and returned the question.

"Just come down to shop. We have a house up in the hills—you must come and see it. Darling, look who's here."

A bronzed Jimmy Purchase approached across the square. Like Sylvia he seemed in fine spirits, and endorsed enthusiastically the suggestion that Bertie should come out to their house. It was a few miles from the city on the slopes of Mount Ortobene, a long low white modern house at the end of a rough road. They sat in a courtyard and ate grilled fish, and drank a hard dry local white wine.

Bertie felt his natural curiosity rising. How could he ask questions without appearing to be—well—nosy? Over coffee he said that he supposed Jimmy was out here on an assignment.

It was Sylvia who answered. "Oh, no, he's given all that up since the book was published."

"The book?"

"Show him, Jimmy." Jimmy went into the house. He returned with a book which said on the cover *My Tempestuous Life. As told by Anita Sorana to Jimmy Purchase.*

"You've heard of her?"

It would have been difficult not to have heard of Anita Sorana. She was a screen actress famous equally for her temperament, her five well-publicized marriages, and the variety of her love affairs.

"It was fantastic luck when she agreed that Jimmy should write her autobiography. It was all very hush-hush and we had to pretend that he was off on assignments when he was really with Anita."

Jimmy took it up. "Then she'd break appointments, say she wasn't in the mood to talk. A few days afterwards she'd ask to see me at a minute's notice. Then Sylvia started to play up—"

"I thought he was having an affair with her. She certainly fancied him. He swears he wasn't, but I don't know. Anyway, it was worth it." She yawned.

"The book was a success?"

Jimmy grinned, teeth very white in his brown face. "I'll say. Enough for me to shake off the dust of Fleet Street."

So the quarrel was explained, and Jimmy's sudden absences, and his failure to return. After a glass of some fiery local liqueur Bertie felt soporific, conscious that he had drunk a little more than usual. There was some other question he wanted to ask, but he did not remember it until they were driving him down the mountain, back to his hotel in Nuoro.

"How is your cousin?"

Jimmy was driving. "Cousin?"

"Mr. Wallington, Sylvia's cousin from South Africa."

Sylvia, from the back of the car, said, "Alf's dead."

"Dead!"

"In a car accident. Soon after he got back to South Africa. Wasn't it sad?"

Very few more words were spoken before they reached the hotel and said good-bye. The heat of the hotel room and the wine he had drunk made Bertie fall asleep at once. After a couple of hours he woke, sweating, and wondered if he believed what he had been told. Was it possible to make enough money from "ghosting" (he had heard that was the word) a life story to retire to Sardinia? It seemed unlikely. He lay on his back in the dark room, and it seemed to him that he saw with terrible clarity what had happened.

Wallington was one of the Small Bank Robbers, and he had come to the Purchases looking for a safe place to stay. He had his money, what Holmes had called the loot, with him, and they had decided to kill him for it. The quarrel had been about when Wallington would be killed, the sound that wakened him in the night had been Wallington's death cry.

Jimmy had merely pretended to go away that night, and had returned to help Sylvia dispose of the body. Jimmy dug the grave and they put Wallington in it. Then the cat had been killed and put into a shallow grave on top of the body. It was the killing of the cat, those savage blows on its head, that somehow horrified Bertie most.

He cut short his holiday and took the next plane back. At home he walked round to the place where he had dug up the cat. The Hobsons had put in bedding plants, and the wallflowers were flourishing. He had read somewhere that flowers always flourished over a grave.

"Not thinking of trespassing again, I hope, Mr. Mays?"

It was P.C. Harris, red-faced and jovial.

Bertie shook his head. What he had imagined in the hotel room might be true, but then again it might not. Supposing that he went to the police, supposing he was able to convince them that there was something in his story, supposing they dug up the flowerbed and found nothing but the cat? He would be the laughingstock of the neighborhood.

Bertie Mays knew that he would say nothing.

"I reckon you was feeling a little bit eccentric that night you was doing the digging," P.C. Harris said sagely.

"Yes, I think I must have been."

"They make a fine show, them wallflowers. Makes you more cheerful, seeing spring flowers."

"Yes," said Bertie Mays meekly. "They make a fine show."

A NICE PLACE TO STAY

by *NEDRA TYRE*

All my life I've wanted a nice place to stay. I don't mean anything grand, just a small room with the walls freshly painted and a few neat pieces of furniture and a window to catch the sun so that two or three pot plants could grow. That's what I've always dreamed of. I didn't yearn for love or money or nice clothes, though I was a pretty enough girl and pretty clothes would have made me prettier—not that I mean to brag.

Things fell on my shoulders when I was fifteen. That was when Mama took sick, and keeping house and looking after Papa and my two older brothers—and of course nursing Mama—became my responsibility. Not long after that Papa lost the farm and we moved to town. I don't like to think of the house we lived in near the C & R railroad tracks, though I guess we were lucky to have a roof over our heads—it was the worst days of the Depression and a lot of people didn't even have a roof, even one that leaked, plink, plonk; in a heavy rain there weren't enough pots and pans and vegetable bowls to set around to catch all the water.

Mama was the sick one but it was Papa who died first—living in town didn't suit him. By then my brothers had married and Mama and I moved into two back rooms that looked onto an alley and everybody's garbage cans and dump heaps. My brothers pitched in and gave me enough every month for Mama's and my barest expenses even though their wives grumbled and complained.

I tried to make Mama comfortable. I catered to her every whim and fancy. I loved her. All the same I had another reason to keep her alive as long as possible. While she breathed I knew I had a place to stay. I was terrified of what would happen to me when Mama died. I had no high school diploma and no experience at outside work and I knew my sisters-in-law wouldn't take me in or let my brothers support me once Mama was gone.

Then Mama drew her last breath with a smile of thanks on her face for what I had done.

Sure enough, Norine and Thelma, my brothers' wives, put their feet down. I was on my own from then on. So that scared feeling of wondering where I could lay my head took over in my mind and never left me.

I had some respite when Mr. Williams, a widower twenty-four years older than me, asked me to marry him. I took my vows seriously. I meant to cherish him and I did. But that house we lived in! Those walls couldn't have been dirtier if they'd been smeared with soot and the plumbing was stubborn as a mule. My left foot stayed sore from having to kick the pipe underneath the kitchen sink to get the water to run through.

Then Mr. Williams got sick and had to give up his shoe repair shop that he ran all by himself. He had a small savings account and a few of those twenty-five-dollar government bonds and drew some disability insurance until the policy ran out in something like six months.

I did everything I could to make him comfortable and keep him cheerful. Though I did all the laundry I gave him clean sheets and clean pajamas every third day and I think it was by my will power alone that I made a begonia bloom in that dark back room Mr. Williams stayed in. I even pestered his two daughters and told them they ought to send their father some get-well cards and they did once or twice. Every now and then when there were a few pennies extra I'd buy cards and scrawl signatures nobody could have read and mailed them to Mr. Williams to make him think some of his former customers were remembering him and wishing him well.

Of course when Mr. Williams died his daughters were johnny-on-the-spot to see that they got their share of the little bit that tumbledown house brought. I didn't begrudge them—I'm not one to argue with human nature.

I hate to think about all those hardships I had after Mr. Williams died. The worst of it was finding somewhere to sleep; it all boiled down to having a place to stay. Because somehow you can manage not to starve. There are garbage cans to dip into—you'd be surprised how wasteful some people are and how much good food they throw away. Or if it was right after the garbage trucks had made their collections and the cans were empty I'd go into a supermarket and pick, say, at the cherries pretending I was selecting some to buy. I didn't slip their best ones into my mouth. I'd take either those so ripe that they should have been thrown away or those that weren't ripe enough and shouldn't have been put out for people to buy. I might snitch a withered cabbage leaf or a few pieces of watercress or a few of those small round tomatoes about the size of hickory nuts—I never can remember their right name. I wouldn't make a pig of myself, just eat enough to ease my hunger. So I managed. As I say, you don't have to starve.

The only work I could get hardly ever paid me anything beyond room and board. I wasn't a practical nurse, though I knew how to take care of sick folks, and the people hiring me would say that since I didn't have the training and qualifications I couldn't expect much. All they really wanted was for someone to spend the night with Aunt Myrtle or Cousin Kate or Mama or Daddy; no actual duties were demanded of me, they said, and they really didn't think my help was worth anything except meals and a place to sleep. The arrangements were pretty makeshift. Half the time I wouldn't have a place to keep my things, not that I had any clothes to speak of, and sometimes I'd sleep on a cot in the hall outside the patient's room or on some sort of contrived bed in the patient's room.

I cherished every one of those sick people, just as I had cherished Mama and Mr. Williams. I didn't want them to die. I did everything I knew to let them know I was interested in their welfare—first for their sakes, and then for mine, so I wouldn't have to go out and find another place to stay.

Well, now, I've made out my case for the defense, a term I never thought I'd have to use personally, so now I'll make out the case for the prosecution.

I stole.

I don't like to say it, but I was a thief.

I'm not light-fingered. I didn't want a thing that belonged to anybody else. But there came a time when I felt forced to steal. I had to have some things. My shoes fell apart. I needed some stockings and underclothes. And when I'd ask a son or a daughter or a cousin or a niece for a little money for those necessities they acted as if I was trying to blackmail them. They reminded me that I wasn't qualified as a practical nurse, that I might even get into trouble with the authorities if they found I was palming myself off as a practical nurse—which I wasn't and they knew it. Anyway, they said that their terms were only bed and board.

So I began to take things—small things that had been pushed into the backs of drawers or stored high on shelves in boxes—things that hadn't been used or worn for years and probably would never be used again. I made my biggest haul at Mrs. Bick's where there was an attic full of trunks stuffed with clothes and doodads from the twenties all the way back to the nineties—uniforms, ostrich fans, Spanish shawls, beaded bags. I sneaked out a few of these at a time and every so often sold them to a place called Way Out, Hippie Clothiers.

I tried to work out the exact amount I got for selling something. Not, I know, that you can make up for theft. But, say, I got a dollar for a feather boa belonging to Mrs. Bick: well, then I'd come back and work at a job that the cleaning woman kept putting off, like waxing the hall upstairs or polishing the andirons or getting the linen closet in order.

All the same I *was* stealing—not everywhere I stayed, not even in most places, but when I had to I stole. I admit it.

But I didn't steal that silver box.

I was as innocent as a baby where that box was concerned. So when that policeman came toward me grabbing at the box I stepped aside, and maybe

I even gave him the push that sent him to his death. He had no business acting like that when that box was mine, whatever Mrs. Crowe's niece argued.

Fifty thousand nieces couldn't have made it not mine.

Anyway, the policeman was dead and though I hadn't wanted him dead I certainly hadn't wished him well. And then I got to thinking: well, I didn't steal Mrs. Crowe's box but I had stolen other things and it was the mills of God grinding exceeding fine, as I once heard a preacher say, and I was being made to pay for the transgressions that had caught up with me.

Surely I can make a little more sense out of what happened than that, though I never was exactly clear in my own mind about everything that happened.

Mrs. Crowe was the most appreciative person I ever worked for. She was bedridden and could barely move. I don't think the registered nurse on daytime duty considered it part of her job to massage Mrs. Crowe. So at night I would massage her, and that pleased and soothed her. She thanked me for every small thing I did—when I fluffed her pillow, when I'd put a few drops of perfume on her earlobes, when I'd straighten the wrinkled bedcovers.

I had a little joke. I'd pretend I could tell fortunes and I'd take Mrs. Crowe's hand and tell her she was going to have a wonderful day but she must beware of a handsome blond stranger—or some such foolishness that would make her laugh. She didn't sleep well and it seemed to give her pleasure to talk to me most of the night about her childhood or her dead husband.

She kept getting weaker and weaker and two nights before she died she said she wished she could do something for me but that when she became an invalid she had signed over everything to her niece. Anyway, Mrs. Crowe hoped I'd take her silver box. I thanked her. It pleased me that she liked me well enough to give me the box. I didn't have any real use for it. It would have made a nice trinket box, but I didn't have any trinkets. The box seemed to be Mrs. Crowe's fondest possession. She kept it on the table beside her and her eyes lighted up every time she looked at it. She might have been a little girl first seeing a brand-new baby doll early on a Christmas morning.

So when Mrs. Crowe died and the niece on whom I set eyes for the first time dismissed me, I gathered up what little I had and took the box and left. I didn't go to Mrs. Crowe's funeral. The paper said it was private and I wasn't invited. Anyway, I wouldn't have had anything suitable to wear.

I still had a few dollars left over from those things I'd sold to the hippie place called Way Out, so I paid a week's rent for a room that was the worst I'd ever stayed in.

It was freezing cold and no heat came up to the third floor where I was.

In that room with falling plaster and buckling floorboards and darting roaches, I sat wearing every stitch I owned, with a sleazy blanket and a faded quilt draped around me waiting for the heat to rise, when in swept Mrs. Crowe's niece in a fur coat and a fur hat and shiny leather boots up to her knees. Her face was beet red from anger when she started telling me that she had traced me through a private detective and I was to give her back the heirloom I had stolen.

Her statement made me forget the precious little bit I knew of the English language. I couldn't say a word, and she kept on screaming that if I returned the box immediately no criminal charge would be made against me. Then I got back my voice and I said that box was mine and that Mrs. Crowe had wanted me to have it, and she asked if I had any proof or if there were any witnesses to the gift, and I told her that when I was given a present I said thank you, that I didn't ask for proof and witnesses, and that nothing could make me part with Mrs. Crowe's box.

The niece stood there breathing hard, in and out, almost counting her breaths like somebody doing an exercise to get control of herself.

"You'll see," she yelled, and then she left.

The room was colder than ever and my teeth chattered.

Not long afterward I heard heavy steps clumping up the stairway. I realized that the niece had carried out her threat and that the police were after me.

I was panic-stricken. I chased around the room like a rat with a cat after it: Then I thought that if the police searched my room and couldn't find the box it might give me time to decide what to do. I grabbed the box out of the top dresser drawer and scurried down the back hall. I snatched the back door open. I think what I intended to do was run down the back steps and hide the box somewhere, underneath a bush or maybe in a garbage can.

Those back steps were steep and rose almost straight up for three stories and they were flimsy and covered with ice.

I started down. My right foot slipped. The handrail saved me. I clung to it with one hand and to the silver box with the other hand and picked and chose my way across the patches of ice.

When I was midway I heard my name shrieked. I looked around to see a big man leaping down the steps after me. I never saw such anger on a person's face. Then he was directly behind me and reached out to snatch the box.

I swerved to escape his grasp and he cursed me. Maybe I pushed him. I'm not sure—not really.

Anyway, he slipped and fell down and down and down, and then after all that falling he was absolutely still. The bottom step was beneath his head like a pillow and the rest of his body was spreadeagled on the brick walk.

Then almost like a pet that wants to follow its master, the silver box jumped from my hand and bounced down the steps to land beside the man's left ear.

My brain was numb. I felt paralyzed. Then I screamed.

Tenants from that house and the houses next door and across the alley pushed windows open and flung doors open to see what the commotion was about, and then some of them began to run toward the back yard. The policeman who was the dead man's partner—I guess you'd call him that—ordered them to keep away.

After a while more police came and they took the dead man's body and drove me to the station where I was locked up.

From the very beginning I didn't take to that young lawyer they assigned to me. There wasn't anything exactly that I could put my finger on. I just felt uneasy with him. His last name was Stanton. He had a first name of course, but he didn't tell me what it was; he said he wanted me to call him Bat like all his friends did.

He was always smiling and reassuring me when there wasn't anything to smile or be reassured about, and he ought to have known it all along instead of filling me with false hope.

All I could think was that I was thankful Mama and Papa and Mr. Williams were dead and that my shame wouldn't bring shame on them.

"It's going to be all right," the lawyer kept saying right up to the end, and then he claimed to be indignant when I was found guilty of resisting arrest and of manslaughter and theft or robbery—there was the biggest hullabaloo as to whether I was guilty of theft or robbery. Not that I was guilty of either, at least in this particular instance, but no one would believe me.

You would have thought it was the lawyer being sentenced instead of me, the way he carried on. He called it a terrible miscarriage of justice and said we might as well be back in the eighteenth century when they hanged children.

Well, that was an exaggeration, if ever there was one; nobody was being hung and nobody was a child. That policeman had died and I had had a part in it. Maybe I had pushed him. I couldn't be sure. In my heart I really hadn't meant him any harm. I was just scared. But he was dead all the same. And as far as stealing went, I hadn't stolen the box but I had stolen other things more than once.

And then it happened. It was a miracle. All my life I'd dreamed of a nice room of my own, a comfortable place to stay. And that's exactly what I got.

The room was on the small side but it had everything I needed in it, even a wash basin with hot and cold running water, and the walls were freshly painted, and they let me choose whether I wanted a wing chair with a chintz slipcover or a modern Danish armchair. I even got to decide what color bedspread I preferred. The window looked out on a beautiful lawn edged with shrubbery, and the matron said I'd be allowed to go to the greenhouse and select some pot plants to keep in my room. The next day I picked out a white gloxinia and some russet chrysanthemums.

I didn't mind the bars at the windows at all. Why, this day and age some of the finest mansions have barred windows to keep burglars out.

The meals—I simply couldn't believe there was such delicious food in the world. The woman who supervised their preparation had embezzled the funds of one of the largest catering companies in the state after working herself up from assistant cook to treasurer.

The other inmates were very friendly and most of them had led the most interesting lives. Some of the ladies occasionally used words that you usually see written only on fences or printed on sidewalks before the cement dries, but when they were scolded they apologized. Every now and then somebody would get angry with someone and there would be a little scratching or hair pulling, but it never got too bad. There was a choir—I can't sing but I love music—and they gave a concert every Tuesday morning at chapel, and Thursday night was movie night. There wasn't any admission charge. All you did was go in and sit down anywhere you pleased.

We all had a special job and I was assigned to the infirmary. The doctor and nurse both complimented me. The doctor said that I should have gone into professional nursing, that I gave confidence to the patients and helped them get well. I don't know about that but I've had years of practice with sick people and I like to help anybody who feels bad.

I was so happy that sometimes I couldn't sleep at night. I'd get up and click on the light and look at the furniture and the walls. It was hard to believe I had such a pleasant place to stay. I'd remember supper that night, how I'd gone back to the steam table for a second helping of asparagus with lemon and herb sauce, and I compared my plenty with those terrible times when I had slunk into supermarkets and nibbled overripe fruit and raw vegetables to ease my hunger.

Then one day here came that lawyer, not even at regular visiting hours, bouncing around congratulating me that my appeal had been upheld, or whatever the term was, and that I was as free as a bird to leave right that minute.

He told the matron she could send my belongings later and he dragged me out front where TV cameras and newspaper reporters were waiting.

As soon as the cameras began whirring and the photographers began to aim, the lawyer kissed me on the cheek and pinned a flower on me. He made a speech saying that a terrible miscarriage of justice had been rectified. He had located people who testified that Mrs. Crowe had given me the box —she had told the gardener and the cleaning woman. They hadn't wanted to testify because they didn't want to get mixed up with the police, but the lawyer had persuaded them in the cause of justice and humanity to come forward and make statements.

The lawyer had also looked into the personnel record of the dead policeman and had learned that he had been judged emotionally unfit for his job, and the psychiatrist had warned the Chief of Police that something awful might happen either to the man himself or to a suspect unless he was relieved of his duties.

All the time the lawyer was talking into the microphones he had latched onto me like I was a three year old that might run away, and I just stood and stared. Then when he had finished his speech about me the reporters told him that like his grandfather and his uncle he was sure to end up as governor but at a much earlier age.

At that the lawyer gave a big grin in front of the camera and waved good-bye and pushed me into his car.

I was terrified. The nice place I'd found to stay in wasn't mine any longer. My old nightmare was back—wondering how I could manage to eat and how much stealing I'd have to do to live from one day to the next.

The cameras and reporters had followed us.

A photographer asked me to turn down the car window beside me, and I overheard two men way in the back of the crowd talking. My ears are sharp. Papa always said I could hear thunder three states away. Above the congratulations and bubbly talk around me I heard one of those men in back say, "This is a bit too much, don't you think? Our Bat is showing himself the champion of the Senior Citizen now. He's already copped the teenyboppers and the under thirties using methods that ought to have disbarred him. He should have made the gardener and cleaning woman testify at the beginning, and from the first he should have checked into the policeman's history. There ought never to have been a case at all, much less a conviction. But Bat wouldn't have got any publicity that way. He had to do it in his own devious, spectacular fashion." The other man just kept nodding and saying after every sentence, "You're damned right."

Then we drove off and I didn't dare look behind me because I was so heartbroken over what I was leaving.

The lawyer took me to his office. He said he hoped I wouldn't mind a little excitement for the next few days. He had mapped out some public appearances for me. The next morning I was to be on an early television show. There was nothing to be worried about. He would be right beside me to help me just as he had helped me throughout my trouble. All that I had to say on the TV program was that I owed my freedom to him.

I guess I looked startled or bewildered because he hurried on to say that I hadn't been able to pay him a fee but that now I was able to pay him back

—not in money but in letting the public know about how he was the champion of the underdog.

I said I had been told that the court furnished lawyers free of charge to people who couldn't pay, and he said that was right, but his point was that I could repay him now by telling people all that he had done for me. Then he said the main thing was to talk over our next appearance on TV. He wanted to coach me in what I was going to say, but first he would go into his partner's office and tell him to take all the incoming calls and handle the rest of his appointments.

When the door closed after him I thought that he was right. I did owe my freedom to him. He was to blame for it. The smart alec. The upstart. Who asked him to butt in and snatch me out of my pretty room and the work I loved and all that delicious food?

It was the first time in my life I knew what it meant to despise someone. I hated him.

Before, when I was convicted of manslaughter, there was a lot of talk about malice aforethought and premeditated crime.

There wouldn't be any argument this time.

I hadn't wanted any harm to come to that policeman. But I did mean harm to come to this lawyer.

I grabbed up a letter opener from his desk and ran my finger along the blade and felt how sharp it was. I waited behind the door and when he walked through I gathered all my strength and stabbed him. Again and again and again.

Now I'm back where I want to be—in a nice place to stay.

PAUL BRODERICK'S MAN

by THOMAS WALSH

Flanagan was warned in good time. Which meant, following Paul Broderick's advice, that he was not stupid enough to retire abruptly on the pension. At such a time that action would have been markedly suspicious, and
so, in its place, a police-doctor friend of Broderick's put it down that
because of a bad back Captain Anthony Vincent Flanagan was granted a
necessary period of sick leave.

There were no hitches or awkward moments. There never were, with
Paul Broderick handling things. True enough, half a dozen men were questioned later by a Grand Jury, but they were all pretty small fish, as is usual
in such matters, and in the end the investigation fizzled out with nothing
changed. Captain Flanagan, of course, was unable to testify: medical reasons. The bad back confined him on strict bed rest to an upstate sanitarium,
and there he remained, again on Broderick's advice, until after the election
in the fall.

And after that there was nothing at all for Flanagan to worry about. He
had it made. A widower with four grown children, he sold the old brick
house in Bay Ridge where he had raised them all, bought himself a fine
new $12,000 car, and rented a small but elegantly luxurious apartment in
the East Seventies. His son Frank, the doctor, was set up in an impressive
midtown office; Flanagan bought a fine new house up in Westchester, cash
on the barrelhead, for his daughter Mamie and her family; and Paul Broderick, who always knew the right people, just as he had known where to
locate an obliging police doctor, enrolled Flanagan's younger son Jerry in
what was reputed to be the best law school in the country.

The only child for whom he was not permitted to buy anything was his
other daughter Maureen. Damned queer notions of life, that one. There
were times, Flanagan thought grimly, when it seemed to him that about all
she was suited for was the convent.

"But I really don't want anything," she tried to excuse herself when
Flanagan asked her straight out. "Jack and I have everything we need, Papa.
Don't worry about us."

"Have you now?" Flanagan demanded, his lips tightening noticeably. "Well, well, well. Isn't that just wonderful? Everything you need: a satisfied woman. You don't even want a check from me, then?"

"Nothing at all, sir," the husband chimed in; the damned stick of a social worker, whatever the hell they were, up in East Harlem. "But thank you very much."

Maureen, who knew Flanagan much better than her husband did, tried to pass it off lightly.

"Now don't get all huffy," she said. "Don't be that silly, Papa. All we mean—"

"Maybe I know what you mean," Flanagan said, turning his back curtly. "So don't bother explaining yourself. Good day to you both."

Yet the incident irritated him more than was sensible on his part. He had always been an extremely practical man, with very little patience for fine, sensitive consciences; but Maureen, after all, had always been his favorite, the very image of her dead mother.

But after that day, whenever they met at Mamie's house for Sunday dinner, or at Frank's, there was nothing at all of the old closeness between them—and that was more due to Flanagan himself, he had to admit, than to Maureen. In certain matters Flanagan had long been aware that he had the pride of the devil in him.

All right, then. Why bother his head about anyone now, even Maureen? He had everything in the world. No money worries; damned good health for his age; the finest of food and drink; and a drawerful of medals and commendations for meritorious police work. There was no one who could say a word about Flanagan, at least not openly. So right after Christmas, still on sick leave, he went to Florida for the winter. Very pleasant, too. Fine sunny weather; breakfast at poolside every day—lamb chops, hashed brown potatoes, and imported Canadian ale, or grilled kidneys and one or two Bloody Marys; and in the afternoons friends to be met, his or Broderick's, at the $50 Clubhouse window in Gulfstream Park.

Yes, Maureen would learn about life one day. The answer might be that he had always made things a little too easy for her. She had never been forced to fight her way up out of the dirt the way her father had; to see when an opportunity presented itself and to have brains enough to grab hold of it. But the hurt remained in him, deep down, and when her first child was born that spring, even though she named it Anthony after him, he went to see it one day when Frank took him, but never bought it a present of any kind—not a toy, not a feeding cup, not a rattle. Flanagan had never been a forgiving man. He had been struck to the heart once, and for no reason; he did not intend to place himself in that vulnerable a position ever again.

But one night not long afterward, in a well-known Third Avenue bar, he got himself into a tussle. There was a drunk who kept pushing at him, to get his place, and when Flanagan jabbed a resentful elbow into the man's side, the drunk muttered something to the tart with him.

Flanagan did not actually hear the remark, and yet he knew what it was; there was something about the drunk's sly contemptuous smile that informed Flanagan. So he yanked the drunk around, slapped him back and forth across the mouth, and pitched him headlong into the nearest wall.

Joe Martin, Mamie's husband, was much amused by that at the next family dinner.

"You'd better watch out," he grinned, "or they'll be throwing you into the ring with Muhammed Ali one of these days. I hear you knocked out three of his teeth. What did you hit the guy for anyway, Pop? What did he say to you?"

"What could he say?" Flanagan said, with a certain cold dangerous note in his voice. "Let's have your opinion, Joe. What do you think? What would you suggest, eh?"

"Oh, who cares?" Maureen said, moving behind him and putting both hands on his shoulders; so she knew, of course, and a lot quicker than any of them. "I wouldn't pay any attention to people like that, Papa. They simply don't know what they're talking about. When are you ever going to come up to the Bronx and see the baby again?"

So he did go up there a few days later and solemnly permitted little Anthony to curl a tiny paw around big Anthony's finger. But something had changed. It was a very effortful evening both for him and for Maureen. There fell long silences, and when they talked it seemed to Flanagan it was always about something that neither of them was thinking about.

He felt unaccountably depressed when he got home, whatever the reason might have been, and decided to have a drink for himself. In the end, however, it was more than one, and he woke up at four in the morning, very drunk, and still in his clothes, sitting up in the easy chair and with the television still blaring away.

He had never been much of a drinker before. Now he was. When fall came he had got into the habit of taking his first drink of the day even before breakfast, and had to buy three or four new suits for himself. The old ones had got too small around the waist. Always a trim, leanly built man, in good hard fettle, it shocked him to discover that he had put on something like 30 pounds.

Have to do something, Flanagan decided; time to get hold of myself. He must have forgotten who he was—a police captain, a respected police captain named Anthony Vincent Flanagan. There was no one who told him what to do. He told them. Yet, if that were true, why had he avoided facing up to Paul Broderick for month after month now? He was not afraid, surely; not Captain Flanagan. Then, damn it to hell, why was he letting it go on and on?

So next morning he shaved and dressed very carefully, had nothing to drink, and took a cab downtown to Broderick's office.

And with the old iron toughness and independence stiffening his back, he was the old Flanagan that day, blunt and forceful as a rifle bullet.

"I'll tell you what I came to see you about," he announced, as soon as they had shaken hands and sat down. "I'd like my job back. I'd say it's about time, Paul. Will you see to it, then? I'm still on the sick leave, you know."

"Thought you were enjoying yourself," Broderick murmured gently, pushing his fine Cuban cigars over. "Don't know any reason why you wouldn't be. You're a very lucky man, Anthony. You're a man who started out with nothing at all and who's got himself everything in the world now. Just think it over a little. You've put your time in. Get out on the pension. What's to prevent?"

"At my age?" Flanagan demanded, sitting forward an inch. "No, no, Paul. There's a year or two yet until I hit fifty. I don't care for the job itself, you understand. It's a dog's life, and I hate it. But I want to stop this loose talk that's going around concerning me. It's getting a bit bothersome. Even my own daughter Maureen seems to think—but of course that's no matter. I just want the job again. It's all I'm fitted for. So give me the plain answer, Paul. Yes or no?"

Broderick, sitting very low in the leather desk chair, did not look at Flanagan. He looked at the long cigar in his fingers.

"Then I'm sorry," he said at last, raising world-weary and palely untouchable blue eyes. "It's no, Anthony. It has to be. You're well out of it now, and I'd say you're a lot better off that way. I managed to smooth it out for all of us, or for most of us, but it was a damned close thing. I can see no point at all in stirring it up again. There's another Grand Jury in session now and they might get just a little curious as to why your back trouble came up at such a convenient time last year—convenient for you and for me, at any rate. Why risk that? Don't you see what a fool's game it would be?"

"Yes, I do see," Flanagan heard himself gritting. "At least I see what a damned fool I was. Don't forget that I could have come back and talked about that construction contract we each had a piece of—and if I had, there was no one in God's world who could have kept even you out of the box."

"True enough," Broderick agreed, nodding tranquilly. "We'd have gone down the drain, all right, the whole shooting match—and you with us."

The flesh under Flanagan's eyes darkened. Again he leaned forward, his big fist clenching itself tightly on the desk blotter.

"I'm telling you to fix it for me!" he declared thickly. "I'm owed that! I was a damned good police officer before I ever met up with you, but you ran the whole department then from behind the curtain—and you still do. To get on in the department I had to do what you asked me—or else I had to get out. Now is that true as the Book, or isn't it?"

"As far as it goes," Broderick admitted. "But you've forgotten one thing. For what you did for me you were paid—and paid damned well. We did business for a long time, and very satisfactory business. I understand you're worth something like three-quarters of a million dollars now. A great saver on your police salary, weren't you?"

"And if I am"—but with his voice beginning to shake—"how much are you worth? With your cab companies and your plumbing supply houses and your building construction firms? And with every one of them having first say on any city contract that ever comes up? I'm not denying that I did what I did. I'd have been the fool of the world to turn my back on the thing. But—"

"Yes, you would have been," Broderick agreed calmly once more. "But remember, Anthony, you made your own decision. Nobody forced you. Think of that for a moment, and don't stand there shouting at me in my own office like a mad bull. I won't have it. You're not your own man any more, and you haven't been for a good many years. You're Paul Broderick's man, and you'll do as you're told here, as you always have. Is that quite clear now?"

"Me?" Flanagan said, on his feet suddenly and gripping the edge of the desk with both hands. "Is that it? Your man, am I? A Broderick office boy, to fetch and carry for you? Well, by God—"

He moved so abruptly that he knocked over the inkwell. Broderick clicked his tongue and rang for the girl.

"My fine rug," he mourned. "Damn it, Anthony, what the hell is the matter with you? I'll never get that spot out of it now. Come back and see me again when you've thought out this business. I'll put you down for lunch at the club next Tuesday. And then we'll—"

But Flanagan, shoving the girl to one side, had lunged out through the office doorway. Down in the street a flood of bright summer sunshine burst over him, but had he come down in the elevator moments ago or had he walked? It was impossible for him to remember. Broderick's man! Not Flanagan's man, not for years now—never Flanagan's man. But Broderick's. Was that true? Could it be true?

In the $12,000 car he sat motionless, trying to decide on the answer. Only there was a numbed thickness in his head, presenting to him not steady and consecutive reasoning, but scraps and fragments. You never knew what was really being asked of you the first time—that was one fragment. You were only a sergeant then, and a man came around to the precinct house shortly before Christmas with his overcoat pockets full of envelopes. An envelope for the sergeant, an envelope for the lieutenant, an envelope for the captain, and all with Season's Greetings from Paul Broderick. So you had taken your envelope, as the others had taken theirs, and from then on, wherever Broderick's big black Cadillac was left parked, you looked out for it.

Soon it was "Good morning, Mr. Broderick, sir," to the great man, and then it was a couple of tickets pressed into your hand for the next Yankee game at the Stadium, or the Ranger game that night at the Garden. Mr. Broderick liked your style, he said, and one day, when he noticed a dent in your old jalopy, he had one of his men take it downtown to his taxicab garage. Might as well let them hammer that dent out, you were told, only when you got the car back the next day, they had repainted the whole thing. They had also put in new slipcovers and an expensive FM radio and substituted whitewall tires. They had tuned the motor and put in new sparkplugs, a new air filter, and a new fly belt. The old jalopy ran like a charm and looked like a new car.

"Just between us," Broderick had said, "I like your style, Anthony. You've got a good level head on your shoulders, and you've done me many a favor. What's holding your name up on the lieutenants' list? I think I'd better find out about that. I'll let you know in a few days. The bill for your car? What bill? What are you talking about? Favor for favor, that's all. I've got a friend at court now, and so do you. So let's keep it that way, eh? How was the game last night?"

And it had been kept that way. After that there had always been a friend at court for Mr. Broderick in times of need, and also, since Sergeant Flanagan made lieutenant in another month, the fair exchange had been no robbery. Now and again a stock tip, always a good stock tip; later on a chance to buy in as a silent partner in one of the Broderick Construction firms a few days before it landed a $38,000,000 city contract; but never even the hint of Broderick's man, or not until today.

But today, if you had never realized it before, or had insisted stubbornly to yourself that you didn't realize it, the thing had come out in plain words, the plainest possible. Not his own man, Flanagan remembered—and not for years. Was it possible? And at last, forcing himself to look back, he saw that it was not only possible, it was true.

He drove home with that queer numbness still inside his head, parked his car in the apartment-house garage, went upstairs, and began to drink. He drank steadily for eight days, the first time in his life, and came out of it to find himself in a private hospital suffering from acute alcoholism, with Maureen crying beside him and holding his hand.

And that shamed him. When he was permitted home again, he emptied every bottle of whiskey in the place, and to get through the hours of the day in one fashion or another forced himself to take long walks, even late-at-night walks, on the many occasions when he could not sleep. Broderick's man? Never! Not if he fought it out now. There was a way back for him. He had only to find the right door, wherever it was. Now he knew. Now he could understand how true were those couple of lines from Omar Khayyam. How did they go?

"I wonder often what the Vintners buy
One half so precious as the stuff they sell."

And what had Anthony Vincent Flanagan sold? Himself? His work, his manhood, his pride, his reason for living? He knew now, and had to find the way back. There must still be a chance to start all over again for himself, to reshape his life. That was all he had left now, and it was necessary to hold fast to it. The way back existed. But where could he find it? Precisely where had he left it behind him?

He did not know. He had to search. So sometimes very late at night he walked desolate and deserted areas along the river, in the same district that Captain Flanagan had once held in the palm of his hand, with a power almost of life and death over it. The dark alleys; the gloomy warehouse walls on each side; the high coldly indifferent street lamps; the sneaking wind-driven shadows. What did Captain Flanagan expect there? What was he looking for? But still he knew, somehow or other. Patience, it came to him. He had been a man in those days and he would be again. Here was the way back—right here waiting for him. Only where and when?

On the night he found out he had stopped briefly to rest, looking out over the river, when a prowl car pulled in to the curb beside him.

"Hey, old-timer," a voice said out of the passenger side. "What are you doing in this neighborhood night after night? It's a hell of a section to get mugged in, in case you don't know. What's your name, Pop? Where do you live? Just come over here to the car now and speak up. You've got us interested. We've been watching you every night for the past week."

"Where do I live?" Flanagan repeated. "Not around here. How are you, Boudreau? How have you been, Mahoney?"

Boudreau got out of the car at that, peering more closely.

"Gee," he said then. "Captain Flanagan! But you got so old-looking—or—I mean—well, I just didn't happen to recognize you, Captain, not with your back turned. How you been, Captain? Can we give you a lift someplace? Where you headed for?"

But Captain Flanagan did not know that himself. He got into the prowl car, however, and all at once he seemed to be back in time about 20 years or more. This car might have been the same car he had known then, and it might have been a patrolman named Flanagan who was back of the steering wheel, not Harry Mahoney; just as it might have been Flanagan's partner Bert Bailey in the passenger seat, not Phil Boudreau. Flanagan and Bailey had been partners then, but there came a time when only Flanagan had come back from another spell of night duty.

They had chanced upon a liquor-store holdup in East Seventy-ninth Street. A night much like this, Flanagan remembered, with the same kind of clear lazy rain trickling down the car windows, and then, beyond it, three men suddenly bursting out of the liquor store with their guns waving. Bailey, always the quicker of them, was out at once, shouting the necessary warning; but it had been an unheeded warning, and even yet Flanagan could see the sudden tiny spurt of flame over there in the liquor-store doorway. The bullet had knocked Bailey back onto the car, spinning him around on it, and Flanagan could see again the sudden surprised look on his face, the kind of frightened and realizing half smile that had followed it. Bailey had touched himself on the chest, then looked at his hand. The smile had wavered.

"Holy God," he had said. "I'm hit bad. I feel all—they got me. I'm going, Tony. So long, fella. Tell Agnes and the kid—"

Then he had pitched forward, and a young Flanagan had been out of the car and after the three men. One he had dropped right away, with the first shot he fired; the second he had got around the street corner; and the third he had trapped in a dark alleyway.

But the alleyway had not frightened young Flanagan, nor had the bullets that had whistled out of it past his head. There was a company to which young Flanagan belonged, and so there was a thing that had to be done by him. He had not thought about it at all. He had just raced ahead, into the dark alleyway, and had done it. But of course all that was a long time ago. Oh, yes, old Flanagan remembered. Twenty years or more.

"We were talking about you the other night at the precinct," Harry Mahoney told him. "They give us a new guy that ain't too bad, but lemme tell you he ain't no Tony Flanagan, Captain. How you feeling these days? You coming back on the job soon?"

"I don't know," Flanagan replied slowly. "It's pretty hard to say, Harry. But I've been thinking, since I've got my time in—" Outside the window Bailey's terrified white face wisped away under a curl of three-in-the-morning fog, so that Flanagan could no longer see it even when he brushed mist from the glass. But it had been there, surely. Flanagan had seen it as plain as—

"Can't blame you a bit," Boudreau said. "Get the hell out of the department while you still got a lot of good years to expect, that's the way I see it. You got it made, Captain. You got everything in the world now, so why not enjoy it, huh?"

"Right on," Mahoney agreed. "But I got to take a break down at that diner, Phil. Give me a couple of minutes, huh? I'll be right back."

They swung in to the curb and Mahoney trotted off. Boudreau got out, too, yawning and stretching. Then, glancing along the other side of the street, he suddenly froze.

"Look at that car," he told Flanagan. "Over there by the loading dock, Captain. Black Dodge, isn't it?"

And it was, Flanagan could see, twisting his head around in the car to look at it.

"But I bet," Boudreau said, hurriedly checking his revolver holster, "it isn't the same license plate. Of course. They change that on every job they pull. Smart cookies, these fellas. They've been hitting the warehouses around here for the past six months. Guess I better make a quick check over there, Captain. Tell Harry, will you? He said he'd be right back."

Boudreau moved quickly and quietly off, into the deep shadows around the loading dock and the parked Dodge. Flanagan stayed where he was. He had better, something whispered to him. It would be time enough to help after Boudreau had made the identification. Now he would only be in the way. His wristwatch showed him that it was 4:25, and the street ahead shone emptily, with a black glisten of pavement, under the arc lights. Even on the elevated highway down at the end of it, only an occasional car whizzed by.

Flanagan, sitting edgily forward on the back seat, felt a sudden cold prickle along the spine. Was he afraid? Captain Flanagan? There was a company to which he belonged, as he had belonged to it more than 20 years ago outside that liquor store, so not to worry now. Still, he had to admit that he felt damned queer—a brief dryness in the throat, a slight quiver of the arm muscles, a sudden unsteadiness in the way his heart had begun to beat. What the hell bothered him? It could not be fear. It had never been that before. Then what?

He got out of the prowl car. Up on the highway a night-hawk taxi raced by, but around him all other sounds seemed to be cushioned in thick velvet. He rubbed his mouth, roughly passing the back of his hand over it three or four times, and moved ahead hurriedly to shelter himself in a garage doorway. But he was only obeying a proper caution here, that was all. Flanagan had attended to matters like this before and by God he could attend to them again!

It was annoying, however, not to be sure of what was going on. He could see no one, not even Boudreau, and not even a small telltale sound could be heard anywhere. What had happened to Harry Mahoney? Why wasn't he back yet? But trust a rotten time-serving little cringer of that type. He knew well when and where to make himself scarce. Let Flanagan and Boudreau attend to this matter. Mahoney would do the sensible thing. He would post himself down in the corner diner, safe and secure there, until he knew it was all over.

The thought of it brought up in Flanagan a wild surge of fury. Damn it, why had he met them tonight? Why had he been stupid enough to get into the car with them? Trapped now—and it might be, very soon, a bullet in the head for his pains. No matter then that Tony Flanagan had got everything in God's world for himself. Dead and destroyed here in the gutter if he so much as poked his nose out of the garage doorway. Keep it in, then. Look out for himself. Who the hell else? Where was Boudreau? What was he doing?

It was impossible to say. He must be moving along in the shadows, silently, with great care, and peering vainly for him. Flanagan became aware of a rapid and persistent tic under the lower lid of his right eye. He had his police revolver out, and it seemed to him that his hand clung to it with desperate tightness, as if his fingers had become frozen in that position, as if from the shoulder down his whole arm had become paralyzed. Sudden cold sweat broke out on his forehead and on his chest. Why?

The thing was incomprehensible. When had Tony Flanagan been afraid of anyone or anything in the world? It had to be only a stupid idea that had come into his head—that he stood all alone now, with no one to care what happened to him, because there was a company of which he was no longer a member. He felt the sweat drop into his eyes at that and shook his head savagely. Was that why, more than 20 years ago, he had been able to plunge into that dark alley after a man with a gun without even thinking about it —and why tonight he could not move even a step out of this doorway? Once there had been the fellowship of the department for him—but tonight there was not. Could that be the answer?

No, never! He had lost nothing. What he had to do here was simple enough—follow Boudreau and no matter what happened, stand shoulder to shoulder with him. But there was an open area in the street before he could reach that loading dock where the Dodge was parked, and Flanagan discovered that he could not force himself out into it. He simply could not. Twice he tried. Twice, as if by the grasp of a physical hand from behind, he was pulled back.

He lifted his head, eyes squeezed shut tightly, an agonized expression twitching the corners of his lips. But he did not try to move out into the open a third time. He felt a shudder deep inside him, and then, little by little, felt it ripple down through his whole body. He did nothing. He just waited.

"What is it?"—and Harry Mahoney's anxious voice was just beside him. "Where's Phil, Captain? What's going on?"

Flanagan, averting his face, managed to gesture with the gun—up ahead —and as he did so a door rasped open at the loading dock. No light was turned on, but four men could be seen gathered now in the loading doorway. One of them jumped down quickly and opened the car trunk. The three on the platform, deftly and rapidly, in perfect silence, passed down carton after carton. Then one by one the three men jumped down also, not bothering to close the loading door after them. But Boudreau used his head. He was one against four, so far as he knew, and it must have seemed to him that about the only chance he had was to let them get into the car before he revealed himself.

"Hold it right there!" Flanagan heard. "I got you covered. Don't start that car!"

But they did. Apparently they started it with the gas pedal down to the floor, rocketing it straight ahead, and when Boudreau ran out into the street, gun drawn, they fired at him. Yellow flares as tiny as fireflies spat at him, and Boudreau was hit. He spun around in the headlights, staggered to one side, and crashed head-on into an areaway railing.

Flanagan saw all that, felt the cold sweat once more, and stayed right where he was. Harry Mahoney did not. At the first shot he was out in the street, on one knee, firing back, and Flanagan found himself making an altogether foolish attempt to force his body back. The car rushed on drunkenly at him, windshield shattered, and for the fraction of a moment he could see the two men in the front seat and the two in the back. So they would all have been sitting ducks, in that breath of time under the street light, for Tony Flanagan who twice in earlier years had made the police rifle team.

But he did not fire at them. All he did was to fall to his knees and cross his two arms over his face. It was Harry Mahoney who never gave an inch, who fired a second time, a third time, a fourth time as the black Dodge roared by, straight across the street, and smashed into a parked truck. There was a squeal of tires, a whining of brakes, then the crash and then stinging quiet. The Dodge lay on its side. One of the doors had popped open. An arm reached out of it, groped around vaguely, and flopped back.

Harry Mahoney, letting out a long shaky breath, swung around to Flanagan.

"You all right?" he demanded. "You didn't get hit, did you?"

"No, fine," Flanagan croaked. Still on his knees, he lowered his arms dazedly and realized that he had dropped his police revolver. Mahoney retrieved it out of the gutter and ran down to check on Boudreau.

"Not too bad," he yelled back. "Just in the shoulder, Captain. But we had a pretty good ruckus there for a while, didn't we?"

Flanagan did not answer him. He was peering ahead down the long narrowing street, empty and rain-washed under the street lights, and it seemed to him that he could see a figure dwindling away down there, getting smaller and smaller, farther and farther away; a figure all by itself. It did not turn its head to him, but he knew who it was. It was Anthony Vincent Flanagan.

He pushed himself up dumbly. But that couldn't be true. He needed another chance. He wanted one! It had not been a deliberate thing. He had just failed to understand in time that the bargain with Broderick had been all or nothing. So listen up there. Please, please! There was more to his life still than walking into a dead end. There was a company that still existed and Flanagan was still a member. Even if just now he—

"Better sit down in the car," Mahoney suggested. "You look kind of shaken up, Captain. Let me give you a hand."

But Flanagan backed off at that, shaking his head quickly and thrusting out both arms. There was no room in the prowl car for Tony Flanagan, it came to him; in that company his place was now forever forfeited. A certain problem had arisen. So he turned blindly, before the others would get there, and with one arm still extended, as if groping, he lurched around the street corner.

After that he was all alone. He moved hurriedly in whatever direction the pavement took him. He knew what he had become at last. He was the ex-police captain who had got everything in the world for himself—and who, in return, had been clever enough to trade off for that nothing more vitally needful to a man than his honor.

WHEN NOTHING MATTERS
by *FLORENCE V. MAYBERRY*

It was a long tiring walk from the top of Mount Carmel to the shore of the sea, but Solange had taken it again, as she had for the past week, every day since Thorwald was gone. Gone. No longer her husband.

The tiring was good. She yearned for a fatigue so sodden and compelling that she would sleep, stop thinking.

She crossed the highway, stumbled over rough ground to the railroad tracks, stepped over them down to the sandy beach. She kicked off her loafers, rolled up her slacks, and let the waves lick her feet. She shaded her eyes, gazing at the water. Near the shore, the Mediterranean was a brilliant turquoise. A few meters out it deepened into dark blue, almost cobalt. In the distance a white ship, contrasting sharply against the sea, moved slant-wise from the horizon toward Haifa's harbor.

Perhaps she should take a ship, go to Greece, Italy, America. Anywhere but Haifa and Israel.

She faced southward, in the direction of Tel Aviv. No ship to be seen there, only the empty horizon. "Like me. Empty. Alone with itself," Solange said aloud. Vaguely she realized that it was aloud, and vaguely she was troubled because it was. For the past week, and only for the past week, she had been holding conversations with herself. "It's because I'm alone. Alone!" she shouted at the sea. The rush and thud of the waves against the shore blotted up the sound, leaving her even more lonely.

She moved away from the soothing touch of the warm sea, rubbed the sand from her damp feet, slipped on her shoes, and continued on down the beach, past a service station, past the public beach, on and on. When she considered she was sufficiently tired she crossed the highway to a weedy space of ground where an Arab shepherd guarded a straggle of black goats and began the long slow climb up the steep height of Carmel. "Surely you'll sleep tonight," she assured herself.

Short of the mountain top she turned along a narrow slanting lane, went down a flight of stairs past terraced gardens, turned the key in the lock of her ground-floor apartment, shut the door behind her. She hesitated, not wanting to go farther into the empty room. "Empty," she said aloud. "Not even a cat or a dog or a bird. Nothing but you." She looked at herself in the hall mirror, watched her mouth twist in a grimace, its bitterness intensified by contrast with the delicate blossoms of the potted plant beneath the mirror. On impulse she picked up the plant, walked through the living room to the window area, pushed aside the glass of one window, and hurled the pot into the deep wadi below. "Nothing," she repeated.

She went to the kitchen, thinking: *boil the water, put in the filter paper, measure the coffee, pour the water, drink it and you'll feel better. Anything else, Solly—a poached egg? No? Corn flakes? Yes, corn flakes. Eat.*

"Why?" she asked.

She removed the bowl she had filled with brown flakes and the bluish Israeli milk from the table, carried it to the sink, poured its contents into the drain. She returned to the living room and lay down on the sofa, her face pressed against an embroidered Indian pillow. Its little metal mirrors scratched her cheek as though to sharpen memory of when she and Thorwald had bought the pillow covers in India, almost in the shadow of the Taj Mahal.

Almost as if she were taking it again, the long taxi drive from New Delhi to Agra ribboned through her mind. Passing crews of women in dull-colored saris as they scrabbled in dirt to build a highway, male supervisors idly watching. Past painted elephants, monkeys chattering in trees above strange long protuberances that their driver said were birds' nests, dangling from branches to protect their eggs from marauders. At Thorwald's request the taxi stopped and laughingly he pulled her toward a painted elephant, insisted she clamber onto it and have her picture taken. "You looked like a princess riding to meet your lover," he said, once they were back in the taxi.

"I am," she said confidently, snuggling close to him. "And I've met him." How long had they been married then? Six months? No, a year but it was still like a honeymoon, traveling continually to Thorwald's engineering assignments in exotic, wonderful places. That was what he liked, a constant change, and so did she as long as he was with her.

That day they had stopped at village rest stations where men charmed snakes out of baskets, where scraggly Himalayan bears danced pathetically to reedy music, where men wandered casually in and out of open-doored relief sheds. The heat throbbed over the land and crescendoed into a blinding, staggering white blaze as they walked past reflecting pools toward the scalding noon beauty of the Taj Mahal. It was so hot she thought she might faint, and she clung to Thorwald to steady herself against the swirling vertigo in her head. He hurried her forward, fleeing from the heat into the shadowed protection of the exquisite mausoleum that the Shad Jahan had built for the wife he loved so dearly.

She had gazed, fascinated, at the jeweled final token of adoration a king
had given his beloved, yearning not for it but for the love that caused it.
"Thorwald, if you were king and I had died, would you build me a Taj
like this?"

"Of course," he said easily. "Now let's find a restaurant. I'm famished."
As they walked back past the pools he added, "Jewels are easy to give when
they are only promises. Even a poor man can give them."

And she had answered, "But promises like that *are* jewels."

She sat up and asked the empty room, "Are they?" She walked again to
the window to distract the memory, but it would not leave. It kept reeling
on, like a film, with the rest of that day's journey as they drove back to
New Delhi, traveling the same road, past the same houses, trees with monkeys and birds. But the late golden sun changed the scene, made it into a
new road, a new country and people. Now the village women were clean
and fresh, dressed in brilliant saris, like butterflies freed from the chrysalis of
the dusty morning's work. They walked gracefully beside the highway,
copper pots of water balanced on their heads, calling to children, laughing
with neighbors, their staccato chatter rising like fragmented music. Happy,
serene, gentle.

But then, so soon after, she had become tearful, almost hysterical from
the awful proof that happiness is fragile, fleeting. Ahead of them a crowd
was gathered on the highway. The taxi slowed, then veered sharply to
hasten past the group with its terrible center. A body's crumpled figure was
flat on the road, face down, one leg askew, a jagged white bone glistening
from mangled flesh and torn trousers, the road beneath him streaked red.

"Don't cry," Thorwald had soothed. "Never waste life by crying over
things you can't do anything about. Where shall we have dinner tonight?
At the hotel, or go adventuring?"

Her stomach had turned at the thought of food, but she forced down the
repugnance. This was their continuing honeymoon, it must be kept happy,
not spoiled. She leaned against him, drawing on his cool control. For yes,
Thorwald was as controlled as the engineering graphs he produced for his
company. She determined to learn from him, to become pragmatic, objective.

She had not learned.

"Solly, you're all emotion, no control. And I might add, that's damned
wearing," he had told her a week ago. "No, I will not tell you who she is,
I'll not have you messing about with some crazy, useless confrontation. It
wouldn't change a thing, only make everything more difficult. I've told
you before and I tell you again, don't waste strength on things you can't
change. Because frankly, Solly, you haven't got what it takes to change
what I'm going to do."

But she couldn't stop trying; she was driven to know about the woman who was taking Thorwald away from her. "Thorwald, what is she that I'm not? Prettier? Poised, controlled the way you want me to be? I'll change, truly I will, but don't leave me, Thorwald."

"Oh, God, not that again," he had answered. Turned his back on her. Zipped up his shaving kit, stuffed it in his travel case, snapped the case shut. Snapped her out of his life.

New York. Thorwald's head office. Sooner or later Thorwald would be intending to go to his New York office. "I'll call Simon, that's the thing to do," she said aloud. She sat again on the sofa, reached for the telephone on the low teak table beside it, slowly dialed a familiar number. A secretary in New York answered. "This is Mrs. Thorwald Jensen, calling from Israel," Solange said. "Please connect me right away with Mr. Simon, it's important."

The voice of Simon, Thorwald's chief, came over the wire as clearly as though he was on a telephone in the next apartment. "Hello, hello? Solange? Good to hear your voice. Where is Thorwald anyway, we've been expecting him every day. We need a briefing on that Negev Desert job. Here in New York? No, no sign of him, I said we're waiting for him."

"But he said New York." Her mouth was dry. "I thought . . . I haven't heard . . . where do you suppose . . ."

"Take it easy, Solange, don't go getting upset," Simon was saying. "You ought to know by now how crazy survey engineers can be. Any place they land is home and they never think anybody should be notified, especially bosses and wives. Thorwald's probably stopped off in London to catch some shows, yeah, I'd bet on London. I'll put in a call to the hotel he usually stays at, or have you called there already? No? Well, leave it to me, I'll track him down. Listen, go out on the town yourself. Where are you? Tel Aviv?"

"Haifa," she said. And for no particular reason she added, "It's a quiet town."

"Go to a movie," Simon said. "And listen, the minute I catch Thorwald I'll have him phone you."

A few more soothing words. A click. And she was alone with herself again. Thorwald call her? Never.

She lay on the sofa until the summer sky changed from afternoon brightness to twilight, to dark, and even after that for a long time. "Why not a movie?" she finally asked herself. She rose, chose a light shawl, and went outdoors. As she walked up the stone stairs, from far behind her came the ecstatic hungering cries of animals in the zoo located at the head of the wadi in Gan Ha'em, the Mothers' Park. She shivered, an unbidden primitive fear tightening the muscles of her back. She moved rapidly up the steep lane, pursued by the sounds, gasped with relief as she reached the sidewalk and saw the piercing headlights of cars speeding by.

A last faint, almost laughing howl came from the animals. Then silence. The silence and the howling told her it was too late for the movie. Each night, for what reason she did not know, the animals cried briefly, at almost ten o'clock. And again in the dark early morning before dawn. Not feeding hours surely. Perhaps a check by caretakers; it didn't matter, did it? Nothing mattered, Thorwald was gone.

Even though she decided against the movie she continued up the steeply sloping street toward Central Carmel, the clustered shopping district on the crest of Mount Carmel. There she moved among laughing, noisy groups of youth clustered in front of restaurants, ice-cream stands, fellafel counters. Although so different, yet it made her think of other crowds of youth on Shaftsbury and Piccadilly in London where she and Thorwald had strolled after the theater, window-gazing at shops she might visit the following day. Standing in front of a china shop choosing table settings she would never have. How could birds of passage possess china, or silver, having no home other than hotels, leased apartments, pensions? A few weeks here, a few months there, never a year, then off on another exciting journey, the adventure of change that Thorwald craved.

"I'll go, I'll leave Haifa, I can't stay here any longer," she told herself. Then clapped her hand over her mouth, fearful to be noticed talking to herself.

She walked swiftly back down the mountainside, running the last few steps into her apartment. She turned the key and leaned, panting, against the door.

In the night, near morning, she heard the animals cry again and she moaned as she struggled to recapture sleep. With eyes staring into the dark she tried to imagine how the woman, Thorwald's unknown love, might look. Dark hair and violet eyes, like a movie actress? No, Thorwald liked blondes; that was why she had lightened her own red-brown hair, had become a titian blonde. She fretted with the idea of perhaps getting up, turning on the light to see again how well her titian hair contrasted with sage-green eyes. "You're unreal," Thorwald had said when he first saw the change of color. "Absolutely not real, Solly, I must be imagining you. Eyes of an Egyptian cat and hair of an angel. Come here, give us a kiss."

He had loved her then. What had changed him?

Face it, be realistic: Thorwald was in love with change, always another project, another country, and now another woman. Sameness bored him. On the go, here, there, anywhere, everywhere.

"God, tell me, where is he now?"

She sat up, arms clasping her shoulders in a comforting hug. She rocked to and fro in a terrible wrestling with God, "Tell me, God, tell me!" Then fell back on the pillow, exhausted, smothered by the dark and the loneliness.

In the morning she tried to eat, couldn't, only drank coffee. She opened the utility cupboard, found the key to her storeroom, picked up a flashlight, went into the open foyer and down the basement stairs. In the storeroom she surveyed the travel cases, selected one of medium size, and carried it upstairs.

She went to the telephone and called their travel agent. "This is Mrs. Thorwald Jensen. I want to make a flight reservation."

"Shalom, shalom, Mrs. Jensen. You going to join Mr. Jensen? By the way, was he able to make his connection in Europe?"

Connection? To New York? Or to some other place where the woman would be waiting to greet him? *I never looked at his ticket. I should have looked at his ticket. I could only think that he was leaving me.*

"He hasn't cabled," she said. "But make my ticket just like Mr. Jensen's, please." *Perhaps I'll find the woman and when I do I'll—*

"Very good. When will you want to leave? And would you like me to make a hotel reservation in Mexico City? Oh, but of course, your husband will be taking care of that."

"Yes. Yes, of course." Mexico City! Then the woman would be there, otherwise Thorwald would have gone directly to New York. "And I want to leave right away, tomorrow. I'll call for the ticket this afternoon."

The arrangements finished, she went into the bedroom with the travel case. "How can I take everything?" she asked, helpless at the thought. It was a leased furnished apartment but the paintings, the books and ornaments were hers. And all the clothes she had delighted to preen herself in before Thorwald. What good had that been?

She sat on the bed beside the case, dully contemplating its limited size. She rose, took the key and flashlight again.

In the foyer that opened directly onto the terraced garden she halted abruptly, startled to see a small deer run across the flagged walkway. Its hoofs spattered on the graveled path which bordered the flower-strewn terrace. In swift succession behind the deer ran a stocky mustached man and two lean youths in work clothes. Tree branches thrashed against the building as the three vanished around the building, their pounding footsteps crescendoing into heavy thuds as they leaped down the last terrace onto the sharply descending sides of the wadi.

She hurried down the basement stairs, picked her way along the narrow hallway beside the row of storerooms to the door that opened onto the side garden. From there she went to the edge of the embankment above the wadi. Dry brush cracked in the canyonlike depths below. She saw, far down, the deer dodging among trees, leaping ahead of its pursuers. *It has run away from the zoo,* she thought, *escaped its prison. Did Thorwald do that?*

She began to tremble.

One of the youths left the group and turned back along the wadi's floor toward the zoo located at its end. She stayed to see how the search progressed, but soon the deer and the other two men vanished, concealed by brush and trees. She sat on the ground, waiting, watching. After a time the youth who had returned to the zoo came back with a second older man who carried a gun, an unusual kind of gun which she recognized from a safari trip in Africa she had taken with Thorwald. A gun to shoot tranquilizing darts.

She felt a momentary pang for the fleeing animal, then hardened against it. "It shouldn't run away, it's safer in the zoo, it's not good to run away."

She rose and went back to the storeroom. There she hesitated beside a large travel case, left it untouched, then chose a smaller one and a duffel bag.

Back upstairs the thought of the deer and the men in the wadi clung and troubled her. She went to the wide living-room window which faced the deep sprawling ravine, pushed aside the glass to let in the air, pulled a chair close, and sat down to see if the searchers would succeed. Shortly before noon one youth, carrying the tranquilizer gun, hurried up the wadi toward the zoo. Behind him, moving slowly with the weight of the sleeping beast, were the man who had brought the gun and the other youth. The first man, the one with the mustache, was not with them.

Solange stood up and went to the bedroom.

In late afternoon she decided she was finished with packing. Too bad about the paintings, the fragile ceramics. But she could return; there were months left on the lease. Only she wouldn't, not ever, never see her charming collections again; too bad, too bad, everything was too bad.

She changed clothes, walked to the shopping district. There she closed out her bank account and picked up her ticket that was made out for Mexico City. Yes, surely the woman would be there. Somehow she would find that woman. And she would kill her.

Back home she remembered that she had not eaten all day. She went to the kitchen, prepared tea and toast, thought vaguely about poaching an egg but gave up the idea. She took her tea and toast into the living room, sat before the window, nibbled and sipped as she stared into the wadi. Not seeing it, seeing only the pictures in her mind, she drifted into sleep.

The excited wailing of the zoo animals awakened her in the night. She switched on the light, looked at her watch. Ten o'clock. Why did the animals cry at this hour? Were they lonely? Was the deer awake too? Or perhaps it was dead, never to join again in the nightly excitement of the animals.

She telephoned a taxi company, made arrangements to be picked up early in the morning. Then she bathed, carefully made up her face, blotting out the dark circles under her eyes, outlining her lips, filling between the lines with provocative color. She assessed the mouth Thorwald had kissed so many times. The vulnerable mouth of a baby, he had said, tantalizing with the cat eyes and the angelic hair. *Thorwald, how could you have left me?*

Briefly the eyes in the mirror flamed, then became shuttered.

When she finished dressing she did not lie down but sat in the chair waiting for morning.

Before dawn she carried the two cases up the steep lane to the sidewalk, tucked them against shrubbery, and returned for the duffel bag. Back again in the open entranceway she hesitated uncertainly, looked down the basement stairs, waited, thinking. Then she returned to the apartment and found the storage-room key.

When she came back up the basement stairs she was carrying the large travel case. She took both it and the duffel bag up to the street to wait for the taxi.

At Lod Airport she joined the passenger queue going through security check. When her turn came she lifted the smaller cases to the checking table. *Did you pack these yourself, did anyone give you anything to carry, did anyone other than yourself have access to these, give you any gifts to transport?* Yes, no, no, no. The girl security officer expertly prodded and lifted clothing, felt inside shoes, tested bottles, finally closed the cases.

"You have another case, Madam. Please lift it to the table."

Solange lifted the large case. "Open it, please." She did. The girl's voice sharpened. "Are you certain you packed this case yourself?"

"Yes."

"But these are men's clothes. Is your husband with you?"

Involuntarily Solange started to look behind her, caught herself. "No. They are my husband's clothes. He left earlier. I'm taking this case to him."

The girl hesitated, then systematically lifted out the clothes, searching pockets, unrolling socks, unzipping the shaving kit, squeezing the shaving-cream tube, turning the razor's handle. Finally she said, "It is all right. Thank you."

Solange went to the ticket check-in station, paid the excess-baggage charge, went upstairs, through customs and the body-and-hand-luggage search. Inside the departure lounge she bought the English-language newspaper, then wandered unseeing past jewelry and souvenir displays to the exit gate. Almost time, almost time to leave Israel, almost time . . .

Her flight was announced and she filed down to the bus, onto the plane, found her seat beside the window. Opened the newspaper. Breath whistled through clenched teeth with her sharp intake of air. Even though the headlines were small, the article sprang at her from the middle of the front page. *Body of American Oil Official Found on Mount Carmel.*

The deer had found him. Staggered by the dart it had floundered into the brush and fallen almost on the body mutilated by wild animals almost beyond recognition. Except for the airline ticket, found in the torn and scattered clothing and finally pieced together, it would have been difficult to identify the man. But when all the ticket fragments were rejoined, there it was: Thorwald Jensen, destination New York via Mexico City.

The plane taxied slowly to the runway. Its engines revved, then quieted as a white car sped toward it. Two men got out of the car, motioned authoritatively at a truck which hurried forward. Workmen leaped from it, rolled mobile stairs against the airliner's side. A stewardess unlocked the exit door.

She waited, hands gripped together, eyes closed as scenes of that last night with Thorwald skimmed through her mind. The frightening, furtive struggle to push and pull Thorwald down the basement stairs, past the storerooms, into the garden. Then along the garden path, rolling him down the wadi's sharp incline, every cracking twig an alarm, every lighted window discovery.

The exit door opened and the two men entered the plane. As they started down the aisle she rehearsed in her mind what she would tell them. The truth, only the truth. *He was straightening his tie before the bathroom mirror. I came behind him, begging him again not to leave me. He smiled and shook his head, not even bothering to answer, as though what I said had no importance, merely a whim to be smiled at. I already had the knife, held behind me. I struck. Hard. It was terrible. Awful. I begged him to come alive. But he couldn't. I knew that, and I was terrified. So I took him into the wadi.*

As the men stopped in the aisle beside her row she stood up, almost in welcome.

THIS IS DEATH

by *DONALD E. WESTLAKE*

It's hard not to believe in ghosts when you are one. I hanged myself in a fit of truculence—stronger than pique, but not so dignified as despair—and regretted it before the thing was well begun. The instant I kicked the chair away I wanted it back, but gravity was turning my former wish to its present command; the chair would not right itself from where it lay on the floor, and my 193 pounds would not cease to urge downward from the rope thick around my neck.

There was pain, of course, quite horrible pain centered in my throat, but the most astounding thing was the way my cheeks seemed to swell. I could barely see over their round red hills, my eyes staring in agony at the door, *willing* someone to come in and rescue me, though I knew there was no one in the house, and in any event the door was carefully locked. My kicking legs caused me to twist and turn, so that sometimes I faced the door and sometimes the window, and my shivering hands struggled with the rope so deep in my flesh I could barely find it and most certainly could not pull it loose.

I was frantic and terrified, yet at the same time my brain possessed a cold corner of aloof observation. I seemed now to be everywhere in the room at once, within my writhing body but also without, seeing my frenzied spasms, the thick rope, the heavy beam, the mismatched pair of lit bedside lamps throwing my convulsive double shadow on the walls, the closed locked door, the white-curtained window with its shade drawn all the way down. *This is death,* I thought, and I no longer wanted it, now that the choice was gone forever.

My name is—was—Edward Thornburn, and my dates are 1938–1977. I killed myself just a month before my fortieth birthday, though I don't believe the well-known pangs of that milestone had much if anything to do with my action. I blame it all (as I blamed most of the errors and failures of my life) on my sterility. Had I been able to father children my marriage would have remained strong, Emily would not have been unfaithful to me, and I would not have taken my own life in a final fit of truculence.

The setting was the guestroom of our house in Barnstaple, Connecticut, and the time was just after seven p.m.; deep twilight, at this time of year. I had come home from the office—I was a realtor, a fairly lucrative occupation in Connecticut, though my income had been falling off recently—shortly before six, to find the note on the kitchen table: "Antiquing with Greg. Afraid you'll have to make your own dinner. Sorry. Love, Emily."

Greg was the one; Emily's lover. He owned an antique shop out on the main road toward New York, and Emily filled a part of her days as his ill-paid assistant. I knew what they did together in the back of the shop on those long midweek afternoons when there were no tourists, no antique collectors to disturb them. I knew, and I'd known for more than three years, but I had never decided how to deal with my knowledge. The fact was, I blamed myself, and therefore I had no way to *behave* if the ugly subject were ever to come into the open.

So I remained silent, but not content. I was discontent, unhappy, angry, resentful—truculent.

I'd tried to kill myself before. At first with the car, by steering it into an oncoming truck (I swerved at the last second, amid howling horns) and by driving it off a cliff into the Connecticut River (I slammed on the brakes at the very brink, and sat covered in perspiration for half an hour before backing away) and finally by stopping athwart one of the few level crossings left in this neighborhood. But no train came for 20 minutes, and my truculence wore off, and I drove home.

Later I tried to slit my wrists, but found it impossible to push sharp metal into my own skin. Impossible. The vision of my naked wrist and that shining steel so close together washed my truculence completely out of my mind. Until the next time.

With the rope; and then I succeeded. Oh, totally, oh, fully I succeeded. My legs kicked at air, my fingernails clawed at my throat, my bulging eyes stared out over my swollen purple cheeks, my tongue thickened and grew bulbous in my mouth, my body jigged and jangled like a toy at the end of a string, and the pain was excruciating, horrible, not to be endured. I can't endure it, I thought, it can't be endured. Much worse than knife slashings was the knotted strangled pain in my throat, and my head ballooned with pain, pressure outward, my face turning black, my eyes no longer human, the pressure in my head building and building as though I would explode. Endless horrible pain, not to be endured, but going on and on.

My legs kicked more feebly. My arms sagged, my hands dropped to my sides, my fingers twitched uselessly against my sopping trouser legs, my head hung at an angle from the rope, I turned more slowly in the air, like a broken windchime on a breezeless day. The pains lessened, in my throat and head, but never entirely stopped.

And now I saw that my distended eyes had become lusterless, gray. The moisture had dried on the eyeballs, they were as dead as stones. And yet I could see them, my own eyes, and when I widened my vision I could see my entire body, turning, hanging, no longer twitching, and with horror I realized I was dead.

But *present.* Dead, but still present, with the scraping ache still in my throat and the bulging pressure still in my head. Present, but no longer in that used-up clay, that hanging meat; I was suffused through the room, like indirect lighting, everywhere present but without a source. What happens now? I wondered, dulled by fear and strangeness and the continuing pains, and I waited, like a hovering mist, for whatever would happen next.

But nothing happened. I waited; the body became utterly still; the double shadow on the wall showed no vibration; the bedside lamps continued to burn; the door remained shut and the window shade drawn; and nothing happened.

What *now?* I craved to scream the question aloud, but I could not. My throat ached, but I had no throat. My mouth burned, but I had no mouth. Every final strain and struggle of my body remained imprinted in my mind, but I had no body and no brain and no *self,* no substance. No power to speak, no power to move myself, no power to *re*move myself from this room and this suspended corpse. I could only wait here, and wonder, and go on waiting.

There was a digital clock on the dresser opposite the bed, and when it first occurred to me to look at it the numbers were 7:21—perhaps twenty minutes after I'd kicked the chair away, perhaps fifteen minutes since I'd died. Shouldn't something happen, shouldn't some *change* take place?

The clock read 9:11 when I heard Emily's Volkswagen drive around to the back of the house. I had left no note, having nothing I wanted to say to anyone and in any event believing my own dead body would be eloquent enough, but I hadn't thought I would be *present* when Emily found me. I was justified in my action, however much I now regretted having taken it, I was justified, I knew I was justified, but I didn't want to see her face when she came through that door. She had wronged me, she was the cause of it, she would have to know that as well as I, but I didn't want to see her face.

The pains increased, in what had been my throat, in what had been my head. I heard the back door slam, far away downstairs, and I stirred like air currents in the room, but I didn't leave. I couldn't leave.

"Ed? Ed? It's me, hon!"

I know it's you. I must go away now, I can't stay here, I must go away. Is there a God? Is this my soul, this hovering presence? *Hell* would be better than this, take me away to Hell or wherever I'm to go, don't leave me here!

She came up the stairs, calling again, walking past the closed guestroom door. I heard her go into our bedroom, heard her call my name, heard the beginnings of apprehension in her voice. She went by again, out there in the hall, went downstairs, became quiet.

What was she doing? Searching for a note perhaps, some message from me. Looking out the window, seeing again my Chevrolet, knowing I must be home. Moving through the rooms of this old house, the original structure a barn nearly 200 years old, converted by some previous owner just after the Second World War, bought by me twelve years ago, furnished by Emily—and Greg—from their interminable, damnable, awful antiques. Shaker furniture, Colonial furniture, hooked rugs and quilts, the old yellow pine tables, the faint sense always of being in some slightly shabby minor museum, this house that I had bought but never loved. I'd bought it for Emily, I did everything for Emily, because I knew I could never do the one thing for Emily that mattered. I could never give her a child.

She was good about it, of course. Emily *is* good, I never blamed her, never completely blamed *her* instead of myself. In the early days of our marriage she made a few wistful references, but I suppose she saw the effect they had on me, and for a long time she has said nothing. But I have known.

The beam from which I had hanged myself was a part of the original building, a thick hand-hewed length of aged timber eleven inches square, chevroned with the marks of the hatchet that had shaped it. A strong beam, it would support my weight forever. It would support my weight until I was found and cut down. Until I was found.

The clock read 9:23 and Emily had been in the house twelve minutes when she came upstairs again, her steps quick and light on the old wood, approaching, pausing, stopping. "Ed?"

The doorknob turned.

The door was locked, of course, with the key on the inside. She'd have to break it down, have to call someone else to break it down, perhaps she wouldn't be the one to find me after all. Hope rose in me, and the pains receded.

"Ed? Are you in there?" She knocked at the door, rattled the knob, called my name several times more, then abruptly turned and ran away downstairs again, and after a moment I heard her voice, murmuring and unclear. She had called someone, on the phone.

Greg, I thought, and the throat-rasp filled me, and I wanted this to be the end. I wanted to be taken away, dead body and living soul, taken away. I wanted everything to be finished.

She stayed downstairs, waiting for him, and I stayed upstairs, waiting for them both. Perhaps she already knew what she'd find up here, and that's why she waited below.

I didn't mind about Greg, about being present when he came in. I didn't mind about *him*. It was Emily I minded.

The clock read 9:44 when I heard tires on the gravel at the side of the house. He entered, I heard them talking down there, the deeper male voice slow and reassuring, the lighter female voice quick and frightened, and then they came up together, neither speaking. The doorknob turned, jiggled, rattled, and Greg's voice called, "Ed?"

After a little silence Emily said, "He wouldn't— He wouldn't *do* anything, would he?"

"Do anything?" Greg sounded almost annoyed at the question. "What do you mean, do anything?"

"He's been so depressed, he's— Ed!" And forcibly the door was rattled, the door was shaken in its frame.

"Emily, don't. Take it easy."

"I shouldn't have called you," she said. "Ed, *please!*"

"Why not? For heaven's sake, Emily—"

"Ed, *please* come out, don't scare me like this!"

"Why *shouldn't* you call me, Emily?"

"Ed isn't stupid, Greg. He's—"

There was then a brief silence, pregnant with the hint of murmuring. They thought me still alive in here, they didn't want me to hear Emily say, "He *knows,* Greg, he knows about us."

The murmurings sifted and shifted, and then Greg spoke loudly, "That's ridiculous. Ed? Come out, Ed, let's talk this over." And the doorknob rattled and clattered, and he sounded annoyed when he said, "We must get in, that's all. Is there another key?"

"I think all the locks up here are the same. Just a minute."

They were. A simple skeleton key would open any interior door in the house. I waited, listening, knowing Emily had gone off to find another key, knowing they would soon come in together, and I felt such terror and revulsion for Emily's entrance that I could feel myself shimmer in the room, like a reflection in a warped mirror. Oh, can I at least stop seeing? In life I had eyes, but also eyelids, I could shut out the intolerable, but now I was only a presence, a total presence, I *could not* stop my awareness.

The rasp of key in lock was like rough metal edges in my throat; my memory of a throat. The pain flared in me, and through it I heard Emily asking what was wrong, and Greg answering, "The key's in it, on the other side."

"Oh, dear God! Oh, Greg, what has he done?"

"We'll have to take the door off its hinges," he told her. "Call Tony. Tell him to bring the toolbox."

"Can't you push the key through?"

Of course he could, but he said, quite determinedly, "Go *on,* Emily," and I realized then he had no intention of taking the door down. He simply wanted her away when the door was first opened. Oh, very good, *very* good!

"All right," she said doubtfully, and I heard her go away to phone Tony. A beetle-browed young man with great masses of black hair and an olive complexion, Tony lived in Greg's house and was a kind of handyman. He did work around the house and was also (according to Emily) very good at restoration of antique furniture; stripping paint, reassembling broken parts, that sort of thing.

There was now a renewed scraping and rasping at the lock, as Greg struggled to get the door open before Emily's return. I found myself feeling unexpected warmth and liking toward Greg. He wasn't a bad person; an opportunist with my wife, but not in general a bad person. Would he marry her now? They could live in this house, he'd had more to do with its furnishing than I. Or would this room hold too grim a memory, would Emily have to sell the house, live elsewhere? She might have to sell at a low price; as a realtor, I knew the difficulty in selling a house where a suicide has taken place. No matter how much they may joke about it, people are still afraid of the supernatural. Many of them would believe this room was haunted.

It was then I finally realized the room *was* haunted. With me! *I'm a ghost,* I thought, thinking the word for the first time, in utter blank astonishment. I'm a ghost.

Oh, how dismal! To hover here, to be a boneless fleshless aching *presence* here, to be a kind of ectoplasmic mildew seeping through the days and nights, alone, unending, a stupid pain-racked misery-filled observer of the comings and goings of strangers—she *would* sell the house, she'd have to, I was sure of that. Was this my punishment? The punishment of the suicide, the solitary hell of him who takes his own life. To remain forever a sentient nothing, bound by a force greater than gravity itself to the place of one's finish.

I was distracted from this misery by a sudden agitation in the key on this side of the lock. I saw it quiver and jiggle like something alive, and then it popped out—it seemed to *leap* out, itself a suicide leaping from a cliff—and clattered to the floor, and an instant later the door was pushed open and Greg's ashen face stared at my own purple face, and after the astonishment and horror, his expression shifted to revulsion—and contempt?—and he backed out, slamming the door. Once more the key turned in the lock, and I heard him hurry away downstairs.

The clock read 9:58. *Now* he was telling her. *Now* he was giving her a drink to calm her. *Now* he was phoning the police. *Now* he was talking to her about whether or not to admit their affair to the police; what would they decide?

"Noooooooooo!"

The clock read 10:07. What had taken so long? Hadn't he even called the police yet?

She was coming up the stairs, stumbling and rushing, she was pounding on the door, screaming my name. I shrank into the corners of the room, I *felt* the thuds of her fists against the door, I cowered from her. She can't come in, dear God don't let her in! I don't care what she's done, I don't care about anything, just don't let her see me! *Don't let me see her!*

Greg joined her. She screamed at him, he persuaded her, she raved, he argued, she demanded, he denied. "Give me the key. Give me the key."

Surely he'll hold out, surely he'll take her away, surely he's stronger, more forceful.

He gave her the key.

No. *This* cannot be endured. *This* is the horror beyond all else. She came in, she walked into the room, and the sound she made will always live inside me. That cry wasn't human; it was the howl of every creature that has ever despaired. *Now* I know what despair is, and why I called my own state mere truculence.

Now that it was too late, Greg tried to restrain her, tried to hold her shoulders and draw her from the room, but she pulled away and crossed the room toward . . . not toward *me*. I was everywhere in the room, driven by pain and remorse, and Emily walked toward the carcass. She looked at it almost tenderly, she even reached up and touched its swollen cheek. "Oh, Ed," she murmured.

The pains were as violent now as in the moments before my death. The slashing torment in my throat, the awful distension in my head, they made me squirm in agony all over again; but I *could not* feel her hand on my cheek.

Greg followed her, touched her shoulder again, spoke her name, and immediately her face dissolved, she cried out once more and wrapped her arms around the corpse's legs and clung to it, weeping and gasping and uttering words too quick and broken to understand. Thank *God* they were too quick and broken to understand!

Greg, that fool, did finally force her away, though he had great trouble breaking her clasp on the body. But he succeeded, and pulled her out of the room, and slammed the door, and for a little while the body swayed and turned, until it became still once more.

That was the worst. Nothing could be worse than that. The long days and nights here—how long must a stupid creature like myself *haunt* his death-place before release?—would be horrible, I knew that, but not so bad as this. Emily would survive, would sell the house, would slowly forget. (Even I would slowly forget.) She and Greg could marry. She was only 36, she could still be a mother.

For the rest of the night I heard her wailing, elsewhere in the house. The police did come at last, and a pair of grim silent white-coated men from the morgue entered the room to cut me—it—down. They bundled it like a broken toy into a large oval wicker basket with long wooden handles, and they carried it away.

I had thought I might be forced to stay with the body, I had feared the possibility of being buried with it, of spending eternity as a thinking nothingness in the black dark of a casket, but the body left the room and I remained behind.

A doctor was called. When the body was carried away the room door was left open, and now I could plainly hear the voices from downstairs. Tony was among them now, his characteristic surly monosyllable occasionally rumbling, but the main thing for a while was the doctor. He was trying to give Emily a sedative, but she kept wailing, she kept speaking high hurried frantic sentences as though she had too little time to say it all. "I did it!" she cried, over and over. "I did it! I'm to blame!"

Yes. That was the reaction I'd wanted, and expected, and here it was, and it was horrible. Everything I had desired in the last moments of my life had been granted to me, and they were all ghastly beyond belief. I *didn't* want to die! I *didn't* want to give Emily such misery! And more than all the rest I didn't want to be here, seeing and hearing it all.

They did quiet her at last, and then a policeman in a rumpled blue suit came into the room with Greg, and listened while Greg described everything that had happened. While Greg talked, the policeman rather grumpily stared at the remaining length of rope still knotted around the beam, and when Greg had finished the policeman said, "You're a close friend of his?"

"More of his wife. She works for me. I own The Bibelot, an antique shop out on the New York road."

"Mm. Why on earth did you let her in here?"

Greg smiled; a sheepish embarrassed expression. "She's stronger than I am," he said. "A more forceful personality. That's always been true."

It was with some surprise I realized it *was* true. Greg was something of a weakling, and Emily was very strong. *(I had been something of a weakling, hadn't I? Emily was the strongest of us all.)*

The policeman was saying, "Any idea why he'd do it?"

"I think he suspected his wife was having an affair with me." Clearly Greg had rehearsed this sentence, he'd much earlier come to the decision to say it and had braced himself for the moment. He blinked all the way through the statement, as though standing in a harsh glare.

The policeman gave him a quick shrewd look. "Were you?"

"Yes."

"She was getting a divorce?"

"No. She doesn't love me, she loved her husband."

"Then why sleep around?"

"Emily wasn't sleeping *around,*" Greg said, showing offense only with that emphasized word. "From time to time, and not very often, she was sleeping with me."

"Why?"

"For comfort." Greg too looked at the rope around the beam, as though it had become me and he was awkward speaking in its presence. "Ed wasn't an easy man to get along with," he said carefully. "He was moody. It was getting worse."

"Cheerful people don't kill themselves," the policeman said.

"Exactly. Ed was depressed most of the time, obscurely angry now and then. It was affecting his business, costing him clients. He made Emily miserable but she wouldn't leave him, she loved him. I don't know what she'll do now."

"You two won't marry?"

"Oh, no." Greg smiled, a bit sadly. "Do you think we murdered him, made it look like suicide so we could marry?"

"Not at all," the policeman said. "But what's the problem? You already married?"

"I am homosexual."

The policeman was no more astonished than I. He said, "I don't get it."

"I live with my friend; that young man downstairs. I am—capable—of a wider range, but my preferences are set. I am very fond of Emily, I felt sorry for her, the life she had with Ed. I told you our physical relationship was infrequent. And often not very successful."

Oh, Emily. Oh, poor Emily.

The policeman said, "Did Thornburn know you were, uh, that way?"

"I have no idea. I don't make a public point of it."

"All right." The policeman gave one more half-angry look around the room, then said, "Let's go."

They left. The door remained open, and I heard them continue to talk as they went downstairs, first the policeman asking, "Is there somebody to stay the night? Mrs. Thornburn shouldn't be alone."

"She has relatives in Great Barrington. I phoned them earlier. Somebody should be arriving within the hour."

"You'll stay until then? The doctor says she'll probably sleep, but just in case—"

"Of course."

That was all I heard. Male voices murmured a while longer from below, and then stopped. I heard cars drive away.

How complicated men and women are. How stupid are simple actions. I had never understood anyone, least of all myself.

The room was visited once more that night, by Greg, shortly after the police left. He entered, looking as offended and repelled as though the body were still here, stood the chair up on its legs, climbed on it, and with some difficulty untied the remnant of rope. This he stuffed partway into his pocket as he stepped down again to the floor, then returned the chair to its usual spot in the corner of the room, picked the key off the floor and put it in the lock, switched off both bedside lamps and left the room, shutting the door behind him.

Now I was in darkness, except for the faint line of light under the door, and the illuminated numerals of the clock. How long one minute is! That clock was my enemy, it dragged out every minute, it paused and waited and paused and waited till I could stand it no more, and then it waited longer, and *then* the next number dropped into place. Sixty times an hour, hour after hour, all night long. I couldn't stand one night of this, how could I stand eternity?

And how could I stand the torment and torture inside my brain? That was much worse now than the physical pain, which never entirely left me. I had been right about Emily and Greg, but at the same time I had been hopelessly brainlessly wrong. I had been right about my life, but wrong; right about my death, but wrong. How *much* I wanted to make amends, and how impossible it was to do anything any more, anything at all. My actions had all tended to this, and ended with this: black remorse, the most dreadful pain of all.

I had all night to think, and to feel the pains, and to wait without knowing what I was waiting for or when—or if—my waiting would ever end. Faintly I heard the arrival of Emily's sister and brother-in-law, the murmured conversation, then the departure of Tony and Greg. Not long afterward the guestroom door opened, but almost immediately closed again, no one having entered, and a bit after that the hall light went out, and now only the illuminated clock broke the darkness.

When next would I see Emily? Would she ever enter this room again? It wouldn't be as horrible as the first time, but it would surely be horror enough.

Dawn grayed the window shade, and gradually the room appeared out of the darkness, dim and silent and morose. Apparently it was a sunless day, which never got very bright. The day went on and on, featureless, each protracted minute marked by the clock. At times I dreaded someone's entering this room, at other times I prayed for something, anything—even the presence of Emily herself—to break this unending boring *absence*. But the day went on with no event, no sound, no activity anywhere—they must be keeping Emily sedated through this first day—and it wasn't until twilight, with the digital clock reading 6:52, that the door again opened and a person entered.

At first I didn't recognize him. An angry-looking man, blunt and determined, he came in with quick ragged steps, switched on both bedside lamps, then shut the door with rather more force than necessary, and turned the key in the lock. Truculent, his manner was, and when he turned from the door I saw with incredulity that he was *me*. Me! I wasn't dead, I was alive! But how could that be?

And what was that he was carrying? He picked up the chair from the corner, carried it to the middle of the room, stood on it—

No! No!

He tied the rope around the beam. The noose was already in the other end, which he slipped over his head and tightened around his neck.

Good God, *don't!*

He kicked the chair away.

The instant I kicked the chair away I wanted it back, but gravity was turning my former wish to its present command; the chair would not right itself from where it lay on the floor, and my 193 pounds would not cease to urge downward from the rope thick around my neck.

There was pain, of course, quite horrible pain centered in my throat, but the most astounding thing was the way my cheeks seemed to swell. I could barely see over their round red hills, my eyes staring in agony at the door, *willing* someone to come in and rescue me, though I knew there was no one in the house, and in any event the door was carefully locked. My kicking legs caused me to twist and turn, so that sometimes I faced the door and sometimes the window, and my shivering hands struggled with the rope so deep in my flesh I could barely find it and most certainly could not pull it loose.

I was frantic and horrified, yet at the same time my brain possessed a cold corner of aloof observation. I seemed now to be everywhere in the room at once, within my writhing body but also without, seeing my frenzied spasms, the thick rope, the heavy beam, the mismatched pair of lit bedside lamps throwing my convulsive double shadow on the walls, the closed locked door, the white-curtained window with its shade drawn all the way down. *This is death*

WOODROW WILSON'S
NECKTIE
by PATRICIA HIGHSMITH

The façade of MADAME THIBUALT'S WAXWORK HORRORS glittered and throbbed with red and yellow lights, even in the daytime. Knobs of golden balls—the yellow lights—pulsated amid the red lights, attracting the eye and holding it.

Clive Wilkes loved the place, the inside and the outside equally. Since he was a delivery boy for a grocery store, it was easy for him to say that a certain delivery had taken him longer than had been expected—he'd had to wait for Mrs. So-and-so to get home because the doorman had told him she was due back any minute, or he'd had to go five blocks to find some change because Mrs. Smith had had only a twenty-dollar bill. At these spare moments—and Clive managed one or two a week—he visited MADAME THIBAULT'S WAXWORK HORRORS.

Inside the establishment you went through a dark passage—to be put in the mood—and then you were confronted by a bloody murder scene on the left: a girl with long blond hair was sticking a knife into the neck of an old man who sat at a kitchen table eating his dinner. His dinner consisted of two wax frankfurters and wax sauerkraut. Then came the Lindbergh kidnapping scene, with Hauptmann climbing down a ladder outside a nursery window; you could see the top of the ladder out the window, and the top half of Hauptmann's figure, clutching the little boy. Also there was Marat in his bath with Charlotte nearby. And Christie with his stocking, throttling a woman.

Clive loved every tableau, and they never became stale. But he didn't look at them with the solemn, vaguely startled expression of the other people who looked at them. Clive was inclined to smile, even to laugh. They were amusing. So why not laugh?

Farther on in the museum were the torture chambers—one old, one modern, purporting to show Twentieth Century torture methods in Nazi Germany and in French Algeria. Madame Thibault—who Clive strongly suspected did not exist—kept up to date. There were the Kennedy assassination and the Tate massacre, of course, and some murder that had happened only a month ago somewhere.

Clive's first definite ambition in regard to MADAME THIBAULT'S WAX-WORK HORRORS museum was to spend a night there. This he did one night, providently taking along a cheese sandwich in his pocket. It was fairly easy to accomplish. Clive knew that three people worked in the museum proper—down in the bowels, as he thought of it, though the museum was on street level—while a fourth, a plumpish middle-aged man in a nautical cap, sold tickets at a booth in front. The three who worked in the bowels were two men and a woman; the woman, also plump and with curly brown hair and glasses and about 40, took the tickets at the end of the dark corridor, where the museum proper began.

One of the inside men lectured constantly, though not more than half the people ever bothered to listen. "Here we see the fanatical expression of the true murderer, captured by the supreme wax artistry of Madame Thibault"—and so on. The other inside man had black hair and black-rimmed glasses like the woman, and he just drifted around, shooing away kids who wanted to climb into the tableaux, maybe watching for pickpockets, or maybe protecting women from unpleasant assaults in the semidarkness. Clive didn't know.

He only knew it was quite easy to slip into one of the dark corners or into a nook next to one of the Iron Molls—maybe even into one of the Iron Molls; but slender as he was, the spikes might poke into him, Clive thought, so he ruled out this idea. He had observed that people were gently urged out around 9:15 P.M., as the museum closed at 9:30 P.M. And lingering as late as possible one evening, Clive had learned that there was a sort of cloakroom for the staff behind a door in one back corner, from which direction he had also heard the sound of a toilet flushing.

So one night in November, Clive concealed himself in the shadows, which were abundant, and listened to the three people as they got ready to leave. The woman—whose name turned out to be Mildred—was lingering to take the money box from Fred, the ticket seller, and to count it and deposit it somewhere in the cloakroom. Clive was not interested in the money. He was interested only in spending a night in the place and being able to boast he had.

"Night, Mildred—see you tomorrow," called one of the men.

"Anything else to do? I'm leaving now," said Mildred. "Boy, am I tired! But I'm still going to watch Dragon Man tonight."

"Dragon Man," the other man repeated, uninterested.

Evidently the ticket seller, Fred, left from the front of the building after handing in the money box, and in fact Clive recalled seeing him close up

the front once, cutting the lights from inside the entrance door, then locking the door and barring it on the outside.

Clive stood in a nook by an Iron Moll. When he heard the back door
shut and the key turn in the lock, he waited for a moment in delicious
silence, aloneness, and suspense, and then ventured out. He went first, on
tiptoe, to the room where they kept their coats, because he had never seen
it. He had brought matches—also cigarettes, though smoking was not allowed, according to several signs—and with the aid of a match he found
the light switch. The room contained an old desk, four metal lockers, a tin
wastebasket, an umbrella stand, and some books in a bookcase against a
grimy wall that had once been white. Clive slid open a drawer and found
the well-worn wooden box which he had once seen the ticket seller carrying in through the front door. The box was locked. He could walk out
with the box, Clive thought, but he didn't care to, and he considered this
rather decent of himself. He gave the box a wipe with the side of his hand,
not forgetting the bottom where his fingertips had touched. That was
funny, he thought, wiping something he wasn't going to steal.

Clive set about enjoying the night. He found the lights and put them on
so that the booths with the gory tableaux were all illuminated. He was
hungry, took one bite of his sandwich, then put it back in the paper napkin
in his pocket. He sauntered slowly past the John F. Kennedy assassination—
Mrs. Kennedy and the doctors bending anxiously over the white table on
which JFK lay. This time, Hauptmann's descent of the ladder made Clive
giggle. Charles Lindbergh, Jr.'s face looked so untroubled that one would
think he might be sitting on the floor of his nursery, playing with blocks.

Clive swung a leg over a metal bar and climbed into the Judd-Snyder
tableau. It gave him a thrill to be standing right *with* them, inches from the
throttling-from-behind which the lover of the woman was administering to
the husband. Clive put a hand out and touched the red-paint blood that was
seeming to come from the man's throat where the cord pressed deep. Clive
also touched the cool cheekbones of the victim. The popping eyes were of
glass, vaguely disgusting, and Clive did not touch those.

Two hours later he was singing church hymns, *Nearer My God to Thee*
and *Jesus Wants Me for a Sunbeam*. Clive didn't know all the words. And he
smoked.

By two in the morning he was bored and tried to get out by both the
front door and back, but couldn't—both were barred on the outside. He
had thought of having a hamburger at an all-night diner between here and
home. However, his enforced incarceration didn't bother him, so he finished the now-dry cheese sandwich and slept for a bit on three straight
chairs which he arranged in a row. It was so uncomfortable that he knew
he'd wake up in a while, which he did—at 5 A.M. He washed his face, then

went for another look at the wax exhibits. This time he took a souvenir—
Woodrow Wilson's necktie.

As the hour of 9:00 approached—MADAME THIBAULT'S WAXWORK
HORRORS opened at 9:30 A.M.—Clive hid himself in an excellent spot,
behind one of the tableaux whose backdrop was a black-and-gold Chinese
screen. In front of the screen was a bed and in the bed lay a wax man with a
handlebar mustache, who was supposed to have been poisoned by his wife.

The public began to trickle in shortly after 9:30 A.M., and the taller, more
solemn man began to mumble his boring lecture. Clive had to wait till a
few minutes past ten before he felt safe enough to mingle with the crowd
and make his exit, with Woodrow Wilson's necktie rolled up in his pocket.
He was a bit tired, but happy—though on second thought, who would he
tell about it? Joey Vrasky, that dumb cluck who worked behind the counter
at Simmons' Grocery? Hah! Why bother? Joey didn't deserve a good story.
Clive was half an hour late for work.

"I'm sorry, Mr. Simmons, I overslept," Clive said hastily, but he thought
quite politely, as he came into the store. There was a delivery job awaiting
him. Clive took his bicycle and put the carton on a platform in front of the
handlebars.

Clive lived with his mother, a thin highly strung woman who was a
saleswoman in a shop that sold stockings, girdles, and underwear. Her
husband had left her when Clive was nine. She had no other children. Clive
had quit high school a year before graduation, to his mother's regret, and
for a year he had done nothing but lie around the house or stand on street
corners with his pals. But Clive had never been very chummy with any of
them, for which his mother was thankful, as she considered them a worthless lot. Clive had had the delivery job at Simmons' for nearly a year now,
and his mother felt that he was settling down.

When Clive came home that evening at 6:30 P.M. he had a story ready
for his mother. Last night he had run into his old friend Richie, who was in
the Army and home on leave, and they had sat up at Richie's house talking
so late that Richie's parents had invited him to stay over, and Clive had
slept on the couch. His mother accepted this explanation. She made a supper
of baked beans, bacon, and eggs.

There was really no one to whom Clive felt like telling his exploit of
the night. He couldn't have borne someone looking at him and saying,
"Yeah? So what?" because what he had done had taken a bit of planning,
even a little daring. He put Woodrow Wilson's tie among his others that
hung over a string on the inside of his closet door. It was a gray silk tie,
conservative and expensive-looking. Several times that day Clive imagined
one of the two men in the museum, or maybe the woman named Mildred,
glancing at Woodrow Wilson and exclaiming, "Hey! What happened to
Woodrow Wilson's tie, I wonder?"

Each time Clive thought of this he had to duck his head to hide a smile.

After twenty-four hours, however, the exploit had begun to lose its charm and excitement. Clive's excitement only rose again—and it could rise two or three times a day—whenever he cycled past the twinkling façade of MADAME THIBAULT'S WAXWORK HORRORS. His heart would give a leap, his blood would run a little faster, and he would think of all the motionless murders going on in there, and all the stupid faces of Mr. and Mrs. Johnny Q. Public gaping at them. But Clive didn't even buy another ticket—price 65 cents—to go in and look at Woodrow Wilson and see that his tie was missing and his collar button showing—his work.

Clive did get another idea one afternoon, a hilarious idea that would make the public sit up and take notice. Clive's ribs trembled with suppressed laughter as he pedaled toward Simmons', having just delivered a bag of groceries.

When should he do it? Tonight? No, best to take a day or so to plan it. It would take brains. And silence. And sure movements—all the things Clive admired.

He spent two days thinking about it. He went to his local snack bar and drank beer and played the pinball machines with his pals. The pinball machines had pulsating lights too—*More Than One Can Play* and *It's More Fun To Compete*— but Clive thought only of MADAME THIBAULT'S as he stared at the rolling, bouncing balls that mounted a score he cared nothing about. It was the same when he looked at the rainbow-colored jukebox whose blues, reds, and yellows undulated, and when he went over to drop a coin in it. He was thinking of what he was going to do in MADAME THIBAULT'S WAXWORK HORRORS.

On the second night, after a supper with his mother, Clive went to MADAME THIBAULT'S and bought a ticket. The old guy who sold tickets barely looked at people, he was so busy making change and tearing off the stubs, which was just as well. Clive went in at 9:00 P.M.

He looked at the tableaux, though they were not so fascinating to him tonight as they had been before. Woodrow Wilson's tie was still missing, as if no one had noticed it, and Clive chuckled over this. He remembered that the solemn-faced pickpocket-watcher—the drifting snoop—had been the last to leave the night Clive had stayed, so Clive assumed he had the keys, and therefore he ought to be the last to be killed.

The woman was the first. Clive hid himself beside one of the Iron Molls again, while the crowd ambled out, and when Mildred walked by him, in her hat and coat, to leave by the back door, having just said something to one of the men in the exhibition hall, Clive stepped out and wrapped an arm around her throat from behind.

She made only a small *ur-rk* sound.

Clive squeezed her throat with his hands, stopping her voice. At last she slumped, and Clive dragged her into a dark, recessed corner to the left of the cloakroom. He knocked an empty cardboard box of some kind over, but it didn't make enough noise to attract the attention of the two men.

"Mildred's gone?" one of the men asked.

"I think she's in the office."

"No, she's not." The owner of this voice had already gone into the corridor where Clive crouched over Mildred and had looked into the empty cloakroom where the light was still on. "She's left. Well, I'm calling it a day too."

Clive stepped out then and encircled this man's neck in the same manner. The job was more difficult, because the man struggled, but Clive's arm was thin and strong; he acted with swiftness and knocked the man's head against the wooden floor.

"What's going on?" The thump had brought the second man.

This time Clive tried a punch to the man's jaw, but missed and hit his neck. However, this so stunned the man—the little solemn fellow, the snoop—that a quick second blow was easy, and then Clive was able to take him by the shirtfront and bash his head against the plaster wall which was harder than the wooden floor. Then Clive made sure that all three were dead. The two men's heads were bloody. The woman was bleeding slightly from her mouth. Clive reached for the keys in the second man's pockets. They were in his left trousers pocket and with them was a penknife. Clive also took the knife.

Then the taller man moved slightly. Alarmed, Clive opened the pearl-handled penknife and plunged it into the man's throat three times.

Close call, Clive thought, as he checked again to make sure they were all dead. They most certainly were, and that was most certainly real blood, not the red paint of Madame Thibault's Waxwork Horrors. Clive switched on the lights for the tableaux and went into the exhibition hall for the interesting task of choosing exactly the right places for the three corpses.

The woman belonged in Marat's bath—not much doubt about that. Clive debated removing her clothing, but decided against it, simply because she would look much funnier sitting in a bath wearing a fur-trimmed coat and hat. The figure of Marat sent him off into laughter. He'd expected sticks for legs, and nothing between the legs, because you couldn't see any more of Marat than from the middle of his torso up; but Marat had no legs at all and his wax body ended just below the waist in a fat stump which was planted on a wooden platform so that it would not topple. This crazy waxwork Clive carried into the cloakroom and placed squarely in the middle of the desk. He then carried the woman—who weighed a good deal —onto the Marat scene and put her in the bath. Her hat fell off, and he pushed it on again, a bit over one eye. Her bloody mouth hung open.

Good lord, it *was* funny!

Now for the men. Obviously, the one whose throat he had knifed would look good in the place of the old man who was eating wax franks and sauerkraut, because the girl behind him was supposed to be stabbing him in the throat. This took Clive some fifteen minutes. Since the figure of the old man was in a seated position, Clive put him on the toilet off the cloakroom. It was terribly amusing to see the old man seated on the toilet, throat apparently bleeding, a knife in one hand and a fork in the other. Clive lurched against the door jamb, laughing loudly, not even caring if someone heard him, because it was so comical it was even worth getting caught for.

Next, the little snoop. Clive looked around him and his eye fell on the Woodrow Wilson scene which depicted the signing of the armistice in 1918. A wax figure sat at a huge desk signing something, and that was the logical place for a man whose head was almost split open. With some difficulty Clive got the pen out of the wax man's fingers, laid it to one side on the desk, and carried the figure—it didn't weigh much—into the cloak-room, where Clive seated him at the desk, rigid arms in an attitude of writing. Clive stuck a ballpoint pen into his right hand. Now for the last heave. Clive saw that his jacket was now quite spotted with blood and he would have to get rid of it, but so far there was no blood on his trousers.

Clive dragged the second man to the Woodrow Wilson tableau, lifted him up, and rolled him toward the desk. He got him onto the chair, but the head toppled forward onto the green-blottered desk, onto the blank wax pages, and the pen barely stood upright in the limp hand.

But it was done. Clive stood back and smiled. Then he listened. He sat down on a straight chair and rested for a few minutes, because his heart was beating fast and he suddenly realized that every muscle in his body was tired. Ah, well, he now had the keys. He could lock up, go home, and have a good night's rest, because he wanted to be ready to enjoy tomorrow.

Clive took a sweater from one of the male figures in a log-cabin tableau of some kind. He had to pull the sweater down over the feet of the waxwork to get it off, because the arms would not bend; it stretched the neck of the sweater, but he couldn't help that. Now the wax figure had a sort of bib for a shirtfront, and naked arms and chest.

Clive wadded up his jacket and went everywhere with it, erasing finger-prints from whatever he thought he had touched. He turned the lights off, made his way carefully to the back door, locked and barred it behind him, and would have left the keys in a mailbox if there had been one; but there wasn't, so he dropped the keys on the rear doorstep. In a wire rubbish basket he found some newspapers; he wrapped up his jacket in them and walked on with it until he found another wire rubbish basket, where he forced the bundle down among candy wrappers, beer cans, and other trash.

"A new sweater?" his mother asked that night.

"Richie gave it to me—for luck."

Clive slept like the dead, too tired even to laugh again at the memory of the old man sitting on the toilet.

The next morning Clive was standing across the street when the ticket seller arrived just before 9:30 A.M. By 9:35 A.M. only four people had gone in; but Clive could not wait any longer, so he crossed the street and bought a ticket. Now the ticket seller was doubling as ticket taker, and telling people, "Just go on in. Everybody's late this morning."

The ticket man stepped inside the door to put on some lights, then walked all the way into the place to put on the display lights for the tableaux, which worked from switches in the hall that led to the cloakroom. And the funny thing, to Clive who was walking behind him, was that the ticket man didn't notice anything odd, didn't even notice Mildred in her hat and coat sitting in Marat's bathtub.

The other customers so far were a man and a woman, a boy of fourteen or so in sneakers, alone apparently, and a single man. They looked expressionlessly at Mildred in the tub as if they thought it quite "normal," which would have sent Clive into paroxysms of mirth, except that his heart was thumping madly and he could hardly breathe for the suspense. Also, the man with his face in franks and sauerkraut brought no surprise either. Clive was a bit disappointed.

Two more people came in, a man and a woman.

Then at last, in front of the Woodrow Wilson tableau, there was a reaction. One of the women, clinging to her husband's arm, asked, "Was someone shot when the armistice was signed?"

"I don't know. I don't *think* so," the man replied vaguely.

Clive's laughter pressed like an explosion in his chest; he spun on his heel to control himself, and he had the feeling he knew *all* about history, and that no one else did. By now, of course, the real blood had turned to a rust color. The green blotter was now splotched, and blood had dripped down the side of the desk.

A woman on the other side of the room, where Mildred was, let out a scream.

A man laughed, but only briefly.

Suddenly everything happened. A woman shrieked, and at the same time a man yelled, "My God, it's *real!*"

Clive saw a man climbing up to investigate the corpse with his face in the frankfurters.

"The blood's *real!* It's a *dead* man!"

Another man—one of the public—slumped to the floor. He had fainted.

The ticket seller came bustling in. "What's the trouble here?"

"Coupla corpses—*real* ones!"

Now the ticket seller looked at Marat's bathtub and fairly jumped into the air with surprise. "Holy Christmas! *Holy* cripes!—it's *Mildred!*"

"And this one!"

"And the one here!"

"My God, got to—got to call the police!" said the ticket seller.

One man and woman left hurriedly. But the rest lingered, shocked, fascinated.

The ticket seller had run into the cloakroom, where the telephone was, and Clive heard him yell something. He'd seen the man at the desk, of course, the wax man, and the half body of Marat on the desk.

Clive thought it was time to drift out, so he did, sidling his way through a group of people peering in the front door, perhaps intending to come in because there was no ticket seller.

That was good, Clive thought. That was all right. Not bad. Not bad at all.

He had not intended to go to work that day, but suddenly he thought it wiser to check in and ask for the day off. Mr. Simmons was of course as sour as ever when Clive said he was not feeling well, but as Clive held his stomach and appeared weak, there was little old Simmons could do. Clive left the grocery. He had brought with him all his ready cash, about $23.

Clive wanted to take a long bus ride somewhere. He realized that suspicion might fall on him, if the ticket seller remembered his coming to MADAME THIBAULT'S often, or especially if he remembered Clive being there last night; but this really had little to do with his desire to take a bus ride. His longing for a bus ride was simply, somehow, irresistible. He bought a ticket westward for $8 and change, one way. This brought him, by about 7:00 P.M., to a good-sized town in Indiana, whose name Clive paid no attention to.

The bus spilled a few passengers, Clive included, at a terminal, where there was a cafeteria and a bar. By now Clive was curious about the newspapers, so he went to the newsstand near the street door of the cafeteria. And there were the headlines:

Triple Murder in Waxworks

Mass Murder in Museum

Mystery Killer Strikes: Three Dead in Waxworks

Clive liked the last one best. He bought the three newspapers, and stood at the bar with a beer.

"This morning at 9:30 A.M., ticket man Fred J. Carmody and several of the public who had come to see Madame Thibault's Waxwork Horrors, a noted attraction of this city, were confronted by three genuine corpses among the displays. They were the bodies of Mrs. Mildred Veery, 41; George P. Hartley, 43; and Richard K. McFadden, 37, all employed at the waxworks museum. The two men were killed by concussion and stabbing, and the woman by strangulation. Police are searching for clues on the premises. The murders are believed to have taken place shortly before 10:00 P.M. last evening, when the three employees were about to leave the museum. The murderer or murderers may have been among the last patrons of the museum before closing time at 9:30 P.M. It is thought that he or they may have concealed themselves somewhere in the museum until the rest of the patrons had left. . . ."

Clive was pleased. He smiled as he sipped his beer. He hunched over the papers, as if he did not wish the rest of the world to share his pleasure, but this was not true. After a few minutes Clive stood up and looked to the right and left to see if anyone else among the men and women at the bar was also reading the story. Two men were reading newspapers, but Clive could not tell if they were reading about him, because their newspapers were folded.

Clive lit a cigarette and went through all three newspapers to see if any clue to him was mentioned. He found nothing. One paper said specifically that Fred J. Carmody had not noticed any person or persons entering the museum last evening who looked suspicious.

". . . Because of the bizarre arrangement of the victims and of the displaced wax figures in the exhibition, in whose places the victims were put, police are looking for a psychopathic killer. Residents of the area have been warned by radio and television to take special precautions on the streets and to keep their houses locked."

Clive chuckled over that one. Psychopathic killer! He was sorry about the lack of detail, the lack of humor in the three reporters' stories. They might have said something about the old guy sitting on the toilet. Or the fellow signing the armistice with the back of his head bashed in. Those were strokes of genius. Why didn't they appreciate them?

When he had finished his beer, Clive walked out onto the sidewalk. It was now dark and the streetlights were on. He enjoyed looking around in the new town, looking into shop windows. But he was aiming for a hamburger place, and he went into the first one he came to. It was a diner made up to look like a crack railway car.

Clive ordered a hamburger and a cup of coffee. Next to him were two Western-looking men in cowboy boots and rather soiled broad-brimmed hats. Was one a sheriff, Clive wondered? But they were talking, in a drawl, about acreage somewhere. Land. They were hunched over hamburgers and coffee, one so close that his elbow kept touching Clive's. Clive was reading his newspapers all over again and he had propped one against the napkin container in front of him.

One of the men asked for a napkin and disturbed Clive, but Clive smiled and said in a friendly way, "Did you read about the murders in the wax-works?"

The man looked blank for a moment, then said, "Yep, saw the head-lines."

"Someone killed the three people who worked in the place. Look." There was a photograph in one of the papers, but Clive didn't much like it because it showed the corpses lined up on the floor. He would have pre-ferred Mildred in the bathtub.

"Yeah," said the Westerner, edging away from Clive as if he didn't like him.

"The bodies were put into a few of the exhibits. Like the wax figures. They say that, but they don't show a picture of it," said Clive.

"Yeah," said the Westerner, and went on eating.

Clive felt let down and somehow insulted. His face grew a little warm as he stared back at his newspapers. In fact, anger was growing quickly inside him, making his heart go faster, as it always did when he passed MADAME THIBAULT'S WAXWORK HORRORS, though now the sensation was not at all pleasant.

Clive put on a smile, however, and turned to the man on his left again. "I mention it, because I did it. That's my work there." He gestured toward the picture of the corpses.

"Listen, boy," said the Westerner casually, "you just keep to yourself tonight. Okay? We ain't botherin' you, so don't you go botherin' us." He laughed a little, glancing at his companion.

His friend was staring at Clive, but looked away at once when Clive stared back.

This was a double rebuff, and quite enough for Clive. He got out his money and paid for his unfinished food with a dollar bill. He left the change and walked to the sliding-door exit.

"But y'know, maybe that guy ain't kiddin'," Clive heard one of the men say.

Clive turned and said, "I *ain't* kiddin'!" Then he went out into the night.

Clive slept at a Y.M.C.A. The next day he half-expected he would be picked up by a passing cop on the beat, but he wasn't. He got a lift to another town, nearer his hometown. The day's newspapers brought no mention of his name, and no mention of clues. In another café that evening, almost the identical conversation took place between Clive and a couple of fellows his own age. They didn't believe him. It was stupid of them, Clive thought, and he wondered if they were pretending? Or lying?

Clive hitched his way home and headed for the police station. He was curious as to what *they* would say. He imagined what his mother would say after he confessed. Probably the same thing she had said to her friends sometimes, or that she'd said to a policeman when he was sixteen and had stolen a car.

"Clive hasn't been the same since his father went away. I know he needs a man around the house, a man to look up to, imitate, you know. That's what people tell me. Since he was fourteen Clive's been asking me questions like, 'Who am I, anyway?' and 'Am I a person, mom?'" Clive could see and hear her in the police station.

"I have an important confession to make," Clive said to a deskman in the front.

The man's attitude was rude and suspicious, Clive thought, but he was told to walk to an office, where he spoke with a police officer who had gray hair and a fat face. Clive told his story.

"Where do you go to school, Clive?"

"I don't. I'm eighteen." Clive told him about his job at Simmons' Grocery.

"Clive, you've got troubles, but they're not the ones you're talking about," said the officer.

Clive had to wait in a room, and nearly an hour later a psychiatrist was brought in. Then his mother. Clive became more and more impatient. They didn't believe him. They were saying his was a typical case of false confession in order to draw attention to himself. His mother's repeated statements about his asking questions like "Am I a person?" and "Who am I?" only seemed to corroborate the opinions of the psychiatrist and the police.

Clive was to report somewhere twice a week for psychiatric therapy.

He fumed. He refused to go back to Simmons' Grocery, but found another delivery job, because he liked having a little money in his pocket, and he was fast on his bicycle and honest with the change.

"You haven't *found* the murderer, have you?" Clive said to the police psychiatrist. "You're all the biggest bunch of jackasses I've ever seen in my life!"

The psychiatrist said soothingly, "You'll never get anywhere talking to people like that, boy."

Clive said, "Some perfectly ordinary strangers in Indiana said, 'Maybe that guy ain't kidding.' They had more sense than *you!*"

The psychiatrist smiled.

Clive smoldered. One thing might have helped to prove his story—Woodrow Wilson's necktie, which still hung in his closet. But these dumb clucks damned well didn't deserve to see that tie. Even as he ate his suppers with his mother, went to the movies, and delivered groceries, he was planning. He'd do something more important next time—like starting a fire in the depths of a big building or planting a bomb somewhere or taking a machine gun up to some penthouse and letting 'em have it down on the street. Kill a hundred people at least, or a thousand. They'd have to come up in the building to get him. *Then* they'd know. *Then* they'd treat him like somebody who really existed, like somebody who deserved an exhibit of himself in MADAME THIBAULT'S WAXWORK HORRORS.

The Eighties

THE JACKAL AND THE TIGER
by *MICHAEL GILBERT*

On the evening of April 15th, 1944, Colonel Hubert, of Military Intelligence, said to the Director of Public Prosecutions, "The only mistake Karl made was to underestimate young Ronnie Kavanagh."

That afternoon, Karl Muller, who sometimes called himself Charles Miller, had been shot in the underground rifle range at the Tower of London, which was the place being used at that time for the execution of German spies.

"A fatal mistake," agreed the Director.

Jim Perrot, late of the Military Police, wrote to his friend, Fred Denniston:

"Dear Denny,

"Do you remember those plans we talked over so often in North Africa and Italy? Well, I've got an option on a twenty-one-year lease of a nice first-floor office in Chancery Lane. That's bang in the middle of legal London, where the legal eagles are beginning to flap their wings and sharpen their claws again. Lots of work for an Enquiry Agency and not much competition—as yet. The lease is a snip. I've commuted my pension and got me a bit of capital. I reckon we'll have to put in about £2,000 each to get going. Denny's Detectives! How about it?"

And Denny's Detectives had turned out to be a success from the start.

As Perrot had said, there was no lack of work. Much of it was divorce work, the sad byproduct of a long war. It was in connection with this branch of their activities, which neither of the partners liked, that they acquired Mr. Huffin. He was perfectly equipped for the role he had to play. He was small, mild-looking, and so insignificant that many businessmen, departing to alleged conferences in the Midlands, had failed to recognize the little man who traveled in the train with them and occupied a table in an obscure corner of their hotel dining room until he stood up in court and swore to tell the truth, the whole truth, and nothing but the truth about the lady who had shared the businessman's table, and, later, his bedroom.

Jim Perrot's job was the tracing of elusive debtors. His experience as a policeman was useful to him here. Fred Denniston, for his part, rarely left the office. His specialty was estimating the credit-worthiness of companies. He gradually became expert at reading between the lines of optimistic profit-and-loss accounts and precariously balanced balance sheets. He developed, with experience, a quite uncanny instinct for over-valued stocks and under-depreciated assets. Perrot would sometimes see him holding a suspect document delicately between his fingers and sniffing at it, as though he could detect, by smell alone, the odor of falsification.

One factor that helped them to show a steady profit was their absurdly small rent. When Perrot had described the lease as a "snip" he was not exaggerating. At the end of the war, when no one was bothered about inflation, twenty-one-year leases could be had without the periodical reviews which are commonplace today. As the end of their lease approached, the partners did become aware that they were paying a good deal less than the market rent. Indeed, they could hardly help being aware of it—their landlords, the Scotus Property Company, commented on it with increasing bitterness.

"It's no good complaining about it," said Perrot genially. "You should have thought about that when you granted the lease."

"Just you wait till the end of next year," said Scotus.

Denniston said, "I suppose we shall have to pay a bit more. Anyway, they can't turn us out. We're protected tenants."

When a friendly valuer from the other end of Chancery Lane learned what their rent was, he struggled to control his feelings. "I suppose you realize," he said, "that you're paying a pound a square foot—"

"Just about what I made it," said Denniston.

"And that the going rate in this area is between five and six pounds."

"You mean," said Perrot, "that when our lease comes to an end, we'll have to pay five times the present rent."

"Oh, at least that," said the valuer cheerfully. "But I imagine you've been putting aside a fund to meet it."

The partners looked at each other. They were well aware that they had been doing nothing of the sort.

That was the first shock.

The second shock was Perrot's death. He had been putting on weight and smoking too much, but had looked healthy enough. One afternoon he complained of not feeling well, went home early, and died that night.

Denniston had been fond of him and his first feelings were of personal loss. His next feeling was that he was going to need another partner and additional capital; and that fairly quickly.

He considered and rejected the idea of inviting Mr. Huffin to become a partner. The main drawback was that Denniston disliked him. And he was so totally negative. He crept into the office every morning on the stroke of nine and, unless he had some outside business, stayed in his room, which had been partitioned off from Denniston's, until half past five. The partition was so thin that Denniston could hear him every time he got up from his chair.

Not partner material, said Denniston to himself.

He tried advertising, but soon found that the limited number of applicants who had capital would have been unsuitable as partners, while the rather greater number who might have been acceptable as partners had no capital.

After some months of fruitless effort he realized two other things. The first was that they were losing business. Jim Perrot's clients were taking their affairs elsewhere. The second was that the day of reckoning with his landlords was looming.

It was at this point that Andrew Gurney turned up. Denniston liked him at sight. He was young. He was cheerful. He seemed anxious to learn the business. And he made a proposal.

In about a year's time, when he attained the ripe old age of twenty-five, he would be coming into a bit of capital under a family trust. By that time he would have a fair idea whether the business suited him and he suited them. All being well, he was prepared to invest that capital in the firm.

They discussed amounts and dates and came to a tentative agreement. Gurney took over Perrot's old room. Denniston breathed a sigh of relief and turned his mind to the analysis of a complex set of group accounts.

It was almost exactly a month later when Mr. Huffin knocked on his door, put his head round, blinked twice, and said, "If you're not too busy, I wonder if I might have a word with you."

"I'm doing nothing that can't wait," said Denniston.

Mr. Huffin slid into the room, advanced toward the desk, and then, as if changing his mind at the last moment, seated himself in the chair that was normally reserved for clients.

Denniston was conscious of a slight feeling of surprise. Previously when Mr. Huffin had come to see him, he had stood in front of the desk and had waited, if the discussion was likely to be lengthy, for an invitation to sit down.

He was even more surprised when Mr. Huffin spoke. He said, "You're in trouble, aren't you?"

It was not only that Mr. Huffin had omitted the "sir" which he had previously used when addressing his employer. It was more than that. There was something sharp and cold in the tone of his voice. It was like the sudden unexpected chill which announces the end of autumn and the beginning of winter.

"You haven't seen fit to take me into your confidence," Mr. Huffin continued, "but the wall between our offices is so thin that it's impossible for me not to hear every word that's said."

Denniston had recovered himself sufficiently to say, "The fact that you can overhear confidential matters doesn't entitle you to trade on them."

"When the ship's sinking," said Mr. Huffin, "etiquette has to go by the board."

This was followed by a silence which Denniston found difficult to break. In the end he said, "It's true that Mr. Perrot's death has left us in a difficult position. But as it happens, I have been able to make arrangements which should tide us over."

"You mean young Gurney? In the month he's been here, he's earned less than half you pay him. And speaking personally, I should have said that he's got no real aptitude for the work. What you need is someone without such nice manners, but with a thicker skin."

Denniston said, "Look here, Mr. Huffin—" and stopped. He was on the point of saying, "If you don't like the way I run this firm, we can do without you." But could they?

As though reading his thoughts, Mr. Huffin said, "In the old days, Mr. Perrot, you, and I earned roughly equal amounts. Recently the proportions have been slipping. Last year I brought in half our fees. At least those were the figures you gave our auditor, so I assume they're correct."

"You listened to that discussion also?"

"I felt I was an interested party."

Mr. Denniston said, "All right. I accept that your services have been valuable. If that's your point, you've made it. I imagine it's leading up to something else. You want an increase in salary?"

"Not really."

"Then perhaps you had it in mind that I should make you a partner?"

"Not exactly."

"Then—"

"My proposal was that I should take over the firm."

In the long silence that followed, Denniston found himself revising his opinion of Mr. Huffin. His surface meekness was, he realized, a piece of professional camouflage, as meaningless as the wigs of the barristers and the pin-striped trousers of the solicitors.

Mr. Huffin added, "Have you thought out what would happen if I did leave? Maybe you could make enough to cover expenses. Until your lease expires. But what then? Have you, I wonder, overlooked one point. At the conclusion of a twenty-one-year lease there is bound to be a heavy bill for dilapidations."

"Dilapidations?" said Denniston slowly. The five syllables chimed together in an ominous chord. "Surely, there's nothing much to do."

"I took the precaution of having a word with an old friend, a Mr. Ellen. He's one of the surveyors used by the Scotus Property Company. He's a leading expert in his field and his calculations are very rarely challenged by the court. Last weekend I arranged for him to make an inspection. He thought that the cost of carrying out all the necessary work in a first-class fashion would be between six and eight thousand pounds."

"For God's sake!" said Denniston. "It can't be!"

"He showed me the breakdown. It could be more."

To give himself time to think, Denniston said, after a pause, "If you have such a poor opinion of the prospects of the firm, why would you want to buy me out?"

"I'm sorry," said Mr. Huffin gently. "You've misunderstood me. I wasn't proposing to pay you anything. After all, what have you got to sell?"

It was not Denniston's habit to discuss business with his wife, but this was a crisis. He poured out the whole matter to her as soon as he got home that evening.

"And I know damned well what he'll do," he said. "As soon as he's got me out, he'll bring in some accomplice of his own. They won't stick to divorce work. That's legal, at least. The real money's in dirty work. Finding useful witnesses and bribing them to say what your client wants. Faking evidence. Fudging expert reports."

His wife said, "He seems to be prepared to pay eight thousand pounds for the privilege of doing it."

"Of course he won't: that's a put-up job between him and his old pal, Mr. Ellen, of Scotus. He'll pay a lot less and be allowed to pay it in easy installments."

"What happens if you say no?"

"I'd have to challenge the dilapidations. It'd mean going to court and that's expensive."

"If you used some of Gurney's money—" Mrs. Denniston stopped.

They were both straightforward people. Denniston put what she was thinking into words. "I can't take that boy's money and put it into a legal wrangle."

"And there's no other way of raising it?"

"None that I can think of."

"Then that's that," said his wife. "I'd say cut your losses and clear out. We're still solvent. We'll think of something to do."

It took a lot of talk to persuade him, but in the end he saw the force of her arguments. "All right," he said. "No sense in dragging it out. I'll go in tomorrow and tell Huffin he can have the firm. I'll also tell him what I think of him."

"It won't do any good."
"It'll do me a lot of good."

On the following evening, Denniston arrived back on the stroke of six. He kissed his wife and said to her, "Whatever you were thinking of cooking for supper, think again. We're going out to find the best dinner London can provide. We'll drink champagne before it, burgundy with it, and brandy after it."

His wife, who had spent the day worrying about how they were going to survive, said, "Really, Fred. Do you think we ought—"

"Certainly we ought. We're celebrating."

"Celebrating what?"

"A miracle."

It had happened at nine o'clock that morning. While Denniston was polishing up the precise terms in which he intended to say good-bye to Mr. Huffin, his secretary came into his room. She was looking ruffled. She said, "Could you be free to see Mr. Kavanagh at ten?"

Denniston looked at his diary and said, "Yes. That'll be all right. Who is Mr. Kavanagh?"

"Mr. Ronald Kavanagh," said his secretary. While he was still looking blank, she added, "Kavanagh Lewisohn and Fitch. He's the chairman."

Denniston said, "Good God!" And then, "How do you know that?"

"Before I came here, I worked in their head office."

"Do you know Mr. Kavanagh?"

His secretary said, "I was in the typing pool. I caught a glimpse of him twice in the three years I was there."

"Did he say what he wanted?"

"He wanted to see you."

"You're sure he didn't ask me to go and see him? He's coming here?"

"That's what he said."

"It must be some mistake," said Denniston.

Kavanagh Lewisohn and Fitch were so well known that people said KLF and assumed you would understand what they meant. They were one of the largest credit-sale firms in London, so large that they rarely dealt with individual customers. They sold everything from computer banks to motor cars and television sets and washing machines to middle men, who in turn sold them to retailers. If Ronald Kavanagh was really planning to visit a small firm of enquiry agents, it could hardly be in connection with business matters. It must be private trouble. Something that needed to be dealt with discreetly.

When Kavanagh arrived, he turned out, surprisingly, to be a slight, quiet, unassuming person in his early fifties. Denniston was agreeably surprised. Such managing directors of large companies as he had come across in the past had been intimidating people, assertive of their status and conscious of their financial muscle. A further surprise was that he really had come to talk business.

He said, "This is something I wanted to deal with myself. Some time ago you did credit-rating reports for us on two potential customers." He mentioned their names.

"Yes," said Denniston, wondering what had gone wrong.

"We were impressed by the thorough way you tackled them. I assume, by the way, that you did the work yourself."

Denniston nodded.

"You gave a good rating to one, although it was a new company. The other, which was older and apparently sound, you warned us against. In both cases, you were absolutely right. That's why I'm here today. Up to the present we've been getting the reports we needed from half a dozen different sources. This is now such an important part of our business that the Board has decided that it would like to concentrate it in one pair of hands. Our first idea was to offer you the work on a retainer basis. Then we had a better idea." Mr. Kavanagh smiled. "We decided to buy you. That is, of course, if you're for sale."

Denniston was incapable of speech.

"We had it in mind to purchase your business as a going concern. We would take over the premises as they stand. There is, however, one condition. It's *your* brains and *your* flair that we're buying. We should have to ask you to enter into a service contract, at a fair salary, for five years certain, with options on both sides to renew. Your existing staff, too, if they wish. But you are the one we must have."

The room, which had shown signs of revolving on its axis, slowed down. Denniston took a grip of himself. He said, "Your offer is more than fair, but there is one thing you ought to know. You spoke of taking over these premises. There is a snag—"

When he had finished, Kavanagh said, "It was good of you to tell me. It accords, if I may say so, with your reputation. We are not unacquainted with Scotus." He smiled gently. "We had some dealings with them over one of our branch offices last year. Fortunately, we have very good solicitors and excellent surveyors. The outcome was a lot happier for us than it was for them. However, in this case it doesn't arise. Our own service department will carry out such repairs and redecoration as *we* consider necessary. If Scotus object, they can take us to court. I don't think they will. They're timid folk when they're up against someone bigger than themselves."

"Like all bullies," said Denniston. As he said it, he reflected with pleasure that Mr. Huffin had undoubtedly got his ear glued to the wall.

*   *   *

It soon became apparent that Ronald Kavanagh was not a man who delegated to others things that he enjoyed doing himself.

On the morning after the deal had been signed, he limped into the room, accompanied by the head of his service department and a foreman. They inspected everything and made notes. The next morning, a gang of workmen arrived and started to turn the office upside down.

Kavanagh arrived with the workmen. He said to Denniston, "We'll start with your room. Strip and paint the whole place. They can do it in two days. What colors do you fancy?"

"Something cheerful."

"I agree. My solicitor's office looks as if it hasn't been dusted since Charles Dickens worked there. What we want is an impression of cheerful reliability. Cream paint, venetian blinds, and solid-brass light fittings. And we'll need a second desk. I propose to establish a niche here for myself. I hope you don't mind."

"I don't mind at all," said Denniston. It occurred to him that one cause of his depression had been that since Perrot's death he had really had no one to talk to. "I'll be glad of your company, though I don't suppose you'll be able to spare us a lot of time."

"It's a common fallacy," said Kavanagh, sitting on a corner of the table, swinging his damaged leg ("a relic of war service," he had explained), "widely believed, but quite untrue, that managing directors are busy men. If they are, it's a sign of incompetence. I have excellent subordinates who do the real work. All I have to do is utter occasional sounds of approval or disapproval. It's such a boring life that a new venture like this is a breath of fresh air. Oh, you want to move this table. We'd better shift into young Gurney's office.

"As I was saying," he continued when they had established themselves in Gurney's room, "I have an insatiable curiosity about the mechanics of other people's business. When we went into the secondhand car market, we took over a motor-repair outfit. I got so interested that I put on overalls and started to work there myself. The men thought it was a huge joke, but they soon got used to it. And the things I learned about faking repair bills, you wouldn't believe. Oh, sorry—I'm afraid they want to start work in here, too. Let's go to my club and get ourselves an early luncheon."

Denniston found the new regime very pleasant. Kavanagh did not, of course, spend all his time with them, but he managed to put in a full hour on most days. His method of working was to have copies made, on the modern photocopying machine which had been one of his first innovations, of all of Denniston's reports. These he would study carefully, occasionally asking for the working papers. The questions he asked were shrewd and could not be answered without thought.

"Really," he said, "we're in the same line of business. Success depends on finding out who to trust. I once turned down a prosperous-looking television wholesaler because he turned up in a Green Jackets' tie. I'm damned certain he'd never been near the Brigade. Quite the wrong shape for a Rifleman."

"Instinct, based on experience," agreed Denniston. He already felt years younger. It was not only the steady flow of new work and the certainty of getting a check at the end of each month, the whole office seemed to have changed. Even Mr. Huffin appeared to be happy. Not only had his room been repainted, it had been furnished with a new desk and a set of gleaming filing cabinets equipped with Chubb locks. These innovations seemed to have compensated him for the setback to his own plans and he went out of his way to be pleasant to Kavanagh when he encountered him.

"Slimy toad," said Denniston to his wife. "When I asked Kavanagh if he planned to keep him, he laughed and said, 'Why not? I don't much like the sort of work he's doing, but it brings in good money. As long as he keeps within the law. If you hear any complaints of sharp practice, that's another matter.' "

"Mr. Kavanagh sounds terrific."

"Terrific's not quite the right word. He's honest, sensible, and unassuming. Also, he's still a bit of a schoolboy. He likes to see the wheels go round."

"I don't believe a single word of it," said his wife.

"Well, Uncle," said Andrew Gurney. "What next?"

Kavanagh said, "Next, I think, a glass of port."

"Then it must be something damned unpleasant," said Gurney.

"Why?"

"If it wasn't, you wouldn't be wasting the Club port on me."

"You're an irreverent brat," said Kavanagh.

"When you wangled me into the firm I guessed you were up to something."

"Two large ports, please, Barker. Actually, Andrew, all I want you to do is to commit a burglary."

"I said it was going to be something unpleasant."

"But this is a very safe burglary. You're to burgle the offices of Denny's Detectives. Since the firm belongs to me, technically hardly a burglary at all, would you say?"

"Well—," said Gurney cautiously.

"I will supply you with the key of the outer door, the key of Mr. Huffin's room, and a key for each of his new filing cabinets and his desk. Mr. Huffin is a careful man. When the desk and cabinets were installed, he asked for the duplicate keys to be handed to him. Fortunately, I had a second copy made of each. Nevertheless, I was much encouraged by his request. It showed me that I might be on the right track."

"What track?"

Kavanagh took a sip of his port and said, "It's Warre '63. Don't gulp it. I suggest that you start around eleven o'clock. By that time, Chancery Lane should be deserted except for the occasional policeman. In case you should run into trouble, I'll supply you with a note stating that you are working late with my permission."

"Yes, Uncle, but—"

"When you get into Mr. Huffin's room, take all the files from his cabinets and all the papers from his desk and photograph them. Be very careful to put them back in the order you found them."

"Yes, but—"

"I don't imagine you'll be able to finish the job in one night, or even in two. When you leave, bring the photocopies round to my flat. You can use my spare room and make up for your lost nights by sleeping by day. I'll warn my housekeeper. As far as the office is concerned, you're out of town on a job for me. I think that's all quite straightforward."

"Oh, quite," said Gurney. "The only thing is you haven't told me what you're up to."

"When I've had a chance of examining Mr. Huffin's papers, I may have a clearer idea myself. As soon as I do, I'll put you in the picture."

Andrew sighed. "When do you want me to start?"

"It's Monday today. If you start tomorrow night, you should be through by the end of the week. I suggest you go home now and get a good night's rest."

As his uncle had predicted, it took Andrew exactly four nights to finish the job. If he expected something dramatic to happen, he was disappointed. For a week his uncle failed to turn up at the office.

"Our owner," said Mr. Huffin with a smirk, "seems to have lost interest in us."

Andrew smiled and agreed. He had just had an invitation to dinner at his uncle's flat in Albany and guessed that things might be moving.

During dinner, his uncle spoke only of cricket. He was a devotee of the Kent team, most of whom he seemed to know by name. After dinner, which was cooked and served by the housekeeper, they retired to the sitting room. Kavanagh said, "And how did you enjoy your experience as a burglar?"

"It was a bit creepy at first. After nightfall, Chancery Lane seems to be inhabited by howling cats."

"They're not cats. They're the spirits of disappointed litigants."

"Did I produce whatever it was you were looking for?"

"The papers from the cabinets related only to Mr. Huffin's routine work. They showed him to be a thorough, if somewhat unscrupulous operator. A model trufflehound. Ninety-nine percent of his private papers likewise. But the other one percent—two memoranda and a bundle of receipts—were worth all the rest put together. They demonstrated that Mr. Huffin has a second job. He's a moonlighter."

"He's crooked enough for anything. What's his other job? Some sort of blackmail, I suppose."

"Try not to use words loosely, Andrew. Blackmail has become a portmanteau word covering everything from illegal intimidation to the use of lawful leverage."

"I can't imagine Mr. Huffin intimidating anyone."

"Personally, probably not. But he has a partner. And that man we must now locate. Those scraps of paper are his footprints."

Andrew looked at his uncle. He knew something of the work he had done during the war, but he found it hard to visualize this mild grey-haired man pursuing, in peace, the tactics which had brought Karl Muller and others to the rifle range in the Tower. For the first time, he was striking the flint under the topsoil and it was a curiously disturbing experience. He said, "You promised—"

"Yes, I promised. So be it. Does the name David Rogerson mean anything to you?"

"I know he was one of your friends."

"More than that. During the retreat to Dunkirk, he managed to extract me from a crashed and burning lorry—which was, incidentally, full of explosives. That was when I broke my right leg in several places and contracted this limp which ended my service as an Infanteer. Which was why I went into Intelligence.

"I kept up with David after the war. Not as closely as I should have liked. He had married a particularly stupid woman. However, we met once or twice a year for lunch in the City. We were both busy. I was setting up KLF and he was climbing the ladder in Clarion Insurance. About six months ago, he asked me to lend him some money—a thousand pounds. Of course I said yes and didn't ask him what he wanted it for. But I suppose he felt he owed me some sort of explanation. When he was leaving he said, with something like a smile, 'Do you play draughts?' I said I did when I was a boy. 'Well,' he said, 'I've been huffed. By Mr. Huffin.' Those were his last words to me. The next news I had was of his death."

Gurney said, "I read about that. No one seemed to know why he did it."

"You may recall that at the inquest his wife was asked whether he had left a note. She said no. That was a lie. He did leave a note, as I discovered later. David had made me executor. My first job was to look after his wife. I soon saw that Phyllis Rogerson had one objective. To live her own life on

the proceeds of some substantial insurance policies David had taken out—
and to forget about him. I accepted that this was a natural reaction. Women
are realists. It was when I was clearing up his papers that she told me the
truth. He *had* left a letter and it was addressed to me. She said, 'I guessed it
was something to do with the trouble he'd been having. I knew that if you
read it all the unpleasantness would have to come out into the open, so I
burnt it. I didn't even read it.' I said, 'If it was some sort of blackmailer,
David won't have been his only victim. He must be caught and punished.'
She wouldn't listen. I haven't spoken to her since."

"But you located Mr. Huffin."

"That wasn't difficult. The Huffin clan isn't large. A clergyman in Shropshire, a farmer in Wales, a maiden lady in Northumberland. Little Mr.
Huffin of Denny's Detectives was so clearly the first choice that I had no
hesitation in trying him first."

"Clearly enough for you to spend your company's money in buying the
agency?"

"We were on the lookout for a good credit-rating firm. My Board was
unanimous that Denniston was the man for the job. So I was able to kill
two birds with one stone—always an agreeable thing to do. My first idea
was to expose Huffin as a blackmailer. I felt that there would be enough
evidence in his files to convict him. I was wrong. What those papers show
is that a second man is involved—possibly the more important villain of
the two. I see Huffin as the reconnaissance unit, the other man as the heavy
brigade."

"Do you know his name?"

"The only lead I have to him is that Mr. Huffin used to communicate
privately with a Mr. Angus. The address he wrote to was a small news-
agent's shop in Tufnell Park, an accommodation address, no doubt. Receipts
for the payments he made to the shopkeeper were among his papers. I
visualize Mr. Angus calling from time to time to collect his letters. Or he
may send a messenger. That is something we shall have to find out."

"And you want me to watch the shop?"

"It's kind of you to offer. But no. Here I think we want professional
help. Captain Smedley will be the man for the job. You've never heard of
him? He's the head of a detective agency." Rather unkindly, Kavanagh
added, "A *real* detective agency, Andrew."

Captain Smedley said, "I shall need exactly a hundred, in ones and fives.
That's what it will cost to buy the man in the shop. I'll pay it to him
myself. He won't play silly buggers with me."

Kavanagh looked at Captain Smedley, who had a face like a hank of
wire rope, and agreed that no one was likely to play silly buggers with him.

"I'll have a man outside," Smedley said. "All the shopkeeper's got to do is tip him the wink when the letter's collected. Then my man follows him back to wherever he came from."

"Might it be safer to have two men outside?"

"Safer, but more expensive."

"Expense no object."

"I see," said the Captain. He looked curiously at Mr. Kavanagh, whom he had known for some time. "All right. I'll fix it up for you."

On the Wednesday of the third week following this conversation, Kavanagh got a thick plain envelope addressed to him at his flat. It contained several pages of typescript, which he read carefully. The look on his face was partly enlightenment and partly disgust. "What a game," he said. "I wonder how they work it."

After breakfast, he spent some time in the reference section of the nearest public library browsing among Civil Service lists and copies of *Whittaker's Almanac*. Finally he found the name he wanted. Arnold Robbins. Yes, Arnold would certainly help him if the matter was put to him in the right way. But it would need devilish careful handling. "A jackal," he said, "and a tiger. Now all we need is a tethered goat to bring the tiger under the rifle. But it will have to be tethered very carefully, in exactly the right spot. The brute is a man-eater, no question."

A lady touched him on the shoulder and pointed to the notice which said SILENCE, PLEASE. He was not aware that he had spoken aloud.

During the months that followed, Kavanagh resumed his regular visits to the office in Chancery Lane, but Denniston noticed that his interest in the details of the work seemed to be slackening. He would still read the current reports and comment on them, but more of his time seemed to be spent in conversation.

In the old days, Denniston might have objected to this as being a waste of time which could better have been spent in earning profits. Now it was different. He was being paid a handsome salary, and if it pleased the owner of the firm to pass an occasional hour in gossip why should he object? Moreover, Kavanagh was an excellent talker, with a rich fund of experience in the byways of the jungle which lies between Temple Bar and Aldgate Pump. Politics, economics, finance; honesty, dishonesty, and crime. Twenty years of cut-and-thrust between armies whose soldiers wore lounge suits and carried rolled umbrellas—warfare in which victory could be more profitable and defeat more devastating than on any field of battle.

On one occasion, Kavanagh, after what must have been an unusually good luncheon, had devoted an entertaining hour to a dissertation on the tax system.

"At the height of their power and arrogance," he said, "the Church demanded one-tenth of a man's income. The government of England exacts six times as much. The pirate who sank an occasional ship, the highwayman who held up a coach, was a child compared to the modern taxman."

"You can't fight the State," said Denniston.

"It's been tried. Poujade in France. But I agree that massive tax resistance is self-defeating. Each man must fight for himself. There are lawyers and accountants who specialize in finding loopholes in the tax laws, but such success can only be temporary. As soon as a loophole is discovered, the next Finance Act shuts it up. The essentials of guerrilla warfare are concealment and agility."

Really interested now, Denniston said, "Have you discovered a practical method of sidestepping tax? I've never made excessive profits, but I do resent handing over a slab of what I've made to a government who spends most of it on vote-catching projects."

"My method isn't one which would suit everyone. Its merit is simplicity. I arrange with my Board that they will pay me only two-thirds of what I ought to be getting. The other third goes to charities nominated by me. They, of course, pay no tax. That part of it is quite legitimate. Our constitution permits gifts to charity."

"Then how—?"

"The only fact which is *not* known is that I set up and control the charities concerned. One is a local village affair. Another looks after our own employees. A third is for members of my old Regiment. I am chairman, secretary, and treasurer of all three. Some of the money is devoted to the proper objects of the charity. The balance comes back, by various routes, to me. A lovely tax-free increment."

"But," said Denniston, "surely—"

"Yes?"

"It seems too simple."

"But, I assure you, effective."

And later, to himself, Kavanagh asked, I wonder if that was too obvious. I can only wait and see.

"There's something stirring," said Captain Smedley. "My men tell me those two beauties have got a regular meeting place. Top of the Duke of York's Steps. It isn't possible to get close enough to hear what they're saying—no doubt that's why they chose it—but they're certainly worked up about something. Licking their lips, you might say."

"The bleating of the goat," said Kavanagh, "excites the tiger."

The letter which arrived at his flat a week later was in a buff envelope, typed on buff paper. It was headed *Inland Revenue Special Investigation Branch.* It said, "Our attention has been drawn by the Charity Commissioners to certain apparent discrepancies in the latest accounts submitted to them of the undermentioned charities, all of which have been signed by you as treasurer. It is for this reason that we are making a direct approach to you before any further action is considered. The charities are the Lamperdown Village Hall Trust, the City of London Fusiliers' Trust, and the KLF Employees' Special Fund. You may feel that an interview would clarify the points at issue, in which case the writer would be happy to call on you, either at your place of business or at your residence, as you may prefer."

The writer appeared to be a Mr. Wagner.

Kavanagh observed with appreciation the nicely judged mixture of official suavity and concealed threat. A queen's pawn opening.

Before answering it, he had a telephone call to make. The man he was asking for was evidently important since he had to be approached through a secretary and a personal assistant, with suitable pauses at each stage. When contact had been made, a friendly conversation ensued, conducted on christian-name terms. It concluded with Ronnie inviting Arnold to lunch at his club on the following Monday.

He then composed a brief letter to Mr. Wagner, suggesting a meeting at his flat at seven o'clock in the evening on the following Wednesday. He apologized for suggesting such a late hour, but daytime commitments made it difficult to fix anything earlier.

"I wonder if it really is a tiger," said Kavanagh, "or only a second jackal. That would be disappointing."

When he opened the door to his visitor, his fears were set at rest. Mr. Wagner was a big man, with a red-brown face. There was a tuft of sandy hair growing down each cheekbone. He had the broad, flattened nose of a pugilist. His eyes were so light as to be almost yellow and a deep fold ran down under each eye to form a fence round the corners of an unusually wide mouth. His black coat was glossy, his legs decorously striped. He was a tiger. A smooth and shining tiger.

"Come in," said Kavanagh. "I'm alone this evening. Can I get you a drink?"

"Not just now," said Mr. Wagner.

He seated himself, opened his briefcase, took out a folder of papers, and laid it on the table. This was done without a word spoken. The folder was tied with tape. Mr. Wagner's spatulate fingers toyed with the tape and finally untied it. With deliberation, he extracted a number of papers and arranged them in two neat lines. Kavanagh, who had also seated himself, seemed hypnotized by this methodical proceeding.

When everything was to his satisfaction, Mr. Wagner raised his heavy head, fixed his yellow eyes on Kavanagh, and said, "I'm afraid you're in trouble." An echo. Had not Mr. Huffin said the same thing to Fred Denniston?

"Trouble?"

"You're in trouble. You've been cheating."

Kavanagh said, "Oh!" Then, sinking a little in his chair: "You've no right to say a thing like that."

"I've every right to say it, because it's true. I've been studying the accounts of the three charities I mentioned in my letter. In particular, the accounts you submitted last month. They proved interesting indeed." The voice had become a purr. "Previously, your accounts were in such general terms that they might have meant—or concealed—anything. The latest accounts are, fortunately, much fuller and much more specific."

"Well," said Kavanagh, trying out a smile, "the Commissioners did indicate that they wanted rather more detail as to where the money went."

"Yes, Mr. Kavanagh. And where *did* it go?"

"It's—" Kavanagh waved a hand feebly toward the table. "It's all here. In the accounts."

"Then shall we look at them? These are the accounts of the Fusiliers' Trust. Previously the accounts only showed a lump sum, described as 'Grants to disabled Fusiliers and to the widows and dependents of deceased Fusiliers.' "

"Yes. Yes, that's right."

"In the latest accounts you supply a list of their names." The voice deepened even further. The purr became a growl. The tiger was ready to spring. "A very interesting list, because on reference to the Army authorities we have been unable to find any record of any of the people you mentioned as having served with the Fusiliers."

"Possibly—"

"Yes, Mr. Kavanagh?"

"Some mistake—"

"Thirty names. *All* of them fictitious?"

Kavanagh seemed incapable of speech.

"On the other hand, when we look at the KLF Fund we find that the names you have given do correspond to the names of former employees of the firm. But a further question then presents itself. Have these people in fact received the sums shown against their names? Well? Well? Nothing to say? It would be very simple to find out. A letter to each of them—"

This seemed to galvanize Kavanagh into action for the first time. He half rose in his seat and said, "No. I absolutely forbid it."

"But are you in any position to forbid it?"

Kavanagh considered this question carefully, conscious that Mr. Wagner's yellow eyes were watching him. Then he said, "It does seem that there may have been some irregularity in the presentation of these accounts. I cannot attend to all these matters myself, you understand. Income may not always go where it should. There may be some tax which ought to have been paid—"

Mr. Wagner had begun to smile. The opening of his lips displayed a formidable set of teeth.

"I had always understood," went on Kavanagh, "that in these circumstances, if the tax was paid, together with a sum by way of penalties—"

Mr. Wagner's mouth shut with a snap. He said, "Then you misunderstood the position. It is not simply a question of payment. When you sign your tax return, the form is so arranged that if you make a deliberate misstatement you can be charged before the court with perjury."

There was a long silence. Kavanagh was thinking, So this is how he does it. Poor old David. I wonder what slip-ups he made. I'm sure it was unintentional, but a charge of perjury. Good-bye to his prospects with the Clarion. And a lot of other things, too.

He said, in a voice which had become almost a bleat, "You must understand how serious that would be for me, Mr. Wagner. I'd be willing to pay any sum rather than have that happen. Is there no way—" He let the sentence tail off.

Mr. Wagner had taken a silver pencil from his pocket and seemed to be making some calculations. He said, "If, in fact, the sums of money shown as going to the beneficiaries of these three trusts ended up in your own pocket, I would estimate—a rough calculation only—that you have been obtaining at least ten thousand pounds a year free of tax. I am not aware of how long this very convenient arrangement has been going on. Five years? Possibly more? Had you declared this income, you would have paid at least thirty thousand pounds in tax."

"Exactly," said Kavanagh eagerly. "That's the point I was making. Isn't this something that could more easily be solved by a money payment? At the moment I have considerable resources. If a charge of perjury was brought, they would largely disappear. What good would that do anyone?"

Mr. Wagner appeared to consider the matter. Then he smiled. It was a terrible smile. He said, "I have some sympathy with that point of view, Mr. Kavanagh. Allow me to make a suggestion. It is a friendly suggestion and you can always refuse it. At the moment, the file is entirely under my control. The information came from a private source. It is known only to me. You follow me?"

"I think so. Yes."

Mr. Wagner leaned forward and said with great deliberation, "If you will pay me ten thousand pounds, the file will be destroyed."

"Ten thousand pounds?"

"Ten thousand pounds."

"How would the payment be made?"

"You would pay the money into an account in the name of M. Angus at the Westminster Branch of the London and Home Counties Bank."

"That should be enough for you," said Kavanagh. He was addressing the door leading into the next room, which now opened to admit Sir Arnold Robbins, the Deputy Head of Inland Revenue, and two other men.

Robbins said, "You are suspended from duty. These gentlemen are police officers. They will accompany you and will impound your passport. It will be for the Director of Public Prosecutions to decide on any further action."

Mr. Wagner was on his feet. His face was engorged. A trickle of blood ran from one nostril down his upper lip. He dashed it away with the back of his hand and said, in a voice thick with fury, "So it was a trap!"

"You must blame your accomplice for that," said Kavanagh. "He saw the writing on the wall and sold you to save his own skin. There's not much honor among thieves."

When Wagner had gone, Sir Arnold said, "I apologize for not believing you. I suppose the fact is that we give these special-investigation people too much rope. Incidentally, I've had a look at Rogerson's file. It was as you thought. A minor omission, not even his own income. Some money his wife got from Ireland. She may not even have told him about it."

"Probably not," said Kavanagh. He switched off the microphone, which connected with the next room. "We've got all this on tape if you need it."

"Good. And, by the way, I take it those donations of yours are in order?"

"Perfectly. Every penny that went into these charities has gone to the beneficiaries. I'll show you the receipts. The only thing I fudged was that list of Fusilier names. I'll have to apologize to the Charity Commissioners and send them the correct list."

As Sir Arnold was going, he said, "Why did you tell Wagner it was his accomplice who had shopped him? Was it true?"

"It was untrue," said Kavanagh. "But I thought it might have some interesting results. It's going to be very difficult to get at Mr. Huffin. He really was only the jackal. He picked up scraps of information when he was doing his job and fed them to Wagner, who moved in for the kill. Wagner will be at liberty until the Director makes up his mind. I felt we should give him a chance to ask Mr. Huffin for an explanation."

"He didn't say anything," said Captain Smedley. "He just hit him. Huffin's not a big man. It lifted him off his feet and sent him backward down the steps. Cracked his skull. Dead before he got to hospital."

"And Mr. Wagner?"

"I had a policeman standing by, like you suggested. I thought he was going to put up a fight, but he seemed dazed. When they got him to the station, he just keeled over."

"You don't mean he's dead, too?"

"No. But near enough. And if he does recover from whatever it is—a stroke of kinds—he's in every sort of trouble. A good riddance to a nasty pair."

But that was not their real epitaph. That had been spoken by Colonel Hubert on the evening of April 15th in the year 1944.

THE FIX

by ROBERT TWOHY

Stremberg got the word on the third race at Peninsula Meadows. It came from Vassily, a part-time private guard at the track who knew things. Vassily had given Stremberg three tips in the past five years and they had all paid off. Vassily wasn't a klutz or a juicehead and he knew the race game— and he liked Stremberg who had driven him for years and had done some favors for him. They weren't buddies but they could trust each other.

Vassily said that he knew the trainer of Bugle Call. Bugle had been held back his last six outings to set up a payday. The payday was today, Thursday the 9th. All the jocks were in on it. Bugle would get off at least 20 to 1. He'd run away from the field in the stretch.

Stremberg went to the Tropical Club, which on Thursday morning was pretty full of track fans having a few before taking off for the track. He had two one-dollar bills, three quarters, and two dimes in his pocket. That was all he had to his name. He wasn't working. He'd quit when the horses had come to Peninsula Meadows nearly two months ago. When Ray behind the bar put his beer in front of him Stremberg said, "Ray, you want in on a big one?"

Ray didn't look like he did. Stremberg went on talking, low, "The third is set up. I got the word."

"That a fact."

"Stake me ten and we'll split. I'll bring you back over a hundred."

Ray looked thoughtful. He stroked his thick chin. Stremberg felt hopeful.

Then Ray said, "Nah," and walked away.

Stremberg lit a cigarette. He looked along the mirror behind the bar, sizing up who was there.

Big Otto. He had the money. But Stremberg was scared of him. Otto was said to be the local syndicate man. He operated a chauffeur service, wore black suits, smoked thin cigars, and was always at the Tropical or the Moondust, drinking cola—never went near his chauffeur service. He had dark patches under tired-looking eyes that looked like he never slept, like

maybe he couldn't sleep because the faces of victims and their beat-up
bodies kept coming between him and sleep. Stremberg didn't want anything to do with Big Otto.

Graveyard Flo. Tall and skinny with big weird eyes who when you
drove her home in the cab sat beside you and stroked your hand with her
clammy claws and whispered, "Thank you for being you." Sometimes she
threw a fit and went rigid and more than a few times Stremberg had carried
her like a plank up the stairs to her second-floor apartment off Floribunda
and her husband Curly, who was a railroad accountant with a gimpy leg,
would open the door and say, "Oh, damn. Dump her on the couch," and
give Stremberg five bucks over the fare.

Flo was sitting alone at a table sipping something foamy in a long-
stemmed glass and looking over the daily form. It was worth a shot.

He went over to her with his beer. "How's it going, Flo?"

She looked at him with her big weird eyes.

"You, uh, see anything good going today?" He indicated the form.

She said, in a loud voice, "Do I know you?"

"Sure. Stremberg. You know, the cab driver."

"Ray, do I know this person?"

Everybody turned to look. Ah, hell, thought Stremberg, she's in one of
her goofy moods.

"Quit yelling, Flo," said Ray.

"Is this the kind of place where a ratty-looking individual comes up and
fersts himself off on a lady? Is that the kind of dump you run here?"

She was starting to breathe funny. Her eyes had begun to roll. She was
stiffening.

Ray called, "Stremberg, get the hell away from her."

"Yeah," said Stremberg. He went back to the bar.

Ray said, "Stay away from her."

"I will."

"She's ready to throw one. She went out of here last night with a guy
whose wife caught up with them in the Moondust and bopped her on the
head five times with a beer glass."

Stremberg shook his head, and sipped his beer. He looked in the mirror
and saw that Flo had stopped going stiff, and was quietly sipping her drink
and flicking her fingernail over the form.

He said when Ray came back up the bar, "Say, Ray, are you sure—"

"I'm sure."

Tiny Jane, about 70, with a face all blown up from drinking, slid up to
Stremberg. She held her little green coin purse in both spotty hands. "I
heard what you said to Ray when you came in. You need backing?"

"Hello, Tiny," he said, suddenly very weary.

"You're a nice little fella." Her voice was a creaky whisper. "You ain't a bad little fella at all. I'll stake you fifty dollars."

"Fine, Tiny."

She struggled the snaps of her purse open, stuck shaky fingers in, pulled out a nickel and a penny. He took them. "Thanks, Tiny."

"I trust you. You can bring me the money tonight. Now you can buy me a drink." Her face parted in a horrible grin.

She climbed like somebody climbing a fence up on the stool next to him. Ah, hell, thought Stremberg, and felt defeated. "Ray," he said, and thumbed at Tiny.

Ray poured her a shot of brandy, water back, and took all Stremberg's money except one buck and Tiny's six cents.

Hell, he thought, I'm out $1.95 already and I still don't have any backing.

Tiny took the brandy down in one loud suck. She moaned and sighed and tears ran down her swollen cheeks that looked ready to split open and spray liquor all over the place.

Stremberg looked at the clock. Past 11:30. Some of the fans were drifting out, to get down to the track—first post, 12:30.

The guy that always wore two hats, a dark regular hat and a kind of straw hat under it, and a pair of woman's dark glasses, came up on the other side of Stremberg. He was the guy who had once been a dentist with a big practice in town, and an estate on the hill. He said, sharp and low, "I got a good one going today."

"Yeah?" said Stremberg.

"Yeah. In the sixth. Split ten and I'll bring you back over $100."

"I'm not working. I only got a buck."

"Well, give me the buck then." The dentist sounded irritated.

Stremberg heard Tiny sighing on his left. The dentist had his hand out, was jiggling his fingers, getting impatient. Stremberg got a sudden strange and sinking feeling that he had no will of his own. He gave the dentist his last buck.

"Okay." The dentist went down the bar to hit up someone else.

Stremberg shook his head. I don't even know him, he said to himself. Why the hell did I give him my last buck?

He had the impulse to go after the ex-dentist and get his buck back, but that was stupid. You don't go chasing after a guy in a bar where you're known and argue about a buck.

But now all he had left was Tiny's six cents, half a pack of butts, and about an inch of beer.

Tiny said, "I could handle another."

"I'm sorry, Tiny."

"You're *sorry!*" Her voice was thin with amazement. She shook her blown-out cheeks at him. "Ray," she shrilled. "Ray!"

Ray happened to be three feet away, drawing a beer. "Yeah, Tiny," he said, not looking up.

"Can you imagine anyone as mean as this? I sit and talk with this man and he won't even buy me a drink!"

"Yeah, Tiny." Ray looked at Stremberg and there was a twist to his lips. "It don't seem like your day."

"Not yet it don't."

Tiny said, "That's dirty pool, mister! You know what? I'm a friend of Big Otto. He's right down the bar there."

"I know."

"You could be found in the alley with big red holes in your head."

She half slid, half fell from the stool. "Don't get smart with me," she said, and departed.

Ray drew a beer and put it in front of Stremberg.

Stremberg nodded, and drank half of it.

Ray lingered. "You really got something in the third?"

"Yeah. From Vassily."

"I don't know him. Do I?"

"Prob'ly not. He don't make the bars. But he's on the inside. He knows his stuff."

Ray reached in his pocket. "Okay." He handed over a $10 bill.

"Thanks, Ray. But now I need $3.50 more."

"Why?"

"Two-fifty to get in, buck for bus fare."

"Okay," said Ray, reaching again. "But that's a loan. You owe me $3.50."

"Thanks, Ray."

"Which horse?"

The bar was emptying, nobody was near, but you don't take chances. You want to keep the odds up. Stremberg put a hand to the side of his face, just scratching his cheek if anyone on that side was watching. He said low, "Bugle Call."

Ray raised his eyebrows, pursed his lips. "What's he done?"

"Nothing—never been close. They been setting it up for today. All the jocks are in on it."

Ray shook his head. Then he said, "Well, what do *I* know? I ain't had a winner all meet."

Stremberg finished his beer and pushed back from the bar.

As he got off the stool he realized he was being stared at. He turned. Graveyard Flo was the starer.

"Wait a minute!" she yelled, and her eyes started to roll. "Ray," she screamed, "who *is* that little rat?"

Ray said, "Get out of here, Stremberg."

"I'm going." He hurried out, as Flo kept screaming.

Ten minutes later he caught the bus. It was crowded. He stood in the aisle. A man pressed against him with a hard fat stomach. The man started to look at him, and Stremberg looked away. But there was no room to look away. To his right was someone's red neck with blisters. To his left was a woman's coiled blue hair. He couldn't turn his head far enough either way to avoid the fat man's stare.

He looked down, then up. Finally there was nothing to do but look back at the man.

The eyes were glazed, yellow-green. Under them was a pitted nose and under that a mouth which, as Stremberg helplessly stared, began to curve in a smile that got wider and wider, until Stremberg got a feeling the tongue was going to come looping out, like a soft sticky pink hook, and clamp around his neck.

He shuddered, tried to close his eyes—but they wouldn't close. The guy is hypnotizing me, he thought helplessly. Now why in hell is he doing that?

Then the bus slammed to a stop and everybody staggered around and fell into each other, and the hypnotist fell and staggered like everyone else, and Stremberg was freed from his spell. He stayed behind him as they all got off and from the rear the man seemed to be just an ordinary person, just a normal sloppy fat man hurrying to the track.

Stremberg thought suddenly, I'm pretty light-headed. He couldn't remember when he'd last had a meal.

He ran the gauntlet of hot-sheet touts, shouting and snarling in their booths, paid his entrance fee, and was in under the grandstand. He stood smoking cigarettes and watching while the first two races were run, with a Daily Double payoff of $42.60. Then the morning line started flashing for the third.

He copped a look at someone's program. Bugle Call was post position 6. The morning line was 15 to 1.

Stremberg waited, jumping around, smoking more cigarettes. The tote odds were climbing. Big Otto and his henchmen, who of course knew when a fix was on, were letting this one go by. They did that a lot—they knew what they were doing. Get too greedy and jump in on every boat ride and the public starts to catch on when the price dip shows suddenly on the tote, and then everyone's jumping in and it's a messed-up situation. The syndicate knows when to lie low.

40 to 1, the tote said now. $400 to split with Ray. Stremberg tried to keep his face masklike, but realized that he was walking around in a tight

quick circle and smacking his palms together. A man and a girl were looking at him. The girl giggled.

Stremberg hit his palms together a few more times, with a serious expression on his face like someone with a circulation problem who knows what he's doing, then walked away flopping his hands like checking to be sure the blood was flowing again. He thought he had done it in a cool way but as he walked away the girl seemed to be giggling louder.

He saw it was four minutes to post and hurried to the parimutuel lineup. The flashboard on the wall showed that Bugle Call was now 50 to 1. $500 to split with Ray. The syndicate hadn't jumped in on this one, just like he'd figured they wouldn't.

He put Ray's $10 on Number 6 to win, went back outside, and stood there tense and still, watching as they loaded the horses into the starting gate. Bugle Call went in prancing. He looked fit and sharp. His jock seemed to wear a tight, knowing grin. The grin was to let those in on the fix know that everything was set, on target.

The starting bell yanged, the gates whanged open.

Bugle broke good, and hitting the first turn of the mile race the jock had him tucked in at the rail in third place, two lengths back and running low and easy. Stremberg felt the deep joy he had been waiting to feel since the meet started 51 racing days ago beginning to build inside him.

Bugle ran smooth and easy through the back stretch and around the far turn, holding fourth now, five lengths back, and came out of the turn near the middle of the track with room on the outside, in perfect position—all the jocks had done their job, all cooperating to get Bugle positioned like this. Just like Vassily had said, he was going to run away from the field, a clear sweep down the stretch. The jock got ready to unload with the whip, and the deep joy swelled in Stremberg.

Then the horse hung.

Stremberg couldn't believe it. He watched it and couldn't believe it. It was like the animal had run into an 80-mile head wind. His legs moved like each shoe weighed 35 pounds. Everyone sailed past him up the stretch.

He couldn't believe it. Everything had gone just right all the way from the start.

And the jock had had that tight little grin.

Stremberg was walking toward the exit, fingering the six cents in his pocket, when it all came clear to him.

For reasons of its own the syndicate, which hadn't got in on this one, wanted the fix off. Maybe they'd got a flash that some Congressional committee investigating rackets in sports had got wind of the Bugle Call fix and was busy rigging up evidence that would make it look like the syndicate was behind the fix. So the syndicate flashed the word to the track to the guys behind the fix to take it off, and right now—and seconds from the finish, when he was starting up the stretch, the jock got the flash from the stands: It's off, pull him.

So the jock, hip as all jocks are, did as he was ordered.

Near the exit Stremberg saw Vassily, sagging against a wall, with a kind of stunned look on his face.

Vassily didn't duck away. He looked Stremberg in the eyes and mumbled, "I sure thought I was giving you the straight goods."

"You were," said Stremberg. "You couldn't know it would get called off."

Vassily rubbed his hand over his mouth. His eyes looked kind of stunned again. Then he said, "Yeah. Right. That's something you can't figure on."

"The syndicate does what they have to do."

"Right. They do what they have to do."

Stremberg fingered the six cents in his pocket. "Got a buck I can borrow for bus fare?"

Vassily went through his pockets. He had 23 cents. "I put all I had, $27, on Bugle Call."

Stremberg churned up a smile, to let Vassily know that Stremberg knew that if Vassily had a buck he'd lend it to Stremberg. "See you around." He turned away.

Vassily said, "You want the twenty-three cents?"

"No, that's okay."

"How you going to get home?"

"I'll probably run into someone I know with a car." He said good-bye to Vassily, and went out the exit.

In the parking lot he stopped to light his last butt. He stood and smoked it, then dropped it, and started walking the four miles home.

About four o'clock he got to the room he had at Mrs. Mustie's, and was glad to see her car gone, so she couldn't hassle him about the rent being eight days late. He locked his door, took off his shoes and jacket, stretched out on the bed, and went to sleep.

He woke up to hammering on the door. It was dark outside the window. Mrs. Mustie's terrible voice yelled, "Stremberg! I know you're in there! Open the door!" She kept on hammering and yelling as he lay quiet.

Finally her husband called from downstairs, "Oh, for Pete's sake, knock it off."

"The door's locked! He's in there!"

"So he's in there. So he ain't got the dough, so he ain't answering—what's the good hollering?"

"You know what's going to happen tomorrow, Stremberg?" she yelled. "Tomorrow a padlock goes on this door!"

Stremberg waited until she had lumped away down the stairs. Then he got up and stood at the window. He hoped she'd go out again. She spent most of every day going out somewhere or coming back. In a little while her mean-looking little white car rolled away down the drive.

He got his shoes and jacket back on, and put socks, shorts, two shirts, pants, comb, toothbrush, and razor, which were all the things he had in the world except what he was wearing, in the big grocery bag he carried them in when he moved. He opened the door and called, "Mr. Mustie?"

"Yeah, Stremberg."

"I'll be going. You better take a look so she won't yell I've swiped something."

A chair wheezed and Mr. Mustie came in sight, holding his evening *Courier.* He climbed the stairs while Stremberg waited. He said, "Where you going to go?"

"I'll find a place. I'll bring her the dough when I get it."

"Yeah." Mr. Mustie looked around the room, picked up the painted china ashtray that was a nicely shaped pair of woman's hands, looked at it, looked surprised that he was looking at it, then set it down. "Okay, Stremberg. Take it easy."

"Yeah," said Stremberg.

He went downstairs and out the door.

He walked eight blocks to the Tropical. There was a good crowd. Big Otto was there, drinking cola and rolling poker dice with some guys Stremberg didn't know, at a dollar a flop. Flo was at the bar with a short punk who looked like bad news. Tiny wasn't in sight. He was glad of that.

He got a stool near the door. Ray come over. Stremberg laid the $10 win ticket on Bugle Call in front of him. "Everything was great and then the fix came off."

Ray tossed the ticket behind the bar. "You owe me $3.50."

"Right. How about a beer?"

Ray shrugged and drew one.

"Got a cigarette?"

Ray gave him one.

Stremberg sat there drinking and smoking. He looked in the mirror and saw the dentist with two hats sitting at a table with a couple of women and laughing, his mouth wide showing a few whole teeth but mostly yellow stumps. He wore the woman's dark glasses that he always wore. There was a pile of money by his hand. The three of them looked pleased with life.

The dentist raised his glass. "To Trader Jack and Vinnie Espinosa, the best damn jockey at the meet!" The women said, "Hurray!" and laughed and drank, while the dentist grinned at them with his stumps.

Stremberg called, "Ray."

Ray came over.

"Who won the sixth?"

Ray was silent. Then he walked away. He conferred with Big Otto, and came back.

"Trader Jack. Paid 60 to 1."

Stremberg went over to the dentist. "Remember me?"

"Sure. You're the cab driver."

"I split a bet with you today on Trader Jack."

"Did you?" The dark glasses caught the light and gave a sparkle. "No, not Trader Jack. Little Steamy."

Stremberg looked at the money on the table. "Little Steamy?"

"Yeah, that was my tip. He run a damn fine race, but didn't have it in the stretch."

Stremberg nodded at the money. "Didn't you win that betting on Trader Jack?"

"Yeah, I did actually. But I put your buck and another guy's dough on Little Steamy, which was my tip. Trader Jack was just a wild hunch I played because one of my ex-wives is named Jacqueline."

Stremberg nodded. What was the use?

"Have a beer," the dentist invited.

"Thanks, I got one at the bar."

"You need money or anything? You want a buck?"

"That's okay." Stremberg went back to his drink. He said to Ray, who was near, "I ought to have my butt kicked. I split a bet with him and didn't get the name of the horse."

Ray pulled his lips in and shook his head slowly, like someone looking at a pitiful specimen.

Stremberg nodded, agreeing with Ray's shake. "I just ain't been with it today."

He finished his beer, picked up his bag, and walked down the block to the hole-in-the-wall Red & Black cab office. All the cabs were off the stand. A sharp-faced old Swede lounged behind the counter.

"Hello, Oscar."

"Hello, Stremberg."

"How's it going?"

"Not too bad."

Stremberg leaned on the counter, setting his bag on it. "Got a smoke?"

Oscar gave him a cigarette. Stremberg lit it.

"Need a driver?"

Oscar looked at him a while with his pale blue eyes. "You figure to go back to work?"

"Yeah."

"Horses not treating you so good?"

Stremberg fished in his pocket and laid his six cents on the counter.

Oscar said, "You had nearly three thousand bucks when you quit. You said you was going to make a killing, you'd never drive cab again."

"I guess I did say that."

"You'll never beat the horses, Stremberg."

Stremberg didn't answer. It wasn't the time to argue about it.

Oscar smoked, and eyed him. "Okay, I'll put you back on. You ain't a drunk and you're honest, or reasonably honest, and you ain't smashed up any of my cabs. Next time you quit me though, don't bother coming back."

"Okay," said Stremberg. "Listen, Oscar, can I sleep in a cab tonight?"

"Throw you out of your room?"

"Yeah."

Oscar said, "All right." Then he reached in a pocket. "Here's three bucks. Go get yourself something to eat, you look like someone's been dug up."

"Okay."

"And clean up in the washroom before you start on shift tomorrow."

"Okay."

A man came in. "You got the racing form?"

"Sure." There was a pile on the desk behind the counter. Oscar handed one to the man and accepted a buck, which he dropped in a cigar box.

The man leaned on the counter, slit the paper open with the side of his hand, worked a cigar around in his mouth, and said, "You got anything for tomorrow?"

"I ain't a horse player," Oscar said.

The man glanced at Stremberg. *"You're* a horse player. I've seen you down at the track."

"I used to be," Stremberg said. "I gave it up."

"You're smarter than I am." The man went out.

Stremberg walked up the block past the Tropical Club toward the bowling alley where they had a lunch counter. He'd get a pack of cigarettes from the machine there, and still have enough for a burger and coffee. It had been a long time since he'd eaten.

He thought of Bugle Call, and shook his head. He didn't blame Otto, or the syndicate—they only did what they had to do. They had to protect themselves when Congressional committees got too nosey.

He took a few deep breaths of the crisp autumn night air. He glanced in a store window as he passed and was surprised how pale and seedy and caved-in he looked.

Driving cab in the winter months ain't a bad job. You can make a buck.

By the time the thoroughbreds came back in the spring, he should have a nice stake.

ONE MOMENT OF MADNESS

by EDWARD D. HOCH

The rain had stopped but the night air was still muggy with August heat. Leopold stood by the window in his pajamas, silently cursing the window air-conditioner that still hummed loudly but delivered only warm air. Across town there was a fire burning, and as he listened to the distant sound of sirens he tried to pinpoint its location. Something in the Mill Road Shopping Center, he guessed—one of the stores.

He was glad he wasn't a fireman.

For a time he watched the flames reflecting off the low clouds, casting an orange glow over one whole end of the city. He was just turning to get back into bed when the telephone rang.

"Leopold here."

"Captain, you'd better get down here." It was Fletcher's voice, talking too loud.

"What's up? Is it the fire?"

"Hank Schultz just went berserk in the squadroom and shot four people!"

"I'll be right down! You got it under control?"

"I shot Hank, Captain. There was no other way."

"All right. I'll be there in ten minutes."

He was dressed and down to his car in less than five. The highrise building where he lived was generally a fifteen-minute drive away from headquarters, but at three in the morning traffic was light. He stuck the magnetized flasher on the roof of his car and turned it on, and held his speed steady at fifty-five all the way downtown.

There were ambulances and cars all over the street in front of the aging headquarters building. He recognized a couple of reporters trying to buck the hastily erected police line. "What's up, Captain?" one of them shouted, recognizing him, but Leopold ignored him. At the moment he couldn't imagine what was up. Hank Schultz was a nine-year veteran of the Force who'd done various sorts of undercover work in addition to regular patrol duty. Though he'd never been on Leopold's Violent Crimes Squad, Leopold knew him well.

"Coming through!" a white-coated stretcher-bearer shouted, and Leopold stepped aside. The man on the stretcher, who seemed to be unconscious, was Hank Schultz. Leopold hurried up the steps to the second floor and found Lieutenant Fletcher standing in the middle of the squadroom surveying the damage. A chair was overturned and there was blood on the floor and one of the walls. The police photographer was snapping pictures of one uniformed body, but Leopold couldn't see who it was.

"How many dead?" he asked grimly.

Fletcher glanced up as if surprised that Leopold had arrived so soon. "One. Sam Bentley over there. We think he took the first shot."

Leopold had known Sergeant Bentley since the day twenty years earlier when Leopold came up from New York to join the Force in the city where he grew up. Bentley was on the Force already then. Now he was only a year from retirement. "Who else did Hank shoot?"

"Unidentified white male prisoner and the two detectives who brought him in. Sweeney and Gross. They're not bad, but the prisoner has two wounds. Hank emptied his service revolver before I could stop him."

"Is Hank alive?"

"Just barely. All four of them are at the hospital."

Leopold walked over and stared down at the body of Sam Bentley. He felt like hell. "You'd better tell me the whole thing, from the beginning." The Police Commissioner would be arriving soon and he wanted to have some answers.

"We don't know a great deal, Captain. I was in my office. Things were fairly quiet and Bentley was at his desk typing up an arrest report. A little after two-thirty Sweeney and Gross came in with their prisoner. Then Hank Schultz came in."

"Was he in uniform?"

"No, civilian clothes. I don't think he was on duty. I heard them talking but I didn't pay much attention. Sam had just gotten a report on the Crown SuperShopper fire out at the shopping center and was telling them about it. I happened to look out through my glass partition just as Hank drew the revolver from under his jacket and fired. I couldn't believe what I was seeing! But then Sam fell against the wall and went down. Hank kept firing at the others and everybody was yelling at once. I ran out of the office, drawing my gun. Sweeney and Gross were both on the floor by now, along with their prisoner—I hadn't counted the shots. Hank turned and pointed his revolver at me and—I had to shoot him, Captain! His gun was already empty but I didn't know that." Fletcher's voice was trembling.

"You had no choice," Leopold said, resting a hand on his shoulder. "I would have done the same thing."

"I was drinking coffee with him just last night—"

Others were arriving now—the Commissioner and someone from the District Attorney's office. Leopold didn't have any answers for them. He greeted them briefly and said he was on his way to the hospital.

"This will look terrible in the papers," the Commissioner said.

"It *is* terrible."

"How could a rational man just flip out like that? Could he be on drugs?"

"I'm going to find out," Leopold promised.

The Commissioner stared bleakly at the blood on the floor and the wall. It seemed to bother him more than the sight of Sam Bentley's body.

Leopold went downstairs to his car. It was a short drive to the hospital and the four wounded men were still in Emergency when he arrived. He found a doctor named Rice working with an intern over Milt Sweeney, who seemed to be the least injured of the four.

"Can I speak to him?" Leopold asked when the doctors came out of the curtained cubicle for a moment.

"As soon as we get him stitched up. He's lucky—the bullet passed through the fleshy part of his thigh."

"How are the others?"

The doctor consulted an admissions sheet. "Schultz is bad. We're preparing him for surgery now. The other officer, Gross, has an abdominal wound but I think he'll pull through. The woman is unconscious—"

"What woman?"

"Beats me. Unidentified. A woman dressed in man's clothing."

"She was brought in with the others? From Police headquarters?"

"That's right. We didn't know she was a woman at first. She's fairly young, I'd say—under thirty."

He excused himself and went back into the cubicle, and Leopold paced the floor. Perhaps Sweeney could shed some light on this craziness. He certainly hoped so.

Some minutes later the doctor emerged and motioned to Leopold. "You can have five minutes with him, no more. He's still weak from loss of blood."

Leopold nodded, pushed aside the white curtain, and went in. "Hi, Milt," he said. "How're you feeling?"

Sweeney managed a lopsided grin. "I'll live. What about the others?"

"Gross will be all right, I understand. Sam Bentley's dead."

"God!"

"I'm sorry I had to tell you like this."

"What about Schultz? I didn't see a thing after he shot my leg out from under me."

"Fletcher got him in the chest. They're taking him to the operating room now."

"Why in hell did he do it!"

Leopold sighed. "I was hoping you could tell me."

"We'd just come in with our prisoner. Sam was behind his desk talking about a fire somewhere and all of a sudden there was Hank Schultz out of nowhere, taking his gun from the belt holster under his jacket."

"What did he say?"

"Nothing I can remember. I think Bentley put out his hand to grab for the gun. Schultz shot him first and then turned on me and kept on firing. I felt a blow to my leg and just went down."

"What about the suspect you'd brought in?"

"Was he hit too?"

"Yes. But the doctor says it's a woman dressed in men's clothes."

"What?" Sweeney struggled to sit up, but winced in pain and abandoned the effort. "A *woman?*"

Leopold nodded. "What did you arrest her for?"

"Gross and I were checking the after-hours bars on Field Avenue. We were parked in front of the Old Athens when this guy—we thought it was a guy—came along and threw an empty bottle through the front window of the bar. We jumped out and grabbed him. We figured we had a drunk on our hands and we drove downtown to book him."

"Did Hank seem to know your prisoner?"

"I wouldn't know. Like I said, I didn't even see him until he was there pulling out his gun."

The doctor appeared at the curtain. "Better let him get some rest now. You can see him again in the morning."

Leopold squeezed Sweeney's shoulder. "Take it easy, Milt. I'll be back."

"Right, Captain. Find out why he did it, huh?"

"I'm trying."

Outside, Leopold asked the doctor, "How's the woman?"

"Not so good, but we think she's got a better than even chance. Any luck on identification?"

"Not a thing. Let me look at her clothes."

The doctor led him to a little cubicle and opened a garment bag bearing a numbered label and the single word UNIDENTIFIED. Leopold noticed the fresh blood around the hole in the front of the coat and shirt. Otherwise the man's suit was reasonably clean and nondescript, with a label from a cut-rate men's store downtown. "Did the clothes seem to fit her?" Leopold asked.

"I guess so, yes. But I wasn't really paying attention to their fit," Rice answered.

"I'm wondering if she bought them for herself or got them from somebody," Leopold murmured, going through the pockets. They were empty except for a handkerchief, a few coins, and a crumpled five-dollar food stamp. "Any sign of drug addiction on her?" Leopold asked.

"Not that I noticed."

A young intern poked his head in. "Dr. Rice, they're waiting for you in the operating room."

Rice told Leopold, "I'm assisting at the operation on Schultz. I have to scrub now."

"Good luck," Leopold said, meaning it.

He waited in the corridor until they wheeled Hank Schultz past him. The young detective's eyes were closed and his breathing seemed irregular. An intern with an intravenous bottle walked alongside.

Damn it, Hank, Leopold asked silently, why did you do it?

In the morning, while Fletcher dealt with the press as best he could, Leopold began the arduous task of reconstructing Hank Schultz's recent activities. He had been, Leopold learned, doing some undercover narcotics work, but his superior officer believed he'd veered away into something else.

"He was onto a new line," Lieutenant Maxwell told Leopold. "On one of his drug busts he discovered the shipment had been paid for with a hundred thousand dollars in stolen food stamps."

Food stamps.

Leopold remembered the crumpled food stamp in the unidentified woman's pocket. "When was this?"

"About two months ago. He told me he had a line on the source of the stolen stamps and asked to be taken off the narcotics angle to pursue it. I contacted the proper federal agencies and they gave me the go-ahead. In fact, Schultz was supposed to meet with a man from the Justice Department today regarding his investigation."

"It doesn't sound as if he was having emotional problems of any sort."

"No apparent ones," Maxwell agreed. "He was doing his job. I'm as dumbfounded as anyone else by what happened this morning."

"And yet something caused him to draw his revolver and shoot four people. What was it?"

"Damned if I know. In this business, sometimes the strain builds up over weeks and months until suddenly it explodes."

"I know," Leopold agreed. "But that answer won't be good enough for the Commissioner."

"What are Hank's chances of living to tell us about it?"

"He was still in the operating room when I left the hospital at four o'clock. I'm going back over there now."

*   *   *

With the coming of morning the emergency room had quieted down to its usual summer pace of children with broken arms and cut feet. Leopold asked for Dr. Rice and was directed to an office on the second floor, where he found the surgeon staring bleakly into an empty coffee cup.

"A long night?" Leopold asked.

Rice nodded. "We lost Schultz a half hour ago. He survived the surgery but died in the recovery room."

Leopold shook his head sadly. "Can I use your phone?"

"I've already called the Police Commissioner."

"I want to tell the man who shot him," Leopold said.

He dialed the squadroom number but was told Fletcher had finally gone home for some sleep. Leopold hesitated a moment and then dialed Fletcher's home number, hoping Fletcher would answer instead of his wife. He was in luck.

"Hello, Fletcher. How are you?"

"I'm exhausted, Captain. I'm going to sleep for a week."

"Hank Schultz died a half-hour ago," Leopold told him. "I thought you'd want to know."

"Thanks. I guess he's been dead for me since the minute I shot him."

"Try to get some sleep."

Leopold hung up and turned back to Dr. Rice. "How about the others?"

"Gross is coming along, and the woman is conscious now. Do you want to see her?"

"I certainly do."

Rice escorted him to a private room on the third floor. "I'll want a guard posted here," he told the doctor. "I'll arrange for it."

"Okay. You can have five minutes alone with her."

Leopold entered the room and walked over to the bed. He saw at once that the woman was awake, watching him with deep-blue eyes that he might have found attractive in other circumstances. She must have been in her late twenties. Her brown hair was cut short as a man's, but Leopold couldn't imagine that Sweeney and Gross had failed to realize she was a woman. Her high cheekbones and soft features contributed to a decidedly feminine appearance.

"I'm Captain Leopold," he told her, "investigating last night's shooting."

"I don't know what happened," she said, closing her eyes.

"Let's start with your name. Who are you and why were you dressed as a man?"

"I'm Cathy Wright. I'm an artist and I wasn't dressed as a man. I was wearing my usual clothes. They had no right to arrest me."

"You broke the window of the Old Athens with a bottle," Leopold pointed out. "And unfortunately you did it right in front of an unmarked police car."

"Whatever I did, I didn't deserve being shot."

"No," he agreed, "you didn't. The man who shot you was a detective named Hank Schultz. Does that name mean anything to you?"

"No. Should it?"

"He opened fire on you and several others without warning. I'm trying to find the reason."

"What happened to him?"

"He was shot by one of my men. He died a short time ago. But the doctor assures me you're going to be all right."

"Thanks," she said. Her eyes began to mist.

"I'll need your address for the records. I don't think you need to worry about the charges against you, though. Under the circumstances they'll probably be dropped."

She gave him an address in one of the older downtown areas, not far from where she'd been arrested. "I'd like to be alone now," she told him.

"Certainly," Leopold agreed. "But one other thing—there was a five-dollar food stamp in your pocket. Where'd you get it?"

"At the bank. Artists don't always make enough to live on."

Leopold nodded and left the room. He wasn't satisfied with the answers she'd given, but she was too weak to pursue it now. He'd come back later and maybe get some answers then. Maybe he'd find out why she seemed about to cry when he told her Hank Schultz was dead.

Detective Irving Gross was a middle-aged man with too much weight and too little hair. He'd been more seriously wounded than Sweeney. Lying flat on his back with a tube up his nose and another in his arm, he seemed wounded by more than Schultz's bullet.

"Schultz is dead," Leopold told him.

"That's no great loss, Captain. He was always an odd sort."

"In what way?"

"Oh, suspicious of everyone. Ever since his divorce a few years back after he caught his wife cheatin' he thought everybody was out to betray him or something. Beats me how Maxwell put up with him all these years."

"I never realized that. Maybe I didn't know him as well as I thought. But why'd he start shooting last night, Irving?"

"I thought maybe you came here to tell me."

"What about the suspect you and Sweeney arrested?"

"Guy broke a window with a bottle."

"It was a woman, dressed more like a man."

"Yeah? Nothing surprises me in that neighborhood."

"Did Hank Schultz see her before he started shooting?"

"Sure, he saw her. She was standing right there with us."

"In handcuffs?"

"No, we took them off when we got her inside."

"Did Schultz speak to her?"

"Not a word."

"What was your impression when you arrested her—that she was high, drunk, or what?"

"Tell you the truth, Captain, it was none of those. My impression was that he—we thought it was a he—wanted to be arrested. You know, like the guy in the O. Henry story who wanted a warm cell for the winter?"

"I know," Leopold said. "Only this is summer."

He tried not to read the newspapers that night, with their screaming black headlines about the shooting. There were big pictures of Schultz and Bentley, smaller photos of Sweeney and Gross. They didn't have a picture of Cathy Wright, but a subhead referred to her as the "mystery woman" in the case. The story was given so much play on the front page that the fire at the Crown SuperShopper had been relegated to an inside page.

Leopold stayed late at headquarters in order to see Fletcher when he came on duty. That was how he happened to be at his desk when the man from the Justice Department arrived. His name was Arnold Ellis and he was a light-skinned black man with a tiny mustache.

He smiled as he shook hands and said, "Lieutenant Maxwell said you're the one to see. I understand you're in charge of the investigation into last night's tragic events."

"I seem to be," Leopold admitted.

"I flew up from Washington this afternoon to meet with Hank Schultz. That was before I knew he'd been killed."

"Maxwell told me you were working in the same area."

The man from Washington nodded. "Stolen food stamps. It's gotten to be a major problem, especially in urban areas. The underworld uses them like money, to buy narcotics and guns and just about everything else. For all practical purposes they are money, but in most instances they're a great deal easier to steal."

"But what finally happens to all these food stamps?" Leopold asked. "At the end of the line someone must redeem them for cash, knowing they're stolen."

"That's what Schultz was working on. We believe they're funneled into large supermarkets, probably at about twenty-five to fifty cents on the dollar. The store managers are happy to pocket the profit, with very little risk."

"Supermarkets," Leopold repeated. "Did you happen to hear about our fire last night?"

"Where was that?"

"At the Crown SuperShopper. It broke out just a little while before the shooting."

"Arson?"

"I don't know," Leopold said. "But I intend to find out."

"Let me come with you. I have to do something to justify my trip up here."

Leopold picked up a copy of the arson squad's report, which showed evidence that the Crown fire was of suspicious origin. He and Arnold Ellis drove out to look at the scene, but in the darkness there was little they could do or see. "Roof caved in," Leopold observed as they walked around the ruined building. "Looks like a total loss."

"A good way to destroy the evidence," Ellis remarked.

"What evidence?"

"A hundred thousand dollars in stolen food stamps. Someone knocked over our local distribution center last month, but we kept it out of the papers. It was no big deal. The place was in a parking garage behind the federal building. Someone who knew the setup just walked in during the lunch hour and helped himself. With a duplicate key all he had to do was stay out of the sight line of one television camera and he was home free."

This brought a whistle from Leopold. "Schultz was working on it?"

Ellis nodded. "His contacts told him the stamps were being redeemed through local supermarkets. I did a computer graph on the number of redemptions per market plotted against the relative income of the surrounding neighborhoods. Crown here had too many redemptions for its area. That's why I came here to meet Schultz today. I wanted to raid the place tomorrow on the strong possibility these latest stolen stamps were on the premises. I told Schultz on the phone we'd probably go after a search warrant tomorrow."

Leopold sighed and kicked at a piece of charred wood. "The trouble is, your Hank Schultz was a tough undercover cop who got results, but I'm left with one who went berserk in the squadroom and shot four people."

"It does sound like two different men. What about the supermarket manager? His name must be in the arson-squad report."

They went back to the car and checked. The name was there—Titus Kern, with an address in one of the better suburbs. "Business must be pretty good," Leopold remarked. "Let's go see him."

Arnold Ellis hesitated. "Not me. At this point in my investigation it's probably better if we don't meet. Keep it on a local level, but find out what you can."

Leopold dropped Ellis at his hotel downtown and drove out to see Titus Kern alone. It was nearly eleven when he reached the house, and it was dark. He was about to abandon the idea till morning when a taxi turned into the street and pulled up in front of the house. A man opened the door and paid the driver. Leopold got out. "Pardon me," he called as the man headed up the walk toward the darkened house. "Mr. Kern?"

The man hesitated, perhaps fearing a robbery. "Yes?"

"Captain Leopold, police. I'd like to ask you a few questions about last night's fire."

As he came closer, Leopold saw that Titus Kern was a man in his fifties, slim and gray-haired, with a high-cheekboned face that seemed vaguely familiar. "I've had a very trying day, Captain. I'm sure you understand. My store was destroyed by fire and I've just come from visiting my daughter who is ill. I'm sure I can't tell you anything you don't already know."

"I promise it won't take more than a few minutes."

Titus Kern sighed. "Very well. You can come in for a minute."

Leopold followed him into the large colonial house and waited while he turned on a few lamps in the living room. "My wife's away," he explained. "I'm something of a bachelor these days. Please sit down."

Leopold sat opposite the piano, where a number of family portraits were on display. "You must realize that last night's fire had a suspicious origin," he began. "The arson squad found evidence of a timing device—"

"I know nothing of that. I manage the store, I don't own it. The fire causes me grief, but the corporation collects the insurance."

"It's been suggested that the fire might have been set, not to collect the insurance but to destroy evidence of a felony."

"What? What are you talking about?"

But before Leopold could reply, his eyes focused on the large middle portrait in the grouping on the piano. Suddenly he knew why Titus Kern's face was familiar. "That must be your daughter in the picture," he said. "She looks very much like you."

"I'm afraid she's a bit wild, like so many young people today."

"You said she was ill?"

"I—yes, that's correct."

"In the hospital, I imagine."

"Did I say that?"

"I met your daughter today, Mr. Kern. The picture is a very good likeness. She's using the name Cathy Wright and the newspapers call her a mystery woman."

"I told her to stop that foolishness and tell the truth."

Suddenly the pieces of the puzzle were beginning to fall into place. "What about Hank Schultz, Mr. Kern?"

"What about him? I never heard of him until he shot my daughter. And you can be sure the city's going to find itself with a very large lawsuit on its hands over this."

"How did you know it was your daughter in the hospital?"

"She telephoned me earlier this evening. I suppose she feared I'd report her missing to the police."

"Does she live here?"

"No, she has an apartment where she works as an artist. But she helps with some of my bookkeeping at the store." He glanced pointedly at his watch. "I'm very tired, and I can't see how these questions about my daughter have a bearing on the fire."

"There may be a connection between the fire and the shooting of your daughter," Leopold said. He got to his feet. "Thank you for your help, Mr. Kern."

In the morning Leopold went back to the hospital. He waited outside Cathy's door while Dr. Rice examined her. "She's coming along," the doctor said as he departed. "But try not to tire her with your questions."

Leopold went in and sat by the bed. "How are you feeling?"

"A little better than yesterday," she replied.

"I talked to your father last night."

Her face seemed to freeze. "I don't—"

"There's no point in denying your identity."

"All right, so you talked to my father. So what?"

"I thought you might have something to tell me—about yourself and Hank Schultz."

"What are you talking about?"

"It was seeing you in the squadroom that set him off, wasn't it? He knew you well enough to recognize you even in men's clothes. Your handcuffs were off and he didn't realize you'd been arrested. He thought you were there to betray him, as another woman—his wife—had once betrayed him in a different way."

She started crying then, not holding back the tears that had threatened the day before, and Leopold turned for a moment to stare out the window. He remembered how he'd seen the fire burning from the window of his bedroom, and that reminded him of why he was here. He had a job to do. Hank Schultz had forgotten about his job and that had been his fatal flaw. He turned back to the sobbing girl.

"When Schultz stumbled onto the stolen-food-stamp racket he met you, didn't he? The two of you had the last couple of months for your special form of insanity."

"It wasn't insanity! It was love!"

"Hank stole that last batch of food stamps from the federal building garage, didn't he? And you helped. He needed your help because the stamps had to be funneled through your father's store. But a man named Ellis at the Justice Department used a computer and pinpointed Crown as redeeming more than its share of stamps for the income area it was in. Ellis wanted to get a search warrant and raid the store today. The stolen stamps were there and you couldn't get them out in time, so you had to burn the place down. If your father had been involved he could have removed them, but for some reason you couldn't reach them in time."

"I'd hidden them in the storeroom," she said listlessly, wiping her eyes with a tissue, "until it was safe to turn them in to the government. I had one in my pocket because we were trying to sell them elsewhere—but everyone was scared after the robbery, especially when there was nothing in the papers about it. We didn't know what the Justice Department was up to. So the stamps were there in my father's storeroom, and then Hank heard that Ellis had pinpointed Crown and wanted a search warrant. I could get in only when the store was open, and they were doing an inventory back there. I was helpless till Friday, and that would have been too late."

"How did you manage all this without your father knowing?"

"When I was doing the bookkeeping I handled things like foodstamp redemptions. I'd been buying them from people in my neighborhood for the past two years and selling them back to the government through his store. He never asked questions. He trusted me."

"And you were willing to burn down the store rather than lose that trust." When she didn't answer he went on. "You dressed in men's clothes to disguise yourself in case you were seen planting the firebombs behind the store. Then you broke a window while a couple of plainclothes cops were watching to give yourself a perfect alibi. If the fire was ever traced to you, you could claim you were in jail when it started. Of course, the arson squad recovered the remains of the timing device so the alibi wouldn't have held water, but you didn't know that."

"I wasn't thinking straight," she admitted. "Neither was Hank."

"He certainly wasn't. He walked into the squad room night before last and saw you with Sweeney and Gross. He probably never noticed what you were wearing. He'd probably gone through the day on the edge of insanity, fearful of what Ellis might do when he arrived from Washington. Then he saw you and thought you'd betrayed him, sold him out to save your own skin. He didn't wait for words. He drew his revolver and when Sergeant Bentley made a dive for it he got the first bullet. Then he shot you twice, and Gross and Sweeney, before Lieutenant Fletcher killed him."

"One moment of madness," she said, the tears spilling over again.

"Are you willing to talk about it?" Leopold asked. "Before a grand jury?"

"It'll be rough on me, won't it?"

"Not half as rough as it was on Hank Schultz."

LOOPY

by RUTH RENDELL

At the end of the last performance, after the curtain calls, Red Riding
Hood put me on a lead and with the rest of the company we went across to
the pub. No one had taken makeup off or changed, there was no time for
that before the George closed. I remember prancing across the road and
growling at someone on a bicycle.

They loved me in the pub—well, some of them loved me. Quite a lot
were embarrassed. The funny thing was that I should have been embarrassed
myself if I had been one of them. I should have ignored *me* and drunk up
my drink and left. Except that it is unlikely I would have been in a pub at
all. Normally, I never went near such places. But inside the wolf skin it was
very different, everything was different in there.

I prowled about for a while, sometimes on all-fours—though this isn't
easy for us who are accustomed to the upright stance—sometimes loping,
with my forepaws held close up to my chest. I went over to tables where
people were sitting and snuffled my snout at their packets of crisps. If they
were smoking I growled and waved my paws in air-clearing gestures. Lots
of them were forthcoming, stroking me and making jokes or pretending
terror at my red jaws and wicked little eyes. There was even one lady who
took hold of my head and laid it in her lap.

Bounding up to the bar to collect my small dry sherry, I heard Bill
Harkness (the First Woodcutter) say to Susan Hayes (Red Riding Hood's
Mother): "Old Colin's really come out of his shell tonight."

And Susan, bless her, said, "He's a real actor, isn't he?"

I was one of the few members of our company who was. I expect this is
always true in amateur dramatics. There are one or two real actors, people
who could have made their livings on the stage if it wasn't so overcrowded
a profession, and the rest who just come for the fun of it and the social side.

Did I ever consider the stage seriously? My father had been a civil
servant, both my grandfathers in the ICS. As far back as I can remember it
was taken for granted I should get my degree and go into the Civil Service.
I never questioned it. If you have a mother like mine, one in a million,

more a friend than a parent, you never feel the need to rebel. Besides, Mother gave me all the support I could have wished for in my acting. Acting as a hobby, that is. For instance, though the company made provision for hiring all the more complicated costumes for that year's Christmas pantomime, Mother made the wolf suit for me herself. It was ten times better than anything we could have hired. The head we had to buy, but the body and the limbs she made from a long-haired grey-fur fabric such as is manufactured for ladies' coats.

Moira used to say I enjoyed acting so much because it enabled me to lose myself and become, for a while, someone else. She said I disliked what I was and looked for ways of escape. A strange way to talk to the man you intend to marry! But before I approach the subject of Moira or, indeed, continue with this account, I should explain what its purpose is.

The psychiatrist attached to this place or who visits it (I'm not entirely clear which), one Dr. Vernon-Peak, has asked me to write down some of my feelings and impressions. That, I said, would only be possible in the context of a narrative. Very well, he said, he had no objection. What will become of it when finished I hardly know. Will it constitute a statement to be used in court? Or will it enter Dr. Vernon-Peak's files as another case history? It's all the same to me. I can only tell the truth.

After the George closed, then, we took off our makeup and changed and went our several ways home. Mother was waiting up for me. This was not invariably her habit. If I told her I should be late and to go to bed at her usual time she always did so. But I, quite naturally, was not averse to a welcome when I got home, particularly after a triumph like that one. Besides, I had been looking forward to telling her what an amusing time I'd had in the pub.

Our house is late-Victorian, double-fronted, of grey limestone, by no means beautiful, but a comfortable, well built place. My grandfather bought it when he retired and came home from India in 1920. Mother was ten at the time, so she has spent most of her life in that house.

Grandfather was quite a famous shot and used to go big-game hunting before that kind of thing became, and rightly so, very much frowned upon. The result was that the place was full of "trophies of the chase." While Grandfather was alive, and he lived to a great age, we had no choice but to put up with the antlers and tusks that sprouted everywhere out of the walls, the elephant's-foot umbrella stand, and the snarling maws of *tigris* and *ursa*. We had to grin and bear it, as Mother, who has a fine turn of wit, used to put it.

But when Grandfather was at last gathered to his ancestors, reverently and without the least disrespect to him, we took down all those heads and horns and packed them away in trunks. The fur rugs, however, we didn't disturb. These days they are worth a fortune and I always felt that the tiger skins scattered across the hall parquet, the snow leopard draped across the back of the sofa, and the bear into whose fur one could bury one's toes before the fire gave to the place a luxurious look. I took off my shoes and snuggled my toes in it that night.

Mother, of course, had been to see the show. She had come on the first night and seen me make my onslaught on Red Riding Hood, an attack so sudden and unexpected that the whole audience had jumped to its feet and gasped. (In our version we didn't have the wolf actually devour Red Riding Hood. Unanimously, we agreed this would hardly have been the thing at Christmas.) Mother, however, wanted to see me wearing her creation once more, so I put it on and did some prancing and growling for her benefit. Again I noticed how curiously uninhibited I became once inside the wolf skin. For instance, I bounded up to the snow leopard and began snarling at it. I boxed at its great grey-white face and made playful bites at its ears. Down on all fours I went and pounced on the bear, fighting it, actually forcing its neck within the space of my jaws.

How Mother laughed! She said it was as good as anything in the pantomime and a good deal better than anything they put on television.

"Animal crackers in my soup," she said, wiping her eyes. "There used to be a song that went like that in my youth. How did it go on? Something about lions and tigers loop the loop."

"Well, *lupus* means a wolf in Latin," I said.

"And you're certainly loopy! When you put that suit on again I shall have to say you're going all loopy again!"

When I put that suit on again? Did I intend to put it on again? I had not really thought about it. Yes, perhaps if I ever went to a fancy-dress party—a remote enough contingency. Yet what a shame it seemed to waste it, to pack it away like Grandfather's tusks and antlers after all the labor Mother had put into it. That night I hung it up in my wardrobe and I remember how strange I felt when I took it off that second time, more naked than I usually felt without my clothes, almost as if I had taken off my skin.

Life kept to the "even tenor" of its way. I felt a little flat with no rehearsals to attend and no lines to learn. Christmas came. Traditionally, Mother and I were alone on the Day itself, we would not have had it any other way, but on Boxing Day Moira arrived and Mother invited a couple of neighbors of ours in as well. At some stage, I seem to recall, Susan Hayes dropped in with her husband to wish us the compliments of the season.

Moira and I had been engaged for three years. We would have got married some time before, there was no question of our not being able to afford to marry, but a difficulty had arisen over where we should live. I think I may say in all fairness that the difficulty was entirely of Moira's making. No mother could have been more welcoming to a future daughter-in-law than mine. She actually wanted us to live with her at Simla

House—she said we must think of it as our home and of her simply as our housekeeper. But Moira wanted us to buy a place of our own, so we had reached a deadlock, an impasse.

It was unfortunate that on that Boxing Day, after the others had gone, Moira brought the subject up again. Her brother (an estate agent) had told her of a bungalow for sale halfway between Simla House and her parents' home that was what he called "a real snip." Fortunately, *I* thought, Mother managed to turn the conversation by telling us about the bungalow she and her parents had lived in in India, with its great collonaded veranda, its English flower garden, and its peepul tree. But Moira interrupted her.

"This is *our* future we're talking about, not your past. I thought Colin and I were getting married."

Mother was quite alarmed. "Aren't you? Surely Colin hasn't broken things off?"

"I suppose you don't consider the possibility *I* might break things off?"

Poor Mother couldn't help smiling at that. She smiled to cover her hurt. Moira could upset her very easily. For some reason this made Moira angry.

"I'm too old and unattractive to have any choice in the matter, is that what you mean?"

"Moira," I said.

She took no notice. "You may not realize it," she said, "but marrying me will be the making of Colin. It's what he needs to make a man of him."

It must have slipped out before Mother quite knew what she was saying. She patted Moira's knee. "I can quite see it may be a tough assignment, dear."

There was no quarrel. Mother would never have allowed herself to be drawn into that. But Moira became very huffy and said she wanted to go home, so I had to get the car out and take her.

All the way to her parents' house I had to listen to a catalogue of her wrongs at my hands and my mother's. By the time we parted I felt dispirited and nervous. I even wondered if I was doing the right thing, contemplating matrimony in the "sere and yellow leaf" of forty-two.

Mother had cleared the things away and gone to bed. I went into my bedroom and began undressing. Opening the wardrobe to hang up my tweed trousers, I caught sight of the wolf suit and on some impulse I put it on.

Once inside the wolf I felt calmer and, yes, happier. I sat down in an armchair but after a while I found it more comfortable to crouch, then lie stretched out on the floor. Lying there, basking in the warmth from the gas fire on my belly and paws, I found myself remembering tales of man's affinity with wolves, Romulus and Remus suckled by a she-wolf, the ancient myth of the werewolf, abandoned children reared by wolves even in these modern times. All this seemed to deflect my mind from the discord between Moira and my mother and I was able to go to bed reasonably happily and to sleep well.

Perhaps, then, it will not seem so very strange and wonderful that the next time I felt depressed I put the suit on again. Mother was out, so I was able to have the freedom of the whole house, not just of my room. It was dusk at four, but instead of putting the lights on I prowled about the house in the twilight, sometimes catching sight of my lean grey form in the many large mirrors Mother is so fond of. Because there was so little light and our house is crammed with bulky furniture and knickknacks, the reflection I saw looked not like a man disguised but like a real wolf that has somehow escaped and strayed into a cluttered Victorian room. Or a werewolf, that animal part of man's personality that detaches itself and wanders free while leaving behind the depleted human shape.

I crept up upon the teakwood carving of the antelope and devoured the little creature before it knew what had attacked it. I resumed my battle with the bear and we struggled in front of the fireplace, locked in a desperate hairy embrace. It was then that I heard Mother let herself in at the back door. Time had passed more quickly than I had thought. I escaped and whisked my hind paws and tail round the bend in the stairs just before she came into the hall.

Dr. Vernon-Peak seems to want to know why I began this at the age of forty-two, or rather why I had not done it before. I wish I knew. Of course, there is the simple solution that I didn't have a wolf skin before, but that is not the whole answer. Was it perhaps that until then I didn't know what my needs were, though partially I had satisfied them by playing the parts I was given in dramatic productions?

There is one other thing. I have told him that I recall, as a very young child, having a close relationship with some large animal, a dog perhaps or a pony, though a search conducted into family history by this same assiduous Vernon-Peak has yielded no evidence that we ever kept a pet. But more of this anon.

Be that as it may, once I had lived inside the wolf I felt the need to do so more and more. Erect on my hind legs, drawn up to my full height, I do not think I flatter myself unduly when I say I made a fine handsome animal. And having written that, I realize that I have not yet described the wolf suit, taking for granted, I suppose, that those who see this document will also see it. Yet this may not be the case. They have refused to let *me* see it, which makes me wonder if it has been cleaned and made presentable again or if it is still—but, no, there is no point in going into unsavory details.

I have said that the body and limbs of the suit were made of long-haired grey-fur fabric. The stuff of it was coarse, hardly an attractive material for a coat, I should have thought, but very closely similar to a wolf's pelt. Mother made the paws after the fashion of fur gloves but with the padded and stiffened fingers of a pair of leather gloves for the claws. The head we bought from a jokes-and-games shop. It had tall prick ears, small yellow eyes, and a wonderful, half open mouth—red, voracious-looking, and with a double row of white fangs. The opening for me to breathe through was just beneath the lower jaw where the head joined the powerful hairy throat.

As Spring came I would sometimes drive out into the countryside, park the car, and slip into the skin. It was far from my ambition to be seen by anyone. I sought solitude. Whether I should have cared for a "beastly" companion, that is something else again. At that time I wanted merely to wander in the woods and copses or along a hedgerow in my wolf's persona. And this I did, choosing unfrequented places, avoiding anywhere that I might come in contact with the human race.

I am trying, in writing this, to explain how I felt. Principally, I felt *not human*. And to be not human is to be without human responsibilities and human cares. Inside the wolf, I laid aside my apprehensiveness about getting married, my apprehensiveness about *not* getting married, my fear of leaving Mother on her own, my justifiable resentment at not getting the leading part in our new production. All this got left behind with the depleted sleeping man I left behind to become a happy mindless wild creature.

Our wedding had once again been postponed. The purchase of the house Moira and I had finally agreed upon fell through at the last moment. I cannot say I was altogether sorry. It was near enough to my home, in the same street in fact as Simla House, but I had begun to wonder how I would feel passing our dear old house every day knowing it was not under that familiar roof I should lay my head.

Moira was very upset.

Yet, "I won't live in the same house as your mother even for three months," she said in answer to my suggestion. "That's a certain recipe for disaster."

"Mother and Daddy lived with Mother's parents for twenty years," I said.

"Yes, and look at the result!" It was then that she made that remark about my enjoying playing parts because I disliked my real self.

There was nothing more to be said except that we must keep on house-hunting.

"We can still go to Malta, I suppose," Moira said. "We don't have to cancel that."

Perhaps, but it would be no honeymoon. Anticipating the delights of matrimony was something I had not done up till then and had no intention of doing. And I was on my guard when Moira—Mother was out at her bridge evening—insisted on going up to my bedroom with me, ostensibly to check on the shade of the suit I had bought to get married in. She said she wanted to buy me a tie. Once there, she reclined on my bed, cajoling me to come and sit beside her.

I suppose it was because I was feeling depressed that I put on the wolf skin. I took off my jacket—but nothing more, of course, in front of Moira —stepped into the wolf skin, fastened it up, and adjusted the head. She watched me. She had seen me in it when she came to the pantomime.

"Why have you put that on?"

I said nothing. What could I have said? The usual contentment filled me, though, and I found myself obeying her command, loping across to the bed where she was. It seemed to come naturally to fawn on her, to rub my great prick-eared head against her breast, to enclose her hands with my paws. All kinds of fantasies filled my wolfish mind and they were of an intense piercing sweetness. If we had been on our holiday then, I do not think moral resolutions would have held me back.

But unlike the lady in the George, Moira did not take hold of my head and lay it in her lap. She jumped up and shouted at me to stop this nonsense, stop it at once, she hated it. So I did as I was told, of course I did, and got sadly out of the skin and hung it back in the cupboard. I took Moira home. On our way we called in at her brother's and looked at fresh lists of houses.

It was on one of these that we eventually settled after another month or so of picking and choosing and stalling, and we fixed our wedding for the middle of December. During the summer the company had done *Blithe Spirit* (in which I had the meager part of Dr. Bradman, Bill Harkness being Charles Condomine) and the pantomime this year was *Cinderella* with Susan Hayes in the name part and me as the Elder of the Ugly Sisters. I had calculated I should be back from my honeymoon just in time.

No doubt I would have been. No doubt I would have married and gone away on my honeymoon and come back to play my comic part had I not agreed to go shopping with Moira on her birthday. What happened that day changed everything.

It was a Thursday evening. The stores in the West End stay open late on Thursdays. We left our offices at five, met by arrangement and together walked up Bond Street. The last thing I had in view was that we should begin bickering again, though we had seemed to do little else lately. It started with my mentioning our honeymoon. We were outside Asprey's, walking along arm-in-arm. Since our house wouldn't be ready for us to move into till the middle of January, I suggested we should go back for just two weeks to Simla House. We should be going there for Christmas in any case.

"I thought we'd decided to go to a hotel," Moira said.

"Don't you think that's rather a waste of money?"

"I think," she said in a grim sort of tone, "I think it's money we daren't not spend," and she drew her arm away from mine.

I asked her what on earth she meant.

"Once get you back there with Mummy and you'll never move."

I treated that with the contempt it deserved and said nothing. We walked along in silence. Then Moira began talking in a low monotone, using expressions from paperback psychology which I'm glad to say I have never heard from Dr. Vernon-Peak. We crossed the street and entered Selfridge's. Moira was still going on about Oedipus complexes and that nonsense about making a man of me.

"Keep your voice down," I said. "Everyone can hear you."

She shouted at me to shut up, she would say what she pleased. Well, she had repeatedly told me to be a man and to assert myself, so I did just that. I went up to one of the counters, wrote her a check for, I must admit, a good deal more than I had originally meant to give her, put it into her hands, and walked off, leaving her there.

For a while I felt not displeased with myself, but on the way home in the train depression set in. I should have liked to tell Mother about it but Mother would be out, playing bridge. So I took recourse in my other source of comfort, my wolf skin. The phone rang several times while I was gamboling about the rooms but I didn't answer it. I knew it was Moira. I was on the floor with Grandfather's stuffed eagle in my paws and my teeth in its neck when Mother walked in.

Bridge had ended early. One of the ladies had been taken ill and rushed to the hospital. I had been too intent on my task to see the light come on or hear the door. She stood there in her old fur coat, looking at me. I let the eagle fall and bowed my head—I wanted to die I was so ashamed and embarrassed. How little I really knew my mother! My dear faithful companion, my only friend! Might I not say, my other self?

She smiled. I could hardly believe it but she was smiling. It was that wonderful, conspiratorial, rather naughty smile of hers. "Hallo," she said. "Are you going all loopy?"

In a moment she was down on her knees beside me, the fur coat enveloping her, and together we worried at the eagle, engaged in battle with the bear, attacked the antelope. Together we bounded into the hall to pounce upon the sleeping tigers. Mother kept laughing (and growling too) saying, "What a relief, what a relief!" I think we embraced.

Next day when I got home she was waiting for me, transformed and ready. She had made herself an animal suit. She must have worked on it all day, out of the snow-leopard skin and a length of white-fur fabric. I could see her eyes dancing through the gap in its throat.

"You don't know how I've longed to be an animal again," she said. "I used to be animals when you were a baby. I was a dog for a long time and then I was a bear, but your father found out and he didn't like it. I had to stop."

So that was what I dimly remembered. I said she looked like the Queen of the Beasts.

"Do I, Loopy?" she said.

We had a wonderful weekend, Mother and I. Wolf and leopard, we breakfasted together that morning. Then we played. We played all over the house, sometimes fighting, sometimes dancing, hunting of course, carrying off our prey to the lairs we made for ourselves among the furniture. We went out in the car, drove into the country, and there in a wood got into our skins and for many happy hours roamed wild among the trees.

There seemed no reason, during those two days, to become human again at all, but on the Tuesday I had a rehearsal and on the Monday morning I had to go off to work. It was coming down to earth, back to what we call reality, with a nasty bang. Still, it had its amusing side too. A lady in the train trod on my toe and I had growled at her before I remembered and turned it into a cough.

All through that weekend neither of us had bothered to answer the phone. In the office I had no choice and it was there that Moira caught me. Marriage had come to seem remote, something grotesque, something that others did, not me. Animals do not marry. But that was not the sort of thing I could say to Moira. I promised to ring her. I said we must meet before the week was out.

I suppose she did tell me she'd come over on the Thursday evening and show me what she'd bought with the money I had given her. She knew Mother was always out on Thursdays. I suppose Moira did tell me and I failed to take it in. Nothing was important to me but being animals with Mother—Loopy and the Queen of the Beasts.

Each night as soon as I got home we made ourselves ready for our evening's games. How harmless it all was! How innocent! Like the gentle creatures in the dawn of the world before man came. Like the Garden of Eden after Adam and Eve had been sent away.

The lady who had been taken ill at the bridge evening had since died, so this week it was cancelled. But would Mother have gone anyway? Probably not. Our animal capers meant as much to her as they did to me, almost more perhaps, for she had denied herself so long.

We were sitting at the dining table, eating our evening meal. Mother had cooked, I recall, a rack of lamb so that we might later gnaw the bones. We never ate it, of course, and I have since wondered what became of it. But we did begin on our soup. The bread was at my end of the table, with the bread board and the long sharp knife.

Moira, when she called and I was alone, was in the habit of letting herself in by the back door. We did not hear her, neither of us heard her, though I do remember Mother's noble head lifted a fraction before Moira came in, her fangs bared and her ears pricked. Moira opened the dining-room door and walked in. I can see her now, the complacent smile on her lips fading and the scream starting to come. She was wearing what must have been my present, a full-length white sheepskin coat.

And then? This is what Dr. Vernon-Peak will particularly wish to know but what I cannot clearly remember. I remember that as the door opened I was holding the bread knife in my paws. I think I remember letting out a low growling and poising myself to spring. But what came after?

The last things I can recall before they brought me here are the blood on my fur and the two wild predatory creatures crouched on the floor over the body of the lamb.

THE PLATEAU

by CLARK HOWARD

Tank Sherman felt his daughter's hand shaking him gently. "Tank. Tank, wake up. Bruno's dead."

Tank sat up, moving his legs off the side of the cot where he had been napping, fully clothed except for his boots. Bruno? Bruno dead?

"You mean Hannah," he said, automatically reaching for his boots.

"No, Tank, I mean Bruno. Hannah's still alive. It's Bruno that died."

Tank frowned. That was not the way it was supposed to happen. He pushed first one foot, then the other, into black Atlas boots with riding heels. He had owned the boots for eighteen years, and they were as soft as glove leather. After he got them on, he sat staring at the floor, still confused. Bruno dead? How could that be? Bruno was supposed to have survived Hannah. Bruno was young; Hannah was old. And it was on Bruno that the lottery had been held.

"What happened?" he asked Delia, his daughter.

"I don't know. Doc Lewis is on his way over to check him." She crossed the little one-room cabin to the stove and turned on a burner under the coffee pot. Getting out a cup, she poured a shot of peach brandy into it. "Will they still have the hunt, do you think? Since it's Hannah and not Bruno?"

"No," Tank said emphatically, "they couldn't. Hannah's too old. It wouldn't be a hunt; it would be a target shoot."

When the coffee was ready, Delia poured it in with the brandy and brought it to him. As he sipped it, Tank studied his daughter. She had the dark hair of her mother: thick and black as a crow's wing. And the high cheekbones of her mother's people, the Shoshone. Her light halfbreed coloring and blue eyes she got from him. All her life she had called him "Tank" instead of "Daddy." At nineteen, her body was round and strong. She lived in her own mobile home down the road, and dealt blackjack for a living in an illegal game behind the Custer's Last Stand restaurant. Tank himself still lived in the cabin where Delia had been born. He had been alone for a year, since Delia left; and lonely for six years, since her mother had died of bone disease.

"Are you going down to the concession?" Delia asked.

"In a minute." He held the coffee cup with both hands, as if warming his palms, and smiled at his daughter. "Remember how your Ma used to raise hell when she caught you lacing my coffee with brandy?"

"Yes." Delia smiled back.

"She always wanted me to make something of myself, your Ma. Always wanted me to do something important. But I guess it just isn't in the cards. If Hannah had died first, like she was supposed to, why, I could have done something important for the first time in my life. Important to your Ma, at least. And to Bruno. But Bruno ups and dies first, so I'm left with nothing important to do. If your Ma was still alive, she'd swear on her medicine bag that I arranged it this way."

Shaking his head wryly, Tank drank a long swallow from his cup. At fifty, he was a rangy, well-worn man with not an ounce of fat on him. His face showed the results of a hundred fists, maybe more. Twenty years earlier he had come to town as part of a traveling boxing show, whites against Indians. Dan Sherman, his name had been, but they billed him as "Tank" because he was so tough. Tank Sherman, after the Sherman tank. A hide like armor. Took punches like Jake LaMotta. But he had taken too many by then. In their little Montana town, a Northern Cheyenne who hated whites had beaten him to a pulp, and when the outfit moved on it took the Northern Cheyenne with it and left Tank behind. Delia's mother had found him sitting behind the 7-Eleven, trying to eat some crackers and Vienna sausage he had bought with his last dollar. His lips were swollen so grotesquely he could barely chew, his eyes puffed to slits through which he could hardly see. Delia's mother took him home with her. They were never to part. Delia was their only child.

"Let's go on down to the concession," Tank said when he finished his coffee.

His cabin was on the slope of a low hill, and as Tank and Delia walked down its path they could see a small crowd already beginning to gather at the concession's corral. The concession itself was nothing more than a small barn next to the corral, with a gaudy red sign over its door which read: LAST TWO LIVING BUFFALO—ADMISSION $1. Tourists bought tickets and lined up around the corral, then the barn doors were opened and Bruno and Hannah were driven out to be viewed. They were the last two remaining buffalo in North America.

Now there was only one.

Old Doc Lewis, the reservation veterinarian from the nearby Crow agency, had just finished examining Bruno when Tank and Delia eased their way through the crowd to him.

"What killed him, Doc?" asked Tank, looking down at the great mass of animal spread out on the ground.

"Stroke," the vet said, brushing off his knees. "He was carrying too much weight. Must have been upwards of two thousand pounds."

Tank nodded. "Can't run off much fat in a corral," he observed.

Doc Lewis was making notes in a small book. "How old was he, do you know?"

"Nine," Tank said. "My wife helped deliver him." His scarred boxer's face saddened as he noticed his daughter reach out and pat the dead buffalo's massive head. Then he glanced over to a corner of the corral and saw Hannah, standing quietly, watching. Unlike Bruno, a young bull, Hannah was a cow and much older: at least thirty. She had thinner, lighter hair than most buffalo, and a triangular part of her neck and shoulder cape was almost blond, indicating the presence somewhere in her ancestry of a white buffalo. Much smaller than Bruno, she stood only five feet at her shoulders and weighed a shade over seven hundred pounds.

"I guess this means the big hunt is off, doesn't it, Doc?" Tank asked. It was the same question Delia had asked him, and Doc gave the same answer.

"Of course. There wouldn't be any sport at all going after Hannah. She's much too old."

The three of them walked over to Hannah and, as if compelled by some irresistible urge, they all patted her at once. "Well, old girl," Doc said, "you made the history books. The last North American plains buffalo."

"Maybe they'll put her on a stamp or something," said Delia.

"Maybe," Doc allowed. "They already had the buffalo on a nickel, but that was before your time."

From the barn, a pretty young woman in the tan uniform of a state park ranger walked over to them. White, educated, poised, she was everything Delia was not. "Hello, Dr. Lewis—Mr. Sherman," she said. "Hello there, Delia." She snapped a lead rein onto the collar Hannah wore. "I just got a call from headquarters to close down the concession. And to trim Hannah's hooves. Isn't it exciting?"

Doc and Tank exchanged surprised looks. "Isn't what exciting?" Doc asked, almost hesitantly. Instinctively, both he and Tank already knew what her answer would be.

"The hunt, of course. Oh, I know it won't be the same as it would have been with Bruno as the prey. But it will still be the last buffalo hunt ever. That's history in the making!"

"That," Doc rebuked, "is barbarism."

"Are you saying the hunt's still on?" Tank asked. "With Hannah as the prey?"

"Of course." She shrugged her pretty shoulders. "I mean, how else can it be? The tickets have been sold, the lottery has been held. You don't expect the state to go back on its word, do you?"

"No," Delia said, "definitely not. Never. Not the state."

"Well, there you are," the young ranger said, missing Delia's sarcasm entirely. "But, listen, they *have* changed the rules a little to make it fairer. Bruno was only going to be given a twelve-hour start, remember? Well, Hannah gets a full *twenty-four.*" She smiled, apparently delighted by the allowance.

Doc Lewis turned and walked away, thoroughly disgusted. Tank and Delia left also. Walking back up the path to Tank's cabin, Delia said, "Looks like you're getting your chance to do something important, after all."

Tank, thinking about his dead wife, nodded. "Looks like . . ."

When it had become clear that the plains buffalo had finally reached the threshold of extinction, when it was absolutely certain that no new calves would be born because the remaining cows were too old to conceive, the state had immediately done two things: penned up the few remaining members of the species and put an admission on their viewing, and devised a nationwide lottery to select the persons who would be allowed to hunt— and take the head and hide of—the last American buffalo.

Both moves proved enormously successful. The Last Remaining Buffalo concession, let by the state to one of its own departments, the Bureau of Parks, was open nine months of the year. Managed by park rangers, it operated under very low overhead and was the most profitable tourist attraction in the state. All around the corral where the buffalo were exhibited, there were coin-operated machines where for a quarter visitors could purchase cups of processed food pellets to toss into the corral for the buffalo to eat. Like peanuts to caged monkeys. Except that the buffalo refused to do tricks. Despite considerable effort in the beginning, including the use of a whip, the buffalo had remained stoic and refused to be trained. Finally, the park rangers had to resign themselves to simply leading their charges into the corral and letting them stand there while small children pelted them with synthetic food. The attraction, nevertheless, was popular.

As profitable as the concession was, however, its earnings were modest compared to the proceeds of the lottery. In a scheme devised by one of the General Accounting Office's young financial wizards, two million numbered tickets had been sold throughout the state and through the mail nationally, for five dollars a chance. The ticket supply was exhausted within a month, and the state had made a quick ten million dollars. Even people who had no interest whatever in hunting bought a ticket for investment speculation. Even before the drawing, advertisements had been run by people offering to buy a winning ticket from anyone whose number was picked.

The drawing, wherein three winners were selected, was by the use of a single, predesignated digit each day from the total shares traded on the New York Stock Exchange. The lucky ticket holders were a piano tuner from Boston, a waiter in Memphis, and a ranch hand in Nevada. The piano tuner sold his ticket for ten thousand dollars to Gregory Kingston, the actor. The waiter sold his for eighty-five hundred to bestselling author Harmon Langford. Lester Ash, the ranch hand, kept his, deciding that the head and hide would be worth far more than the ticket. He was counting on being a better hunter and shot than the actor and author were.

Within two hours of the untimely death of Bruno, the three registered owners of the winning tickets were notified to come claim their prize. Hannah, the last surviving plains buffalo, would be released fifty miles out on the prairie at noon on Friday.

At noon on Saturday, the three lottery winners would be free to hunt her.

By midnight on Thursday, Tank Sherman was ready to go. Hitched to the rear of his Ford pickup truck was a double-stall horse trailer from which he had removed the center divider, creating one large stall.

Parking the rig on the prairie some one hundred yards behind the concession corral, he and Delia slipped through the quiet night to the barn, snipped the padlock with bolt-cutters, and led Hannah out. The old buffalo cow was as docile as a rabbit and made no noise whatever as Delia fed her a handful of fresh meadow grass and Tank slipped a braided halter over her head.

After walking the buffalo aboard the trailer and quietly closing her in, Tank handed Delia an envelope. "Here's the deed to the cabin and lot. And the passbook to your ma's savings account. She had six hundred and forty dollars saved when she died; it was supposed to be yours when you were twenty-one. Oh, and the title to the pickup is there, too, just in case. Guess that's about all."

Delia got a paper bag and thermos jug from her Jeep. "Sandwiches," she said. "And coffee. With, uh—"

"Yeah." He put the bag and jug on the seat of the pickup and sniffed once as if he might be catching cold. But he wasn't catching cold. "Listen, take care of yourself, kid," he said brusquely, and started to get into the truck. Then he turned back. "Look, I know I ain't never won no Father-of-the-Year prize and I never gave you noplace to live but that cabin and I never sent you to college or nothing, but those things don't have nothing to do with caring. You understand?"

"Sure," Delia said. She shrugged. "After all, you did teach me when to fold in poker. And how to change a flat. And how to get a squirrel to eat out of my hand. Lots of girls never learn those things." She had to struggle to control her voice. She was not able to control her tears. But she knew that Tank couldn't see the tears in the darkness.

"Okay," he said. "I'll be hitting the road then."

He eased the door of the pickup shut, quietly started the engine, and slowly pulled away without headlights.

Behind him, Delia waved in the darkness and said, "Bye—Daddy."

When he reached the highway, turned on his headlights, and increased speed, Tank thought: *Okay, Rose, this is for you, honey.*

Rose was Tank's dead wife, the woman who had always wanted him to do something important. Her Shoshone name was Primrose, given to her by her father because she had been born on a day in early July when the evening primrose had just blossomed. Later, when she moved into town and took up the ways of the white woman, she shortened it to Rose.

Tank always remembered Rose as being beautiful, but she was not; she was not even pretty. Her face was very plain, her eyes set too close together, her nose too long, and one cheek was pitted with pockmarks. Only her hair, lustrous as polished onyx, could truly be called beautiful. But Tank saw so much more of her than was outside. He saw her hopes and dreams, her pride, her nakedness when they made love, her secret joys. He saw everything about her, and it was all of those things combined which made her beautiful to him.

The first time she had shown him the buffalo was three months after she had taken him to live with her, after she had nursed him back to health from the beating he had taken. They got up early one morning on Rose's day off from the sugar-beet processing plant, and in her old Jeep they drove thirty miles out onto the raw prairie. There, on an isolated meadow, was a small buffalo herd: three bulls, a cow, and six calves. They were the beginning of the last migration, when the ocean of tourists had started driving them north and west from the Black Hills.

"See how noble they look," Rose had said. "See the dignity with which they stand and observe." Her eyes had become water and she had added, "They are watching their world come to an end."

Once, Rose explained to him, there had been sixty *million* plains buffalo. Their presence on the Northern Plains had been the greatest recorded aggregation of large land animals ever known to man. To the red man of the prairie, the vast herds had been the mainstay of his economy. That single species provided food, clothing, shelter, and medicine for an entire race— the only time in history that such a natural balance between man and beast had ever been achieved.

"Then, of course, the whites came," Rose said. "At first, they killed the buffalo for meat and hides, as our people did, and that was acceptable because the herds were many. Later they killed them only for hides, leaving the carcasses to rot in the sun. Even that act, although it was without honor, could have been tolerated. But then they began killing them for what they called 'sport.' Fun. Recreation.

"They killed them first by the tens of thousands. The butcher Cody, whom they called 'Buffalo Bill,' personally recorded more than forty-two-thousand kills in one seventeen-month period. Soon they were being slaughtered with total wantonness, by the hundreds of thousands. Today there are only a few hundred left. Most of them are in the Black Hills. But they're slowly migrating back up here again."

"Why?" Tank asked, fascinated.

"They know the end is nearing for them. A species can tell when their breed is running out. Each year they see fewer and fewer calves, the herds become smaller and smaller. So they look for a place to end their line. They look for a grassy meadow unspoiled by humans. A place to lie down and die with dignity."

For all the years Tank Sherman knew and lived with the Shoshone woman Rose, she had loved the great buffalo and mourned its diminishing number. As much as Tank missed her in death, he was glad that she had not lived to see Bruno and Hannah, the last two of the breed, penned up and put on display—or known about the lottery for the privilege of hunting the survivor.

So this is for you, honey, he thought as he headed southeast with Hannah in the horse trailer. He would have about five hours' head start. Possibly two hundred-fifty miles. Maybe it would be enough.

Maybe not.

Two hours after dawn, a tall, very handsome man, livid with anger, was stalking back and forth in the empty concession corral.

"What the hell do you mean, *missing?* How can something as large as a buffalo be *missing?*" His name was Gregory Kingston. An Academy Award-winning actor, he was not acting now; he was truly incensed.

"The state guaranteed this hunt," said a second man. Smaller, plumper, not as handsome but with a good deal more bearing, this was Harmon Langford, internationally known bestselling author. Like Kingston, he was dressed in expensive hunting garb, carrying a fine, hand-tooled, engraved, foreign-made rifle. "Exactly who's in charge here?" he quietly demanded.

A third man, Lester Ash, the ranch hand from Nevada, stood back a step, not speaking, but observing everything. He wore hardy working clothes: denim, twill, roughout leather.

"Gentlemen," a Bureau of Mines spokesman pleaded, "please believe me, we're trying to get to the bottom of this as quickly as we can. All we know right now is that some person or persons apparently abducted Hannah sometime during the night. The highway patrol has been notified and a statewide search is getting underway at this very moment—"

"Why in hell would anyone want to abduct a *buffalo?*" Kingston inquired loudly of the world at large, throwing his arms up in bewilderment. Now he *was* acting.

"Oh, come, Kingston," said Harmon Langford, "we're not talking about *a* buffalo, we're talking about *this* buffalo. Unlike ourselves, there *are* those—" and here he glanced at Lester Ash "—who are interested in this animal not for sport but for profit." Lester Ash grinned but remained silent. Langford continued, "At any rate, we cannot waste time on *why*—we must concentrate on *where*. *Where* is our great, hairy prize? And how do we get to it?"

The Bureau of Parks man said, "We should be hearing from the highway patrol any time now. Every road in the state is covered."

"What do we do now?" asked Gregory Kingston, directing the question at Langford.

"We must be prepared to get to the animal as quickly as possible after it's located," the author declared. "Before some outsider decides to take an illegal shot at it. This part of the country is crawling with would-be cowboys. Pickup trucks, rifle racks in the back window, old faded Levis— that sort of thing. I'm sure there are a few of them who would like to be remembered as the man who gunned down the last buffalo."

"Like you, you mean?" Lester Ash said, speaking for the first time.

A smirk settled on Langford's lips. "Yes," he acknowledged. Adding, "And you." They locked eyes in a moment of mutual understanding and then Langford said, "What we need, of course, is fast, flexible transportation." He turned to the Parks man. "How far is the nearest helicopter service?"

"Fifty miles."

"I suggest we start at once. If we have a helicopter at our disposal by the time the buffalo is located, we can hurry there at once. I presume the state would have no objection to that?"

The Parks man shrugged. "Not so long as all three of you get an equal start. And don't shoot it from the air."

"Of course not. We aren't barbarians, after all." He looked at Kingston and Lester Ash. "Are we agreed?"

"Agreed," said the actor.

"Let's go," said Ash.

Three hours earlier, Tank had parked the pickup and trailer in a stand of elm and gone on foot deeper into the trees where Otter had his cabin. It had still been dark—the eerie void before dawn. He knocked softly at Otter's door.

"Who disturbs this weak old man at such an hour?" a voice asked from within. "Is it someone evil, come to take advantage of my helplessness?"

"Otter, it's Sherman," said Tank. "Your daughter's man before she passed."

"What is it you want?" asked Otter. "I am destitute and can offer you nothing. I have no money or other valuables. I barely exist from day to day. Why have you come to me?"

"For your wisdom, Otter. For your words."

"Perhaps I can give you that, although I am usually so weak from hunger that each breath could well be my last. How many others have you brought with you?"

Tank smiled in the darkness. "I am alone, Otter." Maybe now the old scoundrel would stop acting.

"You may enter," Otter said. "There are candles by the door."

Inside the front door, Tank lighted a candle that illuminated patches of an incredibly dirty and impoverished room. In one corner, an ancient cot with torn sagging mattress; in another, a rusted iron sink filled with dirty pots and pans; in a third, an old chifforobe with a broken door hanging loose to reveal a few articles of ragged clothing. Everywhere in between there was dirt, grime, clutter.

Tank didn't pause in the room. He lit his way directly to a door which led to a second room, and in that room he found Otter sitting up in a king-size bed, a cigar in his mouth, a bottle of whiskey at his side. As Tank closed the door behind him, the old Indian uncocked a double-barrel shotgun on the bed beside him and put it on the floor. "How are you, Soft Face?" he asked. The first time he had seen Tank, the young fighter's face had been beaten to pulp. Otter had called him "Soft Face" ever since.

"I'm okay," Tank said. "You look the same."

The old Indian shrugged. "There is no reason for something perfect to change."

Tank grinned and glanced around the room. It was a self-contained little world, holding everything Otter needed or wanted for his personal comfort. Portable air-conditioner, color television, microwave oven, upright freezer, power generator, small bathroom in one corner, indoor hot tub and jacuzzi in another. "How's the bootlegging business?" Tank asked.

"My customers are loyal. I make ends meet." Otter got out of bed and put a Hopi blanket around his shoulders. "Is my granddaughter still dealing cards in the white man's game?"

"Yes."

"Does she cheat them when the opportunity presents itself?"

"Yes, if they are tourists."

Otter nodded in approval. "That is good. Even a half-Indian should cheat the whites whenever possible." At a two-burner hotplate, Otter set water to boil. "Sit here at the table," he said, "and tell me your problem."

Tank explained to the old Indian what he had done, and why. When he got to the part about Rose and her love for the buffalo, Otter's eyes became misty. When Tank stopped talking, Otter rose, poured coffee and brandy for them, and brought it to the table. "How can I help you?" he asked.

"I need a safe place to put the old buffalo. Someplace where she can live out her days in peace without fear of being hunted and shot. Someplace where she will be able to die quietly, like your daughter Primrose would want her to die."

Otter sipped his coffee and pondered the problem. Several times he shook his head, as if first considering, then dismissing, a possibility. Finally he tapped a forefinger on the table and said, "Do you remember the place where Ditch Creek runs beside Bear Mountain?"

"In the Black Hills?" said Tank. "Where you used to take us on picnics when Delia was a little girl?"

"That's the place. There's a grassy meadow far above Ditch Creek that belongs to the few remaining people of the Deerfield tribe. It's within the Black Hills National Park, but the federal government deeded it to the Deerfields because there was no road into it and they must have figured the tourists wouldn't be able to get to it anyway. The Deerfield use it for religious ceremonies—it's sacred ground to them. The buffalo would be protected once it got there. But there are only dirt paths leading up to the meadow. I don't know if the buffalo could climb it or not."

"How high is it?" Tank asked.

"About seven thousand feet. There's a gravel road to about six thousand, but the rest of the way would be on footpaths. It would have been better if you'd stolen a mountain goat—you never were very smart, Soft Face."

"Can you draw me a map?" Tank asked.

"Of course. I am a man of many talents."

Otter got paper and pencil and from memory sketched a map and gave it to Tank. It was daylight now and the two of them walked out to the horse trailer.

Tank backed Hannah out to exercise and feed her.

"She's a fine old buffalo," Otter observed. "Only your people would think of shooting her."

"Just because they're the same color doesn't mean they're my people," Tank replied.

Tank tethered the buffalo to a tree and returned to the cabin with Otter. The old Indian cooked breakfast and they ate together. Then it was time for Tank to leave. Otter walked back to the rig and helped him load Hannah. After Tank got in and started the truck, Otter put a hand on the door.

"In each man's life, there is a plateau," he said. "Every man reaches that plateau. He may be there for a day or a year, or only for a moment. But his time there is the meaning of his life. It is the reason the Great One put him here on earth. I think, Soft Face, that your plateau might be that grassy meadow above Ditch Creek." He touched Tank's shoulder. "Go with the wind, son."

Tank swallowed dryly, nodded, and drove off.

The helicopter was flying a checkerboard search pattern two hundred miles from where the buffalo had been stolen. Harmon Langford sat next to the pilot. Gregory Kingston and Lester Ash occupied jumpseats behind them. All three men scanned the ground below with binoculars.

"This is maddening," Kingston muttered. He tapped Langford on the shoulder. "Tell me again!" he yelled through the noise of the rotor. "Why are we looking in this direction?"

The author yelled back, "The highway patrol reported that a pickup truck pulling a horse trailer filled up with gas in Dayton at four o'clock this morning! The station attendant said the animal in the trailer had a blanket over it and the man driving the truck said it was a rodeo bull! But he thinks it was our buffalo! They were headed toward Gillette! We're searching the area south of Gillette!"

The actor shrugged, as if it were all totally meaningless to him. Lester Ash leaned close to his ear and said, "Highway Patrol thinks he might be headed toward Thunder Basin! That's a big grassland area! Be a perfect place to set a buffalo loose!"

"I see!" Kingston said, smiling. "Now *that* makes sense!" He patted Ash fondly on the knee. Ash drew back suspiciously.

The helicopter continued to checkerboard, its pilot crossing out squares on a plot map on the console. They flew well into the grasslands, twenty miles deep, and began a random searching pattern, following shadows, wind movement, wild game—anything that attracted their attention. But they didn't find what they were looking for.

After an hour, the pilot advised Langford, "We'll have to land for fuel soon."

No sooner had he spoken, they received a radio message from the Parks man back at the concession. "The trailer has been sighted by a Civil Air Patrol scout plane. It's on Route 16, south of Osage, heading toward the Black Hills. It's sure to make it across the state line, so we're requesting the South Dakota state police to set up roadblocks. I'll keep you advised."

"How far is Osage?" Langford asked the pilot.

"Fifty miles, give or take."

"Can we make it?"

"Yessir, but that'll be the limit. We'll have to refuel in Osage."

"Go," Harmon Langford ordered.

*   *   *

Tank had his CB tuned to the law-enforcement band, so he heard the South Dakota state police order go out for roadblocks. They were being set up in Custer, Four Corners, and at the junction of Routes 85 and 16. Pulling onto the shoulder of the road, Tank shifted to neutral and unfolded a map he'd picked up at a service station near Sundance, where Otter lived. When he'd stopped at the station, the tarp flaps on the trailer had been down so no one could see inside. He was sure it hadn't been the station attendant who put the law on him. Probably that low-flying two-seater that had come in over him outside Osage.

Studying the map, Tank saw that the locations selected for the roadblocks gave him considerably more leeway than he had expected. Apparently they thought he was going to try to drive well into the Black Hills. He wasn't. He needed to penetrate them only a few miles before reaching a secondary road that ran north and then east to Ditch Creek. Smiling, he saw that he would reach all three roadblocks. Getting out of the truck for a moment, he lifted one of the trailer flaps and reached in to pat Hannah's thick, hairy cape.

"We're going to beat the sons of bitches, old girl," he said happily.

It hadn't occurred to him that they might use a helicopter.

At Osage, Harmon Langford conferred by telephone with the authorities responsible for the roadblock. "Of course, I very much appreciate your help in containing this man, Captain, and I assure you that when I write about this incident, you and your men will be prominently featured. Now if you'd just be good enough to keep your forces in place and let my associates and me handle it from here, I think justice will be properly served. We really don't consider this a criminal matter. It's more mischief than anything else—a nuisance, but we can handle it."

Then he talked with the pilot of the scout plane. "Are you keeping him in sight?"

"Yes, Mr. Langford. He's moving up a secondary road toward a place called Ditch Creek."

"Fine. Keep circling and don't lose him. We'll be airborne again in a few minutes and should be there shortly. Of course, I'll expect to see you after this is all over, for photographs and such. Over and out."

As Langford turned to face them, Kingston and Lester Ash saw a look of gleeful triumph on his face. Almost an evil look.

"In a very short while, gentlemen," he said, "we should be in position to take our buffalo back. I trust both of you are prepared to deal with this abductor if he resists us?"

Kingston frowned. "What do you mean?"

Langford did not answer. Instead, he picked up his rifle and jacked a round into the chamber.

Watching him, Lester Ash smiled.

Turning off the secondary road into the inclining gravel road, Tank was aware that the patrol plane was following him. But he wasn't overly concerned. The two men in the light plane couldn't get to him. There was noplace in the surrounding hills they could land. All they could do was radio his position and he was too close to his goal now for that to matter. He knew where the roadblocks were—no one from there could catch up with him. Only one obstacle remained in his way: the thousand feet of footpath from the end of the gravel road up to the meadow.

Frowning, he wondered if old Hannah was going to be able to make it. A lot would depend on how steep the trail was and what kind of footing it offered. Good dirt footing was what he hoped for—Hannah's freshly trimmed hooves would slide too much on rock.

At the end of the gravel road, Tank drove the rig as far into the trees as he could. Part of the trailer still stuck out and he knew it could be seen from the air. No matter, he thought, they can't catch us now.

"Come on, old girl," he said as he backed Hannah out of the trailer and rubbed her neck. Studying the terrain above them, he selected the least steep path he could find and gently pulled Hannah onto it. Moving about four feet ahead of her, he drew the halter rope tight and urged her forward. She stepped nimbly up the trail and followed him without resistance.

This might be easier than I thought, Tank told himself hopefully.

The helicopter rendezvoused with the scout plane an hour after Tank and Hannah began their climb.

"Where are they?" Langford asked the air-patrol pilot on the radio.

"In those trees on the side of the mountain, sir. You can't see them right now because of the overgrowth. They're probably about halfway up to that grassy meadow on the plateau there."

Langford praised the two men in the plane for exemplary work, dismissed them, and turned to the helicopter pilot. "Set down on that grassy meadow," he ordered.

"I can't do that, sir," said the pilot, who was half Nez Percé. "That's sacred land belonging to the Deerfield tribe. Outsiders aren't permitted there."

Langford shifted the barrel of his rifle until it pointed toward the pilot. "I really do want you to land," he said pointedly.

The Nez Percé smiled. "I'd be careful with that rifle if I were you, sir. Unless you or your friends know how to fly one of these babies. They go down mighty fast."

Pursing his lips, Langford shifted the barrel back. He reached into his pocket, extracted a roll of currency, and peeled off five one-hundred-dollar bills. "If you could just hover a few feet from the ground. Long enough for us to drop off."

"That," the pilot said, taking the money, "I can do."

The last few hundred feet were the worst for both the man and the buffalo. The trail, after an easy beginning, had become narrow, steep, rutted, and treacherous. Three times, Hannah's hooves slipped on loose rocks or concealed roots and she went sliding back fifteen or twenty feet, dragging Tank with her. Each time, she rolled over onto her side and mooed anxiously as dirt from above displaced and shifted down to half bury her. Each time, Tank had to stroke and soothe her, help her dig out and regain her balance and patiently urge her forward again.

Twice Tank himself slipped badly, the leather of his old boots reacting just as Hannah's hooves did to the hostile ground under them. The first time he fell, his left foot came out from under him and he pitched onto both knees, puncturing one trouser leg on a sharp rock and cutting his knee badly enough to bleed. The second time, he lost his balance completely and went plunging downhill, sliding helplessly past Hannah, his face, shirt, and boots catching the avalanche of loose dirt that followed him. He had the presence of mind to let go of the halter rope, and didn't upset Hannah with his spill, but he slid all of forty feet. When he straightened himself, he was filthy with dirt stuck to his sweaty clothes and body and his face and hands showed nicks and cuts seeping blood through the dirt. Cursing mightily, Tank clawed his way back up to where Hannah, watching him curiously, waited with infinite patience.

Late in the climb, perhaps two hundred feet from the plateau, Tank thought he heard the roar of a motor. It was hard to tell with the thick treetops insulating the ground from noise and the constant wind whipping about now that they were so high. Maybe it was that light plane coming in low to search the meadow. If so, he thought craftily, they would find nothing there.

We're beating them, Rose—Hannah and me. And it's important that we beat them. Important that we make that plateau.

They kept climbing, the man and the buffalo, struggling against the total environment around them—the height aloof above them, the ground resistant under them, the air thin and selfish, the dirt and dust, the rocks and roots. Blood and sweat burned their eyes, both of them, for Hannah now had cuts on her old face as well. Foam coated her lips, saliva and tears wet the man's cheeks.

They climbed until their muscles came close to locking, their lungs close to bursting, their hearts close to breaking. With no resource left but blind courage, they climbed.

Finally, they made it to the top and together crawled onto the edge of the grassy meadow.

The three hunters were waiting there for them.

Only when he saw the hunters did Tank Sherman realize that the motor roar he heard had not been the scout plane but a helicopter. As he and the buffalo struggled together to drag their bodies over the lip of the plateau, both had fallen onto their knees, Tank pitching forward so that he was on all fours, Hannah with her front legs bent, great head down. Both were panting, trying to suck enough oxygen out of the thin air to cool lungs that felt as if they had been singed. For one brief instant, as they knelt side by side, Tank's shoulder brushing Hannah's neck, both their heads hung, as if man and beast were one.

Then Tank looked up and saw the hunters. They stood in a row, the sun reflecting on their rifles.

"No," he said softly, shaking his head. "No," a little louder as he got to his feet. "No!" he yelled as he walked toward them.

Harmon Langford, standing in the middle, said, "Stop where you are— come any closer and we'll shoot!"

Eyes fixed like a madman, jaw clenched like a vise, his big fists closed, Tank stalked toward them. "No!" he kept shouting. "No! No! No!"

"You've been warned!" snapped Langford.

Tank kept coming.

"All right, shoot him!" Langford ordered, shouldering his own rifle and aiming.

No shots were fired. Langford lowered his rifle and looked frantically from Kingston to Lester Ash. "Shoot! Why don't you shoot?"

"Why don't you?" Lester Ash asked evenly.

Langford didn't have time to reply. Tank reached him, snatched the rifle from his hands, and hurled it away. Then he drove a crushing right fist into Langford's face, smashing his nose and lips, sending him reeling back in shock.

As Langford fell, Tank turned on Gregory Kingston. "Now just a minute," the actor pleaded, "I had no intention of shooting you—" He threw down the rifle as evidence of his sincerity, but that didn't deter Tank. The old fighter dug a solid right fist deep into Kingston's midsection and the actor folded up like a suitcase, the color draining from his face, his eyes bulging. Dropping to his knees, he pitched forward onto his face, the juicy meadow grass staining it green.

When Tank looked for the third man, he found that Lester Ash, experienced hunter that he was, had flanked his adversary and moved around behind him. It was now Tank standing on the meadow, Lester Ash facing him with his back to the sun.

"We can do it the easy way or the hard way, bud," said Lester. "Either way, that buffalo's mine."

Tank shook his head. "No." He moved toward Ash.

"I ain't no loud-mouthed writer or sissy actor, bud," the Nevadan said. "Mess with me and I'll put you in the hospital. That buff is *mine!*"

"No." Tank kept coming.

"Please yourself," Lester said disgustedly. He snapped the rifle to his shoulder and fired.

The round ripped all the way through the fleshy part of Tank's left thigh and knocked him off his feet. Instincts two decades old still lived in his mind, and as if someone were counting ten over him Tank rolled over and got back up. Clutching his thigh, he limped toward Ash.

"You're a damned fool, bud," said Lester Ash. He fired again.

The second slug tore a hole in Tank's right thigh and he was again spun to the ground. He moaned aloud, involuntarily, and sat up, one hand on each wound. Pain seared his body, hot and relentless, and he began to choke, cough, and cry. I'm done for, he thought.

Then at his feet he saw something white and yellow. Pawing the tears from his eyes, he managed to focus. It was a clump of wildflowers—white petals with yellow nectaries. Primroses.

Tank dragged himself up one last time. He started forward again, weaving and faltering like a drunk man. His eyes fixed on Lester Ash and held.

"Okay, bud," said Lester, "now you lose a kneecap—"

Before Lester could fire, Hannah charged. Massive head down, hooves almost soundless on the thick meadow grass, she was upon Lester Ash before he realized it. Catching him from the left side, her broad forehead drove into his chest, crushing his left rib cage, collapsing the lung beneath it. With his body half bent over her face, Hannah propelled him to the edge of the plateau and hurled him over the side.

Lester Ash screamed as his body ricocheted off the first three trees, then was silent for the rest of the way down.

The Deerfield tribe marshal and his deputy, who rode up to the meadow on horseback at the first sound of gunfire, secured the area and arranged for Harmon Langford and Gregory Kingston to be escorted down to the reservation boundary. They were released with a stern warning never to violate Deerfield land again. Some men with a rescue stretcher retrieved Lester Ash's body. His death was officially attributed to an accidental fall from the plateau.

A Deerfield medicine man named Alzada, who resided in a lodge back in the trees next to the meadow, was consulted by the marshal as to the disposition of the buffalo.

"If the Great One put the buffalo here," Alzada decreed, "then the buffalo must be sacred. It shall be allowed to graze on the sacred meadow until the Great One summons it back."

The marshal looked over at the edge of the meadow where Tank sat under a tree, exhausted and bleeding. "What about the man?"

"What man?" said Alzada. "I see no man. I see only a sacred buffalo, grazing contentedly. If you see something else, perhaps it is a spirit."

The marshal shook his head. "If Alzada sees nothing, then I see nothing. Only Alzada can see spirits."

The marshal and his deputy rode back down the mountain.

When they were gone, the medicine man went over and helped Tank into the trees to his lodge.

THE BUTCHERS

by *PETER LOVESEY*

He had passed the weekend in the cold-store of Pugh the Butcher's. It was now Monday morning. The door was still shut. He was unconcerned. Quite early on Saturday evening he had given up beating his fists on the door and screaming for help. He had soon tired of jumping and arm-swinging to keep his circulation going. He had become increasingly drowsy as his brain had succumbed to the deprivation of oxygen. He had lain on the tiled floor below the glistening carcases and by Sunday morning he had frozen to death.

On the other side of the door, Joe Wilkins filled two mugs with instant coffee. It was still only 8:00 A.M. and the shop didn't open until 8:30. He was Mr. Pugh's shop manager, forty-four, a master butcher, dark and good-looking, with an old-fashioned Clark Gable mustache and quick laughing eyes that had a way of involving everyone in the shop each time he passed a joke with a customer.

The second mug was for Frank, the apprentice butcher. Frank was eighteen and useful for heavy work. He earned extra money on Saturday nights as a bouncer in Stacey's, the disco across the street. When the deliveries came from the slaughterer's, Frank would take the sides of beef on his back as if they were pieces of polystyrene. The girls from Woolworth's next door often came into the shop on their lunch hour and asked Frank for rides on his motorbike. Frank got embarrassed when Joe Wilkins teased him about it.

Frank hung up his leather jacket and put on a clean apron. Joe was already wearing his straw boater. He watched the young man struggle awkwardly with the apron strings, tying a bow so loose it was sure to fall apart as soon as he stretched up to lift a carcase off its hook.

"Another heavy weekend, lad?"

"Not really," answered Frank, taking his coffee and slopping some on the chopping block. "Same as usual."

"That's good to hear. Looks as if we've got a busy morning ahead of us."

Frank gave a frown.

Joe snapped his fingers. "Come on, lad, what's different this morning, or haven't you noticed yet?"

Frank looked around the shop. "Meat's not out yet."

"Right. And why not?"

"Percy isn't in."

"Right again. By Jove, I was wrong about you. You ought to be on the telly with a mind as sharp as that. Why spend the rest of your life hacking pieces of meat when you could earn millions sitting in an armchair answering questions? And now for five hundred and a holiday for two in the Bahamas, Mr. Dobson. What do you think has happened to Percy?"

"Dunno," answered Frank.

"You don't know? Come on, lad. You're not trying."

"He could have fallen off his bike again."

"That's more like it," said Joe as he took his knives and cleavers from the drawer behind the counter and started sharpening them. "Get the window ready, will you?"

Frank put down his coffee and looked for the enamel trays that usually stood in the shop window.

Joe said, "You're probably right about Percy. He's too old to be in charge of a bike. Seven miles is a long way on a morning like this, with ice all the way up Bread and Cheese Hill and the motorists driving like lunatics. He was knocked in the ditch last week, poor old devil."

"Where does he put the trays?" asked Frank.

"Trays?"

"For the meat—in the window."

"Aren't they there then?" Joe put down his knife and went to look. "Well, I suppose he puts them away somewhere. By the time I arrive, they're always here. Have a look behind the deep-freeze cabinet. —Got 'em? Good. Blowed if I understand why he bothers to do that."

"Dust, I expect," said Frank.

"Quite right. Wipe them over with a cloth, lad. I used to wonder what Percy did with himself before we arrived in the morning. He's in by six, you know, regular. How about that? He must be up at five. Could you do that six mornings a week? And it gets no easier as you get older. He must be pushing seventy by now."

"What *does* he do before we get in?" asked Frank.

"Well, it's always spotless, isn't it?"

"I thought that was because he stays on of a night to clean up after we close."

"So he does—but there's always more dust by morning. Percy wipes all the surfaces clean. He puts out the trays, and the cuts from the cold-store. He hangs up the poultry and opens a tin of liver and checks everything against the price list, puts out the tags and the plastic parsley and the new-laid eggs and the packets of stuffing and bread sauce. I hope you're listening, lad, because I want all those jobs done before we open."

Frank gave another frown. "You want me to do all that?"

"Who else, lad?" said Joe in a reasonable voice. "It's obvious that Percy isn't going to make it this morning, and I've got the orders to get out."

"He hasn't had a day off since I started last year," said Frank, still unable to believe his bad luck.

"He hasn't had a day off in the twenty years I've been working here. Six in the morning till seven at night, six days a week. And what for? Boy's work. He does the work you ought to be doing, lad. No one else but Percy would stand for it. Fetching and carrying and sweeping up. Do you know, he's never once complained to me or Mr. Pugh or anyone else? You've seen him bent nearly double carrying in the carcasses. A man of his age shouldn't be doing work like that. It's exploitation, that's what it is."

"Why does he do it then? He's old enough to draw his pension."

Joe shook his head. "He wouldn't be happy with his feet up. He's spent the best years of his life working in this shop. He was here before Mr. Pugh took it over. It was Slater's in those days. —Yes, Percy can tell you some tales about the old days. It means a lot to him, working in this shop."

Frank went to the cold-store to get out the small joints left over from Saturday. The cold-store consisted of two chambers, one for the chilled meat, the other for the frozen. He opened the door of the chiller and started taking out legs of lamb. He needed to hurry to fill the trays in the window by opening time.

Joe was still sharpening knives. He continued telling Frank about the injustices heaped on Percy. "He gets no recognition for all the work he puts in. Blind loyalty, I call it, but there are some that would call it plain stupidity. Do you think Mr. Pugh appreciates what Percy does? Of course he doesn't."

"He's never here, is he?" contributed Frank, who was becoming quite skillful at fueling Joe's maledictions against their employer.

"That's a fact. To be fair to Mr. Pugh, he has to look in at the market and collect the meat from the slaughterhouse, but that shouldn't take all day. It wouldn't hurt him to show his face here more often."

Frank gave a sly grin. "It might hurt someone else."

"What do you mean by that?" asked Joe, taking offense.

"Well, you and me. We don't want the boss breathing down our necks, do we?"

Joe said in a curt tone, "Speak for yourself, boy. I'm not ashamed of my work." He put down the knife he was holding and went to the window to rearrange the tray of lamb chops Frank had just put there. "Haven't you any idea how to put meat on a tray to make it look attractive?"

"I was trying to be quick."

"You can't hurry a job like this. That's why Percy starts so early. He's an artist in his way. His windows are a picture. I wonder what's happened to him."

"He could be dead."

Joe turned to look at Frank with clear disfavor. "That's a very unpleasant suggestion."

"It's a possibility. He's always falling off that old bike. Well, he could have been taken to hospital, anyway."

"Someone would have phoned by now."

"All right, perhaps he died in the night," persisted Frank. "He could be lying in his bed. He lives alone, doesn't he?"

"You're talking nonsense, lad."

"Can you think of anything better?"

"Any more lip from you, young man, and I'll see you get your cards. Get the chickens out—I'll attend to this."

"Do you mean the frozen birds, Mr. Wilkins?"

"The farm birds. I'll tell you if we need any frozen in a minute or two."

"Do you think we ought to phone the hospital, Mr. Wilkins, just in case something happened to Percy?"

"What good would that do?"

Frank took seven capons from the chiller and hung them on the rail above the window. "That's all there is," he told Joe. "Shall I get out some frozen ones?"

Joe shook his head. "It's Monday, isn't it? There isn't much call for poultry on a Monday."

"We'll need them for tomorrow. They need to thaw. We won't be getting any farm birds this week with Mr. Pugh on holiday."

Joe hesitated in his rearrangement of the window display. "You've got a point there, lad."

Frank waited.

"Yes," said Joe. "We shall want some frozen birds."

"Have you got the key?"

"The key?"

"There's a padlock on the freezer door."

Joe crossed the shop to take a look. It was a heavy padlock. It secured the hasp on the freezer door over an iron staple. He said, "Silly old beggar. What does he want to lock it for?"

"There's a lot of good meat in there," said Frank, in Percy's defense. "Have you got the key?"

Joe shook his head. "I reckon he takes it home with him."

Frank swore. "What are we going to do? We've got to get in there. It's not just the chickens. It's the New Zealand. We're right down on lamb."

"We'd better look for the key—he might leave it somewhere," said Joe, opening one of the drawers under the counter.

Their short search did not turn up the key.

"I think I could force it with that old file of yours," suggested Frank.

"No, lad, you might damage the door. You don't want to get your marching orders from Mr. Pugh. I've got one of those small hacksaws in my toolbag in the car. We can use that to cut through the padlock."

A short time later he returned with the saw. He held the padlock firm while Frank started sawing through the staple.

"All this trouble because of Percy," said Frank. "I'd like to strangle the old git."

"It might not be his fault after all," said Joe. "Mr. Pugh might have given him orders to use a padlock. He's dead scared of the boss. He does exactly what he's told, and I don't blame him. I heard Mr. Pugh laying into him on Saturday night after you left to deliver those orders. It was vicious, it really was."

Frank continued sawing. "What was it about?"

"Well, you were here when Mr. Pugh walked in out of nowhere, saying he wanted to see that things were straight before he went off for his week in Majorca—that was before you left with the orders."

"He'd just picked up his tickets from the travel agent."

"Right. You'd think he'd be on top of the world, wouldn't you, just about to push off for a week in the sun? Not Mr. Pugh. He happened to catch old Percy putting away the cuts we hadn't sold."

"There's nothing wrong with that, is there?"

"No, but Percy left the door of the chiller open while he was doing it. We all do it, but Percy got caught. You should have heard Mr. Pugh go for him, ranting and raving about the cost of running a cold chamber with employees who are so idle they let the cold air out because they can't be bothered to open and close the door a few times. He really laid it on thick. He was quoting things about cubic feet of air and thermal units as if old Percy had done it deliberately."

"Almost there," said Frank. "Mind it doesn't catch your hand."

The hacksaw blade cut cleanly through the staple.

Joe said, "Good." But he was determined to finish his story. "He told Percy he was too old for the job and he ought to retire soon. Percy started pleading with him. I tell you, Frank, I was so embarrassed I didn't want to hear any more. I left them to it and went home."

"I'll bring out those frozen birds," said Frank, slipping the padlock from the hasp.

"You'd have a job to find a meaner man than Mr. Pugh," Joe continued as Frank swung back the door of the freezer chamber. "Going on like that at an old man who's worked here all his life, and all for the sake of a few pence more on his electricity bill when we all know he makes enough profit to have holidays in Spain. —What's the matter, lad?"

Frank had uttered a strange cry as he entered the chamber.

Joe looked in and saw him standing over the huddled, hoar-white figure of a dead man. He went closer and crouched to look at the face. It was glistening with a patina of frost.

It was the face of Mr. Pugh.

Joe placed his hand on Frank's shoulder and said, "Come away, lad. There's nothing we can do."

From somewhere Joe produced a hip flask and poured some scotch for Frank as they sat in the shop and stared at the door of the freezer.

"We'll have to call the police," said Frank.

"I'll do it presently."

"He must have been trapped in there all the weekend."

"He wouldn't have known much about it," said Joe. "He must have died inside a few hours."

"How could it have happened?"

Joe stared into space and said nothing.

"There's a handle on the inside of that door," said Frank, speaking his thoughts as they rushed through the implications. "Anyone caught in there can open the door and walk out, usually. But he couldn't get out because the padlock on the outside was on. Someone must have put it there. It must have been Percy. Why would Percy do a thing like that?"

Joe gave a shrug and kept silent.

Frank supplied his own answer: "He must have panicked when he thought he would lose his job. He'd been in fear of losing it for years. He found some way of persuading Mr. Pugh to go into the freezer and then locked him inside.

"I know what he did! He told Mr. Pugh the handle on the inside was too stiff to move and he liked to leave the door open because he was scared of being trapped. Mr. Pugh said he was making excuses and stepped inside to show how easy it was to get out." Frank began to smile. "Mr. Wilkins, I think I'm going to laugh."

The tension relaxed a little.

"I'll tell you something funnier than that," said Joe. "Why do you think Percy hasn't come in this morning?"

"Well, it's obvious. He knew we'd open that door and find the body."

"Yes, but where do you think he is?"

Frank frowned and shook his head. "At home?"

Joe grinned and said, "Majorca."

"No!" Frank rocked with laughter. "The crafty old beggar!"

"When Mr. Pugh came in on Saturday he had a large brown envelope containing his travel tickets."

"I remember. I saw it. He put it on the counter by the cash register."

"Well, it isn't there now, is it?"

Frank said, "You can't help admiring the old man. He's probably sitting on the hotel terrace at this minute, ordering his breakfast and thinking of you and me finding Mr. Pugh in the freezer."

"I'd better phone the police," said Joe, getting up.

"You know, if it wasn't for that padlock on the door no one would suspect what happened," said Frank. "Mr. Pugh might have just felt ill and fainted in there. They'd call it misadventure, or something."

"And Percy would get away with it," said Joe reflectively. "It isn't as if he's a vicious murderer. He's no danger to anyone else."

"I could get rid of it," offered Frank. "I could put it in the pannier on my bike and get rid of it lunchtime."

"We'd have to stick to the same story," said Joe. "We just opened the door and found him lying there."

"It's the truth," said Frank. "We don't need to say a word about the padlock. Shall we do it? Poor old Percy—he hasn't had many breaks."

"All right," confirmed Joe. "We'll do it."

After they had shaken hands, he picked up the phone and called the police. Frank took the padlock to his motorbike in the yard at the back of the shop and secreted it under the toolbag in the pannier.

A squad car drew up outside the shop within five minutes of Joe's call. A bearded sergeant and a constable came in and Joe opened the freezer chamber and showed them Mr. Pugh's body. Frank described how he had found it, omitting to mention the padlock. Joe confirmed Frank's statement.

"So it looks as if the body's been lying in there since you closed on Saturday," said the sergeant after they had withdrawn to the warmer air of the shop. "You say that Mr. Pugh looked in late in the afternoon. What did he want?"

"He was just making sure everything was in order before he went on holiday," said Joe.

"He was off to Majorca for a week," added Frank.

"Lucky man," put in the constable.

The sergeant gave him a withering look. "Was Mr. Pugh in good health?" he asked Joe.

"I thought he looked rather off-color," answered Joe. "He drove himself hard, you know."

"He needed the holiday," said Frank, quick to see the point of what Joe was suggesting.

"Well, he didn't get it," said the sergeant. "He must have collapsed.

Heart, I expect. The doctor will tell us. There's an ambulance on the way. I suggest you keep the shop closed for a couple of hours. I shall want statements from both of you. Was there anyone else working here on Saturday?"

"Only Percy—Mr. Maddox," answered Joe. "He isn't in this morning. I believe he was going to ask Mr. Pugh for a few days off."

"I see. We'll want a statement from him. Have you got his address?"

"He told me he was hoping to go away," said Joe.

"We'll catch up with him later then. Which of you was the last to leave on Saturday?"

"That was Percy," said Joe.

"He stays behind to clear up," explained Frank.

"He puts things away, you mean?"

"That's right," said Joe. "He's getting on a bit. He's worked here for years. A bit slow now, but he likes to be useful. He puts everything away at the end of the day."

"In the freezer?"

Joe shook his head. "We don't refreeze meat. It has to be put in the chiller at the end of the day."

"So he wouldn't have opened the freezer door?"

"It's unlikely," said Joe. "If he had, he'd have found Mr. Pugh, wouldn't he?"

They took a statement from Frank. He said nothing to incriminate Percy. He simply explained how he had seen Mr. Pugh come into the shop late on Saturday afternoon shortly before he, Frank, had left to deliver the orders. As for this morning, he had opened the freezer door and found Mr. Pugh dead on the floor. The constable read the statement back and Frank signed it. "Would you like some coffee and a fresh doughnut?" he asked the policeman. "We always have a doughnut in the morning. It's my job to collect them from Jonquil's. I go on my bike and they're still warm when I get back."

"I like the sound of that," said the sergeant, putting his hand in his pocket. "How much are they?"

Frank felt an exhilarating sense of release as he wheeled his motorcycle into the street and started the engine. He rode up the hill toward the baker's, stopping a few yards short, by the place where the front of the delicatessen was being renovated. Outside was a builder's skip containing old wood and masonry. Frank took the padlock from his basket and dropped it unobtrusively into the skip. He collected the bag of doughnuts from the baker's and drove back to the shop.

An ambulance had drawn up outside. As Frank approached, one of the attendants was closing the rear door. The man walked round the side of the vehicle and got in. It moved away. The few bystanders who had collected outside the shop moved on.

When Frank went in, Joe had already made the coffee. He was talking to the police about football.

"We should have gone by now," the sergeant told Frank. "We've got both your statements and the body's been collected, but we didn't want to miss those doughnuts."

Frank handed them around.

"Still warm," said the sergeant. "I hope you observed the speed limit, lad."

Frank smiled.

The police finished their coffee and doughnuts and left the shop.

Frank heaved a huge breath of relief.

Joe took out his handkerchief and mopped his forehead. "Did you get rid of it?"

Frank nodded.

"Well done," said Joe. "Well done, Frank."

"I reckon old Percy owes us both a beer after that," said Frank.

"It's worth more than that," said Joe.

"We couldn't have turned him in," said Frank.

They opened the shop. Customers who had seen the shop closed earlier now returned in force. They all wanted to know what the police had been doing here and whether it was a body that the ambulance men had collected. Joe and Frank explained that they were unable to comment. The inquiries persisted and the queue got longer.

"If you ask me," one woman notorious for voicing her opinions said, "it was that old boy who sweeps the floor. He was far too old to be working in a shop."

"If you mean Percy Maddox, you're wrong," said the woman next in line. "There's nothing wrong with Percy. There he is coming up the street on his bike."

Joe dropped the cleaver he was using and went to the window. He was joined by Frank, who gave a low whistle of amazement.

"Crazy old man," said Joe angrily. "What does he think he's up to? He ought to be in Spain."

They watched through the window as Percy came to a halt outside the shop, dismounted, removed his cycle-clips, and wheeled his bicycle up the side passage. A moment later he appeared in the shop, a slight, bald-headed, worried-looking man in a faded grey suit. He picked his apron off the hook and started getting into it. "Morning, ladies," he said to the queue, then turned to Joe and said, "Morning, Joe. Shall I tidy up the window? It's a bit of a mess."

Joe said, "What are you doing, coming in here?"

"Sorry I'm late," said Percy. "The police kept me waiting."

"You've been to the police?" said Joe in a shrill voice. "What did you tell them?"

Frank said, "Listen, I've just thought of something. I'd better go and fetch it." He started untying his apron.

But he was slower than Joe, who was already out of his. He said, "You stay. I'll go."

While Frank was saying, "But you don't know where I put it," Joe was round the counter and out to the street.

He didn't get far. Apparently from nowhere, two policemen grabbed him. A squad car drew up and he was bundled into the back. It drove away, its blue light flashing.

"Who's next?" said Percy, who had taken Joe's place behind the counter.

An hour or so later, when there was no queue left and Frank and Percy had the shop to themselves, Frank said, "What's going to happen to Joe?"

"Plenty of questions, I should think," answered Percy. "You know about Mr. Pugh being found dead, don't you?"

"I was the one who found him."

"Well, Joe must have murdered him."

"Joe? We thought it was you."

Percy blinked. "Me, son?"

"When you didn't come in this morning, we thought you must have bunked off to Spain with that ticket Mr. Pugh left on the counter."

"But why should I want to kill Mr. Pugh after all these years?"

"Well, because of the bad time he gave you—all those long hours without a word of thanks. Exploitation, Joe called it."

"Did he, by George," said Percy with a smile.

"He said there was a bit of a scene on Saturday because you left the freezer door open. He said he felt so embarrassed he cleared off home while Mr. Pugh was still laying into you."

Percy shook his head. "Son, that isn't true. I left before Joe on Friday. Mr. Pugh had told me it might be better if I wasn't around while he did some stocktaking with Joe. We had our suspicions about Joe, you see. The books weren't right. There were big discrepancies. Mr. Pugh and I decided to check things carefully for a week and confront him with the evidence on Saturday after we closed."

Frank's eyes widened.

"Mr. Pugh and *you?*"

"Yes. You weren't to know this, and nor was Joe, but Mr. Pugh made me a partner last year, after I'd done fifty years in the shop. Nice of him, wasn't it? I told him I wouldn't ever make a manager, and I certainly didn't want to upset Joe, so we agreed to keep the partnership a secret and I carried on the same as ever, with the work I know best. But as things have turned out, with me the surviving partner, I can't keep it a secret any longer, can I? It's my shop now. I'm the boss."

Frank was shaking his head, trying to understand. "So did you put the police onto Joe?"

Percy nodded. "But I didn't mean to. I didn't know what had happened. On Sunday morning Joe drove over to see me. He told me Mr. Pugh had changed his mind about going to Spain because the auditors were coming to look at the books and he'd asked Joe to offer the ticket to me. I believed him. I thought he wanted me out of the way to spare me any unpleasantness."

"When it was really Joe who wanted you out of the way," said Frank. He recollected the events of the morning, the way Joe had tricked him into covering up the crime out of sympathy for Percy, when in reality Percy was innocent. The trick had almost succeeded too. The police had gone away convinced Mr. Pugh had died by misadventure. They hadn't suspected murder, and they certainly hadn't suspected Joe of committing it. But now he was under arrest.

"Well, if you weren't suspicious of Joe," Frank said to Percy, "why aren't you in Spain? What made you go to the police?"

Percy picked up Joe's straw boater.

"You know how it is with me, son. I haven't had a holiday in years, let alone a holiday abroad. I haven't got a passport. I dropped in at the police station to ask where I can get one, and—" He handed the boater to Frank. "I need a new manager now, don't I?"

BURNING BRIDGES

by JAMES POWELL

As soon as Barber hit the ball off the tee on the sixth hole, he suspected that Billy Hicks was no longer among the living. Barber's stance, swing, and follow-through, all the despair of the club pro, all the reason he golfed alone, had come together perfectly. The high lofting ball cleared the water trap at the end of the fairway to drop like a ripe plum onto the green. Yes, Hicks was dead. When the ball rolled toward the pin and fell into the cup, well, that was just a little something extra. Barber knew enough about golf to know a hole-in-one was luck. But that was Hicks, a great athlete and a real lucky bastard. Up till now. Barber gave a small, sad smile.

He trundled back toward the clubhouse in the gold cart without retrieving his ball. And he wouldn't mention the hole-in-one. That would only start heads shaking again. People had been doing that for as long as Barber could remember. At first they'd shaken their heads in amazement that the apple had fallen so far from the tree, that Titus Barber had sired so bland, awkward, and undriven a son. Then they tut-tutted over the wild crowd he ran with in high school. But more recently Barber had given those same heads another reason to shake, by totally confounding their early estimates of him. Ten years out of college, not only had he restructured his father's company but he'd come up with a product line that placed Barber Textiles among the country's top three producers of casual stockings for women. Looking back on it, perhaps Barber was more baffled than anyone else by the transformation. Recently he'd come to suspect what Hicks's death now seemed to confirm: that it had something to do with the Four Musketeers.

They'd been best of friends since high school—Billy Hicks, the jock of the group; Sterne, the ringleader, the brain, the one who came up with the ideas; hotshot Hagerdorn, with his bray of a laugh and a knack for organizing things; Lundeen, who, when he wasn't fighting off the girls, would do anything on a dare. And Barber. The Four Musketeers, they called themselves. All for one and one for all. Sterne picked the name, meaning it as a joke on Barber's shortcomings in the personality department. They used to call him "the little man who almost wasn't there." Barber had never minded. Alone, he'd been shy, clumsy, tongue-tied, and not so much un-popular as ignored or overlooked. But with them he'd felt full of life and purpose.

He could still remember his excitement after the prom their sophomore year when Sterne came up with the idea of burning one of the old covered bridges that still served the narrower, less-traveled roads in that corner of the county. The one they chose was a fifty-footer tucked away in a small valley. They came in one car. When the fire was going well, they drew lots and took their turns driving across the burning bridge and back again. It was a variation on the old road game called Chicken, the winner being the one who dared to make the last run. That was usually Lundeen, who never seemed to give a damn—which might have been part of his charm with women. After that, burning a covered bridge became a regular prom-night event for the Four Musketeers. And they always got away with it, although bridge number three had been a close call.

When Barber graduated from high school, his father had wanted to send him to one of the big colleges out East. In a rare show of determination, Barber insisted on joining his friends at the state college nearby. Barber didn't do very well there. He wasn't lazy, he was just a plodder. When Sterne put two ideas together, Barber could see them catch fire. When Hagerdorn talked mathematics, it made sense. And when the popular Billy Hicks introduced him around or Lundeen demonstrated the art of charming the ladies (or "wowing the dollies" as Lundeen called it), they made it look like the easiest thing in the world. But when Barber was on his own, no ideas gave off the merest spark, nothing seemed to add up, and people made him nervous—women most of all. In fact, he stood so much in awe of Lundeen's prowess with women that one time Sterne had bounced a paper-back off his head from across the room with the angry remark, "Remember, even Don Juan takes off his pants one leg at a time."

But at last, college days came to an end, sending all five of the Four Musketeers on their separate ways. Sterne, who'd been active in theater on campus, traveled to Cape Cod to work as a stagehand in summer stock and later to New York, where he set about writing plays. Hagerdorn enrolled at Wharton for an MBA. Hicks, who'd been at college on a football scholar-ship, was picked up by a major professional team. Lundeen traveled south to work for an uncle who owned a share in an insurance agency. Barber returned home to Barber Textiles.

Those next few years had been the unhappiest in Barber's life. His father shunted him around from department to department to acquaint him with every aspect of the company over which he would one day preside. Barber plodded from Sales to Raw Materials, from the mill floor to Personnel, leaving many a shaking head in his wake. In his fifth year, he was assigned to the Comptroller's office, which he found slightly more congenial because the Comptroller, a relation of the family by marriage, was a plodder, too.

Then one day, out of the blue, Barber came up with a plan for restructuring the company's long-term debt that was so ingenious he couldn't at first believe the numbers. The Comptroller stared down at the calculations, drummed his fingers, and admitted he couldn't see why it wouldn't work, either. Barber gave a high-pitched laugh. Then the two men hurried off down the hall to Barber Senior. That afternoon the company learned that young Barber had been named to the newly created post of Assistant to the President in Charge of Reorganization.

The next morning Barber came down to breakfast mulling over a shakeup in mid-level management. Without looking up from his grapefruit and newspaper, his father said, "Says here a friend of yours died. That young Hagerdorn, the one with the whinny, fell down dead getting out of a cab on Wall Street. Heart attack."

Barber surprised himself by how easily he took Hagerdorn's death. He tried to mourn, but felt no real sense of loss. Strange as it seemed, Barber felt closer to Hagerdorn now than he ever had.

During the next few years, Barber made something of a name for himself in the textile industry. A profile of him in *Modern Yarn and Spindle* spoke of the "new lean look at Barber Textiles." Sterne was making the papers, too. He'd had a couple of plays produced Off Broadway, married an actress of reputation, and gotten a divorce. Meanwhile, Billy Hicks, retired from football now with a bad knee, had gone into stock-car racing. And Lundeen had arrived back in town and used an inheritance from his uncle to open up his own insurance agency. Barber and Lundeen met occasionally for lunch. Lundeen hadn't changed a bit. He always looked like he could use a good night's sleep. Barber made sure he got the Barber Textiles business. A year later, Hicks moved back to town with his wife and kids and started a small air-freight company out at the airport.

One summer Hicks rented a beach house on North Carolina's Outer Banks just above Cape Hatteras. Whenever Barber could get away, he would go down for surf-fishing. One long weekend they were joined by Lundeen and a striking redhead named Maura, who wore a big floppy hat to protect her skin from the sun. It was windy the afternoon they arrived and Maura'd had to anchor down the hat with her forearm, which was quickly the color of boiled lobster. By Saturday, she didn't venture out from under the deck umbrella. But she fell sleep in the shade on the deckchair and the sun swung around. She awoke with angry red legs, one marked with a diagonal of white skin where the other leg had crossed over it. Barber remarked to himself that that leg looked something like a candy cane or like the nearby lighthouse except that the diagonals on the lighthouse were black and white.

It wasn't until the fall of that year, on a chilly day with wet leaves in the gutter, that Barber remembered that candy-cane leg and the Hatteras Light and got the idea that that would make Barber Textiles a national name. Lighthouse Legs, they would call them, a line of casual stockings for women based on the unique patterns of shape and color of the coastal lighthouses. Everyone in Design thought it was a great idea.

At breakfast the next morning, Barber's father said, "It says here your friend Sterne passed away on Martha's Vineyard. 'By his own hand,' it says." Barber took the paper from his father and read Sterne's short obituary. When he came to the line that referred to the playwright as a maker of "brittle concoctions of vespine dialogue and one-dimensional characterizations," he threw the paper against the wall with an angry force that surprised him.

But he had little time to mourn Sterne. He was busy with the advertising and sales-promotion campaigns for Lighthouse Legs, which he based on a map of the country divided into "lighthouse sectors" instead of states and mock proclamations in the media of penalties for women whose stockings didn't match the nearest lighthouse. The buying public accepted the whole thing as good fun. Two television sitcoms in the same time slot worked Lighthouse Legs into their plots on the same night, a coincidence that made parallel issues of *Time* and *Newsweek*. Lighthouse Legs became the novelty sensation of the women's apparel industry that year. And after their initial popularity, they were as successful a basic in the standard wardrobe as the little black dress and the tweed skirt.

Barber Senior was so pleased with his son's performance that he retired from the company, naming Barber as his successor. At the end of his first year as president, Barber married. While he and his wife were honeymooning in Europe, Barber's father died in his sleep.

Barber met his wife Laurel in the design department at Barber Textiles, where she was attached to the Lighthouse Legs project. She was a tall, vigorous woman with frank, self-confident eyes and a restless air. She had a considerable reputation locally as an artist in her own right and was starting to attract attention on the East Coast with her "charged mobile sculptures," as she called them—like the elaborate remote-controlled construction of firecrackers, pinwheels, and screaming rockets she'd put together for the Fourth of July Statue of Liberty Centennial.

The first time Barber asked her out she refused, seeming genuinely surprised by the invitation. And she kept saying no until he decided it was hopeless. But when work threw them together again a few months later, he asked her out again, he didn't know why—perhaps because she seemed a bit down. She countered with an invitation of her own. That coming Friday there would be a show of her work at a gallery in town. Would he take her?

The gallery was bright, and crowded with people and Laurel's charged mobile sculptures. Her work was all electronically programmed now. The one she'd christened "The Answering Machine," for example, responded with raucous noises and mechanical agitation when spoken to. Another, "Twittering Pie a la Mode de Paul Klee," resembled a covered casserole with a divided lid which it fluttered while emitting peeping sounds when approached. If the intrusion persisted, squawking metal bird-heads popped out from inside and finally the lid began to flap as if struggling to make the casserole airborne. Barber thought them very clever, and he was pleased to find Lundeen there with Dixie Thomas—a town beauty, married to one of his agency's biggest clients—proud that for once he was with an attractive woman, too.

After the gallery opening, Barber took Laurel out any chance he got. He told himself that her coolness toward him would change in time. He knew she liked to live well, admired fast cars, and dreamed of leaving Barber Textiles to give all her time to her own work. He told himself he had to be careful not to overwhelm her with an offer of these things. But having given himself all this good advice, he proposed to her within two months of the gallery show. He was almost surprised when she accepted. Billy Hicks was best man at the wedding. Barber would have asked Lundeen, but he'd just run off with Dixie Thomas.

As Mrs. Barber, Laurel played the charming hostess and represented her husband on several civic committees working for good causes. She even made love to him now and then with a kind of hurried frenzy. But time worked no magic. Worse than that, by the end of the fifth year of their marriage Barber could tell that it cost his wife a great deal of effort to tolerate him at all. Unfortunately, he now loved her more than he had in the beginning. When he sold Barber Textiles to an international conglomerate, he told people he meant to read Dickens and manage his investments. But much of his reason was the desperate hope that spending more time with Laurel might turn the situation around.

Gold had come later. The truth was that Laurel complained about having him underfoot all the time. She also told him he was putting on weight. So he took up golf, playing his solitary nine holes every morning. The game gave him his first chance to think about the changes in his life brought about by the deaths of Hagerdorn and Sterne. And as he did, his mind kept returning to the words of the old policeman that night so many years before when they'd almost been caught burning down their third bridge.

Sterne had figured people would start to be on the lookout by the third prom night, so, to draw off the local fire companies, he sent in a false alarm about another covered bridge burning about twenty miles away. But while they were standing around drinking beer and waiting for the flames to get far enough along for their game, a township police car pulled up behind them. After speaking into his car radio, a fat old policeman got out and, hitching up his trousers, headed slowly over to them.

"Relax," Sterne had whispered and nodded around significantly. Barber and the others understood what he meant. They'd left everything they'd used to start the fire out there on the bridge.

"What the hell's going on here?" demanded the policeman.

"You tell us, officer," said Sterne. "We just got here." He nodded gravely at the bridge as though the fire was a terrible thing.

The old policeman looked from Sterne to the rest of them. In that moment, they all saw that the old man knew underage drinking was the most he could charge them with. They all waited solemnly for the policeman to say something. Then Hagerdorn stretched his palms out to warm them at the fire and said, "It sure takes the chill off the night." The others tried to keep a straight face, but then the laughter came—with Hagerdorn's bray leading all the rest.

The old policeman took off his hat and, holding it, wiped his brow with the crook of his arm. Barber remembered the man's face mottled by flickering flame and darkness. And he never forgot what he told them.

"You're really something," he'd said. "I expect a person'd have to roll all five of you young men together to make one passable human being."

"It just came over the radio, Mr. Barber," said Roy, the locker-room man, holding out a fresh towel and soap. "Your friend Mr. Hicks was killed in a crash out at the airport."

"Yes, I know," said Barber solemnly and headed for the showers.

As he lathered up, he told himself that the old policeman's words offered the only explanation for what had happened to him. That made "all for one" the operative part of the Four Musketeers' motto now, with Barber the "one"—the one passable human being the five of them would make if they were all rolled together. But Barber put a different spin on what the old policeman had said. He saw Sterne, Hagerdorn, and Hicks as if they were parts of himself that he'd loaned out but didn't get paid back until death took a hand in things. And when Lundeen died, he'd be paid back in full—Lundeen's attraction for women would be his. At least enough of it, Barber was sure, for him to hold onto Laurel. Provided Lundeen died soon enough. Hicks' death gave Barber the perfect opportunity to hasten that event.

Barber drove home intending to call Lundeen as soon as he got there. But when he pulled into the circular driveway, a mournful Lundeen was getting out of his car at the front door. "I think Hicks needs a sendoff," said Barber.

Lundeen understood and liked the idea. "One Musketeer's funeral pyre coming up, good buddy," he agreed.

They left the cemetery right after Billy Hicks's funeral and drove back to Barber's separately. They'd bought an old car a couple of days before and left it parked behind the house. The bridge they'd chosen spanned the hundred-foot bed of a river—a mere trickle among the boulders, for it had been unusually dry that year. The bridge would probably burn without much smoke.

Just before the bridge, a small service road angled uphill to the transmission tower of a local television station. But there wasn't any other reason for anyone to come that way except to see the covered bridge itself, the longest in the county. It had escaped the Four Musketeers in their high-school days because a retired farmer and his wife lived right across the way in a small house which, as was the local custom, had been built for them when their children took over the farm. But when the old people died some years back, the house had been sold and moved to a site closer to town. The bridge had board-and-batten walls and a pitched shingle roof. It was painted red.

Driving up onto it was like entering a long, open-ended barn. The planking gave off a low rumble beneath the tires. Halfway across, Barber and Lundeen stopped and unloaded two three-gallon cans of paint thinner, setting them up on the foot-square beams that formed the skeleton of the structure. When they'd parked the car off to the side of the road facing the bridge, they walked back to the two cans. They drenched the middle third of the bridge and gave the liquid a minute or two to soak in. Flame skated across the wood when Lundeen tossed down the torch of rolled up newspaper.

Back at the car, Lundeen reached in and pulled out a six-pack which he offered to Barber. Barber tore off the nearest can, they bumped metal and toasted Billy Hicks, then they sat on the hood of the car, watching the fire's progress.

After a bit, Lundeen said, "Billy Hicks buying the farm like that really makes a guy stop and think about back when. And whenever I do that, do you know what gets me? No offense, old buddy, but when it comes to 'back when,' I always start remembering how you were, well, such a royal nothing back in those days. Man, have you changed! You're a different guy. Hell, a couple of different guys. And me, here I am still doing business at the same old stand."

"Still wowing the dollies, you mean?" said Barber quickly, afraid for a moment that Lundeen was beginning to understand.

Sighing like a man who'd just given up trying to put something important into words, Lundeen took a swallow of beer and said quietly, "Sure, still wowing the dollies."

Barber was surprised to find he'd drunk all his own beer. He was nervous. Simple as his plan was, it was not without risk. Of course, he had Billy Hicks's luck and skill going for him. He intended to use Lundeen's daredevil recklessness to make his friend kill himself. No matter how many runs across the bridge Lundeen made, Barber would make one more, until Lundeen—who could never let himself be beaten like that—would be forced to make the fatal run.

Barber threw his empty beer can into the ditch and jumped to the ground. "Musketeers, start your engines!" he said loudly, for he had won the toss to make the first run. Lundeen got down, too, and stood watching the flames with an absent look. Barber slid behind the wheel, pulled the car back onto the road, and hit the accelerator. He'd done the thing enough times to know that the first few runs wouldn't be anything at all. But when he got there, he was surprised to see how fast the flames had spread and to feel how hot the wind was on his cheek as the car raced through the fire. He reached the other end, spun the car around with all Hicks's skill, and drove back through the flames again.

Lundeen didn't get behind the wheel right away. He stood with his hand on the doorhandle, finishing his beer. Then he looked at Barber and said, "We're getting too old for games like this. No, I mean it. Remember, it's only the two of us left now, good buddy." He got into the car. "So I don't want anything to happen to you. I want you to take care of yourself." Lundeen smiled. "Starting tomorrow." Then he hit the accelerator and rushed the bridge in a shower of gravel.

Barber watched him go with real affection. He could no more bear Lundeen ill will than he could hate his own arm or leg. I'm doing us both a favor, he was telling himself as the car reappeared through the flames, its tires smoking.

"It's going up real fast," said Lundeen. But he still insisted they have another beer. "To Hagerdorn," he named the toast.

"To Hagerdorn," Barber agreed, raising the fresh can of beer. The fire had broken out onto the roof now—the flames seemed wind-fed. As he watched, an updraft of hot air burst out through the roof, carrying burning shingles high into the air. They fluttered down into the dry riverbed like spent fireworks. Barber averted his eyes. But he could hear the flames crack and the structure hum like a pipe organ. He took a long drink and forced himself to say, "And how about you? I hear the agency's not doing well. I hear you're planning on leaving town."

"More than thinking," said Lundeen. "Leaving."

"If it's money—," offered Barber. Funny that he could mean this offer, even while trying to get Lundeen to kill himself. When Lundeen shook his head, Barber threw away the beer can and got behind the wheel. He'd meant to drag things out, but the flames were licking up above the entrance now, he couldn't wait any longer. He put his foot on the gas and the burning bridge rushed to meet him.

Half the bridge, roadbed, and walls, was burning. Barber felt the shock of the heat as the speeding car barreled into the flames. He smelled the blistering paint. A section of boards collapsed behind him as he passed. Then he was out of the flames and down onto the road again. He clenched his teeth, spun the car around, and sped right back into the flames. Halfway across the bridge, a flaming rafter fell, turning the windshield on the passenger's side into a web of shattered glass before bouncing off to the side. In the next instant, Barber was out on the road again. His whole body was shaking when he pulled himself out of the car.

"Thanks for offering the money," said Lundeen as if he'd never left. "But I can't take it. There's nothing or nobody keeping me around here." He shared the last of the beers with Barber, adding, "A change of place may change my luck." Lundeen took his beer with him into the car and looked back. "Here's to Sterne," he said with a smile. "And, listen—no matter what anybody says, remember I never meant to do you any harm."

A puzzled Barber had to fight to keep from calling him back. He watched Lundeen accelerate the blackened car into the inferno of the bridge. The roof was completely engulfed in flames now. The structure crackled and groaned. Suddenly a section of rafters collapsed onto the bridge. Barber shook his head, mourning his friend. An instant later, the car roared out of the flames, scorched and smoking, shouldering a flaming rafter aside as it came.

Lundeen was white as a ghost when he got out of the car. "There's no way you can make it," he insisted, grabbing Barber's arm when he tried to get behind the wheel. "Old Lundeen's won again, right?" But Barber cursed and pushed him aside. He got into the car and put it into reverse for a good running start. "Don't be a damn fool!" shouted Lundeen.

Gritting his teeth, Barber launched the car at the bridge. Ahead of him everything was twisting flames and falling, burning wood. The bridge roared like an animal and Barber roared right back. His anger carried him into the fire and out the other end, where a kind of calm descended on him. As he spun the car around, he knew for a certainty he was going to make it back and that Lundeen would have to make another run and be killed.

He was smiling as he drove back onto the bridge. But suddenly, just as he reached the flames, he heard a sharp bang and the engine cut out. He pumped the gas, but nothing happened. Momentum carried the car halfway out of the flames. Fighting the smoke and the heat, Barber struggled with the unfamiliar doorhandle. Beyond the windshield, beyond the flames, he saw Lundeen's horrified eyes as he dashed onto the bridge trying to get to him. Poor Lundeen, thought Barber affectionately. He understands. In that same moment Barber got the car door open.

Laurel Barber had chaired the fund-raising committee for the hospital's new surgery wing. Now, pale and wearing a small bandage on her forehead, she sat alone in its small waiting room. When the police arrived at her door, she'd expected to be told her husband was dead. Instead they'd said her husband and his friend Mr. Lundeen had been in a bad accident. Lundeen? That was when she'd fainted, striking her head on the corner of the entranceway table. But it hadn't worked out badly. She had only seemed the stricken wife.

She felt better now. The doctor had just come by to discuss her husband's condition. He was on the operating table. The doctor said the next few minutes would be critical. He said her husband wouldn't have been alive at all if the explosion hadn't blown out the side of the bridge and him after it —she could see they had little hope for his recovery. Lundeen was another matter. He'd been hit by some flying debris while trying to get to Barber. A bad concussion. Nothing worse than that. He was unconscious but all vital signs were good.

Laurel thanked the doctor. But when he'd gone, she hadn't sat back down. Instead, she went to the window and looked out across the flat roofs, with their collections of air-conditioning and heating equipment. She found it a comforting view, resembling one of her own creations.

Well, after a frightening start, it looked like everything was working out. She hadn't wanted to kill her husband. In a way, she felt grateful for the way he'd let her use him against Lundeen. God knows he never suspected anything, though he'd almost walked in on them, coming home early like that the day Hicks died. They'd been lucky Lundeen's secretary had called when the plane crash came over the radio.

Laurel would have been content to let things go on the way they'd been going since Lundeen had come back to town, but then Lundeen started up again about leaving for good to make a new start somewhere. They'd fought and broken up many a time—never over his one-night stands, she knew the way he was, but over the longer ones like that silly cow, Dixie Thomas. But this time it wasn't another woman. He simply wanted to go away, to walk out of her life. Frantic, she'd convinced herself that it was Barber who stood in the way of their happiness. With him out of the picture and with his money hers, she was sure Lundeen would stay. Or they could go off *together*. Or, if it came to that, she could follow after him.

So even before Hicks died, Laurel had been trying to come up with a way to kill her husband. When Lundeen first told her about the bridge-burning business, their stupid Musketeer funeral pyre, she'd been furious he'd risk his life like that. But all of a sudden she saw it as a tailormade opportunity. She'd made the small detonating device from leftover Statue of Liberty Centennial parts and wired it to the gas pump of the old car they were going to use. She didn't tell Lundeen. He'd never do anything to harm his good buddy Barber. In fact, her most desperate hold over him these last few months had been her threat to tell Barber about them if he ever went off without her again.

While Lundeen and her husband played out their grim little ritual, Laurel had been watching from her car on the road leading up to the television transmission tower, the remote-control detonator in her lap. Each time Lundeen drove on the bridge, she thought she'd die. But she waited. The fire had to be just right, large enough so that the car's momentum wouldn't carry her husband out of the flames. The instant after she pushed the button, she heard the fire engines. She couldn't let herself be found there. She drove back down the hill as quickly as she could and didn't even look back when she heard the explosion on the bridge.

Someone was standing in the waiting-room doorway. It was the doctor. He shook his head with regret. "I'm sorry, Mrs. Barber," he said. "There was really nothing we could do."

"I'm sure you did your best, Doctor," she said, in a meek widow's voice.

The doctor gave a small bow and looked away. "It's Mr. Lundeen's case that baffles me," he admitted. "As I told you, all the vital signs were strong."

"Lundeen?" she managed to say.

"Mr. Lundeen died without regaining consciousness," said the doctor. "A blood clot, we expect."

Laurel Barber turned ash-gray. The doctor eased her down into a chair, adding, "The intensive-care people spoke to me just as I was coming here. Funny thing about the time of death they gave me. It's the same as we recorded for your husband's death—I mean, down to the second."

A GOOD TURN

by ROBERT BARNARD

In the darkness, the young man couldn't find a bell or a knocker, so he
banged with his fist on the front door. Then he leaned his head against the
cool brickwork of the strange house, his stomach heaving. Inside, all was
still, and he stood up and banged again. This time his fuddled brain became
aware of a dim light appearing in an upstairs window, then of the window
opening. It was just then that his gut began audibly churning.

"What the hell do you want?"

"Mr. Jacklin? Fred Jacklin?"

"No, it's not. What do you mean, banging on my door at this time of
night?"

"It is number fifty-seven, isn't it?"

"No, it's thirty-seven. Why, you filthy young bugger—"

For his stomach had finally risen in revolt and was emptying itself over
the gladioli by the front door. As more lights came on in the house, the boy
fled down the path, out the front gate, and down the road.

Fifty-seven. It must be on this side of the road. His head seemed clearer
now. Funny that—that clearing out your stomach like that should affect
the brain. Nice houses. Bigger than your average semi. A damned sight
better than Mam's back-to-back in Gateshead—all the rooms so poky, with
damp on the bedroom walls, and the two of them getting under each
other's feet and on each other's nerves.

Unemployment, that's what did it. Sitting around all day with no
money, no hope. He'd had a friend—a nice, normal kid—who'd gone and
strung himself up under the strain. In his own case, there'd just been one
big, explosive row.

Number fifty-seven. That was in darkness, too. Went to bed early round
these parts, didn't they? He looked at his cheap wristwatch. Half past
eleven. No time. No time when you didn't have to get up early in the
morning. When you didn't have to get up at all. This is a nice house, he
thought. A semi, but a big, substantial one. Room to move about, be

yourself, keep yourself to yourself if you wanted to. Garden could do with a bit of attention, though.

He went up the path, and in the darkness felt around the heavy wood front door till he found the bell. It played the first notes of "Home Sweet Home."

Again there was silence on the other side of the door. Well, he supposed, if you were in bed the natural thing was to hope that whoever it was would go away. He rang again. This time there were stirrings on the other side of the door—a light upstairs in the distance, then the sound of someone shuffling slowly down the stairs. The door did not open.

"Who is it?"

"Mr. Jacklin? Dad?"

"What did you say?"

"Dad? It's Steve. Your son, Steve."

There was silence on the other side of the door. Well there might be, Steve was sober enough now to realize. Then he heard the sound of bolts being drawn across. The porch light came on, but no lights inside the house. The door was opened, but only to the limits of its chain, which was left on. Dimly he perceived a face appear in the crack.

"What do you want?"

"Dad—it's Steve. I'm your son."

"So you said. Bloody funny time to pay a visit."

"I was in Birmingham. I had a row with me Mam and hitched a lift down."

"You been drinking?"

"Yes. I was a bit sloshed. I knocked on the door of number thirty-seven. But I'm all right now. I just wanted to see you."

The scrutiny continued.

"I can see your mother in you. I suppose it's all right." The figure on the other side fiddled with the chain and the door was opened. Now a light was put on in the hall. "Go through to the kitchen. We'll have a cup of tea."

As Steve went through to the kitchen and found the light switch, the hall light was extinguished. He smiled briefly. He knew North Country people, his people—they were "near." He and his mother had to be. His father originated, he knew, in Bradford. So if he was careful with electricity, it was only to be expected.

His father came into the kitchen now and pottered over to the sink, filling up a kettle and setting it down on the gas ring. When he turned, it was Steve's first view, first proper view, of him. It was something of a shock. He had known that he'd be older than his mother, but this man was about sixty, an old man. And he looked it, too, to Steve's eyes. He was wearing an old-fashioned woolly vest, buttoned at the neck, and grubby flannel trousers with braces, hastily pulled on when the doorbell rang, no doubt. His face was wrinkled, and there was a heavy stubble on chin and cheeks that suggested that his last shave had been the day before. But he was at least wide awake. There was a sharp glint in his eyes.

"So you're Steven." He seemed to have difficulty finding anything to say. Not surprising in the circumstances. "Last time I saw you, you were—how old?"

"Two. Me Mam says you left when I was just over two."

"That'd be about it. Women remember these things. What do you do, then, Steve?"

"Nothing. I'm unemployed. I've been on schemes—youth employment schemes and that. But they're all fakes—nothing comes out of them. There's nothing in Gateshead at all. Twenty-five percent out of work. It's diabolical."

"It's bad here, too. Very bad. You need to go south, the southeast. That's where the work is."

"I know."

He hadn't expected a warm invitation to make this his home, though he had wondered whether he mightn't stop here for a week or two, maybe a month—getting to know his father, helping in the garden. But the drift of the old man's remarks thoroughly chilled the impulse. There was silence again.

"How's your mother?"

"All right. We just about manage. She has a couple of cleaning jobs, but they're a bit dicey. She helps out at the corner shop if they're short-staffed now and again. We're both around the house most of the time, so we get on each other's nerves. We had a big bust-up last night."

His father screwed up his face. "Always had a temper, your mother."

"It were me as well."

"Nasty tongue with it."

"Is that why you moved out?"

It came out more baldly than he had intended. He had always had a curiosity about his father and what had happened before and after his birth, but he hadn't intended to show it by any sort of inquisition. But the old man did not seem disconcerted.

"I never moved in." A cunning smile twisted the gnarled face and Steve saw blackened stumps of teeth. "I know a trick worth two of that. Living with her would practically have been admitting the brat was mine."

"Me."

"That's right. I never lived with your mother. I just slept with her, and slipped her money now and again. She was all right. She inherited that house when your grandparents died."

"It's not a bloody stately home!"

"She was all right," repeated the old man. He poured the tea into two cups and came across to hand one to Steve. His body smelt of meanness and neglect. When Steve tasted the tea, he found it had not been sugared. Seeing a packet on the table he went over and spooned some in, then he squatted on the edge of the table, watching the old man, his father, rolling a cigarette.

"You got a dog?" he asked, fingering a dog lead that was lying on the table. "Not much of a watchdog."

"He's in the garage. He's old, and lost control of his bowels. I'm sick of clearing up his bloody messes. He's deaf, too. I'd have him put down, but it all costs money."

"Sounds like he'd be happier."

The old man shrugged. The boy felt a sudden turn in his stomach which was not due to drink.

"So when I was two you just took off down here?"

"I didn't take off. I sold the business up there and bought a business down here. What's that fancy word the Yanks use? Relocated. That's what I did—I relocated."

"You never told me Mam, though, did you?"

"Oh, she *has* fed you a line, hasn't she? Well, there was no cause to tell her. She was the girl at the counter, the girl behind the cash register, that's all *she* bloody was. Did she expect to be treated like she was co-director? It was a nice little business selling plumbers' supplies, but she was about the smallest cog in the outfit."

"You didn't tell her until it was all wrapped up, then you said she needn't bother to come in on Monday."

"Saved a bloody scene, didn't it?"

"And that was the last she saw of you."

"It was. Mind you, I sent her a bit of money from time to time—has she told you that?"

"Peanuts."

"Money doesn't grow on trees."

Steve looked around. "You seem to have done all right."

"Anyway, if I'd sent her anything big, or sent money regular, that would have been practically acknowledging you were my son. I never did that."

"I am, though?"

"Oh, aye. I can say that now you're grown up."

"Oh, yeah—marvelous! Thanks! You acknowledge me now I'm grown up and no one's going to grant a maintenance order against you."

"That's right." The old man smiled a smile of horrible complacency. "Let me give you a bit of advice, free, gratis, and for nothing, son. There's always folk out there waiting to take you for a ride. You'll never get anywhere if you sit back and let 'em. In this world, there's mugs and there's them that take advantage of the mugs. In my book, there's nothing to be said for being one of the mugs."

"I could kill you."

The words came out flatly. They sprang unbidden from disillusion, from the shattering of hopes he didn't know he had cherished, from a sudden, overpowering distaste.

The old man took no notice. He shrugged and turned to wash up his cup. "Well, that's my philosophy, like it or leave it. I didn't ask you to turn up here, and if you were expecting a tearful family reunion you were off your rocker."

Possessed by a new desire thoroughly to frighten this miserable, mean-spirited old man who was his father, Steve spelt it out, speaking low and intensely. "I could kill you. I could put that doglead round your scrawny throat and I could pull it tight and throttle you and no one in this world would care a damn that you were gone."

Still the old man was more puzzled than frightened. He stubbed out his cigarette in an overfull ashtray. "What would you do that for? I never done you no harm."

"Fathers are supposed to do their sons good." Steve reached out and took up the dog lead. "It would almost be a public service. You'd have been done away with, like that old dog that you're too mean to put out of its misery. And no one would think of coming after me, because you haven't got a son, have you? You've never been mug enough to acknowledge you've got a son."

"Don't be daft." There was a tiny quaver of fear now in the old man's voice, showing that Steve's intensity had got through to him. "Your finger-prints'd be all over this kitchen."

"I've never been in trouble with the police. My prints won't be on their files."

"You said yourself you knocked at number thirty-seven. You'll have been seen."

"I was spewing my guts up over their gladdies. They didn't see my face. And what if they had? I'm not known here, and I wouldn't be here by the time the police found you." He tested the leather leash in his strong young hands and slipped off the table he had been sitting on. "I could strangle the life out of you and you'd probably lie on this floor till your body rotted and the stink was so foul that someone outside got a whiff of it. I could snuff you out like a candle—use the life you gave me to put an end to yours."

"Why?" There was open fear now in his face as the boy took a step toward him.

"Because of the way you treated my mother. You didn't just treat her bad, you treated her mean—and you thought yourself bloody smart while you were doing it. And because of the way you treated me. You can't just bring life into the world and slope off as if it's no concern of yours."

"People are doing it all the time."

"They shouldn't." He was now very close to the man, could smell his body, smell his breath. "And because I've never existed for you, I could kill you and nobody'd be any the wiser, nobody'd come after me, and my name wouldn't even come up."

Now he was standing over him, undeniably threatening.

"You young thug! Keep away from me!"

"*You're* the thug. Hit and run, f——and run—it's the same principle."

"You're dirt! That's what your mother has brought up—a lump of s——!"

Possessed by he no longer knew what compulsion, to frighten or to kill, the boy suddenly put the lead over the man's head, got his ducking body firmly under his, and tightened the leather around his neck, pulling, pulling.

"Stop! You can't—!" The voice was thick, choked, almost petering out. The boy kept pulling.

"I've left you everything!"

The words got through what seemed like a blanket of blood around the boy's brain. His hands paused.

"I've left you everything! There was no one else—you're my heir! The police will be coming after you, all right!"

Steve's hands slackened—the leather relaxed its throttlehold on the old man's windpipe. As the attack faltered, his father lay there very still. Suddenly, the boy stumbled over the pathetic heap, ran through the kitchen and out to the front door. As he pulled the door to, he heard from the kitchen a hoarse, scraggly laugh.

Next day, standing on the motorway, thumbing a lift from the cars streaming north, Steve felt almost lighthearted. From time to time, he did in fact laugh. He would never know whether he had been his father's heir, but he sure as hell would not be it much longer. That was right. He had had nothing from him, wanted nothing of him. He would go back to Gateshead, make it up with his mother, then head south looking for work. He'd see if one of his mates who'd gone down to London could put him up. Failing that, he'd get a bed in a hostel. There was work, if you could keep clear of the people who wanted to get you on drugs or into prostitution. He'd survive. He had a life ahead of him.

And it would be a life unstained by—that act. He would never know whether he would have gone through with it to the end, but a terrible gut feeling told him he would have gone on pulling tighter. It was that cunning old sod that had stopped him. His father had saved him. For once in his life, he had done someone a good turn.

CLAP HANDS, THERE GOES CHARLIE

by GEORGE BAXT

At nine o'clock one Wednesday morning Alice Carruthers sat at the neatly laid table in the breakfast nook, toying with a withered piece of buttered toast. She stared into her third cup of black coffee as though it were a crystal ball, but it told her nothing she didn't already suspect. She was positive Charles, her husband, was having an affair with another woman.

She propped up her chin with the palm of her left hand and stared out the window at the East River. In the background a garbage scow drifted lazily past her line of vision; in the foreground two men were jogging side by side on the path that occasionally invited the attentions of the friendly neighborhood muggers. If she craned her neck, she could see a bit of Gracie Mansion, the mayor's residence, but to Alice it was just an ugly relic that New York should have demolished years ago.

"Clap hands, there goes Charlie." Alice smiled at the memory of her older and wiser sister Rita on that Sunday ten years ago when Alice had married Charles Carruthers. "That's a long winding trail of broken hearts he's leaving behind. How come you drew the lucky number?"

"I was hard to get," Alice remembered replying, also remembering those months before he proposed when every nerve in her body seemed to scream, "Charlie, Charlie, give me Charlie, I must have Charlie." He was so handsome. He still is, but add ten years to the portrait. Not quite six feet tall, amazingly muscular for someone in publishing who was known only to exercise with glasses containing very dry vodka martinis or very wet bloody Marys. And those blue blue eyes. Those incredible blue blue eyes against which, in Alice's prejudiced observation, Paul Newman's paled. Ten years later Charlie was still a formidable presence now much given to absence, such as like where was he last night until three a.m.? And why did he sleep in the guestroom?

Poor sister Rita. Poor dead sister Rita, "Rita," Alice had asked her during a confrontation in Rita's apartment, "have you been having an affair with Charlie?"

She remembered Rita sitting at the vanity table trying to make her sallow face healthy through the aid of any number of cosmetics. "Past tense, sweetheart. I was the penultimate fling before he married you. After me came that peculiar authoress from Canada, you know, the one with three names and one plot." Alice couldn't remember any of the three names because after two books Charlie's publishing house dropped her and she hadn't been heard from since. "Then Mother died and you decided to repatriate yourself from London," where Alice's affair with a notorious Shakespearian star had come to an end—"and Charlie's big eyes lighted you up and here you are, Mrs. Charles Carruthers."

Alice remembered Rita's eyes locking with hers in the vanity-table mirror. "My God, you haven't been married a year yet and you suspect he's cheating?" Alice nodded solemnly. Rita then shrugged, resumed applying the unbecoming shade of rouge, and said through a hollow chuckle, "Clap hands, there goes Charlie."

Five years and seven suspected extracurricular Charlie-affairs later Alice made peace with herself about Charlie. She wanted him and she got him and she would make do with what she had. In his own way Charlie loved her. He never flaunted those clandestine romances in her face and as his star ascended in the world of publishing, so did their financial status and their social rating.

They always got preferential treatment from Elaine at her celebrated Eastside watering hole, and the heads of many a maître d' in the city's most expensive restaurants seemed to barely miss scraping the floor as the toadies bowed them to a table. Charlie was now a partner in the firm of Dickens and Welles, and the authors he continued to edit were a superb Who's Who in the world of literature.

Alice sighed and glanced at her wristwatch. It was past nine a.m. Normally Charlie would be in his office by now going through the mail and dictating to his faithful and loving and unattractive secretary, Clara Kule. Then Alice had a thought: maybe Charlie had left the house before she awakened. But after only three hours of sleep? Then Alice had another thought and this one almost made the blood drain from her face. Maybe Charlie's dead.

"Clap hands, there goes Charlie."

She left the breakfast nook and went into the living room. Charlie's topcoat and his briefcase were on the divan where he had flung them when he came home. The briefcase was open and several manuscript pages had fallen on the carpet. Alice picked them up. The pages had been heavily edited. She read some of the top sheet and shook her head in disbelief. What junk. What trash. Conversations with the dead.

Charlie had explained to her months ago that he had to take on certain books he disliked but he knew the public wanted to read. He knew because smarter publishers had recognized the trend earlier and were saving themselves from bankruptcy by publishing books that boasted lurid dust jackets and screaming two-word titles such as "The Scream," "The Shriek," and one called "The Thumb," which she never had the courage to investigate.

Alice carefully replaced the manuscript pages in the briefcase and was about to enter the guest bedroom when the telephone rang. It was three more shrill rings before she intercepted the nearest extension which was on a table next to the divan.

"It's me!" trilled the gay voice at the other end. Alice recognized Minna Walsh, one of the few friends left from the "old gang," the starry-eyed aspirants to theatrical celebrity of those wonderful days (were they really?) before she became the British Shakespearian star's idiotic camp follower and trailed him to his home in London. "Can we meet a little earlier today? I've got something special on for both of us at two o'clock promptly and I'm sure it's going to be a hoot."

Minna frequently came up with "hoots." A wealthy widow, she gave up the theater when she married Herman Walsh, a successful Westchester dentist who, Minna explained when they became engaged, "Looked in my mouth and it was love at first sight."

"What kind of hoot?" asked Alice.

"I'll tell you when I see you. Right now I'll be late for the beauty parlor and they need all the time I can give them. So twelve thirty at Joe's, okay?"

"Fine by me." Alice replaced the phone on the receiver when Charlie entered from the guestroom. He was naked except for a bath towel strategically tied around his waist. His left cheek was raked with four nasty scratches. "What happened to you?" she asked even though her mouth had gone dry. Charlie continued on to the kitchen. As he went past her she heard him mutter, "Nothing serious."

"Those scratches look ugly!" she called after him. "Let me put some peroxide on them."

"I already have." He turned in the doorway of the kitchen. "Do me a favor. Call the office. Tell Clara I'm not coming in today. I'm working at home. You having your usual lunch with Minna?"

"Yes." He went into the kitchen and she dutifully went to the phone. The usual lunch with Minna. Every Wednesday. Lunch with Minna at Joe's, a theatrical hangout in the theater district, and then a matinee. The usual lunch. The usual Minna. The usual Wednesday.

"What usual Wednesday?" asked Clara at the other end of the phone.

Alice was startled. "Did I say that?"

Clara cleared her throat and said, "You said, the usual Wednesday. Maybe it's the title of a book?"

"Not that I know of."

"He's not sick or anything, is he?"

"No . . . not sick . . . or anything. He's just decided to work at home."

"Well, that's an awful lot of appointments I've got to reschedule. And Mrs. D. due at twelve is hell on wheels about punctuality. I better get on to her right away. Okay, Mrs. C., I'll take care of everything." Good old dependable Clara. Had she opted for spinsterhood because she preferred being dependable to being married? Should Alice have tested for that television series instead of marrying Charlie?

"I'd probably be a has-been by now."

"What the hell are you talking about?" She had entered the kitchen where Charlie stood at the counter drinking a cup of black coffee.

"Do you want some eggs or something? Some fresh toast?"

"Nothing, thanks."

"What's wrong?"

"For Pete's sake lay off!" He slammed the cup onto the saucer and left the kitchen. Alice knew better than to pursue and worry him. Instead, she examined both pieces of china to see if they'd been damaged, and they hadn't been. She tidied up because this was the maid's day out. She wondered about preparing some lunch for her husband. She continued wondering while she bathed, then anointed herself, carefully made up her face, and carefully chose her wardrobe.

When she was ready to leave to meet Minna, she found Charlie seated on the divan in the living room wearing slacks, sports shirt, and scuffed loafers. He was making notes in the manuscript he'd brought home the night before.

"Any good?" asked Alice.

"This?" Charlie indicated the manuscript. "Unadulterated junk."

"I read a page this morning. Some of the manuscript fell on the floor when you came home last night."

"No, I threw them on the floor. I hate this book. I hate myself for publishing it. I hate myself lately for a lot of things and I owe you a world of apologies for how badly I've been behaving lately, but now isn't the time. So you'll forgive me if I return to this pile of tripe. I'm expecting the author at twelve thirty."

Alice stared at him and then asked, "Shall I prepare some lunch? I could do a salad or something light like that."

"No, thanks. I'll phone out and have something delivered. Give my love to Minna."

"Will do." She was in the foyer when he shouted her name. She crossed back to the living room and stood in the entrance with a quizzical expression on her face.

"How's about dinner tonight? Someplace downtown for a change. Let's go to Little Italy. I've got a sudden craving for some rich Italian food."

"It's a date," she said, favoring him with what she hoped was one of her most delicious smiles.

Five minutes later, seated in the back of the taxi heading downtown, she wondered why he told her he was expecting the author of that junk at twelve thirty. Did he really consider her such a fool? Did Charlie really think she was an idiot? Didn't he realize by now she was a past master at putting two and two together?

The author of that junk about life after death was his current sweetie. It was her fingers that had raked his cheek last night. And then after they kissed and made up, he remembered that the next day was Wednesday, Alice's usual lunch day with Minna, and that the coast would be clear. How could he? She clenched her fist as she stared out the window. How could he bring her into our home? To her knowledge, he had never done that before. But today he was entertaining the author of that junk.

Alice had a feeling of déjà vu. (How had Minna once put it? "Tippecanoe and déjà vu!") Over a decade ago in London, Alice had returned to the pied-à-terre she occasionally shared with her Shakespearian superstar to find him in a compromising situation (to put it delicately) with one of the juveniles in his company. "I don't know what you're so upset about!" he had sputtered, showering spittle all over the sitting room. (His spray was almost as famous as he was. His devoted audiences were wise enough to book their seats at least five rows away from the stage apron. It remained for the tourists to sit up front and get drenched.) "I mean as an American you should quite understand what I'm up to. What do you call it there? Of course! Diversification!"

Ten minutes later, seated across from Minna at their favorite table near the bar, Minna asked, "Why so down in the mouth?" Alice told her. She could always trust Minna. Minna didn't find Charlie in the least bit sexy and said so aloud, especially when Charlie was within earshot. "That calls for some bloody Marys." Minna flagged a waiter, gave him instructions, then redirected her words at Alice. "Listen. If he's making such a thing about taking you to dinner in Little Italy tonight, then he's giving the other one her walking papers."

"You're sure?"

"Very sure. He couldn't very well do it in the office, could he, not with Clara tuning in. Obviously he let her have the bad news last night which won him his stripes." She glanced at her wristwatch. "At this very moment he's giving her the *coup de* Grace or whatever the hell her name is. Forget it. You knew what Charlie was all about when you married him. You got what you wanted and you've lived with it this long. Believe me, there's little better out there. My late darling did plenty of kadoodling of his own.

I was no fool. While he grew hot I kept my cool. Our doctor kept warning him he was overtaxing his heart, but, oh, well, he went and here I am, rich and cosy and guess where I'm taking you at two p.m. sharp."

"I give up," said Alice while the waiter served their drinks.

"We're going to a séance."

Alice roared with laughter. "Are you mad?"

"No, just looking for some fun. Don't be a spoilsport. Say you'll come with me."

"Well, of course I'm going. I wouldn't miss it for the world."

What a weird day this is, Alice suddenly realized. It's a day that's completely out of focus. It's surreal, with settings by the late Jean Cocteau.

"You've heard of Monica Duval, of course."

"Of course." Alice sipped her drink.

"She's got this marvelously bizarre studio over at Carnegie Hall."

"You've been there before?"

"For drinks. Not to a séance."

"You know this Duval woman socially?"

"Just the one time for drinks. She was at that do at the Gastons a couple of weeks ago. We were introduced, got to talking"—Minna's voice was now singsong—"realized we had some people in common, she invited me for drinks and then this morning called and invited me to the séance."

"Does she know I'm coming?"

"Oh, sure. I told her last week about our Wednesday ritual. When she invited me for lunch on Wednesday and I said, sorry not on Wednesday, because Wednesday belongs to my good old buddy Alice and me." Minna patted Alice's hand. "And we certainly are good old buddies, aren't we, darling."

"We certainly are." Alice lifted her glass in a toast. "Here's to us. The good old buddies."

At promptly two p.m., Alice and Minna arrived at Monica Duval's studio above Carnegie Hall. The door was opened by a middle-aged woman who spoke with a trace of French accent. She led them into the main room where there was a round table which accommodated six chairs. Alice counted the chairs and thought to herself, Madam Duval likes to keep her séances intimate.

There were three people already seated at the table, two middle-aged men and a dumpy woman so badly dressed she had to be uncommonly wealthy. She was obviously married to the man on her right who kept referring impatiently to a very old and very grand pocket watch. Alice and Minna took two seats and then Alice whispered to Minna, "I thought our hostess was very strict about punctuality." It was ten minutes past two.

"How did you know that?" asked Minna.

"I remember reading it someplace." Monica Duval had given interviews to the women's page editor of the *Daily News* and to a feature writer for *New York* magazine. Alice read them both. The other clients stirred as what seemed like a cyclone came hurrying into the room.

"I am so so sorry, my darlings! But I had an urgent appointment at the other side of town and traffic is horrendous when it's normal, but on a Wednesday when all those taxis are hurtling pell-mell to the theater district it is simply *incroyable,* absolutely incredible, but here I am and ready to begin!"

Alice studied the amazing woman as she greeted Minna and the three others, exchanging meaningless pleasantries with the four, as though knowing Alice would require some time to study her. Monica Duval seemed to be in her early thirties. She was of medium height, seemed beautifully proportioned, and had exquisite skin. Her eyes were a seductive sepia and she wore a plain but beautifully cut black dress with a single strand of pearls around her neck. Alice heard Minna introduce her name.

"Mrs. Carruthers," said Madam Duval with a gracious, welcoming nod of her head. "How nice to meet you."

"Thank you. I'm looking forward to this meeting."

"I'm so glad. Is there anyone in particular you'd like to reach in the afterworld?" Alice thought of all the people she couldn't get hold of in this world and wished Madam Duval could materialize an elusive plumber. "Perhaps your sister Rita?" coaxed Madam Duval.

Alice was glad her hands were clasping her purse under the table, out of sight of the others. She was positive her knuckles had gone ivory white. She managed what she hoped was a clever smile. "Did you know my sister Rita? She was a brilliant dress designer."

"I know all about your sister. Would you like me to try and contact her?"

"Yes. By all means."

Madam Duval was looking inscrutable. Her assistant, an old woman, had drawn all the curtains and there was solitary red light strategically situated over Madam Duval's head. Now Madam Duval's eyes closed as she instructed everyone to join hands, which they dutifully did. Very dramatically Madam Duval emitted a ghostly sigh as her head flew back and her mouth fell open.

Minna squeezed Alice's hand. Alice's eyes never left the medium's face. Madam Duval was making strange noises but none of them sounded like Rita. They sounded more to Alice like screechy hinges badly in need of oiling. The unpleasant noises continued and Alice, knowing her sister Rita, was positive if there was an afterlife, Rita was off somewhere having a matinee of her own with some good-looking young man.

And then a voice came from Monica Duval's mouth that made Alice's blood freeze.

"I'm sorry about tonight, honey."

Charlie!

Had Minna recognized it too? Is that why her nails were digging into Alice's palm, although Alice felt no pain?

"I'm sorry, sweetie, but it's off. I can't make dinner." Alice stared at the medium. She had to be in a genuine trance. Her body was unnaturally rigid, almost as though she had died and rigor mortis had set in. "I love you, Alice. I only loved you, Alice. I . . ."—and then Monica Duval's body went into a convulsion. Her hands flew up, her eyes opened, she lurched to her feet, and from her mouth came what Alice and Minna would always remember as a hideous ungodly screeching such as no mortal could ever have uttered.

The lights went on and Madam Duval's assistant hurried to her side. Monica Duval collapsed into her arms and with the help of one of the men the medium was led to a sofa. They stretched her out and after a moment she seemed to have fallen into a sleep deep enough to be mistaken for a coma.

Her assistant said to the clients, "You must go. Madam is not well. She hasn't been well for some time now. She shouldn't be working. Please go. I will look after her."

Minna grabbed Alice's hand and started to hurry her out of the room when the dumpy woman stepped in front of them and said to Alice, "Was that your husband?" Her eyes were like bright kindling, her voice was drenched with anxiety. "Was that your dead husband?"

"My husband is *not* dead," Alice informed her and then her hand flew to her mouth.

"What's wrong?" whispered Minna sounding like the Ghost of Christmas Past.

"Oh, my God, Minna, come home with me! Come home with me!"

"Why? What is it?"

"Hurry, Minna, hurry!"

In the taxi going uptown Minna held tightly to Alice's hand. Alice wouldn't speak. She kept shaking her head and biting her lip, and Minna was worried that the séance might have brought on a nervous breakdown. Life with Charlie was always a strain and maybe the séance was the straw that broke Alice's back. Now what the hell was Charlie doing at the séance, Minna wondered. I mean it was Rita whom Madam Duval was trying to contact—how did Charlie get into the act? Do mediums contact the living too?

The taxi pulled up in front of Alice's apartment building on East End Avenue. Alice had a five-dollar bill ready and thrust it at the driver. She and Minna hurried into the building, into the elevator, and up to the penthouse apartment.

The police were already there.

Detective Jack Becker explained that a neighbor had seen the front door to the apartment ajar, thought it strange, and entered the apartment to investigate. The neighbor, a Mr. Alfred Wayne, a retired chiropodist, found Charlie lying face down on the divan. Protruding from his back was a pair of ornamental shears that usually lay on Charlie's desk. The shears had penetrated his heart. Death must have been instantaneous.

"Clap hands," whispered Alice, and Detective Becker, startled, looked at the freshly minted widow with suspicion.

"What did you say?"

Alice repeated, "Clap hands," then added, "there goes Charlie." She turned to Detective Becker. "It's something my late sister said to me on my wedding day. Detective Becker, I think I can name my husband's murderer."

Scattered on the floor was the manuscript that Charlie Carruthers had been working on that morning. Alice knelt to gather up the pages. Detective Becker spoke to her sharply, "Please don't touch those. We haven't dusted them yet for fingerprints."

Alice got to her feet and crossed to console Minna who stood by a window sobbing. She had really liked Charlie. Alice was glad Minna had taken her to the séance. She was glad Monica Duval had phoned Minna to invite her and to be sure to bring Alice with her. That proved premeditation, as Alice explained it all to Detective Becker who at first was skeptical and then found chills going up his spine when Alice told him about Charlie's voice coming from Monica Duval's mouth.

"I have a feeling Charlie knew Monica Duval intended to kill him. I think she tried to kill him last night but did not succeed. And I think the murder was still so fresh in Monica's mind that instead of invoking the spirit of my sister Rita, she brought in poor Charlie instead. You see, Mr. Becker, those pages scattered on the floor are from a manuscript about life after death written by Monica Duval who has been having an affair with my husband." Minna kept bobbing her head up and down in agreement. "It's a terrible piece of trash, but now that she's murdered my poor Charlie, it will sell millions in hardcover and paperback, and then there are serializations and foreign editions, and it'll make a hell of a television series."

Detective Becker phoned his precinct to have them bring in Monica Duval. He seemed to be hearing some startling news from the precinct. "Are you sure it's the same woman?" Alice and Minna exchanged glances and then moved nearer to the detective. "Okay, if that's what her mother told you, we've got to take it for gospel." Was Duval's assistant her mother?

"Monica Duval confessed killing your husband to her mother shortly before she died."

"She's dead?" gasped Alice. "But . . . what happened?"

"Her mother said she thought she was having a fit. It's as though some-one was choking her to death. But she managed to say she'd killed your husband, then collapsed and died."

"Oh, God, oh, God," said Alice.

"It's just too terrible," said Minna.

"It's worse than you think," said Alice. "Because if there's an afterlife, oh, God, Minna, if there's an afterlife then they're together!"

BIG BOY, LITTLE BOY

by SIMON BRETT

Under normal circumstances he would have thrown away the letter as soon as he recognized the cramped handwriting, but Larry Renshaw was in the process of murdering his wife and needed to focus his mind on something else. So he read it.

Mario, the barman, had handed it over. Having a variety of postal addresses in pubs and bars all over London was a habit Larry had developed in less opulent days, and one that he had not attempted to break after his marriage to Lydia. The sort of letters he received had changed, though; there were fewer instructions from "business associates," fewer guilty wads of notes buying other people's extramarital secrets. Their place had been taken by confirmations of his own sexual assignations, correspondence that could, by the widest distension of the category, be classed as love letters. Marriage had not meant an end of secrets.

But it had meant an upgrading of some of the "postes restantes." Gaston's Bar in Albemarle Street was a definite advance on the Stag's Head in Kilburn. And the Saville Row suit, from which he flicked the salt shed by Mario's peanuts, was more elegant than a hotel porter's uniform. The gold identity bracelet that clinked reassuringly on his wrist was more comfortable than a handcuff—and, Larry Renshaw sincerely believed, much more his natural style.

Which was why he had to ensure that he continued to live in that style. He was nearly fifty. He resented the injustices of a world which had kept him so long from his natural milieu, and now that he had finally arrived there he had no intentions of leaving.

Nor was he going to limit his lifestyle by removing those elements—other women—of which Lydia disapproved.

Which was why, while he sipped Campari and vodka in Gaston's Bar, he was murdering his wife.

And why he read Peter Mostyn's letter to take his mind off what he was doing.

*   *   *

"—and those feelings for you haven't changed. I know over thirty years have passed, but those nights we spent together are still the memories I most treasure. I have never had any other *friends*. Nothing that has happened and no one I have met since has meant as much to me as the pleasure I got, not only from being with you, but also from being known as *yours,* from being made fun of at school as your Little Boy.

"I know it didn't mean as much to you, but I flatter myself that you felt *something* for me at the time. I remember how once we changed pyjamas and you let me sleep in yours in *your* bed all night. I've never felt closer to you than I did that night, as if I didn't just take on your clothes, but also a bit of you—as if I became you for a little while. I had never felt so happy. Because, though we always looked a little alike, though we were the same height and had the same colouring, I never had your strength of character. Just then, for a moment, I knew what it was like to be Larry Renshaw.

"It was wonderful for me to see you last week. I'm only sorry it was for such a short time. Remember, if there's ever *anything* I can do for you, you have only to ask. If you want to meet up again, do ring. I'm only over here sorting out some problem on my uncle's will and as I'm pretty hard up, I spend most of my time in my room at the hotel. But if I *am* out when you ring, they'll take a message. I'll be going back to France at the end of the week, but I'd really like to see you before then. I sometimes think I'll take my courage in both hands and come round to your flat, but I know you wouldn't really like it, particularly now you're *married to that woman*. It was quite a shock when you told me about your marriage. I had always had a secret hope that the reason you never *had* married was—"

Larry stopped reading. Not only had the mention of his marriage brought his mind back to the murder of Lydia, he also found the letter distasteful.

It wasn't being the object of a homosexual passion that worried or challenged him. He had no doubt where his own tastes lay. He didn't even think he had gone through a homosexual phase in adolescence, but he had always had a strong libido, and what other outlet was there in a boys' boarding school? All the other Big Boys had had Little Boys, so he had played the games tradition demanded. But as soon as he had been released from that particular prison, he had quickly discovered, and concentrated on, the instinctive pleasures of heterosexuality.

But Peter Mostyn hadn't changed. He'd make contact every few years, suggesting a lunch, and Larry, aware that a free meal was one he didn't have to pay for, would agree to meet. Their conversation would be stilted, spiralling round topics long dead, and Larry would finish up his brandy and leave as soon as the bill arrived. Then, within a week, one of the "poste restante" barmen would hand over a letter full of closely written obsequious gratitude and assurances of continuing devotion.

For Mostyn the dormitory grappling had obviously meant more and he had frozen like an insect in the amber of adolescence. That was what depressed Larry. He hated the past, he didn't like to think about it. For him there was always the hope of the big win just around the next corner, and he would rather concentrate on that than on the disasters behind him.

He could forget the past so easily, instinctively sloughing off the skin of one shady failure to slither out with a shining new identity ready for the next infallible scheme. This protean ability had enabled him to melt from stockbroker's clerk to Army recruit (after a few bounced cheques), from Army reject to mail-order manager (after a few missing boxes of ammunition), from mail-order manager to pimp (after a few prepaid but undelivered orders), and from pimp to hotel porter (after a police raid). And it had facilitated the latest metamorphosis, from hotel porter to Savile-Row-suited husband of a rich neurotic dipsomaniac (just before the inevitable theft inquiry). For Larry, change and hope went hand in hand.

So Peter Mostyn's devotion was an unpleasant intrusion. It suggested that, whatever his current identity, there remained in Larry an unchanging core that could still be loved. It threatened his independence in a way the love of women never had. His heterosexual affairs were all brisk and physical, soon ended, leaving in him no adverse emotion that couldn't be erased by another conquest and, in the women, undiluted resentment.

But Peter Mostyn's avowed love was something else—an unpleasant reminder of his continuing identity, almost a *memento mori*. And Peter Mostyn himself was even more of a *memento mori*.

They had met the previous week for the first time in six years. Once again, old habits had died hard, and Larry had instinctively taken the bait of a free meal in spite of his new opulence.

As soon as he saw Peter Mostyn, he knew it was a bad idea. He felt like Dorian Gray meeting his picture face to face. The Little Boy had aged so unattractively that his appearance was a challenge to Larry's vigour and smartness. After all, they were about the same age—no, hell, Mostyn was younger. At school he had been the Little Boy to Larry's Big Boy. A couple of forms behind, so a couple of years younger.

And yet to see him, you'd think he was on the verge of death. He had been ill, apparently; Larry seemed to remember his saying something over the lunch about having been ill. Perhaps that explained the long tubular crutches and the general air of debility. But it was no excuse for the teeth and the hair—the improvement of those was quite within his power. Okay, most of us lose some teeth, but that doesn't mean we have to go around with a mouth like a drawstring purse. Larry prided himself on his own false teeth. One of the first things he'd done after marrying Lydia had been to set up a series of private dental appointments and have his mouth filled with the best replacements money could buy.

And the hair. Larry was thinning a bit and would have been greying but for the discreet preparation he bought from his Jermyn Street hairdresser. But he liked to think that, even if he had been so unfortunate as to lose all his hair, he wouldn't have resorted to a toupé that looked like a small brown mammal that had been run over by a day's traffic on the M1.

And yet that was how Peter Mostyn had appeared, a hobbling creature with concave lips and hair that lacked any credibility. And, to match his physical state, he had demonstrated his emotional crippledom with the same adolescent infatuation and unwholesome self-pity, the same constant assertions that he would do anything for his friend, that he felt his own life to be without value and only likely to take on meaning if it could be used in the service of Larry Renshaw.

Larry didn't like any of it. Particularly he didn't like the constant use of the past tense, as if life from now on would be an increasingly crepuscular experience. He thought in the future tense, and of a future that was infinite now that he had Lydia's money.

Now that he had Lydia's money . . . He looked at his watch. A quarter to eight. She should be a good five hours dead. Time to put thoughts of that tired old queen Mostyn behind him and get on with the main business of the day. Time for the dutiful husband to go home and discover his wife's body. Or if he was really lucky, discover that his sister-in-law had just discovered his wife's body.

He said good-bye loudly to Mario, and made some quip about the barman's new apron. He also asked if the barroom clock was right and checked his watch against it.

After a lifetime of obscuring details of timing and squeezing alibis from forgotten minutes, it was an amusing novelty to draw attention to time. And to himself.

For the same reason, he exchanged memorable banter with the driver of the taxi he picked up in a still-light Piccadilly Circus before settling back for the journey to Abbey Road.

Now he felt supremely confident. He was following his infallible instinct. The plan was the work of a mastermind. He even had a twinge of regret to think that when he had all Lydia's money that mind would be lost to crime. But no, he didn't intend to hazard his newfound fortune by doing anything mildly risky. He needed freedom to cram into his remaining rich life what he had missed out on in poorer days.

Which was why the murder plan was so good. It contained no risk at all.

In fact, although he didn't consciously realize it at the time he had got the murder plan at the same time he had got Lydia. She had come ready-packed with her own self-destruct mechanism. The complete kit.

*　　　　*　　　　*

Lydia had fallen in love with Larry when he saved her life, and had married him out of gratitude.

It had happened two years previously. Larry Renshaw had been at the lowest ebb of a career that had known many freak tides. He had been working as a porter at a Park Lane hotel, whose management was beginning to suspect him of helping himself from the wallets, handbags, and jewel cases of the guests. One afternoon he had received a tipoff that they were on to him, and determined to make one last reasonable-sized haul before another sudden exit and change of identity.

Observation and staff gossip led him to use his passkey on the door of a Mrs. Lydia Phythian, a lady whose Christmas-tree appearances in the bar left no doubts about her possession of a considerable stock of jewellery, and whose consumption of gin in the same bar suggested that she might be a little careless in locking away her decorations.

So it proved. Necklaces, brooches, bracelets, and rings lay among the pill bottles on the dressing table as casually as stranded seaweed. But there was also in the room something that promised a far richer and less risky haul than a fence's grudging prices for the gems.

There was Mrs. Lydia Phythian, in the process of committing suicide.

The scene was classic to the point of being corny. An empty gin bottle clutched in the hand of the snoring figure on the bed, on the bedside table an empty pill bottle dramatically on its side, and propped against the lamp a folded sheet of crisp blue monogrammed notepaper.

The first thing Larry did was to read the note.

This was the only way out. Nobody cares whether I live or die and I don't want to go on just being a burden. I've tried, but life's too much.

It was undated. Instinctively, Larry put it in his pocket before turning his attention to the figure on the bed. She was deeply asleep, but her pulses were still strong. Remembering some movie with this scene in it, he slapped her face.

Her eyes came woozily open. "I want to die. Why shouldn't I die?"

"Because there's so much to live for," he replied, possibly remembering dialogue from the same movie.

Her eyes rolled shut again. He rang for an ambulance. Instinct told him to get an outside line and ring the Emergency Services direct; he didn't want the manager muscling in on his act.

Then, again following the pattern of the movie, he walked her sagging body up and down, keeping her semiconscious until help arrived.

Thereafter he just followed instinct. Instinct told him to accompany her in the ambulance to the hospital; instinct told him to return (out of his hotel uniform) to be there when she came round after the ministrations of the stomach pump; instinct told him to continue his visits when she was moved to the recuperative luxury of the Avenue Clinic. And instinct provided the words which assured her that there really was a lot to live for, and that it was insane for a woman as attractive as her to feel unloved, and that he at least appreciated her true worth.

So their marriage three months after she came out of the clinic was really a triumph of instinct.

A couple of days before the registry-office ceremony, Larry Renshaw had fixed to see her doctor. "I felt, you know, that I should know her medical history now that we're going to be together for life," he said in a responsible voice. "I mean, I'm not asking you to give away any professional secrets, but obviously I want to ensure that there isn't a recurrence of the appalling incident which brought us together."

"Of course." The doctor was bald, thin, and frankly sceptical. He did not seem to be taken in by Larry's performance as the concerned husband-to-be. "Well, she's a very neurotic woman, she likes to draw attention to herself. Nothing's going to change her basic character."

"I thought, being married . . ."

"She's been married a few times before, you must know that."

"Yes, of course, but she seems to have had pretty bad luck and been landed with a lot of bastards. I thought, given someone who really loves her for herself . . ."

"Oh yes, I'm sure she'd be a lot more stable, given *that.*" The scepticism was now so overt as to be insulting, but Larry didn't risk righteous anger, as the doctor went on, "The trouble is, Mr. Renshaw, women as rich as Mrs. Phythian tend to meet up with rather a lot of bastards."

Larry ignored the second insult. "What I really wanted to know was—"

"What you really wanted to know," the doctor interrupted, "was whether she was likely to attempt suicide again."

Larry nodded gravely.

"Well, I can't tell you. Someone who takes as many pills and who drinks as much as she does is rarely fully rational. This wasn't her first attempt, though it was different from the others."

"How?"

"The previous ones were more obviously simply demands for attention —she made pretty sure that she'd be found before anything too serious happened. In this case—well, if you hadn't walked into the room I think she'd have gone the distance. Incidentally—"

But Larry spoke before the inevitable question about why he came to be in her room. "Were there any other differences this time?"

"Small ones. The way she crushed up all the pills into the gin before she started suggested a more positive approach. And the fact that there was no note . . ."

Larry didn't respond to the quizzical look. When he left, the doctor shook him by the hand and said with undisguised irony, "I wouldn't worry. I'm sure everything will work out *for you.*"

The insolent distrust was back in that final emphasis, but mixed in the doctor's voice with another feeling, one of relief. At least a new husband would keep Mrs. Phythian out of his surgery for a little while. There would just be a series of repeat prescriptions for tranquillisers and sleeping pills, and he could still charge her for those.

Subconsciously, Larry knew that the doctor had confirmed how easy it would be for him to murder his wife, but he didn't let himself think about it. After all, why should it be necessary?

At first it wasn't. Mrs. Lydia Phythian changed her name again—she was almost rivalling her husband in the number of identities she had taken on— and become Mrs. Lydia Renshaw. At first the marriage worked pretty well. She enjoyed kitting out her new husband and he enjoyed being taken round to expensive shops and being treated by her. He found her a surprisingly avid sexual partner and, although he couldn't have subsisted on that diet alone, secret snacks with other women kept him agreeably nourished and he began to think marriage suited him.

Certainly it brought him a lifestyle he had never before experienced. Having been brought up by parents whose middle-class insistence on putting him through minor public school had dragged their living standards down to working-class and below, and then having never been securely wealthy for more than a fortnight, he was well placed to appreciate the large flat in Abbey Road, the country house in Uckfield, and the choice of driving a Bentley or a little Mercedes.

In fact, there were only two things about his wife that annoyed him— her unwillingness to let him see other women and the restricted amount of pocket money she allowed him.

He had found ways around the second problem; in fact, he had reverted to his old ways to get round the second problem. He had started, very early in their marriage, stealing from his wife.

At first he had done it indirectly. She had trustingly put him in charge of her portfolio of investments, which made it very easy for him to cream off what he required for his day-to-day needs. However, a stormy meeting with Lydia's broker and accountant, who threatened to disclose all to their employer, persuaded him to relinquish these responsibilities.

So he started robbing his wife directly. The alcoholic haze in which she habitually moved made this fairly easy. Mislaying a ring or a small necklace, or even finding her wallet empty within a few hours of going to the bank, were common occurrences and not ones to which she liked to draw attention since they raised the question of how much her drinking affected her memory.

Larry spent a certain amount of this loot on other women, but the bulk of it he consigned to a suitcase, which every three or four weeks was moved discreetly to another Left Luggage office—premarital habits again dying hard. Over some twenty months of marriage, he had accumulated between twelve and thirteen thousand pounds, which was a comforting hedge against adversity.

But he didn't expect adversity. Or at least he didn't expect adversity until he discovered that his wife had put a private detective onto him and had compiled a dossier of a fortnight's infidelities.

It was then that he knew he had to murder her, and had to do it quickly, before the meeting with her solicitor she had mentioned when confronting him with the detective's report. Larry Renshaw had no intention of being divorced from his wife's money.

As soon as he had made the decision, the murder plan that he had shut up in the Left Luggage locker of his subconscious was revealed by a simple turn of a key. It was so simple, he glowed from the beauty of it.

He went through it again as he sat in the cab on the way to Abbey Road. The timing was perfect; there was no way it could fail.

Every three months Lydia spent four days at a health farm. The aim was not primarily to dry her out but to put a temporary brake on the runaway deterioration of her physical charms. However, the strictness of the fashionable institution chosen to take on this hopeless task meant that the visit did have the side-effect of keeping her off alcohol for its duration. The natural consequence of this was that on the afternoon of her return she would, regular as clockwork, irrigate her parched system with at least half a bottle of gin.

And that was all the plan needed. His instinct told him it couldn't fail.

He had made the preparations that morning, almost joyously. He had whistled softly as he worked. There was so little to do. Crush up the pills into the gin bottle, place the suicide note in the desk drawer, and set out to spend his day in company. No part of that day was to be unaccounted for. Gaston's Bar was only the last link in a long chain of alibi.

During the day he had probed at the plan, testing it for weaknesses, and found none.

Suppose Lydia thought the gin tasted funny? She wouldn't, in her haste. Anyway, in her descriptions of the previous attempt, she had said there was no taste. It had been, she said, just like drinking it neat and getting gently drowsier and drowsier. A quiet end. Not an unattractive one.

Suppose the police found out about the private detective and the appointment with the solicitor? Wouldn't they begin to suspect the dead woman's husband? No, if anything, that strengthened his case. Disillusioned by yet another man, depressed by the prospect of yet another divorce, she had taken the quickest way out. True, it didn't put her husband in a very good light, but Larry was not worried about that. So long as he inherited, he didn't care what people thought.

Suppose she had already made a will which disinherited him? He knew she hadn't. That was what she'd set up with the solicitor for the next day. And Larry had been present when she made her previous will that named him, her husband, as sole legatee.

No, his instinct told him nothing could go wrong . . .

He paid off the taxi driver and told him a joke he had heard in the course of the day.

He then went into their block of flats, told the porter the same joke, and asked if he could check the right time. Eight-seventeen. Never had there been a better-documented day.

As he went up in the lift, he wondered if the final refinement to the plan had happened. It wasn't essential, but it would have been nice. Lydia's sister had said she would drop round for the evening. If she could actually have discovered the body . . . Still, she was notoriously bad about time and you can't have everything. But it would be nice . . .

Everything played into his hands. On the landing he met a neighbour just about to walk his chihuahua. Larry greeted them cheerfully and checked the time. His confidence was huge. He enjoyed being a criminal mastermind.

For the benefit of the departing neighbour and because he was going to play the part to the hilt, he called out cheerily, "Good evening, darling!" as he unlocked the front door.

"Good evening, *darling,*" said Lydia.

As soon as he saw her, he knew that she knew everything. She sat poised on the sofa, and on the glass coffee table in front of her were the bottle of gin and the suicide note. If they had been labelled in a courtroom, they couldn't have been more clearly marked as evidence. On a table to the side of the sofa stood a half-empty bottle of gin. The bloody, boozy bitch—she couldn't even wait until she got home, she'd taken on new supplies on the way back from the health farm.

"Well, Larry, I dare say you're surprised to see me."

"A little," he said lightly, and smiled what he had always believed to be a charming smile.

"I think I'll have quite a lot to say to my solicitor tomorrow."

He laughed lightly.

"After I've been to the police," she continued.

His next laugh was more brittle.

"Yes, Larry, there are quite a few things to talk about. For a start, I've just done an inventory of my jewellery. And do you know, I think I've suddenly realized why you appeared in my hotel room that fateful afternoon. Once a thief, always a thief. But murder—that's going up a league for you, isn't it?"

The gin hadn't got to her; she was speaking with cold coherence. Larry slowed down his mind to match her logical deliberation. He walked over to his desk in the corner by the door. When he turned round, he was holding the gun he kept in its drawer.

Lydia laughed, loudly and unattractively, as if in derision of his manhood. "Oh, come on, Larry, that's not very subtle. No, your other little scheme was quite clever, I'll give you that. But to shoot me . . . They'd never let you inherit. You aren't allowed to profit from a crime."

"I'm not going to shoot you." He moved across and pointed the gun at her head. "I'm going to make you drink from that other gin bottle."

Again he got the harsh, challenging laugh. "Oh, come on, sweetie. What kind of threat is that? There's a basic fault in your logic. You can't make people kill themselves by threatening to kill them. If you gotta go, who cares about the method? And if you intend to kill me, I'll ensure that you do it the way that gives you most trouble. Shoot away, sweetie."

Involuntarily, he lowered the arm holding the gun.

She laughed again.

"Anyway, I'm bored with this." She rose from the sofa. "I'm going to ring the police. I've had enough of being married to a criminal mastermind."

The taunt so exactly reflected his self-image that it stung like a blow. His gun arm stiffened again and he shot her in the temple as she made her way towards the telephone.

There was a lot of blood. At first he stood there mesmerized by how much blood there was, but then, as the flow stopped, his mind started to work again.

Its deliberations were not comforting. He had blown it. The best he could hope for now was escape.

Unnaturally calm, he went to the telephone. He rang Heathrow. There was a ten o'clock flight. Yes, there was a seat. He booked it.

He took the spare cash from Lydia's handbag. Under ten pounds. She hadn't been to the bank since her return from the health farm. Still, he could use a credit card to pay for the ticket.

He went into the bedroom, where her jewellery lay in its customary disarray. He reached out for a diamond choker.

But no. Supposed the Customs searched him. That was just the sort of trouble he had to avoid. For the same reason, he couldn't take the jewellery from his case in the Left Luggage office. Where was it now, anyway? Oh, no! Liverpool Street! Fumes of panic rose to his brain. There wouldn't be time. Or would there? Maybe if he just got the money from the case and—

The doorbell rang.

Oh, my God! Lydia's sister!

He grabbed a suitcase, threw in his pyjamas and a clean shirt, then rushed into the kitchen, opened the back door, and ran down the fire escape.

Peter Mostyn's cottage was in the Department of the Lot. The nearest large town was Cahors, the nearest small town was Montaigu-de-Quercy, but neither was very near. The cottage itself was small and primitive. Mostyn was not a British trendy making a fashionable home in France; he had moved there in search of obscurity and lived very cheaply, constantly calculating how many years he could remain there on the dwindling capital he had been left by a remote uncle and hoping it would last out his lifetime. He didn't have more contact with the locals than weekly shopping demanded, and both sides seemed happy with this arrangement.

Larry Renshaw arrived there on the third night after Lydia's death. He had travelled unobtrusively by local trains, thumbed lifts, and long stretches of cross-country walking, sleeping in the fields by night. He had sold his Savile Row suit for a tenth of its value in a Paris secondhand clothes shop, where he had bought a set of stained blue overalls, which made him less conspicuous tramping along the sun-baked roads of France. His passport and gold identity bracelet were secure in an inside pocket.

If there was any chase, he reckoned he was ahead of it.

It had been dark for about four hours when he reached the cottage. It was a warm summer night. The countryside was dry and brittle, needing rain. Although the occasional car had flashed past on the narrow local roads, he had not met any pedestrians.

There was a meager slice of moon which showed him enough to dash another hope. In the back of his mind had lurked the possibility that Mostyn, in spite of his constant assertions of poverty, lived in luxury and would prove as well fleshed a body as Lydia to batten on. But the crumbling exterior of the cottage told him that the long-term solution to his problems would have to lie elsewhere. The building had hardly changed at all through many generations of peasant owners.

And when Mostyn came to the door, he could have been the latest representative of that peasant dynasty. His wig was off, he wore a shapeless sort of nightshirt and clutched a candleholder out of a Dickens television serial. The toothless lips moved uneasily and in his eye was an old peasant distrust of outsiders.

That expression vanished as soon as he recognized his visitor.

"Larry. I hoped you'd come to me. I read about it in the papers. Come inside. You'll be safe here."

* * *

Safe he certainly was. Mostyn's limited social round meant that there was no danger of the newcomer being recognized. No danger of his even being seen. For three days the only person Larry Renshaw saw was Peter Mostyn.

And Peter Mostyn still hadn't changed at all. He remained a pathetic cripple, rendered even more pathetic by his cringing devotion. For him Renshaw's appearance was the answer to a prayer. Now at last he had the object of his affections in his own home. He was in seventh heaven.

Renshaw wasn't embarrassed by the devotion; he knew Mostyn was far too diffident to try and force unwelcome attentions on him. For a little while at least he had found sanctuary and was content for a couple of days to sit and drink his host's brandy and assess his position.

The assessment wasn't encouraging. Everything had turned sour. All the careful plans he had laid for Lydia's death now worked against him. The elaborate fixing of the time of his arrival at the flat no longer established his alibi; it now pointed the finger of murder at him. Even after he'd shot her, he might have been able to sort something out but for that bloody sister of hers ringing the bell and making him panic. Everything had turned out wrong.

On the third evening, as he sat silent at the table, savagely drinking brandy while Mostyn watched him, Renshaw shouted out against the injustice of it all. "That bloody bitch!"

"Lydia?" asked Mostyn hesitantly.

"No, you fool. Her sister. If she hadn't turned up just at that moment, I'd have got away with it. I'd have thought of something."

"At what moment?"

"Just after I'd shot Lydia. She rang the bell."

"What—about eight-thirty?"

"Yes."

Mostyn paled beneath his toupé. "That wasn't Lydia's sister."

"What? How do you know?"

"It was me." Renshaw looked at him. "It was me. I was flying back the next morning. You hadn't *rung*. I so wanted to see you before I left, so I came to the flats. I didn't *intend* to go in. But I just asked the porter if you were there and he said you'd just arrived."

"It was you! You bloody fool, why didn't you say?"

"I didn't know what had happened. I just—"

"You idiot! You bloody idiot!" The frustration of the last few days and the brandy came together in a wave of fury. Renshaw seized Mostyn by the lapels and shook him. "If I had known it was you . . . You could have saved my life! You bloody fool! You . . ."

"I didn't know, I didn't know," the Little Boy whimpered. "When there was no reply, I just went back to the hotel. Honestly, if I'd known what

was happening . . . I'd do anything for you, you *know* I would. Anything . . ."

Renshaw slackened his grasp on Mostyn's lapels and returned to Mostyn's brandy.

It was the next day that he took up the offer. They sat over the debris of
lunch. "Peter, you said you'd do anything for me . . ."

"Of course, and I meant it. My life hasn't been much. You're the only
person that matters to me. I'd do anything for you. I'll look after you here
for as long as—"

"I'm not staying here. I have to get away."

Mostyn's face betrayed his hurt. Renshaw ignored it and continued. "For
that I need money."

"I've told you, you can have anything I—"

"No, I know you haven't got any money. Not real money. But I have.
In the Left Luggage office at Liverpool Street Station I have over twelve
thousand pounds in cash and jewellery." Renshaw looked at Mostyn with
the smile he had always believed to be charming. "I want you to go to
England to fetch it for me."

"What? But I'd never get it back over here."

"Yes, you would. You're the ideal smuggler. You put the stuff in your
crutches. They'd never suspect someone like you."

"But I—"

Renshaw looked hurt. "You said you'd do anything for me."

"Well, I would, but—"

"You can go into Cahors tomorrow and fix the flight."

"But—but that means you'll leave me again."

"For a little while, yes. I'd come back," Renshaw lied.

"I—"

"Please do it for me." Renshaw put on an expression he knew to be
vulnerable. "Please."

"All right, I will."

"Bless you, bless you. Come on, let's drink to it."

"I don't drink much. It makes me sleepy. I haven't got the head for it.
I—"

"Come on, drink."

Mostyn hadn't got the head for it. As the afternoon progressed, he
became more and more embarrassingly devoted. Then he fell into a coma-
tose sleep.

The day after next, the plane ticket was on the dining-room table next to
Peter Mostyn's passport. Upstairs his small case was packed ready. He was
to fly from Paris in three days' time, on the Wednesday. He would be back

at the cottage by the weekend with the money and jewels which would be Renshaw's lifeline.

Renshaw's confidence started to return. With money in his pocket, everything would once more become possible. Twelve thousand pounds was plenty to buy a new identity and start again. Talent like his, he knew, could not be kept down for long.

Mostyn was obviously uneasy about the task ahead of him, but he had been carefully briefed and he'd manage it all right. The Big Boy was entrusting him with a mission and the Little Boy would see that it was efficiently discharged.

A new harmony came into their relationship. Now that his escape had a date on it, Renshaw could relax and even be pleasant to his protector. Mostyn glowed with gratitude for the attention. It didn't take much to make him happy, Renshaw thought contemptuously. Once again, as he looked at the prematurely aged and crippled figure, he found it incongruous that their bodies had ever touched. Mostyn had never been other than pathetic.

Still, he was useful. And though it was making huge inroads into his carefully husbanded wealth, he kept the supply of brandy flowing. Renshaw topped up his tumbler again after lunch on the Monday afternoon. It was then that there was a knock at the door. Mostyn leapt nervously to the window to check out the visitor. When he looked back at Renshaw, his face had even less colour under its thatch. "It's a gendarme."

Moving quickly and efficiently, Larry Renshaw picked up his dirty plate, together with the brandy bottle and tumbler, and went upstairs. His bedroom window was above the sloping roof of the porch. If anyone came up, he would be able to make a quick getaway.

He heard conversation downstairs, but it was too indistinct and his knowledge of French too limited for him to understand it. Then he heard the front door shut. From his window he saw the gendarme go to his bike and cycle off towards Montaigu-de-Quercy.

He gave it five minutes and went downstairs. Peter Mostyn sat at the table, literally shaking.

"What the hell's the matter?"

"The gendarme—he asked if I'd seen you."

"So you said you hadn't."

"Yes, but . . ."

"But what? That's all there is to it, surely. There's been an Interpol alert to check out any contacts I might have abroad. They got your name from my address book back at the flat. So now the local bobby here has done his bit and will report back that you haven't seen me since last week in London. End of story. I'm glad it's happened. At least now I don't have to wait for it."

"Yes, but, Larry, look at the state I'm in."

"You'll calm down. Come on, okay, it was a shock, but you'll get over it."

"That's not what I mean. What I'm saying is, if I'm in this state now, I just won't be able to go through with what I'm supposed to be doing on Wednesday."

"Look, all you have to do is to catch a plane to London, go to the Liverpool Street Left Luggage office, get the case, go to somewhere conveniently quiet, load the stuff into your crutches, and come back here! There's no danger!"

"I can't do it, Larry. I *can't.* I'll crack up. I'll give myself away somehow. If I were like you, I could do it. You've always had a strong nerve for that sort of thing. I wish it were you who was going to do it, because I know you *could*. But I just . . ."

He petered out. Anger invaded Renshaw. "Listen, you little worm, you've got to do it! Good God, you've said enough times you'd do anything for me—and now the first time I ask for something you're bloody chicken!"

"Larry, I would do anything for you, I would. But I just don't think I *can* go through with this. I'd mess it up somehow. Honestly, Larry, if there were anything *else* I could do . . ."

"Anything else? How about getting me off the murder charge? Maybe you'd like to do that instead?" Renshaw asked with acid sarcasm.

"If I could . . . Or if I had enough money to be any use . . . Or if . . ."

"Oh, shut up, you useless little queen!" Larry Renshaw stomped savagely upstairs with the brandy bottle.

They did not speak to each other for over twenty-four hours.

But the next evening, as he lay on the bed drinking brandy, watching the declining sun tinge the scrubby oak trees of the hillside with gold, Renshaw's instinct started to take over again. It was a warm feeling. Once more he felt protected. His instinct was an Almighty Big Boy, looking after him, guiding him, showing him the way forward, as it always had done before.

After about an hour, he heard the front door and saw Mostyn setting off down the road that led to Montaigu-de-Quercy. Again. He'd been out more than once since their row. No doubt going to buy more brandy as a peace offering. Poor little sod. Renshaw chuckled to himself at the aptness of the description.

Alone in the cottage, he dozed. The bang of the door on Mostyn's return woke him. And he was not surprised to wake up with his plan of campaign worked out in every detail.

* * *

Peter Mostyn looked up like a mongrel fearing a kick, but Larry Renshaw smiled at him and was amused to see how gratefully the expression changed. Mostyn had all the weakness of the sort of women Renshaw had spent his life avoiding.

"Larry, look, I'm terribly sorry about yesterday afternoon. I was just a coward. Look, I really *do* want to do something for you. You know I'd give my life for you if I thought it'd be any use. It's been a pretty wasted life—I'd like it to do *something* valuable."

"But not go to London and pick up my things?" Renshaw asked lightly.

"I just don't think I *could*, Larry, I don't think I have it *in me*. But I will go to London tomorrow. There's something else I can do for you. I *can* help you. I *have* helped you already. I—"

"Never mind." Renshaw spread his hands in a magnanimous gesture of forgiveness. "Never mind. Listen, Peter," he went on intimately, "I behaved like a swine yesterday and I want to apologize. I'm sorry, this whole thing's been a dreadful strain and I just haven't been appreciating all you're doing for me. Please forgive me."

"You've been fine. I . . . ." Mostyn's expression hovered between surprise and delight at his friend's change of behaviour.

"No, I've been being a swine. Peace offering." He drew his hand out of his pocket and held it towards Mostyn.

"But you don't want to give me that. It's your identity bracelet, it's got your name on. And it's gold. I mean, you'd—"

"Please . . ."

Mostyn took the bracelet and slipped it onto his thin wrist.

"Listen, Peter, I've been so confused I haven't been thinking straight. Forget the money in London. Maybe I'll get it someday, maybe I won't. The important thing is that I'm safe at the moment, with a *friend*. A very good friend. Peter, what I want to ask is—can I stay here for a bit?" He looked up humbly. "If you don't mind."

"Mind? Look, you know, Larry, I'd be delighted. *Delighted.* You don't have to ask that."

"Bless you, Peter." Renshaw spoke softly, as if choked by emotion. Then he perked up. "If that's settled then, let's drink on it."

"I won't, thank you, Larry. You know it only makes me sleepy."

"Oh, come on, Peter. If we're going to live together, we've got to learn to enjoy the same hobbies." And he filled two tumblers with brandy.

The prospect opened up by the words "live together" was too much for Mostyn. There were tears in his eyes as he drained the first drink.

It was about an hour and a half later when Renshaw judged the moment to be right. Mostyn was slurring his words and yawning, but still conscious.

His eyes focused in pleasure for a moment when Renshaw murmured, "Why don't we go upstairs?"

"Whaddya mean?"

"You know what I mean." He giggled.

"Really? Really?"

Renshaw nodded.

Mostyn rose, swaying, to his feet. "Where are my crutches?"

"They won't help you stand up straight in the state you're in." Renshaw giggled again, and Mostyn joined in. Renshaw ruffled his Little Boy's hair, and the toupé came off in his hand.

"Gimme thaback."

"When I come upstairs," Renshaw murmured softly. Then, in an even lower whisper, "Go up to my room, get my pyjamas, put them on, and get into my bed. I'll be up soon."

Mostyn smiled with fuddled pleasure and started off up the stairs. Renshaw heard the uneven footsteps in his room above, then the hobbling noises of undressing, the thump of a body hitting the bed, and soon, predictably, silence.

He sat for about a quarter of an hour finishing his drink. Then, whistling softly, he started to make his preparations.

He moved slowly, but efficiently, following the infallible dictates of his instinct. First he went into the little bathroom and shaved off his remaining hair. It took a surprisingly short time. Then he removed his false teeth and put them in a glass of water.

He went cautiously up the stairs and inched open the door of his bedroom. As expected, Mostyn lay unconscious from the unaccustomed alcohol.

Unhurriedly, Renshaw placed the glass of teeth on the bedside table. Then he changed into the clothes Mostyn had just abandoned on the floor. He went into the other bedroom, picked up the overnight case that had been packed, and returned downstairs.

He picked up the air ticket and passport, which still lay accusingly on the dining table. He put on the toupé and compared his reflection with the passport photograph. The picture was ten years old and the resemblance quite sufficient. He picked up the crutches and tried them until he could reproduce the limp that appeared in the "Special Peculiarities" section.

Then he picked up the half-full brandy bottle, another unopened one, and the candle on the table, and went upstairs.

The Little Boy lay on his Big Boy's bed, in his Big Boy's pyjamas, even wearing his Big Boy's gold identity bracelet, but was in no state to appreciate this longed-for felicity. He did not stir as his Big Boy sprinkled brandy over the bedclothes, the rush matting, and the wooden floorboards. Nor did he stir when his Big Boy set the lighted candle on the floor and watched its flames spread.

Larry Renshaw felt the usual confidence that following his instinct produced as he travelled back to London in the identity of Peter Mostyn. He even found there were compensations in being a pathetic, toothless cripple on crutches. People made way for him at the airport and helped him with his bags.

On the plane he mused comfortably about his next movements. Certainly his first port of call must be the Left Luggage office at Liverpool Street. And then probably one of the fences he already knew, to turn the jewellery into cash. Then, who could say? Possibly abroad again . . . Certainly a new identity . . .

But there was no hurry. That was the luxury his instinct had achieved for him. In Mostyn's identity he was safe for as long as he could stand being such a pathetic figure. There was no hurry.

He felt tense as he approached Passport Control at Heathrow. Not frightened—he was confident his instinct would see him through—but tense. After all, if there was a moment when his identity was most likely to be questioned, this was it. But if he was accepted here as Peter Mostyn, then he had nothing more to worry about.

It was slightly unnerving, because the Passport Officer seemed to be expecting him. "Ah, Mr. Mostyn," he said. "If you'd just take a seat here for a moment, I'll tell them you've arrived."

"But I—" No, better not to make a scene. Reserve righteous indignation for later. Must be some minor mix-up. He imagined how feebly Peter Mostyn would whine at the nuisances of bureaucracy.

He didn't have long to wait. Two men in raincoats arrived and asked him to go with them to a small room. They did not speak again until they were all seated.

"Now," said the man who seemed to be senior, "let's talk about the murder of Mrs. Lydia Renshaw."

"Mrs. Lydia Renshaw?" echoed Larry Renshaw, bemused. "But I'm Peter Mostyn."

"Yes," said the man, "we know that. There's no question about that. And that's why we want to talk to you about the murder of Mrs. Lydia Renshaw."

"But . . . why?" Larry Renshaw asked, quite as pathetically as Peter Mostyn would have done.

"Why?" The man seemed puzzled. "Well, because of your letter of confession that arrived this morning."

*　　　*　　　*

It was some time before he actually saw the document that had incriminated him, but it didn't take him long to imagine its contents:

Because of his long-standing homosexual attraction to Larry Renshaw, Peter Mostyn had gone round to see him the evening before he was due to return to his home in France. At the block of flats in Abbey Road—where he was seen by the porter—he had found, not Renshaw, but Renshaw's wife, the woman who, in his eyes, had irrevocably alienated the affections of his friend. An argument had ensued, in the course of which he had shot his rival. Larry Renshaw, returning to his flat, seeing his wife's body and guessing what had happened, had immediately set off for France in pursuit of the murderer. It was Renshaw's arrival at his home that had prompted Peter Mostyn to make a clean breast of what he had done . . .

This put Larry Renshaw in a rather difficult position. Since he was now innocent, he could in theory claim back his own identity. But he had a nasty feeling that that would raise more questions than it would answer.

His instinct, now diminished to a limping, apologetic, pathetic thing, advised him to remain as Peter Mostyn, the Little Boy who has made the supreme sacrifice to protect his Big Boy.

So it was as Peter Mostyn that he was charged with, and found guilty of, the murder of Mrs. Lydia Renshaw.

And it was as Peter Mostyn that he was later charged with, and found guilty of, the murder of Larry Renshaw.

About the author

Respected wine critic and vigneron James Halliday AM has a career that spans over forty years, but he is most widely known for his witty and informative writing about wine. As one of the founders of Brokenwood in the Lower Hunter Valley, New South Wales, and thereafter of Coldstream Hills in the Yarra Valley, Victoria, James is an unmatched authority on every aspect of the wine industry, from the planting and pruning of vines through to the creation and marketing of the finished product. His winemaking has led him to sojourns in Bordeaux and Burgundy, and he has had a long career as a wine judge in Australia and overseas. In 1995 he received the wine industry's ultimate accolade, the Maurice O'Shea Award.

James has written or contributed to more than 65 books on wine since he began writing in 1979. His books have been translated into Japanese, French, German, Danish, Icelandic and Polish, and have been published in the UK and the US, as well as in Australia. He is the author of *James Halliday's Wine Atlas of Australia* and *The Australian Wine Encyclopedia*. In 2010 James was made a Member of the Order of Australia.

Wine zones and regions of Australia

NEW SOUTH WALES			
WINE ZONE		**WINE REGION**	
Big Rivers	(A)	Murray Darling	1
		Perricoota	2
		Riverina	3
		Swan Hill	4
Central Ranges	(B)	Cowra	5
		Mudgee	6
		Orange	7
Hunter Valley	(C)	Hunter	8
		Upper Hunter	9
Northern Rivers	(D)	Hastings River	10
Northern Slopes	(E)	New England	11
South Coast	(F)	Shoalhaven Coast	12
		Southern Highlands	13
Southern New South Wales	(G)	Canberra District	14
		Gundagai	15
		Hilltops	16
		Tumbarumba	17
Western Plains	(H)		

SOUTH AUSTRALIA			
WINE ZONE		**WINE REGION**	
Adelaide Super Zone includes Mount Lofty Ranges, Fleurieu and Barossa wine regions			
Barossa		Barossa Valley	18
		Eden Valley	19
Fleurieu	(J)	Currency Creek	20
		Kangaroo Island	21
		Langhorne Creek	22
		McLaren Vale	23
		Southern Fleurieu	24
Mount Lofty Ranges		Adelaide Hills	25
		Adelaide Plains	26
		Clare Valley	27
Far North	(K)	Southern Flinders Ranges	28
Limestone Coast	(L)	Coonawarra	29
		Mount Benson	30
		Mount Gambier	31
		Padthaway	32
		Robe	33
		Wrattonbully	34
Lower Murray	(M)	Riverland	35
The Peninsulas	(N)	Southern Eyre Peninsula*	36

VICTORIA			
WINE ZONE		**WINE REGION**	
Central Victoria	(P)	Bendigo	37
		Goulburn Valley	38
		Heathcote	39
		Strathbogie Ranges	40
Gippsland	(Q)	Upper Goulburn	41
		Alpine Valleys	42
North East Victoria	(R)	Beechworth	43
		Glenrowan	44
		King Valley	45
		Rutherglen	46
North West Victoria	(S)	Murray Darling	47
		Swan Hill	48
Port Phillip	(T)	Geelong	49
		Macedon Ranges	50
		Mornington Peninsula	51
		Sunbury	52
		Yarra Valley	53
Western Victoria	(U)	Ballarat*	54
		Grampians	55
		Henty	56
		Pyrenees	57

* For more information see page 52.

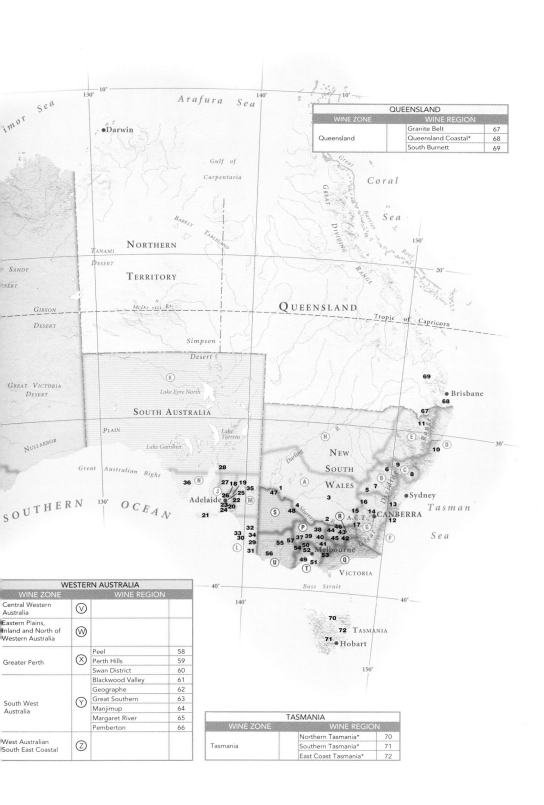

QUEENSLAND		
WINE ZONE	WINE REGION	
Queensland	Granite Belt	67
	Queensland Coastal*	68
	South Burnett	69

WESTERN AUSTRALIA			
WINE ZONE		WINE REGION	
Central Western Australia	Ⓥ		
Eastern Plains, Inland and North of Western Australia	Ⓦ		
Greater Perth	Ⓧ	Peel	58
		Perth Hills	59
		Swan District	60
South West Australia	Ⓨ	Blackwood Valley	61
		Geographe	62
		Great Southern	63
		Manjimup	64
		Margaret River	65
		Pemberton	66
West Australian South East Coastal	Ⓩ		

TASMANIA		
WINE ZONE	WINE REGION	
Tasmania	Northern Tasmania*	70
	Southern Tasmania*	71
	East Coast Tasmania*	72

SAVE OVER 50%

When you subscribe to the Wine Companion Magazine & website today

For only $39 you will receive:

- Six entertaining and advice-packed issues of the Wine Companion Magazine (RRP $59.70)

- A one-year membership to Wine Companion website with access to over 70,000 tasting notes and much more (RRP $39)

Subscribing is simple:

Visit www.winecompanion.com.au/become-a-member

Enter unique code wcb2013 at checkout to redeem this offer. Ends 30 November 2012

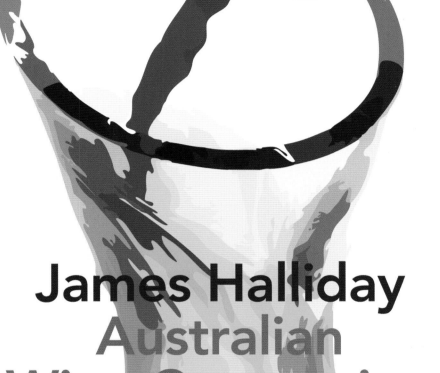

James Halliday
Australian
Wine Companion

2013 Edition

hardie grant books
MELBOURNE · LONDON

**THE BESTSELLING AND DEFINITIVE
GUIDE TO AUSTRALIAN WINE**

www.winecompanion.com.au

Published in 2012 by Hardie Grant Books

Hardie Grant Books (Australia)
Ground Floor, Building 1
658 Church Street
Richmond, Victoria 3121
www.hardiegrant.com.au

Hardie Grant Books (UK)
Dudley House, North Suite
34–35 Southampton Street
London WC2E 7HF
www.hardiegrant.co.uk

ISBN 978 1 74270 306 0

Typeset by Megan Ellis
Cover design by Heather Menzies
Printed and bound in Australia by Ligare Book Printers

Contents

Introduction

We are told that our economy is the envy of the developed world, the balance of payments running unprecedented surpluses month after month, our dollar is worth more than twice its nadir at the time Paul Keating unveiled his banana republic warning, and unemployment is half of what it was in the 1980s, close to bedrock.

Yet despite this, all winemakers share the view it is a difficult market in which to operate, and it is small consolation that virtually all sectors of the domestic retail market are facing similar sales resistance.

So where now? The larger than expected 2011 vintage in South Eastern Australia resulted in generally good white wines, but it was a struggle with the red wines. Western Australia and Tasmania had no problems, nor, as the snapshot of the '12 vintage shows, did they in '12. Moreover, there will be a stream of outstanding '12 red wines from South Australia and southern Victoria coming onto the market over the next two years. The reduced yields from the premium regions is at once good (meeting the surplus bogeyman head on) and bad (lesser production and cash flow).

While consumers' purse strings will loosen sooner or later, congestion on the routes to market will continue to increase as Coles' and Woolworths' market share continues to grow, exacerbated by their direct imports of wines from Europe and the ubiquitous New Zealand Sauvignon Blanc.

E-commerce is one answer, but websites and e-newsletters need constant attention and points of difference. All of this said and done, the consumer who is prepared to spend money will have a seriously good array of keenly priced/discounted wines to choose from over the coming year.

Australia's two largest export markets have long been the UK and the US. While some of Australia's best small wineries have an ongoing presence in the UK, the long shadow of a hostile government raising the duty on all forms of alcohol every year, partly to raise revenue, partly to abate binge drinking; an economy in recession; and supermarkets intent on driving supply prices downwards, mean the importance of the UK will dwindle year after year.

The outlook for the US, and notably Canada, is less sombre, particularly if the economies continue to recover. But the strong Australian dollar is an issue in these markets and, of course, in the UK. It highlights – and exacerbates – the need for a new paradigm. The seemingly inexhaustible appetite for cheap and cheerful Australian wine over the last 15 years of the 20th century has disappeared with disconcerting and irreversible speed.

And so to the two hopes for the future: Australia+, and Asia, with China to the fore. Australia+ is the new marketing mantra, putting all the focus on our 'super-premium' wines, those that have a retail price in excess of $20 in Australia. China has so much potential it is difficult to comprehend it: a country with 90 cities having a population equal to or larger than Sydney, and a rapidly growing middle class looking for ways to spend money. Australia exports more bottles with an FOB price of $10 or more (more or less equal to $20 RRP in Australia) than to any other country. But we don't know how much is pipeline filling, how much finds its way into the households of the so-called middle class, how much they consume with or without a coca cola infusion, and how much knowledge they have.

Shortly put, the Asian markets have huge potential for sales, and equally large traps for the unwary or over-optimistic exporters. Shortly prior to this book going to press, Wine Intelligence (the leading market research group) pointed to an (overdue) increase in the demand for white wine, and – wait for it – sweet red wine.

How to use this book

Wineries

Kilikanoon ★★★★★

Penna Lane, Penwortham, SA 5453 Region Clare Valley
T (08) 8843 4206 **www**.kilikanoon.com.au **Open** Thurs–Mon 11-5
Winemaker Kevin Mitchell **Est.** 1997 **Dozens** 40 000 **Vyds** 330ha
Kilikanoon has travelled in the fast lane since winemaker Kevin Mitchell established it in 1997 on the foundation of 6ha of vines owned by him and father Mort. It made its first entry in the 2001 *Wine Companion* with a 4-star rating for its 3000-dozen production of Riesling, Cabernet Sauvignon and Grenache. With the aid of investors its 40 000-dozen production comes from over 300ha of estate-owned vineyards, and access to the best grapes from a total of 2266ha across South Australia. It is tied to Seppeltfield (see separate entry), two of the principal players being Nathan Waks, formerly principal cellist of the Sydney Symphony Orchestra, and winemaker-cum-entrepreneur Warren Randall. Its galaxy of top-rated wines are made in small batches of outstanding grapes, in the onsite winery built in 2004.

Winery name   Kilikanoon

Although it might seem that stating the winery name is straightforward, this is not necessarily so. To avoid confusion, wherever possible I use the name that appears most prominently on the front label of the wine.

Winery rating   ★★★★★

The effort to come up with a fair winery rating system continues. As last year, I looked at the ratings for this and the previous two years; if the wines tasted this year justified a higher rating than last year, that higher rating has been given. If, on the other hand, the wines are of lesser quality, I took into account the track record over the past two years (or longer where the winery is well known) and made a judgement call on whether it should retain its ranking, or be given a lesser one. Where no wines were submitted by a well-rated winery which had a track record of providing samples, I used my discretion to roll over last year's rating.

While there are (only) 1381 wineries profiled in this edition there are more than 2750 wineries to be found on www.winecompanion.com.au.

The precise meanings attached to the winery star rating is as follows; the percentages at the end of each rating is that of the total number of wineries in the Wine Companion database at the time of going to print. Two caveats: first, I retain a discretionary right to depart from the normal criteria. Second, the basis of the rating will best be understood on the website, where all wine ratings appear.

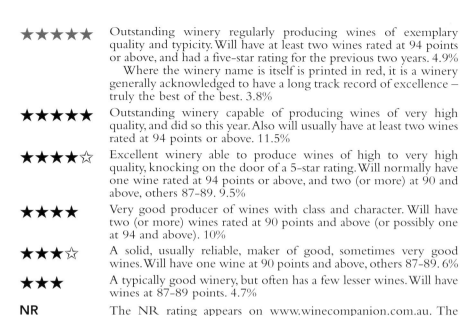

★★★★★ Outstanding winery regularly producing wines of exemplary quality and typicity. Will have at least two wines rated at 94 points or above, and had a five-star rating for the previous two years. 4.9%

Where the winery name is itself is printed in red, it is a winery generally acknowledged to have a long track record of excellence – truly the best of the best. 3.8%

★★★★★ Outstanding winery capable of producing wines of very high quality, and did so this year. Also will usually have at least two wines rated at 94 points or above. 11.5%

★★★★☆ Excellent winery able to produce wines of high to very high quality, knocking on the door of a 5-star rating. Will normally have one wine rated at 94 points or above, and two (or more) at 90 and above, others 87–89. 9.5%

★★★★ Very good producer of wines with class and character. Will have two (or more) wines rated at 90 and above (or possibly one at 94 and above). 10%

★★★☆ A solid, usually reliable, maker of good, sometimes very good wines. Will have one wine at 90 points and above, others 87–89. 6%

★★★ A typically good winery, but often has a few lesser wines. Will have wines at 87–89 points. 4.7%

NR The NR rating appears on www.winecompanion.com.au. The rating is given in a range of circumstances: where there have been no tastings in the 12-month period; where there have been tastings, but with no wines scoring more than 86 points; or where the tastings have, for one reason or another, proved not to fairly reflect the reputation of a winery with a track record of success. 49.6%

Contact Details Penna Lane, Penwortham, SA 5453 T (08) 8843 4206

The details are usually those of the winery and cellar door, but in a few instances may simply be a postal address; this occurs when the wine is made at another winery or wineries, and is sold only through the website and/or retail.

Region Clare Valley

A full list of Zones, Regions and Subregions appears on pages 52 to 55. Occasionally you will see 'Various' as the region. This means the wine is made from purchased grapes, from a number of regions, often a winery without a vineyard of its own.

www.kilikanoon.com.au

An increasingly important reference point, often containing material not found (for space reasons) in this book.

Open Thurs–Mon 11–5

Although a winery might be listed as not open or only open on weekends, some may in fact be prepared to open by appointment. Many will, some won't; a telephone call will establish whether it is possible or not.

Winemaker Kevin Mitchell

In all but the smallest producers, the winemaker is simply the head of a team; there may be many executive winemakers actually responsible for specific wines in the medium to large companies (80 000 cases and upwards).

Est. 1997

Keep in mind that some makers consider the year in which they purchased the land to be the year of establishment, others the year in which they first planted grapes, others the year they first made wine, and so on. There may also be minor complications where there has been a change of ownership or break in production.

Vyds 330ha

Shows the hectares of vineyard/s owned by the winery.

Dozens 40 000

This figure (representing the number of 9-litre (12-bottle) cases produced each year) is merely an indication of the size of the operation. Some winery entries do not feature a production figure: this is either because the winery (principally, but not exclusively, the large companies) regards this information as confidential.

Summary Kilikanoon has travelled in the fast lane since winemaker Kevin Mitchell established it in 1997 on the foundation of 6ha of vines owned by him and father Mort …

My summary of the winery. Little needs be said, except that I have tried to vary the subjects I discuss in this part of the winery entry.

New wineries

 The vine leaf symbol indicates the 66 wineries that are new entries in this year's *Wine Companion.*

Tasting notes

While the points and glass symbols given below remain unchanged, the ever-increasing number of wineries (there are still more births than deaths) and increased total number of tasting notes has necessitated the move to www.winecompanion.com.au of some tasting notes that in prior years would have appeared in the Wine Companion book as well as the website. These tasting notes will be for wines that have scored 87 points or above. A summary of the criteria used to determine the ratings to follows.

Ratings

94–100	🍷🍷🍷🍷🍷	**Outstanding.** Wines of the highest quality, often with a distinguished pedigree. Tasting notes will usually appear in the *Wine Companion* and also on www.winecompanion.com.au.
90–93	🍷🍷🍷🍷🍷	**Highly recommended.** Wines of great quality, style and character, worthy of a place in any cellar. If the highest-pointed wines fall into this group, the tasting notes appear in full, otherwise the wines will be listed with rating, price and drink-to details, with the full entry on www.winecompanion.com.au.
87–89	🍷🍷🍷🍷	**Recommended.** Wines of above-average quality, fault-free, and with clear varietal expression. If the highest-pointed wines fall in this group, the tasting notes appear in full, otherwise the wines will be listed with rating, price and drink-to details, with the full entry on www.winecompanion.com.au.
87–97	✪	**Special value.** Wines considered to offer special value for money. If the special value wines fall into the winery's top two groups, the tasting notes appear in full, otherwise the wines will be listed with rating, price and drink-to details, with the full entry on www.winecompanion.com.au.
87–97	◉	**1001 Wines Under $20.** These wines were included (with tasting notes) in the 2012 edition of *1001 Wines Under $20*, and may still be available. Tasting notes appear on www.winecompanion.com.au.
84–86	🍷🍷🍷	**Acceptable.** Wines of fair commercial quality, free of any significant fault. Tasting notes will only appear on www.winecompanion.com.au.
80–83	🍷🍷🍷	**Over to you.** Everyday wines, usually cheap and with little or no future, needing more character and flavour. No Tasting notes are published.
75–79	🍷🍷🍷	**Not recommended.** Wines with one or more significant winemaking faults. No tasting notes are published, but points and price are shown.

🍷🍷🍷🍷🍷 **Attunga 1865 Clare Valley Shiraz 2009** As the name suggests, the vines were planted in 1865, very early in the history of the Clare Valley; the crimson-purple colour is excellent, and the wine cries out for 20 years in bottle, for while the fruit is intense, there is a ghetto blast of oak. Cork. 14.5% alc. **Rating** 96 **To** 2050 $250

The tasting note opens with the vintage of the wine tasted. This tasting note will have been made within the 12 months prior to publication. Even that is a long time, and during the life of this book the wine will almost certainly change. More than this, remember the tasting is a highly subjective and imperfect art. The price of the wine is listed where information is available. Tasting notes for wines 94 points and over are printed in red.

Where BE appears at the end of a wine listing, this signifies that Ben Edwards tasted the wine and wrote the note and allocated the score.

To 2050

Rather than give a span of drinking years, I have simply provided a (conservative) 'best by' date. Modern winemaking is such that, even if a wine has 10 or 20 years' future during which it will gain greater complexity, it can be enjoyed at any time over the intervening months and years.

Cork

This is the closure used for this particular wine. The closures in use for the wines tasted are (in descending order): screwcap 87% (last year 85%), one-piece natural cork 7% (last year 8%), Diam 5% (last year 5%). The remaining 1% (in approximate order of importance) are ProCork, Twin Top, Crown Seal, Zork, Vino-Lok and Synthetic. I believe the percentage of screwcap will continue to rise for red wines; over 97.5% of white wines are screwcapped, leaving little room for any further increase.

14.5% alc

As with closures, I have endeavoured to always include this piece of information, which is in one sense self-explanatory. What is less obvious is the increasing concern of many of Australian winemakers about the rise in levels of alcohol, and much research and practical experiment (picking earlier, higher fermentation temperatures in open fermenters, etc) is occurring. Reverse osmosis and yeast selection are two of the options available to decrease higher than desirable alcohol levels. Recent changes to domestic and export labelling mean the stated alcohol will be within a maximum of 0.5% of that obtained by analysis.

Australian vintage 2012: a snapshot

Western Australia was, as usual, blessed by the weather from start to finish, as was South Australia, the only issue for the latter significantly reduced yields. Tasmania and southern Victoria joined the band with a great vintage, but the centre and north of Victoria shared damaging rainfall in late February/early March with the whole of New South Wales and Queensland following suit. The question was what did you pick before the rain, what after? The other recurring theme was lower alcohol levels thanks to the generally cool weather.

SOUTH AUSTRALIA

I cannot remember a vintage having received such hyperbolic praise right across the board, covering all regions and all varieties, as there is for 2012. Words that came up repeatedly were *'fantastic'*, *'outstanding'*, *'sensational'*, *'best in my lifetime'*, *'perfect in every way'*, *'density of colour'*, and *'development of flavour at moderate alcohol levels'*, and one winemaker, who couldn't wait to give it a numeric rating for next year, gave it 11/10. The only sour note is the low yields, seldom less than 20% below average, and for some half of the average. **Adelaide Hills** had crops down 30% to 50% in some vineyards, but one of the great years with outstanding flavour and natural acidity for all varieties, notably chardonnay, sauvignon blanc and shiraz. Following the overall pattern, the **Barossa Valley** had a wet winter and spring, only a few hot days scattered here and there, and March a picture postcard perfect rendition of autumn; cold nights were followed by wonderful mild but bright days. All the red varieties are outstanding, although yields of some varieties fell below two tonnes to the acre. **Clare Valley**'s riesling will be absolutely outstanding, one of the greatest years in living memory, shiraz and cabernet sauvignon not far behind, with enormous depth of colour and power without excess alcohol. While veraison in **Coonawarra** commenced two weeks earlier than average, ripening occurred at a leisurely pace, with cabernet still being picked in mid-April in balmy conditions, giving winemakers a degree of latitude they have not seen for many years. Small berries were part of the picture, with glorious varietal expression, and all of the Coonawarra makers with prestige labels will be making those this year. The winter was dry in the **Eden Valley**, though fruit-set and yield were affected by wet, drizzly weather in mid- to late November. Good rain in late January and late February was ideally timed, particularly with the general warming from March through to an Indian summer in April. This resulted in a long window of picking and amazing maturities, purity, intense varietal expression, length and balance are the key words. **Kangaroo Island** continued the good news story, with adequate rain up to mid-December, and then cool and dry from late December until mid- to late March, vintage coming 10 to 15 days later than a normal year (global warming missing in action). Outstanding red wines will be made. Good subsoil moisture in **Langhorne Creek** carried over from 2011, was supplemented by average summer rainfall, maintaining good canopy health, daily temperatures moderate to below average. Crop levels were below average for shiraz and tempranillo, malbec going the other way. Overall, the red wines are every bit as good as the best years over the past two decades, with alcohol in a 13% to 13.5% alc/vol range rather than the usual 14.5% to 15% range. **McLaren Vale** was harder and more uniformly hit by reduced yields (30% to 50% less than normal), but the quality of the grapes more than compensated. Shiraz is the real standout, displaying amazing fruit intensity; cabernet and merlot are also extremely concentrated with exceptional colour and varietal expression, grenache following suit with peppery/spicy red berry fruits. A very early budburst in **Mount Benson**, and good growth, brought the whole ripening period forward by two to three weeks, yet not shortening the hang time. The white varieties are all very promising, and while shiraz was amazing, cabernet sauvignon may be the standout variety when the shouting dies down. **Padthaway** had one of its driest, warmest and earliest growing seasons for many years. Yields were lower than normal, the two standout varieties shiraz and chardonnay. **Riverland** provided yet more good news with the best year since 2005; once past a slightly tricky spring the cooler than usual summer meant all varieties ripened gradually, chardonnay and shiraz star performers, cabernet sauvignon and merlot also very good. **Southern Fleurieu** provided more of the same, emulating the perfect growing conditions in **Wrattonbully** with warm and dry weather but no heat spikes, nor untimely rain. Yields of cabernet sauvignon in particular are down, well below 20%, but has that extra something, with outstanding blackcurrant and briar notes with ripe seed tannins.

VICTORIA

For many of the regions in Victoria, though by no means all, it was a vintage in two halves: before significant rain events at the end of February and again a week later in March, grape quality was very good to outstanding, but those who were unable to pick before the rain had to be very selective in what was picked, and what was not. The **Alpine Valleys** had the earliest start to vintage on record, with a dream run until 300 mm of rain fell in early March turned the season on its head. The early ripeners of tempranillo, pinot noir and chardonnay are excellent, riesling and pinot gris also good. **Beechworth** had above normal rainfall right through summer, but no heat waves, making it one of its best vintages in years. Chardonnay, shiraz and even pinot noir are of exceptional quality. A classic vintage in two halves for **Bendigo**, with outstanding chardonnay and shiraz picked early, the rest variable, except for some with cabernet sauvignon that paid no attention to the rain. One of those regions with a nigh-on perfect vintage was **Geelong**, rainfall simply beneficial in slowing down vintage. Pinot noir and shiraz both looked to have the potential of 'best ever', the vintage as a whole every bit as good as the great 2010 year. **Glenrowan** received the late February rain and heavy falls in March, but is very happy with the quality of shiraz, cabernet sauvignon and nero d'Avola. Yields in **Heathcote** were diminished by heavy rain during flowering, but January and most of February were warm and mild with average rainfall, and the northern and central parts of the region had basically completed a standout vintage for shiraz before the rain arrived, the wines reminiscent of 2010, strongly coloured and flavoured with lovely purity. Heavy rain during flowering, reduced **Henty**'s yields by 30%, but thereafter it was a smooth run to the finish of well above average quality. **Macedon Ranges** picks later than almost any other region (perhaps Henty is in the same boat), and for those who were able to keep disease at bay until mid-March, an Indian summer arrived allowing virtually all varieties to shine, for a change, with above average yields. The **Mornington Peninsula** had the same foreboding as the Yarra Valley when it seemed the rain of 2011 was never going to stop, but it did, with the driest December for 10 years, and a similarly dry January with ideal ripening conditions. The lower altitude vineyards picked high quality pinot noir and chardonnay before the mid-March rainfall, but the hillside vineyards on the top of the ridges dried out well. Several vineyards reported outstanding quality. **Murray Darling** was put into perspective by Phil Spillman (of Deakin Estate) who wrote 'This is the best overall quality I've seen in my nine Murray Darling vintages. The standout varieties were sauvignon blanc, chardonnay, riesling, viognier, merlot, cabernet sauvignon and tempranillo; average was sparkling base, moscato (too cool) and pinot grigio (why bother)'. Ideal conditions in **Nagambie Lakes** right through to the first week of February resulted in high quality grapes, but then heavy rain on February 26/27 and again March 1 and 4 caused substantial problems for some. Riesling, chardonnay and shiraz will be the picks. The **Pyrenees** provided more of the same, a magnificent first half of the growing season, then rain tried to spoil the party. However, all reports point to excellent shiraz and very good cabernet sauvignon. Winter rainfall in the **Strathbogie Ranges** was persistent, keeping good levels of moisture in the soil, while conditions were generally dry, it was a wet, windy and overcast period for flowering and fruit-set, reducing yields significantly. End-February and mid-March rainfall tested patience and skill, but the overall quality is expected to be good to very good, with outstanding cabernet sauvignon. **Upper Goulburn** had on-and-off weather up to the start of February when the weather systems stabilised, allowing cabernet sauvignon and riesling to fully ripen with very good varietal character and overall flavour. The **Yarra Valley** had a wet end to the 2011 calendar year, causing frayed nerves, but the weather cleared, and ideal conditions prevailed through the whole of January and February, with only one or two hot days, and a little hail (back in December) causing any concern. Endless days through to April (and only one period of rain) with clear skies and temperatures in the mid-20s were reminiscent of 1992, and virtually every winemaker in the Valley is ecstatic about the quality of the pinot noir, with exceptional colour, flavour and structure, and no weak spots with the other varieties.

NEW SOUTH WALES

Overall, a difficult vintage, with rainfall dashing hopes time and again. Heavy rain in mid-November prompted excellent vine growth in the **Canberra District**, some of the best for a decade. Late November rain and thunder storms upset fruit-set and eventual yield, but then a long and very cool growing season followed with only four days over 30°C. When a vintage in a lifetime loomed, two weeks from harvest hail and 100-400 mm of rain in three days hit some vineyards, leading to splitting and botrytis. Selective hand-picking reduced riesling yield by 40%, but the wine that was made is quite outstanding, with low alcohol (10% alc/vol) but intense flavours and balanced acids. Cabernet sauvignon cruised through and was picked later in ideal conditions. **Gundagai** had a similar story to tell, although there cabernet sauvignon (followed by shiraz and merlot) are the most important varieties in the region. The **Hastings**

River inevitably felt the brunt of the tropical downpours affecting Queensland and northern New South Wales, with heavy rains during January; again as in the Hunter, semillon fared best, along with the hybrid, mould-resistant chambourcin. Summer went missing in action in the **Hunter Valley**, leaving vignerons to struggle with two issues: high crops of semillon and slow ripening of small crops of red varieties, notably shiraz. Vintage got underway on January 31 with drizzling rain (last year 43°C and sunshine), and the rain continued through February with 170 mm falling. It was a question of picking and choosing vineyards, and once choosing a vineyard, to be ultra-selective in harvesting. As always, there will be small amounts of very good wine made, but these will be the exceptions to prove the rule. **Mudgee** had to deal with constant rainfall in the lead up to and during harvest, chardonnay the one bright light for the best-managed vineyards. While 133 mm of rain during the crucial flowering weeks reduced yield in **Orange**, the real problem stemmed from 268 mm falling between February 1 to March 19, combined with very cool conditions. Only the best viticulturists were able to coax modest yields of fine quality, balanced musts in a low alcohol mode. Those on the heavier soils, with heavy crops were left lamenting. In the **Riverina**, too, timing was everything. Moderate rainfall in spring and early summer was followed by mild summer temperatures with cooler than usual evenings that provided some of the best flavour seen for many years in chardonnay, verdelho and sauvignon blanc. Somewhat lower than normal yields also helped. Durif, shiraz and merlot harvested before the late February rain have wonderful depth of varietal flavour. **Shoalhaven Coast** relies both on locally grown fruit, and grapes coming from the Southern Highlands, Tumbarumba and even the Yarra Valley. Only the last came through with good grapes (arneis); local semillon, chardonnay and sauvignon blanc that were protected from the constant disease pressure have produced elegant wines. The **Southern Highlands** had a year it would prefer to forget with continuous rain from winter through to much of the (theoretical) ripening phase. Cloud-cover and over 500 mm of rain between January and mid-March not only meant a constant battle with disease, but inadequate warmth to ripen the red wines. Sparkling wine base and pinot gris are (somewhat dismal) highlights. **Tumbarumba** had, if anything, a more difficult season than 2011, chardonnay and small parcels of pinot noir and sauvignon blanc rescued by hand-picking and selective sorting.

WESTERN AUSTRALIA

Yet again, it's all good news from the west. The season in Western Australia started off on the back of good winter and spring rains across all regions, and continued through to December, with short-lived disease pressure. Thereafter there was a very warm and dry summer, January the hottest for 11 years, but not to the extent of damaging the grapes, and simply bringing the growing season back into line with prior years after a slow start. For **Great Southern** the standout out varieties were riesling, pinot noir and cabernet sauvignon. In **Margaret River** the usual suspects of chardonnay and cabernet sauvignon, generally described as exceptional, and very close to the excellent '11 vintage. For **Pemberton** the standouts were riesling, chardonnay and shiraz. Even in the **Swan Valley**, often a pressure cooker, vintage progressed at a leisurely rate, producing very good white wines and outstanding shiraz.

TASMANIA

Northern Tasmania had average winter rainfall, increasing to above average in late spring, setting the scene for excellent growth as the weather warmed. Pinot gris, riesling, sauvignon blanc and pinot noir all have vibrant flavours, lingering and persistent, crisp acids and overall very good, ripe flavours. The **East Coast** had different conditions for the first half of the growing season (no surprise in Tasmania), then a very cold July, promptly followed by one of the warmest Augusts on record promoting early budburst. Summer continued mild and warm except for some cold spells in January, before the Indian summer arrived for glorious autumn days providing superb pinot noir with excellent colour, concentration, structure and balance. Riesling and chardonnay are good to very good, albeit with lower than normal acidity. **Southern Tasmanian** yields were reduced by poor fruit set, localised severe spring frosts and a February bushfire in the Upper Derwent Valley, but the quality of riesling and pinot noir is outstanding.

QUEENSLAND

The **Granite Belt** had a topsy-turvy vintage, with a very cold spring and some light frosts after budburst, the real damage coming with hail in mid-October taking half the crop from some vineyards. Thereafter the vintage continued cool, with February rainfall, the picking considerably delayed. The reduced crops, however, helped the quality of the shiraz in particular. A warmer winter and spring in **South Burnett** saw vintage starting January 6 (extremely early) and all the white grapes were harvested in top condition prior to heavy rain that commenced on January 25 and continued into February, with 130 mm causing real problems with some of the red varieties.

Winery of the year

Kilikanoon

Kilikanoon has travelled in the fast lane since its establishment in 1997, gaining 5-star status in the 2004 Wine Companion, five red stars in '08, moving to the ultimate red star/red name in 2012. This placed it among the best 100 wineries in Australia, yet this year ('13) it surpassed its prior history with 12 of its wines receiving 94 points or above.

Kevin Mitchell has been the winemaker since day one; in the 2001 Wine Companion its production was 3000 dozen, its vineyards six hectares in the Clare Valley, and it received a 4-star rating. One sign of the future may have been its exports to seven major markets, however small the quantities may have been.

Without any fanfare (although the Clare Wine Show '02 where it won six of the seven trophies on offer must have been a catalyst), production increased to 15000 dozen (2005 Wine Companion), then 25000 dozen (2006). Behind the scenes vineyards leapt from 20ha to over 300ha, and in August '07 Seppeltsfied was acquired by what I describe as the Kilikanoon Group, production of the latter rising to is present level of 40000 dozen.

The investors who purchased Seppeltsfield via their control of Kilikanoon were led by Nathan Waks, Sydney Symphony principal cellist, and included Janet Holmes a Court. When she decided to sell her share in July 2009, Warren Randall struck, completing the circle started in the 1980s when he was enfant terrible at Seppelt (Great Western).

The Warren Randall wine group now has what has been called a 'cat's cradle' of 16 interlocking entities with 2266ha of vineyards, a crush of 16000 tonnes and global sales of 117 000 dozen. Tinlins (McLaren Vale) and Fleurieu Vintners supply the volume, Kilikanoon and Seppeltsfield the icon wines, drawing on its own vineyards, supplemented by access to the Randall group's vineyards.

The prices for the top 12 Kilikanoon red wines range from $33 (Clare Grenache) to $250 for 145-year-old Attunge Vineyard Clare Valley Shiraz, the majority at a financially comfortable $80. Kilikanoon has become a golden goose thanks to exceptional vineyard resources and small production runs of its best wines.

Best of the best wines

I make my usual disclaimer: while there are two periods of intense tasting activity in the 12 months during which the tasting notes for this edition were made, and while some wines are tasted more than once, an over-arching comparative tasting of all the best wines is simply not possible, however desirable it might be.

So the points for the individual wines scoring 94 or above stand uncorrected by the wisdom of hindsight. Nonetheless, the link between variety and region (or, if you prefer, between variety and terroir) is in most instances strikingly evident. It is for this reason that I have shown the region for each of the best wines. Medium and longer term prosperity will depend on a sense of place, of regional identity. It is also the reason for the overview of the varietal/regional mosaic (page 56).

Brand Australia has been the foundation upon which the success of the past 20 years has been built, but all recognise the need to move on. While some naysayers may regard this as marketing rhetoric, the truth is that Australia is blessed with an unmatched range of terroir (including climate in that deceptively simple term) enabling it to make wines ranging from the uniquely complex fortified wines of Rutherglen (fashioned from frontignac and muscadelle, known locally as muscat and tokay), to the 100-year-old Para Liqueur of Seppelt in the Barossa Valley, all the way through to the exceptional sparkling wines of Tasmania, grown in a climate every bit as cool as that of Champagne.

This is one of the principal reasons for the wines with the same points to be arranged by region, even though the main text is alpha-ordered. I should also point out that the cut-off for listing the wines of each variety differs considerably, depending on the strength of the class concerned.

There is now a second string to the bow of exports: Australia+ Australian Wine (www.apluswines.com). It is a reflection of two realities. First, the honeymoon days of ever-rising value and volume exports year-on-year are – for a variety of short and longer term reasons – are gone forever. Second, it is essential that far more focus is directed on the type of wines that follow over the next 18 pages if exports are to reach their full potential.

Best of the best by variety

Riesling

These wines show that the Clare and Eden Valleys remain at the head of the regional pack, but the regions of South West Australia and Tasmania are nipping at their heels. Only three other regions contribute (in a small but impressive way) to the mix: Canberra District, Henty and Grampians.

RATING	WINE	REGION
97	2011 Grosset Polish Hill	Clare Valley
97	2011 Wines by KT Melva Wild Fermented	Clare Valley
97	2011 Best's Great Western	Grampians
97	2011 Seppelt Drumborg Vineyard	Grampians
97	2011 Crawford River	Henty
97	2006 Pressing Matters R9	Southern Tasmania
96	2011 Clonakilla	Canberra District
96	2011 Gallagher	Canberra District
96	2011 Atlas 172° Watervale	Clare Valley
96	2007 Leasingham Classic Clare	Clare Valley
96	2001 Taylors Bottle Aged St Andrews	Clare Valley
96	2011 Henschke Julius	Eden Valley
96	2011 Rolf Binder Veritas	Eden Valley
96	2011 Seppeltsfield	Eden Valley
96	2011 Tim Smith	Eden Valley
96	2011 Frankland Estate Netley Road Vineyard	Frankland River
96	2011 Howard Park Porongurup	Great Southern
96	2011 Castle Rock Estate	Great Southern
96	2011 Duke's Vineyard Magpie Hill Reserve	Great Southern
96	2011 Duke's Vineyard Porongurup	Great Southern
96	2011 Larry Cherubino Cherubino Porongurup	Great Southern
96	2011 Bay of Fires	Northern Tasmania
96	2009 Hardys HRB	Pemberton/ Adelaide Hills
96	2011 Leo Buring Leopold Derwent Valley	Tasmania
96	2010 Pressing Matters R9	Tasmania
96	2011 Stefano Lubiana	Tasmania
96	2011 Third Child Ella Mae	Tasmania

Chardonnay

Chardonnay is a marvellously flexible variety, performing well almost everywhere it is grown. But four regions stand apart, in alpha order, Adelaide Hills, Margaret River, Mornington Peninsula and Yarra Valley. It is strongly arguable modern Australian chardonnay is our best varietal wine.

RATING	WINE	REGION
98	2010 By Farr	Geelong
97	2010 Giaconda	Beechworth
97	2010 Marchand & Burch Porongurup	Great Southern
97	2009 Cullen Kevin John	Margaret River
97	2010 Cullen Kevin John	Margaret River
97	2009 Devil's Lair 9th Chamber	Margaret River
97	2009 Leeuwin Estate Art Series	Margaret River
97	2010 Xanadu Reserve	Margaret River
97	2010 Galli Estate Pamela	Sunbury
97	2010 Heemskerk Coal River Valley	Tasmania
96	2011 Casa Freschi Altezza	Adelaide Hills
96	2010 Grosset Piccadilly	Adelaide Hills
96	2010 Penfolds Reserve Bin A	Adelaide Hills
96	2009 Penfolds Yattarna	cool climate blend
96	2009 Petaluma Tiers Piccadilly Valley	Adelaide Hills
96	2010 Shaw & Smith M3	Adelaide Hills
96	2009 Yalumba FDW[7c]	Adelaide Hills
96	2009 Tomboy Hill Ruby's Picking Goldfields	Ballarat
96	2010 A. Rodda	Beechworth
96	2010 Hardys Eileen Hardy	Cool climate blend
96	2009 Heggies Reserve	Eden Valley
96	2009 Lethbridge Allegra Geelong	Geelong
96	2010 Willow Bridge Estate	Geographe
96	2011 Marchand & Burch Porongurup	Great Southern
96	2011 Penfolds Bin 311	Henty
96	2010 First Creek Winemaker's Reserve	Hunter Valley
96	2010 Brookland Valley Reserve	Margaret River
96	2010 Cape Mentelle	Margaret River
96	2010 Flametree	Margaret River
96	2010 Flametree S.R.S.	Margaret River
96	2010 Lenton Brae Wilyabrup	Margaret River
96	2010 Robert Oatley Finisterre	Margaret River
96	2010 Stella Bella Serie Luminosa	Margaret River
96	2010 Streicker Ironstone Block Old Vine	Margaret River
96	2009 Victory Point	Margaret River
96	2009 Voyager Estate	Margaret River
96	2010 Dexter	Mornington Peninsula

96	2009 Montalto Vineyards The Eleven	Mornington Peninsula
96	2010 Yabby Lake Vineyard Block 6	Mornington Peninsula
96	2010 Yabby Lake Vineyard Single Vineyard	Mornington Peninsula
96	2010 Bellarmine Pemberton	Pemberton
96	2010 Dawson & James	Tasmania
96	2008 Stefano Lubiana Collina	Tasmania
96	2010 Barwang 842	Tumbarumba
96	2011 Clonakilla	Tumbarumba/ Canberra District
96	2010 Bird on a Wire	Yarra Valley
96	2010 Domaine Chandon Yarra	Yarra Valley
96	2010 Giant Steps Tarraford Vineyard	Yarra Valley
96	2010 Hoddles Creek Estate 1er	Yarra Valley
96	2011 Oakridge 864 Charlie's Block J&J D'Aloisio Vineyard	Yarra Valley
96	2010 Seville Estate Reserve	Yarra Valley
96	2010 Seville Estate	Yarra Valley
96	2010 Toolangi Vineyards Estate	Yarra Valley
96	2011 YarraLoch	Yarra Valley
96	2010 Yering Station Reserve	Yarra Valley

95 points

2009 Bannockburn, 2009 Barwang 842, 2010 Bird in Hand Nest Egg, 2011 Brookland Valley, 2009 Brown Brothers Patricia, 2009 Cannibal Creek, 2011 Castelli Estate, 2010 Centennial Single Vineyard Reserve, 2010 Chalice Bridge The Chalice Limited Release, 2010 Chapman Grove Atticus, 2010 Charles Sturt University Cellar Reserve Tumbarumba, 2010 Clairault Estate, 2010 Coldstream Hills Deer Farm Vineyard, 2010 Cowaramup Reserve Limited Edition, 2010 David Franz Brother's Ilk, 2010 Devil's Lair, 2010 Dorrien Estate Bin 1A, 2010 Evoi Reserve, 2010 Forest Hill Block 8, 2011 Fraser Gallop Estate, 2010 Freycinet, 2008 Gembrook Hill, 2010 Geoff Weaver, 2010 Giant Steps Sexton Vineyard, 2009 Hoddles Creek, 2010 Hoddles Creek, 2010 Kooyong Farrago, 2011 Lenton Brae Southside, 2010 Marq Wild Ferment, 2010 Merum Estate Premium Reserve, 2010 Montalto Estate, 2010 Montgomery's Hill The Mulberry Block Reserve, 2010 Moorooduc Estate The Moorooduc, 2010 Moss Wood, 2010 Mountadam High Eden Estate, 2011 Oakridge 864 Drive Block Funder & Diamond Vineyard, 2011 Oakridge Local Barkala Ridge Vineyard, 2011 Oakridge Denton Vineyard, 2011 Oakridge Guerin Vineyard, 2011 Oakridge Lusatia Park Vineyard, 2010 Pierro, 2010 Pike & Joyce, 2010 Polperro Mill Hill, 2010 Port Phillip Estate, 2010 Punch Lance's Vineyard, 2010 Punters Corner, 2010 Riversdale Estate Crater, 2011 Sandalford Prendiville Reserve, 2010 Shelmerdine, 2010 Spence, 2010 Staniford Wine Co. Reserve, 2009 Stonier KBS Vineyard, 2010 Ten Minutes by Tractor McCutcheon, 2010 Ten Minutes by Tractor Wallis, 2010 Treasury Wine Estates Abel's Tempest, 2010 Tuck's Ridge Buckle, 2010 Tuck's Ridge Turramurra, 2010 Vasse Felix, 2010 Warner Glen Estate, 2007 Wolf Blass White Label Specially Aged Release, 2010 Woodlands Chloe Reserve, 2010 Xanadu Stevens Road.

Semillon

Little needs to be said, except to repeat Bruce Tyrrell's comment on the impact of screwcaps: 'Hunter Valley semillon is entering a golden age.' These wines are all screw–capped, and span 2002 to 2011; I strongly suspect they will easily see out 20 years, the best 50 years.

RATING	WINE	REGION
97	2005 Audrey Wilkinson Museum Reserve	Hunter Valley
97	2006 McGuigan Bin Series No. 9000	Hunter Valley
97	2011 Pepper Tree Alluvius Single Vineyard Reserve	Hunter Valley
97	2002 Thomas Cellar Reserve Braemore	Hunter Valley
97	2005 Warraroong Estate Warraroong Estate	Hunter Valley
96	2011 Bimbadgen Signature	Hunter Valley
96	2006 Brokenwood ILR Reserve	Hunter Valley
96	2005 Chateau Francois Pokolbin	Hunter Valley
96	2006 Margan Family Aged Release	Hunter Valley
96	2007 Margan Family Aged Release	Hunter Valley
96	2011 McLeish Estate	Hunter Valley
96	2007 McWilliam's Mount Pleasant Lovedale	Hunter Valley
96	2007 Meerea Park Alexander Munro	Hunter Valley
96	2011 Pepper Tree Tallawanta Limited Release	Hunter Valley
96	2007 Thomas Cellar Reserve Braemore	Hunter Valley
96	2011 Tower Estate Coombe Rise Vineyard	Hunter Valley
96	2011 Two Rivers Stones Throw	Hunter Valley
96	2007 Tyrrell's Futures Selection	Hunter Valley
96	2011 Tyrrell's Johnno's Basket Pressed	Hunter Valley
96	2006 Tyrrell's Museum Release Vat 1	Hunter Valley
96	2011 Tyrrell's Vat 1	Hunter Valley
96	2006 Warraroong Estate	Hunter Valley

Sauvignon Blanc

Sauvignon blanc has held its ground as the waves of Marlborough Sauvignon Blanc continue to flood the market. Happily, Australia has stuck to its knitting, producing wines that have structure, and do not seek to emulate the Marlborough style. This variety is not going to go away any time soon. Adelaide Hills leads Margaret River at the head of the pack.

RATING	WINE	REGION
96	2011 SC Pannell	Adelaide Hills
96	2011 Shaw & Smith	Adelaide Hills
96	2011 Larry Cherubino Cherubino	Pemberton
95	2011 Willoughby Park	Great Southern
95	2011 Millbrook Winery	Margaret River

95	2011 Belgravia Vineyards	Orange
95	2011 Limbic	Port Phillip Zone
95	2009 Domaine A Lady A Sauvignon Blanc	Tasmania

Sauvignon Semillon Blends

If there is to be a challenge to the monopoly the Hunter Valley has with semillon, it is Margaret River's hold on sauvignon/semillon blends. The maritime climate replicates that of Bordeaux, the Old World home of the blend (the percentage of muscadelle is rapidly decreasing in Bordeaux).

RATING	WINE	REGION
96	2011 Harewood Estate Reserve Semillon Sauvignon Blanc	Great Southern
96	2009 Cape Mentelle Wallcliffe Sauvignon Blanc Semillon	Margaret River
96	2010 Cape Mentelle Wallcliffe Sauvignon Blanc Semillon	Margaret River
96	2011 Cullen Vineyard Sauvignon Blanc Semillon	Margaret River
96	2011 Fraser Gallop Estate Semillon Sauvignon Blanc	Margaret River
96	2007 Suckfizzle Sauvignon Blanc Semillon	Margaret River
96	2008 Suckfizzle Sauvignon Blanc Semillon	Margaret River
96	2011 Vasse Felix Sauvignon Blanc Semillon	Margaret River
95	2011 Grosset Semillon Sauvignon Blanc	Clare Valley/ Adelaide Hills
95	2011 Harewood Estate Sauvignon Blanc Semillon	Great Southern
95	2011 Cape Mentelle Sauvignon Blanc Semillon	Margaret River
95	2011 Cullen Mangan Vineyard Sauvignon Blanc Semillon	Margaret River
95	2011 Lenton Brae Wilyabrup Semillon Sauvignon Blanc	Margaret River
95	2011 Moss Wood Ribbon Vale Semillon Sauvignon Blanc	Margaret River
95	2011 Pierro LTC Semillon Sauvignon Blanc	Margaret River
95	2011 Sandalford Estate Reserve Sauvignon Blanc Semillon	Margaret River
95	2011 Wise Margaret River Sauvignon Blanc Semillon	Pemberton
95	2011 Larry Cherubino The Yard Pedestal Vineyard Semillon Sauvignon Blanc	Western Australia

Other White Wines and blends

This group of wines shows that the 'alternative' varieties' Charge of the Light Brigade is yet to inflict many casualties on viognier, pinot gris, marsanne and gewurztraminer. The cause of the newer alternatives was not helped by the embarrassing discovery that the CSIRO-supplied albarino is in fact savagnin, a gewurztraminer clone grown in the Jura region of France. It is true that the 42 wines that received 94 points do take in a much broader range of varieties.

RATING	WINE	REGION
96	2010 Yalumba The Virgilius Viognier	Eden Valley
96	2002 Tahbilk 1927 Vines Marsanne	Nagambie Lakes
95	2011 Riposte The Stiletto Pinot Gris	Adelaide Hills

95	2011 Clonakilla Viognier	Canberra District
95	2011 Rymill GT Gewurztraminer	Coonawarra
95	2011 Casa Freschi La Signorina	Langhorne Creek
95	2011 Paradigm Hill Pinot Gris	Mornington Peninsula
95	2011 Scorpo Pinot Gris	Mornington Peninsula
95	2011 Yabby Lake Vineyard Pinot Gris	Mornington Peninsula
95	2011 Bay of Fires Pinot Gris	Northern Tasmania

Sparkling

The best sparkling wines are now solely sourced either from Tasmania or from the coolest sites in the southern parts of the mainland, with altitude playing a major role. They are all fermented in the bottle, and the best have had extended lees contact prior to disgorgement, giving them great complexity.

White and rose

RATING	WINE	REGION
97	2001 Freycinet Radenti Chardonnay Pinot Noir	Tasmania
96	2001 Arras Blanc de Blanc	Tasmania
96	NV Arras Brut Elite Chardonnay Pinot Noir	Tasmania
96	2000 Arras EJ Carr Late Disgorged	Tasmania
96	1996 Domaine Chandon Prestige Cuvee	Yarra Valley
96	2004 Yarrabank Late Disgorged	Yarra Valley
95	2009 Romney Park Blanc de Blancs	Adelaide Hills
95	2006 Brown Brothers Patricia Pinot Noir Chardonnay Brut	King Valley
95	2004 Mount William	Macedon Ranges
95	2006 Jansz Premium Vintage Cuvee	Tasmania
95	2008 Mitchell Harris Sabre	Pyrenees
95	NV Centennial Vineyards Blanc de Blancs	Southern Highlands
95	2008 Domaine Chandon Tasmanian Cuvee	Tasmania
95	2007 Heemskerk Coal River Valley Chardonnay Pinot Noir	Tasmania
95	2008 Domaine Chandon Blanc de Blancs	Yarra Valley
95	2007 Domaine Chandon Blanc de Noirs	Yarra Valley
95	2008 Domaine Chandon Brut Rose Vintage	Yarra Valley
95	2007 Yarrabank Cuvee	Yarra Valley
95	2008 Yarrabank Cuvee	Yarra Valley

Sparkling red

A tiny group of wines, eagerly sought by the small percentage of wine drinkers who understand the peculiarities of the style and who, better still, are prepared to cellar them for a year or more, the longer the better.

RATING	WINE	REGION
95	NV Rockford Black Shiraz	Barossa Valley
95	NV Primo Estate Joseph Sparkling Red	McLaren Vale

94	2005 Barossa Valley Estate E&E Black Pepper Sparkling Shiraz	Barossa Valley
94	2007 Peter Lehmann Black Queen Sparkling Shiraz	Barossa Valley
94	2006 Teusner MC Sparkling Shiraz	Barossa Valley
94	NV Turkey Flat Sparkling Shiraz	Barossa Valley
94	NV Buller Family Reserve Reginald Langdon Buller Sparkling Shiraz	Rutherglen

Sweet
Riesling

Tasmania may have been under-represented in the dry riesling group, but it comes into its own here: from gently sweet Kabinett styles through to Auslese-equivalent or above, its truly cool climate gives the wines tremendous zest and length to the piercing lime-accented flavours of riesling.

RATING	WINE	REGION
96	2011 Grosset Noble Riesling	Clare Valley
96	2008 Brown Brothers Patricia Noble Riesling	King Valley
96	2010 Frogmore Creek FGR Riesling	Tasmania
96	2011 Oakridge Limited Release Riesling	Yarra Valley
95	2011 Clonakilla Riesling Auslese	Canberra District
95	2011 Heggies Vineyard Botrytis Riesling	Eden Valley
95	2011 Bellarmine Riesling Select	Pemberton
95	2011 Frogmore Creek FGR Riesling	Tasmania
95	2009 Josef Chromy Botrytis Riesling	Tasmania
95	2011 Pressing Matters R69 Riesling	Tasmania
95	2010 Pressing Matters R69 Riesling	Tasmania
94	2010 Bress Gold Chook The Kindest Cut Riesling	Bendigo
94	2011 Lerida Estate Lake George Botrytis Pinot Gris	Canberra District
94	2011 Mount Horrocks Cordon Cut Riesling	Clare Valley
94	2010 Plantagenet Wyjup Vineyard Ringbark Riesling	Mount Barker
94	2009 Tertini Reserve Noble Riesling	Southern Highlands
94	2009 Home Hill Kelly's Reserve Late Harvest Sticky	Tasmania
94	2010 Milton Vineyard Iced Riesling	Tasmania
94	2010 Moores Hill Estate CGR Late Harvest Riesling	Tasmania
94	2011 Pooley Late Harvest Riesling	Tasmania

Semillon and others

It makes no sense to put the semillons into the same group as the rieslings and other varieties. Altogether different dynamics are in play with the semillon, which largely come from the Riverland; these are barrel-feremented, highly botrytised wines with vanilla bean, peaches and cream, crème brulee, apricot or cumquat flavours – take your pick.

RATING	WINE	REGION
95	2008 Rymill Coonawarra June Traminer	Coonawarra
95	2008 McGuigan Miranda Golden Botrytis	Hunter Valley
95	2010 Lillypilly Estate Family Reserve Noble Blend	Riverina
95	2010 Westend Estate 3 Bridges Golden Mist Botrytis	Riverina
95	2011 Terre à Terre Botrytis	Wrattonbully
94	2011 Riposte Reserve Noble 'Traminer	Adelaide Hills
94	2010 Crawford River Serendipitous Selection	Henty
94	2010 Brown Brothers Noble Chardonnay	King Valley
94	2010 Hand Crafted by Geoff Hardy Botrytis Noble Intent	Limestone Coast
94	2007 di Lusso Estate Passito	Mudgee
94	2011 Cargo Road Five Rows Botrytis Gewurztraminer	Orange
94	2009 McWilliam's Morning Light Botrytis Semillon	Riverina
94	2010 Barambah First Grid Rack Dried Semillon	South Burnett
94	2010 Frogmore Creek Iced Gewurztraminer	Tasmania
94	2010 Delatite Catherine Gewurztraminer	Upper Goulburn

Rose

The number of roses on the market continues to grow, seemingly unabated and unstoppable. There are no rules: they can be bone-dry, slightly sweet, or very sweet. They can be and are made from almost any red variety, red blends or red and white blends. They may be a convenient way of concentrating the red wine left after the rose is run off (bleeding or saignee) from the fermenter shortly after the grapes are crushed, or made from the ground up using grapes and techniques specifically chosen for the purpose. The vast majority fall in the former camp; those listed mainly come from the latter.

RATING	WINE	REGION
96	2010 Ashton Hills Armen and Benen Pinot Noir Saignee	Adelaide Hills
95	2011 Willow Bridge Estate Madam Dragonfly Rose	Geographe
95	2011 Dandelion Vineyards Fairytale of the Barossa Rose	Barossa Valley
94	2011 Charles Melton Rose of Virginia	Barossa Valley
94	2011 Spinifex Rose	Barossa Valley
94	2011 Turkey Flat Rose	Barossa Valley
94	2011 Foster e Rocco Rose	Heathcote
94	2011 Walter Clappis The Hedonist Sangiovese Rose	McLaren Vale
95	2011 Greedy Sheep Rose	Margaret River

94	2011 Sandalford Rose	Margaret River
94	2011 Tuck's Ridge Pinot Rose	Mornington Peninsula
94	2011 Domaine Chandon Pinot Noir Rose	Yarra Valley

Pinot Noir

The three regions that produce 90% of Australia's best Pinot Noirs are (in alpha order) the Mornington Peninsula, Tasmania and Yarra Valley. Tasmania is under–represented in the following list, partly because their points mainly come from the most contested battleground of all, the Tasmanian Wine Show.

RATING	WINE	REGION
97	2010 Ashton Hills Reserve	Adelaide Hills
97	2009 Paringa Estate The Paringa	Mornington Peninsula
97	2010 Scorpo	Mornington Peninsula
97	2009 Ten Minutes by Tractor 10X	Mornington Peninsula
97	2010 Tuck's Ridge Buckle	Mornington Peninsula
97	2010 Yabby Lake Vineyard Block 6	Mornington Peninsula
97	2010 Yabby Lake Vineyard Single Block Release Block 2	Mornington Peninsula
97	2010 Hillcrest Vineyard Premium	Yarra Valley
97	2010 Mayer Close Planted	Yarra Valley
96	2010 Tomboy Hill The Tomboy Goldfields	Ballarat
96	2010 Freycinet	East Coast Tasmania
96	2010 Farr Rising	Geelong
96	2010 Farrside by Farr	Geelong
96	2009 Curly Flat	Macedon Ranges
96	2010 Kooyong Single Vineyard Selection Haven	Mornington Peninsula
96	2010 Paringa Estate Estate	Mornington Peninsula
96	2010 Ten Minutes by Tractor Judd Vineyard	Mornington Peninsula
96	2010 Ten Minutes by Tractor McCutcheon	Mornington Peninsula
96	2010 Yabby Lake Vineyard Single Vineyard	Mornington Peninsula
96	2010 Dawson & James	Tasmania
96	2010 Stoney Rise Holyman	Tasmania
96	2010 Tower Estate Panorama Vineyard Tasmania	Tasmania
96	2010 De Bortoli Riorret The Abbey	Yarra Valley
96	2010 Giant Steps Sexton Vineyard	Yarra Valley
96	2010 PHI Single Vineyard	Yarra Valley
96	2010 Punch Lance's Close Planted	Yarra Valley
96	2010 Serrat	Yarra Valley
96	2010 The Wanderer Upper	Yarra Valley
96	2010 Yering Station Reserve	Yarra Valley

Shiraz

The number of wines receiving 96 points or more may seem extreme, but in fact expressed as a percentage of the total number of wines tasted, it is no greater than that for riesling, semillon and chardonnay. Moreover, there is tremendous diversity of style from the resurgent Hunter Valley, thence through the whole of Victoria, most of South Australia and thence to the southwest of Western Australia. Finally, the 2010 vintage was exceptional in almost all regions, '09 more than useful in most.

RATING	WINE	REGION
97	2009 Kaesler Old Bastard	Barossa Valley
97	2009 Penfolds RWT	Barossa Valley
97	2006 Torbreck The Laird	Barossa Valley
97	2010 Turkey Flat	Barossa Valley
97	2010 Clonakilla Murrumbateman Syrah	Canberra District
97	2010 Best's Thomson Family	Grampians
97	2009 Moppity Vineyards Reserve	Hilltops
97	2010 Tyrrell's Vat 9 Hunter	Hunter Valley
97	2010 Pepper Tree Random Acts of Winemaking	Hunter Valley/ Grampians
97	2006 Tahbilk 1860 Vines	Nagambie Lakes
97	2010 Seville Estate Dr McMahon	Yarra Valley
96	2010 Atlas 516°	Barossa Valley
96	2010 BK Cult Single Vineyard Lobethal Syrah	Adelaide Hills
96	2009 Scott	Adelaide Hills
96	2010 Shaw & Smith	Adelaide Hills
96	2010 Patritti JPB Single Vineyard	Adelaide Zone
96	2009 Dutschke Oscar Semmler	Barossa Valley
96	2010 Elderton Neil Ashmead Grand Tourer	Barossa Valley
96	2009 Glen Eldon Black Lady	Barossa Valley
96	2010 Head The Contrarian Single Vineyard Greenock Syrah	Barossa Valley
96	2010 Hentley Farm Clos Otto	Barossa Valley
96	2010 Hentley Farm The Beauty	Barossa Valley
96	2009 Kalleske Eduard Old Vine	Barossa Valley
96	2009 Kalleske Johann Georg Old Vine Single Vineyard	Barossa Valley
96	2009 Kilikanoon R	Barossa Valley
96	2008 Laughing Jack Limited Two	Barossa Valley
96	2008 Laughing Jack Moppa Block	Barossa Valley
96	2010 Linfield Road Stubborn Patriarch Single Vineyard	Barossa Valley
96	2008 Peter Lehmann Stonewell	Barossa Valley
96	2008 Ross Estate JDR	Barossa Valley
96	2009 St Hallett Old Block Barossa	Barossa Valley
96	2009 Smidge Magic Dirt Greenock	Barossa Valley
96	2010 Smidge Magic Dirt Stonewell	Barossa Valley

96	2008 Teusner Righteous FG	Barossa Valley
96	2010 Teusner The Riebke	Barossa Valley
96	2009 Tim Smith	Barossa Valley
96	2010 Torbreck The Gask	Barossa Valley
96	2009 Tower Estate Horse Paddock Vineyard	Barossa Valley
96	2005 Trevor Jones JP Belle-Terroir	Barossa Valley
96	2008 Turkey Flat Single Vineyard The Conqueror	Barossa Valley
96	2009 Turkey Flat Single Vineyard The Conqueror	Barossa Valley
96	2009 Turkey Flat Single Vineyard The Twist	Barossa Valley
96	2009 Westlake Vineyards Eleazar	Barossa Valley
96	2009 Wolf Blass Platinum Label	Barossa Valley
96	2010 Bendigo Wine Estate Gold Nugget	Bendigo
96	2010 Atlas 429°	Clare Valley
96	2009 Kilikanoon Attunga 1865	Clare Valley
96	2009 Kilikanoon Oracle	Clare Valley
96	2009 Wynns Estate Michael Limited Release	Coonawarra
96	2009 Sons of Eden Remus Old Vine	Eden Valley
96	2009 Maverick Old Ben	Eden Valley
96	2007 Henschke Hill Of Grace	Eden Valley
96	2009 Henschke Mount Edelstone	Eden Valley
96	2006 Hutton Vale Vineyard	Eden Valley
96	2010 Paradise IV Moorabool Estate Dardel	Geelong
96	2010 Willow Bridge Estate Black Dog Geographe	Geographe
96	2010 Clayfield Grampians	Grampians
96	2009 Mount Langi Ghiran Cliff Edge	Grampians
96	2010 The Story Henty Estate Vineyard	Grampians
96	2010 Boireann Granite Belt	Granite Belt
96	2010 Larry Cherubino Cherubino Frankland River	Great Southern
96	2010 Graillot Syrah	Heathcote
96	2009 Heathcote Estate Single Block Release Block F	Heathcote
96	2009 Munari Black Lady	Heathcote
96	2010 Paul Osicka Moormbool Reserve	Heathcote
96	2010 Audrey Wilkinson The Lake	Hunter Valley
96	2010 Audrey Wilkinson Selection	Hunter Valley
96	2009 Chateau Pâto Old Pokolbin Vineyard	Hunter Valley
96	2006 Drayton's Family William	Hunter Valley
96	2010 Lambloch Estate The Loch	Hunter Valley
96	2009 Lambloch Estate The Loch	Hunter Valley
96	2010 McWilliam's Mount Pleasant Maurice O'Shea	Hunter Valley
96	2010 Pepper Tree Single Vineyard Reserve Coquun	Hunter Valley
96	2010 Tyrrell's Johnno's	Hunter Valley
96	2010 Tyrrell's Single Vineyard Old Patch 1867	Hunter Valley
96	2008 Antipodean Vintners Tilly Devine	McLaren Vale
96	2009 Angove Warboys Vineyard	McLaren Vale

96	2010 Angove Warboys Vineyard	McLaren Vale
96	2009 Clarendon Hills Astralis	McLaren Vale
96	2009 Clarendon Hills Brookman Clarendon Syrah	McLaren Vale
96	2009 Clarendon Hills Piggot Range Clarendon Syrah	McLaren Vale
96	2008 Gemtree Vineyards Obsidian	McLaren Vale
96	2004 Geoff Merrill Henley	McLaren Vale
96	2007 Hardys Eileen Hardy	McLaren Vale
96	2009 Hewitson The Mad Hatter	McLaren Vale
96	2009 Kangarilla Road Scarce Earth Project	McLaren Vale
96	2010 Marius Symphony Single Vineyard	McLaren Vale
96	2005 Reynella Cellar No. One Reserve	McLaren Vale
96	2010 Richard Hamilton Centurion Old Vine	McLaren Vale
96	2008 SC Pannell	McLaren Vale
96	2008 Tintara	McLaren Vale
96	2010 Wirra Wirra RSW	McLaren Vale
96	2010 Cape Mentelle	Margaret River
96	2009 Churchview The Bartondale Reserve	Margaret River
96	2010 Deep Woods Block 7	Margaret River
96	2010 Voyager Estate	Margaret River
96	2010 Paradigm Hill Col's Block	Mornington Peninsula
96	2008 Paringa Estate The Paringa Single Vineyard	Mornington Peninsula
96	2009 Huntington Estate Special Reserve	Mudgee
96	2006 Tahbilk Eric Stevens Purbrick	Nagambie Lakes
96	2010 Printhie MCC	Orange
96	2010 Dalwhinnie Moonambel	Pyrenees
96	2010 Dalwhinnie Southwest Rocks	Pyrenees
96	2010 Dalwhinnie The Pinnacle	Pyrenees
96	2010 Ochota Barrels The Shellac Vineyard Syrah	Various SA
96	2010 Giant Steps/Innocent Bystander Mea Culpa	Yarra Valley
96	2010 Luke Lambert Reserve Syrah	Yarra Valley
96	2010 Oakridge 864 Single Block Release Winery Block Syrah	Yarra Valley
96	2010 Seville Estate Old Vine Reserve	Yarra Valley

95 points

2010 A.T. Richardson Chockstone, 2010 Amelia Park Reserve, 2009 Angove The Medhyk, 2009 Anvers The Warrior, 2009 Atlas 429°, 2009 Atlas 516°, 2007 Bannockburn, 2010 Bellarmine, 2009 Best's Bin No. 0, 2010 Best's Bin No. 0, 2009 Bird in Hand Nest Egg, 2010 Bird on a Wire Syrah, 2009 BlackJack Vineyards Block 6, 2010 Bleasdale The Powder Monkey, 2010 Bress Le Grand Coq Noir, 2008 Brown Brothers Patricia, 2010 Farr Rising, 2010 Cape Barren Native Goose, 2009 Cardinham Estate The Stradbrooke, 2009 Chain of Ponds The Ledge, 2010 Chapel Hill The Chosen House Block, 2010 Chapel Hill The Vicar, 2009 Charles Cimicky The Autograph, 2010 Chateau Pâto DJP, 2010 Chateau Tanunda Terroirs of the Barossa Ebenezer District, 2010 Chateau Tanunda Terroirs of the Barossa Greenock, 2009 Chateau Tanunda The Chateau 100 Year Old Vines, 2010 Chateau Tanunda The Chateau Single Vineyard, 2010 Chatsfield, 2010 Churchview Estate The Bartondale Reserve, 2009 Clarendon Hills Domaine Clarendon Syrah, 2009 Clarendon Hills

Hickinbotham Clarendon Syrah, 2009 Clarendon Hills Onkaparinga Clarendon Syrah, 2008 Clarnette & Ludvigsen, 2009 Clayfield, 2010 Clayfield Massif, 2010 Clayfield Moyston, 2010 Claymore Dark Side of the Moon, 2008 Clyde Park Reserve, 2010 Coldstream Hills Reserve Yarra Valley, 2004 David Franz Benjamin's Promise Cellar Release, 2010 De Iuliis, 2009 De Iuliis Limited Release, 2010 Dominique Portet, 2009 Dorrien Estate Bin 1, 2008 Downing Estate Reserve, 2009 Dutschke St Jakobi Single Vineyard, 2008 Echelon Zeppelin Ferdinand, 2010 Eden Road Gundagai, 2010 Eden Road Hilltops, 2009 Enigma Variations Syrah, 2010 Epsilon 1994 Greenock, 2010 First Creek Winemaker's Reserve, 2009 First Drop Fat of the Land Ebenezer, 2009 First Drop Fat of the Land Seppeltsfield, 2009 First Drop The Cream, 2008 Forest Hill Block 9, 2009 Fox Gordon Hannah's Swing, 2010 Foxeys Hangout, 2010 Gemtree Uncut, 2008 Gibson Reserve, 2010 Glaetzer Amon-Ra, 2006 Glenguin Aristea, 2008 Gralyn Reserve, 2009 Greenstone, 2010 Head The Brunette Syrah, 2010 Heathcote Estate, 2010 Hentley Farm The Beast, 2009 Honey Moon Vineyard, 2010 Hugh Hamilton The Original Church Block, 2006 Huntington Estate Signature Tim Stevens, 2009 Jim Barry The Armagh, 2009 John Duval Eligo, 2009 John Duval Entity, 2009 Kaesler, 2010 Kangarilla Road Vineyard Scarce Earth Project, 2009 Kay Brothers Amery Vineyards Block 6, 2009 Kilikanoon Attunga 1865, 2009 Kilikanoon M, 2010 Landhaus Estate Classics, 2006 Landhaus Estate Rare, 2008 Landhaus Estate Rare, 2010 Larry Cherubino The Yard Riversdale Vineyard, 2008 Leasingham Classic Clare, 2010 Leconfield, 2010 Leogate Estate Reserve, 2009 Magpie Estate The Election, 2010 Mandala, 2007 Margan Family Aged Release, 2009 Margan Family Limited Release, 2009 Massena The Eleventh Hour, 2009 Maverick Greenock Rise, 2008 Maverick Trial Hill, 2009 Mayford Porepunkah, 2010 McWilliam's Mount Pleasant Original Vineyard OP&OH, 2010 Merum Premium Reserve, 2009 Michael Hall Stonewell Valley, 2009 Mitolo Savitar, 2010 Montalto Pennon Hill, 2008 Mount Langi Ghiran Moyston Hills Vineyard, 2008 Mount Langi Ghiran Nowhere Creek, 2009 Mountadam Patriarch, 2009 Munari Ladys Pass, 2009 Murray Street Black Label, 2010 Norton Estate Wendy's Dedication, 2010 Oakdene William, 2010 Oakridge Local Vineyard Series Whitsend & Oakridge, 2010 Palmarium Exemplar, 2010 Patritti Lot 3, 2010 Paul Osicka Majors Creek Vineyard, 2007 Penfolds Grange, 2009 Penfolds Magill Estate, 2010 Penny's Hill Cracking Black, 2010 Pepper Tree Tallavera, 2009 Pertaringa Over The Top, 2009 Peter Lehmann VSV Orrock, 2010 Pfeiffer, 2009 Pikes The EWP Reserve, 2009 Pokolbin Estate Limited Release Reserve, 2009 Poole's Rock, 2009 Primo Estate Joseph Angel Gully, 2009 Purple Hands, 2010 Radford Bio-Dynamically Grown, 2009 Red Edge Degree, 2009 Red Edge, 2009 Reynella, 2011 Robert Oatley Finisterre, 2010 Robert Stein Reserve, 2009 Rockford Basket Press, 2010 Salo Hawke's Bay Syrah, 2010 Samuel's Gorge, 2009 Schwarz The Schiller, 2008 Scorpiiion The Scorpiiion, 2010 Shadowfax Pink Cliffs, 2010 Shingleback D Block Reserve, 2009 Smidge Magic Dirt Moppa, 2010 St Hallett Garden of Eden, 2010 St Hallett Dawkins, 2010 St Hallett Materne, 2010 St Hallett Mattschoss, 2010 St Hallett Scholz, 2009 Summerfield Jo, 2010 Summerfield Reserve, 2010 Tallavera Grove Carillion The Feldspars Orange, 2010 Tallavera Grove Fenestella, 2010 Taylors St Andrews Old Block, 2009 Teusner Albert, 2009 The Lane Vineyard Reunion, 2010 The Story Garden Gully Vineyard, 2010 The Story Rice's Vineyard, 2010 The Wanderer, 2010 Thomas Kiss Limited Release, 2010 Tim Smith, 2009 Torbreck RunRig, 2004 Trevor Jones JP Belle-Terroir, 2002 Trevor Jones JP Belle-Terroir, 2009 Turkey Flat The Conqueror, 2008 Turkey Flat The Great, 2009 Turkey Flat The Great , 2008 Were Estate The Moorabbin, 2009 Westlake 717 Convicts The Warden, 2009 WineSA Kalimna, 2009 Woodstock The Stocks, 2009 Wynns Coonawarra Estate V&A Lane Selected Vineyards, 2010 Wynns Coonawarra Estate V&A Lane Selected Vineyards, 2009 Xanadu, 2007 Yalumba Craneford, 2007 Yalumba Spring Gully, 2010 Yering Station Old Beenak Road.

Shiraz Viognier

In best Australian Tall Poppy Syndrome fashion, it has already become fashionable in some quarters to challenge the remarkable synergy obtained by co-fermenting around 5% of viognier with shiraz. When used in cool to temperate regions, the enhancement of colour, aroma and flavour is remarkable, as is the softening and smoothing of texture. It is not a panacea for lesser quality grapes, and yes, it is and should remain a subtext to the thrust of shiraz's flavour. Nonetheless, the wines in this group offer pleasure second to none.

RATING	WINE	REGION
96	2010 Head The Blonde Single Vineyard Stonewell	Barossa Valley
96	2008 Syrahmi La La	Heathcote
96	2010 Yering Station	Yarra Valley
95	2010 Turner's Crossing	Bendigo
95	2011 Clonakilla	Canberra District
95	2010 Serrat	Yarra Valley
95	2010 Yering Station Reserve	Yarra Valley

Cabernet Sauvignon

The affinity of cabernet sauvignon with a maritime climate is put beyond doubt by its home in Bordeaux's Medoc region. So it comes as no surprise to find that most (but not all) of Australia's top quality cabernets come from regions with climates similar to Bordeaux (conspicuously Coonawarra and Margaret River) and/or which are within 50 kms of the sea with no intervening mountain. The far greater number of Margaret River cabernet sauvignons is due to four excellent vintages from 2007 to '10 inclusive (and '11 and '12 to follow in the same vein when ready). Coonawarra has not had the same fortune.

RATING	WINE	REGION
97	2008 Penfolds Bin 169	Coonawarra
97	2008 Houghton Gladstones	Margaret River
97	2008 Stella Bella Serie Luminosa	Margaret River
96	2002 David Franz Georgie's Walk Cellar Release	Barossa Valley
96	2009 Grant Burge Corryton Park	Barossa Valley
96	2009 Bellwether	Coonawarra
96	2008 Jamiesons Run Mildara	Coonawarra
96	2009 Wynns Estate	Coonawarra
96	2009 Wynns Estate John Riddoch	Coonawarra
96	2009 Devil's Lair	Margaret River
96	2010 Hay Shed Hill	Margaret River
96	2007 Heydon Estate W.G. Grace Single Vineyard	Margaret River
96	2010 Houghton Wisdom	Margaret River
96	2010 Larry Cherubino Cherubino	Margaret River
96	2008 Moss Wood	Margaret River

96	2010 Pedestal Vineyard Elevation	Margaret River
96	2009 Robert Oatley Finisterre	Margaret River
96	2009 Stella Bella Serie Luminosa	Margaret River
96	2009 Woodlands Alma May	Margaret River
96	2010 Howard Park Abercrombie	Margaret River
96	2010 Chalk Hill Alpha Crucis	McLaren Vale
96	2010 Wirra Wirra The Angelus	McLaren Vale
96	2006 Tahbilk Eric Stevens Purbrick	Nagambie Lakes
96	2009 Kerrigan + Berry	Mount Barker/ Margaret River
96	2010 Hillcrest Vineyard Premium	Yarra Valley
96	2010 Yering Station	Yarra Valley

Cabernet and Family

This group revolves around the grapes of Bordeaux, and primarily blends thereof, but with some single varieties most notably merlot, the majority from moderately cool regions, Margaret River once again the leader of the band. Also included are the classic Australian cabernet and shiraz (or vice versa) blends.

RATING	WINE	REGION
98	2008 Penfolds Bin 620 Cabernet Shiraz	Coonawarra
98	2008 Houghton Jack Mann Cabernet Sauvignon	Swan Valley
96	2009 Yalumba FDR1A Cabernet Sauvignon Shiraz	Barossa
96	2009 Grosset Gaia	Clare Valley
96	2009 Primo Estate Joseph Moda Cabernet Sauvignon Merlot	McLaren Vale
96	2009 Cape Mentelle Trinders Cabernet Merlot	Margaret River
96	2009 Cape Mentelle Wilyabrup	Margaret River
96	2010 Cullen Diana Madeline	Margaret River
96	2008 Voyager Estate Cabernet Sauvignon Merlot	Margaret River
96	2004 Harewood Estate Aged Release Cabernet Merlot	Mount Barker
96	2010 Belgravia Merlot	Orange
96	2008 McWilliam's 1877 Cabernet Sauvignon Shiraz	Riverina
96	2009 Yarra Yering Dry Red No. 3	Yarra Valley
95	2009 Penfolds Bin 389 Cabernet Shiraz	Barossa Valley
95	2008 Peter Lehmann Mentor Cabernet	Barossa Valley
95	2009 Thorn-Clarke Shotfire Quartage	Barossa Valley
95	2008 Wolf Blass Black Label Cabernet Sauvignon Shiraz Malbec	Barossa Valley
95	2010 Balnaves The Blend	Coonawarra
95	2009 Katnook Estate The Caledonian	Coonawarra
95	2010 Leconfield Petit Verdot	Coonawarra
95	2008 Parker Terra Rossa First Growth	Coonawarra
95	2009 Mountadam The Red	Eden Valley
95	2008 Yalumba The Signature Cabernet Shiraz	Barossa

95	2010 Briarose Estate Blackwood Cove	Margaret River
95	2009 Brookland Valley Cabernet Sauvignon Merlot	Margaret River
95	2009 Cape Mentelle Zinfandel	Margaret River
95	2009 Celestial Bay Zenith	Margaret River
95	2010 Credaro Family Estate Cabernet Merlot	Margaret River
95	2009 Cullen Diana Madeline	Margaret River
95	2007 Laurance Merlot	Margaret River
95	2010 Moss Brothers The Wilyabrup	Margaret River
95	2010 Pedestal Vineyard Cabernet Merlot	Margaret River
95	2009 Brangayne Tristan Cabernet Sauvignon Shiraz Merlot	Orange
95	2010 Pyren Vineyard Yardbird Union	Pyrenees
95	2010 All Saints Estate Durif	Rutherglen
95	2010 Larry Cherubino Ad Hoc Etcetera Cabernet Merlot	Margaret River
95	2009 Larry Cherubino Pedestal Cabernet Merlot	Margaret River
95	2010 Pepper Tree Single Vineyard Strandlines Grand Reserve Cabernet Shiraz	Wrattonbully
95	2010 Giant Steps Harry's Monster	Yarra Valley
95	2010 Hillcrest Vineyard Premium Merlot	Yarra Valley

Shiraz and Family

A South Australia stronghold, mostly with some or all of shiraz, grenache and mourvedre.

RATING	WINE	REGION
97	2009 Hewitson Private Cellar Shiraz Mourvedre	Barossa Valley
96	2009 Atlas Shiraz Mataro	Barossa Valley
96	2009 Hewitson Old Garden Mourvedre	Barossa Valley
96	2009 Chateau Tanunda The Everest Grenache	Barossa Valley
96	2009 Angove Warboys Vineyard Shiraz Grenache	McLaren Vale
96	2010 Angove Warboys Vineyard Shiraz Grenache	McLaren Vale
95	2010 Atlas Shiraz Mataro	Barossa Valley
95	2009 Charles Melton Richelieu	Barossa Valley
95	2010 Head Old Vine Single Vineyard Greenock Grenache	Barossa Valley
95	2010 Jacob's Creek St Hugo Grenache Shiraz Mataro	Barossa Valley
95	2010 Maverick Twins Grenache Shiraz Mourvedre	Barossa Valley
95	2010 Seppeltsfield GST Grenache Shiraz Touriga	Barossa Valley
95	2010 Seppeltsfield SGC Shiraz Grenache Carignan	Barossa Valley
95	2010 Teusner Joshua	Barossa Valley
95	2009 Yelland & Papps Divine Grenache	Barossa Valley
95	2010 Mount Majura TSG Tempranillo Shiraz Graciano	Canberra District
95	2010 PHI Single Vineyard Syrah Grenache	Heathcote
95	2009 Clarendon Hills Romas Clarendon Grenache	McLaren Vale
95	2010 Paxton AAA Shiraz Grenache	McLaren Vale

95	2008 SC Pannell Shiraz Grenache	McLaren Vale
95	2010 Willunga 100 Grenache	McLaren Vale
95	2010 Wirra Wirra The Absconder Grenache	McLaren Vale
95	2010 Angove Warboys Vineyard Grenache	McLaren Vale
95	2010 DogRock Degraves Road	Pyrenees

Other Reds

95	2010 Hahndorf Hill Blueblood Blaufrankisch	Adelaide Hills
95	2010 Nepenthe Tempranillo	Adelaide Hills
95	2010 Mayford Porepunkah Tempranillo	Alpine Valleys
94	2010 Hand Crafted by Geoff Hardy Teroldego	Adelaide
94	2009 First Drop Minchia Montepulciano	Adelaide Hills
94	2010 Massena Tannat	Barossa Valley
94	2008 Sons of Eden Stauros Old Vine Mourvedre	Barossa Valley
94	2010 Tim Smith Mataro	Barossa Valley
94	2010 Best's Old Vine Pinot Meunier	Grampians
94	2009 Buckshot Vineyard The Square Peg Zinfandel	Heathcote
94	2010 Greenstone Vineyard Colorino	Heathcote
94	2009 Red Edge Limited Edition Mataro	Heathcote
94	2008 Cobaw Ridge Lagrein	Macedon Ranges
94	2010 Cape Mentelle Zinfandel	Margaret River
94	2010 Woodlands Reserve de la Cave Cabernet Franc	Margaret River
94	2009 Xanadu Graciano	Margaret River
94	2010 Hugh Hamilton The Odd Ball Saperavi	McLaren Vale
94	2010 La Curio The Original Zin Primitivo	McLaren Vale
94	2010 Samuel's Gorge Mourvedre	McLaren Vale
94	2010 Yangarra Estate Vineyard Mourvedre	McLaren Vale
94	2009 Lowe Mudgee Zinfandel	Mudgee

Fortified Wines

A relatively small but absolutely sensational group of magnificent wines, as quintessentially Australian as a Drizabone, and of unique style.

RATING	WINE	REGION
100	1912 Seppeltsfield 100 Year Old Para Liqueur	Barossa Valley
98	NV Baileys Winemaker's Selection Old Muscat	Glenrowan
98	NV Bleasdale Fortis et Astutus Rare Liqueur Tawny	Langhorne Creek
98	NV All Saints Estate Rare Muscat	Rutherglen
98	NV Campbells Isabella Rare Topaque	Rutherglen
98	NV Chambers Rosewood Rare Muscadelle	Rutherglen
98	NV Pfeiffer Rare Muscat	Rutherglen
97	NV David Franz Old Redemption X.O. Tawny	Barossa Valley
97	NV Penfolds Grandfather Fine Old Liqueur Tawny	Barossa Valley
97	NV Penfolds Great Grandfather Limited Release Rare Tawny	Barossa Valley
97	NV Baileys Winemaker's Selection Rare Old Topaque	Glenrowan
97	NV All Saints Rare Topaque	Rutherglen
97	NV Campbells Merchant Prince Rare Muscat	Rutherglen
97	NV Morris Old Premium Liqueur Muscat	Rutherglen
97	NV Pfeiffer Grand Muscat	Rutherglen
97	NV Pfeiffer Rare Topaque	Rutherglen

Best wineries of the regions

The nomination of the best wineries of the regions has evolved into a three-level classification (further explained on page 10). At the very top are the wineries with their names and stars printed in red, these have been generally recognised for having a long track record of excellence – truly the best of the best. Next are wineries with their stars (but not their names) printed in red, and which have had a consistent record of excellence for at least the last three years. Those wineries with black stars have achieved excellence this year (and sometimes longer).

ADELAIDE HILLS
Ashton Hills ★★★★★
Barratt ★★★★★
Bird in Hand ★★★★★
Birdwood Estate ★★★★★
BK Wines ★★★★★
Chain of Ponds ★★★★★
Fox Gordon ★★★★★
Geoff Weaver ★★★★★
Honey Moon Vineyard ★★★★★
K1 by Geoff Hardy ★★★★★
La Linea ★★★★★
Mount Torrens Vineyards ★★★★★
Mt Lofty Ranges Vineyard ★★★★★
Murdoch Hill ★★★★★
Nepenthe ★★★★★
Nova Vita Wines ★★★★★
Paracombe Wines ★★★★★
Petaluma ★★★★★
Pike & Joyce ★★★★★
Riposte ★★★★★
Romney Park Wines ★★★★★
Scott ★★★★★
Setanta Wines ★★★★★
Shaw & Smith ★★★★★
Warwick Billings ★★★★★

ADELAIDE ZONE
Heirloom Vineyards ★★★★★
Hewitson ★★★★★
Patritti Wines ★★★★★
Penfolds Magill Estate ★★★★★

ALBANY
Montgomery's Hill ★★★★★
Oranje Tractor ★★★★★

ALPINE VALLEYS
Mayford Wines ★★★★★

BALLARAT
Tomboy Hill ★★★★★

BAROSSA VALLEY
Barossa Valley Estate ★★★★★
Caillard Wine ★★★★★
Charles Cimicky ★★★★★
Charles Melton ★★★★★
Chateau Tanunda ★★★★★
David Franz ★★★★★
Deisen ★★★★★
Dorrien Estate ★★★★★
Dutschke Wines ★★★★★
Elderton ★★★★★
Eperosa ★★★★★
First Drop Wines ★★★★★
Gibson Barossavale/Loose End ★★★★★
Glaetzer Wines ★★★★★
Glen Eldon Wines ★★★★★
Grant Burge ★★★★★
Hare's Chase ★★★★★
Head Wines ★★★★★
Hentley Farm Wines ★★★★★
Jacob's Creek ★★★★★
John Duval Wines ★★★★★

Kaesler Wines ★★★★★
Kalleske ★★★★★
Kellermeister ★★★★★
Kurtz Family Vineyards ★★★★★
Landhaus Estate ★★★★★
Langmeil Winery ★★★★★
Laughing Jack ★★★★★
Linfield Road Wines ★★★★★
Magpie Estate ★★★★★
Massena Vineyards ★★★★★
Maverick Wines ★★★★★
Murray Street Vineyard ★★★★★
Penfolds ★★★★★
Peter Lehmann ★★★★★
Purple Hands Wines ★★★★★
Rockford ★★★★★
Rolf Binder Veritas Winery ★★★★★
Rosenvale Wines ★★★★★
Ross Estate Wines ★★★★★
Saltram ★★★★★
Schubert Estate ★★★★★
Scorpiiion ★★★★★
Seabrook Wines ★★★★★
Seppeltsfield ★★★★★
Smallfry Wines ★★★★★
Sons of Eden ★★★★★
Spinifex ★★★★★
St Hallett ★★★★★
Teusner ★★★★★
Thorn-Clarke Wines ★★★★★
Tim Smith Wines ★★★★★
Torbreck Vintners ★★★★★
Trevor Jones Fine Wines ★★★★★
Turkey Flat ★★★★★
Two Hands Wines ★★★★★
Two Way Range ★★★★★
Westlake Vineyards ★★★★★
Wolf Blass ★★★★★
Yelland & Papps ★★★★★

BEECHWORTH
A. Rodda Wines ★★★★★
Fighting Gully Road ★★★★★
Giaconda ★★★★★
Smiths Vineyard ★★★★★

BENDIGO
BlackJack Vineyards ★★★★★
Bress ★★★★★
Killiecrankie Wines ★★★★★
Pondalowie Vineyards ★★★★★
Turner's Crossing Vineyard ★★★★★

BLACKWOOD VALLEY
Hillbillé ★★★★★
Nannup Ridge Estate ★★★★★

CANBERRA DISTRICT
Capital Wines ★★★★★
Clonakilla ★★★★★
Collector Wines ★★★★★
Eden Road Wines ★★★★★
Helm ★★★★★
Lark Hill ★★★★★
Lerida Estate ★★★★★
Mount Majura Vineyard ★★★★★
Nick O'Leary Wines ★★★★★

CENTRAL VICTORIA ZONE
Mt Terrible ★★★★★

CLARE VALLEY
Annie's Lane ★★★★★
Atlas Wines ★★★★★
Crabtree Watervale Wines ★★★★★
Gaelic Cemetery Wines ★★★★★
Grosset ★★★★★
Jim Barry Wines ★★★★★
Kilikanoon ★★★★★
Knappstein ★★★★★
Koonowla Wines ★★★★★
Leasingham ★★★★★
Mitchell ★★★★★
Mount Horrocks ★★★★★
O'Leary Walker Wines ★★★★★
Paulett ★★★★★
Pikes ★★★★★
Rhythm Stick Wines ★★★★★
Skillogalee ★★★★★
Taylors ★★★★★
Tim Adams ★★★★★
Wendouree ★★★★★
Wilson Vineyard ★★★★★
Wines by KT ★★★★★

COONAWARRA
Balnaves of Coonawarra ★★★★★
Bellwether ★★★★★
Brand's Laira Coonawarra ★★★★★
Hollick ★★★★★
Katnook Estate ★★★★★
Leconfield ★★★★★
Lindemans ★★★★★
Majella ★★★★★
Parker Coonawarra Estate ★★★★★
Patrick of Coonawarra ★★★★★
Penley Estate ★★★★★
Punters Corner ★★★★★
Rymill Coonawarra ★★★★★
Wynns Coonawarra Estate ★★★★★
Zema Estate ★★★★★

DENMARK
Harewood Estate ★★★★★
Matilda's Estate ★★★★★
Moombaki Wines ★★★★★

EDEN VALLEY
Flaxman Wines ★★★★★
Gatt Wines ★★★★★
Heggies Vineyard ★★★★★
Henschke ★★★★★
Leo Buring ★★★★★
Mountadam ★★★★★
Pewsey Vale ★★★★★
Poonawatta Estate ★★★★★
Radford Wines ★★★★★
Yalumba ★★★★★

FRANKLAND RIVER
Alkoomi ★★★★★
Ferngrove ★★★★★
Frankland Estate ★★★★★

GEELONG
Amietta Vineyard ★★★★★
Austin's Wines ★★★★★
Banks Road ★★★★★
Bannockburn Vineyards ★★★★★
Barrgowan Vineyard ★★★★★
Brown Magpie Wines ★★★★★
By Farr/Farr Rising ★★★★★
Clyde Park Vineyard ★★★★★

Curlewis Winery ★★★★★
Lethbridge Wines ★★★★★
Leura Park Estate ★★★★★
Oakdene Vineyards ★★★★★
Paradise IV ★★★★★
Provenance Wines ★★★★★
Scotchmans Hill ★★★★★
Shadowfax ★★★★★

GEOGRAPHE
Capel Vale ★★★★★
Hackersley ★★★★★
Willow Bridge Estate ★★★★★

GIPPSLAND
Bass Phillip ★★★★★
Bellvale Wines ★★★★★
Narkoojee ★★★★★

GLENROWAN
Baileys of Glenrowan ★★★★★

GRAMPIANS
A.T. Richardson Wines ★★★★★
Armstrong Vineyards ★★★★★
Best's Wines ★★★★★
Clayfield Wines ★★★★★
Grampians Estate ★★★★★
Mount Langi Ghiran Vineyards
   ★★★★★
Seppelt ★★★★★
The Story Wines ★★★★★

GRANITE BELT
Boireann ★★★★★
Symphony Hill Wines ★★★★★

GREAT SOUTHERN
Castelli Estate ★★★★★
Forest Hill Vineyard ★★★★★
Marchand & Burch ★★★★★
Staniford Wine Co. ★★★★★
Trevelen Farm ★★★★★
Willoughby Park ★★★★★

HEATHCOTE
Domaine Asmara ★★★★★
Downing Estate Vineyard ★★★★★
Foster e Rocco ★★★★★
Greenstone Vineyard ★★★★★

Heathcote Estate ★★★★★
Jasper Hill ★★★★★
Munari Wines ★★★★★
Paul Osicka ★★★★★
Red Edge ★★★★★
Sanguine Estate ★★★★★
Shelmerdine Vineyards ★★★★★
Tellurian ★★★★★

HENTY
Crawford River Wines ★★★★★

HILLTOPS
Barwang ★★★★★
Chalkers Crossing ★★★★★
Freeman Vineyards ★★★★★
Moppity Vineyards ★★★★★

HUNTER VALLEY
Audrey Wilkinson Vineyard ★★★★★
Bimbadgen ★★★★★
Briar Ridge Vineyard ★★★★★
Brokenwood ★★★★★
Chateau Francois ★★★★★
Chateau Pâto ★★★★★
Corduroy ★★★★★
De Iuliis ★★★★★
First Creek Wines ★★★★★
Gartelmann Hunter Estate ★★★★★
Glenguin Estate ★★★★★
Keith Tulloch Wine ★★★★★
Lake's Folly ★★★★★
Lambloch Estate ★★★★★
Leogate Estate Wines ★★★★★
Margan Family ★★★★★
McGuigan Wines ★★★★★
McLeish Estate ★★★★★
McWilliam's Mount Pleasant ★★★★★
Meerea Park ★★★★★
Mistletoe Wines ★★★★★
Mount Eyre Vineyards ★★★★★
Mount View Estate ★★★★★
Noonji Estate ★★★★★
Pepper Tree Wines ★★★★★
Pokolbin Estate ★★★★★
Tallavera Grove Vineyard & Winery
   ★★★★★

Tamburlaine ★★★★★
Thomas Wines ★★★★★
Tintilla Wines ★★★★★
Tower Estate ★★★★★
Tulloch ★★★★★
Tyrrell's ★★★★★
Wandin Hunter Valley ★★★★★
Warraroong Estate ★★★★★

KANGAROO ISLAND
The Islander Estate Vineyards
   ★★★★★

KING VALLEY
Brown Brothers ★★★★★

LANGHORNE CREEK
Angas Plains Estate ★★★★★
Beach Road ★★★★★
Bleasdale Vineyards ★★★★★
Bremerton Wines ★★★★★
Casa Freschi ★★★★★
John's Blend ★★★★★
Lake Breeze Wines ★★★★★

MACEDON RANGES
Bindi Wine Growers ★★★★★
Curly Flat ★★★★★
Hanging Rock Winery ★★★★★
Mount William Winery ★★★★★

MANJIMUP
Chestnut Grove ★★★★★

MARGARET RIVER
Amelia Park Wines ★★★★★
Ashbrook Estate ★★★★★
Brookland Valley ★★★★★
Brygon Reserve ★★★★★
Cape Mentelle ★★★★★
Cape Naturaliste Vineyard ★★★★★
Celestial Bay ★★★★★
Chalice Bridge Estate ★★★★★
Chapman Grove Wines ★★★★★
Churchview Estate ★★★★★
Clairault ★★★★★
Cowaramup Wines ★★★★★
Credaro Family Estate ★★★★★
Cullen Wines ★★★★★

Deep Woods Estate ★★★★★
Della Fay Wines ★★★★★
Devil's Lair ★★★★★
Evans & Tate ★★★★★
Evoi Wines ★★★★★
Fermoy Estate ★★★★★
Flametree ★★★★★
Forester Estate ★★★★★
Fraser Gallop Estate ★★★★★
Gralyn Estate ★★★★★
Happs ★★★★★
Hay Shed Hill Wines ★★★★★
Heydon Estate ★★★★★
Howard Park/MadFish ★★★★★
Hutton Wines ★★★★★
Juniper Estate ★★★★★
Laurance of Margaret River ★★★★★
Leeuwin Estate ★★★★★
Lenton Brae Wines ★★★★★
McHenry Hohnen Vintners ★★★★★
Merops Wines ★★★★★
Miles from Nowhere ★★★★★
Moss Brothers ★★★★★
Moss Wood ★★★★★
Night Harvest ★★★★★
Palmer Wines ★★★★★
Peccavi Wines ★★★★★
Pedestal Vineyard Wines ★★★★★
Pierro ★★★★★
Redgate ★★★★★
Rockfield Estate ★★★★★
Rosabrook Margaret River Wine
  ★★★★★
Sandalford ★★★★★
Stella Bella Wines ★★★★★
Streicker ★★★★★
Thompson Estate ★★★★★
Umamu Estate ★★★★★
Vasse Felix ★★★★★
Voyager Estate ★★★★★
Warner Glen Estate ★★★★★
Were Estate ★★★★★
Wills Domain ★★★★★
Windows Estate ★★★★★
wine by brad ★★★★★
Wise Wine ★★★★★

Woodlands ★★★★★
Woodside Valley Estate ★★★★★
Xanadu Wines ★★★★★

MCLAREN VALE
2 Mates ★★★★★
Antipodean Vintners ★★★★★
Cape Barren Wines ★★★★★
Chalk Hill ★★★★★
Chapel Hill ★★★★★
Clarendon Hills ★★★★★
Coriole ★★★★★
d'Arenberg ★★★★★
Dandelion Vineyards ★★★★★
DogRidge Wine Company
  ★★★★★
Fox Creek Wines ★★★★★
Gemtree Vineyards ★★★★★
Geoff Merrill Wines ★★★★★
Hardys ★★★★★
Hugh Hamilton Wines ★★★★★
Kangarilla Road Vineyard ★★★★★
Kay Brothers Amery Vineyards
  ★★★★★
Marius Wines ★★★★★
Maxwell Wines ★★★★★
Mitolo Wines ★★★★★
Mr Riggs Wine Company ★★★★★
Paxton ★★★★★
Penny's Hill ★★★★★
Pertaringa ★★★★★
Primo Estate ★★★★★
Reynella ★★★★★
Richard Hamilton ★★★★★
Rosemount Estate ★★★★★
Samuel's Gorge ★★★★★
SC Pannell ★★★★★
Serafino Wines ★★★★★
Shingleback ★★★★★
Shottesbrooke ★★★★★
The Old Faithful Estate ★★★★★
Ulithorne ★★★★★
Walter Clappis Wine Co. ★★★★★
Willunga 100 Wines ★★★★★
Wirra Wirra ★★★★★
Woodstock ★★★★★

Yangarra Estate Vineyard ★★★★★
Zonte's Footstep ★★★★★

MORNINGTON PENINSULA
Crittenden Estate ★★★★★
Dexter Wines ★★★★★
Eldridge Estate of Red Hill
   ★★★★★
Elgee Park ★★★★★
Foxeys Hangout ★★★★★
Hurley Vineyard ★★★★★
Jones Road ★★★★★
Kooyong ★★★★★
Main Ridge Estate ★★★★★
Merricks Creek Wines ★★★★★
Merricks Estate ★★★★★
Montalto Vineyards ★★★★★
Moorooduc Estate ★★★★★
Ocean Eight Vineyard & Winery
   ★★★★★
Paradigm Hill ★★★★★
Paringa Estate ★★★★★
Port Phillip Estate ★★★★★
Prancing Horse Estate ★★★★★
Red Hill Estate ★★★★★
Scorpo Wines ★★★★★
Stonier Wines ★★★★★
T'Gallant ★★★★★
Ten Minutes by Tractor ★★★★★
Tuck's Ridge ★★★★★
Willow Creek Vineyard ★★★★★
Yabby Lake Vineyard ★★★★★

MOUNT BARKER
3 Drops ★★★★★
Plantagenet ★★★★★
Poacher's Ridge Vineyard ★★★★★
West Cape Howe Wines ★★★★★
Xabregas ★★★★★

MOUNT LOFTY RANGES ZONE
Michael Hall Wines ★★★★★

MUDGEE
Huntington Estate ★★★★★
Logan Wines ★★★★★
Lowe Wines ★★★★★
Quilty Wines ★★★★★

Robert Oatley Vineyards ★★★★★
Robert Stein Vineyard ★★★★★

NAGAMBIE LAKES
Mitchelton ★★★★★
Tahbilk ★★★★★

ORANGE
Belgravia Vineyards ★★★★★
Bloodwood ★★★★★
Mayfield Vineyard ★★★★★
Philip Shaw Wines ★★★★★
Printhie Wines ★★★★★
Ross Hill Wines ★★★★★

PEMBERTON
Bellarmine Wines ★★★★★
Fonty's Pool Vineyards ★★★★★
Lillian ★★★★★
Lost Lake ★★★★★
Merum Estate ★★★★★
Silkwood Wines ★★★★★

PERTH HILLS
Millbrook Winery ★★★★★

PORONGURUP
Castle Rock Estate ★★★★★
Duke's Vineyard ★★★★★

PORT PHILLIP ZONE
Limbic ★★★★★
Onannon ★★★★★

PYRENEES
Dalwhinnie ★★★★★
DogRock Winery ★★★★★
M. Chapoutier Australia ★★★★★
Mitchell Harris Wines ★★★★★
Mount Avoca ★★★★★
Pyren Vineyard ★★★★★
Pyrenees Ridge Winery ★★★★★
Quartz Hill Vineyard ★★★★★
Summerfield ★★★★★
Warrenmang Vineyard & Resort
   ★★★★★

RIVERINA
De Bortoli ★★★★★
McWilliam's ★★★★★
Nugan Estate ★★★★★

RUTHERGLEN
All Saints Estate ★★★★★
Buller ★★★★★
Campbells ★★★★★
Chambers Rosewood ★★★★★
Morris ★★★★★
Pfeiffer Wines ★★★★★
Stanton & Killeen Wines ★★★★★
Warrabilla ★★★★★

SHOALHAVEN COAST
Coolangatta Estate ★★★★★

SOUTH AUSTRALIA
Angove Family Winemakers ★★★★★
Hand Crafted by Geoff Hardy
  ★★★★★
Tapanappa ★★★★★
Tollana ★★★★★
WineSA ★★★★★

SOUTH WEST AUSTRALIA ZONE
Kerrigan + Berry ★★★★★
Snake + Herring ★★★★★

SOUTHERN FLEURIEU
Madeleines Wines ★★★★★
Mt Billy ★★★★★
Salomon Estate ★★★★★

SOUTHERN HIGHLANDS
Centennial Vineyards ★★★★★
Tertini Wines ★★★★★

SUNBURY
Craiglee ★★★★★
Galli Estate ★★★★★
The Hairy Arm ★★★★★

SWAN VALLEY
Faber Vineyard ★★★★★
Houghton ★★★★★
John Kosovich Wines ★★★★★

UPPER GOULBURN
Delatite ★★★★★
Rocky Passes Estate ★★★★★

TASMANIA
Barringwood Park ★★★★★
Bay of Fires/House of Arras ★★★★★

Bream Creek ★★★★★
Clover Hill ★★★★★
Craigow ★★★★★
Darlington Vineyard ★★★★★
Dawson & James ★★★★★
Delamere Vineyard ★★★★★
Derwent Estate ★★★★★
Domaine A ★★★★★
Freycinet ★★★★★
Frogmore Creek ★★★★★
Heemskerk ★★★★★
Holm Oak ★★★★★
Jansz Tasmania ★★★★★
Josef Chromy Wines ★★★★★
Kate Hill Wines ★★★★★
Lake Barrington Vineyard
  ★★★★★
Moorilla Estate ★★★★★
Pipers Brook Vineyard ★★★★★
Pooley Wines ★★★★★
Pressing Matters ★★★★★
Resolution Vineyard ★★★★★
Richard Meyman Wines ★★★★★
Riversdale Estate ★★★★★
Stefano Lubiana ★★★★★
Stoney Rise ★★★★★
Tasmanian Estates ★★★★★
Waterton Vineyards ★★★★★

VARIOUS/SOUTH EASTERN AUSTRALIA
Accolade Wines ★★★★★
Echelon ★★★★★
Palmarium ★★★★★
Smidge Wines ★★★★★
Treasury Wine Estates ★★★★★
Twofold ★★★★★

WESTERN AUSTRALIA
Larry Cherubino Wines ★★★★★

WESTERN VICTORIA ZONE
Michael Unwin Wines ★★★★★
Norton Estate ★★★★★

WRATTONBULLY
Terre à Terre ★★★★★

YARRA VALLEY

Bird on a Wire Wines ★★★★★
Carlei Estate & Carlei Green Vineyards
  ★★★★★
Coldstream Hills ★★★★★
De Bortoli ★★★★★
Domaine Chandon ★★★★★
Dominique Portet ★★★★★
Elmswood Estate ★★★★★
Gembrook Hill ★★★★★
Giant Steps/Innocent Bystander
  ★★★★★
Helen's Hill Estate ★★★★★
Hillcrest Vineyard ★★★★★
Hoddles Creek Estate ★★★★★
Jamsheed ★★★★★
Long Gully Estate ★★★★★
Luke Lambert Wines ★★★★★
macforbes ★★★★★
Mandala ★★★★★
Mayer ★★★★★
Medhurst ★★★★★
Mount Mary ★★★★★
Oakridge Wines ★★★★★
PHI ★★★★★

Pimpernel Vineyards ★★★★★
Punch ★★★★★
Punt Road ★★★★★
Rochford Wines ★★★★★
Salo Wines ★★★★★
Serrat ★★★★★
Seville Estate ★★★★★
Squitchy Lane Vineyard ★★★★★
Steels Creek Estate ★★★★★
Sticks Yarra Valley ★★★★★
Tarrawarra Estate ★★★★★
The Wanderer ★★★★★
Thick as Thieves Wines ★★★★★
Toolangi Vineyards ★★★★★
Trellis ★★★★★
Wantirna Estate ★★★★★
William Downie ★★★★★
Yarra Yarra ★★★★★
Yarra Yering ★★★★★
Yarrabank ★★★★★
YarraLoch ★★★★★
Yering Station ★★★★★
Yeringberg ★★★★★

Ten of the best new wineries

Each one of these wineries making its debut in the *Wine Companion* has earnt a five-star rating. They are thus the pick of the 66 new wineries in this edition. A list of other five-star inductees follows; my choice of the 10 has been largely driven by the larger volume of wines made by them, but that should not stop you seeking out the smaller wineries.

A. Rodda Wines, Antipodean Vintners, Bird on a Wire Wines, Corduroy, Echelon, Night Harvest, Palmarium, Richard Meyman Wines, Salo Wines, Staniford Wine Co. and Warwick Billings.

ATLAS WINES Clare Valley, SA / PAGE 85
Owner/winemaker Adam Barton had a wide-ranging apprenticeship before establishing Atlas Wines, working at Scarpantoni Estate in McLaren Vale, Rolf Binder Wines in the Barossa Valley, Wynns Coonawarra Estate and the iconic Bonny Doon Vineyard in California. Currently, he is winemaker at Reillys Wines in the Clare Valley, as well as making Atlas wines from 6ha of shiraz and 2ha of cabernet sauvignon grown on a stony ridge at the eastern end of the valley. He also buys Watervale riesling and shiraz and mataro from the Barossa Valley. These are all seriously good wines, with a maximum price tag of $35.

DAWSON & JAMES Southern Tasmania / PAGE 210
Looked at one way, this is a case of teaching old dogs new tricks; on the other view, you might think only Tasmania, and the lure of pinot noir and chardonnay, could entice industry veterans Peter Dawson and Tim James out of the safety of post-retirement consultancy work. As a sad postscript, fire ravaged the Meadowbank vineyard, meaning there will be no 2013 wines.

DELLA FAY WINES Margaret River, WA / PAGE 219
Here is yet another old dog (perhaps industry veteran is kinder), Michael Kelly, successfully taking the plunge with his family in establishing his own business. Experience at Seville Estate, Mount Mary, Domaine Louis Chapuis in Burgundy, Leeuwin Estate and Sandalford was accumulated before he became long-term winemaker at Fermoy Estate. The groundwork for Della Fay began back in 1999 with the purchase of 8ha of land in Caves Road, Yallingup.

ECHELON Various / PAGE 236
This is the brainchild of Nicholas Crampton, a wine marketer who has always been driven by quality, and a gift for lateral thinking. The business is owned by McWilliam's, but Nicholas and his winemaking cohorts are given free rein, making wines under the Zeppelin, Last Horizon, Partisan, Armchair Critic and Under & Over labels. The marriage of climate, site and variety has been foremost in establishing this impressive venture.

HAND CRAFTED BY GEOFF HARDY Various SA / **PAGE 301**
This is a very different operation to Geoff Hardy's other brands of K1 (Adelaide Hills) and Pertaringa (McLaren Vale). Here Langhorne Creek and Limestone Coast come into play, but more relevant is the remarkable varietal spread of Graciano, Lagrein, Primitivo, Roussanne, Savagnin, Teroldego and Verdelho. There are also staples such as Chardonnay, Pinot Noir and Cabernet Sauvignon from the Adelaide Hills.

LAMBLOCH ESTATE Hunter Valley, NSW / **PAGE 377**
Why Drayton's Family Wines was prepared to sell the 8ha vineyard allowing Jas Khara to establish Lambloch Estate, I am not sure. What I do know is that it has an impeccable address, adjoining Lake's Folly, with McWilliam's Rosehill Vineyard directly opposite on Broke Road. This red volcanic soil supports some of the very best Hunter plantings, but it is rare. Securing Scott Stephens as winemaker has got the venture off to a flying start.

MERUM ESTATE Pemberton, WA / **PAGE 436**
Strictly speaking, this is not a new winery, having oscillated between grape growing and winemaking since the vineyard was established in 1996. After the 2006 vintage winemaking ceased under the Merum label, but in '10 Mike Melsom (the viticulturist co-owner) and partner Julie Roberts once again made wines from the 10ha vineyard, adding the multi-region Curious Nature Remarkable Red and Wondrous White as entry points wines at a mere $15.

PURPLE HANDS WINES Barossa Valley, SA / **PAGE 542**
This is a busman's holiday for Craig Stansborough, whose real job is chief winemaker at Grant Burge. He owns an 8ha vineyard in the coolest corner of the southern Barossa Valley planted to shiraz, supplementing the fruit from that vineyard (part is sold, I would guess to Grant Burge) with contract-grown grenache. His partner in crime is Mark Slade, who, so they say, 'provides the passion'.

SNAKE + HERRING South West Australia Zone / **PAGE 611**
The name is unusual and catchy, and the labels are, if anything, even more so. But it's not just marketing window dressing: it brings together one of the most experienced winemakers in Western Australia, Tony Davis (Snake), and a chartered accountant with international accounting experience allied with financial advice and planning for Forrester Estate in partnership with Kevin McKay, Redmond Sweeny (Herring). The exceptionally good wines are sourced from Mount Barker, Porongurup and Margaret River.

TREVOR JONES FINE WINES Barossa Valley, SA / **PAGE 676**
In 2010 Trevor Jones (the person) was winemaker and production manager for Kellermeister, many of which were in fact released under his name. There was then a parting of the ways, and he now concentrates on the eponymous business he owns with his wife Mandy. Since 1998 he has owned 5ha of vineyard, and has four vintages spanning 2002–05 labelled Belle-Terroir available. The wines are made at Torbreck, but plans to have his own winery operations for the 2014 vintage.

Ten dark horses

For the first time, this year's wines come from ten different regions. A primary qualification was the first time recognition of five stars, although in many instances, the producers have been knocking at the door with 4.5 stars for some years. In many instances the wines are attractively priced.

BK WINES Adelaide Hills, SA / PAGE 118
Established by Brendon and Kirsty Keys in 2007, Brendon having worked in the US, Argentina and NZ before moving to SA. The Keys established their winery with the intriguing name Altamont Premium Studio, where they make wines for some of the top Adelaide Hills producers as well as their own BK Wines label. Syrah and Chardonnay are the key varieties.

BROWN MAGPIE WINES Geelong, Vic / PAGE 138
Shane and Loretta Breheny planted their 9ha vineyard over 2001-02, astutely choosing pinot noir, pinot gris and shiraz, all three producing first-class wines at very attractive prices. Loretta looks after the vineyard, and Shane (with help from Chris Sargeant) the winemaking. High quality Pinot and Shiraz are no surprise, but compelling Pinot Grigio and Pinot Gris are.

CAPE NATURALISTE VINEYARD Margaret River, WA / PAGE 153
I can't explain why Cape Naturaliste has not previously been elevated to five stars, because Bruce Dukes was (deservedly if belatedly) named Winemaker of the Year at the WA Wine Industry Awards '11. As well as producing the estate wines, Bruce and Ian Bell in fact make the wines for a bevy of five-star wineries across Margaret River. On the home front they score bulls eyes with Cabernet Sauvignon, Merlot and Shiraz either as blends or single varietals.

ELMSWOOD ESTATE Yarra Valley, Vic / PAGE 245
Elmswood Estate is situated in the beautiful Wandin area of the Yarra Valley, noted for its vivid volcanic soils, plantings dating back to 1981. A particular feature is the pavilion, a glass room on a ridge-top with 180° views of the Upper Yarra Valley, seating up to 110 guests, making it a popular wedding venue. Dylan McMahon of Seville Estate contract-made excellent red wines in 2010, showing his expertise in coaxing shiraz and cabernet sauvignon to fully ripen on red soils, no easy task.

HILLBILLÉ Blackwood Valley, WA / PAGE 322
With contract winemakers at talented as Stuart Watson of Woodlands Wines and Bruce Dukes of Cape Naturaliste, it is no surprise to find a portfolio of wines that are either of very high quality, or offer impressive value for money. If you make a trip to the winery, the RAC advises it is 'the most scenic drive in the southwest of WA', with delicious Chardonnay and Shiraz Viognier (not common in the West) the reward.

HOLM OAK Northern Tasmania / PAGE 327

Holm Oak is one of the most senior wineries in Northern Tasmania, dating back to 1983. In '04 the Wilson family purchased the property, with daughter Rebecca (complete with winemaking experience from Australia and California) becoming winemaker in '06, husband Tim Duffy the viticulturist, and onsite winery completed just prior to the '07 vintage. It has all paid big dividends for Riesling and Pinot Noir, and sophisticated, 20% barrel-fermented Sauvignon Blanc.

RYMILL COONAWARRA, SA / PAGE 572

The Rymills are descendants of John Riddoch, and have been growing grapes in Coonawarra since 1970, now with 137ha on prime viticultural land, winemaking since 1974. The elevation of Champagne-trained Flying Winemaker Sandrine Gimon to chief winemaker has seen Rymill take the last step with a range of attractively priced wines, its success with Gewurztraminer adding spice to the sauce.

SALOMON ESTATE Southern Fleurieu, SA / PAGE 577

I have to confess to greatly enjoying the affable Austrian winemaker/owner Bert Salomon (who also runs the family winery in Austria), but I am in good company: he is universally liked. The current range of reds from '09 and '10 are irresistible, spanning Shiraz, Syrah Viognier, Shiraz Cabernet, Grenache Shiraz Mourvedre and Cabernet Sauvignon.

SILKWOOD WINES Pemberton, WA / PAGE 603

Silkwood stands first amongst this year's Dark Horses with its wonderful range of table wines all selling for $20 or less, most less. Silkwood is the venture of third-generation farmers Pam and John Allen, who use a large flock of guinea fowl to eliminate insect pests from their substantial 23.5ha vineyard. The wines are made in the onsite winery built in 2006. The Sauvignon Blanc and Pinot Noir are particularly impressive.

WILLOW BRIDGE ESTATE Geographe, WA / PAGE 714

With two wines at 96 points, two at 95 points and four at 94 (three of those with an $18 price tag), Willow Bridge might have been a contender for Winery of the Year; as a consolation prize it won the trophy for Most Successful WA Exhibitor Processing Under 300 tonnes at the Perth Wine Show '11. Black Dog Shiraz is an outstanding leader of the pack.

Australia's geographical indications

The process of formally mapping Australia's wine regions is all but complete, although will never come to a complete halt – for one thing, climate change is lurking in the wings. The division into States, Zones, Regions and Subregions follows; those Regions or Subregions marked with an asterisk are not yet registered, and may never be, but are in common usage. The bizarre Hunter Valley GI map now has Hunter Valley as a Zone, Hunter as the Region and the sprawling Upper Hunter as a Subregion along with Pokolbin (small and disputed by some locals). Another recent official change has been the registration of Mount Gambier as a new Region in the Limestone Coast Zone.

I am still in front of the game with Tasmania, dividing it into Northern, Southern and East Coast, and, to a lesser degree, have anticipated that the Darling Downs and coastal hinterland region of Queensland will seek recognition under this or some similar name. In similar vein, I have included Ballarat (with 17 wineries); and the Southern Eyre Peninsula (three wineries).

State/Zone	Region	Subregion
AUSTRALIA		
Australia Australian South Eastern Australia ★	★The South Eastern Australia Zone incorporates the whole of the states of NSW, Vic and Tasmania and only part of Qld and SA.	
NEW SOUTH WALES		
Big Rivers	Murray Darling Perricoota Riverina Swan Hill	
Central Ranges	Cowra Mudgee Orange	
Hunter Valley	Hunter	Broke Fordwich Pokolbin Upper Hunter Valley

State/Zone	Region	Subregion
Northern Rivers	Hastings River	
Northern Slopes	New England Australia	
South Coast	Shoalhaven Coast Southern Highlands	
Southern New South Wales	Canberra District Gundagai Hilltops Tumbarumba	
Western Plains		

SOUTH AUSTRALIA

Adelaide (Super Zone, includes Mount Lofty Ranges, Fleurieu and Barossa)

State/Zone	Region	Subregion
Barossa	Barossa Valley Eden Valley	High Eden
Far North	Southern Flinders Ranges	
Fleurieu	Currency Creek Kangaroo Island Langhorne Creek McLaren Vale Southern Fleurieu	
Limestone Coast	Coonawarra Mount Benson Mount Gambier Padthaway Robe Wrattonbully	
Lower Murray	Riverland	
Mount Lofty Ranges	Adelaide Hills Adelaide Plains Clare Valley	Lenswood Piccadilly Valley Polish Hill River★ Watervale★
The Peninsulas	Southern Eyre Peninsula★	

State/Zone	Region	Subregion
VICTORIA		
Central Victoria	Bendigo	
	Goulburn Valley	Nagambie Lakes
	Heathcote	
	Strathbogie Ranges	
	Upper Goulburn	
Gippsland		
North East Victoria	Alpine Valleys	
	Beechworth	
	Glenrowan	
	King Valley	
	Rutherglen	
North West Victoria	Murray Darling	
	Swan Hill	
Port Phillip	Geelong	
	Macedon Ranges	
	Mornington Peninsula	
	Sunbury	
	Yarra Valley	
Western Victoria	Ballarat★	
	Grampians	Great Western
	Henty	
	Pyrenees	
WESTERN AUSTRALIA		
Central Western Australia		
Eastern Plains, Inland and North of Western Australia		
Greater Perth	Peel	
	Perth Hills	
	Swan District	Swan Valley

State/Zone	Region	Subregion
South West Australia	Blackwood Valley	
	Geographe	
	Great Southern	Albany
		Denmark
		Frankland River
		Mount Barker
		Porongurup
	Manjimup	
	Margaret River	
	Pemberton	
West Australian South East Coastal		

QUEENSLAND

Queensland	Granite Belt	
	Queensland Coastal★	
	South Burnett	
	Darling Downs★	

TASMANIA

Tasmania	Northern Tasmania★	
	Southern Tasmania★	
	East Coast Tasmania★	

AUSTRALIAN CAPITAL TERRITORY

NORTHERN TERRITORY

Varietal wine styles and regions

For better or worse, there simply has to be concerted action to highlight the link between regions, varieties and wine styles. It's not a question of creating the links: they are already there, and have been in existence for periods as short as 20 years or as long as 150 years. So here is an abbreviated summary of those regional styles (in turn reflected in the Best of the Best lists commencing on page 20).

Riesling

The link with the **Eden Valley** dates back at least to when Joseph Gilbert planted his Pewsey Vale vineyard, and quickly made its way to the nearby **Clare Valley**. These two regions stood above all others for well over 100 years, producing wines that shared many flavour and texture characteristics: lime (a little more obvious in the Eden Valley), apple, talc and mineral, lightly browned toasty notes emerging with five to 10 years bottle age. Within the last 20 or so years, the subregions of the **Great Southern** of Western Australia have established a deserved reputation for finely structured, elegant wines with wonderful length, sometimes shy when young, bursting into song after five years. The subregions are (in alpha order) **Albany**, **Denmark**, **Frankland River**, **Mount Barker** and **Porongurup**. **Tasmania**, too, produces high class rieslings, notable for their purity and intensity courtesy of their high natural acidity. Finally, there is the small and very cool Victorian region of **Henty** (once referred to as Drumborg) with exceptional riesling sharing many things in common with Tasmania.

Semillon

There is a Siamese-twin relationship between semillon and the **Hunter Valley**, producing a wine style like no other in the world for well over 100 years. The humid and very warm climate (best coupled with sandy soils not common in the region) results in wines that have a median alcohol level of 10.5% and no residual sugar, cold-fermented in stainless steel and bottled within three months of vintage. They are devoid of colour and have only the barest hints of grass, herb and mineral wrapped around a core of acidity. Over the next five to 10 years they develop a glowing green-gold colour, a suite of grass and citrus fruit surrounded by buttered toast and honey notes. Like rieslings, screwcaps have added decades to their cellaring life. The **Adelaide Hills** and **Margaret River** produce entirely different semillon, more structured and weighty, its alcohol 13% to 14%, and as often as not blended with sauvignon blanc, barrel fermentation of part or all common. Finally, there is a cuckoo in the nest: Peter Lehmann in the **Barossa/Eden Valley** has adapted Hunter Valley practices, picking early, fermenting in steel, bottling early, and holding the top wine for five years before release – and succeeding brilliantly.

Chardonnay

This infinitely flexible grape is grown and vinified in all 63 regions, and accounts for half of Australia's white wine grapes and wine. Incredibly, before 1970 it was all but unknown, hiding its promise here and there (**Mudgee** was one such place) under a cloak of anonymity. It was there and in the **Hunter Valley** that the first wines labelled chardonnay were made in 1971 (by Craigmoor and Tyrrell's). Its bold yellow colour, peaches and cream flavour and vanilla oak was unlike anything that had gone before and was accepted by domestic and export markets with equal enthusiasm. When exports took off into the stratosphere between 1985 and 1995, one half of Brand Australia was cheap and cheerful oak-chipped chardonnay grown in the **Riverina** and **Riverland**. By coincidence, over the same period chardonnay from the emerging cool climate regions was starting to appear in limited quantities, its flavour and structure radically different to the warm-grown, high-cropped wine. Another 10 years on, and by 2005/06 the wine surplus was starting to build rapidly, with demand for chardonnay much less than its production. As attention swung from chardonnay to sauvignon blanc, the situation became dire. Lost in the heat of battle were (and to a degree still are) supremely elegant wines from most cool regions, **Margaret River** and **Yarra Valley** the leaders of the large band. Constant refinement of the style, and the adoption of the screwcap, puts these wines at the forefront of the battle to re-engage consumers here and abroad with what are world-class wines.

Sauvignon Blanc

Two regions, the **Adelaide Hills** and **Margaret River** stood in front of all others until recently joined by **Orange**; these three produce Australia's best sauvignon blanc, wines with real structure and authority. It is a matter of record that Marlborough sauvignon blanc accounts for one-third of Australia's white wine sales; all one can say (accurately) is that the basic Marlborough style is very different, and look back at what happened with Australian chardonnay. Margaret River also offers complex blends of sauvignon blanc and semillon in widely varying proportions.

Shiraz

Shiraz is by far the most important red variety and is tremendously flexible in its ability to adapt to virtually any combination of climate and soil/terroir. Unlike chardonnay, a recent arrival, shiraz was the most important red variety throughout the 19th and 20th centuries. Its ancestral homes were the **Barossa Valley**, the **Clare Valley**, **McLaren Vale** and the **Hunter Valley**, and it still leads in those regions. With the exception of the Hunter Valley, it was as important in making fortified wine as table wine over the period 1850 to 1950, aided and abetted by grenache and mourvedre (mataro). In New South Wales the **Hilltops** and **Canberra District** are producing elegant, cool-grown wines that usually conceal their power (especially when co-fermented with viognier) but not their silky length. Further north, but at a higher altitude, **Orange** is also producing fine, fragrant and spicy wines. All the other New South Wales regions are capable of producing good shiraz of seriously good character and quality; shiraz ripens comfortably, but quite late in the season. Polished, sophisticated wines are the result. Victoria has a cornucopia of regions at the cooler end of the spectrum; the coolest (though not too cool for comfort) are the **Yarra Valley**, **Mornington Peninsula**, **Sumbury** and **Geelong**, all producing fragrant, spicy medium-bodied wines. **Bendigo**, **Heathcote**, **Grampians** and **Pyrenees**, more or less running east-west across the centre of Victoria are producing some of the most exciting medium-bodied shirazs in Australia, each with its own terroir stamp, but all combing generosity and elegance. In Western Australia, **Great Southern** and three of its five subregions, **Frankland River**, **Mount Barker** and **Porongurup**, are making magical shirazs, fragrant and spicy, fleshy yet strongly structured. **Margaret River** has been a relatively late mover, but it, too, is producing wines with exemplary varietal definition and finesse.

Cabernet Sauvignon

The tough-skinned cabernet sauvignon can be, and is, grown in all regions, but it struggles in the coolest (notably **Tasmania**) and loses desirable varietal definition in the warmer regions, especially in warmer vintages. Shiraz can cope with alcohol levels in excess of 14.5%, cabernet can't. In South Australia, **Coonawarra** stands supreme, its climate (though not its soil) strikingly similar to that of Bordeaux, the main difference lower rainfall. Perfectly detailed cabernets are the result, with no need of shiraz or merlot to fill in the mid-palate, although some excellent blends are made. **Langhorne Creek** (a little warmer) and **McLaren Vale** (warmer still) have similar maritime climates, doubtless the reason why McLaren Vale manages to deal with the warmth of its summer/autumn weather. The **Eden Valley** is the most reliable of the inner regions, the other principal regions dependent on a cool summer. From South Australia to Western Australia, and **Margaret River**, with its extreme maritime climate shaped by the warm Indian Ocean, stands tall. It is also Australia's foremost producer of cabernet merlot et al in the Bordeaux mix. The texture and structure of both the straight varietal and the blend is regal, often to the point of austerity when the wines are young, but the sheer power of this underlying fruit provides the balance and guarantees the future development of the wines over a conservative 20 years, especially if screwcapped. The **Great Southern** subregions of **Frankland River** and **Mount Barker** share a continental climate that is somewhat cooler than Margaret River, and has a greater diurnal temperature range. Here cabernet has an incisive, dark berry character and firm but usually fine tannins – not demanding merlot, though a touch of it and/or malbec can be beneficial. It is grown successfully through the centre and south of Victoria, but is often overshadowed by shiraz. In the last 20 years it has ceased to be a problem child and become a favourite son of the **Yarra Valley**; the forward move of vintage dates has been the key to the change.

Pinot Noir

The promiscuity of shiraz (particularly) and cabernet sauvignon is in sharp contrast to the puritanical rectitude of pinot noir. One sin of omission or commission, and the door slams shut, leaving you on the outside. **Tasmania** is the El Dorado for the variety, and the best is still to come with better clones, older vines and greater exploration of the multitude of mesoclimates that Tasmania has to offer. While it is north of Central Otago (New Zealand), its vineyards are all air-conditioned by the Southern Ocean and Tasman Sea, and it stands toe-to-toe with Central Otago in its ability to make deeply-coloured, profound pinot with all the length one could ask for. Once on the mainland, Victoria's Port Phillip Zone, encompassing the **Geelong**, **Macedon Ranges**, **Sunbury**, **Mornington Peninsula** and **Yarra Valley** is the epicentre of Australian pinot noir, **Henty** a small outpost. The sheer number of high quality, elegant wines produced by dozens of makers put the **Adelaide Hills** and **Porongurup** (also capable of producing quality pinot) into the shade.

Sparkling Wines

The patter is eerily similar to that of pinot noir, **Tasmania** now and in the future the keeper of the Holy Grail, the **Port Phillip Zone** the centre of activity on the mainland.

Fortified Wines

Rutherglen and **Glenrowan** are the two (and only) regions that produce immensely complex, long-barrel-aged muscat and muscadelle, the latter called tokay for over a century, now renamed topaque. These wines have no equal in the world, Spain's Malaga nearest in terms of lusciousness, but nowhere near as complex. The other producer of a wine without parallel is Seppeltsfield in the **Barossa Valley**, which each year releases an explosively rich and intense tawny liqueur style that is 100% 100 years old.

Australian vintage charts

Each number represents a mark out of 10 for the quality of vintages in each region.

red wine   white wine

2008	2009	2010	2011

NSW

Hunter Valley
2008	2009	2010	2011
2	7	7	6
7	10	9	7

Mudgee
8	8	6	6
7	9	8	8

Cowra
9	7	7	4
7	8	6	6

Orange
8	8	9	6
7	9	9	7

Riverina/Griffith
7	7	7	6
8	6	8	7

Canberra District
8	9	8	8
9	9	9	9

Southern Highlands
9	6	7	6
8	9	7	7

Hilltops
9	8	8	7
8	8	9	6

Tumbarumba
7	8	8	6
9	8	9	7

Shoalhaven
7	8	5	7
7	8	7	8

VIC

Yarra Valley
2008	2009	2010	2011
7	2	9	6
7	7	9	9

Mornington Peninsula
9	9	10	5
8	9	9	6

Geelong
7	9	9	6
7	9	9	7

Macedon Ranges
7	7	8	7
7	8	7	8

Sunbury
8	9	9	6
7	8	8	7

Grampians
7	8	9	7
7	9	8	8

Pyrenees
8	7	8	5
8	7	7	8

Henty
9	8	9	8
8	8	8	8

Bendigo
8	4	8	6
8	7	9	6

Heathcote
9	7	9	7
7	6	7	8

Goulburn Valley
2008	2009	2010	2011
8	7	8	6
9	8	8	8

Upper Goulburn
7	6	9	5
8	8	8	9

Strathbogie Ranges
8	6	8	2
7	7	9	6

Glenrowan & Rutherglen
7	-	8	4
6	-	7	6

King Valley
7	8	8	5
9	7	8	7

Alpine Valleys
7	8	8	4
7	8	8	6

Beechworth
7	2	7	6
6	7	6	8

Gippsland
8	6	8	-
7	8	7	-

Murray Darling
8	8	7	1
8	8	7	4

	2008	2009	2010	2011

SA

Barossa Valley

2008	2009	2010	2011
8	7	9	5
7	7	8	7

Eden Valley

2008	2009	2010	2011
7	9	8	5
8	8	9	7

Clare Valley

2008	2009	2010	2011
6	9	8	5
8	8	9	7

Adelaide Hills

2008	2009	2010	2011
7	9	9	3
7	9	9	6

Adelaide Plains

2008	2009	2010	2011
8	-	9	5
7	-	7	6

Coonawarra

2008	2009	2010	2011
9	7	9	6
7	8	8	8

Padthaway

2008	2009	2010	2011
6	6	8	6
6	8	8	8

Mount Benson & Robe

2008	2009	2010	2011
8	7	8	5
8	8	8	7

Wrattonbully

2008	2009	2010	2011
7	6	9	5
8	7	8	7

McLaren Vale

2008	2009	2010	2011
7	8	8	7
7	7	7	8

Southern Fleurieu

2008	2009	2010	2011
8	7	8	7
7	7	8	8

Langhorne Creek

2008	2009	2010	2011
-	-	10	7
-	-	9	8

Kangaroo Island

2008	2009	2010	2011
8	9	8	6
8	10	9	8

Riverland

2008	2009	2010	2011
6	6	8	5
8	7	8	5

WA

Margaret River

2008	2009	2010	2011
9	9	9	9
9	9	8	8

Great Southern

2008	2009	2010	2011
8	8	8	9
8	9	8	8

Manjimup

2008	2009	2010	2011
8	7	8	8
9	8	9	8

Pemberton

2008	2009	2010	2011
8	8	8	8
9	9	7	8

Geographe

2008	2009	2010	2011
8	8	9	9
7	8	8	8

Swan District

2008	2009	2010	2011
8	10	8	8
8	10	8	7

Peel

2008	2009	2010	2011
8	8	8	-
5	7	7	-

Perth Hills

2008	2009	2010	2011
7	10	8	-
8	8	8	-

QLD

Granite Belt

2008	2009	2010	2011
6	-	7	5
8	-	7	4

South Burnett

2008	2009	2010	2011
6	-	9	5
7	-	8	8

TAS

Northern Tasmania

2008	2009	2010	2011
8	8	8	7
7	8	9	8

Southern Tasmania

2008	2009	2010	2011
7	8	9	8
7	8	8	9

Acknowledgements

It is, I suppose, inevitable that the production of a book such as this should involve many people in a long chain of events, some seemingly trivial, others of fundamental importance.

The starting point is the making of the thousands of bottles of wine Ben Edwards and I taste each year, and the end point is the appearance of the book on retailers' shelves across Australia on 1 August 2012. Well prior to that date, many hundreds of tasting notes for the 2014 edition will have been made, and details of yet more new wineries will have been entered.

My foremost thanks must go to the winemakers for sending the wines to me at their cost, and in particular those who treat submission dates as serious deadlines rather than an approximate wish-list on my part. Those who ignored the deadlines are increasingly likely to fall on their own sword as the competition for space in the book intensifies.

Next are those responsible for getting the wine to me, whether by the excellent parcel delivery service of Australia Post, by courier or by hand delivery. I am reliant on the goodwill and tolerance of many people involved in what may seem as a warped version of trivial pursuits as the wines arrive, are placed in bins, in due course fork-lifted up one story and removed from those bins, unpacked, listed, entered into the database, with precise names cross-checked, alcohol, price, and closure type recorded, tasting sheets printed for the day's tasting of 120 wines, initially arranged by producer, but the re-sorted by variety, moved onto a long tasting bench, opened, poured at the same pace I taste, the Riedel glasses returned to washing racks, washed, rinsed and dried, the tasting notes typed, the database now returning the notes to a winery-by-winery sequence, proof-checked by me (and at least three others at subsequent stages before going to print).

In the meantime, my office team of Paula Grey and Beth Anthony has been busy chasing up new, missing or inconsistent details regarding the winery and the wines. To those who remember to provide the price (and if a lab label, the alcohol) my special thanks. I only wish I could extend those thanks more often.

Then there is the ever-patient, but deadline-conscious, team at Hardie Grant, working on cover design (surely brilliant), page design, paper type, two-colour printing, which give rise to the galley pages for proof-reading again and again.

To my team of Ben Edwards, Paula Grey, Beth Anthony; Coldstream Post Office (Barry, Trevor and Val); Pam Holmes (and others at Coldstream Hills); John Cook (Programmer); and the Hardie Grant team led by believer-in-chief Sandy Grant, Hannah Koelmeyer and Sarah Shrubb (Editors), Megan Ellis (Typesetter) and Heather Menzies (cover design). This is as much their book as it is mine.

96 POINTS

James Halliday Australian Wine
Companion newsletter
April 19, 2012

WOLF BLASS®

Platinum Label

MEDLANDS ESTATE
BAROSSA VALLEY

S H I R A Z

2009

SOURCED FROM WOLF BLASS MEDLANDS ESTATE
'THE ORCHARD' VINEYARD, CELEBRATED FOR ITS
INTENSE, FRAGRANT AND STRUCTURAL SHIRAZ

WOLF BLASS®

L U X U R Y   R E L E A S E

2012

LUXURY RELEAS

Australian wineries and wines

A note on alphabetical order
Wineries beginning with 'The' are listed under 'T'; for example,
'The Wanderer'. Winery names that include a numeral are treated
as if the numeral is spelt out; for example, '2 Mates'
is listed under 'T'.

A. Retief   ★★★★☆

PO Box 2503, Strawberry Hills, NSW 2012 **Region** Southern New South Wales Zone
T 0400 650 530 **www**.aretief.com.au **Open** Not
Winemaker Alex Retief **Est.** 2008 **Dozens** 3000
Owner and winemaker Alex Retief's wine career was prompted by his parents planting a
vineyard near Ladysmith, in the Gundagai region, in 1997. The following year he enrolled
in the wine science course at CSU, and in 2001 was accepted as the trainee winemaker at
the university's winery under Greg Gallagher. In mid '02 he went to California's Sonoma
Valley for four months, working at Fetzer Vineyards, returning to the Hunter Valley for
the '03 vintage with Andrew Margan. He was winemaker there for two and a half years,
punctuated by a harvest in Languedoc in '04, before heading back to France in '05 for a
two-year appointment as winemaker at Chateau de Lagarde in Bordeaux. Since then he has
worked for Peter Lehmann Wines in Sydney as a sales representative, thereafter starting his
own boutique wine distribution company. Its portfolio includes A. Retief, imported wines
from Chateau de Lagarde, and local wines Eden Road, Cape Bernier, Capanno and Lawsons.
The A. Retief wines are made from contract-grown grapes in the Canberra District/Hilltops/
Gundagai regions.

ΨΨΨΨΨ **Tumbarumba Chardonnay 2011** If you enjoy racy chardonnay, assembled in
the Chablis mould, then this may be the wine for you; loaded with lemon, quartz
and laced with well-handled spicy oak, the palate is incredibly pure and long;
it would seem that Alex Retief has a handle on Tumbarumba fruit. Screwcap.
13% alc. **Rating** 94 **To** 2020 $45 BE

ΨΨΨΨΨ **Sauvignon Blanc Semillon 2011 Rating** 90 **To** 2015 $28 BE

ΨΨΨΨ **The Alias Hilltops Mataro 2010 Rating** 88 **To** 2016 $45 BE
Botrytis Grenache 2010 Rating 88 **To** 2014 $28 BE

A. Rodda Wines   ★★★★★

PO Box 589, Beechworth, Vic 3747 **Region** Beechworth
T 0400 350 135 **Open** Not
Winemaker Adrian Rodda **Est.** 2010 **Dozens** 600
Adrian Rodda has been winemaking since 1998, almost entirely working with David
Bicknell at Oakridge. He was thus involved in the development of the superb Oakridge 864
Chardonnay, his final contribution to 864 coming in 2009. At the start of 2010 he and his
wife Christie, a doctor, and their small but growing family, decided to move to Beechworth,
and it was no coincidence that he was a long-term friend of viticulturist Mark Walpole. Yet
further coincidences came with the Smith Vineyard and winery being available for lease; he
now shares it with Mark Walpole, who makes his Beechworth wines there. Even more, was
the availability of Smith Vineyard chardonnay, planted in 1974, and thus the release of the first
A. Rodda wine. One should hardly be surprised that it is so good. Further down the track
there will be a Yarra chardonnay from Murramong Vineyard, a single vineyard Tempranillo
from Mark Walpole's vineyard in Beechworth, and a Bordeaux blend sourced predominantly
from the old plantings on the Smith Vineyard.

ΨΨΨΨΨ **Beechworth Chardonnay 2010** The grapes were whole bunch-pressed direct
to barrel for a full solids, wild yeast fermentation; following fermentation the
wine was immediately sulphured to prevent the onset of mlf and retain natural
acidity. This is a totally delicious wine, with intense white peach, grapefruit and
French oak seamlessly married on the long palate and aftertaste. Screwcap. 13% alc.
Rating 96 **To** 2020 $40

A.T. Richardson Wines   ★★★★★

94 Hard Hill Road, Armstrong, Vic 3377 **Region** Grampians
T +1 925 321 6941 **www**.atrichardsonwines.com **Open** Not
Winemaker Adam Richardson **Est.** 2005 **Dozens** 1000 **Vyds** 6ha

Perth-born Adam Richardson began his winemaking career in 1995, along the way working for Normans, d'Arenberg and Oakridge Estate. Since that time he has been appointed Director of Global Winemaking for the international premium wines division of The Wine Group, the third-largest producer in the US. He is responsible for an annual production of more than five million dozen from Argentina, Australia, Austria, California, Chile, France, Germany, Italy, NZ, Oregon, Spain, South Africa and Washington. In 2005 he put down small roots in the Grampians region, acquiring a vineyard with shiraz from old clones from the 19th century, and riesling. Until early '10 all of his wines were exported to the US, but the Shirazs and Riesling are now being sold in Australia. They are exceptionally good wines, and given his experience and the quality of the vineyard, that should not come as a surprise. Exports to the US.

ŸŸŸŸŸ **Chockstone Grampians Shiraz 2010** Clear but deep crimson-purple; takes up
✪ where the '09 left off, with a bewitching assemblage of spice, pepper, licorice and black fruits, fine but persistent tannins and quality oak – all with an elegant, quasi-French, touch. Screwcap. 14.1% alc. **Rating** 95 **To** 2030 $25
Chockstone Grampians Riesling 2011 Light quartz-green; the floral, blossom-filled bouquet heralds a palate full to the brim with succulent lime juice flavours that may or may not have a hint of residual sugar; whichever way, the acid balance is spot on. Now or later. Screwcap. 12% alc. **Rating** 94 **To** 2020 $20

Abbey Creek Vineyard ★★★★☆
2388 Porongurup Road, Porongurup, WA 6324 **Region** Porongurup
T (08) 9853 1044 **F** (08) 9454 5501 **Open** By appt
Winemaker Castle Rock Estate (Robert Diletti) **Est.** 1990 **Dozens** 850 **Vyds** 1.6ha
This is the family business of Mike and Mary Dilworth, the name coming from a winter creek that runs alongside the vineyard and a view of The Abbey in the Stirling Range. The vineyard is equally split between riesling, pinot noir, sauvignon blanc and cabernet sauvignon planted in 1990 and '93. The Rieslings have had significant show success for a number of years, occasionally joined by the Pinot Noir at the top of the tree.

ŸŸŸŸŸ **Porongurup Riesling 2011** Pale quartz; a delicate, flowery bouquet and a
similarly delicate but perfectly balanced palate, lifting and expanding on the lime/citrus finish is archetypal Porongurup. Few white wines in Australia can match the development of these over 5–10 years. Screwcap. 12.5% alc. **Rating** 94
To 2021 $25

ŸŸŸŸŸ **Porongurup Sauvignon Blanc 2011 Rating** 92 **To** 2013 $24
Porongurup Pinot Noir 2009 Rating 91 **To** 2015 $30
Porongurup Cabernet Sauvignon 2003 Rating 90 **To** 2014 $25

Accolade Wines ★★★★★
Reynell Road, Reynella, SA 5161 **Region** Various
T (08) 8392 2300 **www.**accolade-wines.com **Open** Not
Winemaker Various **Est.** 2011 **Dozens** NFP
Accolade Wines is the newly created and named business that was acquired by a private equity group (CHAMP) from Constellation Wines of the US in June 2011. The principal Australian brands owned by Accolade are Amberley, Banrock Station, Bay of Fires/House of Arras, Brookland Valley, Goundrey, Hardys, Houghton, Leasingham, Moondah Brook, Reynella, Tintara and Yarra Burn. Exports to all major markets.

Ada River ★★★☆
2330 Main Road, Neerim South, Vic 3831 **Region** Gippsland
T (03) 5628 1661 **F** (03) 5628 1661 **Open** W'ends & public hols 10–6
Winemaker Peter Kelliher **Est.** 1983 **Dozens** 500 **Vyds** 10ha
The Kelliher family first planted vines on their dairy farm at Neerim South in 1983, extending the vineyard in '89 and increasing plantings further by establishing the nearby Manilla Vineyard

in '94. Until 2000, Ada River leased a Yarra Valley vineyard; it relinquished that lease and in its place established a vineyard at Heathcote in conjunction with a local grower.

ΨΨΨΨ **Heathcote Shiraz 2010** Purple-crimson; has fragrant plum, black cherry and blackberry fruit aromas on the bouquet; the full-bodied plate offers more of the same, but lacks line and enough structure. Screwcap. 14.4% alc. **Rating** 89 **To** 2018 $25

Heathcote Merlot 2010 Mid red-purple; has what seems to be the plummy fruit that many regard as the benchmark for merlot (I don't), but has been crippled by the over-enthusiastic use of oak. Screwcap. 14.7% alc. **Rating** 87 **To** 2015 $25

Adelaide Winemakers ★★★★☆

PO Box 72, Blackwood, SA 5051 **Region** Various SA
T (08) 8383 5500 **www.**adelaidewinemakers.com.au **Open** Not
Winemaker Nick Haselgrove **Est.** 2010 **Dozens** 25 000 **Vyds** 418ha
As a result of various sales, amalgamations and disposals of particular brands, Adelaide Winemakers is now owned (equally) by Nick Haselgrove, David Watkins and Warren Randall. It either owns, part-owns or is in the process of absorbing some of the external part-ownerships of some of the brands (The Old Faithful – see separate entry – Quorum, Blackbilly, James Haselgrove, The Old Gentlemen, Clarence Hill, Ace High and Martins Road). Adelaide Winemakers works with World Wine Headquarters (with old friend John Larchet) for the Wishing Tree, Hill of Content and Tir na N'og brands. Adelaide Winemakers has over 400ha of vines across Adelaide Hills (5ha), McLaren Vale (27ha), Langhorne Creek (216ha) and Currency Creek (170ha), giving the interconnected businesses a great deal of flexibility. Exports to the UK, the US and other major markets.

ΨΨΨΨΨ **Tir na N'og Old Vines McLaren Vale Grenache 2008** Has retained good colour given the vintage; has the power, focus and concentration of the best McLaren Vale grenache, seldom equalled in the Barossa; while only medium-bodied, its energy drives the mix of red and black fruits through a long and vibrant palate, with just the right amount of tannins to carry it forward. Diam. 14.5% alc. **Rating** 94 **To** 2018 $35

ΨΨΨΨΨ **Clarence Hill Adelaide Chardonnay 2011** Light straw-green; an exceptionally
✪ classy chardonnay at this price point; the varietal fruit is pure and intense, building flavour all the way through to the back-palate and finish, with white peach and cashew to the fore. Screwcap. 14.5% alc. **Rating** 93 **To** 2014 $14

James Haselgrove Futures McLaren Vale Shiraz 2009 **Rating** 93 **To** 2024 $40

✪ **Blackbilly McLaren Vale Grenache Shiraz Mourvedre 2010** Deep crimson; a fragrant and spicy bouquet of blackberry pastille, licorice and tar; the palate is medium-bodied, fleshy and fragrant, with plenty of stuffing and interest for the price. Screwcap. 14.5% alc. **Rating** 91 **To** 2018 $20 BE

✪ **Clarence Hill Adelaide Shiraz 2010** Deeply coloured, its full-bodied palate has layer upon layer of blackberry and bitter chocolate fruit, the tannins ripe and balanced, oak in a support role. Outstanding value. Screwcap. 14.5% alc. **Rating** 90 **To** 2020 $14

✪ **Blackbilly McLaren Vale Shiraz 2010** Deep colour and showing bright and fragrant black fruits, with licorice and mocha in abundance; the palate is juicy and vibrant, with tangy acidity playing the foil to such dense fruit. Screwcap. 14.5% alc. **Rating** 90 **To** 2018 $20 BE

ΨΨΨΨ **Clarence Hill Adelaide Grenache Shiraz 2010** **Rating** 89
✪ **To** 2015 $14

Clarence Hill Adelaide Cabernet Sauvignon 2009 **Rating** 88 **To** 2016 $14
The Wishing Tree Shiraz 2008 **Rating** 87 **To** 2014 $14
Blackbilly SB4 Sparkling Shiraz NV **Rating** 87 **To** 2013 $20

After Hours

455 North Jindong Road, Margaret River, WA 6285 **Region** Margaret River
T 0438 737 587 **www**.afterhours.com.au **Open** By appt
Winemaker Phil Potter **Est.** 2006 **Dozens** 1000 **Vyds** 8.6ha
In December 2005 Warwick and Cherylyn Mathews acquired the long-established Hopelands
Vineyard, planted to cabernet sauvignon (2.6ha), shiraz (1.6ha), merlot, semillon, sauvignon
blanc and chardonnay (1.1ha each). The first wine was made in '06, after which they decided
to completely rework the vineyard, requiring many hours of physical labour. The vines were
cut right and retrained, with a consequent reduction in yield and rise in wine quality.

ΨΨΨΨΨ **Margaret River Chardonnay 2010** Bright straw-green; the timing of the
✿   decision to pick was spot on, and everything followed on from that point, barrel
         fermentation and the choice of oak simply reinforcing the validity of the first
         decision; white peach, creamy cashew and tight acidity all make this a bargain.
         Screwcap. 13% alc. **Rating** 93 **To** 2018 $19

ΨΨΨΨ **Margaret River Sauvignon Blanc Semillon 2011** **Rating** 88 **To** 2013 $18

Aldersyde Estate

226 Aldersyde Road, Bickley, WA 6076 **Region** Perth Hills
T (08) 9293 3309 **www**.aldersyde.com.au **Open** Sat 1–5, Sun, public hols 10–5 & by appt
Winemaker Lara Bray **Est.** 1974 **Dozens** 600 **Vyds** 2.5ha
Aldersyde Estate is the mother and daughter venture of Di and Lara Bray, formerly known
as Piesse Brook. Lara Bray has joined the business as winemaker after an impressive career
as a Flying Winemaker with top producers around the world as well as at Mount Mary,
Brokenwood, Vasse Felix and Cape Mentelle in Australia. She was also dux of the Len Evans
Tutorial in 2008, named as one of the 50 stars of that year in *Wine Business Magazine*, and has
since judged at the Margaret River, Swan Valley, Perth and Perth Hills shows, and the Qantas
Wine Show of WA, Geographe and at the Air New Zealand Awards. All this came after she
had obtained her law degree. Wines were received after this issue went to print; tasting notes
appear on www.winecompanion.com.au.

Alkoomi

Wingebellup Road, Frankland River, WA 6396 **Region** Frankland River
T (08) 9855 2229 **www**.alkoomiwines.com.au **Open** 7 days 10–5
Winemaker Andrew Cherry, Dougal Herd **Est.** 1971 **Dozens** 90 000 **Vyds** 103.5ha
For those who see the wineries of WA as suffering from the tyranny of distance, this most
remote of all wineries shows there is no tyranny after all. It is a story of unqualified success due
to sheer hard work, and no doubt to founders Merv and Judy Lange's aversion to borrowing
a single dollar from the bank. The substantial production is entirely drawn from the estate
vineyards – now over 100ha. Wine quality across the range is impeccable, always with precisely
defined varietal character. In April '10 Merv and Judy announced that from July '10 their
daughter Sandy Hallett would assume full ownership and control of Alkoomi, having been an
integral part of the business for many years. She and husband Rod, together with daughters
Laura, Emily and Molly, represent the second and third generations to be involved in this
remarkably successful family business. Exports to all major markets.

ΨΨΨΨΨ **Black Label Frankland River Chardonnay 2010** Bright straw-green; you
✿   get the whole kit and caboodle with this wine, which marries the entire range
         of chardonnay aromas and flavours with barrel fermentation in French oak:
         grapefruit, white and yellow peach, fig, lychee and citrus/mineral acidity to close.
         Screwcap. 13% alc. **Rating** 94 **To** 2017 $22.34

ΨΨΨΨΨ **Frankland River Semillon Sauvignon Blanc 2010** An estate-grown blend
✿   with a powerful, albeit unusual, fuzzy peach skin aroma on the bouquet, moving
         more to tropical fruit on the palate, cut grass and herbs ever present in the
         background of the long finish. Screwcap. 11.5% alc. **Rating** 92 **To** 2015 $21

○   **White Label Frankland River Shiraz 2010** Bright crimson-purple; the
     medium-bodied palate is full of fresh red and black fruits courtesy of the estate
     vines; the finish is long and persuasive thanks to fine-grained tannins, the aftertaste
     confirming what has gone before. Screwcap. 13.9% alc. **Rating** 91 **To** 2017 $16
     White Label Frankland River Sauvignon Blanc 2011 **Rating** 90
     To 2013 $15.89

♥♥♥♥   **White Label Frankland River Chardonnay 2011** **Rating** 89 **To** 2014 $16
        White Label Frankland River Late Harvest 2011 **Rating** 88 **To** 2014 $16 BE

All Saints Estate   ★★★★★

All Saints Road, Wahgunyah, Vic 3687 **Region** Rutherglen
T (02) 6035 2222 **www**.allsaintswine.com.au **Open** Mon–Sat 9–5.30, Sun 10–5.30
Winemaker Dan Crane **Est.** 1864 **Dozens** 30 500 **Vyds** 33.46ha
The winery rating reflects the fortified wines, but the table wines are also in the top drawer.
The Terrace restaurant makes this a most enjoyable stop for any visitor to Northeast Victoria.
The faux castle, modelled on a Scottish castle beloved by the founder, is classified by the
Historic Buildings Council. All Saints and St Leonards are owned and managed by fourth-
generation Brown family members Eliza, Angela and Nicholas. Eliza is an energetic and
highly intelligent leader, wise beyond her years, and highly regarded by the wine industry. Dan
Crane's winemaking skills across the whole portfolio are very impressive. Exports to the UK.

♥♥♥♥♥   **Rare Rutherglen Muscat NV** A highly aromatic perfumed bouquet, then
         a palate that, while holding firm to the raisin aromas and flavours expected
         of muscat, dares to introduce the idea of elegance into this level of intensity.
         Remarkable wine, marching to the tune of its own drum. 375ml. Vino-Lok.
         18% alc. **Rating** 98 **To** 2013 $115
         Rare Rutherglen Topaque NV Burnt umber grading to olive on the rim; apart
         from a highly perfumed array of spices on the bouquet, it is the sheer intensity and
         complexity of the wine that tells of its very long time in wood, and the consequent
         development of rancio; the final magic of the wine is its semi-dry finish that
         cleanses the mouth. 375ml. Vino-Lok. 18% alc. **Rating** 97 **To** 2013 $115
         Durif 2010 Once again, this is an outstanding example of balanced, fresh,
         complex and compelling durif; the bouquet is loaded with ample sweet black
         fruits, layers of spice and a little gamey complexity; the palate is full-bodied and
         fresh, with an expansive profile and a myriad of possibilities for interesting food
         and wine pairing; lovely stuff. Screwcap. 14% alc. **Rating** 95 **To** 2025 $28 BE
         Alias II 2007 A blend of 95% shiraz and 5% muscadelle, used in the 19th century
         at All Saints. The blend works seriously well here, the texture a mix of silk and
         taffeta, the flavours of black fruits, earth and spice, the tannins fine and persistent.
         Vino-Lok. 14.8% alc. **Rating** 94 **To** 2020 $35

♥♥♥♥♀   **Rutherglen Muscat NV** Amber-brown; full-on potent raisin flavours, the spirit,
○   treacle and butterscotch also adding to the weight and concentration of the
         flavour. 375ml. Vino-Lok. 17% alc. **Rating** 93 **To** 2013 $22
         Family Cellar Durif 2009 **Rating** 92 **To** 2018 $60 BE
○   **Rutherglen Tokay NV** Light gold-amber; has strong varietal character, with a
         mix of honey, singed toffee and tea leaf; overall has greater weight and complexity
         than many in this bottom-of-the-range classification. 375ml. Vino-Lok. 17% alc.
         Rating 92 **To** 2013 $22
         Marsanne 2010 **Rating** 91 **To** 2018 $22 BE
         Chenin Blanc 2011 **Rating** 90 **To** 2015 $22 BE

♥♥♥♥   **Family Cellar Marsanne 2010** **Rating** 89 **To** 2016 $30 BE
        Limited Release Ruby Cabernet 2010 **Rating** 89 **To** 2018 $30 BE
        Chardonnay 2011 **Rating** 88 **To** 2014 $22 BE
        Rosa 2011 **Rating** 88 **To** 2014 $18 BE
        Sangiovese Cabernet 2009 **Rating** 88 **To** 2015 $22 BE
        Riesling 2011 **Rating** 87 **To** 2016 $22 BE

Allies Wines

15 Hume Road, Somers, Vic 3927 (postal) **Region** Mornington Peninsula
T 0412 111 587 **F** (03) 5983 1523 **www**.allies.com.au **Open** Not
Winemaker David Chapman **Est.** 2003 **Dozens** 900
Founders Barney Flanders and David Chapman have had an amicable business separation.
David will be making the wines under the Allies brand, Barney taking on the Garagiste
label. Henceforth, David will concentrate on wines from the Mornington Peninsula and, in
particular, pinot noir. He plans to release a range of pinot noirs reflecting the diverse sites
(climate and soil) of the Peninsula. The wines will be line-priced: in other words, the aim is
to highlight differing site characters, rather than differing wine quality.

♥♥♥♥♀ **Merricks Mornington Peninsula Pinot Noir 2010** Clear purple-red; a
remarkably round and generous pinot given its alcohol, with plum to the fore,
supported by red cherry pip and an airbrush of savoury tannins. Will gain more
complexity over the next 3-4 years. Screwcap. 13% alc. **Rating** 93 **To** 2017 $32

Allusion Wines

Smith Hill Road, Yankalilla, SA 5203 **Region** Southern Fleurieu
T (08) 8558 3333 **F** (08) 8558 3333 **Open** Thurs–Sun 11–5
Winemaker Contract **Est.** 1996 **Dozens** NA
Steve and Wendy Taylor purchased the property on which Allusion Wines is established in
1980, and have since planted 4ha of vines and 35 000 trees. Steve Taylor's 20 years as a chef
has strongly influenced both the varietal plantings and the wine styles made: not altogether
surprisingly, they are designed to be consumed with good food. The wine is fermented offsite,
then matured onsite before being contract-bottled.

♥♥♥♥ **Semillon Sauvignon Blanc 2011** Ripe fruit aromas and flavours run right
through until falling away slightly on the finish. Screwcap. 12.5% alc. **Rating** 87
To 2013 $18

Alta Vineyards

102 Main Street, Hahndorf, SA 5245 **Region** Adelaide Hills
T (08) 8388 7155 **www**.altavineyards.com.au **Open** 7 days 10.30–5
Winemaker Sarah Fletcher **Est.** 2003 **Dozens** 10 000 **Vyds** 23ha
Sarah Fletcher came to Alta with an impressive winemaking background: a degree from
Roseworthy, and thereafter seven years working for Orlando Wyndham. There she came face
to face with grapes from all over Australia, and developed a particular regard for those coming
from the Adelaide Hills. So she joined Alta, which had already established a reputation for its
Sauvignon Blanc. The portfolio has been progressively extended with varieties suited to the
cool climate of the Adelaide Hills. Exports to the UK, Canada and Hong Kong.

♥♥♥♥♀ **Adelaide Hills Sauvignon Blanc 2011** Pale straw-green; has significantly
greater structure than most due to small portions fermented on skins, and in oak
vats; selected sauvignon blanc yeasts also played a role in a herb and mineral-
accented palate. Screwcap. 12.5% alc. **Rating** 93 **To** 2013 $20

♥♥♥♥ **Adelaide Hills Pinot Grigio 2011 Rating** 89 **To** Now $20
for Elsie Pinot Noir Rose 2011 Rating 88 **To** Now $20

Amadio Wines

461 Payneham Road, Felixstow, SA 5070 **Region** Adelaide Hills
T (08) 8337 5144 **www**.amadiowines.com.au **Open** Mon–Fri 9–6, Sat 9–5.30
Winemaker Danniel Amadio **Est.** 2004 **Dozens** 75 000 **Vyds** 200ha
Danniel Amadio says he has followed in the footsteps of his Italian grandfather, selling wine
from his cellar (cantina) direct to the consumer, cutting out wholesale and distribution.
He also draws upon the business of his parents, built not in Italy, but in Australia. Amadio
Wines has substantial vineyards, primarily in the Adelaide Hills, and also small parcels of

contract- grown grapes from Clare Valley, McLaren Vale and Langhorne Creek, covering just about every variety imaginable, and with a very strong representation of Italian varieties. Exports to the UK, the US, Canada, Russia, South Korea, Singapore, Hong Kong and China.

ŸŸŸŸŸ **Block 2a Shiraz 2008** Good retention of colour; a very intense and complex wine, a little oaky on the bouquet, but expanding on the palate with dark berry and plum fruit, licorice and spice; tannins help to disguise the oak, and extend the finish. Cork. 14.5% alc. **Rating** 93 **To** 2023 $45

✪ **Adelaide Hills Sauvignon Blanc 2011** Pale straw-green; both the bouquet and palate offer a mix of citrus, kiwi fruit, lychee and stone fruit underpinned by crisp acidity. The cool vintage shows well. Screwcap. 12.5% alc. **Rating** 92 **To** Now $20

✪ **Adelaide Hills Cabernet Sauvignon 2007** Holding its hue well; has some attractive cassis varietal fruit, and the tannins are finer and riper than most from this tough vintage; good length and balance. Screwcap. 14.5% alc. **Rating** 92 **To** 2016 $20

✪ **Adelaide Hills Pinot Grigio 2011** Pale straw-pink; an attractive wine, and my only quarrel with the back label description of 'nashi pear and lemon citrus on the nose and guava, green lime and hints of honey on the palate in the offing' is that this is a description not of grigio, but of gris. Screwcap. 13% alc. **Rating** 91 **To** 2013 $20

Sebastien's Adelaide Hills Cabernet Sauvignon 2008 Good, clear red-purple, excellent given its age; the bouquet is fragrant, with cassis aromas, oak and tannins coming through on the blackcurrant palate. The cork permitting, should be long lived, and will benefit from further time in bottle. Cork. 14.5% alc. **Rating** 91 **To** 2023 $45

Barossa Valley Aglianico 2010 Light crimson-red; there is a chamber orchestra of fruit aromas and flavours, yet all encompassed in a reasonably limited space, with none of the fearsome tannins predicted by the back-palate. Moreover, there are some really charming red fruit notes to be found. Screwcap. 14% alc. **Rating** 91 **To** 2018 $33

Barossa Valley Sagrantino 2010 The colour is distinctly less brilliant than that of the Aglianico, losing the tinge of purple; the bouquet has dark fruit aromas that carry through in a slightly altered fashion to the palate; here there are flavours of stewed plum, spiced cake and glace cherries; the tannins are soft and in balance. Screwcap. 14% alc. **Rating** 91 **To** 2016 $33

● **Adelaide Hills Sangiovese 2009 Rating** 90 **To** 2016 $20

ŸŸŸŸ **Adelaide Hills Shiraz 2009 Rating** 89 **To** 2016 $20
Rosso Quattro 2009 Rating 88 **To** Now $17
Vino di Famiglia Adelaide Hills Rossa Superiore 2009 Rating 87 **To** 2013 $15
Biljana Brut NV Rating 87 **To** 2014 $20

Ambar Hill   ★★★

364 Mt Stirling Road, Glen Aplin, Qld 4381 **Region** Granite Belt
T 0409 631 292 **www**.ambarhill.com.au **Open** Not
Winemaker Jim Barnes **Est.** 2001 **Dozens** 500 **Vyds** 2.5ha
Graham and Judy Dalton have planted 2.5ha of shiraz, cabernet sauvignon, cabernet franc, merlot, verdelho, chardonnay and semillon, with the first wine produced in 2003. Both have varied backgrounds stretching back to Canberra in the Whitlam era. Graham is an economist-turned-restaurateur, previously a prison reform consultant and running the Qld Farmers' Federation. The wines, incidentally, are sold wholesale through Fino Food + Wine of Bulimba, Qld.

ŸŸŸŸ **Reserve Chardonnay 2008** Hand-picked and barrel-fermented in new French oak; has considerable presence and texture, the fruit powerful enough to largely absorb the oak. No hurry to drink it. Screwcap. 12.5% alc. **Rating** 89 **To** 2018 $18

Amberley

10460 Vasse Highway, Nannup, WA 6275 **Region** Margaret River
T 1800 088 711 **www**.amberley-estate.com.au **Open** Not
Winemaker Lance Parkin **Est.** 1986 **Dozens** NFP

Initial growth was based on its ultra-commercial, fairly sweet Chenin Blanc, which continues to provide the volume for the brand. However, the quality of all the other wines has risen markedly over recent years as the 31ha of estate plantings have become fully mature. Became part of CWA (now Accolade Wines) following Constellation Wines' acquisition of Canadian winemaker Vincor, which had in turn acquired Amberley Estate in early 2004. Accolade sold the vineyard, cellar and restaurant facility to family interests associated with Stephen Tobin, a Perth-based businessman, in 2010, but retained the brand; the wines are now made elsewhere. Exports to the UK, the US and Pacific Islands.

Secret Lane Margaret River Cabernet Merlot 2010 The fragrant and silky bouquet and the positive oak contribution will please many consumers as much as the judges at the Perth and National Wine Shows '11, who gave it a gold medal; the plum and mint flavours add pheromones to the call of a wine full of soft red and black fruits. Screwcap. 13.5% alc. **Rating** 94 **To** 2017 $20

Merlot 2010 If all merlots were like this, you could understand why they are so popular in the marketplace; it is medium-bodied, supple and smooth, with notes of cassis, plum and red cherry, with seductive mouthfeel, and welcoming the faintly savoury tannins on the finish. Screwcap. 13.5% alc. **Rating** 93 **To** 2018 $19

Secret Lane Margaret River Semillon Sauvignon Blanc 2011 The wine has notable structure and grip, which are positives, for they support the kiwi fruit, citrus and stone fruit flavours, the grip coming from the minerality that runs through from start to finish. Screwcap. 13% alc. **Rating** 90 **To** 2014 $20

Secret Lane Margaret River Sauvignon Blanc 2011 Rating 89 **To** 2013 $20
Chenin Blanc 2011 Rating 89 **To** 2013 $19

Amelia Park Wines

PO Box 749, Dunsborough, WA 6281 **Region** Margaret River
T (08) 9756 7007 **www**.ameliaparkwines.com.au **Open** Not
Winemaker Jeremy Gordon **Est.** 2009 **Dozens** 20 000

This brings together Jeremy Gordon, wife Daniela and business partner Peter Walsh. Jeremy had a winemaking career starting with Evans & Tate and thereafter Houghton, before moving to the eastern states to broaden his winemaking experience. After several years, he returned to the west to co-found Flametree Wines in 2007. In its first year, Flametree was awarded six trophies and over 30 medals. Amelia Park has no vineyards of its own, but that has not stopped its rapid growth. Exports to the UK, Russia, China, Hong Kong, Singapore, Thailand, South Korea, Macau, Indonesia, Japan and NZ.

Reserve Frankland River Shiraz 2010 Strong purple-crimson; in that finely structured yet intensely flavoured style that Frankland River does so well; spice, plum and black cherry fruit are interwoven through outstanding silky tannins, oak adding a contribution. Excellent line, length and balance. Screwcap. 14.5% alc. **Rating** 95 **To** 2025 $49

Margaret River Chardonnay 2010 An aromatic display of grapefruit and melon on the bouquet feeds into the lively palate that adds some stone fruit and cashew/almond to the flavour spectrum; the oak is restrained, and fruit flavours and acidity do the hard yards. Screwcap. 13.5% alc. **Rating** 94 **To** 2016 $29

Margaret River Cabernet Merlot 2010 Good colour; a serious yet elegant medium-bodied cabernet merlot, perfectly framed and balanced, the blend wholly synergistic and seamless. After a year in French oak, it will loosen up nicely over the next few years, and go on from there. Screwcap. 14.5% alc. **Rating** 94 **To** 2020 $29

ΨΨΨΨΨ **Mishmash Margaret River Red 2010** Light, bright red-purple; a silky and
✪   seductuve fruit-driven wine from start to finish, with red and black berry fruits,
        and an airbrush of oak and tannins. In a remarkable double, both this wine and the
        '10 Cabernet Merlot won gold medals in class 25 at the National Wine Show '11.
        Screwcap. 14% alc. **Rating** 93 **To** 2013 $15
✪   **Margaret River Sauvignon Blanc Semillon 2011** Pale quartz; an elegant
        light-bodied wine that creeps up on you, gently unfolding lime, apple and
        passionfruit on the palate, the acidity precise and balanced. Screwcap. 13% alc.
        Rating 92 **To** 2013 $22
        Frankland River Shiraz 2010 Rating 92 **To** 2020 $29
        Reserve Margaret River Cabernet Sauvignon 2010 Rating 91 **To** 2025 $49

ΨΨΨΨ   **Mishmash Margaret River White 2011 Rating** 89 **To** 2013 $15

Amherst Winery   ★★★★☆

Talbot-Avoca Road, Amherst, Vic 3371 **Region** Pyrenees
T (03) 5463 2105 **www.**amherstwinery.com **Open** W'ends & public hols 10–5
Winemaker Andrew Koerner (Consultant), Luke Jones **Est.** 1989 **Dozens** 3000 **Vyds** 4.5ha
Norman and Elizabeth Jones have planted vines on a property with an extraordinarily rich
history, which is commemorated in the name Dunn's Paddock Shiraz. Samuel Knowles was
a convict who arrived in Van Diemen's Land in 1838. He endured continuous punishment
before fleeing to SA in 1846 and changing his name to Dunn. When, at the end of 1851, he
married 18-year-old Mary Therese Taaffe in Adelaide, they walked from Adelaide to Amherst
pushing a wheelbarrow carrying their belongings, arriving just before gold was discovered.
The lease title of the property shows that Amherst Winery is sited on land once owned by
Samuel Dunn. Exports to China.

ΨΨΨΨΨ **Chinese Gardens Pyrenees Cabernet Sauvignon 2010** Light, bright
        crimson-purple; fragrant cassis aromas on the bouquet lead into a fresh, light- to
        medium-bodied palate, with cassis again to the fore, French oak, fine tannins
        and crisp acidity bringing up the rear. Cabernet sauvignon a la mode. Screwcap.
        12.5% alc. **Rating** 93 **To** 2020 $28
        Dunn's Paddock Pyrenees Shiraz 2010 Bright, clear crimson; the fragrant
        bouquet leads into a medium-bodied palate with ripe black cherry and blackberry
        fruit; 15 months in French oak has coated the palate with a veneer of oak, which
        is more likely than not to dissipate over the next few years. Screwcap. 13% alc.
        Rating 92 **To** 2019 $28

ΨΨΨΨ   **Daisy Creek Pyrenees Chardonnay 2010** Light straw-green; has been picked
✪   very early, but avoided green fruit or quasi-sauvignon blanc flavours; that said, it
        is true that citrus and grapefruit are the players, with only a hint of oak in the
        background. Screwcap. 12% alc. **Rating** 89 **To** 2015 $16
        Daisy Creek Pyrenees Shiraz Cabernet 2010 Rating 87 **To** 2013 $16

Amietta Vineyard   ★★★★★

30 Steddy Road, Lethbridge, Vic 3332 **Region** Geelong
T (03) 5281 7407 **www.**amietta.com.au **Open** 1st Sun each month 10–4 or by appt
Winemaker Nicholas Clark, Janet Cockbill **Est.** 1995 **Dozens** 450 **Vyds** 2.77ha
Janet Cockbill and Nicholas Clark are multi-talented. Both are archaeologists, but Janet is a
multi-tasking genius, combining archaeology, radiography, organic viticulture and wrangling
their two small sons. Nicholas studied viticulture at CSU, and both he and Janet worked
vintage at Michel Chapoutier's biodynamic Domaine des Béates in Provence in 2001.
Plantings include lagrein and carmenere. In 2012 Janet (aged 43) and Nicholas (aged 54)
were presented with a surprise baby girl, who arrived prematurely. Chaos has been restored,
but they are limited to a 'subsistence' living with their winemaking, only releasing one wine
a year. Taking a leaf from JJ Prum, the level of SO_2 is deliberately high to guarantee the long
life ahead of the wine.

ŶŶŶŶŶ **Biodynamic Geelong Riesling 2010** Bright green-yellow; a beautifully made wine, with fruit, residual sugar and acid in harmonious balance; the net result is a wine bursting with sweet lime fruit. The ultimate style for Chinese or Japanese food. Screwcap. 11% alc. **Rating** 95 **To** 2025 $31

Anderson ★★★☆

Lot 13 Chiltern Road, Rutherglen, Vic 3685 **Region** Rutherglen
T (02) 6032 8111 **www**.andersonwinery.com.au **Open** 7 days 10–5
Winemaker Howard and Christobelle Anderson **Est.** 1992 **Dozens** 1500 **Vyds** 8.8ha
Having notched up a winemaking career spanning over 50 years, including a stint at Seppelt (Great Western), Howard Anderson and family started their own winery, initially with a particular focus on sparkling wine but now extending across all table wine styles. The original estate plantings of shiraz, durif and petit verdot (6ha) were expanded in 2007–08 with tempranillo, saperavi, brown muscat, chenin blanc and viognier.

ŶŶŶŶŶ **Rutherglen Shiraz Rose 2011** Pale pink; fresh red fruit and spice bouquet, with fennel and citrus; the palate is fleshy, clean and dry. Screwcap. 10.2% alc. **Rating** 90 **To** 2013 $19 BE

ŶŶŶŶ **Cellar Block Durif 2006 Rating** 87 **To** 2013 $33 BE

Angas Plains Estate ★★★★★

Lot 52 Angas Plains Road, Langhorne Creek, SA 5255 **Region** Langhorne Creek
T (08) 8537 3159 **www**.angasplainswines.com.au **Open** 7 days 11–5
Winemaker Peter Douglas **Est.** 1994 **Dozens** 3000 **Vyds** 15.2ha
In 1994 Phillip and Judy Cross began planting a vineyard on their 40ha property, situated on the old flood plains of the Angas River, which only flows after heavy rains in its catchment of the Adelaide Hills. With the assistance of son Jason they manage the property to minimise water use and maximise the accumulation of organic matter. Skilled contract winemaking has resulted in some excellent wines from the estate-grown shiraz (14ha), cabernet sauvignon (10ha) and chardonnay (1.2ha). Exports to China.

ŶŶŶŶŶ **PJ's Special Langhorne Creek Shiraz 2008** The gold braid knotted on the neck of this and the Special Reserve certainly catches the eye. Healthy garnet-red; the wine has the mouthfilling fruit that Langhorne Creek so often achieves, at once medium- to full-bodied but soft, with luscious red and black fruits, it looks to McLaren Vale for a touch of dark chocolate, and to the winery for the ample oak. Diam. 14.5% alc. **Rating** 94 **To** 2020 $28
Special Reserve Langhorne Creek Shiraz 2008 The taller, heavier bottle and finer braid around the neck of the bottle make the same statement as PJ's. The best parcels of fruit and the best barrels went to make this wine, the lower alcohol in no way restricting the depth of flavour; it fills the mouth with supple tannins, plum and red and black berries, the finish long and balanced. Diam. 14% alc. **Rating** 94 **To** 2023 $40

Angelicus ★★★☆

Lot 9 Catalano Road, Burekup, WA 6227 **Region** Geographe
T 0429 481 425 **www**.angelicus.com.au **Open** W'ends & public hols 11–4 or by appt
Winemaker John Ward, Sue Ward **Est.** 1997 **Dozens** 500 **Vyds** 0.8ha
Dr John and Sue Ward moved from Sydney to WA with the aim of establishing a vineyard and winery, settling first on a property in the Middlesex Valley of Pemberton. Despite the success of that venture, they have decided to move to the Geographe region, where they have purchased a 51ha block of granite-strewn rocky hillside facing north and west at Burekup, 200m above sea level, looking towards the Indian Ocean. They have retained the Angelicus label and the stock from their previous vineyard. In 2009 they began the planting of their vines, the lion's share to grenache (bush vines, managed biodynamically), five clones of tempranillo, and verdelho. In the interim, they are purchasing grenache, mourvedre, shiraz and tempranillo from growers in the region.

ŸŸŸŸŸ Garnacha Shiraz Monastrell 2010 Bright, clear red; strongly savoury spicy aromas and flavours are the first impression, but red fruits also come through on retasting, plus a hint of eucalypt. The firm structure is admirable. Screwcap. 14.5% alc. Rating 92 To 2015 $24

ŸŸŸŸ Tempranillo 2010 Rating 89 To 2020 $24

Angove Family Winemakers ★★★★★

Bookmark Avenue, Renmark, SA 5341 **Region** South Australia
T (08) 8580 3100 **www**.angove.com.au **Open** Mon–Fri 9–5, Sat 10–4, Sun & pub hols 10–3
Winemaker Tony Ingle, Paul Kernich, Ben Horley, Amelia Hildebrand **Est.** 1886
Dozens 1.5 million **Vyds** 480ha
Exemplifies the economies of scale achievable in the Riverland without compromising potential quality. Very good technology provides wines that are never poor and sometimes exceed their theoretical station in life. The vast Nanya Vineyard is currently being redeveloped with changes in the varietal mix, row orientation and a partial move to organic growing. Angove's expansion into Padthaway (chardonnay), Watervale (riesling) and Coonawarra (cabernet sauvignon) via long-term contracts, and the purchase of the Warboys Vineyard in McLaren Vale in 2008, have resulted in outstanding premium wines to back up its Riverland wines. In 2012 Angove celebrated its 125th anniversary, with the opening of a large, modern cellar door and cafe on the Medyk Vineyard at the corner of Chalk Hill Rd/Olivers Rd, open 10–5 daily. Exports to all major markets.

ŸŸŸŸŸ Warboys Vineyard McLaren Vale Shiraz 2010 Deep purple-crimson; the bouquet exudes sultry black fruits, spice and dark chocolate, the luscious multilayered palate has exceptional mouthfeel, the fruit on a soft swan's down pillow of tannins, and a lingering finish. 176 dozen made. Screwcap. 14% alc. Rating 96 To 2030 $35

Warboys Vineyard McLaren Vale Shiraz 2009 Sourced from vines on the northwestern corner of the estate Warboys Vineyard, with a southerly aspect exposed to breezes from the Gulf of St Vincent, and matured in French oak; a barrel selection of 176 dozen bottles ex French oak. It has exceptional mouthfeel, superb fruit in a soft swan's down pillow of tannins, and a lingering finish. Screwcap. 14% alc. Rating 96 To 2030 $35

Warboys Vineyard McLaren Vale Shiraz Grenache 2010 A role model for those seeking to combine elegance with intense red fruit and spice (ex grenache) with savoury blackberry and dark chocolate (ex shiraz). 386 dozen made. Screwcap. 14.5% alc. Rating 96 To 2025 $35

Warboys Vineyard McLaren Vale Shiraz Grenache 2009 Good colour; a 60%/40% blend from two sections of the vineyard, each suited to the variety in question; the viticultural and winemaking choices have been exceptional. This is a role model for those seeking elegance to accompany intense varietal flavours of the red fruits of the grenache and the black of the shiraz. 386 dozen made. Screwcap. 14% alc. Rating 96 To 2029 $25

Rare Average Age 15 Years Tawny NV Burnt umber colour; a lusciously rich yet nimble mix of fruitcake, mocha, toffee, bitter chocolate and brandy snap. Another major surprise, winning the top gold medal in the small volume, aged fortified tawny class in the National Wine Show '11, causing the judges to comment 'a classic example of the style'. 500ml. Screwcap. 19.8% alc. Rating 96 To 2013 $45

The Medhyk Old Vine McLaren Vale Shiraz 2009 Excellent colour; fermented in half-tonne fermenters over an extended period, basket-pressed, and matured for 18 months in French barriques and puncheons; only 208 dozen bottles made. A very impressive '09 wine (how good will the '10 be?) with black fruits, licorice, dark chocolate and cedary French oak all in balance, alcohol contributing. Screwcap. 14.5% alc. Rating 95 To 2030 $50

○ **Warboys Vineyard McLaren Vale Grenache 2010** Very good colour as expected; another dimension of flavour from the great '10 vintage, but I am not convinced the oak use has not been a little too enthusiastic. It's a carping criticism, for this is a wonderful wine, and a fascinating contrast to the '09. Screwcap. 14% alc. **Rating** 95 **To** 2030 $35

♟♟♟♟♀
○ **Vineyard Select Adelaide Hills Sauvignon Blanc 2011** Light straw-green; a flowery, apple and citrus blossom bouquet is quickly overwhelmed by the intensity of the palate with green, zesty fruit flavours wrapped in minerally acidity. Excellent food style. Screwcap. 12.5% alc. **Rating** 92 **To** 2013 $18

○ **Vineyard Select Coonawarra Cabernet Sauvignon 2010** Deep garnet, bright; the bouquet is pure cassis, overlaid with a hint of eucalypt; the palate is young and very firm, with tannins playing a pivotal role to the fresh fruit on offer; unresolved at this early stage, time will see a vast improvement as the tannins soften. Screwcap. 13.5% alc. **Rating** 91 **To** 2018 $19 BE

Grand Average Age 10 Years Tawny NV Rating 91 **To** 2013 $25

○ **Butterfly Ridge Riesling Gewurztraminer 2011** A cleverly made wine, with a deliberate touch of residual sweetness making it a walk-up match for Chinese food, lime and lemon the driving flavours. Absurdly good at the price, for it has finesse and length. Screwcap. 11% alc. **Rating** 90 **To** 2013 $8

Nine Vines Grenache Shiraz Rose 2011 Rating 90 **To** Now $15

○ **Vineyard Select McLaren Vale Shiraz 2010** Strong crimson-purple; wild-fermented in 70-year-old open fermenters and spent 18 months in oak; the result is a medium- to full-bodied wine with an abundance of blackberry and plum fruit, plus good tannin structure for ageing. Screwcap. 14.5% alc. **Rating** 90 **To** 2020 $18

McLaren Vale Grenache Shiraz Mourvedre 2010 Rating 90 **To** 2018 $25

Angullong Wines   ★★★★☆

Victoria Street, Millthorpe, NSW 2798 **Region** Orange
T (02) 6366 4300 **www.**angullong.com.au **Open** W'ends & public hols 11–5
Winemaker Jon Reynolds **Est.** 1998 **Dozens** 15 000 **Vyds** 216.7ha
The Crossing family (Bill and Hatty, and third generation James and Ben) has owned a 2000ha sheep and cattle station for over half a century. Located 40km south of Orange, overlooking the Belubula Valley, more than 200ha of vines have been planted since 1998. In all, there are 15 varieties, with shiraz, cabernet sauvignon and merlot leading the way. Most of the production is sold to Hunter Valley wineries. Exports to Finland.

♟♟♟♟♟
○ **Fossil Hill Orange Pinot Gris 2011** Pale quartz; without question, one of the better pinot gris going around, with an intense mix of nashi pear, citrus, apple and honeysuckle, the pear dominant; has considerable length and a commendably dry palate. Screwcap. 13.5% alc. **Rating** 94 **To** 2014 $22

♟♟♟♟♀
○ **Orange Sauvignon Blanc 2011** Quartz-green; in the usual Angullong style, with tropical fruit aromas and flavours to the fore, ranging from passionfruit to more citrussy notes; has good acidity and length. Screwcap. 13% alc. **Rating** 92 **To** 2013 $17

The Pretender Central Ranges Savagnin 2011 Rating 90 **To** 2014 $22
Bull's Roar Central Ranges Tempranillo 2010 Rating 90 **To** 2015 $25

♟♟♟♟ **Fossil Hill Orange Cabernet Merlot 2009 Rating** 88 **To** 2015 $22
Orange Verdelho 2011 Rating 87 **To** Now $17

Angus the Bull   ★★★★

PO Box 611, Manly, NSW 1655 **Region** South Eastern Australia
T (02) 8966 9020 **www.**angusthebull.com **Open** Not
Winemaker Hamish MacGowan **Est.** 2002 **Dozens** 20 000
Hamish MacGowan has taken the virtual winery idea to its ultimate conclusion, with a single wine (Cabernet Sauvignon) designed to be drunk with premium red meat, or, more

particularly, a perfectly cooked steak. Parcels of grapes are selected from regions across Victoria and SA each year, the multiregional-blend approach designed to minimise vintage variation. Exports to the UK and other major markets.

🍷🍷🍷🍷🍷 **Cabernet Sauvignon 2010** Good purple hue; excellent varietal character; cassis/blackcurrant, ripe tannins, and subtle oak doing no more than is needed. Best in this line since it was started, an ideal full-bodied match for a rich, rare rump steak. Screwcap. 14.5% alc. **Rating** 92 **To** 2020 $20

Annie's Lane   ★★★★★

Quelltaler Road, Watervale, SA 5452 **Region** Clare Valley
T (08) 8843 2320 **www**.annieslane.com.au **Open** Mon–Fri 9–5, w'ends & public hols 10–4
Winemaker Alex MacKenzie **Est.** 1851 **Dozens** NFP
The Clare Valley brand of TWE, the name coming from Annie Weyman, a turn-of-the-century local identity. The brand consistently offers wines that over-deliver against their price points, with both wine show success and critical acclaim. Copper Trail is the flagship release, and there are some very worthy cellar door and on-premise wines. Exports to the UK, the US and Europe.

🍷🍷🍷🍷🍷 **Quelltaler Watervale Riesling 2011** Mid gold, bright green hue; a generous bouquet of nectarine, lime juice and musk; the palate is fleshy and at the rich end of the young Clare Valley riesling spectrum, yet the acidity is lively and direct; more pleasure than pain compared with many young wines of this style. Screwcap. 12.5% alc. **Rating** 94 **To** 2018 $25 BE
Quelltaler Watervale Shiraz Cabernet 2010 Vibrant purple hue; on the bouquet the cedar and cassis with a leafy edge shows a dominant cabernet personality, yet the spicy warm-fruited palate with licks of toasty new oak leans towards the shiraz; young and unevolved, a classic Australian blend executed seamlessly. Screwcap. 14.5% alc. **Rating** 94 **To** 2020 $25 BE
Clare Valley Riesling 2011 Rating 94 **To** 2021 $20

🍷🍷🍷🍷🍷 **Clare Valley Cabernet Merlot 2009** Has retained excellent hue; the expressive bouquet has cassis and black fruits plus a touch of spice, the medium-bodied palate building as it moves from the mid palate towards the finish. A few years in the cellar will see all the components settle down. Screwcap. 14% alc. **Rating** 91 **To** 2019 $21
Quelltaler Watervale Sparkling Shiraz NV Rating 91 **To** 2015 $25 BE
Clare Valley Semillon Sauvignon Blanc 2011 Rating 90 **To** 2013 $21

🍷🍷🍷🍷 **Clare Valley Rose 2011 Rating** 89 **To** Now $21
Botrytis Riesling 2009 Rating 89 **To** 2014 $25
Clare Valley Chardonnay 2011 Rating 87 **To** 2015 $21

Ansted & Co.   ★★★★☆

11 Flood Street, Bendigo, Vic 3550 (postal) **Region** Bendigo
T 0409 665 005 **www**.anstedandco.com.au **Open** Not
Winemaker Tobias Ansted **Est.** 2008 **Dozens** 300
Ansted & Co. was started as a busman's holiday by Tobias Ansted – then and now winemaker at Balgownie Estate – in 2003. Pressure of work and family commitments led to the sale of the vineyard in 2006, but with an agreement to buy back the grapes, and to manage the vineyard. While syrah was the initial planting, marsanne, roussanne and viognier will follow.

🍷🍷🍷🍷🍷 **North Harcourt Vineyard Syrah 2009** This is a selection of the best barrels, effectively splitting the vintage into two halves of 150 dozen bottles each. This is clearly the superior wine; the colour is excellent, and although the wine enters the mouth with a fanfare of trumpets and drums, it manages to gain finesse and drive on the back-palate and finish, the flavours covering a similar spectrum to Variation No. 1. Screwcap. 14.5% alc. **Rating** 94 **To** 2025 $35

♟♟♟♟♀ **Variation No. 1 Syrah 2009** From the same north Harcourt vineyard that
✪ provided the grapes for its sibling, it has exemplary crimson-purple colour, and
a considerable depth to the mix of black fruits, licorice, spice and oak on the
medium- to full-bodied palate. Will repay cellaring, and best left for a couple of
years if you can keep your hands off it. Screwcap. 14% alc. **Rating** 90 **To** 2019 $20

Antcliff's Chase

RMB 4510, Caveat via Seymour, Vic 3660 **Region** Strathbogie Ranges
T (03) 5790 4333 **F** (03) 5790 4333 **Open** W'ends 10–5
Winemaker Chris Bennett, Ian Leamon **Est.** 1982 **Dozens** 800
A small family enterprise that began with planting the vineyards at an elevation of 600m in
the Strathbogie Ranges in 1982; wine production from the 4ha vineyard commenced in the
early 1990s. After an uncertain start, wine quality has stabilised at a commendable level.

♟♟♟♟♀ **Strathbogie Ranges Lagrein 2008** Deep purple; a particularly potent and
concentrated wine with a fusion of black fruits, a whisper of bitter chocolate
before the palate breaks free on the finish, for the expected tannins simply aren't
there. Screwcap. 13.4% alc. **Rating** 90 **To** 2017 $30

♟♟♟♟ **Top Top Strathbogie Ranges Riesling 2010 Rating** 88 **To** 2014 $18
Strathbogie Ranges Riesling 2008 Rating 88 **To** 2014 $18
Strathbogie Ranges Botrytis Riesling 2010 Rating 88 **To** 2014 $24

Antipodean Vintners

82a Northgate Street, Unley Park, SA 5061 (postal) **Region** McLaren Vale
T (08) 8271 4546 **F** (08) 8377 7827 **Open** Not
Winemaker Matthew Rechner **Est.** 2008 **Dozens** 550
Antipodean Vintners started in 2008 as a venture between five friends – Mark and Simone
Perks, Jamie Craig, Sarah Matthews and Angelo Tsirbas – all self-confessed wine enthusiasts.
Their goal is to produce small batches of wine that best represent the location and vintage
from where the grapes are sourced. They buy the grapes for their wine from 95-year-old vines
in McLaren Vale. The first release from 2008 was an outstanding wine.

♟♟♟♟♟ **Tilly Devine McLaren Vale Shiraz 2008** From 90-year-old vines, hand-
picked, cold soaked in open fermenters and matured in French oak, 30% new.
Deep crimson-purple, the wine certainly shows the French oak, but there is
more than enough blackberry, plum and licorice fruit to accommodate that oak;
the mouthfeel is velvety, the finish soft but very long; no issue whatsoever with the
alcohol. Vino-Lok. 14.9% alc. **Rating** 96 **To** 2028 $36

Anvers

Cnr Chalk Hill Road/Foggo Road, McLaren Vale, SA 5171 **Region** Adelaide Hills
T (08) 8323 9603 **www.**anvers.com.au **Open** Not
Winemaker Kym Milne MW **Est.** 1998 **Dozens** 10 000 **Vyds** 24.5ha
Myriam and Wayne Keoghan established Anvers with the emphasis on quality rather than
quantity. The principal vineyard is in the Adelaide Hills at Kangarilla (16ha of cabernet
sauvignon, shiraz, chardonnay, sauvignon blanc and viognier), the second (96-year-old)
vineyard at McLaren Vale (shiraz, grenache and cabernet sauvignon). Winemaker Kym Milne
has experience gained across many of the wine-producing countries in both northern and
southern hemispheres. Exports to the UK and other major markets.

♟♟♟♟♟ **The Warrior Adelaide Hills McLaren Vale Langhorne Creek Shiraz
2009** Deep colour, slightly less bright than the McLaren Vale Shiraz; a regional
blend that works very well, although the Adelaide Hills drives the wine with its
spicy, lively, almost urgent thrust of black cherry/berry fruit, and the fine tannins
that underpin the long palate and finish. Especially pleasing to see the flagship
screwcapped, the standard wine cork-finished. So often it's the other way around.
Screwcap. 14.5% alc. **Rating** 95 **To** 2034 $47

♀♀♀♀♀ 20 Years Old Rare Tawny NV Rating 93 To Now $55
McLaren Vale Shiraz 2009 Rating 92 To 2019 $28
Langhorne Creek Cabernet Sauvignon 2009 Rating 92 To 2019 $28
✪ Adelaide Hills Sauvignon Blanc 2011 Pale quartz; in the gooseberry/grassy/
nettle end of the spectrum, but is fragrant, has good mouthfeel, and a long,
cleansing finish. Screwcap. 12.5% alc. **Rating** 90 To Now $20
Adelaide Hills Chardonnay 2010 Rating 90 To 2013 $24

♀♀♀♀ Razorback Road Adelaide Hills Shiraz Cabernet Sauvignon 2009
Rating 89 To 2015 $20
Adelaide Hills Sauvignon Blanc 2010 Rating 88 To Now $20

Aramis Vineyards   ★★★★
29 Sir Donald Bradman Drive, Mile End South, SA 5031 **Region** McLaren Vale
T (08) 8352 2900 **www**.aramisvineyards.com **Open** Mon–Fri 8–4, or by appt
Winemaker Contract **Est.** 1998 **Dozens** 15 000 **Vyds** 26ha
The estate vineyards have been planted to just two varieties: shiraz and cabernet sauvignon.
Viticulturist David Mills is a third-generation McLaren Vale resident and has been involved in
the establishment of the vineyards from the beginning. Winemaker Scott Rawlinson was with
Mildara Blass for eight years before joining the Aramis team under the direction of owner
Lee Flourentzou. Exports to the UK, the US, Canada, Singapore, Malaysia, Thailand, Vietnam,
Japan and Hong Kong.

♀♀♀♀♀ Single Vineyard McLaren Vale Shiraz 2010 Deep, dense crimson; it comes as
no surprise to find a full-bodied palate, the fruit amplified by 21 months in French
oak; flavours of highly concentrated blackberry, chocolate, licorice and earth are
given balance by savoury, but ripe, tannins. When it slims down in a decade or so,
will be even better than it is today. Screwcap. 14.5% alc. **Rating** 93 To 2030 $28
Single Vineyard McLaren Vale Cabernet Sauvignon 2010 Deep, dense
colour; a potent wine speaking as loudly about its varietal origin as the place
in which it lives; there is a cascade of black fruits, dark chocolate, French oak
(21 months) and tannins, all culminating in a long, earthy finish. Screwcap.
14.5% alc. **Rating** 93 To 2025 $25
Black Label McLaren Vale Cabernet Sauvignon 2009 Deep crimson-
purple; a powerful, full-bodied wine with everything correct except for one thing:
the tannins should have been fined, or the wine held even longer before release.
It's now up to you to make the decision; the one option I would not recommend
is to drink it now or soon. Screwcap. 14.5% alc. **Rating** 90 To 2019 $25

♀♀♀♀ White Label Eden Valley Riesling 2011 Rating 88 To 2014 $20
White Label Adelaide Hills Sauvignon Blanc 2011 Rating 88 To Now $20

Arete Wines   ★★★★☆
1 Banyan Court, Greenwith, SA 5125 (postal) **Region** Barossa Valley
T 0418 296 969 **www**.aretewines.com.au **Open** Not
Winemaker Richard Bate **Est.** 2008 **Dozens** 500
The name chosen by owner Richard Bate comes from Greek mythology, describing the
aggregate of all the qualities of valour, virtue and excellence that make up good character.
Having graduated with a Bachelor of Science (wine science major) from CSU, Richard
worked at Barossa Valley Estate, then Saltram, Wolf Blass and Penfolds. His next move was to
work for the Burgundian cooper François Frères distributing barrels within Australia, before
venturing into the challenging world of the small winemaker. His intention is to make single
vineyard wines wherever possible, with small quantities of each wine part of the strategy.

♀♀♀♀♀ Greenock Barossa Valley Shiraz 2009 A single vineyard selection, with
good red-purple colour; the intensity to its fruit has reacted well to a sojourn
of 20 months in François Frères oak (60% new), the blackberry, licorice and
plum fruit in a velvet slipper of quality oak, finishing with fine tannins. Screwcap.
14.5% alc. **Rating** 94 To 2019 $45

♀♀♀♀ The Chatterbox Barossa Valley Shiraz 2010 Rating 89 To 2020 $20

Argyle Estate Vineyards ★★★★☆

PO Box 486, Echunga, SA 5153 **Region** Adelaide Hills
T 0432 787 041 **Open** Not
Winemaker Linda Domas **Est.** 2007 **Dozens** 2000 **Vyds** 18.6ha
The Argyle Estate vineyard has a rich history. It was once part of a much larger property originally owned by one of SA's viticultural pioneers, John Barton Hack. He grew grapes on his Echunga property in the 1840s, and even sent a sample of his 'Hock' to Queen Victoria, following in the footsteps of Walter Duffield, who had earlier sent Queen Victoria a case of 1844 white, and was promptly prosecuted for making wine without the requisite licence. Re-establishment of the vineyard began in 1999 (by former owner Jock Calder and family), with sauvignon blanc, shiraz and riesling planted. Subsequent plantings have taken the area under vine to its present level. The vineyard was purchased by Paul Freer and Dennis Clift in 2007, with a name change from Cawdor Wines to Argyle Estate. Exports to China.

ΥΥΥΥ **Adelaide Hills Shiraz 2009** Deep crimson-purple; a supple, medium- to full-
✪   bodied wine that has a complex web of interacting flavours and texture, with multi-spice, plum cake, blackberry and a twist of pepper, all of which carry the warmth of the alcohol with ease. Screwcap. 15% alc. **Rating** 93 **To** 2024 $20

✪   **Adelaide Hills Cabernet Sauvignon 2009** Clear, bright red-purple; the fragrant blackcurrant fruit of the Adelaide Hills, with its nuances of mint and earth, has been offset by 15 months in American oak, designed – presumably – to contribute some softer, sweeter influences. I'm not sure I would make the same call. Screwcap. 14.5% alc. **Rating** 92 **To** 2019 $20

Arimia Margaret River ★★★★

Quininup Road, Wilyabrup, WA 6280 **Region** Margaret River
T (08) 9287 2411 **www.**arimia.com.au **Open** By appt
Winemaker Mark Warren **Est.** 1998 **Dozens** 3685 **Vyds** 5.9ha
Anne Spencer and Malcolm Washbourne purchased their 55ha property overlooking the Indian Ocean in 1997, its northern boundaries marked by the Cape Naturaliste National Park. Quininup Creek meanders through the property, providing the water source for its blue-green dam. The name is a combination of daughters Ariann and Mia. They have planted a Joseph's coat array of varieties, including semillon, sauvignon blanc, verdelho, chardonnay, cabernet sauvignon, merlot, petit verdot, shiraz, grenache, mourvedre and zinfandel. A new cellar door is planned for 2011.

ΥΥΥΥ **Shiraz Viognier 2009** Bright crimson-purple; has a fragrant bouquet of spiced
✪   plums, then a change of pace on the energetic palate, with its assemblage of pepper and red and black berries, the tannins particularly fine. Screwcap. 13.9% alc. **Rating** 93 **To** 2019 $22

Arlewood Estate ★★★★

Cnr Bussell Highway/Calgardup Road, Forest Grove, WA 6286 **Region** Margaret River
T (08) 9755 6267 **www.**arlewood.com.au **Open** Sat 11–5 or by appt
Winemaker Bill Crappsley **Est.** 1988 **Dozens** 7000 **Vyds** 9.7ha
A series of events in 2007 led to major changes in the Arlewood Estate structure. The Gosatti family sold the Harmans Road vineyard to Vasse Felix, but retained ownership of the brand and all stock. In mid '08 Arlewood acquired the former Hesperos Estate vineyard, 10km south of Margaret River, and Bill Crappsley, already a partner with the Gosattis in Plan B (see separate entry), became full-time winemaker for Arlewood and Plan B. Exports to the UK, the US, Canada, Switzerland, Singapore, Malaysia, Hong Kong, Philippines and China.

ΥΥΥΥ **La Bratta 2009** No indication of the blend is given on the label, yet there is
✪   a distinctly savoury character to the bouquet of sandalwood, spice, anise and bramble; the palate is taut and full of nervy acidity, prominent tannins and finishing with a lingering note of tar. A very interesting wine. Screwcap. 14% alc. **Rating** 93 **To** 2020 $60 BE

Reserve Margaret River Semillon Sauvignon Blanc 2010 Bright colour, and effusive, with a balanced blend of toasted cashew, straw and tropical fruit notes in the background; the fleshy palate offers vibrant acidity and a clean toasty finish. Screwcap. 12% alc. **Rating** 92 **To** 2016 $35 BE

Reserve Margaret River Semillon Sauvignon Blanc 2009 Vibrant green hue; the forward nature and rich bouquet is testament to the age and the vintage of 2009; deeply toasty with a fresh backbone of acidity, this is at optimum drinking right now. Screwcap. 13.5% alc. **Rating** 90 **To** 2013 $35 BE

♟♟♟♟ **Margaret River Cabernet Merlot 2010 Rating** 89 **To** 2018 $20 BE
Margaret River Shiraz 2009 Rating 88 **To** 2018 $20 BE
Margaret River Semillon Sauvignon Blanc 2011 Rating 87 **To** 2014 $20 BE

Armstead Estate   ★★★☆

366 Moorabbee Road, Knowsley, Vic 3523 **Region** Heathcote
T (03) 5439 1363 **www**.armsteadestate.com.au **Open** W'ends & public hols 11–5
Winemaker Peter Armstead **Est.** 2003 **Dozens** 500 **Vyds** 0.6ha

Peter Armstead had been a lifelong wine collector and consumer when he was caught up in the Ansett collapse; he had been an aircraft engineer and technical instructor. While he and partner Sharon Egan have full-time day jobs, they were able to purchase a property on the shores of Lake Eppalock, beautiful even when the lake was empty. Now it is full, and they have a very attractive cellar door. They were determined to have a small vineyard, and proceeded to sequentially plant shiraz, marsanne and cabernet sauvignon, deliberately keeping the size of the plantings manageable. Within months of arriving in 2003, the first planting stage had been completed, Peter had joined the Heathcote Winegrowers Association and, before he knew it, had become secretary. He has used all of his numerous local contacts to learn as much as possible about viticulture and winemaking, and has also been able to buy grapes from well-known vineyards in the region. At first he was an observer and cellar assistant, but in 2009 he took the plunge and took over winemaking, but, he says, 'still with a little help from my friends'.

♟♟♟♟♟ **Roxy's Paddock Heathcote Shiraz 2009** Good colour; a voluptuous, full-flavoured, full-bodied shiraz with blackberry, stewed plum and licorice flavours interwoven on the well-balanced palate. The tannins are soft, and the oak largely integrated, making it a drink now or later proposition. Screwcap. 14.5% alc. **Rating** 90 **To** 2020 $28

Armstrong Vineyards   ★★★★★

2 Abbottshall Road, Hawthorn, SA 5062 (postal) **Region** Grampians
T 0419 815 735 **F** (08) 8447 7491 **Open** Not
Winemaker Tony Royal **Est.** 1989 **Dozens** 1000

Armstrong Vineyards is the brain- or love-child of Tony Royal, former Seppelt (Great Western) winemaker, former CEO of Seguin Moreau Australia, and now CEO and joint owner of Portavin Integrated Wine Services. Armstrong Vineyards has 6.7ha of shiraz, the first 2ha planted in 1989, the remainder in '95–96. Low yields (4.5–5.5 tonnes perha) mean the wine will always be produced in limited quantities. Exports to the UK, Hong Kong and China.

♟♟♟♟♟ **Shiraz 2009** The cork can only mean one thing: the lion's share of the wine is headed offshore, most likely to the US. The wine is a classic cool-climate medium-bodied style, with abundant spice, pepper and licorice running through the black fruits and fine tannins; excellent length and balance. 14.5% alc. **Rating** 94 **To** 2019 $32

ArtWine   ★★★★

ArtWine House, Springfarm Road, Clare, SA 5453 **Region** Clare Valley
T 0411 422 450 **www**.artwine.com.au **Open** By appt
Winemaker Joanne Irvine **Est.** 1997 **Dozens** 1500 **Vyds** 25ha

This may be a relative newcomer on the winemaking front, but it has substantial vineyards dating back to 1997. It is the venture of Glen Kelly, owner of Harrison Research, who previously had senior roles with the Commonwealth Bank. Wife Judy also had many years in senior marketing roles in Australia and New York before the establishment of ArtWine. It has two vineyards, one on Springfarm Road, Clare, the other on Sawmill Road, Sevenhill. The Springfarm Road vineyard has a most interesting portfolio of grapes, the largest planting being 3.64ha of tempranillo, followed by (in descending order of size) riesling, pinot gris, cabernet sauvignon, grenache, cabernet franc, fiano, viognier and graciano. A further 2ha of fiano and 1.75ha of graciano were planted in the spring of 2011, replacing part of the cabernet block and the contoured section of the riesling block. The remainder of the cabernet sauvignon and riesling (plus cabernet franc) will be replanted over the next few years, the varieties yet to be decided. This is definitely a lateral approach by any standards. A second cellar door will open in 2012 in the Adelaide Hills (Bird in Hand Road, Woodside). Exports to Singapore.

ΨΨΨΨΨ **Clare Valley Riesling 2009** Light straw-green; the 18 months in bottle, plus
✪ some skin contact introduces layers of complexity, with spiced lime fruit and highly unusual touches of honeysuckle. Demands to be drunk soon. Screwcap. 13.7% alc. **Rating** 92 **To** 2014 $18

○ **Clare Valley Riesling 2011 Rating** 93 **To** 2020 $20

ΨΨΨΨ **Clare Valley Pinot Grigio 2011 Rating** 89 **To** Now $20
○

Ascella Pure Wine   ★★★★☆

203 Thompsons Road, Milbrodale, NSW 2330 **Region** Hunter Valley
T (02) 6574 5275 **www.**ascellawine.com **Open** By appt
Winemaker First Creek Wines (Liz Jackson) **Est.** 1999 **Dozens** 20 000 **Vyds** 32.4ha
This is a very substantial business that has only come into public focus since 2009. Ten years earlier Geoff and Barb Brown had begun to plant an organically grown vineyard; most was planted in 1999, a small amount in 2001. The grapes were sold under an ongoing contract to Tamburlaine, but in late '08 the owners turned to First Creek Wines, with Liz Jackson the lead winemaker for the new brand, Ascella Pure Wine. The name reflects the Browns' belief that organically grown grapes are inherently superior to conventionally-grown grapes, and that the benefit flows through to the wines. Both have fascinating backgrounds outside of the wine industry. Exports to the UK, Canada, Sweden, Japan and China.

ΨΨΨΨΨ **Hunter Valley Semillon 2011** Lemon blossom aromas lead into a palate that neatly encapsulates the ability of the Hunter to produce exceptional flavour in low alcohol, dry table wine, for this is positively juicy, and cheekily borrows lemon citrus flavours from riesling. Screwcap. 10% alc. **Rating** 94 **To** 2026 $24

ΨΨΨΨΨ **Hunter Valley Chardonnay 2011 Rating** 93 **To** 2017 $24
Reserve Hunter Valley Chardonnay 2009 Rating 91 **To** 2015 $30
Hunter Valley Verdelho 2010 Rating 90 **To** 2015 $24

Ashbrook Estate   ★★★★★

379 Tom Cullity Drive, Wilyabrup via Cowaramup, WA 6284 **Region** Margaret River
T (08) 9755 6262 **www.**ashbrookwines.com.au **Open** 7 days 10–5
Winemaker Catherine Edwards, Tony and Brian Devitt **Est.** 1975 **Dozens** 14 000
Vyds 17.4ha
This fastidious producer of consistently excellent estate-grown table wines shuns publicity and the wine show system alike, and is less well known than is deserved, selling much of its wine through the cellar door and to an understandably very loyal mailing list clientele. The white wines are of the highest quality, year in, year out. Exports to the UK, Canada, Germany, Indonesia, Japan, Singapore, Hong Kong, Taiwan and China.

ΨΨΨΨΨ **Margaret River Semillon 2011** Light straw-green; a wine full of flavour, a
✪ fleeting glimpse of fresh-cut grass before ripe citrus and some tropical fruit takes over; with an almost succulent mouthfeel; simply can't be compared to Hunter Valley semillon, and delicious now. Screwcap. 14% alc. **Rating** 94 **To** 2016 $22

Margaret River Chardonnay 2010 Mid gold; a big and ripe wine showing grapefruit, fresh fig, pineapple and plenty of spice; the palate is richly textured on entry, with the backbone of vibrant acidity cleaning it up and delivering a full flavoured, yet lively conclusion. Screwcap. 14% alc. **Rating** 94 **To** 2018 $32 BE

✪   Margaret River Verdelho 2011 Pale straw-green; a compelling blend of citrus, spice and tropical fruit comes through strongly on the bouquet and palate alike, supported on the palate by perfectly balanced acidity. Margaret River verdelho has always had a little bit extra. Screwcap. 14% alc. **Rating** 94 **To** 2015 $22

Margaret River Cabernet Merlot Cabernet Franc 2007 To be precise, it is 'a blend mostly of cabernet sauvignon, with the remainder merlot, cabernet franc and petit verdot'; it has an elegant but complex medium-bodied palate with fine-grained tannins rippling through the blackcurrant/cassis flavours, finishing with touches of cedar, spice and earth. Screwcap. 14% alc. **Rating** 94 **To** 2020 $29

🍷🍷🍷🍷🍷 Margaret River Sauvignon Blanc 2011 **Rating** 90 **To** Now $22
Margaret River Shiraz 2007 **Rating** 90 **To** 2017 $29

🍷🍷🍷🍷 Margaret River Riesling 2011 **Rating** 89 **To** 2013 $22

Ashton Hills   ★★★★★

Tregarthen Road, Ashton, SA 5137 **Region** Adelaide Hills
T (08) 8390 1243 **Open** W'ends & most public hols 11–5.30
Winemaker Stephen George **Est.** 1982 **Dozens** 1500 **Vyds** 3ha

Stephen George wears three winemaker hats: one for Ashton Hills, drawing upon an estate vineyard high in the Adelaide Hills; one for Galah Wines; and one for Wendouree. It would be hard to imagine three wineries with more diverse styles, from the elegance and finesse of Ashton Hills to the awesome power of Wendouree. After years of selecting the best pinot noir vines to provide grafting material, in the spring of 2011, all of the white vines (other than riesling) were grafted to pinot noir. The outcome is that Ashton Hills now has 2.65 of pinot noir, and 0.35ha of riesling.

🍷🍷🍷🍷🍷 Reserve Adelaide Hills Pinot Noir 2010 Bright purple-red, with some depth; a beautiful wine that takes the best characters of the Estate and the Piccadilly Valley, and then multiplies them many times. It is awash with cherry and plum fruit, and has a superb mouthfeel, allowing harmonious access to every nuance, every corner, of the flavours. Screwcap. 13.5% alc. **Rating** 97 **To** 2020 $66

Armen and Benen Pinot Noir Saignee 2010 Made from the first free-run juice of the best of the 18 clones of pinot noir that Ashton Hills has planted. It's light coloured, not pink, not salmon – its own special colour. The bouquet is exquisitely fragrant, the palate perfectly balanced, with its own range of rose petal, spice, crushed strawberry, leaves and flesh. If it's not the most expensive Australian rose, it should be, because it is the best. Screwcap. 13% alc. **Rating** 96 **To** 2014 $33

Estate Adelaide Hills Pinot Noir 2010 Clear, light purple-red; very much in the Ashton Hills style, fragrant and elegant, the flavours capturing elements of red fruits, spice and forest floor, without any one dominating; this is length at work. Screwcap. 13.5% alc. **Rating** 94 **To** 2017 $44

Piccadilly Valley Pinot Noir 2010 Similar colour to the Estate, with just a little less purple; has more primary pinot expression, the red fruits a little warmer and riper, the forest floor and stem notes less obvious. Some may prefer this to the Estate because it is easier to understand. Screwcap. 14% alc. **Rating** 94 **To** 2018 $33

Mount Lofty Ranges Shiraz 2006 Good colour retention; a solitary, isolated vineyard in the Burra Burra district northeast of the Clare Valley; severe frost in the spring of '06 reduced the crop to less than a kilo per vine (less than ½ a tonne per acre). This has resulted in an intensely flavoured wine with excellent balance and acidity that will live for as long as you wish it to. Screwcap. 14% alc. **Rating** 94 **To** 2026 $28

Salmon Brut Adelaide Hills Pinot Noir 2009 Pink, with the slightest touch of salmon; whole bunch-pressed pinot noir bottle-fermented, with red pinot noir wine added for colour. Strawberry and cherry fruit flavours are crystal clear, and the wine has a haunting delicacy. Cork. 13.5% alc. **Rating** 94 **To** 2015 $39

Tardy Riesling 2011 Reduction provides a closed bouquet, with struck match and green apple on display; the palate is off dry and full of mineral interest, with plenty of texture; lovely purity and precision, and excellent length. Manfred Prum would approve. Screwcap. 10.2% alc. **Rating** 94 **To** 2016 $33 BE

♔♔♔♔♔ **Adelaide Hills Chardonnay 2010** **Rating** 92 **To** 2015 $44 BE

Atlas Wines   ★★★★★

PO Box 458, Clare, SA 5453 **Region** Clare Valley
T 0419 847 491 **www**.atlaswines.com.au **Open** Not
Winemaker Adam Barton **Est.** 2008 **Dozens** 1200 **Vyds** 8ha
Owner and winemaker Adam Barton had an extensive winemaking career before establishing Atlas Wines. It took him from Scarpantoni Estate in McLaren Vale, to Rolf Binder Wines in the Barossa Valley, Wynns Coonawarra Estate and the iconic Bonnydoon Vineyard in California. Most recently he has been winemaker at Reillys Wines in the Clare Valley, and continues in that role while working on Atlas Wines. He has 6ha of shiraz and 2ha of cabernet sauvignon grown on a stony ridge on the eastern slopes of the region, and also sources small batches from other distinguished sites in the Clare and Barossa Valleys; all the riesling is purchased. The quality, and the consistency of the quality, of his initial releases is exceptional. Exports to China and Singapore.

♔♔♔♔♔ **172° Watervale Riesling 2011** Bright, light green-straw; a highly perfumed, floral bouquet with citrus blossom aromas leads into an intense and incisive palate, with lime and lemon flavours running through to the tingling acidity on the finish. No green notes here. Screwcap. 12.5% alc. **Rating** 96 **To** 2026 $27
516° Barossa Valley Shiraz 2010 Full crimson-purple; from a single old vine vineyard in the Ebenezer district of the Barossa Valley. A very different wine from 429°, with a more lacy and open texture, travelling to spice and pepper flavours more typical of much cooler regions. Once again, it is the lightness of touch on the finish that makes the wine. Screwcap. 14.5% alc. **Rating** 96 **To** 2025 $35
429° Clare Valley Shiraz 2010 Made from a single batch of a single estate vineyard in the White Hut district on the northeastern ranges of the Clare Valley. Deep crimson-purple; the bouquet is profound, but does not prepare you for the multiple layers of the full-bodied palate; blackberry, anise, bitter chocolate and cedary oak are among some of the flavours; others will no doubt find more, and I won't complain. The most unexpected feature of an unexpected wine is the freshness and elegance of the finish; this is masterful winemaking. Screwcap. 14.5% alc. **Rating** 96 **To** 2035 $35
Barossa Valley Shiraz Mataro 2009 Based on the same grape resources as the '10, but has a slightly finer mouthfeel, perhaps reflecting the lower alcohol, but also the richness of the vintage; there is no question this wine should be drunk now, the '10 cellared for as long as possible. Screwcap. 14% alc. **Rating** 96 **To** 2020 $35
516° Barossa Valley Shiraz 2009 Strong crimson-purple, although not as deep as 429°; medium- to full-bodied, the bouquet has black fruits, spices and a touch of mocha seamlessly leading into the palate, which has the elegant and supple flavour and structure that seem natural to Adam Barton, finishing with seductively sweet fruit. Screwcap. 14.2% alc. **Rating** 95 **To** 2030 $35
429° Clare Valley Shiraz 2009 Made from a single batch of a single estate vineyard in the White Hut district on the northeastern ranges of the Clare Valley. Deep purple-crimson; an extremely rich, full-bodied shiraz with layer upon layer of black fruits, spice and oak that literally draw the saliva from the mouth, the finish with the focus on the fruit, not the tannins, nor the oak, although there are plenty of both in the wine. Screwcap. 14.5% alc. **Rating** 95 **To** 2034 $35
Barossa Valley Shiraz Mataro 2010 Sourced from small, old vine vineyards in the Ebenezer district of the Barossa Valley. Shiraz mourvedre/mataro is less frequently encountered than either shiraz grenache or shiraz grenache mataro, adding interest to a wine with a very long life span; it has great perfume and texture emanating from fruit, with tannins and oak playing perfectly balanced support roles. Screwcap. 14.5% alc. **Rating** 95 **To** 2025 $35
Section 32 Clare Valley Shiraz 2010 **Rating** 94 **To** 2025 $25

ŶŶŶŶŶ **172° Watervale Riesling 2010** Rating 93 To 2020 $27
Section 32 Clare Valley Cabernet Malbec 2010 Rating 90 To 2025 $25

Atze's Corner Wines ★★★★

Box 81, Nuriootpa, SA 5355 **Region** Barossa Valley
T 0407 621 989 **www**.atzescornerwines.com.au **Open** By appt
Winemaker Contract, Andrew Kalleske **Est.** 2005 **Dozens** 600 **Vyds** 30ha
The seemingly numerous members of the Kalleske family have widespread involvement in grapegrowing and winemaking in the Barossa Valley. This particular venture is that of Andrew Kalleske, son of John and Barb Kalleske. In 1975 they purchased the Atze Vineyard, which included a small block of shiraz planted in '12, but with additional plantings along the way, including more shiraz in '51. Andrew purchases some grapes from the family vineyard. It has 20ha of shiraz, with small amounts of mataro, petit verdot, grenache, cabernet sauvignon, tempranillo, viognier, petite sirah, graciano, montepulciano, vermentino and aglianico. Local boutique winemakers provide the physical facilities for the winemaking, with Andrew involved.

ŶŶŶŶŶ **Eddies Old Vine Barossa Valley Shiraz 2007** Shows developed leather, bacon bones and dark fruit on the bouquet; the palate delivers a firm and rugged wine, with plenty of life and finishing with long mocha and bitter chocolate notes. Particularly good for an '07. Cork. 14.5% alc. **Rating** 90 **To** 2016 $55 BE

Audrey Wilkinson Vineyard ★★★★★

Oakdale, De Beyers Road, Pokolbin, NSW 2320 **Region** Hunter Valley
T (02) 4998 7411 **www**.audreywilkinson.com.au **Open** Mon–Fri 9–5, w'ends & public hols 9.30–5
Winemaker Jeff Byrne **Est.** 1866 **Dozens** 30 000 **Vyds** 35.33ha
One of the most historic properties in the Hunter Valley, set in a particularly beautiful location and with a very attractive cellar door, has been owned by Brian Agnew and family since 2004. The wines are made from estate-grown grapes, the lion's share to shiraz, the remainder (in descending order) to semillon, malbec, verdelho, tempranillo, merlot, cabernet sauvignon, muscat and traminer; the vines were planted between the 1970s and '90s. More recently, a small McLaren Vale vineyard of 3.45 ha, planted to merlot and shiraz, was acquired. Exports to Canada, China and NZ.

ŶŶŶŶŶ **Museum Reserve Semillon 2005** Bright straw-green; a great example of a great vintage moving inexorably towards its full majesty; in the meantime its honeyed lemon flavours reach every corner of the mouth. A truly beautiful wine now, and will be so in the years to come. A prime example of the magic of screwcaps. 11.6% alc. **Rating** 97 **To** 2020 $65
Winemakers Selection Hunter Valley Shiraz 2010 Excellent purple-crimson, deep but clear; a wine of great complexity and power that will flower magnificently over the next three decades and beyond; blackberry, plum, licorice and French oak are all there, but it's the tannins that will steer the wine into the far future. Screwcap. 14% alc. **Rating** 96 **To** 2025 $35
The Lake Shiraz 2010 Vibrant deep magenta; while no expense has been spared with high levels of fine French oak, lurking beneath is a complex, multilayered and generous wine; built for the long haul, the freshness of acidity is the perfect foil for this deeply fruited, finely textured and extraordinarily long shiraz. Screwcap. 13.5% alc. **Rating** 96 **To** 2025 $65 BE
The Ridge Semillon 2011 Light straw-green; made from 40-year-old estate vines at the top of the vineyard; it says 'anything you can do I can do better' to the Winemakers Selection with its layer upon layer of citrus, green apple and minerally acidity. Screwcap. 11% alc. **Rating** 95 **To** 2026 $35
Winemakers Selection Verdelho 2011 Rating 94 **To** 2016 $25 BE
Winemakers Selection McLaren Vale Shiraz 2010 Rating 94 **To** 2025 $30

ŶŶŶŶŶ **Winemakers Selection Semillon 2011** Rating 93 **To** 2021 $25
O   **Hunter Valley Semillon 2011** Rating 93 **To** 2020 $20 BE
Reserve Chardonnay 2010 Rating 93 **To** 2015 $35
Coonawarra Cabernet Sauvignon 2009 Rating 91 **To** 2019 $20

Winemakers Selection Gewurztraminer 2011 Rating 90 To 2017 $25
Hunter Valley Verdelho 2011 Rating 90 To 2013 $20
Hunter Valley Shiraz 2010 Rating 90 To 2030 $20
Great Western Merlot 2010 Rating 90 To 2015 $20 BE
Hunter Valley Tempranillo 2011 Rating 90 To 2014 $20 BE

ŶŶŶŶ   Winemakers Selection Merlot Cabernet 2010 Rating 89 To 2020 $30
O   Hunter Valley Tempranillo 2010 Rating 89 To 2014 $20

Austin's Wines   ★★★★★

870 Steiglitz Road, Sutherlands Creek, Vic 3331 **Region** Geelong
T (03) 5281 1799 **www**.austinswines.com.au **Open** 1st Sun each month by appt
Winemaker Scott Ireland **Est.** 1982 **Dozens** 20 000 **Vyds** 61.5ha
Pamela and Richard Austin have quietly built their business from a tiny base, and it has
flourished. The vineyard has been progressively extended to over 60ha. Scott Ireland is
full-time resident winemaker in the capacious onsite winery, and the quality of the wines
is admirable. Exports to the UK, Canada, Hong Kong, Japan and China.

ŶŶŶŶŶ Chardonnay 2010 Bright straw-green; a bracing blend of white peach,
       grapefruit and nutty oak has produced a chardonnay with considerable attitude
       and length. Screwcap. 13% alc. **Rating** 94 **To** 2017 $30
✪   Shiraz 2008 Very good hue for age; an elegant, fresh and fragrant, light- to
       medium-bodied wine in polar opposite style to that of full-bodied Barossa shiraz.
       Red berry/cherry fruit has a tapestry of spice, licorice and white pepper, tannins
       in a minor role. Screwcap. 13.5% alc. **Rating** 94 **To** 2022 $30

ŶŶŶŶŶ Riesling 2011 Pale quartz-green; has some flowery notes to the bouquet, but it
✪   is the palate that grabs attention with the intensity, drive and length to its citrus
       flavours; great outcome for the region. Screwcap. 12% alc. **Rating** 93 **To** 2020 $20
       Pinot Noir 2010 **Rating** 92 **To** 2018 $33
✪   Six Foot Six Pinot Gris 2011 The King Valley climate is ideal for bringing out
       a complex array of aromas and flavours from poached pear, to apple, lime and
       even a hint of honeysuckle. In genuine gris style. Screwcap. 12.5% alc. **Rating** 91
       To 2014 $20
✪   Saignee Rose 2011 Pale salmon-pink; made from estate-grown grapes; the
       bouquet is fragrant, with strawberry aroma, and a hint of spice that continues on
       into the very appealing soft strawberry flavours, balanced by good acidity and a
       near-dry finish. Screwcap. 13.5% alc. **Rating** 91 **To** 2013 $20
O   Six Foot Six Pinot Gris 2010 **Rating** 90 **To** 2013 $20

ŶŶŶŶ   Sauvignon Blanc 2011 **Rating** 89 **To** 2013 $20
       Six Foot Six Shiraz 2008 **Rating** 89 **To** 2020 $20
       Six Foot Six Pinot Noir 2010 **Rating** 88 **To** 2016 $20

Australian Domaine Wines   ★★★☆

PO Box 13, Walkerville, SA 5081 **Region** South Australia
T (08) 8234 5161 **www**.ausdomwines.com.au **Open** By appt
Winemaker Pikes (Neil Pike), Charles Wish **Est.** 1998 **Dozens** 5000
Australian Domaine Wines is a business owned by Ben and Mario Barletta, who started
their own brand business for leading Adelaide retailer Walkerville Cellars, which they then
owned. The wines are made at Pikes using tanks and barrels owned by the Barlettas. Grapes
are sourced from the Clare Valley, McLaren Vale and the Barossa Valley. Exports to the US,
Germany, Switzerland, Sweden, France, Japan and Sweden.

ŶŶŶŶŶ Deaf Galah McLaren Vale Red 2009 A sweet confection raspberry fruit
       bouquet, offset by licorice and thyme; the palate is unctuous, fleshy and accessible,
       with a backbone of drying tannins lingering on the finish. Shiraz/Grenache/
       Cabernet Sauvignon/Tempranillo. Screwcap. 14.5% alc. **Rating** 91 **To** 2018 $22 BE

ŶŶŶŶ   The Hattrick 2009 **Rating** 89 **To** 2017 $50 BE

Avenue Wines

124 Seventh Avenue, Joslin, SA 5070 (postal) **Region** South Australia
T (08) 8362 4032 **www**.avenuewines.com.au **Open** Not
Winemaker George Ochota **Est.** 2004 **Dozens** 2000
The Ochota family established a vineyard in the Clare Valley in the 1960s, which eventually
led to George Ochota becoming an amateur winemaker in the mid '90s; after winning
numerous medals he decided it was time to take the plunge into commercial winemaking,
buying grapes from the Clare Valley (including the former family vineyard), Langhorne Creek,
McLaren Vale and Barossa.

ŸŸŸŸŸ **Clare Valley Riesling 2011** The fragrant lime blossom bouquet and the intense,
✪   long and full-flavoured palate are the markers of a wine that has most definitely
           benefited from the cool vintage; the flavours of ripe lime and lemon fruit are
           balanced by crisp acidity. Screwcap. 11.5% alc. **Rating** 92 **To** 2021 $20

ŸŸŸŸ **Clare Valley Shiraz 2008 Rating** 89 **To** 2020 $25
        McLaren Vale Shiraz 2008 Rating 87 **To** 2016 $25

BackVintage Wines

2/177 Sailors Bay Road, Northbridge, NSW 2063 **Region** Various
T (02) 9967 9880 **F** (02) 9967 9882 **www**.backvintage.com.au **Open** Mon–Fri 9–5
Winemaker Michael Dijrstra, Nick Bulleid MW, Rob Moody (Contract) **Est.** 2003
Dozens 10 000
BackVintage Wines is a virtual winery with a difference; not only does it not own vineyards,
nor a winery, but also it sells only through its website, or by fax or phone. The team of Michael
Dijrstra, Nick Bulleid and Rob Moody source parcels of bulk wines they consider to represent
excellent quality and value for money. They are then responsible for the final steps before the
wine goes to bottle. In times of surplus they are able to pick and choose, and it looks as if the
days of surplus will extend well into the current decade.

ŸŸŸŸŸ Margaret River Cabernet Sauvignon 2007 Rating 95 To 2020 $13
❍

ŸŸŸŸ Barossa Shiraz 2008 Rating 88 To 2013 $13
❍

Baddaginnie Run

PO Box 579, North Melbourne, Vic 3051 **Region** Strathbogie Ranges
T (03) 9348 9310 **www**.baddaginnierun.net.au **Open** Not
Winemaker Contract **Est.** 1996 **Dozens** 3000 **Vyds** 24ha
Winsome McCaughey and Professor Snow Barlow (Professor of Horticulture and Viticulture
at the University of Melbourne) spend part of their week in the Strathbogie Ranges, and part
in Melbourne. The business name, Seven Sisters Vineyard, reflects the seven generations of the
McCaughey family associated with the land since 1870; Baddaginnie is the nearby township.
The vineyard is one element in a restored valley landscape, 100 000 indigenous trees having
been replanted. Exports to Canada and China.

ŸŸŸŸŸ **Reserve Strathbogie Ranges Shiraz 2009** Deep colour; loaded with black
           fruits, tar and licorice also showing a charcuterie note; medium–bodied and fresh,
           with a savoury spicy note lingering on the finish. Screwcap. 13.5% alc. **Rating** 92
           To 2016 $35 BE

ŸŸŸŸ **Strathbogie Ranges Viognier 2010** Ripe and fragrant, apricot and spice
✪   bouquet; soft and fleshy, with just enough acidity and grip to provide freshness
           and depth on the finish. Screwcap. 13.4% alc. **Rating** 89 **To** 2013 $18 BE

Badger's Brook ★★★★

874 Maroondah Highway, Coldstream, Vic 3770 **Region** Yarra Valley
T (03) 5962 4130 **www**.badgersbrook.com.au **Open** Wed–Sun 11–5
Winemaker Michael Waview, Gary Baldwin (Consultant) **Est.** 1993 **Dozens** 1500
Vyds 4.8ha
Situated next door to the well-known Rochford, the vineyard is planted to chardonnay, sauvignon blanc, pinot noir, shiraz (1ha each), cabernet sauvignon (0.35ha), merlot, viognier (0.2ha each), with a few rows each of roussanne, marsanne and tempranillo. The Badger's Brook wines, made onsite since 2012, are 100% estate-grown; the second Storm Ridge label has used only Yarra Valley grapes since 2009. Also houses the smart brasserie restaurant/bakery/cooking school Bella Vedere with well-known chef Gary Cooper in charge. Exports to Asia.

ϓϓϓϓϓ **Yarra Valley Shiraz 2008** Excellent bright crimson; an elegant cool climate shiraz with red fruits contributing more than black, but both are in the mix; fine, gently savoury, tannins run through from the mid palate to the finish. Screwcap. 14% alc. **Rating** 92 **To** 2020 $25

❍ **Storm Ridge Yarra Valley Shiraz 2010** Rating 90 **To** 2020 $18

ϓϓϓϓ **Yarra Valley Shiraz Viognier 2008** Rating 89 **To** 2015 $22
Yarra Valley Cabernet Sauvignon 2010 Rating 89 **To** 2019 $25
Storm Ridge Yarra Valley Pinot Noir 2011 Rating 88 **To** 2013 $18
Yarra Valley Pinot Noir 2010 Rating 88 **To** 2013 $28

Bagdad Hills ★★★★☆

1557 Midland Highway, Bagdad, Tas 7030 **Region** Southern Tasmania
T 0408 127 004 **Open** By appt
Winemaker Winstead (Neil Snare) **Est.** 2001 **Dozens** 140 **Vyds** 2ha
Graeme and Pip Roberts, long-time residents of Tasmania, ventured into wine later in life than many. Graeme is a retired civil engineer, Pip a registered nurse, who moved to Bagdad from Hobart. The vineyard is predominantly planted to pinot noir, with smaller amounts of sauvignon blanc, riesling and shiraz. The vineyard has been managed biodynamically since planting began in 2001, and Graeme is on the Council of Biodynamics Tasmania.

ϓϓϓϓϓ **Shiraz 2010** Deep crimson-purple; excellent texture and structure; judging was very difficult in warm conditions, but the sheer class of the wine shone through, with spicy nuances. Gold Tas Wine Show '12. Screwcap. 13.2% alc. **Rating** 94 **To** 2020 $48

ϓϓϓϓϓ **Pinot Noir 2010** Rating 90 **To** 2016 $30

Baileys of Glenrowan ★★★★★

3675 Taminick Gap Road, Glenrowan, Vic 3675 **Region** Glenrowan
T (03) 5766 1600 **www**.baileysofglenrowan.com.au **Open** 7 days 10–5
Winemaker Paul Dahlenburg **Est.** 1870 **Dozens** 15 000 **Vyds** 143ha
Just when it seemed that Baileys would remain one of the forgotten outposts of the Foster's group, the reverse has occurred. Since 1998, Paul Dahlenburg has been in charge of Baileys and has overseen an expansion in the vineyard and the construction of a 2000-tonne winery. The cellar door has a heritage museum, winery-viewing deck, contemporary art gallery and landscaped grounds, preserving much of the heritage value. Baileys has also picked up the pace with its Muscat and Tokay, reintroducing the Winemaker's Selection at the top of the tree, while continuing the larger-volume Founder series. After briefly flirting with the idea of selling Baileys, Foster's changed tack, with all winemaking reverting to the winery, including the return of vats and barrels for the red wines, Tokay and Muscat. Exports to the UK and NZ.

ŦŦŦŦŦ **Winemaker's Selection Old Muscat NV** In a world where 'rare', 'reserve', 'special selection' and so forth are often meaningless, it is a pleasure to come across a wine that is all these things and more. The colour is mahogany, grading to olive on the rim, the aromatic bouquet and palate redolent of highly spiced Christmas pudding. The most remarkable achievement is the freshness of the wine, bordering on delicate, and inciting the desire to scoff it down, a vinous crime worthy of capital punishment. Cork. 17.5% alc. **Rating** 98 **To** 2013 $75
Winemaker's Selection Rare Old Topaque NV Olive-brown; exceptionally complex in that lighter/more refined style than Rutherglen; the high-toned aromas and flavours range through tea leaf, heavily spiced cake, toffee, mandarin zest and honey. Cork. 17.5% alc. **Rating** 97 **To** 2013 $75
VP140 2010 Youthful, bright purple; made from a mix of traditional Portuguese varieties and shiraz, and looks to the future, rather than the past, with its outstanding balance. It is much less sweet than the wines of past decades, its wonderful array of spices enticing immediate consumption, but it will mature over many years in bottle. Screwcap. 19% alc. **Rating** 94 **To** 2030 $30

ŦŦŦŦŦ **Founder Series Classic Muscat NV** The colour has developed past any hint of
✪   red; a good example of the more elegant style that Paul Dahlenburg is seeking to make, with a perfumed bouquet, and without sacrificing fruit intensity or flavour; the spirit is part of the answer, as are blending decisions. Cork. 17% alc. **Rating** 93 **To** 2013 $25
✪   **Founder Series Classic Topaque NV** Amber with a slight grading to light olive on the rim; abundant flavour, with Christmas cake, singed toffee and abundant spice; the long finish is well-balanced, although the sweetness continues to the very end. Cork. 17% alc. **Rating** 92 **To** 2013 $25

Baillieu Vineyard   ★★★★☆

32 Tubbarubba Road, Merricks North, Vic 3926 **Region** Mornington Peninsula
T (03) 5989 7622 **www.**baillieuvineyard.com.au **Open** At Merricks General Store
Winemaker Kathleen Quealy **Est.** 1999 **Dozens** 2500 **Vyds** 10ha
Charlie and Samantha Baillieu have re-established the former Foxwood Vineyard, growing chardonnay, viognier, pinot gris, pinot noir and shiraz. The north-facing vineyard is part of the 64ha Bulldog Run property owned by the Baillieus, and is immaculately maintained without financial constraints.

ŦŦŦŦŦ **Mornington Peninsula Pinot Gris 2011** A great vintage for pinot gris with unusually low yields; there is real aroma (not a normal characteristic of pinot gris), and it has very good texture and depth, almost into red berry and honey; a 16-hour press cycle a la Alsace paid big dividends, and echoes of Zind Humbrecht, one of its leading lights. Screwcap. 14% alc. **Rating** 94 **To** 2014 $25

ŦŦŦŦŦ **Mornington Peninsula Shiraz 2009 Rating** 92 **To** 2019 $25
✪   **Mornington Peninsula Rose 2011** Pale but bright colour; a spicy and savoury red-fruited, bouquet reflecting its pinot noir/pinot meunier origins; the palate is taut, finishing dry and full of texture and interest; fits seamlessly into the current trend of dry and savoury Rose in the marketplace. Screwcap. 13% alc. **Rating** 91 **To** 2013 $20

ŦŦŦŦ **Mornington Peninsula Pinot Noir 2010 Rating** 89 **To** 2014 $35 BE
Mornington Peninsula Chardonnay 2010 Rating 88 **To** 2014 $25

Balgownie Estate   ★★★★☆

Hermitage Road, Maiden Gully, Vic 3551 **Region** Bendigo
T (03) 5449 6222 **www.**balgownieestate.com.au **Open** 7 days 10–5
Winemaker Tony Winspear **Est.** 1969 **Dozens** 21 000 **Vyds** 29.45ha
Balgownie Estate continues to grow in the wake of its acquisition by the Forrester family, and celebrated its 40th vintage at Maiden Gully in 2012. A $3 million winery upgrade coincided

with a doubling of the size of the vineyard, and Balgownie Estate also has a cellar door in the Yarra Valley (Yarra Glen). The Yarra Valley operation of Balgownie Estate neatly fits in with the Bendigo wines, each supporting the other. Balgownie has the largest vineyard-based resort in the Yarra Valley, with over 65 rooms and a limited number of spa suites. It specialises in catering for conferences and functions, and Rae's Restaurant is open seven days for breakfast and lunch. Exports to the UK, the US, Canada, the Netherlands, Fiji, Hong Kong, Singapore and NZ.

ŶŶŶŶŶ **Bendigo Chardonnay 2010** Hand-picked grapes from the 31-year-old estate plantings were crushed and fermented in new and used French oak, spending 11 months in barrel with lees stirring; has plenty going for it, but is fractionally short. Screwcap. 13% alc. **Rating** 91 **To** 2015 $45

Yarra Valley Chardonnay 2009 The paradox of the '09 bushfire year was the cool summer either side of 10 days of hell; moreover, the skins of white grapes are removed before fermentation, the smoke taint in the skins remains bound in those skins and does not affect the wine. This chardonnay has soft stone fruit and melon flavours coupled with toasty oak and a shaft of citrussy acidity. Screwcap. 13.5% alc. **Rating** 91 **To** 2015 $24

Black Label Bendigo Cabernet Merlot 2009 Crimson-red; the aromas of savoury black fruits are intensified on the medium- to full-bodied palate, with notes of earth and graphite; this is definitely a wine for generous charcoal-grilled red meat. Screwcap. 14.5% alc. **Rating** 90 **To** 2018 $24

Bendigo Cabernet Sauvignon 2009 Medium purple-red; has come through a difficult vintage well, even though the normal richness and depth of the cabernet fruit are lacking, and the savoury notes are made more obvious by that lack, yet the old vines provide an undercurrent of nobility. Medium-term cellaring will do no harm. Screwcap. 13.5% alc. **Rating** 90 **To** 2016 $45

ŶŶŶŶ **Black Label Yarra Valley Sauvignon Blanc 2011 Rating** 89 **To** Now $24
Bendigo Viognier 2010 Rating 89 **To** 2013 $40
Bendigo Shiraz 2009 Rating 88 **To** 2020 $45
Black Label Bendigo Shiraz 2009 Rating 87 **To** 2015 $24

Ballabourneen   ★★★★☆

2347 Broke Road, Pokobin, NSW 2320 **Region** Hunter Valley
T (02) 4998 6505 **www.**ballabourneen.com.au **Open** 7 days 10–5
Winemaker Daniel Binet **Est.** 2008 **Dozens** 5000
In December 2008, young gun Daniel Binet, until that time winemaker at Capercaillie, formed a partnership with Alex Stuart OAM. The formerly low profile of Ballabourneen has lifted, the cellar door having been established in what was previously the Evans Family Wines cellar door on what is known locally as 'The Golden Mile' of the Broke Road. Ballabourneen also provides contract winemaking for Wandin Hunter Valley, Warraroong and Tatler wines. Exports to China.

ŶŶŶŶŶ **Alexander the Great Shiraz 2010** Deep crimson; while the oak dominates the fruit at this early juncture, the future looks promising, with ample levels of sweet black fruits and sweet spices lurking beneath; the palate is fleshy, fresh and almost luscious in nature, and once the oak fully integrates with the fruit will be long and generous. Screwcap. 13.8% alc. **Rating** 92 **To** 2018 $50 BE

The Three Amigo's Cabernet Merlot Petit Verdot 2009 Red-purple, bright and clear; the three varieties were sourced from the Hunter Valley, McLaren Vale and Wrattonbully, and open-fermented and matured in new and old French oak for 20 months; it has a complex array of black and redcurrant fruit, and positive tannins that will soften in due course. Screwcap. 14% alc. **Rating** 92 **To** 2019 $35

Major's Lane Semillon 2011 Pale colour; zesty lemon and talc bouquet, with a lively and fresh lemon-drop palate; fresh, vibrant and clean. Screwcap. 10.8% alc. **Rating** 91 **To** 2017 $25 BE

The Three Amigo's Cabernet Merlot Petit Verdot 2010 Friends is the motto, and the end result is a fleshy, fragrant and friendly wine, with good concentration, zesty acidity and an even, easy-drinking personality. Screwcap. 14.5% alc. **Rating** 90 **To** 2016 $35 BE

♟♟♟♟ **Gamay Noir 2011 Rating** 89 **To** 2014 $25

Ballandean Estate Wines ★★★★☆

Sundown Road, Ballandean, Qld 4382 **Region** Granite Belt
T (07) 4684 1226 **www.**ballandeanestate.com **Open** 7 days 9–5
Winemaker Dylan Rhymer, Angelo Puglisi **Est.** 1970 **Dozens** 12 000 **Vyds** 32ha
A rock of ages in the Granite Belt, owned by the ever-cheerful and charming Angelo Puglisi and wife Mary. Mary has introduced a gourmet food gallery at the cellar door, featuring foods produced by local food artisans as well as Greedy Me gourmet products made by Mary herself. 2009 saw Ballandean wines appearing on the wine lists of Vue de Monde in Melbourne and Aria in Brisbane. One of the specialties of the winery has always been Sylvaner. A devastating fire in December '11 destroyed a large part of the bottled wine stock, but did not affect the winery, and hence the wine in barrel, and there are sufficient bottles of the current releases for the business to continue daily operation as usual. Exports to Taiwan.

♟♟♟♟♟ **Josephine's Liqueur Muscat 1986** An ode to Josephine Puglisi from three generations of her descendants, chronicling her life when she came to Australia in 1927, aged 12, to join her father. There is no question muscat has been left to progressively build its flavours of Christmas cake, oatmeal biscuit and burnt toffee (plus a hundred others) all coalescing. Cork. 17.5% alc. **Rating** 94 **To** 2013 $65

♟♟♟♟♟ **S.S.B Semillon Sauvignon Blanc 2011** Bright straw-green; there is no specific
✪   mention of the region of origin, and the wine has quite startling intensity to its mix of lemon citrus and tropical fruit flavours; in a sense, the origin is irrelevant, for this is a particularly enjoyable SSB. Screwcap. 11.1% alc. **Rating** 92 **To** 2014 $18

Ballast Stone Estate Wines ★★★★

Myrtle Grove Road, Currency Creek, SA 5214 **Region** Currency Creek
T (08) 8555 4215 **www.**ballaststonewines.com **Open** 7 days 10.30–5
Winemaker John Loxton **Est.** 2001 **Dozens** 80 000 **Vyds** 461ha
Richard and Marie Shaw ventured into the wine industry by planting shiraz in the early 1970s at McLaren Flat. They still have the original vineyards and during the Vine Pull Scheme of the 1980s saved several neighbours' valuable old shiraz and grenache. Their three sons are also involved in the family business. Extensive vineyards are now held in McLaren Vale (60ha) and Currency Creek (350ha), with a modern winery in Currency Creek. The family produces around 80 000 dozen under the Ballast Stone Estate label as well as supplying others. The wine portfolio impressively over-delivers on value. Ballast Stone opened a second cellar door and café at Signal Point, Goolwa in 2011. Exports to the UK, the US and other major markets.

♟♟♟♟♟ **Currency Creek Estate The Black Swamp Fleurieu Peninsula Cabernet**
✪   **Sauvignon Malbec Petit Verdot Merlot 2010** An 81/9/8/2% blend, with a vibrant, youthful crimson-purple colour; the medium- to full-bodied palate has a feast of red and black fruits, supported by tannins yet to fully integrate; needs a couple of years. Screwcap. 14.5% alc. **Rating** 91 **To** 2016 $17
✪   **Currency Creek Rose 2011** Made from sangiovese, not obvious given the light, but bright pink colour; raspberry fruit fills the fore-palate, and it's not until the finish that you find the slight touch of sweetness balanced by acidity. Screwcap. 11.5% alc. **Rating** 90 **To** 2013 $17
✪   **Currency Creek Rose 2010 Rating** 90 **To** Now $17
✪   **McLaren Vale Grenache 2010 Rating** 91 **To** 2016 $17

♟♟♟♟ **McLaren Vale Merlot 2010 Rating** 89 **To** 2017 $17
✪   **Stonemason Currency Creek Cabernet Sauvignon 2010 Rating** 89 **To** 2015 $12

○ Steeple Jack Shiraz 2010 Rating 88 To 2015 $10
  McLaren Vale Shiraz 2010 Rating 88 To 2015 $17
○ Stonemason Currency Creek Shiraz 2010 Rating 87 To 2013 $12
  Currency Creek Estate Ostrich Hill Fleurieu Peninsula Shiraz Viognier 2010 Rating 87 To 2014 $17
  McLaren Vale Cabernet Sauvignon 2010 Rating 87 To 2015 $17

Ballycroft Vineyard & Cellars ★★★

1 Adelaide Road, Greenock, SA 5360 **Region** Barossa Valley
T (08) 8562 8184 **www**.ballycroft.com **Open** By appt
Winemaker Joseph Evans **Est.** 2005 **Dozens** 125 **Vyds** 3ha
This micro-business is owned by Joe and Sue Evans. Joe's life on the land started in 1984 with a diploma of horticulture in nursery management, followed three years later by a viticulture degree from Roseworthy/Adelaide University. Between '92 and '99 he had various responsibilities at Rockford Wines, '92–'95 in the cellar door, '96 vintage cellarhand, and '97–'99 vineyard manager. Since that time he has been a man for all seasons at Greenock Creek Wines. A cheesery is also on the property, operated by Sue and sister Tracey Skepper. Water and waste recycling is a major focus of the business, with a vegetable garden supplying local restaurants and selling through the Barossa Farmers Market.

ΨΨΨΨ **Small Berry Langhorne Creek Cabernet Sauvignon 2009** A light- to medium-bodied cabernet with sweet cassis fruit, that spent 28 months in shaved French oak barrels, and has good length and overall balance; only 55 dozen made from the tiny 39-year-old estate block. Screwcap. 14% alc. **Rating** 88 **To** 2019 $33

Balnaves of Coonawarra ★★★★★

Main Road, Coonawarra, SA 5263 **Region** Coonawarra
T (08) 8737 2946 **www**.balnaves.com.au **Open** Mon–Fri 9–5, w'ends 12–5
Winemaker Pete Bissell 1975 **Dozens** 10 000 **Vyds** 53.7ha
Grapegrower, viticultural consultant and vigneron, Doug Balnaves has over 50ha of high-quality estate vineyards. The wines are invariably excellent, often outstanding, notable for their supple mouthfeel, varietal integrity, balance and length; the tannins are always fine and ripe, the oak subtle and perfectly integrated. Coonawarra at its best. Exports to the UK, the Netherlands, Germany, Denmark, Canada, Vietnam, Japan, Indonesia and Hong Kong.

ΨΨΨΨΨ **Cabernet Sauvignon 2010** A heavily stained ProCork is a worry. The strong purple-crimson colour signals no problems yet, the rich bouquet and medium-to full-bodied palate bursting with intense, perfectly ripened blackcurrant fruit; despite 19 months in quality French oak, it is this fruit, and the well-weighted tannins, which are the primary drivers. 14.5% alc. **Rating** 95 **To** 2025 $39
○ **The Blend 2010 Rating** 95 **To** 2030 $19
  Chardonnay 2010 Hand-picked and whole bunch-pressed, then barrel-fermented in deluxe Louis Latour barriques, 25% wild yeast-fermented, then 11 months on lees. The cohesion and balance of the resultant wine is remarkable, grapefruit, stone fruit and fig coalescing with the oak and natural acidity. Screwcap. 13.5% alc. **Rating** 94 **To** 2016 $28
  Shiraz 2010 Medium purple-crimson; a welcoming bouquet of perfumed black fruits and perfectly balanced oak leads into a medium-bodied palate, the balance good, the length better still; fine tannins intermingle with lighter fruit notes on the finish and aftertaste. Screwcap. 14.5% alc. **Rating** 94 **To** 2020 $26
  Cabernet Merlot 2010 A 92/8% blend that spent 17 months in new and used French oak from topflight coopers; the crimson colour leads into a bouquet and palate with blackcurrant and cassis to the fore; the oak adds to both texture and flavour, but it is the lifted fruit on the finish that really puts the stamp of quality on the wine. Screwcap. 14.5% alc. **Rating** 94 **To** 2025 $26

The Tally Reserve Cabernet Sauvignon 2010 Has a similar ProCork issue to the Cabernet Sauvignon. The grapes were hand-picked and received a long post-fermentation maceration on skins, extracting every bit of flavour and tannins from those skins. The wine spent 19 months in new, top-quality, barriques from top cooperages. The final judgement on this wine can't be made until it is at least 10 years old (ProCork permitting), when the issue of the oak balance can be resolved. Right now, it seems too much of a good thing; hopefully, time will prove otherwise. 14.5% alc. **Rating** 94 **To** 2030 $95

Banks Road   ★★★★★
600 Banks Road, Marcus Hill, Vic 3222 **Region** Geelong
T (03) 5258 3777 **www**.banksroad.com.au **Open** Fri–Sun 11–5
Winemaker Peter Kimber, William Derham **Est.** 2001 **Dozens** 2000 **Vyds** 6ha
Banks Road, owned and operated by William Derham, has two vineyards: the first (2.5ha) is on the Bellarine Peninsula at Marcus Hill, planted to pinot noir, chardonnay, pinot gris, shiraz and sauvignon blanc; the second is at Harcourt in the Bendigo region, planted to shiraz and cabernet sauvignon.

♀♀♀♀♀   Geelong Sauvignon Blanc 2011 Light straw-green; a very fragrant burst of
✪   tropical/passionfruit aromas on the bouquet is followed by mouthwatering flavours
         on the long, well-balanced palate. Great bargain. Screwcap. 12% alc. **Rating** 94
         To 2014 $20
         Geelong Chardonnay 2010 Bright, light straw-green; a complex and
         powerful wine, with striking drive and energy to its display of fig, white peach
         and grapefruit, tied together by minerally acidity. Screwcap. 13% alc. **Rating** 94
         To 2014 $28

♀♀♀♀♀   Geelong Pinot Noir 2010 **Rating** 93 **To** 2018 $30
         Will's Selection Bellarine Peninsula Pinot Noir 2009 **Rating** 93 **To** 2017 $45

♀♀♀♀   Geelong Pinot Gris 2011 **Rating** 88 **To** 2013 $28
         Geelong Pinot Grigio 2011 **Rating** 88 **To** Now $20

Banks Thargo Wines   ★★★★☆
920 Racecourse Road, Penola, SA 5277 **Region** Coonawarra
T (08) 8736 3313 **www**.banksthargo.com.au **Open** By appt
Winemaker Contract **Est.** 1980 **Dozens** 2000 **Vyds** 23.6ha
The unusual name comes from family history. One branch of the Kidman family moved to the Mount Gambier district in 1858, but Thomas Kidman (who had been in the foster care of the Banks family from the age of two to 13) moved to Broken Hill/southwest Qld to work for the famous Kidman Bros pastoral interests. He 'retired' from the outback, and in 1919 bought this property. His second son was named Banks Thargomindah Kidman, and it was he and wife Genny who decided to diversify their grazing activities by planting vines in the 1980s: most is under contract, leaving 1ha each of merlot and cabernet sauvignon for the Banks Thargo brand. Ownership has now passed to Genny, Jon and Heather Kidman.

♀♀♀♀♀   Coonawarra Cabernet Sauvignon 2008 Excellent hue and clarity; the
✪   fragrant bouquet of cassis and black fruits leads into a medium-bodied palate with
         perfect balance between the blackcurrant and mint flavours, fine, ripe tannins and
         quality French oak. Screwcap. 15% alc. **Rating** 94 **To** 2028 $22

♀♀♀♀♀   Racecourse Red Coonawarra Cabernet Sauvignon Merlot 2009 Medium
✪   red-purple; it has an appealingly fragrant fruit-driven bouquet, and a lively palate
         with blackcurrant, cassis and plum flavours, the French and American oak in
         which it was matured not assertive, the tannins fine. Ready to drink any time you
         fancy. Screwcap. 14.3% alc. **Rating** 90 **To** 2018 $17

♀♀♀♀   Coonawarra Merlot 2010 **Rating** 88 **To** 2015 $19

Bannockburn Vineyards ★★★★★

Midland Highway, Bannockburn, Vic 3331 (postal) **Region** Geelong
T (03) 5281 1363 **www.**bannockburnvineyards.com **Open** By appt
Winemaker Michael Glover **Est.** 1974 **Dozens** 4000 **Vyds** 30ha
With the qualified exception of the Douglas, which can be a little leafy and gamey,
Bannockburn produces outstanding wines across the range, all with individuality, style, great
complexity and depth of flavour. The low-yielding estate vineyards play their role. Winemaker
Michael Glover is determined to enhance the reputation of Bannockburn. Exports to Canada,
China, Singapore and Hong Kong.

ｹｹｹｹｹ **Geelong Chardonnay 2009** Mid gold, bright; a complex and surprisingly
understated bouquet of peach, cashew, charcuterie and spice; the palate reveals silky
texture and true breeding, with a long and expansive journey from start to finish;
will stand the test of time with aplomb. Cork. 13% alc. **Rating** 95 **To** 2018 $52 BE
Geelong Pinot Noir 2009 Mid garnet, slight bricking; the use of stems is de
rigeur for Bannockburn, and the perfume of sap, cold tea and spices dominates the
bouquet; the palate reveals the dark fruit beneath, with freshness in terms of acidity
and silky tannins providing a very complex and thoroughly intriguing pinot noir.
Cork. 12.5% alc. **Rating** 95 **To** 2018 $57 BE
Serre 2008 The bricking colour is an indication of the heavy use of stems in a
relatively young pinot noir, and the perfume is compelling for its undergrowth
complexity, while the new oak that is in use is devoured in totality; the palate is
super fine and lacy, with slippery, silky tannins and fresh acidity dragging the finish
out to a peacock's tail of flavour; this style looks older than it is, but will remain
in this state for a considerable time to come. 100 dozen made. Cork. 12% alc.
Rating 95 **To** 2020 $95 BE
Geelong Shiraz 2007 Michael Glover's shiraz is like a souped-up version of his
pinot, where grace and power combine to provide yet another intriguing wine;
spice, game, roasted meats and clove mingle with sweet black fruits and ripe silky
tannins; finding descriptors is easy, yet the wine remains a little challenging, just as
the maker desires; the possibilities for matching with food are practically endless.
Cork. 13.5% alc. **Rating** 95 **To** 2020 $42 BE
Geelong Riesling 2011 Vivid green hue; highly perfumed and somewhat exotic
on the bouquet, with quince, lime, spices and quartz; the palate is lively and fresh,
yet offers depth and richness at its core; long, linear and certainly an interesting
prospect to watch evolve. Screwcap. 13.5% alc. **Rating** 94 **To** 2022 $27 BE
3 Years on Lees Geelong Chardonnay 2008 Mid gold, vibrant green hue;
the bouquet is surprisingly fresh and vibrant, showing nectarine, citrus blossom,
almond meal and spicy oak notes; the palate is very concentrated, showing life and
vitality, tangy acidity and a creamy texture that can only have come through such
extended maturation on lees. Cork. 13.5% alc. **Rating** 94 **To** 2020 $65 BE

ｹｹｹｹｹ **S.R.H. 2008 Rating** 93 **To** 2017 $75 BE
Stuart Geelong Pinot 2009 Rating 93 **To** 2016 $72 BE
Geelong Sauvignon Blanc 2011 Rating 92 **To** 2016 $28 BE
Geelong Shiraz 2008 Rating 92 **To** 2018 $45 BE
Douglas 2008 Rating 90 **To** 2017 $28 BE

Banrock Station

Holmes Road (off Sturt Highway), Kingston-on-Murray, SA 5331 **Region** Riverland
T (08) 8583 0299 **www.**banrockstation.com.au **Open** Mon–Fri 9–4, w'ends &
public hols 9–5
Winemaker Paul Burnett **Est.** 1994 **Dozens** NFP **Vyds** 240ha
The eco-friendly $1 million visitor centre at Banrock Station is a major tourist destination.
Owned by Accolade, the Banrock Station property covers over 1700 ha, with 240ha of
vineyard and the remainder being a major wildlife and wetland preservation area. Recycling of
all waste water and use of solar energy add to the preservation image. Each bottle of Banrock
Station wine sold generates funds donated to environmental projects around the world. The

wines have consistently offered good value, even the more expensive alternative variety releases that have recently come onto the market. Exports to all major markets.

ŶŶŶŶ   **Mediterranean Collection Pinot Grigio 2011** An altogether superior example
✪   of the variety notwithstanding its breeding, with drive to the palate and abundant pear and ripe apple flavours. Screwcap. 12% alc. **Rating** 89 **To** 2013 $16
✪   **Chardonnay 2011** It must have taken exceptional care of the vineyards and in the winemaking to produce a wine such as this from the '11 vintage, especially difficult for Riverland winemakers. It has utterly authentic citrus and stone fruit flavours, aided and abetted by light oak maturation – which if you don't like oak, shouldn't put you off. Screwcap. 13% alc. **Rating** 88 **To** 2013 $10

Bantry Grove   ★★★☆

519 Three Brothers Road, Newbridge, NSW 2795 **Region** Orange
T (02) 6368 1036 **www**.bantrygrove.com.au **Open** By appt
Winemaker Richard Parker **Est.** 1990 **Dozens** 1200 **Vyds** 12ha
Terrey and Barbie Johnson (and family) raise beef cattle on a property at the southern end of Orange. Seeking to diversify, and to lessen the impact of drought through the establishment of an irrigated perennial crop, the Johnsons have planted a vineyard at an elevation of 960 m, making it one of the coolest in the region. The plantings began in 1990 with chardonnay and cabernet sauvignon, the latter now grafted or removed because the climate is simply too cool. Most of the 80–85-tonne production from the chardonnay, merlot, sauvignon blanc, pinot noir and pinot gris is sold to various producers making Orange-designated wines. A steadily increasing portion of the grapes is retained for the Bantry Grove label, with Pinot Gris added in 2012. The wines are sold through membership of Bantry Grove's Inner Circle Wine Club and local outlets, with some Sydney distribution.

ŶŶŶŶŶ   **Orange Chardonnay 2010** Straw-green; a wine with above-average texture and structure, and with white peach and nectarine fruit, some creamy cashew notes on the finish. Screwcap. 13% alc. **Rating** 90 **To** 2017 $24
    Orange Pinot Noir 2010 Light, bright crimson; a rich and quite luscious pinot, with sweet fruit pushing all the way to the finish; it's not easy to tell whether this is fruit sweetness, pure and simple, or whether there is a trace of residual sugar in the wine. Screwcap. 14.5% alc. **Rating** 90 **To** 2017 $24

ŶŶŶŶ   **Orange Rose 2011 Rating** 89 **To** 2013 $18

Barambah Wines   ★★★★☆

79 Goshnicks Road, off Redgate Road, Moffatdale, Qld 4605 **Region** South Burnett
T (07) 3392 0011 **F** (07) 3392 0055 **www**.barambah.com.au **Open** Thurs–Sun 10–5
Winemaker Peter Scudamore-Smith MW (Contract) **Est.** 1995 **Dozens** 1000 **Vyds** 7ha
Barambah is owned by Jane and Steve Wilson, who live there in a historic 19th century home. During the time they owned the large cattle property Barambah Station, they found themselves next-door neighbours to Barambah Wines. They purchased the winery and vineyard, retaining them after they sold their cattle station. The 2011 vintage was devastated in the South Burnett region, with total annual rainfall occurring in three months leading up to and including vintage. A gallant decision to double-prune the cabernet sauvignon was hit by hail, eliminating that venture. Other left-field winemaking techniques have been inspired and managed by Peter Scudamore-Smith MW, and the outlook for 2012 was much better.

ŶŶŶŶŶ   First Grid Rack Dried Semillon 2010 Made using the techniques perfected in Tokaji in Hungary; bunches of '10 semillon were dried on racks for five weeks, then refermented with dry white semillon from the same vintage. The wine is very well balanced, and very attractive, but it would be interesting to see whether, given five or so years' bottle age, it will develop the complexity of a Tokaji of similar age. 375ml. Screwcap. 10.5% alc. **Rating** 94 **To** 2016 $34

ŶŶŶŶŶ   **First Grid Shiraz 2010 Rating** 91 **To** 2020 $34

Barley Stacks Wines

Minlaton Road, Maitland, SA 5573 **Region** The Peninsulas Zone
T (08) 8834 1258 **www**.barleystackswines.com **Open** 7 days 10–5
Winemaker John Zilm **Est.** 1997 **Dozens** 3000 **Vyds** 10ha

Lyall and Cynthia Schulz have an organically managed vineyard near Maitland, on the western side of the Yorke Peninsula, planted to chardonnay, viognier, shiraz and cabernet sauvignon. The wines are made onsite; there are also facilities to cater for concerts or festivals, and tours by arrangement. Exports to Canada.

ǷǷǷǷ **The Peninsulas Shiraz 2008** Deep, dense red-purple; the full-bodied palate has layers of black fruits and ripe tannins, and even greater warmth on the back palate and finish imparted by the alcohol. It seems the grapes could have been picked earlier. Screwcap. 15% alc. **Rating** 87 **To** 2018 $25

Barnadown Run

390 Cornella Road, Toolleen, Vic 3551 **Region** Heathcote
T (03) 5433 6376 **www**.barnadownrun.com.au **Open** 7 days 10–5
Winemaker Andrew Millis **Est.** 1995 **Dozens** 1200 **Vyds** 5ha

Named after the original pastoral lease of which the vineyard forms part, established on the rich terra rossa soil for which Heathcote is famous. Owner Andrew Millis carries out both the viticulture and winemaking at the vineyard, which is planted to cabernet sauvignon, merlot, shiraz and viognier. Exports to Canada, Norway, Hong Kong, Singapore and China.

ǷǷǷǷǷ **White Lanyard Heathcote Cabernet Sauvignon 2008** Good colour for age; a plush and velvety palate with layers of blackcurrant, plum and mint is balanced by lively acidity on the finish, which provides significant extra length to the palate. Screwcap. 14% alc. **Rating** 93 **To** 2018 $29
Heathcote Merlot 2008 Strong crimson-purple; a juicy palate full of delicious red fruits and some plum; has excellent length and balance, the finish with fine tannins supporting, not detracting from, the fruit. Screwcap. 14% alc. **Rating** 92 **To** 2016 $29
Heathcote Rose 2011 Salmon-pink; the colour, the spicy notes to the fruit, and the mouthfeel suggest barrel fermentation, but none has in fact been used; the technique has worked well to present a rose with good flavour, good balance and good attitude. Screwcap. 13.5% alc. **Rating** 90 **To** 2014 $24

Barokes Wines

111 Cecil Street, South Melbourne, Vic 3205 (postal) **Region** Various
T (03) 9675 4349 **F** (03) 9675 4594 **www**.wineinacan.com **Open** Not
Winemaker Steve Barics **Est.** 2003 **Dozens** 300 000

Barokes packages its wines in aluminium cans. The filling process is patented, and the wine has been in commercial production since 2003. The wines show normal maturation and none of the cans used since start-up shows signs of corrosion. Wines are supplied in bulk by large wineries in South Eastern Australia, with Peter Scudamore-Smith acting as blending consultant. Year after year, my tastings give rise to tasting notes with no mention of reduction or any other fault. The technology has now been licensed by global packaging company Ball Packaging Europe, which will see more producers selling wines in cans in Europe; in Australia Barokes is offering customised canning for Australian companies. Barokes has now won a series of awards, with gold medals and a trophy in wine competitions in California and Europe. The day Barokes wins a gold medal, let alone a trophy, in an Australian wine show, I will be the first to congratulate it. Exports to all major markets with increasing success, with production rising to 300 000 cases (24 cans per case).

Barossa Valley Estate
★★★★★

Seppeltsfield Road, Marananga, SA 5352 **Region** Barossa Valley
T (08) 8568 6900 **F** (08) 8568 6999 **www**.bve.com.au **Open** 7 days 10–4.30
Winemaker Mark Jamieson **Est.** 1985 **Dozens** 50 000 **Vyds** 40.12ha

Barossa Valley Estate is now solely owned by Barossa Growers Holdings Limited, the latter representing the grower shareholders of the original co-operative. The 40ha of vines directly owned by Barossa Valley Estate (shiraz, cabernet sauvignon, merlot, grenache, chardonnay and marsanne) contribute only a small part of the production, most of the grapes coming from the grower shareholders. Across the board, the wines are full-flavoured and honest. E&E Black Pepper Shiraz is an upmarket label with a strong reputation and following; the Ebenezer range likewise. Exports to the UK, the US and other major markets.

♟♟♟♟♟ **Ebenezer Shiraz 2007** Vibrant, fresh and focused, showing classic Barossa generosity with a firm backbone of structure for the future; mulberry, bitter chocolate and a little black olive, with a long, fragrant, fresh finish; excellent value as an aged release. Screwcap. 14.1% alc. **Rating** 94 **To** 2020 $35 BE
E&E Black Pepper Sparkling Shiraz 2005 Made using the traditional method, and is, as one would expect, very complex, with flavours of plum, mocha and even a touch of dark chocolate; the finish has been carefully managed so that it is not heavy or sweet. One of the best examples at the present time. Cork. 14% alc. **Rating** 94 **To** 2014 $50

♟♟♟♟♟ **Entourage Cellar Reserve Shiraz 2010** Bright crimson; the bright bouquet
✪ is followed by a palate brimming with red and black fruits, fine tannins and subtle oak; a brilliant example of shiraz flavour at modest alcohol, although how a '10 red wine can be a 'cellar reserve' is beyond me. Screwcap. 13.5% alc. **Rating** 93 **To** 2020 $20

Barratt ★★★★★
Uley Vineyard, Cornish Road, Summertown, SA 5141 **Region** Adelaide Hills
T (08) 8390 1788 **www.**barrattwines.com.au **Open** W'ends & most public hols 11.30–5 (closed Jun–Jul)
Winemaker Lindsay Barratt **Est.** 1993 **Dozens** 2000 **Vyds** 8.7ha
This is the venture of former physician Lindsay Barratt. Lindsay has always been responsible for viticulture and, following his retirement in 2001, has taken full, hands-on responsibility for winemaking (receiving a graduate diploma in oenology from the University of Adelaide in '02). The quality of the wines is beyond reproach. Limited quantities are exported to the UK, Malaysia and Singapore.

♟♟♟♟♟ **Piccadilly Valley Chardonnay 2010** Pale, bright straw-green; comes from 27-year-old estate vineyards, the juice wild yeast-fermented in a mix of new and used French barriques. It is a very elegant and finely detailed wine, easy to overlook in the company of fleshier wines, and totally at odds with its 14% alcohol. Screwcap. **Rating** 94 **To** 2019 $32
The Reserve Piccadilly Valley Pinot Noir 2010 Crystal clear crimson; a radically different wine from the Bonython, with far more structure, texture and complexity, deriving in large measure from whole bunch/stem characters; the savoury/foresty notes underpinning the red and black fruits point to the need for some further bottle age before the wine reaches its peak. Screwcap. 13.5% alc. **Rating** 94 **To** 2018 $49

♟♟♟♟♟ **Piccadilly Valley Sauvignon Blanc 2011 Rating** 93 **To** 2014 $23
The Bonython Piccadilly Valley Pinot Noir 2010 Rating 92 **To** 2019 $28

Barrgowan Vineyard ★★★★★
30 Pax Parade, Curlewis, Vic 3222 **Region** Geelong
T (03) 5250 3861 **www.**barrgowanvineyard.com.au **Open** By appt
Winemaker Dick Simonsen **Est.** 1998 **Dozens** 150 **Vyds** 0.5ha
Dick and Dib (Elizabeth) Simonsen began planting their shiraz (with five clones) in 1994, intending to make wine for their own consumption. With all five clones in full production, the Simonsens have a maximum production of 200 dozen, and accordingly release small quantities

of Shiraz, which sell out quickly. The vines are hand-pruned, the grapes hand-picked, the must basket-pressed, and all wine movements are by gravity. The quality is exemplary.

ΨΨΨΨΨ Simonsens Bellarine Peninsula Shiraz 2010 Vivid purple hue; saturated dark fruits on the bouquet, with lots of pepper and spice; the palate is young and juicy, almost like a barrel sample at this point in time, showing lots of flavour generosity and freshness on the finish. Diam. 13.4% alc. **Rating** 94 **To** 2016 $25 BE

Barringwood Park ★★★★★

60 Gillams Road, Lower Barrington, Tas 7306 **Region** Northern Tasmania
T (03) 6492 3140 **www**.barringwoodpark.com.au **Open** Wed–Sun & public hols 10–5
Winemaker Josef Chromy Wines (Jeremy Dineen) **Est.** 1993 **Dozens** 1700 **Vyds** 5ha
Judy and Ian Robinson operate a sawmill at Lower Barrington, 15 minutes south of Devonport on the main tourist trail to Cradle Mountain, and when they planted 500 vines in 1993 the aim was to do a bit of home winemaking. In a thoroughly familiar story, the urge to expand the vineyard and make wine on a commercial scale soon occurred, and they embarked on a six-year plan, planting 1ha per year in the first four years and building the cellar and tasting rooms during the following two years. Another 1.2ha have recently been planted, and I think I must acknowledge some responsibility for urging the Robinsons to do so.

ΨΨΨΨΨ Barrel Selection Chardonnay 2010 Given its barrel fermentation, this has an extraordinarily pale colour, and the intense fruit has, as the saying goes, eaten the (flavour of the) oak. Very long and fine, it will be fascinating to watch its development, underpinned by its typical Tasmanian acidity. Due for release late 2012. Screwcap. 13.2% alc. **Rating** 94 **To** 2018 $40

❂ Northbank Chardonnay 2010 Estate-grown, whole bunch-pressed and barrel-fermented in French oak; classic cool-grown chardonnay with fresh, intense grapefruit and white peach flavours complexed by a touch of grilled nut/mealy oak inputs. Screwcap. 13% alc. **Rating** 94 **To** 2017 $28
Mill Block Pinot Noir 2010 Significantly deeper colour than Forest Raven; while far from full-bodied, has attractive red cherry and plum aromas that flow directly into the palate, backed by superfine tannins. Elegance personified. Screwcap. 13.2% alc. **Rating** 94 **To** 2017 $40

ΨΨΨΨΨ Jessica 2009 **Rating** 93 **To** 2015 $35
Pinot Grigio 2011 **Rating** 92 **To** 2014 $26
Pinot Noir 2009 **Rating** 91 **To** 2018 $29
Schonburger 2011 **Rating** 90 **To** 2013 $25

ΨΨΨΨ Forest Raven Pinot Noir 2010 **Rating** 89 **To** 2015 $29
Rose 2011 **Rating** 87 **To** Now $21

Barristers Block

141 Onkaparinga Valley Road, Woodside, SA 5244 **Region** Adelaide Hills
T (08) 8389 7706 **www**.barristersblock.com.au **Open** 7 days 10.30–5
Winemaker Contract **Est.** 2004 **Dozens** 7500 **Vyds** 18.5ha
Owner Jan Siemelink-Allen has over 20 years in the industry, and spent five years in SA's Supreme Court in a successful battle to reclaim ownership of 10ha of cabernet sauvignon and shiraz in Wrattonbully after a joint venture collapsed; it is not hard to imagine the origin of the name. In 2006 she and her family purchased an 8ha vineyard planted to sauvignon blanc and pinot noir near Woodside in the Adelaide Hills, adjoining Shaw & Smith's vineyard. Exports to the UK, Germany, Vietnam, Malaysia, South Korea, Hong Kong, Singapore and China.

ΨΨΨΨΨ Limited Release Wrattonbully Cabernet Sauvignon 2009 Mid crimson; a bright bouquet of red and black fruits, offset by a touch of floral complexity; medium-bodied, fresh and vibrant on the palate, juicy and generous. Screwcap. 14% alc. **Rating** 90 **To** 2018 $30 BE

Barton Estate

2307 Barton Highway, Murrumbateman, NSW 2582 **Region** Canberra District
T (02) 6230 9553 **www**.bartonestate.com.au **Open** W'ends by appt
Winemaker Capital Wines, Canberra Winemakers **Est.** 1997 **Dozens** 600 **Vyds** 8ha
Bob Furbank and wife Julie Chitty are both CSIRO plant biologists: he is a biochemist
(physiologist) and she is a specialist in plant tissue culture. In 1997 they acquired the 120ha
property forming part of historic Jeir Station, and have since planted 15 grape varieties. The
most significant plantings are to cabernet sauvignon, shiraz, merlot, riesling and chardonnay,
the Joseph's coat completed with micro quantities of other varieties.

ΤΤΤΤΤ **Canberra Sauvignon Blanc 2011** Light straw-green; the intense tropical fruits
✪   on the palate seem to have been lifted by the retention of a small amount of
                 residual sugar, justified to balance the acidity. A very interesting wine, likely to have
                 wide appeal. Screwcap. 11.1% alc. **Rating** 92 **To** 2013 $18

ΤΤΤΤ **Canberra Sangiovese 2010 Rating** 89 **To** 2017 $22

Barton Jones Wines

39 Upper Capel Road, Donnybrook, WA 6239 **Region** Geographe
T (08) 9731 2233 **www**.bartonjoneswines.com.au **Open** Fri–Mon 10.30–4.30
Winemaker Contract **Est.** 1978 **Dozens** 2500 **Vyds** 3ha
The 22ha property on which Blackboy Ridge Estate is established was partly cleared and
planted to 2.5ha of semillon, chenin blanc, shiraz and cabernet sauvignon in 1978. When
current owners Adrian Jones and Jackie Barton purchased the property in 2000 the vines were
already some of the oldest in the region. The vineyard and the owners' house are on gentle
north-facing slopes, with extensive views over the Donnybrook area. A straw-bale cellar door
was completed in 2010. Wines are released under the Barton Jones and Blackboy Ridge labels.

ΤΤΤΤΤ **Blackboy Ridge Geographe Sauvignon Blanc Semillon 2011** Light straw-
✪   green; a wine with drive and power, with a mix of grass and snow pea presumably
                 from the semillon, and tropical/pineapple notes from the sauvignon blanc; the two
                 parts work well together. Screwcap. 13.5% alc. **Rating** 90 **To** 2014 $17

ΤΤΤΤ **The Brilliant Cut Semillon Sauvignon Blanc 2010 Rating** 89 **To** 2014 $22

Barton Vineyard

2464 Macquarie Road, Campbell Town, Tas 7210 **Region** Northern Tasmania
T (03) 6398 5114 **www**.bartonvineyards.com **Open** Last Sun each month or by appt
Winemaker Rebecca Wilson, Winemaking Tasmania **Est.** 2001 **Dozens** 300 **Vyds** 2ha
This is the venture of Milly and Frank Youl. Frank is a sixth-generation Tasmanian with a
farming background on a merino sheep stud; the property, long known as Barton, is adjacent
to the Macquarie River. After planting a few trial vines in 1987, the Youls finally took the
plunge (ignoring most advice) and planted pinot noir and riesling on a north-facing slope in
2001. They have a small cottage for fly fishers near the Macquarie River, and I believe I stayed
in it one year with fellow judges from the Tasmanian Wine Show. The cottage brings the Youl
family history full circle, as forebear James Youl introduced trout into Australia. A new cellar
door is planned.

ΤΤΤΤ **Pinot Noir 2010** Bright, clear crimson; this is a pretty wine with appealing small
                 red berry flavours; may develop more character with time in bottle, but good for
                 simple drinking right now. Screwcap. 13.1% alc. **Rating** 88 **To** 2016 $23

Barwang ★★★★★

Barwang Road, Young, NSW 2594 (postal) **Region** Hilltops
T (02) 9722 1299 **www**.mcwilliamswinesgroup.com **Open** Not
Winemaker Andrew Higgins **Est.** 1969 **Dozens** NFP **Vyds** 100ha

Peter Robertson pioneered viticulture in the Young area when he planted his first vines in 1969 as part of a diversification program for his 400ha grazing property. When McWilliam's acquired Barwang in 1989, the vineyard amounted to 13 ha; today the plantings are 100ha. Wine quality has been exemplary from the word go, value for money no less so. The Barwang label also takes in 100% Tumbarumba wines, as well as Hilltops/Tumbarumba blends. Exports to Asia.

ŢŢŢŢŢ **842 Tumbarumba Chardonnay 2010** Pale gold, vibrant hue; year in and year out this high altitude wine excels in shows around the country; this vintage is tightly wound and unevolved, showing pure nectarine and charcuterie notes; the palate is linear and finely detailed, slowly opening up to reveal layers of flavour; beautifully poised and harmonious. Screwcap. 13% alc. **Rating** 96 **To** 2020 $35 BE
842 Tumbarumba Chardonnay 2009 The McWilliam's winemaking team responsible for 842 has got the style nailed, its near–delicacy utterly misleading, for the citrus and white peach fruit has great intensity, and simply soaks up the French oak. It still has all the indicia of a very young wine, and will continue to and probably past the end of this decade. Screwcap. 14% alc. **Rating** 95 **To** 2020 $35

✪ **Hilltops Cabernet Sauvignon 2010** Deep crimson; a fragrant and pure-fruited bouquet of redcurrant, cassis and violets; the palate is elegantly constructed, with fine-grained tannins aplenty, fresh acidity and fine persistence on the finish. Screwcap. 14% alc. **Rating** 94 **To** 2022 $20 BE

ŢŢŢŢŢ
✪ **Tumbarumba Chardonnay 2011** Bright straw-green; light-bodied, crisp and fresh, albeit with good intensity to the citrus and melon fruit of the palate; early picking has not diminished the varietal character or overall appeal of the wine, which won a gold medal at the National Wine Show '11. Screwcap. 12.5% alc. **Rating** 93 **To** 2015 $20

The Stables Cabernet Sauvignon 2009 Rating 93 **To** 2024 $40

✪ **Granite Track Tumbarumba Riesling 2010** Without warning, Tumbarumba produces a top-class riesling winning gold in class 500 (yes 500) and the trophy for Champion Sweet Wine at the Bathurst Cool Climate Wine Show '10, backing up with a gold medal at the Canberra Regional and Perth Wine Shows '11. For some obscure reason, there is no mention of the distinct touch of sweetness on the finish, even if it is perfectly balanced by acidity; yet another Mosel lookalike. Screwcap. 10.5% alc. **Rating** 93 **To** 2018 $23

✪ **Hilltops Shiraz 2009** Good hue of medium depth; strongly regional, with blackberry and plum fruit leavened by spice, pepper and licorice, savoury tannins in support. Much better than its meagre haul of two bronze medals would suggest. Screwcap. 14% alc. **Rating** 90 **To** 2017 $20

ŢŢŢŢ **Hilltops Cabernet Sauvignon 2009 Rating** 89 **To** 2017 $20

Barwick Wines   ★★★★☆

283 Yelverton North Road, Yelverton, WA 6281 **Region** Margaret River
T (08) 9755 7100 **www.**barwickwines.com **Open** By appt
Winemaker Nigel Ludlow **Est.** 1997 **Dozens** 120 000 **Vyds** 188ha
The production gives some guide to the size of the three estate vineyards. The first is the Dwalganup Vineyard in the Blackwood Valley region; the second is St John's Brook Vineyard in Margaret River; and the third is the Treenbrook Vineyard in Pemberton. Taken together, the three holdings place Barwick in the top 10 wine producers in WA. The wines are released under four labels, The Collectables at the top, from small parcels of estate-grown grapes. Last year's rating is maintained in the absence of a representative submission of its wines. Exports to the UK, the US, Canada, Africa, the Middle East, Laos and Singapore.

ŢŢŢŢ **Margaret River Sauvignon Blanc 2011** Vivid green hue; a pungent and expressive bouquet of nettle and pea pod, with citrus in tow; the palate is zesty and fresh, and should be enjoyed thoroughly chilled and as young as possible. Screwcap. 12.5% alc. **Rating** 88 **To** 2013 $25 BE

Bass Fine Wines

16 Goodman Court, Invermay, Launceston, Tas 7250 **Region** Northern Tasmania
T (03) 6331 0136 **Open** Mon–Fri 9–5, w'ends 9–4
Winemaker Guy Wagner **Est.** 1999 **Dozens** 3000
Owner/winemaker Guy Wagner has built the scope of his business over a period of 10 years, the greater expansion starting in 2007–08. He now makes wines for 17 small vineyards in Northern Tasmania in addition to his own wines; the 2008 crush was over 220 tonnes, with just one cellar hand to assist him. At the end of that year his partnership in the Rosevears winery ended, and a new winery was constructed prior to the '09 vintage at Invermay, well inside the city of Launceston. The cellar door at this location has glass walls, allowing visitors to observe the workings of a small winery. Retail distribution in Tas, Vic, NSW and ACT. Exports to the US.

 Strait Sauvignon Blanc 2011 Has more length and complexity than most of its Tasmanian peers; the varietal expression is mainly at the herbal/mineral end of the spectrum. Screwcap. 12.5% alc. **Rating** 90 **To** 2013 $25
Barrel Fermented Pinot Gris 2011 Straw-green; we are told the wine was made 'in our special French puncheons and left on lees' but given no further explanation; in fact not needed, for the wine has considerable depth and textural complexity, finishing with a blinding flash of Tasmanian acidity. It is nothing if not different. Screwcap. 13.5% alc. **Rating** 90 **To** 2014 $25
Strait Pinot Noir 2011 Purple, with just a touch of crimson; a powerful, full-bodied pinot noir with an abundance of ripe plum and black cherry fruit, finishing with a faint savoury edge to the tannins to give balance. Time to go. Screwcap. 13.5% alc. **Rating** 90 **To** 2018 $25

 Strait Gewurztraminer 2009 Rating 88 **To** 2014 $25
Strait Pinot Noir 2011 Rating 87 **To** 2014 $25

Bass Phillip ★★★★★

Tosch's Road, Leongatha South, Vic 3953 **Region** Gippsland
T (03) 5664 3341 **F** (03) 5664 3209 **Open** By appt
Winemaker Phillip Jones **Est.** 1979 **Dozens** 1500
Phillip Jones retired from the Melbourne rat-race to handcraft tiny quantities of superlative Pinot Noir which, at its best, has no equal in Australia. Painstaking site selection, ultra-close vine spacing and the very, very cool climate of South Gippsland are the keys to the magic of Bass Phillip and its eerily Burgundian Pinots. No wines were received for this edition; the rating is that of last year.

Bass River Winery ★★★

1835 Dalyston Glen Forbes Road, Glen Forbes, Vic 3990 **Region** Gippsland
T (03) 5678 8252 **www.**bassriverwinery.com **Open** Thurs–Tues 9–5
Winemaker Pasquale Butera, Frank Butera **Est.** 1999 **Dozens** 850 **Vyds** 4ha
The Butera family has established pinot noir (1ha), chardonnay (0.75ha), riesling, sauvignon blanc, pinot gris (0.5ha each) and cabernet sauvignon (0.25ha), with both the winemaking and viticulture handled by the father and son team of Pasquale and Frank. The small production is principally sold through the cellar door plus to some retailers and restaurants in the South Gippsland area. Exports to Singapore.

 Gippsland Iced Riesling 2011 Bright straw-green; made by partly freezing the juice, removing the ice that forms, leaving the sugar, acid and all of the fruit in more concentrated solution. Thoroughly deserved its silver medal at the Gippsland Wine Show '11. Screwcap. 10% alc. **Rating** 90 **To** 2014 $25

battely wines ★★★★

1375 Beechworth-Wangaratta Road, Beechworth, Vic 3747 **Region** Beechworth
T (03) 5727 0505 **F** (03) 5727 0506 **www.**battelywines.com.au **Open** By appt
Winemaker Russell Bourne **Est.** 1998 **Dozens** 500 **Vyds** 5ha

Dr Russell Bourne is an anaesthetist and former GP at Mt Beauty who has always loved the food, wine and skiing of Northeast Victoria. He completed his oenology degree at CSU in 2002 following his 1998 acquisition of the former Brown Brothers Everton Hills Vineyard. He has since planted 1.6ha of shiraz and viognier, more recently adding counoise, the first planting of this variety in Australia. All wines are estate-grown. Exports to the UK, the US and Hong Kong.

🍷🍷🍷🍷 **Beechworth Syrah 2010** Excellent colour and clarity; the medium-bodied palate has both flavour and structural complexity, with a beguiling mix of blackberry, black cherry, licorice, spice and black pepper; this has been achieved without burdening the finish. Cork. 14.5% alc. **Rating** 93 **To** 2018 $58
Beechworth Durif 2010 Has the durif tannins, but they are largely balanced by the display of black fruits and touches of licorice and spice. That said, don't feel stressed if you leave it a year or two before seeing what it tastes like. Cork. 14.5% alc. **Rating** 90 **To** 2017 $44

Battle of Bosworth

Gaffney Road, Willunga, SA 5172 **Region** McLaren Vale
T (08) 8556 2441 **F** (08) 8556 4881 **www**.battleofbosworth.com.au **Open** Fri–Mon 11–5
Winemaker Joch Bosworth **Est.** 1996 **Dozens** 5000 **Vyds** 80ha
Battle of Bosworth is owned and run by Joch Bosworth (viticulture and winemaking) and partner Louise Hemsley-Smith (sales and marketing). The wines take their name from the battle which ended the War of the Roses, fought on Bosworth Field, Leicestershire in 1485. The vineyards were established in the early 1970s by parents Peter and Anthea Bosworth, in the foothills of the Mt Lofty Ranges in McLaren Vale. Conversion to organic viticulture began in 1995, with vines now 20 years and older, fully certified A-grade organic by ACO. The label depicts the yellow soursob (*Oxalis pes-caprae*), hated by gardeners everywhere, but whose growth habits make it an ideal weapon for battling weeds in organic viticulture. Shiraz, cabernet sauvignon and chardonnay account for 75% of the plantings, with 10 more varieties making up the numbers. The Spring Seeds Wine Co. wines are made from estate vineyards. Exports to the UK, the US, Canada, the Czech Republic, Hong Kong and Singapore.

🍷🍷🍷🍷 **Braden's McLaren Vale Shiraz 2010** Only two 300-litre, 4-year-old French oak barrels were used to make this hand-bottled, unfiltered wine designed to fully reflect its place of origin, which it handsomely does with its lush plum, black cherry, blackberry and mocha flavours; the tannins are there, but it's the fruit that's talking. Screwcap. 14.5% alc. **Rating** 93 **To** 2025 $45
McLaren Vale Cabernet Sauvignon 2010 Medium purple-crimson; one of many wines to demonstrate the synergy between McLaren Vale's Mediterranean climate and cabernet sauvignon; only medium-bodied, and the tannins are a little adrift, but will come together in a year or so. Organically grown. Screwcap. 14.5% alc. **Rating** 90 **To** 2018 $25

🍷🍷🍷🍷
✪ **Spring Seed Wine Co. Forget-Me-Not McLaren Vale Sauvignon Blanc Semillon 2011** Quartz-white; a lively wine with fresh-mown grass and minerally components, with a hint of spice (from non-existent oak); has a good finish, and is a very snappy wine given the year. Screwcap. 12% alc. **Rating** 89 **To** 2013 $18
McLaren Vale Shiraz 2010 Rating 89 **To** 2016 $25
Puritan McLaren Vale Shiraz 2011 Rating 88 **To** 2014 $20
Spring Seed Wine Co. Scarlet Runner McLaren Vale Shiraz 2010 Rating 87 **To** 2014 $20

Bawley Vale Estate

226 Bawley Point Road, Bawley Point, NSW 2539 **Region** Shoalhaven Coast
T (02) 4457 2555 **www**.bawleyvaleestate.com.au **Open** W'ends & public hols 11–4.30
Winemaker Crooked River Winery (Michelle Crockett) **Est.** 2003 **Dozens** 600
Vyds 2.4ha

Bawley Vale Estate sits on 40ha of prime south coast land acquired by Raymond and Loris McLoughlin in 2003. They have planted 0.7ha of cabernet sauvignon, 0.4ha each of verdelho, chardonnay and shiraz, 0.3ha of chambourcin, 0.2ha of arneis, plus small plantings of merlot, along with citrus and olive groves. The wines are sold through local restaurants and bottle shops and (of course) via the cellar door and website.

🍷🍷🍷🍷 **Murramarang Vineyard Shoalhaven Coast Shiraz 2010** Light red-purple; it is very surprising that the flavours, while light, are not green; likewise, handling in the winery has been gentle, with just enough tannins to sustain the wine. Screwcap. 11.5% alc. **Rating** 87 **To** 2014 $25
Bawley Storm 2010 A blend of cabernet sauvignon, malbec, merlot, cabernet franc and petit verdot. The colour is bright, and here, too, the flavours are fresher than they are green, although there is some of that in the make-up of the wine. Screwcap. 11.9% alc. **Rating** 87 **To** 2014 $25

Bay of Fires/House of Arras ★★★★★
40 Baxters Road, Pipers River, Tas 7252 **Region** Northern Tasmania
T (03) 6382 7622 **www**.bayoffireswines.com.au **Open** 7 days 10–5
Winemaker Peter Dredge **Est.** 2001 **Dozens** NFP
Hardys purchased its first grapes from Tasmania in 1994 with the aim of further developing and refining its sparkling wines, a process that quickly gave birth to Arras. The next stage was the inclusion of various parcels of chardonnay from Tasmania in the 1998 Eileen Hardy, then the development in 2001 of the Bay of Fires brand, offering wines sourced from various parts of Tasmania. The winery was originally that of Rochecombe, then Ninth Island, and now, of course, Bay of Fires. Its potential has now been fully realised in the most impressive imaginable fashion. Exports to all major markets.

🍷🍷🍷🍷🍷 **Bay of Fires Riesling 2011** Pale straw-green; intense lime blossom and lime zest aromas lead into a superb palate with lime juice flavours a la the Mosel Valley lengthened by perfectly balanced acidity. Something quite special. Screwcap. 12% alc. **Rating** 96 **To** 2026 $32
Arras Blanc de Blanc 2001 Traditional method and many years on yeast lees have resulted in a wine that marries finesse and flavour, with the flavours in the grapefruit/white peach spectrum, but softened by the brioche characters from the long time on lees. Cork. 12.5% alc. **Rating** 96 **To** 2014 $80
Arras Brut Elite Chardonnay Pinot Noir NV Cuvee no. 401 A traditional method blend of multi-Tasmanian region pinot noir and chardonnay given many years on lees prior to disgorgement. Pale straw-green, it is at once intense yet fine, with brioche and toast nuances in a creamy web, the acidity perfect, the palate long and harmonious. Cork. 12.5% alc. **Rating** 96 **To** Now $55
Arras EJ Carr Late Disgorged 2000 Pale green-straw/gold; very good, fine and focused; given its age, amazingly youthful, on the way to creamy. Top Gold Tas Wine Show '12. Cork. 12.5% alc. **Rating** 96 **To** 2015 $198
Bay of Fires Pinot Gris 2011 Pale straw-green; a striking bouquet of pear, spice and ginger leads into an exceptional palate with quince added to the already complex array of flavours; the texture of the finish is also exceptional. Screwcap. 13.5% alc. **Rating** 95 **To** 2014 $32
Bay of Fires Pinot Noir 2010 Bright crimson-purple; a pure evocation of pinot noir, with red cherry and ripe strawberry aromas and flavours; while French oak is part of the picture, it is strictly secondary to the fruit on the long, lingering finish. From the Derwent River, East Coast and Coal River areas. Screwcap. 13.5% alc. **Rating** 95 **To** 2017 $38
Bay of Fires Riesling 2010 Rating 94 **To** 2030 $39

🍷🍷🍷🍷♀ **Tasmanian Cuvee Brut Pinot Noir Chardonnay NV Rating** 93 **To** Now $32
Tasmanian Cuvee Rose NV Rating 93 **To** 2016 $37
Bay of Fires Sauvignon Blanc 2011 Rating 92 **To** 2014 $32

🍷🍷🍷🍷 **Bay of Fires Chardonnay 2010 Rating** 88 **To** 2015 $40

Bay of Shoals ★★★★☆

Cordes Road, Kingscote, Kangaroo Island, SA 5223 **Region** Kangaroo Island
T (08) 8553 0289 **www**.bayofshoalswines.com.au **Open** 7 days 11–5
Winemaker Jonothan Ketley **Est.** 1994 **Dozens** NA **Vyds** 10ha
John Willoughby's vineyard overlooks the Bay of Shoals, which is the northern boundary of
Kingscote, Kangaroo Island's main town. Planting of the vineyard began in 1994 and it now
comprises riesling, chardonnay, sauvignon blanc, cabernet sauvignon and shiraz. In addition,
460 olive trees have been planted to produce table olives.

ⵣⵣⵣⵣⵣ **Kangaroo Island Riesling 2011** A bright and fragrant bouquet of fresh lime,
✪ sea spray and a ripe candied orange exotic note; the palate reveals a sweet-fruited
core, and while it is 14.2% alc, there is little trace of such warmth on the finish.
Screwcap. **Rating** 90 **To** 2017 $18 BE
✪ **Kangaroo Island Shiraz 2009** Deep garnet; a spicy bouquet of blackberry, pea
pod, black pepper and juniper; the palate is driven by racy acidity and savoury
charcuterie flavours to finish; certainly a big step away from 'traditional' Australian
shiraz, and interesting for it. Screwcap. 14.2% alc. **Rating** 90 **To** 2018 $20 BE

ⵣⵣⵣⵣ **Kangaroo Island Chardonnay 2011** A fragrant and energetic wine, showing
✪ citrus, fennel and mineral complexity; the palate is taut and racy, refreshing and
direct, with a fine lemony finish, in a style akin to Chablis. Screwcap. 12.5% alc.
Rating 89 **To** 2015 $18 BE
Limited Edition Kangaroo Island Sparkling Chardonnay 2011 Rating 88
To 2014 $20 BE

Beach Road ★★★★★

PO Box 1106, McLaren Flat, SA 5171 **Region** Langhorne Creek/McLaren Vale
T (08) 8327 4547 **www**.beachroadwines.com.au **Open** Not
Winemaker Briony Hoare **Est.** 2007 **Dozens** 1000
This is the thoroughly impressive venture of winemaker Briony Hoare and viticulturist Tony
Hoare, who began their life partnership after meeting while studying wine science at the
Roseworthy campus of Adelaide University. Their involvement in the industry dates back to
the early 1990s, Briony working around Australia with many of the flagship wines of (then)
Southcorp, Tony gaining extensive experience in Mildura, the Hunter Valley and McLaren
Vale (it was in McLaren Vale that he spent five years as viticulturist for Wirra Wirra). In 2005
the pair decided to go it alone, setting up a wine consultancy, and in '07 launching Beach
Road. An early focus on Italian varieties stemmed from Briony's vintage in Piedmont, where
she worked with barbera, nebbiolo, gavi and moscato. Along the way, however, they both
had a lot of exposure to grenache, shiraz and mourvedre; it is not surprising that one of the
first wines to be released was a Shiraz Grenache, joined by Petit Verdot, Fiano, Greco di Tufo
and Primitivo (the Italian name for zinfandel). Last year's rating has been retained given the
challenges of the '12 vintage.

ⵣⵣⵣⵣⵣ **Fiano 2011** Pale, bright straw-green; a fragrant bouquet of orange zest, spice and
orange blossom is followed by a lively palate with a surge of sweet citrus flavour
on the finish and aftertaste, actively drawing saliva from the mouth. A variety full
of potential from the south of Italy. Screwcap. 13% alc. **Rating** 94 **To** 2014 $25

ⵣⵣⵣⵣⵣ **Vermentino 2011 Rating** 92 **To** 2015 $25

Beattie Wines ★★★★☆

53 Andrew Street, Windsor, Vic 3181 (postal) **Region** Yarra Valley
T 0411 187 871 **www**.beattie.tv **Open** Not
Winemaker Brendon Beattie **Est.** 1998 **Dozens** 200
Brendon Beattie makes chardonnay, cabernet sauvignon and merlot, the small production sold
through the Swords Select shops at Prahran Market, Queen Victoria Market, Clifton Hill and
South Melbourne Market.

🍷🍷🍷🍷🍷 **Yarra Valley Cabernet Sauvignon 2008** Deeply coloured, this is a very good cabernet, with a cross-weave of earthy/briary notes, and juicy, vibrant cassis, the finish bringing it all together with fine, polished tannins and quality oak. Diam. 13.5% alc. **Rating** 94 **To** 2020

🍷🍷🍷🍷 **Yarra Valley Cabernet Sauvignon 2010 Rating** 89 **To** 2018 $26

Beckingham Wines

6–7/477 Warrigal Road, Moorabbin, Vic 3189 **Region** Mornington Peninsula
T 0400 192 264 **www**.beckinghamwines.com.au **Open** W'ends 10–5
Winemaker Peter Beckingham **Est.** 1998 **Dozens** 3000
Peter Beckingham is a chemical engineer who has turned a hobby into a business, moving operations from the driveway of his house to a warehouse in Moorabbin. The situation of the winery may not be romantic, but it is eminently practical, and more than a few winemakers in California have adopted the same solution. His friends grow the grapes, and he makes the wine, both for himself and as a contract maker for others.

🍷🍷🍷🍷 **Blanc de Noir 2005 Rating** 89 **To** 2013 $20
◎

Beelgara

Farm 576 Rossetto Road, Beelbangera, NSW 2680 **Region** Riverina
T (02) 6966 0200 **www**.beelgara.com.au **Open** Mon–Sat 10–3
Winemaker Rod Hooper, Danny Toaldo **Est.** 1930 **Dozens** 500 000
Beelgara Estate was formed in 2001 after the purchase of the 60-year-old Rossetto family winery by a group of shareholders, mostly the Toohey family. The emphasis has changed significantly, with a concerted effort to go to the right region for each variety (in the Regional Reserve range), while still maintaining very good value for money. Exports to Ireland, Canada and Asia.

🍷🍷🍷🍷🍷 **Regional Reserve Watervale Riesling 2011** Lime, unsweetened lemon and slatey mineral characters define both the bouquet and palate; the acidity provides a steely backbone that will see the wine live for many years, although precisely how it will develop is not easy to see. Screwcap. 12% alc. **Rating** 92 **To** 2021 $25

Regional Reserve Yarra Valley Chardonnay 2010 Pale colour, bright; a restrained and elegant bouquet of pear, nectarine and fine spices; lively acidity, with bath talc, quartz and a splash of lemon providing lift and line. Screwcap. 12.5% alc. **Rating** 91 **To** 2017 $25 BE

✪ **Black Label Mount Lofty Grenache Rose 2011** Bright fuchsia-pink; the Mt Lofty Ranges includes the disparate Adelaide Hills, Adelaide Plains and Clare Valley regions, and this wine must surely come from either or both of the latter two. It is lively, fresh and crisp, with red fruits to the fore, backed up by good acidity; dry finish. Screwcap. 13.5% alc. **Rating** 90 **To** Now $18

✪ **Black Label Clare Valley Shiraz 2009** A ripe and fragrant blend of mulberry fruits and fruitcake spices; the charry oak is a strong factor on the finish, yet the fruit balances it with aplomb Screwcap. 13.5% alc. **Rating** 90 **To** 2016 $18

🍷🍷🍷🍷 **Black Label Adelaide Hills Sauvignon Blanc 2011** A fragrant, fresh and
✪ juicy sauvignon, showing tropical fruits, and a vibrant mix of fresh-cut grass herbaceousness; made for early drinking. Screwcap. 12.5% alc. **Rating** 89 **To** 2013 $18 BE

✪ **Black Label Clare Valley Cabernet Sauvignon 2009** Showing a little development of leather alongside a healthy dose of cassis and olive; the palate is soft, forward and accessible, ready for drinking in the short term. Screwcap. 14% alc. **Rating** 89 **To** 2015 $18 BE

Black Label Mount Lofty Pinot Grigio 2011 Rating 87 **To** Now $18

✪ **Estate Range Shiraz 2010** Mid crimson; a simple, fresh and direct red-fruited wine; clean and well made, and certainly offering good value at this price point. Screwcap. 12.5% alc. **Rating** 87 **To** 2014 $9 BE

Black Label Adelaide Hills Merlot 2010 Rating 87 **To** 2015 $18 BE

Belgravia Vineyards ★★★★★

84 Byng Street, Orange, NSW 2800 **Region** Orange
T (02) 6360 0495 **www**.belgravia.com.au **Open** 7 days 10–4
Winemaker Phil Kerney (Contract) **Est.** 2001 **Dozens** 10 000 **Vyds** 193ha
Belgravia is an 1800ha mixed farming property (sheep, cattle and vines) 20km north of Orange, established and owned by the Hattersley family. There are now over 190ha of vineyard, with 10ha devoted to the Belgravia brand. In 2006 Belgravia opened its cellar door at the heritage-listed former Union Bank building in Orange, which also operates as a wine bar and restaurant. Exports to the UK, Denmark, Germany and Hong Kong.

ŸŸŸŸŸ **Orange Merlot 2010** Impressive colour and bouquet with a distinct bramble aroma and perhaps wild rose; the palate lifts the wine another notch, with blackcurrant fruit, powerful but balanced tannins, and quality oak all in play. An Australian merlot that a Left Bank producer in Bordeaux would instantly relate to, sweet plum fruit nowhere in the profile. Screwcap. 13.5% alc. **Rating** 96 To 2025 $30

✪ **Orange Sauvignon Blanc 2011** Light straw-green; it only takes an instant to realise this is a delicious sauvignon, the bouquet and palate unfolding a full array of tropical fruits headed by passionfruit, guava and kiwi fruit, the finish given special impact with its lemony acidity. Screwcap. 12.5% alc. **Rating** 95 To 2013 $22

Orange Riesling 2011 Quartz-green; the floral bouquet introduces a palate with echoes of the orange blossom of the bouquet, together with lime, passionfruit and a shaft of acidity. Screwcap. 12.5% alc. **Rating** 94 To 2021 $22

The Apex Orange Chardonnay 2011 Pale straw-green; The Apex is the title given to the best wine produced each vintage: here it is a chardonnay that is both very subtle yet very complex; it is hand-picked, whole bunch-pressed, the juice wild yeast-fermented in new French oak; that oak is part of the single stream of white peach, grapefruit and cashew flavours underpinned by citrussy acidity. The overall texture and balance are impeccable, so much so it's not easy to unbundle the wine. Screwcap. 12.5% alc. **Rating** 94 To 2018 $30

ŸŸŸŸŸ **Orange Gewurztraminer 2011 Rating** 91 To 2017 $22
Orange Roussanne 2011 Rating 90 To 2016 $22

ŸŸŸŸ **Orange Cabernet Sauvignon 2009 Rating** 89 To 2015 $22
Orange Pinot Gris 2011 Rating 87 To 2013 $22

Bellarine Estate ★★★★☆

2270 Portarlington Road, Bellarine, Vic 3222 **Region** Geelong
T (03) 5259 3310 **www**.bellarineestate.com.au **Open** 7 days 11–4
Winemaker Anthony Brain **Est.** 1995 **Dozens** 4500 **Vyds** 12ha
Anthony Brain, with six vintages under his belt at Bellarine Estate's onsite winery, is now a district veteran. With the second string of the Bellarine Brewing company (which makes the only micro-brewed beer on the Bellarine Peninsula) also situated in the winery, and the extended operating hours of Julian's Restaurant, it is a popular meeting place. The vineyard is planted to chardonnay, pinot noir, shiraz, merlot, viognier and sauvignon blanc. Exports to the US.

ŸŸŸŸ **James' Paddock Geelong Chardonnay 2010** Light straw-green; has clearly defined cool-grown chardonnay characters of pink grapefruit and white peach on the bouquet and palate; barrel-fermented in French oak and 10 months' maturation have added a touch of toasty cashew, the finish lifted by crisp acidity. Screwcap. 13.4% alc. **Rating** 93 To 2017 $28

Bellarmine Wines ★★★★★

1 Balyan Retreat, Pemberton, WA 6258 **Region** Pemberton
T (08) 9776 0667 **www**.bellarmine.com.au **Open** By appt
Winemaker Dr Diane Miller **Est.** 2000 **Dozens** 6000 **Vyds** 20.2ha

This vineyard is owned by German residents Dr Willi and Gudrun Schumacher. Long-term wine lovers, the Schumachers decided to establish a vineyard and winery of their own, using Australia partly because of its stable political climate. The vineyard is planted to merlot, pinot noir, chardonnay, shiraz, riesling, sauvignon blanc and petit verdot. Following the departure of long-term winemaker Mike Bewsher, Diane Miller, previously head of the Vintage Wineworx contract winemaking facility, was appointed winemaker and operations manager. Exports to the UK, Canada, Germany and China.

🍷🍷🍷🍷🍷 **Pemberton Chardonnay 2010** Glowing straw-green; as ever with Bellarmine,
✪ a beautifully focused and balanced wine, with great length to its perfectly ripened nectarine and citrus palate, subtle oak totally integrated. Screwcap. 14% alc. **Rating** 96 **To** 2020 $20

● **Pemberton Riesling Half Dry 2011 Rating** 95 **To** 2015 $20
Pemberton Shiraz 2010 Deep purple-crimson; the class of wine shines through from the first whiff to the long finish and aftertaste; multi-spice, licorice and black pepper are woven through the blackberry and plum fruit, with fine-grained tannins in support. Screwcap. 14.5% alc. **Rating** 95 **To** 2030 $35

● **Pemberton Riesling Select 2011 Rating** 95 **To** 2030 $20
● **Pemberton Riesling Dry 2011 Rating** 94 **To** 2020 $20
Pemberton Pinot Noir 2010 Very good colour, verging on ruby; the bouquet is highly aromatic and strongly varietal, its promise fulfilled on the palate. Here there is a mix of cherry, plum and spice set in a savoury, forest floor spectrum; thanks to the depth of the primary fruit, these characters simply add to the appeal of the wine. Screwcap. 14.5% alc. **Rating** 94 **To** 2017 $25

🍷🍷🍷🍷🍷 **Pemberton Sauvignon Blanc 2011 Rating** 93 **To** 2013 $20
●

 # Bellevue Estate
797 Main Road, McLaren Vale, SA 5171 **Region** McLaren Vale
T 0413 082 358 **www**.bellevueestate.com.au **Open** By appt
Winemaker Corey Vandeleur **Est.** 2007 **Dozens** 1000 **Vyds** 4ha
Corey and Michelle Vandeleur's venture may be a small one, but it has been planned to the last degree, and backed by Corey's very impressive history in winemaking. While he has no formal qualifications, he was born and bred in McLaren Vale, and began as a cellarhand at Maglieri Winery in 1990, where he remained for the next seven years before heading overseas to do vintage at Geyser Peak, in California, thence to South Africa, and eventually for three vintages in Bordeaux in wineries owned by the Despagne family. A decade at Hardys Tintara followed before creating the Bellevue Estate label. However, he had looked to the future by planting 4ha of shiraz on his family's property – fronting the main street of McLaren Vale – in 1997, and is still the only person involved in the care of the vineyard. In 2007, declining prices for contract-grown grapes led to the decision to build a winery on the main street. The inevitable litigation duly followed, but the Vandeleurs persisted and in that same year made their first vintage, selling most of the wine on the bulk market, but bottling 300 dozen for their own label. The wine is made in using typical small-batch processes with small open fermenters and minimum interference.

🍷🍷🍷🍷🍷 **McLaren Vale Shiraz 2010** Inky purple-crimson; a lush, plush, concentrated
✪ regional style with blackberry, blackcurrant and dark chocolate flavours, the tannins appropriately lined up in support. Good cellaring prospect. Screwcap. 14.5% alc. **Rating** 90 **To** 2020 $18

Bellvale Wines
95 Forresters Lane, Berrys Creek, Vic 3953 **Region** Gippsland
T (03) 5668 8230 **www**.bellvalewine.com.au **Open** By appt
Winemaker John Ellis **Est.** 1998 **Dozens** 2500 **Vyds** 18ha
John Ellis is the third under this name to be actively involved in the wine industry. His background as a former 747 pilot, and the knowledge he gained of Burgundy over many

visits, sets him apart from the others. He has established pinot noir (10ha), chardonnay (5ha) and pinot gris (3ha) on the red soils of a north-facing slope. He chose a density of 7150 vines per ha, following as far as possible the precepts of Burgundy, but limited by tractor size, which precludes narrower row spacing and even higher plant density. Exports to the UK, the US, Denmark, Germany, Singapore and Japan.

ɭɭɭɭɭ **Athena's Vineyard Gippsland Chardonnay 2009** Medium straw-green; fills the mouth, as do many Gippsland chardonnays, with fleshy stone fruit and cashew flavours supported by balanced acidity and well-integrated French oak. Screwcap. 13% alc. **Rating** 94 **To** 2016 $35

The Quercus Vineyard Gippsland Pinot Noir 2010 Produced from John Ellis's close-planted, dry-grown vineyard; the colour and clarity are beyond reproach, although on the light side. This is a wine of finesse, but, more than that, shows how pinot that initially appears light-bodied can and does expand dramatically on the finish and aftertaste, here with a mix of berries and bramble characters. Diam. 13% alc. **Rating** 94 **To** 2016 $35

Bellwether ★★★★★

PO Box 344, Coonawarra, SA 5263 **Region** Coonawarra
T 0417 080 945 **www.**bellwetherwines.com.au **Open** Not
Winemaker Sue Bell **Est.** 2009 **Dozens** 1000
Sometimes good things come from bad. When Constellation decided to sell (or mothball) its large Padthaway winery, built by Hardys little more than 10 years previously at a cost of $20 million, chief winemaker Sue Bell was summarily retrenched. In quick succession she received a $46,000 wine industry scholarship from the Grape and Wine Research Development Council to study the wine industry in relation to other rural industries in Australia and overseas, and its interaction with community and society. She also became Dux of the Len Evans Tutorial, her prize an extended trip through Bordeaux and Burgundy. She had decided to stay and live in Coonawarra, and the next stroke of good fortune was that a beautiful old shearing shed at Glenroy in Coonawarra came on the market, and will be her winery and cellar door. She is making two wines: a Coonawarra Cabernet and a Tasmanian Chardonnay, having had the opportunity to work with chardonnay from Tasmania, the Yarra Valley and SA while at Stonehaven.

ɭɭɭɭɭ **Coonawarra Cabernet Sauvignon 2009** Crimson-purple; a rare example of a producer in Coonawarra hand-pruning, hand-picking, open-fermenting with indigenous yeast, basket-pressing and using French oak. The modest alcohol, while not unique, is not common, yet is the key to the freshness and purity of the wine; blackberry is part of the make-up, but so are black and red cherry; the tannins are superfine and supple, the oak totally integrated. A beautiful wine. Screwcap. 13% alc. **Rating** 96 **To** 2030 $50

Coonawarra Cabernet Sauvignon 2008 Good colour for age; has the same degree of fragrance as the '09, with traditional Coonawarra blackcurrant, earth and mint characters; once again, the bouquet and palate are fresh and precise, the palate with immaculate balance and length. Screwcap. 13% alc. **Rating** 95 **To** 2028 $50

ɭɭɭɭɭ **Tamar Valley Chardonnay 2010 Rating** 93 **To** 2020 $50

Belvoir Park Estate

39 Belvoir Park Road, Big Hill, Vic 3453 **Region** Bendigo
T (03) 5435 3075 **www.**belvoirparkestate.com.au **Open** W'ends 11–5 or by appt
Winemaker Greg McClure **Est.** 1996 **Dozens** 1000 **Vyds** 3ha
When Greg and Mell McClure purchased Belvoir Park Estate in November 2010 from founders Ian and Julie Hall, it was in excellent condition. The house, guarded by 200-year-old redgums, overlooks the vineyard gently sloping away from the house, planted to riesling, merlot, shiraz and cabernet sauvignon. It was very much a lifestyle change for the McClures and their three young children. The one continuing thread has been Greg's involvement in

the marketing side of many businesses, evident in the renovation of the cellar door that now includes a gallery for local artists.

🍷🍷🍷🍷 **Symphony Bendigo Shiraz Cabernet Merlot 2009** The colour isn't convincing, but the wine is pleasant enough, the three varieties in tune; that said, it seems the shiraz has been the conductor. Diam. 13.9% alc. **Rating** 89 **To** 2016 $29 **Single Vineyard Bendigo Shiraz 2010** Good hue, although not 100% bright; a firm wine with notes of forest and briar to the blackberry fruit of the medium-bodied palate; needs a touch more flesh. Screwcap. 13.1% alc. **Rating** 88 **To** 2015 $28

Ben Haines Wine Co.   ★★★★☆
7/211 Gold Street, Clifton Hill, Vic 3068 (postal) **Region** Various
T 0417 083 645 **www**.benhaineswine.com **Open** Not
Winemaker Ben Haines **Est.** 2010 **Dozens** 500
Ben Haines graduated from the University of Adelaide in 1999 with a degree in viticulture, waiting a couple of years (immersing himself in music) before focusing on his career. An early interest in terroir led to a deliberate choice of diverse regions, including the Yarra Valley, McLaren Vale, Adelaide Hills, Langhorne Creek, Tasmania and Central Victoria, as well as time in the US and France. Most recently, he worked at Mitchelton as senior winemaker, and in 2008 won The Wine Society Young Winemaker of the Year Award.

🍷🍷🍷🍷🍷 **Warramunda Vineyard Yarra Valley Marsanne 2011** Pale straw-green; made with the philosophy that good things can't be hurried, and the hope that at least some of those who buy this wine will give it at least 5 years, and preferably 10, to allow it to reach its full expression; the balance and length, and the history of the variety here and overseas, all point to its longevity. The points are for today, not for 5 or 10 years hence. Screwcap. 13% alc. **Rating** 93 **To** 2026 $28

Ben Potts Wines   ★★★☆
Wellington Road, Langhorne Creek, SA 5255 **Region** Langhorne Creek
T (08) 8537 3029 **www**.benpottswines.com.au **Open** 7 days 10–5
Winemaker Ben Potts **Est.** 2002 **Dozens** 800
Ben Potts is the sixth generation to be involved in grapegrowing and winemaking in Langhorne Creek, the first being Frank Potts, founder of Bleasdale Vineyards. Ben completed the oenology degree at CSU, and ventured into winemaking on a commercial scale in 2002 (aged 25). Fiddle's Block Shiraz is named after great-grandfather Fiddle; Lenny's Block Cabernet Sauvignon Malbec after grandfather Len; and Bill's Block Malbec after father Bill. Exports to Switzerland, Hong Kong, Singapore and China.

🍷🍷🍷🍷🍷 **Lenny's Block Langhorne Creek Cabernet Sauvignon 2009** Medium red-purple; made from 50-year-old vines; it is full-bodied and rich, with black fruits and thick, chewy tannins. The hope is that time will slim it down somewhat. Cork. 15% alc. **Rating** 91 **To** 2024 $40

🍷🍷🍷🍷 **Fiddle's Block Langhorne Creek Shiraz 2009** Rating 88 To 2019 $40

Bended Knee Vineyard   ★★★★
PO Box 334, Buninyong, Vic 3357 **Region** Ballarat
T (03) 5341 8437 **www**.bendedknee.com.au **Open** Not
Winemaker Peter Roche **Est.** 1999 **Dozens** 250 **Vyds** 1.2ha
Peter and Pauline Roche have 0.5ha each of chardonnay and pinot noir planted at moderately high density, and 0.2ha of ultra-close-planted pinot noir at the equivalent of 9000 vines perha. Here four clones have been used: 114, 115, G5V15 and 777. The Roches say, 'We are committed to sustainable viticulture and aim to leave the planet in better shape than we found it.' Ducks, guinea fowl and chooks are vineyard custodians, and all vine canopy management is done by hand, including pruning and picking. Although production is tiny, Bended Knee wines can be found at some of Melbourne's best restaurants.

ŸŸŸŸ♀ **Pinot Noir 2010** Light, bright crimson-purple; part wild, part inoculated yeast in the ferment; clear-cut varietal fruit ranges through strawberry to red cherry to black cherry, all with a faint bramble character. Well made, with time to go. Screwcap. 14% alc. **Rating** 91 **To** 2017 $35

Bendigo Wine Estate ★★★★☆

682 Axedale-Goornong Road, Axedale, Vic 3551 **Region** Bendigo
T (03) 5439 7444 **F** (03) 5439 7433 **Open** Mon–Fri 9–3, w'ends by appt
Winemaker Various contract **Est.** 2000 **Dozens** 920 **Vyds** 39ha
A quite substantial operation, with plantings of shiraz (21ha) and cabernet sauvignon (10ha) having the lion's share, together with smaller plantings of merlot, malbec, verdelho, chardonnay, mataro and riesling producing both table and sparkling wines. The wines are chiefly sold by mail order and through the cellar door, which has bbq and picnic facilities, and periodically stages events.

ŸŸŸŸŸ **Gold Nugget Shiraz 2010** Deep purple-red; the ultra-fragrant bouquet doesn't warn you of the wine's formidable power, but just when you think this may be too much comes the realisation that the palate is beautifully balanced, and there is almost limitless supple black and red fruit under that power. Great now, it will become even greater with a couple of decades under its belt. Screwcap. 13.5% alc. **Rating** 96 **To** 2035 $30

ŸŸŸŸ♀ **Campaspe Valley Chardonnay 2008** Pale straw-green; the wine is travelling very well given its vintage, with white and yellow peach fruit doing much of the heavy lifting; there is no obvious oak, the mouthfeel sourced entirely from the fruit. Ready and waiting for you. Screwcap. 13% alc. **Rating** 90 **To** 2015 $16
Bennett's Run Shiraz 2009 Rating 90 **To** 2019 $22

ŸŸŸŸ **Cabernet Sauvignon 2010 Rating** 87 **To** 2020 $22

Bent Road ★★★

535 Bents Road, Ballandean, Qld 5382 **Region** Granite Belt
T 0418 190 104 **www.**bentroadwine.com.au **Open** By appt
Winemaker Glen Robert **Est.** 2004 **Dozens** 2500 **Vyds** 4ha
Bent Road is owned by winemaker Glen Robert and vineyard manager Robert Richter. Glen is a former medical research chemist, but moved into winemaking simply because he (and Robert) fell under the spell of wine around 2000. Glen put together vintage experience at Cakebread Cellars in the Napa Valley ('04), Clovely Estate ('04–'06) and Heritage Estate ('05). He has also found time to work for Sirromet, Symphony Hill and Granite Ridge wineries. Robert moved from photography, engineering, catering and property development to focus on the organic management of the vineyard, which is planted to tempranillo, shiraz, merlot, marsanne, semillon and verdelho. Chardonnay and cabernet sauvignon are purchased from local growers. Exports to Hong Kong.

ŸŸŸŸ **Estate 2BC Marsanne 2011** Mid gold; a fragrant blend of fresh-cut lemon, honeysuckle and straw; fresh acidity provides line and a chalky, simple-fruited finish. Screwcap. 10.7% alc. **Rating** 88 **To** 2014 $30 BE

Berton Vineyards ★★★★☆

55 Mirrool Avenue, Yenda, NSW 2681 **Region** Riverina
T (02) 6968 1600 **www.**bertonvineyards.com.au **Open** Mon–Fri 10–4, Sat 11–4
Winemaker James Ceccato, Sam Trimboli **Est.** 2001 **Dozens** 1 million **Vyds** 12.5ha
The Berton Vineyard partners – Bob and Cherie Berton, Paul Bartholomaeus, James Ceccato and Jamie Bennett – have almost 100 years' combined experience in winemaking, viticulture, finance, production and marketing. 1996 saw the acquisition of a 30ha property in the Eden Valley and the planting of the first vines. It took two years for the dam to fill, and the vines struggled on the white rock soil. This is only a small part of the business, which sources bulk wine from regions across South Eastern Australia. Wines are released under the FoundStone,

Head Over Heels and Berton Vineyard (varietals, Soldier Farms and Reserve) labels. Exports to the UK, the US and other major markets.

ŸŸŸŸŸ   **Bonsai High Eden Shiraz 2009** Medium red-purple; 300 dozen made of what is a very good wine, with intense red and black fruits interleaved with spice and oak nuances, persistent but fine tannins extending the long finish. Screwcap. 15% alc. **Rating** 94 **To** 2024 $60

ŸŸŸŸŸ   **High Eden Sauvignon Blanc 2011 Rating** 92 **To** 2014 $20
O   **Reserve Barossa Shiraz 2008 Rating** 90 **To** 2015 $20
    High Eden Cabernet Sauvignon 2008 Rating 90 **To** 2020 $35

ŸŸŸŸ   **Sauvignon Blanc 2011 Rating** 89
✪   **To** 2013 $12
✪   **Foundstone Unoaked Chardonnay 2011 Rating** 88 **To** 2013 $8
    Reserve Eden Valley Chardonnay 2010 Rating 88 **To** 2014 $17 BE
    Reserve Eden Valley Chardonnay 2009 Rating 88 **To** 2013 $17
    Reserve Tasmania Pinot Noir 2010 Rating 88 **To** 2015 $20 BE
O   **The Black Shiraz 2010 Rating** 88 **To** 2014 $15
    Reserve Coonawarra Cabernet Sauvignon 2009 Rating 87 **To** 2014 $17 BE

Best's Wines   ★★★★★

111 Best's Road, Great Western, Vic 3377 **Region** Grampians
T (03) 5356 2250 **F** (03) 5356 2430 **www.**bestswines.com **Open** Mon–Sat 10–5, Sun 11–4
Winemaker Justin Purser **Est.** 1868 **Dozens** 20 000 **Vyds** 30ha
Best's winery and vineyards are among Australia's best-kept secrets. Indeed the vineyards, with vines dating back to 1868, have secrets that may never be revealed: for example, one of the vines planted in the Nursery Block has defied identification and is thought to exist nowhere else in the world. Part of the cellars, too, go back to the same era, constructed by butcher-turned-winemaker Henry Best and his family. Since 1920, the Thomson family has owned the property, with Ben, the fifth generation, having taken over management from father Viv. Best's consistently produces elegant, supple wines; the Bin No. 0 is a classic, the Thomson Family Shiraz (from vines planted in 1868) magnificent. Very occasionally a Pinot Noir (with 15% Pinot Meunier) is made solely from the 1868 plantings of those two varieties; there is no other pinot of this vine age made anywhere else in the world. In '12 Justin Purser was appointed winemaker to succeed Adam Wadewitz; he brings with him a remarkable CV with extensive experience in Australia, NZ and (most recently) Burgundy at Domaine de Montille. Exports to the UK, Ireland, Canada, Sweden Singapore, Hong Kong and China.

ŸŸŸŸŸ   **Great Western Riesling 2011** Light straw-green; fragrant, floral/blossom aromas are followed by an exceptionally intense palate, with wonderful drive to its lime, lemon and apple fruit; has revelled in the cool conditions. Screwcap. 11.5% alc. **Rating** 97 **To** 2025 $25
    Thomson Family Great Western Shiraz 2010 Deep crimson-purple; made predominantly from vines planted in 1868, and genuinely a wine that is only made in the best vintages. I can't help but think when I taste a wine such as this that my ashes will have been scattered decades before it fulfils all of its potential. It has lashings of blackberry, plum, blackcurrant and touches of licorice and mint; the tannins are quite obvious, but ripe and in balance for a wine so blessed with great fruit. Bottle no. 833 of 4200. Screwcap. 14% alc. **Rating** 97 **To** 2040 $180
    Bin No. 0 Great Western Shiraz 2010 Crimson-purple; a very high quality wine made from a mix of old and younger vines matured in French oak. A great definition of what a medium-bodied shiraz should present. A fragrant bouquet of plum, black cherry and a touch of blackberry sliding seamlessly into a perfectly moulded palate, delivering all of the flavours promised by the bouquet, tannins and oak in precisely tailored amounts. Screwcap. 13.5% alc. **Rating** 95 **To** 2030 $75

Bin No. 0 Great Western Shiraz 2009 Deep purple-crimson; this includes the grapes from the 1868 shiraz vines normally reserved for the Thomson Family Shiraz (none made), but the yield and volume made was much less than usual. The wine is very full-bodied, but not jammy, for the tannins provide excellent texture and structure as the foundations of a long-lived wine. Screwcap. 14.5% alc. Rating 95 To 2040 $75
Bin No. 1 Great Western Shiraz 2010 Rating 94 To 2030 $25
Old Vine Great Western Pinot Meunier 2010 Rating 94 To 2035 $60 BE

🍷🍷🍷🍷 Great Western Cabernet Sauvignon 2010 Rating 92 To 2025 $25
White Gravels Hill Great Western Shiraz 2010 Rating 90 To 2020 $35 BE

🍷🍷🍷🍷 Great Western Pinot Gris 2011 Rating 89 To 2014 $22 BE
Great Western Chardonnay 2010 Rating 88 To 2016 $25 BE

Bethany Wines   ★★★★☆

Bethany Road, Tanunda, SA 5352 **Region** Barossa Valley
T (08) 8563 2086 **www**.bethany.com.au **Open** Mon–Sat 10–5, Sun 1–5
Winemaker Geoff and Robert Schrapel **Est.** 1981 **Dozens** 25 000 **Vyds** 38ha
The Schrapel family has been growing grapes in the Barossa Valley for over 140 years, but the winery has only been in operation since 1981. Nestled high on a hillside on the site of an old bluestone quarry, Geoff and Rob Schrapel produce a range of consistently well-made and attractively packaged wines. Bethany has vineyards in the Barossa and Eden Valleys. Exports to the UK, Europe and Asia.

🍷🍷🍷🍷 Eden Valley Riesling 2011 Pale quartz; a fragrant, faintly spicy, bouquet leads into a juicy, well-balanced palate with citrus and green apple; still to fully open up, with its best days in front of it. Screwcap. 11% alc. Rating 92 To 2021 $18
Barossa Semillon 2010 Rating 92 To 2015 $18
Barossa Eden Valley Riesling 2011 A bright, fragrant and floral-accented bouquet, showing lemon pith and struck quartz; tangy and lively on the palate, and with enough flesh for enjoyment in the immediate to medium term. Screwcap. 11.5% alc. Rating 90 To 2017 $14 BE
Barossa Shiraz 2008 Medium red-purple; right in the mainstream of traditional Barossa Valley shiraz with generous plum cake and blackberry fruit, sweet oak, and soft tannins. A go anywhere wine, ready now or soonish. Screwcap. 14.8% alc. Rating 90 To 2015 $28

🍷🍷🍷 Barossa Cabernet Sauvignon 2009 Rating 89 To 2018 $28 BE
G6 Barossa Riesling 2011 Rating 88 To 2014 $18
Barossa Cabernet Merlot 2008 Rating 88 To 2016 $22 BE
Barossa Chardonnay 2010 Rating 87 To 2013 $20
Barossa Valley Grenache 2009 Rating 87 To 2014 $20

Bidgeebong Wines   ★★★☆

352 Byrnes Road, Wagga Wagga, NSW 2650 **Region** Gundagai
T (02) 6931 9955 **www**.bidgeebong.com.au **Open** Mon–Fri 9–4
Winemaker Andrew Birks **Est.** 2000 **Dozens** 20 000
Encompasses what the founders refer to as the Bidgeebong triangle – between Young, Wagga Wagga, Tumbarumba and Gundagai – which provides grapes for the Bidgeebong brand. The onsite winery will eventually handle 2000 tonnes of grapes for Bidgeebong's own needs, and those of other local growers and larger producers who purchase grapes from the region. Exports to Canada, Singapore and China.

🍷🍷🍷🍷 Kyeamba Lot Tempranillo by Birks 2008 Good retention of colour, still in the red spectrum; has the varietal mix of black and red cherries, and also that touch of lemon/citrus that I find on the finish of many tempranillos. Screwcap. 13.9% alc. Rating 90 To 2016 $22

ᵀᵀᵀᵀ   **Regional Selection Gundagai Shiraz 2009** Rating 89 To 2019 $22
        Regional Selection Gundagai Shiraz 2008 Rating 89 To 2014 $22
✪   **Triangle Shiraz 2010** Medium red-purple; a nicely composed wine, with an
        assemblage of red and black fruits, spice and a hint of oak on the bouquet and
        the medium-bodied palate. Screwcap. 14.8% alc. **Rating** 88 **To** 2016 $13

big shed wines   ★★★★

1289 Malmsbury Road, Glenlyon, Vic 3461 **Region** Macedon Ranges
T (03) 5348 7825 **www**.bigshedwines.com.au **Open** 7 days, winter 10–6, summer 10–7
Winemaker Ken and Miranda Jones **Est.** 1999 **Dozens** 1200 **Vyds** 2ha
Founder and winemaker Ken Jones was formerly a geneticist and molecular biologist at
Edinburgh University, so the chemistry of winemaking comes easily. The estate-based wine
comes from 2ha of pinot noir (clones MV6 and D5V12); the other wines are made from
purchased grapes grown in various parts of Central Victoria. Exports to China.

ᵀᵀᵀᵀᵀ   **Cabernets 2009** An 80/20% blend of cabernet sauvignon and cabernet franc;
        is unashamedly full-bodied, with luscious blackcurrant fruit, and a considerable
        amount of oak in tandem with that fruit. A few years in the cellar would do this
        wine no end of good. Screwcap. 14% alc. **Rating** 92 **To** 2020 $30
        Macedon Pinot Chardonnay 2007 Bottle-fermented and four years on lees,
        and won the trophy for Best Sparkling Wine at the Daylesford Wine Show '11;
        bronze with a trace of pink, it is a complex wine, with strong bready/yeasty
        characters balanced by a shaft of steely acidity. Diam. 12.5% alc. **Rating** 92
        To 2014 $40

Billanook Estate   ★★★☆

280 Edward Road, Chirnside Park, Vic 3116 **Region** Yarra Valley
T (03) 9735 4484 **www**.billanookestate.com.au **Open** W'ends & public hols 10–6,
or by appt
Winemaker Domenic Bucci, John D'Aloisio **Est.** 1994 **Dozens** 1200 **Vyds** 15.5ha
The D'Aloisio family has been involved in the agricultural heritage of the Yarra Valley since
the late 1960s, and in '94 planted the first vines on their 36ha property. The vineyard is planted
to cabernet sauvignon (4.4ha), shiraz (3.3ha), chardonnay (3.2ha), sauvignon blanc (1.7ha),
pinot noir (1.4ha) and merlot (1.1ha). Most of the grapes are sold to various wineries in the
Valley, leaving a small percentage for the Billanook Estate label.

ᵀᵀᵀᵀᵀ   **Methode Champenoise Yarra Valley Chardonnay Pinot Noir 2008** Pale
        pink-bronze; a 60/40% blend, the pinot responsible for the pink tinge; the wine
        has almost certainly spent more than two years on yeast lees, and this has led to
        an attractive rounding of the fruit, and the introduction of some yeasty brioche
        characters. Diam. 12.5% alc. **Rating** 92 **To** 2016 $25

Billy Pye Vineyard   ★★★☆

PO Box 229, Ashton, SA 5137 **Region** Adelaide Hills
T (08) 8390 1332 **F** (08) 8390 3435 **Open** Not
Winemaker Contract **Est.** 1997 **Dozens** 80 **Vyds** 2.1ha
The history of Billy Pye Vineyard is fascinating. It dates back to 1858, when William Grasby
began establishing an apple orchard on a property near Balhannah on the upper reaches of
the Onkaparinga River. The neighbouring property on the southern side had been owned
since 1868 by colourful local character WH (Billy) Pye, a surveyor and engineer. His property
contained the largest hill in the area, known locally as Billy Pye Hill, where he built his house.
In 1997 Sandra Schubert, a fifth-generation Grasby, began to plant a vineyard on the northern
slopes of Billy Pye Hill in partnership with John Bowley, leaving the top of the hill with the
native vegetation Billy had loved. The wines currently available are made from grapes grown
on a small site on the eastern slopes of the vineyard. The Glengyle Red is named after a variety
of apple developed by the Grasby family.

🍷🍷🍷🍷🍷 **Eleanor 2010** A blend of merlot, cabernet franc, shiraz and cabernet sauvignon, the fresh colour with none of the uncertainty of the other Billy Pye wines; the aromas and flavours are complex, ranging through juicy cassis, red cherry, plum, blackberry and blackcurrant; the palate is well balanced, with enough oak and tannins to sustain the cornucopia of fruits. Screwcap. 14.3% alc. **Rating** 90 **To** 2018 $25

🍷🍷🍷🍷 **Leo Shiraz 2010 Rating** 89 **To** 2019 $25
Glengyle Red 2010 Rating 88 **To** 2016 $28

Bimbadgen ★★★★★
790 McDonalds Road, Pokolbin, NSW 2320 **Region** Hunter Valley
T (02) 4998 4600 **www.**bimbadgen.com.au **Open** Fri–Sat 10–7, Sun–Thurs 10–5
Winemaker Sarah Crowe, Mike De Garis (Consultant) **Est.** 1968 **Dozens** 40 000
Vyds 25ha
Established as McPherson Wines, then successively Tamalee, Sobels, Parker Wines and now Bimbadgen, this substantial winery has had what might be politely termed a turbulent history. It has vineyards in McDonalds Road and Palmers Lane, Pokolbin, and these produce the Bimbadgen Signature range at the top of the tree. Next comes the Regions range of a diverse selection of varietals from regions known for their ability to produce high-quality wines of a given variety or varieties. The Bimbadgen Ridge range is for wines in the lower price tier. The team of Sarah Crowe and Mike de Garis is proving to be a potent one. Exports to all major markets.

🍷🍷🍷🍷🍷 **Signature Hunter Valley Semillon 2011** Similar colour to the Estate; has the flavour spectrum of the Estate, but doubled (or more) intensity; it is a wine of real authority and structure, and a long finish. Screwcap. 11% alc. **Rating** 96 **To** 2030 $40

✪ **Estate Hunter Valley Semillon 2011** Very pale quartz-green; it has a fragrant, aromatic bouquet, then a well-balanced palate, with a juicy mix of lemon, lemongrass, and grass (three quite distinct flavours). Screwcap. 10% alc. **Rating** 94 **To** 2021 $20

🍷🍷🍷🍷🍷 **Art Series Shiraz 2010 Rating** 93 **To** 2020 $25
Signature McDonalds Road Vineyard Shiraz 2007 Rating 92 **To** 2032 $50
Estate Hunter Valley Shiraz 2010 Rating 90 **To** 2020 $23
Estate Hunter Valley Shiraz Viognier 2010 Rating 90 **To** 2020 $25

🍷🍷🍷🍷 **Regions Tasmania Sauvignon Blanc 2011 Rating** 89 **To** 2014 $25
Estate Hunter Valley Chardonnay 2011 Rating 89 **To** 2014 $22
Ridge Rose 2010 Rating 89 **To** Now $15
Art Series Gewurztraminer 2011 Rating 88 **To** 2016 $25
Ridge Rose 2011 Rating 88 **To** 2013 $15
Estate Hunter Valley Verdelho 2011 Rating 87 **To** Now $20
Ridge Semillon Verdelho Chardonnay 2009 Rating 87 **To** 2014 $15

binbilla ★★★★
Good Friday Gully Road, Maimuru, NSW 2594 (postal) **Region** Hilltops
T (02) 6383 3305 **www.**binbillawines.com **Open** Not
Winemaker Nick O'Leary (Contract) **Est.** 2001 **Dozens** 1000 **Vyds** 6ha
Gerard and Berenice Hines planted their vineyard in 2001, with 4ha of cabernet sauvignon (since grafted over to viognier), 2ha of shiraz and 1ha of riesling, which produced the first wines in '04. The more recent grafting of some vines to viognier has seen the release of a Shiraz Viognier. The only wine that is not estate-grown is the Chardonnay, which is sourced from a nearby Hilltops vineyard. The quantity made will increase as the vines come into full bearing, but is unlikely to exceed 1000 dozens a year, with limited retail and restaurant listings in Melbourne, Sydney and Brisbane.

ŢŢŢŢ♀ **Special Steps Hilltops Cabernet Sauvignon 2010** A cool example of
cabernet, with redcurrant and sage on display, beside ample fine-grained tannins
and a brambly, savoury note that lingers on the conclusion. Screwcap. 13.3% alc.
Rating 90 **To** 2016 $25 BE

ŢŢŢŢ   **Good Friday Shiraz 2009 Rating** 87 **To** 2014 $25 BE

Bindi Wine Growers   ★★★★★

343 Melton Road, Gisborne, Vic 3437 (postal) **Region** Macedon Ranges
T (03) 5428 2564 **Open** Not
Winemaker Michael Dhillon, Stuart Anderson (Consultant) **Est.** 1988 **Dozens** 2000
One of the icons of Macedon. The Chardonnay is top-shelf, the Pinot Noir as remarkable
(albeit in a very different idiom) as Bass Phillip, Giaconda or any of the other tiny-production,
icon wines. The addition of Heathcote-sourced Shiraz under the Pyrette label confirms Bindi
as one of the greatest small producers in Australia. Notwithstanding the tiny production, the
wines are exported (in small quantities, of course) to the UK, the US and other major markets.
No wines were received for this edition; the rating is that of last year.

Bird in Hand   ★★★★★

Bird In Hand Road, Woodside, SA 5244 **Region** Adelaide Hills
T (08) 8389 9488 **www.**birdinhand.com.au **Open** 7 days 11–5
Winemaker Andrew Nugent, Kym Milne (MW), Peter Ruchs **Est.** 1997 **Dozens** 70 000
Vyds 29ha
This very successful business took its name from a 19th-century gold mine. It is the venture of
the Nugent family, headed by Dr Michael Nugent; son Andrew is a Roseworthy graduate. The
family also has a vineyard in the Clare Valley, the latter providing both riesling and shiraz (and
olives from 100-year-old wild trees). A state-of-the-art winery and a straw and mud barrel
cellar were completed in 2007. The estate plantings (merlot, pinot noir, cabernet sauvignon,
sauvignon blanc, riesling and shiraz) provide only part of the annual crush, the remainder
coming from contract growers. In November 2010, a replica Bird in Hand cellar door was
opened in Dalian in China's northeastern Laioning province, a second following in Yingkou.
Exports to all major markets.

ŢŢŢŢŢ **Nest Egg Adelaide Hills Chardonnay 2010** Bright straw-green; a wine
with exceptional mouthfeel that marries intensity and finesse; barrel ferment, mlf
and lees stirring all played a role, but at the end of the day, it is the white peach
and grapefruit flavours of first-quality grapes that make the difference. Screwcap.
13.5% alc. **Rating** 95 **To** 2020 $60
Nest Egg Adelaide Hills Shiraz 2009 Strong red-purple; 400 dozen made of
this concentrated, full-bodied, black-fruited wine with intense spice, pepper and
licorice nuances woven throughout, together with significant oak. Not for the
faint-hearted. Screwcap. 14.5% alc. **Rating** 95 **To** 2034 $75
Adelaide Hills Cabernet Sauvignon 2010 Clear, full crimson; the bouquet
accurately suggests a generous, well-ripened palate with blackberry, cassis and
cedary oak all contributing equally, backed up by fine, ripe tannins and quality
oak. A pleasure to drink now, or for many years to come. Screwcap. 14.5% alc.
Rating 95 **To** 2030 $35
Clare Valley Riesling 2011 Pale green-quartz; the floral blossom-filled bouquet
leads into an intense palate with citrus and apple built on the backbone of steely
acidity that continues through to the aftertaste. Will be long lived. Screwcap.
12.5% alc. **Rating** 94 **To** 2026 $25
Mt Lofty Ranges Shiraz 2010 Deep crimson-purple; the bouquet of red and
black berry fruits augmented by spice promises much, and the medium- to full-
bodied palate duly delivers, with depth to the supple fruit, ripe tannins and quality
French oak. Screwcap. 14.5% alc. **Rating** 94 **To** 2025 $35
Nest Egg Adelaide Hills Cabernet Sauvignon 2009 The colour is not
entirely convincing, but the full-bodied palate brooks no argument with its display
of cassis, blackberry and black plum flavours strongly supported by quality oak
and fine tannins. Given the benefit of the colour doubt. Screwcap. 14.5% alc.
Rating 94 **To** 2024 $85

🍷🍷🍷🍷🍷 **Adelaide Hills Chardonnay 2010** Rating 93 To 2017 $28
Adelaide Hills Merlot 2010 Rating 93 To 2020 $35

✪ **Two in the Bush Adelaide Hills Chardonnay 2010** Bright, light straw-green; a fruit-driven style from start to finish, with white flesh stone fruit, melon and citrus rind flavours, fermentation and maturation in old oak imparting structure and length. Impressive. Screwcap. 13.5% alc. Rating 92 To 2015 $20

✪ **Two in the Bush Mt Lofty Ranges Shiraz 2010** Bright crimson-purple; multi-spice and pepper overtones on the bouquet attest to the cool climate, as does the black cherry and blackberry fruit of the palate; American and French oak contribute as much to texture as flavour. Screwcap. 14.5% alc. Rating 91 To 2020 $20

✪ **Two in the Bush Adelaide Hills Merlot Cabernet 2010** Bright colour; ripe cassis and redcurrant fruit bouquet, with a touch of cedar and black olive; the palate is firm and fleshy, varietal and poised, certainly existing at the savoury end of the spectrum, a consistent character for the Adelaide Hills. Screwcap. 14.5% alc. Rating 91 To 2016 $20 BE
Adelaide Hills Sauvignon Blanc 2011 Rating 90 To Now $25

✪ **Two in the Bush Adelaide Hills Semillon Sauvignon Blanc 2011** Pale, bright quartz; a gently fragrant bouquet of cut grass and flowers leads into a fresh palate assisted by a subliminal touch of sweetness. Screwcap. 11.5% alc. Rating 90 To Now $20

🍷🍷🍷🍷 **Honeysuckle Clare Valley Riesling 2011** Rating 89 To 2016 $25
Adelaide Hills Pinot Rose 2011 Rating 89 To Now $20

Bird on a Wire Wines

51 Symons Street, Healesville, Vic 3777 (postal) **Region** Yarra Valley
T 0439 045 000 **www.**birdonawirewines.com.au **Open** By appt
Winemaker Caroline Mooney **Est.** 2008 **Dozens** 500
This is the out-of-hours labour of love business of winemaker husband and wife Caroline Mooney and Paul Bridgeman, both of whom grew up in the Yarra Valley and who have had (other full-time) winemaking jobs in the valley for 10 years. The focus is on small, single vineyard sites owned by growers committed to producing outstanding grapes. Having worked at the legendary Domaine Jean-Louis Chave in the 2006 vintage, they have a special interest in shiraz and marsanne, both grown from distinct sites on a single vineyard in the Yarra Glen area. They also make a Chardonnay from the upper Yarra Valley, now generally accepted as a perfect environment for the finest of chardonnay styles. Exports to the UK.

🍷🍷🍷🍷🍷 **Chardonnay 2010** Pale straw-green; a complex structure and mouthfeel to a wine with initially restrained fruit aromas and flavours succeeds very well; the natural acidity is part of the story, as is the way the white flesh stone fruit progressively builds on multiple retastings. Screwcap. 13% alc. Rating 96 To 2018 $40
Syrah 2010 Good colour; a particularly rich and complex full-bodied wine, belying the minimalism of the clever label and the 1% addition of marsanne; has multiple layers of ripe black cherry and plum fruit with quality oak woven throughout. Screwcap. 14% alc. Rating 95 To 2030 $40
Marsanne 2010 This wine has all of the grainy texture – like a nashi pear – that marsanne provides in the Rhône Valley; the flavours are as much minerally/savoury as fruity, but you can see where the wine will be in another 10 years. So fasten your seat belts, and hang on. Screwcap. 14.5% alc. Rating 94 To 2020 $35

🍷🍷🍷🍷🍷 **Syrah 2011** Rating 92 To 2026 $40

Birdwood Estate ★★★★★

Mannum Road, Birdwood, SA 5234 (postal) **Region** Adelaide Hills
T (08) 8263 0986 **F** (08) 8263 0986 **Open** Not
Winemaker Oli Cucchiarelli **Est.** 1990 **Dozens** 1000 **Vyds** 7.5ha

Birdwood Estate draws upon estate vineyards progressively established since 1990 (pinot noir, riesling and sauvignon blanc). The quality of the white wines has generally been good. The tiny production is principally sold through retail in Adelaide and a small amount is exported to Canada. No wine was made in 2011 due to mildew caused by incessant rain.

Birthday Villa Vineyard ★★★

19 Mollison Street, Malmsbury, Vic 3446 **Region** Macedon Ranges
T (03) 5423 2789 **www**.birthdayvilla.com.au **Open** W'ends or by appt 11–5
Winemaker Greg Dedman (Contract) **Est.** 1968 **Dozens** 350 **Vyds** 2ha
The Birthday Villa name comes from the 19th-century Birthday Mine at nearby Drummond discovered on Queen Victoria's birthday. Gewurztraminer (1.5ha) was planted in 1962; cabernet sauvignon (0.5ha) followed later. The quality of the Gewurztraminer comes as no surprise, as the very cool climate is suited to the variety. On the other hand, the Cabernet Sauvignon comes as a major surprise, although there are likely to be vintages where the variety will provide a major challenge as it struggles for ripeness.

ΨΨΨΨ   **Malmsbury Cabernet Sauvignon 2008** Good hue; a light- to medium-bodied cabernet with juicy red fruit aromas and flavours that are still fresh; no need to wait for the tannins to soften, because they are so fine anyway. Screwcap. 13% alc. **Rating** 87 **To** 2014 $25

Bishops Vineyard ★★★☆

86 Acton Road, Acton Park, Tas 7170 (postal) **Region** Southern Tasmania
T (03) 6248 7342 **www**.bishopsvineyard.com.au **Open** Not
Winemaker Julian Alcorso (Contract) **Est.** 1999 **Dozens** 350
Phillip and Maree Bishop planted the first vines on their property in 1999, keeping things under control with 0.5ha each of chardonnay and pinot noir. The property overlooks Frederick Henry Bay and Ralph's Bay, a 15-min drive from Hobart.

ΨΨΨΨΨ   **Pinot Noir Chardonnay 2008** Bright green-straw; fresh and lively, with citrus flavours to the fore; good length and finesse; high acidity is in no small measure a function of its place of origin. Cork. 12.5% alc. **Rating** 91 **To** 2015 $30

ΨΨΨΨ   **Pinot Noir 2010 Rating** 88 **To** 2015 $26

BK Wines ★★★★★

18 Wattle Street, Lobethal, SA 5241 **Region** Adelaide Hills
T 0410 124 674 **www**.bkwines.com.au **Open** By appt
Winemaker Brendon Keys **Est.** 2007 **Dozens** 2000
BK Wines is owned by Brendon and Kirsty Keys. Brendon came from NZ, and has worked in the US, Argentina, NZ and SA. The wines are made at their own winery, Altamont Premium Studio, along with contract-made wines for a number of business in and around the Adelaide Hills. Exports to Singapore.

ΨΨΨΨΨ   **Cult Single Vineyard Lobethal Adelaide Hills Syrah 2010** Strong colour;
✪   I suppose the retro label suits the cult imagery, but the quality of the wine could be lost in the story. It has a wonderful bouquet of black cherry fruit and quality oak, and the palate builds on the promise of the bouquet in an effortless display of cool-climate shiraz at its best. Bargain. Diam. 14% alc. **Rating** 96 **To** 2025 $27
    One Ball Single Vineyard Kenton Valley Adelaide Hills Chardonnay 2010 As the saying goes, this is a very smart wine, with nectarine, white peach and grapefruit lining the palate with a silky stream of fruit flavour, barrel ferment oak and bright acidity there to add support, not to complicate the message. Diam. 14% alc. **Rating** 94 **To** 2017 $27
    Swaby Single Vineyard Piccadilly Valley Adelaide Hills Chardonnay 2010 Light straw-green; an elegant and perfectly balanced chardonnay with white peach, melon and grapefruit swathed in a fine touch of French oak. An excellent example of Adelaide Hills chardonnay. Diam. 14% alc. **Rating** 94 **To** 2016 $35

Mazi Whole Bunch Blewitt Springs McLaren Vale Syrah 2009 Whole bunches are mentioned on the label, but the use of them doesn't appear on the liqueur-soaked plum, blackberry and fruitcake bouquet; the palate is warm and unctuous, with good acidity and chewy tannins complementing the ample fruit. Diam. 14% alc. **Rating** 94 **To** 2017 $85 BE

𝒴𝒴𝒴𝒴𝒴 Gumeracha Adelaide Hills Syrah Nouveau 2011 This has plenty of appeal,
✪ and is clearly made in a youthful, drink-early style; loaded with spice and red fruits, the medium-bodied palate is super fresh, almost racy and refreshing; fun packaging with a wine in the bottle to match. Screwcap. 12.5% alc. **Rating** 92 **To** 2016 $21 BE
Neyle Single Vineyard Mount Torrens Adelaide Hills Syrah 2010
Rating 90 **To** 2016 $38 BE

𝒴𝒴𝒴𝒴 **Rosetta Single Vineyard Lenswood Adelaide Hills Pinot Gris 2010**
Rating 89 **To** Now $27
Rosetta Single Vineyard Lenswood Adelaide Hills Pinot Noir 2010
Rating 89 **To** 2015 $38 BE
Saignee of Pinot Noir Lenswood Adelaide Hills Rose 2011 Rating 88
To 2013 $21 BE
Inox Lenswood Adelaide Hills Pinot Grigio 2011 Rating 87 **To** Now $21 BE

Black Estate Vineyard ★★★

Patons Road, Axe Creek, Vic 3551 **Region** Bendigo
T (03) 5442 8048 **www**.blackestate.com.au **Open** By appt
Winemaker Greg Dedman (Contract) **Est.** 1999 **Dozens** 250 **Vyds** 1.5ha
Robert and Leanne Black purchased their 8ha property in 1997, part of a larger block that in the latter part of the 19th century was home to the then-renowned 14ha Hercynia Vineyard. After a trial planting of 100 shiraz cuttings in 1998, they completed planting of their vineyard in the spring of '99. Future plantings of cabernet sauvignon and possibly riesling or verdelho will depend on water availability.

𝒴𝒴𝒴𝒴 Shiraz 2009 Slightly turbid colour; a rustic full-bodied wine, with abundant black fruits, but also tannins. Good bbq red to cut back greasy fingers, etc. Screwcap. 14% alc. **Rating** 87 **To** 2017 $20
Shiraz 2008 Light colour; well made given the continuing drought conditions in Central Victoria, with red and black fruits and a typical touch of eucalypt on the light- to medium-bodied palate. Screwcap. 14% alc. **Rating** 87 **To** 2015 $20

BlackJack Vineyards ★★★★★

Cnr Blackjack Road/Calder Highway, Harcourt, Vic 3453 **Region** Bendigo
T (03) 5474 2355 **www**.blackjackwines.com.au **Open** W'ends & most public hols 11–5
Winemaker Ian McKenzie, Ken Pollock **Est.** 1987 **Dozens** 4000 **Vyds** 6ha
Established by the McKenzie and Pollock families on the site of an old apple and pear orchard in the Harcourt Valley, Blackjack is best known for some very good Shirazs. Ian McKenzie, incidentally, is not to be confused with Ian McKenzie formerly of Seppelt (Great Western). Despite some tough vintage conditions, BlackJack has managed to continue to produce supremely honest, full-flavoured and powerful wines, all with a redeeming edge of elegance. Exports to Canada and China.

𝒴𝒴𝒴𝒴𝒴 Block 6 Bendigo Shiraz 2009 Similar colour to the standard wine, although with a touch more purple. Like its sibling, 100% estate-grown, but has a brighter and more focused palate, with more spice and less leather; excellent finish. Screwcap. 14.5% alc. **Rating** 95 **To** 2034 $35
Bendigo Shiraz 2009 The colour isn't entirely clear, suggesting no filtration. A powerful full-bodied wine that derives its power from fruit rather than tannins or oak, with black fruits, licorice and leather running from the bouquet to the finish of the palate. Screwcap. 15% alc. **Rating** 94 **To** 2029 $35

ΨΨΨΨ♀ **Major's Line Bendigo Shiraz 2009** Rating 93 To 2024 $25
Bendigo Cabernet Merlot 2009 Rating 92 To 2017 $25

ΨΨΨΨ **Chortle's Edge Bendigo Shiraz 2009** Rating 89 To 2014 $18
O

Blackwood Crest Wines   ★★★☆

RMB 404A, Boyup Brook, WA 6244 **Region** Blackwood Valley
T (08) 9767 3029 **F** (08) 9767 3029 **Open** By appt 10–5
Winemaker Max Fairbrass **Est.** 1976 **Dozens** 3000 **Vyds** 8ha
Blackwood Crest has been holding a low profile while developing its vineyards (cabernet
sauvignon, shiraz, riesling, semillon, sauvignon blanc, pinot noir and merlot) and a 100-tonne
winery. It has been an ongoing project, and progresses as time allows, which is fitting, as Max
Fairbrass's grandparents took up the property as virgin bush in 1908.

Bleasdale Vineyards   ★★★★★

Wellington Road, Langhorne Creek, SA 5255 **Region** Langhorne Creek
T (08) 8537 3001 **www**.bleasdale.com.au **Open** Mon–Sun 10–5
Winemaker Paul Hotker, Ben Potts, Matt Laube **Est.** 1850 **Dozens** 100 000 **Vyds** 47ha
This is one of the most historic wineries in Australia, in 2010 celebrating 160 years of
continuous winemaking by the direct descendants of the Potts founding family. Not so long
prior to arrival of the 21st century, its vineyards were flooded every winter by diversion of the
Bremer River, which provided moisture throughout the dry, cool growing season. In the new
millennium, every drop of water was counted. Bleasdale has taken the opportunity presented
by these challenges and removed under-performing vineyard blocks. Shiraz now represents
35% of plantings, cabernet 20%, malbec 15% and petit verdot 1.5%. Other reds include 1ha
of tempranillo and 1.5 of old vine grenache. Verdelho is the leader of the whites with 10%,
plus a small amount of chardonnay also used for table wines. The net result is a rebound in
vineyard plantings to 47 ha, with more to be planted over coming years. Concurrently with
all this, Bleasdale has had a complete revamp of its labels and packaging, and has headed to the
Adelaide Hills for sauvignon blanc, pinot gris and chardonnay. Exports to all major markets.

ΨΨΨΨΨ **Fortis et Astutus Rare Liqueur Tawny NV** Packaged in the most original
and striking bottle-cum-decanter I have seen. The wine has an average age of
over 20 years and is entitled to the 'Rare' name. Full golden tawny; it has been
brilliantly blended so that the complex mosaic of aged fruit flavours are not stale,
nor is the alcohol aggressive; it has perfect rancio, and the flavours of Christmas
cake, brandysnap, honey, dried fruits and glace fruits are all part of the picture, none
dominating. In terms of sheer drinkability, this is quite exceptional. Cork. 17% alc.
Rating 98 To 2013 $125
The Powder Monkey Langhorne Creek Shiraz 2010 Purple-crimson; an
intense and powerful wine that at no stage shows any overripe fruit characters; the
accent is on blackberry, licorice and bitter chocolate, with savoury tannins running
through the length of the palate. A great future lies ahead. Screwcap. 14.5% alc.
Rating 95 To 2035 $65
Frank Potts 2009 A 70/14/8/4/4% blend of cabernet sauvignon, malbec,
petit verdot, merlot and cabernet franc. The colour is bright crimson and, despite
18 months in French oak, is foremost a combination of red and black berry fruits;
the tannins are firm, but fundamentally in balance, and will see the wine safely sail
through the next 15+ years. Screwcap. 13.9% alc. Rating 94 To 2025 $29

ΨΨΨΨ♀ **Premium Langhorne Creek Malbec 2010** Rating 93 To 2018 $24
✪ **Adelaide Hills Sauvignon Blanc 2011** Bright straw-green; a delicious
sauvignon blanc, with a mouthwatering mix of citrus, passionfruit and gooseberry,
held in place by balanced, crisp acidity. Screwcap. 12.5% alc. Rating 92 To 2014 $18
✪ **Adelaide Hills Chardonnay 2011** Hand-picked and pressed directly to barrel
for wild yeast fermentation. Pale straw-green, it is a wine of considerable elegance
and balance; grapefruit and melon flavours run through the bouquet and palate,
with a clean and crisp finish. Screwcap. 12.5% alc. Rating 92 To 2016 $18

✪ **Bremerview Langhorne Creek Shiraz 2010** Medium purple-red; a medium-bodied wine with plenty of activity on both the bouquet and palate; blackberry, plum, spice and fruitcake are augmented by a touch of smoky oak and attractive, savoury tannins. Screwcap. 13.9% alc. **Rating** 91 **To** 2016 $18

✪ **Adelaide Hills Pinot Gris 2011** Hand-picked and whole bunch-pressed, part fermented in stainless steel, part in old oak; this has built structure, but not subdued the fresh apple aromas and flavours, nor the crisp acidity on the finish. Screwcap. 12.5% alc. **Rating** 90 **To** 2014 $18
Petrel Reserve Langhorne Creek Shiraz Cabernet Malbec 2009 **Rating** 90 **To** 2029 $23

✪ **Mulberry Tree Langhorne Creek Cabernet Sauvignon 2010** Mid crimson; an elegant medium-bodied wine with clear-cut varietal presence on both the bouquet and palate, skewed towards red fruits rather than black, and with fine-grained tannins on the finish. The moderate alcohol gives the wine freshness and vitality. Screwcap. 13.5% alc. **Rating** 90 **To** 2016 $18

✪ **Second Innings Langhorne Creek Malbec 2010** A light- to medium-bodied version of the Premium, tracking that wine in terms of colour, flavour and texture, with its plum and red berry fruit and tannins beyond normal expectations for this variety. Screwcap. 13.5% alc. **Rating** 90 **To** 2015 $18

♟♟♟♟ **The Broad-Side Langhorne Creek Shiraz Cabernet Sauvignon Malbec 2010** **Rating** 89 **To** 2015 $15
T&M McLaren Vale Langhorne Creek Tempranillo Malbec 2010 **Rating** 89 **To** 2018 $24
The Wise One Wood Matured Verdelho NV **Rating** 89 **To** 2013 $15

Bloodwood ★★★★★

231 Griffin Road, Orange, NSW 2800 **Region** Orange
T (02) 6362 5631 **www**.bloodwood.biz **Open** By appt
Winemaker Stephen Doyle **Est.** 1983 **Dozens** 4000 **Vyds** 8.43ha
Rhonda and Stephen Doyle are two of the pioneers of the Orange district. The estate vineyards (chardonnay, riesling, merlot, cabernet sauvignon, shiraz, cabernet franc and malbec) are planted at an elevation of 810–860 m, which provides a reliably cool climate; frost can be an issue, but heat seldom is. The wines are sold mainly through the cellar door and by an energetic, humorous and informatively run mailing list (see, for example, the tasting note for Big Men in Tights). Has an impressive track record across the full gamut of varietal (and other) wine styles, especially Riesling, in a variety of styles; all of the wines have a particular elegance and grace. Very much part of the high-quality reputation of Orange.

♟♟♟♟♟ Schubert 2010 A typically savoury example from this producer, with inspiration coming from the old world; savoury fennel, lemon pith and a little grapefruit are on display; the palate is generous and fine boned, with a long blanched almond finish, and lingering fine acidity. Chardonnay. Screwcap. 13% alc. Rating 94 To 2015 $28 BE

♟♟♟♟♟ **Riesling 2011** **Rating** 92 **To** 2021 $20 BE
Chardonnay 2011 **Rating** 90 **To** 2016 $25 BE

♟♟♟♟ **Pinot Noir 2011** **Rating** 89 **To** 2014 $35 BE
Shiraz 2008 **Rating** 88 **To** 2014 $27 BE

Blue Pyrenees Estate ★★★★☆

Vinoca Road, Avoca, Vic 3467 **Region** Pyrenees
T (03) 5465 1111 **www**.bluepyrenees.com.au **Open** Mon–Fri 10–4.30, w'ends & public hols 10–5
Winemaker Andrew Koerner, Chris Smales **Est.** 1963 **Dozens** 60 000 **Vyds** 149ha
Forty years after Remy Cointreau established Blue Pyrenees Estate (then known as Chateau Remy), the business was sold to a small group of Sydney businessmen. Former Rosemount

senior winemaker Andrew Koerner heads the winery team. The core of the business is the very large estate plantings, most decades old, but with newer arrivals including viognier. Blue Pyrenees has a number of programs designed to protect the environment and reduce its carbon footprint: all wines are 100% estate-grown and made, including onsite bottling. Last year's rating is maintained in the absence of a representative submission of its wines. Exports to Asia, primarily China.

ҰҰҰҰ **Cellar Door Series Botrytis Riesling 2010** Deep gold; lots of botrytis is in evidence, with dried apricot, marmalade and a little toffee brittle complexity; even, rich and very sweet, this will satisfy those with a predilection for sugar. Screwcap. 10% alc. **Rating** 89 **To** 2016 $18 BE

Cellar Door Series Grenache 2011 A pungent and gamey bouquet of red fruits, salt bush and red licorice and lavender; medium-bodied with firm tannins and fresh acidity to finish; at the firm end for the variety. Screwcap. 14.5% alc. **Rating** 88 **To** 2016 $18 BE

 # Blue Rock Wines

PO Box 692, Williamstown, SA 5351 **Region** Eden Valley
T 0419 817 017 **www**.bluerockwines.com.au **Open** Not
Winemaker Zissis Zachopoulos **Est.** 2005 **Dozens** 4000 **Vyds** 58ha
This is the venture of the brothers Zachopoulos: Nicholas, Michael and Zissis, the last with a double degree – viticulture and wine sciences – from CSU gained in 2009. Brothers Michael and Nicholas manage the 104ha property situated in the Eden Valley at an elevation between 415m and 475m. The majority of the blocks have a north-facing aspect, with some southern and western aspects. The slopes provide good frost protection with their natural air drainage, the soils likewise rich and free-draining. Fifty ha of vineyards have been planted so far to mainstream varieties, with an ongoing planting program extending to 8ha of tempranillo, pinot gris, pinot noir, grenache and mataro. Establishment of the vineyard began in 1998/99, and by far the major proportion of the 450- to 500-tonne grape production is the subject of a sales agreement with Grant Burge up to and including the 2013 vintage. So far 75 tonnes has been retained each year to make the Blue Rock wines.

ҰҰҰҰҰ **Barossa Ranges Vineyards Eden Valley Shiraz 2008** Deep colour, and very
✪ good hue; bursting with complex fruit, spice, mocha and anise fruit aromas and flavours; adroit footwork to pick the grapes before the March heatwave took hold; a very attractive full-bodied shiraz, with good texture and structure ex ripe tannins. Screwcap. 14% alc. **Rating** 93 **To** 2028 $20

✪ **Barossa Ranges Vineyards Eden Valley Shiraz Viognier 2008**
Co-fermented with viognier; this and the lower alcohol has produced a fresh and spicy wine with black and red cherry fruit to the fore, then a distinctly savoury finish; the French oak has been well integrated and the tannins will support the wine over the years ahead. Screwcap. 13.5% alc. **Rating** 92 **To** 2020 $20

ҰҰҰҰ **Barossa Ranges Vineyards Eden Valley Sauvignon Blanc 2010** Light
✪ straw-green; the gentle tropical fruit of the bouquet sets the scene for the pleasant flavours of the palate, all running within the tropical framework. Easy to drink style. Screwcap. 13.5% alc. **Rating** 89 **To** Now $15

Barossa Ranges Vineyards Eden Valley Cabernet Sauvignon 2007
Rating 88 **To** 2015 $20
Barossa Ranges Vineyards Eden Valley Riesling 2010 Rating 87
To 2013 $15
VR Barossa Ranges Vineyards Eden Valley Moscato Viognier Riesling 2010 Rating 87 **To** Now $15

Blue Wren

433 Ulan Road, Mudgee, NSW 2850 **Region** Mudgee
T (02) 6372 6205 **www**.bluewrenwines.com.au **Open** 7 days 10.30–4.30
Winemaker Michael Slater **Est.** 1998 **Dozens** 4000 **Vyds** 5.5ha

Roy Hofmeier and Vikki Williams purchased Blue Wren from the Anderson family in 2005. They have since slimmed down the vineyards to 5.5ha of shiraz, verdelho and merlot, and retained Michael Slater as contract winemaker.

ΨΨΨΨ   **Mudgee Shiraz 2010** The hue is good, although slightly weak; a pleasant shiraz for everyday drinking, gently sweet fruit and vanillin oak the drivers. Screwcap. 13.5% alc. **Rating** 87 **To** 2014 $22

Boat O'Craigo   ★★★★
458 Maroondah Highway, Healesville, Vic 3777 **Region** Yarra Valley
T (03) 5962 6899 **www**.boatocraigo.com.au **Open** Fri–Mon 10.30–5.30
Winemaker Al Fencaros, The Yarra Hill (Contract) **Est.** 1998 **Dozens** 3000 **Vyds** 21.63ha
Steve Graham purchased the property, which is now known as Boat O'Craigo (a tiny place in a Scottish valley where his ancestors lived), in 2003. It has two quite separate vineyards: a hillside planting on one of the highest sites in the Yarra Valley, and one at Kangaroo Ground on the opposite side of the valley. Exports to Finland, China and Hong Kong.

ΨΨΨΨΨ   **Black Spur Yarra Valley Chardonnay 2010** Thirty per cent was barrel-fermented in French oak and matured in that oak for nine months; the remainder kept in stainless steel. The wine is every bit as fresh as that elevage should deliver, with delicate but intense flavours of grapefruit and white peach. Will develop slowly, and has good potential. Screwcap. 13.8% alc. **Rating** 91 **To** 2018 $24
Yarra Valley Blanc de Blanc 2010 The traditional method was used for this 100% estate-grown chardonnay; bright straw-green, it has fresh, bright and zesty grapefruit and white peach flavours, with the finish long and dry. The acidity is quite high, and the wine will benefit from two or three years on cork. Diam. 12.5% alc. **Rating** 90 **To** 2015 $32

ΨΨΨΨ   **Black Spur Yarra Valley Gewurztraminer 2011** Pale quartz-green; elegant
✪   and fresh, with good length and balance; what it lacks is overt varietal character other, perhaps, than some spicy notes, and a hint of rose petal. Screwcap. 11.5% alc. **Rating** 89 **To** 2015 $20
Rob Roy Yarra Valley Pinot Noir 2010 Rating 89 **To** 2017 $24

Bobar   ★★★
253 Gulf Road, Yarra Glen, Vic 3775 **Region** Yarra Valley
T (03) 9730 2668 **F** (03) 9730 2668 **Open** By appt
Winemaker Tom and Sally Belford **Est.** 2010 **Dozens** 250
Tom and Sally Belford have worked full-time for vineyards and wineries in the cooler hilly parts of NSW, Macedon Ranges and Heathcote, but mostly and more recently in the Yarra Valley, where Tom is a winemaker at Sticks. Along the way they also managed to spend 15 months in France (with their two children), dividing their time between Champagne, Beaujolais, Provence, Cahors and Sauternes. In 2010 they decided to make a little wine for the hell of it, and purchased shiraz from the Yarraland Vineyard at Chirnside Park, run by the D'Aloisio family. It comes as close to natural wine as is possible, with whole bunches in an open fermenter, no crushing or destemming , no pigeage or pumping over, and no yeast. After eight days of carbonic maceration it was pressed to tank where it completed its alcoholic and malolactic fermentations, and remained on lees for four months before it was racked for the first and last time, and bottled without fining or filtration; prior to bottling a small sulphur dioxide addition of 20 ppm was made. It is sold by mail list via tomeb@iprimus.com.au and in a few bottle shops and restaurants in the Yarra Valley and Melbourne. Exports to the UK.

ΨΨΨΨ   **Yarra Valley Chardonnay 2011** As much as the Syrah is light-coloured, this is a developed colour and flavour role reversal; it runs from full peach flavours on the fore-palate to grapefruit pith on the finish. Screwcap. 13% alc. **Rating** 87 **To** 2014 $27
Yarra Valley Syrah 2011 Very light colour, almost rose, but good hue; pleasant light-bodied red wine/rose cross, ready to drink right now. Screwcap. 12.5% alc. **Rating** 87 **To** 2013 $27

Boireann   ★★★★★

26 Donnellys Castle Road, The Summit, Qld 4377 **Region** Granite Belt
T (07) 4683 2194 **www.**boireannwinery.com.au **Open** Fri–Sun 10–4
Winemaker Peter Stark **Est.** 1998 **Dozens** 800 **Vyds** 1.6ha
Peter and Therese Stark have a 10ha property set among the great granite boulders and trees
that are so much a part of the Granite Belt. They have planted no fewer than 11 varieties,
including four that go to make the Lurnea, a Bordeaux blend; shiraz and viognier; grenache
and mourvedre providing a Rhône blend, and a straight merlot. Tannat, pinot noir (French)
and sangiovese, barbera and nebbiolo (Italian) make up the viticultural League of Nations.
Peter is a winemaker of exceptional talent, producing cameo amounts of quite beautifully
made red wines that are of a quality equal to Australia's best.

ΨΨΨΨΨ **Granite Belt Shiraz 2010** Vivid purple-crimson; this is yet another beautifully
balanced, beautifully structured shiraz from Boireann, with astute selection of fruit
from across the Granite Belt conjured by the inspired winemaking of Peter Stark
into a wine sitting comfortably with the best wines of the southern and western
states of Australia. Screwcap. 13.5% alc. **Rating** 96 **To** 2025 $40
Granite Belt Shiraz Mourvedre 2010 Good colour; the typically fragrant
bouquet leads into a medium-bodied palate, shiraz and mourvedre taking turns to
express their respective personalities. Gives every indication it will flourish in the
years ahead. Screwcap. 14.5% alc. **Rating** 94 **To** 2025 $30
The Lurnea 2010 A 50/35/15% blend of merlot, cabernet sauvignon and petit
verdot with very good crimson colour; all of Peter Stark's skills come to the fore as
he balances blackcurrant, blackberry and redcurrant fruit with savoury tannins and
a dab of French oak; he is particularly successful with the bouquet, and also comes
through on the palate. Screwcap. 13% alc. **Rating** 94 **To** 2018 $28
Le Cima Granite Belt Barbera 2010 Boireann has certainly lifted its skirts
with this very different, a la mode label design; the grapes come from the Golden
Grove Vineyard; the wine matches the label, bright – lively and juicy, with pure red
cherry fruit, intriguing acidity, and the finest possible tannins. Absolutely ready to
go. Screwcap. 13.2% alc. **Rating** 94 **To** 2014 $25

ΨΨΨΨΨ **Granite Belt Cabernet Sauvignon 2010** **Rating** 92 **To** 2020 $28

ΨΨΨΨ **Granite Belt Cabernet Sauvignon Merlot 2010** **Rating** 87 **To** 2014 $18

Borrodell on the Mount   ★★★★☆

Lake Canobolas Road, Orange, NSW 2800 **Region** Orange
T (02) 6365 3425 **www.**borrodell.com.au **Open** 7 days 11–5
Winemaker Peter Logan, Phil Kerney, Simon Gilbert **Est.** 1995 **Dozens** 3000 **Vyds** 6ha
Borry Gartrell and Gaye Stuart-Nairne have planted pinot noir, sauvignon blanc, pinot
meunier, gewurztraminer and chardonnay adjacent to a cherry, plum and heritage apple
orchard and truffiere. It is a 10-min drive from Orange, and adjacent to Lake Canobolas, at
an altitude of 1000m. The wines have been consistent medal winners at regional and small
winemaker shows.

ΨΨΨΨΨ **Orange Sauvignon Blanc 2011** Pale straw-green; has aromas of guava and
passionfruit on the bouquet that also flow through to the juicy, full-flavoured
palate; balanced acidity helps tie up the flavours in a neat package with a zesty
finish. Screwcap. 11.5% alc. **Rating** 94 **To** 2013 $25

ΨΨΨΨΨ **Orange Gewurztraminer 2011** **Rating** 93 **To** 2017 $30

Botobolar   ★★★

89 Botobolar Road, Mudgee, NSW 2850 **Region** Mudgee
T (02) 6373 3840 **www.**botobolar.com **Open** Mon–Sat 10–5, Sun 10–3
Winemaker Kevin Karstrom **Est.** 1971 **Dozens** 3000 **Vyds** 19.4ha

One of the first (possibly the first) fully organic vineyards in Australia, with present owner Kevin Karstrom continuing the practices established by founder Gil Wahlquist. Preservative-free reds and low-preservative dry whites extend the organic practice of the vineyard to the winery. Dry Red is consistently the best wine to appear under the Botobolar label, with gold-medal success at the Mudgee Wine Show. Its preservative-free red wines are in the top echelon of this class. In winter 2010 a solar generator was installed on the hill behind the winery in their first step towards lowering their carbon footprint. Exports to Denmark and Japan.

Preservative Free Mudgee Shiraz 2011 Deep crimson hue; this is a vibrant and juicy young wine, with fresh blackberry, spice and a splash of tar on display; medium-bodied and best enjoyed in the full flush of youth. Screwcap. 13% alc. **Rating** 88 **To** 2014 $20 BE

Bou-saada ★★★

Kells Creek Road, Mittagong, NSW 2575 **Region** Southern Highlands
T (02) 4878 5399 **www.**bousaada.com **Open** Thurs–Mon 10.30–5
Winemaker High Range Vintners (Jonathan Holgate) **Est.** 1997 **Dozens** 500 **Vyds** 6.2ha
Alastair and Michele Graham purchased the 40ha property in 1996, planting the vineyard the following year with sauvignon blanc, followed by merlot, chardonnay and riesling. The wines are estate grown. The name, incidentally, is a pilgrimage town in Algeria built around an oasis: 'Bou' means father and 'saada' peace and happiness. The cellar door is made from Sydney blue gum and local stringybark.

First Fruits Fume Blanc 2008 Given the age of the wine and its 12 months in oak the colour is still remarkably light; I suspect its low pH (and high acidity) are part of the explanation; certainly the wine has unsweetened lemon juice notes, but in the end, is varietal. Screwcap. 12.5% alc. **Rating** 89 **To** 2013 $22

Bowen Estate ★★★★☆

Riddoch Highway, Coonawarra, SA 5263 **Region** Coonawarra
T (08) 8737 2229 **www.**bowenestate.com.au **Open** 7 days 10–5
Winemaker Emma Bowen **Est.** 1972 **Dozens** 12 000 **Vyds** 33ha
Bluff-faced regional veteran Doug Bowen, now with daughter Emma at his side in the winery, presides over one of Coonawarra's landmarks. Doug has now handed over full winemaking responsibility to Emma, 'retiring' to the position of viticulturist. It is to be hoped that the quality of the '09 reds will point the way for the future for a winery with so much potential. Exports to Indonesia, the Maldives, Singapore, China, Japan and NZ.

Coonawarra Cabernet Sauvignon 2009 Strong, bright purple-crimson; like the Shiraz, a great return to form, with pristine cabernet varietal fruit on the medium-bodied palate, the finish lengthened and strengthened by fine, ripe tannins. Screwcap. 14.5% alc. **Rating** 94 **To** 2024 $30

Coonawarra Shiraz 2009 **Rating** 92 **To** 2029 $30

Coonawarra Chardonnay 2010 **Rating** 87 **To** 2013 $20

Bowman's Run ★★★

1305 Beechworth-Wodonga Road, Wooragee, Vic 3747 **Region** Beechworth
T (03) 5728 7318 **Open** Most w'ends & by appt
Winemaker Daniel Balzer **Est.** 1989 **Dozens** 250 **Vyds** 1ha
Struan and Fran Robertson have cabernet sauvignon, riesling and small plots of shiraz and traminer dating back to 1989. The tiny winery came on-stream in 2000, and is part of a larger general agricultural holding.

Seven Springs Beechworth Riesling 2010 Light straw-green; a combination of gently ripe citrus and tropical fruit contrasts with minerally acidity; the length and balance are good. Screwcap. 12.3% alc. **Rating** 88 **To** 2015 $25

Box Grove Vineyard

PO Box 86, Avenel, Vic 3664 **Region** Nagambie Lakes
T (03) 5796 2626 **www.**boxgrovevineyard.com.au **Open** Not
Winemaker Sarah Gough **Est.** 1995 **Dozens** 1500 **Vyds** 26ha
This is the venture of the Gough family, with industry veteran (and daughter) Sarah Gough managing the vineyard, winemaking and marketing. In 1995, having worked for Brown Brothers' marketing department for 10 years, Sarah told Ross Brown she was leaving to get married and establish a family-owned farm near Tabilk. He immediately offered a 10-year contract to buy the grapes from 10ha each of shiraz and cabernet sauvignon; nervous about the long-term future, Sarah also planted 2.8ha of roussanne, promptly becoming the largest grower of the variety in the state. In 2007 Sarah decided to take a pre-emptive step of having five tonnes each of roussanne and shiraz roussanne made at Plunkett Fowles from the '08 vintage. Prior to the '09 vintage the supply agreement with Brown Brothers was not renewed (no surprise), leaving Sarah with a number of difficult decisions. The solution was to graft over 6ha of cabernet to 2ha of prosecco and 1ha each of viognier, vermentino, savagnin and primitivo, and manage Box Grove Vineyard as a fully fledged wine and verjus producer. Exports to China.

🍷🍷🍷🍷🍸 **Savagnin 2011** However accidental the commercial planting of savagnin may have been, it is a variety that continues to impress, particularly given the very young status of most of the vines. This has positive zesty flavours, with nuances of grapefruit on the one hand, spice on the other; the finish is dry and inviting. Screwcap. 13.8% alc. **Rating** 91 **To** 2014 $22

Roussanne 2010 Bright yellow-green; wild yeast-fermented, it spent one year on lees, with periodic stirring. Its wild flower and honeysuckle overtones, built on a structure of firm acidity, suggest that it could become even more interesting with more time in bottle, although I don't doubt that most will be consumed sooner rather than later. Screwcap. 14% alc. **Rating** 90 **To** 2015 $25

🍷🍷🍷🍷 **Vermentino 2011 Rating** 88 **To** 2013 $22

Box Stallion

64 Turrarubba Road, Merricks North, Vic 3926 **Region** Mornington Peninsula
T (03) 5989 7444 **www.**boxstallion.com.au **Open** 7 days 11–5
Winemaker Alex White **Est.** 2001 **Dozens** 9000 **Vyds** 16ha
Box Stallion is the joint venture of Stephen Wharton, John Gillies and Garry Zerbe, who have linked two vineyards at Bittern and Merricks North, with 16ha of vines planted between 1997 and 2003. What was once a thoroughbred stud has now become a vineyard, with the Red Barn (in their words) 'now home to a stable of fine wines'. Exports to the US, Canada, Japan and China.

🍷🍷🍷🍷🍷 **Mornington Peninsula Shiraz 2009** Bright, clear crimson; the spiced red fruits of the bouquet open the curtains for an elegant, medium-bodied palate with impeccable length and balance, more akin to a mare than a stallion. Diam. 14% alc. **Rating** 94 **To** 2020 $30

🍷🍷🍷🍷🍸 ✪ **Mornington Peninsula Gewurztraminer 2010** Pale straw-green; the bouquet has classic varietal aromas of spice, rose petal and lychee, the delicate palate following suit. One of the better from a small field from Australia. Screwcap. 13% alc. **Rating** 93 **To** 2014 $25

✪ **Mornington Peninsula Arneis 2009** A striking bouquet of clove-spiced pear straight from my childhood 65 years ago; the palate retains those flavours, with the finish appropriately soft. Screwcap. 14% alc. **Rating** 90 **To** 2013 $20

Mornington Peninsula Tempranillo 2009 Rating 90 **To** 2017 $40

🍷🍷🍷🍷 **Blaze Mornington Peninsula Rose 2011 Rating** 89 **To** 2013 $20

Boynton's Feathertop ★★★★

Great Alpine Road, Porepunkah, Vic 3741 **Region** Alpine Valleys
T (03) 5756 2356 **www**.boynton.com.au **Open** 7 days 10–5
Winemaker Kel Boynton **Est.** 1987 **Dozens** 12 500 **Vyds** 18ha
Kel Boynton has a beautiful vineyard, framed by Mt Feathertop rising above it. Overall, the red wines have always outshone the whites. The initial very strong American oak input has been softened in more recent vintages to give a better fruit–oak balance. The wines are released under the Boynton Reserve and Feathertop labels. Kel has planted a spectacular array of varieties, headed by shiraz and pinot gris, merlot, savagnin and nebbiolo, cabernet sauvignon and sangiovese, with smaller plantings of tempranillo, pinot noir, pinot meunier, vermentino, chardonnay, riesling, friulano, fiano, prosecco and semillon, culminating with a combined half-hectare of malbec, dornfelder and petit verdot. Exports to Austria.

 Alpine Valleys Merlot 2010 Light, bright, clear crimson-purple; an exemplary, fresh wine that has clearly expressed varietal character built around cassis, black olive and a touch of plum; the length and balance are also good. Screwcap. 13.5% alc. **Rating** 90 **To** 2017 $25

Brand's Laira Coonawarra ★★★★★

Riddoch Highway, Coonawarra, SA 5263 **Region** Coonawarra
T (08) 8736 3260 **www**.mcwilliamswinegroup.com **Open** Mon–Fri 9–4.30, w'ends & public hols 10–4
Winemaker Peter Weinberg **Est.** 1966 **Dozens** NFP **Vyds** 278ha
Part of a substantial investment in Coonawarra by McWilliam's, which first acquired a 50% interest from the Brand family, then increased to 100%, and followed this with the purchase of 100ha of additional vineyard land. Significantly increased production of the smooth wines for which Brand's is known has followed. The estate plantings include the 100-year-old Stentiford block. Further tasting notes appear on www.winecompanion.com.au. Exports to select markets.

 Chardonnay 2010 Bright straw-green; has more intensity, line and length than
✪ the majority of Coonawarra chardonnays; the grapefruit and white peach flavours have a crosscut of subtle oak, and the wine has obvious development potential. Screwcap. 14% alc. **Rating** 93 **To** 2020 $22

ΤΤΤΤ **Blockers Cabernet Sauvignon 2009** Rating 89 **To** 2019 $28

Brandy Creek Wines ★★★★

570 Buln Buln Road, Drouin East, Vic 3818 **Region** Gippsland
T (03) 5625 4498 **www**.brandycreekwines.com.au **Open** Thurs–Sun & public hols 11–5, Thurs–Sat nights
Winemaker Peter Beckingham (Contract) **Est.** 2005 **Dozens** 2000 **Vyds** 3ha
Marie McDonald and Rick Stockdale purchased the property on which they have since established their vineyard, cellar door and restaurant in 1997. Pinot gris and tempranillo have been progressively planted, with other varieties purchased from local growers. The café (and surrounding vineyard) is situated on a northeast-facing slope with spectacular views out to the Baw Baw Ranges.

ΤΤΤΤΤ **Gippsland Cabernet Sauvignon 2010** Bright, clear purple shot through with crimson; a lively, intense wine full of energy and drive to its blackcurrant/cassis fruit, neatly balanced by ripe, gently savoury tannins. Screwcap. 14.2% alc. **Rating** 93 **To** 2020 $22
Wooded Gippsland Chardonnay 2008 Rich, peachy fruit offset by nice acidity; complex bouquet. Screwcap. 13.5% alc. **Rating** 90 **To** 2015 $25

ΤΤΤΤ **Gippsland Sauvignon Blanc 2011** Rating 88 **To** 2013 $25
Gippsland Tempranillo 2009 Rating 87 **To** 2015 $28
Blanc de Noir 2008 Rating 87 **To** 2014 $30 BE

Brangayne of Orange

837 Pinnacle Road, Orange, NSW 2800 **Region** Orange
T (02) 6365 3229 **www**.brangayne.com **Open** Mon–Fri 11–1, 2–4, Sat 10–5, Sun 11–4
Winemaker Simon Gilbert **Est.** 1994 **Dozens** 3000 **Vyds** 25.7ha
The Hoskins family (formerly orchardists) decided to move into grapegrowing in 1994 and have progressively established high-quality vineyards. Right from the outset, Brangayne has produced excellent wines across all mainstream varieties, remarkably ranging from Pinot Noir to Cabernet Sauvignon. Son David has been managing the business since 2005; it sells a substantial part of its crop to other winemakers. Exports to the UK, Canada and Spain.

♀♀♀♀♀ **Tristan Cabernet Sauvignon Shiraz Merlot 2009** Bright crimson-purple; a fragrant bouquet is upstaged by the surge of juicy red and black cherry and berry fruits on the medium-bodied palate; it is in turn supported by fine-grained tannins and cedary oak. Attractive wine. Screwcap. 14.5% alc. **Rating** 95 **To** 2024 $30

♀♀♀♀♀ **Isolde Reserve Chardonnay 2010 Rating** 92 **To** 2015 $30
Late Harvest Riesling 2011 Rating 92 **To** 2015 $24
Sauvignon Blanc 2011 Rating 91 **To** 2013 $22

♀♀♀♀ **Chardonnay 2011 Rating** 89 **To** 2013 $20
Pinot Noir 2010 Rating 89 **To** 2015 $30
Pinot Grigio 2011 Rating 88 **To** Now $20

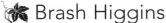 Brash Higgins ★★★★

242 California Road, McLaren Vale, SA 5171 **Region** McLaren Vale
T (08) 8556 4237 **www**.brashhiggins.com **Open** By appt
Winemaker Brad Hickey, Tim Geddes **Est.** 2010 **Dozens** 750 **Vyds** 7ha
Move over Treasury Estate's 'vintrepreneurs', for Brad Hickey has come up with 'creator' and 'vinitor' to cover his role (together with partner Nicole Thorpe) in establishing Brash Higgins. The one thing rather less clearly explained is how you move from Brad Hickey, bypass vintrepeneur, and come up with vinitor. His varied background, including 10 years as head sommelier at some of the best New York restaurants, then a further 10 years of baking, brewing and travelling to the best-known wine regions of the world, may provide some clue. More tangibly, he planted 4ha of shiraz, 2ha of cabernet sauvignon, and recently grafted 1ha of shiraz to nero d'Avola on his Omensetter Vineyard looking over the Willunga Escarpment and on to the Gulf of St Vincent. He has used his New York experience to set up distribution of the wine in the US.

♀♀♀♀♀ **NDV Amphora Project McLaren Vale Nero d'Avola 2011** The bright, clear light magenta colour is flawless; on this test alone, this natural wine, fermented with wild yeast and kept on its skins for seven months in 200-litre beeswax-lined amphoras specially made for the winery, is remarkable. It really does have an aroma of lavender, and flavours of red cherry, with an ever-so-slight savoury undercurrent. If all natural wines were half as good as this, I would have to do a major rethink. My only concern is that it should be drunk as soon as you get your hands on a bottle, for I doubt its staying capacity. 113 dozen made. Screwcap. 13% alc. **Rating** 92 **To** 2014 $37

GR/M Co-Ferment McLaren Vale Grenache Mataro 2011 The idea of co-fermentation is not as novel as winemaker Brad Hickey would have us believe, with some of the greatest cabernet shiraz blends made over the last decades using this principle, not to mention viognier with shiraz. However that may be, this 70/30% blend has juicy red berry flavours promised by the bright, clear colour; needless to say, tannins are not an issue, with the undertow of savoury fruit from the mataro. 116 dozen made. Screwcap. 14.5% alc. **Rating** 90 **To** 2015 $37

CBSV McLaren Vale Cabernet Sauvignon 2009 Red-purple; the wine spent 24 months in French oak, the bouquet with nuances of leather, earth and dark chocolate that feed through into the savoury black fruits of the medium- to full-bodied palate; ripe, persistent tannins help lengthen the finish. Screwcap. 14.5% alc. **Rating** 90 **To** 2020 $37

♥♥♥♥ **SHZ McLaren Vale Shiraz 2009 Rating** 89 **To** 2020 $37

Brave Goose Vineyard ★★★★

PO Box 633, Seymour, Vic 3660 **Region** Central Victoria
T (03) 5799 1229 **www**.bravegoosevineyard.com.au **Open** By appt
Winemaker John and Nina Stocker **Est.** 1988 **Dozens** 400
Dr John Stocker and wife Joanne must be among the most highly qualified boutique vineyard and winery operators in Australia. John is the former chief executive of CSIRO and was chairman of the Grape and Wine Research & Development Corporation for seven years, while daughter Nina has completed the Roseworthy postgraduate oenology course. Moreover, they established their first vineyard (while living in Switzerland) on the French/Swiss border in the village of Flueh. On returning to Australia in 1987 they found a property on the inside of the Great Dividing Range with north-facing slopes and shallow, weathered ironstone soils. Here they have established 2.5ha each of shiraz and cabernet sauvignon, and 0.5ha each of merlot and gamay, selling the majority of grapes from the 20-year-old vines, but making small quantities of Cabernet Merlot, Merlot and Gamay. The brave goose in question was the sole survivor of a flock put into the vineyard to repel cockatoos and foxes.

♥♥♥♥♀ ✪ **Cabernet Merlot 2005** Clean and firm, with crystal-clear blackcurrant and cassis fruit supporting fine, ripe, lingering tannins and good oak. Picked at the perfect point of ripeness. Screwcap. 14.7% alc. **Rating** 93 **To** 2020 $20
Shiraz 2008 Crimson-purple; an elegant medium-bodied shiraz, clearly picked before the heatwave took hold; spicy blackberry and plum fruit has both precision and length; the supporting tannins are fine, the oak subtle. Screwcap. 13.5% alc. **Rating** 92 **To** 2018 $25
✪ **Merlot 2008** Bright colour; an elegant merlot with sweet plum and cassis fruit; the tannins are fine, and underwrite the finish. Screwcap. 13.2% alc. **Rating** 90 **To** 2016 $20

Bream Creek ★★★★★

Marion Bay Road, Bream Creek, Tas 7175 **Region** Southern Tasmania
T (03) 6231 4646 **www**.breamcreekvineyard.com.au **Open** At Dunally Waterfront Café
Winemaker Winemaking Tasmania (Julian Alcorso) **Est.** 1973 **Dozens** 7000 **Vyds** 7.6ha
Until 1990 the Bream Creek fruit was sold to Moorilla Estate, but since then the winery has been independently owned and managed by Fred Peacock, legendary for the care he bestows on the vines under his direction. Fred's skills have seen both an increase in production and also outstanding wine quality across the range, headed by the Pinot Noir. The list of trophies and gold, silver and bronze medals won extends for nine neatly typed A4 pages. The Tamar Valley vineyard has been sold, allowing Fred to concentrate on the southern vineyards, where he is still a consultant/manager of non-estate plantings. Exports to Canada and Sweden.

♥♥♥♥♥ **Riesling 2011** Light straw-green; has beeswax and honey on the bouquet, then a long, lingering sweet-fruited palate; won't let go; good aftertaste. Screwcap. 12% alc. **Rating** 94 **To** 2021 $27
Tashinga Chardonnay 2010 Light to medium straw-green; fragrant, fresh and fine stone fruit flavours drive the palate, with oak in a minor role; almost, but not quite, too elegant. Screwcap. 13% alc. **Rating** 94 **To** 2016 $50

♥♥♥♥♀ **Pinot Rose 2010 Rating** 92 **To** 2014 $24
Pinot Noir 2010 Rating 91 **To** 2018 $35
Sauvignon Blanc 2011 Rating 90 **To** 2013 $27
Cellar Selection Pinot Noir 2008 Rating 90 **To** 2015 $40

♥♥♥♥ **Chardonnay 2010 Rating** 88 **To** 2016 $30
Pinot Chardonnay 2007 Rating 87 **To** 2013 $46

Bremerton Wines ★★★★★

Strathalbyn Road, Langhorne Creek, SA 5255 **Region** Langhorne Creek
T (08) 8537 3093 www.bremerton.com.au **Open** 7 days 10–5
Winemaker Rebecca Willson **Est.** 1988 **Dozens** 40 000 **Vyds** 101.5ha
The Willsons have been grapegrowers in the Langhorne Creek region for some considerable time but their dual business as grapegrowers and winemakers has expanded significantly. Their vineyards have more than doubled (predominantly cabernet sauvignon and shiraz), as has their production of wine. In 2004 sisters Rebecca and Lucy (marketing) took control of the business, marking the event with (guess what) revamped label designs. Can fairly claim to be the best producer in Langhorne Creek. Exports to all major markets.

🍷🍷🍷🍷🍷 Old Adam Shiraz 2009 Before I go further, this is a very good wine. The question is, how much better it might have been with 1% less alcohol. Given the newly inserted cork, it must have spent two years in barrel. All this goes to define the wine, with its generous, but soft regional flavours; oak and tannins are good, and the wine will bring pleasure to many. 15.5% alc. **Rating** 94 **To** 2019 $50
B.O.V. 2009 B.O.V. stands for 'best of vintage', and in this instance is a blend of shiraz and cabernet sauvignon, brim-full of blackberry, blackcurrant, blood plum and dark chocolate flavours supported throughout by soft but persistent tannins, plus a level of oak justified by the generosity of the fruit. Cork. 15% alc. **Rating** 94 **To** 2019 $75

🍷🍷🍷🍷🍷 Special Release Langhorne Creek Malbec 2010 **Rating** 91 **To** 2015 $24 BE
Selkirk Langhorne Creek Shiraz 2010 **Rating** 90 **To** 2016 $22 BE
Coulthard Langhorne Creek Cabernet Sauvignon 2010 **Rating** 90 **To** 2020 $22
Wiggy Methode Champenoise Sparkling Chardonnay 2007 **Rating** 90 **To** 2013 $28

🍷🍷🍷🍷 Reserve Langhorne Creek Chardonnay 2010 **Rating** 89 **To** 2014 $32 BE
○ Langhorne Creek Sauvignon Blanc 2011 **Rating** 89 **To** Now $17
Langhorne Creek Racy Rose 2011 **Rating** 87 **To** Now $16
Tamblyn Langhorne Creek Cabernet Shiraz Malbec Merlot 2010 **Rating** 87 **To** 2015 $18
Special Release Langhorne Creek Tannat 2009 **Rating** 87 **To** 2013 $24 BE

Bress ★★★★★

3894 Calder Highway, Harcourt, Vic 3453 **Region** Bendigo
T (03) 5474 2262 www.bress.com.au **Open** W'ends & public hols 11–5 or by appt
Winemaker Adam Marks **Est.** 2001 **Dozens** 5000 **Vyds** 23ha
Adam Marks has made wine in all parts of the world since 1991, and made the brave decision (during his honeymoon in 2000) to start his own business. Having initially scoured various regions of Australia for the varieties best suited to those regions, the focus has switched to three Central Victorian vineyards, in Bendigo, Macedon Ranges and Heathcote. The Harcourt vineyard in Bendigo is planted to riesling (2ha), shiraz (1ha) and 3ha of cabernet sauvignon and cabernet franc; the Macedon vineyard to chardonnay (6ha) and pinot noir (3ha); and the Heathcote vineyard to shiraz (2ha). Exports to the Maldives.

🍷🍷🍷🍷🍷 Le Grand Coq Noir Unfiltered Harcourt Valley Shiraz 2010 The colour is fractionally more developed than the Gold Chook, but there is a greater volume of dark plum, blackberry and spice-accented fruit; the medium-bodied palate has great mouthfeel, halfway between silk and velvet, the tannins supple, the oak balanced. Screwcap. 14% alc. **Rating** 95 **To** 2025 $60
Gold Chook Macedon Chardonnay 2010 Light straw-green; the tight and incisive nature of well-grown Macedon chardonnay sets the scene; fine white peach and grapefruit are set in a fine web of oak from barrel fermentation and 12 months' maturation in French barrels. Screwcap. 13% alc. **Rating** 94 **To** 2017 $30

Gold Chook Heathcote Shiraz 2010 Purple-crimson hue, not especially deep; the bouquet is full of fragrant spice, licorice and dark berry fruit plus harmonious oak; the long palate is sustained by persistent powdery tannins underpinning the complex black fruit flavours. Screwcap. 14% alc. **Rating** 94 **To** 2020 $40

Gold Chook The Kindest Cut Harcourt Valley Riesling 2010 Bright green-gold; this luscious wine comes from cordon-cut canes left on the vine until the grapes begin to dehydrate. The telltale honey/banana points to the absence of botrytis. 375ml. Screwcap. 12.5% alc. **Rating** 94 **To** 2016 $30

ＹＹＹＹＹ **Gold Chook Macedon Pinot Noir 2010 Rating** 91 **To** 2015 $40

ＹＹＹＹ **Gold Chook Harcourt Valley O.D. Riesling 2011 Rating** 88 **To** 2018 $30

Briar Ridge Vineyard ★★★★★

Mount View Road, Mount View, NSW 2325 **Region** Hunter Valley
T (02) 4990 3670 **www**.briarridge.com.au **Open** 7 days 10–5
Winemaker Luke Watson, Karl Stockhausen **Est.** 1972 **Dozens** 15 000 **Vyds** 39ha
Semillon and Shiraz have been the most consistent performers, underlying the suitability of these varieties to the Hunter Valley. The Semillon, in particular, invariably shows intense fruit and cellars well. Briar Ridge has been a model of stability, and has the comfort of substantial estate vineyards from which it is able to select the best grapes. It also has not hesitated to venture into other regions, notably Orange. Exports to Canada.

ＹＹＹＹＹ **Dairy Hill Single Vineyard Hunter Valley Shiraz 2010** Deep crimson; deep and dark-fruited with spicy, toasty oak a prominent feature; the palate reveals taut acidity, fresh fragrant blue and black fruits, and a long, generous and evenly balanced oaky finish. Screwcap. 14.5% alc. **Rating** 94 **To** 2020 $48 BE

ＹＹＹＹＹ **Dairy Hill Single Vineyard Hunter Valley Semillon 2011 Rating** 92 **To** 2022 $30 BE
Currawong Single Vineyard Orange Cabernet Sauvignon 2009 Rating 92 **To** 2020 $38 BE
Signature Release Karl Stockhausen Hunter Valley Shiraz 2010 Rating 91 **To** 2018 $28 BE
Signature Release Karl Stockhausen Hunter Valley Semillon 2011 Rating 90 **To** 2016 $26 BE
Briar Hill Single Vineyard Hunter Valley Chardonnay 2011 Rating 90 **To** 2017 $30 BE

ＹＹＹＹ **Signature Release Karl Stockhausen Hunter Valley Chardonnay 2011 Rating** 89 **To** 2015 $28 BE
Homestead Verdelho 2011 Rating 88 **To** 2014 $19 BE

Briarose Estate ★★★★☆

13245 Bussell Highway, Augusta, WA 6290 **Region** Margaret River
T (08) 9758 4160 **www**.briarose.com.au **Open** 7 days 10–4.30
Winemaker Stella Bella Wines (Stuart Pym), Bill Crappsley (Consultant) **Est.** 1998
Dozens 6000 **Vyds** 13.56ha
Brian and Rosemary Webster began developing the estate plantings in 1998. They now comprise sauvignon blanc (2.33ha), semillon (1.33ha), cabernet sauvignon (6.6ha), merlot (2.2ha) and cabernet franc (1.1ha). The winery is situated at the southern end of the Margaret River region, where the climate is distinctly cooler than that of northern Margaret River.

ＹＹＹＹＹ **Blackwood Cove 2010** Bright, clear crimson-red; a blend of cabernet franc, cabernet sauvignon and merlot matured in high-quality French oak; a truly impressive wine, with great balance and mouthfeel to the seamless sway of blackcurrant, redcurrant and cedar flavours of the fruit and oak; has good tannin structure and support. Screwcap. 13.5% alc. **Rating** 95 **To** 2025 $32

♀♀♀♀♀ **Margaret River Semillon 2008** Glowing yellow-green; 100% barrel-fermented
✪ and matured on lees for 10 months. How this expensive upbringing can be
reconciled with the price I don't know, but don't look a gift horse in the mouth,
for this is a most attractive lemon-accented wine that has woven the fruit through
the oak (or vice versa) with great skill. Screwcap. 12% alc. **Rating** 93 **To** 2016 $22

✪ **Margaret River Semillon Sauvignon Blanc 2011** Straw-green; a complex and
generous wine, with citrus, snow pea and tropical fruits running through to the
long, well-balanced finish. Screwcap. 13.5% alc. **Rating** 92 **To** 2018 $20

✪ **Margaret River Sauvignon Blanc 2011** Pale straw-green; an interesting
bouquet, with light but distinct touches of tomato leaf; the palate is back in centre
field, with snow pea, grass and gooseberry flavours supported by crisp acidity.
Screwcap. 13.5% alc. **Rating** 91 **To** 2013 $20

Reserve Margaret River Cabernet Sauvignon 2010 Rating 90 **To** 2020 $30

Brick Kiln ★★★★☆

21 Greer St, Hyde Park, SA 5061 **Region** McLaren Vale
T (08) 8357 2561 **www**.brickkiln.com.au **Open** At Red Poles Restaurant
Winemaker Linda Domas, Phil Christiansen **Est.** 2001 **Dozens** 1800 **Vyds** 8ha
This is the venture of Malcolm and Alison Mackinnon, Garry and Nancy Watson, and Ian and
Pene Davey. They purchased the Nine Gums Vineyard in 2001, it had been planted to shiraz
in 1995–96. The majority of the grapes are sold, with a lesser portion contract-made for the
partners under the Brick Kiln label, which takes its name from the Brick Kiln Bridge adjacent
to the vineyard. Exports to the UK, Canada, China, Hong Kong and Singapore.

♀♀♀♀♀ **McLaren Vale Shiraz 2010** Deep purple-crimson; it was matured for 21 months
✪ in American (85%) and French hogsheads; it is an impressive full-bodied wine
showing the best of the vintage and the best of the region with a panoply of black
fruits, licorice, spice, dark chocolate and plum cake, firm tannins giving the wine
the structure it needs. Screwcap. 14.5% alc. **Rating** 94 **To** 2025 $20

Brindabella Hills ★★★★☆

156 Woodgrove Close, via Hall, ACT 2618 **Region** Canberra District
T (02) 6230 2583 **www**.brindabellahills.com.au **Open** W'ends, public hols 10–5
Winemaker Dr Roger Harris, Brian Sinclair **Est.** 1986 **Dozens** 1800 **Vyds** 5ha
Distinguished research scientist Dr Roger Harris presides over Brindabella Hills, which
increasingly relies on estate-produced grapes, with small plantings of riesling, shiraz, chardonnay,
sauvignon blanc, merlot, sangiovese, cabernet sauvignon, cabernet franc and viognier. Wine
quality has been consistently impressive, although the problems the region poses for red wines
means the focus has switched for the time being to whites. Exports to Hong Kong.

♀♀♀♀♀ **Canberra District Riesling 2011** Quartz-green; a complex spice and herb
bouquet is followed by an almost crunchy palate, anchored by minerally acidity,
but with citrus and apple fruit providing flesh. Died-in-the-wool stayer. Screwcap.
11.2% alc. **Rating** 94 **To** 2021 $25

♀♀♀♀♀ **Canberra District Sauvignon Blanc 2011** Pale quartz; a fragrant and flowery
✪ bouquet with hints of passionfruit, then a very zippy, zesty palate driven by
crunchy acidity; cool grown and early picked, and comes again on the aftertaste.
Screwcap. 11.6% alc. **Rating** 91 **To** 2013 $20

⊙ **Canberra District Cabernet Merlot 2009 Rating** 91 **To** 2019 $20

🍂 Brockenchack ★★★★☆

13/102 Burnett Street, Buderim, Qld 4556 (postal) **Region** Eden Valley
T (07) 5458 7710 **www**.brockenchack.com.au **Open** Not
Winemaker Shawn Kalleske **Est.** 2007 **Dozens** 3400 **Vyds** 16ha
Trevor (and wife Marilyn) Harch have long been involved in liquor distribution in Qld,
owning one of Australia's leading independent liquor wholesalers, servicing licensed premises

throughout Qld. Over the years, he became a regular visitor to the Barossa/Eden Valley region, and in 1999 purchased the historic Tanunda Cellars Wine Store. This encouraged him to purchase a wine store at Maleny, renamed Purple Palate, and spawning four other Purple Palate retail bottle shops across Brisbane and the Sunshine Coast, plus the premier wine bar in Brisbane city, known as Bar Barossa. But that is only part of the story: in 2007, Trevor and Marilyn purchased a 16ha vineyard in the Eden Valley and retained friend Shawn Kalleske as winemaker. The vineyard has 8ha of shiraz, 2ha each of riesling and cabernet sauvignon, and 1.3ha each of pinot noir, pinot gris and chardonnay. The name of the business is appropriately Delphic. While every wine so far released, and those planned for the future, are labelled in honour of one or other of the March's family, Brockenchack comes from the Christian names of the four grandchildren: Bronte, Mackenzie, Charli and Jack.

🍷🍷🍷🍷🍷 **William Frederick Single Vineyard Eden Valley Shiraz 2009** Identical colour to the Jack Harrison Single Vineyard Shiraz; the overall style is also similar, but this wine does have even greater intensity. Both wines are to be approached with caution, and will repay a decade or two in the cellar. The price is courageous for a new kid on the block. Screwcap. 14.5% alc. **Rating** 94 **To** 2039 $170

🍷🍷🍷🍷 **Jack Harrison Single Vineyard Eden Valley Shiraz 2009** **Rating** 93 **To** 2034 $57

✪ **Mackenzie William 1896 Single Vineyard Eden Valley Riesling 2010** Light straw-green; has started to develop the appearance of 'normal' riesling in contradistinction to the 2011s; has good intensity, grip, length and texture; drink now or later, whenever the mood takes you. Screwcap. 12.5% alc. **Rating** 91 **To** 2020 $19

✪ **Mackenzie William 1896 Single Vineyard Eden Valley Riesling 2011** Light green-straw; a fragrant and flowery bouquet with citrus and apple blossom signals a crisp and lively palate, with the hallmark acidity of the vintage. Screwcap. 11% alc. **Rating** 90 **To** 2017 $19

Broken Gate Wines ★★★★

57 Rokeby Street, Collingwood, Vic 3066 **Region** South Eastern Australia
T (03) 9417 5757 **www**.brokengate.com.au **Open** Mon–Fri 8–5
Winemaker Josef Orbach **Est.** 2001 **Dozens** 50 000

Broken Gate is a Melbourne-based multi-regional producer, specialising in cool-climate reds and whites. Founder Josef Orbach lived and worked in the Clare Valley from 1994 to '98 at Leasingham Wines, and is currently studying wine technology and viticulture at the University of Melbourne. His is a classic negociant business, buying grapes and/or wines from various regions; the wines may be either purchased in bulk, then blended and bottled by Orbach, or purchased as cleanskins. The wine glut has been a great boon for his business. Last year's rating has been retained. Exports to Canada, Thailand, Singapore and China.

Brokenwood ★★★★★

401–427 McDonalds Road, Pokolbin, NSW 2321 **Region** Hunter Valley
T (02) 4998 7559 **www**.brokenwood.com.au **Open** 7 days 9.30–5
Winemaker Iain Riggs, Simon Steele **Est.** 1970 **Dozens** 100 000 **Vyds** 64ha

This deservedly fashionable winery, producing consistently excellent wines, has kept Graveyard Shiraz as its ultimate flagship wine, while extending its reach through many of the best eastern regions for its broad selection of varietal wine styles. Its big-selling Hunter Semillon provides the volume to balance the limited quantities of the flagships ILR Semillon and Graveyard Shiraz. Next there is a range of wines coming from regions including Beechworth (a major resource from the associated Indigo Vineyard), Orange, Central Ranges, McLaren Vale, Cowra and elsewhere. The two-storey Albert Room tasting facility (named in honour of the late Tony Albert, one of the founders) was opened in 2006. In 2012 Iain Riggs celebrated his 30th vintage at the helm of Brokenwood, offering a unique mix of winemaking skills, management of a diverse business, and an unerring ability to keep Brokenwood's high profile fresh and newsworthy. He has also contributed a great deal to various wine industry organisations. Exports to all major markets.

ΨΨΨΨΨ ILR Reserve Hunter Valley Semillon 2006 Straw-green, still bright and relatively light; at the first moment of the emergence of honey and toast from its lime and mineral womb, but has many years before it becomes an adult. Thus you have the best of all worlds; drink it now, tomorrow, or in 10 years or more, by which time the honey, toast and nut characters will be at their zenith. Screwcap. 11% alc. **Rating** 96 **To** 2026 $48

✪ Hunter Valley Semillon 2011 Pale quartz; the bouquet is clean and pure, with cut grass and apple/citrus aromas, the palate fresh and lively, building impact on the back-palate and finish, yet doing so with delicate, rather than phenolic, flavours. Made to be enjoyed young, but still able to repay medium-term cellaring. Screwcap. 11% alc. **Rating** 94 **To** 2016 $20

Forest Edge Vineyard Orange Chardonnay 2011 Vivid green hue; tightly wound citrus blossom, nectarine and clove bouquet; the acidity is rapier-like and racy, yet the fruit offers generosity and a well-balanced dollop of fine oak to balance the end result; long and fine. Screwcap. 12.5% alc. **Rating** 94 **To** 2018 $32 BE

Indigo Vineyard Beechworth Chardonnay 2010 Pale green-gold; astute winemaking led to part fermentation in tank and part in older French oak barrels using wild yeast; this has kept the wine under control and fresher than the alcohol might suggest; despite all this, its overall message is generosity and complexity. Screwcap. 14% alc. **Rating** 94 **To** 2016 $30

Mistress Block Vineyard Hunter Valley Shiraz 2009 From a single dry-grown, 41-year-old vineyard owned by the McGeoch family. Vivid, clear crimson colour introduces a medium-bodied wine with fragrant berry fruits on the bouquet plus a punch of earth, and an elegant palate shaped by the savoury tannins that run through its length. Born and bred to stay. Screwcap. 14.5% alc. **Rating** 94 **To** 2034 $65

Wade Block 2 Vineyard McLaren Vale Shiraz 2009 Deep garnet; mocha positively jumps out of the glass with blackberry peering out from behind its coat tails; the palate offers a mass of sweet dark fruit, travelling alongside a refreshing core of mineral, fine tannins and fresh acidity. Screwcap. 14.5% alc. **Rating** 94 **To** 2020 $48 BE

ΨΨΨΨΩ McLaren Vale Beechworth Shiraz 2009 **Rating** 92 **To** 2016 $32 BE

Beechworth Pinot Gris 2011 **Rating** 91 **To** 2013 $25

McLaren Vale Cabernet Sauvignon Merlot 2010 **Rating** 91 **To** 2030 $32

✪ Cricket Pitch Sauvignon Blanc Semillon 2010 A stalwart of the Brokenwood portfolio, it appears generosity and texture are sought and found; ripe nectarine and citrus notes are accompanied by straw on the bouquet; the palate is soft-centred, fleshy and accessible, with a complex barrel-derived blanched almond note lingering on the finish. Screwcap. 13% alc. **Rating** 90 **To** 2013 $19 BE

✪ Cricket Pitch Cabernet Sauvignon Shiraz Merlot Petit Verdot 2010 Bright mid garnet; highly perfumed, fragrant and attractive red and black fruit bouquet, with olive and cedar thrown in for good measure; juicy and refreshing, designed for maximum appeal as a young wine, and should be enjoyed as such. Screwcap. 13.5% alc. **Rating** 90 **To** 2016 $19 BE

ΨΨΨΨ Beechworth Nebbiolo 2010 **Rating** 89 **To** 2015 $32 BE

🍇 Bromley Wines   ★★★★☆

PO Box 571, Drysdale, Vic 3222 **Region** Geelong
T 0487 505 367 **Open** Not
Winemaker Darren Burke **Est.** 2010 **Dozens** 300

In his previous life, Darren Burke worked as an intensive care nurse around Australia and in the UK, but at the age of 30 he fell to the allure of wine and enrolled in the Bachelor of Applied Science (Oenology) at Adelaide University. Thereafter he successively became graduate winemaker at Orlando, then Alkoomi Wines (he had done a vintage there during his undergraduate studies), fitting in a vintage in Chianti. With two successful vintages in 2005 and '06 completed, and the impending birth of Darren and wife Tammy's first child, they decided to move back to the east coast. There he worked at several wineries on the Bellarine Peninsula before taking up his full-time winemaking post at Leura Park Estate. Says Darren, 'The essence of Bromley is is family. All our wines carry names drawn from our family history. Family is about flesh and blood, sweat and tears, love and laughter. It is all of these things that we bring to the table when we make our wines.'

♙♙♙♙♙ **Errington Geelong Pinot Noir 2010** Medium red; an exceptionally expressive bouquet full of black cherry and plum fruit aromas, and it doesn't deceive; the same flavours drive the palate, but with the support of spicy tannins on the long, well-balanced finish. Screwcap. 13% alc. **Rating** 94 **To** 2018 $30

♙♙♙♙ **Joy Geelong Pinot Gris 2011 Rating** 89 **To** 2015 $30

Brook Eden Vineyard ★★★★

Adams Road, Lebrina, Tas 7254 **Region** Northern Tasmania
T (03) 6395 6244 **www.**brookeden.com.au **Open** Thurs–Tues 11–5 (Jun–Jul by appt)
Winemaker Winemaking Tasmania **Est.** 1988 **Dozens** 1200 **Vyds** 2.1ha
Peter McIntosh and Sue Stuart purchased Brook Eden from Sheila Bezemer in 2004. At 41° south and an altitude of 160m it is one of the coolest sites in Tasmania, and (in the words of the new owners) 'represents viticulture on the edge'. While the plantings remain small (1ha pinot noir, 0.8ha chardonnay and 0.3ha pinot gris), yield has been significantly reduced, resulting in earlier picking and better-quality grapes. Exports to Canada.

♙♙♙♙♙ **Riesling 2011** Pale straw-green; a fine, elegant and intense palate, balanced and long; still building flavour. Silver Tas Wine Show '12. Screwcap. 12.1% alc. **Rating** 93 **To** 2021 $25
Chardonnay 2010 Light green-yellow; the barrel fermentation impact on the bouquet seems to have been enhanced by the early picking of the grapes, but the grapefruit and white peach flavours of the fruit on the palate do fight back. Screwcap. 12.7% alc. **Rating** 91 **To** 2016 $32
Pinot Gris 2011 Full straw-green; full structure, texture and complexity; very much in the Alsace gris style. Silver Tas Wine Show '12. Screwcap. 13.2% alc. **Rating** 91 **To** 2014 $23

♙♙♙♙ **Water's Edge Pinot Noir 2010 Rating** 89 **To** 2014 $26

Brookland Valley ★★★★★

Caves Road, Wilyabrup, WA 6280 **Region** Margaret River
T (08) 9755 6042 **www.**brooklandvalley.com.au **Open** 7 days 10–5
Winemaker Pete Dillon **Est.** 1984 **Dozens** NFP
Brookland Valley has an idyllic setting, plus its café and Gallery of Wine Arts, which houses an eclectic collection of wine, food-related art and wine accessories. After acquiring a 50% share of Brookland Valley in 1997, Hardys moved to full ownership in 2004; it is now part of Accolade Wines. The quality, and consistency, of the wines has been exemplary. The 2009 Cabernet Merlot was one of two gold medals in a class of 50 wines at the Margaret River Wine Show '10. Exports to Hong Kong and Pacific Islands.

♙♙♙♙♙ **Reserve Margaret River Chardonnay 2010** Pale green-straw; maybe it's the super-elegant style that takes it away from mainstream Margaret River chardonnay, but it's curious it is seldom mentioned when the top wines of the region are listed. The perfect balance, line and length mean the grapefruit and white peach flavours that drive the wine will still be on full display a decade hence. Screwcap. 13% alc. **Rating** 96 **To** 2020 $68
Margaret River Chardonnay 2011 Pale, bright green-straw; a wine of great varietal purity and intensity, the fruit rather than the barrel-ferment French oak inputs driving the character and quality of the wine; the flavours are predominantly white peach and grapefruit, which linger on the palate long after the wine has been swallowed. Screwcap. 13.5% alc. **Rating** 95 **To** 2019 $38

Margaret River Cabernet Sauvignon Merlot 2009 Vivid crimson-purple; shows yet again why Margaret River is unchallenged as the greatest region in Australia for this classic blend. The fruit aromas and flavours are vivid and vital, ranging through black and redcurrant, plum and black olive, the tannins firm but fine and ripe, the finish long. Screwcap. 13.5% alc. **Rating** 95 **To** 2030 $45

Margaret River Cabernet Sauvignon Merlot 2010 Bright purple-crimson; a classy blend, with blackcurrant and redcurrant fruit to the fore, contrasting plum and black olive notes on the back-palate; overall, medium-bodied, balanced and lively. Screwcap. 13.5% alc. **Rating** 94 **To** 2020 $45

✪ **Verse 1 Margaret River Cabernet Merlot 2010** Deep crimson; a detailed and highly perfumed bouquet, revealing succulent black fruits in abundance; the medium-bodied palate reveals fine-grained tannins, black olive and a completely harmonious conclusion; meticulously crafted and excellent value as a result. Screwcap. 13.5% alc. **Rating** 94 **To** 2020 $20 BE

♟♟♟♟♟ **Verse 1 Margaret River Chardonnay 2011** A textbook introduction to
✪ Margaret River chardonnay for those first venturing there; it is all about depth and texture, with flavours ranging from zesty grapefruit through to tropical, and hints of honey and brioche. Screwcap. 13.5% alc. **Rating** 91 **To** 2016 $20

Verse 1 Margaret River Semillon Sauvignon Blanc 2011 **Rating** 90 **To** Now $18

✪ **Verse 1 Margaret River Shiraz 2009** Mid crimson; lively, spicy red fruits guide the wine from the start of the palate through to the finish, with nuances of spice and fine tannins providing support. Screwcap. 13.5% alc. **Rating** 90 **To** 2019 $20

Brookwood Estate   ★★★☆

Treeton Road, Cowaramup, WA 6284 **Region** Margaret River
T (08) 9755 5604 **www**.brookwood.com.au **Open** 7 days 11–5
Winemaker Matt Dermody, Peter Stanlake **Est.** 1996 **Dozens** 3500 **Vyds** 5.5ha
Trevor and Lyn Mann began the development of their 50ha property in 1996, and now have 1.3ha each of semillon, sauvignon blanc and chenin blanc; 1.2ha of shiraz and 1ha of cabernet sauvignon.

♟♟♟♟♟ **Margaret River Semillon Sauvignon Blanc 2011** Pale straw-green; the two
✪ varieties have joined in joyful synergy, the wine alive with tropical fruits and a strong shaft of lemony acidity. Totally delicious now, but will stand up to a year or more in bottle. Screwcap. 11.5% alc. **Rating** 93 **To** 2013 $20

♟♟♟♟ **Margaret River Shiraz 2010** **Rating** 88 **To** 2015 $25
Margaret River Cabernet Sauvignon 2010 **Rating** 88 **To** 2015 $25
Margaret River Sauvignon Blanc 2011 **Rating** 87 **To** 2013 $20
Margaret River Chenin Blanc 2011 **Rating** 87 **To** 2013 $20

Brothers in Arms   ★★★☆

Lake Plains Road, Langhorne Creek, SA 5255 **Region** Langhorne Creek
T (08) 8537 3182 **F** (08) 8537 3383 **www**.brothersinarms.com.au **Open** By appt
Winemaker Jim Urlwin, Justin Lane **Est.** 1998 **Dozens** 18 000 **Vyds** 80ha
The Adams family has been growing grapes at Langhorne Creek since 1891, when the first vines at the famed Metala vineyards were planted. Guy Adams is the fifth generation to own and work the vineyard, and over the past 20 years has both improved the viticulture and expanded the plantings. It was not until 1998 that they decided to hold back a small proportion of the production for vinification under the Brothers in Arms label, and now they dedicate 80ha to the Brothers in Arms wines (shiraz, cabernet sauvignon, malbec and petit verdot); the grapes from the remaining 200ha are sold. Exports to the UK, the US and other major markets account for 60% of total sales.

ΨΨΨΨ♀ **6th Generation 2010** Mid garnet; lively red and black fruits, offset by a splash of cedar and lots of spice; the palate is fleshy and fragrant, medium-bodied, and shows nice balance and harmony on the finish; it is not surprising that this is one of the lowest alcohol wines from this producer, and one of the best. Cabernet Sauvignon/Shiraz. Screwcap. 14.5% alc. **Rating** 91 **To** 2016 $30 BE

ΨΨΨΨ **Formby & Adams Leading Horse Cabernet Sauvignon 2008** Rating 88 **To** 2014 $19 BE

Brown Brothers   ★★★★★

Milawa-Bobinawarrah Road, Milawa, Vic 3678 **Region** King Valley
T (03) 5720 5500 **www**.brownbrothers.com.au **Open** 7 days 9–5
Winemaker Wendy Cameron, Joel Tilbrook, Cate Looney, Geoff Alexander, Chloe Earl
Est. 1885 **Dozens** 1 million **Vyds** 662ha
Draws upon a considerable number of vineyards spread throughout a range of site climates, ranging from very warm to very cool. A relatively recent expansion into Heathcote has added significantly to its armoury. It is known for the diversity of varieties with which it works, and the wines represent good value for money. Deservedly one of the most successful family wineries – its cellar door receives the greatest number of visitors in Australia. In 2010 Brown Brothers took a momentous step, acquiring Tasmania's Tamar Ridge for $32.5 million. It is intended that there will be no changes to Tamar Ridge until all of the opportunities and possible synergies have been carefully considered. An onsite airstrip is an (unusual) extra. Exports to all major markets.

ΨΨΨΨ♀ **Patricia Noble Riesling 2008** Glowing gold; has the wonderful intensity and length of high-quality botrytised riesling, and Brown Brothers have more expertise in making this wine than any other Australian producer. The flavours are of honey, cumquat, marmalade, tangerine, plus whatever else you like. Now on the plateau of perfection. 375ml. Screwcap. 11% alc. **Rating** 96 **To** 2014 $35
Patricia Chardonnay 2009 Bright, light green-straw; still as fresh as a daisy approaching three years of age; the oak and fruit balance is perfect, resulting in an unbroken line from the fore-palate through to the finish and aftertaste; the flavours of the fruit are in a stone fruit and rock melon spectrum, with grapefruit also contributing. Screwcap. 13% alc. **Rating** 95 **To** 2016 $40
Patricia Shiraz 2008 Clear red-purple; the fragrant bouquet of red and black fruits sets the scene for the medium-bodied, but very long and lively, palate; it demonstrates its quality on the finish and aftertaste with fruit and cleansing acidity leaving the mouth fresh and demanding another glass. Screwcap. 14.5% alc. **Rating** 95 **To** 2023 $56
Patricia Cabernet Sauvignon 2008 Clear, bright crimson-purple; this is an immaculately balanced wine. The bouquet is fragrant; fine-grained tannins running through the length of the palate in classic cabernet fashion and combining with the fruit to provide a savoury finish. Screwcap. 14.5% alc. **Rating** 95 **To** 2025 $56
Patricia Pinot Noir Chardonnay Brut 2006 Pale straw-green; made using the traditional method; it is still vibrantly alive and beautifully balanced; so good is the balance that it is easy to overlook the complexity of the wine, and its creamy/yeasty characters held within the fruit. Cork. 12.5% alc. **Rating** 95 **To** 2014 $45
Noble Chardonnay 2010 Gleaming golden-yellow with glints of green; complex and well balanced, giving it a wider spread of use, although fruit-based desserts loom large. There's not a lot of point in cellaring it. 375ml. Screwcap. 9.5% alc. **Rating** 94 **To** 2014 $20

ΨΨΨΨ♀ **Cellar Door Release Single Vineyard King Valley Graciano 2009**
✪ Won Best Red Mediterranean Style at the Melbourne Wine Show '11 (in the alternative style category, despite being planted by Ross Brown's grandfather John Francis Brown in the 1920s). Sold exclusively through the cellar door, it has abundant fruit and good tannin structure. Screwcap. 14.5% alc. **Rating** 92 **To** 2019 $20

King Valley Pinot Noir Chardonnay & Pinot Meunier NV Rating 92
To 2015 $23 BE
Sparkling Shiraz 2008 Rating 92 To 2015 $26
Limited Release King Valley Prosecco 2011 Rating 91 To 2013 $23 BE
Limited Release Single Vineyard Heathcote Shiraz 2010 Rating 90
To 2025 $30

✪   Tempranillo Graciano 2007 Light, but bright, hue; it would seem Brown
Brothers has decided to hold this wine back for release; although the tannins
are (now) well integrated and balanced, there are abundant red fruit aromas and
flavours ranging through the full spectrum, but with cherry to the fore. The acidity
on the finish is very refreshing. Screwcap. 14.5% alc. Rating 90 To 2018 $20

🍷🍷🍷🍷   Montepulciano 2010 Rating 89
✪   To 2016 $20
Limited Release Single Vineyard Banksdale King Valley Chardonnay
2011 Rating 88 To 2015 $25
Crouchen Riesling 2010 Rating 87 To Now $15
Victoria Tempranillo 2010 Rating 87 To 2015 $18
King Valley Prosecco NV Rating 87 To Now $18
Special Late Harvested Orange Muscat & Flora 2010 Rating 87
To 2013 $16

Brown Hill Estate   ★★★★☆

Cnr Rosa Brook Road/Barrett Road, Rosa Brook, WA 6285 **Region** Margaret River
T (08) 9757 4003 www.brownhillestate.com.au **Open** 7 days 10–5
Winemaker Nathan Bailey, Sean Ambrose **Est.** 1995 **Dozens** 3000 **Vyds** 22ha
The Bailey family is involved in all stages of wine production, with minimum outside help.
Their stated aim is to produce top-quality wines at affordable prices, via uncompromising
viticultural practices emphasising low yields. They have shiraz and cabernet sauvignon (8ha
each), semillon, sauvignon blanc and merlot (2ha each). By the standards of Margaret River,
the prices are indeed affordable.

🍷🍷🍷🍷🍷   Perseverance Margaret River Cabernet Merlot 2009 Medium red-purple;
by some distance the best of the '09 releases; there is clearly articulated and
fragrant red and blackcurrant fruit on the bouquet and medium-bodied palate,
with oak evident but balanced and integrated; the tannins are also well balanced.
Screwcap. 14.2% alc. Rating 94 To 2025 $50

🍷🍷🍷🍷♀   Ivanhoe Reserve Margaret River Cabernet Sauvignon 2009 Rating 92
To 2024 $30
Great Boulder Margaret River Cabernet Shiraz Merlot Malbec 2009
Rating 91 To 2020 $40

✪   Lakeview Margaret River Sauvignon Blanc Semillon 2011 Light straw-
green; a fresh, lively and juicy blend, with attractive passionfruit and gooseberry
flavours, the length and balance both good thanks to citrussy acidity. Screwcap.
13.5% alc. Rating 90 To 2013 $17
Croesus Reserve Margaret River Merlot 2009 Rating 90 To 2019 $35
Perseverance Margaret River Cabernet Merlot 2008 Rating 90
To 2015 $45

🍷🍷🍷🍷   Chaffers Margaret River Shiraz 2010 Rating 89
✪   To 2016 $18
Fimiston Reserve Margaret River Shiraz 2009 Rating 87 To 2015 $30

Brown Magpie Wines   ★★★★★

125 Larcombes Road, Modewarre, Vic 3240 **Region** Geelong
T (03) 5266 2147 **F** (03) 5266 2147 www.brownmagpiewines.com **Open** 7 days Jan
11–4, w'ends Nov–Apr 11–4
Winemaker Loretta and Shane Breheny, Chris Sargeant **Est.** 2000 **Dozens** 3500 **Vyds** 9ha

Shane and Loretta Breheny's 20ha property is situated predominantly on a gentle, north-facing slope, with cypress trees on the western and southern borders providing protection against the wind. Vines were planted over 2001–02, with pinot noir (4ha) taking the lion's share, followed by pinot gris and shiraz (2.4ha each) and 0.1ha each of chardonnay and sauvignon blanc. Viticulture is Loretta's love; winemaking (and wine) is Shane's.

Single Vineyard Geelong Pinot Grigio 2011 There is no suggestion the wine was anything other than stainless steel-fermented and taken to bottle in the usual way; nonetheless, it has exceptional intensity and varietal presence on both the bouquet and palate with its blend of pear, apple and citrus, the last making a major contribution on the way through and also to the finish. A pinot gris with attitude. Screwcap. 12.5% alc. **Rating** 94 **To** 2014 $22

Single Vineyard Geelong Pinot Gris 2011 The difference between this wine and the Pinot Grigio is the alcohol: the grapes for this were picked substantially later. This wine has unusual richness, bordering on outright voluptuousness, and bringing some tropical fruits into play; unless you had tasted the two wines, you might suspect this wine had residual sugar, but it doesn't. Screwcap. 13.5% alc. **Rating** 94 **To** 2014 $22

Geelong Pinot Noir 2010 Excellent crimson-purple colour, deep and clear; full of varietal fruit expression from the first whiff of the bouquet through to the finish; rich plum and cherry fruit is supported by balanced French oak; all up, warm and generous. Screwcap. 13% alc. **Rating** 94 **To** 2016 $22

Geelong Shiraz 2010 Strong red-purple; the complex and expressive bouquet is replete with black fruits and the lurking spice and smoked meat come through strongly on the long and intense palate; oak is a constant companion, and the tannins are firm but ripe. Screwcap. 14% alc. **Rating** 94 **To** 2020 $27

Single Vineyard Geelong Rose 2011 Pale, bright pink; hand-picked, estate-grown pinot noir is the base; crisp, vibrant and fresh strawberries have a few drops of lemon juice to bring out the flavour, that touch of citrus lingering on the dry finish. Desperately hard work covering production costs on this wine. Screwcap. 11.5% alc. **Rating** 89 **To** 2013 $12

Bruny Island Premium Wines ★★★

4391 Main Road, Lunawanna, Bruny Island, Tas 7150 (postal) **Region** Southern Tasmania
T 0409 973 033 **www**.brunyislandwine.com **Open** Most days 11–4
Winemaker Bernice Woolley **Est.** 1998 **Dozens** 830 **Vyds** 2ha
Richard and Bernice Woolley have established the only vineyard on Bruny Island, the southernmost commercial planting in Australia (1ha each of chardonnay and pinot noir). Bernice has a degree in marketing from Curtin University, and she and Richard operate budget and deluxe holiday accommodation on the property.

Pinot Noir 2010 Light colour; in fact, the wine has unexpected drive and length, with good varietal expression. Screwcap. 13.6% alc. **Rating** 89 **To** 2015 $30

Brygon Reserve ★★★★★

PO Box 281, Cowaramup, WA 6284 **Region** Margaret River
T 0404 432 878 **www**.brygonreservewines.com.au **Open** Not
Winemaker David Longden **Est.** 2009 **Dozens** NFP
This is one of a portfolio of brands under the corporate umbrella of Australian Fermenters, founded and owned by Robert and Laurie Fraser-Scott. The other brands are Third Wheel, Birds of a Feather and Winston Lake Estate. Each has numerous labels, some as subsets (thus Birds of a Feather has six Reserve varietal wines and eight Humming Bird wines). In March 2012 the number of labels had risen from 52 to 60, precisely the opposite to what I had expected. Extraordinary show success continues, including the trophy for Best Semillon Sauvignon Blanc at the Margaret River Wine Show '11 for the Brygon Reserve Bin 828 Semillon Sauvignon Blanc '11. The remarkable price range of $15 to $30 continues, and the business has now opened an office in China. Exports to the US, Vietnam, Macau, Taiwan, Thailand, Hong Kong and China.

TTTTT Brygon Reserve Bin 828 Margaret River Semillon Sauvignon Blanc 2011
✪ Light straw-green; the fragrant bouquet is followed by a delicious palate with passionfruit, guava and peach all flowing seamlessly through to the clean finish. Trophy Best Semillon Sauvignon Blanc Margaret River Wine Show '11 besting a star-studded field. Screwcap. 12.5% alc. **Rating** 94 **To** 2014 $15

Brygon Reserve Epitome Margaret River Shiraz 2009 Medium crimson; a new label for the stable, and at a higher price point than any prior wines; it is well made, with a well-constructed and balanced palate, the flavours running through blackberry, plum, licorice and cedary French oak. Has good overall balance and length. Screwcap. 13.5% alc. **Rating** 94 **To** 2024 $30

TTTTY Birds of a Feather Reserve Collection Margaret River Semillon
✪ Sauvignon Blanc 2011 Has an abundance of tropical fruit aromas and flavours filling the bouquet and palate respectively; the balance is good, as is the length, which no doubt led to its silver medal in the Sydney Wine Show '12. Screwcap. 12.5% alc. **Rating** 91 **To** 2013 $20

❍ Third Wheel Reserve Margaret River Sauvignon Blanc 2009 **Rating** 90 **To** Now $20

Brygon Reserve Epitome Margaret River Semillon Sauvignon Blanc 2011 **Rating** 90 **To** 2014 $30

❍ Winston Lake Estate Margaret River Chardonnay 2010 **Rating** 90 **To** 2015 $15

✪ Third Wheel Reserve Margaret River Chardonnay 2010 Mid straw-gold; has developed layers of white and yellow peach, nectarine and melon; citrussy acidity provides balance and length on the finish. Screwcap. 12.5% alc. **Rating** 90 **To** 2014 $20

✪ Winston Lake Estate Margaret River Cabernet Merlot 2009 Light, clear red-purple; the aromas and flavours of red and blackcurrant fruit, allied with a touch of cherry, have a more sustained finish than initially anticipated, with a pleasing savoury touch. Screwcap. 13.5% alc. **Rating** 90 **To** 2016 $15

❍ Birds of a Feather Humming Bird Series Margaret River Cabernet Sauvignon 2009 **Rating** 90 **To** 2019 $18

TTTT Brygon Reserve The Bruce Margaret River Sauvignon Blanc 2009
❍ **Rating** 89 **To** Now $18
❍ Third Wheel Margaret River Semillon Sauvignon Blanc 2010 **Rating** 89 **To** 2013 $15
❍ Brygon Reserve Bin 828 Margaret River Semillon Sauvignon Blanc 2010 **Rating** 89 **To** Now $17
❍ Birds of a Feather Reserve Collection Margaret River Semillon Sauvignon Blanc 2009 **Rating** 89 **To** 2013 $18
❍ Birds of a Feather Humming Bird Series Margaret River Semillon Sauvignon Blanc 2009 **Rating** 89 **To** 2013 $18
❍ Third Wheel Margaret River Chardonnay 2009 **Rating** 89 **To** 2016 $15
✪ Brygon Reserve Bin 882 Margaret River Shiraz 2010 **Rating** 89 **To** 2014 $15
✪ Brygon Reserve The Bruce Margaret River Cabernet Sauvignon 2010 **Rating** 89 **To** 2018 $18

Brygon Reserve The Bruce Margaret River Chardonnay 2010 **Rating** 88 **To** Now $18
❍ Third Wheel Reserve Margaret River Chardonnay 2009 **Rating** 88 **To** 2015 $20
❍ Birds of a Feather Humming Bird Series Margaret River Chardonnay 2009 **Rating** 88 **To** 2015 $18

Birds of a Feather Reserve Collection Margaret River Merlot 2009 **Rating** 88 **To** 2017 $20

Brygon Reserve Mirror Image Margaret River Chardonnay 2010 **Rating** 87 **To** 2013 $15

B3 Wines ★★★★

Light Pass Road (via Basedow Road), Tanunda, SA 5352 **Region** Barossa Valley
T (08) 8363 2211 **www.b3wines.com.au Open** By appt
Winemaker Richard Basedow; Craig Stansborough and Rob Gibson (Consultants)
Est. 2001 **Dozens** NA
Peter, Michael and Richard Basedow are the three Brothers Basedow (as they call themselves), fifth-generation Barossans with distinguished forefathers. Grandfather Oscar Basedow established the Basedow winery (no longer in family ownership) in 1896, while Martin Basedow established the Roseworthy Agricultural College. Their father, John Oscar Basedow, died in the 1970s, having won the 1970 Jimmy Watson Trophy for his '69 Cabernet Sauvignon, a high point for the family. As well as retaining consultant winemaker Rob Gibson, the brothers constructed a winery in the old Vine Vale Primary School property in 2008, using the schoolrooms as a cellar door. Exports to the US, Canada, Sweden, Denmark, India, South Korea, Taiwan, Hong Kong, Singapore, Thailand, Japan and China.

John Oscar Barossa Shiraz 2008 Deep colour; a fresh and lively bouquet of black fruits, licorice and toasty oak; the palate shows surprisingly high levels of acidity, providing light and energy to the dense nature of the fruit; long and luscious. Cork. 14.5% alc. **Rating** 92 **To** 2016 $50 BE
John Oscar Barossa Shiraz 2009 Deep colour; a brooding mass of black fruits, fruitcake, tar and chocolate are on display on the bouquet; the palate is warm, thickly textured and generous, almost to a fault, yet the palate provides freshness and ripe well-rounded tannins. Screwcap. 14.8% alc. **Rating** 91 **To** 2024 $50 BE
Barossa Grenache Shiraz Mourvedre 2009 Mid garnet; vine sap and red fruits display themselves, with the medium-bodied palate offering a silky and finely structured experience; fleshy, forward and eminently drinkable as a young wine, and will be best enjoyed as such. Screwcap. 14.5% alc. **Rating** 90 **To** 2014 $22 BE

Buckshot Vineyard ★★★★☆

PO Box 119, Coldstream, Vic 3770 **Region** Heathcote
T 0417 349 785 **www.buckshotvineyard.com.au Open** Not
Winemaker Rob Peebles **Est.** 1999 **Dozens** 800 **Vyds** 2ha
This is the venture of Meegan and Rob Peebles, which comes on the back of Rob's 15-plus-year involvement in the wine industry, including six vintages in Rutherglen, starting in 1993, followed by 10 years at Domaine Chandon, and squeezing in weekend work at Coldstream Hills' cellar door in '93. It is the soils of Heathcote, and a long-time friendship with John and Jenny Davies, that sees the flagship Shiraz, and a smaller amount of Zinfandel (with some shiraz) coming from a small block, part of a 40ha vineyard owned by the Davies just to the southwest of Colbinabbin. The wines are made by Rob at Domaine Chandon. Exports to the US.

 The Square Peg Heathcote Zinfandel 2009 Clear purple-crimson; the sweet fruit bouquet leads into a delicious light- to medium-bodied palate with red berries and some warm Asian spice notes, the slightly savoury tannins silky. The length and balance are spot on, and there is no sign of alcohol heat. Screwcap. 15% alc. **Rating** 94 **To** 2015 $26

 Heathcote Shiraz 2009 Rating 92 **To** 2019 $31

Buller (Rutherglen) ★★★★★

Three Chain Road, Rutherglen, Vic 3685 **Region** Rutherglen
T (02) 6032 9660 **www.bullerwines.com.au Open** Mon–Sat 9–5, Sun 10–5
Winemaker Andrew Buller **Est.** 1921 **Dozens** 10 000 **Vyds** 32ha
Andrew Buller controls this division of the family company, concentrating on Rutherglen regional wines, headed by Shiraz and Durif, and on the high-quality fortified wines that give rise to the winery's five-star rating. He sources the grapes from the family's 90-year-old Calliope Vineyard, and his own Inigo Vineyard. Some attractive table wines have also joined the roster in more recent years. Exports to all major markets.

ŢŢŢŢŢ **Calliope Grand Rutherglen Tokay NV** Dense olive-brown/mahogany;
✪   sublimely rich and focused, with obvious age, but magically fresh on the finish and
         aftertaste (as it should be) courtesy of a touch of much younger material. Cork.
         18% alc. **Rating** 96 **To** Now $59

✪   **Calliope Grand Rutherglen Muscat NV** More brown evident, but as old as
         the Topaque; glorious raisin, toffee, Christmas pudding and who knows what more
         flavours. Great style. Cork. 18% alc. **Rating** 96 **To** Now $59

         Family Reserve Reginald Langdon Buller Sparkling Shiraz NV Dark
         garnet; a very complex wine that is neither oaky nor sweet, and spent time on lees
         after blending; in the classic heartland of Australian sparkling shiraz, one of half a
         dozen top examples. Diam. 14.5% alc. **Rating** 94 **To** 2016 $39

ŢŢŢŢŢ **Classic Old Vine Tokay NV Rating** 93 **To** Now $24
✪   **Cellar Selection Tokay NV** Pale walnut colour; has good varietal character, with
         a tea leaf/butterscotch bouquet, and cleansing rancio notes on the spicy palate do
         not diminish the varietal lift. Cork. 18% alc. **Rating** 92 **To** Now $15
         Classic Old Vine Muscat NV Rating 92 **To** Now $24
         Classic Old Vine Frontignac NV Rating 92 **To** Now $24

ŢŢŢŢ **Calliope Shiraz 2006 Rating** 89 **To** 2021 $35
      Calliope Durif 2006 Rating 89 **To** 2016 $35
      Classic Old Vine Tawny NV Rating 89 **To** Now $24
      Cellar Selection Sauvignon Blanc 2010 Rating 87 **To** Now $15
      Calliope Traditional Method Pinot Chardonnay 2008 Rating 87
      To Now $35

Buller (Swan Hill)   ★★★★

1374 Murray Valley Highway, Beverford, Vic 3590 **Region** Swan Hill
T (03) 5037 6305 **www**.bullerwines.com.au **Open** Mon–Fri 9–5, Sat 10–4, Sun 10–4
(school & public hols only)
Winemaker Richard Buller **Est.** 1951 **Dozens** 250 000 **Vyds** 22ha
Controlled by Richard and Susan Buller, along with their children Richard Jr, Angela and
Kate, Buller offers traditional wines that in the final analysis reflect both their Riverland origin
and a fairly low-key approach to style in the winery. The estate vineyard is planted to a wide
variety of grapes, and additional grapes are purchased from growers in the region. Brands
include the value-for-money Beverford range, Caspia, Black Dog Creek from the King Valley
and Fine Old fortifieds. Production has soared from 120 000 to 250 000 dozen off the back
of exports, especially to China. Exports also to the UK, the US and NZ.

ŢŢŢŢŢ **Langdon Heathcote Durif 2010** Excellent deep crimson-purple; a potent,
         concentrated and focused black-fruited wine, although why does Buller have to
         go to Heathcote to buy it (at considerable expense) when there is plenty in North
         East Victoria and the Riverland? No need to worry about the tannins, for they are
         balanced. Screwcap. 15% alc. **Rating** 92 **To** 2020 $50

✪   **Fine Old Muscat NV** Has elected to remain outside the four-tier Rutherglen
         Classification structure; has a vast haul of awards, mainly from overseas wine
         competitions. There is a lightness of touch to the wine that is most appealing, with
         spice and raisin aromas and flavours to the fore, and without heating the finish.
         Screwcap. 18% alc. **Rating** 92 **To** 2013 $22

✪   **Fine Old Topaque NV** Deep colour for a wine of this price; the bouquet and
         palate are rich and complex, no doubt contributing to a string of gold and silver
         medals (some less prestigious than others) on the label. To be enjoyed for what it is,
         rather than what it is not. Cork. 18% alc. **Rating** 90 **To** 2013 $22

ŢŢŢŢ **Beverford Cabernet Sauvignon 2009** Bright purple-crimson; an attractive
✪   light- to medium-bodied cabernet that is equally attractively priced; has good
         cassis varietal character, and the tannins are well-balanced and fine. Thoroughly
         commendable. Screwcap. 14% alc. **Rating** 89 **To** 2014 $13
         Black Dog Creek King Valley Shiraz 2009 Rating 87 **To** Now $15

Bulong Estate ★★★★☆

70 Summerhill Road, Yarra Junction, Vic 3797 (postal) **Region** Yarra Valley
T (03) 5967 1358 **F** (03) 5967 1350 **www**.bulongestate.com.au **Open** 7 days 11–4
Winemaker Matt Carter **Est.** 1994 **Dozens** 2000 **Vyds** 31ha

Judy and Howard Carter's beautifully situated 45ha property looks down into the valley below and across to the nearby ranges, with Mt Donna Buang at their peak. Most of the grapes from the immaculately tended vineyard are sold, with limited quantities made onsite for the Bulong Estate label.

♥♥♥♥♀ **Yarra Valley Sauvignon Blanc 2011** A bright and pungent blend of tropical fruit, nettle and citrus are exhibited on the bouquet; the palate is fleshy on entry, with tangy acidity providing life and verve on the finish; excellent varietal definition. Screwcap. 12% alc. **Rating** 93 **To** 2014 $21 BE
Yarra Valley Merlot 2010 Mid crimson; a lifted mulberry, plum and spice bouquet, with a little briary complexity; light to medium-bodied, fresh, lively and accessible; easy drinking and elegant. Screwcap. 13.5% alc. **Rating** 90 **To** 2016 $24 BE

♥♥♥♥ **Yarra Valley Pinot Gris 2011 Rating** 88 **To** 2014 $21 BE

Bundaleer Wines ★★★☆

PO Box 41, Hove, SA 5048 **Region** Southern Flinders Ranges
T (08) 8294 7011 **F** (08) 8294 7009 **www**.bundaleerwines.com.au **Open** At North Star Hotel, Melrose Wed–Sun 11–5
Winemaker Angela Meaney **Est.** 1998 **Dozens** 4000 **Vyds** 7ha

Bundaleer is a joint venture between the Meaney and Spurling families, situated in an area known as Bundaleer Gardens, on the edge of the Bundaleer Forest, 200km north of Adelaide. The red wines are produced from estate plantings (equal quantities of shiraz and cabernet sauvignon are planted), the white wines from purchased grapes from the Clare Valley. Exports to Taiwan, China and Hong Kong.

♥♥♥♥ **North Star Southern Flinders Ranges Rose 2011 Rating** 89
◐ **To** Now $19
Clare Valley Riesling 2011 Vibrant green hue; ripe lime, ginger and musk bouquet; a fresh and generous wine, with ample texture and refreshing acidity; accessible and made for early consumption. Screwcap. 12% alc. **Rating** 88 **To** 2016 $17 BE
Golden Spike Clare Valley Chardonnay 2011 Vibrant colour; nectarine and clove accents on the bouquet; soft and fleshy on entry, with a fine backbone of acidity providing freshness and detail on the finish. Screwcap. 13% alc. **Rating** 88 **To** 2013 $17 BE
Southern Flinders Ranges Shiraz 2010 Bright colour; spicy blackberry fruits, mixed with wood smoke and fresh herbs; medium-bodied with juicy fruit and a distinct mineral edge; a savoury style. WAK screwcap. 14% alc. **Rating** 88 **To** 2014 $19 BE

Bunkers Margaret River Wines ★★★★

1142 Kaloorup Roadm Kaloorup, WA 6280 **Region** Margaret River
T (08) 9368 4555 **F** (08) 9368 4566 **www**.bunkerswines.com.au **Open** Not
Winemaker Brian Fletcher **Est.** 1997 **Dozens** 3500 **Vyds** 34ha

Over the past 20+ years, Mike Calneggia has had his fingers in innumerable Margaret River viticultural pies. He has watched ventures succeed, others fail, and while Bunkers Wines (owned by Mike and Sally Calneggia) is only a small part of his viticultural undertakings, it has been carefully targeted from the word go. It has the five mainstream varieties (cabernet, semillon, merlot, chardonnay and shiraz) joined by one rising star, tempranillo, in the warm and relatively fertile northern part of the Margaret River. He has secured the services of the immensely experienced Brian Fletcher as winemaker, and Murray Edmonds as viticulturist (both formerly at Evans & Tate). Mike and daughter Amy are responsible for sales and marketing, supported by direct sales specialist Cat Duncan. They say, 'The world of wine is full of serious people making serious wines for an ever-decreasing serious market ... Bunkers wines have been created to put the "F" word back into wine: "FUN", that is.' Exports to Canada and Hong Kong.

ɣɣɣɣɣ Honeycombs Chardonnay 2010 Rating 90 To 2014 $18
O   The Box Tempranillo 2010 Rating 92 To 2015 $18

ɣɣɣɣ Bears Cabernet Merlot 2010 Rating 89 To 2018 $20
O   Windmills Rose 2010 Rating 88 To Now $18

Bunnamagoo Estate   ★★★★☆
603 Henry Lawson Drive, Mudgee, NSW 2850 **Region** Central Ranges Zone
T 1300 304 707 **F** (02) 6377 5231 **www**.bunnamagoowines.com.au **Open** 7 days 10–4
Winemaker Robert Black **Est.** 1995 **Dozens** 50 000 **Vyds** 102ha
Bunnamagoo Estate (on one of the first land grants in the region) is situated near the historic town of Rockley. Here a 6ha vineyard planted to chardonnay, merlot and cabernet sauvignon has been established by Paspaley Pearls, a famous name in the WA pearl industry. The winery and cellar door are located at the much larger (and warmer) Eurunderee vineyard at Mudgee. Exports to the US and China.

ɣɣɣɣɣ Semillon 2010 Barrel fermentation in used French oak barriques and hogsheads,
✪   plus nine months' maturation on lees, has significantly added to the texture of the
         wine, but without impinging on its freshness or varietal expression; lemon and
         lemongrass flavours drive through the length of the palate, the finish crisp and
         clean. Should develop very well. Screwcap. 11% alc. Rating 94 To 2020 $22

ɣɣɣɣ 1827 Handpicked Cabernet Sauvignon 2009 Rating 89 To 2019 $50
         Merlot 2010 Rating 88 To 2015 $22
         Cabernet Sauvignon Merlot 2010 Rating 88 To 2015 $22 BE
         Kids Earth Fund Autumn Semillon 2010 Rating 88 To 2014 $18 BE
         Riesling 2011 Rating 87 To 2017 $22 BE
         Chardonnay 2010 Rating 87 To 2014 $22

Burge Family Winemakers   ★★★★☆
Barossa Way, Lyndoch, SA 5351 **Region** Barossa Valley
T (08) 8524 4644 **F** (08) 8524 4444 **www**.burgefamily.com.au **Open** Fri, Sat, Mon 10–5
Winemaker Rick Burge **Est.** 1928 **Dozens** 3500 **Vyds** 10ha
Rick Burge and Burge Family Winemakers (not to be confused with Grant Burge, although the families are related) has established itself as an icon producer of exceptionally rich, lush and concentrated Barossa red wines. 2008 marked 80 years of continuous winemaking by three generations of the family, and the red wines previously tasted will be available for sale throughout '12, and the tasting notes are thus repeated below. Exports to Canada, Germany, Belgium, the Netherlands, Hong Kong, Singapore and Japan.

ɣɣɣɣɣ Olive Hill Barossa Valley Shiraz Grenache Mourvedre 2008 Deep purple-
         red; a rich and opulent wine, with a complex array of black and red fruits, licorice,
         fruitcake and dark chocolate; the tannins are balanced, and by some miracle,
         you don't feel the alcohol until the aftertaste – with a hearty red meat dish you
         wouldn't see it at all. Cork. 15.5% alc. Rating 93 To 2020 $32
         Draycott Barossa Valley Shiraz 2008 Medium purple-red; the generous
         bouquet has blackberry, plum, chocolate and French oak on display; the palate
         full of sweet fruit, so sweet you wonder whether the finish will be dry (it is). In
         transition from old to modern in style. Cork. 14.5% alc. Rating 92 To 2020 $36
         Olive Hill Barossa Valley Mourvedre Shiraz Grenache 2008 Good hue; a
         special blend, based on the quality of Mourvedre in '08, and indeed, there is a very
         attractive juicy character to the wine without any confection notes. Cork. 15% alc.
         Rating 91 To 2018 $25

Garnacha Dry Grown Barossa Valley Grenache 2008 Good hue, although relatively light; fragrant red berry, almost flowery, aromas, then confectionery overtones to the berry fruit of the palate. Very regional/varietal. Cork. 15% alc. **Rating** 90 **To** 2016 $25

ΨΨΨΨ **Olive Hill Barossa Valley Semillon 2011** **Rating** 88 **To** 2015 $22

Burke & Wills Winery ★★★★☆

3155 Burke & Wills Track, Mia Mia, Vic 3444 **Region** Heathcote
T (03) 5425 5400 **www**.wineandmusic.net **Open** By appt
Winemaker Andrew Pattison, Gary Baldwin (Consultant) **Est.** 2003 **Dozens** 1500
Vyds 5ha
After 18 years at Lancefield Winery in the Macedon Ranges, Andrew Pattison moved his operation a few miles north in 2004 to set up Burke & Wills Winery at the southern edge of Heathcote, continuing to produce wines from both regions. While establishing 2ha of shiraz, 0.5ha of gewurztraminer and 0.5ha of merlot, malbec and petit verdot at Burke & Wills, he still retains a 20-year-old vineyard at Malmsbury at the northern end of the Macedon Ranges, with 1ha each of cabernet sauvignon, merlot, malbec, cabernet franc, and 0.5ha each of chardonnay and pinot noir. Additional grapes come from contract growers in Heathcote.

ΨΨΨΨΨ **Vat 1 French Oak Heathcote Shiraz 2009** Deep garnet, bright; a fragrant and savoury offering of red fruits, sage and briary complexity; the palate is medium-bodied and full of red fruits, lively acidity and a fine mineral edge to finish; plenty of energy and not as massively concentrated as many from the region. Screwcap. 13.5% alc. **Rating** 94 **To** 2022 $28 BE

ΨΨΨΨ **Mia Mia Heathcote Gewurztraminer 2011** **Rating** 90 **To** 2014 $25 BE

ΨΨΨΨ **Vat 2 American Oak Heathcote Shiraz 2009** **Rating** 87 **To** 2018 $25 BE

Burnbrae ★★★

548 Hill End Road, Mudgee, NSW 2850 **Region** Mudgee
T (02) 6373 3504 **www**.burnbraewines.com.au **Open** Mon–Sat 9–5, Sun 9–4
Winemaker Frank Newman **Est.** 1968 **Dozens** 4500 **Vyds** 16ha
Tony and Jill Bryant were broadacre farmers who had a long-held dream of having a vineyard and winery. Following the sale of the family farm in the 1990s Tony studied viticulture and marketing, and went on to manage wineries in the Mudgee area before starting his own viticultural consultancy business. In 2004 he and Jill were able to take the final step by purchasing Burnbrae, and acquiring the services of industry veteran Frank Newman as winemaker. Burnbrae also provides contract winemaking services for others, and Tony is currently president of the Mudgee Wine and Grape Growers Association. Exports to Singapore.

ΨΨΨΨ **Mudgee Pinot Gris 2011** Light straw-green; some musk and honeysuckle
✪ aromas are attractive, and the palate does not disappoint. Amazing how the cool, wet vintage has assisted white wines. Screwcap. 11.5% alc. **Rating** 89 **To** 2013 $18
Mudgee Viognier 2010 Light straw-green; has authentic varietal aromas of apricot and a hint of ginger, backing off somewhat on the palate, but at least avoiding oily phenolics. Screwcap. 13% alc. **Rating** 89 **To** 2014 $20
Mudgee Shiraz 2008 Medium red-purple, some development; open-fermented, then basket-pressed; the American oak has been significantly overplayed, but that won't displease some, as there is plenty of all-up flavour. Screwcap. 14% alc. **Rating** 87 **To** 2014 $28
Mudgee Botrytis Semillon 2011 A crowd-pleasing soft, rich botrytis semillon; it seems age as much as botrytis has given the flavour. Screwcap. 13% alc. **Rating** 87 **To** 2013 $25

By Farr/Farr Rising

27 Maddens Road, Bannockburn, Vic 3331 **Region** Geelong
T (03) 5281 1733 **www**.byfarr.com.au **Open** Not
Winemaker Gary and Nick Farr **Est.** 1994 **Dozens** 5000 **Vyds** 14ha
Father Gary and son Nick Farr have merged their businesses, although the two labels (By Farr and Farr Rising) will continue. The estate plantings of pinot noir, chardonnay, shiraz and viognier cover the varieties made under the labels; wines under other regions fall under the Regional Dirt Banner. The combined production represents an even split for each of the two brands. The Farrs make exceptionally complex Pinot Noir and Chardonnay, the Shiraz and Viognier equally meritorious. Exports to the UK, Canada, Denmark, Sweden, Hong Kong, Singapore, Taiwan, Maldives and Japan.

ΨΨΨΨΨ **By Farr Geelong Chardonnay 2010** Vibrant green hue; a simply stunning array of nectarine, spices, charcuterie and well-handled oak are on the bouquet; the palate is rich and generous on entry, tightening up across the palate, with a complex texture that lingers elegantly on the extraordinarily long finish; this is one of the most exciting and complete chardonnays to have come out of Australia. Cork. 13.5% alc. **Rating** 98 **To** 2025 $60 BE

Farr Rising Geelong Pinot Noir 2010 Excellent pinot noir colour; the first of four regional wines made in identical fashion to explore the impact of different terroir; a strikingly fragrant, richly robed pinot with dark plum and spice aromas and flavours, tannins and French oak promising a long life. Cork. 13.5% alc. **Rating** 96 **To** 2019 $40

Farrside by Farr Pinot Noir 2010 Deep crimson, bright; a deeply complex and compelling bouquet of dark cherry, plum, vine sap and cold tea stemmy notes in harmony with the fruit; the palate is fleshy and seductively textured, with silky tannins a feature, drawing out the palate to a crescendo of exotic flavours; a beautiful wine that will enthral from the start to the finish. Cork. 13.5% alc. **Rating** 96 **To** 2022 $65 BE

Farr Rising Regional Dirt Berrys Creek Gippsland Pinot Noir 2010 Clear crimson-purple; a wine with very different mouthfeel and flavour spectrum from the Geelong Pinot: more stemmy/spicy and with a finely detailed, almost slippery, palate. Cork. 13.5% alc. **Rating** 95 **To** 2017 $40

Tout Pres by Farr Pinot Noir 2009 Deep garnet; a deeply fruited and brooding wine offering ripe black cherry, hoi sin, thyme and brambly complexity in spades; the palate reveals incredible concentration and muscle, with the tannins certainly ruling the roost at this stage; clearly made to age, this wine will reward patient cellaring. Cork. 13% alc. **Rating** 95 **To** 2024 $110 BE

Farr Rising Geelong Shiraz 2010 The bouquet reflects a style of wine utilising whole-bunch spiciness and complexity to offset the rich red and black fruits on offer; the texture is verging on velvety, with fine tannins and an unctuousness that is complemented ably by lively acidity; a beautifully executed wine in every respect. Cork. 13.5% alc. **Rating** 95 **To** 2022 $35 BE

Farr Rising Regional Dirt Tarrington Henty Pinot Noir 2010 **Rating** 94 **To** 2016 $40

Farr Rising Regional Dirt Merricks Mornington Pinot Noir 2010 **Rating** 94 **To** 2016 $40

Sangreal by Farr Pinot Noir 2010 **Rating** 94 **To** 2022 $70 BE

ΨΨΨΨΨ **Farr Rising Geelong Chardonnay 2010** **Rating** 93 **To** 2018 $35 BE
By Farr Geelong Viognier 2010 **Rating** 92 **To** 2015 $55 BE
Farr Rising Geelong Saignee 2011 **Rating** 90 **To** 2014 $24 BE

 By Jingo!

★★★★

Barker Road, Mount Barker, SA 5251 **Region** Various
T 0418 713 947 **www**.byjingowines.com **Open** By appt
Winemaker John Gilbert **Est.** 2011 **Dozens** NFP **Vyds** 6.5ha

John Gilbert's interest in wine began while working in the pay TV industry; tasting a bottle of 1996 Kangarilla Road Old Vine Zinfandel in '97 led directly to purchasing a small block (1.5ha) overlooking Mount Barker township and partly planting it with zinfandel and shiraz. At the same time he studied at the University of Adelaide, Roseworthy Campus, graduating in 2000. With remarkable alacrity he left for vintages in Sicily and Alto Adige in '01; this fanned the flames, and he instigated the importation of grillo, and planted it and montepulciano, nero d'Avola and negro amaro on the Mount Barker plot. With equal alacrity he created a number of brands, including Jardim do Bomfim, with a production of 20 000 dozen, and was able to sell this in early 2011 to concentrate on his alternative varieties, offered at attention-getting prices.

ŸŸŸŸŸ **The Great Barossa Shiraz 2008** Medium purple-red; ticks all the boxes: open-fermented, basket-pressed, and spent three years in French oak, then was held for a further 10 months prior to release. Has considerable intensity and complexity to its savoury black fruits within the cocoon of French oak. Should develop well. 100 dozen made. Screwcap. 14.2% alc. **Rating** 93 **To** 2028 $60
Adelaide Hills Montepulciano Zinfandel 2009 The two varieties (an 82/18% blend from 15-year-old vines – surprising to find montepulciano so mature) were co-fermented (with 5% whole bunches) in open fermenters, then spent two years in older French oak barriques. It is a lively wine, with fresh red berry fruits and contrasting spicy/savoury tannins that persist well into the finish and aftertaste. 180 dozen made. Screwcap. 14.2% alc. **Rating** 92 **To** 2016 $48

ŸŸŸŸ **Adelaide Hills Montepulciano 2006 Rating** 89 **To** 2015 $120
Southern Fleurieu Mendoza 2009 Rating 87 **To** 2015 $42

Byrne Vineyards

PO Box 15, Kent Town BC, SA 5071 **Region** South Australia
T (08) 8132 0022 **www.**byrnevineyards.com.au **Open** Not
Winemaker Tom White, Phil Reedman **Est.** 1999 **Dozens** NFP **Vyds** 508.79ha
Byrne Vineyards is a family-owned wine business. The Byrne family has been involved in the SA wine industry for three generations, with vineyards spanning over 500ha in SA's prime wine-producing regions, including Clare Valley, Eden Valley, Adelaide Plains and Riverland. The vines vary from 20 to over 40 years of age. The portfolio includes Thomson Estate, Scotts Creek, Devlin's Mount, Boutique Wildflower and Karoola Ridge. Exports to the UK, Canada, Germany, Denmark, Sweden, Thailand, the Philippines, Singapore and China.

ŸŸŸŸ **Thomson Estate Back Blocks Clare Valley Shiraz 2010** Mid crimson; a blend of spicy black fruit and brine on the bouquet; the palate follows suit with a savoury, almost rustic note; ruggedly charming. Screwcap. 14.5% alc. **Rating** 89 **To** 2015 $25 BE
Thomson Estate Old Pumphouse Shiraz 2010 Bright colour; lifted black cherry, plum and dried herb bouquet; medium-bodied, fleshy and generous to conclude. Screwcap. 14.5% alc. **Rating** 87 **To** 2015 $15 BE

Caillard Wine ★★★★★

Sannelsley Street, Leichhardt, NSW 2040 (postal) **Region** Barossa Valley
T 0433 272 912 **www.**caillardwine.com **Open** Not
Winemaker Dr Chris Taylor, Andrew Caillard MW **Est.** 2008 **Dozens** 320
Andrew Caillard MW has had a long and varied career in wine, including vintage work at Brokenwood and elsewhere, but has only just taken the final step of making his own wine, with the support of wife Bobby. Andrew says the inspiration to make Mataro came while writing the background for the various editions of the Penfolds' The Rewards of Patience tastings. Apart from anything else, he learnt that both Max Schubert and John Davoren had experimented with the variety, and that the original releases of Penfolds St Henri comprised a fair percentage of mataro. For good measure, Andrew's great (times four) grandfather, John Reynell, planted one of Australia's first vineyards: at Reynella, around 1838. No wines were received for this edition, so the rating is that of last year.

Calulu Park Vineyard

1800 Warburton Highway, Woori Yallock, Vic 3139 **Region** Yarra Valley
T (03) 5964 7450 **Open** Nov–Mar 7 days 9–5; April–Oct by appt
Winemaker Franco D'Anna (Hoddles Creek Estate) **Est.** 1982 **Dozens** 3000 **Vyds** 7ha
Joe and Helen Tricarico purchased a bushland lot in 1974, first establishing a berry farm, followed in '82 by a small vineyard. The first purchaser of the grapes was Coldstream Hills in '86, which continued to buy the grapes for some years thereafter. Since that time the vineyard has been expanded to 7 ha, with the majority of the fruit being sold. The first Calulu Park wines were made in 2002.

▼▼▼▼   **Yarra Valley Merlot 2010** Good hue, although faintly turbid; a medium–bodied wine with abundant plum/cassis fruit and the barest hint of black olive. An easy–access style that will have broad appeal among merlot lovers. Screwcap. 13.2% alc. **Rating** 89 **To** 2015 $19

Cambewarra Estate

520 Illaroo Road, Cambewarra, NSW 2540 **Region** Shoalhaven Coast
T (02) 4446 0170 **www**.cambewarraestate.com.au **Open** Thurs–Sun 10–5 & public & school hols
Winemaker Tamburlaine **Est.** 1991 **Dozens** 3000 **Vyds** 4ha
Louise Cole owns and runs Cambewarra Estate, near the Shoalhaven River on the coast of NSW; the wines are made at Tamburlaine in the Hunter Valley. Cambewarra continues to produce attractive wines that have had significant success in wine shows. Exports to Hong Kong.

▼▼▼▼▼   **Louise Late Harvest Chardonnay 2008** Deep yellow-gold; luscious yellow peach fruit flavours, backed by clean acidity. Tasted three years ago, and the expectation was that the palate would now be past its best; in fact it is not, although further cellaring will be pointless. Right now, it's a delicious mouthful of peach with a gentle touch of alcohol. Screwcap. 8.7% alc. **Rating** 92 **To** 2014 $26

▼▼▼▼   **Amanda Verdelho 2011 Rating** 88 **To** 2013 $22
Michael Chambourcin 2011 Rating 88 **To** 2013 $24

Campania Hills

447 Native Corners Road, Campania, Tas 7026 **Region** Southern Tasmania
T (03) 6260 4387 **Open** By appt
Winemaker Winemaking Tasmania (Julian Alcorso) **Est.** 1994 **Dozens** 500
This is the former Colmaur, purchased by Jeanette and Lindsay Kingston in 2005. They had just sold their business, built up over 22 years, and thought they were returning to country life and relaxation when they purchased the property, with 1.5ha of vines equally split between pinot noir and chardonnay (plus 700 olive trees). Says Lindsay, somewhat wryly, 'We welcome visitors. The last lot stayed three hours.'

▼▼▼▼▼   **Pinot Noir 2010** Strong colour; a potent medium- to full-bodied pinot, with supple, round and ripe dark fruits. Screwcap. 13.8% alc. **Rating** 90 **To** 2016 $22

Campbells ★★★★★

Murray Valley Highway, Rutherglen, Vic 3685 **Region** Rutherglen
T (02) 6033 6000 **www**.campbellswines.com.au **Open** Mon–Sat 9–5, Sun 10–5
Winemaker Colin Campbell, Tim Griel **Est.** 1870 **Dozens** 36 000 **Vyds** 72ha
Campbells has a long and rich history, with five generations of the family making wine in the same place for 140 years. There were difficult times: phylloxera's arrival in the Bobbie Burns Vineyard in 1898; the Depression of the 1930s; and premature deaths along the way. But the Scottish blood of founder John Campbell has ensured that the business has not only survived, but quietly flourished. Indeed, there have been spectacular successes in unexpected quarters (white table wines, especially Riesling) and expected success with Muscat and Topaque.

But even here, 99-point scores from Robert Parker and a 100-point score from Harvey Steiman (*Wine Spectator*) put Campbells in a special position, dramatically underlined with its Merchant Prince Rare Muscat receiving trophies in 2008 and '10 from the Rutherglen Wine Show as Best Australian Fortified Wine and Best Australian Muscat. It is fair to say that the nigh-on half-century fourth-generation stewardship of Malcolm and Colin Campbell has been the most important in the history of the winery, but the five members of the fifth generation all working in various capacities in the business are well equipped to move up the ladder when Colin and/or Malcolm decide to retire. This is not a decision under consideration right now, although as with any successful family business, succession planning is underway. Exports to the UK, the US and other major markets.

ΨΨΨΨΨ **Isabella Rare Topaque NV** Deep burnt amber and olive on the rim; exceptionally luscious, intense and rich, its density more like very old Seppelt Paras, but with the unique topaque suite of flavours. Impossible to resist, although espresso coffee and walnuts would be a great match. 375ml. Screwcap. 18% alc. **Rating** 98 **To** 2013 $136

Merchant Prince Rare Muscat NV As with the Isabella Topaque, is more viscous and more luscious than its peers, with the most complex array of flavours adding to the usual raisin, burnt toffee and hints of tar. 375ml. Cork. 18% alc. **Rating** 97 **To** 2013 $136

Grand Rutherglen Topaque NV Olive-brown, especially on the rim; gloriously intense and complex, yet satin smooth; burnt honey/toffee carries the spice and Christmas cake flavours; 375ml. Cork. 17.5% alc. **Rating** 95 **To** Now $74

Limited Release Rutherglen Durif 2009 Excellent red-crimson; a very good example of the variety, mouthfilling and velvety, yet not too ripe; the flavours are of plum, blackberry and a touch of dark chocolate, the tannins ripe and round. Screwcap. 14.5% alc. **Rating** 94 **To** 2024 $28

Grand Rutherglen Muscat NV Mahogany-brown; high-toned aromas of raisin, multi-spice, the palate very complex, rancio and sheer richness competing with each other; great balance and length; 375ml. Cork. 17.5% alc. **Rating** 94 **To** Now $74

ΨΨΨΨΨ **The Brothers Rutherglen Shiraz 2009** **Rating** 93 **To** 2024 $60
✪ **Rutherglen Topaque NV** An outstanding wine at this bottom-of-the-range category; bright, light amber; it has great detail to its mix of honey, tea leaf, toffee and cake on the back-palate, and a very lively finish. The only problem is a half-bottle won't be big enough. 375ml. Screwcap. 17.5% alc. **Rating** 93 **To** 2013 $19

Classic Rutherglen Muscat NV **Rating** 93 **To** 2013 $40

Bobbie Burns Rutherglen Shiraz 2010 **Rating** 92 **To** 2030 $23

✪ **Rutherglen Muscat NV** Light, vibrant colour; the palate is crammed with a mix of raisins, burnt toffee and glace fruits, the finish long and harmonious. Gold medal Decanter International Wine Challenge '10. Screwcap. 17.5% alc. **Rating** 92 **To** 2013 $19

The Sixties Block 2010 **Rating** 91 **To** 2017 $29

The Barkly Rutherglen Durif 2009 **Rating** 90 **To** 2020 $54

Rutherglen Sparkling Shiraz NV **Rating** 90 **To** 2017 $30

Cannibal Creek Vineyard ★★★★☆

260 Tynong North Road, Tynong North, Vic 3813 **Region** Gippsland
T (03) 5942 8380 **www**.cannibalcreek.com.au **Open** 7 days 11–5
Winemaker Patrick Hardiker **Est.** 1997 **Dozens** 3000 **Vyds** 5ha

Patrick and Kirsten Hardiker moved to Tynong North in 1988, initially grazing beef cattle, but aware of the viticultural potential of the sandy clay loam and bleached subsurface soils weathered from the granite foothills of the Black Snake Ranges. Plantings began in 1997, using organically based cultivation methods; varieties include pinot noir, chardonnay, sauvignon blanc, merlot and cabernet sauvignon. The family decided to make its own wine, and established the winery in an old farm barn built in the early 1900s by the Weatherhead family, with timber from Weatherhead Hill (visible from the vineyard) that also houses the cellar door. Exports to Hong Kong.

🍷🍷🍷🍷🍷 Chardonnay 2009 Very good green-gold; very attractive and harmonious wine; fruit-forward, with subtle oak, and a long finish. Top gold Winewise '11. Screwcap. 13.2% alc. **Rating** 95 **To** 2017 $28

🍷🍷🍷🍷🍷 Pinot Noir 2009 **Rating** 92 **To** 2015 $28 BE
Cabernet Sauvignon 2010 **Rating** 90 **To** 2016 $28 BE

🍷🍷🍷🍷 Sauvignon Blanc 2011 **Rating** 88 **To** 2013 $28 BE
Chardonnay 2008 **Rating** 88 **To** 2014 $28 BE
Methode Champenoise 2009 **Rating** 88 **To** 2013 $28 BE

Capanno   ★★★★

PO Box 1310, Double Bay, NSW 1360 **Region** Southern Highlands
T 0417 569 544 **www**.capanno.com.au **Open** Not
Winemaker Eden Road Wines (Nick Spencer) **Est.** 2004 **Dozens** 230 **Vyds** 1.2ha
This is the weekend and holiday retreat of Cameron Jones and Jody Williams. Capanno is the Italian word for 'shed', and is an allusion to the series of architect-designed (almost industrial) pavilions that together make up the house. The vineyard was planted close to and around the house, a foreground to the mountains beyond which, in their words, 'provide a fantastic backdrop for afternoon drinks around the bocce court with great friends'. It seems that wine, food and entertaining friends rate high on the Jones and Williams' priorities. The vineyard gives equal space to pinot gris and pinot noir clones 115 and 777. The wines are contract-made by one of the best young winemakers going around, and grown with the help of an expert viticulturist. Notwithstanding the small production, the wines are sold to restaurants and wine bars in Sydney, Melbourne and Canberra.

🍷🍷🍷🍷🍷 Single Vineyard Pinot Noir 2010 Ruby red; it overflows with small red fruits and a degree of plum that fill the mouth with unequivocal varietal flavour; the palate is particularly well balanced and long, and the wine needs several years to really show its best. A singular achievement for the Southern Highlands. Screwcap. 13.8% alc. **Rating** 93 **To** 2017 $35
Single Vineyard Pinot Gris 2011 Distinct pale pink-bronze; fermentation in French puncheons has given the wine texture and structure without obliterating the pear and peach notes, the finish dry and with good acidity. Screwcap. 13.6% alc. **Rating** 92 **To** 2013 $28

Cape Barren Wines   ★★★★★

PO Box 738, North Adelaide, SA 5006 **Region** McLaren Vale
T (08) 8267 3292 **www**.capebarrenwines.com **Open** By appt
Winemaker Rob Dundon **Est.** 1999 **Dozens** 6500 **Vyds** 10ha
Cape Barren was founded in 1999 by Peter Matthews, who worked tirelessly to create wines of distinction from some of the oldest vineyards in McLaren Vale. Peter sold the business in late 2009 to Rob Dundon and Tom Adams, who together have amassed in excess of 50 years' experience in winemaking, viticulture and international sales. Wines are sourced from 3ha of 80–85-year-old grenache at Blewitt Springs, 4.5ha of 120-year-old unirrigated shiraz at McLaren Flat, and 4ha of chardonnay plus 3ha of sauvignon blanc in the Adelaide Hills. Exports to the UK, the US and other major markets.

🍷🍷🍷🍷🍷 Native Goose McLaren Vale Shiraz 2010 Strong, deep crimson-purple; all the desired elements of medium-bodied McLaren Vale shiraz are here, and are in perfect balance; soft, dark fruits, a whirl of dark chocolate, cedary oak and spices are all given their say, and do so eloquently, backed by fine, ripe tannins. Screwcap. 14.5% alc. **Rating** 95 **To** 2025 $23
Native Goose McLaren Vale GSM 2010 A blend of 58% grenache, 38% shiraz and 4% mourvedre. Bright red-purple, it has the innate fruit freshness of '10, a freshness that will not disappear quickly, and which highlights the fragrant red fruits of the grenache mid- to back-palate from the shiraz and mourvedre. Attractive medium-bodied wine. Screwcap. 14.5% alc. **Rating** 94 **To** 2020 $24

ƎƎƎƎƎ **Silly Goose Adelaide Hills Sauvignon Blanc Semillon 2011** A pale quartz
✪ 93/5/2% blend of sauvignon blanc, semillon and verdelho; the gently floral
bouquet is followed by an intense, highly focused and very long palate with zesty
lemon and potent minerally acidity. Screwcap. 11% alc. **Rating** 93 **To** 2013 $18
Old Vine Reserve Release McLaren Vale Shiraz 2010 Rating 90
To 2018 $40 BE

Cape Bernier Vineyard ★★★★☆

230 Bream Creek Road, Bream Creek, Tas 7175 **Region** Southern Tasmania
T (03) 6253 5443 **www**.capebernier.com.au **Open** 7 days 9–5 or by appt
Winemaker Winemaking Tasmania (Julian Alcorso) **Est.** 1999 **Dozens** 2000 **Vyds** 4ha
Alastair Christie and family have established 2ha of pinot noir (including three Dijon clones),
another 1.3ha of chardonnay and 0.7ha of pinot gris on a north-facing slope overlooking
historic Marion Bay. The property is not far from the Bream Creek vineyard, and is one of
several developments in the region changing the land use from dairy and beef cattle to wine
production and tourism. In 2010 Cape Bernier won the title 'Tasmanian Vineyard of the Year',
an award conducted by the Royal Agricultural Society of Tasmania in association with the
State Government and Wine Industry Tasmania.

ƎƎƎƎƎ **Pinot Noir 2010** Very good clear crimson-purple colour; a totally delicious pinot,
with beautifully defined red and black cherry fruit, superfine tannins and balanced
oak. Not a hair out of place. Screwcap. 13.5% alc. **Rating** 94 **To** 2016 $35

ƎƎƎƎƎ **Chardonnay 2010 Rating** 92 **To** 2016 $34
Pinot Noir 2009 Rating 91 **To** 2024 $34
Pinot Gris 2011 Rating 90 **To** 2013 $29
Pinot Rose 2011 Rating 90 **To** Now $29

ƎƎƎƎ **Cabernet Merlot 2009 Rating** 89 **To** 2014 $30

Cape Grace ★★★★

281 Fifty One Road, Cowaramup, WA 6284 **Region** Margaret River
T (08) 9755 5669 **F** (08) 9755 5668 **www**.capegracewines.com.au **Open** 7 days 10–5
Winemaker Mark Messenger (Consultant) **Est.** 1996 **Dozens** 2000 **Vyds** 6.25ha
Cape Grace can trace its history back to 1875 when timber baron MC Davies settled at
Karridale, building the Leeuwin lighthouse and founding the township of Margaret River;
120 years later, Robert and Karen Karri-Davies planted the vineyard to chardonnay, shiraz
and cabernet sauvignon, with smaller amounts of merlot, semillon and chenin blanc. Robert
is a self-taught viticulturist; Karen has over 15 years of international sales and marketing
experience in the hospitality industry. Winemaking is carried out on the property; consultant
Mark Messenger is a veteran of the Margaret River region. Exports to Singapore.

ƎƎƎƎƎ **Margaret River Chardonnay 2010** A deep-fruited wine, with grapefruit,
pineapple and fresh fig; the palate is full of toasty oak, grilled cashew and
lemony acidity; big-boned chardonnay for lovers of flavour. Screwcap. 13.5% alc.
Rating 90 **To** 2016 $38 BE

ƎƎƎƎ **Margaret River Chenin Blanc 2011 Rating** 88 **To** 2015 $20 BE
Margaret River Shiraz Cabernet 2010 Rating 87 **To** 2016 $24 BE

Cape Horn Vineyard ★★★☆

Stewarts Bridge Road, Echuca, Vic 3564 **Region** Goulburn Valley
T (03) 5480 6013 **www**.capehornvineyard.com.au **Open** 7 days 11–5
Winemaker Ian Harrison, John Ellis (Contract) **Est.** 1993 **Dozens** 3500 **Vyds** 11ha
The unusual name comes from a bend in the Murray River considered by riverboat owners of
the 19th century to resemble Cape Horn, which is depicted on the wine label. The property
was acquired by Echuca GP Dr Sue Harrison and her schoolteacher husband Ian in 1993.
Ian has progressively planted their vineyard to chardonnay (3ha), shiraz, cabernet sauvignon
(2ha each), durif, marsanne (1.5ha each) and zinfandel (1ha).

ԲԲԲԲꝒ **Echuca Goulburn Valley Durif 2009** Has retained very good crimson colour, and excellent balance and structure on the bouquet and palate, the latter with abundant plum and blackberry fruit. Screwcap. 13.5% alc. **Rating** 93 **To** 2020 $26

ԲԲԲԲ **Echuca Goulburn Valley Shiraz 2009** Rating 87 To 2014 $22
Echuca Sparkling Durif Shiraz 2007 Rating 87 To 2014 $30

Cape Jaffa Wines   ★★★★

Limestone Coast Road, Mount Benson via Robe, SA 5276 **Region** Mount Benson
T (08) 8768 5053 **www**.capejaffawines.com.au **Open** 7 days 10–5
Winemaker Derek Hooper **Est.** 1993 **Dozens** 12 000 **Vyds** 24.9ha
Cape Jaffa was the first of the Mount Benson wineries and all of the production now comes from the estate plantings, which include three major Bordeaux red varieties, plus shiraz, chardonnay, sauvignon blanc, semillon and pinot gris. The winery, built from local rock, crushes between 800 and 1000 tonnes a year, with a significant proportion of contract winemaking. In 2008 Cape Jaffa became a fully certified biodynamic vineyard, and has installed solar panels to partly offset electricity usage. It received the Advantage SA Regional Award for its sustainable initiatives in the Limestone Coast in both '09 and '10. It has also discontinued the use of heavy glass bottles. Exports to the UK, Canada, Thailand, Cambodia, the Philippines, Hong Kong and Singapore.

ԲԲԲԲꝒ **Mount Benson Pinot Gris 2011** A live-wire pinot gris, bursting with vitality
✪ and flavours that run along the citrus and pear spectrum, the finish long, clean and balanced. Screwcap. 12% alc. **Rating** 92 **To** 2013 $19
La Lune Mount Benson Rose de Syrah 2011 Pale crimson-pink; biodynamically grown, and made from grapes specifically dedicated to rose; a clean, bright and crisp wine with red cherry fruit, and cleansing acidity on the dry finish. Screwcap. 13% alc. **Rating** 90 **To** 2014 $30

ԲԲԲԲ **The Set Limestone Coast Shiraz Cabernet Merlot 2010** Medium red-
✪ purple; the bouquet and palate offer a complex array of ripe fruit aromas and flavours; as well as some oak influence, there is a touch of sweetness on the finish, both of which add to the appeal of the wine for those cruising around a $15 price point. Screwcap. 14.5% alc. **Rating** 88 **To** 2015 $16
La Lune Mount Benson Botrytis Semillon 2009 Rating 88 To 2014 $25 BE
The Set Limestone Coast Unwooded Chardonnay 2010 Rating 87
To 2013 $16

Cape Mentelle   ★★★★★

Wallcliffe Road, Margaret River, WA 6285 **Region** Margaret River
T (08) 9757 0888 **www**.capementelle.com.au **Open** 7 days 10–4.30
Winemaker Robert Mann, Paul Callaghan, Evan Thompson **Est.** 1970 **Dozens** 100 000
Vyds 154.4ha
Part of the LVMH (Louis Vuitton Möet Hennessy) group. Cape Mentelle is firing on all cylinders, with the winemaking team fully capitalising on the extensive and largely mature vineyards, which obviate the need for contract-grown fruit. It is hard to say which of the wines is best; the ranking, such as it is, varies from year to year. That said, Sauvignon Blanc Semillon, Chardonnay, Shiraz and Cabernet Sauvignon lead the portfolio. Exports to all major markets.

ԲԲԲԲꝒ **Wallcliffe Sauvignon Blanc Semillon 2010** Bright colour, showing the hallmarks of a complex, layered and meticulously detailed blend inspired by the best the Bordelaise can muster; fragrant tropical fruits, nettle, fine toasty oak and a tightly wound palate that is both complex and refreshing; long, layered and impeccable. Screwcap. 13% alc. **Rating** 96 **To** 2022 $45 BE
Wallcliffe Sauvignon Blanc Semillon 2009 A paradigm of barrel-fermented sauvignon blanc (68%) and semillon (32%); a marriage of fruit generosity and intensity with its long, elegant, layered palate. It is remarkable, too, for the relatively low alcohol that gives rise to this cornucopia of flavours. Screwcap. 13% alc.
Rating 96 To 2019 $45

Margaret River Chardonnay 2010 Bright, light green-gold; an intense, vibrant and tightly structured wine primarily driven by its grapefruit, lime and white peach fruit, less by its barrel fermentation in French oak. It has great drive to the palate, and outstanding length, all the fruit flavours still wrapped around its natural acidity. Screwcap. 13% alc. **Rating** 96 **To** 2022 $42

Margaret River Shiraz 2010 Deep but clear purple-crimson; the bouquet calmly announces its cool-grown origins, with fragrant, almost flowery, red fruits and spices; the medium-bodied palate is supple and smooth, building impressively on the finely structured finish thanks to exactly poised tannins. Screwcap. 13.5% alc. **Rating** 96 **To** 2030 $40

Trinders Margaret River Cabernet Merlot 2009 A blend of 60% Cabernet Sauvignon, 26% Merlot, 8% Cabernet Franc and 6% Petit Verdot, with an extended ferment of up to 40 days, all the components matured separately for 18 months in French oak, 25% new, 75% one year old. Vibrant crimson-purple, this is a beautifully structured and balanced wine, with red and black berry fruits, touches of violets and cedar on the bouquet and palate alike, the finish long and fresh. Screwcap. 14% alc. **Rating** 96 **To** 2025 $32

Wilyabrup 2009 A blend of cabernet sauvignon, merlot and cabernet franc from vines planted in 1970, some of the first in the Wilyabrup area; the bright and crystal clear crimson colour introduces a beautifully modulated wine, with layers of red and black fruits, superfine tannins and cedary French oak. Screwcap. 13.5% alc. **Rating** 96 **To** 2029 $49

Margaret River Sauvignon Blanc Semillon 2011 Bright quartz-green; this is the unwooded version of Cape Mentelle's Sauvignon Blanc Semillon, but shows the fruit intensity and complexity that allows the (oaked) Wallcliffe version to succeed so well. Here there is a panoply of aromas and flavours spanning citrus/grapefruit, stone fruit and tropical fruits (whatever you care to mention), sustained by lovely natural acidity. Screwcap. 13% alc. **Rating** 95 **To** 2017 $28

Margaret River Cabernet Sauvignon 2009 Deep crimson; a classic bouquet of redcurrant, blackcurrant, cedar, olive and finely tuned French oak; medium-bodied and certainly no blockbuster, the palate is elegantly textured, silky and fine, building to a real crescendo of flavour; long, elegant and harmonious Screwcap. 13.5% alc. **Rating** 95 **To** 2025 $85 BE

Margaret River Zinfandel 2009 Even richer and fuller in the mouth than the '10, but bringing the same raft of flavours into play. Its colour retention is excellent, as is the tapestry of tannins on the finish, making it an even better wine. Screwcap. 15% alc. **Rating** 95 **To** 2017 $55

Margaret River Shiraz 2009 Rating 94 **To** 2020 $40
Margaret River Zinfandel 2010 Rating 94 **To** 2017 $55

 \u00a0\u00a0\u00a0\u00a0\u00a0 **Margaret River Chardonnay 2011** Rating 93 **To** 2016 $42 BE
○ **Marmaduke Margaret River Shiraz 2009** Rating 92 **To** 2017 $19
  Margaret River Zinfandel 2008 Rating 91 **To** 2015 $55
○ **Georgiana Margaret River Sauvignon Blanc 2011** Rating 90 **To** 2013 $19

  Trinders Margaret River Cabernet Merlot 2010 Rating 88 **To** 2014 $30

Cape Naturaliste Vineyard ★★★★★

1 Coley Road (off Caves Road), Yallingup, WA 6282 **Region** Margaret River
T (08) 9755 2538 **www**.capenaturalistevineyard.com.au **Open** 7 days 10.30–5
Winemaker Ian Bell, Bruce Dukes **Est.** 1997 **Dozens** 4000 **Vyds** 9.7ha
Cape Naturaliste Vineyard has a long and varied history going back 150 years, when it was a coach inn for travellers journeying between Perth and Margaret River. Later it became a dairy farm, and in 1970 a mining company purchased it, intending to extract nearby mineral sands. The government stepped in and declared the area a national park, whereafter (in 1980) Craig Brent-White purchased the property. The vineyard is planted to cabernet sauvignon, shiraz, merlot, semillon and sauvignon blanc, and is run on an organic/biodynamic basis. The quality of the wines would suggest the effort is well worthwhile, especially with Bruce Dukes' skills

recognised when he was named Winemaker of the Year at the WA Wine Industry Awards '11. Exports to Singapore and Indonesia.

🍷🍷🍷🍷🍷 **Torpedo Rocks Reserve Margaret River Cabernet Sauvignon 2008** In the full-bodied Cape Naturaliste style, with blackcurrant fruit, cedary oak and tannins in an indivisible line; the balance of flavours, and of texture, is such that the wine will live for decades to come. Screwcap. 14.5% alc. **Rating** 95 **To** 2033 $50

✪ **Margaret River Semillon Sauvignon Blanc 2011** Pale green–quartz; the tropical aromas and flavours have a delicacy and attraction reminiscent of a shimmering butterfly, making it easy to overlook the intensity and length of the palate. Screwcap. 12.8% alc. **Rating** 94 **To** 2013 $20

Torpedo Rocks Margaret River Shiraz 2009 Strong crimson; the power and intensity of the wine reflects the yield of 1.2 tonnes per acre; spice and dark fruits on the bouquet and palate reflect the two years the wine spent in French oak barriques, but it is the black fruits and licorice that dominate proceedings in a classy, full-bodied wine. Screwcap. 14.8% alc. **Rating** 94 **To** 2024 $35

Torpedo Rocks Margaret River Merlot 2009 This is a serious face of merlot, the vineyard yielding little more than a tonne to the acre, and the wine spending 24 months in French oak; the outcome is a strong bouquet and substantial structure to the palate; the aromas and flavour range through black cherry, cassis and a touch of black olive, the tannins firm but balanced and not dry; oak has, of course, left its calling card. Screwcap. 14.7% alc. **Rating** 94 **To** 2024 $35

Torpedo Rocks Margaret River Cabernet Merlot 2009 The low yields are very obvious, building blackcurrant and plum fruit, but so is the French oak and the tannins. It has had to venture to the International Wine & Spirit Competition in London, where its affinities to a young Bordeaux might be more easily recognised to win a trophy. The multilayered, full-bodied nature of the wine underwrites its long-term development. Screwcap. 13.6% alc. **Rating** 94 **To** 2034 $60

Torpedo Rocks Margaret River Cabernet Shiraz 2009 A 60/40% blend, matured for 24 months in French oak barriques. Crimson-red; the bouquet is flooded with sweet red and black fruit aromas, leading to a repeat performance on the medium-bodied palate with blackberry and redcurrant fruit playing tag, plum and blackcurrant watching on from the sidelines; oak and tannin management is exactly as required. Screwcap. 14.7% alc. **Rating** 94 **To** 2020 $35

🍷🍷🍷🍷🍷 **Torpedo Rocks Reserve Margaret River Shiraz 2008** **Rating** 93 **To** 2033 $50

🍷🍷🍷🍷 **Margaret River Sauvignon Blanc 2011** **Rating** 89 **To** 2013 $20

Capel Vale   ★★★★★

118 Mallokup Road, Capel, WA 6271 **Region** Geographe
T (08) 9727 1986 **www**.capelvale.com **Open** 7 days 10–4
Winemaker Justin Hearn **Est.** 1974 **Dozens** 70 000 **Vyds** 165.27ha

Established by Perth-based medical practitioner Dr Peter Pratten and wife Elizabeth in 1974. The first vineyard adjacent to the winery was planted on the banks of the quiet waters of Capel River. The very fertile soil gave rise to extravagant vine growth, providing 95% of the winery's intake until the mid 1980s. The viticultural empire has since been expanded, spreading across Capel (35.66ha), Mount Barker (25.06ha), Pemberton (76.65ha) and Margaret River (27.9ha), with 18 varieties planted; the most recent arrivals are petit verdot, sangiovese, tempranillo and nebbiolo. Unfavourable weather conditions in 2010 meant that Capel Vale did not makes its icon single vineyard wines in that year. Exports to all major markets.

🍷🍷🍷🍷🍷 **Single Vineyard Series Whispering Hill Mount Barker Riesling 2011** A decidedly exotic, fragrant and multilayered wine, with fresh lemon myrtle, lime and spice in abundance; the palate is taut and minerally, with racy acidity providing a pure line that extends the palate for a very long, even and graceful finish. Screwcap. 12% alc. **Rating** 95 **To** 2020 $33 BE

Regional Series Margaret River Cabernet Sauvignon 2010 Deep garnet; a ripe and pure bouquet of cassis, olive and a little leafy complexity; the palate is full-bodied and layered with ample levels of black fruit, gravelly tannins and a long and even finish; generous cabernet. Screwcap. 14% alc. **Rating** 94 **To** 2020 $25 BE

ΨΨΨΨΩ   Regional Series Mount Barker Riesling 2011 **Rating** 92 **To** 2018 $25 BE
Regional Series Pemberton Sauvignon Blanc 2011 **Rating** 90 **To** 2013 $25 BE
Regional Series Pemberton Chardonnay 2010 **Rating** 90 **To** 2016 $25 BE

✪   Debut Verdelho 2010 Bright, light green-yellow; the wine has unusual but attractively lush and tactile mouthfeel, akin to that of sweet white wine, but is dry, with plenty of the usual fruit salad flavours running through to the long finish. Screwcap. 13% alc. **Rating** 90 **To** 2013 $18

✪   Debut Merlot 2010 Mid crimson; an attractively floral perfumed bouquet with plum and thyme; the palate is fleshy, juicy and accessible, with good concentration and length; a very good example of merlot for the price. Screwcap. 14% alc. **Rating** 90 **To** 2018 $18 BE

ΨΨΨΨ   Regional Series Pemberton Semillon Sauvignon Blanc 2011 **Rating** 89 **To** 2013 $25 BE

✪   Debut Merlot 2009 **Rating** 89 **To** 2015 $18
Debut Sauvignon Blanc Semillon 2011 **Rating** 87 **To** 2013 $18 BE
Debut Chardonnay 2010 **Rating** 87 **To** Now $18
Debut Cabernet Merlot 2009 **Rating** 87 **To** 2014 $18

Capital Wines   ★★★★★

Grazing Restaurant, Royal Hotel, Cork Street, Gundaroo, NSW 2620
Region Canberra District
T (02) 6236 8555 **www.**capitalwines.com.au **Open** 7 days 10–5
Winemaker Andrew McEwin **Est.** 1986 **Dozens** 5000 **Vyds** 5ha
This is the venture of Mark and Jenny Mooney (of the Royal Hotel at Gundaroo) and Andrew and Marion McEwin (of Kyeema Wines). They joined forces to found Capital Wines, which purchased Kyeema Wines and related contract winemaking in 2008. The venture has seen the creation of The Ministry Series wines, with clever graphic design and generally invigorated marketing efforts. The estate vineyard is still an important source, supplemented by grape purchases. Whether by coincidence or not, consecutive releases of the wines are of impressive quality, and have led to a substantial increase in production and sales. The cellar door operates in conjunction with the Grazing Restaurant in Gundaroo, in the 1830s stone stables. Exports to Singapore.

ΨΨΨΨΨ   The Whip Riesling 2011 Pale straw-green; the flowery bouquet is attractive, but it is the intensity and focus of the palate that makes the wine what it is, drawing saliva from the mouth with its lime juice and mineral spice; long, satisfying finish. Screwcap. 11.3% alc. **Rating** 94 **To** 2020 $19
Kyeema Vineyard Reserve Canberra District Merlot 2010 Bright, clear, purple-crimson; a bright, fresh medium-bodied merlot that has responded well to the cool growing conditions; cassis, red cherry, spice and whispers of olive and of oak result in a wine of style and exemplary varietal character. Screwcap. 13.5% alc. **Rating** 94 **To** 2020 $46

ΨΨΨΨΩ   Kyeema Vineyard Reserve Canberra District Shiraz 2010 **Rating** 92 **To** 2019 $52
The Backbencher Merlot 2010 **Rating** 90 **To** 2018 $25
The Foreign Minister Canberra District Sangiovese 2010 **Rating** 90 **To** 2014 $25
The Ambassador Canberra District Tempranillo 2010 **Rating** 90 **To** 2017 $27

ΨΨΨΨ   The Swinger Sauvignon Blanc 2011 **Rating** 89 **To** 2014 $19
The Frontbencher Shiraz 2010 **Rating** 89 **To** 2017 $25 BE

Kyeema Vineyard Chardonnay Viognier 2011 Rating 88 To 2015 $36 BE
The Abstainer Rose 2011 Rating 87 To 2013 $19
The Black Rod 2008 Rating 87 To 2016 $36

Cappa Stone Wines   ★★★

PO Box 14, Red Cliffs, Vic 3496 **Region** Murray Darling
www.cappastonewines.com.au **Open** Not
Winemaker Contract **Est.** 2009 **Dozens** 3000
Cappa Stone takes its name from a mountain in Calabria that provided a refuge for those
fleeing the Second World War. It is a symbol of life, fulfilment and opportunity that owners
Reg Cua and Dale Stephens wish to bring to the business and the wines it makes. It is a virtual
winery, the cornerstone being the white frontignac Moscato.

🍷🍷🍷🍷 Adelaide Hills Sauvignon Blanc 2011 A fresh, restrained and vibrant example
of the variety, showing a glimpse of tropical fruit; open knit, forward and made for
early consumption. Screwcap. 12.5% alc. **Rating** 87 **To** 2013 $16 BE

 # Captain Barossa   ★★★☆

PO Box 900, Lyndoch, SA 5351 **Region** Barossa Zone
T 0477 440 014 **www**.captainbarossa.com.au **Open** Not
Winemaker Captain Barossa **Est.** 2011 **Dozens** 1000
This is an unusual form of virtual winery. The owners are James MacKenzie and Captain
Barossa, the latter a nom de plume. The good captain is also the winemaker for the business.
Grapes or wines are purchased from leading growers, the prices reflecting the absence of
investment in vineyards, winery and cellar door. The pool of suppliers may well fluctuate from
one year to the next, but the source is always identified on the label of the bottles. On average,
between 60 and 250 dozen bottles of each wine will be available.

🍷🍷🍷🍷🍷 AK Ebenezer Barossa Valley Petit Verdot 2009 Deep colour; once again,
✪ demonstrates the willingness, if not the desire, of petit verdot to grow and crop
well wherever it is planted. Very attractive blackberry and spiced plum fruit, with
soft tannins. Screwcap. 14% alc. **Rating** 90 **To** 2016 $18

🍷🍷🍷🍷 AK Koonunga Barossa Valley Durif 2009 Dense, opaque colour; full-bodied,
✪ with layers of black fruits, yet avoiding the tannin trap. Despite its weight and
generosity of flavour, best drunk sooner rather than later. Screwcap. 15% alc.
Rating 89 **To** 2014 $18
Mackenzie Williamstown Single Vineyard Barossa Valley Shiraz 2010
Rating 88 **To** 2018 $18
Elytra Eden Valley Shiraz Cabernet 2009 **Rating** 87 **To** 2015 $18

Cardinham Estate   ★★★★☆

Main North Road, Stanley Flat, SA 5453 **Region** Clare Valley
T (08) 8842 1944 **www**.cardinham.com **Open** 7 days 10–5
Winemaker Scott Smith, Brett Stevens **Est.** 1981 **Dozens** 8000 **Vyds** 50ha
Cardinham Estate was founded by Fred Dinham as a single 24ha vineyard in 1981. Now
known as the Home Block, continuous improvement and land availability has seen the
vineyards expand to 50ha. Noel Smith and wife Heather moved to Clare to run the vineyards, eventually living on the Home Block. With falling grape prices and an oversupply of the
wrong varieties, things were very tight, but hard work prevailed and the rewards were realised
when Noel was able to purchase more land and sons Scott and Shane returned to help. By
the 1990s the whole family was involved in the venture, which now includes the Stradbrooke,
Russ' Block and Carters vineyards. Their work was rewarded when they won three trophies
at the Canberra International Riesling Challenge '09, including the coveted Best Riesling in
the World Trophy (for the '03 Riesling), the first awarded to an Australian winery. Exports to
the US, Hong Kong and China.

♟♟♟♟♟ **The Stradbrooke Clare Valley Shiraz 2009** Dense, inky purple-crimson; like a distilled essence of the standard shiraz, jam-packed full of black fruits, licorice and spice, characters that overwhelm the alcohol; 100 dozen made. Diam. 15% alc. Rating 95 **To** 2029 $50

♟♟♟♟♀ **Clare Valley Shiraz 2009** Rating 91 **To** 2019 $25

♟♟♟♟ **The Stradbrooke Clare Valley Cabernet Sauvignon 2009** Rating 88 **To** 2039 $50
Clare Valley Sangiovese 2009 Rating 87 **To** 2013 $20

Cargo Road Wines ★★★★☆

Cargo Road, Orange, NSW 2800 **Region** Orange
T (02) 6365 6100 **www**.cargoroadwines.com.au **Open** W'ends & public hols 11–5, or by appt
Winemaker James Sweetapple **Est.** 1983 **Dozens** 3000 **Vyds** 14.65ha
Originally called The Midas Tree, the vineyard was planted in 1984 by Roseworthy graduate John Swanson, who established a 2.5ha vineyard that included zinfandel – 15 years ahead of his time. The property was acquired in 1997 by Charles Lane, James Sweetapple and Brian Walters. Since then they have rejuvenated the original vineyard and planted more zinfandel, sauvignon blanc, cabernet and riesling. Exports to the UK and Singapore.

♟♟♟♟♟ **Old Vine Five Rows Orange Botrytis Gewurztraminer 2011** Gleaming gold-green; intensely luscious, with lime, honey and lemon curd flavours, the lusciousness balanced by bright acidity. It's a lot of money to pay for a half-bottle of botrytis sweet wine (so far as I know the highest in Australia), but it is seriously good. Screwcap. 11% alc. Rating 94 **To** 2017 $50

♟♟♟♟♀ **Orange Riesling 2011** Rating 91 **To** 2021 $25
Orange Gewurztraminer 2011 Rating 90 **To** 2016 $25

♟♟♟♟ **Orange Cabernet Sauvignon 2010** Rating 89 **To** 2025 $35
Orange Sauvignon Blanc 2011 Rating 88 **To** 2013 $22
Dessert Zinfandel 2010 Rating 87 **To** 2013 $45
Primitivo Love NV Rating 87 **To** 2013 $25

Carlei Estate & Carlei Green Vineyards ★★★★★

1 Alber Road, Upper Beaconsfield, Vic 3808 **Region** Yarra Valley
T (03) 5944 4599 **www**.carlei.com.au **Open** W'ends 11–6 or by appt
Winemaker Sergio Carlei **Est.** 1994 **Dozens** 10 000 **Vyds** 2.25ha
Sergio Carlei has come a long way in a short time: graduating from home winemaking in a suburban garage to his own (commercial) winery in Upper Beaconsfield; Carlei Estate falls just within the boundaries of the Yarra Valley. Along the way Carlei acquired a Bachelor of Wine Science from CSU, and established a vineyard with organic and biodynamic accreditation adjacent to the Upper Beaconsfield winery. His contract winemaking services are now a major part of the business, and showcase his extremely impressive winemaking talents. Exports to the US, Canada, Sweden, China, Singapore and Malaysia.

♟♟♟♟♟ **Estate Tasmania Riesling 2010** Said to come from south of the Tamar Valley, which is a puzzle, but also coming from an unirrigated vineyard yielding 1 tonne to the acre. Given the extraordinary volume of fruit flavour, that makes eminent sense; rich citrus and ripe apple characters are wound around a core of racy acidity, giving the wine great length. Screwcap. 13% alc. Rating 95 **To** 2020 $25
Green Vineyards Yarra Valley Chardonnay 2008 Lighter colour and counterintuitively lighter-bodied than the Carlei Estate; here white peach and melon are joined by a light squeeze of grapefruit and barrel-ferment oak has been well judged. Ageing slowly and impressively. Screwcap. 13% alc. Rating 94 **To** 2018 $29

Estate Directors' Cut Central Victoria Shiraz 2008 Medium to full purple-crimson, the wine not needing a dreadnought bottle to convince consumers of its quality; dark forest fruits are an introduction to the wine, spice and licorice another step, and distinctly savoury tannins the finale. Aged for 24 months in selected barrels out of a considerably larger number. Diam. 14.9% alc. Rating 94 To 2030 $90

ŸŸŸŸç Estate Yarra Valley Chardonnay 2008 Rating 93 To 2014 $49
Estate Directors' Cut Central Victoria Shiraz 2006 Rating 93 To 2020 $90
Green Vineyards Central Victoria Shiraz 2002 Rating 93 To 2015 $49
Green Vineyards Cardinia Ranges Pinot Noir 2010 Rating 92 To 2017 $30
Tre Amici Sangiovese Cabernet Merlot 2007 Rating 92 To 2015 $39
Estate Nebbiolo 2009 Rating 92 To 2019 $59
Green Vineyards Cardinia Ranges Pinot Gris 2011 Rating 91 To 2013 $25
Estate Central Victoria Mourvedre 2007 Rating 91 To 2017 $59
Estate Sud Heathcote Shiraz 2008 Rating 90 To 2030 $59

ŸŸŸŸ Estate Pinot Noir 2010 Rating 89 To 2015 $49
Estate Nord Heathcote Shiraz 2008 Rating 87 To 2016 $59
Estate Yarra Valley Cabernet Sauvignon 2008 Rating 87 To 2018 $49

Carpe Diem Vineyards   ★★★★

213 Johnson Road, Wilyabrup, WA 6280 **Region** Margaret River
T (08) 9755 6118 **www**.carpediemvineyards.com.au **Open** By appt
Winemaker Gianfranco Anderle **Est.** 2003 **Dozens** 2500 **Vyds** 12.2ha
When Gianfranco and Francesca Anderle first visited WA in 2000, they immediately fell in love with the Margaret River region. They promptly returned to Italy, sold up, and returned to purchase their 30ha Wilyabrup property in 2001. Vineyard plantings began in 2003 and continued until '05, with a mix of Margaret River staples (5.5ha of sauvignon blanc and semillon, and 3.3ha of cabernet sauvignon and merlot), the Italian connection cemented with further plantings of sangiovese, nebbiolo, malbec, vermentino and pinot grigio. Gianfranco is a qualified oenologist from Conegliano (northern Italy), the oldest wine school in Europe, and already had 22 years of winemaking experience when he arrived in Australia. The wines are made and bottled onsite.

ŸŸŸŸ Schiaffo Margaret River Sauvignon Blanc 2011 Mid straw; a ripe example
of the variety, with guava, straw and fresh grassy notes; the palate is at the generous
end of the sauvignon spectrum, with flesh overtaking freshness. Screwcap.
12.9% alc. Rating 88 To 2013 $24 BE
Margaret River Shiraz 2009 Deep colour; a savoury bouquet of game, black
fruits and licorice; the palate is dense, with gravelly tannins the focal point on the
finish. Screwcap. 13.8% alc. Rating 87 To 2014 $24 BE
Decantato Margaret River Sangiovese Merlot Cabernet Sauvignon
2011 A pungent bouquet of char and red fruits; the palate follows suit with a
savoury nuance that is hard to deny; fresh acidity provides some interest. Screwcap.
13.5% alc. Rating 87 To 2013 $24 BE

Casa Freschi   ★★★★★

PO Box 45, Summertown, SA 5141 **Region** Langhorne Creek
T 0409 364 569 **www**.casafreschi.com.au **Open** Not
Winemaker David Freschi **Est.** 1998 **Dozens** 2000 **Vyds** 7.55ha
David Freschi graduated with a degree in oenology from Roseworthy College in 1991 and spent most of the decade working in California, Italy and NZ. In 1998 he and his wife decided to trade in the corporate world for a small family-owned winemaking business, with a core of 2.4ha of vines established by his parents in '72; an additional 1.85ha of nebbiolo has now been planted adjacent to the original vineyard. Says David, 'The names of the wines were chosen to best express the personality of the wines grown in our vineyard, as well as to express our heritage.' A second 3.2ha vineyard has subsequently been established in the Adelaide Hills, planted to chardonnay, pinot gris, riesling and gewurztraminer. Exports to Canada and Singapore.

ΨΨΨΨΨ **Altezza Adelaide Hills Chardonnay 2011** The blue blood credentials of this wine cannot be challenged: a high-density planting of Burgundy clones, plus Mendoza clone, on a 1.6ha very steep, organically managed, north-facing amphitheatre slope. Barrel-fermented in used French barriques, two-thirds going through mlf, and left without lees stirring for 10 months. Exceptional intensity and length, the flavours in a grapefruit spectrum, the acidity perfectly balanced, the finish long and penetrating. Screwcap. 12.5% alc. **Rating** 96 **To** 2021 $45
La Signorina 2011 A blend of 85% riesling and small amounts of gewurztraminer, chardonnay and pinot gris grown on a steep slope near Mt Lofty in the Adelaide Hills; whole bunch-pressed and 100% barrel-fermented in used French oak barriques; it remained on yeast lees for 10 months and was filtered before bottling. Takes the riesling story to another dimension, and a great outcome for left-field vineyard planting and winemaking. Screwcap. 12% alc. **Rating** 95 **To** 2020 $30
Ragazzi Adelaide Hills Pinot Grigio 2011 The grapes are grown on a single, low-yielding vineyard near Mt Lofty (560–580m), and were whole bunch-pressed, then fermented in old French oak barriques, 27% going through mlf. Even with that mlf, the wine is bracing and cleansing, its pear and grapefruit flavours backed by pronounced acidity. A grigio loaded with personality. Screwcap. 12% alc. **Rating** 94 **To** 2015 $25

ΨΨΨΨ **Ragazzi Langhorne Creek Nebbiolo 2011 Rating** 89 **To** 2016 $25

Cascabel

★★★★☆

Rogers Road, Willunga, SA 5172 (postal) **Region** McLaren Vale
T (08) 8557 4434 **www**.cascabelwinery.com.au **Open** Not
Winemaker Susana Fernandez, Duncan Ferguson **Est.** 1997 **Dozens** 2500 **Vyds** 4.9ha
Cascabel's proprietors, Duncan Ferguson and Susana Fernandez, have planted a mosaic of southern Rhône and Spanish varieties. The choice of grapes reflects the winemaking experience of the proprietors in Australia, the Rhône Valley, Bordeaux, Italy, Germany and NZ – and also Susana's birthplace, Spain. Production has moved steadily towards the style of the Rhône Valley, Rioja and other parts of Spain. Exports to the UK, the US, Canada, Switzerland, Spain, Hong Kong and Japan.

ΨΨΨΨΨ **McLaren Vale Tempranillo Graciano 2009** Light red, showing some development; a 70/30% blend, with a fragrant red and black cherry bouquet (ex the tempranillo) and distinctly spicy/savoury tannins (ex the graciano). The resultant mouthfeel is very good, with an unusual but good tactile quality. Only 50 dozen made. Screwcap. 14% alc. **Rating** 93 **To** 2017 $44
Eden Valley Riesling 2011 Bright pale straw; has green apple and lemon/citrus aromas that lead into an intense and long palate, with marked lemon zest acidity on the finish. 190 dozen made from a single, dry-grown, mature vineyard. Will flourish in bottle. Screwcap. 11% alc. **Rating** 92 **To** 2019 $20
El Sendero 2010 Like its younger sibling (Joven), is bright, clear red; from the best block of tempranillo on the estate, and with 15 months in French oak; the mix of red and sour (or if you prefer, savoury) cherries is very compelling; the tannins are certainly present, but are fine and supportive. 165 dozen made. Screwcap. 14% alc. **Rating** 92 **To** 2018 $32
Couloir 2011 A 50/50 blend of roussanne and viognier, planted next to each other and ending in a steep gully ('couloir' in French). It has already developed some colour, but not to an alarming extent, and I am perfectly happy with the idea that the roussanne gives elegance and length, and the viognier highlights quince and peach. 150 dozen made. Screwcap. 13% alc. **Rating** 90 **To** 2016 $25
Compose McLaren Vale Sparkling Shiraz 1998 Developed, light brick-red; the base wine was matured in oak for 12 months before going to bottle using the traditional method, spending two years before disgorgement in Oct '11. A complex wine with both oak and fruit characters playing a role, the sweetness of the dosage on the finish needed to balance the phenolics. Will repay further time on cork. 13% alc. **Rating** 90 **To** 2015 $32

ΨΨΨΨ   **Joven 2011** Bright clear crimson; estate-grown tempranillo, made in the Joven
✪   (or young) style, spending only three months in used oak. It has been particularly
successful in this challenging vintage, and 541 dozen produced, a big number by
Cascabel's standards. Screwcap. 13.5% alc. **Rating** 89 **To** 2013 $20
El Sendero 2009 Rating 89 **To** 2014 $32

Casella Wines   ★★★★☆
Wakely Road, Yenda, NSW 2681 **Region** Riverina
T (02) 6961 3000 **www**.casellawines.com.au **Open** Not
Winemaker Alan Kennett, Frank Mallamace, Randy Herron **Est.** 1969
Dozens 12 million **Vyds** 1397ha
A modern-day fairytale success story, transformed overnight from a substantial, successful
but non-charismatic business making 650 000 dozen in 2000. Its opportunity came when
leading US distributor WJ Deutsch & Sons formed a partnership with Casella and, for the
first time, imported wines as well as distributing them. The partners built their US presence
at a faster rate than any other brand in history. It has been aided in all markets by making
small batches (500 dozen or so) of gold medal-standard Reserve and Limited Release wines.
It is not generally realised just how large its estate vineyards are, with pinot noir (53.76ha),
merlot (59.87ha), semillon (62.92ha), sauvignon blanc (83.96ha), riesling (114.77ha), pinot gris
(192.67ha), cabernet sauvignon (218.44ha) and shiraz (380.78ha). Exports to all major markets.

ΨΨΨΨΨ   **1919 Cabernet Sauvignon 2006** The grapes come from Wrattonbully
and Coonawarra, not − as you might imagine − contract-grown, but from
Casella's own vineyards. It has retained vibrant colour, and has a potent palate of
blackcurrant and mulberry fruit sustained by balanced tannins and integrated oak.
Only 500 dozen made. Cork. 14% alc. **Rating** 94 **To** 2021 $40

ΨΨΨΨΨ   **yellow tail Reserve Special Selection Pinot Grigio 2010** My points might
✪   seem miserly given that the wine won the Trophy for Best Other Varietal White
or Rose at the Adelaide Wine Show '11, and it's an example of the skill of the
winemaking team. It is batch-bottled, kept at 2°C to 3°C in tank until required,
thus ensuring its freshness. It also contains some sauvignon blanc that further lifts
its flavour profile, as does the slightly higher alcohol than the core Pinot Grigio
at $10. Screwcap. 12% alc. **Rating** 90 **To** Now $15

ΨΨΨΨ   **yellow tail Special Selection Reserve Cabernet Sauvignon 2010**
✪   **Rating** 89 **To** 2015 $15

Cassegrain   ★★★★
764 Fernbank Creek Road, Port Macquarie, NSW 2444 **Region** Hastings River
T (02) 6582 8377 **www**.cassegrainwines.com.au **Open** 7 days 9–5
Winemaker John Cassegrain (Chief), Michelle Heagney (Senior) **Est.** 1980
Dozens 60 000 **Vyds** 34.9ha
Cassegrain has continued to evolve and develop. It still draws on the original Hastings River
vineyard of 4.9 ha, the most important varieties being semillon, verdelho and chambourcin,
with pinot noir and cabernet sauvignon making up the numbers. However, Cassegrain now
part-owns and manages Richfield Vineyard (see separate entry) in the New England region,
with 30ha of chardonnay, verdelho, semillon, shiraz, merlot, cabernet sauvignon and ruby
cabernet. These estate vineyards are supplemented by grapes purchased from Tumbarumba,
Orange and the Hunter Valley. Exports to the UK, the US, and other major markets.

ΨΨΨΨΨ   **Limited Release Gewurztraminer 2005** Amazing pale green colour; from
a single vineyard at 900m in the New England GI, the wine has slowly evolved
since first tasted five years ago, and fulfilled the promise it then had. In texture,
has overtones of Alsace, and also spice, lavender and lychee aromas and flavours.
Screwcap. 14.5% alc. **Rating** 93 **To** 2017 $35

Verdelho 2011 You would not guess it from the mix of citrus blossom and herb on the bouquet and palate, nor the refreshing crisp finish, but the wine comes from the Hunter Valley. Mind you, you pay for it. Screwcap. 13.5% alc. **Rating** 90 **To** Now $20

♟♟♟♟ **Stone Circle Sparkling Rose NV Rating** 87 **To** Now $15

Castagna   ★★★★☆

88 Ressom Lane, Beechworth, Vic 3747 **Region** Beechworth
T (03) 5728 2888 **www**.castagna.com.au **Open** By appt
Winemaker Julian Castagna, Adam Castagna **Est.** 1997 **Dozens** 1800 **Vyds** 4ha
Julian Castagna is an erudite and totally committed disciple of biodynamic grapegrowing and winemaking. He acknowledges that at least part of the belief in biodynamics has to be intuitive, while also seeking to understand and explain how and why the principles and practises enunciated by Rudolf Steiner in 1924 actually work. A recent move has been the purchase of two egg-shaped, food-grade concrete tanks, each holding 900 litres. They are, he says, 'the most perfect shape in physics', and in the winery reduce pressure on the lees and deposit the lees over a larger surface area, which, he believes, will eliminate the need for battonage. He has been joined by son Adam, who is responsible for the 400 dozen or so of Adam's Rib made each year, complementing the production of Castagna. Exports to the UK, France, Spain, Denmark, South Korea, Hong Kong, China and Japan.

♟♟♟♟♟ **Genesis Syrah 2009** Julian Castagna has very definite ideas about viticulture (biodynamic), winemaking (minimal interference), and a belief that too many wines are homogenised. He also thinks this may be his best Genesis yet, and it certainly has personality; it overflows with dark berry to full-on black, with herbs, spices, polished leather and bramble, yet is finely drawn and perfectly balanced. It will live for as long as your patience lasts. Diam. 14% alc. **Rating** 94 **To** 2030 $75

♟♟♟♟♟ **Adam's Rib The White 2009 Rating** 90 **To** 2015 $35

Castelli Estate   ★★★★★

380 Mount Shadforth Road, Denmark, WA 6333 **Region** Great Southern
T (08) 9364 0400 **www**.castelliestate.com.au **Open** By appt
Winemaker Mike Garland, Andrew Hoadley **Est.** 2007 **Dozens** 5000
Castelli Estate will cause many small winery owners to go green with envy. When Sam Castelli purchased the property in late 2004, he was intending simply to use it as a family holiday destination. But because there was a partly constructed winery he decided to complete the building work and lock the doors. However, wine was in his blood courtesy of his father, who owned a small vineyard in Italy's south. The temptation was too much, and in 2007 the winery was commissioned, with 20 tonnes of Great Southern fruit crushed under the Castelli label, with annual increases thereafter. There is room for expansion because the winery actually has a capacity of 500 tonnes, and the underground cellar is fully climate controlled. Fruit is sourced from some of the best vineyards in WA, including the Hadley Hall, Kalgan River, Whispering Hill and Omodei vineyards. These are geographically distributed across WA's southern regions, including Frankland River, Mount Barker, Pemberton and Porongurup.

♟♟♟♟♟ **Pemberton Chardonnay 2011** Vibrant green hue; the bouquet is a complex blend of grapefruit, cashew, citrus blossom and charcuterie; the medium-weighted palate is fresh and zesty on entry, with a strong mineral accent and savoury note in harmony with the fruit; long, linear and toasty on the finish. Screwcap. 13.8% alc. **Rating** 95 **To** 2022 $28 BE
Porongurup Riesling 2011 Pale straw, vibrant green hue; a fine and fragrant bouquet of lemon, coriander and lime; the palate is taut, dry and racy, with enough ripe fruit to provide generosity and finesse on the finish; long and evenly balanced. Screwcap. 12.5% alc. **Rating** 94 **To** 2022 $25 BE

Pemberton Merlot 2010 Deep crimson; a dark, savoury and seriously complex bouquet of cassis, black olive and thyme; the palate is medium-bodied and shows plenty of tannin, with firmness giving the tightly wound black fruit a long and harmonious ride to the long finish. Screwcap. 13.5% alc. **Rating** 94 **To** 2020 $25 BE

Frankland River Cabernet Sauvignon 2010 A lovely and bright, pure-fruited bouquet showing mulberry, spice and a little ironstone complexity; the palate is medium-bodied and the acidity has real crunch and texture; long, supple and accessible, with time in the tank for patient cellaring. Screwcap. 13.9% alc. **Rating** 94 **To** 2025 $28 BE

ΤΤΤΤΤ Cerca Sauvignon Blanc Semillon 2011 Vibrant green hue; a bright, fresh and
✪ focused bouquet of citrus, tropical fruit notes and a splash of fresh pea pod; the palate is linear and minerally, with engaging acidity and depth of fruit; long, even and poised. Screwcap. 13.5% alc. **Rating** 93 **To** 2015 $18 BE

Frankland River Shiraz 2010 **Rating** 90 **To** 2025 $28 BE

✪ Cerca Cabernet Merlot 2010 Deep crimson, purple hue; the bouquet offers essency black fruits with a smoky background of toasty oak; the full-bodied palate is oaky and richly textured, yet the racy acidity cuts through, providing freshness and a red fruit highlight on the finish. Screwcap. 13.6% alc. **Rating** 90 **To** 2022 $18 BE

ΤΤΤΤ Pemberton Denmark Pinot Noir 2010 **Rating** 88 **To** 2015 $28 BE

Castle Rock Estate   ★★★★★

2660 Porongurup Road, Porongurup, WA 6324 **Region** Porongurup
T (08) 9853 1035 www.castlerockestate.com.au **Open** 7 days 10–5
Winemaker Robert Diletti **Est.** 1983 **Dozens** 4500 **Vyds** 11.2ha
An exceptionally beautifully sited vineyard (riesling, pinot noir, chardonnay, sauvignon blanc, cabernet sauvignon and merlot), winery and cellar door on a 55ha property with sweeping vistas from the Porongurups, operated by the Diletti family. The standard of viticulture is very high, and the vineyard itself ideally situated (quite apart from its beauty). The two-level winery, set on a natural slope, maximises gravity flow, in particular for crushed must feeding into the press. The Rieslings have always been elegant and have handsomely repaid time in bottle; the Pinot Noir is the most consistent performer in the region; the Shiraz is a great cool-climate example; and Chardonnay has joined a thoroughly impressive quartet, elegance the common link. Rob Diletti's excellent palate and sensitive winemaking mark Castle Rock as one of the superstars of WA. Exports to China.

ΤΤΤΤΤ Great Southern Riesling 2011 A flowery, blossom-filled bouquet is the foreplay
✪ for an explosive palate of lime and lime zest, spice and mineral flavours that dance along an almost painfully long spine of acidity, absolutely guaranteeing the future of the wine. Ludicrously cheap. Screwcap. 12% alc. **Rating** 96 **To** 2026 $23

Great Southern Pinot Noir 2010 Light, bright crimson; confit plum aromas lead into a palate with abundant varietal fruit in a blood plum spectrum; a thoroughly impressive and beautifully made pinot in similar style to the excellent '09; the tannins do need to soften. Screwcap. 13.5% alc. **Rating** 95 **To** 2017 $30

Diletti Chardonnay 2009 Bright green-straw; barrel-fermented and aged in French oak for 10 months, the aromas and flavours are fruit-driven, oak merely playing a support role for the grapefruit pith, stone fruit and melon flavours, with minerality added through the acidity. Screwcap. 13% alc. **Rating** 94 **To** 2016 $30

ΤΤΤΤΤ Great Southern Sauvignon Blanc 2010 Notwithstanding its extra year in
✪ bottle (compared to the '11 vintage), is deceptively tightly wound, the bouquet clean except for a hint of the flinty character of the palate, then underlying nuances of gooseberry and herb that build on the finish. Screwcap. 13% alc. **Rating** 92 **To** Now $20

✪   **Great Southern Chardonnay 2011** Light straw-green; here low alcohol from early picking has worked well, without leaving the trail of swingeing acidity found in many; instead there is a gentle fusion of nectarine, melon and citrus, with subtle oak adding a complementary touch. Screwcap. 12.5% alc. **Rating** 92 **To** 2016 $20

Catherine Vale Vineyard   ★★★

656 Milbrodale Road, Fordwich, NSW 2330 **Region** Hunter Valley
T (02) 6579 1334 **www.**catherinevale.com.au **Open** W'ends & public hols 10–5, or by appt
Winemaker Hunter Wine Services (John Hordern) **Est.** 1994 **Dozens** 1500 **Vyds** 4.45ha
Former schoolteachers Bill and Wendy Lawson have established Catherine Vale as a not-so-idle retirement venture. The lion's share of the vineyard planting is chardonnay and semillon, with smaller amounts of verdelho, arneis, dolcetto and barbera. The Lawsons chose to plant the latter three varieties after visiting the Piedmont region of Italy, pioneering the move to these varieties in the Hunter Valley. Exports to Japan.

🍷🍷🍷🍷   **Chardonnay 2010** Has relatively advanced colour. While there are abundant yellow peach, cashew/cream and butter flavours, the wine has redeeming citrussy acidity unexpectedly freshening the finish. Screwcap. 12.5% alc. **Rating** 89 **To** Now $18
Semillon 2010 Mid gold; developed and already toasty for such a young Hunter Semillon; fleshy and toasty on the palate, this should be drunk sooner rather than later. Screwcap. 12% alc. **Rating** 87 **To** 2013 $15 BE
Gabrielle Dolcetto 2010 Very light red, with spicy, savoury, earthy aromas and flavours, the acidity accentuated by early picking. A fresh, halfway house between rose and dry red – perhaps closer to the latter. Ready now. Screwcap. 11.5% alc. **Rating** 87 **To** 2013 $17

Celestial Bay

33 Welwyn Avenue, Manning, WA 6152 (postal) **Region** Margaret River
T (08) 9450 4191 **www.**celestialbay.com.au **Open** Not
Winemaker Bernard Abbott **Est.** 1999 **Dozens** 8000 **Vyds** 60ha
Michael and Kim O'Brien had a background of farming in the Chittering Valley when they purchased their 104ha property. It is very much a family enterprise, with son Aaron studying viticulture and oenology at Curtin University, and daughter Daneka involved in marketing and sales. Under the direction of vineyard manager Sam Juniper, vines have been rapidly planted. The plantings are totally logical: semillon, sauvignon blanc, chardonnay, shiraz, cabernet sauvignon, merlot, malbec and petit verdot. More than half of the grape production is sold at attractive (for Celestial Bay) prices. Winemaker Bernard Abbott celebrated his 27th Margaret River vintage in 2012. The 2010 red wines were received after this issue went to print; tasting notes appear on www.winecompanion.com.au. Exports to the UK, the US, Canada, China, Singapore and Hong Kong.

🍷🍷🍷🍷🍷   **Zenith 2009** Dense purple-crimson; a Petit Verdot/Cabernet Sauvignon/Shiraz blend; an aristocratic wine, justifiably taking offence at being tasted two weeks after being bottled, but its breeding and class obvious; deep black fruits are married to powerful but ripe tannins, the future already easy to see, although don't bother it for a minimum of three years. Screwcap. 14% alc. **Rating** 95 **To** 2030 $35

✪   **Margaret River Cabernet Sauvignon 2009** Strong crimson-purple; a potent bouquet with strong blackcurrant fruit is followed by a full-bodied palate with black fruits and powerful earthy tannins; tasted two weeks after bottling, still shaken up, and will improve radically prior to its release. Screwcap. 14.5% alc. **Rating** 94 **To** 2025 $22

🍷🍷🍷🍷   **Margaret River Chardonnay 2011** **Rating** 87 **To** 2015 $22 BE

Centennial Vineyards

'Woodside', 252 Centennial Road, Bowral, NSW 2576 **Region** Southern Highlands
T (02) 4861 8722 **www.**centennial.net.au **Open** 7 days 10–5
Winemaker Tony Cosgriff **Est.** 2002 **Dozens** 10 000 **Vyds** 28.65ha

Centennial Vineyards, a substantial development jointly owned by wine professional John Large and investor Mark Dowling, covers 133ha of beautiful grazing land, with the vineyard planted to pinot noir (6.21ha), chardonnay (7.14ha), sauvignon blanc (4.05ha), tempranillo (3.38ha), pinot gris (2.61ha) and smaller plantings of savagnin, riesling, arneis, gewurztraminer and pinot meunier. Production from the estate vineyards is supplemented by purchases of grapes from other regions, including Orange. The consistency of the quality of the wines is wholly commendable, reflecting the skilled touch of Tony Cosgriff in a region that often throws up climatic challenges. Exports to the US, Denmark, Singapore, China and Korea.

Single Vineyard Reserve Chardonnay 2010 Gleaming straw-green; from the Bantry Grove vineyard, at an altitude of 900 m, in Orange; total barrel fermentation, part wild, lees stirring and partial mlf all used; the wine has absorbed all of these inputs, none obvious, and has excellent intensity, length and focus to its white peach and nectarine fruit, backed by some creamy cashew notes. Will age with distinction. Screwcap. 13.6% alc. **Rating** 95 **To** 2016 $30

Blanc de Blancs NV Gleaming green-gold; 100% Bowral chardonnay, whole bunch-pressed free-run; 20% barrel-fermented in old oak; 10% mlf, multi-vintage blend, 65% ex '06; five years on lees. Intense, highly focused citrus and apple fruit, high dosage and high acidity perfectly balanced. Trophy Best Sparkling Canberra Regional Wine Show '11, gold medal National Wine Show '11. Diam. 12% alc. **Rating** 95 **To** 2015 $35

Single Vineyard Reserve Riesling 2011 Sourced from the 850m altitude Mayfield Vineyard in Orange. The floral, blossom-filled bouquet leads into a palate with intense lime flavours, and an unusual touch of grapefruit; it has great drive and length, and an assured future. Screwcap. 12% alc. **Rating** 94 **To** 2020 $25

Reserve Single Vineyard Pinot Noir 2010 Mid garnet, bright; a fragrant and perfumed black cherry, plum and bramble bouquet, with savoury nuances; the palate is soft and accessible, ready to go as a young wine, and will be best enjoyed in the full flush of youth. Received a gold medal at the National Wine Show '11 alongside wines from the Yarra Valley and Mornington Peninsula. Screwcap. 13% alc. **Rating** 94 **To** 2016 $30

Reserve Single Vineyard Shiraz Viognier 2009 Mid crimson; a bright, fragrant and spicy black-fruited bouquet, with a splash of tar and licorice; medium-bodied, with fine-grained tannins and taut acidity providing lots of freshness and vibrancy from start to finish. Screwcap. 14.5% alc. **Rating** 94 **To** 2020 $30 BE

Reserve Wild Ferment Sauvignon Blanc 2010 Pushes the envelope to extremes, with wild fermentation, partial mlf, and ageing on yeast lees for nine months. The aim was to produce complexity and texture, rather than youthful fruit and zesty acidity, and winemaker Tony Cosgriff has succeeded admirably. The wine has uncommon texture without, however, the loss of varietal fruit, retaining flavours of gooseberry and ripe citrus, finishing with cleansing acidity. Screwcap. 12.7% alc. **Rating** 93 **To** 2015 $25

Woodside Winery Block Single Vineyard Chardonnay 2010 This has the extra degree of ripeness and depth to the flavour that the Old Block lacks, and the temptation to blend the two parcels must have been difficult to resist. Here nectarine and white peach, together with creamy cashew notes, do the talking; the acidity on the finish is not only integrated, but perfectly balanced. Screwcap. 13.3% alc. **Rating** 93 **To** 2017 $23

Woodside Shiraz 2010 Deep crimson; a spicy blend of fresh blackberry, pepper, nutmeg and vine sap; medium-bodied with savoury tannins and an intriguing thread of quartz and earth; a fine, fragrant and food-friendly example of the variety. Screwcap. 14.5% alc. **Rating** 93 **To** 2020 $25 BE

Single Vineyard Reserve Cabernet Sauvignon 2009 Rating 93 **To** 2029 $30
Pinot Noir Chardonnay NV Rating 93 **To** 2015 $28
Sparkling Shiraz NV Rating 93 **To** 2015 $25
Brut Rose NV Rating 92 **To** 2014 $28

✪ **Woodside Single Vineyard Sauvignon Blanc 2011** Just how much the small percentage of wild fermentation in old barrels has added to the texture and grip of this stainless steel-fermented wine isn't easy to tell, but it certainly has grip and texture – indeed, it is all about texture in much the same way as white Bordeaux and emphatically not Marlborough. Screwcap. 12.7% alc. **Rating** 91 **To** 2013 $22

✪ **Bong Bong Red 2010** A blend of shiraz and tempranillo sourced from the Hilltops and Southern Highlands makes a mockery of its price with the array of spicy red and black fruits; the bouquet and medium- to full-bodied palate are doubtless intended for current drinking, but will prove ageworthy. Screwcap. 14% alc. **Rating** 91 **To** 2018 $19

Woodside Single Vineyard Tempranillo 2010 Rating 91 To 2015 $25 BE

✪ **Woodside Old Block Single Vineyard Chardonnay 2010** Made from grapes grown on the estate vineyards at Bowral, and given the full suite of Tony Cosgriff's techniques. Light straw-green, it is both highly focused and intense; some may find the acidity intimidating, others as simply refreshing. Screwcap. 12.4% alc. **Rating** 90 **To** 2016 $20

Woodside Single Vineyard Pinot Grigio 2011 Rating 90 To 2013 $22

Finale Late Autumn Chardonnay 2010 Rating 90 To 2014 $25

Ceravolo Estate

Suite 5, 143 Glynburn Road, Firle, SA 5070 (postal) **Region** Adelaide Plains
T (08) 8336 4522 **F** (08) 8365 0538 **www**.ceravolo.com.au **Open** Not
Winemaker Joe Ceravolo, Michael Sykes, Colin Glaetzer, Ben Glaetzer (Contract) **Est.** 1985 **Dozens** 25 000 **Vyds** 30ha

Dentist turned vigneron and winemaker Joe Ceravolo, and his wife Heather, have been producing single vineyard wines from their 23ha estate on the Adelaide Plains since 1999. Significant wine show success, particularly with Shiraz, Petit Verdot, Merlot and Sangiovese, has added to the reputation of their brand. Their son Antony, with wife Fiona, is now working with them to take their family business into the next generation. The Ceravolos have also established vineyards (6.5ha) around their home in the Adelaide Hills, focusing on cooler-climate Italian varieties such as primitivo, piccolit, pinot grigio, dolcetto, barbera and cortese. Wines are released under Ceravolo, St Andrews Estate and export-only Red Earth labels. Exports to all major markets.

🍷🍷🍷🍷🍷 **Adelaide Plains Sangiovese 2009** Mid garnet; a lifted perfume of sweet red
✪ cherry, red licorice and sage; the palate is soft and supple on entry, finishing with a little savoury firmness in the tail. Screwcap. 14% alc. **Rating** 90 **To** 2015 $18 BE

Adelaide Plains Petit Verdot 2009 Deep colour, vibrant hue; a perfumed and highly polished bouquet of liqueur-soaked plums, mulberry and thyme; the palate is unctuous and sweet-fruited, leaving a licorice note lingering on the finish. Screwcap. 15% alc. **Rating** 90 **To** 2016 $22 BE

🍷🍷🍷🍷 **Adelaide Plains Pinot Grigio 2011** Quite literally, water white; the cool season
✪ has conserved the fresh pear and apple aromas and flavours of a pleasant wine with good mouthfeel and balance. Screwcap. 12% alc. **Rating** 89 **To** Now $16
✪ **Adelaide Plains Sangiovese Rose 2011** Pale pink; cherry aromas with some spicy nougat notes come through on the palate, which has good balance (neither sweet nor dry) and length. Nice wine. Screwcap. 12% alc. **Rating** 89 **To** Now $17

The Emigrant Adelaide Hills Primitivo 2011 Rating 89 To 2014 $22 BE

Adelaide Plains Sauvignon Blanc 2011 Rating 87 To Now $16

Ceres Bridge Estate

84 Merrawarp Road, Stonehaven, Vic 3221 **Region** Geelong
T (03) 5271 1212 **F** (03) 5271 1212 **Open** By appt
Winemaker Challon Murdock **Est.** 1996 **Dozens** 500 **Vyds** 7.4ha

Challon and Patricia Murdock began the long, slow and at times very frustrating process of establishing their vineyard in 1996. They planted 1.8ha of chardonnay in that year, but 50% of the vines died over the next two years in the face of drought and inadequate water supply. Instead of deciding it was all too difficult, they persevered by planting 1.1ha of pinot noir in 2000, with replanting in '01, and then in '05 signified the intention to become serious by planting between 0.5ha and 1ha each of shiraz, nebbiolo, sauvignon blanc, viognier, tempranillo and pinot grigio.

ΨΨΨΨ **Geelong Chardonnay 2010** Glowing yellow-green; has a very good textural
✪   play, with grainy acidity, and barrel fermentation and maturation in French
           oak (largely used) all leaving the fruit intact. Screwcap. 13% alc. **Rating** 89
           To 2015 $18
           Geelong Pinot Noir 2010 Strong red-purple, showing the first signs of
           development; totally at odds with its low alcohol, with dense and chewy black
           cherry and anise aromas and flavours, plus oak impact on top of the fruit. Where
           now? Screwcap. 12.5% alc. **Rating** 88 **To** 2015 $18

Chaffey Bros Wine Co.   ★★★★☆

26 Campbell Road, Parkside, SA 5063 (postal) **Region** Barossa Valley
T 0417 565 511 **www**.chaffeybros.com **Open** Not
Winemaker Daniel Chaffey Hartwig **Est.** 2008 **Dozens** 10 000
This is a negociant/virtual winery business, co-founded by Daniel Chaffey Hartwig, the fifth generation of the Chaffey family in the Australian wine business. Daniel's great-uncle Bill Chaffey founded Seaview Wines in McLaren Vale, and he in turn was a descendant of the Chaffey brothers who came to Australia to create the Sunraysia and Riverland regions as we know them today by designing and implementing the original irrigation schemes. Daniel, born and raised in the Barossa Valley, picked grapes during school holidays, and later on worked at Penfolds' cellar door. After eight years of selling and helping other people create wine labels, he became a bulk wine merchant dealing both in Australian and overseas wines and wineries. Now Chaffey Bros Wine Co. uses the experience he has gained in developing a range of wines including Cornucopia's Finest, Hero Series, Rivers of Gold, The Killer and the Nosey Parker (the last two exclusive to Dan Murphy). Exports to Canada.

ΨΨΨΨΨ **The Super Barossa Is Shiraz Cabernet Sauvignon 2009** Good crimson-
           purple; despite its relatively modest alcohol, the wine is awash with blackberry,
           blackcurrant and plum fruit on a velvety, richly textured cushion, tannins and
           oak purely incidental to the main game. Eye-catching label. Screwcap. 14.3% alc.
           Rating 94 To 2024 $32

ΨΨΨΨ **This Is Not Your Grandma's Eden Valley Riesling 2010** Bright green-
✪   quartz; a generous offering of lime and lemon fruit with the typical support of
           steely acidity providing balance now and well into the future. Screwcap. 13% alc.
           Rating 92 To 2018 $20

ΨΨΨΨ **The Barossa Is Shiraz 2009** Rating 89 To 2019 $24

Chain of Ponds   ★★★★★

Adelaide Road, Gumeracha, SA 5233 **Region** Adelaide Hills
T (08) 8389 1415 **www**.chainofponds.com.au **Open** Fri–Sun 11–4
Winemaker Greg Clack **Est.** 1993 **Dozens** 35 000
The Chain of Ponds brand has been separated from the now-sold 200ha of vineyards, which were among the largest in the Adelaide Hills. Now owned by Chris Milner, Tony Johnson and Graeme Lowe, it has contract growers throughout the Adelaide Hills for the label, two single vineyard reds from Kangaroo Island, and the Novello wines with a SA appellation. Exports to the UK, the US, Canada, Singapore, Hong Kong, the Philippines and China.

ΨΨΨΨΨ **The Ledge Adelaide Hills Shiraz 2009** Purple-crimson; follows in the footsteps
           of the very good '08; the medium- to full-bodied palate revels in its wanton
           display of licorice, spice, blackberry and dark plum fruit balanced by positive, ripe
           tannins and integrated oak. Screwcap. 14.5% alc. Rating 95 To 2024 $35

First Lady Barrel Fermented Adelaide Hills Sauvignon Blanc 2010
The formidable face of Mary Anne Newman on the neck label is easy to understand given that she had 20 children, one of whom settled in the Chain of Ponds area. None of which is relevant to the quality of this barrel-fermented sauvignon blanc, with its exceptional texture and balance between fruit and oak. Top wine style for almost all food. Screwcap. 13% alc. **Rating** 94 **To** 2014 $30

✪ **Novello Adelaide Hills Semillon Sauvignon Blanc 2011** Quartz-white in Dec '11; has a truly delicious palate of lime, lemongrass, kiwi fruit and passionfruit, the acidity juicy and mouthwatering. A total contrast to First Lady, begging to be drunk right now. Screwcap. 11% alc. **Rating** 94 **To** Now $16

The Amadeus Adelaide Hills Cabernet Sauvignon 2009 Good hue; a medium-bodied cabernet sauvignon (with 4% shiraz) has been well handled; its bouquet is fragrant, and the blackcurrant fruit on the palate has precisely managed oak and tannin support. Screwcap. 14.5% alc. **Rating** 94 **To** 2020 $35

♟♟♟♟♟ **Black Thursday Adelaide Hills Sauvignon Blanc 2011** Quartz-white; aromas
✪ of kiwi fruit and herb lead into a well-balanced palate that brings more fruit into play, with a subtle tropical gloss to the flavour profile and finish. Screwcap. 11.5% alc. **Rating** 91 **To** 2013 $20

Diva Bottle Fermented Adelaide Hills Pinot Noir Chardonnay 2008 Rating 91 **To** 2013 $50

Amelia's Letter Adelaide Hills Pinot Grigio 2011 Rating 90 **To** Now $20

Innocence Adelaide Hills Pinot Noir Rose 2011 Rating 90 **To** 2013 $25

✪ **Grave's Gate Adelaide Hills Shiraz 2009** Good hue; a fresh and lively light- to medium-bodied shiraz with aromatic spice, pepper and red and black small berry/cherry fruits; oak and tannins are in appropriately delicate balance. Screwcap. 14.5% alc. **Rating** 90 **To** 2017 $20

The Cachet Adelaide Cabernet Sauvignon Shiraz Merlot 2007 Rating 90 **To** 2017 $50

✪ **The Stopover Adelaide Hills Barbera 2010** Light colour likely to develop quickly; open fermentation and maturation in older French barriques has produced a light- to medium-bodied, fresh, cherry-flavoured palate finishing with good acidity in place of tannins. Screwcap. 13% alc. **Rating** 90 **To** 2014 $20

♟♟♟♟ **Section 400 Adelaide Hills Pinot Noir 2010 Rating** 89
● **To** 2014 $20
● **Novello Adelaide Hills Rose 2011 Rating** 89 **To** Now $16
● **Novello Adelaide Hills Cabernet Merlot 2010 Rating** 89 **To** 2013 $16

Morning Star Adelaide Hills Pinot Noir 2010 Rating 88 **To** 2014 $50

Diva NV Rating 88 **To** Now $20

Chalice Bridge Estate ★★★★★

796 Rosa Glen Road, Margaret River, WA 6285 **Region** Margaret River
T (08) 9319 8200 **www.**chalicebridge.com.au **Open** By appt
Winemaker Janice McDonald, Bob Cartwright (Consultant) **Est.** 1998 **Dozens** 15 000
Vyds 122ha
Planting of the vineyard (now fully owned by the Edinger family) began in 1998; there are now over 28ha each of cabernet sauvignon and shiraz, 27ha of chardonnay, 12.5ha of semillon, 18ha of sauvignon blanc and 7.5ha of merlot; it is the second-largest single vineyard in Margaret River. Sensible pricing helps, cross-subsidised by the sale of the major part of the annual crop. Exports to the UK, Macau, Hong Kong and China.

♟♟♟♟♟ **The Chalice Limited Release Margaret River Chardonnay 2010** Glowing yellow-green, more developed than many from this vintage; a rich and complex wine with white peach to the fore, grapefruit tucked in close behind; excellent oak handling; very good length and balance. Screwcap. 13.5% alc. **Rating** 95 **To** 2015 $56

The Quest Single Vineyard Margaret River Chardonnay 2010 Similar colour to The Chalice; less complex, but arguably more elegant; fresh grapefruit and nectarine fruit flavours infused with subtle oak; has good length and focus. Screwcap. 14% alc. **Rating** 94 **To** 2017 $26

✪ The Estate Margaret River Cabernet Merlot 2008 Developed colour, consistent with its age; the bouquet is a fragrant offering of red and black fruits plus a waft of oak, the palate following suit with a seductive mix of cherry, cassis, cedary oak and fine tannins. Close on perfect balance given the ripeness of the fruit. Ready now. Screwcap. 14% alc. **Rating** 94 **To** 2015 $20

🍷🍷🍷🍷🍷 **The Chalice Limited Release Margaret River Cabernet Sauvignon 2008 Rating** 92 **To** 2020 $56

Chalk Hill   ★★★★★
56 Field Street, McLaren Vale, SA 5171 **Region** McLaren Vale
T (08) 8323 6400 **www**.chalkhill.com.au **Open** Not
Winemaker Emmanuelle Bekkers **Est.** 1973 **Dozens** 35 000 **Vyds** 120ha
The growth of Chalk Hill has accelerated after passing from parents John and Diana Harvey to grapegrowing sons Jock and Tom. Both are heavily involved in wine industry affairs in varying capacities (Tom was a participant in the second intake of the Wine Industry Future Leaders Program) and the business has strong links with Greening Australia. (Chalk Hill donates 25c for each bottle sold, the highest per-bottle donation in the Australian wine industry.) Further acquisitions mean the vineyards now span each subregion of McLaren Vale, and have been planted to both the exotic (savagnin, vermentino barbera and sangiovese) and the mainstream (shiraz, cabernet sauvignon, grenache, chardonnay and cabernet franc). A new cellar door is planned for 2013. Exports to all major markets; exports to the UK, the US and Canada under the Alpha Crucis label.

🍷🍷🍷🍷🍷 Alpha Crucis McLaren Vale Cabernet Sauvignon 2010 Deep purple-crimson; reaffirms the bond between McLaren Vale and cabernet sauvignon; here blackcurrant fruit, with a subtext of earth and bitter chocolate, has great length, focus and concentration, yet retains elegance. Screwcap. 14% alc. **Rating** 96 **To** 2035 $75

✪ McLaren Vale Shiraz 2010 Deep, dense purple-crimson; the aromatic bouquet of black fruits leads into a bold, full-bodied palate which adds a slice of McLaren Vale dark chocolate and potent, but ripe, tannins. A very good example of full-bodied shiraz for those on vinous bodybuilding exercises. Screwcap. 14.5% alc. **Rating** 94 **To** 2030 $22

⬤ Sidetrack 2010 **Rating** 94 **To** 2020 $19

🍷🍷🍷🍷🍷 **McLaren Vale Cabernet Sauvignon 2010 Rating** 92 **To** 2025 $22
McLaren Vale Barbera 2010 Rating 92 **To** 2015 $28
⬤ **The Procrastinator 2010 Rating** 91 **To** 2018 $19

🍷🍷🍷🍷 **McLaren Vale Sangiovese 2010 Rating** 89 **To** 2018 $22
McLaren Vale Vermentino 2011 Rating 87 **To** 2014 $18
Moscato 2011 Rating 87 **To** Now $18

Chalkers Crossing   ★★★★★
285 Grenfell Road, Young, NSW 2594 **Region** Hilltops
T (02) 6382 6900 **www**.chalkerscrossing.com.au **Open** Mon–Fri 9–5
Winemaker Celine Rousseau **Est.** 2000 **Dozens** 7000 **Vyds** 10ha
Owned and operated by Ted and Wendy Ambler, Chalkers Crossing's Rockleigh Vineyard was planted in 1997–98. It also purchases grapes from Tumbarumba and Gundagai. Winemaker Celine Rousseau was born in France's Loire Valley, trained in Bordeaux and has worked in Bordeaux, Champagne, Languedoc, Margaret River and the Perth Hills. This Flying Winemaker (now an Australian citizen) has exceptional skills and dedication. Exports to the UK, Canada, Germany, Denmark, Sweden, Singapore, China and Hong Kong.

ŶŶŶŶŶ **Tumbarumba Chardonnay 2010** Light, bright straw-green; French oak barrel-
✪ fermented and kept on lees for 12 months, the wine is a handsome demonstration
of Celine Rousseau's skills. The grapes were harvested at precisely the right time,
the flavours offering both grapefruit and white peach, the oak contributing both
to texture and flavour. Screwcap. 13.5% alc. **Rating** 94 **To** 2017 $22
Hilltops Cabernet Sauvignon 2010 Red-purple of medium depth; an elegant
and complex wine that shows the characters gained by finishing the fermentation
in oak (American and French); it has very good cassis and briar flavours, the
tannins soft and lingering. Its balance should ensure a long life. Screwcap. 14% alc.
Rating 94 **To** 2020 $30

ŶŶŶŶŶ **Hilltops Shiraz 2010 Rating** 91 **To** 2020 $30

ŶŶŶŶ **Hilltops Riesling 2011 Rating** 87 **To** 2015 $18

Chalmers ★★★☆

PO Box 2263, Mildura, Vic 3502 **Region** Murray Darling/Heathcote
T 0400 261 932 **www.**chalmerswine.com.au **Open** Not
Winemaker Sandro Mosele (Contract) **Est.** 1989 **Dozens** 4000 **Vyds** 19ha
Following the March 2008 sale of their very large vineyard and vine nursery propagation
business, Bruce and Jenny Chalmers have established twin wine businesses, both commenced
in '08. They have an 80ha property on the Mt Camel Range at Colbinabbin, with the
wines released under the Montevecchio label: Bianco is a co-fermented field blend made
from vermentino, fiano and a splash of moscato giallo; Rosso is a co-fermented field blend
of shiraz, lagrein, nero d'Avola and sagrantino; Moscato is made from 100% moscato giallo.
The second property is a 10ha vineyard at Merbein, just outside Mildura, with commercial
blocks of vermentino, sagrantino and nero d'Avola. The fourth block contains every single
clone and variety Chalmers imported over its decades-long involvement in the industry. With
a couple of additional direct imports, micro-vinification will see wines made from varieties
never previously made in Australia. The plans are to make the wines onsite, with minimal
winemaking intervention, and make exclusive releases, some as small as 20 or 50 litres. Exports
to the UK and Denmark.

ŶŶŶŶŶ **Montevecchio Bianco 2011** A blend of vermentino, fiano and moscato giallo;
whether the total is greater than the sum of the parts I have no idea, but there are
some interesting flavours here, including spiced baked apple. For the wine nerds,
for sure. Screwcap. 12.5% alc. **Rating** 90 **To** Now $23

ŶŶŶŶ **Heathcote Rosato 2011 Rating** 89 **To** Now $22
Montevecchio Rosso 2011 Rating 89 **To** Now $23
Aglianico 2009 Rating 89 **To** 2014 $32
Nero d'Avola 2011 Rating 88 **To** 2013 $29
Montevecchio Heathcote Moscato 2011 Rating 87 **To** Now $21

Chambers Rosewood ★★★★★

Barkly Street, Rutherglen, Vic 3685 **Region** Rutherglen
T (02) 6032 8641 **www.**chambersrosewood.com.au **Open** Mon–Sat 9–5, Sun 10–5
Winemaker Stephen Chambers **Est.** 1858 **Dozens** 10 000 **Vyds** 50ha
Chambers' Rare Muscat and Rare Muscadelle (or Topaque or Tokay, what's in a name?) are the
greatest of all in the Rutherglen firmament, the other wines in the hierarchy also magnificent.
Stephen Chambers comes into the role as winemaker, the sixth generation of the Chambers
family. Exports to the UK, the US, Belgium, Sweden and NZ.

ŶŶŶŶŶ **Rare Rutherglen Muscadelle NV** Deep, dark burnt umber, with an olive
rim; exceedingly complex, and contains some very old material contributing
to the rancio characters. Adheres to the sides of the glass as you swirl it, but,
notwithstanding its concentration, the innumerable flavours come together on a
very long, yet effortless, finish. 375ml. Screwcap. 18% alc. **Rating** 98 **To** 2013 $250

Grand Rutherglen Muscat NV Has moved well into the brown spectrum, with olive starting to appear on the rim; here the raisin fruit has concentrated and developed strong Christmas pudding, liqueured plum, and Asian spices, wrapped up in a viscous drum roll of flavour. 375ml. Screwcap. 18% alc. **Rating** 96 **To** 2013 $60

Grand Rutherglen Special Muscadelle NV Mahogany, with olive rim; intense tea leaf, toffee, fish oil and coffee varietal character, the flavours blazing in the mouth. Chambers' Grand is almost anyone else's Rare; 375ml. Cork. 18% alc. **Rating** 96 **To** Now $100

Old Vine Rutherglen Muscadelle NV Chambers has chosen to use the grape varietal name, rather than Topaque (the approved substitute for the incorrect 'Tokay'). Bright golden-brown; the wine is, as expected, very complex, with a mix of vanilla, tea, spice, mocha and toffee characters; part of the secret of the wine is the perfectly balanced finish. 375ml. Screwcap. 18.5% alc. **Rating** 96 **To** 2013 $60

✪ **Classic Rutherglen Muscat NV** Is old enough to have lost any red hues, but is still fresh and youthful, with raisins and warm spices illuminating the bouquet and palate alike. It is one of those wines that is so well balanced and inviting, you might well regret the following morning how much you drank the night before. 375ml. Screwcap. 18% alc. **Rating** 94 **To** 2013 $20

🍷🍷🍷🍷½ ✪ **Rutherglen Botrytis Muscadelle 2011** Golden yellow; a very attractive, very well made wine; luscious yellow fruit is balanced by acidity and the botrytis cut; good length. 375ml Screwcap. 11.3% alc. **Rating** 91 **To** 2015 $18

🍷🍷🍷🍷 **American Oak Shiraz 2007 Rating** 87 **To** 2015 $15

Chanters Ridge ★★★★☆

440 Chanters Lane, Tylden, Vic 3444 **Region** Macedon Ranges
T 0427 511 341 **www**.chantersridge.com.au **Open** W'ends 10–4 and by appt
Winemaker Hanging Rock Winery **Est.** 1995 **Dozens** 300 **Vyds** 2ha

Orthopaedic surgeon Barry Elliott, as well as running the surgery unit at Melbourne's Alfred Hospital, has became involved with the Kyneton Hospital. He and his wife acquired the 24ha property without any clear idea of what they might do with it; later his lifelong interest in wine steered him towards the idea of establishing a vineyard. He retained John Ellis as his consultant, and this led to the planting of pinot noir, and the first tiny make in 2000.

🍷🍷🍷🍷🍷 **Macedon Vintage Sparkling Pinot Noir 2004** Produced from estate-grown pinot noir, aged on lees for over two years prior to being tiraged in Dec '05, and disgorged almost six years later, in Sept '11. Light green-gold, it has fine, persistent mousse, the length and balance of the elegant palate excellent. Very well priced for a wine of this provenance and age. Diam. 12.5% alc. **Rating** 94 **To** 2014 $35

🍷🍷🍷🍷½ **Macedon Ranges Pinot Noir 2008 Rating** 93 **To** 2015 $30
Macedon Pinot Noir Chardonnay NV Rating 91 **To** 2014 $30
Macedon Ranges Pinot Noir 2007 Rating 90 **To** 2014 $30

🍷🍷🍷🍷 ✪ **Macedon Sparkling Red Pinot Noir NV** Produced from several vintages of estate-grown pinot noir, blended and tiraged in Feb '07, disgorged in Oct '10. The colour is red, not pink, albeit with some development; red cherry and plum pinot flavours run into some tannins on the finish not covered by sweetness; find suitable food. Diam. 13.5% alc. **Rating** 89 **To** 2014 $20

Chapel Hill ★★★★★

1 Chapel Hill Road, McLaren Vale, SA 5171 **Region** McLaren Vale
T (08) 8323 8429 **www**.chapelhillwine.com.au **Open** 7 days 11–5
Winemaker Michael Fragos, Bryn Richards **Est.** 1979 **Dozens** 50 000 **Vyds** 44ha

A leading medium-sized winery in the region. In 2000 Chapel Hill was sold to the Swiss Thomas Schmidheiny group, which owns the respected Cuvaison winery in California as well as vineyards in Switzerland and Argentina. Wine quality is as good as, if not better, than ever. Winemaker Michael Fragos was named Winemaker of the Year at London's International Wine & Spirit Competition '08. The production comes from the estate plantings of shiraz, cabernet sauvignon, chardonnay, verdelho, savagnin, sangiovese and merlot, together with purchased grapes from McLaren Vale. Exports to all other major markets.

ŸŸŸŸŸ The Chosen House Block McLaren Vale Shiraz 2010 Deep magenta; the bouquet offers an elegant array of red and black fruits, nestled alongside violets and licorice; the palate is medium-bodied and finely detailed, with fine-grained tannins, lacy fruit and a long and expansive, harmonious finish. At the elegant end of the McLaren Vale spectrum. Screwcap. 14% alc. **Rating** 95 **To** 2030 $55 BE
The Vicar McLaren Vale Shiraz 2010 Impenetrable colour, dark and brooding in character with concentrated black fruits, spice and toasty oak all playing a major role on the bouquet; the palate is densely packed with absolutely everything but the kitchen sink, yet manages to relay a sense of lightness on the finish; an essay in contained power. Screwcap. 14.5% alc. **Rating** 95 **To** 2035 $75 BE
McLaren Vale Shiraz 2010 Dark colour, with a densely packed bouquet of black fruits, bitter chocolate, fruitcake and blackberry all in balance with well-handled oak; the palate is concentrated and fresh, medium-bodied and generous; approachable as a young wine, with plenty of time in the tank. Screwcap. 14.5% alc. **Rating** 94 **To** 2025 $32 BE
Road Block McLaren Vale Shiraz 2010 This is a dense, dark, brooding and inky black wine, full of bitter chocolate, licorice, tar and black fruits; big, rugged and muscular in structure, with firm chewy tannins a prominent character; this has been constructed to go the distance and to have a commanding presence in every respect. Screwcap. 14% alc. **Rating** 94 **To** 2030 $55 BE

ŸŸŸŸŸ Il Vescovo McLaren Vale Sangiovese Rose 2011 **Rating** 93 **To** 2013 $22
✪ The Vicar McLaren Vale Shiraz 2009 **Rating** 93 **To** 2034 $75
Bush Vine McLaren Vale Grenache 2010 **Rating** 92 **To** 2016 $35
Il Vescovo McLaren Vale Sangiovese 2010 **Rating** 91 **To** 2017 $25
◐ Il Vescovo Adelaide Hills Tempranillo 2010 **Rating** 91 **To** 2014 $20
Gorge Block McLaren Vale Chardonnay 2010 **Rating** 90 **To** 2015 $25
McLaren Vale Cabernet Sauvignon 2010 **Rating** 90 **To** 2020 $32 BE
McLaren Vale Mourvedre 2010 **Rating** 90 **To** 2020 $35

ŸŸŸŸ The Chosen Gorge Block McLaren Vale Cabernet Sauvignon 2010 **Rating** 89 **To** 2016 $55 BE
✪ McLaren Vale Adelaide Hills Chardonnay 2011 **Rating** 89 **To** 2014 $16
✪ McLaren Vale Verdelho 2011 **Rating** 89 **To** Now $16
il Vescovo McLaren Vale White 2011 **Rating** 88 **To** 2013 $22

Chapman Grove Wines ★★★★★

PO Box 1460, Margaret River, WA 6285 **Region** Margaret River
T (08) 9364 3885 **www**.chapmangrove.com.au **Open** Not
Winemaker Bruce Dukes (Contract) **Est.** 2005 **Dozens** 10 000 **Vyds** 32ha
A very successful venture under the control of managing director Ron Fraser. The contract-made wines come from the extensive estate vineyards planted to chardonnay, semillon, sauvignon blanc, shiraz, cabernet sauvignon and merlot. The wines are released in three price ranges: at the bottom end, the Dreaming Dog red varietals and blends; in the middle, the standard Chapman Grove range; and, at the top, ultra-premium wines under the Atticus label. Exports to Canada, Hong Kong, Singapore, Taiwan and China.

ŸŸŸŸŸ Atticus Margaret River Chardonnay 2010 Vibrant green hue; nectarine, grapefruit and lots of attractive oak from judicious oak handling; the zesty acidity provides a lively palate that is direct and long, powerful and precise; a complex and heady blend of power and finesse the west is becoming famous for. Screwcap. 13.8% alc. **Rating** 95 **To** 2018 $60 BE

✪   **Margaret River Sauvignon Blanc 2011** Light straw-green; Margaret River seemingly effortlessly provides sauvignon blanc with a perfect balance between ripe/tropical fruit on the one hand and refreshing citrussy acidity on the other. This wine is in the latter camp, notable for its extreme length. Screwcap. 12.8% alc. **Rating** 94 **To** 2014 $20

    Atticus Wood Aged La Croyance Sauvignon Blanc Semillon 2010 The judicious use of oak has added complexity to the fresh and fragrant nature of the variety; the palate is lively and direct, with only a little toastiness lingering on the very long and complex finish. Screwcap. 12.8% alc. **Rating** 94 **To** 2018 $60 BE

✪   **Reserve Margaret River Chardonnay 2010** Glowing green-yellow; this is a complete chardonnay: stone fruit, some citrus, cashew, and great length thanks to balanced acidity. Screwcap. 13.6% alc. **Rating** 94 **To** 2018 $25

🍷🍷🍷🍷🍷   **Reserve Margaret River Shiraz 2010 Rating** 93 **To** 2020 $25

    Atticus Margaret River Shiraz 2010 Rating 91 **To** 2018 $60 BE

✪   **Dreaming Dog Margaret River Classic Red 2010** A blend of merlot and cabernet sauvignon, the colour clear light crimson; has delicious, albeit light-bodied, cassis and redcurrant aromas and fruit flavours, neither oak nor tannins making a contribution, thus enhancing the drinkability of the wine. Screwcap. 13.5% alc. **Rating** 91 **To** 2014 $15

    Atticus Margaret River Cabernet Sauvignon 2010 Rating 90 **To** 2016 $60 BE

🍷🍷🍷🍷   **Margaret River Cabernet Merlot 2010 Rating** 89 **To** 2019 $20

○   **Dreaming Dog Margaret River Classic White 2011 Rating** 89 **To** 2013 $15

Charles Cimicky   ★★★★★

Gomersal Road, Lyndoch, SA 5351 **Region** Barossa Valley
T (08) 8524 4025 **Open** Tues–Sat 10.30–4.30
Winemaker Charles Cimicky **Est.** 1972 **Dozens** 15 000 **Vyds** 24.5ha
These wines are of very good quality, thanks to the sophisticated use of good oak in tandem with high-quality grapes. Historically, Cimicky was happy to keep an ultra-low profile, but has relented sufficiently to send some (very impressive) wines. Exports to the US, Switzerland, Canada, Finland, China, Malaysia and Hong Kong.

🍷🍷🍷🍷🍷   **The Autograph Barossa Valley Shiraz 2009** Dense, opaque colour; the bouquet and palate live up to the colour, but it is not over-extracted, and has very good balance between its abundant black fruits, oak and tannins; there is a very attractive earthy/savoury character to the palate that positively adds to the wine. Cork. 14.5% alc. **Rating** 95 **To** 2030 $40

✪   **Trumps Barossa Valley Shiraz 2009** Strong crimson-purple; a rich and complex wine, with plush plum, dark chocolate and blackberry fruit, positive oak, and a swathe of ripe tannins rounding up the finish. Screwcap. 14.5% alc. **Rating** 94 **To** 2024 $18

Charles Melton   ★★★★★

Krondorf Road, Tanunda, SA 5352 **Region** Barossa Valley
T (08) 8563 3606 **www.**charlesmeltonwines.com.au **Open** 7 days 11–5
Winemaker Charlie Melton **Est.** 1984 **Dozens** 15 000 **Vyds** 31ha
Charlie Melton, one of the Barossa Valley's great characters, with wife Virginia by his side, makes some of the most eagerly sought a la mode wines in Australia. Inevitably, the Melton empire has continued to grow in response to the insatiable demand. There are now 7ha at Lyndoch, 9ha at Krondorf and 1.6ha at Light Pass, the lion's share shiraz and grenache, and a small planting of cabernet sauvignon. An additional 30ha property was purchased in High Eden, with 10ha of shiraz planted in 2009, and a 5ha field planting of grenache, shiraz, mataro, carignan, cinsaut, picpoul and bourboulenc planted in '10. The expanded volume has had no adverse effect on the wonderfully rich, sweet and well-made wines. The original Krondorf village church (circa 1864) has been acquired and converted to guest accommodation. Exports to all major markets.

♟♟♟♟♟ Richelieu 2009 Pure dark fruits abound in the bouquet, with an intriguing Provençal herb complexity, offset by ironstone minerality; long, luscious, pure and poised, and given the 26 months in French oak barriques, a massive departure from traditional Barossa grenache. Screwcap. 14% alc. **Rating** 95 **To** 2020 $70 BE

✪ **Barossa Valley Rose of Virginia 2011** Vivid puce; after a brief period of skin contact before pressing, the free-run juice was cold-fermented for six weeks and has svelte sweet fruit (not sugar-sweet) flavours that provide great mouthfeel, length and balance. Food style; forget the '11 demons. Screwcap. 12.5% alc. **Rating** 94 **To** 2013 $24

Voices of Angels Shiraz 2009 A classic bouquet of fruitcake spice, blackberry, liqueur-soaked fruits and chocolate; the palate has ample levels of sweet fruits, generous in every regard, with fine tannins and a long fleshy finish. Screwcap. 14% alc. **Rating** 94 **To** 2020 $70 BE

Nine Popes 2009 The bouquet offers a hedonistic blend of sweet red and black fruits, liqueur-soaked plums, licorice and bramble; the palate is sweet-fruited and certainly warm, with a long and succulent finish. Shiraz/Grenache. Screwcap. 14.5% alc. **Rating** 94 **To** 2015 $70 BE

Charles Sturt University Winery   ★★★★☆

McKeown Drive, Wagga Wagga, NSW 2650 **Region** Big Rivers Zone
T (02) 6933 2435 **www.**csu.edu.au/winery **Open** Mon–Fri 11–5, w'ends 11–4
Winemaker Andrew Drumm **Est.** 1977 **Dozens** 12 000 **Vyds** 25.1ha
A new $2.5 million commercial winery was opened in 2002, complementing the $1 million experimental winery opened in '01. The commercial winery was funded through the sale of wines produced under the CSU brand, which always offer exceptional value. Following the University's acquisition of the former University of Sydney campus in Orange (Leeds Parade, open Fri-Sun 11–4 or by appt), it now has 7.1ha of estate plantings at Wagga Wagga and 18ha of mature vineyards at Orange, the latter planted to chardonnay, sauvignon blanc, shiraz, cabernet sauvignon and merlot. Interestingly, this teaching facility is using screwcaps for all its wines, white and red, recalling its pioneering use in 1977. Moreover, since 2005 its sparkling wines have been released under crown seal.

♟♟♟♟♟ Cellar Reserve Tumbarumba Chardonnay 2010 Bright, pale green-gold; a wine reflecting the high quality of the Tumbarumba chardonnay in the '10 vintage and astute winemaking; the flavours are at a midpoint between citrus and stone fruit, and barrel fermentation in large oak has added both texture and subtle flavour to a high-quality wine. Screwcap. 13.5% alc. **Rating** 95 **To** 2017 $28

♟♟♟♟♟ R Rose 2011 The grapes for this wine come from Tumbarumba; clear, light pink,
✪ its fresh palate is replete with flavours of strawberry and red cherry; the finish is dry, the balance good. Screwcap. 10.6% alc. **Rating** 90 **To** 2013 $20

♟♟♟♟ **Orange Chardonnay 2011 Rating** 89
✪ **To** 2014 $15
✪ **Gundagai Shiraz 2010 Rating** 89 **To** 2016 $15
T Tempranillo 2010 Rating 88 **To** 2014 $20
NV Sparkling NV Rating 87 **To** 2013 $20
Cellar Reserve Sparkling Red NV Rating 87 **To** 2013 $28

Charlotte Plains   ★★★

RMB 3180 Dooleys Road, Maryborough, Vic 3465 **Region** Bendigo
T (03) 5361 3137 **Open** By appt
Winemaker Graeme Jukes **Est.** 1990 **Dozens** 100 **Vyds** 0.3ha
Charlotte Plains is a classic example of miniaturism: Ian Kemp has 0.3ha of ultra close-planted shiraz, at a density of almost 5000 perha. The minuscule production is sold solely via the cellar door, mailing list (and by phone).

♟♟♟♟ **Maryborough Sparkling Shiraz 2010** A well-balanced wine, with the dosage kept appropriately low; the base wine, too, was of good quality, with spicy black fruits and just the right amount of tannins. Diam. 13% alc. **Rating** 88 **To** 2014 $25

Chartley Estate   ★★★☆

38 Blackwood Hills Road, Rowella, Tas 7270 **Region** Northern Tasmania
T (03) 6394 7198 **www**.chartleyestatevineyard.com.au **Open** Not
Winemaker Winemaking Tasmania (Julian Alcorso) **Est.** 2000 **Dozens** 1250
The Kossman family began the establishment of 2ha each of pinot gris, sauvignon blanc and
pinot noir, and 1ha of riesling in 2000. Although the vines are still relatively young, some
attractive wines from each variety have been made. Exports to Taiwan.

ŢŢŢŢŢ **Riesling 2011** Bright green-yellow; both the bouquet and palate have focus,
intensity, grip and great length; finishes with a lingering aftertaste. Silver Tas Wine
Show '12. Screwcap. 12% alc. **Rating** 92 **To** 2021 $22

ŢŢŢŢ **Pinot Gris 2011 Rating** 89 **To** 2013 $23
Off Dry Riesling 2011 Rating 87 **To** 2016 $22

Chateau Dorrien   ★★★☆

Cnr Seppeltsfield Road/Barossa Valley Way, Dorrien, SA 5352 **Region** Barossa Valley
T (08) 8562 2850 **www**.chateaudorrien.com.au **Open** 7 days 10–5
Winemaker Ramon Martin **Est.** 1985 **Dozens** 20 000 **Vyds** 28ha
The Martin family, headed by Fernando and Jeanette, purchased the old Dorrien winery from
the Seppelt family in 1984; in '90 the family purchased Twin Valley Estate and moved the
winemaking operations of Chateau Dorrien to the Twin Valley site. All the Chateau Dorrien
group wines are sold at Chateau Dorrien; Twin Valley is simply a production facility. In 2006
the family purchased a 32ha property at Myponga, with mature vineyards that now provide
the grapes for San Fernando Estate, the new name of the vineyard.

ŢŢŢŢŢ **Barossa Valley Shiraz 2008** Excellent crimson-purple; full to the brim with
✪   character, albeit in the full-bodied mode of most of the '08s; the bouquet is very
good, heralding the spiced, ripe plum fruit and licorice flavours of the palate. The
only question is the alcohol, but it has to be accepted as an integral part of the
style. Diam. 14.8% alc. **Rating** 93 **To** 2023 $28
Barossa Valley Cabernet Sauvignon 2010 Good colour; the wine lives up to
the claim that Chateau Dorrien has found some cool-climate sites in the Barossa
Valley, for it does have some savoury black olive adjuncts to its blackcurrant fruit;
French oak also plays a role. Screwcap. 14.5% alc. **Rating** 90 **To** 2018 $25

ŢŢŢŢ **San Fernando Estate Cross Winds Merlot 2010 Rating** 88 **To** 2015 $15

Chateau Francois   ★★★★★

Broke Road, Pokolbin, NSW 2321 **Region** Hunter Valley
T (02) 4998 7548 **F** (02) 4998 7805 **Open** W'ends 9–5, or by appt
Winemaker Don Francois **Est.** 1969 **Dozens** 200
I have known former NSW Director of Fisheries Dr Don Francois for almost as long as I
have been involved with wine, which is a very long time indeed. I remember his early
fermentations of sundry substances other than grapes (none of which, I hasten to add, was
the least bit illegal) in the copper bowl of an antiquated washing machine in his laundry.
He established Chateau Francois one year before Brokenwood, and our winemaking and
fishing paths have crossed many times since. Some years ago Don suffered a mild stroke, and
no longer speaks or writes with any fluency, but this has not stopped him from producing a
range of absolutely beautiful semillons that flourish marvellously with age. I should add that
he is even prouder of the distinguished career of his daughter, Rachel Francois, at the NSW
bar. The semillon vines are now over 40 years old, producing exceptional wine that is sold for
the proverbial song year after year. Five-star value.

ŢŢŢŢŢ **Pokolbin Semillon 2005** Pale, bright green-straw; beautiful in its youth, this
✪   Peter Pan has retained that beauty, and built on the flavour, adding an extra layer
of lemon citrus, still balanced by perfect acidity. If there is a better value wine in
Australia, I am yet to taste it. Screwcap. 11% alc. **Rating** 96 **To** 2025 $14

✪   **Pokolbin Shiraz 2009** Excellent hue and clarity; an extremely well-made shiraz that perfectly showcases the excellent vintage, the varietal expression of the blackberry and plum fruits, and its place of origin. An absurdly low price. Screwcap. 12.5% alc. **Rating** 94 **To** 2029 $14

♟♟♟♟♟ **Pokolbin Semillon 2010** Bright straw-green; yet another in an unbroken
✪   stream of high-quality semillons from Don Francois at a ridiculously low price, unchanged for many years. This wine has a touch more body than some, and may be at its best inside five years. Screwcap. 11% alc. **Rating** 93 **To** 2017 $14

Chateau Pâto   ★★★★★

67 Thompsons Road, Pokolbin, NSW 2321 **Region** Hunter Valley
T (02) 4998 7634 **F** (02) 4998 7860 **Open** By appt
Winemaker Nicholas Paterson **Est.** 1980 **Dozens** 500 **Vyds** 2.5ha
Nicholas Paterson took over responsibility for this tiny winery following the death of father David during the 1993 vintage. The lion's share of plantings is shiraz (the first plantings), with smaller blocks of chardonnay, marsanne, roussanne, viognier and mourvedre; most of the grapes are sold, with a tiny quantity of shiraz being made into a marvellous wine. David's legacy is being handsomely guarded.

♟♟♟♟♟ **Hunter Wine Country Old Pokolbin Vineyard Shiraz 2009** Medium red-purple; the complex, fragrant bouquet has black cherry and hints of sage, the intense palate with multiple layers of flavour building further on the bouquet; line, length and balance are impeccable. This is a remarkable wine. Screwcap. 13.9% alc. **Rating** 96 **To** 2040 $35
Hunter Wine Country DJP Shiraz 2010 Full, clear red-purple; from vines planted 30 years ago by the long-departed DJ Paterson. The mantle of winemaker has fallen on son Nicholas, who has established an enviable reputation for this wine, with its plum and blackberry fruits, superfine, persistent tannins and integrated oak. Screwcap. 13.7% alc. **Rating** 95 **To** 2025 $50

Chateau Tanunda   ★★★★★

9 Basedow Road, Tanunda, SA 5352 **Region** Barossa Valley
T (08) 8563 3888 **www.**chateautanunda.com **Open** 7 days 10–5
Winemaker Stuart Bourne **Est.** 1890 **Dozens** 50 000 **Vyds** 95ha
This is one of the most historically significant winery buildings in the Barossa Valley, built from bluestone quarried at nearby Bethany in the late 1880s. It has been restored by the Geber family and a new basket-press winery has been installed. Chateau Tanunda owns almost 100ha of vineyards in Bethany, Eden Valley, Tanunda and Vine Vale, with additional fruit sourced from a group of 30 growers, including descendants of the Barossa's original settlers, covering the panoply of Barossan subregions. The wines are made from hand-picked grapes, basket-pressed, and are neither fined nor filtered. There is an emphasis on single vineyard and single-subregion wines under the Terroirs of the Barossa label. The grand building houses the cellar door and Barossa Small Winemakers Centre, offering wines made by boutique winemakers. The Chateau hosts conferences, conventions and weddings, catering for groups of up to 500, and there is a competition-standard croquet lawn. The acclaimed charity Masters Cricket match played biennially on the CCG (Chateau Cricket Ground) sees many of the world's greats grace its pitch. Exports to the UK, Germany, Switzerland, Sweden, Denmark, Belgium and China.

♟♟♟♟♟ **The Everest Old Bushvine Grenache 2009** Good colour; it would seem that only one barrique was made of this wine, and I have to admit this is an exceptional Barossa Valley grenache, with real depth to the flavour, the red fruits having swallowed up the oak, having spent 20 months in the barrique on lees. The points awarded also reflect the degree of difficulty inherent in achieving this result. Cork. 15% alc. **Rating** 96 **To** 2025 $195

The Chateau Single Vineyard Shiraz 2010 Impenetrable colour; this is dark and dense Barossa Shiraz with fruitcake spice, black fruits and a tarry aspect that provides complexity and interest; long, warm and with ample chewy tannins, tailor-made for lovers of rich wines. Diam. 14.5% alc. **Rating** 95 **To** 2025 $28 BE
Terroirs of the Barossa Ebenezer District Shiraz 2010 The wine was neither fined nor filtered (a badge of honour) and is faintly turbid, although the colour is deep; all of the usual feel-good techniques are elaborated on the back label; it has almost frightening power, with a fireworks display of black fruits, licorice, spice and oak; improbable though it may seem, the wine is very well balanced and will richly repay cellaring; keep under lock and key for the next five years at least. Cork. 14% alc. **Rating** 95 **To** 2035 $48
Terroirs of the Barossa Greenock Shiraz 2010 Deep, dense crimson-purple; made in the same way as all three wines in the Terroirs of the Barossa series, given 18 months in a mix of new and used American and French oak. The higher alcohol does introduce another level of flavours and focus, and, as long as the wine has been given a reasonable period to mature and is drunk with food, it should suit those who like long-lived, full-bodied shiraz. Cork. 15% alc. **Rating** 95 **To** 2035 $48
The Chateau 100 Year Old Vines Shiraz 2009 Comes from three vineyards in the Eden Valley, Marananga and Vine Vale areas of the Barossa, and given Rolls Royce treatment in the winery; the smooth and supple palate is no more than medium-bodied, but is beautifully balanced and structured; black fruits, mocha, fruitcake, spice and licorice are all woven into the whole, French oak also adding a touch of class. Cork. 14.5% alc. **Rating** 95 **To** 2029 $145
The Everest The Chateau Cru Barossa Shiraz 2009 Neither fined nor filtered, with some impact on the brightness of the colour; it is the best wine of the vintage, and the vintage itself has to be 'truly exceptional'. Some would question whether '09 could be thus regarded, but this is certainly a wine full of power, character and flavour, the last coming in part from 22 months in new French and American oak; there are interesting changes in flavour as the wine moves across the palate, from black fruits to red to spicy/savoury nuances. Dauntingly complex, and I would love to see it in 10 years. Cork. 14.5% alc. **Rating** 95 **To** 2030 $195
Terroirs of the Barossa Lyndoch Shiraz 2010 **Rating** 94 **To** 2030 $48

ΨΨΨΨΨ **Barossa Tower Shiraz 2010** Red-purple; a junior brother to the single area
✪ shiraz range of Chateau Tanunda Terroirs of the Barossa, the same routine of 18 months' maturation in new and used French and American oak; medium-bodied, rather than full-bodied, arguably it's the best value of all of the Chateau Tanunda red wines. Screwcap. 14.5% alc. **Rating** 92 **To** 2025 $18
The Chateau Eden Valley Riesling 2011 **Rating** 91 **To** 2021 $20
✪ Grand Barossa Shiraz 2009 A true medium-bodied Barossa shiraz, with red fruits, fruitcake spice and a trail of warmth that is typical of the region; fresh focused, and holds its 14.5% alc. with aplomb. Diam. **Rating** 91 **To** 2018 $20 BE
The Chateau Barossa Cabernet Sauvignon 2009 **Rating** 91 **To** 2019 $28
Old Vine Barossa Shiraz 2010 **Rating** 90 **To** 2023 $24
The Old Cooperage Barossa Shiraz Mataro 2010 **Rating** 90 **To** 2014 $24
✪ Barossa Tower Shiraz Primitivo 2009 Bright colour; an intriguing blend, showing fresh blackberry aromas and sweet confiture generosity blending together; the palate is vibrant and medium-bodied, with generosity and sweet fruit the driving factor on the finish. Screwcap. 14.5% alc. **Rating** 90 **To** 2014 $18 BE
The Three Graces Barossa Cabernet Sauvignon Cabernet Franc Merlot 2009 **Rating** 90 **To** 2015 $28 BE

Chatsfield   ★★★★☆
O'Neil Road, Mount Barker, WA 6324 **Region** Mount Barker
T (08) 9851 1704 **www.chatsfield.com.au Open** By appt
Winemaker Mt Shadforth Contract Crush **Est.** 1976 **Dozens** 3500 **Vyds** 19ha
Irish-born medical practitioner Ken Lynch can be proud of his achievements at Chatsfield, as can the various contract winemakers, who have taken the high-quality estate-grown material

and made some impressive wines, notably the Riesling and spicy, licorice Shiraz. Exports to the UK and Singapore.

ŸŸŸŸŸ **Mount Barker Shiraz 2010** Bright crimson-purple; a delicious, medium-bodied
✪ shiraz overflowing with regional character built around black cherry, warm spices and a touch of smoked meat. The palate has excellent length, the finish inviting the second glass. Screwcap. 13.3% alc. **Rating** 95 **To** 2025 $24

ŸŸŸŸŸ **Mount Barker Sauvignon Blanc 2011** The warm vintage in the west was in
✪ stark contrast to that of the east of the continent, and it's no surprise to find the wine absolutely overflowing with every form of tropical fruit you care to name; on the other hand, it has crisp acidity to lengthen and tighten the finish. Great bargain. Screwcap. 13% alc. **Rating** 93 **To** 2013 $18
Mount Barker Riesling 2011 Rating 90 **To** 2015 $22
Mount Barker Cabernet Merlot 2009 Rating 90 **To** 2016 $22

ŸŸŸŸ **Mount Barker Rose 2011 Rating** 89
✪ **To** 2013 $16

Cherry Tree Hill   ★★★☆
Hume Highway, Sutton Forest, NSW 2577 **Region** Southern Highlands
T (02) 8217 1409 **www.**cherrytreehill.com.au **Open** 7 days 9–5
Winemaker Anton Balog (Contract) **Est.** 2000 **Dozens** 4000 **Vyds** 13.5ha
The Lorentz family, then headed by Gabi Lorentz, began the establishment of the Cherry Tree Hill vineyard in 2000 with the planting of 3ha each of cabernet sauvignon and riesling; 3ha each of merlot and sauvignon blanc followed in '01, and, finally, 2ha of chardonnay in '02. The inspiration was childhood trips on a horse and cart through his grandfather's vineyard in Hungary, and Gabi's son (and current owner) David completes the three-generation involvement as manager of the business.

ŸŸŸŸŸ **Sauvignon Blanc 2011** The wine has been well made, with partial barrel
✪ fermentation adding both flavour and texture, but not diminishing the gently tropical varietal fruit flavour. Screwcap. 12% alc. **Rating** 91 **To** 2013 $20

ŸŸŸŸ **Chardonnay 2011 Rating** 89 **To** 2015 $20
Riesling 2011 Rating 88 **To** 2014 $20

Chestnut Grove   ★★★★★
Chestnut Grove Road, Manjimup, WA 6258 **Region** Manjimup
T (08) 9722 4255 **www.**chestnutgrove.com.au **Open** Mon–Sat 10–4
Winemaker David Dowden **Est.** 1988 **Dozens** 15 000 **Vyds** 40ha
A substantial vineyard that commenced in 1987, with an onsite winery constructed in '98, Chestnut Grove has come full circle from founder Vic Kordic and sons Paul and Mark, to Australian Wine Holdings in 2002, and back to the Kordics in '09 under the umbrella of Manjimup Wine Enterprises Pty Ltd. Mark is general manager of the wine business, the cellar door has reopened and Chestnut Grove has resumed exports, currently to the US and Canada.

ŸŸŸŸŸ **Manjimup Pinot Noir 2010** Strong colour; warm (in the best sense) red and
✪ black cherry aromas expand further on the palate, with spice and forest floor notes adding to the complexity, but not diminishing the juicy fruit core of the wine. Fantastic bargain. Screwcap. 13.5% alc. **Rating** 94 **To** 2016 $20
Reserve Manjimup Merlot 2010 Medium purple-crimson; Chestnut Grove has always had the X factor in its merlots, whether clone or style, I don't know; this is a very elegant wine, with redcurrant driving a medium-bodied palate complexed by spicy/savoury, fine-grained tannins. Screwcap. 14% alc. **Rating** 94 **To** 2018 $40

ŸŸŸŸŸ **Reserve Manjimup Chardonnay 2009 Rating** 93 **To** 2017 $30
Shiraz Viognier 2011 Rating 93 **To** 2017 $30

✪ **Manjimup Cabernet Sauvignon Merlot 2010** Purple-crimson; blackcurrant, olive and briar aromas are largely reflected in the medium-bodied palate; here the fruit characters become dominant, adding greatly to the appeal of a very good wine at an enticing price. Screwcap. 13.5% alc. **Rating** 93 **To** 2019 $20

✪ **Manjimup Cabernet Sauvignon Merlot 2009** Bright hue; a 55/45% blend; real overtones of Bordeaux, with its black olive nuances behind the blackcurrant fruit, and the 18 months in French oak doing its part well. Screwcap. 13.5% alc. **Rating** 91 **To** 2019 $20
Reserve Pinot Noir 2010 Rating 90 **To** 2018 $35

♟♟♟♟ **Shiraz 2010 Rating** 89 **To** 2016 $30 BE
Reserve Manjimup Merlot 2009 Rating 89 **To** 2016 $40 BE
Pinot Noir Chardonnay 2009 Rating 89 **To** 2015 $40
Manjimup Verdelho 2011 Rating 88 **To** 2013 $20 BE
Viognier Liqueur 2011 Rating 87 **To** Now $35

Cheviot Bridge   ★★★
9th Floor, 564 St Kilda Road, Melbourne, Vic 3004 (postal) **Region** Various
T (03) 8656 7000 **www**.cheviotbridge.com.au **Open** Not
Winemaker Shane Virgo, Hugh Cuthbertson **Est.** 1998 **Dozens** 350 000
Cheviot Bridge made headlines when it purchased the Tyrrell's Long Flat range of wines in 2003, but the nature of the business has changed substantially since then. In late 2010 Cheviot Bridge acquired the InWine Group and its principal wineries, Arrowfield Estate and Red Hill Estate. While the production of these two wineries is less than that of Cheviot Bridge, the brands thus acquired are well known, and add depth to the Cheviot Bridge portfolio. In its own right, Cheviot Bridge produces 350 000 dozen from the Clare, Barossa and Yarra valleys, utilising custom-make facilities in various places. The brands also include Cheviot Bridge Yea Valley, Long Flat, Long Flat Destinations, La Vie and Kissing Bridge. Exports to all major markets.

♟♟♟♟ **Destinations Barossa Shiraz 2009** Light, although bright, red-purple; an open and easily accessed light- to medium-bodied wine with black cherry and plum fruit, fine savoury tannins and a tremor of oak. Screwcap. 14.5% alc. **Rating** 88 **To** 2014 $16

○ **La Vie Pinot Noir Chardonnay NV Rating** 89 **To** Now $17

Chrismont   ★★★★☆
251 Upper King River Road, Cheshunt, Vic 3678 **Region** King Valley
T (03) 5729 8220 **www**.chrismont.com.au **Open** 7 days 11–5
Winemaker Warren Proft **Est.** 1980 **Dozens** 23 000 **Vyds** 100ha
Arnold (Arnie) and Jo Pizzini's substantial vineyards in the Whitfield area of the upper King Valley have been planted with riesling, sauvignon blanc, chardonnay, pinot gris, cabernet sauvignon, merlot, shiraz, barbera, marzemino and arneis. The La Zona range ties in the Italian heritage of the Pizzinis and is part of the intense interest in all things Italian. It also produces a Prosecco, contract-grown in the King Valley. A second cellar door also operates 7 days 10–5 at Shop 1, 1605 Glenrowan-Myrtleford Road, Milawa. Exports to the UK.

♟♟♟♟♟ **King Valley Riesling 2011** Light straw-green; has a highly aromatic, floral, citrus
✪ bouquet, and a long and intense palate, sweet lime flavours complemented by bright acidity on the finish. Perhaps a touch of botrytis, but no mould. Screwcap. 11.5% alc. **Rating** 93 **To** 2015 $16
La Zona King Valley Tempranillo 2010 Good colour; the rich and full bouquet is matched by the complexity of the medium- to full-bodied palate, with a baseline of black and red cherry varietal fruit, and a host of other things, not the least oak in which the wine was matured. The plus side is the integration of that oak, and the soft tannins. Screwcap. 13% alc. **Rating** 91 **To** 2017 $26
La Zona King Valley Arneis 2011 Arneis, vermentino, fiano and savagnin are four of the most interesting alternative white varieties; here you see the apple and peach opening flavours, then the streak of citrus pith acidity that enlivens and cleanses the finish. Screwcap. 12% alc. **Rating** 90 **To** 2014 $22

Arnaldo 2006 Interesting wine in many ways: the overall appearance of the cork suggests the wine has not been long in bottle, and there are two streams of wine that have come up on opposite sides of the cork, stopping just short of the end. Yet the wine has only just been released, and the price is hefty; moreover, it has a distinctly bitter finish that needs to soften. The points are intended to give the wine the benefit of the doubt, but are a compromise. Sangiovese/Cabernet Sauvignon. 14% alc. **Rating** 90 **To** 2021 $75

Il Re' King Valley Nebbiolo 2006 Here there is no issue with a high-quality cork that has done its job to this point of time without a blemish; the colour of the wine is already turning to brick, and is not deep, but that is not so unusual for nebbiolo. I have to admit to tasting it with a degree of apprehension, but found it to be spicy and savoury, with some fleeting notes of cherry; the finish, however, let the tannins loose. Yet another cowardly compromise with the points. 14.5% alc. **Rating** 90 **To** 2016 $75

✪ **La Zona King Valley Prosecco NV** The attraction of prosecco to those who drink it is the fresh palate and crisp, dry finish. In a sense, it serves a similar purpose to manzanilla in the food context: it simply doesn't compete with the food, but, of course, is more proactive than sparkling water, and this is distinctly more than that. Crown seal. 12% alc. **Rating** 90 **To** Now $22

🍷🍷🍷🍷 **La Zona King Valley Pinot Grigio 2011** Rating 89 **To** 2014 $22
King Valley Merlot 2009 Rating 89 **To** 2014 $24

Chuan Wines ★★★☆

11 Station Road, Rosanna, Vic 3084 (postal) **Region** Yarra Valley
T 0413 949 948 **www**.chuan-wines.com **Open** Not
Winemaker Han Tao Lau **Est.** 2009 **Dozens** 500
Owner and winemaker Han Tao Lau was born and raised in Hong Kong, but caught the wine bug, leading to studies in wine business, and then oenology at the University of Adelaide. He accumulated substantial vintage experience working for Hewitson and Paracombe Wines in SA, Chateau Valandraud in St Emilion, France, Weingut Rebholz in the Pfalz, Germany, and Coldstream Hills and Domaine Chandon in the Yarra Valley. Thereafter he became assistant winemaker at Yarra Yering and then Carlei Green Vineyards, and is currently winemaker at Long Gully Estate. He buys the grapes for his wines from several Yarra Valley vineyards. Exports to Hong Kong and China.

🍷🍷🍷🍷 **Yarra Valley Cabernet Sauvignon Merlot Cabernet Franc 2010** Light red-purple; bright blackcurrant/redcurrant/cassis fruit on the bouquet comes through with precisely the same message on the light- to medium-bodied palate; savoury tannins do populate the finish, but are in balance and will soften quickly. Screwcap. 12.5% alc. **Rating** 90 **To** 2019 $32

Churchview Estate ★★★★★

Cnr Bussell Highway/Gale Road, Metricup, WA 6280 **Region** Margaret River
T (08) 9755 7200 **www**.churchview.com.au **Open** Mon–Sat 10–5
Winemaker Greg Garnish **Est.** 1998 **Dozens** 20 000 **Vyds** 65ha
The Fokkema family, headed by Spike Fokkema, immigrated from the Netherlands in the 1950s. Business success in the following decades led to the acquisition of the 100ha Churchview Estate property in '97, and to the progressive establishment of substantial vineyards (65ha planted to 15 varieties). Exports to Europe and Asia.

🍷🍷🍷🍷🍷 **The Bartondale Reserve Margaret River Shiraz 2009** Good hue and depth; 4% viognier, 60% new oak, 40% one-year-old; perhaps it is the vintage, perhaps the extra year in bottle, but this is a more seamless and elegant wine than the '10, although very much in the family. Here the viognier does brighten the flavours, and the tannins are silky, the line, length and balance impeccable. WAK screwcap. 14% alc. **Rating** 96 **To** 2030 $50

The **Bartondale Reserve Margaret River Shiraz 2010** Dense crimson-purple; an incredibly powerful full-bodied wine, with blackberry, plum, licorice and French oak all clamouring to be heard; the tannins are also powerful, but in balance. The 5% viognier seems almost an afterthought. Will live for decades. WAK screwcap. 15% alc. **Rating** 95 **To** 2035 $50

The **Bartondale Reserve Margaret River Chardonnay 2010** Mid gold hue; ripe grapefruit, spice, straw and a dollop of toasty oak on the bouquet; fleshy and ripe, with a zesty backbone of acidity and some grip on the complex, grilled nut finish; long and generous. Screwcap. 14.1% alc. **Rating** 94 **To** 2015 $35 BE

ŶŶŶŶŶ **St Johns Limited Release Grenache Shiraz Mourvedre 2010 Rating** 90 **To** 2015 $35 BE
Margaret River Cabernet Merlot 2009 Rating 90 **To** 2016 $20 BE

ŶŶŶŶ **Margaret River Sauvignon Blanc Semillon 2011 Rating** 88 **To** 2013 $20 BE
O **Silverleaf Margaret River Merlot 2010 Rating** 89 **To** 2016 $13
O **Silverleaf Margaret River Semillon Sauvignon Blanc 2011 Rating** 88 **To** Now $13
Margaret River Shiraz 2009 Rating 88 **To** 2016 $20 BE

Ciavarella Oxley Estate ★★★★☆

Evans Lane, Oxley, Vic 3678 **Region** King Valley
T (03) 5727 3384 **www**.oxleyestate.com.au **Open** Mon–Sat 9–6, Sun 10–6
Winemaker Cyril and Tony Ciavarella **Est.** 1978 **Dozens** 2500 **Vyds** 1.6ha
Cyril and Jan Ciavarella's vineyard was begun in 1978, with plantings being extended over the years. One variety, aucerot, was first produced by Maurice O'Shea of McWilliam's Mount Pleasant 60 or so years ago; the Ciavarella vines have been grown from cuttings collected from an old Glenrowan vineyard before the parent plants were removed in the mid 1980s. Tony Ciavarella left a career in agricultural research in mid 2003 to join his parents at Ciavarella. The family is justifiably proud of the breadth of the range of wines it offers, albeit in small quantities.

ŶŶŶŶŶ **Durif 2010** Bright mid crimson; a fresh and vibrant bouquet, dare it be mentioned, but elegant and seductive; while not the classic characters of the variety, the generous perfume and spice is poised and precise; clearly excellent winemaking at work. Gold medal Victorian Wine Show '11. Screwcap. 13.7% alc. **Rating** 94 **To** 2017 $29 BE

ŶŶŶŶŶ **Noble Sweet Aucerot 2010 Rating** 93 **To** 2016 $80 BE
Shiraz 2010 Rating 92 **To** 2020 $38 BE

ŶŶŶŶ **Cabernet Sauvignon 2010 Rating** 88 **To** 2015 $20 BE
Fortified White NV Rating 88 **To** 2015 $18 BE

Circe Wines ★★★★☆

PO Box 22, Red Hill, Vic 3937 **Region** Mornington Peninsula
T 0417 328 142 **www**.circewines.com.au **Open** Not
Winemaker Dan Buckle **Est.** 2010 **Dozens** 800 **Vyds** 2.9ha
Circe Wines (Circe was a seductress and minor goddess of intoxicants in Homer's *Odyssey*) is the partnership of winemaker Dan Buckle and marketer Aaron Drummond. It is very much a weekend and holiday venture, inspired by their mutual love of pinot noir. They have obtained a long-term lease on a vineyard in Hillcrest Road, not far from Paringa Estate, Tucks Ridge and Montalto. 'Indeed,' says Dan, 'it is not far from the Lieu-dit "Buckle" Vineyard my Dad planted in the 1980s.' The Hillcrest Road property has 1.2ha of vines, half chardonnay and half MV6 pinot noir. They are also planting 1.7ha of pinot noir (MV6, Abel, 777, D2V5 and Bests' Old Clone) at a vineyard in William Road, Red Hill. Dan Buckle's real job is chief winemaker at Domaine Chandon. Exports to the UK.

𑀟𑀟𑀟𑀟𑀟 **Red Hill South Vineyard Pinot Noir 2011** Light, bright and clear crimson; at this stage, at least, more expressive than Hillcrest Road, with a greater range of fruit flavours, hints of plum sidling up to the dominant red cherry flavours. Here the extra level of fruit flavour liberates the wine, and, in particular, the seductive finish. Screwcap. 12.5% alc. **Rating** 94 **To** 2017 $40

𑀟𑀟𑀟𑀟𑀟 **Hillcrest Road Vineyard Chardonnay 2011 Rating** 93 **To** 2019 $60
Hillcrest Road Vineyard Pinot Noir 2011 Rating 90 **To** 2017 $60
Pinot Noir 2010 Rating 90 **To** 2014 $60

𑀟𑀟𑀟𑀟 **Pinot Noir Rose 2011 Rating** 89 **To** 2013 $25
Red Hill South Vineyard Chardonnay 2011 Rating 87 **To** 2016 $40

Clair de Lune Vineyard   ★★★☆

8805 South Gippsland Highway, Kardella South, Vic 3951 **Region** Gippsland
T (03) 5655 1032 **www**.clairdelune.com.au **Open** 7 days 11.30–5.30
Winemaker Brian Gaffy **Est.** 1997 **Dozens** 500 **Vyds** 4ha
Brian Gaffy married a successful 20-year career in civil engineering with a long-term involvement in the Bundaburra Wine & Food Club in Melbourne. His interest in wine grew, leading to studies at the Dookie Agricultural College, with particular input from Denise Miller. He has planted a vineyard on the rolling hills of the Strzelecki Range to sauvignon blanc, chardonnay, pinot noir and a mixed block of shiraz/merlot/cabernet.

𑀟𑀟𑀟𑀟 **South Gippsland Oaked Chardonnay 2010** Some slightly premature colour development, possibly due to full barrel fermentation, heralds a wine where the fruit needed a lighter touch in the winery. It does have complexity, but needs to be drunk now, not later. Screwcap. 13.5% alc. **Rating** 88 **To** 2014 $30
South Gippsland Shiraz 2010 Mid garnet, showing a little leathery development, alongside a decent level of peppery spice; medium-bodied with a savoury, dry and mineral accented finish. Screwcap. 12.4% alc. **Rating** 88 **To** 2015 $27 BE

Clairault   ★★★★★

3277 Caves Road, Wilyabrup, WA 6280 **Region** Margaret River
T (08) 9755 6225 **www**.clairaultwines.com.au **Open** 7 days 10–5
Winemaker Will Shields **Est.** 1976 **Dozens** 20 000 **Vyds** 36.44ha
Bill and Ena Martin, with sons Conor, Brian and Shane, acquired Clairault several years ago and expanded the vineyards on the 120ha property, but in April 2012 were finalising an agreement for sale to John Streicker, already a substantial vineyard owner, with his eoponymous wines (see separate entry) made by Naturaliste Vintners. The 12ha of vines established by the former owners (most now over 35 years old) have been supplemented by another 24ha or so of vines, with a ratio of roughly 70% red varieties to 30% white. Deeply concerned about the environment and consumer health, Clairault has joined with ERA (Environmentally Responsible Agriculture) to implement the elimination of chemical use and the introduction of biological farming. Exports to the UK, the US and other major markets.

𑀟𑀟𑀟𑀟𑀟 **Estate Margaret River Chardonnay 2010** Bright straw-green; hand-picked and sorted grapes are whole bunch-pressed, wild yeast-fermented in French barriques with lees stirring and partial mlf; the wine has a rapier-like bouquet and palate, the mouthfeel zesty and crunchy. Cries out for time in bottle to reveal all within, and deserve even higher points. Gold medal National Wine Show '11. Screwcap. 13% alc. **Rating** 95 **To** 2017 $39
B79 Margaret River Semillon Sauvignon Blanc 2011 Five hundred and eighty two dozen made of this very attractive blend. The fruit flavours are generous, with a seamless union of the two varieties, snow pea, gooseberry, citrus and passionfruit all intermingling. WAK screwcap. 12% alc. **Rating** 94 **To** 2015 $35

𑀟𑀟𑀟𑀟𑀟 **Cellar Release Margaret River Cabernet Merlot 2007 Rating** 93
To 2022 $60

A76 Margaret River Cabernet Sauvignon 2010 Rating 93 To 2025 $65
Cellar Release Margaret River Cane Cut Riesling 2011 Rating 92
To 2014 $35
Margaret River Chardonnay 2010 Rating 91 To 2014 $25
Margaret River Sauvignon Blanc Semillon 2011 Rating 90 To 2014 $27

♀♀♀♀   Margaret River Cabernet Sauvignon 2009 Rating 89 To 2017 $28

Clare Wine Co.   ★★★☆

PO Box 852, Nuriootpa, SA 5355 **Region** Clare Valley
T (08) 8562 4488 **www**.clarewineco.com.au **Open** Not
Winemaker Reid Bosward, Stephen Dew **Est.** 2008 **Dozens** 2500 **Vyds** 30.5ha
An affiliate of Kaesler Wines, its primary focus is on exports to China, Singapore and Hong
Kong. Its vines are predominantly given over to shiraz (15ha) and cabernet sauvignon (9.5ha).
It also has 3.8ha of riesling and 2.2ha of semillon, but no chardonnay, which is presumably
purchased from other Clare Valley growers.

♀♀♀♀♀ **Rose 2011** Light magenta; shiraz grown in the Polish Hill River area was cold-
✪   soaked for five days, then pressed off for fermentation to begin. It has a fragrant red
        cherry/morello cherry bouquet, then a full-flavoured, red fruit, including raspberry,
        palate. For a full-bodied rose, it ticks the boxes. Screwcap. 14% alc. **Rating** 90
        To 2013 $18

♀♀♀♀   **Cabernet Sauvignon 2010** Rating 88 To 2020 $18
        Shiraz 2010 Rating 87 To 2014 $18

Clarence House Wines   ★★★★☆

193 Pass Road, Cambridge, Tas 7170 (postal) **Region** Southern Tasmania
T (03) 6247 7345 **Open** Not
Winemaker Winemaking Tasmania (Julian Alcorso), Frogmore Creek (Alain Rousseau)
Est. 1998 **Dozens** 3000 **Vyds** 12ha
Clarence House was built in 1830 at Clarence Vale, Mt Rumney. The house has been kept
in great condition, and in 1998 present owner, David Kilpatrick, began planting vines on a
northeast-sloping block opposite the house. While pinot noir and chardonnay account for
over 8ha of the total plantings, the remainder includes pinot blanc and tempranillo, rare in
Tasmania. The wines are released under three labels: at the bottom Clarence Plains, made for
early drinking; Clarence House Estate, complex wines reflecting the terroir of the region; and
Clarence House Reserve, occasional releases from exceptional vintages.

♀♀♀♀♀ **Reserve Chardonnay 2008** Has that indelible acid stamp of Tasmania that
        sustains all its white wines; the intense grapefruit and white peach fruit has all
        but absorbed the oak in which it was fermented. A wine of character, with the
        promise of further longevity. Screwcap. 13% alc. **Rating** 94 To 2016 $32

♀♀♀♀♀ **Pinot Noir 2008** Rating 91 To 2016 $30

♀♀♀♀   **Sauvignon Blanc 2010** Rating 89 To 2013 $25
        Pinot Blanc 2010 Rating 89 To 2014 $26
        Tempranillo 2007 Rating 89 To 2015 $25
        Reserve Merlot 2008 Rating 88 To 2015 $32

Clarendon Hills   ★★★★★

Brookmans Road, Blewitt Springs, SA 5171 **Region** McLaren Vale
T (08) 8363 6111 **www**.clarendonhills.com.au **Open** By appt
Winemaker Roman Bratasiuk **Est.** 1990 **Dozens** 15 000 **Vyds** 63ha
Age and experience, it would seem, have mellowed Roman Bratasiuk – and the style of his
wines. Once formidable and often rustic, they are now far more sculpted and smooth, at
times bordering on downright elegance. Roman has taken another major step by purchasing

a 160ha property high in the hill country of Clarendon at an altitude close to that of the Adelaide Hills. Here he has established a vineyard with single-stake trellising similar to that used on the steep slopes of Germany and Austria, which produces the Domaine Clarendon Syrah. He makes up to 20 different wines each year, all consistently good, a tribute to the old vines. Exports to the US and other major markets.

🍷🍷🍷🍷🍷 **Brookman Clarendon Syrah 2009** Deep, dark crimson-purple; an exceptionally complex bouquet with nuances of the roasted meats I normally find so elusive, together with tobacco and blackberry; the impact of 18 months in 70% new French oak is obvious, as it is across all of the Clarendon Syrah and Cabernet range. The long and supple palate has lifted black fruit flavours supported by fine, ripe tannins. All in all, a lovely wine; 595 dozen made from 90-year-old vines. Cork. 14.5% alc. **Rating** 96 **To** 2035 $125

Piggot Range Clarendon Syrah 2009 Virtually impenetrable crimson-purple; this is the most savoury of the four top-end Clarendon Syrahs, with the mix of partial whole berry and whole bunch wild yeast fermentation departing from the normal whole berry approach; likewise, 18 months in 100% new French oak adds an exclamation mark to the lingering flavours of the finish and aftertaste, where perfectly weighted tannins come into their own; 560 dozen made. Cork. 14.5% alc. **Rating** 96 **To** 2045 $300

Astralis 2009 Ever controversial, because of its self-endowed classification of '1er Grand Cru'. Sourced from a single vineyard in the Blewitt Springs area, with 90-year-old shiraz vines, open-fermented with partial whole berry and whole bunch inclusion; ultimately spending 18 months in 100% new French oak. Deep, bright purple-crimson; strong overtones of bitter chocolate and licorice to the foundation of black fruits on the bouquet steer the same course on the massive, full-bodied palate; the tannins are very obvious, but soft and ripe, leaving the wine with excellent balance; 650 dozen made. Cork. 14.4% alc. **Rating** 96 **To** 2040 $500

Domaine Clarendon Syrah 2009 From the unique estate-owned, steep hillside vineyard, each vine trained upright on a single stake, a la German riesling; first crop from the 14ha site planted in 2005. Vibrant crimson, its bouquet has developed wonderfully fragrant red and black fruit aromas since first tasted shortly after it was bottled; the intense, fresh palate offers plum, blackberry, licorice and spice; fine tannins and balanced oak to close. Cork. 14% alc. **Rating** 95 **To** 2034 $55

Hickinbotham Clarendon Syrah 2009 Very deep crimson; the bouquet exudes black fruits, licorice and spice, coupled with cedary notes from 18 months' maturation in 85% new French oak; a massive wine on the palate, filled with blackberry fruit supported by strong tannins; relaxes a little with its spicy, savoury finish; 740 dozen made. Cork. 14.5% alc. **Rating** 95 **To** 2029 $125

Onkaparinga Clarendon Syrah 2009 Deep crimson-purple; strongly regional aromas of dark chocolate, licorice, blackberry and cardamom spice lead into a mirror image on the palate, with lots of licorice, some bitter chocolate, black fruits and significant cedary French oak (18 months, 85% new); has a textured finish with polished tannins; 680 dozen made from 70-year-old vines. Cork. 14.5% alc. **Rating** 95 **To** 2030 $125

Romas Clarendon Grenache 2009 Brighter purple-crimson than Onkaparinga; the spicy fruit aromas cover both black and red fruits, and the palate is fuller-bodied, with very good length and tannin balance; is wild yeast-fermented in new to 5-year-old French oak; 650 dozen made. Cork. 14.5% alc. **Rating** 95 **To** 2030 $125

Hickinbotham Clarendon Cabernet Sauvignon 2009 As with all the '09 Clarendon wines, the yield was down by 40% on average. Deep, dense colour, the complex bouquet with the 100% new French oak seamlessly woven through the range of black fruits; the palate full-bodied with all of the structure expected of cabernet sauvignon, the blackcurrant fruit flavours supported by pronounced tannins that are not the least dry; 620 dozen made. Cork. 14.5% alc. **Rating** 95 **To** 2040 $125

Onkaparinga Clarendon Grenache 2009 **Rating** 94 **To** 2025 $100

🍇 Clarnette & Ludvigsen Wines ★★★★☆

Westgate Road, Armstrong, Vic 3377 **Region** Grampians
T 0427 971 835 **www**.ludvigsen.com.au **Open** By appt
Winemaker Leigh Clarnette **Est.** 2003 **Dozens** 1000 **Vyds** 14ha
This brings together two vastly experienced wine professionals, Leigh Clarnette as winemaker,
and Kym Ludvigsen as viticulturist. Their career paths crossed in late 1993 when both were
working for Seppelt. Kym has a 14ha vineyard in the heart of the Grampians, all but 1ha of
chardonnay, 0.5ha of viognier and 0.25ha of riesling planted to rare clones of shiraz, sourced
from old plantings in the Great Western area. Kym is presently the Chairman of the Australian
Vine Improvement Association and a board member (and past Chairman) of the Victorian
and Murray Vine Improvement Association. He operates a formal consultancy service (details
on the website). In 2005 the wheel turned full circle when both were employed by Taltarni.

🍷🍷🍷🍷🍷 **Grampians Shiraz 2008** Has a bright purple edge to its crimson colour; the
flavours are complex, black fruits swirling around spice and pepper, the texture also
excellent, but it is the length of this wine which is so striking. (Note: this wine was
tasted in March '11 before the winery details became available and hence has not
been previously published.) Screwcap. 14.8% alc. **Rating** 95 **To** 2035 $25

🍷🍷🍷🍷🍷 **Ampersand Grampians Chardonnay 2010** Picked at 12° baume for its
✪ acid and elegance, then aged on lees in 2-year-old barrels for nine months; no
mlf. The wine is crisp and vital, with grapefruit and white peach to the fore,
oak contributing more to the texture than to the flavour. Screwcap. 12.5% alc.
Rating 92 **To** 2017 $19
Grampians Shiraz 2009 Rating 90 **To** 2019 $25

Clayfield Wines ★★★★★

25 Wilde Lane, Moyston, Vic 3377 **Region** Grampians
T (03) 5354 2689 **www**.clayfieldwines.com **Open** Mon–Sat 10–5, Sun 11–4
Winemaker Simon Clayfield **Est.** 1997 **Dozens** 1000 **Vyds** 2.1ha
Former long-serving Best's winemaker Simon Clayfield and wife Kaye are now doing their
own thing. They planted 2ha of shiraz and merlot between 1997 and '99, later adding 0.1ha of
durif. Additional grapes are purchased from local growers and, when the quality is appropriate,
incorporated in the Grampians Shiraz. Production is modest, but the quality is high.

🍷🍷🍷🍷🍷 **Grampians Shiraz 2010** Deep purple with a crimson rim; a very, very classy
example of Grampians shiraz, with that lifted spice and licorice able to let light
and shade play through the full-bodied, yet elegant, palate; oak and tannins have
been expertly managed. Screwcap. 14.4% alc. **Rating** 96 **To** 2035 $65
Grampians Shiraz 2009 Part estate-grown, and part from Mt Ararat Vineyard, it
spent 31 months in oak; 100 dozen made. A voluptuous, medium- to full-bodied
palate with velvety black fruits, rounded tannins and integrated oak. Screwcap.
14.5% alc. **Rating** 95 **To** 2030 $65
Massif Grampians Shiraz 2010 Vivid crimson-purple; the mainstay of the
Clayfield releases from the Rosebank Vineyard near Moyston; the fragrant bouquet
has gently spiced red and black fruits, setting the template for the medium-bodied
palate, likewise full of fruit, with rounded, soft tannins and carefully controlled oak
inputs. Screwcap. 15.1% alc. **Rating** 95 **To** 2025 $30
Moyston Shiraz 2010 Deep purple-crimson; Clayfield's first 100% estate-grown
shiraz, matured in new American and French hogsheads for 19 months; here black
fruits, licorice and spice come through strongly, and are not the least intimidated
by the oak, although this, too contributes significantly to the overall package.
100 dozen made, available exclusively through cellar door. Screwcap. 14.5% alc.
Rating 95 **To** 2035 $50
Massif Reserve Grampians Shiraz 2009 Crimson-purple; from three local
vineyards, and spent 28 months in French and American oak; a more juicy and
medium-bodied wine than the standard version, with a mix of red and black
fruits, regional spice and licorice, finishing with fine tannins; the modest alcohol is
particularly appealing. Screwcap. 13.6% alc. **Rating** 94 **To** 2024 $35

Claymore Wines

91 Main North Road, Leasingham, SA 5452 **Region** Clare Valley
T (08) 8843 0200 **www**.claymorewines.com.au **Open** 7 days 10–5
Winemaker Donna Stephens **Est.** 1998 **Dozens** 12 000 **Vyds** 27ha
Claymore Wines is the venture of a medical professional imagining that it would lead the way
to early retirement (which, of course, it did not). The starting date depends on which event
you take: the first 4ha vineyard at Leasingham purchased in 1991 (with 70-year-old grenache,
riesling and shiraz); '96, when a 16ha block at Penwortham was purchased and planted to
shiraz, merlot and grenache; '97, when the first wines were made; or '98, when the first releases
came onto the market. The labels are inspired by U2, Pink Floyd and Lou Reed. Exports to
Canada, Denmark, Sweden, Malaysia, Taiwan, Hong Kong and China.

ΨΨΨΨΨ **Dark Side of the Moon Clare Valley Shiraz 2010** A deep, dark and sultry
wine, or is that just the label? In fact the wine displays masses of dense black fruits,
licorice, fruitcake and a gentle seasoning of toasty oak; full-bodied and full throttle,
the winemaking has skilfully kept all components evenly keeled and harmonious;
big and beautiful. Screwcap. 14.8% alc. **Rating** 95 **To** 2020 $25 BE

ΨΨΨΨΨ **Joshua Tree Clare Valley Riesling 2011** Pale colour, vibrant hue; a restrained
⊙   and elegant bouquet of lime, spice and minerals; the palate is racy, taut and dry,
understated and precise; elegance and poise at a very attractive price. Screwcap.
11.5% alc. **Rating** 93 **To** 2018 $18 BE

⊙   **Holy Grail Clare Valley Cabernet Sauvignon 2010** Deep garnet; a fragrant
bouquet of red and black fruits, violets and a splash of cedary complexity;
medium- to full-bodied, evenly balanced and poised. Cork. 14.5% alc. **Rating** 92
To 2018 $20 BE

ΨΨΨΨ **Walk on the Wild Side Clare Valley Shiraz 2009** **Rating** 89 **To** 2020 $20
Lucille Clare Valley Late Harvest Riesling 2011 **Rating** 88 **To** 2014 $18 BE
Nirvana Reserve Clare Valley Shiraz 2009 **Rating** 87 **To** 2016 $40 BE

Clearview Estate Mudgee

Cnr Sydney Road/Rocky Water Hole Road, Mudgee, NSW 2850 **Region** Mudgee
T (02) 6372 4546 **www**.clearviewwines.com.au **Open** Fri 10–3
(Mar–Dec), w'ends & public hols 10–4
Winemaker Contract **Est.** 1995 **Dozens** 1000 **Vyds** 11ha
Paul and Michelle Baguley acquired the vineyard from the founding Hickey family in 2006.
Paul brings 10 years' experience as a viticulturist, and Paul and Michelle have introduced
additional wine styles. Plantings include shiraz, chardonnay, cabernet sauvignon and semillon.

ΨΨΨΨ **Rocky Waterhole Cabernet Sauvignon 2010** Deep garnet; a spicy blend
of mulberry, clove and cinnamon are exhibited on the bouquet; the palate is
medium-bodied, soft and fleshy, with an easygoing user-friendly personality.
Screwcap. 14% alc. **Rating** 87 **To** 2015 $20 BE

Cleggett Wines

Langhorne Creek Road, Langhorne Creek, SA 5255 **Region** Langhorne Creek
T (08) 8537 3133 **www**.cleggettwines.com.au **Open** 7 days 10–6
Winemaker Peter Leske (Consultant) **Est.** 2000 **Dozens** 2000 **Vyds** 74.86ha
The Cleggett family first planted grape vines at Langhorne Creek in 1911. In 1977 a sport
(a natural mutation) of cabernet sauvignon produced bronze-coloured grapes; cuttings were
taken and increasing quantities of the vine were gradually established, and called malian. Ten
years later one of the malian vines itself mutated to yield golden-white bunches, and this in
turn was propagated with the name shalistin. There are now 4ha of shalistin and 2ha of malian
in bearing. Shalistin is made as a full-bodied but unoaked white wine; malian produces both
an early- and a late-harvest rose-style wine. Exports to Malaysia.

ᵠᵠᵠᵠᵠ **Men of Kent 2010** Crimson-purple; a co-fermented cabernet sauvignon
✪   and 4% shalistin, matured in French oak for 12 months. It has attractive juicy
             redcurrant fruit complexed by fine, savoury tannins; worth every penny. Screwcap.
             14.5% alc. **Rating** 91 **To** 2017 $20

✪   **Illawarra Block Langhorne Creek Shiraz 2010** Crimson colour, with a
             cherry-dominated bouquet leading into a supple and smooth palate; here cherry
             is joined by plum and some influence from the 12 months spent in French oak;
             finishes with soft tannins. Screwcap. 14.5% alc. **Rating** 90 **To** 2018 $18

ᵠᵠᵠᵠ   **Shalistin White Cabernet Sauvignon 2011** The white cabernet sauvignon
✪   story and its registration under the name 'shalistin' by the proprietors of Cleggett
             is a complicated one. The wine is good, with fresh citrus and apple flavours,
             the acidity on the finish firm but balanced. Screwcap. 12.5% alc. **Rating** 89
             To 2015 $17

✪   **Legend Series Langhorne Creek Cabernet Sauvignon 2008** Medium
             purple-red; powered by a V8 engine, and fuelled with lashings of black fruit, dark
             chocolate and French oak. You certainly get maximum bang for your buck, but
             don't look for finesse. Diam. 14.5% alc. **Rating** 88 **To** 2020 $18
             Sparkling Malian Bronze Cabernet Sauvignon 2011 Rating 87 **To** 2013 $15

Clemens Hill   ★★★★☆

686 Richmond Road, Cambridge, Tas 7170 **Region** Southern Tasmania
T (03) 6248 5985 **www.**clemenshill.com.au **Open** By appt
Winemaker Winemaking Tasmania **Est.** 1994 **Dozens** 2200 **Vyds** 5.3ha
The Shepherd family acquired Clemens Hill in 2001 after selling their Rosabrook winery
in the Margaret River. They also have a shareholding in Winemaking Tasmania, the contract
winemaking facility run by Julian Alcorso, who makes the Clemens Hill wines. The estate
vineyard includes pinot noir (3.3 ha; 1.5ha replanted in '09) and sauvignon blanc (2ha).

ᵠᵠᵠᵠᵠ **Wild Ferment Fume Blanc 2010** Wild-fermented and spent two months in
             oak; these inputs haven't caused the wine to bat an eyelid, tangy citrus and herb
             driving the incredibly long and intense palate. At the apex of Tasmanian sauvignon
             blanc. Screwcap. 13% alc. **Rating** 94 **To** 2014 $30

ᵠᵠᵠᵠᵠ **Pinot Noir 2010 Rating** 93 **To** 2017 $35

ᵠᵠᵠᵠ   **Sauvignon Blanc 2011 Rating** 89 **To** 2013 $26
             Reserve Pinot Noir 2009 Rating 88 **To** 2015

Clonakilla   ★★★★★

Crisps Lane, Murrumbateman, NSW 2582 **Region** Canberra District
T (02) 6227 5877 **www.**clonakilla.com.au **Open** 7 days 10–5
Winemaker Tim Kirk, Bryan Martin **Est.** 1971 **Dozens** 10 000 **Vyds** 12ha
The indefatigable Tim Kirk, with an inexhaustible thirst for knowledge, is the winemaker
and manager of this family winery founded by Tim's father, scientist Dr John Kirk. It is not
at all surprising that the quality of the wines is excellent, especially the Shiraz Viognier, which
has paved the way for numerous others to follow, but remains the best example in Australia.
Exports to all major markets.

ᵠᵠᵠᵠᵠ **Murrumbateman Syrah 2010** Bright, clear colour, fractionally more advanced
             (less purple) than the O'Riada; the bouquet is so perfectly balanced one is tempted
             to describe it as silky, which is a nonsense; whether or not that be the case, the
             palate certainly takes off in dramatic fashion, with exceptionally intense and
             energetic flavours of spice, red berries, blackberry and black pepper; if all this were
             not enough, the texture is outstanding, fruit, oak and tannins all harmoniously
             contributing. Screwcap. 14% alc. **Rating** 97 **To** 2030 $100
             Canberra District Riesling 2011 Pale straw-green; a floral bouquet of apple
             blossom and spice yields to a palate with great drive to its lime juice flavours,
             which last long after the wine is swallowed. Right up there with the best of them.
             Screwcap. 12% alc. **Rating** 96 **To** 2025 $30

Tumbarumba Canberra District Chardonnay 2011 Bright straw-green; while principally sourced from a high-altitude vineyard in Tumbarumba, has a small amount of estate-grown chardonnay included; hand-picked, whole bunch-pressed, warm fermentation and lees stirred during ageing in French oak; a wonderfully intense, largely fruit-driven, wine with layers of white and yellow peach, grapefruit and a hint of oak; the intensity and drive of the palate are outstanding. Screwcap. 12% alc. **Rating** 96 **To** 2019 $35

Canberra District Viognier 2011 Tim Kirk's mastery of all facets of winemaking allows him to thread the needle of viognier with disarming ease. The wine has the full suite of viognier varietal characters, including the X factor of ginger that neatly balances the apricot and peach, and (joined with barrel-ferment complexity) leaves the wine vital and alive on the back-palate and finish. Screwcap. 13% alc. **Rating** 95 **To** 2018 $50

Shiraz Viognier 2011 Transparently clear purple-crimson; the perfumed bouquet of predominantly red fruits leads into a superfine palate with some darker fruit nuances; it is only on the finish and aftertaste that the quality of the wine fully expresses itself. Screwcap. 13% alc. **Rating** 95 **To** 2025 $100

Riesling Auslese 2011 Bright, light straw-green; I suspect Tim Kirk has used the Auslese term (why haven't the Germans moved to outlaw this?) to denote the total potential alcohol if fully fermented rather than the amount of residual sugar in the wine. That said, it is seductive, like a lime juice ice-block dipped in honey; the acidity draws out the exceptionally long finish. 375ml. Screwcap. 10% alc. **Rating** 95 **To** 2017 $30

O'Riada Canberra District Shiraz 2011 **Rating** 94 **To** 2021 $45

Clos Clare ★★★★

Old Road, Watervale, SA 5452 **Region** Clare Valley
T (08) 8843 0161 **www**.closclare.com.au **Open** W'ends & public hols 11–5
Winemaker Sam and Tom Barry **Est.** 1993 **Dozens** 1000 **Vyds** 2ha
Clos Clare was acquired by the Barry family in 2008. Riesling continues to be made from the 2ha unirrigated section of the original Florita Vineyard (the major part of that vineyard was already in Barry ownership) and newly introduced red wines are coming from a 49-year-old vineyard beside the Armagh site. Exports to the UK.

ΨΨΨΨΨ **Cemetery Block Shiraz 2009** Deep crimson-purple; the bouquet and palate have a complex array of black fruits, red fruits and spices; has good tannin structure and integrated oak. Screwcap. 14% alc. **Rating** 92 **To** 2024 $26

The Hayes Boy Grenache 2010 While the colour is the usual Clare light red-purple, the bouquet and palate have greater stature than the normal offering; there is more structure courtesy of fine, savoury tannins and more plum and raspberry fruit. Screwcap. 14.5% alc. **Rating** 90 **To** 2018 $26

ΨΨΨΨ **Watervale Riesling 2011** **Rating** 88 **To** 2014 $24

Clovely Estate

Steinhardts Road, Moffatdale via Murgon, Qld 4605 **Region** South Burnett
T (07) 3876 3100 **F** (07) 3876 3500 **www**.clovely.com.au **Open** Tues–Sat 11–7
Winemaker Luke Fitzpatrick, Kieran Carney **Est.** 1997 **Dozens** 25 000 **Vyds** 174ha
Clovely Estate has the largest vineyards in Qld, having established over 170ha of immaculately maintained vines at two locations just to the east of Murgon in the Burnett Valley. There are 120ha of red grapes (including 60ha of shiraz) and 54ha of white grapes. The attractively packaged wines are sold in six tiers: Double Pruned at the top; followed by Estate Reserve; Left Field, featuring alternative varieties and styles; then the White Label and Shed ranges for everyday drinking, distributed through the Qld retail market; and at the bottom, First Picked, primarily designed for the export market at low price points. The estate also has a second cellar door and B&B at 210 Musgrave Road, Red Hill. Exports to Denmark, Papua New Guinea, Taiwan and China.

ŶŶŶŶŶ **South Burnett Shiraz Merlot Cabernet 2010** Clear red-purple; the blend
✪ succeeds admirably with an array of red and black fruit flavours from plum to
cherry and redcurrant; the tannins are balanced, as is the oak. Exceptional bargain.
Screwcap. 14.5% alc. **Rating** 91 **To** 2015 $14

✪ **Left Field South Burnett Semillon 2010** Quartz-white; not to be released
until July '13, by which time it will have significantly changed; its bracing bitter
lemon acidity will serve it well in the years ahead. The points are largely nominal.
Screwcap. 9.7% alc. **Rating** 90 **To** 2020 $20

ŶŶŶŶ **Left Field Pinot Gris 2011** Pale quartz; has clear-cut varietal character, with
✪ pear in the lead, and some stone fruit in support; well balanced, with a long palate
and dry finish. Screwcap. 13.5% alc. **Rating** 89 **To** 2013 $20

✪ **Left Field South Burnett Grenache Shiraz Mourvedre 2010** Light colour,
typical of the blend; spicy, savoury nuances run through the red fruits of the
bouquet and light- to medium-bodied palate, the all-up balance good; 290 dozen
made. Screwcap. 14% alc. **Rating** 89 **To** 2015 $20

✪ **South Burnett Semillon Sauvignon Blanc 2011** Very early picking has
heightened the herbaceous, lemongrass flavours of the semillon, but does leave
room for the sauvignon blanc to express itself with flavours of gooseberry
and passionfruit. Fully chilled (or with ice blocks) on a summer's day, fish and
chips close by, would make it taste like nectar. Screwcap. 10.9% alc. **Rating** 88
To 2013 $14

✪ **South Burnett Verdelho 2011** Straw-green; a moderately fragrant, floral
bouquet leads into a palate with some structure to the fruit salad flavours; certainly
right up there with other verdelhos at a fraction of the price. Screwcap. 13.5% alc.
Rating 88 **To** 2013 $14

◍ **South Burnett Verdelho 2010 Rating** 88 **To** 2013 $14
✪ **South Burnett Rose 2011** Pale red tinged with purple; made from grenache
and shiraz, the former impacting on the colour; the wine is light and soft, with
cherry and raspberry flavours on the mid palate, followed by a pleasantly dry finish.
Excellent value. Screwcap. 12% alc. **Rating** 88 **To** 2013 $14

South Burnett Chardonnay 2009 Rating 87 **To** 2014 $14
◍ **South Burnett Semillon Chardonnay 2010 Rating** 87 **To** 2014 $14
◍ **Left Field South Burnett Barbera 2010 Rating** 87 **To** 2015 $20
◍ **Left Field South Burnett Nebbiolo 2009 Rating** 87 **To** 2014 $20

Clover Hill　　　　　　　★★★★★

60 Clover Hill Road, Lebrina, Tas 7254 **Region** Northern Tasmania
T (03) 6395 6114 **www**.cloverhillwines.com.au **Open** By appt
Winemaker Karina Dambergs **Est.** 1986 **Dozens** 8000 **Vyds** 23.9ha
Clover Hill was established by Taltarni in 1986 with the sole purpose of making a premium
sparkling wine. It has 23.9ha of vineyards (chardonnay, pinot noir and pinot meunier) and
its sparkling wine quality is excellent, combining finesse with power and length. In 2009
American owner and founder of Clos du Val (Napa Valley), Taltarni and Clover Hill brought
the management of these businesses and Domaine de Nizas (Languedoc) under the one
management roof; the group is known as Goelet Wine Estates. Exports to the UK, the US
and other major markets.

ŶŶŶŶŶ **Cuvee Exceptionnelle Rose 2008** Pale salmon blush; a reserved and complex
bouquet, showing poise, red fruits and plenty of complexity; the palate is evenly
balanced and long, with freshness and complexity seamlessly interwoven; excellent
rose. Cork. 12.5% alc. **Rating** 94 **To** 2016 $55 BE

Clyde Park Vineyard　　　　★★★★★

2490 Midland Highway, Bannockburn, Vic 3331 **Region** Geelong
T (03) 5281 7274 **www**.clydepark.com.au **Open** Mon–Fri 11–5, w'ends & public hols 12–4
Winemaker Terry Jongebloed, Scott Gerrard **Est.** 1979 **Dozens** 6000

Clyde Park Vineyard, established by Gary Farr but sold by him many years ago, has passed through several changes of ownership. Now owned by Terry Jongebloed and Sue Jongebloed-Dixon, it has significant mature plantings of pinot noir (3.4ha), chardonnay (3.1ha), sauvignon blanc (1.5ha), shiraz (1.2ha) and pinot gris (0.9ha), and the quality of its wines is exemplary. Exports to the UK.

🍷🍷🍷🍷🍷 **Reserve Geelong Shiraz 2008** Deep purple-red; effortlessly combines intensity and elegance with the purity of the black fruits, spice and exceptional tannins running through the palate; completely destroys the stereotype image of jammy/oaky Australian reds. Screwcap. 14.5% alc. **Rating** 95 **To** 2028 $49

⦿ **Sauvignon Blanc 2011 Rating** 94 **To** Now $20
Reserve Geelong Pinot Noir 2010 Bright crimson; a powerful, potent pinot with dark fruit and forest on the bouquet and palate; good tannin and oak support and no sign of early picking despite low alcohol. Should cellar very well. Screwcap. 12.5% alc. **Rating** 94 **To** 2018 $49

🍷🍷🍷🍷🍷 **Geelong Pinot Gris 2011 Rating** 91 **To** 2014 $30
✪ **Locale Geelong Pinot Noir 2010** The colour is distinctly hazy, suggesting no filtration. However, the wine has complexity to both its spicy/foresty bouquet and palate, and pinot varietal character is clearly expressed. Screwcap. 13.5% alc. **Rating** 90 **To** 2015 $20

🍷🍷🍷🍷 **Locale Geelong Pinot Grigio 2011 Rating** 88 **To** Now $20

Coal Valley Vineyard   ★★★★

257 Richmond Road, Cambridge, Tas 7170 **Region** Southern Tasmania
T (03) 6248 5367 **www**.coalvalley.com.au **Open** Thurs–Sun 10–4
Winemaker Alain Rousseau, Todd Goebel **Est.** 1991 **Dozens** 1000 **Vyds** 4.5ha
Since acquiring Coal Valley Vineyard in 1999, Gill Christian and Todd Goebel have increased the original 1ha hobby vineyard to pinot noir (2.3ha), riesling, cabernet sauvignon, merlot, chardonnay and tempranillo. More remarkable were Gill and Todd's concurrent lives: one in India, the other in Tasmania (flying over six times a year), and digging 4000 holes for the new vine plantings. Todd makes the Cabernet Sauvignon onsite, and dreams of making all the wines. Exports to Canada.

🍷🍷🍷🍷🍷 **Sparkling Pinot Noir 2009** Pale salmon; has fine, persistent mousse; the palate is well-balanced, with gentle spice and ample fruit; good length, finish and aftertaste. Gold Tas Wine Show '12. Diam. 12% alc. **Rating** 94 **To** 2025 $34

🍷🍷🍷🍷🍷 **FGR Riesling 2011 Rating** 93 **To** 2021 $27

🍷🍷🍷🍷 **Pinot Noir 2010 Rating** 89 **To** 2016 $32
Riesling 2011 Rating 88 **To** 2017 $26

Cobaw Ridge   ★★★★☆

31 Perc Boyers Lane, Pastoria, Vic 3444 **Region** Macedon Ranges
T (03) 5423 5227 **www**.cobawridge.com.au **Open** Thurs–Mon 12–5
Winemaker Alan Cooper **Est.** 1985 **Dozens** 1000 **Vyds** 4.85ha
When the Coopers started planting in the early 1980s there was scant knowledge of the best varieties for the region, let alone the Cobaw Ridge site. They have now settled on four varieties, chardonnay and syrah always being part of the mix. Lagrein and pinot noir are more recent arrivals to thrive; cabernet sauvignon (long ago) and vermentino (more recently) have been removed. In their place a close-planted, multi-clonal block of pinot noir, with a 1.25m × 1.25m spacing, was established. Son Joshua has breezed through the wine science degree at Adelaide University with multiple distinctions; his immediate career has been with Tyrrell's, then Heathcote Estate/Yabby Lake and thereafter winemaking in Domaine de la Vougeraie (Burgundy) courtesy of leading UK wine author Andrew Jefford's introduction, all in vintage 2012. Exports to Canada and China.

YYYYY Lagrein 2008 While I gave this wine 93 points when I tasted it for the 2012 *Wine Companion* 10 months before its release, I am not happy with the points or that tasting note, for the wine has developed very well indeed. It is on a par with the lovely '05, with its deep black and red cherry fruit, and a pleasing touch of cherry pip bitterness on the finish. Diam. 13% alc. **Rating** 94 **To** 2020 $60

Cockatoo Ridge   ★★★
PO Box 631, Riverton, SA 5412 **Region** South Eastern Australia
T (08) 8563 6400 **www**.cockatooridge.com.au **Open** Not
Winemaker Rod Hooper **Est.** 1990 **Dozens** 110 000
Cockatoo Ridge has been part of the scenery of SA viticulture and winemaking since 1990. During that time its fortunes have waxed and waned; a substantial injection of capital by its new investors is important, but no more significant than the role of Fine Wine Partners, who are responsible for managing the brand and formulating sales strategies in retail and on-premise channels. The package is completed with the appointment of the experienced and skilled Rod Hooper as winemaker. Exports to Germany, Japan and China.

YYYY Limited Release Mount Lofty Shiraz 2009 Light, clear red; has gone some way to making a silk purse from a sow's ear, with sensitive winemaking walking around the limitations of the fruit; a light- to medium-bodied wine for casual consumption. Screwcap. 13.5% alc. **Rating** 87 **To** 2015 $18

✪ Cabernet Merlot 2010 A light-bodied but well-flavoured wine, with varietal fruit flavours, and enough tannins to provide length and balance. For the budget conscious. Screwcap. 13% alc. **Rating** 87 **To** 2014 $10

Cofield Wines   ★★★★☆
Distillery Road, Wahgunyah, Vic 3687 **Region** Rutherglen
T (02) 6033 3798 **www**.cofieldwines.com.au **Open** Mon–Sat 9–5, Sun 10–5
Winemaker Damien Cofield **Est.** 1990 **Dozens** 13 000 **Vyds** 15.4ha
Sons Damien (winery) and Andrew (vineyard) have taken over responsibility for the business from parents Max and Karen. Collectively, they have developed an impressively broad-based product range with a strong cellar door sales base. The Pickled Sisters Café is open for lunch Wed–Mon (tel (02) 6033 2377). A 20ha property at Rutherglen, purchased in 2007, is planted to shiraz, durif and sangiovese. Exports to China.

YYYYY Minimal Footprint Quartz Vein Vineyard Organic Durif 2010 Youthful crimson-purple; I believe implicitly in the value of organic growing, and this wine is a wonderful example to prove the tangible benefits that can flow. It is hard to imagine a more elegant, balanced and flavourful durif than this; both its length and balance are outstanding. Screwcap. 13.8% alc. **Rating** 94 **To** 2020 $32

YYYYY Victorian Marsanne Viognier 2010 Bright green-yellow; the blend works very
✪   well, marsanne providing the structure and chalky acidity, viognier the apricot and peach; sometimes these can cancel each other out, but here the union is synergistic. Screwcap. 12.5% alc. **Rating** 92 **To** 2015 $20
        Provincial Parcel Rutherglen Durif 2010 **Rating** 92 **To** 2018 $39
        Rutherglen Muscat NV **Rating** 92 **To** 2013 $25
        Minimal Footprint Quartz Vein Vineyard Organic Malbec 2009
        Rating 91 **To** 2024 $35
        Minimal Footprint Quartz Vein Vineyard Organic Shiraz 2010 **Rating** 90
        To 2019 $30
        Cabernet Sauvignon 2009 **Rating** 90 **To** 2019 $24
✪   Rutherglen King Valley Sangiovese 2009 Light, bright, clear red; a few steps, then one or two back, but slowly we are seeing sangiovese appeal more frequently that is worthy of the name; this is not a world beater, but has been well-assembled, and the classic cherry/sour cherry fruits are there in abundance, the tannins remarkably well behaved. Screwcap. 13.5% alc. **Rating** 90 **To** 2017 $22

ΨΨΨΨ   Shiraz 2009 **Rating** 89 **To** 2019 $24
King Valley Riesling 2011 **Rating** 88 **To** 2016 $18

Coldstream Hills   ★★★★★

31 Maddens Lane, Coldstream, Vic 3770 **Region** Yarra Valley
T (03) 5960 7000 **www.**coldstreamhills.com.au **Open** 7 days 10–5
Winemaker Andrew Fleming, Greg Jarratt, James Halliday (Consultant) **Est.** 1985
Dozens NA **Vyds** 100ha
Founded by the author, who continues to be involved as a consultant, but acquired by
Southcorp in mid 1996, Coldstream Hills is now a small part of Treasury Wine Estates, with
100ha of owned or managed estate vineyards as its base. Chardonnay and Pinot Noir continue
to be the principal focus; Merlot came on-stream in 1997, Sauvignon Blanc around the same
time, Reserve Shiraz later still. Vintage conditions permitting, Chardonnay, Pinot Noir and
Cabernet Sauvignon are made in both varietal and Reserve form, the latter in restricted
quantities. In 2010 an entirely new, multimillion dollar winery was erected around the original
winery buildings and facilities; it has a capacity of 1500 tonnes. There is a plaque in the
fermentation area commemorating the official opening on 12 October 2010 and naming the
facility the 'James Halliday Cellar'. Tasting notes are written by Andrew Fleming (AF) or Ben
Edwards (BE). Exports to the UK, the US and Singapore.

ΨΨΨΨΨ   **Deer Farm Vineyard Chardonnay 2010** Pale straw; attractive citrus notes
of lemon pith and lime, with underlying hints of matchflint and stonefruit. The
French oak used is seamless and complements the wine beautifully. Classic Upper
Yarra fruit characters of lemon peel, lime and hints of nectarine. The palate is
fine, with great length and finely balanced acidity. Gold medal National Wine
Show '11. Screwcap. 13.5% alc. **Rating** 95 **To** 2019 $40
Reserve Yarra Valley Shiraz 2010 Deep crimson, purple hue; a heady
concoction of ripe red and black fruits, overlaid by spice and seductive floral
aromas; the palate is medium-bodied and full of silky, fine-grained tannins, lively
acidity and a thoroughly expansive conclusion; a wine of purity and power
seamlessly portrayed. Screwcap. 14% alc. **Rating** 95 **To** 2024 $45 BE

ΨΨΨΨΩ   **Yarra Valley Merlot 2010 Rating** 93 **To** 2020 $35 BE
Cabernet Sauvignon 2010 Rating 92 **To** 2022 $35 BE
Yarra Valley Sauvignon Blanc 2011 Rating 91 **To** 2015 $33 BE
Yarra Valley Chardonnay 2011 Rating 91 **To** 2018 $33 BE
Pinot Noir Chardonnay 2008 Rating 91 **To** 2016 $35 BE

Coliban Valley Wines   ★★★★

313 Metcalfe-Redesdale Road, Metcalfe, Vic 3448 **Region** Heathcote
T 0417 312 098 **www.**colibanvalleywines.com.au **Open** W'ends 10–5
Winemaker Helen Miles **Est.** 1997 **Dozens** 400 **Vyds** 4.4ha
Helen Miles, who has a degree in science, and partner Greg Miles have planted 2.8ha of
shiraz, 1.2ha of cabernet and 0.4ha of merlot near Metcalfe, in the cooler southwest corner of
Heathcote. The granitic soils and warm climate allow organic principles to be used successfully.
The shiraz is dry-grown, while the cabernet sauvignon and merlot receive minimal irrigation.

ΨΨΨΨΩ   **Heathcote Shiraz 2009** Good hue and depth; while not entirely free of the
prolonged drought, this wine seems to have far more vibrancy and fragrance
than prior, drought-affected years; it is medium-bodied, but the palate has a
really attractive array of spice, red and black fruits, and a minor twist of licorice;
the finish and aftertaste are particularly attractive. Screwcap. 14% alc. **Rating** 93
To 2020 $30

Collector Wines   ★★★★★

12 Bourke Street, Collector, NSW 2581 (postal) **Region** Canberra District
T (02) 6116 8722 **www.**collectorwines.com.au **Open** Not
Winemaker Alex McKay **Est.** 2007 **Dozens** 2000

Owner and winemaker Alex McKay makes two Canberra District Shirazs, the Marked Tree Red from parcels of shiraz from vineyards in and around Murrumbateman, and the Reserve from a single patch of mature shiraz grown on an elevated granite saddle near Murrumbateman. No shirazs were received for this edition; the rating is that of last year. Exports to the Netherlands.

ŸŸŸŸŸ **Lamp Lit Marsanne 2010** Crisp, firm, vibrant, lively, and fresh. A very smart wine that will develop very well. Gold medal Winewise '11. Screwcap. 12.8% alc. Rating 94 To 2020 $33

Colvin Wines   ★★★★☆

19 Boyle Street, Mosman, NSW 2088 (postal) **Region** Hunter Valley
T (02) 9908 7886 **www.**colvinwines.com.au **Open** Not
Winemaker Andrew Spinaze, Mark Richardson **Est.** 1999 **Dozens** 500 **Vyds** 5.2ha
In 1990 Sydney lawyer John Colvin and wife Robyn purchased the De Beyers Vineyard, which has a history going back to the second half of the 19th century. By 1967, when a syndicate headed by Douglas McGregor bought 35ha of the original vineyard site, no vines remained. The syndicate planted semillon on the alluvial soil of the creek flats and shiraz on the red clay hillsides. When the Colvins acquired the property the vineyard was in need of attention. Up to 1998 all the grapes were sold to Tyrrell's, but since '99 quantities have been made for the Colvin Wines label. These include Sangiovese, from a little over 1ha of vines planted by John in 1996 because of his love of the wines of Tuscany.

ŸŸŸŸŸ **De Beyers Vineyard Hunter Valley Semillon 2010** Bright green-straw; has just embarked on the journey that will ultimately fill it with lemon/lime fruit enriched by honey and lightly browned toast. At the moment, the delicious pure fruit holds sway, which is no bad thing. Screwcap. 11% alc. Rating 94 To 2025 $25

ŸŸŸŸŸ **De Beyers Vineyard Hunter Valley Sangiovese 2009** Rating 93 To 2017 $28
De Beyers Vineyard Hunter Valley Shiraz 2009 Rating 91 To 2020 $35

Condo Wines   ★★★

3 Ward Street, Torrensville, SA 5031 (postal) **Region** Lower Murray Zone
T (08) 8443 7551 **www.**condowines.com.au **Open** Not
Winemaker Jo Irvine, David Norman (Contract) **Est.** 1997 **Dozens** 2500 **Vyds** 36.7ha
The Condo family, headed by Frank Condo, purchased their Allawah property at Swan Reach on the Murray River in 1981, but it was not until the mid '90s that they established their vineyard, planted predominantly to cabernet sauvignon and shiraz, with small amounts of merlot and chardonnay. The winemaking is simple, designed to keep production costs to a minimum. The major focus of the business is on exports (Singapore, Hong Kong and China), price being the obvious attraction.

ŸŸŸŸ ✪ **Chardonnay 2010** Full yellow-green; the best by some distance of the Condo wines, with attractive, ready-to-go peachy fruit, a hint of cashew, and good acidity to close. Screwcap. 13.5% alc. Rating 88 To 2013 $14
Merlot 2010 Light, relatively developed red; completely counter to expectations. Where the Shiraz has failed, the Merlot has succeeded, largely a function of choosing the right moment to pick the grapes; here the result is the retention of enough merlot character to satisfy, with a faint savoury twist to seal the deal. Diam. 13% alc. Rating 87 To 2014 $14

Constable Estate Vineyards   ★★★☆

205 Gillards Road, Cessnock, NSW 2320 **Region** Hunter Valley
T (02) 4998 7887 **www.**constablevineyards.com.au **Open** 7 days 10–5
Winemaker Liz Jackson (Contract) **Est.** 1981 **Dozens** 3000 **Vyds** 5.55ha
The business was created by long-term friends David Constable and Michael Hershon; one of its points of attraction is its spectacular formal gardens: the Rose, Knot and Herb, Secret

and Sculpture. When Michael died in 2007, David purchased his interests in the property from his estate; he has since replanted half the vineyard, and is actively engaged in a program to increase the quality of the wines and the profile of the business. The varieties planted are cabernet sauvignon, verdelho, semillon, shiraz and chardonnay.

ŸŸŸŸŸ **Premium Hunter Valley Chardonnay 2009** Only made in better vintages; this is in the modern, restrained-alcohol style of the Hunter Valley designed to retain as much natural acidity as possible, and keep the French oak influence secondary to the fruit, here with a distinct grapefruit edge. Screwcap. 13% alc. **Rating** 90 **To** 2016 $25

ŸŸŸŸ **Hunter Valley Verdelho 2011 Rating** 89 **To** 2014 $22
Hunter Valley Shiraz 2010 Rating 88 **To** 2015 $25
Matilda Hunter Valley Sparkling Shiraz 2010 Rating 88 **To** 2013 $25

Cooks Lot ★★★

Cassilis Road, Mudgee, NSW 2850 **Region** Mudgee
T (02) 9550 3228 **www**.cookslot.com.au **Open** Not
Winemaker Duncan Cook **Est.** 2002 **Dozens** 4000
Duncan Cook began making wines for his eponymous brand in 2002, while undertaking his oenology degree at CSU. He completed his degree in 2010, and now works with a number of small growers from the Mudgee and Orange regions wishing to be part of the production of wines with characteristic/distinctive regional character. Exports to China.

ŸŸŸŸ **Mudgee Chardonnay 2010** Vibrant green hue; an expressive melon and citrus bouquet, with a touch of nutty complexity; the palate is racy and shows plenty of lemony acidity and minerals to conclude. Screwcap. 11.5% alc. **Rating** 88 **To** 2014 $20 BE
Mudgee Riesling 2010 Mid gold; pungent lemon zest and cookie dough bouquet; fleshy and showing blanched almonds, and appears rather heavy set on the finish; plenty of flavour, but ultimately lacking precision. Screwcap. 12% alc. **Rating** 87 **To** 2014 $20 BE
Orange Pinot Gris 2011 A citrus-driven example of the style, relying on freshness and finding the desired result; clean, minerally and vibrant. Screwcap. 11.8% alc. **Rating** 87 **To** 2013 $20 BE
Orange Late Harvest 2010 Deep burnt orange; a super-sweet wine, with burnt toffee, marmalade, and copious amounts of sugar for those in need of a sugar hit; not so balanced, but clean and well made; a question of sugar tolerance. 375ml. Screwcap. 8.5% alc. **Rating** 87 **To** 2015 $25 BE

Coolangatta Estate ★★★★★

1335 Bolong Road, Shoalhaven Heads, NSW 2535 **Region** Shoalhaven Coast
T (02) 4448 7131 **www**.coolangattaestate.com.au **Open** 7 days 10–5
Winemaker Tyrrell's **Est.** 1988 **Dozens** 5000 **Vyds** 10.5ha
Coolangatta Estate is part of a 150ha resort with accommodation, restaurants, golf course, etc; some of the oldest buildings were convict-built in 1822. It might be thought that the wines are tailored purely for the tourist market, but in fact the standard of viticulture is exceptionally high (immaculate Scott Henry trellising), and the contract winemaking is wholly professional. Coolangatta has a habit of bobbing up with gold medals at Sydney and Canberra wine shows. Its 2001 Semillon was a prolific gold-medal winner up to '08, the '02 and more recent vintages likewise shining with age.

ŸŸŸŸŸ **Estate Grown Wollstonecraft Semillon 2011** Light straw-green; the oldest planting at Coolangatta Estate that has accumulated an awe-inspiring 71 trophies and 100 gold medals over the years, at large and small wine shows – a tribute to the vineyard and to Tyrrell's, which makes the wine. It has a slightly richer palate than the Estate, but retains all important citrussy acidity. Screwcap. 11% alc. **Rating** 95 **To** 2019 $25

Estate Grown Semillon 2011 Light straw-green; a fresh, tangy semillon with a delicious combination of lemon and a little lime on the bouquet and palate; the finish is long and even; finer than the Wollstonecraft. Screwcap. 10.7% alc. Rating 94 To 2018 $25

Aged Release Estate Grown Semillon 2004 Bright green-straw, youthful and vibrant; the original back labels for its release in '04 said 'drink now or cellar for over five years'. Its intense lemony acidity gives the wine great length, and another five years will be no problem. Screwcap. 11% alc. Rating 94 To 2016 $35

ℙℙℙℙℙ
✪   **Estate Grown Savagnin 2011** Made, as usual for Coolangatta, by Tyrrell's; has the layers of flavour and fruit texture that make savagnin so interesting; while no one flavour dominates, has nuances of tropical (lychee), stone fruit (apricot), citrus (lime) and rose petal (traminer-like). It is relatively full-bodied, but there are no phenolics. Screwcap. 12.6% alc. Rating 93 To 2015 $22

Fortified Verdelho 1998 Rating 92 To Now $35

✪   **Estate Grown Sauvignon Blanc Semillon 2011** 'Etate-grown' is particularly important given the dominance of sauvignon blanc in the blend; both varieties were picked on 17 Feb, the strong grassy notes of the sauvignon blanc seamlessly married with the semillon. Unusually, should have a good cellaring option. Screwcap. 10.7% alc. Rating 90 To 2015 $19

Coombe Farm Estate Wines   ★★★★

11 St Huberts Road, Coldstream, Vic 3770 **Region** Yarra Valley
T (03) 9739 1131 **www.**coombefarm.com.au **Open** Thurs–Mon 10–5, Tues–Wed by appt
Winemaker Nicole Esdaile **Est.** 1999 **Dozens** 6000 **Vyds** 60ha
Coombe Farm Vineyard is owned by Pamela, Lady Vestey (Dame Nellie Melba's granddaughter), Lord Samuel Vestey and The Right Honourable Mark Vestey. The vineyard is planted to pinot noir (22ha), chardonnay (18ha), pinot gris (2.6ha), cabernet sauvignon (2ha), with smaller amounts of merlot and arneis; the rest of the vineyard is currently under development. The vast majority of the fruit is sold to eager winemakers in the region, with a small amount made for Coombe Farm. Exports to the UK.

ℙℙℙℙℙ
     Yarra Valley Pinot Noir 2010 Clear red colour; the bouquet is complex, with French oak playing an obvious role; the spicy tannins are especially appealing, lifting and lengthening the finish. Screwcap. 13% alc. Rating 93 To 2016 $29

Yarra Valley Chardonnay 2010 Bright, clear greenish colour; an interesting chardonnay, very tightly wound within a rocky, minerally shell that allows only a few wisps of the nectarine fruit within to escape. Needs and will repay several years before any serious consumption. Screwcap. 13% alc. Rating 92 To 2016 $25

✪   **Yarra Valley Arneis 2010** Fragrant and fresh, with a distinct flash of sherbet on entering the mouth, extending into a mix of apple, citrus and pear running through to the lively finish. Screwcap. 13.5% alc. Rating 90 To 2015 $19

Nellie Melba Yarra Valley Blanc de Blancs 2009 This is the inaugural vintage of the Nellie Melba Blanc de Blancs, made by the traditional method from estate-grown chardonnay, clones 76 and 96, aged on lees in the bottle for a minimum of 15 months. It has good balance and mouthfeel; the finish is crisp and dry. Diam. 13.5% alc. Rating 90 To 2014 $29

ℙℙℙℙ
✪   **Yarra Valley Pinot Gris 2011** Has more texture than many, derived not from the use of oak, but from several picking dates, and ultimate blending of the components. Whether you like gris or grigio, this will fit the bill. Screwcap. 12.5% alc. Rating 89 To 2013 $19

Yarra Valley Merlot 2009 Rating 89 To 2015 $25

Coombend Estate   ★★★★☆

16017 Tasman Highway, Swansea, Tas 7190 **Region** East Coast Tasmania
T (03) 6257 8881 **Open** 7 days 10–5
Winemaker Tom Ravech **Est.** 1985 **Dozens** 1650 **Vyds** 160ha

In 2005 Tamar Ridge acquired Coombend Estate, including all the assets and the business name. Tamar Ridge has immediately commenced the establishment of a large vineyard that will dwarf the existing 1.75ha of cabernet sauvignon, 2.25ha of sauvignon blanc, 0.5ha of pinot noir and 0.3ha of riesling. Now part of Brown Brothers' Tasmanian empire. Exports to the Netherlands and Sweden.

ŸŸŸŸŸ The Mail Run 2010 A blend of cabernet sauvignon, merlot and cabernet franc; the colour is a light, brilliantly clear crimson; the cascade of red fruit and blackcurrant flavours is delicious, and absolutely totally against expectations. Chapeau. (In French, well done!) Screwcap. 14% alc. Rating 94 To 2020 $25

ŸŸŸŸŸ Sauvignon Blanc 2010 Rating 91 To 2013 $25
Sauvignon Blanc 2009 Rating 90 To Now $24

Coral Sea Wines ★★★

PO Box 538, Bangalow, NSW 2479 **Region** South Australia
T 0417 010 066 **www.coralseawines.com** **Open** Not
Winemaker Contract **Est.** 1993 **Dozens** 6000
Coral Sea Wines is the virtual winery venture of John Cooley. The modestly priced range of Sauvignon Blanc, Chardonnay, NV Cuvee, Merlot, Shiraz and Cabernet Merlot comes from grapes 'grown in South Australia's premier regions'. The business is a passionate supporter of the World Wildlife Fund's 'Save the Coral Sea Appeal'. Exports to Tonga, Fiji, the Solomon Islands, Vietnam and China.

ŸŸŸŸ Cabernet Merlot 2010 Good colour; the best of the Coral Sea releases, with
✪ good flavour and balance at this price point. Drink now. Screwcap. 13.5% alc. Rating 87 To Now $13

 # Corduroy ★★★★★

GPO Box 4249, Sydney, NSW 2001 **Region** Hunter Valley
T 0405 123 272 **www.corduroywines.com.au** **Open** Not
Winemaker Phillip LeMessurier **Est.** 2009 **Dozens** 300
Having worked with Andrew Thomas at Thomas Wines for six years, Phillip LeMessurier has taken the next step by establishing Corduroy and making his own wines from single vineyards, the first vintage being made in 2009. The quality of the wines is exemplary, underscoring the skills learnt at Thomas Wines, and the quality of the vineyards from which the grapes have been purchased.

ŸŸŸŸŸ Hunter Valley Semillon 2011 Brilliant light green–quartz; a vibrant bouquet and palate, with lemon, lemongrass and racy acidity tightly bonded; has enough generosity of flavour to be enjoyed now, but will richly repay prolonged cellaring. Sourced from a vineyard in the Lovedale area for the first time; previously made from a different vineyard. The wine was kept on gross lees post fermentation to build textural palate weight. Screwcap. 10.9% alc. Rating 94 To 2026 $25
Hunter Valley Shiraz Cabernet 2009 The colour is very good, better than that of the '10, signalling a wine with considerable energy and drive to the mix of red and black fruits presenting an elegant character. Screwcap. 13.5% alc. Rating 94 To 2029 $30

ŸŸŸŸŸ Hunter Valley Semillon 2010 Rating 93 To 2017 $25
Hunter Valley Shiraz Cabernet 2010 Rating 93 To 2030 $30

Coriole ★★★★★

Chaffeys Road, McLaren Vale, SA 5171 **Region** McLaren Vale
T (08) 8323 8305 **www.coriole.com** **Open** Mon–Fri 10–5, w'ends & public hols 11–5
Winemaker Simon White, Alex Sherrah **Est.** 1967 **Dozens** 35 000 **Vyds** 48.5ha
While Coriole was not established until 1967, the cellar door and gardens date back to 1860, when the original farm houses that now constitute the cellar door were built. The oldest shiraz

forming part of the estate plantings dates back to 1917, and since '85, Coriole has been an Australian pioneer of sangiovese and – more recently – the Italian white variety fiano, plus barbera and nero d'Avola have joined the fold. Shiraz has 65% of the plantings, and it is for this variety that Coriole is best known, led in turn by the super-premium Lloyd Reserve, the flagship. Exports to all major markets.

ΦΦΦΦΦ McLaren Vale Fiano 2011 Mid straw, green hue; savoury aromas of fennel and sea salt combine with citrus blossom on the bouquet; the palate is generous and lively with a personality that is fresh on the one hand and textured and long on the other; Trophy McLaren Vale Wine Show. Screwcap. 13% alc. **Rating** 94 **To** 2013 $25 BE

Estate Grown McLaren Vale Shiraz 2009 Good purple-red hue; the grapes are hand-plunged in open fermenters, then matured in French oak; the wine is positively plush and richly textured, with black fruits, bitter chocolate and licorice supported by French oak and ripe tannins. A long life ahead. Screwcap. 14% alc. **Rating** 94 **To** 2024 $28

Lloyd Reserve McLaren Vale Shiraz 2009 Deep crimson; a massively full-bodied wine, shrouded in dense, dark fruits, the tannins and oak providing no release; the wine is balanced, but really has to be left for no less than 10 years to reduce it to manageable proportions. With the parameters of its style, very good. Screwcap. 14% alc. **Rating** 94 **To** 2040 $85

Mary Kathleen Reserve McLaren Vale Cabernet Merlot 2009 Bright colour; understated as always, with ripe cassis and a savoury brambly edge to the bouquet; fresh red fruits and fine tannins are in abundance, with a long and expressive conclusion the result. Screwcap. 13.5% alc. **Rating** 94 **To** 2020 $50 BE

○   McLaren Vale Sangiovese Shiraz 2009 **Rating** 94 **To** 2016 $16

ΦΦΦΦႳ Estate McLaren Vale Cabernet Sauvignon 2009 **Rating** 93 **To** 2024 $28
✪   McLaren Vale Sangiovese 2010 Coriole planted its first sangiovese in 1985, pioneering the variety in Australia. This wine has above-average depth of colour and excellent hue; it is very powerful and extremely savoury, more than expected at this alcohol. Certainly demands food – bistecca fiorentina to the fore. Screwcap. 14% alc. **Rating** 91 **To** 2015 $22

The Soloist Single Vineyard McLaren Vale Shiraz 2009 **Rating** 90 **To** 2020 $45 BE

The Dancing Fig McLaren Vale Shiraz Mourvedre 2010 **Rating** 90 **To** 2018 $22

McLaren Vale Barbera 2010 **Rating** 90 **To** 2014 $30 BE

ΦΦΦΦ The Optimist Reserve McLaren Vale Chenin Blanc 2010 **Rating** 89 **To** 2015 $30 BE
○   Redstone McLaren Vale Shiraz 2009 **Rating** 89 **To** 2014 $18

Vita Reserve McLaren Vale Sangiovese 2009 **Rating** 89 **To** 2014 $50 BE

McLaren Vale Chenin Blanc 2011 **Rating** 88 **To** 2017 $16

Prosecco NV **Rating** 88 **To** 2014 $25 BE

Redstone McLaren Vale Cabernet Sauvignon 2009 **Rating** 87 **To** 2013 $18

🍇 Cosmo Wines   ★★★★☆

32 Warrs Avenue, Preston, Vic 3072 (postal) **Region** Yarra Valley
T 0408 519 461 **www**.cosmowines.com.au **Open** Not
Winemaker Lindsay Corby **Est.** 2008 **Dozens** 1500
Lindsay Corby started with fruit winemaking while still at high school, but it was not until 1985 that he began to study at CSU, gaining qualifications in viticulture and wine science. Thereafter he gained practical experience in various roles, including cellar door sales, laboratory work and vineyard management, leading in turn to teaching 'the art and science of the vine and wine' at La Trobe University and managing the small campus vineyard. Just prior to Christmas 2008 he found his first (and hopefully permanent) home at Bianchet Winery, where he makes the Bianchet wines, and the Cosmo wines (all of which are made from purchased grapes). Exports to China.

ŢŢŢŢ Yarra Valley Shiraz 2010 Strong red-purple; a very attractive wine that has
✪ absorbed the 50% new French oak (the remainder older American) in which it
was matured. It has excellent texture, balance and length to its mix of blackberry,
spice and plum fruit supported by fine, ripe tannins. Screwcap. 14% alc. **Rating** 94
To 2025 $25

ŢŢŢŢŢ Gippsland Lakes Pinot Noir 2010 Bright and clear red-purple; the bouquet is
✪ fragrant, with spicy/sappy red fruits that surge on entry to the mouth, maintaining
a fruit-sweet red cherry flavour unhindered by oak. Totally delicious drink-now
style. Screwcap. 13.7% alc. **Rating** 92 **To** 2014 $21
✪ Yarra Valley Cabernet Sauvignon 2010 Youthful purple-crimson colour;
has been well-made, with cassis fruit holding its own against French oak, and
the tannins are appropriately fine for a light- to medium-bodied wine. Peculiar
decision to use cork of no great quality. 13% alc. **Rating** 90 **To** 2017 $21
Gippsland Lakes Sparkling Pinot Noir NV Rating 90 **To** 2013 $27

ŢŢŢŢ Yarra Valley Sauvignon Blanc 2011 **Rating** 89 **To** Now $18
Sparkling Chardonnay NV Rating 89 **To** 2013 $27

Cowaramup Wines ★★★★★

19 Tassel Road, Cowaramup, WA 6284 **Region** Margaret River
T (08) 9755 5195 **www**.cowaramupwines.com.au **Open** By appt
Winemaker Naturaliste Vintners (Bruce Dukes) **Est.** 1995 **Dozens** 5000 **Vyds** 17ha
Russell and Marilyn Reynolds run a biodynamic vineyard with the aid of sons Cameron
(viticulturist) and Anthony (assistant winemaker). Plantings began in 1996 and have been
expanded to cover merlot, cabernet sauvignon, shiraz, semillon, chardonnay and sauvignon
blanc. Notwithstanding low yields and the discipline that biodynamic grapegrowing entails,
wine prices are modest. Wines are released under the Cowaramup Wines, Clown Fish and
New School labels.

ŢŢŢŢ Reserve Limited Edition Margaret River Chardonnay 2010 Light straw-
green; a wine of intensity and finesse; it stares down critics who would suggest it
needed riper fruit, pointing to the ease with which is has absorbed 12 months in
new French oak, the latter simply contributing another degree to the length of the
palate. Screwcap. 12.5% alc. **Rating** 95 **To** 2016 $35
Reserve Limited Edition Margaret River Cabernet Sauvignon 2010 From
estate biodynamic vineyards, and includes a small portion of merlot, cabernet franc
and petit verdot. A wine notable for its elegance and effortless balance, the black
and red berry fruits framed by superfine tannins and subtle oak. Screwcap. 13% alc.
Rating 94 **To** 2025 $35

ŢŢŢŢŢ Clown Fish Margaret River Semillon Sauvignon Blanc 2011 The
✪ components were separately fermented in stainless steel and then blended; the
wine has tremendous drive and energy, with passionfruit and gooseberry to the
fore, and a lingering finish. Screwcap. 12.5% alc. **Rating** 93 **To** 2014 $20
Clown Fish Margaret River Chardonnay 2011 Rating 92 **To** 2017 $23
Clown Fish Margaret River Shiraz 2010 Rating 92 **To** 2023 $23
Clown Fish Margaret River Cabernet Merlot 2010 Rating 91 **To** 2017 $25

Coward & Black Vineyards ★★★★

448 Tom Cullity Drive, Wilyabrup. WA 6280 **Region** Margaret River
T (08) 9755 6355 **www**.cowardandblack.com.au **Open** 7 days 9–5
Winemaker Clive Otto (Contract) **Est.** 1998 **Dozens** 3000 **Vyds** 9.5ha
Patrick Coward and Martin Black have been friends since they were five years old. They
acquired a property directly opposite Ashbrook and in the same road as Vasse Felix, and
began the slow establishment of a dry-grown vineyard. A second block was commenced five
years later, by which time water was available to both of the blocks, but it is seldom used.
In all there are 2.5ha each of cabernet sauvignon and shiraz, and 1.5ha each of chardonnay,
semillon and sauvignon blanc. The cellar door is integrated with another of their businesses,

the Margaret River Providore. The result is an organic vegetable garden, 1000 olive trees and an 80-seat restaurant serving food that has attracted praise from all and sundry since the word go, incorporating vegetables and fruit straight from the organic garden.

♈♈♈♈♈ **Margaret River Semillon Sauvignon Blanc 2011** What the Lord giveth (admirably clear, uncluttered front label), the Lord taketh away (excruciatingly difficult to read back label). Pale straw-green, this is most attractive wine, with well-balanced and expressive fruit flavours from the lemon-accented semillon through to the passionfruit and pineapple of the sauvignon blanc. Screwcap. 12.4% alc. **Rating** 93 **To** 2015 $23

✪ **Show Margaret River Shiraz 2007** Light, clear red-purple; while only medium-bodied at best, the wine offers the full suite of aromas and flavours of predominantly red fruits and an array of spices; the fine and soft tannins extend the palate and finish. Screwcap. 14% alc. **Rating** 91 **To** 2017 $21

The Brothers Margaret River Cabernet Sauvignon 2009 Uncertain colour tells of a savoury wine with a stream of tannins partly coming from 20 months in French oak, and partly from the inherent nature of the fruit; the wine has length and persistence, which may well carry it forward to a less confrontational future. Screwcap. 14.5% alc. **Rating** 90 **To** 2020 $35

♈♈♈♈ **Sweetness & Light 2011 Rating** 87 **To** 2014 $19

Crabtree Watervale Wines ★★★★★
North Terrace, Watervale SA 5452 **Region** Clare Valley
T (08) 8843 0069 **www**.crabtreewines.com.au **Open** 7 days 10.30–4.30
Winemaker Kerri Thompson **Est.** 1979 **Dozens** 5000 **Vyds** 13.2ha
Wine industry executives Richard Woods and Rasa Fabian purchased Crabtree in 2007 and left Sydney corporate life for the ultimate seachange. Collectively, they had decades of sales and marketing experience, and remain adamant that Crabtree should be an estate brand, and therefore limited in volume. Kerri Thompson (see Wines by KT) is a highly talented and very experienced winemaker, having a great record with Riesling. Last year's rating is maintained in the absence of a representative submission of its wines.

♈♈♈♈♈ **Riesling 2011** Has more tension, focus and drive than Hilltop Vineyard, although the character of the fruit flavours is similar until the emphatic finish and its lime sherbet. Screwcap. 12% alc. **Rating** 94 **To** 2021 $25

♈♈♈♈♈ **Hilltop Vineyard Riesling 2011 Rating** 90 **To** 2015 $22

Craiglee ★★★★★
Sunbury Road, Sunbury, Vic 3429 **Region** Sunbury
T (03) 9744 4489 **www**.craiglee.com.au **Open** Sun, public hols 10–5, or by appt
Winemaker Patrick Carmody **Est.** 1976 **Dozens** 2500 **Vyds** 9.5ha
A winery with a proud 19th-century record, Craiglee recommenced winemaking in 1976 after a prolonged hiatus. Produces one of the finest cool-climate shirazs in Australia, redolent of cherry, licorice and spice in the better (warmer) vintages, lighter-bodied in the cooler ones. Mature vines and improved viticulture have made the wines more consistent (and even better) over the past 10 years or so. No wines were received for this edition; the rating is that of last year. Exports to the UK, the US, Hong Kong and Italy.

Craigow ★★★★★
528 Richmond Road, Cambridge, Tas 7170 **Region** Southern Tasmania
T (03) 6248 5379 **www**.craigow.com.au **Open** 7 days Christmas to Easter (except public hols), or by appt
Winemaker Winemaking Tasmania (Julian Alcorso) **Est.** 1989 **Dozens** 800 **Vyds** 8.75ha
Hobart surgeon Barry Edwards and wife Cathy have moved from being grapegrowers with only one wine to a portfolio of several wines, while continuing to sell most of their grapes. Craigow has an impressive museum release program; the best are outstanding, while others

show the impact of sporadic bottle oxidation (a diminishing problem with each vintage now under screwcap). In 2008 Craigow won the Tasmanian Vineyard of the Year Award. There is a degree of poetic history: the first settler, who arrived in the 1820s, was a Scottish doctor (James Murdoch) who, among other things, grew opium poppies for medical use; by 1872 his descendants were making wine from grapes, gooseberries and cherries. There is some suggestion that the grapes, known then as black cluster, were in all probability pinot noir.

ΨΨΨΨΨ **Riesling 2010** Glowing yellow-green; a clean, richly robed bouquet; good length and focus; ripe lime-accented fruit. Screwcap. 11.5% alc. **Rating** 90 **To** 2020 $28
Pinot Noir 2010 Strong colour; full-on ripe, luscious, rounded fruit in the heartland of Tasmanian pinot noir in '10; has good development potential. Screwcap. 13.8% alc. **Rating** 90 **To** 2017 $38

ΨΨΨΨ **Gewurztraminer 2010 Rating** 88 **To** 2014 $27
Gewurztraminer 2011 Rating 87 **To** 2013 $23

Craneford

Moorundie Street, Truro, SA 5356 **Region** Barossa Valley
T (08) 8564 0003 **www**.cranefordwines.com **Open** Mon–Fri 10–5, w'ends by appt
Winemaker Carol Riebke, John Glaetzer (Consultant) **Est.** 1978 **Dozens** 50 000
Since Craneford was founded in 1978 it has undergone a number of changes of both location and ownership. The biggest change came in 2004 when the winery, by then housed in the old country fire station building in Truro, was expanded and upgraded. In 2006 John Glaetzer joined the team as consultant winemaker, with Carol Riebke the day-to-day winemaker. Quality grapes are sourced from contract growers, and production has doubled – amazing in these tough times. Exports to all major markets.

ΨΨΨΨΨ **Basket Pressed Barossa Valley Shiraz 2009** Strong crimson-purple; has a full range of black fruits, the grapes having been picked at their optimum; the palate is supple and smooth until the back-palate and finish, when savoury notes and beautifully balanced tannins take it into another dimension. Screwcap. 14.5% alc. **Rating** 93 **To** 2029 $28

Crawford River Wines

741 Hotspur Upper Road, Condah, Vic 3303 **Region** Henty
T (03) 5578 2267 **www**.crawfordriverwines.com **Open** By appt
Winemaker John and Belinda Thomson **Est.** 1975 **Dozens** 4000 **Vyds** 11.5ha
Time flies, and it seems incredible that Crawford River celebrated its 35th birthday in 2010. Once a tiny outpost in a little-known wine region, Crawford River is now one of the foremost producers of Riesling (and other excellent wines) thanks to the unremitting attention to detail and skill of its founder and winemaker, John Thomson (and moral support from wife Catherine). His exceptionally talented elder daughter Belinda has returned part-time after completing her winemaking degree and working along the way in Marlborough (NZ), Bordeaux, Ribera del Duero (Spain), Bolgheri and Tuscany, and the Nahe (Germany), with Crawford River filling in the gaps. She continues working in Spain, effectively doing two vintages each year. Younger daughter Fiona is in charge of national sales and marketing. Exports to the UK, Ireland, Canada, Japan and South-East Asia.

ΨΨΨΨΨ **Riesling 2011** Bright straw-green; unsurprisingly, has many things in common with the Young Vines, but has distinctly deeper and slightly riper lime/citrus fruit on the very long palate. Henty often gets forgotten in discussion of the best Riesling areas in Australia simply because there are only two producers of commercial volumes of the variety (Seppelt the other). Has tremendous length and aftertaste. Screwcap. 13% alc. **Rating** 97 **To** 2026 $37
Young Vines Riesling 2011 The fragrant lime-infused bouquet leads into a palate jumping with lime juice flavours, and with the hallmark core of steely acidity that Crawford River always has, and which gives the wines such a long lease of life. Screwcap. 12.5% alc. **Rating** 95 **To** 2026 $27

Serendipitous Selection 2010 Brilliant green-straw; a very interesting Riesling, made in the Rheingau style rather than Mosel, with varietal fruit, some sweetness, and acidity tightly woven together. The decision not to stop the fermentation earlier was brave, but paid off. A guaranteed 20 years in front of it. Screwcap. 12.5% alc. **Rating** 94 **To** 2030 $43

ŸŸŸŸŸ **Rose 2011 Rating** 90 **To** 2013 $25

Credaro Family Estate ★★★★★

2175 Caves Road, Yallingup, WA 6282 **Region** Margaret River
T (08) 9755 1111 **www**.credarowines.com.au **Open** 7 days 10–5
Winemaker Dave Johnson **Est.** 1993 **Dozens** 10 000 **Vyds** 93ha
The Credaro family first settled in Margaret River in 1922, migrating from Northern Italy. Initially a few small plots of vines were planted to provide the family with wine in the European tradition. However, things moved significantly in the '80s and '90s, and today the family has three separate vineyards, one previously known as Vasse River Wines. Roughly 25% of the grapes are vinified by the family, the remainder sold under contract to larger local producers. The estate produces two ranges: Beach Head and Credaro Family Estate. In recent years Credaro has had significant success in wine shows for both ranges; skilled winemaking and mature vines are the foundation. This in turn has led to the opening of a new cellar door.

ŸŸŸŸŸ **Margaret River Cabernet Merlot 2010** Clear, bright red-purple; although the alcohol is only 14%, this is a medium- to full-bodied wine of considerable power that is founded on the intensity of the blackcurrant, red berry fruits, substantial albeit fine-grained tannins, and French oak. Will richly repay cellaring. Screwcap. 14% alc. **Rating** 95 **To** 2025 $22
Margaret River Sauvignon Blanc Semillon 2011 Pale colour; a lightly pungent and expressive blend of herbaceous green nettle aromas, coupled with tropical fruit notes; the palate is lively and energetic, with tangy and chalky acidity lingering on the even finish. Screwcap. 12.5% alc. **Rating** 94 **To** 2014 $22 BE

ŸŸŸŸŸ
○ **Beach Head Margaret River Sauvignon Blanc Semillon 2011 Rating** 93
To Now $17
Margaret River Chardonnay 2011 Rating 92 **To** 2016 $30 BE
○ **Beach Head Margaret River Shiraz 2010 Rating** 92 **To** 2020 $19
○ **Beach Head Margaret River Cabernet Merlot 2010 Rating** 90
To 2016 $19
Margaret River Cabernet Sauvignon 2010 Rating 90 **To** 2017 $40 BE

ŸŸŸŸ **Margaret River Fragola 2011 Rating** 87 **To** 2014 $24 BE

Crittenden Estate ★★★★★

25 Harrisons Road, Dromana, Vic 3936 **Region** Mornington Peninsula
T (03) 5981 8322 **www**.crittendenwines.com.au **Open** 7 days 11–4
Winemaker Rollo Crittenden **Est.** 2003 **Dozens** 7000 **Vyds** 14ha
The wheel of fortune has turned full circle with son Rollo Crittenden returning to the (new) family wine business established by father Garry in 2003. In so doing, both father and son have severed ties with Dromana Estate, the old family business. For good measure, the Crittendens have taken a lease on a modern winery in Patterson Lakes, approximately 20 mins north of their Dromana property. Capable of handling 200 tonnes of grapes, more than that required by Crittenden Estate, it has enabled Rollo to develop Latitude 38, a contract winemaking business. He was named Young Gun Australian Winemaker of the Year '10. Exports to the UK.

ŸŸŸŸŸ **The Zumma Chardonnay 2010** Made using very similar techniques to the
✪ standard wine, except the mlf is 30%. The far greater intensity and focus of this wine comes from the selection of the best portion of the home vineyard, now 24 years old; the wine flows through the mouth with controlled intensity, the flavours of nectarine and white peach joined by a hint of fig, and oak in the background. Screwcap. 13.5% alc. **Rating** 94 **To** 2017 $50

The Zumma Pinot Noir 2010 Sourced entirely from the home vineyard planted in 1987, the clonal mix increased in '93. Bright, clear colour, the aromatic bouquet with red cherry and spice to the fore; the powerful palate has abundant cherry and plum fruit with fine, persistent tannins drawing out the finish. Screwcap. 13.5% alc. Rating 94 To 2017 $50

ŸŸŸŸŸ Mornington Peninsula Chardonnay 2010 Rating 93 To 2016 $35
Mornington Peninsula Pinot Noir 2010 Rating 92 To 2018 $35
Les Adieux Cabernet 2009 Rating 91 To 2019 $45
Los Hermanos Homenaje 2010 Rating 90 To 2014 $34

ŸŸŸŸ Los Hermanos Tempranillo 2010 Rating 88 To 2017 $30

Cruickshank Callatoota Estate ★★★

5058 Golden Highway, Denman, NSW 2328 **Region** Hunter Valley
T (02) 6547 1088 **www**.cruickshank.com.au **Open** 7 days 9–5
Winemaker John Cruickshank, Laurie Nicholls **Est.** 1973 **Dozens** 6000 **Vyds** 26.63ha
The change of address marks the fact that the Cruickshanks have purchased a substantial existing vineyard near Denman; the original vineyard is now a coal-mining site. The new vineyard is predominantly planted to cabernet sauvignon, verdelho, shiraz, chardonnay and cabernet franc. Exports to China.

ŸŸŸŸ ✪ Hunter Valley Cabernet Sauvignon 2007 Something of a surprise packet, although the vintage certainly helped; still quite fresh; the blackcurrant/plum fruit is framed by balanced tannins. Screwcap. 13.5% alc. Rating 89 To 2014 $18
Hunter Valley Shiraz 2009 Not quite made to a formula, but all the Cruickshank red wines are matured in large American oak casks for up to two years, and then held for up to two years prior to release. Medium red-purple; a medium-bodied wine with black fruits and earthy notes, the oak restrained. Screwcap. 13.5% alc. Rating 88 To 2016 $21

Cullen Wines ★★★★★

4323 Caves Road, Wilyabrup, WA 6280 **Region** Margaret River
T (08) 9755 5277 **www**.cullenwines.com.au **Open** 7 days 10–4.30
Winemaker Vanya Cullen, Trevor Kent **Est.** 1971 **Dozens** 20 000 **Vyds** 49ha
One of the pioneers of Margaret River, which has always produced long-lived wines of highly individual style from the mature estate vineyards. The vineyard has progressed beyond organic to biodynamic certification and, subsequently, has become the first vineyard and winery in Australia to be certified carbon neutral. This requires the calculation of all of the carbon used and carbon dioxide emitted in the winery; the carbon is then offset by the planting of new trees. Winemaking is now in the hands of Vanya Cullen, daughter of the founders; she is possessed of an extraordinarily good palate. It is impossible to single out any particular wine from the top echelon; all are superb. Exports to all major markets.

ŸŸŸŸŸ Kevin John Margaret River Chardonnay 2010 Hand-picked, whole bunch-pressed, and wild yeast-fermented in two-thirds new French barriques, one-third 1-year-old, before spending a further five months in those barrels. The texture and mouthfeel are supple and round, the white peach, cashew and fig flavours coursing in an unbroken stream through to the finish and aftertaste. The length of the finish is prodigious. Screwcap. 13.5% alc. Rating 97 To 2020 $105
Kevin John Margaret River Chardonnay 2009 The 23–35-year-old vines were hand-picked over two weeks; the wine was wild yeast-fermented and spent nine months in new French oak that barely intrudes, so intense and focused is the mix of grapefruit, white peach and mineral flavours of the magnificently long and fresh palate. A wine of exceptional poise and purity. Screwcap. 13.5% alc. Rating 97 To 2024 $105

Cullen Vineyard Margaret River Sauvignon Blanc Semillon 2011 The typical complex make-up of 69% sauvignon blanc and 31% semillon, with 47% of the wine fermented in French oak, 74% new. The ultra-fragrant bouquet and intense palate are most remarkable for the way they have absorbed the barrel fermentation; it's also virtually impossible to decide whether the aromas and flavours are on the citrus/herbal side, or the riper passionfruit spectrum. Does that matter? I sincerely doubt it. Screwcap. 11.5% alc. **Rating** 96 **To** 2021 $35

Diana Madeline 2010 A 77/10/6/4/3% blend of cabernet sauvignon, merlot, petit verdot, malbec and cabernet franc. Confident with the quality of her biodynamically-grown estate grapes, Vanya Cullen is taking a gently gently approach with all aspects of the wine. Thus it is medium-bodied at best, but is perfectly balanced and its array of blackcurrant, redcurrant, earth and spice fruit flavours are clearly varietal. Above all else, it is certain the wine will develop beautifully over the next 20–30 years. Screwcap. 13% alc. **Rating** 96 **To** 2040 $115

Mangan Vineyard Margaret River Sauvignon Blanc Semillon 2011 A blend of 58% sauvignon blanc and 42% semillon; 20% fermented in French oak, 25% new. Like the Cullen Vineyard, made without any acid addition, the multiple components seamlessly woven together; slightly fuller in the mouth, perhaps reflecting the slightly higher alcohol and the greater percentage of semillon; once again, this is an exercise in harmony that no man should put asunder. Screwcap. 12% alc. **Rating** 95 **To** 2021 $35

Diana Madeline 2009 The usual complex blend of Cabernet Sauvignon/ Cabernet Franc/Merlot/Malbec, wild yeast-fermented and matured for 13 months in French oak. It has excellent colour, and is made in the 'new' medium-bodied Cullen style; the texture is silky, and the tannins are not the least aggressive, making it a very elegant and fresh wine that will doubtless age for as long as you wish. Screwcap. 12.5% alc. **Rating** 95 **To** 2030 $112

Mangan Margaret River Malbec Petit Verdot Merlot 2010 **Rating** 94 **To** 2020 $45

ΨΨΨΨΩ   **Mangan Margaret River Malbec Petit Verdot Merlot 2011** **Rating** 92 **To** 2021 $45

○   **Margaret River Red 2009** **Rating** 93 **To** 2017 $20
○   **Margaret River White 2011** **Rating** 92 **To** 2015 $20
✪   **Margaret River Red 2010** A 48/36/16% blend of malbec, petit verdot and merlot with only 21% of the wine having oak contact (eight months in 2-year-old French oak). It is a compelling demonstration of the quality of the fruit that Cullen receives, leaving others shaking their heads in envy. It is full of red and blackcurrant fruit and with emphasis on plum, and has a soft, inviting palate. Screwcap. 13% alc. **Rating** 92 **To** 2017 $20

Cumulus Wines   ★★★★☆

PO Box 41, Cudal, NSW 2864 **Region** Orange
T (02) 6390 7900 **www**.cumuluswines.com.au **Open** During Orange Food Week (Apr) and Wine Week (Oct)
Winemaker Debbie Lauritz **Est.** 2004 **Dozens** 200 000 **Vyds** 508ha
Cumulus Wines was established in 2004, and is now majority owned by the Berardo Group of Portugal (which has numerous wine investments in Portugal, Canada and Madeira). Over 500ha of vineyards, planted in the late 1990s, focus on shiraz, cabernet sauvignon, chardonnay and merlot. The wines are released under three brands: Rolling, from the Central Ranges Zone; Climbing, solely from Orange fruit; and the third, Cumulus, super-premium from the best of the estate vineyard blocks. One of an increasing number of wineries to use lightweight bottles. Exports to the UK, the US and other major markets.

ΨΨΨΨΨ   **Rolling Sauvignon Blanc Semillon 2011** Pale straw-green; the bouquet
✪   offers kiwi fruit and citrus, but it is on the palate that the wine really shines; it is intensely juicy and tangy, the finish and aftertaste bright and cleansing, encouraging the next glass. Screwcap. 12.5% alc. **Rating** 94 **To** Now $18

♈♈♈♈♍ Orange Chardonnay 2011 Rating 93 To 2018 $30
Orange Shiraz 2009 Rating 93 To 2029 $30
Orange Shiraz 2010 Rating 91 To 2020 $30

✪ Climbing Orange Merlot 2010 Clear crimson-red; the bouquet has fragrant red fruit aromas, the light- to medium-bodied palate with red cherry, plum and a twist of black olive on the gently savoury, fine tannins of the finish. Orange provides a good climate for the variety. Screwcap. 13% alc. Rating 91 To 2017 $22

✪ Climbing Orange Chardonnay 2011 The bouquet is clean and moderately aromatic, but gives no hint of the intensity of the palate; grapefruit and nectarine flavours drive through to a long, crisp finish with steely acidity balancing the lush fruit. No oak apparent. Screwcap. 12.5% alc. Rating 90 To 2016 $22
Climbing Orange Pinot Gris 2011 Rating 90 To Now $22

♈♈♈♈ Climbing Orange Cabernet Sauvignon 2010 Rating 89 To 2018 $22
Rolling Central Ranges Chardonnay 2011 Rating 88 To Now $18
Rolling Pink 2011 Rating 88 To Now $18
Rolling Shiraz 2010 Rating 87 To 2014 $18
Rolling Sparkling Pinot Grigio Chardonnay 2011 Rating 87 To 2013 $18

Curlewis Winery ★★★★★

55 Navarre Road, Curlewis, Vic 3222 **Region** Geelong
T (03) 5250 4567 **www.**curlewiswinery.com.au **Open** By appt
Winemaker Rainer Breit **Est.** 1998 **Dozens** 2000 **Vyds** 2.8ha
Rainer Breit and partner Wendy Oliver purchased their property in 1996 with 1.6ha of what were then 11-year-old pinot noir vines. Rainer, a self-taught winemaker, uses the full bag of pinot noir winemaking tricks: cold soaking, hot fermentation, post-ferment maceration, part inoculated and part wild yeast use, prolonged lees contact, and bottling the wine neither fined nor filtered. While self-confessed 'pinotphiles', they planted some chardonnay, supplemented by a little locally grown shiraz and chardonnay. Rainer and Wendy sold the business in May 2011 to Leesa Freyer and Stefano Marasco, but Rainer will stay on as winemaker until 2014, with a phased exit strategy. Leesa and Stefano are passionate pinot noir drinkers, and also own and operate the Yarra Lounge in Yarraville, Melbourne. Exports to Canada, Sweden, the Maldives, Malaysia, Singapore and Hong Kong.

♈♈♈♈♈ Reserve Geelong Pinot Noir 2010 Deep garnet; a very ripe and savoury bouquet of dark fruits, spices and briary complexity; the palate reveals the wine's true personality, with an unctuous texture, silky tannins and a soft, generous and fleshy conclusion. Screwcap. 13% alc. Rating 94 To 2018 $60 BE

♈♈♈♈♍ Geelong Pinot Noir 2010 Rating 91 To 2018 $40 BE
Bel Sel Geelong Pinot Noir 2010 Rating 90 To 2017 $25 BE

♈♈♈♈ Bel Sel Geelong Chardonnay 2011 Rating 89 To 2016 $25 BE

Curly Flat ★★★★★

263 Collivers Road, Lancefield, Vic 3435 **Region** Macedon Ranges
T (03) 5429 1956 **www.**curlyflat.com **Open** W'ends 12–5 or by appt
Winemaker Phillip Moraghan, Matt Regan **Est.** 1991 **Dozens** 6000 **Vyds** 13ha
Phillip Morahan and Jenifer Kolkka began developing Curly Flat in 1992, drawing in part on Phillip's working experience in Switzerland in the late 1980s, and with a passing nod to Michael Leunig. With ceaseless help and guidance from the late Laurie Williams (and others), they have painstakingly established 8.5ha of pinot noir, 3.5ha of chardonnay and 1ha of pinot gris, and a multi-level, gravity-flow winery. Exports to the UK, Japan and Hong Kong.

♈♈♈♈♈ Pinot Noir 2009 Bright mid garnet; a heady and hedonistic array of red and black fruits, Asian spices and subtle floral notes blend together on the bouquet; the palate is silky, deeply textured and layered, with a tightly wound core of super fresh fruit and mouth-watering acidity; long, silky and beautifully detailed, this will reward careful cellaring, but will be hard to leave alone. WAK screwcap. 13.9% alc.
Rating 96 To 2020 $48 BE

Chardonnay 2010 Mid gold-green hue; the bouquet offers a ripe array of nectarine, grapefruit, lemon blossom and struck quartz; the palate reveals a healthy touch of toasty oak that is in balance with the generous fruit and nervy spine of acidity; the length and complexity are both commendable and harmonious. Screwcap. 13.6% alc. **Rating** 94 **To** 2020 $42 BE

Pinot Grigio 2011 This is about as savoury as pinot grigio gets, with a struck match character offset by pure pear and fresh-cut lemon; the palate is racy and dry, linear and eceptionally long, and the opportunities for creative food pairings are an exciting prospect. Screwcap. 13% alc. **Rating** 94 **To** 2018 $26 BE

ΨΨΨΨΩ **Williams Crossing Pinot Noir 2010 Rating** 92 **To** 2018 $25 BE
Williams Crossing Chardonnay 2010 Rating 90 **To** 2015 $22 BE
Rose 2011 Rating 90 **To** 2014 $26 BE

Currency Creek Winery ★★★

Winery Road, Currency Creek, SA 5214 **Region** Currency Creek
T (08) 8555 4069 **www**.currencycreekwinery.com.au **Open** 7 days 10–5
Winemaker John Loxton, Phil Christenson, Graham Phillips **Est.** 1969 **Dozens** 1250
Vyds 12ha
For over 40 years this family-owned vineyard and relatively low-profile winery has produced some outstanding wood-matured whites and pleasant, soft reds selling at attractive prices. The vineyards have roughly equal plantings of shiraz, cabernet sauvignon, mourvedre and chardonnay. It will be apparent from this that the essential part of the grape production is sold. Graham Phillips and Jan Curzon purchased Currency Creek Winery in Nov 2009. Exports to the UK, the US and China.

ΨΨΨ
○ **The Viaduct Fleurieu Peninsula Roussanne Viognier 2010 Rating** 88
To 2015 $17
○ **Ostrich Hill Fleurieu Peninsula Shiraz Viognier 2009 Rating** 88
To 2014 $17
○ **Water Ribbon Fleurieu Peninsula Gewurztraminer 2010 Rating** 87
To 2013 $17

Cuttaway Hill Wines ★★★★

PO Box 881, Mittagong, NSW 2575 **Region** Southern Highlands
T 0409 902 982 **www**.cuttawayhillwines.com.au **Open** By appt
Winemaker Mark Bourne **Est.** 1998 **Dozens** 10 000 **Vyds** 23.5ha
While the Bourne family did not acquire Cuttaway Hill from the founding O'Neil family until 2011, Mark Bourne produced the region's first sparkling wines in '04 under the Cuttaway Hill Laurence label. Until '11 Mark's principal focus was viticulture, and he was the founding president of the Southern Highlands Vignerons Association, and chief organiser of the Australian Highlands Wine Show. While he continues those involvements, he is now in charge of all aspects of the Cuttaway Hill business. Exports to the US, Canada and China.

ΨΨΨΨΩ **Southern Highlands Pinot Noir 2010** Good colour; the fragrant bouquet of red and black cherry leads into a well-constructed palate, with clear varietal fruit flavours, finishing with fine tannins. An impressive example of pinot noir from this not-always-easy region, and – within the context of that region – well priced. Screwcap. 13.5% alc. **Rating** 92 **To** 2016 $25

ΨΨΨΨ
✪ **Southern Highlands Sauvignon Blanc 2011** Pale quartz; citrus and gooseberry fruit play tag with ripe tropical/guava notes, the finish fruity rather than showing acidity. Screwcap. 12% alc. **Rating** 89 **To** 2013 $20
Southern Highlands Chardonnay 2010 Rating 87 **To** 2014 $20
Southern Highlands Merlot 2008 Rating 87 **To** 2014 $20
Laurence Cuvee Prestige Brut Chardonnay Pinot Noir NV Rating 87
To 2013 $32

D'Angelo Estate ★★★☆

41 Bayview Road, Officer, Vic 3809 **Region** Yarra Valley
T 0417 055 651 **www**.dangelowines.com.au **Open** W'ends 12–5 or by appt
Winemaker Benny D'Angelo **Est.** 1994 **Dozens** 3000 **Vyds** 15ha
The business dates back to 1994 when Benny D'Angelo's father planted a small block of pinot noir for home winemaking. One thing led to another, with Benny taking over winemaking and doing well in amateur wine shows. This led to the planting of more pinot and some cabernet sauvignon. Expansion continued with the 2001 acquisition of a 4ha site at Officer, which has been planted to six clones of pinot noir, and small parcels of cabernet sauvignon and shiraz. Grapes are also purchased from a wide range of vineyards, stretching from Gippsland to Langhorne Creek.

🍷🍷🍷🍷🍷 **il Berardino Reserve Officer Pinot Noir 2010** Light, bright and clear crimson-purple, it is relatively light-bodied, yet has good structure and length; red and black cherry, spice and fine tannins build on the finish; has the presence that eludes the Fugiastro Yarra Valley. Screwcap. 13.8% alc. **Rating** 90 **To** 2016 $40
Sab's Langhorne Creek Shiraz 2008 Good colour; the wine spent 18 months in new French and American oak, leaving a strong oak thumbprint; mocha, fruitcake and plum fruit have enough tannins to provide structure. Oak lovers will greatly enjoy the wine. Screwcap. 14% alc. **Rating** 90 **To** 2017 $25

🍷🍷🍷🍷 **Officer Sauvignon Blanc 2010 Rating** 89 **To** 2013 $25
Ben's Officer Shiraz 2010 Rating 89 **To** 2014 $25
GTR Langhorne Creek Cabernet Sauvignon 2008 Rating 89 **To** 2016 $30
Officer Lady Chardonnay 2010 Rating 87 **To** 2014 $25
Officer Pinot Grigio 2010 Rating 87 **To** 2013 $25
Fugiastro Yarra Valley Pinot Noir 2010 Rating 87 **To** 2014 $30
Late Disgorged Blanc de Noir 2008 Rating 87 **To** 2013 $35
Officer Blanc de Noir NV Rating 87 **To** 2013 $25

d'Arenberg ★★★★★

Osborn Road, McLaren Vale, SA 5171 **Region** McLaren Vale
T (08) 8329 4888 **www**.darenberg.com.au **Open** 7 days 10–5
Winemaker Chester Osborn, Jack Walton **Est.** 1912 **Dozens** 270 000 **Vyds** 197.2ha
Nothing, they say, succeeds like success. Few operations in Australia fit this dictum better than d'Arenberg, which has kept its almost 100-year-old heritage while moving into the 21st century with flair and elan. At last count the d'Arenberg vineyards, at various locations, have 24 varieties planted, as well as 120 growers in McLaren Vale. There is no question that its past, present and future revolve around its considerable portfolio of richly robed red wines, Shiraz, Cabernet Sauvignon and Grenache being the cornerstones, but with over 20 varietal and/or blend labels spanning the gulf between Roussanne and Mourvedre. The quality of the wines is unimpeachable, the prices logical and fair. It has a profile in both the UK and the US that far larger companies would love to have, underlined by the *Wine & Spirits Magazine* (US) accolade of Winery of the Year in 2009. d'Arenberg celebrated 100 years of family grapegrowing in '12 on the property that houses the winery, cellar door and restaurant (together with some of the oldest estate vines). Exports to all major markets.

🍷🍷🍷🍷🍷 **The Footbolt McLaren Vale Shiraz 2009** Superb, bright clear crimson; it's not
✪ the first thing that normally comes to mind with d'Arenberg, but this is an elegant, fine, medium-bodied wine; the fruits are more in the red than black spectrum, and it is spice more than dark chocolate that joins the fruit, oak and tannins, all perfectly weighted. Screwcap. 14.4% alc. **Rating** 94 **To** 2020 $19
The Dead Arm Shiraz 2009 Deep, inky purple-crimson; in archetypal Dead Arm style, powerful and rich, but given some welcome lift by the mix of bitter chocolate and savoury/spicy notes on the palate. This is a style that will not change any time soon, and, within that context, is a good example. Screwcap. 14.5% alc. **Rating** 94 **To** 2030 $65

The Wild Pixie McLaren Vale Shiraz Roussanne 2010 Bright crimson-purple; the bouquet has a very interesting and unusual combination of spice and cured meat, characters than continue on the lively, open texture of the medium-bodied palate; the finish is very long, yet balanced. A surprise packet. Screwcap. 13.8% alc. **Rating** 94 **To** 2025 $30

The McLaren Sand Hills Grenache 2010 Light but brilliantly clear crimson; a brave call on price, although the wine is of undoubted quality and varietal integrity; its cherry and raspberry fruit flavours are neatly balanced by fine but persistent tannins running through to the long finish. Screwcap. 14% alc. **Rating** 94 **To** 2018 $99

The Blewitt Springs Grenache 2010 A dark and sweet-fruited wine, offering red and black fruits, briar and licorice; the palate is thickly textured, warm and compelling, with the concentration and depth of fruit to satisfy lovers of rich, heady grenache. Screwcap. 14% alc. **Rating** 94 **To** 2023 $99 BE

ɥɥɥɥɥ **The Love Grass McLaren Vale Shiraz 2009 Rating** 93 **To** 2019 $25 BE

The Beautiful View McLaren Vale Grenache 2010 Rating 93 **To** 2022 $99 BE

✪ **The High Trellis McLaren Vale Cabernet Sauvignon 2009** An elegant, medium-bodied wine that sees its first duty to affirm the affinity between variety and region. The tannins are fine, the oak subtle, the overall balance hard to fault. Seriously good value. Screwcap. 14.5% alc. **Rating** 93 **To** 2020 $20

Galvo Garage Cabernet Sauvignon Merlot Petit Verdot Cabernet Franc 2008 Rating 93 **To** 2020 $29

◐ **d'Arry's Original McLaren Vale Shiraz Grenache 2009 Rating** 92 **To** 2020 $19

◐ **The Noble Mud Pie McLaren Vale Viognier Roussanne 2010 Rating** 92 **To** 2015 $20

◐ **The Stump Jump McLaren Vale Shiraz 2009 Rating** 90 **To** 2020 $12

The Coppermine Road Cabernet Sauvignon 2009 Rating 90 **To** 2024 $65 BE

◐ **The Noble Wrinkled McLaren Vale Riesling 2010 Rating** 90 **To** 2014 $20

Dal Zotto Wines ★★★★

Main Road, Whitfield, Vic 3733 **Region** King Valley
T (03) 5729 8321 **www**.dalzotto.com.au **Open** 7 days 10–5
Winemaker Michael Dal Zotto **Est.** 1987 **Dozens** 15 000 **Vyds** 48ha
The Dal Zotto family is a King Valley institution; ex-tobacco growers, then contract grape-growers, they are now primarily focused on their Dal Zotto range. Led by Otto and Elena, and with sons Michael and Christian handling winemaking and sales/marketing respectively, the family is producing increasing amounts of wine of exceptionally consistent quality from its substantial estate vineyard. The cellar door is in the centre of Whitfield, and is also home to their Trattoria (open weekends). One of the first to produce Prosecco in Australia.

ɥɥɥɥɥ **King Valley Riesling 2010** Pale, bright straw-green; a very well made and
✪   constructed wine with exceptional length and purity, the lime juice and lemon zest fruit perfectly balanced by acidity. Screwcap. 12.5% alc. **Rating** 94 **To** 2020 $18

ɥɥɥɥ **King Valley Arneis 2010 Rating** 89 **To** 2014 $27
King Valley Chardonnay 2011 Rating 87 **To** 2014 $38

Dalfarras ★★★☆

PO Box 123, Nagambie, Vic 3608 **Region** Nagambie Lakes
T (03) 5794 2637 **F** (03) 5794 2360 **Open** At Tahbilk
Winemaker Alister Purbrick, Alan George **Est.** 1991 **Dozens** 10 000 **Vyds** 20.97ha
The personal project of Alister Purbrick and artist wife Rosa (née Dalfarra), whose paintings adorn the labels of the wines. Alister, of course, is best known as winemaker at Tahbilk (see separate entry), the family winery and home, but this range of wines is intended to (in Alister's

words) 'allow me to expand my winemaking horizons and mould wines in styles different from Tahbilk'. Exports to Sweden.

🍷🍷🍷🍷 ✪ **Shiraz Grenache Mourvedre 2009** The striking, near-psychedelic label is son Matt's use of three images of mother Rosa's painting, the wine blend assisted by daughter Hayley; the colour is fresh, as are the vibrantly juicy flavours of the wine. Screwcap. 13.5% alc. **Rating** 89 **To** 2015 $16

Dalrymple Vineyards ★★★★☆

1337 Pipers Brook Road, Pipers Brook, Tas 7254 **Region** Northern Tasmania
T (03) 6382 7229 **www**.dalrymplevineyards.com.au **Open** Fri–Sun 10.30–4.30
Winemaker Peter Caldwell **Est.** 1987 **Dozens** 4000 **Vyds** 17ha

Dalrymple was established many years ago by the Mitchell and Sundstrup families; the vineyard and brand were acquired by Hill-Smith Family Vineyards in late 2007. Plantings are split between pinot noir and sauvignon blanc, and the wines are made at Jansz Tasmania. In September 2010 Peter Caldwell was appointed as 'Vigneron', responsible for the vineyard, viticulture and winemaking. He brings with him 10 years' experience at Te Kairanga Wines (Martinborough, NZ), and most recently two years with Josef Chromy Wines. His knowledge of pinot noir and chardonnay is obviously comprehensive.

🍷🍷🍷🍷🍷 **Chardonnay 2010** Bright straw-green; the bouquet has a floral, citrus blossom fragrance; the citrus and stone fruit palate is long and linear; the wine finishes with good acidity and overall finesse. Gold Tas Wine Show '12. Screwcap. 12.5% alc. **Rating** 94 **To** 2017 $35

🍷🍷🍷🍷 **Single Domaine Block T36 Pinot Noir 2009 Rating** 92 **To** 2018 $55
Sauvignon Blanc 2011 Rating 91 **To** 2013 $25
Pinot Noir 2010 Rating 90 **To** 2016 $36

Dalwhinnie ★★★★★

448 Taltarni Road, Moonambel, Vic 3478 **Region** Pyrenees
T (03) 5467 2388 **www**.dalwhinnie.com.au **Open** 7 days 10–5
Winemaker David Jones, Gary Baldwin (Consultant) **Est.** 1976 **Dozens** 4500 **Vyds** 26ha

David and Jenny Jones are making wines with tremendous depth of fruit flavour, reflecting the relatively low-yielding but very well-maintained vineyards. It is hard to say whether the Chardonnay, the Cabernet Sauvignon or the Shiraz is the more distinguished. A further 8ha of shiraz (with a little viognier) were planted in 1999 on a block acquired on Taltarni Road. A 50-tonne contemporary high-tech winery now allows the wines to be made onsite. In 2011 David and Jenny celebrated 30 years of winemaking at Dalwhinnie. Exports to the UK and other major markets.

🍷🍷🍷🍷🍷 **Moonambel Shiraz 2010** Typical deep crimson-purple; intense dark berry fruit aromas join with quality French oak on the bouquet, the svelte palate adding perfectly balanced and integrated tannins; top-class finish and aftertaste; purity and power. Screwcap. 13.5% alc. **Rating** 96 **To** 2035 $58

Southwest Rocks Shiraz 2010 Crimson-purple; black fruits abound on the bouquet and palate, intertwined with spice, pepper and fine tannins; the overall mouthfeel is exceptionally good, emphasising the medium-bodied, elegant nature of the wine. Screwcap. 13% alc. **Rating** 96 **To** 2030 $80

The Pinnacle Shiraz 2010 Slightly deeper colour than Southwest Rocks, with a touch more purple; plum joins the blackberry fruit, and the multifaceted palate is medium- to full-bodied, with balanced, but substantial, tannins. Here power is the key, although it doesn't threaten the balance of the wine. While the two wines are significantly different in style, they can't be separated in terms of quality. Screwcap. 14.5% alc. **Rating** 96 **To** 2040 $80

Moonambel Cabernet 2010 Classic Dalwhinnie style with abundant aromas, fruit on the fore-palate likewise; tightens up on the finish with tannin grip that will relax as the years go by. Screwcap. 14.5% alc. **Rating** 95 **To** 2030 $50

Moonambel Chardonnay 2010 Light, bright green-straw; there is a precision and clarity about the wine that puts it in a class of its own, as its line spears through from the first sip to the aftertaste without any break whatsoever. Screwcap. 13.5% alc. **Rating** 94 **To** 2018 $42

Dandelion Vineyards ★★★★★

PO Box 138, McLaren Vale, SA 5171 **Region** McLaren Vale
T (08) 8556 6099 **www**.dandelionvineyards.com.au **Open** Not
Winemaker Elena Brooks **Est.** 2007 **Dozens** NFP **Vyds** 124.2ha
This is a highly impressive partnership between Peggy and Carl Lindner (40%), Elena and Zar Brooks (40%), and Fiona and Brad Rey (20%). It brings together vineyards spread across the Adelaide Hills, Eden Valley, Langhorne Creek, McLaren Vale, Barossa Valley and Fleurieu Peninsula. Elena is not only the beautiful wife of industry dilettante Zar, but also an exceptionally gifted winemaker. It may be a dauntingly competitive marketplace, but there can be few more promising ventures than this one. Exports to all major markets.

ΨΨΨΨΨ Fairytale of the Barossa Rose 2011 An interesting slant on the vintage: a high
✪ natural acidity of 7.9 g/l, pH of 3.02 and less than 5 g/l of residual sugar. From 85-year-old vines, wild yeast-fermented in old French barrels. Bright pale pink, it is stacked with spicy red berry fruit with a long, lingering finish driven by crisp acidity. A serious wine. Screwcap. 13% alc. **Rating** 95 **To** 2013 $25

✪ Wonderland of the Eden Valley Riesling 2011 Quartz-green; an admirably tight and fine riesling framed by crunchy acidity; lemon, lime and apple fruit will grow with age into a mini-masterpiece. Screwcap. 11.5% alc. **Rating** 94 **To** 2021 $25

ΨΨΨΨΨ Wishing Clock of the Adelaide Hills Sauvignon Blanc 2011 **Rating** 91 **To** 2014 $25

Darlington Vineyard ★★★★★

Holkham Court, Orford, Tas 7190 **Region** Southern Tasmania
T (03) 6257 1630 **www**.darlingtonvineyard.com.au **Open** 7 days 10–5
Winemaker Frogmore Creek **Est.** 1993 **Dozens** 800 **Vyds** 1.6ha
Peter and Margaret Hyland planted a little under 2ha of vineyard in 1993, on the Freycinet coast. The first wines were made from the 1999 vintage, forcing retired builder Peter to complete their home so that the small building in which they had been living could be converted into a cellar door. The vineyard looks out towards the settlement of Darlington on Maria Island, the site of Diego Bernacchi's attempt to establish a vineyard in the 1880s and lure investors by attaching artificial bunches of grapes to his vines. Darlington Vineyard is now owned by Paul and Louise Stranan.

ΨΨΨΨΨ Riesling 2011 Pale straw-green; the bouquet is stacked full of perfumed, exotic
✪ blossom aromas, and the palate is equally intense, with delicious lime juice fruit, and a long, lingering finish. Screwcap. 12.1% alc. **Rating** 95 **To** 2025 $22

TGR Riesling 2011 A delicious wine, its 22 g/l of residual sugar largely covered by the crisp acidity; passionfruit and lime flavours run through to the very long finish. At this stage lies behind the dry version. Screwcap. 10.9% alc. **Rating** 94 **To** 2021 $22

Pinot Noir 2010 Clear purple-crimson; a seamless fusion of red and black cherry and plum on the bouquet flows through onto the silky palate, underpinned by fine tannins and subtle French oak. Classy wine. Screwcap. 13.8% alc. **Rating** 94 **To** 2017 $27

ΨΨΨΨΨ Sauvignon Blanc 2011 **Rating** 93 **To** 2014 $22

ΨΨΨΨ Chardonnay 2011 **Rating** 89 **To** 2014 $22

David Franz ★★★★★

PO Box 677, Tanunda, SA 5352 **Region** Barossa Valley
T 0419 807 468 **www**.david-franz.com **Open** By appt
Winemaker David Franz Lehmann **Est.** 1998 **Dozens** 3500 **Vyds** 29.54ha

David Franz (Lehmann) is one of Margaret and Peter Lehmann's sons, and took a very circuitous path around the world before establishing his eponymous winery. Wife Nicki accompanied him on his odyssey and they, together with three children, two dogs, a mess of chickens and a surly shed cat, all happily live together (albeit privately) in their house and winery. The utterly unique bottles stem from (incomplete) university studies in graphic design (and subsequently interior design); his degree in hospitality business management is less relevant, for visits to the winery, aka, the shed, are strictly by appointment only. An extended family of five share the work in the vineyard and the shed. Exports to the UK, the US, Canada, India, Singapore, Japan, Indonesia, Hong Kong and China.

🍷🍷🍷🍷🍷 **Old Redemption X.O. Tawny NV** Full tawny, grading to light olive on the rim; this '11 blend and bottling has an average age of over 50 years, with a total production of 540 500ml bottles; it is fantastically complex and intense, father Peter Lehmann having acquired the base wine for Old Redemption in 1966 when it was already extremely old. The art of blending is exemplified by this wine, with 2% of '10 riesling added to (very effectively) freshen it up. The rancio is very, very obvious, giving the wine great cut and length; there are some notes of sherry which purists would shake their heads at, but there is no complaint from me. Diam. 19.9% alc. **Rating** 97 **To** 2013 $39

Georgie's Walk Cellar Release Cabernet Sauvignon 2002 A heavily stained cork hardly inspires confidence for this 550-bottle re-release. However, the last bit of the cork was clean, and the wine has held firm, its colour good, and the intense blackcurrant, bitter chocolate and earth flavours bear testament to the very cool, high-quality vintage. David Franz recommends double-decanting this very fine wine. 14.6% alc. **Rating** 96 **To** 2017 $63

Brother's Ilk Adelaide Hills Chardonnay 2010 Pale straw-green; the wine comes from Dijon clones 76 and 96, and although the lengthy back label has a long dissertation, I cannot work out where David's younger brother Phil's contribution starts and finishes, except that he (Phil) made this classically tight and fresh wine with its finely structured grapefruit and mineral flavours. 83 dozen made. Screwcap. 13.7% alc. **Rating** 95 **To** 2017 $42

Benjamin's Promise Cellar Release Shiraz 2004 Eight five per cent from the estate Stonewell Hill Vineyard, 15% from Stelzer Road; 32 dozen of this re-release. A totally delicious wine now on a plateau of perfection that it will hold for years to come, thanks in part to the long, high-quality, perfectly inserted cork; there is a menage of silky red and black fruits, dusted with spice and thoroughly integrated oak. Worth every penny of its price. 14.8% alc. **Rating** 95 **To** 2019 $63

Alternative View Shiraz 2007 Rating 94 **To** 2032 $155
Benjamin's Promise Shiraz 2007 Rating 94 **To** 2022 $43
Plane Turning Right Adelaide Hills Merlot Cabernet Petit Verdot 2010 Rating 94 **To** 2018 $37
Alexander's Reward Cellar Release Cabernet Sauvignon Shiraz 2004 Rating 94 **To** 2019 $63

🍷🍷🍷🍷🍷 **Larrikin IV Grenache Shiraz Cabernet Mataro NV Rating** 93 **To** 2017 $43
Georgie's Walk Cellar Release Cabernet Sauvignon 2004 Rating 93 **To** 2015 $63
Survivor Vine Grenache Shiraz 2009 Rating 92 **To** 2016 $33
Smoking Jim Slaughterhouse Merlot 2009 Rating 92 **To** 2017 $32
Alexander's Reward 2007 Rating 92 **To** 2017 $43
POP Wine Issue 3.1 Cabernet Shiraz 2006 Rating 92 **To** 2021 $66
Cellar Release Red Rose 2006 Rating 91 **To** 2014 $29
Howling Dogue Grenache Shiraz 2009 Rating 90 **To** 2015 $55

ΨΨΨΨ   Blockers Road Pinot Noir 2010 Rating 89 To 2015 $42.90
POP Wine Issue 4.2 Eden Valley Shiraz 2008 Rating 87 To 2014 $65.90

David Hook Wines   ★★★★☆

Cnr Broke Road/Ekerts Road, Pokolbin, NSW 2320 **Region** Hunter Valley
T (02) 4998 7121 **www.**davidhookwines.com.au **Open** 7 days 10–5
Winemaker David Hook **Est.** 1984 **Dozens** 7500 **Vyds** 8ha
David Hook has over 25 years' experience as a winemaker for Tyrrell's and Lake's Folly, also
doing the full Flying Winemaker bit with jobs in Bordeaux, the Rhône Valley, Spain, the US
and Georgia. The estate-owned Pothana Vineyard has been in production for over 25 years,
and the wines made from it are given the 'Old Vines' banner. This vineyard is planted on the
Belford Dome, an ancient geological formation that provides red clay soils over limestone on
the slopes, and sandy loams along the creek flats; the former for red wines, the latter for white.
Exports to the US and Japan.

ΨΨΨΨΨ   Old Vines Pothana Vineyard Belford Semillon 2011 Light quartz colour; a
fresh and lively bouquet and palate has very good length and balance; as is often
the case with young screwcapped semillon, there are more citrus (almost riesling-
like) characters than there were in traditional semillons 10 to 15 years ago. The
change is significant. 10.5% alc. Rating 94 To 2020 $25

ΨΨΨΨΨ   Old Vines Pothana Vineyard Belford Chardonnay 2011 Rating 92
To 2030 $30
Orange Riesling 2011 Rating 90 To 2014 $25
De Novo Bianco 2011 Rating 90 To 2014 $30
○   Hunter Valley + Shiraz 2009 Rating 90 To 2014 $18

ΨΨΨΨ   Hunter Valley Pinot Grigio 2011 Rating 87 To Now $18
○

David Traeger Wines   ★★★

Dromana Estate, 555 Old Moorooduc Road, Tuerong, Vic 3937 **Region** Nagambie Lakes
T (03) 5974 4400 **www.**dromanaestate.com.au **Open** Wed–Sun 11–4
Winemaker David Traeger **Est.** 1986 **Dozens** 3000
David Traeger learned much during his years as assistant winemaker at Mitchelton and
knows Central Victoria well. The red wines are solidly crafted, the Verdelho interesting and
surprisingly long lived. In 2002 the business was acquired by the Dromana Estate group, but
David Traeger continues as winemaker. (See also Baptista entry.) Exports to the UK, Japan,
Italy and Canada.

ΨΨΨΨ   Verdelho 2011 The cool vintage has given the wine energy and a distinct citrus
✪   backbone, both taking it out of the usual rut, leaving the lemon curd and fruit
salad flavours intact. Screwcap. 13% alc. Rating 89 To 2016 $15
Shiraz 2009 Full of contradictions, from the cheap twin-top cork on the one
hand, through to expensive maturation in new American and French oak; the
front label says 'Victoria', the back label the officially recognised Nagambie Lakes
subregion of Goulburn Valley. The red and black fruits have not been able to throw
off their oaky womb, but this is nonetheless as pleasant, well-priced wine. 14% alc.
Rating 89 To 2015 $20

 Dawson & James   ★★★★★

RSD 1470 Brookman Road, Hope Forest via Willunga, SA 5172 (postal)
Region Southern Tasmania
T (08) 8556 7326 **www.**dawsonjames.com.au **Open** Not
Winemaker Peter Dawson, Tim James **Est.** 2010 **Dozens** 750
Peter Dawson and Tim James had long and highly successful careers as senior winemakers
for Hardys/Accolade wines. Tim jumped ship first, becoming managing director of Wirra
Wirra for seven years until 2007, while Peter stayed longer with Constellation. Now both

have consulting roles, and Peter is chairman of the Australian Wine Research Institute, Tim an active consultant. They have both long had a desire to grow and make wine in Tasmania, a desire which came to fruition in '10. Tragically, however, the vineyard on the Derwent River that was supplying them with grapes was hit by the Tasmanian bushfires at the end of February 2012, smoke taint preventing the use of the grapes. Exports to the UK.

ΨΨΨΨΨ **Chardonnay 2010** The wine is super-intense and very long in the mouth, with grapefruit to the fore, white peach following. There is a gentle touch of funk ex partial solids fermentation, the 11 months in 30% new Taransaud oak (what else?) not obvious, and 50% mlf great natural acidity that accelerates the wine on the finish and aftertaste. Screwcap. 12% alc. **Rating** 96 **To** 2023 $42

Pinot Noir 2010 Excellent bright red–purple colour introduces a very fragrant, flowery, scented bouquet, then a supple, elegant and expressive palate with small berries and spices, silky tannins, and great drive; 10% whole bunches and 30% new Taransaud oak are the trimmings for a lovely pinot in which the fruit does all the work. Screwcap. 13.5% alc. **Rating** 96 **To** 2017 $48

Dawson's Patch

71 Kallista-Emerald Road, The Patch, Vic 3792 (postal) **Region** Yarra Valley
T 0419 521 080 **www**.dawsonspatch.com.au **Open** Not
Winemaker Jody Dawson **Est.** 1996 **Dozens** 400 **Vyds** 1.2ha
James and Jody Dawson own and manage this vineyard at the southern end of the Yarra Valley, planted to chardonnay and pinot noir. The climate here is particularly cool, and the grapes do not normally ripen until late April. Jody has completed a degree in viticulture through CSU. The tiny hand-crafted production (Chardonnay and Pinot Noir) is sold through local restaurants and cellars in the Olinda/Emerald/Belgrave area.

ΨΨΨΨΨ **Yarra Valley Chardonnay 2010** Bright pale straw; a pure and fragrant pear and spice bouquet; the palate is lithe and focused, offering a long and complex finish with a generous dollop of toasty oak; clean as a whistle and finely detailed. Screwcap. 13% alc. **Rating** 92 **To** 2016 $27 BE

De Beaurepaire Wines

182 Cudgegong Road, Rylstone, NSW 2849 **Region** Mudgee
T (02) 6379 1473 **F** (02) 6379 0809 **www**.debeaurepairewines.com **Open** At Bridgeview Inn, Rylstone
Winemaker Jacob Stein (Contract) **Est.** 1998 **Dozens** NA **Vyds** 52.34ha
This is the retirement business of former clinical psychologist Janet de Beaurepaire and investment banker Richard de Beaurepaire. Beaurepaire Ridge Vineyard is situated on the 200ha Woodlawn property, one of the oldest properties west of the Blue Mountains, at an altitude of 570–600m. While part of the Mudgee GI, the Rylstone climate is significantly cooler than other parts of the region. The vineyard is planted to shiraz, merlot, cabernet sauvignon, chardonnay, semillon, viognier, petit verdot, verdelho and pinot gris. The property is bounded on two sides by the Cudgegong River, which provides irrigation. Exports to Malaysia, Singapore and China.

ΨΨΨΨ **Captain Starlight Series Rose 2010** Bright pink; made from estate-grown cabernet sauvignon; the precisely measured touch of sweetness becomes more evident each time it is tasted, but not taking it to extremes; true it is that the red berry fruit lying behind that sweetness is not very intense. Screwcap. 12% alc. **Rating** 87 **To** 2013 $18

De Bortoli

De Bortoli Road, Bilbul, NSW 2680 **Region** Riverina
T (02) 6966 0100 **www**.debortoli.com.au **Open** Mon–Sat 9–5, Sun 9–4
Winemaker Darren De Bortoli, Julie Mortlock, John Coughlan **Est.** 1928 **Dozens** 3 million **Vyds** 332ha

Famous among the cognoscenti for its superb Noble One, which in fact accounts for only a minute part of its total production, this winery turns out low-priced varietal and generic wines that are invariably competently made and equally invariably provide value for money. These come in part from estate vineyards, but also from contract-grown grapes. The rating is in part a reflection of the exceptional value for money offered across the range. Exports to all major markets.

ㅜㅜㅜㅜㅜ **Deen Vat 2 Sauvignon Blanc 2011** Pale straw; there is no question the
✪   cool, wet vintage favoured the aromatic white wines if disease was kept at bay; the specific sauvignon blanc yeast seems also to have helped the clear tropical gooseberry aromas and flavours, zesty acidity and the faintest touch of spritz also at work. Drink as fresh as possible. Screwcap. 12% alc. **Rating** 91 **To** Now $13

✪   **Deen Vat 4 Petit Verdot 2009** Medium red–purple; yet another tribute to the ability of petit verdot to produce a wine with good colour and abundant ripe flavour even with a heavy crop; there are layers of plum and black fruits, supported by soft tannins. Two gold medals, including Rutherglen Wine Show '11 in class 216D, I kid you not (most wine shows have less than 60 classes). Screwcap. 14.5% alc. **Rating** 91 **To** 2014 $13

✪   **Sacred Hill Semillon Sauvignon Blanc 2011** Pale straw–green; the bouquet is expressive, with some lemon blossom, the palate with more intensity than others in this price bracket, with citrus and gooseberry fruit, and a clean finish. Screwcap. 11% alc. **Rating** 90 **To** Now $8

ㅜㅜㅜㅜ **DB Family Selection Pinot Grigio 2010** A pleasant and fresh example of the
✪   style with pear flesh, anise and a crisp lemon finish; excellent value. Screwcap. 11.5% alc. **Rating** 89 **To** 2014 $8 BE

✪   **Sacred Hill Chardonnay 2011** Bright, light green-gold, from where I don't know. Yet another tour de force from De Bortoli, with melon and yellow peach fruit making oak totally unnecessary. Screwcap. 13% alc. **Rating** 88 **To** Now $8

●   **Deen De Bortoli Vat 7 Chardonnay 2010 Rating** 88 **To** Now $13
✪   **Deen Vat 9 Cabernet Sauvignon 2009** Light purple-red; part of a consistent portfolio of wines that handsomely over-deliver at their price; only light-bodied, but does have good varietal character, and a gently savoury, not sweet, finish. Screwcap. 14.5% alc. **Rating** 88 **To** 2013 $13

✪   **Sacred Hill Unwooded Colombard Chardonnay 2011** The colombard component adds a shaft of lemony acidity that gives it interest it might not otherwise have. Drink now. Screwcap. 12% alc. **Rating** 87 **To** Now $8

✪   **Sacred Hill Cabernet Merlot 2009** Bright, light red; while unashamedly light-bodied, a very easy, juicy red berry wine; if there is a touch of sweetness on the finish, it is part of the whole. Screwcap. 13.5% alc. **Rating** 87 **To** Now $8

        Emeri Chardonnay Pinot Noir NV Rating 87 **To** Now $13
✪   **Sacred Hill Brut Cuvee NV** A lemon-fruited wine with chalky acidity and a fresh personality; excellent quality for the price. Diam. 11% alc. **Rating** 87 **To** 2013 $8 BE

        Emeri Sparkling Shiraz NV Rating 87 **To** 2013 $13 BE
        Emeri Moscato NV Rating 87 **To** Now $13
        Emeri Pink Moscato NV Rating 87 **To** Now $13

De Bortoli (Hunter Valley)   ★★★☆

532 Wine Country Drive, Pokolbin, NSW 2325 **Region** Hunter Valley
T (02) 4993 8800 **www**.debortoli.com.au **Open** 7 days 10–5
Winemaker Steve Webber **Est.** 2002 **Dozens** 10 000 **Vyds** 36ha
De Bortoli extended its wine empire in 2002 with the purchase of the former Wilderness Estate, giving it an immediate and significant presence in the Hunter Valley courtesy of the 26ha of established vineyards, including semillon vines over 40 years old. The subsequent purchase of the adjoining 40ha property increased the size of the business. The intention is to

convert the vineyards to biological farming practices, with composting and mulching already used to reduce the need for irrigation. Exports to all major markets.

ŤŤŤŤ **Cellar Release Verdelho 2011** Fresh-cut nectarine and lime bouquet, with a zesty palate; soft, simple and lively. Screwcap. 13% alc. **Rating** 87 **To** 2013 $18 BE
Cellar Release Field Blend 2011 Pale straw, bright; a fragrant and accessible bouquet of nectarine, straw and anise; light-bodied, fresh and zesty, made for early consumption. Semillon/Vermentino/Viognier/Verdelho. Screwcap. 11% alc. **Rating** 87 **To** 2014 $18 BE

De Bortoli (Victoria) ★★★★★

Pinnacle Lane, Dixons Creek, Vic 3775 **Region** Yarra Valley
T (03) 5965 2271 **www**.debortoliyarra.com.au **Open** 7 days 10–5
Winemaker Stephen Webber, Sarah Fagan, Andrew Bretherton **Est.** 1987
Dozens 350 000 **Vyds** 242ha
The quality arm of the bustling De Bortoli group, run by Leanne De Bortoli and husband Steve Webber, ex-Lindemans winemaker. The top label (De Bortoli), the second (Gulf Station) and the third label (Windy Peak) offer wines of consistently good quality and excellent value – the complex Chardonnay and the Pinot Noirs are usually of outstanding quality. The volume of production, by many times the largest in the Yarra Valley, simply underlines the quality/ value for money ratio of the wines. This arm of the business has vineyards in the Yarra and King valleys. Steve retired as chairman of judges at the Melbourne Wine Show in 2011, having made many far-sighted changes to the schedule. Exports to all major markets.

ŤŤŤŤŤ **Riorret The Abbey Yarra Valley Pinot Noir 2010** Light, clear, bright red; has the red berry and spice characters of its less expensive sibling (Estate Pinot Noir), except that the volume of fruit is immeasurably greater, the flavours correspondingly more intense and long; cherry and plum have a dusting of savoury spices. Has stupendous length. Diam. 13% alc. **Rating** 96 **To** 2017 $42
Reserve Release Yarra Valley Pinot Noir 2010 Mid garnet; as always, a wine to contemplate, with red fruits mingling among savoury aromas of cold tea, vine sap and Asian spices; light on entry, the underlying structure and lacy acidity take time to unravel across the palate, building to a crescendo of flavour that is both attractive and a little muscular; power contained by elegance. Screwcap. 13% alc. **Rating** 95 **To** 2020 $52 BE
Reserve Release Yarra Valley Riesling 2010 You can't do more than hand pick and sort the bunches in the vineyard, and this wine repays that philosophy of attention to detail. It's the best dry Yarra Valley riesling I've encountered, which still doesn't change the fact that riesling doesn't enjoy moderately cool maritime climates. It's the superb fruit/sweetness/acid balance that makes this wine the exception to prove the rule. Screwcap. 12% alc. **Rating** 94 **To** 2018 $30
Estate Grown Yarra Valley Sauvignon 2010 Full straw-green; the De Bortoli interpretation of sauvignon blanc takes it in the direction of France, the emphasis as much on structure and texture as on ripe flavours of kiwi fruit, herbs and the impact of partial barrel ferment in old oak to add a nutty character. Screwcap. 12.5% alc. **Rating** 94 **To** 2014 $22
Estate Grown Yarra Valley Chardonnay 2011 Winemaker Stephen Webber is an enthusiastic supporter of the quality of the '11 vintage for chardonnay, and many totally agree. This wine reflects the minimalist approach, with no new oak, but significant texture and complexity from the barrel fermentation and maturation. Screwcap. 12.5% alc. **Rating** 94 **To** 2017 $29
Estate Grown Yarra Valley Chardonnay 2010 Pale quartz-green; there is some bright and healthy colour development; the bouquet is complex, but still to open up fully. Steve Webber has succeeded handsomely with his desire to make textural wine, as evident here as it is with red wine. The textural play introduces layers of different flavour nuances with a mix of grilled nuts (not oak-derived), a waft of nectarine, and minerals. Screwcap. 12.5% alc. **Rating** 94 **To** 2017 $29

Estate Grown Yarra Valley Pinot Noir 2010 Light, bright red; a red berry and spice bouquet introduces an intense and savoury palate suggesting some whole bunch when in fact there is none, simply destemmed whole berries. There is a nod to Burgundy in this wine. Screwcap. 13% alc. **Rating** 94 **To** 2019 $36

Estate Grown Yarra Valley Syrah 2010 Light, bright clear crimson; a juicy, light- to medium-bodied syrah, with a texture more akin to pinot noir than conventional shiraz, as is its perfumed aromaticity; effortlessly fine and long on the palate, and good tannins on the finish. Screwcap. 13% alc. **Rating** 94 **To** 2017 $29

Reserve Release Yarra Valley Syrah 2010 The use of whole bunches in shiraz is becoming 'de rigeur' in the Yarra Valley, and the effect on the bouquet is set to divide opinion; in this instance the sappy, cold tea, Asian spice and red fruit qualities jump out of the glass, with the palate having an almost pinot-like silkiness and layered character; long and spicy. Screwcap. 13% alc. **Rating** 94 **To** 2020 $52 BE

Estate Grown Yarra Valley Cabernet Sauvignon 2010 Mid crimson; an elegant and complex bouquet offering redcurrant, cassis, cedar and a little dried herb complexity; the palate is medium-bodied and refined, highly polished and poised, with the palate extension via silky tannins an absolute pleasure; excellent value, high-quality cabernet. Screwcap. 12.5% alc. **Rating** 94 **To** 2025 $32 BE

ŶŶŶŶ♀
✪ **La Boheme Act Two Yarra Valley Rose 2011** Pale salmon; a walk on the wild side, barrel-fermented in old oak, and made bone dry to place emphasis on the savoury/spicy aspects of a wine designed from the ground up to accompany the widest possible range of food. Screwcap. 12.5% alc. **Rating** 93 **To** Now $20

Riorret Balnarring Mornington Pinot Noir 2010 **Rating** 93 **To** 2020 $42 BE

Riorret Merricks Grove Vineyard Pinot Noir 2009 **Rating** 93 **To** 2015 $42

✪ **Melba Mimi Yarra Valley Cabernet Sauvignon Syrah Nebbiolo 2010** Bright, clear, light crimson; an example of the 'different drum' style that Steven Webber seeks to make; very fine and elegant, freshness and balance prized more than depth of flavour. Here cassis, red cherry and spice rule the roost, with oak and tannins barely perceptible. Screwcap. 12.5% alc. **Rating** 93 **To** 2020 $30

Reserve Release Yarra Valley Riesling 2011 **Rating** 92 **To** 2016 $30

⦿ **Gulf Station Yarra Valley Chardonnay 2010** **Rating** 92 **To** 2013 $20

Melba Reserve 2008 **Rating** 92 **To** 2018 $45

✪ **Gulf Station Yarra Valley Cabernet Sauvignon 2010** Light crystal-clear colour; all about finesse and restraint; because the extraction has been gentle, the sweeter fruit components have not been hidden by tannins. Ready now. Screwcap. 13% alc. **Rating** 91 **To** 2014 $20

✪ **Windy Peak Yarra Valley Chardonnay 2011** Taut acidity drives this wine, with pear and a little grilled nut complexity also on show; the style truly sits outside the norm at this price point, and for freshness and food friendliness it represents great value. Screwcap. 12.5% alc. **Rating** 90 **To** 2016 $14 BE

Estate Grown Yarra Valley Pinot Noir Rose 2011 **Rating** 90 **To** Now $22

Riorret Emu Yarra Valley Pinot Noir 2010 **Rating** 90 **To** 2015 $42

✪ **Windy Peak Pinot Noir Chardonnay NV** A clean and fresh red fruit-accented bouquet, with a dry aperitif feel to the palate; an easy and early-drinking style of sparkling. One of five sparkling wines to win gold or silver medals from a field of 35 wines at the National Wine Show '11, this a silver. Diam. 11.5% alc. **Rating** 90 **To** 2013 $14 BE

Estate Grown Off Dry Yarra Valley Riesling 2011 **Rating** 90 **To** 2014 $22

De Iuliis   ★★★★★

21 Broke Road, Pokolbin, NSW 2320 **Region** Hunter Valley
T (02) 4993 8000 **www**.dewine.com.au **Open** 7 days 10–5
Winemaker Michael De Iuliis **Est.** 1990 **Dozens** 10 000

Three generations of the De Iuliis family have been involved in the establishment of their 45ha vineyard. The family acquired the property in 1986 and planted the first vines in 1990, selling the grapes from the first few vintages to Tyrrell's but retaining increasing amounts for release under the De Iuliis label. Winemaker Michael De Iuliis has completed postgraduate studies in oenology at the Roseworthy campus of Adelaide University and was a Len Evans Tutorial scholar. He has lifted the quality of the wines into the highest echelon.

ŦŦŦŦŦ **Hunter Valley Shiraz 2010** Crimson-purple; has everything you could wish for, everything in its right place, everything in balance: expressive blackberry/black cherry fruit; some regional earth and spice; and ripe, balanced tannins to carry it through the coming decades. Screwcap. 14% alc. **Rating** 95 **To** 2030 $25
Limited Release Hunter Valley Shiraz 2009 Deep colour, with a concentrated amalgam of red and black fruits, fresh leather, toasty oak and graphite; the palate is lively, direct, fresh and beautifully contained, structured to go the distance, yet offering plenty of pleasure in the short term. Screwcap. 13.5% alc. **Rating** 95 **To** 2030 $60 BE
Aged Release Hunter Valley Semillon 2005 There is lots of buttered toast and lemon curd, offset by fresh straw on the bouquet; the palate is fine and racy, with tangy acidity providing drive and energy from the lemony start to the toasty finish. Screwcap. 11.5% alc. **Rating** 94 **To** 2020 $30 BE
LDR Vineyard Hunter Valley Shiraz 2010 Deep crimson, bright; a heady and perfumed bouquet of black cherry, plum, spices and a little briary complexity; the medium-bodied palate is fleshy and accessible, ready to go, but also showing enough stuffing and structure to see a little time in the cellar as a good option; lovely craftsmanship. Screwcap. 13% alc. **Rating** 94 **To** 2025 $40 BE

ŦŦŦŦŦ **Hunter Valley Semillon 2011** Light straw-green; the bouquet is crisp and
✪ lifted, with citrus and grass notes, the palate with good drive, length and balance, and zesty, citrussy minerality, the finish bone dry. Screwcap. 11.5% alc. **Rating** 93 **To** 2021 $18
Sunshine Vineyard Hunter Valley Semillon 2011 **Rating** 92 **To** 2020 $25 BE
✪ **Hunter Valley Chardonnay 2011** This is a bright, modern, fragrant and perfumed chardonnay of the Hunter, showing nectarine, quartz, charcuterie and cashew on the bouquet; the palate is forward and open knit on entry, yet tightens up on the finish, with a bit of grip, drawing out the finish to a longer than expected conclusion. Screwcap. 12.5% alc. **Rating** 92 **To** 2016 $20 BE
Hunter Valley Sangiovese 2011 **Rating** 91 **To** 2015 $25 BE
Hunter Valley Tempranillo 2011 **Rating** 91 **To** 2015 $25 BE

De Salis Wines ★★★★

Lofty Vineyard, 125 Mount Lofty Road, Orange, NSW 2800 **Region** Orange
T 0403 956 295 **www**.desaliswines.com.au **Open** W'ends & public hols 11–5, or by appt
Winemaker Charles Svenson **Est.** 1999 **Dozens** 2500 **Vyds** 8.7ha
This is the venture of research scientist Charles (Charlie) Svenson and wife Loretta. Charlie became interested in winemaking when, aged 32, he returned to study microbiology and biochemistry at the University of NSW. His particular area of interest (for his PhD) was the yeast and bacterial fermentation of cellulosic waste to produce ethanol. In '09, after a prolonged search, Charlie and Loretta purchased a vineyard first planted in 1993 and known as Wattleview (now renamed Lofty Vineyard). At an altitude of 1050m it is the highest vineyard in the Orange GI, and their winery was built and equipped in time for the '09 vintage. In '12, De Salis vinified shiraz, cabernet franc and cabernet sauvignon from vineyards in Boree Lane (near Canobolas-Smith).

ŦŦŦŦŦ **St Em M 2009** A 75/20/5% blend of Cabernet Franc/Cabernet Sauvignon/ Merlot. While the colour is light, the hue is bright, and both the bouquet and medium-bodied palate have fresh, lively red berry fruits, the tannins appropriately fine and ripe. Screwcap. 13.8% alc. **Rating** 92 **To** 2019 $38
St Em F 2009 Light, bright crimson; a well-balanced and structured light- to medium-bodied palate, giving free rein to the 65/25/10% blend of cabernet franc, cabernet sauvignon and merlot; the tannin and oak management have been equally well handled. Screwcap. 13.8% alc. **Rating** 92 **To** 2029 $38

Wild Fume Sauvignon Blanc 2010 Bright straw-green; the name implies wild yeast and barrel fermentation; whatever, the wine has both length and complexity, the mouthfeel is good, the flavours underscored by minerally acidity. Screwcap. 12.8% alc. **Rating** 91 **To** 2013 $28

Chardonnay 2010 Light green-straw; has an unusual but not unpleasant nuance of herbs/wild flowers on the bouquet; the palate brings ripe citrus into play (plus oak), but some of the flavours track the bouquet. Intriguing wine. Screwcap. 13.2% alc. **Rating** 91 **To** 2018 $28

Wild Chardonnay 2010 Slightly more colour evident; has a very different texture from its sibling – richer and more mouthfilling, with more cashew; on the other hand, doesn't have as much personality. Screwcap. 13.2% alc. **Rating** 91 **To** 2016 $28

Pinot Noir 2010 Bright, clear crimson; has a fragrant, almost flowery bouquet, with fruit and spice intermingling along with some sappy/stemmy notes suggesting the use of some whole bunches in the ferment. I like the style. Screwcap. 13% alc. **Rating** 91 **To** 2016 $45

Deakin Estate

Kulkyne Way, via Red Cliffs, Vic 3496 **Region** Murray Darling
T (03) 5018 5555 **www**.deakinestate.com.au **Open** Not
Winemaker Dr Phil Spillman **Est.** 1980 **Dozens** 400 000 **Vyds** 373ha
Part of the Katnook Estate, Riddoch and Deakin Estate triumvirate, which constitutes the Wingara Wine Group, now fully owned by Freixenet of Spain. Deakin Estate draws from its own vineyards, making it largely self-sufficient, and produces wines of consistent quality and impressive value, thanks in no small part to the skills and expertise of winemaker Phil Spillman. Exports to all major markets.

Shiraz 2010 Light red-purple, bright and clear; the bouquet has fragrant red berry aromas, the light- to medium-bodied palate with similar fruit enhanced by fine but persistent tannins. Given an extra point for its freshness and elegance. Screwcap. 13.5% alc. **Rating** 90 **To** 2014 $10

Chardonnay 2011 This is all about varietal fruit, not artefact; the flavours range from melon to stone fruit, braced by citrussy acidity. You really don't notice the absence of oak. Outstanding value. Screwcap. 13% alc. **Rating** 89 **To** 2014 $10

Pinot Noir 2010 Given the estate-grown basis of this wine, and the utterly unsuited climate, this is as good as you can possibly expect; light- to medium-bodied, it has good structure, some plummy fruit, and fine tannins on the finish. Outstanding value. Screwcap. 13% alc. **Rating** 89 **To** 2013 $10

Cabernet Sauvignon 2009 Relatively light colour, but holding its crimson hue well; both the bouquet and palate challenge preconceptions about the place of a $10 wine grown in the Riverland, for there is clear-cut varietal fruit on the bouquet and palate; most surprising is the pleasantly savoury nature of the flavours, and the balanced tannins. Screwcap. 13.5% alc. **Rating** 89 **To** 2013 $10

Deep Woods Estate

889 Commonage Road, Yallingup, WA 6282 **Region** Margaret River
T (08) 9756 6066 **www**.deepwoods.com.au **Open** Wed–Sun 11–5, 7 days during hols
Winemaker Julian Langworthy, Ben Rector **Est.** 1987 **Dozens** 25 000 **Vyds** 16ha
The Gould family acquired Deep Woods Estate in 1992, when the first plantings were four years old. In 2005 the business was purchased by Perth businessman Peter Fogarty and family, who also own Lake's Folly in the Hunter Valley, and Millbrook in the Perth Hills. The 32ha property has 16ha plantings of cabernet sauvignon, shiraz, merlot, cabernet franc, chardonnay, sauvignon blanc, semillon and verdelho. Vineyard and cellar door upgrades are underway. Julian Langworthy was appointed winemaker in the wake of Janice McDonald's move to Howard Park. Exports to Belgium, Germany, Malaysia, Singapore, Japan and China.

ŢŢŢŢŢ **Block 7 Margaret River Shiraz 2010** Deep magenta; an impressive bouquet of black and red fruits, violets and a tangible mineral note, surely a result of a mature vineyard planted in 1987; the palate is generous and sweet-fruited on entry, with structure and savoury complexity remaining on the balanced, long and inviting conclusion. Screwcap. 14% alc. **Rating** 96 **To** 2018 $32 BE
Reserve Margaret River Cabernet Sauvignon 2009 Good purple-crimson; the perfect ripeness of the fruit and quality of the oak speak volumes on the bouquet; the medium-bodied palate takes up where the bouquet left off, with the fruit and oak flavours supported by the finest array of tannins, giving a silky mouthfeel to the mid palate and finish. Screwcap. 14% alc. **Rating** 94 **To** 2024 $45

ŢŢŢŢŢ **Margaret River Sauvignon Blanc 2011** Pale quartz-green; a carefully
✪ constructed sauvignon blanc, with partial barrel fermentation; the bouquet has a tantalising touch of snow pea and flowers, then an intensely focused palate with a spray of tropical fruit. Screwcap. 12.5% alc. **Rating** 92 **To** 2013 $20
✪ **Margaret River Chardonnay 2011** Vibrant green hue; fresh nectarine, grapefruit and a splash of cinnamon; the palate is soft and fleshy on entry, yet has real generosity and fine acidity; extremely user friendly and very good value. Screwcap. 13.5% alc. **Rating** 92 **To** 2016 $20 BE
● **Harmony Margaret River Rose 2011** **Rating** 92 **To** 2013 $15
● **Ivory Margaret River Semillon Sauvignon Blanc 2011** **Rating** 90 **To** Now $15
Reserve Margaret River Chardonnay 2009 **Rating** 90 **To** 2017 $35
Margaret River Cabernet Sauvignon Merlot 2009 **Rating** 90 **To** 2016 $32 BE

ŢŢŢŢ **Reserve Margaret River Nebbiolo 2010** **Rating** 89 **To** 2014 $35 BE
Ebony Margaret River Cabernet Shiraz 2010 **Rating** 88 **To** 2014 $15
Margaret River Verdelho Verde 2011 **Rating** 87 **To** Now $20

Deetswood Wines ★★★

Washpool Creek Road, Tenterfield, NSW 2372 **Region** New England
T (02) 6736 1322 **www**.deetswoodwines.com.au **Open** Fri–Mon 10–5, or by appt
Winemaker Deanne Eaton **Est.** 1996 **Dozens** 1600 **Vyds** 2.4ha
Deanne Eaton and Tim Condrick established their micro-vineyard in 1996, planting semillon, chardonnay, pinot noir, shiraz, merlot, viognier and cabernet sauvignon. At the end of the 19th century, German immigrant Joe Nicoll planted vines here and made wines for family use, and there is still one vine surviving on the site from those original plantings. The wines are normally consistent both in quality and style, offering further proof that this is a very interesting area.

ŢŢŢŢ **Tenterfield Viognier 2011** Ripe peach and spice bouquet, with a splash of bath talc on the bouquet; fleshy and generous, low in acid, but showing nice varietal definition and freshness. Screwcap. 12.9% alc. **Rating** 87 **To** 2013 $15 BE
Tenterfield Shiraz 2011 A blend of smoky bacon, salami, dark cherry and plum; a juicy and tangy young red wine, finishing with a strong charry presence; consume in the full flush of youth. Screwcap. 12.4% alc. **Rating** 87 **To** 2014 $17 BE

Deisen ★★★★★

PO Box 61, Tanunda, SA 5352 **Region** Barossa Valley
T (08) 8563 2298 **www**.deisen.com.au **Open** Not
Winemaker Sabine Deisen **Est.** 2001 **Dozens** 1200
Deisen once again proves the old adage that nothing succeeds like success. In the first year, 3.5 tonnes of grapes produced five barrels of Shiraz and two of Grenache. Since that time, production has grown slowly but steadily with bits and pieces of traditional winemaking equipment (small crushers, open tanks and hand-plunging, now housed in a slightly larger tin shed). The number of wines made and the tiny quantities of some (20 dozen is not uncommon) is staggering. The style of all the wines is remarkably similar: sweet and luscious

fruit; soft, ripe tannins; and a warmth from the alcohol (toned down in recent releases). No wines were released prior to publication, but they will become available in August-September 2012; tasting notes will appear on www.winecompanion.com.au. Limited numbers of magnums of back-vintages will also be available. Exports to the US.

del Rios of Mt Anakie ★★★

2320 Ballan Road, Anakie, Vic 3221 **Region** Geelong
T (03) 9497 4644 **www**.delrios.com.au **Open** W'ends 10–5
Winemaker Gus del Rio **Est.** 1996 **Dozens** 5000 **Vyds** 17ha
Gus del Rio, of Spanish heritage, established a vineyard in 1996 on the slopes of Mt Anakie, northwest of Geelong (chardonnay, pinot noir, cabernet sauvignon, sauvignon blanc, shiraz, merlot and marsanne). The vines are hand-pruned, the fruit is hand-picked and the wines are made onsite in the fully equipped winery, which includes a bottling and labelling line able to process over 150 tonnes. Exports to China.

🍷🍷🍷🍷 **Geelong Sauvignon Blanc 2011** Deep colour, and showing lots of texture and complexity, rather than a simple, forward fresh fruit character; spiced grapefruit and fennel, with an Amaro savoury finish. Screwcap. 14% alc. **Rating** 89 **To** 2014 $20 BE

Geelong Rose 2011 Very pale colour, with savoury anise and wild strawberry aromas; very dry, and even a little austere and minerally in character; a lean and dry style. Screwcap. 13% alc. **Rating** 89 **To** 2013 $20 BE

Delamere Vineyard ★★★★★

Bridport Road, Pipers Brook, Tas 7254 **Region** Northern Tasmania
T (03) 6382 7190 **www**.delamerevineyards.com.au **Open** 7 days 10–5
Winemaker Shane Holloway, Fran Austin **Est.** 1983 **Dozens** 3500 **Vyds** 6.5ha
Delamere was one of the first vineyards planted in the Pipers Brook area. It had previously been a diverse fruit orchard and market garden, attesting to the fertile soils. A new chapter has opened for Delamere, with Shane Holloway and wife Fran Austin (ex Bay of Fires) now in charge of viticulture and winemaking. The journey has begun (Delamere was purchased by Shane, Fran and their respective families in 2007), but there are challenges and equally great opportunities lying ahead. The old vines still need some TLC, but there will also be 4ha of pinot noir and chardonnay planted at the end of '12.

🍷🍷🍷🍷🍷 **Pinot Noir 2010** Hand-picked, open-fermented, and matured in Burgundian-coopered French oak, the wine has red-purple colour, and a powerful, layered palate with black cherry, plum, French oak and firm tannins all intermingling. Please give it a few years, as it needs to loosen up. 350 dozen made. Screwcap. 13.5% alc. **Rating** 94 **To** 2018 $42

Blanc de Blanc 2007 Made, obviously enough, from 100% chardonnay, traditionally fermented, and hand-disgorged. Is a lovely example of Tasmanian blanc de blanc style, with a mouthfeel that is at once feathery yet juicy, citrus and brioche to the fore. One glass will lead very quickly to another. Cork. 13% alc. **Rating** 94 **To** 2015 $50

🍷🍷🍷🍷½ **Naissante Pinot Gris 2011** **Rating** 92 **To** 2014 $25
Cuvee 2008 **Rating** 90 **To** 2015 $35

🍷🍷🍷🍷 **Chardonnay 2010** **Rating** 89 **To** 2017 $30
Naissante Pinot Noir 2010 **Rating** 89 **To** 2016 $25

Delatite ★★★★★

26 High Street, Mansfield, Vic 3722 **Region** Upper Goulburn
T (03) 5775 2922 **www**.delatitewinery.com.au **Open** 7 days 11–5
Winemaker Andy Browning **Est.** 1982 **Dozens** 10 000 **Vyds** 26ha

With its sweeping views across to the snow-clad Alps, this is uncompromising cool-climate viticulture, and the wines naturally reflect that. Increasing vine age (many of the plantings are well over 25 years old), and the adoption of organic (and partial biodynamic) viticulture, seems also to have played a role in providing the red wines with more depth and texture; the white wines are as good as ever. In June 2011 Vestey Holdings Limited, the international pastoral giant, acquired a majority holding in Delatite, and has said it represents 'The first of what they hope will be a number of agricultural businesses here.' It coincides with a modest increase in estate plantings. Exports to Denmark, China, Japan and Malaysia.

ፕፕፕፕፕ **Sylvia Riesling 2009** Bright straw-green; a very interesting and well-made wine that is more in the Rhinegau style than the usual Mosel style made in Australia; fruit, acidity and residual sugar are woven together from the first moment, giving the wine more weight and texture than usual. Screwcap. 10% alc. **Rating** 94 To 2019 $23
Catherine Gewurztraminer 2010 Picked four weeks after the normal harvest, but seemingly not affected by botrytis or, for that matter, much dehydration; the palate is very fresh, with excellent fruit/acidity balance, sweetness there but subtle. 375ml. Screwcap. 10% alc. **Rating** 94 To 2017 $25

ፕፕፕፕ **V.S. Limited Edition Riesling 2011** **Rating** 92 To 2018 $40 BE
Dead Man's Hill Gewurztraminer 2011 **Rating** 92 To 2015 $25 BE
Sauvignon Blanc 2010 **Rating** 91 To 2013 $23
Malbec 2009 **Rating** 91 To 2015 $35 BE
Cellar Reserve Pinot Noir 2010 **Rating** 90 To 2014 $50 BE
Pinot Noir 2010 **Rating** 90 To 2014 $30 BE
Late Harvest Riesling 2011 **Rating** 90 To 2018 $23 BE

ፕፕፕፕ **Riesling 2011** **Rating** 89 To 2015 $23 BE
Pinot Gris 2011 **Rating** 88 To 2014 $23 BE
Cellar Reserve Merlot 2010 **Rating** 88 To 2015 $45 BE
Pinot Noir 2009 **Rating** 87 To 2016 $30

 Della Fay Wines ★★★★★

3276 Caves Road, Yallingup, WA 6284 **Region** Margaret River
T (08) 9755 2747 **www**.kellysvineyard.com.au **Open** By appt
Winemaker Michael Kelly **Est.** 1999 **Dozens** 2000 **Vyds** 8ha
This is the venture of the Kelly family, headed by district veteran Michael Kelly, who gained his degree in wine science from CSU before working at Seville Estate and Mount Mary in the Yarra Valley, and Domaine Louis Chapuis in Burgundy, then coming back to WA working for Leeuwin Estate and Sandalford. From there he became the long-term winemaker at Fermoy Estate, but he and his family laid the ground for their own brand, buying prime viticultural land in Caves Road, Yallingup, in 1999. They planted 1.2ha each of cabernet sauvignon, merlot, nebbiolo, vermentino and sauvignon blanc, 1.1ha of chardonnay, and 0.5ha each of malbec and petit verdot. It is an eclectic mix of French, Italian and Spanish varieties, and shiraz from the Geographe region will also be included. 'Della Fay' honours the eponymous Kelly family matriarch.

ፕፕፕፕፕ **Reserve Geographe Shiraz 2010** Healthy crimson-purple; an impressive first-
✪ up wine, medium-bodied, replete with classic and delicious cherry, plum, spice and pepper; the finish is supple and smooth, building on all that has gone before. Screwcap. 14% alc. **Rating** 94 To 2023 $25
✪ **Margaret River Cabernet Sauvignon 2009** Clear crimson-purple; the bouquet is full of the cassis fruit that also arrives first on the palate; precisely judged tannins follow, providing line, length and balance; good oak handling. Screwcap. 13.5% alc. **Rating** 94 To 2019 $25

ፕፕፕፕ **Margaret River Vermentino 2010** **Rating** 89 To 2013 $20

Derwent Estate ★★★★★

329 Lyell Highway, Granton, Tas 7070 **Region** Southern Tasmania
T (03) 6263 5802 **www**.derwentestate.com.au **Open** Mon–Fri 10–4 (Sun–Fri 10–4 Nov–Jan)
Winemaker Winemaking Tasmania (Julian Alcorso) **Est.** 1992 **Dozens** 2500 **Vyds** 10.08ha
Three generations of the Hanigan family are involved in the management of their historic
Mt Nassau property, owned by the family since 1913. Given that over the last 100 years or so
the property has at various times been involved with sheep, cattle, vegetable production, seed
crops, poppies, quarrying and the production of lime, the addition of viticulture in 1992 was
not surprising. The vineyard has grown in stages, doubling to 10ha in 2003, the grapes bound
for Bay of Fires wines and Penfolds Yattarna. The grapes retained by Derwent Estate have
produced consistently good wines.

🍷🍷🍷🍷🍷 **Riesling 2011** Vivid green hue; an array of ripe exotic fruits mingle with fresh
kiwi and lime; the palate is racy and full of energy, with chalky acidity providing
line to the concentrated fruit on offer. Screwcap. 12% alc. **Rating** 94 **To** 2020
$25 BE
Chardonnay 2010 Mid gold; showing rich nectarine, lemon curd, cashew and
spice on the bouquet; the palate continues the theme, with toasty notes drawn out
by fresh lemon acidity; long and nutty to conclude. Screwcap. 13% alc. **Rating** 94
To 2016 $35 BE

🍷🍷🍷🍷🍷 **Pinot Gris 2011** **Rating** 91 **To** 2014 $25 BE
Rose 2011 **Rating** 90 **To** 2013 $22 BE
Pinot Noir 2010 **Rating** 90 **To** 2017 $35

Deviation Road ★★★★

214 Scott Creek Road, Longwood, SA 5153 **Region** Adelaide Hills
T (08) 8339 2633 **www**.deviationroad.com **Open** 7 days 10–5
Winemaker Kate and Hamish Laurie **Est.** 1999 **Dozens** 6000 **Vyds** 11.05ha
Deviation Road was created in 1998 by Hamish Laurie, great-great-grandson of Mary Laurie,
SA's first female winemaker. He initially joined with father Dr Chris Laurie in 1992 to help
build the Hillstowe Wines business; the brand was sold to Banksia Wines in 2001, but the
Laurie family retained the vineyard, which now supplies Deviation Road with its grapes. Wife
Kate joined the business in 2001, having studied winemaking and viticulture in Champagne,
then spent four years at her family's Stone Bridge winery in Manjimup. All the wines come
from the family vineyards, but only account for a small portion of the annual grape production
of those vineyards. It also has 3ha of pinot noir and shiraz at Longwood, where its new cellar
door is situated. Exports to the UK, the US and Hong Kong.

🍷🍷🍷🍷🍷 **Adelaide Hills Methode Champenoise Brut 2009** The Pinot Noir/
Chardonnay base is aged on lees for at least 12 months (disgorged progressively).
It is a sparkling brut with real attitude, penetration and length; green apple is
the driver, with some nutty strawberry notes in the background. Diam. 12% alc.
Rating 93 **To** 2014 $34

🍷🍷🍷🍷 **Adelaide Hills Sauvignon Blanc 2011** **Rating** 88 **To** 2013 $18 BE

Devil's Lair ★★★★★

Rocky Road, Forest Grove via Margaret River, WA 6285 **Region** Margaret River
T (08) 9757 7573 **www**.devils-lair.com **Open** Not
Winemaker Oliver Crawford **Est.** 1981 **Dozens** NFP **Vyds** 130ha
Having rapidly carved out a high reputation for itself through a combination of clever
packaging and impressive wine quality, Devil's Lair was acquired by Southcorp in 1996. The
estate vineyards have been substantially increased since, now with sauvignon blanc, semillon,
chardonnay, cabernet sauvignon, merlot, shiraz, cabernet franc and petit verdot, supplemented
by grapes purchased from contract growers. An exceptionally successful business; production
has increased from 40 000 dozen to many times greater, in no small measure due to its second
label, Fifth Leg. Exports to the UK, the US and other major markets.

ŢŢŢŢŢ **9th Chamber Margaret River Chardonnay 2009** The inaugural release of the 200 dozen estate-grown wine that will only be produced in the best vintages (not made in '10). As at March '12, the colour was still very pale, with just a slight tinge of green; the bouquet takes the varietal chardonnay to another level, but, interestingly, it was entirely fermented and matured in second-use French oak, the lees stirred for 10 months prior to bottling. The bouquet brings grapefruit, nectarine and white peach fruit into play, the oak imparting spicy/nutty characters in the background. The palate is incredibly rich and unctuous, yet somehow retains elegance thanks to the multilayered texture and tight focus. Screwcap. 13% alc. **Rating** 97 **To** 2025 $100

Margaret River Cabernet Sauvignon 2009 Bright crimson; an extremely elegant and fine cabernet, with fruit, oak and tannins in perfect balance; the medium-bodied palate is very long, the blackcurrant and black olive fruit lingering in the mouth long after the wine has been swallowed. Top gold Margaret River Wine Show '10 in one of the blue ribbon (71 wines) classes. Screwcap. 13% alc. **Rating** 96 **To** 2029 $50

Margaret River Chardonnay 2010 Bright, light green-gold; one of Margaret River's classics; marks out its own territory with an extra dimension of elegance, its nectarine and white peach fruit in a fine web of French (40% new) oak from barrel fermentation and nine months' fermentation in barrel. The finish has admirable grip, giving the wine attitude. Screwcap. 13.5% alc. **Rating** 95 **To** 2018 $50

Margaret River Cabernet Sauvignon 2010 The tasting note for the '09 has been rolled over from the '12 Wine Companion. A foretaste of the '10 (already bottled, and due for release in October) is particularly interesting because there was no merlot included, some tempranillo taking its place. The fragrant bouquet leads into a silky palate with red and black cherry and berry fruits, supported by fine tannins and already-integrated oak. Screwcap. 14% alc. **Rating** 95 **To** 2030 $50

ŢŢŢŢŢ **Dance with the Devil Margaret River Shiraz Tempranillo 2010** **Rating** 93 **To** 2020 $25

The Hidden Cave Margaret River Cabernet Shiraz 2010 **Rating** 93 **To** 2018 $23

○ **Fifth Leg White 2011** **Rating** 92 **To** 2013 $18

The Hidden Cave Margaret River Chardonnay 2011 **Rating** 92 **To** 2016 $23

The Hidden Cave Margaret River Sauvignon Blanc Semillon 2011 **Rating** 91 **To** 2014 $23

○ **Fifth Leg Rose 2011** **Rating** 91 **To** Now $18

✪ **Fifth Leg Shiraz Merlot Cabernet Sauvignon 2010** Good colour; once, Fifth Leg was a light- to medium-bodied wine designed for early consumption. Now it demands to be taken more seriously, despite its price. Blackberry, cherry, spice and persistent, albeit ripe and fine tannins take this to the upper end of the medium-bodied spectrum. Screwcap. 14.5% alc. **Rating** 91 **To** 2025 $18

○ **Fifth Leg Shiraz Merlot Cabernet Sauvignon 2009** **Rating** 90 **To** 2014 $18

ŢŢŢŢ **Dance with the Devil Margaret River Sauvignon Blanc Chenin Blanc 2011** **Rating** 89 **To** 2013 $25

○ **Fifth Leg Crisp Chardonnay 2011** **Rating** 89 **To** 2013 $18

Dexter Wines

210 Foxeys Road, Merricks North, Vic 3926 (postal) **Region** Mornington Peninsula **T** (03) 5989 7007 **www.dexterwines.com.au** **Open** Not
Winemaker Tod Dexter **Est.** 2006 **Dozens** 1400 **Vyds** 7.1ha
Through a series of seemingly unrelated events, Tod Dexter arrived in the US with the intention of enjoying some skiing; having done that, he became an apprentice winemaker at Cakebread Cellars, a well-known Napa Valley winery. After seven years he returned to Australia and the Mornington Peninsula, and began the establishment of the vineyard, planted to pinot noir (4ha) and chardonnay (3.1ha). To keep the wolves from the door he became winemaker at Stonier, and leased his vineyard to Stonier, the grapes always used in the Stonier

Reserve range. Having left Stonier to become Yabby Lake winemaker, and spurred on by turning 50 in 2006 (and at the urging of friends), he and wife Debbie decided to establish the Dexter label. Exports to the UK and the US.

🍷🍷🍷🍷🍷 **Mornington Peninsula Chardonnay 2010** Tod Dexter's long experience in the Peninsula shines through in this limited production of 625 dozen bottles. It is refined and elegant from start to finish, with a refreshing skein of acidity running through the grapefruit, nectarine and melon fruit, the impact of barrel fermentation almost negligible. Screwcap. 13.5% alc. **Rating** 96 **To** 2018 $38
Mornington Peninsula Pinot Noir 2010 Light, clear red-purple; very fragrant cherry and strawberry aromas lead into a vibrant and crisp palate, long and pure, with a twist of savoury/spicy tannins, oak restrained. Screwcap. 13.5% alc. **Rating** 94 **To** 2016 $49

🍷🍷🍷🍷 **Route de Van Dolcetto Shiraz 2010 Rating** 88 **To** 2014 $18

Di Fabio Estate

5 Valleyview Drive, McLaren Vale, SA 5171 (postal) **Region** McLaren Vale
T (08) 8383 0188 **www.difabioestatewines.com.au Open** Not
Winemaker Goe Di Fabio **Est.** 1994 **Dozens** 6000 **Vyds** 38.91ha
Di Fabio Estate is the venture of brothers Goe and Tony Di Fabio. Their parents Giovanni and Maria Di Fabio purchased their first vineyard in McLaren Vale in 1966 (with a tradition stretching back further to Italy) and became long-term contract grapegrowers for other winemakers. The business carried on by their sons has a 56ha property at McLaren Vale, and 8.5ha at Waikerie. The plantings are dominated by 12.5ha of grenache, 10.5ha of shiraz, and 3.6ha of mourvedre; petit verdot, merlot, chardonnay, cabernet franc, sauvignon blanc and semillon are also grown. Exports to Macau, Singapore and China.

🍷🍷🍷🍷 **Bush Vine McLaren Vale Shiraz 2009** Mid garnet; toasty oak, red and black fruits and a dollop of liqueur kirsch are at play on the bouquet; medium-bodied with sweet fruits and a developed note that prevails on the finish. Early drinking may be the best option. Screwcap. 14% alc. **Rating** 88 **To** 2014 $34 BE
McLaren Vale Grenache Shiraz 2010 Fresh and fragrant black fruits with a splash of sage and spice; medium-bodied, forward and accessible, ready to go and easy drinking in nature. Screwcap. 14.5% alc. **Rating** 88 **To** 2014 $24 BE

di Lusso Estate

Eurunderee Lane, Mudgee, NSW 2850 **Region** Mudgee
T (02) 6373 3125 **www.dilusso.com.au Open** Wed–Sat 10–5, Sun 10–4, Mon 10–5
Winemaker Julia Conchie, Robert Paul (Consultant) **Est.** 1998 **Dozens** 5000 **Vyds** 6.5ha
Rob Fairall and partner Luanne Hill have brought to fruition their vision to establish an Italian 'enoteca' operation, offering Italian varietal wines and foods. When they began to plant their vineyard in 1998, the Italian varietal craze was yet to gain serious traction. They now have a thoroughly impressive range of barbera, sangiovese, vermentino, aleatico, lagrein, greco di tufo, picolit and nebbiolo. The estate also produces olives for olive oil and table olives, and the range of both wine and food will increase over the years. The decision to focus on Italian varieties has been a major success, the quality of the wines, however, the key to that success.

🍷🍷🍷🍷🍷 **Passito 2007** Golden umber; air-dried on racks before fermentation, then three years in old oak before bottling; very, very luscious and complex, great for biscotti and double espresso. Screwcap. 7.1% alc. **Rating** 94 **To** Now $55

🍷🍷🍷🍷🍷 **Vino Rosato 2011** Pale pink; a blend of sangiovese and lagrein with crushed
✪   lemon leaf aromas; the palate is crisp, dry and full of energy; considerable length. Screwcap. 12.6% alc. **Rating** 92 **To** 2013 $18
Vermentino 2011 Rating 92 **To** 2014 $23
il Palio 2010 Rating 92 **To** 2020 $26
Mudgee Barbera 2010 Rating 91 **To** 2017 $26

Pinot Grigio 2011 **Rating** 90 **To** Now $26
Greco di Tufo 2011 **Rating** 90 **To** 2015 $23
Mudgee Picolit 2010 **Rating** 90 **To** 2016 $23

🍷🍷🍷🍷 **Mudgee Sangiovese 2010** **Rating** 87 **To** 2013 $26

Diamond Creek Estate ★★★☆

292 Diamond Fields Road, Mittagong, NSW 2575 **Region** Southern Highlands
T (02) 4872 3311 **www**.diamondcreekestate.com.au **Open** By appt
Winemaker Eddy Rossi, Jonathan Holgate **Est.** 1997 **Dozens** 2500 **Vyds** 6ha
Helen Hale purchased Diamond Creek Estate in late 2002, by which time the chardonnay, sauvignon blanc, riesling, pinot noir and cabernet sauvignon planted in 1997 by the prior owner had come into bearing. The vineyard is established at 680m on rich basalt soil, the north-facing slope being relatively frost-free. Since Helen acquired the property, some of the grapes have been sold to Southern Highlands Winery, but most have been retained for release under the Diamond Creek Estate label: these include Riesling, Sauvignon Blanc, Pinot Noir, Cabernet Sauvignon and the highly successful Noble Diamond. Exports to Asia.

🍷🍷🍷🍷🍷 ✪ **Riesling 2011** Pale quartz-green; while the floral bouquet is yet to build intensity, the palate has very attractive lime and apple flavours; the balance and length are good. Screwcap. 11.8% alc. **Rating** 92 **To** 2021 $20

🍷🍷🍷🍷 **Chardonnay 2010** **Rating** 87 **To** 2013 $20
Cabernet Sauvignon 2009 **Rating** 87 **To** 2015 $20

Diamond Island Wines ★★★★

PO Box 56, Bicheno, Tas 7215 **Region** East Coast Tasmania
T 0409 003 988 **Open** Not
Winemaker Winemaking Tasmania (Julian Alcorso) **Est.** 2002 **Dozens** 450 **Vyds** 2ha
Owner Derek Freeman has planted pinot noir, and is the personal full-time viticulturist, helped out during peak periods by a part-time employee. It may not seem much, but successfully growing pinot noir (or any other variety, for that matter) in Tasmania requires an enormous degree of attention to debudding, leaf plucking, wire raising and (in the winter months) pruning. Not surprisingly, Freeman says he has no plans to extend the vineyard at the moment.

🍷🍷🍷🍷🍷 **Bicheno Pinot Noir 2010** Bright, strong crimson-purple; in the Australian scene, only Tasmania could produce pinot of this power without losing the elegance and finesse the variety should have. This will definitely repay cellaring. Screwcap. 13.4% alc. **Rating** 93 **To** 2020 $22

DiGiorgio Family Wines ★★★☆

Riddoch Highway, Coonawarra, SA 5263 **Region** Coonawarra
T (08) 8736 3222 **www**.digiorgio.com.au **Open** 7 days 10–5
Winemaker Peter Douglas **Est.** 1998 **Dozens** 45 000 **Vyds** 353.53ha
Stefano DiGiorgio emigrated from Abruzzi, Italy, in 1952. Over the years, he and his family gradually expanded their holdings at Lucindale. In 1989 he began planting cabernet sauvignon (99ha), chardonnay (10ha), merlot (9ha), shiraz (6ha) and pinot noir (2ha). In 2002 the family purchased the historic Rouge Homme winery, capable of crushing 10 000 tonnes of grapes, and its surrounding 13.5ha of vines, from Southcorp. Since that time the Coonawarra plantings have been increased to almost 230 ha, the lion's share to cabernet sauvignon. The enterprise is offering full winemaking services to vignerons in the Limestone Coast Zone. Exports to all major markets.

🍷🍷🍷🍷🍷 **Emporio Coonawarra Merlot Cabernet Sauvignon Cabernet Franc 2008** Deep garnet; a concentrated and essency blackcurrant bouquet with cedar and black olive on display; rich, dense and full-bodied, finishing with a lifted accent of eucalypt, providing freshness and contrast to the dark fruit on offer. ProCork. 14.8% alc. **Rating** 90 **To** 2018 $23 BE

♀♀♀♀   Coonawarra Cabernet Sauvignon 2008 Rating 89 To 2018 $23 BE
Lucindale Limestone Coast Sauvignon Blanc 2011 Rating 87 To Now
$18 BE
Coonawarra Shiraz 2008 Rating 87 To 2016 $23 BE

Dindima Wines   ★★★

859 Cargo Road, Orange, NSW 2800 **Region** Orange
T (02) 6365 3388 **www**.dindima.com.au **Open** Fri 12–5, w'ends & public hols 10–5 or
by appt (7 days Jan)
Winemaker James Bell **Est.** 2002 **Dozens** 400 **Vyds** 3.8ha
In late 2002 the Bell family acquired a property on the northern slopes of Mt Canobolas at
an altitude of approximately 895m. Prior to 1996 the property had been an orchard. With
its redevelopment as a vineyard some of the original muscat vines were retained (now about
45 years old) and new plantings of semillon, merlot, shiraz and cabernet sauvignon occurred.
In '05 a further planting of chardonnay was made and plans to add a similar amount of riesling
are underway. This family team, led by son James, regards attention to detail in all areas of
the winemaking process as essential; theirs is very much a hands-on operation, especially in
relation to vineyard canopy management.

♀♀♀♀   Orange Shiraz 2008 Obvious colour development; the wine is loaded with
multi-spice, licorice and pepper, all of which warm this medium-bodied, earthy
shiraz; has a distinct lift on the finish. Diam. 13% alc. **Rating** 89 **To** 2018 $38

Dinny Goonan   ★★★★

880 Winchelsea-Deans Marsh Road, Bambra, Vic 3241 **Region** Geelong
T 0438 408 420 **www**.dinnygoonan.com.au **Open** 7 days Jan, w'ends & public hols
Nov–Jun or by appt
Winemaker Dinny and Angus Goonan **Est.** 1990 **Dozens** 1200 **Vyds** 5.5ha
The establishment of Dinny Goonan dates back to 1988 when Dinny bought a 20ha property
near Bambra, in the hinterland of the Otway Coast. Dinny had recently completed a viticulture
diploma at CSU, and initially a wide range of varieties was planted in what is now known as the
Nursery Block, to establish those best suited to the area. As these came into production Dinny
headed back to CSU, where he completed a wine science degree. Ultimately, it was decided to
focus production on shiraz and riesling, with more extensive planting of these varieties. In '07
a 'sticky' block was added (semillon, sauvignon blanc), with the first harvest in 2011.

♀♀♀♀♀   Single Vineyard Shiraz 2010 Light, bright crimson; perhaps in part reflecting
the inclusion of a small portion of viognier in the wine, the bouquet is fragrant
and fresh, with abundant red berry fruit flavours on the light- to medium-bodied
palate; superfine tannins on the finish make this a prime candidate for drinking
over the next few years. Screwcap. 13.5% alc. **Rating** 92 **To** 2015 $25
✪   Single Vineyard Riesling 2011 A very attractive wine with hints of passionfruit
travelling alongside the lime and unsweetened lemon juice flavours; a classic drink
now or later proposition. Screwcap. 12.5% alc. **Rating** 91 **To** 2016 $20

♀♀♀♀   Early Harvest Riesling 2011 Rating 88 To 2016 $25
The Bambra Pinot Noir Chardonnay 2005 Rating 87 To 2013 $30

Dionysus Winery   ★★★

1 Patemans Lane, Murrumbateman, NSW 2582 **Region** Canberra District
T (02) 6227 0208 **www**.dionysus-winery.com.au **Open** W'ends & public hols 10–5,
or by appt
Winemaker Michael O'Dea **Est.** 1998 **Dozens** 1000 **Vyds** 4ha
Michael and Wendy O'Dea founded the winery while they had parallel lives as public
servants in Canberra, but they have now retired, and devote themselves full time to the
winery. They purchased their property at Murrumbateman in 1996, and planted chardonnay,
sauvignon blanc, riesling, viognier, merlot, pinot noir, cabernet sauvignon and shiraz between

1998 and 2001. Michael has completed an associate degree in winemaking at CSU, and is responsible for viticulture and winemaking; Wendy has completed various courses at the Canberra TAFE and is responsible for wine marketing and (in their words) 'nagging Michael and being a general slushie'.

🍷🍷🍷🍷 **Canberra District Cabernet Sauvignon 2010** Light red-purple; fragrant cassis/red berry aromas are effectively replayed on the light-bodied palate, there supported by fine tannins; attractive in its class. Screwcap. 13.5% alc. **Rating** 88 **To** 2014 $22
Canberra District Riesling 2011 Light straw-green; has potent, ripe, lime aromas and flavours; a rich, forward style ready right now. Screwcap. 11.5% alc. **Rating** 87 **To** 2014 $20
Maenads NV Pale salmon; the fragrant red berry bouquet is seasoned with cooking spices, the palate laden with the same range of spices plus cooked cherries and lemony acidity. Unconventional. Screwcap. 13% alc. **Rating** 87 **To** Now $18

 Dirt Road Vignerons ★★★

PO Box 594, Greenock, SA 5360 **Region** Barossa Zone
T (08) 8563 4043 **Open** Not
Winemaker Nathan Norman **Est.** 2005 **Dozens** 200 **Vyds** 11.6ha
When Jeff and Lisa Laycock planted 1.6ha of albarino in 2005 they, along with various other enthusiasts around Australia, had no idea the variety was in fact savagnin, no relation whatsoever to the albarino they thought they were planting. After some highly-publicised soul-searching by other growers (all good promotional material anyway) it was clear there was nothing left but to either use the correct name, or simply give a generic. Why did no one use Fool's Gold? Be that as it may, and with 10ha of shiraz as the real business, albeit not for Dirt Road Vignerons at this stage, Nathan Norman made several hundred dozen of savagnin, naming it The Debacle.

🍷🍷🍷🍷 **The Debacle Barossa Valley Savagnin 2011** Pale quartz; on the dilute side, but does have some pear and citrus flavours bolstered by a hint of sugar. Screwcap. 12% alc. **Rating** 87 **To** Now $16

Disaster Bay Wines ★★★☆

133 Oaklands Road, Pambula, NSW 2549 **Region** South Coast Zone
T (02) 6495 6869 **www.**disasterbaywines.com **Open** Not
Winemaker Dean O'Reilly, Capital Wines (Andrew McEwen) **Est.** 2000 **Dozens** 200 **Vyds** 1.2ha
Dean O'Reilly has a background in the distribution of fine table wines, culminating in employment by Möet Hennessy Australia. He has accumulated the UK-based WSET Intermediate and Advanced Certificates, completed various other programs and competitions, and has been associate judge and judge at various Canberra district events. He has also travelled through the wine regions of NZ, Champagne, Bordeaux, Chablis, Piedmont and Tuscany. In 2009 he was one of 12 wine professionals selected to participate in the week-long Len Evans Tutorial. The wines are made at Capital Wines, with Andrew McEwen overseeing Dean's apprenticeship; the grapes come from the block owned by Dean adjacent to the Pambula River.

🍷🍷🍷🍷🍷 **Sauvignon Blanc Semillon 2011** Part barrel-fermented, part stainless steel-fermented, then given brief oak maturation; there is some green acidity that sharpens the herb and grass flavours of the palate, but the upside is unqualified freshness and suitability for seafood. Screwcap. 13% alc. **Rating** 90 **To** 2013 $20

Dog Trap Vineyard ★★★★

262 Dog Trap Road, Yass, NSW 2582 **Region** Canberra District
T (02) 6226 5898 **www.**dogtrapvineyard.com.au **Open** By appt
Winemaker Dr Dennis Hart, Dr Roger Harris, Brian Sinclair, John Leyshon **Est.** 1996
Dozens 1000 **Vyds** 6.1ha

The somewhat ghoulish name and label illustration is a reminder of bygone days when wild dogs were caught in traps in much the same way as rabbits. It certainly means the name of the venture will be remembered. Planting of the vineyard began in 1996, with a smaller addition in '98. The property was purchased by Dr Dennis Hart and Ms Julian White in December 2003, and until '06 the grapes were sold to Constellation's Kamberra winery. In '07 the crop was completely destroyed by a violent but localised hailstorm, so the first wines were not made until '08. Shiraz and cabernet sauvignon were the initial plantings, and more recently, riesling and pinot gris were added.

DogRidge Wine Company   ★★★★★

129 Bagshaws Road, McLaren Flat, SA 5171 **Region** McLaren Vale
T (08) 8383 0140 **www**.dogridge.com.au **Open** 7 days 11–5
Winemaker Fred Howard **Est.** 1991 **Dozens** 9500 **Vyds** 56ha
Dave and Jen Wright had a combined background of dentistry, art and a CSU viticultural degree when they moved from Adelaide to McLaren Flat to become vignerons. They inherited vines planted in the early 1940s as a source for Chateau Reynella fortified wines, and their viticultural empire now ranges from 2001 plantings to some of the oldest vines remaining in the immediate region today. At the McLaren Flat vineyards, DogRidge has 60+-year-old shiraz, as well as 60-year-old grenache. Part of the grape production is retained, but most is sold to other leading wineries. Exports to the UK, the US and other major markets.

ΨΨΨΨΨ Most Valuable Player McLaren Vale Shiraz 2009 Deep and sweet-fruited, with fruitcake, liqueur-soaked black fruits and cinnamon on display; the palate is warm, unctuous and long, with a caress of mocha that lingers for a very long time. Screwcap. 14.5% alc. **Rating** 94 **To** 2016 $65 BE
Grand Old Brand New McLaren Vale Shiraz Petit Verdot Cabernet Sauvignon 2009 Made from 70-year-old shiraz and cabernet plantings, and 9-year-old petit verdot vines, a big mouthful. Excellent purple-crimson; the wine is filled with cassis and cherry fruit, superfine tannins and oak in perfect balance. Screwcap. 15% alc. **Rating** 94 **To** 2024 $40

ΨΨΨΨΨ Canvas McLaren Vale Cabernet Shiraz 2008 Exceptionally clever label with ✪   a smiley face; wine has an unexpectedly and pleasingly fragrant bouquet with cassis to the fore, the medium-bodied palate running in the same path. Delicious bargain. Screwcap. 14.5% alc. **Rating** 90 **To** 2015 $10

ΨΨΨΨ The Pup Sauvignon Blanc 2011 **Rating** 89 **To** 2013 $18
Shirtfront McLaren Vale Shiraz 2009 **Rating** 89 **To** 2015 $25 BE
Fortified Viognier NV **Rating** 88 **To** 2013 $18
The Pup Shiraz 2010 **Rating** 87 **To** 2014 $18 BE
Cadenzia McLaren Vale Grenache 2008 **Rating** 87 **To** 2013 $25
Cadenzia McLaren Vale Grenache Shiraz 2009 **Rating** 87 **To** 2014 $25 BE
The Pup Cabernet Merlot 2010 **Rating** 87 **To** 2014 $18 BE

DogRock Winery   ★★★★★

114 De Graves Road, Crowlands, Vic 3377 **Region** Pyrenees
T (03) 5354 9201 **www**.dogrock.com.au **Open** By appt
Winemaker Allen Hart **Est.** 1999 **Dozens** 1200 **Vyds** 6.2ha
This is the micro-venture (but with inbuilt future growth to something slightly larger) of Allen (now full-time winemaker) and Andrea (viticulturist) Hart. Having purchased the property in 1998, the planting of shiraz, riesling, tempranillo, grenache, chardonnay and marsanne began in 2000. Given Allen's former post as research scientist/winemaker with Foster's, the attitude taken to winemaking is unexpected. The estate-grown wines are made in a low-tech fashion, without gas cover or filtration, the Harts saying 'all wine will be sealed with a screwcap and no DogRock wine will ever be released under natural cork bark'. DogRock installed the first solar-powered irrigation system in Australia, capable of supplying water 365 days a year at night or in cloudy conditions; irrigation can be continued by water taken from a header dam, automatically refilled when sunlight returns.

🍷🍷🍷🍷 **Degraves Road 2010** Vibrant crimson hue; an intriguing blend for the region, yet the strength of personality in this wine is undeniable; crunchy fresh redcurrant, raspberry and blackberry fruits, mingle seamlessly with spice and minerals; the palate is medium-bodied, fresh and fragrant, with a long and engaging spine of acidity and tannin. A 45/40/15% blend of shiraz, grenache and tempranillo. Trophy Victorian Wines Show '11. Screwcap. 14% alc. **Rating** 95 **To** 2018 $75 BE

✪ **Pyrenees Shiraz 2010** Vivid purple hue; attractive floral-accented bouquet with liqueur-soaked black cherry, spice and a strong mineral note; the palate is medium-bodied, lively and spicy, with lots of energy and freshness; longevity will not be an issue. Screwcap. 13.5% alc. **Rating** 94 **To** 2020 $25 BE

🍷🍷🍷🍷🍷 **Pedro's Pyrenees Sparkling Red 2009 Rating** 92 **To** 2014 $30 BE
Reserve Pyrenees Riesling 2011 Rating 90 **To** 2017 $35

🍷🍷🍷🍷 **Pyrenees Riesling 2011 Rating** 88 **To** 2016 $20 BE

Domain Barossa

25 Murray Street, Tanunda, SA 5352 **Region** Barossa Valley
T (08) 8563 2170 **www**.domainbarossa.com **Open** By appt
Winemaker Todd Riethmuller **Est.** 2002 **Dozens** 3000
Todd Riethmuller and family are long-term residents of the Barossa Valley and have the inside running, as it were, when it comes to buying grapes from local growers. Thus they have been able to dispense with the expensive and often frustrating business of having their own winery, yet can make wines of exceptional quality. Exports to the UK, the US and Canada.

🍷🍷🍷🍷🍷 **Black Tongue Shiraz 2010** Deep colour, offering lavish levels of sweet black
✪ fruits, bitter chocolate and dark plums in abundance; a generous and evenly balanced wine. Screwcap. 14.5% alc. **Rating** 90 **To** 2018 $19 BE

✪ **Toddler GSM 2010** Deep colour, and showing masses of sweet black fruits, licorice and a little gamey complexity; the palate is fleshy and generous, forward and accessible; ready to go now, and best for short to medium-term consumption. Screwcap. 14.5% alc. **Rating** 90 **To** 2016 $19 BE

Domaine A

Tea Tree Road, Campania, Tas 7026 **Region** Southern Tasmania
T (03) 6260 4174 **www**.domaine-a.com.au **Open** Mon–Fri 10–4
Winemaker Peter Althaus **Est.** 1973 **Dozens** 5000 **Vyds** 10.7ha
The striking black label of the premium Domaine A wine, dominated by the single, multi-coloured 'A', signified the change of ownership from George Park to Swiss businessman Peter Althaus many years ago. The wines are made without compromise, and reflect the low yields from the immaculately tended vineyards. They represent aspects of both Old World and New World philosophies, techniques and styles. Exports to the UK, Denmark, Switzerland, Germany, France, Belgium, Canada, Taiwan, Hong Kong, China, Japan and Singapore.

🍷🍷🍷🍷🍷 **Lady A Sauvignon Blanc 2009** Mid straw, vibrant green hue; an exotic blend of guava, spice, nectarine and blanched almonds; the palate is unctuous, complex, extremely fresh and long, and there is no denying the strong 'Euro/Bordeaux' accent of this wine; complex sauvignon made with aplomb. Cork. 13.5% alc. **Rating** 95 **To** 2015 $60 BE

Stoney Vineyard Cabernet Sauvignon 2006 A blend of cabernet sauvignon, merlot, cabernet franc and petit verdot that spent 33 months in French barriques. Domain A is the only winery in Tasmania able to produce a wine of this quality from this Bordeaux blend, the secret being closely spaced, dry-grown old vines. It is a black-fruited wine with an autocratic personality, but will loosen up to a degree over the coming years. Diam. 14.5% alc. **Rating** 95 **To** 2026 $35

Stoney Vineyard Sauvignon Blanc 2010 Glowing pale green-gold; a very rich and concentrated sauvignon blanc, its layers of tropical fruit achieved at a modest alcohol level thanks to the small berries of fully matured dry-grown vines; citrussy acidity appears on the finish to provide balance. There is no other Tasmanian sauvignon blanc remotely like this. Cork. 13% alc. **Rating** 94 **To** 2014 $35

Stoney Vineyard Pinot Noir 2010 Strong, clear crimson-purple; combines power and elegance, depth and length — all this in Domaine A's second label; plum, black cherry and some foresty nuances play throughout the long palate. A long life ahead. Diam. 13.5% alc. **Rating** 94 **To** 2018 $35

Pinot Noir 2008 Deep, verging on dense, purple with a scarlet rim; right in the centre of the Domaine A style, more powerful and concentrated than any other Tasmanian pinot, or from parts further north, for that matter. This gravitas has been achieved without limiting pinot varietal character, albeit it is different from all others. Cork. 14% alc. **Rating** 94 **To** 2020 $70

Domaine Asmara   ★★★★★

Gibb Road, Toolleen, Vic 3551 **Region** Heathcote
T (03) 5433 6133 **www**.domaineasmara.com **Open** 7 days 9–6.30
Winemaker Sanguine Estate, Adrian Munari **Est.** 2008 **Dozens** 2500 **Vyds** 12ha
Chemical engineer Andreas Greiving had a lifelong dream to own and operate a vineyard, and the opportunity came along with the global financial crisis. He was able to purchase a vineyard planted to shiraz (7ha), cabernet sauvignon (2ha), cabernet franc, durif and viognier (1ha each), and have the wines contract-made. The venture is co-managed by dentist wife Hennijati. Exports to the UK.

ℙℙℙℙℙ **Reserve Heathcote Shiraz 2009** Bright, deep purple-crimson; a plush, full-bodied but relatively soft wine, with plum and black cherry fruit on the bouquet and palate alike, along with nuances of dried herb and licorice on the finish. Screwcap. 14.8% alc. **Rating** 94 **To** 2024 $45

Reserve Heathcote Cabernet Sauvignon 2010 Full, deep red-purple; the bouquet is full to the brim with rich blackcurrant fruit, the plush and textured medium- to full-bodied palate telling the same tale; oak somewhere in the mix, likewise tannins. Screwcap. 14.5% alc. **Rating** 94 **To** 2025 $45

ℙℙℙℙℙ **Private Collection Heathcote Shiraz 2010 Rating** 93 **To** 2020 $35
The Asmara 2010 Rating 93 **To** 2020 $25

ℙℙℙℙ **Heathcote Viognier 2011 Rating** 87 **To** 2013 $25

Domaine Carlei G2   ★★★★☆

1 Alber Road, Upper Beaconsfield, Vic 3808 **Region** Various Vic
T (03) 5944 4599 **www**.domainecarlei.com **Open** By appt
Winemaker David Carlei **Est.** 2010 **Dozens** 2000
This is the venture of David Carlei, son of Sergio Carlei; the two have worked together for some years, and David is currently studying wine marketing at CSU. His focus is on using organic and/or biodynamic grapes; maceration of white wines on skins for up to 90 days, followed by prolonged lees contact with minimal fining. The reds see a similar process with whole clusters, wild yeast fermentation and prolonged maceration periods with ageing on lees. They are, in short, natural wines, the red wines with more intrinsic quality than most of their peers. Exports to the US, the UK and China.

ℙℙℙℙℙ **Yarra Valley Syrah 2010** Clear, light crimson; a very pure wine reflecting its modest alcohol; finesse and elegance are the key words, the brightness of the red cherry fruit is also important. The oak is more subtle here than in the Reserve Heathcote. Diam. 13.5% alc. **Rating** 94 **To** 2025 $39

ℙℙℙℙℙ **Reserve Heathcote Syrah 2010 Rating** 93 **To** 2025 $39
Heathcote Syrah 2008 Rating 93 **To** 2020 $39
Yarra Valley Nudo Bianco 2011 Rating 91 **To** 2015 $39
Fleur Cardinia Ranges Pinot Noir 2009 Rating 90 **To** 2017 $39

Domaine Chandon   ★★★★★

727 Maroondah Highway, Coldstream, Vic 3770 **Region** Yarra Valley
T (03) 9738 9200 **www**.chandon.com.au **Open** 7 days 10.30–4.30
Winemaker Dan Buckle, Glenn Thompson, Adam Keath **Est.** 1986 **Dozens** 120 000
Vyds 118.6ha
Established by Möet & Chandon, this is one of the two most important wine facilities in
the Yarra Valley; the tasting room has a national and international reputation, having won
a number of major tourism awards in recent years. The sparkling wine product range has
evolved, and there has been increasing emphasis placed on the table wines, now released under
the Domaine Chandon label. An energetic young winemaking team has maintained the high
quality standards set by ex-CEO and mentor Dr Tony Jordan. Exports to all major markets.

🍷🍷🍷🍷🍷 **Yarra Valley Chardonnay 2010** Light straw-green; the wine has a very
expressive and complex bouquet of cashew, grapefruit and nectarine, the palate
picking up this lead-in to perfection, intense and tightly structured, yet nonetheless
allowing the fruit to shine through. Oak is present, but marginalised in a wine that
shows how much flavour can be harnessed at such low alcohol levels. Top-gold
National Wine Show '11. Screwcap. 12.5% alc. **Rating** 96 **To** 2018 $28
Prestige Cuvee 1996 The glowing gold colour is striking, a tribute to the
15 years the wine spent on lees prior to disgorgement; the bouquet gives no hint
of the explosive flavour on the palate, with multilayered complexity of dried fruit
and brioche flavours. Diam. 12.5% alc. **Rating** 96 **To** 2014 $89
Blanc de Blancs 2008 Pale green-straw; traditional method; 15 components
from various sites in the Yarra Valley, Adelaide Hills and Tasmania were included in
this wine. It spent 30 months on yeast lees; has excellent length and balance, with
flavours in the peach and pear spectrum. Diam. 12.5% alc. **Rating** 95 **To** 2014 $40
Tasmanian Cuvee 2008 Entirely sourced from one vineyard, the Tolpuddle
Vineyard in the Coal River area, the final blend 52% chardonnay and 48% pinot
noir. Pale straw-green, it spent 36 months on lees and disgorged Sept '11. The
extra intensity is very obvious, with fruit still dominating the brioche components.
Diam. 12.5% alc. **Rating** 95 **To** 2015 $40
Blanc de Noirs 2007 Largely sourced from the Upper Yarra Valley and Macedon.
A strong straw-gold colour; the bouquet is truly complex, with secondary biscuit/
brioche notes contrasting with crisp red berries; the palate is long, with classy
acidity and no hint of sweetness. Diam. 12.5% alc. **Rating** 95 **To** 2014 $40
Brut Rose Vintage 2008 A 55/45% Pinot Noir/Chardonnay, made from
40 different cuvees deriving from eight regions in four states. No traditional
method sparkling wine made elsewhere in Australia or the world has such a
massive range of terroir. It contains 8% pinot noir table wine, and spent 30 months
on lees prior to disgorgement. It has a delicious strawberries and cream mid palate,
and a long, clean and crisp finish. Diam. 12.5% alc. **Rating** 95 **To** 2016 $40
Pinot Noir Rose 2011 Rating 94 **To** 2013 $25
Heathcote Shiraz 2009 Rating 94 **To** 2020 $34
Z*D Blanc de Blancs 2008 Rating 94 **To** 2015 $40
Vintage Yarra Valley Cuvee 2006 Rating 94 **To** 2016 $40 BE

🍷🍷🍷🍷🍷 **Pinot Gris 2011 Rating** 92 **To** 2014 $28
Brut Rose Non Vintage NV Rating 92 **To** Now $29
Cuvee Riche NV Rating 91 **To** Now $65
Chandon Sparkling Pinot Noir Shiraz NV Rating 91 **To** 2014 $29 BE
Brut NV Rating 90 **To** 2014 $29 BE

🍷🍷🍷🍷 **Yarra Valley Pinot Noir 2010 Rating** 89 **To** 2014 $34
Sauvignon Blanc 2011 Rating 88 **To** 2013 $25 BE

Domaine Rogha Crois Wines   ★★★★

PO Box 436, Bungendore, NSW 2621 **Region** Canberra District
T (02) 6238 0500 **www**.drcwine.com.au **Open** Not
Winemaker Malcolm Burdett, Andrew McEwin **Est.** 1998 **Dozens** 400 **Vyds** 2ha

David and Lyn Crossley purchased their property on the Lake George escarpment in 1998, planting clonally-selected pinot noir, pinot gris, cabernet franc and merlot over the following two years. Their inspiration was the pioneering work done by Dr Edgar Riek. The vineyard is on a steep hillside at 800–840 m, often snow-covered in winter, but is protected from frosts by its slope. The small size of the vineyard facilitates micro-management of the vines throughout the year. The name is gaelic for 'quality cross'.

♉♉♉♉♀ **Pinot Noir 2010** Strong, crystal-bright colour; the bouquet has some interesting spicy notes, and the palate picks up on those with dark cherry and plum fruit; the wine has appropriate body, and a silky mouthfeel, despite the alcohol. Screwcap. 14.5% alc. **Rating** 91 **To** 2016 $30
Conti's Tower 2011 This blend of cabernet franc and merlot is medium-bodied, very much in accord with the blend; rose petal and cedar aromas are followed by a light- to medium-bodied palate with fresh red fruits, the tannins well-handled and weighted. Screwcap. 12.6% alc. **Rating** 90 **To** 2017 $28

♉♉♉♉ **Pinot Gris 2011 Rating** 89 **To** 2014 $28

Domaines Tatiarra   ★★★★☆
2 Corrong Court, Eltham, Vic 3095 (postal) **Region** Heathcote
T 0428 628 420 **www**.cambrianshiraz.com **Open** Not
Winemaker Ben Riggs, Peter Flewellyn **Est.** 1991 **Dozens** 3000 **Vyds** 13.4ha
Domaines Tatiarra Ltd. is an unlisted public company, its core asset being a 60ha property of Cambrian earth identified and developed by Bill Hepburn, who sold to the company in 1991. It produces only one varietal wine: Shiraz. The majority of the wine comes from the Tatiarra (an Aboriginal word meaning 'beautiful country') property, but the Trademark Shiraz is an equal blend of McLaren Vale and Heathcote wine. The wines are made at the Pettavel Winery in Geelong, with Ben Riggs commuting between there and McLaren Vale as required. Exports to the UK, the US, Canada, Denmark, Switzerland, Singapore and China.

♉♉♉♉♉ **Trademark Heathcote McLaren Vale Shiraz 2009** Each year the best two barrels from Heathcote made by Peter Llewellyn are blended with the best two barrels of McLaren Vale shiraz made by Ben Riggs to make this wine. Given its alcohol, it is no surprise to find a full-bodied palate crammed to the gills with spice, dark chocolate, plum cake, blackberry and licorice. The surprise is the absence of heat on the finish. Screwcap. 15.5% alc. **Rating** 94 **To** 2020 $60

Dominique Portet   ★★★★★
870–872 Maroondah Highway, Coldstream, Vic 3770 **Region** Yarra Valley
T (03) 5962 5760 **www**.dominiqueportet.com **Open** 7 days 10–5
Winemaker Ben Portet **Est.** 2000 **Dozens** 10 000 **Vyds** 4.3ha
Dominique Portet was bred in the purple. He spent his early years at Chateau Lafite (where his father was régisseur) and was one of the very first Flying Winemakers, commuting to Clos du Val in the Napa Valley, where his brother was winemaker. He then spent over 20 years as managing director of Taltarni and Clover Hill in Tasmania. After retiring from Taltarni, he moved to the Yarra Valley, a region he had been closely observing since the mid 1980s. In 2001 he found the site he had long looked for and in the twinkling of an eye built his winery and cellar door, planting a quixotic mix of viognier, sauvignon blanc and merlot next to the winery. Son Ben is now executive winemaker, leaving Dominique with a roving role as de facto consultant and brand marketer. Ben (30) has a winemaking CV of awesome scope, covering all parts of France, South Africa, California and four vintages at Petaluma. Exports to Canada, the Netherlands, Denmark, Dubai, Hong Kong, Singapore, Malaysia, China and Japan.

♉♉♉♉♉ **Heathcote Shiraz 2010** Bright crimson-purple; the bouquet·is a fragrant and complex blend of black and red fruits, spice and oak, the palate with great elegance, balance and length. Reflects the excellent vintage. Cork. 13.5% alc. **Rating** 95 **To** 2030 $55

Yarra Valley Cabernet Sauvignon 2010 Bright red-purple; the bouquet is a fragrant and fresh rendition of cabernet, with blackcurrant and redcurrant to the fore; the palate is better still, finely drawn and intense, with the fruit driving the long, lingering finish, oak and tannins in balanced support. The choice of cork is a puzzle. 13% alc. **Rating** 94 **To** 2020 $55

Yarra Valley Brut Rose LD NV A blend of pinot noir and chardonnay grown in the Yarra Valley, and fermented in this bottle; bright pale pink, it has most attractive strawberry fruit flavours, with very good length; the LD signifies light dosage (ie lesser than normal sugar added to the wine after disgorgement). It all works perfectly to result in a wine for all seasons. Cork. 13% alc. **Rating** 94 **To** Now $28

ΨΨΨΨΩ
✪
Fontaine Yarra Valley Pyrenees Rose 2011 A blend of merlot, shiraz and cabernet sauvignon; pale pink, with just a touch of salmon, the wine has an array of delicate red berry flavours, a touch of savoury spice, and a dry finish. Screwcap. 13% alc. **Rating** 90 **To** Now $20

Vendanges Tardives Yarra Valley Sauvignon Blanc 2010 Rating 90 **To** 2014 $28

ΨΨΨΨ
Yarra Valley Sauvignon Blanc 2011 Rating 89 **To** Now $28
Fontaine Yarra Valley Heathcote Shiraz Cabernet 2010 Rating 89 **To** 2016 $20

Donny Goodmac ★★★★

PO Box 467, Healesville, Vic 3777 **Region** Yarra Valley
T (03) 5962 3779 **www**.donnygoodmac.com.au **Open** Not
Winemaker Kate Goodman **Est.** 2002 **Dozens** 500
The improbable name is a typically whimsical invention of the three proprietors: Donny is contributed by Stuart Gregor, whose marketing and PR prowess has hitherto prevented an entry for the venture in the *Wine Companion*. Kate Goodman is the (genuinely) good part of the team, while Cameron MacKenzie is the 'mac'. Kate and Cameron both work full-time at Punt Road, where Kate is chief winemaker. What started as a little bit of fun in 2002 (less than 50 dozen made) has grown to the dizzy heights of 600 dozen, utilising old-vine shiraz from the Pyrenees, and chardonnay and cabernet sauvignon from a couple of old vineyards in the Coldstream area of the Yarra Valley.

ΨΨΨΨΩ
Individual Vineyard Pyrenees Shiraz 2009 Deep garnet; a savoury mixture of mulberry, liqueur-soaked plums, toasty cedary oak and sage; the medium-bodied palate is silky in texture, with fine-grained tannins and lively acidity drawing out the even finish. Screwcap. 13.2% alc. **Rating** 93 **To** 2020 $37 BE

Individual Vineyard Yarra Valley Cabernet Sauvignon 2009 Deep garnet; the bouquet is essency, showing red fruits and blackcurrant, olive and a little lavender; the palate is medium-bodied, with ample tannins pulling the wine into shape on the long finish. Screwcap. 12.8% alc. **Rating** 91 **To** 2020 $33 BE

Individual Vineyard Yarra Valley Chardonnay 2009 Despite the bushfires and the heat, there were many good chardonnays made in the Yarra Valley in '09. This wine was picked at very low baume, and despite wild yeast barrel fermentation (15% new), lees stirring and no mlf, is very light indeed. Only 190 dozen made. Screwcap. 12.2% alc. **Rating** 90 **To** 2014 $29

ΨΨΨΨ
Individual Vineyard Yarra Valley Chardonnay 2010 Rating 87 **To** 2014 $28 BE

Dorrien Estate ★★★★★

Cnr Barossa Valley Way/Siegersdorf Road, Tanunda, SA 5352 **Region** Barossa Valley
T (08) 8561 2200 **www**.cellarmasters.com.au **Open** Not
Winemaker Julie Montgomery, Neil Doddridge, Sally Blackwell, Matt Reimann, Hamish Seabrook **Est.** 1982 **Dozens** 1 million
Dorrien Estate is the physical base of the vast Cellarmasters network that, wearing its retailer's hat, is by far the largest direct-sale outlet in Australia. It also makes wine for many producers

across Australia at its modern winery, which has a capacity of 14.5 million litres of wine in tank and barrel; however, a typical make of each wine will be little more than 1000 dozen. Most of the wines made for others are exclusively distributed by Cellarmasters. (Chateau Dorrien is an entirely unrelated business.) Acquired by Woolworths in May 2011. Exports to the UK and NZ.

🍷🍷🍷🍷🍷 **Dorrien Estate Bin 1A Chardonnay 2010** Sourced from the Coal River Valley, Margaret River and Mount Benson, areas that react synergistically, giving this wine the texture one would normally expect from older wine; a very high-quality wine, and it will be fascinating to observe how it develops over the years ahead with its nectarine and cashew fruit. Screwcap. 13.5% alc. **Rating** 95 **To** 2017 $36
Dorrien Estate Bin 1 Barossa Valley Shiraz 2009 Medium purple-red; a no-holds-barred full-bodied shiraz stacked full of blackberry fruit, ripe tannins and vanillin oak; full-bodied it may be, but it has very good balance, line and length. Screwcap. 14.5% alc. **Rating** 95 **To** 2030 $42
Krondorf Growers Schulz & Scalzi Barossa Valley Shiraz 2010 Deep crimson-purple hue; the bouquet is loaded with sweet black fruits, spices and a splash of licorice; the palate is juicy and direct, medium-bodied and evenly poised; the long finish displays an abundance of fresh fruit; while cellaring will be rewarded, there is a lot to like in this wine at this price. Screwcap. 14.5% alc. **Rating** 94 **To** 2018 $27 BE
Black Wattle Mount Benson Cabernet Sauvignon 2010 Bright colour; a fresh and inviting bouquet of cranberry, bramble and olive; the full-bodied palate is fragrant and focused, with fine tannins aplenty; fresh and savoury personality. Screwcap. 14.5% alc. **Rating** 94 **To** 2016 $41 BE

🍷🍷🍷🍷🍷 **Dorrien Estate Bin 1A Bendito Shiraz 2009** **Rating** 93 **To** 2025 $36
Stonyfell Bin 62 Langhorne Creek Cabernet Sauvignon Shiraz Malbec 2010 **Rating** 93 **To** 2018 $39 BE
Yarra View Yarra Valley Chardonnay 2010 **Rating** 92 **To** 2015 $26 BE
Redemption Canberra District Shiraz 2010 **Rating** 92 **To** 2022 $28
Black Wattle Vineyard Mount Benson Merlot 2010 **Rating** 92 **To** 2015 $41 BE
Yarra View Yarra Valley Pinot Noir 2010 **Rating** 91 **To** 2016 $29 BE
Krondorf Symmetry Barossa Valley Shiraz 2009 **Rating** 91 **To** 2020 $49 BE
Avon Brae New Eden Vineyards Shiraz 2010 **Rating** 90 **To** 2016 $40 BE
Black Wattle Mount Benson Shiraz 2009 **Rating** 90 **To** 2016 $41 BE
Tolley Elite Bendigo Barossa Valley Shiraz 2009 **Rating** 90 **To** 2016 $38 BE
Avon Brae New Eden Vineyards Shiraz 2009 **Rating** 90 **To** 2016 $40 BE

Dowie Doole ★★★★☆

276 California Road, McLaren Vale, SA 5171 **Region** McLaren Vale
T (08) 8323 8875 **www**.dowiedoole.com **Open** By appt
Winemaker Chris Thomas **Est.** 1996 **Dozens** 25 000 **Vyds** 44.35ha
Dowie Doole was born of the frustration following the 1995 vintage, which led friends Norm Doole and Drew Dowie to form a partnership to take control over the destiny of their grapes. In '98, Leigh Gilligan, a McLaren Vale veteran, was appointed to take overall control of the business, and joined the partnership. Founding winemaker Brian Light has stepped back to a consultancy role following the appointment of Chris Thomas as winemaker in 2011. Sami Gilligan, Lulu Lunn and Dave Gartelmann share responsibility for the five vineyards in which Dowie Doole has an interest, all managed using sustainable viticulture practises. Exports to the UK, the US, Canada, Denmark, Germany, Hong Kong and China.

🍷🍷🍷🍷🍷 **Reserve McLaren Vale Shiraz 2010** A deep, dark and dense wine, showing lavish levels of sweet black fruits, mocha oak and a fresh sea salt tang for contrast; full-bodied and full throttle in every regard, yet showing a lightness of touch and fineness of tannin that provides a long and even finish. Diam. 14.5% alc. **Rating** 94 **To** 2020 $60 BE

🍷🍷🍷🍷🍷 **G&T McLaren Vale Garnacha & Tempranillo 2011** **Rating** 90 **To** 2013 $25 BE

ŶŶŶŶ   Cali Road McLaren Vale Shiraz 2010 Rating 89 To 2016 $35 BE
McLaren Vale Merlot 2010 Rating 88 To 2015 $22 BE
Second Nature Adelaide Hills Sauvignon Blanc 2011 Rating 87
To Now $19
Second Nature McLaren Vale Cabernet Shiraz Merlot 2010 Rating 87
To 2013 $19

Downing Estate Vineyard ★★★★★

19 Drummonds Lane, Heathcote, Vic 3523 **Region** Heathcote
T (03) 5433 3387 **www**.downingestate.com.au **Open** Long w'ends & public hols 11–5
or by appt
Winemaker John Ellis **Est.** 1994 **Dozens** 1000 **Vyds** 10ha
Bob and Joy Downing purchased 24ha of undulating land in 1994, and have established a
dry-grown vineyard planted to shiraz (7.2ha), cabernet sauvignon (2.4ha) and merlot (0.4ha).
At any one time, a number of vintages of each wine are available for sale. Exports to Canada,
Singapore and China.

ŶŶŶŶŶ   Reserve Heathcote Shiraz 2008 Outstanding colour for an '08; predominantly
made from a small section of the estate vineyard, and spent 21 months in 100%
new French barriques; it is a measure of the quality of the fruit that it was able to
absorb so much new oak; the palate has a juicy intensity that belies the impact of
the warmth of the vintage and the continuing drought; has great length, and will
be very long lived. Screwcap. 14.7% alc. Rating 95 To 2030 $85
Heathcote Cabernet Sauvignon 2009 Half bottled with screwcap, half with
Diam. Crimson-purple; a very attractive, medium-bodied cabernet, with perfectly
ripened cassis and dark berry flavours, the tannins fine and balanced, oak positive
but integrated. 14.1% alc. Rating 94 To 2024 $39

ŶŶŶŶŶ   Heathcote Shiraz 2009 Rating 93 To 2024 $39

Drayton's Family Wines ★★★★☆

555 Oakey Creek Road, Cessnock, NSW 2321 **Region** Hunter Valley
T (02) 4998 7513 **www**.draytonswines.com.au **Open** Mon–Fri 8–5, w'ends &
public hols 10–5
Winemaker Andrew Leembruggen, Max and John Drayton **Est.** 1853 **Dozens** 60 000
Vyds 72ha
This substantial Hunter Valley producer has suffered more than its share of misfortune over
the years, but has risen to the challenges. Winemaker William (Will) Rikard-Bell, badly
injured in the winery explosion of 2007, retired prior to the '11 vintage to pursue separate
business interests in Orange with wife Kimmy. They parted on good terms, and Drayton's
was able to secure the services of Andrew Leembruggen as chief winemaker after 13 years
with McWilliam's Mount Pleasant. Exports to Ireland, Vietnam, Singapore, Taiwan and China.

ŶŶŶŶŶ   William Shiraz 2006 Exceptional crimson-purple; 100+-year-old vines and
skilled winemaking have produced a seriously good Hunter shiraz; red and black
cherry fruit is fused with oak and tannins, but the fruit remains the driving force
on a long and immaculately balanced medium-bodied palate feasting on its
moderate alcohol. Cork. 13.5% alc. Rating 96 To 2030 $45

ŶŶŶŶŶ   Heritage Vines Semillon 2011 Rating 93 To 2021 $59
Susanne Semillon 2007 Rating 92 To 2017 $35
Vineyard Reserve Pokolbin Chardonnay 2010 Rating 92 To 2015 $30
Heritage Vines Shiraz 2010 Rating 92 To 2035 $49
✪   Bin 5555 Hunter Valley Shiraz 2009 Has retained bright, light crimson colour;
the fragrant bouquet announces a classic Hunter shiraz, only light- to medium-
bodied, but with lovely fresh red fruits that will gradually evolve with more earthy
notes as the wine ages. Screwcap. 12.5% alc. Rating 92 To 2020 $20
Vineyard Reserve Pokolbin Semillon 2009 Rating 90 To 2016 $30

ƳƳƳƳ   Hunter Valley Semillon Sauvignon Blanc 2011 Rating 87 To Now $20
Hunter Valley Verdelho 2011 Rating 87 To 2013 $20

Dromana Estate   ★★★★☆

555 Old Moorooduc Road, Tuerong, Vic 3933 **Region** Mornington Peninsula
T (03) 5974 4400 **www**.dromanaestate.com.au **Open** Wed–Sun 11–5
Winemaker Duncan Buchanan **Est.** 1982 **Dozens** 30 000 **Vyds** 53.9ha
Since it was established thirty years ago, Dromana Estate has always been near or at the
cutting edge, both in marketing terms and in terms of development of new varietals, most
obviously the Italian range under the 'i' label. Dromana Estate is owned by the investors of a
publicly listed company, operating under the name of Mornington Winery Group Limited. It
includes the Dromana Estate, Mornington Estate and David Traeger (see separate entry) labels.
Expanded production has seen export markets increase. Exports to the US, Canada and China.

ƳƳƳƳƳ   30th Anniversary Pinot Noir 2010 Mid garnet; a perfumed and red-fruited
bouquet, offset by layers of spice and well-handled oak; the palate is silky and
fine-boned with lacy tannins, fine acidity and a thoroughly elegant personality; no
blockbuster, but there is much to like in this 30th Anniversary edition. Screwcap.
13.3% alc. Rating 94 To 2018 $55 BE

ƳƳƳƳƳ   Mornington Estate Sauvignon Blanc 2010 Rating 90 To 2013 $22

ƳƳƳƳ   Mornington Estate Pinot Gris 2010 Rating 89 To Now $22
i Mornington Peninsula Arneis 2009 Rating 88 To Now $20

Dryridge Estate   ★★★★

The Six Foot Track, Megalong Valley, NSW 2785 **Region** Central Ranges Zone
T (02) 4787 5625 **www**.dryridge.com.au **Open** Sun from 11 am, or by appt
Winemaker Madrez Wine Services (Chris Derrez, Lucy Maddox) **Est.** 2000 **Dozens**
1500 **Vyds** 3.8ha
Bob and Barbara Tyrrell (no relation to Tyrrell's of the Hunter Valley) have pioneered
commercial viticulture in the Megalong Valley, adjacent to the Blue Mountains National Park.
They have 1.8ha of riesling, 1.1ha of shiraz and 0.9ha of cabernet sauvignon, and a further
0.9ha to be planted (possibly fiano) in due course. The vines are set on typically east-facing
rolling hillsides, with granitic-derived light, sandy clay loam soils of moderately low fertility.
Sunrise Lodge provides 4.5-star accommodation overlooking the vineyard.

ƳƳƳƳƳ   Blue Mountains Riesling 2011 Bright green hue; an attractive array of citrus
with lemon, orange blossom and quartz on the bouquet; the palate is juicy
on entry, tightening up with mineral complexity on the finish; a user-friendly
example of the variety. Screwcap. 12% alc. Rating 90 To 2018 $23 BE
Blue Mountains Cabernet Sauvignon 2011 Mid crimson; a bright red and
blue-fruited bouquet with a splash of sage; the palate is medium-bodied, focused
and fresh, with vibrant acidity and graphite tannins evident in equal proportion to
the fruit. Screwcap. 13.2% alc. Rating 90 To 2018 $27 BE

ƳƳƳƳ   Nellie's Cabernet Rose 2011 Rating 88 To 2013 $18 BE
Six Foot Track Shiraz 2011 Rating 88 To 2014 $25 BE

Dudley Wines   ★★★

1153 Willoughby Road, Penneshaw, Kangaroo Island, SA 5222 **Region** Kangaroo Island
T (08) 8553 1333 **www**.dudleywines.com.au **Open** 7 days 10–5
Winemaker Brodie Howard **Est.** 1994 **Dozens** 3500 **Vyds** 14ha
Jeff and Val Howard own Dudley Wines and its three vineyards on Kangaroo Island's Dudley
Peninsula: the Porky Flat Vineyard, Hog Bay River and Sawyers. It is the quirky vineyard
names that give the wines their distinctive identities. The Howards not only look after
viticulture, but also join in the winemaking process. Most of the wines are sold through
licensed outlets on Kangaroo Island.

ŢŢŢŢ **Hog Bay River Kangaroo Island Cabernet Sauvignon 2009** Developed leather, mocha and bramble are all evident on the bouquet; medium-bodied and savoury, with a sweet core of black fruit and a long tail of mocha and olive to finish. Screwcap. 14.5% alc. **Rating** 88 **To** 2014 $28 BE

Duke's Vineyard ★★★★★

Porongurup Road, Porongurup, WA 6324 **Region** Porongurup
T (08) 9853 1107 **www.**dukesvineyard.com **Open** 7 days 10–4.30
Winemaker Robert Diletti **Est.** 1998 **Dozens** 3500 **Vyds** 10ha
When Hilde and Ian (Duke) Ranson sold their clothing manufacturing business in 1998, they were able to fulfil a long-held dream of establishing a vineyard in the Porongurup subregion of Great Southern with the acquisition of a 65ha farm at the foot of the Porongurup Range. They planted shiraz and cabernet sauvignon (3ha each) and riesling (4ha). Hilde, a successful artist, designed the beautiful, scalloped, glass-walled cellar door sales area, with its mountain blue cladding. The appointment of Rob Diletti as winemaker will, if it were possible, increase the quality of the wines.

ŢŢŢŢŢ **Magpie Hill Reserve Riesling 2011** Hand-picked, whole bunch-pressed, using
✪ only free-run juice; the fragrant blossom-filled bouquet foretells the wonderfully intense and juicy palate, full of lime and lemon flavours before moving through to a long, dry finish. What more can you ask for? WAK screwcap. 12.8% alc. **Rating** 96 **To** 2030 $27

○ **Porongurup Riesling 2011 Rating** 96 **To** 2031 $20
Magpie Hill Reserve Shiraz 2010 Crimson-purple; everything is well with this wine; deserving of its Reserve status, but it does need time for the French oak to settle down as it will over the next 2–3 years; it has abundant black cherry and blackberry fruit on the bouquet and palate, and the length and balance are good. WAK screwcap. 13% alc. **Rating** 94 **To** 2025 $30
✪ **Single Vineyard Porongurup Shiraz 2010** Mid crimson-purple; a very elegant and impeccably balanced medium-bodied shiraz; its cool-climate origins are spelt out to the degree one would expect, with notes of spice and pepper intermingling with fine tannins. WAK screwcap. 13.2% alc. **Rating** 94 **To** 2022 $22

ŢŢŢŢ **Magpie Hill Reserve Sparkling Riesling 2009 Rating** 88 **To** 2013 $27

Dunn's Creek Estate ★★★☆

137 McIlroys Road, Red Hill, Vic 3937 **Region** Mornington Peninsula
T (03) 5989 2011 **www.**dunnscreek.com.au **Open** W'ends 10–5 or by appt
Winemaker Sandro Mosele (Contract) **Est.** 2001 **Dozens** 140 **Vyds** 3.28ha
This is the retirement venture of Roger and Hannah Stuart-Andrews, a former professional couple whose love of Italian and Spanish wines led them to their eclectic choice of varieties. Thus they have planted 1.3ha of pinot gris and 0.66ha each of barbera, arneis and pinot noir.

ŢŢŢŢŢ **Mornington Peninsula Barbera 2010** Medium red-purple; a more than useful barbera, with a tangy range of spice, sour cherry and bramble flavours; the texture and structure are enhanced by fine tannins. Screwcap. 14% alc. **Rating** 90 **To** 2016 $27

Dutschke Wines ★★★★★

PO Box 107 Lyndoch, SA 5351 **Region** Barossa Valley
T (08) 8524 5485 **www.**dutschkewines.com **Open** Not
Winemaker Wayne Dutschke **Est.** 1998 **Dozens** 6000 **Vyds** 17.5ha
Wayne Dutschke spent over 20 years working in Australia and overseas for companies large and small before joining his uncle (and grapegrower) Ken Semmler to form Dutschke Wines. In addition to outstanding table wines, he has a yearly release of fortified wines (doubtless drawing on his time at Baileys of Glenrowan); these sell out overnight, and have received the usual stratospheric points from Robert Parker Jr. The quality of the wines is in fact exemplary. Exports to the US, Canada, Denmark, Germany and the Netherlands.

ɣɣɣɣɣ Oscar Semmler Lyndoch Barossa Valley Shiraz 2009 Deep purple-crimson; an intense yet elegant wine, with a panoply of spice, licorice and black fruits on the bouquet gathering pace and drive on the highly focused and long palate, the finish long and the aftertaste lingering for minutes. Screwcap. 14.8% alc. **Rating** 96 **To** 2030 $60

St Jakobi Single Vineyard Barossa Valley Shiraz 2009 Very good purple-crimson colour; a complex bouquet with black fruits, spice and subtle oak that flow through to the medium-bodied, elegant palate, the tannins fine and ripe, the oak subtle. A lovely Barossa shiraz. Screwcap. 14.8% alc. **Rating** 95 **To** 2024 $38

Single Barrel St Jakobi Vineyard 78 Block Barossa Valley Cabernet Sauvignon 2009 Deep crimson, purple hue; full of sweet cassis fruit on the bouquet, almost pastille-like purity, and offset by cedary complexity from new oak; the palate reveals poised dark fruits, ample fine-grained tannins and a very long and oaky finish; the price and the oak may be a sticking point, but this is sure to reward patient cellaring. Screwcap. 15% alc. **Rating** 95 **To** 2025 $125 BE

GHR Neighbours Barossa Valley Shiraz 2010 Deep colour and loaded with toasty oak, black fruits and cinnamon on the bouquet; the palate is generous and densely packed with fruit and oak, while maintaining freshness and verve; a long and toasty finish, with time sure to settle the oak influence. Screwcap. 14.7% alc. **Rating** 94 **To** 2016 $25 BE

ɣɣɣɣ   Jackson St Jakobi Vineyard Barossa Valley Cabernet Shiraz 2010 **Rating** 87 **To** 2017 $30 BE

Eagle Vale Estate   ★★★★

7087 Caves Road, Margaret River, WA 6285 **Region** Margaret River
T (08) 9757 6477 **www**.eaglevalewine.com **Open** Mon–Fri 10–4.30, w'ends by appt
Winemaker Guy Gallienne **Est.** 1997 **Dozens** 15 000 **Vyds** 11.5ha
Eagle Vale is the venture of Colorado businessman Steve Jacobs, and the operator/winemaking team of Chantal and Guy Gallienne. The Galliennes come from the Loire Valley, although Guy secured his winemaking degree at Roseworthy College/Adelaide University. The vineyard is managed on a low-impact basis, without pesticides (guinea fowls do the work) and with minimal irrigation. All the wines are made from estate-grown grapes. Exports to the UK, the US, the Seychelles, China and Hong Kong.

ɣɣɣɣɣ Margaret River Chardonnay 2010 Vivid green hue; a ripe and expressive bouquet of nectarine, pineapple and a little oak-derived spice; the palate is finely textured, with a dry chalky aspect that provides length and vitality to the finish. Screwcap. 13% alc. **Rating** 91 **To** 2017 $20 BE

Whispering Lake Single Vineyard Margaret River Chardonnay 2006 A big, rich, brassy and toasty bouquet of spicy oak, dried figs and straw; the palate is unctuous and full of buttered brioche, with a long tail of grilled nuts; a somewhat old-fashioned example of the variety, for those still held in thrall by weight and depth, rather than finesse. Screwcap. 14% alc. **Rating** 91 **To** 2016 $45 BE

Margaret River Shiraz 2010 Deep crimson; a fragrant blend of red cherry, liqueur-soaked plums, licorice and ironstone; the palate is medium-bodied and fragrant, with a strong backbone of tannins providing length and simply demanding food to counter the structure. Screwcap. 13.5% alc. **Rating** 90 **To** 2020 $20 BE

 # Echelon   ★★★★★

68 Anzac Street, Chullora, NSW 2190 **Region** Various
T (02) 9790 8567 **www**.echelonwine.com.au **Open** Not
Winemaker Various **Est.** 2009 **Dozens** NFP
Echelon is the brainchild of Nicholas Crampton, a wine marketer who understands wine (by no means a usual occurrence). He persuaded McWilliam's (Echelon's owner) to give free rein to his insights, and enlisted the aid of McWilliam's chief winemaker Corey Ryan. Ryan relinquished that role on 30 June 2012, but continues to have a consultancy role. Brands under the Echelon umbrella are Last Horizon (single vineyard wines from Tasmania, made

by Adrian Sparks), Partisan (from McLaren Vale), Armchair Critic and Under & Over (from established vineyards in the best regions) and Zeppelin (made by Corey Ryan and Kym Teusner, sourced from Barossa vineyards either owned by Teusner or Sons of Eden, and often up to 80 years old). Few wineries in Australia so over-deliver on quality at their price-point.

♥♥♥♥♥ **Zeppelin Ferdinand Barossa Valley Shiraz 2008** From a single vineyard in the Greenock area, and has been made with considerable skill, showing none of the cooked fruit characters of many '08s; open-fermented, the wine was pressed and taken to barrel to finish its fermentation; half the barrels were new French oak, half used. Screwcap. 14.5% alc. **Rating** 95 **To** 2028 $37

Last Horizon Coal River Riesling 2011 Bright, light green-quartz; the promise of the colour and the bouquet is realised on the delicious palate, with lime juice and a hint of more tropical fruit; excellent balance and length. Screwcap. 12.5% alc. **Rating** 94 **To** 2021 $23

✪ **Zeppelin Eden Valley Riesling 2011** Hand-picked and accumulated in small lots before gentle whole bunch-pressing, an expensive way for a wine of this price. Pale quartz-green, it has vibrant citrus flavours built around a core of steely acidity that draws out the long finish. Screwcap. 12% alc. **Rating** 94 **To** 2021 $19

✪ **Partisan McLaren Vale Shiraz 2010** Deep purple-crimson; the bouquet tells of the terroir of McLaren Vale and the shiraz it produces; blackberry, black cherry, licorice, spice and dark chocolate are simply a start; it's more important to talk about the exceptional mouthfeel and structure of this beautifully constructed medium-bodied wine. Screwcap. 14% alc. **Rating** 94 **To** 2025 $19

✪ **Zeppelin Big Bertha Barossa Valley Shiraz 2009** Strong purple-crimson; a great deal of ultra-typical Barossa Valley shiraz here, yet it retains excellent structure, balance and mouthfeel, and the flavours build deliciously on the harmonious back-palate and aftertaste. Screwcap. 14.5% alc. **Rating** 94 **To** 2020 $17

♥♥♥♥♀ **Last Horizon Tamar Valley Pinot Noir 2010** Clear magenta-red; cold-soaked
✪ for six days before transfer to open fermenters and matured for eight months in 30% new French oak. While not flamboyant, has purity and excellent varietal expression, with a haunting aftertaste. Screwcap. 13.5% alc. **Rating** 93 **To** 2015 $19

◉ **Armchair Critic Heathcote Shiraz 2009 Rating** 93 **To** 2020 $19
Partisan Single Vineyard Olivers Road Grenache 2010 Rating 93 **To** 2017 $40 BE

✪ **Partisan Trench Coat 2010** A blend of grenache, shiraz and mourvedre from McLaren Vale. A full-bodied version of the style, with blackberry, plum and red cherry fruit reflecting the three varieties; the tannins give the wine considerable structure, the oak all but hidden. Screwcap. 14.9% alc. **Rating** 93 **To** 2020 $19
Partisan McLaren Vale Shiraz 2009 Rating 92 **To** 2024 $27

✪ **Armchair Critic Tumbarumba Chardonnay 2010** The wine is all about intensity, drive and length, sharply focused by the grapefruit-based flavours, rather than the crosscut of winemaker inputs (next to none). Screwcap. 13% alc. **Rating** 91 **To** 2017 $19
Last Horizon Pinot Gris 2010 Rating 91 **To** 2014 $23

♥♥♥♥ **Under & Over Tumbarumba Chardonnay 2011 Rating** 89
✪ **To** 2014 $13
◉ **Under & Over King Valley Pinot Gris 2010 Rating** 89 **To** Now $13
✪ **Under & Over Heathcote Shiraz 2010 Rating** 89 **To** 2015 $13
Armchair Critic Heathcote Shiraz 2010 Rating 89 **To** 2017 $20
Partisan By Jove McLaren Vale Tempranillo 2010 Rating 89 **To** 2017 $19
Partisan Willunga McLaren Vale Grenache 2009 Rating 87 **To** 2014 $27

 Echo Hill Wines

120 Adams Peak Road, Broke, NSW 2330 (postal) **Region** Hunter Valley
T 0439 462 651 **F** (02) 9868 3686 **Open** Not
Winemaker Nick Paterson (Contract) **Est.** 1998 **Dozens** 1000 **Vyds** 4ha

The Day, Epper and Butler families respectively bring Australian, French and NZ background and heritage to Echo Hill. They retained local vigneron Andrew Margan, with 40 years' hands on experience in growing and making wine, as a consultant in the early stages of the venture, including the selection of varieties and design of the vineyard blocks. They have also very sensibly started small, with only 2ha each of chardonnay and shiraz planted on the property, and virtually unlimited room for expansion. Next, they retained one of the best contract winemakers in the region, Nick Paterson, who guides the making of the wine from the grapes on the vine, to wine in the bottle. Moreover, they have chosen screwcaps rather than corks, joining the vast majority (over 90%) of all current Australian wine. Particularly for the Chinese market, the screwcaps provide far better protection during transport, warehousing, retail sale, and maturation in bottle. Exports to China.

ŸŸŸŸŸ **Hunter Valley Shiraz 2005** The colour is more developed than the '06, as it should be; a medium-bodied regional wine with the classic earth and leather overtones to remarkably fresh cherry and berry fruits on the back of good acidity. Screwcap. 13.2% alc. **Rating** 92 **To** 2017 $25
Hunter Valley Shiraz 2006 Developed colour largely consistent with age; has the features that make Hunter Valley shiraz so enjoyable: moderate alcohol, distinctive regional notes, fine tannins and controlled oak spice, black cherry and a dab of oak. Screwcap. 13.8% alc. **Rating** 91 **To** 2016 $25
Hunter Valley Chardonnay 2010 A well-made Hunter Valley chardonnay in the contemporary style, early-picked to heighten the stone fruit, melon and citrus characters that result, oak used with appropriate discretion. Screwcap. 12.8% alc. **Rating** 90 **To** 2016 $25
Hunter Valley Chardonnay 2009 Pale straw-green; has abundant stone fruit aromas and flavours, oak used judiciously; the palate has rich fruit flavours, and there is no need to cellar the wine. Screwcap. 13.3% alc. **Rating** 90 **To** 2014 $25
Hunter Valley Shiraz 2010 Purple-crimson; a well-made wine that gives equal weight to its place/terroir and to its variety; blackberry and black cherry are the main drivers, but the tannins provide the necessary structure. Screwcap. 13.3% alc. **Rating** 90 **To** 2020 $25

ŸŸŸŸ **Hunter Valley Chardonnay 2011** **Rating** 89 **To** 2016 $25

Eclectic Wines   ★★★★

687 Hermitage Road, Pokolbin, NSW 2320 (postal) **Region** Hunter Valley
T (02) 6574 7201 **www**.eclecticwines.com.au **Open** At Hunter Valley Gardens Cellars
Winemaker First Creek Wines **Est.** 2001 **Dozens** 2500
This is the venture of Paul and Kate Stuart, nominally based in the Hunter Valley, where they live and have a vineyard planted to shiraz and mourvedre; 'nominally', because Paul's 30 years in the wine industry have given him the marketing knowledge to sustain the purchase of grapes from various regions, including the Hunter Valley, Canberra and interstate. He balances the production and sale of his own wines under the Eclectic label while also acting as an independent marketing and sales consultant to other producers, avoiding a conflict of interest by selling his clients' wine in different markets from those in which he sells his own. Exports to Denmark, the Netherlands, Germany and China.

ŸŸŸŸŸ ✪ **Black Label Semillon Sauvignon Blanc 2009** The structure of Hunter Valley semillon from a top vintage has the top spot, however the Central Ranges sauvignon blanc makes a positive contribution with its passionfruit and gooseberry flavours. Screwcap. 12.5% alc. **Rating** 92 **To** 2014 $16
Pewter Label Hunter Valley Chardonnay 2011 In the modern Hunter school, and throws all the attention onto the fruit, which has excellent drive, intensity and energy to its array of tangy stone fruit flavours and lively acidity. Screwcap. 12.5% alc. **Rating** 92 **To** 2018 $23
Pewter Label Hunter Valley Chardonnay 2009 Bright green-straw; has a good bouquet that opens up on the well-balanced palate, with nectarine and grapefruit flavours giving the wine length and a zesty finish. Developing slowly. Screwcap. 13% alc. **Rating** 90 **To** 2016 $25

White Label Hunter Valley Shiraz 2009 Good hue; while evidently picked later than its twin, has many of the same characteristics: piquant red fruit flavours, brisk acidity, minimal tannins and subtle oak. Screwcap. 13.5% alc. **Rating** 90 **To** 2019 $28

Black Label Hunter Valley Shiraz 2009 Good crimson hue, albeit very light; early picking has resulted in a bracing cafeteria style, its piquancy demanding tapas-like food, about the only element not brought into play by the back label of this and the White Label Shiraz. Screwcap. 12.5% alc. **Rating** 89 **To** 2016 $16
Pewter Label Canberra Shiraz Viognier 2007 Rating 89 **To** 2017 $28

Eden Hall ★★★★☆

6 Washington Street, Angaston, SA 5353 **Region** Eden Valley
T (08) 8562 4590 **www.**edenhall.com.au **Open** 7 days 11–5
Winemaker Kym Teusner, Christa Deans, Phil Lehmann (Contract) **Est.** 2002
Dozens 2000 **Vyds** 32.3ha
David and Mardi Hall purchased the historic Avon Brae estate in 1996. The 120ha property has been planted to cabernet sauvignon (the lion's share, with 13ha), riesling (9.2ha), shiraz (5.7ha) and smaller plantings of merlot, cabernet franc and viognier. The majority of the production is contracted to Yalumba, St Hallett and McGuigan Simeon, with 10% of the best grapes held back for the Eden Hall label. The Riesling, Shiraz Viognier and Cabernet Sauvignon are all excellent, the red wines outstanding. Exports to the US, Malaysia and China.

Cabernet Sauvignon 2010 Strong crimson-purple; even in the Eden Valley, cabernet sauvignon of this distinction only makes its presence felt in the best vintages, such as this. While only medium-bodied, and showing strong cassis varietal fruit, it has a certain austerity that is unique to the variety. Screwcap. 14.5% alc. **Rating** 95 **To** 2025 $40

Riesling 2011 Has a proud track record of developing exceptionally well with bottle age; here the aromas and flavours are in a gentle lime spectrum, very correct but soft on the palate. Seems certain to develop more quickly than some of the prior vintages, the upside being the open-access nature of the palate. Screwcap. 11.5% alc. **Rating** 92 **To** 2015 $20
Shiraz 2010 Rating 91 **To** 2020 $40

Eden Road Wines ★★★★★

3182 Barton Highway, Murrumbateman, NSW 2582 **Region** Canberra District
T (02) 6226 8800 **www.**edenroadwines.com.au **Open** Wed–Sun 11–4
Winemaker Nick Spencer, Hamish Young **Est.** 2006 **Dozens** 8000 **Vyds** 4.4ha
The name of this business, now entirely based in the Canberra District, reflects an earlier stage of its development, when it also had a property in the Eden Valley. That has now been separated, and Eden Road's operations since 2008 centre on Hilltops, Canberra District and Tumbarumba. At the Royal Melbourne Wine Show '09 Eden Road's The Long Road Hilltops Shiraz '08 was awarded the Jimmy Watson Memorial Trophy; if it needed a higher profile, it now has one. Eden Road has relocated to Murrumbateman, where it purchased the former Doonkuna winery and mature vineyard. Exports to the UK, the US, the Maldives and Hong Kong.

Gundagai Shiraz 2010 Bright crimson-purple; a pure expression of shiraz, picked at precisely the right moment, the plum, black cherry and blackberry fruit with a spicy, gently savoury foundation thanks to tannins and quality oak. Great line, length and balance. Screwcap. 13% alc. **Rating** 95 **To** 2030 $45
Hilltops Shiraz 2010 Deep crimson; highly spiced and red-fruited on the bouquet, showing glimpses of pepper, licorice, sage and game; the palate is silky and fine, medium-bodied and extremely long and layered; this is the epitome of sophisticated cool-climate shiraz; a sophistication that may not be to everyone's taste. Screwcap. 13.5% alc. **Rating** 95 **To** 2020 $45 BE

ŶŶŶŶ♀ **Canberra Riesling 2011** The challenge of '11 to achieve optimum ripeness in
✿   Canberra has provided what can only be described as a lean and racy framework
       in this wine; the winemaking has provided as much texture as possible, and the
       taut minerally structure is long and fine. Time is essential, and it will be fascinating
       to watch this wine evolve slowly over time. Screwcap. 11% alc. **Rating** 91
       To 2022 $21 BE

✿   **The Seedling Gundagai Shiraz 2010** A blend of red and black fruits, sizzling
       sausage meat, charcuterie and anise; medium-bodied and a little rugged, the
       fresh acidity and tight core of gravelly tannins provide a surprisingly persistent
       finish; rugged in all the right ways, especially for the price. Screwcap. 13.4% alc.
       Rating 91 **To** 2018 $15 BE

ŶŶŶŶ   **The Seedling Tumbarumba Chardonnay 2011** Rating 89 To 2016
✿ $15 BE
       Long Road Gundagai Shiraz 2010 Rating 88 To 2017 $21

 # Edenmae Estate Wines

RSD 567, Mount Pleasant, SA 5235 **Region** Eden Valley
T (08) 8568 2685 **www**.edenmae.com.au **Open** Not
Winemaker Richard Sheedy, Paddy Connors **Est.** 2007 **Dozens** 1000 **Vyds** 12ha
In 2006 David and Michelle Redhead moved from Melbourne to the Barossa, thence moving
to work in various parts of the world but always returning to the Barossa. They purchased
a 36ha property on the southernmost crest of the Eden Valley, for long known as Holmes
Estate Wines. It had fallen on hard times, and been abandoned for three years. Hard work has
restored it to its former glory, with tree lots, dams and open areas for grazing alpaca, lambs,
ponies, geese and hens, and is managed on organic principles, certification some way around
the corner. The varied nature of the property lends itself to farm stay, which is one of its
attractions. There are 4ha each of riesling and shiraz, and 2ha each of pinot noir and cabernet
sauvignon, most 38 years old, with some 10-year-old shiraz and 30-year-old pinot.

ŶŶŶŶ♀ **Shiraz 2008** Strong colour; a rich, potent, concentrated and ripe shiraz with
       layers of black fruits, licorice and spice, the tannins in balance, as is the oak. Good
       outcome for the vintage. Screwcap. 14.2% alc. **Rating** 92 **To** 2020 $26
       Single Vineyard Eden Valley Riesling 2010 The 38-year-old dry-grown,
       hand-picked vines have produced a rich, layered wine with distinct personality and
       awaiting a dish of summer seafood. Screwcap. 12.5% alc. **Rating** 90 **To** 2015 $18
       Riesling 2008 Bright green-quartz colour is a come-on if ever there was one; the
       bouquet and palate have similar depth to the '10, with lime and slate to the fore;
       also asks for food to balance the touch of phenolic toughness. Screwcap. 12.1% alc.
       Rating 90 **To** 2015 $26

ŶŶŶŶ   **Single Vineyard Eden Valley Pinot Noir 2010** Rating 89 To 2017 $28
       Adelaide Vintage Cuvee 2011 Rating 87 To 2013 $18

Edwards Wines

687 Ellensbrook Road, Cowaramup, WA 6284 **Region** Margaret River
T (08) 9755 5999 **www**.edwardswines.com.au **Open** 7 days 10.30–5
Winemaker Michael Edwards **Est.** 1993 **Dozens** 12 000 **Vyds** 24.8ha
Edwards Wines is a family-owned and operated winery. Brothers Michael (formerly a
winemaker at Voyager Estate) and Christo are the winemaker and viticulturist, respectively.
The vineyard includes cabernet sauvignon (7.8ha), shiraz (5.2ha), sauvignon blanc (4.6ha),
chardonnay (3.5ha), semillon (2.7ha) and merlot (1ha). The consistency in the quality of the
wines is admirable. Exports to all major markets.

ŶŶŶŶ♀ **Margaret River Shiraz 2010** Vivid deep crimson in colour, the bouquet offers
       violets, dark cherry, plum, roasted meats, tar and spice; the palate is ample and
       sweet-fruited on entry, with gravelly tannins bringing up the rear; long, savoury
       and refreshing. Screwcap. 14.5% alc. **Rating** 92 **To** 2018 $30 BE

Tiger's Tale Margaret River Semillon Sauvignon Blanc 2011 A fresh, clean, crisp and direct example of this now classic Margaret River blend, showing the drier end of the spectrum to full effect, with a chalky, fresh and fragrant finish; an excellent early-drinking example. Screwcap. 13% alc. **Rating** 91 **To** 2014 $18 BE

Margaret River Semillon Sauvignon Blanc 2011 A pungent and fresh blend of fresh-cut grass herbaceousness and nectarine; the palate is juicy and fresh, with enough depth to see evolution as an interesting possibility. Screwcap. 13% alc. **Rating** 91 **To** 2015 $23 BE

Margaret River Chardonnay 2010 Vibrant hue; the bouquet is polished and pure, revealing nectarine, grapefruit and well-handled toasty oak; the palate is lively and focused, with tangy acidity, liquid minerals and finishing with a healthy mouthful of fragrant fruit. Screwcap. 13.5% alc. **Rating** 90 **To** 2016 $32 BE

BCE Reserve Cabernet Sauvignon 2008 Essency cassis is offset by a leafy, herbaceous complexity on the bouquet; the full-bodied palate is tannic, rugged and needing time to settle down, but the wait should be worthwhile. Screwcap. 14% alc. **Rating** 90 **To** 2020 $60 BE

ŶŶŶŶ
✪ **Tiger's Tale Margaret River Cabernet Merlot 2010** Deep crimson; the bouquet shows cassis, redcurrant and some complex dried herb aromas; medium-bodied with assertive gravelly tannins dominant on the palate; plenty of flavour at the price. Screwcap. 14% alc. **Rating** 89 **To** 2018 $18 BE

Eighteen Forty-Seven   ★★★☆

PO Box 722, Kent Town, SA 5071 **Region** Barossa Valley
T (08) 8524 5328 **www.**eighteenfortyseven.com **Open** By invitation
Winemaker Alex Peel **Est.** 1996 **Dozens** 16 000 **Vyds** 8.62ha
A youthful John Curnow began his career over 30 years ago buying and selling wines from all over the world. He then moved to Coca-Cola, becoming a senior executive or CEO in Hungary, the Czech Republic, NZ, the US and Australia. In 1996 he and wife Sue began Eighteen Forty-Seven, with two vineyards planted to shiraz, semillon, petit verdot and a little sauvignon blanc. The name Eighteen Forty-Seven is derived from the date of the original land grant on the property, which also was the site of the first commercial winery in the Barossa Valley. Until 2002 the grapes were sold to other Barossa Valley producers, but in that vintage the first wines were made. Exports to the US, Germany, Hong Kong, Vietnam and China.

ŶŶŶŶŶ **Pappy's Paddock Barossa Valley Shiraz 2008** Curiously, indeed very curiously, the complexity of the black fruits, bitter chocolate and spice counteract the alcohol until the warmth of the aftertaste; with a haunch of rotisserie beef, could be a winner. Cork. 15.4% alc. **Rating** 90 **To** 2018 $35

ŶŶŶŶ **First Pick Shiraz 2008 Rating** 89 **To** 2016 $95
Home Block Barossa Valley Petit Verdot 2008 Rating 87 **To** 2016 $35

Ekhidna   ★★★★

Cnr Kangarilla Road/Foggo Road, McLaren Vale, SA 5171 **Region** McLaren Vale
T (08) 8323 8496 **www.**ekhidnawines.com.au **Open** 7 days 11–5
Winemaker Matthew Rechner **Est.** 2001 **Dozens** 3500
Matt Rechner entered the wine industry in 1988, spending most of the intervening years at Tatachilla Winery in McLaren Vale, starting as laboratory technician and finishing as operations manager. Frustrated by the constraints of large winery practice, he decided to strike out on his own in 2001 via the virtual winery option. His long experience has meant he is able to buy grapes from high-quality producers. A restructuring has seen the arrival of Ekhidna (the old spelling of echidna) and the disappearance of Paper Eagle brands. Exports to the US, Canada, NZ, India and China.

ŶŶŶŶŶ
✪ **Adelaide Hills Sauvignon Blanc 2011** Pale quartz; the cool and wet vintage has kept the flavours largely within a herb, citrus and mineral spectrum; the finish is clean and fresh. Screwcap. 13% alc. **Rating** 90 **To** 2013 $20

ŸŸŸŸ McLaren Vale Shiraz Rose 2011 Rating 89 To 2014 $20
McLaren Vale Cabernet 2010 Rating 87 To 2016 $20

Elderton   ★★★★★

3–5 Tanunda Road, Nuriootpa, SA 5355 **Region** Barossa Valley
T (08) 8568 7878 **www**.eldertonwines.com.au **Open** Mon–Fri 8.30–5, w'ends, hols 11–4
Winemaker Richard Langford **Est.** 1982 **Dozens** 45 000 **Vyds** 75ha
The founding Ashmead family, with mother Lorraine supported by sons Allister and Cameron, continues to impress with its wines. The original source was 30ha of fully mature shiraz, cabernet sauvignon and merlot on the Barossa floor; subsequently 16ha of Eden Valley vineyards (shiraz, cabernet sauvignon, chardonnay, zinfandel, merlot and roussanne) were incorporated into the business. The Rohrlach Vineyard, with 75-year-old shiraz, is under long-term lease and managed by the Ashmead family. The Command Shiraz is justifiably regarded as its icon wine; energetic promotion and marketing both in Australia and overseas are paying dividends. Elderton has followed in the footsteps of Cullen by becoming carbon neutral. Exports to all major markets.

ŸŸŸŸŸ Neil Ashmead Grand Tourer Barossa Shiraz 2010 Clear scarlet-red; made from the oldest vines on the Elderton vineyard; the bouquet is particularly fragrant, the elegant and lively medium-bodied palate delivering the same red and black berry fruit message; the tannins and oak have been well handled, making this a great example of where the Barossa should head. Six-speed gearbox on top of the capsule is a great logo. Screwcap. 13.5% alc. **Rating** 96 **To** 2030 $70
Barossa Shiraz 2010 Deep crimson, purple hue; a bright and fragrant wine, showing blackberry, licorice, toasty oak and violets on the bouquet; the medium-bodied palate is lively and super fresh, accessible and thoroughly engaging, offering very good value in every respect. Screwcap. 14.5% alc. **Rating** 94 **To** 2022 $27 BE
Command Single Vineyard Barossa Shiraz 2009 Clear purple-crimson; a beautifully balanced wine that effortlessly walks around its alcohol, the medium-bodied palate with blackberry and plum fruit, and substantial built-in oak. History shows that Command takes a number of years to absorb that oak and come into full flower. Screwcap. 15% alc. **Rating** 94 **To** 2024 $95
Ashmead Single Vineyard Barossa Cabernet Sauvignon 2010 Often a wine that challenges the idea that the Barossa is not really suited to cabernet, and does so with a vengeance this vintage. Layer upon layer of cassis, blackcurrant, quality oak and fine tannins are all in utterly harmonious balance. The wine has a very long life ahead. Screwcap. 14.5% alc. **Rating** 94 **To** 2030 $90

ŸŸŸŸ♀ Eden Valley Chardonnay 2011 A prime example of the cool (and wet)
✪ vintage producing many excellent white wines. This has intense white peach and grapefruit flavours; partial fermentation in used French oak hogsheads was precisely the right approach in the winery, building a subtle framework for the fruit and lengthening the palate. Screwcap. 12% alc. **Rating** 93 **To** 2016 $19
Ode to Lorraine Barossa Cabernet Sauvignon Shiraz Merlot 2009 **Rating** 93 **To** 2024 $50
✪ Barossa Botrytis Semillon 2011 Glowing green-gold; it's ironic that Elderton's first vintage should come from a vineyard near Greenock that it purchased in '10, mainly for its shiraz, with plantings dating back to 1915. The wine has masses of juicy cumquat and mandarin flavours, but the rate of colour development suggests it should be enjoyed sooner rather than later, something that will not give too many problems to those who have in fact tasted it. 375ml. Screwcap. 10.5% alc. **Rating** 93 **To** 2014 $20
Barossa Cabernet Sauvignon 2009 **Rating** 92 **To** 2020 $27 BE
Barossa Shiraz 2009 **Rating** 90 **To** 2018 $27 BE

ŸŸŸŸ Barossa Merlot 2010 **Rating** 89 **To** 2015 $27 BE
Barossa Cabernet Sauvignon 2008 **Rating** 89 **To** 2015 $27
✪ Eden Valley Shiraz 2011 **Rating** 89 **To** 2018 $19 BE
Eden Valley Riesling 2011 **Rating** 88 **To** 2015 $19

✪   **Shiraz Cabernet Sauvignon 2010** Rating 88 To 2017 $14
Shiraz Cabernet Sauvignon 2011 Rating 87 To 2014 $14

Eldredge   ★★★☆

Spring Gully Road, Clare, SA 5453 **Region** Clare Valley
T (08) 8842 3086 **www**.eldredge.com.au **Open** 7 days 11–5
Winemaker Leigh Eldredge **Est.** 1993 **Dozens** 3000 **Vyds** 20.96ha
Leigh and Karen Eldredge have established their winery and cellar door in the Sevenhill
Ranges at an altitude of 500m above Watervale. It has a substantial vineyard planted to shiraz,
cabernet sauvignon, merlot, riesling, sangiovese and malbec. Both the Rieslings and red wines
have had considerable wine show success in recent years. Exports to the UK, the US, Canada,
Singapore and China.

♀♀♀♀♀   **Clare Valley Malbec 2009** Deep colour; a sappy bouquet of bramble, red fruits
and roasted meat; the palate is fleshy and direct, with a backbone of taut acidity
and drying tannins; freshness is the key here. WAK screwcap. 14.8% alc. **Rating** 90
To 2015 $25 BE

♀♀♀♀   **RL Clare Valley Cabernet Sauvignon 2009** Rating 88 To 2016 $25 BE

Eldridge Estate of Red Hill   ★★★★★

120 Arthurs Seat Road, Red Hill, Vic 3937 **Region** Mornington Peninsula
T (03) 5989 2644 **www**.eldridge-estate.com.au **Open** Mon–Fri 12–4, w'ends & hols 11–5
Winemaker David Lloyd **Est.** 1985 **Dozens** 800 **Vyds** 2.8ha
The Eldridge Estate vineyard was purchased by Wendy and David Lloyd in 1995. Major
retrellising work has been undertaken, changing to Scott Henry, and all the wines are estate-
grown and made. David has also planted several Dijon-selected pinot noir clones (114, 115
and 777), which have been contributing since 2004, likewise the Dijon chardonnay clone 96.
An interesting move has been the development of the Euroa Creeks range (Early Harvest
Shiraz, Shiraz and Reserve Shiraz), made from contract-grown grapes (a long-term contract)
from the northern end of Heathcote: an interesting grafting of the skills of a cool-climate
pinot noir grower and maker onto the far bigger wine base of Heathcote shiraz. Exports to
the UK, Canada and Singapore.

♀♀♀♀♀   **Clonal Blend Pinot Noir 2010** Mid crimson; a finely detailed and elegant pinot
noir, with red fruits, sap, cold tea and Asian spices on display, alongside some very
fine French oak; the palate is fine, silky and expansive, layered and complex; subtle
and ethereal, long and engaging. Screwcap. 13.5% alc. **Rating** 95 To 2016 $75 BE
Gamay 2010 Light, bright crimson-purple; delicious aromas and flavours of black
cherry and blood plum, with a bewitching touch of warm spice on the finish and
aftertaste. Drink right now. Screwcap. 13.5% alc. **Rating** 94 To 2013 $35
Single Clone Pinot Noir 2010 Clone MV6. Mid garnet; a surprisingly savoury
bouquet of struck match, red fruits and Asian spices for the usually pure-fruited
MV6 clone; the palate is silky, almost seductive on entry, firming up with fine
tannins and a real cut and thrust from the mouth-watering acidity; long and
expansive. Screwcap. 13.5% alc. **Rating** 94 To 2016 $50 BE

♀♀♀♀♀   **Pinot Noir 2010** Rating 92 To 2016 $50 BE
Chardonnay 2010 Rating 90 To 2014 $40 BE

♀♀♀♀   **Single Clone 96 Chardonnay 2010** Rating 89 To 2014 $45 BE
PTG11 2011 Rating 89 To Now $25
Euroa Creeks Central Victoria Shiraz 2008 Rating 88 To 2016 $40 BE
North Patch Chardonnay 2010 Rating 87 To 2014 $30 BE

Elgee Park   ★★★★★

24 Junction Road, Merricks North, Vic 3926 **Region** Mornington Peninsula
T (03) 5989 7338 **www**.elgeeparkwines.com.au **Open** At Merricks General Wine Store
Winemaker Geraldine McFaul (Contract) **Est.** 1972 **Dozens** 1600 **Vyds** 5ha

The pioneer of the Mornington Peninsula in its 20th-century rebirth, owned by Baillieu Myer and family. The vineyard is planted to riesling, chardonnay, viognier (some of the oldest vines in Australia), pinot gris, pinot noir, merlot and cabernet sauvignon. The vineyard is set in a picturesque natural amphitheatre with a northerly aspect looking out across Port Phillip Bay towards the Melbourne skyline.

🍷🍷🍷🍷🍷 **Family Reserve Mornington Peninsula Chardonnay 2010** Light straw-green; a complex wine with above-average texture and structure coming from the mixture of grapefruit and nutty flavours, and the long, brisk and penetrating finish. Screwcap. 13% alc. **Rating** 94 **To** 2018 $40

Family Reserve Mornington Peninsula Viognier 2009 Mid gold, green hue; exotic and pure viognier bouquet with apricot kernel, spice and a little charcuterie complexity; soft and rich, and surprisingly fresh for its age, the depth of personality and freshness of acid and alcohol combined make this an outstanding example of the variety in Australia. Screwcap. 13.5% alc. **Rating** 94 **To** 2013 $25 BE

🍷🍷🍷🍷🍷 **Family Reserve Mornington Peninsula Cabernet Merlot 2009** **Rating** 92 **To** 2019 $30

Mornington Peninsula Cuvee Brut 2008 **Rating** 92 **To** 2016 $45 BE

Family Reserve Mornington Peninsula Riesling 2011 **Rating** 90 **To** 2016 $25 BE

Family Reserve Mornington Peninsula Pinot Noir 2010 **Rating** 90 **To** 2015 $45

Elgo Estate ★★★☆

2020 Upton Road, Upton Hill, via Longwood, Vic 3664 **Region** Strathbogie Ranges
T (03) 9328 3766 **www**.elgoestate.com.au **Open** By appt
Winemaker Dennis Clarke, Craig Lewis **Est.** 1999 **Dozens** 13 000 **Vyds** 57ha
Elgo Estate, owned by the Taresch family, is located high in the hills of the Strathbogie Ranges, 125km northeast of Melbourne, a stone's throw from the southern end of the Heathcote region. With almost 60ha under vine, Elgo Estate is committed to sustainable viticulture reflecting and expressing the characteristics of this cool-climate region. Two distinct wine portfolios via the Allira and Elgo Estate labels are produced. All of the wines are 100% estate-grown from their three vineyards in the region, with plantings dating back to the early 1970s. Elgo Estate was the first winery in Australia to be fully powered by self-generated renewable wind energy. The installation of a 30m tall 150 kW wind turbine in 2007 enables Elgo to save around 400 tonnes of greenhouse gas emissions per year, while generating enough electricity to power the winery twice over, the excess green electricity being fed back into the main power grid. In '12 Elgo purchased the Mount Helen Vineyard from Robert Kirby (previously used for the Cooralook wines).

🍷🍷🍷🍷🍷 **Allira Strathbogie Ranges Chardonnay 2010** A well-made chardonnay with ✪ plenty of peachy fruit and a suitably restrained dab of vanillin oak; won the trophy for Best Chardonnay at the Dookie Wine Show '11 – a pleasant surprise, says Elgo. Screwcap. 13.5% alc. **Rating** 90 **To** 2013 $15

Ellender Estate ★★★☆

Leura Glen, 260 Green Gully Road, Glenlyon, Vic 3461 **Region** Macedon Ranges
T (03) 5348 7785 **www**.ellenderwines.com.au **Open** W'ends & public hols 11–5, or by appt
Winemaker Graham Ellender **Est.** 1996 **Dozens** 1000 **Vyds** 4.1ha
Graham and Jenny Ellender have established pinot noir (2.7ha), chardonnay (1ha), sauvignon blanc (0.2ha) and pinot gris (0.1ha). Wine style is restricted to those varieties true to the ultra-cool climate of the Macedon Ranges: Pinot Noir, Pinot Rose, Chardonnay and sparkling. Exports to the United Arab Emirates.

🍷🍷🍷🍷♀ **Macedon Ranges Pinot Nero NV** A blend of '08 and '09 vintages that works well, with supple plum and cherry fruit flavours, and fine, graceful tannins. Completely at odds with the far more expensive '10 Pinot Noir. Screwcap. 13.5% alc. **Rating** 90 **To** 2015 $28

🍷🍷🍷🍷 **Macedon Ranges Sauvignon Blanc 2011 Rating** 87 **To** 2014 $26

Ellis Wines ★★★★

3025 Heathcote-Rochester Road, Colbinabbin, Vic 3559 (postal) **Region** Heathcote
T 0413 293 796 **www.**elliswines.com.au **Open** Not
Winemaker Greg Flynn, Guy Rathjen **Est.** 1998 **Dozens** 700 **Vyds** 54.6ha
This is a family business in the fullest sense of the term: Bryan and Joy Ellis are the owners, vineyard manager Barney Touhey is Bryan's brother-in-law, and sales manager Paul Flanagan is Bryan's son-in-law. For good measure, seven of the vineyard blocks are named after family members. For 10 years the Ellises were content to sell the grapes to a range of producers including Taltarni, Domaine Chandon, Mount Langi Ghiran and Heathcote Winery. However, since 2009 a portion of the crop has been vinified, with Greg Flynn (of Flynns Wines) as winemaker.

🍷🍷🍷🍷♀ **Signature Label Heathcote Shiraz 2010** Bright crimson-purple; a rich, deeply robed wine that fully expresses its region, with plum, spice and black cherry all contributing, and supported by oak. Screwcap. 15% alc. **Rating** 93 **To** 2025 $26
Signature Label Heathcote Viognier 2010 Medium green-straw; abundant apricot and cumquat aromas and flavours on the bouquet and palate alike; despite this level of flavour, is not phenolic. Screwcap. 14% alc. **Rating** 92 **To** 2015 $23

Elmslie ★★★☆

2 Upper McEwans Road, Legana, Tas 7277 **Region** Northern Tasmania
T (03) 6330 1225 **www.**elmsliewines.com.au **Open** 7 days 8–4
Winemaker Eric Howell **Est.** 1972 **Dozens** 3000 **Vyds** 4.25ha
The estate plantings are some of the oldest in Tasmania, led by cabernet sauvignon (1.5ha) and pinot noir (1.25ha), but also with chardonnay, sauvignon blanc and shiraz. The Lithgow Gallery has installed its large collection of traditional and contemporary Australian paintings and etchings at the fully restored Federation house at Elmslie.

🍷🍷🍷🍷 **Pinot Gris 2010** Bright, pale straw-green; has considerable mid- to back-palate structure and intensity, suggesting some effort in the winery to add interest; is a little phenolic, but if it came from Alsace, the phenolic level would be much higher. Screwcap. 13.4% alc. **Rating** 89 **To** 2013 $32
Sauvignon Blanc 2009 Still quartz-white, extraordinary given its 3+ years of age; grass and green capsicum aromas dominate the bouquet, and the acidity of the palate is still lethal; the extremely low pH is the answer for the lack of colour development – and also, one assumes, some sales resistance. Screwcap. 13.6% alc. **Rating** 87 **To** 2014 $32

Elmswood Estate ★★★★★

75 Monbulk-Seville Road, Wandin East, Vic 3139 **Region** Yarra Valley
T (03) 5964 3015 **www.**elmswoodestate.com.au **Open** 7 days 10–5
Winemaker Mal Stewart (Sparkling), Dylan McMahon (Table) **Est.** 1981 **Dozens** 3000 **Vyds** 8ha
Elmswood Estate has planted cabernet sauvignon, chardonnay, merlot, sauvignon blanc, pinot noir, shiraz and riesling on the red volcanic soils of the far southern side of the Yarra Valley. The cellar door operates from 'The Pavilion', a fully enclosed glass room situated on a ridge above the vineyard, with 180° views of the Upper Yarra Valley. It seats up to 110 guests, and is a popular wedding venue. Music events are held on the third Sunday of each month. Exports to China.

ŸŸŸŸŸ   **Reserve Yarra Valley Shiraz 2010** Crystal clear red-purple; the bouquet is
perfumed by red berry fruits; the light- to medium-bodied palate is full of life and
precision, its red fruits amplified by subtle oak, and the finest imaginable tannins.
Screwcap. 13% alc. **Rating** 94 **To** 2025 $50

Reserve Yarra Valley Cabernet Sauvignon 2010 Bright crimson; the fragrant
bouquet of cassis and a touch of plum is followed by cedar/cigar box nuances; it is
on the aftertaste that the distinction of this wine really impresses – in some ways it
is a throwback to the Yarra cabernets of the '70s that are still very much alive and
kicking 30–40 years after their birth. Screwcap. 13% alc. **Rating** 94 **To** 2040 $60

ŸŸŸŸŸ   **Yarra Valley Merlot 2010 Rating** 93 **To** 2017 $28
Yarra Valley Cabernet Merlot 2010 Rating 92 **To** 2025 $25

ŸŸŸŸ   **Yarra Valley Sauvignon Blanc 2011 Rating** 89 **To** 2013 $23
Yarra Valley Methode Champenoise 2010 Rating 89 **To** 2014 $30
Yarra Valley Riesling 2011 Rating 87 **To** 2016 $20

Eloquesta   ★★★

10 Stroud Avenue, Dubbo, NSW 2830 (postal) **Region** Mudgee
T 0458 525 899 **www**.eloquesta.com.au **Open** Not
Winemaker Stuart Olsen **Est.** 2008 **Dozens** 600 **Vyds** 6ha
The full name of the business is Eloquesta by Stuart Olsen, Stuart being the sole owner and
winemaker. He is a trained scientist and teacher, gaining winemaking experience since 2000,
variously working at Cirillo Estate, Lowe Family Wines and Torbreck, as well as a German
winery in the Rheinhessen. His aim in Mudgee is to make the two varieties that he believes
grow consistently well year after year in the cooler foothills of Mudgee and Rylstone: Shiraz
and Petit Verdot, with an occasional bucket of Viognier.

ŸŸŸŸ   **Mudgee Shiraz Petit Verdot 2009** A blend of 50% shiraz, 47% petit verdot
and 3% viognier. Deep crimson; made using the whole bunch/whole berry foot-
stamping and lengthy hand-plunging techniques espoused by the self-taught Stuart
Olsen; he says his wines are not chemically analysed, so one is left to wonder how
he came up with the alcohol figures for them. Certainly this is riper than the '10,
but it has a certain sharpness on the finish. Bottled Nov '11 at the same time as
the '10. Screwcap. 14% alc. **Rating** 89 **To** 2017 $28

Mudgee Shiraz Petit Verdot 2010 A blend of 55% shiraz, 42% petit verdot
and 3% viognier; an artisanal approach with whole berry/whole bunch ferments,
foot-stamped, then hand-plunged daily for two more weeks, aged in French,
Hungarian and Russian oak. Given the problems of the vintage with persistent
rain, a considerable achievement, with rich red and black fruits and no shortage
of oak; there is a question mark about the sharpness on the finish. Screwcap.
14.5% alc. **Rating** 87 **To** 2015 $28

Enigma Variations   ★★★★☆

Glenelg Highway, Dunkeld, Vic 3294 **Region** Grampians
T (03) 5332 2987 **Open** By appt
Winemaker Tamara Irish **Est.** 2008 **Dozens** 250 **Vyds** 1ha
This is the new venture of former Tarrington winemaker Tamara Irish, who has joined forces
with NZ-born Julia Hailes (a Francophile, violinist and psychodramatist) to buy a small
property near Dunkeld, at the base of the Grampians mountain range. Tamara and Julia are
fiercely committed to biodynamic grapegrowing, and are moving towards the establishment of
a little over 1ha of densely planted, low-yielding and multi-clonal shiraz, and a small winery,
hopefully, to process shiraz to be purchased from the same source as that used for the former
Artemesia label of Tarrington vineyards. The last of the Tarrington wines made by Tamara are
being marketed under the Enigma Variations brand (the site and source acknowledged on the
labels) and are being sold through Enigma, including 2006 and '07 Pinot Noir, and '07 Shiraz.

🍷🍷🍷🍷🍷 Syrah 2009 Deep purple-red; an almost painfully pure rendition of cool-climate shiraz, its black fruit bouquet surrounded by spice, clove and pepper notes balanced by quality oak; the palate is taut and intense, the fruit driving through to a long finish, the tannins neatly controlled. Demands time. Screwcap. 13.7% alc. Rating 95 To 2029 $49

🍷🍷🍷🍷🍷 Phoenix Ysobel Rose 2010 Rating 92 To 2013 $25

Eperosa

24 Maria Street, Tanunda, SA 5352 **Region** Barossa Valley
T 0428 111 121 **www**.eperosa.com.au **Open** By appt
Winemaker Brett Grocke **Est.** 2005 **Dozens** 400
Eperosa owner Brett Grocke qualified as a viticulturist in 2001, and, through Grocke Viticulture, consults and provides technical services to over 200ha of vineyards spread across the Barossa Valley, Eden Valley, Adelaide Hills, Riverland, Langhorne Creek and Hindmarsh Valley. He is ideally placed to secure small parcels of grapes of the highest quality, and treats these with traditional, no-frills winemaking methods: destemmed, macerated prior to fermentation, open-fermented, hand-plunged, basket-pressed, then 18 months in used French oak barrels. The wines are of impeccable quality. Wines were received after this issue went to print; tasting notes appear on www.winecompanion.com.au.

Eppalock Ridge ★★★☆

6 Niemann Street, Bendigo, Vic 3550 (postal) **Region** Heathcote
T (03) 5443 7841 **www**.eppalockridge.com **Open** Not
Winemaker Don Lewis, Narelle King, Rod Hourigan **Est.** 1979 **Dozens** 1500
Sue and Rod Hourigan gave up their careers in fabric design and television production at the ABC in 1976 to chase their passion for fine wine. This took them first to McLaren Vale, with Sue working in the celebrated Barn Restaurant, and Rod starting at d'Arenberg; over the next three hectic years both worked vintages at Pirramimma and Coriole while undertaking the first short course for winemakers at what is now CSU. They then moved to Redesdale in 1979 and established Eppalock Ridge on a basalt hilltop overlooking Lake Eppalock. The 10ha of shiraz, cabernet sauvignon, cabernet franc and merlot are capable of producing wines of high quality. Exports to China.

🍷🍷🍷🍷🍷 Susan's Selection Heathcote Shiraz Cabernet Merlot 2010 Deep purple hue; a vibrant and perfumed bouquet of blackberry, sage and spice; the palate is full-bodied and generous, with lively acidity and a little tar and Amaro savoury complexity on the finish. Screwcap. 14% alc. Rating 90 To 2020 $22 BE

🍷🍷🍷🍷 Heathcote Shiraz 2010 Rating 87 To 2015 $27 BE

Epsilon

Moppa Springs Road, Greenock, SA 5360 **Region** Barossa Valley
T 0417 871 951 **www**.epsilonwines.com.au **Open** Not
Winemaker Aaron Southern, Jaysen Collins **Est.** 2004 **Dozens** 3000 **Vyds** 22ha
Epsilon (the fifth-brightest star in a constellation) takes its name from the five generations of the Kalleske family's involvement in Barossa Valley grapegrowing; Julie Southern is née Kalleske. She and husband Aaron bought back this part of the family farm in 1994, initially selling the grapes, but in 2003 joined forces with close friends Dan Standish and Jaysen Collins to produce the Epsilon wines. Exports to the UK, the US, Canada and South-East Asia.

🍷🍷🍷🍷🍷 1994 Greenock Barossa Valley Shiraz 2010 Impenetrable colour; a deep, dark and intensely concentrated black fruit bouquet with suggestions of lavender and licorice; the palate is thickly textured and impressive in its proportions, yet manages to stay relatively light on its feet, with a tangy backbone of acidity; a long mocha finish is sure to satisfy lovers of big boned shiraz. Screwcap. 14.8% alc. Rating 95 To 2025 $45 BE

🍷🍷🍷🍷 Barossa Valley Shiraz 2010 Rating 87 To 2017 $20 BE

Erin Eyes

13 Main North Road, Auburn, SA 5451 **Region** Clare Valley
T (08) 8849 2260 **www.**erineyes.com.au **Open** Thurs–Sat & Mon 10–5 Sun 11–4
Winemaker Steve Wiblin **Est.** 2009 **Dozens** 1200
Having sold his share of Neagles Rock Vineyards, Steve Wiblin has struck out on his own
with Erin Eyes. He explains the name thus: 'In 1842 my English convict forebear John Wiblin
gazed into a pair of Erin eyes. That gaze changed our family make-up and history forever. In
the Irish-influenced Clare Valley what else would I call my wines but Erin Eyes?' He intends
to focus on the three varieties that he believes are best suited to the region: shiraz, cabernet
sauvignon and riesling. But he has done this with a twist, including a sparkling shiraz as well as
a shiraz table wine, and two versions of what he considers to be the region's most underrated
variety, cabernet sauvignon. One is a Bordeaux blend including malbec and merlot, the other
the time-honoured Australian blend of cabernet and shiraz.

Clare Valley Riesling 2010 Bright straw-green; a classic expression of Clare
riesling, with a balance between minerally acidity on the one hand and citrus,
green apple and herb on the other. Screwcap. 12.5% alc. **Rating** 93 **To** 2020 $22

Limited Release Sparkling Shiraz 2008 Rating 87 **To** 2013 $35

Ernest Hill Wines

307 Wine Country Drive, Nulkaba, NSW 2325 **Region** Hunter Valley
T (02) 4991 4418 **www.**ernesthillwines.com.au **Open** 7 days 10–5
Winemaker Mark Woods **Est.** 1999 **Dozens** 6000 **Vyds** 12ha
This is part of a vineyard originally planted in the early 1970s by Harry Tulloch for Seppelt
Wines; it was later renamed the Pokolbin Creek Vineyard, and later still (in '99) the Wilson
family purchased the upper (hill) part of the vineyard, and renamed it Ernest Hill vineyard.
It is now planted to semillon, shiraz, chardonnay, verdelho, traminer, merlot, tempranillo and
chambourcin.

William Henry Shiraz 2010 There is a sweet red-fruited nature to this wine
that persists from the bouquet to the palate; toasty oak reveals itself on the back-
palate, and the fleshy fruit is accessible and appealing. Diam. 13.8% alc. **Rating** 90
To 2018 $45 BE
The Dam Merlot 2010 The light colour is somewhat misleading, for the wine
has attractive cassis fruit and a fresh finish with just a breath of savoury tannins.
Made for early drinking. Screwcap. 13.5% alc. **Rating** 90 **To** 2014 $25

Shareholders Shiraz 2010 Rating 88 **To** 2015 $30 BE
Over The Hill Unwooded Chardonnay 2011 Rating 87 **To** 2013 $20

Ernest Schuetz Estate Wines

26/24–36 Pacific Highway, Wahroonga, NSW 2076 (postal) **Region** Mudgee
T 0402 326 612 **www.**ernestschuetzestate.com.au **Open** Not
Winemaker Jacob Stein **Est.** 2003 **Dozens** 4000 **Vyds** 4ha
Ernest Schuetz's involvement in the wine industry started in 1988 at the age of 21. Working
in various liquor outlets and as a sales representative for Miranda Wines, McGuigan Simeon
and, later, Watershed Wines, gave him an in-depth understanding of all aspects of the wine
market. In 2003 he and wife Joanna purchased the Arronvale Vineyard (first planted in '91) in
the micro-valley of Menah, at an altitude of 530m. When the Schuetzs acquired the vineyard
it was planted to merlot, shiraz and cabernet sauvignon, and they have since grafted 1ha
to riesling, pinot blanc, pinot gris, zinfandel and nebbiolo. The estate plantings have been
complemented by other varieties purchased from other growers. At the present time, Joanna
manages sales and marketing for the venture, with a cellar door planned. In the meantime,
they live in Sydney, travelling to Mudgee on weekends and for vintage. They aim to build the
business to the point where they can move to Mudgee and start a family. Ernest Shuetz had
outstanding success at the Mudgee Wine Show '11, its four entries winning three gold medals.

ΤΤΤΤΩ **Family Reserve Single Vineyard Mudgee Shiraz 2009** Light, clear red-purple, an attractive, light- to medium-bodied wine with 5% co-fermented viognier adding to the lift of the red fruits that spent two years in used American oak; has real elegance. 100 dozen made. Screwcap. 14.5% alc. **Rating** 91 **To** 2019 $26

✪ **Terra X Mudgee Pinot Gris 2011** Full straw colour; has more weight and texture than many, with ripe pear, lychee, honeysuckle and citrus; falters slightly on the finish, but that's a nitpick. Screwcap. 12.5% alc. **Rating** 90 **To** Now $17
Family Reserve Single Vineyard Mudgee Black Syrah 2009 Deep purple-red; diametrically opposed in style to the Family Reserve, although both wines come from the same estate vineyard; this was obviously picked later. Blackberry and dark cherry fruit, considerable tannins, and vanillin oak (20 months' partial (sic) maturation in new American oak) have all contributed to this full-bodied wine. 200 dozen made. Screwcap. 15% alc. **Rating** 90 **To** 2024 $26
Epica Amarone Method Mudgee Shiraz Cabernet 2009 An epic effort: bunches of shiraz (50%), cabernet sauvignon (40%) and merlot (10%) were air-dried on racks for 36 days before crushing and fermentation, then aged in new Hungarian and new and used French oak for two years. It is very difficult to judge by normal standards, and can only be pointed accepting its premise. 1500 (huge) bottles made. Cork. 15.5% alc. **Rating** 90 **To** 2019 $55

ΤΤΤΤ **Family Reserve Single Vineyard Mudgee Black Merlot 2009 Rating** 89 **To** 2020 $28
Family Reserve Single Vineyard Mudgee Chardonnay 2010 Rating 88 **To** 2013 $26
Moscato 2011 Rating 88 **To** 2013 $17
Family Reserve Single Vineyard Mudgee Black Cabernet Sauvignon 2009 Rating 87 **To** 2014 $26

Estate 807 ★★★★

807 Scotsdale Road, Denmark, WA 6333 **Region** Great Southern
T (08) 9840 9027 **www**.estate807.com.au **Open** Thurs–Mon 10–4, 7 days during school hols
Winemaker Harewood Estate (James Kellie) **Est.** 1998 **Dozens** 2500 **Vyds** 4.2ha
Stephen Junk and Ola Tylestam purchased Estate 807 in 2009; the vineyard had been established in 1998, with plantings of clonally-selected pinot noir and chardonnay, plus small amounts of cabernet sauvignon and more recently-planted sauvignon blanc. Stephen and Ola (who is Swedish) reside in Denmark, and have three generations of English cocker spaniels, some named on the labels. They also have a herd of alpacas, 'amazing animals that are very tame and love human company, always happy when children feed them while their parents are tasting the wines'.

ΤΤΤΤΩ **Reserve Chardonnay 2010** Bright straw-green; a powerful, barrel-fermented wine that seems riper than its alcohol would suggest, with layers of stone fruit, melon and fig, toasty oak adding a further layer. Screwcap. 13.5% alc. **Rating** 91 **To** 2015 $30
Reserve Pinot Noir 2010 Very light, clear, colour; savoury, spicy characters run throughout the bouquet and palate, other characters watching from either side, earthy bramble opposite red and black cherry, plus oak. I would be inclined to drink it sooner rather than later. Screwcap. 14% alc. **Rating** 90 **To** 2014 $40

ΤΤΤΤ **Xena Rose 2011 Rating** 87 **To** 2013 $20
Peb's Red Pinot Noir 2010 Rating 87 **To** Now $35

Evans & Tate ★★★★★

Cnr Metricup Road/Caves Road, Wilyabrup, WA 6280 **Region** Margaret River
T (08) 9755 6244 **www**.mcwilliamswinesgroup.com **Open** 7 days 10.30–5
Winemaker Matthew Byrne, Lachlan McDonald **Est.** 1970 **Dozens** 450 000 **Vyds** 53.33ha

The 40-year history of Evans & Tate has been one of constant change and, for decades, expansion, moving to acquire large wineries in SA and NSW. For a series of reasons, nothing to do with the excellent quality of its Margaret River wines, the empire fell apart in 2005; however, it took an interminable time before McWilliam's finalised its acquisition of the Evans & Tate brand, cellar door and vineyards (although not the winery) in December '07. Remarkably, wine quality was maintained through the turmoil, and shows no sign whatsoever of faltering. Exports to all major markets.

ΨΨΨΨΨ **Metricup Road Margaret River Semillon Sauvignon Blanc 2011** The very
✪   essence of fresh, pungent and pristine Margaret River fruit handled with precision;
       nettle and tropical fruit notes on the bouquet make way for a generously textured
       and linear palate, with depth and freshness in equal measure. Screwcap. 13% alc.
       Rating 94 **To** 2015 $23 BE
✪   **Metricup Road Margaret River Cabernet Merlot 2009** Clear red-crimson;
       the fragrant, cassis-accented bouquet leads into an elegant medium-bodied palate
       with excellent line, length and balance; the tannins are fine, the oak skilfully
       integrated. Screwcap. 14% alc. **Rating** 94 **To** 2024 $23

ΨΨΨΨΨ **Metricup Road Margaret River Sauvignon Blanc 2011** Rating 92
       To 2013 $23
       Porongurup Riesling 2011 Rating 90 **To** 2025 $25 BE
       Metricup Road Margaret River Chardonnay 2010 Rating 90 **To** 2017 $23
✪   **Gnangara Shiraz 2010** Vivid purple-crimson; some very good WA shiraz has
       gone into this wine, and been thoroughly respected in the winery; its balance
       and length are all one could wish for; they simply don't come better at this price.
       Screwcap. 14% alc. **Rating** 90 **To** 2015 $14
✪   **Classic Margaret River Shiraz Cabernet 2010** Bright colour; has a leather
       and red fruit bouquet, with ample gravelly tannins, and a lick of sweet red fruit to
       conclude; juicy, savoury and fresh. Screwcap. 14% alc. **Rating** 90 **To** 2014 $18 BE
✪   **Classic Margaret River Cabernet Merlot 2010** Vibrant colour; a fresh and
       cassis-filled bouquet, showing cedary complexity; medium-bodied and vibrant,
       with good persistence; delivers plenty of flavour at this price point. Screwcap.
       14% alc. **Rating** 90 **To** 2017 $18 BE
       Metricup Road Margaret River Cabernet Sauvignon 2009 Rating 90
       To 2015 $23

ΨΨΨΨ   **Metricup Road Margaret River Shiraz 2009** Rating 89 **To** 2016 $23
       Classic Crisp Margaret River Chardonnay 2010 Rating 88 **To** 2014 $19
       Margaret River Classic White 2011 Rating 88 **To** 2014 $19 BE
✪   **Gnangara Cabernet Merlot 2010** Rating 88 **To** 2014 $14
       Gnangara Cabernet Sauvignon 2010 Rating 87 **To** 2013 $14
       Classic Pink Moscato 2011 Rating 87 **To** Now $19

Evoi Wines   ★★★★★

92 Dunsborough Lakes Drive, Dunsborough, WA 6281 (postal) **Region** Margaret River
T 0407 131 080 **F** (08) 9755 3742 **www**.evoiwines.com **Open** Not
Winemaker Nigel Ludlow **Est.** 2006 **Dozens** 400
NZ-born Flying Winemaker Nigel Ludlow has roosted in the Margaret River for the past nine years, and has no intention of leaving, the beaches, scenery, lifestyle and wine quality all reasons to stay. Evoi's tiny production is dovetailed into Nigel's other winemaking responsibilities in the region. Exports to the UK and Hong Kong.

ΨΨΨΨΨ **Reserve Margaret River Chardonnay 2010** Given the Rolls Royce
       treatment: hand-picked, basket-pressed, fermented in new and 1-year-old French
       barriques, partial wild and mlf and lees stirring. The result is a very elegant wine
       that lingers in the mouth long after it is swallowed, nectarine, white peach and
       creamy cashew all present. Screwcap. 14% alc. **Rating** 95 **To** 2017 $42

The Satyr Reserve 2010 Medium crimson-purple; a complex blend of cabernet sauvignon, petit verdot, merlot and cabernet franc, the components small-batch open-fermented then basket-pressed into new and used French oak to finish primary fermentation and mlf; the fruit aromas and flavours are vibrant and fresh, the oak not obvious; the structure of the wine comes from the firm tannins imparted by the petit verdot and will sustain the wine for years to come. Screwcap. 14.5% alc. **Rating** 94 **To** 2030 $42

Eyre Creek ★★★★

Main North Road, Auburn, SA 5451 **Region** Clare Valley
T 0418 818 400 **F** (08) 8849 2555 **Open** W'ends & public hols 10–5, Mon–Fri as per sign
Winemaker Stephen John, Skillogalee **Est.** 1998 **Dozens** 2500 **Vyds** 2.9ha
John and Glenise Osborne, well-known Auburn hoteliers, established Eyre Creek in 1998. In 2008 they opened their cellar door, a renovated 100-year-old dairy, just north of Auburn. They grow dryland shiraz and grenache; the production is sold at the cellar door, by mail order and at selected bottle shops and restaurants in Adelaide and Sydney.

🍷🍷🍷🍷 Doctor's Paddock Clare Valley Cabernet Sauvignon 2010 Deep purple-red; a potent, full-bodied wine with sombre black fruits, an undergrowth of earth and charry oak, and abundant ripe tannins. Not for the faint-hearted, even if it is no more than the autocratic nature of cabernet. Screwcap. 14.3% alc. **Rating** 93 **To** 2025 $25
The Brookvale Clare Valley Shiraz 2010 Full purple-crimson; the aromatic bouquet has medicinal nuances that are not unpleasant, and merge with spicy characters in turn linked to oak; well balanced, and pushes the envelope without tearing it. Screwcap. 14.5% alc. **Rating** 90 **To** 2020 $25

🍷🍷🍷🍷 Watervale Riesling 2011 **Rating** 88 **To** 2015 $20
Explorers Clare Valley Grenache 2010 **Rating** 87 **To** 2015 $25

Faber Vineyard ★★★★★

233 Haddrill Road, Baskerville, WA 6056 **Region** Swan Valley
T (08) 9296 0209 **www**.fabervineyard.com.au **Open** Sun 11–4
Winemaker John Griffiths **Est.** 1997 **Dozens** 3000 **Vyds** 4.5ha
Former Houghton winemaker, now university lecturer and consultant, John Griffiths teamed with wife, Jane Micallef, to found Faber Vineyard. They have established shiraz, verdelho (1.5ha each), brown muscat, chardonnay and petit verdot (0.5ha each). Says John, 'It may be somewhat quixotic, but I'm a great fan of traditional warm-area Australian wine styles – those found in areas such as Rutherglen and the Barossa, wines made in a relatively simple manner that reflect the concentrated ripe flavours one expects in these regions. And when one searches, some of these gems can be found from the Swan Valley.' Possessed of an excellent palate, and with an impeccable winemaking background, the quality of John's wines is guaranteed, although the rating is also quixotic. As well as the cellar door, opened in 2008, construction of a new barrel store was commenced in late '10.

🍷🍷🍷🍷🍷 Dwellingup Chardonnay 2010 Vibrant green hue; a restrained and mineral-laden bouquet of grapefruit, pear and spicy oak; the palate is taut, fresh and focused, long and refreshing; unevolved and with a healthy life ahead. Screwcap. 13.8% alc. **Rating** 94 **To** 2018 $25 BE
Reserve Swan Valley Shiraz 2009 Deep in colour and dark in character with tar, leather, black fruits and toasty oak all present and accounted for; black fruits and savoury Amaro tannins linger with mocha on the savoury finish; it is a terroir-driven style that John Griffiths aims for, but will split opinions. Cork. 14.5% alc. **Rating** 94 **To** 2016 $54 BE
Swan Valley Liqueur Muscat NV Toffee, grilled nuts, raisins and pain grillee; a lovely, rich and unctuous example, with a baked fruit character that is all Swan Valley in character. 500ml. Cork. 18% alc. **Rating** 94 **To** 2020 $51 BE

ŢŢŢŢ♀ Frankland River Cabernet 2009 Rating 93 To 2016 $48 BE

ŢŢŢŢ Petit Verdot 2010 Rating 87 To 2014 $28 BE

Falls Wines ★★★

Belubula Way, Canowindra, NSW 2804 **Region** Cowra
T (02) 9956 6451 **www**.fallswines.com **Open** By appt
Winemaker Madrez Wine Services (Chris Derrez) **Est.** 1997 **Dozens** 4000 **Vyds** 94.3ha
Falls Wines produces a range of wines from their substantial estate vineyards on the outskirts
of Canowindra, planted to chardonnay, semillon, shiraz, cabernet sauvignon and merlot. The
Falls Vineyard Retreat and Guesthouse adjoins the vineyard, offering full day spa facilities.

ŢŢŢŢ **Merlot 2011** Bright colour; sensibly released early in its life, thus conserving
as much as possible of the primary red fruit flavours; the finish brings a touch
of black olive and superfine tannins into play. Screwcap. 14.5% alc. **Rating** 89
To 2015 $17
Cabernet Sauvignon 2011 Youthful, bright colour; why this wine should have
finer and riper tannins than the '11 Cabernet Merlot I have no idea; while no
more than medium-bodied, it has attractive varietal expression courtesy of its red
and blackcurrant fruits. Screwcap. 14.5% alc. **Rating** 89 **To** 2016 $17

 # Far Ago Hill Wines ★★★★☆

1371 Tugalong Road, Canyonleigh, NSW 2577 **Region** Southern Highlands
T (02) 9557 0089 **www**.faragohill.com **Open** Not
Winemaker Suzanne Little **Est.** 2003 **Dozens** 600 **Vyds** 2.5ha
Katrina Hill lays it on the line when she describes herself as a mad, crazy, female vigneron,
and continues, 'What on earth possessed us (my ex husband and I) to plant a vineyard – I
will never know! "Grape change" seemed like a great idea at the time, and totally different
from interior design (me) and psychiatry (him). I don't think you understand how much
hard work a vineyard is, despite warnings, until you actually do it. Wombats, birds, the worst
sunburn I have ever had, and pruning for 14 weekends through the freezingness of winter!
Not exactly romantic.'

ŢŢŢŢŢ **The George Ellis Reserve Canyonleigh Pinot Gris 2010** Full bronze pink-
copper; 10% barrel-fermented in French oak, the wine has a voluminous bouquet,
and the palate has all the gravitas of Alsace; the flavours are of ripe pear, spice and
strawberry, the balance excellent thanks to crisp acidity on the finish. A rare wine.
Screwcap. 12.5% alc. **Rating** 94 **To** 2013 $30

ŢŢŢŢ♀ **Reserve Canyonleigh Pinot Gris 2011** Rating 93 To 2013 $30

Farmer's Daughter Wines ★★★

791 Ulan Road, Mudgee, NSW 2850 **Region** Mudgee
T (02) 6373 3177 **www**.farmersdaughterwines.com.au **Open** Mon–Fri 9–5, Sat 10–5,
Sun 10–4
Winemaker Greg Silkman, Liz Jackson **Est.** 1995 **Dozens** 8000 **Vyds** 17.6ha
The intriguingly named Farmer's Daughter Wines is a family-owned vineyard, named for
the daughters of Lance and Gwen Smith, who originally planted grapes for sale, looking to
retirement. Retirement, they say, has now become a 10-day week. Part of the production from
the vineyard, planted to shiraz (8ha), cabernet sauvignon, merlot and chardonnay (3.2ha each),
is sold to other makers, but the majority is made for the Farmer's Daughter label. Exports to
the US, Canada and Vietnam.

ŢŢŢŢ **Mudgee Shiraz 2010** Developed spiced plum and leather bouquet; the palate is
soft-centred on entry, and then a shock of tannins bursts through, finishing
dry, savoury and with an Amaro bitter twist. Screwcap. 14.5% alc. **Rating** 87
To 2015 $20 BE

Farmer's Leap Wines ★★★★

PMB 99, Naracoorte, SA 5271 **Region** Padthaway
T (08) 8765 6007 **www**.farmersleap.com **Open** Mon–Fri 10–4 by appt
Winemaker Contract **Est.** 2004 **Dozens** 7100 **Vyds** 295.4ha
Scott Longbottom and Cheryl Merrett are third-generation farmers in the Padthaway region. They commenced planting the vineyard in 1995 on the family property, and there are now 130ha shiraz, 65.5ha cabernet sauvignon, 83.9ha chardonnay and 12.2ha merlot. Initially the majority of the grapes were sold, but increasing quantities held for the Farmer's Leap label have seen production rise from 2500 dozen to its present level. Low prices have doubtless helped drive sales. Exports to Canada, Singapore, South Korea, Japan and China.

ⓉⓉⓉⓉⓉ **Random Shot Padthaway Chardonnay 2011** Has the ultra-fragrant
✪ grapefruit and nectarine aroma of all good Padthaway chardonnay; what is more, the flavours have developed at this level of alcohol. If you like the taste of chardonnay, don't hesitate with this. Screwcap. 12.5% alc. **Rating** 90 **To** 2014 $15
The Brave Padthaway Shiraz 2008 One step further up the mountain than the standard wine thanks to a generous helping of new French and American oak. The cork implies that this wine may be headed to the land of the free, where its many charms will be appreciated. 15% alc. **Rating** 90 **To** 2015 $25
✪ **Padthaway Shiraz 2007** Holding hue very well; the bouquet has that particular berry and plum fruit which is the hallmark of the region, and flows through to the medium-bodied palate; I far prefer alcohol at this level, and fail to see why another 1% alc/vol is needed. Screwcap. 14% alc. **Rating** 90 **To** 2017 $18
✪ **Random Shot Padthaway Cabernet Sauvignon 2010** Do not look a gift horse in the mouth, and wonder how this pristine cabernet, with great texture balance and varietal character, can be $15. Screwcap. 14.5% alc. **Rating** 90 **To** 2017

ⓉⓉⓉⓉ **Random Shot Padthaway Shiraz Cabernet 2008** Has retained full crimson
✪ hue, accurately pointing to the fresh, zesty red cherry, plum and blackberry fruit on the palate. Clever packaging. Screwcap. 14% alc. **Rating** 89 **To** 2016 $15
Padthaway Shiraz 2008 Rating 88 **To** 2018 $18

Fermoy Estate ★★★★★

838 Metricup Road, Wilyabrup, WA 6280 **Region** Margaret River
T (08) 9755 6285 **www**.fermoy.com.au **Open** 7 days 10–5
Winemaker Liz Dawson, Coralie Lewis-Garnier **Est.** 1985 **Dozens** 20 000 **Vyds** 17ha
A long-established estate-based winery with 17ha of semillon, sauvignon blanc, chardonnay, cabernet sauvignon and merlot. Notwithstanding its significant production, it is happy to keep a relatively low profile, however difficult that may be given the quality of the wines Liz Dawson is making. Exports to Europe and Asia.

ⓉⓉⓉⓉⓉ **Reserve Margaret River Cabernet Sauvignon 2010** Vivid magenta; this
is autocratic cabernet sauvignon at its most imperious, lulling you into a sense of false security with its delicious blackcurrant, redcurrant and cassis fruit, then causing you to kneel before the tannins; having done so, the fruit flavours return, and all is forgiven. Screwcap. 14% alc. **Rating** 95 **To** 2035 $65
✪ **Margaret River Semillon Sauvignon Blanc 2010** Still pale quartz-green; a wine built for the long haul, with the lemongrass/herbal/mineral core of semillon dominant, but not smothering the lychee and passionfruit nuances of the sauvignon blanc. Drink now or later. Screwcap. 13.5% alc. **Rating** 94 **To** 2016 $22
Reserve Margaret River Chardonnay 2011 Good colour; a very complex, layered palate exemplifying the great depth of flavour chardonnay achieves in this region; the oak and lees contact characters add notes of grilled cashew to the primary nectarine and white peach fruit; has a long future. Screwcap. 13.5% alc. **Rating** 94 **To** 2019 $50

Reserve Margaret River Chardonnay 2010 The bouquet is fresh and lively, fruit-driven; the palate opens with restraint before accelerating through the mid palate and onto the finish; the flavours are predominantly in the grapefruit and mineral spectrum, acidity more important in providing structure than the French oak in which the wine was fermented. Screwcap. 13.5% alc. Rating 94 To 2018 $50

Margaret River Shiraz 2010 Bright purple-crimson; a notably rich and velvety wine, the array of red and black fruits filling the mouth with flavour; the tannins are soft, the oak balanced, the finish long and satisfying. Screwcap. 14% alc. Rating 94 To 2025 $30

ŦŦŦŦŦ   Margaret River Sauvignon Blanc 2011 Rating 93 To 2014 $25
Margaret River Cabernet Sauvignon Merlot 2010 Rating 92 To 2020 $25
The Partnership Margaret River Semillon Sauvignon Blanc 2011
Rating 91 To 2014 $25
Margaret River Chardonnay 2011 Rating 91 To 2016 $30

ŦŦŦŦ   Margaret River Merlot 2010 Rating 87 To 2017 $30

Fernfield Wines   ★★★★

Rushlea Road, Eden Valley, SA 5235 **Region** Eden Valley
T (08) 8564 1041 **www**.fernfieldwines.com.au **Open** Fri–Mon 11–4
Winemaker Bronwyn Lillecrapp, Shannon Plummer **Est.** 2002 **Dozens** 1500 **Vyds** 27.8ha
The establishment date of 2002 might, with a little poetic licence, be shown as 1864. Bryce Lillecrapp is the fifth generation of the Lillecrapp family; his great-great-great-grandfather bought land in the Eden Valley in 1864, subdividing it in 1866, establishing the township of Eden Valley and building the first house, Rushlea Homestead. Bryce restored this building and opened it in 1998 as a bicentennial project; it now serves as Fernfield Wines' cellar door. He heads up Fernfield as grapegrower, with his wife Bronwyn chief winemaker, son Shannon cellar hand and assistant winemaker, and daughter Rebecca the wine marketer. While all members of the family have married grapegrowing and winemaking with other vocations, they have moved inexorably back to Fernfield, where they have vines dating back three generations of the family (riesling, pinot noir, shiraz, merlot, cabernet sauvignon, traminer and cabernet franc).

ŦŦŦŦŦ   Wayward Blend Eden Valley Cabernet Sauvignon Merlot Cabernet
✪   Franc 2009 Dense colour typical of Fernfield; matured for 25 months in new and used French oak, and – improbably – shakes off its yoke of alcohol. Picked a bit earlier, could have made a great wine; as it is, the opulent red fruits have an unexpected clarity of expression. Screwcap. 15% alc. Rating 91 To 2020 $15
Footstompers Eden Valley Shiraz 2009 Dense, impenetrable purple; a massive, monumental, full-bodied shiraz, foot-stamped by friends from the Eden Valley, and then spending 23 months in new and used French oak. Will undoubtedly have an intensely loyal band of followers, some of whom may cellar some of the wine, a good move. Screwcap. 15% alc. Rating 90 To 2029 $30

ŦŦŦŦ   Pridmore Eden Valley Shiraz 2009 Rating 88 To 2024 $20

Ferngrove   ★★★★★

276 Ferngrove Road, Frankland River, WA 6396 **Region** Frankland River
T (08) 9855 2378 **www**.ferngrove.com.au **Open** 7 days 10–4
Winemaker Kim Horton **Est.** 1997 **Dozens** NFP **Vyds** 210.4ha
After 90 years of beef and dairy farming heritage, Murray Burton ventured into premium grapegrowing and winemaking in 1977. Today the venture he founded has two large vineyards in Frankland River planted to the leading varieties, the lion's share to shiraz, cabernet sauvignon, chardonnay, sauvignon blanc, merlot and semillon, with a small but important planting of malbec. The operation centres around the Ferngrove Vineyard, where a large rammed-earth winery and tourist complex was built in 2000. Part of the vineyard production is sold as grapes, part as juice or must, part as finished wine, and the pick of the crop is made

for the Ferngrove label. The consistency of its wines across a wide range of price points is wholly admirable. Acquired Killerby (Margaret River) in 2008. Exports to the UK, the US and other major markets.

ŸŸŸŸŸ **The Stirlings Shiraz Cabernet Sauvignon 2008** A numbered bottle without also giving the total number has always struck me as a marketing gimmick, pure and simple. However, the brilliant crimson colour betokens a very elegant and fine wine, blackberry and blackcurrant in a cat's cradle of French oak, the tannins long and fine. It is a wine to drink, not just taste, notable for its freshness. Screwcap. 14% alc. **Rating** 96 **To** 2028 $60

Majestic Cabernet Sauvignon 2009 Full crimson; machine-harvested at night, then crushed and cold-soaked before the initiation of an eight-day ferment, racked to 100% new French oak for mlf and then 20 months' maturation. The high-quality grapes have easily handled this regime, providing an intense medium- to full-bodied palate full of blackcurrant fruit, with hints of dark chocolate and ample tannins. Screwcap. 13.5% alc. **Rating** 95 **To** 2030 $30

Cossack Riesling 2011 Pale quartz-green; a wine with a very impressive track record, and all the ingredients present in this vintage: minerals, acidity, lime and apple blossom, spice, length and balance. Has a distinguished track record. Screwcap. 12% alc. **Rating** 94 **To** 2021 $23

ŸŸŸŸŸ **Frankland River Merlot 2009** Light, bright red; this is an impressive merlot; ✪ neatly balances savoury black olive nuances with spicy cassis fruit and cedary French oak; the length and balance are good. Screwcap. 13.5% alc. **Rating** 92 **To** 2015 $20

✪ **Frankland River Sauvignon Blanc 2011** Pale straw-green; this is a firm, crisp and clean wine from start to finish, with citrus, herb and green apple aromas and flavours, and the barest hint of passionfruit in the background. Screwcap. 13.5% alc. **Rating** 91 **To** 2013 $20

✪ **Leaping Lizard Semillon Sauvignon Blanc 2011** A fragrant blend of herbal notes at one extreme, and tropical at the other, the latter dominant, bringing passionfruit, guava and white peach to the party, the mouthfeel without any sharp edges thanks to the balanced acidity. Screwcap. 13% alc. **Rating** 91 **To** 2014 $15

✪ **Leaping Lizard Shiraz 2010** Bright crimson; the light- to medium-bodied palate has juicy plum and blackberry fruit with a generous sprinkling of spice and pepper; there is also a touch of French oak to go along with fine tannins. A great bargain. Screwcap. 14% alc. **Rating** 91 **To** 2018 $15

Dragon Shiraz 2009 Rating 91 **To** 2016 $30 BE
King Malbec 2009 Rating 90 **To** 2014 $30 BE

ŸŸŸŸ **Diamond Frankland River Chardonnay 2010 Rating** 89 **To** 2014 $25
Frankland River Shiraz 2009 Rating 89 **To** 2015 $20 BE
Frankland River Chardonnay 2010 Rating 88 **To** Now $20
Symbols Frankland River Cabernet Merlot 2009 Rating 88 **To** 2014 $16 BE

Fighting Gully Road ★★★★★

319 Whorouly South Road, Whorouly South, Vic 3735 **Region** Beechworth
T (03) 5727 1434 **www**.fightinggully.com **Open** By appt
Winemaker Mark Walpole, Adrian Rodda **Est.** 1997 **Dozens** 800 **Vyds** 8.3ha
Mark Walpole and partner Carolyn De Poi began the development of their Aquila Audax Vineyard in 1997, planting the first vines. It is situated between 530 and 580m above sea level: the upper-eastern slopes are planted to pinot noir and the warmer western slopes to cabernet sauvignon; there are also small quantities of shiraz, tempranillo, sangiovese and merlot.

ŸŸŸŸŸ **Aquila 2010** Full straw; this unique blend (Chardonnay/Viognier/Petit Manseng) was barrel-fermented with wild and cultured yeasts and matured for 10 months; it is full of flavour, and there is an interesting grainy structure. The viognier's presence is the most potent, with ripe apricot fruit, and the petit manseng presumably provided the acidity, chardonnay the missing bits. Unusual, but it works. Screwcap. 12.5% alc. **Rating** 94 **To** 2014 $22

Beechworth Cabernet Sauvignon Merlot 2006 Bright colour; this is amazingly fresh and vibrant for its age, with cassis, loganberry, clove and olive on the bouquet; tightly wound fruits with linear acidity and firm, fine tannins combine seamlessly to provide an even and savoury example of this blend; excellent value for the price. Screwcap. 14% alc. **Rating** 94 **To** 2018 $27 BE

ŸŸŸŸŸ **Beechworth Sangiovese 2010 Rating** 90 **To** 2014 $28 BE

Fire Gully   ★★★★☆
Metricup Road, Wilyabrup, WA 6280 **Region** Margaret River
T (08) 9755 6220 **www**.firegully.com.au **Open** By appt
Winemaker Dr Michael Peterkin **Est.** 1988 **Dozens** 5000 **Vyds** 13.4ha
The Fire Gully vineyard has been established on what was first a dairy and then a beef farm. A 6ha lake created in a gully ravaged by bushfires gave the property its name. In 1998 Mike Peterkin of Pierro purchased the property; he manages the vineyard in conjunction with former owners Ellis and Margaret Butcher. He regards the Fire Gully wines as entirely separate from those of Pierro, being estate-grown: the vineyards are planted to cabernet sauvignon, merlot, shiraz, semillon, sauvignon blanc, chardonnay, viognier and chenin blanc, and have been increased by over 4ha in recent years. Exports to all major markets.

ŸŸŸŸŸ **Margaret River Chardonnay 2010** Vibrant green hue; a restrained and fresh floral and grapefruit-accented bouquet; the palate is zesty and mineral-driven, with grip and texture coming to the fore on the finish; lively and long. Screwcap. 13.5% alc. **Rating** 94 **To** 2015 $30 BE

ŸŸŸŸŸ **Margaret River Semillon Sauvignon Blanc 2010 Rating** 92 **To** 2014 $26 BE
Margaret River Semillon Sauvignon Blanc 2011 Rating 90 **To** 2014 $24
Reserve Margaret River Cabernet Sauvignon 2008 Rating 90 **To** 2014 $42 BE

ŸŸŸŸ **Margaret River Shiraz Viognier 2009 Rating** 89 **To** 2014 $30 BE

First Creek Wines   ★★★★★
600 McDonalds Road, Pokolbin, NSW 2320 **Region** Hunter Valley
T (02) 4998 7293 **www**.firstcreekwines.com.au **Open** 7 days 10–4
Winemaker Liz Jackson, Damien Stevens, Greg Silkman **Est.** 1984 **Dozens** 35 000
First Creek Wines is the brand of First Creek Winemaking Services, a company contract-making wine for over 25 clients. Winemaker Liz Jackson had an exceptional year in 2011: she was a finalist in the Gourmet Traveller Winemaker of the Year awards, winner of the Hunter Valley Winemaker of the Year, and won Best Red Wine of Show at the NSW Wine Awards for the Winemakers Reserve Shiraz 2010. Exports to the UK, Sweden and China.

ŸŸŸŸŸ **Winemaker's Reserve Hunter Valley Chardonnay 2010** Gleaming bright green-yellow; a superb example of elegant, modern Hunter Valley chardonnay that has uncovered the secret to an intense, long wine with all the fragrance and juicy white peach fruit of cool climates. The grapes were picked shortly before torrential rain and were in top condition; thereafter the winemaking surely enhanced the quality. Screwcap. 12.5% alc. **Rating** 96 **To** 2018 $35 BE
Winemaker's Reserve Hunter Valley Shiraz 2010 Strong crimson-purple; the complex bouquet has aromas of spiced plum and oak, the flavours of the medium-bodied palate even more complex, with a swirl of juicy red and black fruits supported by ultra-fine tannins and quality oak. Screwcap. 13.5% alc. **Rating** 95 **To** 2025 $42
Winemaker's Reserve Hunter Valley Chardonnay 2011 A very savoury example of the variety from the Hunter, with charcuterie and grilled nuts sitting alongside nectarine and spice; the palate is surprisingly soft and approachable, but there is steel in the backbone, and the finish is long and satisfying; enjoy in the short to medium term. Screwcap. 13.5% alc. **Rating** 94 **To** 2018 $40

ŶŶŶŶŶ **Winemaker's Reserve Hunter Valley Semillon 2011** Rating 93 To 2020
$35 BE
Hunter Valley Verdelho 2011 Rating 90 To 2015 $22 BE

ŶŶŶŶ **Organic Wine Hunter Valley Bianco Puro 2010** Rating 89 To 2013 $25
Organic Wine Hunter Valley Rosso Puro 2010 Rating 89 To Now $25

First Drop Wines ★★★★★

Home of the Brave, Beckwith Park, Tanunda Road, Nuriootpa, SA 5335
Region Barossa Valley
T (08) 8562 3324 **www**.firstdropwines.com **Open** Not
Winemaker Matt Gant **Est.** 2005 **Dozens** 8000
The First Drop Wines of today bears little resemblance to that of (say) two years ago. It now
has a real winery, part of the old Penfolds winery at Nuriootpa, shared with Tim Smith Wines.
The group of buildings is now called Beckwith Park, in honour of the man who did so much
groundbreaking work for Penfolds (Ray Beckwith OAM, who turned 100 in 2012); his other
recognition came in the form of the Maurice O'Shea Award, rightly recognising that while
Penfolds was his employer, the work he did on wine chemistry and wine bacterial disease was
of huge importance. Various of the wines have had wine show success. Exports to the UK, the
US, Canada, Denmark, Japan, Hong Kong, Singapore and NZ.

ŶŶŶŶŶ **The Cream Barossa Valley Shiraz 2009** The First Drop team seem to be
able to tread the delicate line of power and restraint, while maintaining life and
freshness in impressively concentrated wines; The Cream is a testament to this, as
the layers of dark fruits, roasted meats, tar, bramble and sizzling bacon fat are held
in check by taut tannins and fine acidity; more than just clever winemaking leads
to a long and harmonious finish. Cork. 14.5% alc. **Rating** 96 To 2035 $100 BE
Fat of the Land Ebenezer Single Vineyard Barossa Valley Shiraz 2009
Deep garnet; a ripe, dark and toasty bouquet of mulberry, bitter chocolate and
liqueur-soaked plums; the palate is unctuous and fleshy, and while concentrated
and hedonistic, maintains life and vitality; the long mocha finish frames the fruit
amiably. Cork. 14.5% alc. **Rating** 95 To 2024 $75 BE
**Fat of the Land Seppeltsfield Single Vineyard Barossa Valley Shiraz
2009** Impenetrable colour, and while dark and brooding in character, offers
glimpses of vibrant fresh blackberry, vine sap and bitter chocolate; the palate is full-
bodied and powerful, with a brightness and floral note that engages, and acidity
that lingers evenly on the finish; power with restraint. Cork. 14.5% alc. **Rating** 95
To 2030 $75 BE
Minchia Adelaide Hills Montepulciano 2009 Deep magenta; this is a lovely,
ripe, essency and beguiling wine, combining sweet black fruits with briary
complexity, and doing it with great charm; silky on the palate, lively and layered;
there is a lot to like in this wine, for a great many dining occasions. Screwcap.
14.5% alc. **Rating** 94 To 2018 $38 BE

ŶŶŶŶŶ **Mother's Milk Barossa Shiraz 2010** Medium purple-red; an unashamedly
✪ full-bodied wine, with a super-abundant scrum of blackberry, plum, black cherry,
licorice and ripe tannins, and oak hidden in the middle. Screwcap. 14.5% alc.
Rating 93 To 2025 $25
**JR Gantos Quinta do sul McLaren Vale Cabernet Sauvignon Touriga
Nacional 2009** Rating 93 To 2020 $38 BE
Mere et Fils Adelaide Hills Chardonnay 2010 Rating 90 To 2017 $25 BE
Half & Half Barossa Shiraz Monastrell 2009 Rating 90 To 2016 $25 BE

ŶŶŶŶ **Bella Coppia Adelaide Hills Arneis 2011** Rating 89 To 2014 $25 BE
Two Percent Barossa Shiraz 2009 Rating 89 To 2015 $38 BE
Fat of the Land Single Vineyard Greenock Barossa Valley Shiraz 2009
Rating 89 To 2018 $75 BE
Mother's Ruin McLaren Vale Cabernet Sauvignon 2010 Rating 89
To 2016 $25 BE

The Big Blind Adelaide Hills Nebbiolo Barbera 2009 Rating 88
To 2014 $30 BE
Pintor Barossa Tempranillo 2009 Rating 88 To 2014 $30 BE

Fishbone Wines

Kearney Street, Nannup, WA 6275 **Region** Blackwood Valley
T (08) 9756 0077 www.blackwoodwines.com.au **Open** 7 days 10–4
Winemaker Stuart Pearce **Est.** 1996 **Dozens** 20 000 **Vyds** 5ha
Fishbone Wines, developed by Blackwood Wines, has had significant growth in recent years.
The Blue label is designed to fill the $10–$15 price bracket, with distribution in most
Australian states and exports to the US, Asia and Middle East markets. It also developed the
black label Margaret River range for the $15–$20 domestic and export market. Exports to the
US, the Netherlands, United Arab Emirates, Hong Kong and Singapore.

🍷🍷🍷🍷🍷 **Shiraz 2010** Clear, bright crimson-purple; an opulent, mouthfilling wine with
sumptuous plum and blackberry fruit garnished with licorice and spice; you would
never guess that so much flavour could be achieved at this modest alcohol level,
but remember the gift horse. Screwcap. 13% alc. **Rating** 92 **To** 2030 $25

✪ **Fishbone Margaret River Cabernet Sauvignon Merlot 2009** Clear red-
purple; a deliciously savoury wine, the savoury notes coming from the fruit, not
from its silky tannins; the result is a light- to medium-bodied, but very long, palate.
Screwcap. 14% alc. **Rating** 90 **To** 2016 $20

🍷🍷🍷🍷 **Fishbone Margaret River Semillon Sauvignon Blanc 2011** Rating 89
To 2014 $20

5 Blind Mice

PO Box 243, Basket Range, SA 5138 **Region** Adelaide Hills
T (08) 8390 0206 www.5blindmice.com.au **Open** Not
Winemaker Jodie and Hugh Armstrong **Est.** 2004 **Dozens** 300
Owners Jodie and Hugh Armstrong say, 'What started out as an idea between friends and
family to make something for ourselves to drink at home during the week has blossomed into
a quest for something to stand proudly on its own.' The grapes are chosen from small sections
of three of the vineyards that Jodie manages, and she and Hugh make the wines in garagiste
facilities in the Adelaide Hills and McLaren Vale with the support of local oenological talent.
Exports to Singapore.

🍷🍷🍷🍷🍷 **La Debutante McLaren Vale Shiraz 2010** Deep crimson-purple; all the right
✪ steps have been taken in making this complex and rich wine; it is stacked with
blackberry, licorice and a touch of dark chocolate, the excellent tannin structure
on the finish preventing the fruit going over the top, and guaranteeing its long-
term future. Outstanding value. Screwcap. 14% alc. **Rating** 93 **To** 2025 $19

La Vie en Rose 2011 Pink with just a hint of salmon; a pinot rose with
considerable intensity and structure; the flavours of small red fruits are given
a decided touch of class by the firm, dry, textured finish. Screwcap. 12.5% alc.
Rating 90 **To** 2013 $19

Five Geese

389 Chapel Hill Road, Blewitt Springs, SA 5171 (postal) **Region** McLaren Vale
T (08) 8383 0576 www.fivegeese.com.au **Open** Not
Winemaker Boar's Rock (Mike Farmilo) **Est.** 1999 **Dozens** 3000 **Vyds** 33.88ha
Sue Trott is passionate about her Five Geese wine, which is produced by Hillgrove Wines. The
wines come from vines planted in 1927 and '65. The grapes were sold for many years, but in
1999 Sue decided to create her own label and make a strictly limited amount of wine from
the pick of the vineyards, which are run on organic principles. Exports to the UK, the US,
Hong Kong, South Korea and Singapore.

♟♟♟♟♟ McLaren Vale Shiraz 2010 Rating 94 To 2020 $20
✪

♟♟♟♟♕ Reserve McLaren Vale Shiraz 2009 Rating 90 To 2015 $40 BE
Reserve McLaren Vale Cabernet Sauvignon 2009 Rating 90 To 2016
$40 BE

Flametree   ★★★★★

Cnr Caves Road/Chain Avenue, Dunsborough, WA 6281 **Region** Margaret River
T (08) 9756 8577 **www**.flametreewines.com **Open** 7 days 10–5
Winemaker Cliff Royle, Julian Scott **Est.** 2007 **Dozens** 15 000
Flametree, now owned solely by the Towner family (John, Liz and Rob), has had extraordinary
success since its first vintage in 2007. The usual practice of planting a vineyard and then finding
someone to make the wine was turned on its head: a state-of-the-art winery was built, and
grape purchase agreements entered into with various growers in the region. Gold medal
after gold medal, and trophy after trophy followed, topped by the winning of the Jimmy
Watson Trophy with its first red wine, the 2007 Cabernet Merlot. If all this were not enough,
Flametree has secured the services of former long-serving winemaker at Voyager Estate, Cliff
Royle. Exports to the UK, Sweden, Fiji, Singapore, the Maldives, Indonesia, Hong Kong
and China.

♟♟♟♟♟ Margaret River Chardonnay 2010 From the central Wilyabrup area, and the
✪   cooler southern Wallcliffe area. This is an exceptionally intense wine, with zesty
grapefruit, melon skin and white peach flavours threaded around a high-tensile
chord of acidity running through the palate; oak did the job required of it, but no
more. A very long life ahead. Screwcap. 13.5% alc. **Rating** 96 To 2023 $30
S.R.S. Margaret River Chardonnay 2010 From the 'golden triangle' of the
Wallcliffe area; light, bright straw-green; the wine has exceptional power, presence
and length to its grapefruit, white peach and apple flavours that have eaten the oak
in which it was fermented. Screwcap. 13% alc. **Rating** 96 To 2018 $50
S.R.S. Margaret River Cabernet Sauvignon 2010 In the Sub Regional
Series, coming from Wilyabrup, long regarded as the source of the region's best
cabernets. This is a high-quality, full-bodied wine, with blackcurrant, black olive
and cedar all competing for space, underpinned by tannins that will see the wine
cruise over the next 20+ years. Screwcap. 14% alc. **Rating** 95 To 2030 $50
S.R.S. Margaret River Sauvignon Blanc 2011 S.R.S. denotes Sub Regional
Series wines sourced from optimal regions for the relevant varieties, here the cool,
southern Karridale area. Part was barrel-fermented, impacting as much on texture
as flavour; the mix of snow pea and green citrus fruit is underpinned by firm
acidity on a long palate. Screwcap. 13% alc. **Rating** 94 To 2014 $35
Margaret River Cabernet Merlot 2010 Bright red-purple; the highly fragrant
bouquet of blackcurrant and cedar flows into an elegant medium-bodied palate, the
red and black berry fruits lengthened by exemplary tannins, part berry, part French
oak-derived, but harmonious. Screwcap. 14.2% alc. **Rating** 94 To 2020 $30

♟♟♟♟♕ Embers Margaret River Cabernet Sauvignon 2010 Rating 93
✪   To 2018 $18
Margaret River Sauvignon Blanc Semillon 2011 Rating 92 To 2013 $22
✪   Embers Margaret River Semillon Sauvignon Blanc 2011 Rating 92
To 2013 $18
✪   Margaret River Pinot Rose 2011 Vibrant pale pink; perhaps the best use of
this variety in the region is rose, as this wine has an ebullient personality, full of
vibrant wild strawberry, spice and a slight sea-salt tang that provides extra freshness
and vitality; good fun stuff, excellently constructed. Screwcap. 13% alc. **Rating** 92
To 2013 $19 BE

♟♟♟♟ Frankland River Shiraz 2010 Rating 88 To 2016 $30

Flaxman Wines   ★★★★★

Lot 535 Flaxmans Valley Road, Angaston, SA 5353 **Region** Eden Valley
T 0411 668 949 **www**.flaxmanwines.com.au **Open** By appt
Winemaker Colin Sheppard **Est.** 2005 **Dozens** 1500 **Vyds** 2ha

After visiting the Barossa Valley for over a decade, and working during vintage with Andrew Seppelt at Murray Street Vineyards, Melbourne residents Colin and Fiona Sheppard decided on a seachange and found a small, old vineyard overlooking Flaxmans Valley. It consists of 1ha of 40+-year-old riesling, 1ha of 50+-year-old shiraz and a small planting of 40+-year-old semillon. The vines are dry-grown, hand-pruned and hand-picked, and treated – say the Sheppards – as their garden. Yields are restricted to under 4 tonnes per ha, and small amounts of locally grown grapes are also purchased.

🍷🍷🍷🍷🍷 **Eden Valley Riesling 2011** Light straw-green; a floral, perfumed apple blossom bouquet, then a tightly structured palate, with apple, lime juice and minerally acidity all jousting for space. Only 190 dozen made – technically difficult to manage. Screwcap. 11.5% alc. **Rating** 94 **To** 2025 $27

Eden Valley Shiraz 2009 Deep purple-crimson; the power and concentration of the wine comes from the 80-year-old vines, not from heavy hands in the winery; the flavours are of blackberry, licorice and spice, with tannins and oak evident but balanced; 75 dozen made. Screwcap. 14% alc. **Rating** 94 **To** 2029 $47

The Stranger Barossa Shiraz Cabernet 2010 Bright crimson; a fragrant black cherry and blackcurrant bouquet, then a medium-bodied palate that opens with the same juicy register of fruit flavours, but ends with positive, dusty tannins. It's all in balance and will knit well in a year or two. Screwcap. 14% alc. **Rating** 94 **To** 2020 $37

🍷🍷🍷🍷♀ **Shhh Eden Valley Cabernet 2009 Rating** 93 **To** 2030 $37
Drone Blend 2010 Rating 90 **To** 2016 $25
Barossa Sparkling Shiraz NV Rating 90 **To** 2014 $45

🍷🍷🍷🍷 **Drone Blend 2011 Rating** 89 **To** 2016 $27
✪ **Paladin Barossa Valley Shiraz 2011 Rating** 89 **To** 2015 $20
Barossa Valley Mataro 2009 Rating 88 **To** 2015 $37

🍂 Fletcher Wines   ★★★★

90 Gold Street, Collingwood, Vic 3066 **Region** Various
T 0403 302 729 **www**.fletcherwines.com **Open** By appt
Winemaker David Fletcher **Est.** 2009 **Dozens** 400

David Fletcher has a background that would make any Florentine Renaissance man proud. While completing his oenology course at Adelaide University, he worked filling flagons and tending vines at Tinlins in McLaren Vale. On graduation in 2003, he worked for O'Leary Walker in the Clare Valley for two years; for reasons not entirely self-evident, this inspired him to work in Burgundy, and in '04 he worked harvest at Domaine Chevrot. In love with pinot, he moved to the Yarra Valley at the start of '06, where he stayed for three years as assistant winemaker at Sticks, while fitting in a northern hemisphere vintage each year, once in Kazakhstan, and twice in Italy for Ceretto. In 2009, he became a grape liaison officer with Foster's, with responsibilities extending across Vic and parts of NSW, the object being the assessment of grape quality and determining picking dates. This job then offered him the opportunity to fill the same role in the Napa Valley and Santa Barbara County for Beringer, part of Foster's. Agatha Christie would quickly find the link that led David and wife Eleanor to establish Fletcher Wines, dedicated solely to making Nebbiolo from vines at least 10 years old.

🍷🍷🍷🍷♀ **Malakoff Estate Vineyard Pyrenees Nebbiolo 2010** Slightly deeper colour and a fraction more advanced than the Ann Mary Lees; a more generous, although clearly varietal wine; the fruit has more depth and complexity, the tannins (relatively) less intrusive. Diam. 13.5% alc. **Rating** 93 **To** 2025 $50

Ann Mary Lees Vineyard Adelaide Hills Nebbiolo 2010 Star-bright and clear crimson; strong varietal expression with a spicy/savoury, violet and cherry bouquet, nebbiolo tannins measuring the playing field dimensions of the fruit and combining with the pointed acidity. Diam. 13.5% alc. **Rating** 92 **To** 2020 $50

Flint's of Coonawarra ★★★☆

PO Box 8, Coonawarra, SA 5263 **Region** Coonawarra
T (08) 8736 5046 **www**.flintsofcoonawarra.com.au **Open** Not
Winemaker Contract **Est.** 2000 **Dozens** 3000 **Vyds** 84ha

Six generations of the Flint family have lived and worked in Coonawarra since 1840. Damian Flint and his family began the development of 84ha of cabernet sauvignon, shiraz and merlot in 1989, but it was not until 2000 that they decided to have a small portion of cabernet sauvignon contract-made. Damian and Sue oversee the day-to-day running of both the vineyard and the farm, with Matthew, who studied viticulture in the Barossa, managing the vineyard. Exports to the UK and Hong Kong.

🍷🍷🍷🍷🍷 **Gammon's Crossing Cabernet Sauvignon 2009** Light crimson-purple; fresh and lively, the bouquet aromatic, the palate medium-bodied, with red and black fruits, a touch of mint and supporting tannins. Screwcap. 14.5% alc. **Rating** 90 **To** 2019 $20

Flying Fish Cove ★★★★

Caves Road, Wilyabrup, WA 6284 **Region** Margaret River
T (08) 9755 6600 **www**.flyingfishcove.com **Open** 7 days 11–5
Winemaker Damon Eastaugh, Simon Ding **Est.** 2000 **Dozens** 20 000 **Vyds** 25ha

A group of 20 shareholders acquired the 130ha property on which the Flying Fish Cove winery was subsequently built. It has two strings to its bow: contract winemaking for others, and the development of its own brand, partly based on 25ha of estate plantings, with another 10ha planned. Exports to the US and Singapore.

🍷🍷🍷🍷🍷 **Margaret River Cabernet Sauvignon Merlot 2011** Deep magenta, purple hue; leafy aromas supplemented by cassis, olive, toasty oak and lavender; the palate is full-bodied and generous, layered with chewy tannins and vibrant fruit; a big boned cabernet blend. Screwcap. 14% alc. **Rating** 92 **To** 2022 $22 BE

Wildberry Reserve Margaret River Cabernet Sauvignon 2010 Impenetrable colour; incredibly dark, dense and brooding in every sense, with super-concentrated cassis, black olive, chewy tannins and bright acidity; big-boned, tannic and very dry; will reward a little patient cellaring. Screwcap. 14.5% alc. **Rating** 92 **To** 2025 $35 BE

Wildberry Reserve Margaret River Chardonnay 2010 A fresh melon and nectarine bouquet; soft and very toasty on the palate, with good concentration, sweet fruit on the medium-weighted palate and vibrant acidity providing detail on the finish. Screwcap. 12.5% alc. **Rating** 90 **To** 2016 $35 BE

🍷🍷🍷🍷 **Margaret River Sauvignon Blanc Semillon 2011** **Rating** 89 **To** 2014 $22 BE
Margaret River Pinot Noir Chardonnay 2009 **Rating** 89 **To** 2014 $29
Offshore Margaret River Rose 2009 **Rating** 87 **To** 2013 $15

Flynns Wines ★★★★

Lot 5 Lewis Road, Heathcote, Vic 3523 **Region** Heathcote
T (03) 5433 6297 **www**.flynnswines.com **Open** Mon–Fri 11–2.30
Winemaker Greg and Natala Flynn **Est.** 1999 **Dozens** 2000 **Vyds** 4.12ha

The Flynn name has a long association with Heathcote. In the 1970s John Flynn and Laurie Williams established a 2ha vineyard next door to Mount Ida Vineyard, on the rich, red Cambrian soil. It produced some spectacular wines before being sold in 1983. Greg and Natala Flynn (no relation to John Flynn) spent 18 months searching for their property, 13km north of Heathcote on the same red Cambrian soil. They have established shiraz, sangiovese, verdelho, cabernet sauvignon and merlot. Greg is a Roseworthy marketing graduate, and has had 23 years working at the coalface of retail and wholesale businesses, interweaving nine years of vineyard and winemaking experience, supplemented by the two-year Bendigo TAFE winemaking course. Just for good measure, wife Natala joined Greg for the last eight years of vineyard and winemaking, and likewise completed the TAFE course.

ΨΨΨΨΨ **Irena's Heathcote Verdelho 2010** Pale straw; a short spell in new French oak barriques has made its mark, adding both to the flavour (a note of spice) and texture; the fruit line is razor sharp, acidity a backbone for the mix of citrus and tropical fruit, the finish full of zest. Screwcap. 13.8% alc. **Rating** 93 **To** 2014 $25
Lewis Road Heathcote Shiraz 2009 Open-fermented and basket-pressed, with 5% viognier added and matured in French and American oak. Light, bright, clear colour; the palate is fresh, zesty and light, with fine tannins and touches of herb and eucalypt. Screwcap. 13.2% alc. **Rating** 90 **To** 2015 $22

Fonty's Pool Vineyards

Seven Day Road, Manjimup, WA 6258 **Region** Pemberton
T (08) 9777 0777 **www**.fontyspoolwines.com.au **Open** 7 days 12–4
Winemaker Melanie Bowater, Bernie Stanlake **Est.** 1989 **Dozens** 15 000 **Vyds** 48ha
The Fonty's Pool vineyards are part of the original farm owned by pioneer settler Archie Fontanini, who was granted land by the government in 1907. In the early 1920s a large dam was created to provide water for the extensive vegetable gardens that were part of the farming activities. The dam became known as Fonty's Pool, and to this day remains a famous local landmark and recreational facility. The first grapes were planted in 1989, and the vineyard is one of the region's largest, supplying grapes to a number of leading WA wineries. An increasing amount of the production is used for Fonty's Pool. No wines were received for this edition; the rating is that of last year. Exports to all major markets.

 # Forbes & Forbes ★★★★☆

Mengler Hill Road, Angaston, Tanunda, SA 5352 **Region** Eden Valley
T (08) 8568 2709 **F** (08) 8568 2709 **Open** Sat 11–5
Winemaker Colin Forbes **Est.** 2008 **Dozens** 600 **Vyds** 5ha
This venture is owned by Colin and Robert Forbes, and their respective partners. Colin says 'I have been in the industry for a "frightening" length of time', beginning with Thomas Hardy & Sons in 1974. Currently he is contract winemaking for McLean's Farm, Smallfry, John Dawkins and Partalunga Vineyard, as well as making the wines for Forbes & Forbes. The winemaking is carried out in the shed owned by McLean's Farm. While Colin is particularly attached to riesling, the property owned by the partners in Eden Valley has 2ha each of riesling and merlot, and 1ha of cabernet sauvignon.

ΨΨΨΨΨ **Cellar Matured Eden Valley Riesling 2002** Gleaming green-gold; from a very cool vintage, and has achieved everything expected in the bottle; tangy, toasty nuances to the core of citrus fruit in its web of steely acidity; is at the peak of perfection. Screwcap. 13% alc. **Rating** 94 **To** 2014 $35

ΨΨΨΨΨ **Eden Valley Riesling 2010** Light, bright straw-green; has delicious lime, lemon ✪ and apple flavours couched in the embrace of crunchy acidity. Screwcap. 12.9% alc. **Rating** 93 **To** 2020 $20
Eden Valley Riesling 2011 Rating 90 **To** 2018 $22

ΨΨΨΨ **Eden Valley Cabernet Sauvignon 2008 Rating** 87 **To** 2015 $20

Forest Hill Vineyard

Cnr South Coast Highway/Myers Road, Denmark, WA 6333 **Region** Great Southern
T (08) 9848 0000 **www**.foresthillwines.com.au **Open** 7 days 10–4
Winemaker Clémence Haselgrove **Est.** 1965 **Dozens** 23 000 **Vyds** 65ha
This family-owned business is one of the oldest 'new' winemaking operations in WA, and was the site for the first grape plantings in Great Southern in 1965. The Forest Hill brand

became well known, aided by the fact that a 1975 Riesling made by Sandalford from Forest Hill grapes won nine trophies. The quality of the wines made from the oldest vines on the property is awesome (released under the numbered vineyard block labels). Exports to Taiwan, Hong Kong, Singapore and China.

ŸŸŸŸŸ **Block 1 Mount Barker Riesling 2011** Vibrant pale hue; this is extraordinarily tightly wound on the bouquet, with lashings of minerals, lemon and a dash of spice; the palate reveals the complete picture, with zesty acidity, a tight core of pure citrus fruit and a very long finish; unevolved and needing time to relax and to offer the complete story of the wine within. Screwcap. 13% alc. **Rating** 95 **To** 2025 $40 BE

Springvale Estate Great Southern Riesling 2011 Pure-fruited and fine aromas of lime, nectarine, spice and a little orange zest for added lift; the palate is racy and fine, giving generosity and flesh at the same time for a thoroughly complete and satisfying, long and harmonious young wine. Screwcap. 13% alc. **Rating** 95 **To** 2020 $27 BE

Block 8 Mount Barker Chardonnay 2010 Vibrant green hue; the bouquet is high impact and full of savoury aromas with charcuterie, grilled cashew and grapefruit all coming to the fore; the palate shows good intensity and depth, supported by an electric line of acidity; long, fresh and compelling. Screwcap. 14% alc. **Rating** 95 **To** 2023 $45 BE

Block 9 Mount Barker Shiraz 2008 Mid crimson; a vibrant and perfumed bouquet redolent of red fruits, sea spray, violets and Asian spices; the palate is finely detailed and layered with silky tannins in abundance; the seamless nature of this wine provides a long, coherent and thoroughly engaging experience. Screwcap. 13.5% alc. **Rating** 95 **To** 2025 $65 BE

Estate Great Southern Cabernet Sauvignon 2010 Deep garnet; a dark and brooding bouquet offering cedar, black fruits and fine French oak; the palate shows great intensity, while remaining light on its feet, with tannins that are very fine and polished; a sleeper waiting to awaken. Screwcap. 14% alc. **Rating** 95 **To** 2025 $32 BE

ŸŸŸŸŸ **Estate Great Southern Shiraz 2010** **Rating** 93 **To** 2025 $30 BE
✪ **Highbury Fields Great Southern Cabernet Merlot 2010** Deep crimson; a highly polished and precise blend of red and black fruits, cedar and some fine French oak on display; the palate is almost silky in its structure, with fine tannins and evenly balanced fleshy fruit; delivers well above its price point. Screwcap. 14% alc. **Rating** 93 **To** 2023 $20 BE

Estate Great Southern Chardonnay 2011 **Rating** 92 **To** 2018 $32 BE
✪ **Highbury Fields Great Southern Sauvignon Blanc Semillon 2011** A restrained bouquet of gun flint, guava, grapefruit and anise; the palate is fleshy and textured, with a mineral edge to the fruit, and a very long finish. Screwcap. 13% alc. **Rating** 90 **To** 2014 $20 BE

Block 5 Mount Barker Cabernet Sauvignon 2008 **Rating** 90 **To** 2018 $80 BE

Forester Estate ★★★★★

1064 Wildwood Road, Yallingup, WA 6282 **Region** Margaret River
T (08) 9755 2788 **www**.foresterestate.com.au **Open** By appt
Winemaker Kevin McKay, Todd Payne **Est.** 2001 **Dozens** 25 000 **Vyds** 33.5ha
Forester Estate is owned by Kevin McKay. Kevin has built a 500-tonne winery, half devoted to contract winemaking, the other half for the Forester label. Winemaker Todd Payne has had a distinguished career, starting in the Great Southern, thereafter the Napa Valley, back to Plantagenet, then on to Esk Valley in Hawke's Bay, plus two vintages in the Northern Rhône Valley, one with the esteemed producer Yves Cuilleron in 2008. His move back to WA completes the circle. The estate vineyards are planted to sauvignon blanc, semillon, chardonnay, cabernet sauvignon, shiraz, merlot, petit verdot, malbec and alicante bouschet. Exports to Singapore, China and Japan.

🍷🍷🍷🍷🍷 **Margaret River Sauvignon Blanc 2011** Pale quartz-green; partial barrel fermentation has added a substantial dimension to the wine, without, however, obscuring the attractive tropical fruit flavours that run through the long palate. Screwcap. 13.7% alc. **Rating** 94 **To** 2014 $23
Yelverton Reserve Margaret River Cabernet 2009 The hue is good, although not deep; it has undoubted elegance, finesse and length with excellent balance between the cassis fruits and finely drawn tannins; oak, too, is a comfort. Screwcap. 13.5% alc. **Rating** 94 **To** 2023 $60

🍷🍷🍷🍷🍷 ✪ **Margaret River Semillon Sauvignon Blanc 2011** Pale quartz; a harmonious blend evident from the first whiff, the aromas neither overtly tropical nor herbal, although having some of each; the palate plays along with the same game until the finish and aftertaste, where it flexes its muscles and encourages attention. Screwcap. 13% alc. **Rating** 93 **To** 2014 $20
Margaret River Chardonnay 2010 Rating 92 **To** 2017 $38
✪ **Margaret River Cabernet Merlot 2009** Good colour; its gold medal at the Melbourne Wine Show '11 suggests the judges were looking for elegance rather than depth of fruit; the cassis/blackcurrant fruit flavours are varietal, but the savoury tannins do click in a little earlier than one would hope for; however, that increases its food-friendly character. Screwcap. 13% alc. **Rating** 91 **To** 2019 $20

🍷🍷🍷🍷 **Margaret River Alicante 2010 Rating** 89 **To** 2020 $35

Foster e Rocco   ★★★★★
139 Williams Road, Myers Flat, Vic 3556 (postal) **Region** Heathcote
T 0434 365 504 **Open** Not
Winemaker Adam Foster, Lincoln Riley **Est.** 2008 **Dozens** 750
Long-term sommeliers and friends Adam Foster and Lincoln Riley have established a business that has a very clear vision: food-friendly wine based on the versatility of sangiovese. They make their wine at Syrahmi, building it from the ground up, with fermentation in both stainless steel and a mixture of older French oak barrels.

🍷🍷🍷🍷🍷 **Heathcote Rose 2011** Pale, bright pink; the perfumed bouquet has cherry and wild strawberry aromas, the palate exceptional flavour, texture and structure, again with sangiovese/cherry characters coming through strongly. A top-class rose by any standards. Screwcap. 12.8% alc. **Rating** 94 **To** 2014
Heathcote Sangiovese 2010 Conventional mid red colour; you move straight into conventional sangiovese territory, the aromas and flavours of spiced cherry and sour cherry; the tannins are fine and balanced, presenting no terrors at all. Screwcap. 13.5% alc. **Rating** 94 **To** 2016

🍷🍷🍷🍷🍷 **Nuovo Heathcote Sangiovese 2011 Rating** 92 **To** 2013

Four Winds Vineyard   ★★★★☆
392 Murrumbateman Road, Murrumbateman, NSW 2582 **Region** Canberra District
T 0402 278 371 **www.**fourwindsvineyard.com.au **Open** Not
Winemaker Jaime and Bill Crowe **Est.** 1998 **Dozens** 1500 **Vyds** 14.1ha
Graeme and Suzanne Lunney conceived the idea for Four Winds in 1997, planting the first vines in '98, moving to the property fulltime in '99, and making the first vintage in 2000. Daughter Sarah looks after events and promotions, and youngest daughter Jaime, complete with a degree in Forensic Biology, has joined Bill in the winery. She brings with her several years' experience with the former Kamberra winery, and three vintages in the Napa Valley. Suzanne tends the gardens and the 100 rose bushes at the end of the vine rows.

🍷🍷🍷🍷🍷 ✪ **Canberra District Riesling 2011** Pale quartz-green; a delicious wine that has been made with great skill, pitched precisely on the border between dry and off-dry; the perfect balance between fruit, residual sugar and acidity binds these three characters together, and it's easy to see why it won a gold medal at the Canberra Regional Wine Show '11. Screwcap. 10% alc. **Rating** 94 **To** 2021 $17

🍷🍷🍷🍷🍷 **Canberra District Shiraz 2009 Rating** 91 **To** 2017 $19

Fowles Wine ★★★★☆

Cnr Hume Freeway/Lambing Gully Road, Avenel, Vic 3664 **Region** Strathbogie Ranges
T (03) 5796 2150 **www**.plunkettfowles.com.au **Open** 7 days 9–5
Winemaker Victor Nash, Lindsay Brown **Est.** 1968 **Dozens** 60 000 **Vyds** 140ha
Formerly known as Plunkett Fowles, the Fowles family acquiring the remaining Plunkett family shareholding in the company in April 2012 (Sam Plunkett is taking the opportunity to pursue his Master of Wine degree). The large vineyard is primarily focused on riesling, chardonnay, shiraz and cabernet sauvignon, and also includes chardonnay, shiraz, cabernet sauvignon, sauvignon blanc, pinot noir, merlot, riesling, semillon, viognier, gewurztraminer, savagnin, tempranillo, lagrein, arneis, vermentino, pinot gris and sangiovese. Marketing is energetic, with the well-known Ladies Who Shoot Their Lunch label available as large posters. Exports to the UK, the US, Canada and China.

🍷🍷🍷🍷🍷 **Stone Dwellers Strathbogie Ranges Cabernet Sauvignon 2009** Strong purple-crimson; a wine that sends mixed messages, although none of them bad; while the fruit has a fully ripe blackcurrant core, it is surrounded by more savoury spicy notes partly, but not entirely, from oak; grainy tannins also provide balance to the fruit. Screwcap. 14.5% alc. **Rating** 94 **To** 2019 $25

🍷🍷🍷🍷🍷 **Stone Dwellers Strathbogie Ranges Riesling 2011 Rating** 92 **To** 2018 $22 BE
Ladies Who Shoot Their Lunch Strathbogie Ranges Shiraz 2009 Rating 92 **To** 2020 $35
Ladies who Shoot their Lunch Strathbogie Ranges Riesling 2010 Rating 91 **To** 2020 $35
Ladies Who Shoot Their Lunch Strathbogie Ranges Chardonnay 2011 Rating 91 **To** 2015 $35 BE
✪ **490 m Cabernet Merlot 2008** The colour is still bright and fresh; both the bouquet and palate have clear varietal expression with blackcurrant, black olive and some dried herb on both bouquet and palate; good length and balance underwrite the future. Screwcap. 15% alc. **Rating** 91 **To** 2018 **$15**
Stone Dwellers Strathbogie Ranges Sauvignon Blanc 2011 Rating 90 **To** 2013 $22 BE
490 metres Chardonnay 2011 Rating 90 **To** 2014 $15 BE
The Exception Strathbogie Ranges Riesling 2010 Rating 90 **To** 2015 $30 BE

🍷🍷🍷🍷 **The Exception Strathbogie Ranges Cabernet Sauvignon 2005 Rating** 89 **To** 2015 $50 BE
✪ **490m Sauvignon Blanc Semillon 2010 Rating** 89 **To** 2013 $15
Stone Dwellers Strathbogie Ranges Pinot Gris 2011 Rating 87 **To** 2013 $22 BE
490 metres Shiraz 2009 Rating 87 **To** 2014 $15 BE

Fox Creek Wines ★★★★★

Malpas Road, McLaren Vale, SA 5171 **Region** McLaren Vale
T (08) 8557 0000 **www**.foxcreekwines.com **Open** 7 days 10–5
Winemaker Scott Zrna **Est.** 1995 **Dozens** 40 000 **Vyds** 20.9ha
Fox Creek has made a major impact since coming on-stream late in 1995. It is the venture of the Watts family: Jim (a retired surgeon), wife Helen and son Paul (a viticulturist); and Lyn Roberts. Kristin McLarty (née Watts) is marketing manager and Georgy Rogers (née Watts) is cellar door supervisor. Moves are afoot to introduce organic practices in the vineyards, with trials of an organically registered herbicide derived from pine oil for weed control. Although Fox Creek is not organic, they use sustainable vineyard practices, avoiding all systemic chemicals. The wines have enjoyed considerable show success. Exports to all major markets.

ŸŸŸŸŸ **Short Row McLaren Vale Shiraz 2010** A glass and palate-staining wine, full of saturated black fruits, while also providing some red fruit highlights, and plenty of mocha on the bouquet; the medium-bodied palate is generous and full of ripe fruits, yet maintains freshness and energy from start to finish. Screwcap. 14.5% alc. **Rating** 94 **To** 2025 $29 BE
Reserve McLaren Vale Shiraz 2009 This wine is simply more of everything, with layers of sweet black fruits, mocha, fruitcake and lots of toasty oak; the palate is unctuous and leaves a heady trail of warm alcohol on the finish; pushing the ripeness envelope, but not quite overstepping the mark. Screwcap. 14.5% alc. **Rating** 94 **To** 2020 $70 BE

ŸŸŸŸŸ **Old Vine McLaren Vale Shiraz 2010 Rating** 93 **To** 2022 $50 BE
○ **Red Baron McLaren Vale Shiraz 2010 Rating** 92 **To** 2020 $18
✪ **McLaren Vale Shiraz Grenache Mourvedre 2010** Deep crimson; a decidedly savoury affair of black fruits and bramble on the bouquet; the palate is rugged and charming, with enough freshness and vibrancy to counteract the dense dark fruit on offer; long and savoury. Screwcap. 14.5% alc. **Rating** 92 **To** 2020 $18 BE
Vixen NV Rating 91 **To** 2018 $23 BE
The Circle Single Vineyard McLaren Vale Cabernet Sauvignon 2010 Rating 90 **To** 2020 $28 BE

ŸŸŸŸ **Duet McLaren Vale Cabernet Merlot 2010 Rating** 89 **To** 2018
✪ $19 BE
✪ **Shadow's Run McLaren Vale Shiraz Cabernet Sauvignon 2009 Rating** 88 **To** 2015 $13 BE

Fox Gordon ★★★★★

102 Main Street, Hahndorf, SA 5245 **Region** Barossa Valley/Adelaide Hills
T (08) 8388 7155 **www.**foxgordon.com.au **Open** Not
Winemaker Natasha Mooney **Est.** 2000 **Dozens** 10 000
This is the venture of three very well-known figures in the wine industry: Jane Gordon, Rachel Atkins (née Fox) and Natasha Mooney. Natasha (Tash) has had first-class experience in the Barossa Valley, particularly during her time as chief winemaker at Barossa Valley Estate. The partners wanted to produce high-quality wine, but only small quantities, which would allow them time to look after their children; the venture was planned in the shade of the wisteria tree in Tash's back garden. The grapes come from dry-grown vineyards farmed under biodiversity principles, which, says Tash, makes the winemaker's job easy. Classy packaging adds the final touch, and bargains abound. Exports to the UK, Canada, Germany, India, Singapore, Hong Kong and China.

ŸŸŸŸŸ **Hannah's Swing Barossa Valley Shiraz 2009** Deep crimson-purple; a seductive wine from start to finish, the bouquet and palate both full of black cherry and plum fruit allied with quality, well-integrated and balanced oak, the medium- to full-bodied palate luscious yet fresh. Screwcap. 14% alc. **Rating** 95 **To** 2029 $45
✪ **Eight Uncles Barossa Valley Shiraz 2010** Impenetrable colour, showing layers of black fruits, fruitcake and mulberry; the palate is driven by zesty acidity and gravelly tannins. The freshness makes the wine appealing as a young full-blooded shiraz for relaxed dining. Screwcap. 13.8% alc. **Rating** 94 **To** 2016 $20 BE

ŸŸŸŸŸ **By George Barossa Valley Adelaide Hills Cabernet Tempranillo 2009**
✪ Strong purple-red; has an expressive bouquet, with dark cherry ex the Adelaide Hills tempranillo and blackcurrant ex the Barossa cabernet; these two streams flow through the generous and juicy palate, tannins perfectly balanced to give structure. Will develop well in bottle. Screwcap. 14% alc. **Rating** 93 **To** 2020 $20
✪ **Eight Uncles Barossa Valley Shiraz 2009** Strong crimson-red; plenty going for it, with red and black cherry and damson plum fruit, fine tannins and well-integrated oak. Will go the distance. Screwcap. 14% alc. **Rating** 92 **To** 2020 $20

✪ **Sassy Adelaide Hills Sauvignon Blanc 2011** Pale quartz-green; has a potent bouquet of ripe tropical fruits that are corralled on the palate by mineral and citrus acidity. No shortage of attitude. Screwcap. 12.5% alc. **Rating** 91 **To** 2013 **$15**
Abby Adelaide Hills Viognier 2011 **Rating** 90 **To** 2013 $20 BE

🍷🍷🍷🍷 **Abby Adelaide Hills Viognier 2010** **Rating** 89 **To** Now $20
King Louis Barossa Valley Cabernet Sauvignon 2008 **Rating** 89 **To** 2018 $45 BE
Princess Adelaide Hills Fiano 2010 **Rating** 88 **To** Now $20
Princess Adelaide Hills Fiano 2011 **Rating** 87 **To** 2013 $20 BE

Foxeys Hangout ★★★★★

795 White Hill Road, Red Hill, Vic 3937 **Region** Mornington Peninsula
T (03) 5989 2022 **www**.foxeys-hangout.com.au **Open** W'ends & public hols 11–5
Winemaker Tony Lee, Michael Lee **Est.** 1998 **Dozens** 5000 **Vyds** 3.4ha

This is the venture of Tony Lee and journalist wife Cathy Gowdie. Cathy explains where it all began in 1998: 'We were not obvious candidates for a seachange. When we talked of moving to the country, friends pointed out that Tony and I were hardly back-to-nature types. "Do you own a single pair of shoes without heels?" asked a friend. But at the end of a bleak winter, we bought an old farmhouse on 10 daffodil-dotted acres at Red Hill and planted a vineyard.' They planted pinot noir, chardonnay, pinot gris and shiraz on the north-facing slopes of the old farm. The name (and the catchy label) stems from the tale of two fox-hunters who began a competition with each other in 1936, hanging their kills on the branches of an ancient eucalypt tree to keep count. The corpses have gone, but not the nickname for the area.

🍷🍷🍷🍷🍷 **Mornington Peninsula Shiraz 2010** Laudably, the label makes no mention of the prior vintage winning the Jimmy Watson Trophy. It won't happen again with this vintage, even though it is a very good blood brother, a highly aromatic, beautifully smooth flowing bowl of black cherry fruit, the tannins superfine, the oak exactly weighted. Screwcap. 14.5% alc. **Rating** 95 **To** 2025 $50
White Gates Vineyard Mornington Peninsula Pinot Noir 2010 One hundred dozen only made, all from the 115 clone grown on the home vineyard and sold only through cellar door. Bright, spicy red cherry fruit aromas and flavours run through the bouquet and palate, the latter with silky tannins and very good mouthfeel. Screwcap. 13.5% alc. **Rating** 94 **To** 2018 $60

🍷🍷🍷🍷½ ✪ **The Red Fox Pinot Noir 2010** Clear, light crimson; the third tier and cheapest of the three Foxeys Hangout pinots that nonetheless has a haul of three trophies from the Victorian Wines Show; the fruit is less dense than that of either of its siblings, but is multifaceted, and has good length. Screwcap. 13.5% alc. **Rating** 93 **To** 2017 $20
Mornington Peninsula Pinot Noir 2010 **Rating** 92 **To** 2017 $30
White Gates Vineyard Mornington Peninsula Chardonnay 2010 **Rating** 91 **To** 2020 $45
Mornington Peninsula Late Harvest Pinot Gris 2010 **Rating** 90 **To** 2013 $27

🍷🍷🍷🍷 **Mornington Peninsula Pinot Gris 2010** **Rating** 89 **To** 2013 $27
Mornington Peninsula Sparkling Shiraz 2008 **Rating** 88 **To** 2013 $27

Frankland Estate ★★★★★

Frankland Road, Frankland, WA 6396 **Region** Frankland River
T (08) 9855 1544 **www**.franklandestate.com.au **Open** Mon–Fri 10–4, public hols & w'ends by appt
Winemaker Elizabeth Smith, Hunter Smith, Brian Kent **Est.** 1988 **Dozens** 15 000 **Vyds** 34.5ha

A significant Frankland River operation, situated on a large sheep property owned by Barrie Smith and Judi Cullam. The vineyard has been established progressively since 1988; the recent introduction of an array of single vineyard Rieslings has been a highlight. The venture into the single vineyard wines is driven by Judi's conviction that terroir is of utmost importance, and the soils are indeed different. The climate is not, and the difference between the wines is not as clear-cut as theory might suggest. The Isolation Ridge Vineyard is now organically grown. Frankland Estate has held several important International Riesling tastings and seminars over recent years. Exports to all major markets.

ŸŸŸŸŸ **Smith Cullam Riesling 2011** Light, positive straw-green; made in off-dry mode, with 19 g/l of residual sugar. Just when you think this is merely another Mosel copycat, the astonishing drive and intensity of the palate makes the half-formed words describing the bouquet completely irrelevant. It demonstrates how great riesling (more than any other variety, with the possible exception of semillon) is made in the vineyard. Screwcap. 11% alc. **Rating** 97 **To** 2031 $45
Netley Road Vineyard Riesling 2011 Distinctly deeper straw-green colour; the bouquet has hints of herb and stone which in no way prepare you for the iron fist-in-a-velvet-glove assault of the palate, its power unfolding in waves, mineral, lime zest and rapier-like acidity dominating the back-palate and finish. Screwcap. 12.7% alc. **Rating** 96 **To** 2030 $27
Isolation Ridge Vineyard Riesling 2011 Pale straw-green; it has a shy, floral bouquet with hints of spice and apple, then a beautifully structured, supremely delicate palate; unfolds on the finish and aftertaste with mouth-watering, citrussy acidity. Screwcap. 12% alc. **Rating** 94 **To** 2026 $32
Isolation Ridge Vineyard Chardonnay 2010 Bright colour; a savoury bouquet of charcuterie, grilled nuts and grapefruit; the palate is vibrant and toasty from some new oak; fine, defined and precise, with a long and zesty finish. Screwcap. 13.4% alc. **Rating** 94 **To** 2017 $27 BE
Olmo's Reward 2009 Estate-grown cabernet franc (62%), merlot (17%), malbec (16%) and cabernet sauvignon (5%). The bright crimson colour is an inviting start to a wine with a range of small red and black fruits, plus notes of tobacco, spice and earth, oak playing a restricted role; the tannin support is particularly good, giving the wine distinction. Screwcap. 14% alc. **Rating** 94 **To** 2019 $40

ŸŸŸŸŸ **Isolation Ridge Vineyard Cabernet Sauvignon 2009** **Rating** 93 **To** 2018 $27 BE
O **Rocky Gully Riesling 2011** **Rating** 92 **To** 2015 $18
Poison Hill Vineyard Riesling 2011 **Rating** 92 **To** 2020 $27
Isolation Ridge Vineyard Shiraz 2009 **Rating** 92 **To** 2020 $32 BE
O **Rocky Gully Shiraz 2010** **Rating** 91 **To** 2010 $18

Fraser Gallop Estate ★★★★★

547 Metricup Road, Wilyabrup, WA 6280 **Region** Margaret River
T (08) 9755 7553 **www.**frasergallopestate.com.au **Open** By appt
Winemaker Clive Otto, Kate Morgan **Est.** 1999 **Dozens** 12 000 **Vyds** 18.55ha
Nigel Gallop began the development of the vineyard in 1999, planting cabernet sauvignon, semillon, petit verdot, cabernet franc, malbec, merlot and multi-clone chardonnay. The vines are dry-grown with modest yields, followed by kid-glove treatment in the winery. The first vintage was 2002, the wine being contract-made offsite, but with Clive Otto (formerly of Vasse Felix) on board, a 300-tonne winery was built onsite for the '08 vintage. As well as wines under the Fraser Gallop Estate label, limited amounts of contract wine are made for others. Exports to the UK, Canada, Switzerand and Hong Kong.

ŸŸŸŸŸ **Margaret River Semillon Sauvignon Blanc 2011** A 70/30% blend, 29%
✪ was barrel-fermented and spent two months in new French oak. The bouquet is fragrant and flowery, with passionfruit and citrus, the palate with great purity, line and length, with grapefruit, oak and perfectly balanced acidity in a continuous stream of flavour carrying through to the aftertaste. Will develop superbly. Screwcap. 13% alc. **Rating** 96 **To** 2015 $22

✪　**Margaret River Chardonnay 2011** Light, bright straw-green; an exceptionally intense, tightly focused and long palate, the emphasis on varietal fruit, as only 'limited use' was made of French oak barrels; this has in no way diminished the overall impact of the wine, which has tremendous length to its mix of grapefruit, nectarine, lemon curd and cashew flavours. Exceptional value. Screwcap. 13.5% alc. Rating 95 To 2018 $23

Parterre Wilyabrup Margaret River Cabernet Sauvignon 2010 The wine is in fact 87% cabernet sauvignon, the rest petit verdot, malbec, merlot and cabernet franc. It has excellent, bright crimson colour, its high quality evident from the first whiff of the bouquet, and built on by the palate; perfectly ripened blackcurrant fruit is the driver, with tannins and fully integrated fine French oak bringing up the rear. So perfectly balanced, it will likely be drunk long before its natural best-by date. Screwcap. 14% alc. Rating 95 To 2035 $40

Parterre Margaret River Semillon Sauvignon Blanc 2011 A 58/42% blend, wild yeast-fermented in new French oak and in stainless steel barriques; nine months in oak and stainless steel has built a wine with outstanding drive and intensity, the oak absorbed into both bouquet and palate, the flavours in the mid range between herbal and tropical. Screwcap. 13% alc. Rating 94 To 2018 $36

Parterre Margaret River Chardonnay 2011 An elegantly crafted wine picked at the optimum moment to give flavours of citrus, quince and white peach that are in turn picked up by the barrel-ferment oak inputs; the acidity underwrites the future of the wine to 5+ years. Screwcap. 13.5% alc. Rating 94 To 2017 $31

♟♟♟♟　**Margaret River Cabernet Merlot 2011** Rating 89 To 2017 $23

Fratelli　★★★★

12 Melbourne Road, Yea, Vic 3717 (postal) **Region** Victoria
T 0419 117 858 **www**.fratelliwines.com.au **Open** Not
Winemaker Andrew Santarossa **Est.** 2007 **Dozens** 1500
This is the virtual winery operation of three brothers of Italian heritage with a love of wine: Andrew, Michael and Anthony Santarossa. Andrew, the eldest, is a winemaker with over 10 years' experience making wines in Oregon, the Margaret River and the Yarra Valley. The handsomely packaged wines are sourced from various regions across Victoria; it's a small business as yet, but has the capacity to grow.

♟♟♟♟♟　**Yarra Valley Sauvignon Blanc 2011** Pale straw-green; an excellent
✪　achievement, with layers of citrus and tropical fruits, neatly balanced by bright acidity. As others have found, given appropriate care in the vineyard, the vintage produced excellent white wines. Screwcap. 13% alc. Rating 93 To 2014 $20

RedCote Heathcote Shiraz 2009 Slightly deeper colour than the standard wine; shares many things with its sibling, the main difference being slightly brighter and more intense red berry fruits, in turn balanced by quality oak. Screwcap. 13.6% alc. Rating 93 To 2024 $35

✪　**King Valley Pinot Gris 2011** From the upper reaches of the King Valley, and has admirable varietal character, with clearly expressed pear and apple fruit, together with enlivening acidity; a pinot gris with attitude. Screwcap. 13.5% alc. Rating 91 To 2014 $20

Heathcote Primitivo 2009 The colour is brilliantly clear, albeit somewhat light; the wine has not been forced into ripening, but the inherent nature of the variety has meant that it had to achieve 15% alcohol. This has had no adverse impact on the wine, but experience tells me a maximum of five years will be its life span. Screwcap. 15% alc. Rating 91 To 2016 $30

Heathcote Shiraz 2009 Light colour, although clear and healthy; the medium-bodied palate is predominantly driven by red and black cherry, but with a strong veneer of oak; soft tannins lengthen the finish and aftertaste. Screwcap. 14% alc. Rating 90 To 2019 $25

Freeman Vineyards   ★★★★★

101 Prunevale Road, Prunevale, NSW 2587 **Region** Hilltops
T (02) 6384 4299 **www**.freemanvineyards.com.au **Open** By appt
Winemaker Dr Brian Freeman, Xanthe Freeman **Est.** 2000 **Dozens** 5000 **Vyds** 45ha
Dr Brian Freeman has spent much of his long life in research and education, in the latter role
as head of CSU's viticulture and oenology campus. In 2004 he purchased the 30-year-old
vineyard previously known as Demondrille. He has also established a vineyard next door, and
in all has 14 varieties that range from staples such as shiraz, cabernet sauvignon, semillon and
riesling through to more exotic, trendy varieties such as tempranillo, and on to corvina and
rondinella. He has had a long academic interest in the effect of partial drying of grapes on
the tannins and, living at Prunevale, was easily able to obtain a prune dehydrator to partially
raisin the two varieties.

♈♈♈♈♈ **Rondinella Corvina Secco 2008** The rondinella and corvina grapes are partially
dried (hence secco) prior to fermentation. Typically light colour, but the hue is
good; the bouquet is fragrant and spicy, with cherry and plum fruit sharing the
limelight; prior vintages prove without doubt the ability of this wine to age and
gain yet more complexity. Screwcap. 14.5% alc. **Rating** 94 **To** 2018 $30
Altura Vineyard Tempranillo 2009 Clear red-purple, holding hue well;
fragrant, pure and fresh, with cherry and wild rose bramble aromas and flavours;
Freeman is very sensitive to excess phenolics; spicy savoury red berries are the key.
Screwcap. 13.5% alc. **Rating** 94 **To** 2016 $25

♈♈♈♈♈ **Fortuna Pinot Gris Plus 2010 Rating** 91 **To** 2014 $25

Freycinet   ★★★★★

15919 Tasman Highway via Bicheno, Tas 7215 **Region** East Coast Tasmania
T (03) 6257 8574 **www**.freycinetvineyard.com.au **Open** 7 days 10–5 (Nov–Apr),
10–4 (May–Oct)
Winemaker Claudio Radenti, Lindy Bull **Est.** 1980 **Dozens** 5000 **Vyds** 9.08ha
The Freycinet vineyards are beautifully situated on the sloping hillsides of a small valley. The
soils are brown dermosol on top of Jurassic dolerite, and the combination of aspect, slope, soil
and heat summation produces red grapes with unusual depth of colour and ripe flavours. One
of Australia's foremost producers of pinot noir, with an enviable track record of consistency –
rare in such a temperamental variety. The Radenti (sparkling), Riesling and Chardonnay are
also wines of the highest quality. Exports to the UK.

♈♈♈♈♈ **Radenti Chardonnay Pinot Noir 2001** Bright green-straw; right up there with
preceding vintages, a 60/40% blend fermented in this bottle and spending over
eight years on yeast lees; despite the resultant multilayered complexity and richness,
also has elegance. Cork. 12.5% alc. **Rating** 97 **To** 2015 $70
Pinot Noir 2010 Purple-crimson, slightly deeper than Louis; 31-year-old vines
here (16 years old for Louis, on adjacent sites), a perfect demonstration of the
value of fully mature vines; it has multiple layers of fruit with a silky sweetness to
the flavours; tannins are there, as is the oak, but it is the integrity of the fruit that
makes all the difference. Screwcap. 14.5% alc. **Rating** 96 **To** 2015 $70
Chardonnay 2010 Light straw-green; a complex bouquet with an attractive,
well-controlled touch of Burgundian funk on the bouquet, then a multilayered
palate of white peach, nectarine and creamy cashew. Lovely wine. Gold medal
Winewise '11. Screwcap. 13.5% alc. **Rating** 95 **To** 2018 $38
Louis Pinot Noir 2010 Clear colour; the plum, berry and spice bouquet is
attractive enough, but it is the palate that really defines and drives the quality of
this beautifully structured and balanced wine, combining plum with forest floor
and quality oak adding texture to the package. Screwcap. 14% alc. **Rating** 94
To 2018 $34

♈♈♈♈♈ **Riesling 2011 Rating** 92 **To** 2020 $24
Cabernet Sauvignon Merlot 2007 Rating 90 **To** 2020 $34

Frogmore Creek   ★★★★★

699 Richmond Road, Cambridge, Tas 7170 **Region** Southern Tasmania
T (03) 6248 4484 **www**.frogmorecreek.com.au **Open** 7 days 10–5
Winemaker Alain Rousseau, Nick Glaetzer, John Bown **Est.** 1997 **Dozens** 18000
Vyds 85ha

Frogmore Creek is a Pacific Rim joint venture, the owners being Tony Scherer of Tasmania and Jack Kidwiler of California. The business has grown very substantially, first establishing its own organically managed vineyard, and thereafter by a series of acquisitions. First was the purchase of the Hood/Wellington Wines business previously owned by Andrew Hood; next was the purchase of the large Roslyn Vineyard near Campania; and finally (in October 2010) the acquisition of Meadowbank Estate, where the cellar door is now located. Exports to the US, Japan, Indonesia and South Korea.

♥♥♥♥♥ FGR Riesling 2010 Wow. Leaps into another category. Green-gold; seriously good lime juice/lime zest; acidity/residual sugar balance equally good; has great length and great future. Top gold Tas Wine Show '12. Screwcap. 9.6% alc. Rating 96 To 2020 $24
FGR Riesling 2011 Green-gold; the wine has tremendous intensity, drive and length; the balance is immaculate; Bickford's lime juice flavours abound. Gold medal Tas Wine Show '12. Screwcap. 8.7% alc. Rating 95 To 2021 $24
Cuvee Evermore 2008 A 100% pinot noir blanc de noir, the pale salmon indicating as much. The strawberry fruit is embraced by creamy brioche notes, the acidity perfectly balanced by the dosage. Quality comes easy in Tasmania. Diam. 12% alc. Rating 94 To 2015 $42
Iced Gewurztraminer 2010 Glowing yellow-green; this has been a major success; it's not especially complex, but the balance is excellent, as is the length of the citrus and spice flavours. Screwcap. 10% alc. Rating 94 To 2016 $26

♥♥♥♥♀ Meadowbank Estate Mardi 2007 Rating 92 To 2016 $45
Fume Blanc Sauvignon Blanc 2011 Rating 91 To 2014 $28 BE
Pinot Noir 2010 Rating 91 To 2018 $36
Gewurztraminer 2011 Rating 90 To 2015 $28 BE

♥♥♥♥ 42°S Pinot Noir Rose 2011 Rating 89 To 2013 $22 BE
42°S Premier Cuvee NV Rating 89 To 2014 $26
Iced Riesling 2010 Rating 89 To 2015 $26
42°S Pinot Noir 2010 Rating 87 To 2016 $26

Gaelic Cemetery Wines   ★★★★★

PO Box 54, Sevenhill, SA 5453 **Region** Clare Valley
T (08) 8843 4370 **www**.gaelic-cemeterywines.com **Open** Not
Winemaker Neil Pike, John Trotter, Steve Baraglia **Est.** 2005 **Dozens** 250 **Vyds** 6.5ha

This is a joint venture between winemaker Neil Pike, viticulturist Andrew Pike and Adelaide retailers Mario and Ben Barletta. It hinges on a single vineyard owned by Grant Arnold, planted in 1996, adjacent to the historic cemetery of the region's Scottish pioneers. Situated in a secluded valley of the Clare hills, the low-cropping vineyard, say the partners, 'is always one of the earliest ripening shiraz vineyards in the region and mystifyingly produces fruit with both natural pH and acid analyses that can only be described as beautiful numbers'. The result is hands-off winemaking and maturation for 24 months in new and used Burgundian barriques. Exports to the UK, the US, Canada, Germany, Singapore, Taiwan and China.

♥♥♥♥♥ Clare Valley Shiraz 2009 A massive, full-bodied shiraz made from a single, small low-cropping vineyard yielding 200–250 dozen bottles a year, and headed for export markets relishing the layer upon layer of blackberry, licorice, plum and dark chocolate held in the grip of new French oak. It's a love it or leave it style, pushing the envelope to far extremes. Cork. 14.5% alc. Rating 94 To 2023 $115

Galafrey   ★★★★

Quangellup Road, Mount Barker, WA 6324 **Region** Mount Barker
T (08) 9851 2022 **www**.galafreywines.com.au **Open** 7 days 10–5
Winemaker Kim Tyrer **Est.** 1977 **Dozens** 3000 **Vyds** 13.1ha

Relocated to a purpose-built but utilitarian winery after previously inhabiting the exotic surrounds of the old Albany wool store, Galafrey makes wines with plenty of robust, if not rustic, character, drawing grapes in the main from estate plantings. Following the death of husband/father/founder Ian Tyrer, Kim and Linda Tyrer have taken up the reins, announcing, 'There is girl power happening at Galafrey Wines!' There is a cornucopia of back vintages available, some superb and underpriced, at the cellar door. Exports to China and Japan.

ㅜㅜㅜㅜ **The Jovial 2004** A blend of cabernet sauvignon, merlot and cabernet franc; good colour for age announces a medium-bodied wine now approaching the peak of its development; red and black fruits have a pleasantly savoury finish girdled by fine tannins. Screwcap. 13.5% alc. **Rating** 91 **To** 2014 $35
Dry Grown Mount Barker Cabernet Sauvignon 2009 Good purple-red; has the savoury austerity that should always be accepted as a legitimate varietal expression, but is sometimes misunderstood. Medium-bodied, and tailor-made for any lamb dish. Screwcap. 13.5% alc. **Rating** 90 **To** 2017 $28

ㅜㅜㅜㅜ **Sauvy Mount Barker Sauvignon Blanc 2011 Rating** 87 **To** 2013 $18

Gallagher Wines   ★★★★☆

2770 Dog Trap Road, Murrumbateman, NSW 2582 **Region** Canberra District
T (02) 6227 0555 **www**.gallagherwines.com.au **Open** W'ends & public hols 10–5
Winemaker Greg Gallagher **Est.** 1995 **Dozens** 2000 **Vyds** 2ha

Greg Gallagher was senior winemaker at Taltarni for 20 years, working with Dominique Portet. He began planning a change at much the same time as did Portet, and, together with wife Libby, started establishing a small vineyard at Murrumbateman in 1995, now planted to 1ha each of chardonnay and shiraz. Between 1999 and 2004 Greg was winemaker at Charles Sturt University, and now acts as both winemaker and consultant for a dozen or so wineries in or near to the Canberra District.

ㅜㅜㅜㅜㅜ **Canberra District Riesling 2011** It's not hard to see why this wine should
✪   have been the top gold in its class at the Canberra Regional Wine Show '11. The flavours on the palate are so intense that they seem to come at you, and linger in the mouth for an extraordinarily long time after the wine has gone. Steely acidity is wound through the palate, carrying with it flavours of lime, grapefruit and apple. An exceptional bargain. Screwcap. 11.3% alc. **Rating** 96 **To** 2031 $18

ㅜㅜㅜㅜㅜ **Canberra District Merlot 2009 Rating** 90 **To** 2019 $22

ㅜㅜㅜㅜ **Canberra District Chardonnay 2010 Rating** 88 **To** 2015 $18

Galli Estate   ★★★★★

1507 Melton Highway, Plumpton, Vic 3335 **Region** Sunbury
T (03) 9747 1444 **www**.galliestate.com.au **Open** 7 days 11–5
Winemaker Ben Ranken **Est.** 1997 **Dozens** 10 000 **Vyds** 160ha

Galli Estate, founded in 1997 by (the late) Lorenzo and Pam Galli, is located at Rockbank in Sunbury, with 50ha of vines (chardonnay, shiraz, pinot grigio, cabernet sauvignon and merlot) planted on rich red volcanic soil. The Camelback Vineyard at Heathcote has 110ha planted to a mix of mainstream and Mediterranean varieties (shiraz, cabernet sauvignon, chardonnay, sangiovese, viognier, tempranillo, nebbiolo, merlot, grenache and petit verdot). All wines are estate-grown. Following the death of Lorenzo a decision has been taken to substantially downsize the operation by reducing the make, and selling more of the grapes. Exports to the UK, Canada, Singapore, China and Hong Kong.

ŸŸŸŸŸ **Pamela 2010** From a single block of chardonnay that has only the Burgundy clones; fermented with wild yeast in a dedicated cool room in a mix of French oak, the final wine 33% new, and bottled May '11. A radically different wine from the Artigiano, with great complexity and drive. One out of the ordinary. Screwcap. 13.5% alc. **Rating** 97 **To** 2020 $55

Artigiano Sunbury Chardonnay 2010 A well-crafted chardonnay from two estate blocks; whole bunch-fermented with some solids in a mix of new and used oak plus 20% in stainless steel; very good balance and length. Screwcap. 13% alc. **Rating** 94 **To** 2017 $30

✪ **Artigiano Sunbury Pinot Grigio 2011** While pinot grigio is often accused of having little or no personality, this example shows concentration, lively acidity and a strong mineral accent that is engaging and long; an excellent effort. Screwcap. 13% alc. **Rating** 94 **To** 2013 $20 BE

Il Acquario 2009 Light, bright purple; a fresh and fragrant savoury/spicy red berry assemblage, with well-handled oak and management of tannins; good length, balance and line. Shiraz/Tempranillo/Viognier. Screwcap. 14% alc. **Rating** 94 **To** 2024 $45

Artigiano Heathcote Sangiovese 2009 Light, bright red; fragrant, spicy cherry aromas flow into a most attractive palate with first-class varietal character, both in terms of flavour and structure; fine tannins woven through the savoury cherry fruit. Screwcap. 13% alc. **Rating** 94 **To** 2014 $30

ŸŸŸŸ♀ **Artigiano Heathcote Nebbiolo 2009** **Rating** 93 **To** 2015 $30
Artigiano Sunbury Sauvignon Blanc 2011 **Rating** 92 **To** 2013 $30 BE
● **Camelback Heathcote Sangiovese 2009** **Rating** 90 **To** 2013 $20

ŸŸŸŸ **Camelback Sunbury Sauvignon Blanc 2011** **Rating** 88 **To** 2014 $18 BE

Gallows Wine Co ★★★★

Lennox Road, Carbunup River, WA 6280 **Region** Margaret River
T (08) 9755 1060 **www**.gallows.com.au **Open** 7 days 10–5
Winemaker Charlie Maiolo, Neil Doddridge **Est.** 2008 **Dozens** 10 000 **Vyds** 27ha
This is the venture of the Maiolo family, headed by winemaker Charlie. The macabre name is that of one of the most famous surf breaks on the Margaret River coast. The vineyard is planted to semillon, sauvignon blanc, chardonnay, pinot noir, shiraz, merlot and cabernet sauvignon. The site climate is strongly influenced by Geographe Bay, 5km to the north, and facilitates the production of wines with a large spectrum of flavours and characteristics.

ŸŸŸŸ♀ **The Bommy Margaret River Chardonnay 2010** Vibrant green hue; lemon and grapefruit on the bouquet, with a taut and toasty personality coming through on the palate; at the lean end for Margaret River, but will satisfy those in need of refreshing style over power. Screwcap. 13.5% alc. **Rating** 91 **To** 2015 $28 BE

The Gallows Margaret River Semillon Sauvignon Blanc 2011 Gun flint, tropical fruit and cut grass are on display; the palate is lively, fresh and focused, with a twist of grip on the moderately long and even finish. Screwcap. 12.5% alc. **Rating** 90 **To** 2013 $24 BE

Garagiste ★★★★☆

4 Lawrey Street, Frankston, Vic 3199 (postal) **Region** Mornington Peninsula
T 0439 370 530 **www**.garagiste.com.au **Open** Not
Winemaker Barnaby Flanders **Est.** 2006 **Dozens** 1200 **Vyds** 3ha
Barnaby Flanders was a co-founder of Allies Wines (see separate entry) in 2003, with some of the wines made under the Garagiste label. Allies has now gone its own way, and Barnaby has a controlling interest in the Garagiste brand. The future will focus on the Mornington Peninsula, and in particular grapes from Tuerong and Moorooduc in the north, with sand-based soils, the brown loam/red volcanic soils of Merricks and Merricks North in the middle, and the red volcanic soils of Red Hill and Main Ridge in the most elevated southern sector. Pinot noir and chardonnay will be the varieties used, and the wines will be made with wild yeasts, minimal handling and bottling without fining or filtration.

ŸŸŸŸŸ **Cotier Wines Mornington Peninsula Pinot Noir 2010** Mid crimson, slight CO_2 presence; this is a seductive and elegant pinot, with decidedly more stuffing than first appears; sweet and ripe red fruits are offset by a splash of cold tea and alluring Asian spices; the palate is light on entry, seductively silky and builds in flavour across the palate; lacy and seamlessly integrated. Screwcap. 13.5% alc. Rating 94 To 2018 $45 BE

ŸŸŸŸŸ **Cotier Wines Mornington Peninsula Chardonnay 2010** Rating 90 To 2016 $45 BE

ŸŸŸŸ **Le Stagiaire Mornington Peninsula Pinot Noir 2010** Rating 88 To 2015 $29 BE

Garners

54 Longwood/Mansfield Road, Longwood East, Vic 3666 **Region** Strathbogie Ranges
T (03) 5798 5513 www.garnerswine.com.au **Open** W'ends 10–4, or by appt 0410 649 030
Winemaker Contract **Est.** 2005 **Dozens** 500 **Vyds** 1.8ha
Former Professor of Optometry Leon Garner, and artist wife Rosie, returned to Australia in 2005 after living in NZ since 1979. They intended to settle in Qld, but by pure chance while driving along the Longwood-Mansfield Road, they noticed a 'for sale' sign. The granite house was called Roseleigh (an eerie coincidence) and – when the surrounding scenery was considered – it was too hard to resist. Having purchased the house, they quickly formed a close friendship with Jenny Houghton of neighbouring Maygars Hill Winery, and she provided them with sufficient cuttings to plant 1.8ha of shiraz. Their first vintage followed in 2008.

ŸŸŸŸŸ **Strathbogie Ranges Shiraz 2008** Has held its hue very well; estate-grown,
✪ open-fermented and matured in French and American oak, it is ridiculously good value. It is light- to medium-bodied, with a freshness to the underlying fruit, which is embroidered with nuances of spice, oak and fine tannins. Ready now, but not likely to fall over any time soon. Screwcap. 14.1% alc. Rating 90 To 2018 $16

ŸŸŸŸ **Strathbogie Ranges Shiraz Rose 2011** Rating 87 To 2013 $14

Gartelmann Hunter Estate

701 Lovedale Road, Lovedale, NSW 2321 **Region** Hunter Valley
T (02) 4930 7113 www.gartelmann.com.au **Open** 7 days 10–5
Winemaker Jorg Gartelmann, Liz Jackson **Est.** 1970 **Dozens** 5000
In 1996 Jan and Jorg Gartelmann purchased what was previously the George Hunter Estate – 16ha of mature vineyards, most established by Oliver Shaul in '70. A major change in the business model resulted in the sale of the vineyards after the 2006 vintage, and the grapes are now sourced from other Hunter Valley vineyards, giving the business maximum flexibility. Gartelmann also sources grapes grown in the cool Rylstone area in Mudgee. Exports to Germany.

ŸŸŸŸŸ **Benjamin Semillon 2004** Brilliant green-gold, amazing; has developed beautifully since first tasted in March '05; citrus, lanolin, lemongrass and minerally acidity are fused on the long, vibrantly fresh palate. It hasn't reached the end of the road yet, but is delicious now. Screwcap. 10% alc. Rating 95 To 2017 $30
Benjamin Semillon 2011 Pale quartz-green; has a delicious, albeit unusual, amalgam of sweetened lemon juice, orange peel and near-tropical flavours; the acid balance is excellent, as is the length of the wine. Screwcap. 11% alc. Rating 94 To 2023 $25

ŸŸŸŸŸ **Rylstone Cabernet Sauvignon 2010** Rating 93 To 2025 $35
Diedrich Shiraz 2010 Rating 90 To 2020 $45

ŸŸŸŸ **Sarah Elizabeth Chardonnay 2011** Rating 89 To 2015 $30
Merlot 2010 Rating 89 To 2014 $25
Wilhelm Shiraz 2010 Rating 87 To 2015 $25

Gatt Wines

Boehm Springs Road, Springton, SA 5235 **Region** Eden Valley
T (08) 8564 1166 **www**.gattwines.com **Open** At Taste Eden Valley, Angaston
Winemaker Jo Irvine, David Norman (Contract) **Est.** 1972 **Dozens** 8000 **Vyds** 50.65ha
When you read the hyperbole that sometimes accompanies the acquisition of an existing wine business, about transforming it into a world-class operation, it is easy to sigh and move on. When Ray Gatt acquired Eden Springs, he proceeded to translate words into deeds. As well as the 19.82ha Eden Springs Vineyard, he also acquired the historic Siegersdorf Vineyard (19.43ha) on the Barossa floor, and the neighbouring Graue Vineyard (11.4ha). He then put contract winemakers Joanne Irvine and David Norman in charge, tapping into their long-established credentials. It was hardly surprising that a string of wine show medals should be bestowed on the wines, my personal appreciation of the wines also no surprise. Perhaps the most obvious feature is the exceptional value for money they represent. The change of name from Eden Springs to Gatt Wines in 2011 was sensible, Eden Springs no longer appropriate given the vineyard holdings in the Barossa Valley. Exports to Hong Kong, China and Japan.

♥♥♥♥♥ **Eden Springs High Eden Riesling 2008** Brilliant electric pale-green; this may not have the juicy succulence of the '11, but has started the development that will ultimately lead to honeyed, toasty flavours if you are able to keep your hands off it for a few more years; 12 gold medals between '08 and '11. Screwcap. 11.5% alc. **Rating** 95 **To** 2018 $25
Lady Eleven Cabernet Sauvignon 2009 The name is an anagram of the letters in Eden Valley, and is meant to signal the elegance that has been achieved, as it has handsomely in this wine; it has all the richness of ripe cabernet, with cassis, blackcurrant and plum flavours, coupled with superfine tannins and quality oak. Cork. 13% alc. **Rating** 95 **To** 2030 $250
High Eden Single Vineyard Riesling 2011 The fragrant floral bouquet leads into a deliciously juicy palate with ripe lime and lemon fruit that continues in an unbroken stream through to the finish and aftertaste. Screwcap. 11.5% alc. **Rating** 94 **To** 2021 $30
Single Vineyard Barossa Valley Cabernet Sauvignon 2009 Excellent retention of crimson hue; a fascinating wine that spent 18 months in new French oak barriques that combine with the fruit and tannins, rising to a crescendo on the finish; along the way there are distinct flavours of cassis, mint and cigar box; 310 dozen made. Screwcap. 13.8% alc. **Rating** 94 **To** 2024 $55

♥♥♥♥♡ **High Eden Single Vineyard Shiraz 2009** **Rating** 93 **To** 2024 $55
High Eden Single Vineyard Cabernet Sauvignon 2008 **Rating** 93 **To** 2023 $55
High Eden Single Vineyard Shiraz 2008 **Rating** 92 **To** 2020 $55

♥♥♥♥ **Old Vine Single Vineyard Barossa Valley Shiraz 2010** **Rating** 89 **To** 2020 $100
Single Vineyard Barossa Valley Shiraz 2010 **Rating** 88 **To** 2025 $55

Gembrook Hill

Launching Place Road, Gembrook, Vic 3783 **Region** Yarra Valley
T (03) 5968 1622 **www**.gembrookhill.com.au **Open** By appt
Winemaker Timo Mayer, Andrew Marks **Est.** 1983 **Dozens** 2500 **Vyds** 6ha
Ian and June Marks established Gembrook Hill, one of the oldest vineyards in the coolest part of the upper Yarra Valley, usually harvested some four weeks later than the lower parts of the region. Son Andrew assists Timo Mayer on the winemaking front, each also having their own respective labels (see separate entries for The Wanderer and Mayer). The northeast-facing vineyard is in a natural amphitheatre and most vines are almost 30 years old; the low-yielding vines are not irrigated, are hand-pruned and harvested (plantings consist of sauvignon blanc, chardonnay and pinot noir). The minimal approach to winemaking produces wines of a consistent style with finesse and elegance. Exports to the UK, Denmark, Japan and Malaysia.

ŶŶŶŶŶ **Yarra Valley Chardonnay 2008** Youthful green hue; a fresh and unevolved bouquet with lemon rind, quartz and some complex smoked meat complexity; the palate is racy and fine, long and linear, with a refreshing mineral core driving the very long and fresh finish. Diam. 13% alc. **Rating** 95 **To** 2020 $38 BE
Yarra Valley Pinot Noir 2010 Light colour, but don't be fooled, as the bouquet is seductive and highly expressive, with red fruits in abundance, offset by sappy complexity and an intriguing blend of exotic spices and fresh herbs; light-bodied, silky and layered with a truly expansive and elegant palate that is easy to understand and enjoy. Diam. 13.5% alc. **Rating** 95 **To** 2016 $55 BE
Yarra Valley Sauvignon Blanc 2010 Vivid green hue; as always, a savoury and engaging bouquet of gun flint, exotic fruit and fine herbs; the palate is taut and textural, with zesty acidity and plenty of grip; long and refreshing, and certain to be a pleasure to match with food. Screwcap. 13% alc. **Rating** 94 **To** 2015 $35 BE
Blanc de Blancs 2007 Bright yellow-gold; made from 100% estate-grown chardonnay fermented in this bottle, and given four years on yeast lees prior to disgorgement. It is an intensely flavoured wine, with grapefruit-accented flavours and firm acidity. Food style. Cork. 12.5% alc. **Rating** 94 **To** Now $50

Gemtree Vineyards   ★★★★★

184 Main Road, McLaren Vale, SA 5171 **Region** McLaren Vale
T (08) 8323 8199 **www.**gemtreevineyards.com.au **Open** on–Fri 11–4, w'ends 11–5
Winemaker Mike Brown **Est.** 1998 **Dozens** 30 000 **Vyds** 133.16ha
The Buttery family, headed by Paul and Jill, and with the active involvement of Melissa as viticulturist, have been grapegrowers in McLaren Vale since 1980, when they purchased their first vineyard. The vineyards are managed biodynamically and recently achieved organic certification. The wine portfolio is of high quality, and also full of interest. Exports to the the UK, the US, Canada, South Korea, Vietnam, China and NZ.

ŶŶŶŶŶ **Obsidian McLaren Vale Shiraz 2008** Only 1% of the total Gemtree shiraz intake makes into Obsidian, and then it spends three years in new French oak. The hue is remarkable, still crimson-purple, and the wine is crammed full of flavour, blackberry fruit with its McLaren Vale signature of dark chocolate, and – of course – French oak. Screwcap. 14.5% alc. **Rating** 96 **To** 2030 $55
Uncut McLaren Vale Shiraz 2010 Deep, dense purple-crimson; this is a notably intense and complex shiraz from the start of the bouquet through to the finish and aftertaste; spice, licorice, blackberry, blood plum and dark chocolate powder all have their say while leaving space and air, giving the wine finesse and elegance. Screwcap. 14.5% alc. **Rating** 95 **To** 2025 $25
White Lees McLaren Vale Shiraz 2008 Winemaker Mike Brown hit upon the idea of maturing shiraz in French oak barrels that had the lees of barrel-fermented chardonnay still in place, a practice used here and there in Europe. Here, too, the colour is good, although there is no suggestion of co-fermentation. Just how much it builds the flavour is something only Mike would know, but it is certainly an intensely flavoured, black-fruited wine that has lost none of its regional identity. Screwcap. 14.5% alc. **Rating** 94 **To** 2023 $45

ŶŶŶŶŶ **The Phantom Red 2010 Rating** 93 **To** 2025 $35
The Phantom McLaren Vale Petit Verdot 2009 Rating 93 **To** 2018 $25
Luna Roja McLaren Vale Tempranillo 2011 Rating 92 **To** 2020 $25
○ **Bloodstone McLaren Vale Shiraz 2009 Rating** 90 **To** 2019 $16

ŶŶŶŶ **Bloodstone McLaren Vale Shiraz 2010** Deep purple hue; I suppose you
✪ could say the wine is a bit rustic, but no one could deny the depth of black fruits, licorice, tar and bitter chocolate on the mid palate. Great bbq red now or in a year or two. Screwcap. 14.5% alc. **Rating** 89 **To** 2014 $18
○ **Tigers Eye McLaren Vale Shiraz 2008 Rating** 88 **To** 2014 $14
○ **Moonstone McLaren Vale Savagnin 2011 Rating** 87 **To** Now $16

Geoff Merrill Wines

291 Pimpala Road, Woodcroft, SA 5162 **Region** McLaren Vale
T (08) 8381 6877 **www**.geoffmerrillwines.com.au **Open** Mon–Fri 10–5, w'ends 12–5
Winemaker Geoff Merrill, Scott Heidrich **Est.** 1980 **Dozens** 50 000 **Vyds** 45ha
If Geoff Merrill ever loses his impish sense of humour or his zest for life, high and not-so-high, we shall all be the poorer. The product range consists of three tiers: premium (varietal); Reserve, being the older (and best) wines, reflecting the desire for elegance and subtlety of this otherwise exuberant winemaker; and, at the top, Henley Shiraz. His Mount Hurtle wines are sold exclusively through Vintage Cellars/Liquorland. Exports to all major markets.

ΨΨΨΨΨ **Henley McLaren Vale Shiraz 2004** Medium red-purple, good for age; the bouquet is complex, starting to develop earthy, spicy, cedary/cigar box secondary aromas; I have tasted this wine several times over the years, and I think it is now close to its best, especially if matched with a decent-sized piece of Wagyu steak. Cork. 15% alc. **Rating** 96 **To** 2030 $150
Jacko's Blend McLaren Vale Shiraz 2008 Deep garnet; the perfume is full of succulent sweet red fruits with loganberry conserve, mocha and a light floral note; the medium-bodied palate is juicy and generous, fresh and lively, with ample fine tannins on the finish; an elegant McLaren Vale shiraz by anyone's measure. Screwcap. 14.5% alc. **Rating** 94 **To** 2018 $27 BE
Reserve McLaren Vale Shiraz 2006 Healthy colour; a strict barrel selection after 12 months is returned to barrel for another 10 months, so it is inevitable that both the texture and flavour of the wine are oak-influenced. That said, the fruit flavours have distinct elegance, and carry through to the finish of a wine with a very individual message. Cork. 14.5% alc. **Rating** 94 **To** 2016 $55

ΨΨΨΨΨ **Reserve McLaren Vale Shiraz 2007 Rating** 92 **To** 2018 $55 BE
Bush Vine McLaren Vale Grenache Rose 2011 Rating 91 **To** 2013 $21 BE
Pimpala Vineyard McLaren Vale Cabernet Merlot 2005 Rating 90 **To** 2014 $36 BE

ΨΨΨΨ **Reserve Chardonnay 2007 Rating** 89 **To** 2014 $28 BE
Bush Vine McLaren Vale Shiraz Grenache Mourvedre 2008 Rating 89 **To** 2014 $21 BE
Fleurieu Cabernet Shiraz 2008 Rating 88 **To** 2014 $21 BE
Reserve Coonawarra McLaren Vale Cabernet Sauvignon 2005 Rating 87 **To** 2014 $40 BE

Geoff Weaver

2 Gilpin Lane, Mitcham, SA 5062 (postal) **Region** Adelaide Hills
T (08) 8272 2105 **www**.geoffweaver.com.au **Open** Not
Winemaker Geoff Weaver **Est.** 1982 **Dozens** 3500 **Vyds** 12.3ha
This is the full-time business of former Hardys chief winemaker Geoff Weaver. He draws upon a little over 12ha of vineyard established between 1982 and '88, and invariably produces immaculate Riesling and Sauvignon Blanc, and one of the longest-lived Chardonnays to be found in Australia, with intense grapefruit and melon flavour. The beauty of the labels ranks supreme with Pipers Brook. Exports to Germany and Singapore.

ΨΨΨΨΨ **Lenswood Chardonnay 2010** Bright green-straw; wild yeast-fermented in French oak; mlf and lees contact have given the extra complexity and texture sought by Geoff Weaver, but have also left the vibrant fruit and natural acidity in charge, and the finish very long. Screwcap. 13.5% alc. **Rating** 95 **To** 2018 $39
Lenswood Sauvignon Blanc 2011 Pale quartz-green; the usual immaculately crafted wine from this maker, with passionfruit, lychee and citrus flavours on the clearly defined and pure palate, acidity a given. Screwcap. 11.5% alc. **Rating** 94 **To** 2013 $26

Ghost Rock Vineyard   ★★★★☆

1055 Port Sorrell Road, Northdown, Tas 7307 **Region** Northern Tasmania
T (03) 6428 4005 **www**.ghostrock.com.au **Open** Wed–Sun & public hols 11–5
(7 days Dec–Feb)
Winemaker Jeremy Dineen (Contract) **Est.** 2001 **Dozens** 1800 **Vyds** 16ha
Cate and Colin Arnold purchased the former Patrick Creek Vineyard (planted in 1989) in
2001. They run a printing and design business in Devonport and were looking for a suitable
site to establish a vineyard. The vineyard (pinot gris, pinot noir, sauvignon blanc, chardonnay
and riesling) is planted on a sheltered slope with a northeasterly aspect. The increase in
plantings (and consequent production) has allowed the Arnolds to supply markets throughout
the mainland.

♟♟♟♟♟ Ol' Man's Ghost Pinot Gris 2011 Well balanced; has good line, length and
mouthfeel; equally good varietal character. Gold Tas Wine Show '12. Screwcap.
13% alc. **Rating** 94 **To** 2014 $26

♟♟♟♟ The Pinots Pinot Gris Pinot Noir 2011 **Rating** 89 **To** 2013 $25
Sauvignon Blanc 2011 **Rating** 88 **To** 2013 $25

Giaconda   ★★★★★

30 McClay Road, Beechworth, Vic 3747 **Region** Beechworth
T (03) 5727 0246 **www**.giaconda.com.au **Open** By appt
Winemaker Rick Kinzbrunner **Est.** 1985 **Dozens** 3000
These wines have a super-cult status and, given the tiny production, are extremely difficult
to find; they are sold chiefly through restaurants and by mail order. All have a cosmopolitan
edge befitting Rick Kinzbrunner's international winemaking experience. The Chardonnay is
one of Australia's greatest in normal vintage conditions, and is now made and matured in the
underground wine cellar hewn out of granite. This permits gravity flow, and a year-round
temperature range of 13°C to 17°C, promising even more for the future. Exports to the UK
and the US.

♟♟♟♟♟ Chardonnay 2010 A wine of staggering power, intensity and concentration, all
the components – fruit, acidity, oak – are in perfect balance, albeit as yet tightly
wound, early complexity ex a touch of matchstick. It is the first vintage made
entirely in the cellar, and Kinzbrunner believes it will be better than the '96, a
view I entirely agree with. Screwcap. 13% alc. **Rating** 97 **To** 2030 $125

Giant Steps/Innocent Bystander   ★★★★★

336 Maroondah Highway, Healesville, Vic 3777 **Region** Yarra Valley
T (03) 5962 6111 **www**.innocentbystander.com.au **Open** Mon–Fri 10–10, w'ends 8–10
Winemaker Phil Sexton, Steve Flamsteed, Tim Shand, Emma Holland **Est.** 1997
Dozens 55 000 **Vyds** 32ha
Phil Sexton first made his name in establishing some noted micro-breweries, and later
established Devil's Lair in Margaret River. He sold Devil's Lair to Southcorp in 1996, and the
following year purchased what is now known as the Sexton Vineyard in the Yarra Valley. First
released in 2001, Giant Steps wines focus exclusively on the distinctive expression of single
vineyard sites, drawing grapes from estate, leased and long-term contracted vineyards. Innocent
Bystander wines came on-stream in 2004, and are made from carefully selected vineyards
in the Yarra Valley and beyond, contributing 40 000 dozen to the overall production. Both
Giant Steps and Innocent Bystander wines are handmade in small batches using gravity-flow
principles. Exports to the UK, the US and other major markets.

♟♟♟♟♟ Giant Steps Tarraford Vineyard Yarra Valley Chardonnay 2010 Light
straw-green; the Tarraford Vineyard has some of the oldest chardonnay in the valley,
reflected in the intensity and structure of this wine; has the depth of fruit that can
be obtained at 13%, pointing the way for the future; here the grapefruit, nectarine
and melon skin flavours are prominent, the oak a means to an end. Screwcap.
13% alc. **Rating** 96 **To** 2020 $40

Giant Steps Sexton Vineyard Yarra Valley Pinot Noir 2010 From the estate vineyard, with seven clones, 10% whole bunches, remainder destemmed, not crushed (the same for all four wines); five-day cold soak, 12-day ferment with minimal plunging; 24% new French oak, 25% 1-year-old; like all four wines, 11 months in oak. A highly fragrant bouquet with cherry and wild strawberry fruit that carries through to the silky palate. Very attractive wine. Presumably the price reflects the higher volume of 1750 dozen. Screwcap. 13% alc. **Rating** 96 **To** 2018 $40

Mea Culpa Yarra Valley Shiraz 2010 The back label would do Freud proud, assuming the words can be deciphered. Bright crimson, it is at once elegant and intense, with a rainbow of red and black fruits supported by fine, persistent tannins and quality oak. A seriously good wine. Screwcap. 13% alc. **Rating** 96 **To** 2025 $60

Giant Steps Sexton Vineyard Yarra Valley Chardonnay 2010 The Sexton Vineyard is estate-owned, planted on the slopes of the Warramate Hills (also known as Steels Range) with a northerly aspect. This is a wine of intensity and complexity, the flavours rising in steps like the topography of the vineyard, each sip revealing a new flavour sensation. Screwcap. 13% alc. **Rating** 95 **To** 2018 $35

Giant Steps Tarraford Vineyard Yarra Valley Pinot Noir 2010 Deepest colour of the four; 100% destemmed to small fermenters; six-day cold soak, then half the fermenters plunged regularly, half left untouched; 100% wild yeast; MV6, 114 and 115 clones; 530 dozen made. The most powerful of the four wines, with a strong, albeit ripe, tannin frame for the plum and black cherry fruit; a distinct fruit lift on the finish. Screwcap. 13% alc. **Rating** 95 **To** 2018 $45

Giant Steps Harry's Monster 2010 Vivid crimson-purple; a full-bodied, intense, but very well balanced and structured wine, with cassis, blueberry, blackcurrant and plum fruit held in a gentle embrace of quality French oak and fine, ripe tannins. Screwcap. 13.8% alc. **Rating** 95 **To** 2030 $55

Giant Steps Arthurs Creek Vineyard Yarra Valley Chardonnay 2010 **Rating** 94 **To** 2018 $45

Innocent Bystander Yarra Valley Chardonnay 2011 **Rating** 94 **To** 2016 $25

Giant Steps Applejack Vineyard Yarra Valley Pinot Noir 2010 **Rating** 94 **To** 2017 $45

Innocent Bystander Mule Gateway Vineyard Shiraz 2010 **Rating** 94 **To** 2030 $30

♟♟♟♟♟ **Giant Steps Gladysdale Vineyard Yarra Valley Pinot Noir 2010** **Rating** 93 **To** 2017 $45

Giant Steps Sexton Vineyard Yarra Valley Merlot 2010 **Rating** 93 **To** 2025 $35

Innocent Bystander Mule Gateway Vineyard Sangiovese 2010 **Rating** 93 **To** 2025 $30

Innocent Bystander Yarra Valley Pinot Noir 2011 **Rating** 90 **To** 2014 $25

♟♟♟♟ **Innocent Bystander Mule Gateway Vineyard Viognier 2011** **Rating** 88 **To** 2014 $30

Innocent Bystander Yarra Valley Pinot Gris 2011 **Rating** 87 **To** 2013 $22

Gibson Barossavale/Loose End ★★★★★

Willows Road, Light Pass, SA 5355 **Region** Barossa Valley
T (08) 8562 3193 **www.**gibsonwines.com.au **Open** 7 days 11–5
Winemaker Rob Gibson **Est.** 1996 **Dozens** 10 000 **Vyds** 14.2ha

Rob Gibson spent much of his working life as a senior viticulturist for Penfolds. While at Penfolds he was involved in research tracing the characters that particular parcels of grapes give to a wine, which left him with a passion for identifying and protecting what is left of the original vineyard plantings in wine regions around Australia. He has two vineyards in the Barossa Valley, at Stockwell (shiraz, mataro and grenache) and Light Pass (merlot), and one in the Eden Valley (shiraz and riesling), and also purchases grapes from McLaren Vale and the Adelaide Hills. Loose End is an important 7000-dozen brand launched in 2007, offering wines at lower price points. Exports to the US, Denmark, Hong Kong, Japan, China and Singapore.

ŶŶŶŶŶ   Gibson Reserve Shiraz 2008 Bright red-purple; the fragrant bouquet
has aromas of plum, red cherry and mulberry, the impact of 26 months in
predominantly French oak clear enough, but not over the top; the medium-bodied
palate borders on elegance, the fruit flavours fresh, the tannins fine and spicy. Has a
freshness the Old Vine Shiraz lacks. Screwcap. 14.5% alc. **Rating** 95 **To** 2020 $40

○   Gibson Eden Valley Riesling 2011 **Rating** 94 **To** 2025 $18
Australian Old Vine Collection Barossa Shiraz 2008 Strong red-purple, first
signs of change of hue; concentrated fruit and generous oak is in balance with the
savoury tannins; the flavours of the long palate run from spice and licorice through
to blackberry and plum. Cork. 14.5% alc. **Rating** 94 **To** 2018 $118

ŶŶŶŶŶ   Australian Old Vine Collection Eden Valley Shiraz 2008 **Rating** 93
To 2030 $110
The Dirtman Barossa Shiraz 2009 **Rating** 92 **To** 2024 $28
Botrytis Semillon 2009 **Rating** 92 **To** 2016 $22 BE

✪   Gibson Adelaide Hills Pinot Gris 2011 Pale straw-green; a pinot gris with
attitude and class, particularly on its decisive palate and its mix of lime/citrus, pear
and green apple; balanced finish. Screwcap. 13.4% alc. **Rating** 91 **To** Now $20
Gibson Bin 60 Cabernet Sauvignon Shiraz 2008 **Rating** 91 **To** 2020
$250 BE

ŶŶŶŶ   Loose End Barossa GSM 2007 **Rating** 89 **To** 2014 $19

✪   Loose End Barossa Shiraz 2008 **Rating** 89 **To** 2014 $18
Gibson Isabelle Barossa Adelaide Hills Cabernet Merlot 2006 **Rating** 88
To 2015 $26
Loose End Semillon Sauvignon Blanc 2011 **Rating** 87 **To** 2013 $16 BE
Sparkling Merlot NV **Rating** 87 **To** 2015 $36
Loose End Roscato NV **Rating** 87 **To** 2013 $13 BE

gilbert by Simon Gilbert   ★★★★

PO Box 773, Mudgee, NSW 2850 **Region** Various
T (02) 6373 1371 **www**.thegilbertsarecoming.com.au **Open** Not
Winemaker Simon Gilbert **Est.** 2010 **Dozens** 2050
For some time now Simon Gilbert has devoted himself to his consultancy and wine brokering
business Wineworks of Australia. As that business has grown, and with the sale of the Prince
Hill winery to the Watson Wine Group, Simon has returned to the winery wearing his
Wineworks of Australia hat, overseeing the winemaking of the estate-grown grapes, all of
which will be exported. Separate from his consultancy business, he has established gilbert by
Simon Gilbert, and also makes the wines for this label at the same winery. Grapes are sourced
from premium locations across Australia, and not restricted to the same localities each year.
Distribution is limited to specialist wine retailers and restaurants.

ŶŶŶŶŶ   Mudgee Orange Saignee Sangiovese Shiraz Barbera 2011 Pale pink;
there is a faintly spicy edge to the bouquet, not surprising given the blend; the
palate has excellent mouthfeel and balance to its fruit-sweet red berry flavours,
which lead on to a dry finish. Screwcap. 12.5% alc. **Rating** 91 **To** 2013 $24
Orange Shiraz 2009 Crimson-purple; the fresh and fragrant bouquet and the
light- to medium-bodied palate are full of red and black cherry fruits, oriental
spices and fine-grained tannins; all these come together on the silky, supple, fruit-
driven finish. Screwcap. 14.5% alc. **Rating** 91 **To** 2020 $36

ŶŶŶŶ   Orange Pinot Grigio 2011 **Rating** 89 **To** 2013 $26

Gilberts

30138 Albany Highway, Kendenup via Mount Barker, WA 6323 **Region** Mount Barker
T (08) 9851 4028 **www**.gilbertwines.com.au **Open** Wed–Mon 10–5
Winemaker Plantagenet **Est.** 1980 **Dozens** 4000 **Vyds** 14.5ha

Once a part-time occupation for sheep and beef farmers Jim and Beverly Gilbert, but now a full-time and very successful one. The mature vineyard (shiraz, chardonnay, riesling and cabernet sauvignon), coupled with contract winemaking at Plantagenet, has long produced very high-class Riesling, and now also makes excellent Shiraz. The Three Devils Shiraz is named in honour of their sons.

♀♀♀♀♀ **Mount Barker Riesling 2011** Mid straw; a ripe and exotic bouquet of candied lemon and orange zest, coriander and minerals; the palate is generous on entry, yet has fine acidity and lots of energy from start to finish; both pleasant now and age-worthy. Screwcap. 12.5% alc. **Rating** 94 **To** 2020 $22 BE

♀♀♀♀♀ **3 Lads Mount Barker Cabernet Sauvignon 2009** Good colour; a very good
✪   example of Mount Barker cabernet, with its cool-grown, cedary/earthy nuances to the core of blackcurrant fruit, the tannins firm but ripe, the finish long and well balanced. Will flourish in bottle. Screwcap. 13.5% alc. **Rating** 93 **To** 2024 $23
✪   **Alira 2011** Green apple and lemon myrtle bouquet, with an appealing and linear palate; a very good example of the style (off-dry Riesling) with a mineral backbone, and some exciting possibilities for food and wine matching. Screwcap. 12% alc. **Rating** 91 **To** 2016 $17 BE
         Reserve Mount Barker Shiraz 2009 Rating 90 **To** 2016 $28 BE

Gilligan   ★★★★☆
PO Box 235, Willunga, SA 5172 **Region** McLaren Vale
T (08) 8323 8379 **www**.gilligan.com.au **Open** Not
Winemaker Mark Day, Leigh Gilligan **Est.** 2001 **Dozens** 1200 **Vyds** 5.74ha
Leigh Gilligan is a 20-year marketing veteran, mostly with McLaren Vale wineries (including Wirra Wirra). The Gilligan family has just over 4ha of shiraz and 0.4ha each of grenache, mourvedre, marsanne and roussanne, selling part of the production. In 2001 they persuaded next-door neighbour Drew Noon to make a barrel of Shiraz, which they drank and gave away. Realising they needed more than one barrel, they moved to Maxwell Wines, with help from Maxwell winemaker Mark Day, and have now migrated to Mark's new Koltz Winery at Blewitt Springs. Exports to the UK, the US, Canada, Germany, Denmark, Thailand, Philippines and Hong Kong.

♀♀♀♀♀ **McLaren Vale Shiraz Grenache Mourvedre 2010** Dense purple-crimson;
✪   a powerful, voluptuous, full-bodied wine; the flavours are of black (predominant) and red fruits combined with earthy/chocolatey notes affirming its terroir; the tannins and oak are of the appropriate weight given the density of the black fruit flavours. Will be long lived. Screwcap. 15% alc. **Rating** 94 **To** 2030 $25

Gioiello Estate   ★★★★
PO Box 250, Tullamarine, Vic 3043 **Region** Upper Goulburn
T 0437 240 502 **www**.gioiello.com.au **Open** Not
Winemaker Scott McCarthy (Contract) **Est.** 1987 **Dozens** 4000 **Vyds** 8.97ha
The Gioiello Estate vineyard was established by a Japanese company and originally known as Diawa Nar Darak. Planted between 1987 and '96, it accounts for just under 9ha on a 400ha property of rolling hills, pastures, bushland, river flats, natural water springs and billabongs. The early wines produced were sold only in Japan, but their quality was demonstrated by the 1994 Daiwa Nar Darak Chardonnay, which won the George Mackey Award for Best Wine Exported from Australia in '95. It is now owned by the Schiavello family, which is contemplating increasing the plantings with Italian varieties such as nebbiolo and arneis. The gold medal won by the 2007 Reserve Chardonnay at the 18th Annual Concours des Vins du Victoria in November '08 proved the Mackey Award was no fluke.

♀♀♀♀♀ **Old Hill Upper Goulburn Chardonnay 2010** Vibrant green hue; while the lavish oak attention this wine has received dominates the bouquet, the palate reveals tightly wound nectarine fruit, with quartz and lemony acidity; fresh, long and toasty to conclude. Screwcap. 12.9% alc. **Rating** 91 **To** 2018 $45 BE

Gipsie Jack Wine Co

Wellington Road, Langhorne Creek, SA 5255 **Region** Langhorne Creek
T (08) 8537 3029 **www.**gipsiejack.com.au **Open** 7 days 10–5
Winemaker John Glaetzer, Ben Potts **Est.** 2004 **Dozens** 12 000
One might have thought the partners of Gipsie Jack have enough wine on their plate already, but some just can't resist the temptation, it seems. The two in question are John Glaetzer and Ben Potts, who made a little over 500 dozens from two growers in their inaugural vintage in 2004 (that quantity has increased substantially since). Glaetzer and Potts say, 'We want to make this label fun, like in the "old days". No pretentiousness, no arrogance, not even a back label. A great wine at a great price, with no discounting.' Exports to Switzerland, Hong Kong, Singapore and China.

TTTT **Langhorne Creek Shiraz 2008** Medium red–purple; spent over 42 months in oak, and perhaps tank, not bottled until Dec '11; it is hard to imagine a wine with more chocolate, mocha and vanilla in its make-up; far from unpleasant, but off on a tangent of its own. Screwcap. 14.5% alc. **Rating** 89 **To** 2016 $18

Girraween Estate

41 Hickling Lane, via Wallangarra, Qld 4383 **Region** Granite Belt
T (07) 4684 3186 **www.**girraweenestate.com.au **Open** W'ends & public hols 10–5 or by appt
Winemaker Mike Hayes **Est.** 1985 **Dozens** 10 00 **Vyds** 3.48ha
In 2009 Steve Messiter and wife and Lisa purchased Bald Mountain from its founders, Denis and Jackie Parsons. Steve is a chemical engineer who has a Masters degree and has studied winemaking, and has overseen the complete rejuvenation of the vineyard, including the removal of the lyre trellis and 40% of the vines; some have been grafted over to petit verdot, and albarinho is to follow. Mike Hayes (of Symphony Hill) advises on vineyard management and makes the wine. Underwent a name change to Girraween Estate in 2011.

TTTT **Sauvignon Blanc 2011** I can't compete with the back label descriptors of rose petal, nashi, sweet passionfruit, lychee, guava and gooseberry, but there's no doubting there is an array of flavours in what is a low-alcohol sauvignon blanc with definite freshness. Grab it, and drink it, while the going is good. Screwcap. 11.2% alc. **Rating** 89 **To** 2013 $22
Unwooded Chardonnay 2011 A well-made, pleasant wine that won't frighten the horses; peachy stone fruit is its key note, which clearly won favour with the judges at the Australian Small Makers Wine Show '11, who awarded it the trophy for Best Queensland White Wine. Screwcap. 12.2% alc. **Rating** 88 **To** 2013 $25

GISA   ★★★★

3 Hawke Street, Linden Park, SA 5065 **Region** South Australia
T (08) 8338 2123 **F** (08) 8338 2123 **www.**gisa.com.au **Open** Not
Winemaker Mat Henbest **Est.** 2006 **Dozens** 4000
Mat and Lisa Henbest have chosen a clever name for their virtual winery – GISA stands for Geographic Indication South Australia – neatly covering the fact that their grapes come variously from the Adelaide Hills (Sauvignon Blanc), McLaren Vale (Shiraz Viognier) and Barossa Valley (Reserve Shiraz). It in turn reflects Mat's long apprenticeship in the wine industry, as a child living on his parents' vineyard, then working in retail trade while he pursued tertiary qualifications, and thereafter wholesaling wine to the retail and restaurant trade. He then moved to Haselgrove, where he spent five years working closely with the small winemaking team, refining his concept of style, and gaining experience on the other side of the fence of the marketing equation.

TTTTY
O **Round Adelaide Hills Sauvignon Blanc 2011 Rating** 91
To Now $18
Ellipse Reserve Barossa Valley Shiraz 2008 Deep garnet; a sweet-fruited and soft-centred wine with mulberry, nutmeg and fruitcake on display; fleshy, forward and succulent in style, this is ready to go. Screwcap. 14% alc. **Rating** 90 **To** 2013 $35 BE

🍷🍷🍷🍷 Arc Adelaide Hills Semillon Sauvignon Blanc 2011 Rating 88
⚪ To Now $12

Gisborne Peak ★★★☆

69 Short Road, Gisborne South, Vic 3437 **Region** Macedon Ranges
T (03) 5428 2228 **www**.gisbornepeakwines.com.au **Open** 7 days 11–5
Winemaker John Ellis **Est.** 1978 **Dozens** 1800 **Vyds** 4.55ha
Bob Nixon began the development of Gisborne Peak way back in 1978, planting his dream vineyard row-by-row. (Bob is married to Barbara Nixon, founder of Victoria Winery Tours.) The tasting room has wide shaded verandahs, plenty of windows and sweeping views. The vineyard is planted to chardonnay, pinot noir, semillon, riesling and lagrein.

🍷🍷🍷🍷🍷 Two Blocks Blend Macedon Ranges Pinot Noir 2009 Bright, clear ruby red; has a perfumed bouquet of spicy red and black fruits, the palate initially seeming light, but building power on the way through to the back-palate and finish. Still developing. Screwcap. 12.5% alc. **Rating** 90 **To** 2016 $28

🍷🍷🍷🍷 Macedon Ranges Pinot Rose 2010 Rating 89 To 2013 $24
Macedon Ranges Semillon 2011 Rating 87 To 2015 $24
Allegro Semi-Sweet Macedon Ranges Semillon 2009 Rating 87
To 2014 $22

Glaetzer Wines ★★★★★

Gomersal Road, Tanunda, SA 5352 (postal) **Region** Barossa Valley
T (08) 8563 0947 **www**.glaetzer.com **Open** Not
Winemaker Ben Glaetzer **Est.** 1996 **Dozens** 15 000 **Vyds** 20ha
Colin Glaetzer and son Ben are almost as well known in SA wine circles as Wolf Blass winemaker John Glaetzer, Colin's twin brother. Glaetzer Wines purchases all its grapes from the Ebenezer subregion of the Barossa Valley, principally from fifth-generation growers. Its four wines (Amon-Ra Shiraz, Anaperenna (Shiraz Cabernet Sauvignon), Bishop Shiraz and Wallace Shiraz Grenache) are all made under contract at Barossa Vintners. Exports to all major markets.

🍷🍷🍷🍷🍷 Amon-Ra Unfiltered Barossa Valley Shiraz 2010 This wine is impenetrable in colour; the bouquet is a melange of black fruits, oak, spice, tar and licorice; the palate reveals even more dark fruits, more depth, in fact, more of everything, and that is the essence of the wine; this will go the distance, and if you like impressive wines, then search no further. Cork. 15.1% alc. **Rating** 95 **To** 2050 $100 BE
Anaperenna 2010 Vivid purple hue; saturated black fruits, tar and anise combine with toasty aromas of cinnamon and clove; the palate is powerful and surprisingly lively, with a sappy edge to the fruit that provides light to the massive fruit shade; long and ultimately well balanced, but as always, a big wine for big wine drinkers. Shiraz/Cabernet Sauvignon. Cork. 15.1% alc. **Rating** 94 **To** 2025 $155 BE

🍷🍷🍷🍷🍷 Bishop Barossa Valley Shiraz 2010 Rating 92 To 2025 $33 BE
Wallace Barossa Valley Shiraz Grenache 2010 Rating 92 To 2018 $23 BE

Glen Eldon Wines ★★★★★

Lot 100 Hamiltons Road, Springton, SA 5235 **Region** Barossa Valley
T (08) 8568 2644 **www**.gleneldonwines.com.au **Open** By appt
Winemaker Richard Sheedy **Est.** 1997 **Dozens** 6000 **Vyds** 50ha
Owners Richard and Mary Sheedy (and their four children) have established the Glen Eldon property in the Eden Valley. The shiraz and cabernet sauvignon come from their vineyards in the Barossa Valley; riesling, viognier and merlot from contract-grown fruit; the riesling from the Eden Valley. Exports to the UK, the US, Canada, Switzerland and China.

ŤŤŤŤŤ **Black Lady Shiraz 2009** This is a deluxe blend of Barossa wine made by Richard Sheedy at his Glen Eldon vineyard under the Twisted Arm Reserve label, and Adrian Munari's Lady's Pass Heathcote wine. It is an extremely complex tapestry of predominantly black fruit flavours, dark spices, licorice and quality oak. It is full-bodied, but not corpulent. Cork. 14.5% alc. **Rating** 96 **To** 2029 $110
Midnight Bottling Reserve Barossa Shiraz 2008 The towering magnum bottle with its enamelled front and back label must have cost a fortune, but the fact that there was wine evenly distributed up the sides of the cork and over the top gives real concern about the future of this medium- to full-bodied wine. Nor can I help asking how, if this was taken from the best barrel of Twisted Trunk Reserve, it could have been matured in American and French oak for three years (perhaps it was transferred from one barrel to another). Enough quibbling. Available only from cellar door, it deserves praise for its supple mouthfeel, courtesy of the integration and balance of fruit, oak and tannins. 14.5% alc. **Rating** 94 **To** 2020 $150
Twisted Trunk Reserve Shiraz 2006 Excellent colour for a wine rising six years old; made from 126-year-old vines, matured for two years in new and second-use French and American oak before being transferred to older oak for a further three years; the oak certainly makes its mark, with a strong vanilla understorey; the tannins are likewise fully softened, both aspects reflecting the long period in oak. Would less have been better? Only made twice since 2000. Screwcap. 14.5% alc. **Rating** 94 **To** 2021 $95

ŤŤŤŤŤ **Barossa Cabernet Sauvignon 2009 Rating** 92 **To** 2020 $25
✪ **Kicking Back Barossa Shiraz Cabernet 2009** Full crimson; a rich, generous, medium- to full-bodied blend, driven by black fruits and soft, ripe tannins; designed for early, casual consumption, but there is plenty of horsepower to carry the wine forward for some years. Screwcap. 14.5% alc. **Rating** 91 **To** 2019 $16
✪ **Eden Valley Riesling 2011** Very pale, bordering white; at six months of age, locked in on itself, although the lime/mineral base is evident, pointing to the years ahead as the wine opens up and flowers. Screwcap. 12% alc. **Rating** 90 **To** 2020 $16
✪ **Kicking Back Barossa Shiraz Cabernet 2008** Strong colour; an ample, rich and round wine, with confit black plum and blackberry flavours, spicy nuances also adding interest; ready now. Screwcap. 14% alc. **Rating** 90 **To** 2014 $16

ŤŤŤŤ **Dry Bore Barossa Shiraz 2009 Rating** 89 **To** 2016 $25
Barossa Merlot 2008 Rating 89 **To** 2016 $22

GlenAyr

Back Tea Tree Road, Richmond, Tas 7025 **Region** Southern Tasmania
T (03) 6260 2388 **www**.glenayrwines.com.au **Open** Mon–Fri 8–5
Winemaker Contract **Est.** 1975 **Dozens** 500 **Vyds** 3.1ha
GlenAyr intends to carry on, and indeed expand, its production in the wake of the sale of the Tolpuddle Vineyard to Shaw & Smith in 2011. It has retained its original vineyard (planted in 1975), with chardonnay, pinot noir, shiraz, cabernet merlot and riesling. GlenAyr also has the enviable distinction of selling half of the shiraz that won the Jimmy Watson Trophy '11 to Glaetzer-Dixon Wines for their Mon Pere label.

ŤŤŤŤ **Tolpuddle Vintage Cuvee 2008** Pale bronze; complex, nutty and bready, with a long finish and aftertaste. Cork. 12.5% alc. **Rating** 88 **To** 2015 $29

 # Glenfell ★★★

410/2 Queen Street, Melbourne, Vic 3000 (postal) **Region** Barossa Valley
T (03) 9629 8850 **www**.glenfell.com.au **Open** Not
Winemaker Natasha Mooney **Est.** 2008 **Dozens** 500 **Vyds** 1.6ha
In 2008 Peter Katsoulotos acquired 1.6ha of 20-year-old cabernet sauvignon planted on the sandy, deep, well-drained soils of the Greenock area. Although not declared on the label of the Cabernet Sauvignon, it does in fact contain 3% tempranillo. Exports to Hong Kong and China.

🍷🍷🍷🍷 **Barossa Valley Cabernet Sauvignon 2008** Medium to full red-purple; a very rich and ripe wine that spent two years in 70% new French and 30% American oak. I don't understand 'one of the best Barossa Valley Cabernet Sauvignon No. 5 in the past 20 years' (from the back label). 580 dozen produced; the cork suggests the wine is destined for the export market. 14% alc. **Rating** 89 **To** 2016 $30

Glenguin Estate ★★★★★

Milbrodale Road, Broke, NSW 2330 **Region** Hunter Valley
T (02) 6579 1009 **www**.glenguinestate.com.au **Open** 7 days 10–5
Winemaker Robin Tedder MW, Rhys Eather **Est.** 1993 **Dozens** 3000 **Vyds** 8ha
Glenguin Estate was established by the Tedder family, headed by Robin Tedder MW, close to Broke and adjacent to Wollombi Brook. The backbone of the production comes from 20-year-old plantings of semillon and shiraz. Tannat (1ha) and a new planting of grafted semillon, with cuttings from Braemore/HVD, complete the picture. Vineyard manager Andrew Tedder, who has considerable experience with organics and biodynamics, is overseeing the ongoing development of Glenguin's organic program. Exports to the UK, Hong Kong, Singapore and China.

🍷🍷🍷🍷🍷 **Classic Aged Release Semillon 2006** Gleaming green-gold; has the full array
✪ of aromas and flavours of semillon and has entered what will be a long plateau of maturity; lime marmalade spread on lightly buttered, lightly browned toast; mouth-watering citrussy acidity both extends and refreshes the finish. Screwcap. 10.5% alc. **Rating** 95 **To** 2020 $25
Classic Aged Release Aristea Shiraz 2006 Excellent colour for age; Hunter Valley shiraz at its best, with a perfect balance of plum, blackberry fruit and regional nuances of polished leather, earth and a hint of licorice. Screwcap. 14% alc. **Rating** 95 **To** 2021 $60
Ancestors Semillon 2008 Received high points when first tasted three years ago, and has flourished since then; the colour is starting to develop hints of gold to the green background; an array of flavours have developed on the palate, producing some tropical nuances along with citrus; the acidity then kicks in to both lengthen and tighten the finish. Screwcap. 10% alc. **Rating** 94 **To** 2018 $25

🍷🍷🍷🍷🍷 **Pokolbin Vineyard Shiraz 2002 Rating** 93 **To** 2015 $35

Glenwillow Vineyard ★★★★☆

40 McIntyre Street, White Hills, Vic 3550 (postal) **Region** Bendigo
T 0428 461 076 **www**.glenwillow.com.au **Open** Not
Winemaker Matt Hunter, Greg Dedman (Contract) **Est.** 1999 **Dozens** 1000 **Vyds** 2.8ha
Peter and Cherryl Fyffe began their vineyard at Yandoit Creek, 10km south of Newstead, in 1999, planting 1.8ha of shiraz and 0.3ha of cabernet sauvignon, later branching out with 0.6ha of nebbiolo and 0.1ha of barbera. The vineyard, planted on a mixture of rich volcanic and clay loam interspersed with quartz and buckshot gravel, has an elevated, north-facing aspect, which minimises the risk of frost. Wines are released under the elegantly designed Glenwillow label, the Cyclone Gully label having been discontinued.

🍷🍷🍷🍷🍷 **Bendigo Cabernet Sauvignon 2009** Matured in a mix of new and used
✪ French oak, it has good colour, and clearly benefits from the moderate alcohol that allows expressive aromas of red and blackcurrant fruit on the bouquet, flowing through seamlessly through to the medium-bodied palate; the finish is long and very well balanced. Screwcap. 14% alc. **Rating** 94 **To** 2020 $25

🍷🍷🍷🍷🍷 **Bendigo Nebbiolo d'Yandoit 2009 Rating** 93 **To** 2017 $25
Bendigo Shiraz 2010 Rating 90 **To** 2016 $25

🍷🍷🍷🍷 **Bendigo Barbera d'Yandoit 2009 Rating** 89 **To** 2017 $25

Goaty Hill Wines   ★★★★☆

530 Auburn Road, Kayena, Tas 7270 **Region** Northern Tasmania
T 1300 819 997 **www**.goatyhill.com **Open** 7 days 10–5 (Aug to May)
Winemaker Jeremy Dineen (Contract) **Est.** 1998 **Dozens** 4500 **Vyds** 19.5ha
The partners in Goaty Hill Wines are close friends from two families who moved from
Victoria to make wine in the pristine climate of the Tamar Valley. Partners include Kristine
Grant, Markus Maislinger, and Natasha and Tony Nieuwhof. Most of the estate-grown grapes
are now made into the Goaty Hill brand, although they still sell some of their premium
sparkling fruit to Jansz Tasmania. There aren't any goats on the property, but there is, according
to the owners, a friendly collection of children and dogs.

ȲȲȲȲȲ **Riesling 2011** Bright green-quartz; the gently floral bouquet picks up pace and
intensity the moment the wine is tasted; it exudes lime juice, and has a core of
squeaky acidity taking the palate through to its long, lingering finish; the overall
intensity of the flavours cannot be replicated easily outside Tasmania. Screwcap.
11.9% alc. **Rating** 94 **To** 2025 $25

ȲȲȲȲȲ **Riesling 2010 Rating** 93 **To** 2015 $25
Chardonnay 2010 Rating 93 **To** 2015 $28
Sauvignon Blanc 2010 Rating 91 **To** Now $26
Pinot Gris 2011 Rating 90 **To** 2013 $26

God's Hill Wines   ★★★☆

Lot 211 Gods Hill Road, Lyndoch, SA 5351 **Region** Barossa Valley
T 0412 836 004 **www**.godshillwines.com **Open** By appt
Winemaker Charlie Scalzi **Est.** 1998 **Dozens** 1000 **Vyds** 12ha
Charlie Scalzi arrived in Australia with his parents in 1960, the family settling in Adelaide.
His final education was mechanical engineering, and at the age of 24 he established Monza
Motors, specialising in Italian cars such as Ferrari and Alfa Romeo. In 1998, having followed in
the footsteps of grandfather and father with home winemaking, he purchased a 40ha property
near Lyndoch, planting 4.5ha each of shiraz and cabernet sauvignon, 2ha of merlot and 1ha
of chardonnay. Most of the grapes are taken by Dorrien Estate, with a small amount retained
for the God's Hill label. Exports to China.

ȲȲȲȲȲ **Menzel Single Vineyard Barossa Valley Shiraz 2008** Deep colour, and
dark in personality, with mocha, licorice and black fruits in abundance; the palate
is laden with toasty oak, sweet black fruits and while at the big end of town
and super ripe, expresses a sense of place and time to a 't'. Screwcap. 14.8% alc.
Rating 92 **To** 2020 $43 BE

ȲȲȲȲ **Permanent Arm Single Vineyard Barossa Valley Cabernet Sauvignon
2008 Rating** 87 **To** 2020 $40

Godfrey Wines   ★★★★

PO Box 491, Angaston, SA 5353 **Region** Barossa Zone
T 0417 770 022 **F** (07) 3902 1484 **www**.godfreywines.com.au **Open** Not
Winemaker Sandy Godfrey **Est.** 2008 **Dozens** 1500
You might be tempted to say of the owners that Lisa is a solicitor who runs the administrative
side of the business, while husband Sandy looks after production, sales and marketing, but
there's rather more to it. While Sandy was gaining his BA (History) from the University of
Sydney he worked in several of Sydney's great restaurants, including Bathers Pavilion and
Mezzaluna. He also worked as a fashion model in Sydney, New York and Milan. In 2001 he
moved to Adelaide to undertake the Adelaide University oenology course, graduating with
Honours in 2004. He worked with a number of leading winemakers, including Stephen
Henschke and Tim Adams, but left his position as winemaker at Tim Adams to follow Lisa to
Brisbane, where she had accepted a role as in-house legal counsel for a large property group.
Sandy is now Group Sommelier for the Katarzyna Group, which has Brisbane's largest venue,

Cloudland. Along the way Sandy and Lisa acquired several properties at Springton in the Eden Valley and Gawler in the Barossa Valley, and Sandy spends much of his year travelling between Adelaide and Brisbane, making, blending and bottling the wines. Exports to India.

Poppy Belle Adelaide Hills Chardonnay 2010 An interesting wine, picked very early, whole bunch-pressed, given 12 months in French oak and taken through mlf, all a brave call at this level of alcohol. The retention of varietal character has been sufficient to justify the call. Screwcap. 11.8% alc. **Rating** 92 **To** 2017 $50

Mary I Eden Valley Shiraz 2010 Crimson-purple; this is a deliberate move to a lighter-bodied, lower-alcohol style of shiraz from a single vineyard matured in 100% new French oak. The aim is admirable, and the wine very nearly succeeds, but is just a little thin and minty. Screwcap. 13% alc. **Rating** 91 **To** 2018 $50

Polished Adelaide Hills Pinot Gris 2011 Rating 89 **To** 2014 $25 BE
Alexander I Stone Well Shiraz 2010 Rating 88 **To** 2020 $50 BE
Edward I Barossa Valley Shiraz 2010 Rating 87 **To** 2020 $50 BE
The Doctor's Wife Vintage Sparkling 2011 Rating 87 **To** 2014 $30

Golden Ball

1175 Beechworth Wangaratta Road, Beechworth, Vic 3747 **Region** Beechworth
T (03) 5727 0284 **F** (03) 5727 0294 **www.**goldenball.com.au **Open** By appt
Winemaker James McLaurin **Est.** 1996 **Dozens** 600
The Golden Ball vineyard is on one of the original land grants in the Beechworth region. The 2.4ha vineyard was planted by James and Janine McLaurin in 1996, mainly to cabernet sauvignon, shiraz and merlot, with lesser plantings of grenache and malbec. The wines are vinified separately and aged in one-third new French oak, the remainder 2–3 years old. The low yields result in intensely flavoured wines, which are to be found in a Who's Who of Melbourne's best restaurants and a handful of local and Melbourne retailers, including Randall's at Albert Park. Exports to Singapore.

Beechworth Shiraz 2008 Full purple-red; a rich, complex and concentrated wine that seems higher in alcohol than it in fact is, with licorice, prune and plum fruit in a cross-weave of oak and tannins. Diam. 14.4% alc. **Rating** 91 **To** 2028 $50

e'galitaire Rouge 2008 Good hue, although light; an 80/15/5% blend of merlot, shiraz and malbec; a complex wine with a bramble and wild herb bouquet, the palate more intense than its weight would suggest, bringing small fruits into play; a deceptively long finish. Screwcap. 13.8% alc. **Rating** 90 **To** 2018 $28

Gallice Beechworth Cabernet Merlot Malbec 2008 Has retained a bright hue; the bouquet is fragrant, with red and black fruits waging battle on a complex, medium- to full-bodied palate, with a background of French oak. Still sorting itself out, but will do so. Diam. 14.2% alc. **Rating** 90 **To** 2018 $50

Beechworth Merlot 2008 Rating 89 **To** 2018 $50

Golden Grove Estate

Sundown Road, Ballandean, Qld 4382 **Region** Granite Belt
T (07) 4684 1291 **F** (07) 4684 1247 **www.**goldengroveestate.com.au **Open** 7 days 9–4
Winemaker Raymond Costanzo **Est.** 1993 **Dozens** 4000 **Vyds** 12.4ha
Golden Grove Estate was established by Mario and Sebastian Costanzo in 1946, producing stone fruits and table grapes for the fresh fruit market. The first wine grapes (shiraz) were planted in 1972, but it was not until '85, when ownership passed to son Sam and his wife Grace, that the use of the property began to change. In 1993 chardonnay and merlot joined the shiraz, followed by cabernet sauvignon, sauvignon blanc and semillon. The baton has been passed down another generation to Ray Costanzo, who has lifted the quality of the wines remarkably, and has also planted tempranillo, durif, barbera, malbec, mourvedre, vermentino and nero d'Avola. Its consistent wine show success over recent years with alternative varieties is impressive.

ΥΥΥΥΥ **Granite Belt Semillon Sauvignon Blanc 2011** A very good wine, with all
✪ the potential fruit flavours from the vineyard carefully managed in the winery;
the flavours are on the midpoint between juicy and savoury, the finish long and
lipsmacking. All up, quite exceptional value. Screwcap. 13.2% alc. **Rating** 94
To 2015 $18

ΥΥΥΥΥ **Granite Belt Shiraz 2010** Full purple-crimson; the fragrant and fruit-laden
✪ bouquet reflects the flavours of the medium- to full-bodied palate; here blackberry,
licorice and strong spicy/savoury nuances all come into play, and the oak is
well-handled. Shrugs off its alcohol with ease. Screwcap. 14.8% alc. **Rating** 93
To 2025 $20

✪ **Granite Belt Vintage Fortified 2007** Deep, dense blackish-purple, it has been
made in the new style, with a much lower baume than the traditional style; the
base of shiraz and durif also works well, and even though the alcohol is high, the
spirit is not fiery. Screwcap. 19.8% alc. **Rating** 92 **To** 2020 $20

✪ **Granite Belt Sauvignon Blanc 2011** Pale green-quartz; while not particularly
intense, offers a well-weighted balance of grass and citrus on the one side, and
touches of passionfruit and guava on the other. Screwcap. 12.8% alc. **Rating** 90
To 2013 $18

✪ **Granite Belt Barbera 2011** Youthful vivid purple-crimson; there is no question
barbera should be drunk while it has its full peacock's display of plummy fruit; the
limitation of the variety is its somewhat nebulous structure. Screwcap. 13.5% alc.
Rating 90 **To** 2014 $20
Granite Belt Malbec 2010 **Rating** 90 **To** 2016 $28
Granite Belt Mourvedre 2010 **Rating** 90 **To** 2017 $28

ΥΥΥΥ **Granite Belt Nero d'Avola 2011** **Rating** 89 **To** 2015 $22
◗ **Granite Belt Vermentino 2011** **Rating** 89 **To** 2013 $20
Granite Belt Tempranillo 2010 **Rating** 88 **To** 2015 $28

Golding Wines ★★★★

52 Western Branch Road, Lobethal, SA 5241 **Region** Adelaide Hills
T (08) 8389 5120 **F** (08) 8389 5290 **Open** 7 days 11–4
Winemaker Michael Sykes, Darren Golding **Est.** 2002 **Dozens** 5000 **Vyds** 18.53 ha
The Golding family has lived in the Lobethal area of the Adelaide Hills for several generations,
and has trimmed its once larger viticultural holdings to concentrate on their Western Branch
Road vineyard, planted to sauvignon blanc, savagnin, chardonnay, pinot gris and pinot noir.
The brand was created in 2002, the owners being Darren and Lucy Golding. In 2006 Darren
secured some Marlborough sauvignon blanc, which has resulted in three wines: The Local
(100% estate-grown); The Tourist (100% Marlborough); and The Leap (51% estate-grown/49%
Marlborough). Exports to Hong Kong, Philippines, Malaysia, Singapore and China.

ΥΥΥΥΥ **Lil' Late (Harvest) Adelaide Hills Savagnin 2010** Deep colour; pure botrytis
with pineapple, fresh apricot and a splash of toffee brittle; the palate is very sweet,
but cleaned up with a note of bitterness and fresh acidity in harmony; long and
luscious. 375 ml. Screwcap. 11.7 % alc. **Rating** 91 **To** 2015 $25 BE

✪ **The Local Adelaide Hills Sauvignon Blanc 2011** Pale colour; a fine and
fragrant blend of tropical fruit and fresh cut grass; lively, juicy and direct, with good
concentration and persistence. Screwcap. 12.2% alc. **Rating** 90 **To** 2013 $20 BE

ΥΥΥΥ **The East End Adelaide Hills Rose 2011** Pink, with just a hint of salmon;
✪ produced from pinot noir, with some notes of spice behind the red berry fruits;
the palate has good tension and length, finishing dry. Screwcap. 12.7% alc.
Rating 89 **To** 2013 $20
Block 2 Adelaide Hills Chardonnay 2009 **Rating** 88 **To** 2014 $30 BE
The Handcart Adelaide Hills Shiraz 2010 **Rating** 87 **To** 2016 $20 BE
The Last Hurrah Adelaide Hills Sparkling Non Vintage NV **Rating** 87
To Now $20

Gomersal Wines

Lyndoch Road, Gomersal, SA 5352 **Region** Barossa Valley
T (08) 8563 3611 **www**.gomersalwines.com.au **Open** 7 days 10–5
Winemaker Barry White **Est.** 1887 **Dozens** 5000 **Vyds** 20ha
The 1887 establishment date has a degree of poetic licence. In 1887 Friedrich W Fromm planted the Wonganella Vineyards, following that with a winery on the edge of the Gomersal Creek in 1891 that remained in operation for 90 years, finally closing in 1983. In 2000 a group of friends 'with strong credentials in both the making and consumption end of the wine industry' bought the winery and re-established the vineyard, planting 17ha of shiraz, 2ha of mourvedre and 1ha of grenache via terraced bush vines. The Riesling comes from purchased grapes, the Grenache Rose, Grenache Shiraz Mataro and Shiraz from the replanted vineyard. No samples received (nor information) since the 2011 Rose (tasted in June '11); the rating has been maintained. Exports to the US, Ireland, China and NZ.

ꟼꟼꟼꟽ **Barossa Valley Shiraz Rose 2011** Rating 89 **To** Now $18
O

Good Catholic Girl Wines

Box 526, Clare, SA 5453 **Region** Clare Valley
T 0419 822 909 **www**.goodcatholicgirl.com.au **Open** Not
Winemaker Julie Ann Barry **Est.** 2005 **Dozens** 460 **Vyds** 1ha
Good Catholic Girl is the venture of Julie Ann Barry, one of the many children of the late Jim Barry. She says, 'Having been born into a Catholic wine family, in vintage, my fate was sealed. My Limerick Vineyard was planted in the Armagh area of the Clare Valley in 1997, with cuttings taken from my father's famed Armagh shiraz vines planted across the paddock.' The Shiraz is named The James Brazill, Jim Barry's Christian names. She takes up the story thus: 'In 2008 I made my first Clare Valley Riesling, "Teresa", named after my mother, who is the true GCG (good catholic girl), and loves Clare Riesling, and who may in time consume my entire production of 108 dozen!' 2011 dealt Julie a double blow with the loss of the fruit for the James Brazill Shiraz and the contract-grown Teresa Riesling. Exports to the US.

ꟼꟼꟼꟼꟽ **Teresa Clare Valley Riesling 2010** Light, bright green-straw colour is a promising start; a crisp, dry riesling with a texture that is built around minerally acidity, and has excellent length. The humorous back label alone is worth the bottle price. Screwcap. 12.7% alc. **Rating** 93 **To** 2020 $25

ꟼꟼꟼꟽ **Hail Mary full of grace Clare Valley Cabernet Sauvignon 2009** Rating 87 **To** 2015 $25

Goona Warra Vineyard

790 Sunbury Road, Sunbury, Vic 3429 **Region** Sunbury
T (03) 9740 7766 **www**.goonawarra.com.au **Open** 7 days 10–5
Winemaker John Barnier, Daniel Abotomey **Est.** 1863 **Dozens** 3000 **Vyds** 6.92ha
A historic stone winery, originally established under this name by a 19th-century Victorian premier. A brief interlude as part of The Wine Investment Fund in 2001 is over, the Barniers having bought back the farm. Excellent tasting facilities, an outstanding venue for weddings and receptions, and lunch on Sunday. Exports to Canada, China, Taiwan and South Korea.

ꟼꟼꟼꟼꟽ **Sunbury Shiraz 2009** A nicely balanced shiraz with black cherry, plum and spice fruit; well-handled oak also adds to the appeal and the length. Screwcap. 14% alc. **Rating** 91 **To** 2014 $33

ꟼꟼꟼꟽ **Sunbury Pinot Noir 2008** Rating 89 **To** 2014 $33

🍇 Gordon Hills Estate

1119 Cargo Road, Lidster, NSW 2800 **Region** Orange
T (02) 6361 3429 **www**.gordonhillsestate.com.au **Open** Not
Winemaker Phil Kerney (Contract) **Est.** 1999 **Dozens** 2000 **Vyds** 10ha

Noel and Margie Gordon acquired the Burke & Hills vineyard in 2008, and set about restoring this mature but run-down vineyard (chardonnay, sauvignon blanc, merlot, pinot noir, cabernet franc, cabernet sauvignon, petit verdot and petit meunier). Noel's background as a major property developer on the east coast of Australia, and inaugural chairman of the Brisbane Lions AFL football club (1990-98), overseeing its move from Carrara to the Gabbba, and the merger with the Fitzroy Lions, must have made the task seem like child's play. Moreover, for Margie it was a return to her childhood home, for she grew up in Orange. The retention of Phil Kerney as winemaker was akin to grabbing first pick in the AFL draft.

♀♀♀♀♀ **Orange Chardonnay 2009** Bright, gleaming green-yellow; made in the same way as the '10, whole bunch-pressed to barrel for wild yeast fermentation; it shares the intensity and length of the '10, but without any issues with the oak, and has wonderful length to its grapefruit and nectarine flavours. Screwcap. 12.7% alc. **Rating** 93 **To** 2015 $23
Lidster Hill Orange Cabernet Sauvignon Cabernet Franc Merlot 2010 A 61/22/17% blend, open-fermented with wild yeast and matured in French barriques, 25% new. The bouquet is quite luscious, with juicy, ripe cassis/blackcurrant and tobacco leaf, the tannins fine, the oak making a positive contribution. A really attractive wine. Screwcap. 14.1% alc. **Rating** 93 **To** 2025

● **Orange Sauvignon Blanc 2010 Rating** 90 **To** Now $18
Orange Chardonnay 2011 Very developed colour for its age; given that it was hand-picked, whole bunch-pressed and run directly to French oak barrels, wild yeast-fermented and the mlf suppressed, the source of that colour is a mystery; the palate certainly shows ripe stone fruit with some buttery/toasty/creamy characters, and there is no problem with that. The best answer to the question is to enjoy the wine over the next two years. Screwcap. 13.3% alc. **Rating** 90 **To** 2014

♀♀♀♀ **Orange Chardonnay 2010 Rating** 88 **To** 2014 $23
Orange Pinot Noir 2010 Rating 87 **To** 2015 $32

Goundrey   ★★★☆

Location 10460, Vasse Highway, Nannup, WA 6275 **Region** Western Australia Zone
T 1800 088 711 **www.**goundreywines.com.au **Open** Not
Winemaker Garth Cliff **Est.** 1976 **Dozens** NFP
Goundrey is part of the Accolade Wines group empire. In 2008 it was put on the market by CWA, together with its 237ha of estate vineyards. In 2009 it was purchased by comparative minnow West Cape Howe. The Goundrey brand name has been retained by CWA, and significant quantities of wine will continue to be made from its WA base, with 100% of the Goundrey-grown grapes sold back to CWA pursuant to an ongoing contract with West Cape Howe. Exports to Hong Kong and Pacific Islands.

♀♀♀♀♀ **Homestead Shiraz 2010** Good colour; the bouquet has dark berry fruit, roast
✪ meat and oak aromas; the palate has a pleasing savoury, spicy grip to the dark fruits. Roast meat is a descriptor I used once in a blue moon. A great bargain. Screwcap. 13.5% alc. **Rating** 91 **To** 2018 $17

♀♀♀♀ **Homestead Sauvignon Blanc 2011 Rating** 88 **To** 2014 $17
Homestead Cabernet Merlot 2009 Rating 87 **To** 2015 $17

 Grace Farm   ★★★

45 Keane Street, Peppermint Grove, WA 6011 (postal) **Region** Margaret River
T (08) 9755 9384 **www.**gracefarm.com.au **Open** Not
Winemaker Jonathan Mettam **Est.** 2006 **Dozens** 2000 **Vyds** 8ha
Grace Farm is a 47ha property purchased in 2003 by Perth businessman John Mair and wife Elizabeth. It had remained natural forest until 1952, when it was partially cleared to graze cattle; today the remnant forest adjoins a national park. Vineyard planting commenced in '06, the first stage completed in '11. At the start of '12 only one wine was available commercially,

a Sauvignon Blanc Semillon, but Chardonnay, Cabernet Sauvignon and a cabernet blend will soon join the range.

TTTT **Margaret River Sauvignon Blanc Semillon 2011** Quartz-white; the clean and fresh bouquet leads into citrus and a hint of passionfruit on the moderately long palate. Could develop well. Screwcap. 12.9% alc. **Rating** 88 **To** 2014 $20

Graillot   ★★★★☆

19–21 Russell Street, Abbotsford, Vic 3067 (postal) **Region** Heathcote
T 1300 610 919 **www**.graillotaustralia.com.au **Open** Not
Winemaker Alain Graillot, Sandro Mosele **Est.** 2010 **Dozens** 900
The business is owned by Robert Walters, well known for his role with Bibendum Wine Co., which (inter alia) imports fine wines from various parts of Europe, with France to the fore. He has imported the wines of Alain Graillot, one of the superstars of the northern Rhône Valley (in Crozes-Hermitage) for many years. The two have become good friends during that time, but in 2010 that friendship took a new turn. For a number of years prior, Robert had been making small quantities of Heathcote shiraz with guidance from Sandro Mosele from the Colbinabbin area, but was not satisfied with the results. Having visited the vineyard from which the grapes had been supplied, Alain was sufficiently convinced of the potential to become winemaker/consultant for the business, which is owned and financed by Robert. There will be three wines made each year for the foreseeable future, the first simply labelled Syrah, the second Project Syrah No. 2 and the third (of varying amounts) sold as bulk wine.

TTTTT **Syrah 2010** Bright crimson-purple; a super-elegant medium-bodied syrah that includes 10% whole bunches, plum and black cherry filling the bouquet and palate alike. It has great line, length and balance, but the key to the wine is its texture, built on fine tannins and totally integrated oak. As it turned out, the barrel-by-barrel selection resulted in all the new oak wines going into Project No. 2. Screwcap. 13.5% alc. **Rating** 96 **To** 2025 $50

TTTTT **Project Syrah No. 2 2010 Rating** 93 **To** 2025 $30

Gralyn Estate   ★★★★★

4145 Caves Road, Wilyabrup, WA 6280 **Region** Margaret River
T (08) 9755 6245 **www**.gralyn.com.au **Open** 7 days 10.30–4.30
Winemaker Dr Bradley Hutton **Est.** 1975 **Dozens** 3000 **Vyds** 4.5ha
Under the eagle eye of Merilyn Hutton, Gralyn Estate has established a high reputation for its wines. The primary focus is on the full-bodied red wines, which are made in a distinctively different style from most from Margaret River, with an opulence reminiscent of some of the bigger wines from McLaren Vale. The age of the vines (35+ years) and the site are significant factors. Lesser amounts of chardonnay and fortified wines are also made.

TTTTT **Reserve Margaret River Shiraz 2008** While the price tag is certain to raise eyebrows, there is a deep-seated elegance and refinement to this wine, that may just make it worth while; it is plush and velvety with ample fine-grained tannins and a very long finish – all the hallmarks of high quality. People will vote with their hip pockets. Screwcap. 13.5% alc. **Rating** 95 **To** 2020 $110 BE
Margaret River Chardonnay 2010 Vibrant green hue; rich and oaky on the bouquet, with ripe nectarine, clove, cinnamon and lemon curd; the palate is toasty, full-bodied and unctuous on entry, but the searing spine of acidity provides cut and thrust at the finish line. Screwcap. 12.4% alc. **Rating** 94 **To** 2016 $55 BE

TTTTT **Reserve Margaret River Cabernet Sauvignon 2008 Rating** 93 **To** 2018 $110 BE
Artizan NV Rating 93 **To** 2013 $75
Margaret River Pedro Ximenez NV Rating 91 **To** 2014 $55 BE
Margaret River Tawny Fortified NV Rating 90 **To** 2013 $45

TTTT **Margaret River Cabernet Shiraz 2008 Rating** 89 **To** 2015 $110 BE

Grampians Estate ★★★★★

1477 Western Highway, Great Western, Vic 3377 **Region** Grampians
T (03) 5354 6245 **www**.grampiansestate.com.au **Open** 7 days 12–5
Winemaker Hamish Seabrook, Don Rowe, Tom Guthrie **Est.** 1989 **Dozens** 1200
Vyds 8.6ha

Graziers Sarah and Tom Guthrie began their diversification into wine in 1989, but their core business continues to be fat lamb and wool production. Both activities were ravaged by the 2006 bushfires, but each has recovered, that of their grapegrowing and winemaking rising like a phoenix from the ashes. They have acquired the Garden Gully winery at Great Western, giving them a cellar door presence and a vineyard of 2.4ha of 130-year-old shiraz, and 3ha of 80-year-old riesling vines. A feature of the cellar door is wine tutorials that can be booked at any time; the cellar door offers the full range of Grampians Estate wines and specially chosen wines from smaller local boutique wineries.

🍷🍷🍷🍷♀ **Rutherford Sparkling Shiraz 2008** Estate-grown grapes made in the traditional method; the bouquet is arrestingly spicy, with plum and black cherry fruit, the dosage light, simply because the elegance of the wine in the first place did not need a heavy correction hand. Crown seal. 14.6% alc. **Rating** 92 **To** 2016 $35
Pollyanna's Pinot 2010 Light, clear red; sourced from the Henty region, the fragrant, perfumed bouquet of red cherries and a hint of spice leads into a slinky palate, cherry, spice and a touch of forest all coming together; good length and balance. Screwcap. 13% alc. **Rating** 91 **To** 2018 $26

🍷🍷🍷🍷 **Muirhead Sparkling Rose 2010 Rating** 89 **To** 2014 $25

Granite Hills

1481 Burke and Wills Track, Baynton, Vic 3444 **Region** Macedon Ranges
T (03) 5423 7273 **www**.granitehills.com.au **Open** 7 days 11–6
Winemaker Llew Knight, Ian Gunter **Est.** 1970 **Dozens** 5000 **Vyds** 10.8ha

Granite Hills is one of the enduring classics, pioneering the successful growing of riesling and shiraz in an uncompromisingly cool climate. It is based on riesling, chardonnay, shiraz, cabernet sauvignon, cabernet franc, merlot and pinot noir (the last also used in its sparkling wine). After a quiet period in the 1990s, it has been reinvigorated. The Rieslings age superbly, and the Shiraz is at the forefront of the cool-climate school in Australia. Exports to Canada, Germany, Mauritius, Hong Kong, Singapore and China.

🍷🍷🍷🍷♀ **Knight Macedon Ranges Cabernet Sauvignon 2006** While showing a little development, there is an attractive level of fresh black fruits, licorice and cedar on display; the 'Euro' feel to the palate provides a medium-bodied framework, with a lingering spiciness in harmony with the fine tannins on offer. Screwcap. 14.5% alc. **Rating** 92 **To** 2018 $28 BE
Knight Macedon Ranges Riesling 2011 Deep straw, green hue; an exotic amalgam of lemon juice, ginger, coriander and orange zest; the palate offers depth of fruit, with a tangy acidity that borders on challenging; plenty of flavour that comes at the price of elegance. Screwcap. 12.5% alc. **Rating** 90 **To** 2018 $24 BE
Knight Macedon Ranges Chardonnay 2011 Mid gold; a mixture of ripe melon, citrus blossom and fennel; there is richness on entry, with a tightening of texture as the palate progresses; long and full of grilled nuts to conclude. Screwcap. 13.5% alc. **Rating** 90 **To** 2016 $26 BE
Knight Macedon Ranges Pinot Noir 2008 Mid garnet; showing some development and savoury aromas of roasted game, leather, forest floor and herbaceous notes on the bouquet; medium-bodied and fleshy, with zesty acidity and a prominent mineral quartz-like texture lingering on the finish. Screwcap. 13.5% alc. **Rating** 90 **To** 2016 $28 BE

🍷🍷🍷🍷 **Knight Heathcote Merlot 2006 Rating** 87 **To** 2014 $24 BE

Granite Ridge Wines

Sundown Road, Ballandean, Qld 4382 **Region** Granite Belt
T (07) 4684 1263 **www**.graniteridgewines.com.au **Open** 7 days 9–5
Winemaker Dennis and Juliane Ferguson **Est.** 1995 **Dozens** 1200 **Vyds** 2.5ha
Formerly known as Denlana Ferguson Estate Wines, Granite Ridge had considerable success in the mid 1990s. Its Goldies Unwooded Chardonnay was the first Qld wine to be chosen as the official Parliamentary wine of the Qld Government. Most of the production comes from its estate vineyard, which is planted to tempranillo, petit verdot (1ha each) and merlot (0.5ha), supplemented by purchased grapes.

ΨΨΨΨΨ **First Oak Chardonnay 2010** Mid gold; the bouquet is dominated by a toasty cinnamon perfume offset by melon and grapefruit; the palate is unctuous, with a little warmth noticeable on the finish; lots of flavour. Screwcap. 13.2% alc. **Rating** 90 **To** 2016 $22 BE

ΨΨΨΨ **Granite Rock Shiraz 2009 Rating** 89 **To** 2017 $25 BE

Grant Burge

Krondorf Road, Barossa Valley, SA 5352 **Region** Barossa Valley
T (08) 8563 3700 **www**.grantburgewines.com.au **Open** 7 days 10–5
Winemaker Grant Burge, Craig Stansborough, Matt Pellew, David Horne, Belinda Sinclair **Est.** 1988 **Dozens** 400 000 **Vyds** 356ha
As one might expect, this very experienced industry veteran makes consistently good, full-flavoured and smooth wines based on the pick of the crop of his extensive vineyard holdings; the immaculately restored/rebuilt stone cellar door sales buildings are another attraction. The provocatively named The Holy Trinity joins Shadrach and Meshach at the top of the range. Grant Burge repurchased the farm from Mildara Blass by acquiring the Krondorf winery in Tanunda (not the brand), in which he made his first fortune, in 1999. He renamed it Barossa Vines and opened a cellar door offering casual food. A third cellar door (Illaparra) is open on Murray Street, Tanunda. Exports to all major markets.

ΨΨΨΨΨ **Corryton Park Barossa Cabernet Sauvignon 2009** Good colour, deep but clear; this is one of those wines combining power and finesse, intense blackcurrant fruit with silky tannins and a long finish. From one of the highest vineyards in the Eden Valley; 5% shiraz. Poor cork. 14.5% alc. **Rating** 96 **To** 2020 $40
Miamba Barossa Shiraz 2010 Crimson-purple; a wine that is on one view mainstream Barossa, and on another the new/future Barossa. While the flavours are in the blackberry/plum/dark cherry range, there is considerable texture and light and shade to the mouthfeel, the result finesse and freshness. Deliberately given points beyond the norm. Screwcap. 14.5% alc. **Rating** 94 **To** 2024 $24
Filsell Old Vine Barossa Shiraz 2009 Dense purple-crimson; this is a remarkably balanced and harmonious wine, reflecting the 91-year-old vines; the aromas and flavours revolve around the core of black fruits, adding spice, licorice, quality oak and ripe tannins. Cork. 14.5% alc. **Rating** 94 **To** 2020 $40
Balthasar Eden Valley Shiraz 2008 The high level of toasty oak is evident on the bouquet, but the wealth of sweet and fragrant red fruits, mineral complexity and violet florals is intriguing; the palate is fresh, almost zesty, and the tannins fine and silky smooth; a very good big-boned '08 Shiraz. Diam. 14.5% alc. **Rating** 94 **To** 2018 $37 BE
The Holy Trinity Barossa Grenache Shiraz Mourvedre 2008 Principally made from grapes ex 100-year-old vines in various parts of the Valley, and showing no signs of overripe fruit; indeed, the texture and structure are admirably firm, promising a long life ahead and the continuation of development and complexity. Diam. 14.5% alc. **Rating** 94 **To** 2018 $40
Cameron Vale Barossa Cabernet Sauvignon 2010 Bright crimson-purple; a particularly good example of Barossa cabernet sauvignon, with cassis and redcurrant fruit making the initial impact on the bouquet and palate, followed by plum and cedary oak interspersed with fine, ripe tannins; the overall harmony and balance cannot be faulted. Screwcap. 14% alc. **Rating** 94 **To** 2025 $24

ŢŢŢŢ♀ **Abednego Barossa Shiraz Grenache Mourvedre 2008** Rating 92
To 2018 $62 BE
Summers Eden Valley Adelaide Hills Chardonnay 2011 Rating 91
To 2016 $22 BE

✪ **Daly Road Barossa Shiraz Mourvedre 2010** Clear crimson; has great freshness on the bouquet and medium-bodied palate; clever work in the winery has given a silky, supple mouthfeel to the wine, the focus on red and black cherry inviting early consumption. Screwcap. 14.5% alc. Rating 91 To 2016 $20

✪ **Barossa Shiraz 2010** Good colour; more fruit and depth than one expects at this price; the wine has a comfortable sweetness and softness about it, deriving in part from fruit and in part from fine tannins, oak also in the mix; black cherry, fruitcake and vanilla all intermingle. Screwcap. 14.5% alc. Rating 90 To 2016 $16

✪ **Hillcot Barossa Merlot 2010** If the Barossa barely tolerates cabernet sauvignon, merlot is even further away from where it should be. Despite this, Grant Burge presents a wine with as much plum, cassis and black olive as any cool region you care to name, with oak a strong ally. Screwcap. 14% alc. Rating 90 To 2018 $20

✪ **Barossa Cabernet Sauvignon Merlot 2010** Deep garnet; a ripe blend of cassis, mocha and black olive; the palate is full-bodied and fleshy, with good concentration and varietal integrity; moderately long, but also very moderately priced. Screwcap. 14% alc. Rating 90 To 2018 $16 BE

Grassy Point Wines   ★★★★☆

Coatsworth Farm, 145 Coatsworth Road, Portarlington, Vic 3223 **Region** Geelong
T 0409 429 608 **www**.grassypointwines.com.au **Open** By appt
Winemaker Provenance (Scott Ireland) **Est.** 1997 **Dozens** 600 **Vyds** 6.3ha
Partners David Smith, Robert Bennet and Kerry Jones have established their vineyard at Coatsworth Farm, with sauvignon blanc, chardonnay, pinot noir, shiraz, cabernet franc, malbec and merlot. The vineyard, with its sandy loam soil and a northerly aspect, is influenced by the maritime climate of the Port Phillip and Corio Bays.

ŢŢŢŢŢ **Bellarine Peninsula Chardonnay 2010** Bright green-straw; an impressive
✪ wine with grapefruit, white peach and nectarine to the fore, backed up by barrel-ferment characters on the mid- and back-palate; picked at precisely the right time, the palate has a delicious, juicy character that lifts it out of the ruck. Screwcap. 13% alc. Rating 94 To 2017 $20

ŢŢŢŢ♀ **Bellarine Peninsula Sauvignon Blanc 2010** Bright straw-green; now at its
✪ best, and certainly has a substantial volume of tropical fruit flavours, including pineapple and mango. Screwcap. 11.5% alc. Rating 92 To Now $16

ŢŢŢŢ **Bellarine Peninsula Pinot Noir 2010** Rating 89 To 2014 $25
Bellarine Peninsula Shiraz 2009 Rating 89 To 2017 $20
Bellarine Peninsula Rose 2010 Rating 87 To 2013 $16

Greedy Sheep   ★★★★☆

PO Box 530, Cowaramup, WA 6284 **Region** Margaret River
T (08) 9755 7428 **www**.greedysheep.com.au **Open** Not
Winemaker Dave Johnson **Est.** 2005 **Dozens** 4000 **Vyds** 6ha
Mining engineer Darren Guiney and electrical engineer wife Bridget lived and worked all around Australia in remote locations, but in 2004 decided to find a place to settle permanently. Margaret River was an obvious choice, for it was there they were married in 1999. They purchased the property in '04; it had been planted to cabernet sauvignon, merlot, cabernet franc and malbec in '99. It pays to have a sense of humour, for in January '05 1000 sheep found their way into the vineyard, eating everything green within their reach, including unripe grapes, which must have challenged their digestion. Sauvignon blanc has been purchased from Bridget's twin sister's vineyard, a mere 3km away, semillon from elsewhere.

🍷🍷🍷🍷🍷 ✪ **Margaret River Rose 2011** Has had a spectacular show career, gold medals from Qantas Wine Show WA and Hobart Wine Show, and a at trophy Perth Wine Show '11. Vivid puce, its show success has doubtless hinged on the length of the red berry flavour, and also its balance. Outstanding rose. Screwcap. 13.1% alc. **Rating** 95 **To** 2013 $19

🍷🍷🍷🍷 **Margaret River Cabernet Merlot 2010 Rating** 92 **To** 2018 $24

✪ **Margaret River Sauvignon Blanc Semillon 2011** Pale straw-green; a deceptively powerful wine, with a mix of juicy citrus flavours flowing into white peach and tropical fruits. Screwcap. 12.5% alc. **Rating** 91 **To** 2014 $19

Margaret River Chardonnay 2009 Rating 90 **To** 2015 $24

🍷🍷🍷🍷 **Barrel Select Margaret River Cabernet Sauvignon 2008 Rating** 88 **To** 2017 $24

Greenstone Vineyard ★★★★★

319 Whorouly South Road, Whorouly South, Vic 3735 **Region** Heathcote
T (03) 5727 1434 **www**.greenstoneofheathcote.com **Open** By appt
Winemaker Sandro Mosele (Contract), Alberto Antonini, Mark Walpole **Est.** 2002
Dozens 2500 **Vyds** 20ha

This is one of the most interesting ventures to emerge over the past few years, bringing together David Gleave MW, born and educated in Canada, now a long-term UK resident, who manages an imported wine business and writes widely about the wines of Italy; Alberto Antonini, a graduate of the University of Florence, with postgraduate degrees from Bordeaux and University of California (Davis), and Italian Flying Winemaker; and Mark Walpole, for 20 years manager of Brown Brothers' 700ha of vineyards before retiring in 2010. The partners have chosen what they consider an outstanding vineyard on the red soil of the Heathcote region, planted to 17ha of shiraz, 2ha of sangiovese and 1ha of monastrell (mourvedre). Exports to the UK, the US and other major markets.

🍷🍷🍷🍷🍷 **Heathcote Shiraz 2009** Vibrant colour; the bouquet is loaded with red fruits, violets, spice and sage; medium-bodied and lively on the palate, with silky tannins and linear acidity providing a plush ride from start to finish; unevolved and with plenty in reserve, this will be a wine to watch over the years. Screwcap. 13.5% alc. **Rating** 95 **To** 2020 $35 BE

Heathcote Colorino 2010 Colorino is a minor grape variety found in Tuscany, and this is an Australian first. The colour is purple-crimson, and the bouquet is expressive, almost flowery, with plum and black cherry fruit of the medium-bodied palate, the tannins fine and silky. Screwcap. 13% alc. **Rating** 94 **To** 2018 $28

🍷🍷🍷🍷 **Heathcote Monastrell 2008 Rating** 93 **To** 2018 $32

Greg Cooley Wines ★★★★☆

Main North Road, Clare, SA 5453 **Region** Clare Valley
T (08) 8843 4284 **www**.gregcooleywines.com.au **Open** 7 days 10.30–5
Winemaker Greg Cooley **Est.** 2002 **Dozens** 2800

Greg Cooley says, 'I followed the traditional path to winemaking via accountancy, fraud squad, corporate investigations, running a Wendy's Supa Sundaes franchise and then selling residential property. I left the property market in Brisbane just as the boom started in 2001 and moved to the beautiful Clare just about when the wine glut started.' He explains, 'All my wines are named after people who have been of influence to me in my 45 years and their influence is as varied as the wine styles – from pizza shop owners to my greyhound's vet and South Australian author Monica McInerney.' I have to confess that I am taken by Greg's path to glory because my move through law to wine was punctuated by the part-ownership of two greyhounds that always wanted to run in the opposite direction to the rest of the field. After years of selling direct through wine lunches and internet sales, in April 2011 Greg Cooley and partner Kelli Shanahan took the plunge, establishing a new cellar door on Main North Road, Clare.

🍷🍷🍷🍷 Valerie Beh Watervale Riesling 2011 Pale straw-green; a scented, flowery
✪   bouquet leads into an intense palate, with citrus and lime to the fore, apple in the
           rear. Delicious. Screwcap. 12% alc. **Rating** 94 **To** 2018 $20

🍷🍷🍷🍷 Winna and Toop Clare Valley Cabernet Merlot 2009 **Rating** 90
           To 2024 $25
           Rehbein and Ryan Reserve Clare Valley Cabernet 2009 **Rating** 90
           To 2020 $38

🍷🍷🍷 Five Year Olds and Dogs Clare Valley Rose 2011 **Rating** 88 **To** 2013 $20

Griffin Wines   ★★★★

Tynan Road, Kuitpo, SA 5172 **Region** Adelaide Hills
T (08) 8239 2545 **www**.griffinwines.com **Open** By appt
Winemaker Phil Christiansen, Shaw & Smith, Goe Di Fabio **Est.** 1997 **Dozens** 1500
Vyds 26.12ha
The Griffins (Trevor, Tim, Mark and Val) planted pinot noir, merlot, chardonnay, sauvignon
blanc and shiraz in 1997, having owned the property for over 30 years. Situated 3km from
Kuitpo Hall, its 350m elevation gives sweeping views over the valley below.

🍷🍷🍷🍷 No. 2 Adelaide Hills Sauvignon Blanc 2011 Smoky tropical fruits and a
           suggestion of fresh kiwi on the bouquet; the palate is generous, forward, fleshy and
           approachable and will best be enjoyed thoroughly chilled in the full flush of youth.
           Screwcap. 12% alc. **Rating** 90 **To** 2013 $18 BE
           Reserve Adelaide Hills Shiraz 2009 Dark in colour, and dark in personality,
           with a noticeable lift to the bouquet, providing detail to the dark fruits and toasty
           oak on offer; the palate is warm, thick and tannic, rich and dense; muscle over
           finesse here. Screwcap. 14.5% alc. **Rating** 90 **To** 2016 $35 BE

🍷🍷🍷 No. 1 Adelaide Hills Shiraz 2009 **Rating** 88 **To** 2014 $24 BE

Groom   ★★★★☆

28 Langmeil Road, Tanunda, SA 5352 (postal) **Region** Barossa Valley
T (08) 8563 1101 **www**.groomwines.com **Open** Not
Winemaker Daryl Groom **Est.** 1997 **Dozens** 5000 **Vyds** 27.8ha
The full name of the business is Marschall Groom Cellars, a venture owned by David and
Jeanette Marschall and their six children, and Daryl and Lisa Groom and their four children.
Daryl was a highly regarded winemaker at Penfolds before he moved to Geyser Peak in
California. Years of discussion between the families resulted in the purchase of a 35ha block
of bare land adjacent to Penfolds' 130-year-old Kalimna Vineyard. Shiraz was planted in 1997,
giving its first vintage in '99, the wine blended with the output from two vineyards, one 100
years old, the other 50 years old. The next acquisition was an 8ha vineyard at Lenswood in
the Adelaide Hills, planted to sauvignon blanc. In 2000, 3.2ha of zinfandel was planted on the
Kalimna Bush Block. Not surprisingly, a substantial part of the production is exported to the
US (and also to Canada, Hong Kong and Taiwan).

🍷🍷🍷🍷🍷 Barossa Valley Shiraz 2009 Strong, deep purple-red; the bouquet certainly
            has a generous helping of oak, and the palate follows suit, but in both instances
            there is an abundance of blackberry, plum and licorice fruit in reply. Will age with
            distinction, for the balance is excellent. Cork. 14.5% alc. **Rating** 94 **To** 2024 $49

🍷🍷🍷🍷 Adelaide Hills Sauvignon Blanc 2011 **Rating** 92 **To** 2013 $24
           Bush Block Barossa Valley Zinfandel 2010 **Rating** 90 **To** 2014 $30

Grosset   ★★★★★

King Street, Auburn, SA 5451 **Region** Clare Valley
T (08) 8849 2175 **www**.grosset.com.au **Open** Wed–Sun 10–5 from Sept for approx
6 weeks
Winemaker Jeffrey Grosset, Brent Treloar **Est.** 1981 **Dozens** 11 000 **Vyds** 22.2ha

Jeffrey Grosset has assumed the unchallenged mantle of Australia's foremost riesling maker in the wake of John Vickery stepping back to a consultancy role for Richmond Grove. Grosset's pre-eminence in riesling making is recognised both domestically and internationally; however, he merits equal recognition for the other wines in his portfolio: Semillon Sauvignon Blanc from Clare Valley/Adelaide Hills, Chardonnay and Pinot Noir from the Adelaide Hills; and Gaia, a Bordeaux blend from the Clare Valley. These are all benchmarks. His quietly spoken manner conceals a steely will, exemplified by his long and ultimately successful battle to prevent the use of 'riesling' on flagons and bottles as a generic description, rather than varietal, and his subsequent success in having the Clare Valley riesling makers migrate en masse to screwcaps, unleashing a torrent of change across Australia. Trial plantings (2ha) of fiano, aglianico, nero d'Avola and petit verdot suggest some new wines may be gestating. Exports to all major markets.

ŸŸŸŸŸ **Polish Hill Riesling 2011** Light straw-green; a gently floral, perfumed bouquet is followed by a palate of great purity, with lime juice and a hint of tropical fruit; the sheer intensity and extreme length is awesome, the after-palate persisting for what seems an eternity thanks to its core of minerality. Screwcap. 12.5% alc. **Rating** 97 **To** 2026 $49

Piccadilly Adelaide Hills Chardonnay 2010 The Piccadilly Valley is the coolest part of the Adelaide Hills, always reflected in this wine, but seldom more than this vintage. Has exceptional fruit intensity and focus, the flavours ricocheting around the mouth, drawing saliva as they do so, and covering all the bases from grapefruit through to white peach and nectarine. Obviously, the wine has been barrel-fermented in French oak, but this, at best, provides one part of the structural framework, more coming from the fruit and acidity. Screwcap. 13.5% alc. **Rating** 96 **To** 2019 $53

Gaia 2009 A 75/25% blend of Cabernet Sauvignon and Cabernet Franc, the colour bright crimson-purple, the aromas and flavours circling around cassis. In one sense it is impossibly young, in another juicy and seductive, the dichotomy due to the tannins that will see it through a quarter of a century (and very likely more). They are not dry, and the overall balance, texture and depth of the wine are excellent. It is a wine that Jeffrey Grosset particularly likes. Screwcap. 13.5% alc. **Rating** 95 **To** 2034 $62

Clare Valley Noble Riesling 2011 Glowing yellow-green; very complex and luscious, the result of total botrytis infection; mandarin, lime, cumquat, a hint of creme brulee, then perfect balancing acidity. Will be fascinating to see how it ages. 375ml. Screwcap. 11% alc. **Rating** 96 **To** 2018 $45

Springvale Watervale Riesling 2011 Light straw-green; as ever, has the most exquisitely perfumed bouquet that leaps out of the glass, the palate likewise more effusive, with ripe lime/lemon fruit running through the length of its immaculately balanced palate. Screwcap. 12.5% alc. **Rating** 95 **To** 2021 $36

Clare Valley Adelaide Hills Semillon Sauvignon Blanc 2011 Vivid bright quartz-green; the bouquet is fresh and spotlessly clean, but as at August '11 it was the palate that captured command, with sparkling lemon/grass/citrus ex the semillon, and perfectly integrated pink grapefruit and passionfruit ex the sauvignon blanc. Screwcap. 12.5% alc. **Rating** 95 **To** 2013 $32

Watervale Off-dry Riesling 2011 **Rating** 94 **To** 2026 $32
Adelaide Hills Pinot Noir 2010 **Rating** 94 **To** 2018 $66

Grove Estate Wines   ★★★★☆

Murringo Road, Young, NSW 2594 **Region** Hilltops
T (02) 6382 6999 **www**.groveestate.com.au **Open** Thurs–Sun 10–5
Winemaker Long Rail Gully Wines (Richard Parker) **Est.** 1989 **Dozens** 3000 **Vyds** 46ha
The Grove Estate partners of Brian Mullany, John Kirkwood and Mark Flanders purchased the then unplanted property situated on volcanic red soils at an elevation of 530m with the intention of producing premium cool-climate wine grapes for sale to other winemakers. Over the ensuing years plantings included cabernet sauvignon, shiraz, merlot, zinfandel, barbera, sangiovese, petit verdot, chardonnay, semillon and nebbiolo. In 1997 a decision was taken to

retain a small amount of cabernet sauvignon and have it vinified under the Grove Estate label, and the winemaking gathered pace thereafter. Wine names with apologies to Randall Grahm of Bonnie Doon, California.

ΨΨΨΨΨ **The Cellar Block Hilltops Shiraz Viognier 2010** Light crimson-purple; a vibrantly spicy wine with a mix of red and black berry fruits on the medium-bodied palate that accelerate through to the long, savoury finish. Screwcap. 14% alc. Rating 94 To 2020 $35

ΨΨΨΨΨ **Sommita Hilltops Nebbiolo 2009** Rating 92 To 2019 $35

✪ **The Italian Hilltops Nebbiolo Primitivo 2010** Light, bright red; an interesting blend, the primitivo (zinfandel) contributing positively to the colour, bouquet and palate of the wine, taking it into cherry and raspberry territory, and dealing with the nebbiolo tannins. Not a great wine, but attractive as a young, easy-drinking red. Screwcap. 14% alc. Rating 90 To 2015 $20

ΨΨΨΨ **Wherehaveyou Bin Hilltops Semillon Sauvignon Blanc 2011** Rating 88
✪ To 2014 $15
✪ **Wherehaveyou Bin MCB NV** Rating 88 To 2013 $13
◉ **Zinfamous Hilltops Rose 2011** Rating 89 To Now $15

Guichen Bay Vineyards ★★★

PO Box 582, Newport, NSW 2106 **Region** Mount Benson
T (02) 9997 6677 **www**.guichenbayvineyards.com.au **Open** Not
Winemaker Bird In Hand (White), Mark Day (Red) **Est.** 2003 **Dozens** 600 **Vyds** 120ha
Guichen Bay Vineyards is one of three adjacent vineyards known collectively as the Mount Benson Community Vineyards. Chardonnay, sauvignon blanc, shiraz, merlot and cabernet sauvignon were planted between 1997 and 2001. While the major part of the production is sold, the owners have obtained a producer's licence, and a small quantity of grapes is contract-made for the Guichen Bay Vineyards label.

ΨΨΨΨ **Mount Benson Merlot 2009** Developed colour, and leathery on the bouquet, with earth and olive also on show; rugged and a little rustic, there is a charm and generosity that sits well with the fruit on offer. Screwcap. 14.8% alc. Rating 87 To 2014 $20 BE

Guildford Vineyard ★★★☆

6720 Midland Highway, Guildford, Vic 3451 **Region** Macedon Ranges
T (03) 5476 4457 **www**.guildfordvineyard.com.au **Open** W'ends & public hols 11.30–5
Winemaker Ron Snepp, Brian Jean **Est.** 2003 **Dozens** 650 **Vyds** 4ha
Brian and Mandy Jean decided to establish a vineyard (and winery) in a region with similar growing conditions to the Rhône Valley, with 2.5ha of shiraz and 0.5ha each of viognier, chardonnay and cabernet sauvignon. While they are technically in the Macedon Ranges region, the style of the wines is more typical of the cool end of Bendigo. The winery is cut into the side of a stony ridge, covered by an insulated curved steel roof spanning over 16m. Their property is roughly halfway between Castlemaine and Daylesford, with Malmsbury and Kyneton to the east.

ΨΨΨΨΨ **Shiraz Cabernet 2010** A 60/40% blend with appealing bright crimson colour; the light- to medium-bodied palate is fresh and vibrant, with juicy red fruits and the finest imaginable tannins; a surprise outcome given the very cool climate. Screwcap. 13.9% alc. Rating 90 To 2015 $20

ΨΨΨΨ **North Block Shiraz 2010** Rating 88 To 2013 $20
Chardonnay 2010 Rating 87 To 2014 $18
Shiraz 2009 Rating 87 To 2015 $20
Cabernet Sauvignon 2010 Rating 87 To 2014 $22

Gumpara Wines ★★★★

PO Box 3 Stockwell Road, Light Pass, SA 5355 **Region** Barossa Valley
T 0419 624 559 **www**.gumpara.blogspot.com **Open** At Barossa Museum, Tanunda
Winemaker Mark Mader, Alex Peel, Neville Falkenberg (Consultant) **Est.** 1999
Dozens 500 **Vyds** 21.53ha
In 1856 the Mader family, driven by religious persecution, left Germany to settle in SA, acquiring a 25ha property at Light Pass. Over the generations, farming and fruit growing gave way to 100% grapegrowing; six generations later, Mark Mader produced the first wine under the Gumpara label, in 2000. After success with Shiraz, Mark branched out into Semillon made from a small parcel of almost 90-year-old estate vines. It was judged the top wine in its class in the Barossa Wine Show of that year. The portfolio may be small, but it's certainly diverse, with a Vermentino made in '09 and a range of fortified wines, (Tawny Grenache, Liqueur Semillon and Liqueur Frontignac) made by Mark personally. Exports to Singapore.

ΨΨΨΨΩ **Reserve Barossa Valley Shiraz 2008** The grapes come from 60-year-old estate vines, with partial barrel fermentation in 60% new French oak; the colour is good for an '08, and while the wine is richly flavoured with sweet red and black fruits, the alcohol doesn't threaten the balance or length of the wine, and the tannins give shape to the finish. Screwcap. 14.8% alc. **Rating** 93 **To** 2030 $35
Liqueur Barossa Valley Frontignac NV An attractive blend of juicy fruit, spice, scotch biscuits and nuts, the finish fresh and lively, encouraging another sip. Diam. 18% alc. **Rating** 91 **To** 2013 $33
Barossa Valley Vermentino 2011 Rating 90 **To** 2014 $18

ΨΨΨΨ **Victor's Old Vine Barossa Valley Shiraz 2009** Rating 89 **To** 2015 $25

Gundog Estate ★★★★

101 McDonalds Road, Pokolbin, NSW 2320 **Region** Hunter Valley
T (02) 4998 6873 **www**.gundogestate.com.au **Open** 7 days 10–5
Winemaker Matthew Burton **Est.** 2006 **Dozens** 1000 **Vyds** 5ha
After five years as chief winemaker for Wandin Hunter Valley, Matthew Burton moved on in 2010 in the wake of the exit of Wandin founders James and Philippa Davern. He is now making four different Hunter Semillons, Shiraz from the Hunter Valley (in the course of changing vineyard sources in 2012) and Murrumbateman. He and wife Renee run the leased cellar door space in the historic Pokolbin school house, next to the old Rosemount/ Hungerford Hill building on McDonalds Road. They are also constructing a cellar door at the Gundaroo family property in the Canberra District owned by parents Sharon and Geoff, which has 2.5ha each of chardonnay and cabernet sauvignon.

ΨΨΨΨΩ **Hunter's Semillon 2011** A fine and fragrant example of young Hunter Semillon, with lemon zest, lime and straw; the palate delivers racy acidity, with enough generosity for enjoyment both as a young wine or as a wine to cellar. Screwcap. 12.5% alc. **Rating** 92 **To** 2020 $25 BE
Semi-Sweet Hunter Valley Semillon 2011 Light straw-green; barely off-dry, and doesn't intensify the citrus notes of the semillon quite as much as expected; nonetheless, interesting. Screwcap. 9.5% alc. **Rating** 92 **To** 2013 $25
Canberra District Rose 2011 Pale pink; fresh red fruits and a dollop of rosewater on the bouquet; the palate reveals a savoury, almost leafy, note that weaves through the sweet fruits; while not bone dry, exhibits admirable balance and freshness at its core. Screwcap. 13% alc. **Rating** 91 **To** 2013 $25 BE

ΨΨΨΨ **Wild Hunter Valley Semillon 2011** Rating 89 **To** 2015 $30
Marksman's Limited Release Canberra District Shiraz 2010 Rating 88 **To** 2018 $50 BE
Semillon Sauvignon Blanc 2011 Rating 87 **To** 2013 $25 BE

Haan Wines ★★★★☆

Siegersdorf Road, Tanunda, SA 5352 **Region** Barossa Valley
T (08) 8562 4590 **www**.haanwines.com.au **Open** Not
Winemaker Mark Jamieson (Contract) **Est.** 1993 **Dozens** 4500 **Vyds** 16.3ha
Hans and Fransien Haan established their business in 1993 when they acquired a vineyard
near Tanunda. The plantings are shiraz (5.3ha), merlot (3.4ha), cabernet sauvignon (3ha),
viognier (2.4ha), cabernet franc (1ha) and malbec, petit verdot and semillon (0.4ha each).
Oak undoubtedly plays a role in the shaping of the style of the Haan wines, but it is perfectly
integrated, and the wines have the fruit weight to carry the oak. Exports to the UK, China
and other major markets.

♟♟♟♟♟ Wilhelmus 2009 A 42/21/18/12/7% blend of cabernet sauvignon, merlot,
cabernet franc, malbec and petit verdot that has good colour; against the odds,
perhaps, the wine adds cohesion, balance and length to its precocious display
of black and red berry fruit, positive tannins and good oak. Diam. 14.5% alc.
Rating 94 **To** 2020 $45

♟♟♟♟♟ Barossa Valley Shiraz Prestige 2009 **Rating** 93 **To** 2029 $45
Barossa Valley Merlot Prestige 2009 **Rating** 93 **To** 2019 $45
✪ Barossa Valley Shiraz Cabernet Sauvignon 2009 Oak is an integral part
of the Haan style, here in the guise of American (presumably for the shiraz) and
French (for the cabernet). The fruit flavours run from black cherry for the shiraz
through to a distinct splash of mint ex the cabernet. Ready to roll right now.
Screwcap. 14.5% alc. **Rating** 90 **To** 2015 $20

♟♟♟♟ Barossa Valley Merlot Cabernet Franc 2009 **Rating** 88 **To** 2015 $20
Barossa Valley Semillon Sauvignon Blanc 2011 **Rating** 87 **To** Now $20

Hackersley ★★★★★

1133 Ferguson Road, Dardanup, WA 6236 **Region** Geographe
T (08) 9381 6247 **www**.hackersley.com.au **Open** Thurs–Sun 10–4
Winemaker Jeff Ovens **Est.** 1997 **Dozens** 1500 **Vyds** 12ha
Hackersley is a partnership between the Ovens, Stacey and Hewitt families, friends since their
university days, and with (so they say) the misguided belief that growing and making their own
wine would be cheaper than buying it. They found a 'little piece of paradise in the Ferguson
Valley just south of Dardanup', and in 1998 they planted just under 8 ha, extended since then
to 11.5ha, of the mainstream varieties; interestingly, they turned their back on chardonnay.
Most of the crop is sold to Houghton, but a small quantity is made for the Hackersley label.
No wines were received for this edition; the rating is that of last year.

Hahndorf Hill Winery ★★★★☆

38 Pain Road, Hahndorf, SA 5245 **Region** Adelaide Hills
T (08) 8388 7512 **www**.hahndorfhillwinery.com.au **Open** 7 days 10–5
Winemaker Larry Jacobs **Est.** 2002 **Dozens** 4500 **Vyds** 6.5ha
Larry Jacobs and Marc Dobson, both originally from South Africa, purchased Hahndorf
Hill Winery in 2002. Larry gave up a career in intensive-care medicine in 1988 when he
bought an abandoned property in Stellenbosch, and established the near-iconic Mulderbosch
Wines. When Mulderbosch was purchased at the end of '96, the pair migrated to Australia
and eventually found their way to Hahndorf Hill. In 2006, their investment in the winery
and cellar door was rewarded by induction into the South Australian Great Tourism Hall of
Fame. In '07 they began converting the vineyard to biodynamic status, and they were one
of the first movers in implementing a carbon offset program. Having successfully grown and
made multi medal-winning blaufrankish wines, they have successfully imported three clones
of gruner veltliner from Austria, and their first vintage was made in '10. In the winter of that
year, they successfully propagated several thousand cuttings, and handed these over to five
other Adelaide Hills producers via the Adelaide Hills Vine Improvement Association. Exports
to the UK, Singapore and China.

ΨΨΨΨΨ Blueblood Adelaide Hills Blaufrankisch 2010 The clear colour and highly fragrant bouquet of this highly regarded and widely planted Austrian grape introduces a totally delicious, supple, medium-bodied palate with a Joseph's coat array of flavours ranging from cedar and tobacco through to a silky red cherry finish. Screwcap. 14% alc. **Rating** 95 **To** 2015 $35

ΨΨΨΨΩ **Adelaide Hills Sauvignon Blanc 2011 Rating** 92 **To** 2013 $23
GRU Adelaide Hills Gruner Veltliner 2011 Rating 91 **To** 2018 $28
Single Vineyard Adelaide Hills Shiraz 2009 Rating 91 **To** 2019 $30

ΨΨΨΨ **Adelaide Hills Pinot Grigio 2011 Rating** 89 **To** 2013 $25
Adelaide Hills Rose 2011 Rating 89 **To** 2013 $22

Hamelin Bay ★★★★

McDonald Road, Karridale, WA 6288 **Region** Margaret River
T (08) 9758 6779 **www**.hbwines.com.au **Open** 7 days 10–5
Winemaker Julian Scott **Est.** 1992 **Dozens** 12 000 **Vyds** 23.5ha
The Hamelin Bay vineyard was established by the Drake-Brockman family, pioneers of the region. Richard Drake-Brockman's great-grandmother, Grace Bussell, is famous for her courage when, in 1876 aged 16, she rescued survivors of a shipwreck not far from the mouth of the Margaret River. Exports to the UK, Canada, Malaysia and Singapore.

ΨΨΨΨΩ **Rampant Red Margaret River Shiraz Cabernet Merlot 2009 Rating** 91
o **To** 2018 $19
Five Ashes Vineyard Margaret River Sauvignon Blanc 2011 Pale colour; classic Margaret River nettle and pea pod bouquet; the palate is lively and fresh, with zesty acidity and plenty of life, not to mention a little grip for added interest. Screwcap. 13% alc. **Rating** 90 **To** 2013 $23 BE
Rampant White Margaret River Sauvignon Blanc Semillon 2011 Vibrant hue; a clean, focused and lively example of the blend with nettle, pea pod and a dollop of tropical fruit in support; juicy and zesty, this is made for warm weather and early, chilled drinking. Screwcap. 13% alc. **Rating** 90 **To** 2013 $19 BE
Five Ashes Vineyard Margaret River Semillon Sauvignon Blanc 2011 Vivid hue; a pungent and herbaceous personality of green nettle, pea pod and straw; the palate is taut and racy, with acidity the dominant character; certainly fresh and refreshing; the extremely dry finish may challenge some. Screwcap. 13% alc. **Rating** 90 **To** 2013 $23 BE

ΨΨΨΨ **Five Ashes Vineyard Margaret River Shiraz 2008 Rating** 89 **To** 2015
$31 BE
Traditional Method Margaret River Brut 2010 Rating 89 **To** 2015 $31
Margaret River Rose 2011 Rating 88 **To** 2013 $19 BE
Five Ashes Vineyard Margaret River Chardonnay 2010 Rating 87
To 2014 $29 BE

Hand Crafted by Geoff Hardy ★★★★★

PO Box 2370, McLaren Vale SA 5171 **Region** Various SA
T (08) 8383 2700 **www**.handcraftedbygeoffhardy.com.au **Open** Not
Winemaker Geoff Hardy **Est.** 2005 **Dozens** 4500
Hand Crafted is a collection of wines made from Geoff Hardy's vineyards around SA, including the Angus Vineyard (200ha) at Langhorne Creek, Wirrega Vineyard (160ha) on the Limestone Coast and the Adelaide Hills (45ha); distinctly separate from K1 (Adelaide Hills) and Pertaringa (McLaren Vale).

ΨΨΨΨΨ **Adelaide Teroldego 2010** This is a truly exciting first-up release, with a
✪ sunburst of mulberry and cherry fruit of tremendous length, the finish zesty and lingering. Tannin isn't obvious, and is not needed. Geoff Hardy thinks the wine will develop very well, and adopt further complexity; I'm happy with what there is today. Screwcap. 14.5% alc. **Rating** 94 **To** 2016 $22

Botrytis Noble Intent 2010 I cannot remember ever having tasted a botrytised verdelho, and I've no idea where this came from, but it's an impressive wine, with very luscious fruit, touches of cumquat and marmalade, and balanced acidity. Screwcap. 9.5% alc. **Rating** 94 **To** 2015 $25

♆♆♆♆♀ **Graciano 2009 Rating** 92 **To** 2020 $22
Limestone Coast Lagrein 2009 Rating 92 **To** 2020 $22

✪ **Limestone Coast Shiraz 2009** Good colour; has abundant and rich black cherry, spice, licorice and fruitcake flavours, fruit and oak tannins on the finish extending the length. Has a Vietnamese importer details on the back label. Screwcap. 14.5% alc. **Rating** 91 **To** 2020 $18

✪ **Langhorne Creek Savagnin 2010** Even within the confines of the easy growing conditions of Langhorne Creek, savagnin manages to keep a line of gently mouth-watering fruit, then a textured, structured finish. Well worth a look. Screwcap. 12.5% alc. **Rating** 90 **To** 2014 $18
Langhorne Creek Primitivo 2010 Rating 90 **To** 2015 $22

✪ **Sparkling Red NV** The base wine seems to have spent some time in oak, as there are notes of vanilla, as well as spice, on the red berry fruit; just when you think it will end sweet, it is in fact well balanced, the spicy notes lingering pleasingly. Diam. 13.5% alc. **Rating** 90 **To** 2014 $20

♆♆♆♆ **Adelaide Hills Chardonnay 2009 Rating** 89 **To** 2015 $18
Adelaide Hills Pinot Noir 2010 Rating 89 **To** 2016 $22
Shiraz Viognier 2008 Rating 89 **To** 2015 $18
Adelaide Hills Cabernet Sauvignon 2008 Rating 89 **To** 2017 $18
Sparkling Salmon NV Rating 89 **To** 2013 $20
Langhorne Creek Roussanne 2011 Rating 88 **To** 2015 $18

Hanging Rock Winery ★★★★★

88 Jim Road, Newham, Vic 3442 **Region** Macedon Ranges
T (03) 5427 0542 **www**.hangingrock.com.au **Open** 7 days 10–5
Winemaker John Ellis **Est.** 1982 **Dozens** 40 000 **Vyds** 14.5ha
The Macedon area has proved very marginal in spots, and the Hanging Rock vineyards, with their lovely vista towards the Rock, are no exception. John Ellis has thus elected to source additional grapes from various parts of Victoria to produce an interesting and diverse range of varietals at different price points. In January 2011 John and Anne's children Ruth and Robert returned to the fold: Robert obtained his oenology degree at Adelaide University in 2006, since working as a Flying Winemaker in Champagne, Burgundy, Oregon and Stellenbosch. Most recently he worked as winemaker at Hewitson. Ruth has a degree in wine marketing from Adelaide University, and began work at the winery, before leaving to work with Hanging Rock's Victorian distributors for 18 months. Exports to the UK, the US and other major markets.

♆♆♆♆♆ **Heathcote Shiraz 2009** Bright purple hue; a vibrant and expressive bouquet of blueberry, blackberry, liqueur-soaked plums and toasty oak; the medium-bodied and richly fruited palate is generous, and finishes with savoury flavours of roasted meat and licorice; big-boned red wine, done well. Diam. 14.5% alc. **Rating** 94 **To** 2020 $70 BE
Heathcote Shiraz 2008 Deep crimson-red; the bouquet is rich and deep, with blackberry, spice and dark chocolate intermingling, the hint of vanilla picked up on the palate courtesy of 18 months in new American oak; that oak doesn't overwhelm the fruit on the medium-bodied palate, which has good length and balance; the tannins are particularly fine. Diam. 14.5% alc. **Rating** 94 **To** 2023 $70
Reserve Heathcote Shiraz 2004 Strange, the vintage is shown as '04, but the same piece of label talks of the '00 vintage. Regardless, the bright colour signals a wine of distinct freshness, the red berry fruits backed by a strong streak of acidity, the tannins under strict control. A perfectly inserted Diam may underwrite the life of the wine for a long time to come. 14% alc. **Rating** 94 **To** 2024 $105

ΨΨΨΨ̣ The Jim Jim Macedon Ranges Sauvignon Blanc 2009 Rating 93
To 2014 $27
Jim Jim Macedon Ranges Pinot Noir 2008 Rating 93 To 2014 $45
The Jim Jim Macedon Ranges Sauvignon Blanc 2011 Rating 90
To 2013 $27 BE
Cambrian Rise Heathcote Shiraz 2009 Rating 90 To 2017 $30

ΨΨΨΨ Tarzali Riesling 2010 Rating 88 To 2014 $20 BE
Odd One Out Sauvignon Blanc 2011 Rating 87 To 2013 $20 BE
The Jim Jim Chardonnay 2009 Rating 87 To Now $35 BE
The Jim Jim RS Fifty Macedon Ranges Riesling 2010 Rating 87
To 2013 $27 BE

Happs ★★★★★

575 Commonage Road, Dunsborough, WA 6281 **Region** Margaret River
T (08) 9755 3300 **www**.happs.com.au **Open** 7 days 10–5
Winemaker Erl Happ, Mark Warren, Michael Wheatley **Est.** 1978 **Dozens** 16 000
Vyds 35.2ha
One-time schoolteacher, potter and winemaker Erl Happ is the patriarch of a three-generation family. More than anything, Erl has been a creator and experimenter, building the self-designed winery from mudbrick, concrete form and timber, and designing and making the first crusher. In 1994 he began an entirely new vineyard at Karridale, planted to no less than 28 different varieties, including some of the earliest plantings in Australia of tempranillo. The Three Hills label is made from varieties grown at the 30ha Karridale vineyard. Erl passed on to son Myles a love of pottery, and Happs Pottery now has four potters, including Myles. Exports to Denmark, the Netherlands, Malaysia, Hong Kong, China and Japan.

ΨΨΨΨΨ Three Hills Eva Marie 2011 A very limited production (this bottle no. 876 of 2500) of a remarkably intense and concentrated blend of semillon sauvignon blanc from dry-grown vines, given skin contact (unusual these days), barrel-fermented and lees stirred. Demands food, but is a wine worth seeking out and will cellar for a long time. Screwcap. 13.5% alc. Rating 94 To 2020 $27

✪ Margaret River Chardonnay 2010 Pale, bright straw-green; grown in Karridale, the southernmost and coolest part of the region; a wine of singular intensity and drive, grapefruit and white peach driving the long palate, French oak ex barrel fermentation little more than an ornament. Great value. Screwcap. 13% alc. Rating 94 To 2017 $22

Cabernet Sauvignon 2010 Deep garnet; a dark and brooding wine, showing pronounced leafy complexity, sitting on top of essency cassis fruit and tobacco notes; the palate is firm and backward, needing a fair amount of time to unwind and relax into its bulky framework; excellent concentration and depth of structure augur well for the future. Screwcap. 13.5% alc. Rating 94 To 2030 $24 BE

ΨΨΨΨ̣
✪ Margaret River Pinot Noir 2011 Light but brilliant crimson; has greater purity of varietal flavour than any Margaret River pinot I have ever previously tasted; crisp red fruits and spice are at the heart of a wine tailor-made for immediate drinking. Screwcap. 14% alc. Rating 93 To 2013 $16

✪ Margaret River Merlot 2008 Expected colour development; has more power and depth than most merlots at this price point, its earthy/foresty notes and persistent, fine tannins without any bitterness; has excellent texture, structure and length. Screwcap. 14% alc. Rating 93 To 2017 $20

Three Hills Malbec 2010 Rating 91 To 2015 $36
Margaret River Semillon Sauvignon Blanc 2011 Rating 90 To 2014 $20

ΨΨΨΨ Margaret River Cabernet Merlot 2010 Rating 88 To 2017 $22 BE
Margaret River Verdelho 2011 Rating 87 To 2014 $22
Margaret River Shiraz 2010 Rating 87 To 2016 $22 BE

Harcourt Valley Vineyards ★★★★☆

3339 Calder Highway, Harcourt, Vic 3453 **Region** Bendigo
T (03) 5474 2223 **www**.harcourtvalley.com.au **Open** 7 days 11–5 (11–6 during daylight saving)
Winemaker Quinn Livingstone **Est.** 1976 **Dozens** 2000 **Vyds** 4ha
Harcourt Valley Vineyards (planted 1975) has the oldest planting of vines in the Harcourt Valley. Using 100% estate-grown fruit Quinn Livingstone (second-generation winemaker) is making a number of small-batch wines from the property. The vines are hand-tended and minimal fruit handling is used in the winemaking process. A new tasting area overlooks the vines, and has a large window that allows visitors to see the activity in the winery. In 2011 Harcourt Valley won seven trophies at regional wine shows, four for the 2009 Barbara's Shiraz, others by the 2010 Riesling and 2010 Sightings Shiraz. Exports to China.

🍷🍷🍷🍷🍷 Single Vineyard Old Vine Bendigo Shiraz 2010 A very elegant, although complex, wine that won gold medals at the Ballarat Wine Show '11 and the Sydney Wine Show '12. The moderate alcohol allows the fine red and black fruits free play on the medium-bodied palate, with notes of spice and cedary oak joining fine, ripe tannins on the finish. Screwcap. 14% alc. **Rating** 94 **To** 2025 $60

🍷🍷🍷🍷🍷 Barbara's Bendigo Shiraz 2010 **Rating** 90 **To** 2015 $25
⚫ Sightings Shiraz 2009 **Rating** 91 **To** 2014 $20

🍷🍷🍷🍷 Limited Release Bendigo Cabernet Franc 2010 **Rating** 87 **To** 2013 $25 BE
⚫ Sightings Shiraz 2010 **Rating** 89 **To** 2013 $20
⚫ Bendigo Chardonnay 2010 **Rating** 88 **To** 2013 $20

Hardys ★★★★★

202 Main Road, McLaren Vale, SA 5171 **Region** McLaren Vale
T (08) 8329 4124 **www**.hardys.com.au **Open** Mon–Fri 10–4.30, Sat 10–5, Sun 11–5
Winemaker Paul Lapsley (Chief) **Est.** 1853 **Dozens** NFP
The 1992 merger of Thomas Hardy and the Berri Renmano group may well have had some elements of a forced marriage when it took place, but the merged group prospered mightily over the next 10 years. So successful was it that a further marriage followed in early 2003, with Constellation Wines of the US as the groom, and BRL Hardy the bride, creating the largest wine group in the world (the Australian arm of the business is known as Constellation Wines Australia, or CWA); but it is all now part of the Accolade Wines group. The Hardys wine brands are headed by Eileen Hardy Chardonnay and Shiraz and Thomas Hardy Cabernet Sauvignon; then the Sir James range of sparkling wines; next the HRB Riesling, Chardonnay, Shiraz and Cabernet; then the expanded Oomoo range; and at the bottom of the price pyramid, the Chronicles wines. Exports to all major markets.

🍷🍷🍷🍷🍷 Eileen Hardy Chardonnay 2010 Bright, light straw-green; the very complex bouquet, with its Burgundian funk, has been deliberately built and, for the time being, lords it over the perfectly delineated and weighted stone fruit and citrus of the palate, its future guaranteed. Screwcap. 13% alc. **Rating** 96 **To** 2021 $73
Eileen Hardy Shiraz 2007 There was one immediate question hanging over the head of this wine before I tasted it: could it avoid the toughness of the '07 vintage? The answer is a slightly qualified yes, and more so than many of its peers. It is medium- to full-bodied, with an array of exotic spices running through the blackberry and licorice fruit, the tannins not impeding the flow of the wine in the mouth. Screwcap. 14% alc. **Rating** 96 **To** 2027 $104
Eileen Hardy Pinot Noir 2010 Vivid, crystal clear crimson; the exotic bouquet has a perfumed display of intense red cherry and red fruit aromas, the palate has great texture, setting red fruits against forest fruits and forest floor; immaculate length and balance. Screwcap. 13.5% alc. **Rating** 95 **To** 2018 $78
HRB Riesling 2011 D644. Bright green-straw; a delicious riesling that is a 63/37% blend of Clare Valley and Derwent River (Tasmania) grapes; full of lime juice fruit flavours, it has equally good acidity running through to the finish of the long palate. Screwcap. 12.5% alc. **Rating** 94 **To** 2021 $26

HRB Chardonnay 2010 D638. Is at the forefront of the development of the new Australian style of chardonnay, the oak more a matter of texture than structure, and the fruit prized for its natural acidity; that fruit is locked up in the system at the moment, but will unfurl its wings over the next 5+ years. Screwcap. 13.5% alc. **Rating** 94 **To** 2017 $26

ΨΨΨΨΨ
✪ **Nottage Hill Riesling 2011** It's a sad commentary on the status of riesling in the marketplace when such a delicious wine sells for $10; it has mouthfilling lime and citrus fruit, the balancing acidity finely tensioned, extending all of the flavours through to the finish. Screwcap. 12.5% alc. **Rating** 93 **To** 2017 $10

✪ **Oomoo McLaren Vale Shiraz 2009** Good colour; the bouquet has abundant plum and black cherry fruit, bitter chocolate and savoury tannins joining in on the medium- to full-bodied palate, oak a bit player. Another in a distinguished line under this lovely retro label. Screwcap. 14% alc. **Rating** 93 **To** 2024 $18

Sir James Vintage Pinot Noir Chardonnay 2004 Rating 93 **To** Now $27

✪ **Oomoo Adelaide Hills Sauvignon Blanc 2010** A typically well-made wine, using specific yeast but no other embellishments; the bouquet and palate range between citrus and ripe kiwi fruit flavours, the finish drawn out by good acidity. Screwcap. 13% alc. **Rating** 92 **To** Now $18

Chronicle No. 3 Butcher's Gold Shiraz Sangiovese 2010 Rating 92 **To** 2020

✪ **Oomoo Adelaide Hills Sauvignon Blanc 2011** Pale straw-green; the pungent bouquet is, to say the least, attention-getting, and the lime zest, gooseberry and steely acidity of the palate don't back away. For those who actually like sauvignon blanc; topped its class (with a silver medal) at the National Wine Show '11. Screwcap. 13% alc. **Rating** 90 **To** 2013 $19

HRB Cabernet Sauvignon 2006 Rating 90 **To** 2016 $26

ΨΨΨΨ
✪ **Sir James Brut de Brut Pinot Noir Chardonnay NV Rating** 89 **To** Now $15

Nottage Hill Shiraz 2010 Rating 89 **To** 2014 $10

Oomoo McLaren Vale Shiraz 2010 Rating 88 **To** 2016 $19

Sir James Pinot Noir Chardonnay Cuvee Brut NV Rating 87 **To** 2013 $16

Harewood Estate ★★★★★

Scotsdale Road, Denmark, WA 6333 **Region** Denmark
T (08) 9840 9078 **F** (08) 9840 9053 **www**.harewood.com.au **Open** Fri–Mon 10–4, 7 days during school hols
Winemaker James Kellie, Luke Hipper **Est.** 1988 **Dozens** 15 000 **Vyds** 10ha
In 2003 James Kellie, for many years a winemaker with Howard Park, and responsible for the contract making of Harewood's wines since 1998, purchased the estate with his father and sister as partners. Events moved quickly thereafter: a 300-tonne winery was constructed, offering both contract-winemaking services for the Great Southern region and the ability to expand the Harewood range to include subregional wines that demonstrate the differences in style across the region. In January 2010 James, together with wife Careena, purchased his father's and sister's shares in the business, and are now 100% owners. Exports to the UK, Denmark, Hong Kong, Malaysia, Macau, Singapore, China and Japan.

ΨΨΨΨΨ **Reserve Great Southern Semillon Sauvignon Blanc 2011** Restraint and perfume are not the usual hallmark of this blend in Australia, but this example is fragrant, perfumed and enticing; gun flint, tropical fruits, namely papaya and a fresh edge of nettle; the palate is sweet-fruited, textured and long, fine and evenly poised; restraint is definitely the key here. Screwcap. 13.5% alc. **Rating** 96 **To** 2014 $25 BE

Aged Release Mount Barker Cabernet Merlot 2004 Good colour; a very attractive example of a wine nearing maturity. Both the bouquet and palate give the same message of fresh, fragrant blackcurrant and cassis, subtle oak and great balance for a medium-bodied wine with many years in front of it. Screwcap. 14.5% alc. **Rating** 96 **To** 2024 $50

✪   **Frankland River Riesling 2011** Vibrant pale straw; impeccably clean and focused aromas of lime, minerals and floral notes; the palate is taut on entry with juicy fresh lime and zesty acidity, balanced by a generous mid palate of sweet fruit; will age, but a lovely example as a young wine. Screwcap. 13% alc. **Rating** 95 **To** 2020 $20 BE

✪   **Great Southern Sauvignon Blanc Semillon 2011** An excellent example of concentration and finesse working together in harmony; vibrant tropical fruit, mineral notes and fresh-cut grass on the bouquet; the palate is well rounded and generous on entry, with chalky acidity providing freshness and detail on the finish; surprisingly long and completely refined. Trophy WA Wine Show '11. Screwcap. 13.5% alc. **Rating** 95 **To** 2013 $20 BE

Great Southern Cabernet Sauvignon 2009 From the Denmark and Frankland River subregions, matured for 20 months in new and 1-year-old French oak; has everything one could wish for in a young medium- to full-bodied cabernet, its blackcurrant fruit complexed by touches of spice, earth and oak; great balance, length and texture. Screwcap. 14% alc. **Rating** 95 **To** 2024 $30

✪   **Porongurup Riesling 2011 Rating** 94 **To** 2020 $20 BE
Great Southern Shiraz 2009 Rating 94 **To** 2018 $30 BE

✪   **Great Southern Shiraz Cabernet 2010 Rating** 94 **To** 2018 $20 BE

♥♥♥♥   **Great Southern Pinot Noir 2011 Rating** 89 **To** 2014 $20 BE
Great Southern Chardonnay 2010 Rating 88 **To** 2014 $25 BE
Red Rabbit 2010 Rating 87 **To** 2013 $18

Harrington Glen Estate   ★★★

88 Townsend Road, Glen Aplin, Qld 4381 **Region** Granite Belt
T (07) 4683 4388 **www.**harringtonglenwines.com.au **Open** 7 days 10–4, Sat & public hols 10–5
Winemaker Stephen Oliver **Est.** 2003 **Dozens** 700 **Vyds** 3.44ha
The Ireland family planted cabernet sauvignon, shiraz, merlot and verdelho vines in 1997, with follow-on plantings of muscat, viognier and pinot gris. Red grapes not required for cellar door production are sold to local wine producers, and some white grapes are purchased from other Granite Belt producers. It is somehow appropriate that the accommodation by Harrington Glen is in fact a former Victorian Railways train carriage now embedded within the accommodation building.

♥♥♥♥
✪   **Granite Belt Cabernet Sauvignon 2010** Good colour; is clearly the product of a cool growing season with savoury/minty undertones to the predominantly cassis fruit of the palate. The Granite Belt has no reason to be ashamed of this wine. Screwcap. 13.9% alc. **Rating** 89 **To** 2017 $20

Granite Belt Shiraz 2010 Light purple-crimson; the plum and black cherry fruit on the medium-bodied palate have been enthusiastically supported by oak, and less would have been better. Screwcap. 13.7% alc. **Rating** 87 **To** 2014 $20

Hart & Hunter   ★★★★☆

PO Box 120, Cessnock, NSW 2320 **Region** Hunter Valley
T 0401 605 219 **www.**hartandhunter.com.au **Open** Not
Winemaker Damien Stevens, Jodie Belleville **Est.** 2009 **Dozens** 350
This is the venture of winemaking couple Damien Stevens and Jodie Belleville, together with Daniel and Elle Hart. It is a virtual winery, the grapes being purchased from single vineyards, and made at First Creek Wines, where Damien and Jodie are full-time winemakers. While total production was little more than 300 dozen, half Semillon and half Shiraz, it hit the headlines in 2010 when its Oakey Creek Semillon won two trophies at the Hunter Valley Wine Show, and went on to win a further gold medal at the Hunter Valley Boutique Wine Show. I get the feeling we shall hear more of this venture in the future. Exports to the UK.

ΨΨΨΨΨ Single Vineyard Series Oakey Creek Semillon 2011 Pale straw-green; the
bouquet gives no sign of the intense and vibrant palate, with a flavour profile
with overtones of riesling courtesy of its lime juice aspects, although the purity
and drive of its minerally acidity is all semillon. Screwcap. 10.5% alc. **Rating** 95
To 2021 $27

Hartz Barn Wines   ★★★☆

1 Truro Road, Moculta, SA 5353 **Region** Eden Valley
T 0408 857 347 **www**.hartzbarnwines.com.au **Open** By appt
Winemaker David Barnett **Est.** 1997 **Dozens** 1600 **Vyds** 11ha
Formed in 1997 by Penny Hart (operations director), David Barnett (winemaker/director),
Katrina Barnett (marketing director) and Matthew Barnett (viticulture/ cellar director), which
may suggest that the operation is rather larger than it in fact is. The business name and label
have an unexpectedly complex background too, involving elements from all the partners. The
grapes come from the 11.5ha Dennistone Vineyard, which is planted to merlot, shiraz, riesling,
cabernet sauvignon, chardonnay and lagrein. Exports to Japan and NZ.

ΨΨΨΨΨ **General Store Eden Valley Riesling 2011** Pale straw; a restrained and
mineral-accented lemon pith bouquet, with a taut and racy palate; fine and fresh,
clean and focused. Screwcap. 12% alc. **Rating** 90 **To** 2016 $25 BE

Hartzview Wine Centre   ★★★★

70 Dillons Road, Gardners Bay, Tas 7112 **Region** Southern Tasmania
T (03) 6295 1623 **www**.hartzview.com.au **Open** 7 days 9–5
Winemaker Contract **Est.** 1988 **Dozens** NA
A combined wine centre, offering wines from a number of local Huon Valley wineries;
also offers accommodation for six people in a self-contained house. Hartzview table wines
(produced from 3ha of estate plantings) are preferred to the self-produced Pig & Whistle Hill
fruit wines.

ΨΨΨΨΨ **Reserve Hand Picked Pinot Noir 2008** Has held its colour well; the palate
is rich and full-bodied, but has retained structure and balance; very fruit-driven.
Screwcap. 13.7% alc. **Rating** 90 **To** 2014 $35

Harvey River Bridge Estate   ★★★★

Third Street, Harvey, WA 6220 **Region** Geographe
T (08) 9729 2085 **www**.harveyriverbridgeestate.com.au **Open** 7 days 10–4
Winemaker Stuart Pierce **Est.** 1999 **Dozens** 50 000 **Vyds** 21ha
This highly focused business is owned by the Sorgiovanni and Scolaro families, who also own
the successful fruit juice and dairy product company Harvey Fresh. It has 12 contract growers
throughout the Geographe region, with the wines being made in a company-owned winery
and juice factory. Exports to the UK, the US, Canada and China.

ΨΨΨΨΨ **Joseph River Estate Reserve Margaret River Semillon 2011** Vibrant green
hue; fresh-cut grass, lemon rind and spicy oak notes mingle on the bouquet; the
palate is zesty and fresh, with green nettle and lingering toasty oak; an interesting
and complex style of Semillon. Screwcap. 12.4% alc. **Rating** 90 **To** 2016 $28
**Joseph River Estate Reserve Margaret River Cabernet Sauvignon
Merlot 2010** Deep garnet; blackcurrant pastille, sage and cedar are evident on the
bouquet; the palate is full-bodied and drying, with rugged chewy tannins currently
dominating the fruit; time will see this change for the better. Screwcap. 14.7% alc.
Rating 90 **To** 2018 $38

ΨΨΨΨ **Joseph River Estate Reserve Margaret River Chardonnay 2010**
Rating 88 **To** 2014 $28

Haselgrove Wines ★★★★☆

187 Sand Road, McLaren Vale, SA 5171 **Region** McLaren Vale
T (08) 8323 8706 **www**.haselgrove.com.au **Open** By appt Mon–Fri 10–4
Winemaker Greg Clack, Matthew Copping **Est.** 1981 **Dozens** 40 000 **Vyds** 9.7ha
In 2008 the business was acquired by four Italian-Australian wine stalwarts: Don Totino, Don Luca, Tony Carrocci and Steve Maglieri. The wines are released in four ranges: at the top, the Il Padrone The Boss Series; next the Bella Vigna (Beautiful Vineyard) Series; then the Primo Taglio First Cut Series; and at the entry level, the 'H' by Haselgrove Series. Exports to the UK, Ireland, Denmark, Hong Kong, China and NZ.

♥♥♥♥♥ **First Cut McLaren Vale Cabernet Sauvignon 2010** Bright crimson-purple;
✪ shows (again) what McLaren Vale can do with cabernet sauvignon given the right seasonal climate and intelligent winemaking. Here cassis/blackcurrant fruit has been matured in appropriate oak, and the tannin extraction judged to perfection. Screwcap. 14% alc. **Rating** 94 **To** 2020 $18

♥♥♥♥♀ **First Cut Adelaide Hills Sauvignon Blanc 2010** Light straw-green; the
✪ flowery and fragrant bouquet has touches of passionfruit and citrus, the elegant palate also bringing lychee into play. The finish is long, fresh and clean. Great aperitif style. Screwcap. 11% alc. **Rating** 93 **To** Now $16

✪ **Bella Vigna Premium Selection McLaren Vale Shiraz 2010** Strong purple-crimson; a lush, full-bodied McLaren Vale shiraz, crammed with blackberry, plum and black cherry, indeed Cherry Ripe; the tannins are round and smooth, French and American oak both adding their contribution. Screwcap. 14% alc. **Rating** 93 **To** 2025 $25

✪ **First Cut McLaren Vale Shiraz 2010** Medium red-purple; a generous, soft yet full-bodied McLaren Vale shiraz, filled with blackberry fruit, dark chocolate and a hint of vanilla; the tannins are precisely where they should be. Screwcap. 14% alc. **Rating** 91 **To** 2018 $18

♥♥♥♥ **First Cut Adelaide Hills Pinot Grigio 2011 Rating** 89
○ **To** Now $16
○ **First Cut McLaren Vale Cabernet Sauvignon 2009 Rating** 88
To 2013 $18

Hastwell & Lightfoot ★★★☆

204 Foggos Road, McLaren Vale, SA 5171 **Region** McLaren Vale
T (08) 8323 8692 **www**.hastwellandlightfoot.com.au **Open** By appt
Winemaker James Hastwell **Est.** 1988 **Dozens** 4500 **Vyds** 16ha
Established in 1988 by Mark and Wendy Hastwell and Martin and Jill Lightfoot with a focus on growing quality grapes for McLaren Vale wineries, it has now expanded to 16ha of vines and olive trees. Having initially sold much of the production, they have made a significant commitment to the Hastwell & Lightfoot brand, producing wines from estate-grown varieties (Cabernet Sauvignon, Shiraz, Cabernet Franc, Tempranillo, Chardonnay and Viognier). The vines are grafted onto devigorating American rootstocks that restrain the development of dead fruit characters in warmer seasons. James Hastwell, son of Mark and Wendy, has his winery just 2kms from the vineyard, which means that fruit is moved quickly into the winery. Ferments are conducted in 2- and 3-tonne temperature-controlled open fermenters. Exports to the UK, Canada, Norway, Germany, Malaysia, Taiwan, Singapore and China.

♥♥♥♥ **McLaren Vale Shiraz 2010** Vivid purple hue; the bouquet is full of essency blackberry pastille aromas, with charcuterie and mocha also on display; the palate is medium-bodied and loaded with fruit, tannin and acid, with a little time necessary to see full integration. Screwcap. 14.5% alc. **Rating** 88 **To** 2017 $22 BE
McLaren Vale Cabernet Franc 2009 Mid garnet; the bouquet reveals red fruits, bramble and a touch of earth; the palate is lively and has a distinct savoury edge that provides interesting opportunities for matching with food. Screwcap. 13.5% alc. **Rating** 88 **To** 2016 $22 BE

Fat 'n Skinny Picker's Choice Red 2009 Ripe and concentrated black fruit bouquet, with fruitcake spice and bitter chocolate on display on the medium-bodied and fleshy palate. Screwcap. 14% alc. **Rating** 87 **To** 2015 $15 BE

Hat Rock Vineyard ★★★★

2330 Portarlington Road, Bellarine, Vic 3221 (postal) **Region** Geelong
T (03) 5259 1386 **www**.hatrockvineyard.com.au **Open** By appt
Winemaker Ray Nadeson (Contract) **Est.** 2000 **Dozens** 300 **Vyds** 2ha
Steven and Vici Funnell began the development of Hat Rock in 2000, planting pinot noir. The vineyard derives its name from a hat-shaped rocky outcrop on the Corio Bay shore, not far from the vineyard, a landmark named by Matthew Flinders when he mapped the southern part of Australia.

ΨΨΨΨΨ **Bellarine Peninsula Pinot Noir 2010** Bright colour; a pure-fruited bouquet of blood plum and hoisin on the bouquet; the palate is taut and firm, slowly revealing the fruit lurking beneath, but the intensity speaks of a healthy future; time will see silk and lace, supported by lovely, fine pinot fruit. Screwcap. 13.5% alc. **Rating** 93 **To** 2018 $30 BE

Hay Shed Hill Wines ★★★★★

511 Harmans Mill Road, Wilyabrup, WA 6280 **Region** Margaret River
T (08) 9755 6046 **www**.hayshedhill.com.au **Open** 7 days 9–5
Winemaker Michael Kerrigan **Est.** 1987 **Dozens** 24 000 **Vyds** 18.55ha
Mike Kerrigan, highly regarded former winemaker at Howard Park, acquired the business in late 2006 (with co-ownership by the West Cape Howe syndicate) and is now the full-time winemaker. He had every confidence he could dramatically lift the quality of the wines, which is precisely what he has done. Exports to the UK, the US, Singapore, China and Hong Kong.

ΨΨΨΨΨ **Margaret River Cabernet Sauvignon 2010** Strong purple-crimson; estate-
✪ grown, open-fermented, and 18 months in French oak are the bones; the flesh is beautifully juicy and succulent red berry fruits finishing with fine tannins. Screwcap. 14% alc. **Rating** 96 **To** 2030 $25
Block 2 Margaret River Cabernet Sauvignon 2010 Deep magenta, bright; understated and reserved pure cassis and cedar bouquet, complex and intriguing; the palate is full-bodied and firm, yet with the tannins silky and acidity super fresh; unevolved at the time of tasting, and if patient, will absolutely reward cellaring. Screwcap. 14% alc. **Rating** 95 **To** 2025 $50 BE
Block 6 Margaret River Chardonnay 2011 Mid gold, green hue; restrained aromas of grapefruit, cashew and fine French oak; the palate is lacy, racy and fine, with linear acidity driving the long, even and thoroughly engaging conclusion; unevolved at tasting, but time will reveal the true beauty within. Screwcap. 13% alc. **Rating** 94 **To** 2018 $35 BE
✪ **Margaret River Cabernet Merlot 2010** Medium purple-red; the fragrant red berry bouquet introduces an elegant medium-bodied wine, with structure courtesy of superfine tannins supplemented by French oak and fresh acidity. As good tomorrow as it will be in 10 years. Screwcap. 14% alc. **Rating** 94 **To** 2020 $20

ΨΨΨΨΨ **Margaret River Sauvignon Blanc Semillon 2011** **Rating** 93
○ **To** 2013 $20
Block 1 Margaret River Semillon Sauvignon Blanc 2011 **Rating** 93 **To** 2014 $28 BE
✪ **Margaret River Shiraz Tempranillo 2010** Strong, bright crimson; the percentage of tempranillo is not specified, but its contribution is obvious enough, especially on the tangy finish of the wine; it has bright cherry fruit, attractive French oak inputs, and excellent tannins. Screwcap. 14% alc. **Rating** 93 **To** 2020 $20

✪ **Pitchfork Margaret River Cabernet Merlot 2010** Strong colour; the luscious array of red and black berry fruits on the bouquet and palate are an impressive opening stanza; the palate has considerable structure, deriving from maturation in oak barrels (no staves, no chips) closing with ripe, balanced tannins. Exceptional value. Screwcap. 14% alc. **Rating** 93 **To** 2018 $16
Margaret River Chardonnay 2011 Rating 92 **To** 2016 $25 BE

✪ **Pitchfork Pink 2011** Bright, light reddish-pink; has a delicious array of juicy red cherry/berry fruits with an intriguing fruit lift on the back-palate and finish, more to citrus in character. Screwcap. 13% alc. **Rating** 92 **To** Now $15

✪ **Pitchfork Margaret River Semillon Sauvignon Blanc 2011** Pale quartz; a clean and crisp bouquet, with the herbaceous characters that also drive the palate joined there by a touch of tropical fruit, the finish with bright acidity. Screwcap. 12.5% alc. **Rating** 90 **To** Now $15

✪ **Pitchfork Margaret River Shiraz 2010** Mid crimson; bright fresh red and blueberry, spice and charry oaky bouquet; the medium-bodied palate is rugged and full of wild thyme and fresh acidity; enjoy this in the full flush of youth for maximum enjoyment. Screwcap. 14% alc. **Rating** 90 **To** 2015 $17 BE

🍷🍷🍷🍷 **Block 8 Margaret River Cabernet Franc 2009 Rating** 89 **To** 2014 $35 BE
Pitchfork Margaret River Chardonnay 2011 Rating 87 **To** 2013 $17

Head Wines ★★★★★

Lot 1, Stonewell Road, Stonewell, SA 5352 **Region** Barossa Valley
T 0413 114 233 **www**.headwines.com.au **Open** Not
Winemaker Alex Head **Est.** 2006 **Dozens** 1500
Head Wines is the intriguing, but highly focused, venture of Alex Head, who came into the wine industry in 1997 with a degree in biochemistry from Sydney University. Experience in fine wine retail stores, wholesale importers and an auction house was followed by vintage work at wineries he particularly admired: Tyrrell's, Torbreck, Laughing Jack and Cirillo Estate. The labelling and naming of the wines reflects his fascination with the Northern Rhône Valley, and, in particular, Côte-Rôtie. The two facing slopes in Côte-Rôtie are known as Côte Blonde and Côte Brune, sometimes combining grapes from the two slopes as Côte Brune et Blonde. Head's Blonde comes from an east-facing slope in the Stonewell subregion of the Barossa Valley, while The Brunette comes from a very low-yielding vineyard in the Moppa subregion. In each case, open fermentation (with whole bunches included) and basket-pressing precedes 15 months in seasoned French hogsheads.

🍷🍷🍷🍷🍷 **The Contrarian Single Vineyard Greenock Barossa Valley Syrah 2010** Deep crimson-purple; made using the full natural approach, with 100% whole bunches, foot-stamped, wild yeast-fermented, bottled unfined and unfiltered. An extremely complex wine, oak adding its voice to the sumptuous black fruits and harmonious finish; 250 dozen made. Screwcap. 12.8% alc. **Rating** 96 **To** 2030 $32
The Blonde Single Vineyard Stonewell Shiraz Viognier 2010 Outstanding bright purple-crimson; this proves an exception to the rule that shiraz viognier blends only truly succeed in cool climates, for both the texture and the aromas and flavours of this elegant, medium-bodied wine mark the synergy of the blend; the bouquet is highly fragrant, the palate with vivid spicy cherry and plum fruit, the tannins important but fine. Screwcap. 14% alc. **Rating** 96 **To** 2020 $40
The Brunette Single Vineyard Syrah 2010 A 'Young Gun of Wine' candidate, Alex endeavours to make fragrant and food-friendly wines in the Barossa; while this is the Brunette, the fragrance has a touch of the Blondes (a reference to Côte-Rôtie florals) with a perfume of violets, and lots of silk on the palate; fine, lacy and eminently drinkable, this wine is good to go, but will stand the test of time. Screwcap. 13.8% alc. **Rating** 95 **To** 2030 $45 BE
Old Vine Single Vineyard Greenock Barossa Valley Grenache 2010 One hundred dozen made from partial whole bunch wild yeast fermentation, bottled unfined and unfiltered; the colour is excellent, the juicy berry fruit without any confection characters, the balance excellent, the tannins perfect. Top-class grenache (especially for the Barossa). Screwcap. 14.5% alc. **Rating** 95 **To** 2016 $32
✪ **Head Red Barossa Valley Shiraz Viognier 2010 Rating** 94 **To** 2020 $22

ҮҮҮҮ **Barossa Valley Grenache Mataro Rose 2011** Pale, bright crimson; fragrant
✪   red berry and spice aromas lead into a vibrantly fresh and crisp palate, the finish as
            long as it is bone dry. Impressive. Screwcap. 12.5% alc. **Rating** 92 **To** 2013 $22

ҮҮҮҮ **Head Red Barossa Valley GSM 2011 Rating** 87 **To** 2013 $25

Heafod Glen Winery

8691 West Swan Road, Henley Brook, WA 6055 **Region** Swan Valley
T (08) 9296 3444 **www**.heafodglenwine.com.au **Open** Wed–Sun 10–5
Winemaker Liam Clarke **Est.** 1999 **Dozens** 2500 **Vyds** 3ha
A combined vineyard and restaurant business, each set on outdoing the other, each with
major accolades. Founder Neil Head taught himself winemaking, but in 2007 employed Liam
Clarke (with a degree in viticulture and oenology), and a string of significant show successes
for Verdelho, Viognier and Reserve Chardonnay has followed. Chesters Restaurant, originally
set up by Paul Smith, was awarded Best Tourism Restaurant in '08 and Best Restaurant at a
Winery – Perth and Surrounds '09, chef James Ward having taken over before those awards
were gained. Exports to Japan.

ҮҮҮҮҮ **Swan Valley Cabernet Sauvignon 2009** Bright colour; opens with a ripe and
            essency blackcurrant pastille bouquet; fresh and vibrant, with a moderately long,
            sweet-fruited conclusion. The modest alcohol is the key to a very attractive wine,
            with an emphatic sense of place. Gold medal Winewise '11. Screwcap. 13.6% alc.
            Rating 94 **To** 2016 $35 BE

ҮҮҮҮ **Swan Valley Verdelho 2011 Rating** 90 **To** 2014 $26

Heartland Wines

The Winehouse, Wellington Road, Langhorne Creek, SA 5255 **Region** Langhorne Creek
T (08) 8363 4456 **www**.heartlandwines.com.au **Open** 7 days 10–5
Winemaker Ben Glaetzer **Est.** 2001 **Dozens** 80 000
A joint venture of industry veterans: winemakers Ben Glaetzer and Scott Collett, and wine
industry management specialist Grant Tilbrook. It uses grapes grown in the Limestone Coast
and Langhorne Creek, predominantly from vineyards owned by the partners. It currently
exports 60% of its make to 38 international markets. The wines are principally contract-made
at Barossa Vintners and are excellent value for money. Exports to all major markets.

ҮҮҮҮ **Directors' Cut Langhorne Creek Shiraz 2010** Deep, dense crimson-
            purple; this really is built for the long haul; cedary/spicy French oak is the first
            aroma encountered on the bouquet and is never far away, but there are waves
            of blackberry, plum and dark chocolate fruits, then round tannins to conclude.
            Screwcap. 14.5% alc. **Rating** 94 **To** 2030 $32

ҮҮҮҮ **Langhorne Creek Dolcetto & Lagrein 2010 Rating** 90
❂   **To** 2016 $20

ҮҮҮҮ **Langhorne Creek Pinot Gris 2011 Rating** 89 **To** Now $20

Heathcote Estate ★★★★★

98 High Street, Heathcote, Vic 3523 **Region** Heathcote
T (03) 5433 2488 **www**.yabbylake.com **Open** 7 days 10–5
Winemaker Tom Carson, Chris Forge **Est.** 1988 **Dozens** 5000 **Vyds** 34ha
Heathcote Estate is a thoroughly professional venture, a partnership between Louis Bialkower,
founder of Yarra Ridge, and Robert G. Kirby, owner of Yabby Lake Vineyards, director of
Escarpment Vineyards (NZ) and chairman of Village Roadshow Ltd. They purchased a prime
piece of Heathcote red Cambrian soil in 1999, planting shiraz (30ha) and grenache (4ha),
the latter an interesting variant on viognier. The wines are matured exclusively in French
oak (50% new). The arrival of the hugely talented Tom Carson as Group Winemaker can
only add lustre to the winery and its wines. The cellar door, situated in an old bakery in the

Heathcote township provides a relaxed dining area with indoor/outdoor seating and offers a range of Grossi produce. Exports to the US, the UK, Canada, Sweden, Singapore, Hong Kong and China.

ᵞᵞᵞᵞᵞ **Single Block Release Block F Shiraz 2009** Bright deep crimson; surprisingly understated in style, the bouquet offering an array of fresh red fruits, spices and enticing floral aromas; the medium-bodied palate is lively, focused and shows plenty of detail and interest. While ready to enjoy now, it will continue to deliver perfume and power for years to come. Screwcap. 14.5% alc. **Rating** 96 **To** 2030 $80 BE

Single Vineyard Shiraz 2010 Impenetrable colour; no shrinking violet in any regard, this dense, muscular and deeply fruited wine is full of tar, licorice, sage and a veritable cornucopia of black fruits; the tannins dominate this as a young wine, but the concentration and complexity are undeniable; full-blooded and full throttle, with the stuffing to go the distance. Screwcap. 14.5% alc. **Rating** 95 **To** 2030 $45 BE

Heathcote Winery   ★★★★

183–185 High Street, Heathcote, Vic 3523 **Region** Heathcote
T (03) 5433 2595 **www**.heathcotewinery.com.au **Open** 7 days 10–5
Winemaker Rachel Brooker **Est.** 1978 **Dozens** 8000 **Vyds** 15.25ha
The cellar door of Heathcote Winery is situated in the main street of the region, housed in a restored miner's cottage built by Thomas Craven in 1854 to cater for the huge influx of gold miners. The winery is immediately behind the cellar door, and processed the first vintage in 1983, following the planting of the vineyards in '78. In '97 the winery was purchased by an independent group of wine enthusiasts, led by Stephen Wilkins. When first established, the emphasis was on white wines, but it has since moved decisively in the direction of Shiraz and Shiraz Viognier, with 60% of the total plantings devoted to shiraz. Part of this move came with the establishment of the Slaughterhouse Paddock Vineyard, 3km north of Heathcote, with 4ha of shiraz.

ᵞᵞᵞᵞᵞ **Slaughter House Paddock Shiraz 2010** Deep crimson-purple; the black fruits, anise and spice of the bouquet lead into a medium- to full-bodied palate, the fruit flavours carrying the 20% new American oak well, the tannins ripe. Pushes the alcohol envelope. Screwcap. 14.8% alc. **Rating** 91 **To** 2030 $40

Heathvale   ★★★★

Saw Pit Gully Road, via Keyneton, SA 5353 **Region** Eden Valley
T (08) 8564 8248 **www**.heathvale.com **Open** At Taste Eden Valley, Angaston
Winemaker Trevor March **Est.** 1987 **Dozens** 1500 **Vyds** 10ha
The origins of Heathvale go back to 1865, when William Heath purchased the property, building the homestead and establishing the vineyard. The wine was initially made in the cellar of the house, which still stands on the property (now occupied by owners Trevor and Faye March). The vineyards were re-established in 1987, and consist of shiraz (4.5ha), cabernet sauvignon, riesling and chardonnay (2ha each), and sagrantino (0.5ha). The onsite winery was completed in 2008. Exports to China.

ᵞᵞᵞᵞᵞ **Eden Valley Riesling 2011** Pale green-quartz; has vibrant citrus blossom and apple aromas that translate directly to the palate, with racy acidity providing structure and length. Screwcap. 12% alc. **Rating** 92 **To** 2021 $23

Eden Valley Sagrantino 2010 Good crimson-purple; has similarities to the Amadio Sagrantino, except that there is more of everything, the least difference being the 0.5% more alcohol in this wine; right now the spicy, juicy freshness of the Amadio is more attractive, but this wine has a long life ahead, when some of the corners may be softened, the tannins rounded. Screwcap. 14.5% alc. **Rating** 90 **To** 2025 $55

Hedberg Hill ★★★★

701 The Escort Way, Orange, NSW 2800 **Region** Orange
T (02) 6365 3428 **www**.hedberghill.com.au **Open** W'ends 10–5
Winemaker Wallace Lane Wine Company (Philip Kerney) **Est.** 1998 **Dozens** 1000
Vyds 5.6ha
Peter and Lee Hedberg have established their hilltop vineyard 4km west of Orange, with
0.8ha each of cabernet sauvignon, merlot, tempranillo, chardonnay, viognier, sauvignon blanc
and riesling. The cellar door, opened in June 2010, has great views of Mt Canobolas and the
surrounding valleys. The appointment of Wallace Lane/Phil Kerney as winemaker has seen a
significant increase in quality, however difficult the 2011 vintage proved to be.

 Claudia's Orange Viognier 2010 Rating 94
To 2014 $20

Lara's Orange Chardonnay 2010 Rating 89
To Now $20
Guy's Orange Sauvignon Blanc 2011 Rating 88 To 2013 $16 BE

Heemskerk ★★★★★

131 Cascade Road, South Hobart, Tas 7004 (postal) **Region** Southern Tasmania
T 1300 651 650 **www**.heemskerk.com.au **Open** Not
Winemaker Anna Pooley **Est.** 1974 **Dozens** NFP **Vyds** 5.2ha
The Heemskerk brand established by Graham Wiltshire when he planted the first vines in
1965 (in the Pipers River region) is a very different business these days. It is part of the TWE,
and sources its grapes from three vineyards: the Riversdale Vineyard in the Coal River Valley
for riesling; the Lowestoft Vineyard in the Derwent Valley for pinot noir; and the Tolpuddle
Vineyard in the Coal River Valley for chardonnay. Here there is a link with the past, for
winemaker Anna Pooley was born in the Coal River region, where her parents have their own
vineyard and winery, Pooley Wines, with brother Matt in charge of winemaking.

 Coal River Valley Chardonnay 2010 Made from grapes grown on the mature
Tolpuddle Vineyard, a vineyard purchased by Shaw & Smith in 2011. This is pure
Tasmania, acidity woven through the wine from go to whoa: oak and extended
lees contact have provided a gloss of creamy/nutty nuances, to a wine of extreme
purity, drive and length. Screwcap. 13% alc. Rating 97 To 2018 $50
Coal River Valley Riesling 2011 Light to medium straw-green; very elegant
and fine, but with a lovely touch of passionfruit; great length. Top Gold Tas Wine
Show '12. Screwcap. 11.5% alc. Rating 95 To 2026 $45
Coal River Valley Chardonnay Pinot Noir 2007 Pale straw-green, with
persistent mousse; most, if not entirely, sourced from the Tolpuddle Vineyard and
fermented in its elegant bottle. It has a base of white peach and nectarine fruit, a
sprinkle of spice, and excellent length. Overall, has elegance and harmony. Cork.
12% alc. Rating 95 To Now $60
Coal River Valley Riesling 2010 Light straw-green; a powerful, potent riesling
with strong lime/spice/mineral aromas and flavours; the palate is extremely long
and intense, the finish bone dry. Screwcap. 12.5% alc. Rating 94 To 2020 $45

Heggies Vineyard ★★★★★

Heggies Range Road, Eden Valley, SA 5235 **Region** Eden Valley
T (08) 8561 3200 **www**.heggiesvineyard.com **Open** By appt
Winemaker Peter Gambetta **Est.** 1971 **Dozens** 15 000 **Vyds** 62ha
Heggies was the second of the high-altitude (570 m) vineyards established by the Hill-Smith
family. Plantings on the 120ha former grazing property began in 1973; the principal varieties
are riesling, chardonnay, viognier and merlot. There are then two special plantings: a 1.1ha
reserve chardonnay block, and 27ha of various clonal trials. Exports to all major markets.

ᵀᵀᵀᵀᵀ **Reserve Eden Valley Chardonnay 2009** Light, bright green-gold; made from the distinguished French Dijon clones 76, 95 and 96, planted on a special 1.3ha block within the Heggies vineyard; the wine has outstanding finesse and length, very likely wild yeast-fermented, but that's not the foundation for its quality – it's those clones, and the purity of the chardonnay fruit they deliver. Screwcap. 12.5% alc. **Rating** 96 **To** 2017 $40

✪ **Eden Valley Riesling 2011** Bright straw-green; a flowery and fragrant lime blossom bouquet, then a palate with lime and mineral strands interwoven on the long, balanced palate. Screwcap. 12% alc. **Rating** 95 **To** 2026 $24

✪ **Reserve Eden Valley Riesling 2006** Gleaming green-gold; what a stunningly fresh and vibrant 5-year-old, magically combining youth (mainly) with maturity (less so). Its structure is flawless, the length wonderful. Years still to go. Screwcap. 12.5% alc. **Rating** 95 **To** 2021 $29

Eden Valley Botrytis Riesling 2011 The vintage caused many problems, but it was perfect for the development of botrytis; the wine has wonderfully concentrated and focused lime juice flavours, the residual sugar and acidity perfectly balanced. 375ml. Screwcap. 10% alc. **Rating** 95 **To** 2015 $29

Eden Valley Chardonnay 2010 Hand-picked, wild yeast-fermented and barrel-aged for 11 months. Bright straw-green, it is exceptionally powerful for a chardonnay at this alcohol level, and the flavours are more in the stone fruit than citrus spectrum. Interesting wine in many ways. Screwcap. 12.5% alc. **Rating** 94 **To** 2015 $30

Heidenreich Estate   ★★★☆

PO Box 99, Tanunda, SA 5352 **Region** Barossa Valley
T (08) 8563 2644 **www.**heidenreichvineyards.com.au **Open** By appt
Winemaker Noel Heidenreich, Mark Jamieson **Est.** 1998 **Dozens** 2000 **Vyds** 47.3ha
The Heidenreich family arrived in the Barossa in 1857, with successive generations growing grapes ever since. It is now owned and run by Noel and Cheryl Heidenreich who, having changed the vineyard plantings and done much work on the soil, were content to sell the grapes from their 45ha (at three different sites) of shiraz, cabernet sauvignon, cabernet franc, viognier and chardonnay until 1998, when they and friends crushed a tonne in total of shiraz, cabernet sauvignon and cabernet franc. Since that time, production has increased to around 2000 dozen, much exported to San Diego (US), and a little sold locally, the remainder exported to the US, Hong Kong and China.

ᵀᵀᵀᵀ **The Old School Principals Barossa Valley Shiraz 2007** Colour development normal for age; a thoroughly traditional style with plum and dark berry fruits woven through with vanillin oak; has none of the usual toughness of the vintage. Screwcap. 14.5% alc. **Rating** 88 **To** 2015 $30

Heirloom Vineyards   ★★★★★

PO Box 71, Stirling, SA 5152 **Region** Adelaide Zone
T (08) 8556 6099 **www.**heirloomvineyards.com.au **Open** Not
Winemaker Elena Brooks **Est.** 2006 **Dozens** NFP
This is (yet another) venture for Zar Brooks and his wife Elena. They met during the 2000 vintage, and one thing led to another, as they say. Dandelion Vineyards and Zonte's Footstep came along first, and continue, but other partners are involved in those ventures. The lofty aims here are to preserve the best of tradition, the old world of wine, the unique old vineyards of SA, and to champion the best clones of each variety, embracing the principles of organic and biodynamic farming. I don't doubt for one moment the sincerity of the underlying sentiments, but there's a fair degree of Brooksian marketing spin involved. Having said that, the quality of their first wines is outstanding, easily putting Heirloom Vineyards into the Best New Wineries list. No wines were received for this edition; the rating is that of last year.

Helen's Hill Estate ★★★★★

16 Ingram Road, Lilydale, Vic 3140 **Region** Yarra Valley
T (03) 9739 1573 www.helenshill.com.au **Open** 7 days 10–5
Winemaker Scott McCarthy **Est.** 1984 **Dozens** 10 000 **Vyds** 53ha
Helen's Hill Estate is named after the previous owner of the property, Helen Fraser. Venture partners Andrew and Robyn McIntosh and Roma, Allan and Christine Nalder combined childhood farming experience with more recent careers in medicine and finance to establish and manage the day-to-day operations of the estate. The estate produces two labels: Helen's Hill Estate and Ingram Rd, both labels made onsite by Scott McCarthy. Scott started his career early by working vintages during school holidays before gaining diverse and extensive experience in the Barossa and Yarra valleys, Napa Valley, Languedoc, the Loire Valley and Marlborough. The winery, cellar door complex and elegant 140-seat restaurant command some of the best views in the valley. Exports to Hong Kong and the Maldives.

♀♀♀♀♀ **Single Vineyard Yarra Valley Cabernets 2008** Deep, dense red-purple; a blend of cabernet sauvignon, merlot, cabernet franc, malbec and petit verdot; an unusually full-bodied Bordeaux blend by Yarra Valley standards, yet the depths of the black fruits are not heavy, and the tannins are precisely structured and balanced. This is a certain 40+-year cellar proposition. Screwcap. 13.8% alc. **Rating** 95 **To** 2050 $35
Single Vineyard Yarra Valley Chardonnay 2010 Pale straw-green; has (just) stayed on the right side of ripeness balance; barrel fermentation and maturation in French oak have been perfectly judged, providing support and a degree of complexity to an elegant wine with equal contributions of grapefruit, white peach and nectarine. Screwcap. 11.9% alc. **Rating** 94 **To** 2017 $30
Single Vineyard Yarra Valley Pinot Noir 2010 Strong, clear red-purple; estate-grown MV6, 113 and 114 clone grapes have come together in a top vintage to provide a pinot that has both depth and length to its display of dark plum and cherry fruit, French oak having its say, as do fine tannins – all in tune with each other. Screwcap. 13.9% alc. **Rating** 94 **To** 2017 $30
Single Vineyard Yarra Valley Syrah 2010 Excellent purple-crimson; a very good rendition of Yarra Valley shiraz; both the bouquet and palate have an array of black and red berry fruits; the fine but persistent tannins adding structure, French oak also adding to the length of the palate. Screwcap. 14.6% alc. **Rating** 94 **To** 2025 $30

♀♀♀♀♀ **Ingram Rd Yarra Valley Chardonnay 2010** Rating 93
○   **To** 2016 $18
○   **Ingram Rd Yarra Valley Pinot Noir 2010** Rating 92 **To** 2015 $18
○   **Ingram Rd Yarra Valley Pinot Grigio 2011** Rating 90 **To** Now $18
○   **Ingram Rd Central Victoria Shiraz Cabernets 2009** Rating 90 **To** 2015 $18

♀♀♀♀ **Evolution Single Vineyard Yarra Valley Fume Blanc 2010** Rating 88 **To** 2014 $30

Helm ★★★★★

19 Butts Road, Murrumbateman, NSW 2582 **Region** Canberra District
T (02) 6227 5953 www.helmwines.com.au **Open** Thurs–Mon 10–5
Winemaker Ken and Stephanie Helm **Est.** 1973 **Dozens** 5000 **Vyds** 17ha
Ken Helm is an energetic promoter of his wines and of the Canberra District generally. For some years now his wines have been of the highest standard, the Rieslings receiving conspicuous show success and critical acclaim. Plantings have steadily increased, with riesling (8ha), cabernet sauvignon (6ha), shiraz, gewurztraminer and chardonnay (1ha each), plus smaller plantings of other varieties. Exports to Macau and Hong Kong.

ŶŶŶŶŶ Classic Dry Canberra District Riesling 2011 Pale quartz; the bouquet is as yet restrained, albeit with some citrus and apple blossom, the palate another thing altogether, with an admirable racy/zesty edge carrying the wine through to its long finish and aftertaste. Will develop very well; my points are based on my certainty that this will happen. Screwcap. 11.2% alc. Rating 94 To 2018 $30

ŶŶŶŶŶ Premium Canberra District Cabernet Sauvignon 2009 Rating 93 To 2029 $52
Canberra District Cabernet Sauvignon 2009 Rating 90 To 2024 $35
Half Dry Canberra District Riesling 2011 Rating 90 To 2020 $25

Henley Hill Wines   ★★★★

1 Mount Morton Road, Belgrave South, Vic 3160 (postal) **Region** Yarra Valley
T 0414 563 439 **www**.henleyhillwines.com.au **Open** Not
Winemaker Travis Bush (Contract) **Est.** 2003 **Dozens** 3350 **Vyds** 12.28ha
The history of Henley Hill dates back to 1849, when Rowland Hill began growing crops in the Yarra Valley; the home was built in the 1860s by David Mitchell, Dame Nellie Melba's father. The property adjoined Gulf Station, but when that property was sold in the 1930s the home was moved to Henley and re-erected by Clive and Hilda Hill. Clive then purchased an 80ha property adjoining Gulf Station, completing a full circle for the origins of the Henley name. In 2003 Debbie Hill (Clive's granddaughter), Errol Campbell (Debbie's father-in-law) and Nick and Andrew Peterson planted chardonnay, sauvignon blanc, pinot gris and shiraz. Errol, Nick and Andrew are long-time partners in various business ventures in the hospitality industry and property development.

ŶŶŶŶŶ Yarra Valley Pinot Noir 2010 Clear crimson-purple; attractive spicy red berry aromas run through to the start of the palate, with some forest characters then revealing themselves in a support role for the red cherry and plum fruit. Works well. Screwcap. 12.5% alc. Rating 92 To 2016 $23
Yarra Valley Shiraz 2010 Light, bright and clear red-purple; a fragrant red and black cherry bouquet leads into a light but appealing juicy palate, fusing fruit, oak and fine tannins Screwcap. 13.2% alc. Rating 90 To 2017 $23

Henry's Drive Vignerons   ★★★★

41 Hodgson Road, Padthaway, SA 5271 **Region** Padthaway
T (08) 8765 5251 **www**.henrysdrive.com **Open** 7 days 10–4
Winemaker Renae Hirsch **Est.** 1998 **Dozens** 150 000 **Vyds** 94.9ha
Named after the proprietor of the 19th-century mail coach service that once ran through their property, Henry's Drive Vignerons is the wine operation established by Kim Longbottom and her late husband Mark. Kim is continuing to build the family tradition of winemaking with brands such as Henry's Drive, Parson's Flat, The Trial of John Montford, Dead Letter Office, Pillar Box, Morse Code and The Postmistress. Exports to the UK, the US, Canada, Denmark, Singapore, China and NZ.

ŶŶŶŶŶ Padthaway Shiraz 2009 Deep colour, offering a bouquet of spiced plums, blackberry, liqueur kirsch and bramble; the palate is medium- to full-bodied, with lively acidity and fine tannins; a generous and user-friendly wine. Screwcap. 14% alc. Rating 91 To 2018 $30 BE
Parson's Flat Padthaway Shiraz Cabernet 2009 Deep crimson; a poised blue and black-fruited bouquet, offset by a sprinkling of clove; truly medium-bodied, fleshy and lively; this is easy drinking, but has some cellaring future. Screwcap. 14.5% alc. Rating 91 To 2016 $30 BE

○ Pillar Box Reserve Cabernet Sauvignon 2009 Rating 90 To 2014 $18

ŶŶŶŶ The Trial of John Montford Cabernet Sauvignon 2009 Rating 89 To 2014 $30 BE
Pillar Box Reserve Shiraz 2009 Rating 88 To 2015 $18

✪　**Morse Code Padthaway Chardonnay 2011** Bright and fresh, with melon, spice and lemony acidity; clean, easy and made for early consumption. Screwcap. 12% alc. **Rating** 87 **To** 2014 $12 BE

✪　**Morse Code Padthaway Shiraz 2010** Mid garnet; a soft and juicy wine that is medium-bodied, accessible and fresh, with blackberry, fresh leather and a splash of mint. Screwcap. 14.5% alc. **Rating** 87 **To** 2015 $12
Reserve Padthaway Shiraz 2009 Rating 87 **To** 2014 $55 BE

Henschke ★★★★★

Henschke Road, Keyneton, SA 5353 **Region** Eden Valley
T (08) 8564 8223 **www**.henschke.com.au **Open** Mon–Fri 9–4.30, Sat 9–12, public hols 10–3
Winemaker Stephen Henschke **Est.** 1868 **Dozens** 30 000 **Vyds** 121.72ha
Regarded as the best medium-sized red wine producer in Australia, Henschke has gone from strength to strength over the past three decades under the guidance of winemaker Stephen and viticulturist Prue Henschke. The red wines fully capitalise on the very old, low-yielding, high-quality vines and are superbly made with sensitive but positive use of new small oak: Hill of Grace is second only to Penfolds Grange as Australia's red wine icon (since 2005 sold with a screwcap). Exports to all major markets.

♙♙♙♙♙　**Julius Eden Valley Riesling 2011** Light straw-green; a perfumed wine of outstanding texture and structure that carry the cascade of lime and lime zest fruit through to the long, imperious finish. Great things in store. Screwcap. 11% alc. **Rating** 96 **To** 2021 $33
Mount Edelstone 2009 Deep crimson; a delightful euphony of red fruits, black fruits, quartz, spices and a touch of briary complexity; the medium-bodied palate is poised and precise, offering a velvety armchair ride to a long, even and multilayered conclusion; wonderful nerve and energy, with a very long life ahead indeed. Shiraz. Screwcap. 14.5% alc. **Rating** 96 **To** 2040 $124 BE
Hill of Grace 2007 The colour is relatively light, but the hue clear and youthful. The wine is by no means a blockbuster, and neatly sidesteps the tough tannin issue that dogged many red wines from the vintage. There is a profusion of red and black cherry and plum fruit flavours encircled by fine, gently savoury and ripe tannins. The overall balance is impeccable, as befits a wine of this stature. Screwcap. 14% alc. **Rating** 96 **To** 2030 $620

✪　**Green's Hill Lenswood Riesling 2011** Light straw-green; the bouquet is flowery, with lime and apple blossom leading into a marvellously juicy lime and lemon sherbet palate, the backbone of minerality is there but not overt. Screwcap. 11.5% alc. **Rating** 95 **To** 2026 $25
Keyneton Euphonium 2009 Rating 94 **To** 2025 $54 BE
Henry's Seven 2010 Rating 94 **To** 2018 $38 BE
Lenswood Blanc de Noir NV Rating 94 **To** Now $50

♙♙♙♙♙　**Johann's Garden Grenache 2010 Rating** 92 **To** 2020 $46 BE
Peggy's Hill Eden Valley Riesling 2011 Rating 90 **To** 2018 $23 BE
Tappa Pass Vineyard Selection Eden Valley Shiraz 2009 Rating 90 **To** 2019 $85 BE

♙♙♙♙　**Eleanor's Cottage Eden Valley Adelaide Hills Sauvignon Blanc Semillon 2011 Rating** 88 **To** 2014 $25 BE
Giles Lenswood Pinot Noir 2010 Rating 88 **To** 2018 $56 BE

Hentley Farm Wines ★★★★★

Cnr Jenke Road/Gerald Roberts Road, Seppeltsfield, SA 5355 **Region** Barossa Valley
T (08) 8562 8427 **www**.hentleyfarm.com.au **Open** 7 days 10–5
Winemaker Andrew Quin **Est.** 1999 **Dozens** 10 000 **Vyds** 38.21ha
Keith and Alison Hentschke purchased Hentley Farm in 1997, as an old vineyard and mixed farming property. Keith has thoroughly impressive credentials, having studied agricultural science at Roseworthy, and then wine marketing, obtaining an MBA. During the 1990s he

had a senior production role with Orlando, before moving on to manage one of Australia's largest vineyard management companies, and from 2002 to '06 he worked with Nepenthe. Shiraz (26.83ha), grenache (6.46ha), cabernet sauvignon (4ha), zinfandel (0.78ha) and viognier (0.14ha) are now in production. The vineyard, situated among rolling hills on the banks of Greenock Creek, has red clay loam soils overlaying shattered limestone, lightly rocked slopes and little topsoil. Exports to the US and other major markets.

ŸŸŸŸŸ **The Beauty Barossa Valley Shiraz 2010** Dense crimson-purple; estate-grown and co-fermented with viognier; it is medium-bodied, yet there is an extraordinary array of flavours, as deep seated as they are long; the viognier adds that touch of fruit sweetness, but there is every black fruit you care to name, along with spice, pepper and licorice. The only discordant note is the cork, with substantial staining along the sides. 14.4% alc. **Rating** 96 **To** 2030 $60

Clos Otto Barossa Valley Shiraz 2010 Deep, impenetrable purple, grading all the way to the rim; the bouquet sends wave upon wave of blackberry and black cherry fruit, coupled with licorice, to announce the spectacular palate that follows; oak plus touches of licorice and bitter chocolate join forces with the fruits of the bouquet; despite its massive frame, the wine is well-balanced and, cork permitting, has many decades in front of it. Do remember that this is for lovers of full-bodied Barossa shiraz, and is rated for them. 15% alc. **Rating** 96 **To** 2040 $160

The Beast Barossa Valley Shiraz 2010 The depth of colour of the top-end Hentley Farm wines is unequalled; it seems almost black until you look at the rim, which is purple-crimson. To say the wine is full-bodied is a masterly understatement, I shouldn't play god or de facto winemaker, but I have to wonder what the wine would deliver with only 14.5% alcohol in a year such as '10; having got that off my chest, you cannot separate the tannins from the fruit, or vice versa, and the alcohol only becomes obvious if you go on a mission looking for it. Cork. 15.5% alc. **Rating** 95 **To** 2040 $80

The Creation Barossa Valley Shiraz Cabernet 2010 A unique wine; a blend of shiraz and cabernet from H-block on the vineyard. It has the usual dense, deep colour, and a black hole in space of potent, rich and velvety blackcurrant/blackberry fruits; ripe tannins and oak fulfil their usual role with the Hentley Farm style. Cork. 15% alc. **Rating** 95 **To** 2035 $110

von Kasper Barossa Valley Cabernet Sauvignon 2010 **Rating** 94 **To** 2030 $80

ŸŸŸŸŸ **The Exception Eden Valley Riesling 2011** **Rating** 93 **To** 2021 $23
Barossa Valley Grenache 2010 **Rating** 92 **To** 2020 $60

ŸŸŸŸ
✪ **Barossa Valley Viognier 2011** **Rating** 89 **To** 2014 $45
Dirty Bliss Barossa Valley Grenache Shiraz 2011 **Rating** 89 **To** 2015 $20
Barossa Valley Zinfandel 2011 **Rating** 89 **To** 2015 $35
Caretaker Barossa Valley Shiraz 2011 **Rating** 88 **To** 2015 $20
The Stray Mongrel 2011 **Rating** 87 **To** 2015 $35

Henty Estate   ★★★★☆

657 Hensley Park Road, Hamilton, Vic 3300 (postal) **Region** Henty
T (03) 5572 4446 **www**.henty-estate.com.au **Open** Not
Winemaker Peter Dixon **Est.** 1991 **Dozens** 1500 **Vyds** 7ha
Peter and Glenys Dixon have hastened slowly with Henty Estate. In 1991 they began the planting of 4.5ha of shiraz, 1ha each of cabernet sauvignon and chardonnay, and 0.5ha of riesling. In their words, 'we avoided the temptation to make wine until the vineyard was mature', establishing the winery in 2003. Encouraged by neighbour John Thomson, they have limited the yield to 3–4 tonnes perha on the VSP-trained, dry-grown vineyard.

ŸŸŸŸŸ **Cabernet Sauvignon 2009** Medium crimson-purple; the warm vintage allowed this medium-bodied cabernet to reach full flavour ripeness, albeit in a cassis and red fruit spectrum; controlled French oak maturation has resulted in an elegant, well-balanced wine. Screwcap. 14% alc. **Rating** 91 **To** 2017 $24

Shiraz 2009 Medium red-purple; a spicy, tangy, savoury cool-climate shiraz, with bright, red cherry fruit, and integrated French oak; good length and aftertaste. Screwcap. 14% alc. **Rating** 90 **To** 2019 $24

Herbert Vineyard

Bishop Road, Mount Gambier, SA 5290 **Region** Mount Gambier
T 0408 849 080 **www**.herbertvineyard.com.au **Open** By appt
Winemaker David Herbert **Est.** 1996 **Dozens** 500 **Vyds** 2.4ha
David and Trudy Herbert have planted 1.9ha of pinot noir, and a total of 0.5ha of cabernet sauvignon, merlot and pinot gris (the majority of the pinot noir is sold for sparkling wine). They have built a two-level (mini) winery overlooking a 1300-sq metre maze planted in 2000, which is reflected in the label logo.

ŸŸŸŸŸ **Mount Gambier Chardonnay 2010** Bright straw-green; wild fermented in
✪   French oak, the wine has a striking, funky and complex bouquet that carries through to the intense and long palate. Enticing now, but will develop even greater complexity over the next few years, and continue thereafter. Outstanding bargain. Screwcap. 12.4% alc. **Rating** 94 **To** 2020 $19

ŸŸŸŸŸ **Mount Gambier Pinot Noir 2010** **Rating** 90 **To** 2016 $24

ŸŸŸŸ **Talbot Road Mount Gambier Pinot Noir 2010** **Rating** 89 **To** 2015 $24
✪   **Mount Gambier Cabernet Plus 2010** An 85/12/3% blend of cabernet sauvignon, merlot and cabernet franc; bright, clear crimson; the wine reflects the very cool Mount Gambier climate with its lively redcurrant fruit, tannins playing a back-seat role. Screwcap. 12.5% alc. **Rating** 89 **To** 2017 $19
       Blanc de Blanc 2010 **Rating** 89 **To** 2014 $27

Heritage Estate

Granite Belt Drive, Cottonvale, Qld 4375 **Region** Granite Belt
T (07) 4685 2197 **www**.heritagewines.com.au **Open** 7 days 9–5
Winemaker John Handy **Est.** 1992 **Dozens** 5000 **Vyds** 10ha
Heritage Estate (owned by Bryce and Paddy Kassulke) has two estate vineyards in the Granite Belt, one at Cottonvale (north) at an altitude of 960m, where it grows white varieties, and the other at Ballandean, a slightly warmer site where red varieties and marsanne are planted. Heritage Estate has been a prolific award-winner in various Qld wine shows and (I am pleased to report) it has invested in a new bottling line enabling it to use screwcaps.

ŸŸŸŸŸ **Merlot Cabernet 2011** Deep crimson, bright; a poised, fresh and vibrant bouquet of cassis, olive, herbal complexity and cedar; medium-bodied, fleshy and accessible, the balance of the parts is truly working in harmony as a youthful early-drinking wine. Diam. 13.5% alc. **Rating** 90 **To** 2015 $25 BE

ŸŸŸŸ **Granite Belt Marsanne 2011** A subdued bouquet of lime, nectarine, straw and
✪   anise is followed by a taut palate of citrus fruit and bath talc complexity; fresh and fragrant. Diam. 12.5% alc. **Rating** 89 **To** 2014 $19 BE
      Mourvedre Shiraz 2011 **Rating** 89 **To** 2016 $25 BE
      Granite Belt Savagnin 2011 **Rating** 87 **To** 2013 $25 BE

Heritage Wines

106a Seppeltsfield Road, Marananga, SA 5355 **Region** Barossa Valley
T (08) 8562 2880 **www**.heritagewinery.com.au **Open** Mon–Fri 10–5, w'ends & public hols 11–5
Winemaker Stephen Hoff **Est.** 1984 **Dozens** 5000 **Vyds** 8.3ha
A little-known winery that deserves a far wider audience, for veteran owner/winemaker Stephen Hoff is apt to produce some startlingly good wines. At various times the Riesling (from old Clare Valley vines), Cabernet Sauvignon and Shiraz (now the flag-bearer) have all

excelled. The vineyard is planted to shiraz (5.5ha), cabernet sauvignon (2.5ha) and malbec (0.3ha). Exports to the UK, the US, Thailand, Hong Kong, Malaysia and Singapore.

ΨΨΨΨ **Barossa Semillon 2011 Rating** 89 **To** 2014 $15
O

Hesketh Wine Company ★★★★☆
72 Halifax Street, Adelaide, SA 5000 **Region** Various
T (08) 8232 8622 **F** (08) 8232 8802 **www**.heskethwinecompany.com.au **Open** Not
Winemaker Various **Est.** 2006 **Dozens** 20 000
The Hesketh Wine Company is a New World version of the French négociant éleveur, commonly known in Australia as a virtual winery, and is owned by Jonathon Hesketh, wife Trish and children. Jonathon spent seven years as the Global Sales & Marketing Manager of Wirra Wirra, two and a half years as General Manager of Distinguished Vineyards in NZ working with the Möet Hennessy wine and champagne portfolio, plus the Petaluma group, and also had significant global responsibility for Mars Corporation over a four-year period. He also happens to be the son of Robert Hesketh, one of the key players in the development of many facets of the SA wine industry. The model for Hesketh Wine Company is to find wines that best express the regions they come from and closely monitor their production, but own neither vineyards nor a winery. Exports to the US, Canada and NZ.

ΨΨΨΨΨ **Bright Young Things Adelaide Hills Sauvignon Blanc 2011** Pale quartz;
✪ lively and fresh, with an aromatic bouquet and a zesty fusion of tropical and citrus flavours on the palate; excellent length, finish and aftertaste. Screwcap. 12% alc. Rating 94 **To** 2013 $20

ΨΨΨΨΨ **Scissor Hands Clare Valley Riesling 2010 Rating** 91 **To** 2020 $20

Hewitson ★★★★★
1 Seppeltsfield Road, Dorrien, SA 5355 **Region** Adelaide Zone
T (08) 8212 6233 **www**.hewitson.com.au **Open** 7 days 9–5
Winemaker Dean Hewitson **Est.** 1996 **Dozens** 35 000 **Vyds** 4.5ha
Dean Hewitson was a winemaker at Petaluma for 10 years, during which time he managed to do three vintages in France and one in Oregon as well as undertaking his Masters at the University of California (Davis). It is hardly surprising that the wines are immaculately made from a technical viewpoint. Dean has managed to source 30-year-old riesling from the Eden Valley and 70-year-old shiraz from McLaren Vale; he also makes a Barossa Valley Mourvedre from vines planted in 1853 at Rowland Flat and Barossa Valley Shiraz and Grenache from 60-year-old vines at Tanunda. Between 2008 and '10 Dean progressively established his own winery at Dorrien, completing it in time to process the '10 vintage. A new cellar door opened mid 2012. Exports to the UK, the US and other major markets.

ΨΨΨΨΨ **Private Cellar Barossa Valley Shiraz Mourvedre 2009** Light, clear crimson;
given the medium-bodied weight, the intensity and length of the wine is prodigious; unlike the '08, red fruits, rather than black, are the main theme on the aromatic bouquet and through the palate. Made from very old vines, and comes with a 20-year cellaring guarantee; French oak and fine tannins complete the story of its ultra-limited production. Screwcap. 14% alc. **Rating** 97 **To** 2034 $99
The Mad Hatter McLaren Vale Shiraz 2009 From a single vineyard in the cool Blewitt Springs (unofficial) subregion of McLaren Vale that spent 22 months in new French oak. Its bright crimson colour heralds an elegant medium-bodied wine that has an attractively fragrant bouquet, but soars on the back-palate and finish with its waves of sweet red cherry fruit and gossamer-fine tannins. Screwcap. 14% alc. **Rating** 96 **To** 2030 $70
Old Garden Barossa Valley Mourvedre 2009 Light, clear, but bright red; the mother/daughter relationship with '10 Baby Bush Mourvedre is immediately obvious; this wine has greater intensity to its red fruits, but the same lithe grace and remarkably fine, almost silky, tannins. Will live for a long, long time. Screwcap. 14% alc. **Rating** 96 **To** 2029 $120

Ned & Henry's Barossa Valley Shiraz Mourvedre 2010 Rating 94
To 2025 $25
Miss Harry 2010 Rating 94 To 2030 $23

ꝉꝉꝉꝉꝉ Gun Metal Eden Valley Riesling 2011 Rating 93 To 2024 $26

✪ Baby Bush Barossa Valley Mourvedre 2010 The vineyard was established
with cuttings from the 1853 mourvedre planting (the oldest in the world); light,
bright crimson, the medium-bodied palate has attractive red berry, spicy fruit,
with none of the fearsome tannins the variety can produce. Screwcap. 14% alc.
Rating 93 To 2018 $29

✪ Barossa Valley Rose 2011 A blend of grenache, cinsault and carignan; vivid
puce in colour, it has an aromatic bouquet, then a finely detailed palate, the dry
finish making it an all-purpose wine. Screwcap. 12.5% alc. Rating 92 To 2014 $18

ꝉꝉꝉꝉ LuLu Adelaide Hills Sauvignon Blanc 2011 Rating 89 To Now $22

Heydon Estate

325 Tom Cullity Drive, Wilyabrup, WA 6280 **Region** Margaret River
T (08) 9755 6995 **www**.heydonestate.com.au **Open** Thurs–Mon 10–5
Winemaker Mark Messenger **Est.** 1988 **Dozens** 1500 **Vyds** 10ha
Margaret River dentist George Heydon (and wife Mary) have been involved in the region's
wine industry since 1995. They became 50% partners in Arlewood, and when that partnership
was dissolved in 2004 the Heydons relinquished their interest in the Arlewood brand but
retained the property and the precious 2ha of cabernet sauvignon and 2.5ha of Gingin
clone chardonnay planted in '88. Additional plantings from '95 include Dijon chardonnay
clones, sauvignon blanc, semillon, shiraz and petit verdot. The first cabernet made under
the Heydon ownership, the '04 W.G. Grace Cabernet Sauvignon, won the trophy for Best
Cabernet Sauvignon at the Margaret River Wine Show '06. The estate is now biodynamic,
near-neighbour Vanya Cullen having no doubt inspired the decision. And if it wasn't already
very obvious, George is a cricket tragic. Exports to the UK and Hong Kong.

ꝉꝉꝉꝉꝉ W.G. Grace Single Vineyard Margaret River Cabernet Sauvignon 2007
Excellent clear purple-crimson; a beautifully articulated cabernet, elegant and
medium-bodied, with ripe blackcurrant and redcurrant fruit giving an almost
juicy mouthfeel, the tannins now fully resolved and perfectly balanced. Screwcap.
14% alc. Rating 96 To 2027 $48
The Willow Single Vineyard Margaret River Chardonnay 2007
Outstanding light green-gold; the bouquet and palate are still fresh and tight in
the primary fruit phase of development, but the balance is such that it is irrelevant
how quickly that development takes place; the palate does not disappoint with its
long, highly focused stream of flavour and all-important acidity. Screwcap. 14% alc.
Rating 94 To 2015 $45

ꝉꝉꝉꝉ The Urn Single Vineyard Margaret River Botrytis Semillon 2007
Rating 88 To 2013 $35

Hidden Creek

Eukey Road, Ballandean, Qld 4382 **Region** Granite Belt
T (07) 4684 1383 **www**.hiddencreek.com.au **Open** Mon & Fri 11–3, w'ends 10–4
Winemaker Jim Barnes **Est.** 1997 **Dozens** 2000 **Vyds** 2ha
A beautifully located vineyard and winery at 1000m on a ridge overlooking the Ballandean
township and the Severn River Valley. The granite boulder–strewn hills mean that the 70ha
property only provides 2ha of vineyard, in turn divided into six different blocks planted to
shiraz and merlot. The business is owned by a group of Brisbane wine enthusiasts and Jim
Barnes, who runs a contract winemaking business as well as making the Hidden Creek wines.

ꝉꝉꝉꝉꝉ Granite Belt Chardonnay 2009 Has unexpected sophistication and finesse,
with clever winemaking embellishing the fruit with barrel fermentation and lees
contact, but taking care not to overwhelm what is essentially light-bodied fruit.
Chablis style, if you prefer. Screwcap. 13.5% alc. Rating 90 To 2016 $22

ioro Granite Belt Verdelho 2010 Pale green-quartz; a verdelho with attitude, thanks
 to its crisp citrus component within the generic fruit salad; the result is a wine
with quite complex fruit flavours and a fresh finish. Screwcap. 13% alc. **Rating** 89
To 2014 $18
Granite Belt Shiraz 2009 Rating 89 To 2019 $25

Higher Plane ★★★★☆
165 Warner Glen Road, Forest Grove, WA 6286 **Region** Margaret River
T (08) 9755 9000 **www.**higherplanewines.com.au **Open** At Juniper Estate
Winemaker Mark Messenger **Est.** 1996 **Dozens** 2000 **Vyds** 15ha
In late 2006 Higher Plane was purchased by Roger Hill and family (of Juniper Estate), but
kept as a stand-alone brand, with different distributors, etc. The Higher Plane vineyards are
planted to all of the key varieties, sauvignon blanc foremost, then chardonnay, semillon and
cabernet sauvignon (shiraz, merlot, cabernet franc, malbec, petit verdot and viognier make up
the rest of the plantings). Exports to Canada, Denmark and Hong Kong.

ioroi Margaret River Cabernet Sauvignon 2009 Deep garnet; lifted and fragrant
pure black fruit bouquet, showing cassis and roasted meat complexity; the palate
is unctuous and laden with sweet fruits, soft on entry and firming up on the long
finish. One of five wines to win gold medals in the Cabernet Sauvignon Trophy
class, National Wine Show '11. Screwcap. 14.5% alc. **Rating** 95 To 2019 $45 BE

ioro Margaret River Sauvignon Blanc 2010 Rating 92 To 2016 $27 BE

ioro South by Southwest Margaret River Cabernet Merlot 2010 Rating 87
To 2015 $20 BE

Hill-Smith Estate ★★★★
Flaxmans Valley Road, Eden Valley, SA 5235 **Region** Eden Valley
T (08) 8561 3200 **www.**hillsmithestate.com **Open** By appt
Winemaker Kevin Glastonbury **Est.** 1979 **Dozens** 5000 **Vyds** 12ha
The vineyard sits at an altitude of 510 m, providing a cool climate that extends the growing
season; rocky, acidic soil, coupled with winter rainfall and dry summers, results in modest
crops of highly flavoured sauvignon blanc. As an added bonus, the vineyard is surrounded by
conservation park.

ioro Eden Valley Chardonnay 2010 Bright straw-green; wild fermented, then
matured for 11 months in tight-grained French oak barriques; a sophisticated
wine, its texture shaped in the winery, its white peach and citrus flavours in the
vineyard. Screwcap. 13% alc. **Rating** 93 To 2016 $24
Eden Valley Sauvignon Blanc 2011 Light straw-green; a fresh, crisp and lively
wine; citrus/herb/mineral characters drive the wine; needs more flesh for even
higher points. Screwcap. 11.5% alc. **Rating** 90 To 2013 $24

Hillbillé ★★★★★
Blackwood Valley Estate, Balingup Road, Nannup, WA 6275 **Region** Blackwood Valley
T (08) 9481 0888 **www.**hillbille.com **Open** By appt
Winemaker Woodlands Wines (Stuart Watson), Naturaliste Vintners (Bruce Dukes)
Est. 1998 **Dozens** 5000 **Vyds** 18ha
Gary and Rai Bettridge have planted chardonnay, shiraz, cabernet sauvignon, merlot, semillon,
sauvignon blanc and viognier on their 75ha family property. The vineyard is situated in the
Blackwood Valley between Balingup and Nannup, which the RAC describes as 'the most
scenic drive in the southwest of WA'. Part of the grape production is sold to other makers,
the remainder vinified for the Hillbillé label. Exports to Japan, Singapore. and Hong Kong.

ioroi Signature James Brittain Chardonnay 2011 The complex bouquet and palate
mark a selection of the best barrels of the vintage, even though the oak impact has
been kept under control; the fruit expression has a veneer of grapefruit constructed
around the mid palate of white peach and spiced pear; oak is handled with absolute
precision and sensitivity. Screwcap. 13.5% alc. **Rating** 94 To 2018 $48

Signature James Brittain Shiraz Viognier 2009 Bright crimson; a light-
to medium-bodied wine, its bouquet and palate significantly enhanced by the
co-fermented viognier; the light and supple palate has very seductive red and black
cherry fruit, the viognier imparting a succulence not often found in a wine of this
weight and length. Screwcap. 14.3% alc. **Rating** 94 **To** 2020 $48

ȚȚȚȚȚ **Estate Shiraz 2009** Clear, bright crimson; an elegant, light- to medium-bodied
✪   wine with a fragrant bouquet of peppery red berry aromas that are precisely
the same drivers on the palate; the tannins are silky smooth, the oak restrained.
Sensitive winemaking at work. Screwcap. 14.9% alc. **Rating** 91 **To** 2019 $18
✪   **Estate Chardonnay 2011** Bright, pale green; the intense flavours of white
peach, grapefruit and apple run through the entire length of the palate. Screwcap.
13% alc. **Rating** 90 **To** 2015 $18

ȚȚȚȚ **Estate Semillon Sauvignon Blanc 2011** Rating 89
✪   **To** 2014 $18

Hillbrook Wines

Cnr Hillbrook Road/Wheatley Coast Road, Quinninup, WA 6258 **Region** Pemberton
T (08) 9776 7202 **www**.hillbrookwines.com.au **Open** Not
Winemaker Castle Rock Estate **Est.** 1996 **Dozens** 1500 **Vyds** 8.2ha
When Brian Ede and partner Anne Walsh left Alice Springs in 1996 to move to Pemberton,
they made (in their words) the ultimate tree change. As well as establishing sauvignon blanc
(3.2ha), semillon (2ha), merlot (1.5ha), pinot noir (1ha) and a smattering of chardonnay, they
have 600 olive trees.

ȚȚȚȚȚ **Pemberton Sauvignon Blanc 2011** Pale colour; a very pungent bouquet, with
✪   tropical fruit lurking beneath grassy notes; the palate is lively and zesty, as are the
finish and aftertaste. Screwcap. 12.9% alc. **Rating** 90 **To** 2013 $19 BE
✪   **Pemberton Merlot 2010** Bright colour; a spicy and distinctly leafy bouquet
with varietal green olive aromas and a splash of toast; the palate is medium-bodied
and fresh, with firm tannins providing plenty of backbone. Screwcap. 13.5% alc.
Rating 90 **To** 2015 $19 BE

Hillcrest Vineyard

31 Phillip Road, Woori Yallock, Vic 3139 **Region** Yarra Valley
T (03) 5964 6689 **www**.hillcrestvineyard.com.au **Open** By appt
Winemaker David and Tanya Bryant **Est.** 1970 **Dozens** 1000 **Vyds** 8.1ha
The small, effectively dry-grown vineyard was established by Graeme and Joy Sweet, who
ultimately sold it to David and Tanya Bryant. The pinot noir, chardonnay, merlot and cabernet
sauvignon grown on the property have always been of the highest quality and, when
Coldstream Hills was in its infancy, were particularly important resources for it. For some years
the wines were made by Phillip Jones (Bass Phillip), but the winemaking is now carried out
onsite by David and Tanya Bryant.

ȚȚȚȚȚ **Premium Yarra Valley Pinot Noir 2010** Not only are the colours of the three
Hillcrest pinots identical, but so is the stated alcohol on the label, a statistic that
has a degree of elasticity at the best of times. This is far superior to the other two
wines, however good they may be, with plum and black cherry aromas doing faint
justice to the gorgeous supple, round and mouthfilling palate. I could cry about
the cork. 13.1% alc. **Rating** 97 **To** 2020 $58
Premium Yarra Valley Cabernet Sauvignon 2010 Strong colour; has the
depth (and, to a degree, width) that is the hallmark of Hillcrest cabernet. Intense
blackcurrant fruit and a suggestion of black olive, are just the starting point, the
ultimate strength – and future – of the wine lying with its outstanding tannin
structure. Cork. 13.1% alc. **Rating** 96 **To** 2030 $58

Estate Yarra Valley Pinot Noir 2010 Deep purple-crimson, exceptional for pinot noir, although shared with the other two Hillcrest pinots; the complex bouquet has savoury, dried meat and herb aromas initially swept away by the supple dark cherry and pepper flavours of the palate. Oak has been well calibrated in all three wines. Cork. 13.1% alc. **Rating** 95 **To** 2018 $38

Premium Yarra Valley Merlot 2010 Purple-crimson; estate-grown, 40-year-old vines and a unique site all contribute to the quality of this wine; cassis, plum and all-important superfine gossamer tannins provide both flavour and structural cohesion. At the top end of Australian merlots. If you are going to have a cork, let it be of the quality of this perfectly inserted type. 13.1% alc. **Rating** 95 **To** 2025 $58

Village Yarra Valley Pinot Noir 2010 Rating 94 To 2022 $25

ŸŸŸŸŸ Village Yarra Valley Cabernet Sauvignon 2010 **Rating** 92 **To** 2020 $25

Hirsch Hill Estate   ★★★

2088 Melba Highway, Dixons Creek, Vic 3775 **Region** Yarra Valley
T 1300 877 781 **www**.hirschhill.com **Open** Not
Winemaker Yering Farm (Alan Johns) **Est.** 1998 **Dozens** 3500 **Vyds** 12ha
The Hirsch family has planted a vineyard to pinot noir (predominantly), cabernet sauvignon, chardonnay, merlot and cabernet franc. (New plantings of 2.5ha of sauvignon blanc, shiraz and viognier were lost in the Black Saturday bushfires.) The vineyard is part of a larger racehorse stud, situated in a mini-valley at the northern end of the Yarra Valley.

ŸŸŸŸ Yarra Valley Chardonnay 2010 Bright straw-green; a light-bodied chardonnay, with appealing white peach and rockmelon aromas and flavours, but needing more intensity for higher points. Screwcap. 13% alc. **Rating** 88 **To** 2015 $20

Yarra Valley Pinot Noir 2010 Bright, clear crimson; the red and black cherry fruits are partially out-muscled by the tannins, doubtless the reason why the wine has run up a string of bronze medals. Screwcap. 13.5% alc. **Rating** 88 **To** 2017 $38

Hobbs of Barossa Ranges   ★★★★☆

Cnr Flaxmans Valley Road/Randalls Road, Angaston, SA 5353 **Region** Barossa Valley
T 0427 177 740 **www**.hobbsvintners.com.au **Open** At Artisans of Barossa
Winemaker Pete Schell, Chris Ringland (Consultant) **Est.** 1998 **Dozens** 1100 **Vyds** 6.22ha
Hobbs of Barossa Ranges is the high-profile, if somewhat challenging, venture of Greg and Allison Hobbs. The estate vineyards revolve around 1ha of shiraz planted in 1908, another ha planted in '88, a further ha planted in '97, and 1.82ha planted in 2004. In '09 0.4ha of old white frontignac was removed, giving space for another small planting of shiraz. The viticultural portfolio is completed with 0.6ha of semillon planted in the 1960s, and an inspired 0.6ha of viognier ('88). All of the wines made by Peter Schell (at Spinifex) push the envelope. The only conventionally made wine is the Shiraz Viognier, with a production of 130 dozen. Gregor, an Amarone-style Shiraz in full-blooded table wine mode, and a quartet of dessert wines are produced by cane cutting followed by further desiccation on racks. The Grenache comes from a Barossa floor vineyard, the Semillon, Viognier and White Frontignac from estate-grown grapes.

ŸŸŸŸŸ Shiraz 2008 From old (over 90 years) vines; the wine spent 30 months in French oak; only 250 dozen made. It is every bit as potent as its background and alcohol would suggest, but avoids over-extraction. Cork. 15.4% alc. **Rating** 94 **To** 2023 $130

ŸŸŸŸŸ Gregor Shiraz 2008 **Rating** 90 **To** 2020 $130

ŸŸŸŸ With Freckles Viognier 2009 **Rating** 87 **To** Now $31

Hoddles Creek Estate   ★★★★★

505 Gembrook Road, Hoddles Creek, Vic 3139 **Region** Yarra Valley
T (03) 5967 4692 **www**.hoddlescreekestate.com.au **Open** By appt
Winemaker Franco D'Anna, Lucas Hoorn **Est.** 1997 **Dozens** 20 000 **Vyds** 33.3ha

In 1997, the D'Anna family decided to establish a vineyard on the property that had been in the family since 1960. The vineyards (chardonnay, pinot noir, sauvignon blanc, cabernet sauvignon, pinot gris, merlot and pinot blanc) are hand-pruned and hand-harvested. A 300-tonne, split-level winery was completed in 2003. Son Franco is the viticulturist and winemaker; he started to work in the family liquor store at 13, graduating to chief wine buyer by the time he was 21, then completed a Bachelor of Commerce degree at Melbourne University before studying viticulture at CSU. A vintage at Coldstream Hills, then consulting help from Peter Dredge of Red Edge and Mario Marson (ex Mount Mary), has put an old head on young shoulders. Exports to South Africa, Singapore and Japan.

ᵞᵞᵞᵞᵞ **1er Yarra Valley Chardonnay 2010** Bright straw-green; has all the finesse, complexity and length of Hoddles Creek at its very best. It offers a fragrant mix of white peach, nectarine and grapefruit, the latter providing some of the acidity on the lingering finish. The fruit has entirely absorbed the new French oak used in its elevaged. Screwcap. 13.2% alc. **Rating** 96 **To** 2020 $35

○ **Yarra Valley Chardonnay 2010 Rating** 95 **To** 2017 $19
Yarra Valley Chardonnay 2009 Pale straw-green; immaculately made and proportioned; white peach and nectarine fruit are focused by the natural acidity of the wine; while the fruit is very fine, has easily absorbed the impact of barrel ferment. Screwcap. 13.2% alc. **Rating** 95 **To** 2018 $19

○ **Yarra Valley Pinot Noir 2010 Rating** 94 **To** 2016 $19
1er Yarra Valley Pinot Noir 2010 Light, clear crimson; a superfine and very elegant wine, handled with restraint and respect in the winery; the palate is deceptively long, red fruits, spice and forest floor all intermingling. Drink over the next 4+ years. Screwcap. 13.2% alc. **Rating** 94 **To** 2015 $35

ᵞᵞᵞᵞᵞ **1er Yarra Valley Pinot Blanc 2011 Rating** 93 **To** 2018 $40 BE
✪ **Wickhams Road Yarra Valley Shiraz 2011** Vibrant mid crimson; a young, fresh and somewhat ebullient wine showing lots of spice, smoked meats and dark cherry fruit; the palate is medium-bodied and refreshing and is indicative of some of the exciting developments in Yarra Valley shiraz at this point in time; excellent value and a great opportunity to see what the fuss of stems in shiraz is all about. Screwcap. 12.7% alc. **Rating** 90 **To** 2016 $17 BE

ᵞᵞᵞᵞ **Wickhams Road Gippsland Chardonnay 2011 Rating** 89 **To** 2018
✪ $17 BE
✪ **Wickhams Road Gippsland Pinot Noir 2011 Rating** 88 **To** 2013 $17 BE

Hoeyfield   ★★★★
17 Jetty Road, Birchs Bay, Tas 7162 **Region** Southern Tasmania
T (03) 6267 4149 **F** (03) 6267 4249 **Open** By appt
Winemaker Contract **Est.** 1995 **Dozens** 150 **Vyds** 0.5ha
Richard and Jill Pringle-Jones run a postage stamp-sized vineyard of 0.25ha each of pinot noir and chardonnay, planted on a vine-by-vine basis. When they purchased Hoeyfield in 2004, plantings of chardonnay and pinot noir had spread over 1998, '00, and '02; Richard and Jill added more pinot noir (the new Dijon clone 777) in '04 and '05. Following Richard's retirement from sharebroking, Hoeyfield takes up much of his retirement time.

ᵞᵞᵞᵞᵞ **Pinot Noir 2010** Good purple hue; the aromatic, fruit and spice bouquet is
✪ followed by a palate that combines finesse with flavour; the fruit runs through in a fluid stream, building on the characters of the bouquet. Screwcap. 13.5% alc. **Rating** 93 **To** 2016 $25

✪ **Chardonnay 2011** Light straw-green; aromas of freshly cut white peach, and a soupcon of grapefruit, lead into a palate with a particular squeaky acidity. Screwcap. 13.5% alc. **Rating** 90 **To** 2015 $20

Hollick ★★★★★

Riddoch Highway, Coonawarra, SA 5263 **Region** Coonawarra
T (08) 8737 2318 **www**.hollick.com **Open** Mon–Fri 9–5, w'ends & public hols 10–5
Winemaker Ian Hollick, Matthew Caldersmith **Est.** 1983 **Dozens** 30 000 **Vyds** 80ha
A family business owned by Ian and Wendy Hollick, and winner of many trophies (including
the most famous of all, the Jimmy Watson), its wines are well crafted and competitively
priced. The lavish cellar door and restaurant complex is one of the focal points for tourism
in Coonawarra. The Hollicks have progressively expanded their vineyard holdings: the first
is the Neilson's Block, one of the original John Riddoch selections, but used as a dairy farm
from 1910 to '75, when the Hollicks planted cabernet sauvignon and merlot. The second is
the Wilgha Vineyard, purchased in '87 with established dry-grown cabernet sauvignon and
shiraz. The last is the Red Ridge Vineyard in Wrattonbully, which includes trial plantings of
tempranillo and sangiovese. Exports to most major markets.

♀♀♀♀ **Wilgha Coonawarra Shiraz 2009** A wine with a long and proud history,
estate-grown from selected blocks, and matured for 18 months in predominantly
new French oak. Black fruits, Coonawarra earth and strong cedary oak give the
same message to both the bouquet and medium- to full-bodied palate. Time is on
its side. Screwcap. 14.8% alc. **Rating** 94 **To** 2029 $55
Ravenswood Coonawarra Cabernet Sauvignon 2009 Strong colour; a
full-bodied cabernet sourced from the Hollick vineyards in Coonawarra and
Wrattonbully that finishes its fermentation in new French barriques, then spends
18 months in oak. Powerful blackcurrant, earth, cassis and tannins are all captured
by the palate, and it is difficult to see the end point for the wine, so far distant is it
in the future. Screwcap. 14% alc. **Rating** 94 **To** 2040 $80

♀♀♀♀♀ **Coonawarra Cabernet Sauvignon 2010** Rating 93 **To** 2030 $34
Wrattonbully Shiraz 2010 Rating 92 **To** 2025 $27
Tannery Block Coonawarra Cabernet Sauvignon Merlot 2010 Rating 92
To 2020 $27
Tannery Block Coonawarra Cabernet Sauvignon Merlot 2009 Rating 92
To 2017 $24
The Nectar 2011 Rating 91 **To** 2017 $27 BE
Hollaia Wrattonbully Sangiovese Cabernet Sauvignon 2010 Rating 90
To 2017 $24
Coonawarra Sparkling Merlot 2009 Rating 90 **To** 2014 $32

♀♀♀♀ **Bond Road Chardonnay 2010** Rating 89 **To** 2014 $26
Coonawarra Sauvignon Blanc Savagnin Semillon 2011 Rating 88
To 2014 $21 BE
**Stock Route Coonawarra Wrattonbully Shiraz Cabernet Sauvignon
2010** Rating 87 **To** 2014 $22

Hollydene Estate ★★★★

930 Merriwa Road, Denman, NSW 2328 **Region** Hunter Valley
T (02) 6547 1243 **www**.hollydeneestate.com **Open** By appt
Winemaker Inwine (Barry Koorij) **Est.** 1965 **Dozens** 2000 **Vyds** 40ha
Hollydene Estate has two vineyards, Wybong Estate (established in 1965) and Hollydene
(established in '69, and also producing wheat and beef cattle). It is owned by Karen Williams,
who markets the wines under two brands: Juul and Hollydene Estate. In 2012 Hollydene Estate
purchased the Arrowfield Estate winery and vineyard at Jerrys Plains in the Upper Hunter
Valley,; it plans to open a new cellar door/café in late 2012. Exports to Indonesia and China.

♀♀♀♀♀ **Blanc de Noirs 2006** Pinot noir and pinot meunier from the Mornington
Peninsula were used to make this wine via the traditional method, with up to five
years on lees prior to disgorgement. Pale salmon; the first thing that you note on
tasting the wine is its very low dosage, leaving the acidity and tannins unmasked;
there are spicy wild strawberry flavours wrapped up with steely acidity on the
long finish. Diam. 13.4% alc. **Rating** 91 **To** 2014 $28

Juul Blanc de Blancs 2006 Made from 100% chardonnay grown on the Mornington Peninsula, and made using the traditional method, spending five years on lees prior to disgorgement. Gleaming straw-green, it has strong grapefruit and lemon citrus flavours; like the Blanc de Noirs, the dosage is low, placing a lot of emphasis on the minerally acidity – and the need for food to accompany it. Diam. 13.7% alc. **Rating** 90 **To** 2014 $28

Holm Oak ★★★★★

11 West Bay Road, Rowella, Tas 7270 **Region** Northern Tasmania
T (03) 6394 7577 **www**.holmoakvineyards.com.au **Open** 7 days 11–5 Sept–June,
11–4 Jun–Aug
Winemaker Rebecca Duffy **Est.** 1983 **Dozens** 5000 **Vyds** 11.62ha
Holm Oak takes its name from its grove of oak trees, planted around the beginning of the 20th century and originally intended for the making of tennis racquets. In 2004 Ian and Robyn Wilson purchased the property. The vineyard is planted (in descending order) to pinot noir, cabernet sauvignon, chardonnay, riesling, sauvignon blanc and pinot gris, with small amounts of merlot, cabernet franc and arneis. In 2006 the Wilsons' daughter Rebecca (with extensive winemaking experience in Australia and California) became winemaker, and husband Tim Duffy (a viticultural agronomist) has taken over management of the vineyard. A winery was completed just in time for the 2007 vintage.

ŢŢŢŢŢ **Riesling 2010** Light, bright quartz-green; the floral bouquet has a range of aromas coming together on the mouth-watering palate, with lime juice leading the way; typical Tasmanian acidity provides the great length. Screwcap. 12.5% alc. **Rating** 94 **To** 2020 $25
Sauvignon Blanc 2011 Pale quartz; hints of passionfruit and lychee on the bouquet are the precursor to an intense palate partially shaped by 20% barrel fermentation in old oak; the finish and aftertaste are particularly attractive. Screwcap. 12% alc. **Rating** 94 **To** 2014 $25
Pinot Noir 2010 Clear crimson; the expressive bouquet offers red fruits, spice and floral notes; the silky palate has great texture, balance and length, French oak a backdrop to the delicious display of red fruits and cleansing acidity. Screwcap. 14% alc. **Rating** 94 **To** 2013 $32

ŢŢŢŢŢ **Chardonnay 2010 Rating** 93 **To** 2018 $30
Pinot Gris 2011 Rating 93 **To** 2013 $25
Wild Fermented FGR Riesling 2011 Rating 92 **To** 2021 $22
Riesling 2011 Rating 90 **To** 2021 $25
The Wizard Pinot Noir 2009 Rating 90 **To** 2014 $50
TBR Duffy Moscato 2011 Rating 90 **To** Now $22

ŢŢŢŢ **Sparkling Rose NV Rating** 89 **To** Now $32

Home Hill ★★★★☆

38 Nairn Street, Ranelagh, Tas 7109 **Region** Southern Tasmania
T (03) 6264 1200 **www**.homehillwines.com.au **Open** 7 days 10–5
Winemaker Gilli and Paul Lipcombe **Est.** 1994 **Dozens** 2000 **Vyds** 6ha
Terry and Rosemary Bennett planted their first 0.5ha of vines in 1994 on gentle slopes in the beautiful Huon Valley. Between '94 and '99 the plantings were increased to 3ha of pinot noir, 1.5ha of chardonnay and 0.5ha sylvaner. Home Hill has had great success with its exemplary Pinot Noir, a consistent wine show major award winner.

ŢŢŢŢŢ **Kelly's Reserve Late Harvest Sticky 2009** Developed colour; very rich and unctuous, totally filling the mouth; demands a rich dessert. Riesling. Top Gold Tas Wine Show '12. Screwcap. 9.9% alc. **Rating** 94 **To** 2015 $20

ŢŢŢŢŢ **Kelly's Reserve Pinot Noir 2010 Rating** 92 **To** 2014 $50
White Label Pinot Noir 2010 Rating 90 **To** 2014 $25

ŢŢŢŢ **Pinot Noir 2010 Rating** 88 **To** 2017 $35
Kelly's Reserve Late Harvest Sticky 2010 Rating 88 **To** 2015 $20

Honey Moon Vineyard   ★★★★★

PO Box 544, Echunga SA 5153 **Region** Adelaide Hills
T 0419 862 103 **www**.honeymoonvineyard.com.au **Open** Not
Winemaker Jane Bromley, Hylton McLean **Est.** 2005 **Dozens** 500 **Vyds** 0.8ha
Jane Bromley and Hylton McLean planted 0.4ha each of pinot noir (clones 777, 114 and 115) and shiraz (selected from two old vineyards known for their spicy fruit flavours) in 2003. The moon is a striking feature in the landscape, particularly at harvest time when, as a full moon, it appears as a dollop of rich honey in the sky – hence the name. The first vintage was '05, but Jane has been making wine since '01, with a particular interest in Champagne; Hylton is a winemaker, wine science researcher and wine educator with over 20 years' experience.

ŢŢŢŢŢ **Adelaide Hills Shiraz 2009** Clear purple-crimson; partial crushing and destemming into small open fermenters with cultured yeasts; once finished, racked into 43% new French barriques, bottled after 18 months. It has outstanding balance and great length to its palate, which is full of intense cherry and blackberry fruit, the oak absolutely integrated, harmoniously combining with the fruit flavours. Four gold medals in '11 from important shows. Screwcap. 14.5% alc. **Rating** 95 **To** 2020 $41

Rose Brut 2010 Bright, pale pink; close to a blanc de noir, ie 100% pinot noir, with just a tiny addition of chardonnay; the full traditional method has been used, with tiraging and disgorgement at the winery, disgorgement basically on demand. This bottle was tiraged in Dec '10 and disgorged Jan '12. It is a very fragrant and pretty wine, with strawberry and cherry flavours, the palate already well balanced, clean and fresh. Crown seal. 12.5% alc. **Rating** 94 **To** 2015 $39

ŢŢŢŢŢ **Adelaide Hills Pinot Noir 2009 Rating** 90 **To** 2019 $41

Houghton   ★★★★★

Dale Road, Middle Swan, WA 6065 **Region** Swan Valley
T (08) 9274 9540 **www**.houghton-wines.com.au **Open** 7 days 10–5
Winemaker Ross Pamment **Est.** 1836 **Dozens** NFP
Houghton's reputation was once largely dependent on its (then) White Burgundy, equally good when young or 10 years old. In the last 20 years its portfolio has changed out of all recognition, with a kaleidoscopic range of high-quality wines from the Margaret River, Frankland River, Great Southern and Pemberton regions to the fore. The Jack Mann and Gladstones red wines stand at the forefront, the Wisdom range covering all varietal bases in great style. Nor should the value-for-money brands (Stripe, The Bandit and others) be ignored. To borrow a saying of the late Jack Mann, 'There are no bad wines here.' With a history of 175 years, it's future now lies in the hands of Accolade Wines. Exports to the UK and Asia.

ŢŢŢŢŢ **Jack Mann Cabernet Sauvignon 2008** From the single Justin Vineyard in the Frankland River; this speaks of its place of origin even more eloquently than the Gladstones Margaret River Cabernet Sauvignon. The cabernet is effortlessly focused and powerful, the balance, texture, structure, line and length of this beautiful wine certain to carry it long after I have had my ashes scattered. Screwcap. 14% alc. **Rating** 98 **To** 2040 $110

Gladstones Margaret River Cabernet Sauvignon 2008 Holds a youthful, clear purple-crimson hue; from the Wilyabrup area, this is as near a perfect evocation of this part of Margaret River as you can find, with an all too rare purity to the cassis/blackcurrant fruit, framed by perfectly balanced and integrated French oak and fine, persistent tannins. Screwcap. 14% alc. **Rating** 97 **To** 2030 $70

✪ **Wisdom Margaret River Cabernet Sauvignon 2010** Bright purple-crimson; a significant rise in quality from the varietal; here the cabernet varietal fruit is more intense, and with the autocratic personality shared by the best examples of the variety; it also has cedary French oak, perfectly integrated on the supremely elegant and long palate that finishes with fine-grained tannins. Screwcap. 14% alc. **Rating** 96 **To** 2030 $30

Wisdom Pemberton Chardonnay 2011 The fragrant grapefruit and nectarine bouquet flows directly through to the lively palate, collecting some white peach and French oak along the way; despite its precocious display of flavour, will have a long life. Screwcap. 13.5% alc. **Rating** 94 **To** 2018 $30

ŸŸŸŸŸ ✪ **Wisdom Pemberton Sauvignon Blanc 2011** Pale quartz-green; a tale of three parts: passionfruit aroma and flavour; texture from lees contact; and racy acidity. It all adds up. Screwcap. 13% alc. **Rating** 93 **To** 2013 $19

✪ **Museum Release White Classic 2005 Rating** 93 **To** 2017 $32

✪ **Margaret River Cabernet Sauvignon 2010** Mid crimson-purple; only Houghton could come up with a Margaret River cabernet so flush with blackcurrant/cassis fruit, together with some French oak, at this price point, and quite possibly less in some retail shops; the balance of the medium-bodied palate is perfect, and the length is good. Great bargain. Gold medal at the National Wine Show '11. Screwcap. 13.5% alc. **Rating** 93 **To** 2020 $19

✪ **Stripe White Classic 2011** The forerunner to Margaret River Classic Dry White, with sauvignon blanc, semillon, chardonnay, chenin blanc and verdelho all likely contributors to the blend; vibrant fruit salad flavours on its well-balanced, long palate and fresh finish. Screwcap. 13% alc. **Rating** 90 **To** 2014 $15

ŸŸŸŸ **Limited Release 175th Anniversary Heritage Red Blend 2010 Rating** 89 **To** 2014 $19

✪ **Margaret River Chardonnay 2011 Rating** 89 **To** 2015 $19
✪ **Stripe Cabernet Sauvignon 2010 Rating** 89 **To** 2013 $15
✪ **Sauvignon Blanc Semillon 2011 Rating** 88 **To** 2013 $14
Red Classic Cabernet Shiraz Merlot 2010 Rating 87 **To** 2013 $14

Howard Park/MadFish ★★★★★

Miamup Road, Cowaramup, WA 6284 **Region** Margaret River/Denmark
T (08) 9756 5200 **www**.howardparkwines.com.au **Open** 7 days 10–5
Winemaker Janice McDonald, Mark Bailey **Est.** 1986 **Dozens** NFP **Vyds** 163.07ha
Howard Park has two vineyards: Leston in the Margaret River, and Mt Barrow in Mount Barker; it also manages three vineyards, taking the grapes from these. It practises mainly organic viticulture in its owned and managed vineyards, Mt Barrow with a pinot noir block established and operated using biodynamic practices. The Margaret River winery incorporates feng shui principles, and can welcome large groups for concerts, speaking events, film evenings and private parties. Howard Park also operates a cellar door at Scotsdale Road, Denmark (7 days 10–4). The Margaret River flagships are the Leston Shiraz and Leston Cabernet Sauvignon, but the Margaret River vineyards routinely contribute to all the wines in the range, from multi-region MadFish at the bottom, to the iconic Cabernet Sauvignon Merlot at the top. MadFish is a second label, itself with three price tiers: MadFish Gold Turtle, Sideways and (the original) MadFish. Exports to all major markets.

ŸŸŸŸŸ ✪ **Howard Park Porongurup Riesling 2011** Pale straw-green; each year the evidence increases that Porongurup is one of the best regions for long-lived riesling anywhere in Australia. This wine is typically exceptionally fine, and it (and the track record of the region) tells you greatness awaits around the corner in 5+ years' time, and long thereafter. Do not be fooled by the reticence of its youth. Screwcap. 12% alc. **Rating** 96 **To** 2031 $30

Howard Park Abercrombie Cabernet Sauvignon 2010 Deep crimson; a youthful and effusive wine, displaying the very essence of cassis and cedar, with a fairly hefty dose of new oak; undoubtedly built for the long haul, as the concentration of fruit and the impressive level of tannins simply must have time to settle down and integrate with the oak; the wait will be worth it. Screwcap. 14.5% alc. **Rating** 96 **To** 2040 $100 BE

Howard Park Scotsdale Great Southern Cabernet Sauvignon 2010 Deep crimson, bright; a fragrant and perfumed bouquet of blackcurrant, violets and cedar; the palate is silky and approachable as a young wine, yet the backbone of structure indicates a long journey ahead; excellent purity and plenty of power. Screwcap. 14% alc. **Rating** 95 **To** 2025 $45 BE

✪   **MadFish Grandstand Riesling 2011** Made from a single estate-owned vineyard nicknamed 'The Grandstand' by the vineyard workers because of its elevation and view; has a fragrant, flowery citrus blossom bouquet, then an intense palate with lime and mineral tightly wrapped around each other through to the long finish. Screwcap. 12% alc. **Rating** 94 **To** 2021 $17

Howard Park Sauvignon Blanc 2011 Bright straw-green; a complex wine (due partly to a portion of barrel ferment) with a mix of citrus, stone fruit and tropical fruit, sustained by natural acidity. Screwcap. 13% alc. **Rating** 94 **To** 2013 $29

Howard Park Miamup Margaret River Sauvignon Blanc Semillon 2011 This combines sauvignon blanc from the cool southern end of Margaret River and semillon from the somewhat warmer centre; the varieties mesh well, semillon providing the framework of grass, herb and mineral, sauvignon blanc the swell of tropical fruit that fills the mid- and back-palate. Screwcap. 13% alc. **Rating** 94 **To** 2014 $27

Howard Park Great Southern Chardonnay 2010 Mid gold, green hue; the bouquet offers a blend of grapefruit, melon and spices; the palate follows suit, with ripe fruits, charcuterie and an attractive quartz-like minerality providing spine around the relatively soft acidity; grilled cashews persist on the finish. Screwcap. 13.5% alc. **Rating** 94 **To** 2018 $50 BE

Howard Park Leston Margaret River Shiraz 2010 Deep, dark colour, with a dark and brooding character to match; the ample black fruits, ironstone minerality and licorice are all wound up tightly by well-handled oak; the palate is sweet-fruited and generous on entry, with the backbone of structure providing a long and harmonious ride to the extended finish. Screwcap. 14.5% alc. **Rating** 94 **To** 2025 $45 BE

Howard Park Scotsdale Great Southern Shiraz 2010 Deep magenta; the bouquet is a fragrant, perfumed and spiced array of red and black fruits, offset by a touch of lavender and violets; the palate is soft and fleshy, silky and refined, with lacy acidity making way for some fairly serious tannins and charry oak, characters that will see a long and fruitful existence ahead. Screwcap. 14.5% alc. **Rating** 94 **To** 2025 $45 BE

Howard Park Leston Margaret River Cabernet Sauvignon 2010 Deep crimson; a bright and fragrant, pure-fruited bouquet, showing red and black berries, cedar and violets; the medium-bodied palate provides plenty of punch, fine-grained tannins and a long, even and expansive finish. Screwcap. 14% alc. **Rating** 94 **To** 2024 $45 BE

MadFish Vera's Cuvee Methode Traditionnelle NV Pale straw-yellow-gold; a blend of chardonnay and pinot noir from the coolest sites in southern WA, it is lively and fresh, with fine grapefruit and stone fruit flavours, and attractive nutty/spicy yeast influences; good length and balance. Cork. 12.5% alc. **Rating** 94 **To** Now $29

♟♟♟♟♟   **MadFish Sideways Margaret River Chardonnay 2010** Part tank-, part
✪   barrel-fermented in 1 and 2-year-old French barriques, and kept on lees for nine months; the wine has great energy and drive to its mix of grapefruit and stone fruit flavours, yet has a silky edge to the mouthfeel. Screwcap. 13% alc. **Rating** 93 **To** 2017 $22

●   **MadFish Sangiovese Rose 2011 Rating** 93 **To** 2013 $17
✪   **MadFish Sideways Margaret River Sauvignon Blanc Semillon 2011** Made from estate vineyards, with positive, bright colour and some early complexity building on the bouquet and palate, suggesting some work in the winery (lees or a little oak?). Either way, the varieties have fused so completely it's pointless to analyse them one by one. An all-purpose food wine with a two-year future. Screwcap. 13% alc. **Rating** 92 **To** 2013 $22

Howard Park Flint Rock Mount Barker Chardonnay 2010 Rating 92 **To** 2016 $27

MadFish Gold Turtle Margaret River Chardonnay 2010 Rating 92 **To** 2017 $25 BE

Howard Park Flint Rock Great Southern Pinot Noir 2010 Rating 92
To 2018 $27

● MadFish Shiraz 2009 Rating 92 To 2020 $17

✪ MadFish Grandstand Sauvignon Blanc 2011 Pale straw-green; the bouquet
has interesting stone fruit and lychee nuances, met on the palate by pronounced
grassy/green flavours and crisp acidity. Has attitude. Screwcap. 13% alc. Rating 91
To 2013 $17

Howard Park Miamup Margaret River Cabernet Sauvignon 2008
Rating 91 To 2018 $27

Howard Park Great Southern Riesling 2011 Rating 90 To 2014 $30 BE

✪ MadFish Sauvignon Blanc Semillon 2011 Light straw-green; thoroughly
attractive gentle tropical fruit running across the bouquet and palate is backed by
enough acidity on the finish to keep the wine fresh and lively. Screwcap. 13% alc.
Rating 90 To 2014 $17

Jete Methode Traditionnelle NV Rating 90 To 2014 $30 BE

Jete Methode Traditionnelle Rose NV Rating 90 To 2013 $33 BE

Howard Vineyard ★★★★☆

53 Bald Hills Road, Nairne, SA 5252 **Region** Adelaide Hills
T (08) 8188 0203 **www.**howardvineyard.com **Open** Mon–Fri 11–4, w'ends 10–5
Winemaker Ian Northcott, Mark Swann, Michael Sykes **Est.** 2005 **Dozens** 5000
Vyds 60ha
This venture began in the late 1990s with the establishment of two vineyards at different
locations in the Adelaide Hills. The Schoenthal Vineyard near Lobethal, at an elevation of
440–500 m, is planted primarily to sauvignon blanc and chardonnay, with smaller amounts
of pinot noir and pinot gris. The Howard Vineyard is at a lower elevation, and the slightly
warmer site has been planted (in descending order) to sauvignon blanc, chardonnay, semillon,
cabernet sauvignon, shiraz, viognier and cabernet franc. The substantial quantities of grapes not
required for the Howard Vineyard label are sold to other winemakers. Exports to Hong Kong.

♀♀♀♀♀ Adelaide Hills Cabernet Sauvignon 2010 Clear purple-crimson; an estate-
grown, individual block selection; initially shy, it grows and lengthens on retasting;
cassis/blackcurrant fruit is balanced by fine, savoury/earthy tannins; works very
well. Screwcap. 14.4% alc. Rating 94 To 2025 $25

♀♀♀♀♀ Adelaide Hills Shiraz 2010 Rating 93 To 2020 $25

✪ Adelaide Hills Sauvignon Blanc 2011 Pale quartz; a precisely structured and
weighted Sauvignon Blanc, travelling more on the grass, lemon and citrus side than
the tropical; crisp acidity is a given. Screwcap. 11.5% alc. Rating 91 To 2013 $22

Amos Adelaide Hills Chardonnay 2010 Rating 90 To 2025 $38

♀♀♀♀ Gambol Adelaide Hills Shiraz Cabernet 2010 Bright purple-crimson; a

✪ fragrant and fresh bouquet meshes with the lively black and red cherry fruit of the
palate; firm, spicy tannins provide structure. For enjoyment now or down the track.
Screwcap. 13.9% alc. Rating 89 To 2015 $18

Amos Adelaide Hills Cabernet Franc 2009 Rating 89 To 2017 $60

Amos Adelaide Hills Sauvignon Blanc 2010 Rating 88 To 2013 $30

Hugh Hamilton Wines ★★★★★

94 McMurtrie Road, McLaren Vale, SA 5171 **Region** McLaren Vale
T (08) 8323 8689 **www.**hughhamiltonwines.com.au **Open** 7 days 11–5
Winemaker Peter Leske **Est.** 1991 **Dozens** 30 000 **Vyds** 29.03ha
Hugh Hamilton is the fifth generation of the famous Hamilton family, who first planted
vineyards at Glenelg in 1837. A self-confessed black sheep of the family, Hugh embraces
non-mainstream varieties such as sangiovese, tempranillo and viognier, and is one of only
a few growing saperavi. Production comes from estate plantings and a vineyard in Blewitt
Springs of 85-year-old shiraz and 65-year-old cabernet sauvignon. The irreverent black sheep
packaging was the inspiration of daughter Mary (CEO). The cellar door is lined with the

original jarrah from Vat 15 of the historic Hamilton's Ewell winery, the largest wooden vat ever built in the southern hemisphere. Exports to the UK, the US, Canada, Sweden, Finland, Malaysia and China.

ꝐꝐꝐꝐꝐ **Black Blood II Church Vineyard McLaren Vale Shiraz 2010** The colour is not quite up to that of the of the other Single Vineyard Shirazs, but the texture and flavour profile of the full-bodied palate are quite different; here you'll find sombre black fruits and bitter chocolate emerging the moment the wine enters the mouth; the finish is distinctly savoury, the tannins playing an important role in balancing the alcohol. Screwcap. 15% alc. **Rating** 95 **To** 2030 $50
Shearer's Cut Hand Picked McLaren Vale Shiraz 2010 Healthy crimson hue; while its alcohol is high, the wine largely makes light of its burden; classic McLaren Vale flavours of black and red fruits, and savoury but fine tannins on the finish; oak is evident in a support role. Screwcap. 15% alc. **Rating** 94 **To** 2030 $25
Black Blood I Cellar Vineyard McLaren Vale Shiraz 2010 Bright crimson; the luscious palate is lively and fresh, with nuances of black cherry and licorice to go with the foundation of blackberry, plum and dark chocolate; the length and balance are good despite the alcohol. Screwcap. 15% alc. **Rating** 94 **To** 2030 $50
The Villain McLaren Vale Cabernet Sauvignon 2010 Medium crimson; the varietal signature comprehensively outweighs that of the region, which is a very good start; a medium- to full-bodied cabernet that spent 18 months in French barriques without losing the all-important cabernet tannins to go with the cassis/blackcurrant fruit. Screwcap. 14.5% alc. **Rating** 94 **To** 2025 $25
The Odd Ball McLaren Vale Saperavi 2010 Deep, dense purple-crimson; floods the palate with red and black cherry, warm spices and fine, soft tannins; carries its alcohol with ludicrous ease. Cork. 15.5% alc. **Rating** 94 **To** 2030 $45

ꝐꝐꝐꝐꝐ **The Loose Cannon McLaren Vale Viognier 2011** Pale straw-green; barrel
✪ fermentation for part, and lees stirring of all, of the wine has delivered the complexity desired by winemaker Paul Gordon; moreover, the varietal fruit expression has not been compromised. Fresh and zesty. Screwcap. 13.5% alc. **Rating** 93 **To** 2015 $23
The Rascal McLaren Vale Shiraz 2010 Rating 93 **To** 2020 $25
The Odd Ball McLaren Vale Saperavi 2009 Rating 93 **To** 2029 $45
The Ratbag McLaren Vale Merlot 2010 Rating 92 **To** 2017 $25
Jekyll & Hyde McLaren Vale Shiraz Viognier 2010 Rating 91 **To** 2025 $45
The Floozie McLaren Vale Sangiovese Rose 2011 Rating 90 **To** 2013 $23

Hugo ★★★
246 Elliott Road, McLaren Flat, SA 5171 **Region** McLaren Vale
T (08) 8383 0098 **www**.hugowines.com.au **Open** Mon–Fri 9.30–5, Sat 12–5, Sun 10.30–5
Winemaker John Hugo **Est.** 1982 **Dozens** 7000 **Vyds** 25ha
Came from relative obscurity to prominence in the late 1980s with some lovely ripe, sweet reds, which, while strongly American oak-influenced, were quite outstanding. It picked up the pace again after a dull period in the mid 1990s, but seems to have drifted back again. The estate plantings include shiraz, cabernet sauvignon, chardonnay, grenache and sauvignon blanc, with part of the grape production sold to others. Exports to the UK, the US and Canada.

ꝐꝐꝐꝐ **McLaren Vale Shiraz 2009** Good colour; a warm and inviting melange reflecting place, variety, oak (American) and traditional fermentation. Screwcap. 14.5% alc. **Rating** 89 **To** 2016 $23
McLaren Vale Cabernet Sauvignon 2009 Medium to full red-purple; an interesting outcome from earlier harvesting and regional (bitter chocolate) influences; the variety speaks loudest with savoury dark fruits, and just a touch of green bean tannins. Screwcap. 13.5% alc. **Rating** 88 **To** 2017 $22
McLaren Vale Grenache Shiraz 2010 Includes 60-year-old bush-pruned, dry-grown estate grenache fruit; the hot finish is the wine's Achilles heel. Screwcap. 14.5% alc. **Rating** 87 **To** 2015 $21

Humbug Reach Vineyard ★★★★

72 Nobelius Drive, Legana, Tas, 7277 **Region** Northern Tasmania
T (03) 6330 2875 **www**.humbugreach.com.au **Open** Not
Winemaker Paul McShane, Bass Fine Wines (Guy Wagner) **Est.** 1988 **Dozens** 200
Vyds 1ha

The Humbug Reach Vineyard was established in the late 1980s on the banks of the Tamar River with plantings of pinot noir; riesling and chardonnay followed. Since '99 it has been owned by Paul and Sally McShane, who proudly tend the 6000 vines on the property. After frost decimated the 2007 vintage, Sally and Paul, wanting to become involved in winemaking, brought the process closer to home, with Guy Wagner making the Riesling and Chardonnay, Paul making the Pinot Noir (commuting from the Sustainability Institute at Monash University in Melbourne to do so).

🍷🍷🍷🍷½ **Chardonnay 2010** Bright green-straw; a fragrant, fruit-driven bouquet, then a fresh, zesty palate, the flavour accent in the citrus/grapefruit end of the spectrum, and needing just a touch more ripe fruit to give full flavour balance. Screwcap. 13% alc. **Rating** 90 **To** 2016 $32

Pinot Noir 2010 Clear red-purple; has plenty of weight and concentration to the plum and cherry aromas and flavours; a couple of years away from its best. Screwcap. 13.5% alc. **Rating** 90 **To** 2016 $40

🍷🍷🍷🍷 **Riesling 2011** **Rating** 89 **To** 2018 $25
Chardonnay 2010 **Rating** 89 **To** 2014 $32

Hungerford Hill ★★★★☆

1 Broke Road, Pokolbin, NSW 2320 **Region** Hunter Valley
T (02) 4998 7666 **www**.hungerfordhill.com.au **Open** Sun–Thurs 10–5, Fri–Sat 10–6
Winemaker Michael Hatcher **Est.** 1967 **Dozens** 50 000 **Vyds** 5ha

Hungerford Hill, sold by Southcorp to the Kirby family in 2002, emerged with its home base at the impressive winery previously known as One Broke Road. The development of the One Broke Road complex proved wildly uneconomic, and the rationalisation process has resulted in Hungerford Hill becoming the sole owner. The quality of the wines has seen production rise from 20 000 to 50 000 dozen, reversing the pattern under prior Southcorp ownership. As the notes indicate, Hungerford Hill now focuses its attention on Tumbarumba and the Hunter Valley, with some wines coming from the Hilltops region. Exports to all major markets.

🍷🍷🍷🍷🍷 **Tumbarumba Chardonnay 2010** Bright, light to medium yellow-green; the cool Tumbarumba climate allows the effortless accumulation of varietal flavour, here a beautifully balanced match of white-fleshed stone fruits and grapefruit. French oak plays softly in the background of the long, lingering finish. Screwcap. 13% alc. **Rating** 94 **To** 2018 $29

🍷🍷🍷🍷½ **Hunter Valley Semillon 2011** **Rating** 93 **To** 2020 $25
Collection Hunter Valley Semillon 2010 **Rating** 92 **To** 2020 $35
Hunter Valley Shiraz 2010 **Rating** 90 **To** 2018 $35
Collection Pokolbin Shiraz 2010 **Rating** 90 **To** 2020 $40

🍷🍷🍷🍷 **Tumbarumba Shiraz 2010** **Rating** 89 **To** 2017 $35
✪ **Fishcage Shiraz 2010** **Rating** 89 **To** 2018 $18

Huntington Estate ★★★★★

Cassilis Road, Mudgee, NSW 2850 **Region** Mudgee
T 1800 995 931 **www**.huntingtonestate.com.au **Open** Mon–Sat 10–5, Sun & public hols 10–4
Winemaker Tim Stevens **Est.** 1969 **Dozens** 15 000 **Vyds** 43.8ha

Since taking ownership of Huntington Estate from the founding Roberts family, Tim Stevens has sensibly refrained from making major changes. On the wine side, the policy of having older vintage wines available is continuing, making the cellar door a first port of call for visitors to Mudgee. On the other side, the Music Festival suffers only one problem: there are simply not enough tickets to satisfy the demand. It really has a well-deserved life of its own, and I can see no reason why it should not do so for years to come.

ŸŸŸŸŸ **Special Reserve Mudgee Shiraz 2009** Strong purple-red; right up there with the best of Huntington Estate Special Reserves released over the years; has great structure and balance, fruit, tannins and oak all in harmony, red and black cherry and plum flooding the palate yet not threatening the balance or elegance of the wine. Screwcap. 14.1% alc. **Rating** 96 **To** 2030 $34

Signature Tim Stevens Shiraz 2006 Exceptional hue for age, still youthful crimson; a great example of Mudgee terroir with layers of dark plum and blackberry complexed by ripe tannins and a hint of sweet earth. Screwcap. 14.2% alc. **Rating** 95 **To** 2036 $30

Block 3 Mudgee Cabernet Sauvignon 2008 Medium red-purple; a very good regional example of cabernet sauvignon; Mudgee can disappoint with cabernet, but here the gently earthy/spicy nuances to the mainframe of blackcurrant have worked well. Screwcap. 13.5% alc. **Rating** 94 **To** 2028 $40

Special Reserve Mudgee Cabernet Sauvignon 2008 Slightly deeper colour than Block 3; a more aristocratic version, with an element of briary austerity that is part and parcel of many top-quality cabernets; however, it also has lovely mid- to back-palate flesh, finishing with ripe tannins. Screwcap. 12.9% alc. **Rating** 94 **To** 2030 $36

ŸŸŸŸŸ **Mudgee Semillon 2011** Yet another example of the striking similarity between
✪ Hunter Valley and Mudgee Semillon from mature vines; has a fresh varietal bouquet of lemon and grass, then a very well-structured palate based on firm acidity that will guide the wine over the next 10+ years. Screwcap. 11.3% alc. **Rating** 93 **To** 2021 $17

✪ **Special Reserve Mudgee Shiraz 2008** Similar bright colour to the Bin 18, but the aromas and flavours are very different, with plush dark plum, spicy fruit, and layers of flavour. Screwcap. 13.9% alc. **Rating** 92 **To** 2023 $31

ŸŸŸŸ **Mudgee Shiraz 2008** **Rating** 89 **To** 2018 $21
Mudgee Merlot 2009 **Rating** 88 **To** 2014 $21 BE

Hurley Vineyard   ★★★★★

101 Balnarring Road, Balnarring, Vic 3926 **Region** Mornington Peninsula
T (03) 5931 3000 **www**.hurleyvineyard.com.au **Open** 1st w'end each month 11–5 or by appt
Winemaker Kevin Bell **Est.** 1998 **Dozens** 1000 **Vyds** 3.5ha

It's never as easy as it seems. Despite leading busy city lives, Kevin Bell and wife Tricia Byrnes have done most of the hard work in establishing Hurley Vineyard themselves, with family and friends. Most conspicuously, Kevin has completed the Applied Science (Wine Science) degree at CSU, drawing on Nat White for consultancy advice, and occasionally from Phillip Jones of Bass Phillip and Domaine Fourrier in Gevrey Chambertin.

ŸŸŸŸŸ **Lodestone Mornington Peninsula Pinot Noir 2010** A deep, dark and concentrated wine, showing spiced plums, black cherry and an ironstone minerality that is intriguing and complex; the palate is generous and fleshy, with a firm backbone of refreshing tannins and acidity; a long and expansive finish. Diam. 14.2% alc. **Rating** 95 **To** 2018 $65 BE

Garamond Mornington Peninsula Pinot Noir 2010 Light garnet; the subdued bouquet offers glimpses of red fruits, charcuterie, anise and bramble; the palate reveals more of the story, with the silky texture and light-bodied nature of the wine lingering evenly and gracefully on the finish. Diam. 13.7% alc. **Rating** 94 **To** 2016 $75 BE

Estate Mornington Peninsula Pinot Noir 2010 Mid garnet; this is a soft, fragrant and beguiling wine, exhibiting an elegant and relaxed red-fruited mouthfeel, with a firm backbone of fine-grained tannins drawing out the finish. Diam. 13.5% alc. **Rating** 94 **To** 2016 $45 BE

♀♀♀♀♀ **Hommage Mornington Peninsula Pinot Noir 2010 Rating** 92 **To** 2016 $65 BE

Hutton Vale Vineyard   ★★★★☆

Stone Jar Road, Angaston, SA 5353 **Region** Eden Valley
T (08) 8564 8270 **www.**huttonvale.com **Open** By appt
Winemaker Torbreck Vintners, Murray Street Vineyard (Andrew Seppelt) **Est.** 1960
Dozens 600 **Vyds** 27ha
John Howard Angas (who arrived in SA in 1843, aged 19, charged with the responsibility of looking after the affairs of his father, George Fife Angas) named part of the family estate Hutton Vale. It is here that John Angas, John's great-great-grandson, and wife Jan tend 27ha of vines. Almost all the grapes are sold, but a tiny quantity has been made by the who's who of the Barossa Valley, notably David Powell of Torbreck. Jan is also chair of Regional Food SA.

♀♀♀♀♀ **Eden Valley Shiraz 2006** Good colour for its age, but fades into insignificance compared with the youth and power of the palate; blackberry, prune, plum and bitter chocolate are fused together, framed by ripe, persistent, tannins and quality oak; follows on exactly from the '05. Screwcap. 14% alc. **Rating** 96 **To** 2036 $59

♀♀♀♀♀ **Eden Valley Riesling 2011** Gleaming yellow-green; young rieslings don't
✪ usually have the flavour and structure complexity that this wine has, coming from 50-year-old vines; the aromas and flavours extend beyond citrus through stone fruit and apple, and are thus already mouthfilling, not needing extended cellaring. Screwcap. 11% alc. **Rating** 93 **To** 2016 $20
Eden Valley Grenache Mataro 2009 Rating 90 **To** 2019 $28

Hutton Wines   ★★★★★

PO Box 1214, Dunsborough, WA 6281 **Region** Margaret River
T 0417 923 126 **www.**huttonwines.com **Open** Not
Winemaker Michael Hutton **Est.** 2006 **Dozens** 300
This is another venture of the Hutton family of Gralyn fame, with Michael Hutton, who returned to the Margaret River region in 2005, establishing this micro-business the following year, while continuing his architectural practice. Tiny quantities of Semillon Sauvignon Blanc, Chardonnay and Cabernet Sauvignon are produced, hardly enough to threaten Gralyn.

♀♀♀♀♀ **Triptych Margaret River Chardonnay 2010** Vibrant green hue; a restrained bouquet of citrus blossom, grapefruit, cashew and a light touch of oak; the palate is refined, pure, racy and long, and, frankly, absolutely refreshing; a poised, elegant and balanced example of Margaret River chardonnay. Screwcap. 12.5% alc. **Rating** 94 **To** 2016 $40 BE
Triptych Margaret River Cabernet Sauvignon 2009 Deep garnet; pure cassis and black olive bouquet, showing plenty of purity and a mere suggestion of oak; the palate is fine, silky and fragrant, with a complex lick of cedar remaining on the finish; fine texture is the key in this wine. Screwcap. 13.9% alc. **Rating** 94 **To** 2018 $50 BE

Indigo Wine Company

1221 Beechworth-Wangaratta Road, Everton Upper, Vic 3678 **Region** Beechworth
T (03) 5727 0233 **www.**indigovineyard.com.au **Open** Wed–Sun 11–5
Winemaker Brokenwood (Simon Steele) **Est.** 1999 **Dozens** 1950 **Vyds** 46.15ha
Indigo Wine Company has a little over 46ha of vineyards planted to 11 varieties, including the top French and Italian grapes. The business was and is primarily directed to growing grapes for sale to Brokenwood, but since 2004 small parcels of grapes have been vinified for the Indigo

label. The somewhat incestuous nature of the whole business sees the Indigo wines being made at Brokenwood.

ΨΨΨΨΨ **Secret Village Beechworth Pinot Noir 2010** Brilliant, clear crimson; the vineyard is hidden in a mini-valley at the back of the property, 3km from the cellar door; the bouquet is fragrant, embellished with red berry fruits and spice; the palate has unusual authority in its intensity and power, driven by black cherry and plum fruit, together with positive tannins. Will definitely repay cellaring. Screwcap. 13% alc. **Rating** 94 **To** 2017 $27

ΨΨΨΨΨ **Beechworth Pinot Grigio 2010** Pale straw-quartz; while the bouquet ambles
❂ along, the wine comes alive on the palate, with intense flavours of pear, peach and, above all, citrus; the overall effect of the fruit is doubled by the lance of the steely acid. A very smart grigio. Screwcap. 13.5% alc. **Rating** 93 **To** 2013 $19

Ingoldby

GPO Box 753, Melbourne, Vic 3001 **Region** McLaren Vale
T 1300 651 650 **www.**ingoldby.com.au **Open** Not
Winemaker Kelly Healy **Est.** 1983 **Dozens** NFP
Part of TWE, with the wines now having a sole McLaren Vale source. Over the years, Ingoldby has produced some excellent wines, which can provide great value for money.

ΨΨΨΨΨ **McLaren Vale Shiraz 2010** Deep crimson-purple; a strongly regional bouquet with plush dark berry and dark chocolate aromas, the palate picking up where the bouquet leaves off, with abundant drive and energy, and an overall impression of freshness below the chewy tannins. Screwcap. 14% alc. **Rating** 93 **To** 2025 $20

Ipso Facto Wines ★★★★☆

PO Box 1886, Margaret River, WA 6285 **Region** Margaret River
T 0402 321 572 **Open** Not
Winemaker Kate Morgan 2010 **Dozens** 500
This is the realisation of owner/winemaker Kate Morgan's dream of making her own wine with her own label. After graduating from Curtin University with a degree in viticulture and oenology she worked vintages in Australia (including Coriole, Tamar Ridge and Coldstream Hills) and overseas (Archery Summit, California, and Quinta do Noval, Portugal), before returning to WA. There she worked at Houghton, Stella Bella and for the last three years as assistant winemaker at Fraser Gallop Estate. The wines are made with minimal additions (only SO_2 added), and are wild-fermented.

ΨΨΨΨΨ **Margaret River Chenin 2011** Given the works: whole bunch-pressed, wild-fermented in French oak, lees stirred, and nine months in oak. The wine certainly has considerable texture and structure, and will almost certainly handsomely repay the six or so years winemaker Kate Morgan suggests. Still lean and tart, an appropriate start for cellaring. Screwcap. 13% alc. **Rating** 92 **To** 2021 $28

Iron Pot Bay Wines

766 Deviot Road, Deviot, Tas 7275 **Region** Northern Tasmania
T (03) 6394 7320 **www.**ironpotbay.com.au **Open** Mon–Wed 11–5 (Nov–Mar) or by appt
Winemaker Jeremy Dineen 1988 **Dozens** 1500 **Vyds** 5ha
Iron Pot Bay was established by the Cuthbert family and continues in family ownership. The vineyard takes its name from a bay on the Tamar River (now called West Bay) and is strongly maritime influenced, producing delicate but intensely flavoured unwooded white wines. Over half of the vineyard is planted to chardonnay, the remainder to semillon, sauvignon blanc, pinot gris, gewurztraminer and riesling.

ΨΨΨΨ **Kyra Chardonnay Pinot Noir 2006** Bright straw-green; has a distinctive, although hard to pin down, flavour register; the length and balance are good. Crown seal. 12% alc. **Rating** 87 **To** 2013 $37

Ironwood Estate ★★★★

2191 Porongurup Road, Porongurup, WA 6234 **Region** Porongurup
T (08) 9853 1126 **www**.ironwoodestatewines.com.au **Open** Wed–Mon 11–5
Winemaker Wignalls Wines (Michael Perkins)1996 **Dozens** 2500 **Vyds** 5ha
Ironwood Estate was established in 1996 under the ownership of Mary and Eugene Harma.
An estate vineyard planted to riesling, sauvignon blanc, chardonnay, shiraz, merlot and cabernet
sauvignon (in more or less equal amounts) has been established on a northern slope of the
Porongurup Range. Exports to Japan and Singapore.

Reserve Porongurup Chardonnay 2011 Straw-green; the wines of
Porongurup, irrespective of the variety, have a special brightness and freshness to
the fruit, giving this wine its mouth-watering mix of grapefruit and white peach,
supported by restrained barrel fermentation characters. Screwcap. 14.5% alc.
Rating 93 **To** 2019 $25

Porongurup Shiraz 2009 Deep, bright magenta; a fragrant cherry and plum
bouquet leads into a medium-bodied palate, building on the fruits of the bouquet,
adding spice and a touch of licorice; well balanced and will improve further over
coming years. Screwcap. 13.4% alc. **Rating** 93 **To** 2020 $20

Rocky Rose 2011 Pale pink; the bouquet is full of fragrant sweet fruit aromas,
the palate with well above average mouthfeel, the flavours in the small red berry
spectrum, the finish treading the finest of lines between dry and off-dry. Screwcap.
13% alc. **Rating** 90 **To** 2013 $15

Irvine ★★★★☆

PO Box 308, Angaston, SA 5353 **Region** Eden Valley
T (08) 8564 1046 **www**.irvinewines.com.au **Open** At Taste of Eden Valley, Angaston
Winemaker Joanne Irvine1980 **Dozens** 8000 **Vyds** 9.5ha
Industry veteran Jim Irvine, who has successfully guided the destiny of so many SA wineries,
quietly introduced his own label in 1991. The vineyard from which the wines are sourced was
planted in '83 to an eclectic mix of merlot (4.2ha), chardonnay (3.1ha), pinot gris (1ha), petit
meslier, zinfandel (0.5ha each) and tannat (0.2ha). The flagship is the rich Grand Merlot. Jim
has stepped back to allow daughter Joanne to receive the recognition and praise for the wines
she makes for the brand (and, for that matter, others). Exports to the UK, Germany, Taiwan,
Malaysia, Singapore, Hong Kong and China.

James Irvine Eden Valley Grand Merlot 2009 A wine full of contradictions,
given a luxury bottle, and a long cork that has emerged contorted, reflecting
the interior of the neck of the bottle. The ominously high alcohol is in fact
balanced to a large degree by good acidity, and low pH seems to reflect some
winery adjustment. All of this is framed by oak in the long-established Irvine style.
15.3% alc. **Rating** 91 **To** 2015 $125

Springhill Eden Valley Savagnin 2011 **Rating** 90 **To** Now $18
Stonewell Reserve Barossa Merlot 2009 Plenty of colour; doesn't have
the refinement and complexity of Grand Merlot, but makes up for that with its
sheer volume of flavour. Exclusively available by mail order. Screwcap. 14.5% alc.
Rating 90 **To** 2017 $28

Barossa Merlot Cabernet Franc 2009 **Rating** 88 **To** 2014 $24

Ivanhoe Wines ★★★☆

525 Marrowbone Road, Pokolbin, NSW 2320 **Region** Hunter Valley
T (02) 4998 7325 **www**.ivanhoewines.com.au **Open** 7 days 10–5
Winemaker Stephen Drayton1995 **Dozens** 8000 **Vyds** 19.1ha
Stephen Drayton is the son of the late Reg Drayton and, with wife Tracy, is the third branch
of the family to be actively involved in winemaking in the Hunter Valley. The property on
which the vineyard is situated has been called Ivanhoe for over 140 years, and 30+-year-old
vines provide high-quality fruit for the label. The award-winning cellar door is a replica of the
old homestead (burnt down, along with much of the winery, in the 1968 bushfires).

ㅸㅸㅸㅸㅹ Hunter Valley Traminer 2010 Light straw-green; has more varietal character than many, especially from the Hunter Valley; distinct honey/honeydew and rose petal aromas, then a juicy palate with distinct sweetness on the finish; 500ml. Screwcap. 14% alc. **Rating** 90 **To** 2013 $23

ㅸㅸㅸㅸ Late Picked Hunter Valley Gewurztraminer 2009 **Rating** 89 **To** 2013 $30

Jack Rabbit Vineyard ★★★★

85 McAdams Lane, Bellarine, Vic 3223 **Region** Geelong
T (03) 5251 2223 **www**.jackrabbitvineyard.com.au **Open** 7 days 10.30–5
Winemaker Nyall Condon1989 **Dozens** 4000 **Vyds** 2ha
Jack Rabbit vineyard is the reincarnation of Kilgour Estate following its acquisition by David and Lyndsay Sharp of Leura Park Estate. Its 2ha of vineyards (planted equally to pinot noir and cabernet sauvignon), take second place to its restaurant and event facilities, the restaurant open for dinner on Friday and Saturday nights, but available for special events. Fruit from the estate vineyards is supplemented by contract-grown fruit, and production has increased sharply, each of the six wines winning at least one wine show award in 2011, gold medals to the Chardonnay '10 and Sauvignon Blanc '11 at the Concours des Vins du Victoria '11 heading the field. Unusual one price fits all approach for a small winery.

ㅸㅸㅸㅸㅹ Bellarine Peninsula Shiraz 2010 Good hue, although not deep; the fragrant, spicy bouquet heralds a true cool-climate, medium-bodied shiraz; multi-spice, pepper and high-toned fruits join with well-handled oak to provide a complete wine. Screwcap. 13.2% alc. **Rating** 93 **To** 2020 $30
Bellarine Peninsula Riesling 2011 Quartz-white; has clearly benefited from the cool, wet summer, giving an extra degree of focus and length to its savoury/pithy fruit. Screwcap. 12.5% alc. **Rating** 91 **To** 2018 $30
Bellarine Peninsula Chardonnay 2010 Complex bouquet; attractive fruit/oak on mid palate, but seems to fall away slightly on the finish. Screwcap. 14.5% alc. **Rating** 91 **To** 2018 $30

ㅸㅸㅸㅸ Bellarine Peninsula Sauvignon Blanc 2011 **Rating** 89 **To** 2013 $30
Bellarine Peninsula Rose 2011 **Rating** 88 **To** 2013 $30
Bellarine Peninsula Pinot Grigio 2011 **Rating** 87 **To** 2014 $30

Jacob's Creek ★★★★★

Barossa Valley Way, Rowland Flat, SA 5352 **Region** Barossa Valley
T (08) 8521 3000 **www**.jacobscreek.com **Open** 7 days 10–5
Winemaker Bernard Hickin **Est.** 1973 **Dozens** NFP
Jacob's Creek is one of the largest-selling brands in the world, and the global success of the basic Jacob's Creek range has had the perverse effect of prejudicing many critics and wine writers who fail (so it seems) to objectively look behind the label and taste what is in fact in the glass. Jacob's Creek has four ranges, and all the wines have a connection, direct or indirect, with Johann Gramp, who built his tiny stone winery on the banks of the creek in 1847. The four-tier range consists of Icon (Johann Shiraz Cabernet); then Heritage (Steingarten Riesling, Reeves Point Chardonnay, Centenary Hill Barossa Shiraz and St Hugo Coonawarra Cabernet); then Reserve (all of the major varietals); and finally Classic (ditto). The Reserve range has been superseded by a new Regional Reserve range. Exports to the UK, the US, China, and other major markets.

ㅸㅸㅸㅸㅹ St Hugo Barossa Grenache Shiraz Mataro 2010 A 45/32/23% varietal blend, the grenache from two 40-year-old and one 83-year-old blocks, the mataro from bush-pruned vines at Greenock. An upwards and sideways (and cannibalistic) move for Jacob's Creek, with lifted aromatics, layers of red and black fruits, and supple, fine tannins on the very long finish. Gold medal National Wine Show '11. Screwcap. 14.1% alc. **Rating** 95 **To** 2018 $50

ŶŶŶŶŶ Reserve Adelaide Hills Chardonnay 2010 Light straw-green; initially builds
✪   its character slowly before coming through more strongly on the back-palate and
finish; has good mouthfeel to its white peach fruit and cashew flavours. Screwcap.
13.3% alc. **Rating** 91 **To** 2016 $18

✪   Reserve Chardonnay Pinot Noir 2008 Straw-coloured; sourced from the
Adelaide Hills, and bottle-fermented, although not in this bottle; extended lees
contact has given the wine nutty complexity to go with the long fruit flavours.
Diam. 12% alc. **Rating** 91 **To** 2014 $19

❂   Riesling 2010 **Rating** 90 **To** 2020 $12

ŶŶŶŶ Trilogy Cuvee Brut Pinot Noir Chardonnay Pinot Meunier NV **Rating** 89
✪   To Now $16
✪   Cool Harvest Shiraz Rose 2011 **Rating** 89 **To** Now $15
❂   Shiraz Rose 2010 **Rating** 89 **To** Now $12
❂   Shiraz Cabernet 2008 **Rating** 89 **To** Now $12
     Cool Harvest Sauvignon Blanc 2011 **Rating** 88 **To** Now $15
❂   Chardonnay 2010 **Rating** 88 **To** Now $12
❂   Cabernet Sauvignon 2009 **Rating** 88 **To** 2013 $12
❂   Sauvignon Blanc 2011 **Rating** 87 **To** Now $12
❂   Pinot Noir 2010 **Rating** 87 **To** Now $12

JaJa   ★★★☆

PO Box 3015, Strathmore, Vic 3041 **Region** Barossa Valley
T 0411 106 652 **www**.jaja.com.au **Open** Not
Winemaker Troy Kalleske (Contract) **Est.** 2003 **Dozens** 1200
Brothers Bert and Pierre Werden are the faces behind www.winestar.com.au, which they
describe as Australia's leading online fine wine retailer. While it seemed a natural progression
for them to develop JaJa as a family label, they say, 'Being in retail was a huge advantage in
learning what not to do.' On the positive side was the decision to concentrate on Barossa shiraz,
the Stonewell subdistrict, 50-year-old vines, and the services of Troy Kalleske as winemaker.
The Starlite wines are region-specific, small-batch wines that are sold to on-premise and fine
wine off-premise businesses. Bert and Pierre say, 'The further we delved into the resources of
our partner wineries, the more it became abundantly clear that the recent economic hardship
had slowed the ability of even the biggest names to find a home either domestically or
internationally for their premium fruit. The result was a vintage Mornington Peninsula bubbly,
a single vineyard, high altitude Adelaide Hills chardonnay, and a Barossa shiraz, with more than
a smidgeon of old vine material.' Exports to Singapore and Hong Kong.

ŶŶŶŶŶ Starlite Mornington Peninsula Pinot Noir Chardonnay 2008 From the
✪   Merricks area, this is an intensely juicy/fruity style of sparkling wine with quite
strong citrus and white peach flavours, speaking more of chardonnay than pinot
noir, although that is no complaint. Diam. 12.5% alc. **Rating** 90 **To** 2016 $11

ŶŶŶŶ JaJa Barossa Shiraz 2009 **Rating** 89 **To** 2019 $30
     Starlite Barossa Valley Shiraz 2009 **Rating** 88 **To** 2017 $17
     Starlite Adelaide Hills Chardonnay 2011 **Rating** 87 **To** 2014 $15

James Estate

951 Bylong Valley Way, Baerami, NSW 2333 **Region** Hunter Valley
T (02) 6547 5168 **www**.jamesestatewines.com.au **Open** 7 days 10–4.30
Winemaker Graeme Scott **Est.** 1997 **Dozens** 15 000 **Vyds** 86ha
James Estate has had an unsettled corporate existence at various times since 1997, but has
recently straightened the ship. Graeme Scott has been installed as senior winemaker, having
previously worked with Jim Chatto and Ross Pearson at First Creek, and The Rothbury
Estate before that. The newly appointed winemaking team has appreciably lifted the quality
of the wines, with (I guess) more to come. Exports to China.

⟡⟡⟡⟡⟡ Reserve Hunter Valley Semillon 2011 Pale straw-green; as with so many modern Hunter Valley Semillons, shares many characteristics with young Riesling; this modern style seems to be in part due to yeast selection and screwcaps, a combination enhancing citrus and pear fruit on the bouquet, and reappearing on the finish and aftertaste. Screwcap. 11% alc. **Rating** 93 **To** 2021 $23

Reserve Chardonnay 2011 Vibrant green hue; a fine bouquet of nectarine, citrus blossom and a suggestion of toasty oak; the palate is fleshy and generous, with soft acidity and a long toasty finish. Screwcap. 13% alc. **Rating** 90 **To** 2015 $23 BE

✪ **The Estate Hunter Valley Chardonnay 2009** Partial barrel fermentation in new and 1-year-old French oak makes its mark on this tangy chardonnay that some may see as a Chablis style, others simply as a little light on. Time will tell which view is correct, but I've put my money on Chablis. Screwcap. 13% alc. **Rating** 90 **To** 2015 $16

⟡⟡⟡⟡ The Estate Hunter Valley Verdelho 2011 Pale straw-green; crisp, fresh and
✪ zesty, the wine has a rainbow of flavours that disappear as you try to grab hold of them, but you may see moments of ginger, guava and lime. Does have length and a persistent finish; honey and toast may develop with age. Screwcap. 12.5% alc. **Rating** 89 **To** 2015 $16

The Estate Vitai Semillon 2011 Rating 88 **To** 2015 $16
The Estate Hunter Valley Petit Verdot 2010 Rating 87 **To** 2020 $16

Jamieson Estate   ★★★★☆

PO Box 6598, Silverwater, NSW 2128 **Region** Mudgee
T (02) 9737 8377 **www.**jamiesonestate.com.au **Open** Not
Winemaker Robert Paul **Est.** 1998 **Dozens** 6000 **Vyds** 10ha
Generations of the Jamieson family have been graziers in the region for 150 years, and were able to select 100ha of the most suitable soil from their property on which to establish their vineyard. Beginning in 1998, they planted over 32ha of shiraz, almost 24ha of cabernet sauvignon and 12ha of chardonnay, with smaller amounts of semillon, petit verdot, sauvignon blanc, merlot and barbera. Until 2005 all of the grapes were sold to leading wineries in the region, but beginning in '06 small amounts of chardonnay, sauvignon blanc, semillon, shiraz and petit verdot were held back for the Jamieson Estate label. Due to the lack of continuing grape supply contracts they have removed 79ha of vines and are now producing small quantities of Semillon, Semillon Sauvignon Blanc, Petit Verdot, Shiraz and Cabernet Sauvignon.

Jamiesons Run

Coonawarra Wine Gallery, Riddoch Highway, Coonawarra, SA 5277 **Region** Coonawarra
T (08) 8737 1300 **www.**jamiesonsrun.com.au **Open** 7 days 10–5
Winemaker Andrew Hales **Est.** 1987 **Dozens** NFP
The wheel has turned full circle for Jamiesons Run. It started out as a single-label, mid market, high-volume brand developed by Ray King during his time as CEO of Mildara. It grew and grew until Mildara, having many years since been merged with Wolf Blass, decided to rename the Mildara Coonawarra winery as Jamiesons Run, with the Mildara label just one of a number falling under the Jamiesons Run umbrella. Now the Jamiesons Run winery is no more — Foster's sold it, but retained the brand; the cellar door has moved to shared accommodation at the Coonawarra Wine Gallery. Exports to the UK.

⟡⟡⟡⟡⟡ Mildara Coonawarra Cabernet Sauvignon 2008 This has the famous Mildara white label recalling the fabled '63 Cabernet Sauvignon. Happily, the colour of the wine is very good, the bouquet fragrant with cassis and a touch of mint, the medium-bodied palate quite beautifully balanced and textured. An utterly classic Coonawarra cabernet with a long life ahead, although approachable now. Screwcap. 15% alc. **Rating** 96 **To** 2030 $30

ŶŶŶŶŶ **Limestone Coast Chardonnay 2011** Pale straw-green; a zesty, citrus-driven
✪   style, the low alcohol adding to the freshness. A challenging, polarising style
          blurring the borderline with Sauvignon Blanc, but won a gold medal at the
          National Wine Show '11, the subtle infusion of oak no doubt helping. Fantastic
          value. Screwcap. 12% alc. **Rating** 93 **To** 2013 $16

ŶŶŶŶ **Limestone Coast Shiraz 2011 Rating** 89
✪   **To** 2016 $16
✪   **Limestone Coast Cabernet Sauvignon 2010** Rating 89 **To** 2015 $16
✪   **Limestone Coast Cabernet Shiraz Merlot 2010** Rating 88 **To** 2015 $16

Jane Brook Estate Wines ★★★

229 Toodyay Road, Middle Swan, WA 6056 **Region** Swan Valley
T (08) 9274 1432 **www.**janebrook.com.au **Open** 7 days 10–5
Winemaker Mark Baird **Est.** 1972 **Dozens** 15 000 **Vyds** 18.2ha
Beverley and David Atkinson have worked tirelessly to build up the Jane Brook Estate wine
business over the past 40 years. The most important changes during that time have been the
establishment of a Margaret River vineyard (11.7ha), and sourcing grapes from other southern
wine regions in WA. Exports to Singapore and China.

ŶŶŶŶ **Shovelgate Vineyard Margaret River Chardonnay 2010** Already with
          mid gold colour; a rich wine, with ripe stone fruit and melon flavours along with
          cashew and toasty oak characters; obviously, no shortage of flavour, but should be
          drunk sooner rather rather than later. Screwcap. 13.5% alc. **Rating** 89 **To** 2014 $35
          Atkinson Family Reserve Shiraz 2009 Developed colour for a wine at this
          price; has body and flavour, but looks old-fashioned in the company of other
          red wines from the '09 vintage, whether in the east or the west of the country.
          It has some complexity, coming in part from the warmth of the finish. Screwcap.
          14.9% alc. **Rating** 88 **To** 2017 $50
          Shovelgate Vineyard Margaret River Sauvignon Blanc Semillon 2011
          Curious labelling, the front label proclaiming Margaret River, as does the header
          of the back label, but in the fine print we find '100% Western Australian grapes'.
          An easy-access style, with ripe citrus and stone fruit flavours on a well-balanced
          palate. Screwcap. 12% alc. **Rating** 87 **To** Now $21

Jansz Tasmania ★★★★★

1216b Pipers Brook Road, Pipers Brook, Tas 7254 **Region** Northern Tasmania
T (03) 6382 7066 **www.**jansztas.com **Open** 7 days 10–4.30
Winemaker Natalie Fryar **Est.** 1985 **Dozens** 38 000 **Vyds** 30ha
Jansz is part of Hill-Smith Family Vineyards, and was one of the early sparkling wine labels in
Tasmania, stemming from a short-lived relationship between Heemskerk and Louis Roederer.
Its 15ha of chardonnay, 12ha of pinot noir and 3ha of pinot meunier correspond almost
exactly to the blend composition of the Jansz wines. It is the only Tasmanian winery entirely
devoted to the production of sparkling wine (although the small amount of Dalrymple Estate
wines are also made here), and is of high quality. Exports to all major markets.

ŶŶŶŶŶ **Premium Vintage Cuvee 2006** Bright straw-green; this is a traditional method
          blend of chardonnay and pinot noir that spent 48 months on yeast lees in this
          bottle, resulting in a wine with abundant personality and character, its mix of
          brioche, citrus and stone fruit framed by acidity only partially tamed by malolactic
          fermentation – which is as it should be with Tasmanian sparkling wine. Cork.
          12% alc. **Rating** 95 **To** Now $40
          Premium Vintage Rose 2008 Pale blush pink; traditional method, and obvious
          lees contact for some years, although not so many as would see bronze hints
          influencing the colour; fresh citrus and red berry/strawberry aromas and flavours,
          with a lively, tight finish. Cork. 12.5% alc. **Rating** 94 **To** 2014 $40

ŶŶŶŶŶ **Premium Non Vintage Cuvee NV Rating** 91 **To** 2013 $25

Jasper Hill

Drummonds Lane, Heathcote, Vic 3523 **Region** Heathcote
T (03) 5433 2528 **www**.jasperhill.com **Open** By appt
Winemaker Ron Laughton, Emily McNally **Est.** 1975 **Dozens** 2500 **Vyds** 26.5ha
The red wines of Jasper Hill are highly regarded and much sought after. Over the past decade drought has caused some variation in style and weight, but as long as vintage conditions allow, these are wonderfully rich and full-flavoured wines, albeit with high levels of alcohol. The vineyards are dry-grown (hence drought problems) and are managed organically. Wines were received after this issue went to print; tasting notes appear on www.winecompanion.com.au. Exports to the UK, the US, Canada and Singapore.

jb Wines ★★★☆

PO Box 530, Tanunda, SA 5352 **Region** Barossa Valley
T 0408 794 389 **www**.jbwines.com **Open** By appt
Winemaker Joe Barritt, Tim Geddes **Est.** 2005 **Dozens** 1000 **Vyds** 18ha
The Barritt family has been growing grapes in the Barossa since the 1850s, but this particular venture was established in '05 by Lenore, Joe and Greg Barritt. It is based on shiraz, cabernet sauvignon and chardonnay (with tiny amounts of zinfandel, pinot blanc and clairette) planted between 1972 and '03. Greg runs the vineyard operations; Joe, with a Bachelor of Agricultural Science degree from Adelaide University, followed by 10 years of winemaking in Australia, France and the US, is now the winemaker, together with Tim Geddes at McLaren Vale, where the wines are made. Exports to Hong Kong.

♀♀♀♀♀ **Barossa Valley Syrah Primitivo 2008** Has retained a youthful colour that
✪ gives no hint of the lusciously full-bodied palate that is to follow; here, licorice, savoury spices and fine tannins weave their way through the predominantly black fruits; good length and balance. Exceptional value. Screwcap. 14.2% alc. **Rating** 91 **To** 2018 $15
Joe's Block Barossa Valley Shiraz 2008 Deep colour, and showing lots of oak, struck match and black fruit on the bouquet; rugged and rustic, with gravelly tannins and fresh acidity providing freshness on the finish; mocha remains long after the fruit has gone. Screwcap. 14.6% alc. **Rating** 90 **To** 2023 $25 BE
O **Barossa Valley Cabernet Sauvignon 2005 Rating** 90 **To** 2016 $15

Jeir Creek ★★★☆

122 Bluebell Lane, Murrumbateman, NSW 2582 **Region** Canberra District
T (02) 6227 5999 **www**.jeircreekwines.com.au **Open** Thurs–Mon & hols 10–5
(w'ends only during Aug)
Winemaker Rob Howell **Est.** 1984 **Dozens** 4000 **Vyds** 8ha
Rob and Kay Howell, owner–founders of Jeir Creek, celebrated 25 years of involvement in 2009. Rob runs the technically advanced winery, while Kay looks after the cellar door. Predominantly an estate-based business, the plantings comprise chardonnay, cabernet sauvignon (2ha each), riesling, sauvignon blanc, shiraz (1ha each) and smaller plantings of pinot noir, viognier and muscat.

♀♀♀♀ **Canberra District Sauvignon Blanc 2011** A lean and restrained bouquet, showing minerals and citrus; the palate is taut and focused, with a lingering tail of quartz to finish. Screwcap. 12.3% alc. **Rating** 88 **To** 2014 $20 BE
Canberra District Shiraz 2010 Mid garnet; there is a strong herbal note of green beans sitting alongside red fruits and nutmeg; the palate is medium-bodied and shows a savoury aspect with fine tannins and moderate persistence. Screwcap. 14.4% alc. **Rating** 87 **To** 2018 $25 BE

Jenke Vineyards ★★★☆

Barossa Valley Way, Rowland Flat, SA 5352 **Region** Barossa Valley
T (08) 8524 4154 **Open** 7 days 11–5
Winemaker Kym Jenke **Est.** 1989 **Dozens** 8000 **Vyds** 46ha

The Jenke family have been growing grapes in the southern Barossa continuously since their arrival from Germany in 1854. Today the fifth and sixth generations farm almost 50ha of prime Barossa vineyards, with sixth-generation Kym Jenke making all wines onsite. The vineyards have an average age of 40 years, with the oldest shiraz dating back to 1926. A rejuvenation of new plantings in the early '90s has strengthened the varietal mix of traditional with new varieties. The cellar door is located in the original settlers' cottage built in 1844. Exports to China, Hong Kong and Singapore.

ŸŸŸŸŸ **1926 Vineyard Barossa Shiraz 2008** The vineyard was purchased in 1926 by Kym Jenke's grandfather, suggesting the vines are even older, and the wine is light on its feet given its high alcohol. Open-fermented and given extended maceration, then maturation in French oak, the wine has sweet fruit flavours and graceful tannins. Screwcap. 15% alc. **Rating** 93 **To** 2020 $28

ŸŸŸŸ **Barossa Profile 2010 Rating** 89 **To** 2020 $25
✪ **Barossa Rose 2011** Vivid purple-crimson; made from early-picked cabernet, specifically chosen for this wine; raspberry fruit drives the bouquet and palate, with a touch of fruit sweetness on the finish. Screwcap. 12% alc. **Rating** 88 **To** Now $15
Late Disgorge Barossa Sparkling Shiraz 1998 Rating 88 **To** 2013 $48
Barossa Semillon 2010 Rating 87 **To** 2016 $17

Jester Hill Wines   ★★★☆

292 Mount Stirling Road, Glen Aplin, Qld 4381 **Region** Granite Belt
T (07) 4683 4380 **www.**jesterhillwines.com.au **Open** Mon–Sat 10–5, Sun 10–3
Winemaker James Janda **Est.** 1993 **Dozens** 1500 **Vyds** 6ha
A family-run vineyard situated in the pretty valley of Glen Aplin in the Granite Belt. Owners Michael and Ann Bourke aim to concentrate on small quantities of premium-quality wines reflecting the full-bodied style of the region. Most recently they have planted sangiovese (first vintage 2012) and roussanne, the first vintage due in '13.

ŸŸŸŸŸ **Touchstone Granite Belt Verdelho 2009** Bright green-gold; good bottle development, now at its peak; the good vintage is fully reflected in the wine. Screwcap. 13.9% alc. **Rating** 90 **To** 2013 $20

ŸŸŸŸ **Touchstone Granite Belt Cabernet Sauvignon 2009** Rating 89 **To** 2019 $25

Jim Barry Wines   ★★★★★

Craig's Hill Road, Clare, SA 5453 **Region** Clare Valley
T (08) 8842 2261 **www.**jimbarry.com **Open** Mon–Fri 9–5, w'ends, hols 9–4
Winemaker Peter Barry (leads a team of five) **Est.** 1959 **Dozens** 80 000 **Vyds** 249ha
The patriarch of this highly successful wine business, Jim Barry, died in 2004, but the business continues under the active management of several of his many children. There is a full range of wine styles across most varietals, but with special emphasis on Riesling, Shiraz and Cabernet Sauvignon. The ultra-premium release is The Armagh Shiraz, with the McCrae Wood red wines not far behind. Jim Barry Wines is able to draw upon mature Clare Valley vineyards, plus a small holding in Coonawarra. Exports to all major markets.

ŸŸŸŸŸ **The Lodge Hill Clare Valley Dry Riesling 2011** Rating 95
❂ **To** 2025 $20
The Armagh Shiraz 2009 As is always the case, this is no shrinking violet, but it is no behemoth either; red and dark fruits, earth, spice, sap and toasty oak are on display; the full-bodied palate is lithe, sophisticated and exceptionally long; flagships can often be a caricature of a producer, but in this case it is the elegance and the power combining seamlessly. Cork. 14.5% alc. **Rating** 95 **To** 2030 $250 BE
❂ **Watervale Riesling 2011** Rating 94 **To** 2022 $17
The Florita Clare Valley Riesling 2011 I'm just a simple fellow, and won't argue about the presence (or absence) of all or some of the lime, pink grapefruit, mandarin, lychee, tangelo, frangipani, papaya and rose hip (as per the back label) of what is undoubtedly a richer, riper wine than many of the vintage – and a very good example of that style. Screwcap. 12.5% alc. **Rating** 94 **To** 2021 $45

✪ **The Lodge Hill Shiraz 2010** Vibrant purple hue; elevation of 480m above sea level purports to enhance a wine's elegance, and while elegant in the Jim Barry meaning of the word, there is a powerhouse of dark fruits, chocolate and toasty oak all at play; medium- to full-bodied, young, brash and refreshing, the finish is long, juicy, generous and even a little bit spicy; a lot to like for the price, but beware the oak. Screwcap. 14.5% alc. **Rating** 94 **To** 2020 $23 BE
The McRae Wood Shiraz 2008 A rich and ripe, almost hedonistic display of shiraz's generosity and sweet fruitcake spice and blackberry fruit appeal; fresh and lively on the palate, the fruit handles the not inconsiderable oak with ease, and lingers fragrantly on the finish. Cork. 14.2% alc. **Rating** 94 **To** 2025 $50 BE

♀♀♀♀♀ **The Cover Drive Cabernet Sauvignon 2009** Although there are contradictory
✪ statements in the technical background to the wine, it seems this is a Coonawarra/Clare Valley blend (not 100% Coonawarra) that produces a truly enjoyable, delicious red berry and cassis-fruited wine, the tannins and oak on the boundary. Drink whenever you wish. Screwcap. 14% alc. **Rating** 90 **To** 2014 $20
The Benbournie Cabernet Sauvignon 2006 Rating 90 **To** 2018 $95 BE

♀♀♀♀ **PB Shiraz Cabernet Sauvignon 2009 Rating** 88 **To** 2018 $50 BE
The Cover Drive Cabernet Sauvignon 2010 Rating 88 **To** 2014 $23 BE

Jim Brand Wines ★★★★☆

PO Box 18, Coonawarra, SA 5263 **Region** Coonawarra
T (08) 8736 3252 **www**.jimbrandwines.com.au **Open** Not
Winemaker Brand family, Bruce Gregory (consultant) **Est.** 2000 **Dozens** 2000 **Vyds** 9.5ha
The Brand family story starts with the arrival of Eric Brand in Coonawarra in 1950, when he married Nancy Redman and purchased a 24ha block from the Redman family, relinquishing his job as a baker and becoming a grapegrower. It was not until '66 that the first Brand's Laira wine was made. The Brand family sold the Brand's Laira winery in '94 to McWilliam's, Jim Brand staying on as chief winemaker right up until he died in 2005, after a long battle with cancer, unable to fulfil his ambition to make quality wine under his name. His son Sam, with help from locals, including Bruce Gregory at Majella, has now realised his father's dream, with the release of the '08 and '09 wines, made from the family's holding of 8ha of cabernet sauvignon, and 1.5ha of shiraz.

♀♀♀♀♀ **Jim's Vineyard Coonawarra Shiraz 2009** Crimson-purple; a medium- to full-bodied palate with a complex cascade of shiraz flavours running through blackberry, plum and a touch of spice; good texture and structure. Screwcap. 14.5% alc. **Rating** 93 **To** 2029 $30
Silent Partner Coonawarra Cabernet Sauvignon 2009 Clear red-purple; a blackcurrant bouquet with wisps of mint and earth is followed by a medium- to full-bodied palate delivering more of those classic Coonawarra cabernet characters; the tannins are persistent, but fine, ripe and balanced. Screwcap. 14% alc. **Rating** 93 **To** 2030 $30
Silent Partner Coonawarra Cabernet Sauvignon 2008 Medium purple-red; blackcurrant, blackberry, mulberry and Coonawarra earth fill the bouquet and palate alike; the tannin and oak contribution is balanced, the length good. Screwcap. 14% alc. **Rating** 91 **To** 2023 $30

Joadja Vineyards ★★★★☆

Joadja Road, Berrima, NSW 2577 **Region** Southern Highlands
T (02) 4878 5236 **www**.joadja.com **Open** Fri–Wed 10–5
Winemaker Kim Moginie **Est.** 1983 **Dozens** 1500 **Vyds** 6.5ha
Kim and Francis Moginie were among the pioneers of the Southern Highlands region when they established Joadja, and began planting 6.5ha of vines around the small winery. There was a difficult and protracted learning curve required to work out which varieties were suited to the region, and, having established that, finding the right blocks on the vineyard. Winemaking, too, threw out challenges of its own. All of these have been overcome, and the winery is fully

open for inspection throughout the year, including its 'self-guided winery tour' with signposts explaining the function of each piece or pieces of equipment.

🍷🍷🍷🍷🍷 **Southern Highlands Cabernet Sangiovese 2009** Light colour is no guide (unless it be to sangiovese), for this is an impressive blend that works to perfection; the bouquet is aromatic and fragrant, with redcurrant and cherry to the fore, the palate following suit; the tannins, which might have been the Achilles heel, are also precisely balanced. Screwcap. 12.5% alc. **Rating** 94 **To** 2020 $28

🍷🍷🍷🍷🍷 **Southern Highlands Pinot Gris 2011 Rating** 91 **To** 2013 $25
Reserve Southern Highlands Malbec 2010 Rating 90 **To** 2015 $27

🍷🍷🍷🍷 **Reserve Southern Highlands Fume Blanc 2010 Rating** 88 **To** 2013 $24

John Duval Wines ★★★★★

PO Box 622, Tanunda, SA 5352 **Region** Barossa Valley
T (08) 8562 2266 **www**.johnduvalwines.com **Open** At Artisans of Barossa
Winemaker John Duval **Est.** 2003 **Dozens** 7000
John Duval is an internationally recognised winemaker, having been the custodian of Penfolds Grange for almost 30 years as part of his role as chief red winemaker at Penfolds. These days John is concentrating on his own brand, and providing consultancy services to clients in various parts of the world. On the principle 'if not broken, don't fix', he is basing his business on shiraz and shiraz blends from old-vine vineyards in the Barossa Valley. The brand name Plexus denotes combining the different elements of shiraz/grenache/mourvedre into a coherent structure. Exports to the UK, the US and other major markets.

🍷🍷🍷🍷🍷 **Entity Barossa Shiraz 2009** Crimson-purple; the perfumed bouquet proclaims the class of the wine, its array of blackberry, plum and spice fruit duly delivered on the medium-bodied palate; silky tannins and quality oak complete the picture. Screwcap. 14.5% alc. **Rating** 95 **To** 2030 $48
Eligo Barossa Valley Shiraz 2009 This is the very essence of old-vine Barossa shiraz, made with generosity and warmth as a core value; masses of sweet black fruits, bitter chocolate, graphite tannins and toasty oak combine to deliver a silky mouthful of tannins and plenty of warmth of alcohol; concentration kept in check, and exceptionally long. Cork. 14.5% alc. **Rating** 95 **To** 2020 $105 BE
Plexus Barossa Valley Shiraz Grenache Mourvedre 2010 Bright colour; a beautifully generous, plump and fleshy blend, with a backbone of Provençal garrigue providing light to the masses of sweet red and black fruits shade; the trailing spice and purity of fruit are seamless and very long. Screwcap. 14.5% alc. **Rating** 94 **To** 2018 $38 BE

🍷🍷🍷🍷🍷 **Entity Barossa Shiraz 2010 Rating** 93 **To** 2020 $47 BE

John Gehrig Wines ★★★★☆

Oxley-Milawa Road, Oxley, Vic 3678 **Region** King Valley
T (03) 5727 3395 **www**.johngehrigwines.com.au **Open** 7 days 10–5
Winemaker Ross Gehrig **Est.** 1976 **Dozens** 5600 **Vyds** 6ha
This family-founded and owned winery has passed on to the second generation, headed by Ross Gehrig. The estate vineyard is a patchwork quilt of riesling, chenin blanc, chardonnay, pinot meunier, pinot noir, muscat, lagrein, cabernet sauvignon, merlot, malbec, cabernet franc, petit verdot, durif and gamay, allowing – indeed demanding – Ross to make wines in a wide variety of styles. He continues to enjoy particular success with Riesling and Chenin Blanc.

🍷🍷🍷🍷🍷 **King Valley Riesling 2011** Light straw-green; very cleverly made, with just enough residual sugar to heighten the lime/lemon flavours, and balanced by citrussy acidity. Screwcap. 11% alc. **Rating** 93 **To** 2018 $22
King Valley Pinot Noir 2010 Full crimson-purple; this must be the best King Valley pinot noir I have tasted; it is stacked full of plum and black cherry fruit, and has a savoury structure to give it complexity; it pushes the envelope on the division between pinot noir and dry red, and in my view stays on the right side. Screwcap. 13.6% alc. **Rating** 93 **To** 2018 $30

King Valley Liqueur Muscat NV A very rich and complex muscat, with liqueured raisins to the fore, then Christmas pudding, honey, coffee, burnt toffee and Uncle Tom Cobbly and all. Screwcap. 18% alc. **Rating** 93 **To** 2013 $45

Elizabeth's Block 2009 A bright, light crimson Bordeaux blend; the bouquet is very fragrant, with as much red fruit impact as black; the light- to medium-bodied palate has a similar spray of lively red fruits. I would drink this wine sooner rather than later. Screwcap. 13.4% alc. **Rating** 92 **To** 2015 $32

YYYY   RG King Valley Durif 2010 **Rating** 88 **To** 2016 $35

John Kosovich Wines

Cnr Memorial Avenue/Great Northern Highway, Baskerville, WA 6056 **Region** Swan Valley
T (08) 9296 4356 **www**.johnkosovichwines.com.au **Open** 7 days 10–5.30
Winemaker Anthony Kosovich **Est.** 1922 **Dozens** 4000 **Vyds** 12.5ha
John Kosovich Wines operated as Westfield Wines until 2003, when it changed its name to honour John's 50th vintage. The name change did not signify any change in either philosophy or direction for this much-admired producer of a surprisingly elegant and complex Chardonnay. The other wines are more variable, but from time to time there have been attractive Verdelho and excellent Cabernet Sauvignon. Since 1998, wines partly or wholly from the family's planting at Pemberton have been made, the Swan Valley/Pemberton blends released under the Bronze Wing label.

YYYYY   **Bottle Aged Reserve Swan Valley Chenin Blanc 2007** Pale green-straw; has developed in similar fashion to Hunter Valley Semillon, adding dimensions to its weight and complexity, building on the texture and structure it had as a young wine. The real question is for how many decades will the wine live? Screwcap. 13.5% alc. **Rating** 94 **To** 2017 $32

Liqueur Verdelho NV Tawny brown-gold; '82 base wine, refreshed in '97 and '01; a very complex bouquet then a palate that shines on its own terms, vibrantly fresh yet clearly aged, with burnt butter and shortbread and Christmas cake flavours. 375ml. Diam. 19% alc. **Rating** 94 **To** 2013 $60

YYYYY   **Swan Valley Petit Verdot 2010 Rating** 92 **To** 2025 $28
✪   **Chenin Blanc 2011** Very well made, with more texture and structure than usually encountered, grown in a climate opposite in every way to its home in France's Loire Valley. As the '07 Bottle Aged Reserve shows, will age with grace and distinction. Screwcap. 13.5% alc. **Rating** 91 **To** 2021 $20

Reserve Pemberton Cabernet Malbec 2010 Rating 91 **To** 2020 $38
✪   **Pemberton Verdelho 2011** One of the luxury ends of young Verdelho, brought from the Swan Valley to the estate vineyard in Pemberton, and duly rewarding with its mix of tropical fruit and grainy citrus and mineral undertones. Be patient. Screwcap. 13% alc. **Rating** 90 **To** 2021 $20

John's Blend

18 Neil Avenue, Nuriootpa, SA 5355 (postal) **Region** Langhorne Creek
T (08) 8562 1820 **www**.johnsblend.com.au **Open** At The Winehouse, Langhorne Creek
Winemaker John Glaetzer **Est.** 1974 **Dozens** 2350 **Vyds** 23ha
John Glaetzer was Wolf Blass' right-hand man almost from the word go, the power behind the throne of the three Jimmy Watson trophies awarded to Wolf Blass Wines – in 1974, '75 and '76 – and a small matter of 11 Montgomery trophies for the Best Red Wine at the Adelaide Wine Show. This has always been a personal venture on the side, as it were, by John and wife Margarete, officially sanctioned of course, but really needing little marketing effort. Exports to Canada, Switzerland, Indonesia, Singapore and Hong Kong.

YYYYY   **Margarete's Shiraz 2009** Given the full treatment a la Guigal: 28 months in 100% new oak, 60% American, 40% French; while entirely from two Langhorne Creek vineyards, has (metaphorically) hopped across the border to McLaren Vale to bring back dark chocolate flavours. The primary ferment was finished in oak, thus integrating the oak as only barrel fermentation can do. Everyone's style? No. Most people's? Yes. Cork. 14.5% alc. **Rating** 94 **To** 2025 $35

Individual Selection Langhorne Creek Cabernet Sauvignon 2008
Following the completion of fermentation in new French hogsheads, the wine was matured in those barrels for 40 months; those who have purchased some or all of the preceding 34 vintages will be pleased with the consistency and quality of this wine, one that has to be judged within the parameters of its style. Cork. 14.5% alc. Rating 94 To 2020 $35

Johnston Oakbank ★★★★

18 Oakwood Road, Oakbank, SA 5243 **Region** Adelaide Hills
T (08) 8388 4263 **www**.johnston-oakbank.com.au **Open** Mon–Fri 10.30–4.30, w'ends 11–5
Winemaker David O'Leary (Contract), Geoff Johnston **Est.** 2002 **Dozens** 5000 **Vyds** 49ha
Johnston's has two distinct vineyards: the Galbraith Vineyard (22ha), adjacent to the Oakbank racecourse, was planted in 1993 to chardonnay (12ha) and pinot noir (5ha) for sparkling wine, and cabernet sauvignon (5ha). In '98 40ha was purchased in Balhannah, where 27ha of sauvignon blanc, merlot, pinot noir and shiraz had been planted by the Wenzel family (part of this production is sold to other makers). Exports to the US and Hong Kong.

 Adelaide Hills Cabernet Sauvignon 2009 Rating 93
○   To 2020 $17
○   **Adelaide Hills Shiraz 2009** Rating 93 To 2019 $17

Jones Road ★★★★★

2 Godings Road, Moorooduc, Vic 3933 **Region** Mornington Peninsula
T (03) 5978 8080 **F** (03) 5978 8081 **www**.jonesroad.com.au **Open** W'ends 11–5
Winemaker Sticks (Travis Bush) **Est.** 1998 **Dozens** 10 000 **Vyds** 26.5ha
It's a long story, but after establishing a very large and very successful herb-producing business in the UK, Rob Frewer and family migrated to Australia in 1997. By a circuitous route they ended up with a property on the Mornington Peninsula, promptly planting pinot noir and chardonnay, then pinot gris, sauvignon blanc and merlot; they have since leased another vineyard at Mt Eliza, and purchased Ermes Estate in 2007. Exports to the UK, Canada, Norway, Sweden, Singapore and Japan.

ΨΨΨΨΨ **Nepean Mornington Peninsula Pinot Noir 2010** Mid crimson, bright;
          a pristine and highly fragrant red-fruited bouquet, offering spices, game and a
          touch of vine sap; the palate is silky, fresh, focused and delivers ample fine-grained
          tannins to provide an expansive and harmonious finish; layers of flavour. Screwcap.
          13.5% alc. Rating 95 To 2020 $45 BE
          Nepean Mornington Peninsula Chardonnay 2011 Mid gold, green hue; the
          bouquet is a savoury blend of grapefruit, charcuterie, fine spices and struck quartz;
          the palate is taut and racy, linear and long, with a grace and length that are both
          charming and satisfying. Will be a wine to watch over the short to medium term.
          Screwcap. 13% alc. Rating 94 To 2018 $45 BE

 Mornington Peninsula Pinot Noir 2010 Rating 90 To 2018 $34 BE

Jones Winery & Vineyard ★★★★

Jones Road, Rutherglen, Vic 3685 **Region** Rutherglen
T (02) 6032 8496 **www**.joneswinery.com **Open** Mon, Thurs, Fri 10–4, w'ends 10–5
Winemaker Mandy Jones **Est.** 1860 **Dozens** 1000 **Vyds** 9.22ha
Jones Winery & Vineyard was established in 1860 and stands testament to a rich winemaking tradition. Since 1927, the winery has been owned and operated by the Jones family. Two blocks of old vines have been preserved (including 1.69ha of shiraz), supported by further blocks progressively planted between '75 and 2008. Today, Jones Winery & Vineyard is jointly operated by winemaker Mandy Jones, who brings 14 years of experience working at Chateau Carsin in Bordeaux, France, and her brother Arthur Jones. Together they produce a small range of boutique wines. Exports to Finland.

ΨΨΨΨΩ **Apero NV** Gleaming burnished gold; made from a blend of trebbiano and pedro ximenez, it is of Amontillado style, supple and smooth, and with just the right amount of rancio. Vino-Lok. 19% alc. **Rating** 93 **To** 2014 $25

LJ 2006 First tasted three years ago, and is not so different at this point in its development path; blackberry, plum and some sweet spicy notes run through the length of the medium- to full-bodied palate, the touch of grenache a point of difference. ProCork. 14.8% alc. **Rating** 92 **To** 2016 $70

✪ **Rutherglen Rose 2011** Pale pink; made from shiraz, skilfully matching fleeting red fruit flavours with a more savoury background; the finish is long and dry. Screwcap. 12% alc. **Rating** 90 **To** 2014 $18

ΨΨΨΨ **Rutherglen Marsanne 2010 Rating** 89 **To** 2018 $25
The Winemaker Durif 2009 Rating 88 **To** 2015 $28
Rutherglen Shiraz 2008 Rating 87 **To** 2016 $30

Josef Chromy Wines   ★★★★★

370 Relbia Road, Relbia, Tas 7258 **Region** Northern Tasmania
T (03) 6335 8700 **www**.josefchromy.com.au **Open** 7 days 10–5
Winemaker Jeremy Dineen **Est.** 2004 **Dozens** 30 000 **Vyds** 60ha
Joe Chromy just refuses to lie down and admit that the wine industry in Tasmania is akin to a financial black hole. After escaping from Czechoslovakia in 1950, establishing Blue Ribbon Meats, using the proceeds of sale to buy Rochecombe and Heemskerk vineyards, then selling those and establishing Tamar Ridge before it, too, was sold, Joe is at it again; this time he's invested $40 million in a wine-based but multifaceted business, including a major building development in Launceston. If this were not remarkable enough, Joe has turned 80, and has recovered from a major stroke. Foundation of the new wine business was the purchase of the large Old Stornoway Vineyard at a receivership sale in 2003; in all, there are 60ha of 10-year-old vines, the lion's share to pinot noir and chardonnay. He retained Jeremy Dineen as winemaker, and the winery was completed prior to the '07 vintage. Chromy's grandson Dean Cocker is business manager of the restaurant, function and wine centre, which has spectacular views over White Hills to Ben Lomond, the vineyard and the lakes. The homestead is now a dedicated wine centre and cellar door, offering WSET (Wine & Spirit Education Trust) courses levels 1, 2 and 3. Exports to the UK, the US and other major markets have seen production increase significantly.

ΨΨΨΨΨ **Botrytis Riesling 2009** Classic Botrytis Riesling, leaving the varietal character totally intact with pure lime juice flavours; great sweetness/acid balance and length. Screwcap. 9.8% alc. **Rating** 95 **To** 2018 $25

Pinot Noir Chardonnay 2008 Opens with phenolics and aldehydes, ultimately subsumed in the depth of the very, very complex and layered palate. Gold Tas Wine Show '12. Cork. 12% alc. **Rating** 94 **To** 2014 $38

ΨΨΨΨΩ **Riesling 2010 Rating** 90 **To** 2020 $26

ΨΨΨΨ **PEPIK Chardonnay 2011 Rating** 89 **To** 2014 $20
ZDAR Chardonnay 2008 Rating 88 **To** 2017 $48
PEPIK Sparkling Rose NV Rating 88 **To** Now $27
PEPIK Pinot Noir 2011 Rating 87 **To** 2016 $22

Journeys End Vineyards   ★★★★☆

248 Flinders Street, Adelaide, SA 5000 (postal) **Region** South Eastern Australia
T 0431 709 305 **www**.journeysendvineyards.com.au **Open** Not
Winemaker Ben Riggs (Contract) **Est.** 2001 **Dozens** 13 000
A particularly interesting business in the virtual winery category, which, while focused on McLaren Vale shiraz, also has contracts for other varieties in the Adelaide Hills and Langhorne Creek. The Shiraz comes in four levels and, for good measure, uses five different clones to amplify the complexity that comes from having grapegrowers in many different parts of McLaren Vale. Exports to the UK, the US, Malaysia, Singapore, Hong Kong, China and NZ.

ŶŶŶŶŶ **Arrival McLaren Vale Shiraz 2008** Five clones of shiraz were used in making this wine, the one-piece natural cork strongly suggesting the journey's end will be in the US or China. While also full-bodied like its siblings, it has a more savoury, bitter chocolate cast to the aromas and flavours, and has more drive on the finish. Clearly the best of the shiraz trio. 14.5% alc. **Rating** 94 **To** 2028 $45

ŶŶŶŶŶ **Coonawarra Station Cabernet Sauvignon 2009** The label is very ✪ reminiscent of the famous Woodley Treasure Chest series. Medium red-purple; the wine is medium- to full-bodied, with blackberry, blackcurrant, earth and cedar all in play, the tannins soft, the finish good. Screwcap. 14.5% alc. **Rating** 91 **To** 2023 $22
The Embarkment McLaren Vale Shiraz 2008 Rating 90 **To** 2018 $22
Ascent McLaren Vale Shiraz 2008 Rating 90 **To** 2020 $30

ŶŶŶŶ **The Bobby Dazzler Shiraz 2009** A retro comic book label could not be ✪ more different from the labels of the other Journeys End reds, a curious choice. Red-purple; the medium-bodied palate opens with black fruits before moving speedily into a savoury, somewhat tannin finish. Screwcap. 14.5% alc. **Rating** 89 **To** 2017 $17

✪ **Three Brothers Reunited Shiraz 2010** Good colour; a soft, plushy shiraz with mocha, cocoa and chocolate nuances, and some sweetness that will appeal to many for whom $12 is the right price. Screwcap. 14.5% alc. **Rating** 87 **To** 2013 $12

Juniper Estate ★★★★★
98 Tom Cullity Drive, Cowaramup, WA 6284 **Region** Margaret River
T (08) 9755 9000 **www**.juniperestate.com.au **Open** 7 days 10–5
Winemaker Mark Messenger **Est.** 1973 **Dozens** 13 000 **Vyds** 19.5ha
When Roger Hill and Gillian Anderson purchased the Wrights' vineyard in 1998, the 10ha vineyard was already 25 years old, but in need of retrellising and a certain amount of nursing to bring it back to health. All of that has happened, along with the planting of additional shiraz and cabernet sauvignon. The Juniper Crossing wines use a mix of estate-grown grapes and grapes from other Margaret River vineyards, while the Juniper Estate releases are made only from the estate plantings. Exports to the UK, Ireland, Canada, Denmark, Hong Kong, the Philippines and Singapore.

ŶŶŶŶŶ **Margaret River Semillon 2010** Stylistically speaking, this is an unusual departure for this variety, with a strong oak-aged influence providing a complex and intriguing blend of savoury grilled nut and charcuterie, nestled comfortably alongside fresh tropical fruits; long, unctuous, deep and compelling, with an electric mouthfeel; interesting and a great deal of pleasure, a wonderful combination. Screwcap. 12.5% alc. **Rating** 95 **To** 2017 $27 BE
Margaret River Cabernet Sauvignon 2009 Deep garnet, bright; a graceful and understated bouquet, revealing blackcurrant, lavender, violet and a touch of leafy complexity; the palate is full-bodied, but not full-blooded, with restraint the order of the day; long, expansive and with a long future ahead. Screwcap. 14.5% alc. **Rating** 95 **To** 2025 $50 BE
Margaret River Chardonnay 2010 An elegant and tightly wound expression of the region, with pure grapefruit and nectarine aromas, coupled with fine accents of oak-derived spice; fine and poised, with taut acidity and a long, even and expansive finish; unevolved, and with a healthy future ahead. Screwcap. 13% alc. **Rating** 94 **To** 2022 $35 BE

ŶŶŶŶŶ **Juniper Crossing Margaret River Shiraz 2009** Light to medium red-purple; ✪ an attractive and elegant medium-bodied wine that finished its fermentation in French and American barrels. The red fruit flavours have touches of spice and pepper, and the tannins are of the kind you only get with this type of fermentation. Screwcap. 14.5% alc. **Rating** 93 **To** 2019 $20

✪   **South by Southwest Margaret River Cabernet Merlot 2009** Juniper Estate acquired Higher Plane and the South by Southwest brand some years ago. Bright colour; the fragrant bouquet and lively red and black fruits of the medium-bodied palate reflect the southern area of Margaret River whence this wine comes. Screwcap. 14.5% alc. **Rating** 93 **To** 2020 $21
Margaret River Shiraz 2009 Rating 92 **To** 2025 $35 BE

✪   **Juniper Crossing Margaret River Cabernet Sauvignon Merlot 2009** Deep garnet; a restrained and pure-fruited bouquet of black fruits, olive and cedar; the palate is soft-centred, accessible and fleshy, yet has the backbone to demand attention; restraint and power in equal measure. Screwcap. 14.5% alc. **Rating** 92 **To** 2018 $20 BE
Margaret River Shiraz 2008 Rating 91 **To** 2022 $35 BE

✪   **Juniper Crossing Margaret River Merlot 2010** Mid garnet; a fresh and lively blend of black plum, mulberry and cedar are evident on the bouquet; the palate is fleshy and accessible on entry, with enough stuffing and depth to provide more than a modicum of interest in this fickle variety. Screwcap. 14% alc. **Rating** 91 **To** 2017 $20 BE

✪   **Juniper Crossing Margaret River Chardonnay 2011** Mid gold, green hue; the bouquet is pure grapefruit and oak-derived spice; the palate reveals lacy acidity and plenty of flesh in the form of nectarine and a little grilled nut complexity; freshness and drive are the key. Screwcap. 13% alc. **Rating** 90 **To** 2017 $20 BE

🍷🍷🍷🍷   **Juniper Crossing Tempranillo 2010 Rating** 89 **To** 2016 $20 BE
Margaret River Cane-cut Riesling 2010 Rating 89 **To** 2014 $27 BE

Kabminye Wines   ★★★☆

Krondorf Road, Tanunda, SA 5352 **Region** Barossa Valley
T (08) 8563 0889 **www.**kabminye.com **Open** 7 days 11–5
Winemaker Rick Glastonbury **Est.** 2001 **Dozens** 1500 **Vyds** 1.5ha
Richard and Ingrid Glastonbury's cellar door is on land settled in the 1880s by Ingrid's ancestor, Johann Christian Henschke. Kabminye is an Aboriginal word meaning 'morning star', and was given to the hamlet of Krondorf as a result of the anti-German sentiment during the Second World War (since changed back to the original Krondorf). The cellar door and café opened in 2003; SA Tourism has since used the building as a sustainable tourism case study. The vineyard is planted to durif, shiraz, mourvedre, carignan, cinsaut, princess black muscat and black frontignac. Exports to the UK, Malaysia, Hong Kong and China.

🍷🍷🍷🍷🍷   **Barossa Valley Durif Carignan Shiraz 2009** A 40/40/20% blend that has spent 30 months in French oak barriques, the colour strong purple-red; Kabminye calls it 'this lovely monster' on the back label. It's certainly a monster, but beauty will have to be in the eye of the beholder, because it's all about sombre, savoury black fruits and little else; 110 dozen made. Screwcap. 15% alc. **Rating** 90 **To** 2020 $43

🍷🍷🍷🍷   **Eden Valley Kerner 2010 Rating** 87 **To** 2013 $22

Kaesler Wines   ★★★★★

Barossa Valley Way, Nuriootpa, SA 5355 **Region** Barossa Valley
T (08) 8562 4488 **www.**kaesler.com.au **Open** 7 days 10–5
Winemaker Reid Bosward, Stephen Dew **Est.** 1990 **Dozens** 25 000 **Vyds** 50ha
The first members of the Kaesler family settled in the Barossa Valley in 1845. The vineyards date back to '93, but the Kaesler family ownership ended in 1968. After several changes, the present (much-expanded) Kaesler Wines was acquired by a small group of investment bankers headed by Swiss-born, Singapore-resident, quietly spoken Ed Peter (who has since acquired Yarra Yering), in conjunction with former Flying Winemaker Reid Bosward and wife Bindy. Reid's experience shows through in the wines, which now come from estate vineyards, 40ha adjacent to the winery, and 10ha in the Marananga area. The latter includes shiraz planted in

1899, with both blocks seeing plantings in the 1930s, '60s, then each decade through to the present. Exports to all major markets.

ΨΨΨΨΨ **Old Bastard Barossa Valley Shiraz 2009** From the prime estate vineyard, planted in 1893, with an inimitable Ralph Steadman label. The alcohol is 2.5% lower than that of the '08; it is beautifully supple, fresh and balanced, but retains the intensity, clarity and integrity of very old-vine wine. Bravo. If only it had a screwcap. Cork. 14% alc. **Rating** 97 **To** 2029 $170

Old Vine Barossa Valley Shiraz 2009 From three estate vineyards with 40, 60 and 112-year-old vines, matured for 12 months in French oak. The colour is good, rather than remarkable; the bouquet immediately signals a change from prior vintages: more perfumed, the palate more elegant, but still crammed with plum and blackberry fruit. Cork. 14.5% alc. **Rating** 95 **To** 2029 $80

✪ **Stonehorse Shiraz 2010** Strong, deep colour; how much is the vintage is as yet not certain, but this is a delicious Barossa Valley shiraz hopefully pointing the direction for the future; the flavours are fully ripe and round, and it is the fruit, not the oak, that does the talking. Screwcap. 14.5% alc. **Rating** 94 **To** 2025 $25

Alte Reben Barossa Valley Shiraz 2009 The wine, in its massive eco-unfriendly bottle, comes from the estate 1899 plantings, matured in French oak for 15 months. Has purple-crimson colour, and the underlying fruit shows its distinguished parentage; after several tastings, I decided to accept the alcohol in the overall context of an undoubtedly complex wine. Cork. 15% alc. **Rating** 94 **To** 2024 $120

ΨΨΨΨΨ **The Bogan 2008 Rating** 93 **To** 2018 $50

Barossa Valley Viognier 2010 Rating 90 **To** 2014 $25

ΨΨΨΨ **Rizza Barossa Valley Riesling 2011 Rating** 88 **To** 2014 $18

Kalleske ★★★★★

6 Murray Road, Greenock, SA 5360 **Region** Barossa Valley
T (08) 8563 4000 **www.**kalleske.com **Open** Mon–Fri by appt
Winemaker Troy Kalleske **Est.** 1999 **Dozens** 8000 **Vyds** 42ha

The Kalleske family has been growing and selling grapes on a mixed farming property at Greenock for over 100 years. Sixth-generation Troy Kalleske, with brother Tony, established the winery and created the Kalleske label in 1999. The vineyard is planted to shiraz (27ha), grenache (6ha), mataro (2ha), chenin blanc, durif, viognier, zinfandel, petit verdot, semillon and tempranillo (1ha each). The vines vary in age, with the oldest dating back to 1875, and the overall average age is about 50 years; all grown organically. Exports to all major markets.

ΨΨΨΨΨ **Eduard Old Vine Barossa Valley Shiraz 2009** Dark purple-red; made from three vineyard blocks planted between 1905 and '60; open-fermented and taken to new and used French and American oak hogsheads to conclude its fermentation; an utterly seductive blend of black fruits and licorice, fruitcake, dark chocolate and vanilla, quality tannins present from start to finish. Quite a wine. Screwcap. 14.5% alc. **Rating** 96 **To** 2029 $85

Johann Georg Old Vine Single Vineyard Barossa Valley Shiraz 2009 From a single block of vines planted in 1875, and made in a very small quantity, the product of a single open-top fermenter, finishing that fermentation in French and American oak, where it remained for the next two years. It is very complex and intense, yet little more than medium-bodied, having a tapestry of aromas and flavours similar to Eduard, with great length. How great will the '10 be? Screwcap. 14.5% alc. **Rating** 96 **To** 2034 $100

Greenock Single Vineyard Barossa Valley Shiraz 2010 Deep, dark purple-crimson; a wine literally dripping a stream of flavours, each succeeding the other until the round robin starts again; licoriće, oriental spice, black fruits, mocha and much else are to be found on the bouquet and medium- to full-bodied palate; has outstanding length, augmented by savoury tannins on the finish. Screwcap. 14.5% alc. **Rating** 94 **To** 2024 $38

Greenock Single Vineyard Barossa Valley Shiraz 2009 Deep crimson-purple; from a single vineyard on the western edge of the Greenock Creek, certified biodynamic. Open-fermented, the last stages completed in French and American oak, 30% new. A rich, medium- to full-bodied wine true to the Kalleske style, with black fruits, touches of licorice and spice, and ample, balanced tannins. Will age with aplomb. Screwcap. 14.5% alc. **Rating** 94 **To** 2024 $38

ΥΥΥΥΥ **Moppa Barossa Valley Shiraz 2010 Rating** 93 **To** 2025 $28
✪ **Pirathon by Kalleske Barossa Valley Shiraz 2010** Deep, dense colour; a flagrantly full-bodied wine, sourced from many vineyards, in oak from four countries for 18 months, open-fermented, basket-pressed. This wine (like the Moppa Shiraz) is not hot or alcoholic, nor is there dead fruit; there is lots of oak and extract. Could well slim down with time in bottle. Screwcap. 14.5% alc. **Rating** 92 **To** 2025 $23
✪ **Barossa Valley Rosina 2011** Vivid puce-pink; from 70-year-old grenache vines, wild-fermented and partially barrel-fermented; lively, tangy red fruit pastille flavours supported by brisk acidity drive the palate. Screwcap. 12.5% alc. **Rating** 90 **To** Now $18
Buckboard Single Vineyard Barossa Valley Durif 2010 Rating 90 **To** 2015 $23

ΥΥΥΥ **Merchant Single Vineyard Barossa Valley Cabernet Sauvignon 2009 Rating** 89 **To** 2017 $28
Dodger Single Vineyard Barossa Valley Tempranillo 2010 Rating 89 **To** 2017 $23
Buckboard Single Vineyard Barossa Valley Durif 2009 Rating 89 **To** 2015 $23
Florentine Single Vineyard Barossa Valley Chenin Blanc 2011 Rating 88 **To** 2013 $18

Kangarilla Road Vineyard   ★★★★★

Kangarilla Road, McLaren Vale, SA 5171 **Region** McLaren Vale
T (08) 8383 0533 **www.**kangarillaroad.com.au **Open** Mon–Fri 9–5, w'ends 11–5
Winemaker Kevin O'Brien **Est.** 1997 **Dozens** 65 000 **Vyds** 14ha
Kangarilla Road is owned and operated by long-time industry identity Kevin O'Brien and wife Helen. The estate plantings include shiraz, chardonnay, savagnin and zinfandel, the intake supplemented by purchases from other vineyards in McLaren Vale. Zinfandel is the winery specialty, sold either under that name or as Primitivo; other alternative varieties include sangiovese. Exports to the UK, the US and other major markets.

ΥΥΥΥΥ **Scarce Earth Project McLaren Vale Shiraz 2009** Deep crimson-purple; the scarce earth in this instance is a single vineyard in the Maslin Beach area that is able to provide the grapes for a palate with great intensity to its juicy black fruit flavours while retaining elegance; the wine lingers in the mouth for a long time on the aftertaste. Screwcap. 14% alc. **Rating** 96 **To** 2034 $50
Scarce Earth Project McLaren Vale Shiraz 2010 Full crimson-purple; the vines are grown on the grey and red mottled alluvial soil of Maslin Beach; the wine has exceptional elegance and balance, with spice and licorice nuances of a different tone from the other very good Kangarilla shirazs from this vintage; the finish is long, the balance impeccable. Screwcap. 14.5% alc. **Rating** 95 **To** 2030 $50
The Devil's Whiskers McLaren Vale Shiraz 2010 Deep purple-crimson; a high-quality McLaren Vale shiraz, replete with layers of black fruits, dark chocolate and licorice, firm but fine and ripe tannins, and all the oak that is necessary. Screwcap. 14.5% alc. **Rating** 94 **To** 2030 $35

ΥΥΥΥΥ **McLaren Vale Shiraz 2010** Strong purple-crimson; ticks all the boxes, and then
✪ some, for a wine at this price; the regional influence comes through with notes of bitter chocolate and mocha, varietal character courtesy of the rounded blackberry and licorice fruits; oak and tannins are present, but of less importance. Screwcap. 14% alc. **Rating** 93 **To** 2020 $20

○ **McLaren Vale Sangiovese 2010** Rating 93 To 2018 $25
McLaren Vale Cabernet Sauvignon 2010 Good hue and depth; strong red-purple; proclaims its varietal foundation from the word go; the medium-bodied palate takes the process one step further, with its sombre blackcurrant fruit and firm but ripe tannins; has considerable length and overall balance. Screwcap. 14% alc. **Rating** 92 **To** 2022 $20

ΨΨΨΨ **McLaren Vale Chardonnay 2011** Rating 89 To 2014 $18
McLaren Vale Primitivo Rose 2011 Rating 89 To Now $22
The Veil 2011 Rating 89 To Now $20
Black St Peters McLaren Vale Zinfandel 2009 Rating 87 To 2016 $32

Kangaroo Island Estate ★★★★

Section 37 & 48 HD Seddon, Playford Highway, Kangaroo Island, SA 5220
Region Kangaroo Island
T (08) 8559 6013 **www**.kangarooislandestate.com.au **Open** By appt
Winemaker Greg Wight **Est.** 1999 **Dozens** 800 **Vyds** 8ha
This is the venture of local farmers and entrepreneurs Terry and Cheryl May, who in 1999 decided there was more to life than just sheep and cattle farming, and planted 6ha of shiraz and 2ha of cabernet sauvignon. The vines are hand-pruned and irrigation is minimal, thus ensuring low yields. In 2005 they decided that all wine made from the '07 vintage onwards would be made and bottled onsite, and to this end a farm shed was converted into a winery, and in '06 a climate-controlled barrel storage shed was constructed. The Shiraz and Cabernet are open-fermented and basket-pressed, shiraz into a mixture of old American oak hogsheads, the cabernet into old American and French hogsheads. The wines are aged on lees to keep them fresh while also reducing the oak influence, and are not racked until shortly prior to bottling. The majority of the rose is fermented in stainless steel, a small portion in old French oak quarter-cask barrels. The results speak for themselves.

ΨΨΨΨΨ **Shiraz 2008** Still retains its bright crimson hue; a bright and fresh wine with an array of red fruit flavours, fine tannins and American oak that (counter-intuitively) complements the flavours. Gold medal Cowra Wine Show '10. Screwcap. 13.5% alc. **Rating** 92 **To** 2018 $29
Cabernet Sauvignon 2009 Clear crimson-purple, the fresh bouquet and palate with hints of mint and olive contrasting with the blackcurrant/cassis fruit all point to moderate alcohol; the oak use, too, has been controlled. Screwcap. 15% alc. **Rating** 91 **To** 2020 $29

ΨΨΨΨ ○ **Rose 2010** Strong, clear crimson-purple; a rose with plenty of all-up red berry fruit flavour; a hint of residual sugar is neatly balanced by acidity and some savoury undertones. Screwcap. 12% alc. **Rating** 89 **To** 2013 $17

Kanta ★★★★☆

22–26 Vardon Lane, Adelaide, SA 5000 (postal) **Region** Adelaide Hills
T (08) 8232 5300 **F** (08) 8232 2055 **Open** Not
Winemaker Egon Muller **Est.** 2005 **Dozens** 1000
This is the ultimate virtual winery, a joint venture between famed Mosel-Saar-Ruwer winemaker (and proprietor) Egon Muller, Michael Andrewartha from Adelaide's East End Cellars, and the extraordinarily well-qualified Akos Forczek, with multiple tertiary degrees and fluent in Hungarian, French, English, Russian and Arabic. A three-year search for the perfect riesling site ended almost where the journey began, at the Shaw & Smith Adelaide Hills vineyard. Muller arrived on the day of picking to oversee the whole production of the first vintage, carried out at Shaw & Smith with input from Shaw & Smith's winemaker, Darryl Catlin. The grapes were crushed and cold-soaked for up to 16 hours, the juice settled without enzyme and kept at 12°C until spontaneous fermentation began. Small wonder that the wine is so different from other Australian rieslings, and even more different from the gloriously fine wines that Muller makes at home. Exports to the UK, the US, Canada, Germany and Japan.

ΨΨΨΨ? **Egon Muller Adelaide Hills Riesling 2010** Made in similar style to prior releases, bone-dry and with the fruit initially suppressed by the winemaking methods employed; the expectation is that it will flourish with time in bottle. Screwcap. 13.5% alc. **Rating** 91 **To** 2020 $30

Karatta Wines

Lot 202 Robe-Penola Road, Robe, SA 5276 **Region** Robe
T (08) 8735 7255 **www**.karattawines.com.au **Open** W'ends & hols 11–4 or by appt
Winemaker Duane Coates **Est.** 1994 **Dozens** NFP **Vyds** 39.6ha
Owned by David and Peg Woods, Karatta Wines is named after Karatta House, one of Robe's well-known heritage-listed icons. Built in 1858, Karatta House was occupied by the South Australian Governor Sir James Fergusson during the summers of 1868 to '71. Vineyards include the 12 Mile Vineyard and Tenison Vineyard, both located in the Robe region.

ΨΨΨΨ? **12 Mile Vineyard Robe Shiraz Cabernet Sauvignon 2009** Medium red-
✪   purple; has an array of blackberry, blackcurrant, plum and spice aromas and flavours; the palate is medium- to full-bodied, giving the wine some prospect of further development. Screwcap. 14% alc. **Rating** 90 **To** 2019 $15

ΨΨΨΨ **12 Mile Vineyard Robe Shiraz 2009** **Rating** 89 **To** 2019 $18
12 Mile Vineyard Robe Cabernet Sauvignon 2009 **Rating** 89 **To** 2019 $18

Karra Yerta Wines

Lot 534 Flaxman's Valley Road, Wilton, SA 5353 **Region** Eden Valley
T 0438 870 178 **www**.karrayertawines.com.au **Open** At Collective Barossa, Tanunda
Winemaker James Linke, Peter Gajewski **Est.** 2006 **Dozens** 400 **Vyds** 1.92ha
The name Karra Yerta is derived from the local Aboriginal language, 'karra' the name for the majestic red gum trees, and 'yerta' meaning country or ground. The landscape has changed little (other than the patches of vineyard) since the ancestors of James and Marie Linke arrived (separately) in SA in 1847. Both James and Marie were born in Angaston, but moved to Flaxmans Valley in 1985, and in '87 purchased one of the old stone cottages in the region. Much time has been spent in reviving the largely abandoned vineyard, which provides most of their grapes; plantings now include semillon, riesling, shiraz and frontignac. While most of the grapes were sold, they indulged in home winemaking for many years, but have now moved into commercial winemaking on a micro scale.

ΨΨΨΨ **Bullfrog Flat Eden Valley Shiraz 2008** Deep colour, and showing plenty of mocha prunes and jammy black fruits; sweet-fruited, soft and fully developed, so best to drink soon. Screwcap. 14.5% alc. **Rating** 88 **To** 2015 $35 BE
Barossa Ranges Shiraz Cabernet 2008 Deep colour, with a pastille-like essency dark fruit bouquet; this follows on the palate with blackberry and cassis prominent, supported by mocha notes. Screwcap. 14.5% alc. **Rating** 87 **To** 2016 $25 BE

KarriBindi

RMB 111, Scott Road, Karridale, WA 6288 (postal) **Region** Margaret River
T (08) 9758 5570 **www**.karribindi.com.au **Open** Not
Winemaker Naturaliste Vintners (Bruce Dukes) **Est.** 1997 **Dozens** 1500 **Vyds** 32.05ha
KarriBindi has been established by Kevin, Yvonne and Kris Wealand. The name is partly derived from Karridale and the surrounding karri forests, and from Bindi, the home town of one of the members of the Wealand family. In Nyoongar, 'karri' means strong, special, spiritual, tall tree and 'bindi' means butterfly, hence the label's picture of a butterfly soaring through karri trees. The Wealands have established sauvignon blanc (15ha), chardonnay (6.25ha), cabernet sauvignon (4ha), plus smaller plantings of semillon, shiraz and merlot. The major part of the grape production is sold under contract to Vasse Felix and Leeuwin Estate, with limited amounts released under the KarriBindi label. The core range includes Sauvignon Blanc, Semillon Sauvignon Blanc, Shiraz and Chardonnay Pinot.

ΨΨΨΨΩ **Margaret River Semillon Sauvignon Blanc 2011** Light, bright straw-green;
 the grapes for this blend have been picked at precisely the right time, bestowing
on the one hand crispness and lively acidity, on the other a lovely display of snow
pea, citrus and tropical fruits. Screwcap. 11.8% alc. **Rating** 93 **To** 2015 $20
Margaret River Sauvignon Blanc 2011 Pale quartz-green; lively, bright and
fresh, with a display of effortless citrus and passionfruit flavours; balanced acidity
draws out the finish. Screwcap. 11.8% alc. **Rating** 91 **To** 2013 $20

Kate Hill Wines   ★★★★★

PO Box 343, Sandy Bay, Tas 7006 **Region** Southern Tasmania
T (03) 6281 2330 **www**.katehillwines.com.au **Open** Not
Winemaker Kate Hill **Est.** 2008 **Dozens** 1000
When Kate Hill (and husband Charles) came to Tasmania in 2006, Kate had worked as a
winemaker in Australia and overseas for 10 years. Kate's wines are made from a number of
vineyards across southern Tasmania, the aim being to produce approachable, delicate wines.

ΨΨΨΨΨ **Pinot Chardonnay 2008** Striking label design is a good start, as is the brilliant
green-straw colour; while the time spent on lees is not specified, it has obviously
been substantial, but not to the extent of blunting the wonderfully fresh flavour,
overall mouthfeel and elegance; a mix of citrus and stone fruit is tempered by just
a touch of yeast-derived brioche. Diam. 12% alc. **Rating** 94 **To** 2015 $42

ΨΨΨΨ **Riesling 2011 Rating** 89 **To** 2016 $26

Katnook Estate   ★★★★★

Riddoch Highway, Coonawarra, SA 5263 **Region** Coonawarra
T (08) 8737 0300 **www**.katnookestate.com.au **Open** Mon–Sat 10–5, Sun 11–5
Winemaker Wayne Stehbens **Est.** 1979 **Dozens** 90 000 **Vyds** 198ha
Second in size only to Wynns Coonawarra Estate in the region, Katnook has made significant
strides since its acquisition by Freixinet; at one time selling most of its grapes, it now sells a
maximum of 10%. The historic stone woolshed in which the second vintage in Coonawarra
(1896) was made, and which has served Katnook since 1980, has been restored. Likewise,
the former office of John Riddoch has been fully restored and is now the cellar door, and
the former stables (likewise fully restored) now serve as a function area. Well over half the
total estate plantings are cabernet sauvignon and shiraz, other varieties of importance being
chardonnay, merlot, sauvignon blanc and pinot noir. The Odyssey Cabernet Sauvignon and
Prodigy Shiraz are the icon duo at the top of a multitiered production. Freixenet, the Spanish
Cava producer, now owns 100% of the business. Exports to all major markets.

ΨΨΨΨΨ **The Caledonian 2009** The name is a tribute to the Scottish founder of
Coonawarra, John Riddoch, and for the first time (for Katnook) introduces a
cabernet sauvignon/shiraz/petit verdot blend, a singularly successful move; the
delicious palate has red and blackcurrant fruit flavours, tannins and oak just where
they should be. Screwcap. 13.5% alc. **Rating** 95 **To** 2029 $45
Coonawarra Shiraz 2009 Good crimson-purple; an elegant, medium-bodied
wine, with a harmonious fusion of blackberry, cherry and spice fruit, its sojourn
of 18 months in 20% new French and American oak judged to perfection. Easy
to drink now, but with the option of extended ageing. Screwcap. 13.5% alc.
Rating 94 **To** 2030 $40
Odyssey Coonawarra Cabernet Sauvignon 2008 Has been accorded
the full Odyssey treatment, matured for 34 months in a mixture of French and
American barriques, 70% new; a full-bodied wine, with abundant blackcurrant and
mulberry fruit, and tannins that have not been silenced by the protracted barrel
ageing. High-quality cork. 14.5% alc. **Rating** 94 **To** 2023 $100

ΨΨΨΨΩ **Coonawarra Chardonnay 2010 Rating** 93 **To** 2016 $28
Coonawarra Vintage Brut 2009 Rating 93 **To** 2015 $32

✪ **Founder's Block Coonawarra Cabernet Sauvignon 2010** Good purple-crimson; the fragrant bouquet leads into an elegant, medium-bodied palate with clear-cut varietal character in the blackcurrant/cassis/mint spectrum, along with a hint of earth. Good mouthfeel, length and balance; very impressive at the price. Screwcap. 13.5% alc. **Rating** 92 **To** 2013 $20

✪ **Founder's Block Coonawarra Shiraz 2009** Bright, light crimson; the bouquet is fragrant, with black fruits and attractive oak, the palate focused and long, with fruit, spice, licorice and earthy tannins all woven together. Will repay patience. Screwcap. 13.5% alc. **Rating** 91 **To** 2019 $20

Coonawarra Chardonnay 2008 **Rating** 90 **To** 2015 $28

✪ **Founder's Block Coonawarra Merlot 2009** Light red; the red berry fruits of the bouquet are followed logically by the light- to medium-bodied palate; here plum, cassis and spice flavours have gently savoury tannins that are ideally weighted for the wine. Screwcap. 13.5% alc. **Rating** 90 **To** 2013 $20

Coonawarra Cabernet Sauvignon 2009 **Rating** 90 **To** 2024 $40

🍷🍷🍷🍷 **Coonawarra Riesling 2010** **Rating** 89 **To** 2014 $22
Coonawarra Sauvignon Blanc 2010 **Rating** 89 **To** 2013 $25
Founder's Block Coonawarra Chardonnay Pinot Noir NV **Rating** 89 **To** Now $23
Founder's Block Coonawarra Sparkling Shiraz 2009 **Rating** 89 **To** 2014 $23
Coonawarra Sauvignon Blanc 2011 **Rating** 88 **To** 2013 $25
Founder's Block Coonawarra Shiraz 2010 **Rating** 87 **To** 2014 $20
Founder's Block Coonawarra Merlot 2008 **Rating** 87 **To** 2014 $20

Kay Brothers Amery Vineyards ★★★★★

57 Kays Road, McLaren Vale, SA 5171 **Region** McLaren Vale
T (08) 8323 8211 **www**.kaybrothersamerywines.com **Open** Mon–Fri 9–5, w'ends & public hols 11–5
Winemaker Colin Kay, Andy Coppard **Est.** 1890 **Dozens** 12 000 **Vyds** 22ha

A traditional winery with a rich history and just over 20ha of priceless old vines; while the white wines have been variable, the red wines and fortified wines can be very good. Of particular interest is Block 6 Shiraz, made from 100-year-old vines; both vines and wines are going from strength to strength. Exports to the UK, the US, Canada, Switzerland, France, Hong Kong, Singapore, Japan and NZ.

🍷🍷🍷🍷🍷 **Block 6 Shiraz 2009** Lighter colour than the Hillside, despite coming from the original 1896 1.8ha Hillside block of 117-year-old vines. Hand-picked, fermented in 1896 fermenters, basket-pressed, and matured for over two years in new American and Baltic oak barriques. The intensity of the fruit flavours is remarkable, although I'm not sure about the duck confit flavours ex the back label; the intense fruit has made light work of all that oak, and the tannins are mouth-watering. Screwcap. 13% alc. **Rating** 95 **To** 2040 $75

Rare McLaren Vale Muscat NV Full tawny-gold; halfway between Rutherglen and Barossa (Seppeltsfield); incredibly luscious and rich, with Christmas pudding, pancakes and maple syrup, and most anything you venture to find. And it would be a great topping (in small quantities) on vanilla ice cream. 375ml. Cork. 19.5% alc. **Rating** 94 **To** 2013 $65

🍷🍷🍷🍷½ **Hillside McLaren Vale Shiraz 2009** **Rating** 92 **To** 2024 $45

🍷🍷🍷🍷 **Basket Pressed McLaren Vale Grenache 2010** **Rating** 89 **To** 2016 $25
Hillside McLaren Vale Shiraz 2008 **Rating** 88 **To** 2015 $45

Keith Tulloch Wine ★★★★★

Hermitage Road, Pokolbin, NSW 2320 **Region** Hunter Valley
T (02) 4998 7500 **www**.keithtullochwine.com.au **Open** 7 days 10–5
Winemaker Keith Tulloch **Est.** 1997 **Dozens** 9000 **Vyds** 7.4ha

Keith Tulloch is, of course, a member of the Tulloch family, which has played such a lead role in the Hunter Valley for over a century. Formerly a winemaker at Lindemans and then Rothbury Estate, he has developed his own label since 1997. There is the same almost obsessive attention to detail, the same almost ascetic intellectual approach, the same refusal to accept anything but the best as that of Jeffrey Grosset. Exports to the UK, the US, Canada, Sweden and Hong Kong.

ŸŸŸŸŸ **Hunter Valley Semillon 2011** A pure, fresh and tightly wound bouquet of lemon, lemongrass and ginger; the palate is taut and racy with linear acidity, mineral complexity and a little generosity to make early drinking a fair proposition, cellaring more so. Screwcap. 11% alc. **Rating** 94 **To** 2025 $28 BE
The Kester Hunter Valley Shiraz 2010 Mid crimson, bright; the bouquet shows lifted red fruits, violets and a light dusting of exotic spices; the palate is finely balanced with silky tannins aplenty, red fruits and fine, linear acidity drawing out the evenly balanced, long and harmonious conclusion. Screwcap. 14.5% alc. **Rating** 94 **To** 2025 $60 BE

ŸŸŸŸŸ **Hunter Valley Chardonnay 2011 Rating** 92 **To** 2018 $30 BE
Hunter Valley Shiraz Viognier 2010 Rating 92 **To** 2018 $28 BE
Field of Mars Hunter Valley Shiraz 2010 Rating 91 **To** 2022 $70 BE

ŸŸŸŸ **Field of Mars Block 3 Hunter Valley Semillon 2011 Rating** 88 **To** 2020 $38 BE

Kellermeister ★★★★★

Barossa Valley Highway, Lyndoch, SA 5351 **Region** Barossa Valley
T (08) 8524 4303 **www.**kellermeister.com.au **Open** 7 days 9.30–5.30
Winemaker Matthew Reynolds, Andrew Cockram **Est.** 1976 **Dozens** 35 000 **Vyds** 2ha
Kellermeister is (and always has been) owned by Ralph Wesley Jones. For some considerable time this fact was not known to/acknowledged by the *Wine Companion*. Over and above this, Kellermeister is now the exclusive brand for all wines made by it, including the flagship Wild Witch Shiraz. For a variety of reasons, one being the financial failure of Dan Philips' The Grateful Palate, there have been structural changes to the business, including the appointment of Mark Pearce (most recently ex Wirra Wirra) as CEO, Matt Reynolds as chief winemaker and assistant winemaker Andrew Cockram. Matt began his career with Kay Brothers Amery Vineyards in McLaren Vale, thereafter working with Jeffrey Grosset making Riesling, joining Kellermeister in 2005. Exports to the US, Canada, Switzerland, Denmark, Israel, Taiwan, China and Japan.

ŸŸŸŸŸ **Black Sash Special Release Barossa Valley Shiraz 2006** Bright red, very good for age; Black Sash honours the old vines uprooted in the Vine Pull Scheme, and is itself made from survivors; it has a lush, opulent and rich palate that inevitably reflects its alcohol. Screwcap. 15% alc. **Rating** 93 **To** 2016 $55
Eden Valley Eiswein 2010 Deep gold; a fragrant and intense bouquet of ginger, rosehip, candied orange and apricot; while rich on entry, the finish dries out with a toffee brittle character that is refreshing and engaging; certainly more than just a curio. 375ml. Screwcap. 9% alc. **Rating** 91 **To** 2014 $30 BE
Boots Barossa Shiraz 2010 Deep crimson, purple hue; a bright and fragrant bouquet of red and black fruits, supplemented by choc-mint; the palate is fleshy, forward and full of sweet black fruits; moderately long to conclude. Screwcap. 14.5% alc. **Rating** 90 **To** 2018 $18 BE
⊙ **Boots Barossa Shiraz 2009 Rating** 90 **To** 2017 $18
Chardonnay Pinot Noir NV A well-made blend of Eden Valley chardonnay and pinot noir that spent 15 months on yeast lees; it is well balanced and has some elegance, but lacks the intensity and drive of its price peers. Cork. 12% alc. **Rating** 90 **To** Now $45
The Patriarch Sparkling Shiraz NV A complex and savoury bouquet showing a combination of fresh leather, black fruits tar and spice; the palate is evenly balanced and drying to finish after four years on lees, disgorged in Jan '11. Cork. 14.5% alc. **Rating** 90 **To** 2015 $60 BE

ŶŶŶŶ   **The Pilgrimage McLaren Vale Cabernet Shiraz 2009** Rating 89
To 2018 $25 BE

Kelvedon   ★★★★☆

PO Box 126, Swansea, Tas 7190 **Region** East Coast Tasmania
T (03) 6257 8283 www.kelvedonestate.com.au **Open** Not
Winemaker Winemaking Tasmania (Julian Alcorso) **Est.** 1998 **Dozens** 2000 **Vyds** 9ha
Jack and Gill Cotton began planting the Kelvedon Vineyard with 1ha of pinot noir in 1998.
The Cotton family has owned and managed the historic East Coast property since 1829,
grapegrowing coming very late in the piece. The plantings were extended in 2000–01 by
an additional 5 ha, half to pinot noir and half to chardonnay, followed by a further 2ha of
chardonnay in '10. The chardonnay and 1ha of pinot noir plantings are under contract to
Accolade Wines. One ha of sauvignon blanc has also been established to provide a second wine
under the Kelvedon label; the Pinot Noir can be of excellent quality.

ŶŶŶŶŶ   **Chardonnay 2010** Bottle no. 399/600 underlines the limited release of 50 dozen
bottles; this is a supremely elegant and almost ethereal wine, tangy white fruits
and grapefruit in the driving seat, oak bringing up the rear. Has a long life ahead.
Screwcap. 13.3% alc. **Rating** 94 **To** 2017 $50

ŶŶŶŶŶ   **Sauvignon Blanc 2011** Rating 91 To 2013 $26
Pinot Noir 2010 Rating 91 To 2014 $32

Kennedy   ★★★☆

Maple Park, 224 Wallenjoe Road, Corop, Vic 3559 (postal) **Region** Heathcote
T (03) 5484 8293 www.kennedyvintners.com.au **Open** Not
Winemaker Sandro Mosele (Contract) **Est.** 2002 **Dozens** 1000 **Vyds** 29.2ha
Having been farmers in the Colbinabbin area of Heathcote for 27 years, John and Patricia
Kennedy were on the spot when a prime piece of red Cambrian soil on the east-facing slope
of Mt Camel Range became available for purchase. They planted 20ha of shiraz in 2002. As
they gained knowledge of the intricate differences within the site, and worked with contract
winemaker Sandro Mosele, further plantings of shiraz, tempranillo and mourvedre followed in
'07. The Shiraz is made in small open fermenters, using indigenous yeasts and gentle pigeage
before being taken to French oak (20% new) for 12 months' maturation prior to bottling.

ŶŶŶŶŶ   **Heathcote Shiraz 2008** Excellent retention of hue, although the colour is
light; the fragrant red-fruited bouquet leads into a fine, light- to medium-bodied
palate, the flavours in a spicy red cherry spectrum. Screwcap. 14% alc. **Rating** 90
To 2018 $25

ŶŶŶŶ   **Pink Hills 2011** Rating 87 To 2013 $20

Kerrigan + Berry   ★★★★★

PO Box 221, Cowaramup, WA 6284 **Region** South West Australia Zone
T (08) 9755 6046 www.kerriganandberry.com.au **Open** Not
Winemaker Michael Kerrigan, Gavin Berry **Est.** 2007 **Dozens** 550
Owners Michael Kerrigan and Gavin Berry have been making wine in WA for a combined
period of over 40 years, and say they have been most closely associated with the two varieties
that in their opinion define WA: riesling and cabernet sauvignon. This is strictly a weekend
and after-hours venture, separate from their respective roles as chief winemakers at Hay Shed
Hill and West Cape Howe. They have focused on what is important, and explain, 'We have
spent a total of zero hours on marketing research, and no consultants have been injured in the
making of these wines.' The Riesling is made from the Langton Vineyard in Mount Barker,
with some of the oldest riesling vines in WA (planted in the 1970s). The Cabernet Sauvignon
is a blend of grapes from Mount Barker (the Landsdale Vineyard) and Margaret River (the
Hay Shed Hill vineyard).

♟♟♟♟♟ **Mt Barker Margaret River Cabernet Sauvignon 2009** A 50/50% blend, with excellent colour, a vividly fragrant bouquet and intense medium-bodied palate bringing together the strength and power of Mount Barker and the somewhat fleshier black and redcurrant fruit flavours of Margaret River; the tannin and oak contributions are precisely calibrated. Screwcap. 14% alc. **Rating** 96 To 2029 $55

Mt Barker Great Southern Riesling 2011 Made from nigh-on 40-year-old vines on the Langton Vineyard planted on steep, south-facing (hence cool) slopes. A spotlessly clean bouquet has light wafts of mineral and citrus; the palate is long and bone dry. A wine made without compromise, and all the better for that. Screwcap. 12% alc. **Rating** 94 To 2021 $28

Kersbrook Hill

1498 South Para Road, Kersbrook, SA 5231 **Region** Adelaide Hills
T (08) 8389 3301 **www.**kersbrookhill.com.au **Open** 7 days 10–5.30
Winemaker Simon Greenleaf, Peter Schell **Est.** 1998 **Dozens** 8000 **Vyds** 11ha
Paul and Mary Clark purchased what is now the Kersbrook Hill property, then grazing land, in 1997, planting 0.4ha of shiraz on a reality-check basis. Encouraged by the results, they increased the plantings to 3ha of shiraz and 1ha of riesling two years later. Yet further expansion of the vineyards has seen the area under vine increased to 11 ha, cabernet sauvignon (with 6ha) the somewhat unusual frontrunner. Mark Whisson is consultant viticulturist (Mark has been growing grapes in the Adelaide Hills for over 20 years). Peter Schell makes the Cabernet Sauvignon and Don's Acre Shiraz, Simon Greenleaf the rest of the wines. Exports to the US, Singapore, Hong Kong and China.

♟♟♟♟♟ **Adelaide Hills Cabernet Sauvignon 2010** Deep garnet; a lifted bouquet of redcurrant, cassis and eucalypt is on display; the medium-bodied palate is lively and fresh, with violets, toasty oak and tangy acidity revealing themselves on the forward finish. Screwcap. 14% alc. **Rating** 94 To Now $25

Kidman Wines

Riddoch Highway, Coonawarra, SA 5263 **Region** Coonawarra
T (08) 8736 5071 **www.**kidmanwines.com.au **Open** 7 days 10–5
Winemaker Sid Kidman **Est.** 1984 **Dozens** 6000 **Vyds** 17ha
Sid Kidman planted the first vines on the property in 1971, and has been managing the vineyard ever since. Over the years it has grown to its present, with cabernet sauvignon, shiraz, riesling and sauvignon blanc. The cellar door is housed in the old stables on the Kidman property; they were built in 1859 and are a great link with the district's history. Susie and Sid have recently been joined by their son George, who becomes the fourth generation of the Kidman family to be involved with the property. Exports to Malaysia and China.

♟♟♟♟♟ **Coonawarra Sauvignon Blanc 2011** Pale green-quartz; a pleasant surprise,
✪ with a seductive mix of lemon citrus and tropical fruit on the bouquet and a fresh, lively palate. Screwcap. 11% alc. **Rating** 90 To 2013 $15
✪ **Coonawarra Cabernet Sauvignon 2009** Bright, clear crimson-purple; juicy cassis on the bouquet and palate has been supported, not obliterated, by 18 months in French oak; from the taste of the wine, mainly used. A well-priced way to explore Coonawarra cabernet character. Screwcap. 14% alc. **Rating** 90 To 2019 $20

♟♟♟♟ **Coonawarra Shiraz 2009 Rating** 89 To 2017 $18

Kies Family Wines

Barossa Valley Way, Lyndoch, SA 5381 **Region** Barossa Valley
T (08) 8524 4110 **www.**kieswines.com.au **Open** 7 days 9.30–4
Winemaker Wine Wise Consultancy **Est.** 1969 **Dozens** 5000 **Vyds** 33ha
The Kies family has been resident in the Barossa Valley since 1857; the present generation of winemakers is the fifth. Until 1969 the family sold almost all their grapes, but in that year they

launched their own brand, Karrawirra. The coexistence of Killawarra forced a name change in 1983 to Redgum Vineyard; this business was subsequently sold. Later still, Kies Family Wines opened for business, drawing upon vineyards (up to 100 years old) that had remained in the family throughout the changes, offering a wide range of wines through the 1880 cellar door. Exports to the UK, Singapore, Hong Kong, China and Japan.

ŸŸŸŸ **Hill Block Barossa Valley Riesling 2011** Pale straw-green; generously flavoured and well balanced, with citrus to the fore, and a classic drink now or a few years down the track. Screwcap. 12% alc. **Rating** 88 **To** 2015 $15

SB Limestone Coast Sauvignon Blanc 2011 Light straw-green; an interesting wine, the aromas and flavours in the grass, herb, snow pea and asparagus spectrum, all legitimate aromas and flavours for the variety, less commonly to the exclusion of others. Screwcap. 12% alc. **Rating** 88 **To** 2013 $20

SSB Semillon Sauvignon Blanc 2011 A blend of Barossa Valley semillon and Limestone Coast sauvignon blanc works far better than one might expect, the dominant (in percentage terms) Barossa semillon being swept up by the sauvignon blanc so that ripe tropical fruits, rather than herbaceous characters, carry the day in a slightly rough-hewn palate. Screwcap. 12% alc. **Rating** 88 **To** 2014 $15

Spring Barossa Valley Merlot Rose 2011 Bright pale pink; the fruit flavours are well and truly based on residual sweetness; a strong case for a sweetness chart on the back label as currently used for Riesling. Screwcap. 13% alc. **Rating** 87 **To** 2013 $15

Monkey Nut Tree Barossa Valley Sparkling Merlot 2010 I have to be honest in saying I don't normally enjoy wines such as this, but this has good balance and refreshing red fruit flavours. Cork. 13.5% alc. **Rating** 87 **To** Now $25

Kilikanoon ●   ★★★★★

Penna Lane, Penwortham, SA 5453 **Region** Clare Valley
T (08) 8843 4206 **www**.kilikanoon.com.au **Open** Thurs–Mon 11–5
Winemaker Kevin Mitchell **Est.** 1997 **Dozens** 40 000 **Vyds** 330ha
Kilikanoon has travelled in the fast lane since winemaker Kevin Mitchell established it in 1997 on the foundation of 6ha of vines owned by him and father Mort. It made its first entry in the 2001 *Wine Companion* with a 4-star rating for its 3000-dozen production of Riesling, Cabernet Sauvignon and Grenache. With the aid of investors its 40 000-dozen production comes from over 300ha of estate-owned vineyards, and access to the best grapes from a total of 2266ha across South Australia. It is tied to Seppeltfield (see separate entry), two of the principal players being Nathan Waks, formerly principal cellist of the Sydney Symphony Orchestra, and winemaker-cum-entrepreneur Warren Randall. Its galaxy of top-rated wines are made in small batches of outstanding grapes made in the onsite winery built in 2004.

ŸŸŸŸŸ **Attunga 1865 Clare Valley Shiraz 2009** As the name suggests, the vines were planted in 1865, very early in the history of the Clare Valley; the crimson-purple colour is excellent, and the wine cries out for 20 years in bottle, for while the fruit is intense, there is a ghetto blast of oak. Cork. 14.5% alc. **Rating** 96 **To** 2050 $250

R Barossa Valley Shiraz 2009 From the two estate vineyards in the Barossa Valley, Greens and Crowhurst. The bouquet is admirable in its fruit/oak balance, and the tannins, while potent, play a positive role in giving texture to the layered blackberry fruits. Cork. 14.5% alc. **Rating** 96 **To** 2040 $120

Mort's Reserve Watervale Riesling 2011 Pale straw, vivid hue; an altogether tightly wound and mineral-accented bouquet, offering mere glimpses of lime, florals and riverstone; the palate is beautifully poised and precise, linear and mouth-puckeringly racy, needing some time to reveal its true beauty; certainly worth the wait. Screwcap. 12.5% alc. **Rating** 95 **To** 2020 $35 BE

M McLaren Vale Shiraz 2009 From a single vineyard, and spent 24 months in French and American oak. Deeply coloured, the bouquet speaks first of its place of origin, the full-bodied palate likewise; is arguably the richest and fullest of the range, but lacks the finesse of the best. If you trust the cork gods, time may change the order of these things. 14.5% alc. **Rating** 95 **To** 2040 $80

Oracle Clare Valley Shiraz 2009 Deep crimson-purple; estate-grown, and spent 24 months in French and American oak, which has left a significant impression; more likely than not time will bring balance, and the wine has an appealing texture, full-bodied though it may be. Screwcap. 14.5% alc. **Rating** 95 **To** 2040 $80
Mort's Block Watervale Riesling 2011 Rating 94 To 2018 $22 BE
Parable McLaren Vale Shiraz 2009 Rating 94 To 2029 $45
Green's Vineyard Barossa Valley Shiraz 2009 Rating 94 To 2035 $80
Green's Vineyard Barossa Valley Shiraz 2008 Rating 94 To 2016 $80 BE
Oracle Clare Valley Shiraz 2008 Rating 94 To 2018 $80 BE
The Duke Clare Valley Grenache 2009 Rating 94 To 2016 $33
Reserve Clare Valley Cabernet Sauvignon 2009 Rating 94 To 2020 $49 BE

Barrel Fermented Clare Valley Semillon 2011 Vibrant green hue; a surprisingly pungent and aromatic bouquet given the fact that barrel fermentation has taken place, with pea pod, straw and stone fruit on display; the toastiness reveals itself on the long palate, with racy acidity and taut, almost green fruit providing line and freshness; a very interesting wine. Screwcap. 12.5% alc. **Rating** 93 **To** 2016 $20 BE

Killerman's Run Shiraz 2010 Deep crimson, purple hue; a highly expressive and fragrant bouquet of fresh blackberry, orange rind, spicy oak and thyme; the sweet-fruited medium-bodied palate is warm, generous and fresh, finding a balance between ripeness and savoury complexity; very good drinking for the price. Screwcap. 14.5% alc. **Rating** 93 **To** 2016 $20 BE
Blocks Road Clare Valley Cabernet Sauvignon 2009 Rating 93 **To** 2018 $33 BE
Covenant Clare Valley Shiraz 2009 Rating 92 To 2029 $44
Prodigal Clare Valley Grenache 2009 Rating 92 To 2019 $30

Killerman's Run Cabernet Sauvignon 2009 Rating 88 To 2014 $20 BE

Killara Estate ★★★☆
773 Warburton Highway, Seville East, Vic 3139 **Region** Yarra Valley
T (03) 5961 5877 **www**.killaraestate.com.au **Open** Wed–Sun 11–5
Winemaker Travis Bush, Mac Forbes **Est.** 1997 **Dozens** 8000 **Vyds** 36.02ha
The Palazzo family, headed by Leo, sold its Killara vineyard to Yarragum Agrifoods in November 2010. The family continues to own and run the 36ha Sunnyside Vineyard on the corner of Warburton Highway and Sunnyside Road. Wines produced from the '10 vintage were Pinot Grigio, Sauvignon (Blanc), Dolcino (late-harvest viognier) and Sangiovese (the latter made by Mac Forbes). In the future, Bill Downie will play a lead winemaking role under the Thousand Candles label, pushing the boundaries of wine style and content as he sees fit. Watch this space (or that of a Thousand Candles, launched after this edition was making its way to print). Exports to the UK and China.

Yarra Valley Sparkling Cuvee 2009 Made from 100% estate-grown pinot noir, and given the full traditional method treatment, with fermentation in this bottle; has good mousse and very positive flavours reflecting that red fruit base. Diam. 12% alc. **Rating** 90 **To** 2014 $30

Yarra Valley Rosetta Dolce 2009 Rating 89 To 2013 $30
Racers & Rascals Yarra Valley Merlot 2010 Rating 88 To 2014 $20 BE
Palazzo Yarra Valley Rosetta 2011 Rating 87 To 2013 $20 BE
Yarra Valley Cabernet Merlot 2010 Rating 87 To 2016 $30 BE
Palazzo Frizzante Secco Pinot Grigio 2010 Rating 87 To Now $25

Killerby
Caves Road, Wilyabrup, WA 6280 **Region** Margaret River
T 1800 655 722 **www**.killerby.com.au **Open** Not
Winemaker Vanessa Carson **Est.** 1973 **Dozens** NFP

In June 2008, the winery established by the late Dr Barry Killerby in 1973 was purchased by the Ferngrove wine group, and the estate vineyard was acquired by Sandalford. In 2012 a 13ha vineyard on Caves Road was leased, planted to chardonnay, semillon, sauvignon, blanc, cabernet sauvignon and shiraz, supplementing the 3ha of estate cabernet sauvignon. The wines are made at Ferngrove; a new cellar door is planned.

ΨΨΨΨΨ Margaret River Cabernet Sauvignon 2010 Bright, clear ruby red; Margaret River at its imperious best when it comes to cabernet sauvignon; black fruits, cassis and quality oak come through on the bouquet, feeding into the medium- to full-bodied palate, where perfectly pitched tannins become a major part of the wine, building both structure and flavour. Screwcap. 14% alc. **Rating** 95 **To** 2025 $30

ΨΨΨΨΨ Margaret River Chardonnay 2010 **Rating** 93 **To** 2017 $30
Margaret River Cabernet Sauvignon 2009 **Rating** 93 **To** 2020 $30
Margaret River Semillon 2010 **Rating** 92 **To** 2015 $30
Merchant Trader Margaret River Sauvignon Blanc Semillon 2010 **Rating** 92 **To** Now $24
Margaret River Chardonnay 2009 **Rating** 92 **To** 2016 $30
Margaret River Shiraz 2010 **Rating** 92 **To** 2025 $30
Margaret River Shiraz 2009 **Rating** 91 **To** 2019 $30
Merchant Trader Margaret River Cabernet Sauvignon Merlot 2009 **Rating** 91 **To** 2017 $24

ΨΨΨΨ Margaret River Semillon 2011 **Rating** 89 **To** 2015 $30

Killibinbin   ★★★★☆

PO Box 10, Langhorne Creek, SA 5255 **Region** Langhorne Creek
T (08) 8537 3382 www.killibinbin.com.au **Open** Not
Winemaker Jim Urlwin, Justin Lane **Est.** 1997 **Dozens** 4000 **Vyds** 7.5ha
In late 2010 Guy and Liz Adams (of Metala Vineyards fame) acquired the Killibinbin brand. The wines will continue to be sourced solely from the Metala Vineyards (7.5ha are dedicated to Killibinbin), and the primary market will be the US, currency exchange hurdles permitting. Exports to the UK, the US, Denamrk and China.

ΨΨΨΨΨ Langhorne Creek Scaredy Cat 2008 Intense purple-crimson; a rich, dense
✪   full-bodied blend (Cabernet Sauvignon/Shiraz) with layers of black fruits and oak; there are also ample ripe tannins. Punches well above its weight, and will go the distance. However, don't look for elegance. Screwcap. 15% alc. **Rating** 94 **To** 2030 $24

ΨΨΨΨΨ Langhorne Creek Shiraz 2008 **Rating** 90 **To** 2030 $30

Killiecrankie Wines   ★★★★★

PO Box 6125, Lansell Plaza, Vic 3555 **Region** Bendigo
T (03) 5435 3155 **Open** Not
Winemaker Tony Winspear, John Monteath **Est.** 2000 **Dozens** 120 **Vyds** 1ha
This is the venture of John Monteath and Claire Wills; John moved to the Bendigo region in 1999 to pursue his interest in viticulture and winemaking, and while helping to establish the vineyard from which the grapes are sourced, gained experience at Water Wheel, Heathcote Estate and Balgownie Estate wineries. The non-irrigated vineyard was planted in 2000 to four shiraz clones. The tiny crop is hand-picked, and the wine is made in true garagiste style by local winemaker Tony Winspear, with John his assistant. Further plantings within the Bendigo region, and parcels of premium fruit sourced from other meticulously tended vineyards (including Heathcote), have been added to create a range of individual vineyard wines.

ΨΨΨΨΨ Bendigo Shiraz 2010 Mid garnet; a highly expressive bouquet offering red and black fruits, lots of sage, thyme, licorice and spicy oak notes; the fine palate belies the 15% alcohol, with fine tannins and sweet fruit lingering on the finish. Diam. 15% alc. **Rating** 94 **To** 2018 $39

ΨΨΨΨΨ Heathcote Shiraz 2010 **Rating** 91 **To** 2016 $39 BE

Kimbarra Wines

422 Barkly Street, Ararat, Vic 3377 **Region** Grampians
T (03) 5352 2238 **www**.kimbarrawines.com.au **Open** Mon–Fri 9–4.30 or by appt
Winemaker Peter Leeke, Ian MacKenzie, Adam Wadewitz **Est.** 1990 **Dozens** 900
Vyds 12ha
Peter Leeke has established shiraz, riesling and cabernet sauvignon, varieties that have proved
best suited to the Grampians region. The particularly well-made, estate-grown wines deserve
a wider audience.

♀♀♀♀♀ **Great Western Riesling 2008** Bright, light straw-green; has gained some
weight and complexity since first tasted, and is not finished yet; is built on a
bedrock of slate and mineral, the lime/citrus fruit starting to show the first signs
of toast. Screwcap. 12.9% alc. **Rating** 91 **To** 2018 $30
Great Western Shiraz 2010 Mid purple-crimson; the bouquet comes from
the textbook of moderately cool-grown shiraz, a theme that continues onto the
mid palate; the savoury tannins that then take over were just a little overweight in
Feb '12; needs a couple of years to reveal its undoubted class. Screwcap. 13.8% alc.
Rating 91 **To** 2025 $32

Kimbolton Wines

The Winehouse Cellar Door, Lot 93 Wellington Road, Langhorne Creek, SA 5255
Region Langhorne Creek
T (08) 8537 3359 **www**.kimboltonwines.com.au **Open** 7 days 10–5
Winemaker Greg Follett, Simon Greenleaf (Contract) **Est.** 1998 **Dozens** 750 **Vyds** 54.8ha
The Kimbolton property originally formed part of the Potts Bleasdale estate; in 1946 it was
acquired by Henry and Thelma Case, parents of the current owners, Len and wife Judy Case.
Since that time the grapes from vineyard plantings of cabernet sauvignon, shiraz, chardonnay,
sauvignon blanc, zinfandel and montepulciano have been sold to leading wineries. However,
in '98 the decision was taken to retain a small amount of cabernet sauvignon and shiraz to
supply the Kimbolton Wines label established in that year (the name comes from a medieval
town in Bedfordshire, UK, from which some of Judy's ancestors emigrated).

♀♀♀♀♀ **Fig Tree Langhorne Creek Cabernet Sauvignon 2010** Purple-crimson;
good hue and depth; a fragrant bouquet full of cassis fruit is followed by a
complex palate that sends all the right signals for cabernet: firm blackcurrant fruit,
fine but persistent tannins, and exemplary length and balance. Screwcap. 14.8% alc.
Rating 94 **To** 2025 $24

♀♀♀♀♀ **The Rifleman Langhorne Creek Shiraz 2009** **Rating** 93 **To** 2030 $42
Reserve Block Langhorne Creek Cabernet Sauvignon 2009 **Rating** 93
To 2020 $24

❂ **House Block Langhorne Creek Shiraz 2009** Strong crimson; a plush, rich
palate replete with black fruits, dark chocolate and some fruitcake notes is tied
together by savoury tannins. Screwcap. 14.5% alc. **Rating** 92 **To** 2025 $20

♀♀♀♀ **Fig Tree Langhorne Creek Cabernet Sauvignon 2009** **Rating** 89
To 2015 $24

King River Estate

3556 Wangaratta-Whitfield Road, Wangaratta, Vic 3678 **Region** King Valley
T (03) 5729 3689 **www**.kingriverestate.com.au **Open** 7 days 11–5
Winemaker Trevor Knaggs **Est.** 1996 **Dozens** 3000 **Vyds** 16ha
Trevor Knaggs, with the assistance of his father Collin, began the establishment of King
River Estate in 1990, making the first wines in '96. The initial plantings were 3.3ha each
of chardonnay and cabernet sauvignon, followed by 8ha of merlot and 3ha of shiraz. More
recent plantings have extended the varietal range to include verdelho, viognier, barbera and
sangiovese. Biodynamic practices have been used in the vineyard since 2008. Exports to China
and Singapore.

ҰҰҰҰҰ   King Valley Sangiovese 2009 Full purple-red; a sangiovese with a great deal
of attitude, and not inconsiderable power; savoury tannins are woven through
the black cherry fruit, demanding a plateful of pasta or pizza. Screwcap. 14% alc.
Rating 90 **To** 2016 $25

ҰҰҰҰ   King Valley Merlot 2009 **Rating** 89 **To** 2015 $20
King Valley Shiraz 2009 **Rating** 88 **To** 2015 $28
King Valley Cabernet Sauvignon 2009 **Rating** 88 **To** 2015 $24
King Valley Sparkling Merlot 2004 **Rating** 87 **To** 2013 $30

Kingsdale Wines

745 Crookwell Road, Goulburn, NSW 2580 **Region** Southern New South Wales Zone
T (02) 4822 4880 www.kingsdale.com.au **Open** W'ends & public hols 10–5 or by appt
Winemaker Howard Spark **Est.** 2001 **Dozens** 1500 **Vyds** 2.8ha
Howard and Elly Spark established their vineyard (shiraz, sauvignon blanc, chardonnay, merlot
and semillon) south of the burgeoning Southern Highlands region, falling in the Southern
NSW Zone. It sits 700m above sea level on deep red soils with iron-rich sediments (doubtless
causing the colour) and limestone. The limestone-clad cellar door overlooks Lake Sooley,
7 mins' drive from Goulburn.

ҰҰҰҰ   Goulburn Shiraz Rose 2011 Bright pink; cherry fruit aromas and flavours have
a touch of fresh-squeezed lemon juice that doesn't end up investing the wine with
green fruit flavours, just a zesty mouthfeel (and a hint of residual sugar). Screwcap.
11% alc. **Rating** 89 **To** 2013 $20
Goulburn Semillon 2011 Whether early picking was dictated by the wet season
or simply a deliberate choice is irrelevant; this is a delightfully crisp and easy to
drink style, with a lingering citrussy acid finish. Screwcap. 10.4% alc. **Rating** 88
To 2015 $20

Kingston Estate Wines

Sturt Highway, Kingston-on-Murray, SA 5331 **Region** South Australia
T (08) 8243 3700 www.kingstonestatewines.com **Open** By appt
Winemaker Bill Moularadellis, Brett Duffin, Helen Foggo, Donna Hartwig **Est.** 1979
Dozens 70 000 **Vyds** 500ha
Kingston Estate, under the direction of Bill Moularadellis, has its production roots in the
Riverland region, but has long-term purchase contracts with growers in the Clare Valley,
Adelaide Hills, Coonawarra, Langhorne Creek and Mount Benson. It has also spread its net
to take in a wide range of varietals, mainstream and exotic, under a number of different brands
at various price points. Exports to all major markets.

ҰҰҰҰҰ   Echelon Selected Harvest Petit Verdot 2008 Grown on the estate-owned
Riverland vineyard; typically enough, rises above its birthplace, delivering a
wine with spicy black fruits, persistent but fine tannins, and the ability to handle
American oak. Screwcap. 14.5% alc. **Rating** 91 **To** 2015 $28

ҰҰҰҰ   Shiraz 2010 Mint is the dominant aroma on the bouquet, while also showing
✪   a level of sweet black fruits that is both generous and evenly balanced; a touch of
toast on the finish, and a lick of acid, provides a lot of interest at this price point.
Screwcap. 14% alc. **Rating** 89 **To** 2018 $15 BE
Echelon Selected Harvest Shiraz 2008 **Rating** 89 **To** 2016 $28
●   Cabernet Sauvignon 2010 **Rating** 89 **To** 2014 $14
●   Merlot 2010 **Rating** 88 **To** Now $14
Pinot Gris 2011 **Rating** 87 **To** 2013 $15 BE
Sarantos Soft Press Merlot 2010 **Rating** 87 **To** 2014 $15

Kinloch Wines ★★★★☆

'Kainui', 221 Wairere Road, Booroolite, Vic 3723 **Region** Upper Goulburn
T (03) 5777 3447 **www**.kinlochwines.com.au **Open** 7 days 10–4
Winemaker Al Fencaros, Howard Anderson (Contract) **Est.** 1996 **Dozens** 2000
Vyds 4.42ha
In 1996 Susan and Malcolm Kinloch began the development of their vineyard, at an altitude of 400m on the northern slopes of the Great Dividing Range, 15 mins from Mansfield. The vineyard is planted to chardonnay, pinot noir, pinot meunier (primarily used for sparkling wines), sauvignon blanc, riesling and tempranillo, supplemented by purchases of other varieties from local growers. The grapes are hand-picked and wines contract-made in the Yarra Valley.

ŶŶŶŶŶ **Mansfield Sauvignon Blanc 2011** Pale straw-green; has a highly expressive bouquet and an equally intense palate, both with a virtuoso display of blossom, herb, citrus, asparagus and gooseberry; a hint of sweetness on the finish adds to the pleasure of the wine. Screwcap. 11.5% alc. **Rating** 93 **To** 2013 $24
Mansfield Chardonnay 2009 Speaks clearly of the cool climate of Mansfield in the Upper Goulburn Valley, with its flinty minerality and grapefruit-accented flavours. Moreover, there has not been any misguided attempt to fill any gaps with oak. Screwcap. 12.5% alc. **Rating** 92 **To** 2015 $22
Mansfield Pinot Noir 2010 Very good, bright purple-crimson; a well-made, light-bodied pinot with strong varietal expression on both bouquet and palate; red and black cherry with some spice and French oak nuances are the drivers of a well-priced wine. Screwcap. 12.5% alc. **Rating** 92 **To** 2014 $22
Limited Release Mansfield Riesling 2011 Pale quartz-green; lime and apple blossom aromas lead into a crisp, dry, well-balanced palate and fresh finish. Screwcap. 11.5% alc. **Rating** 90 **To** 2021 $20
Mansfield Pinot Meunier 2010 Light, bright, clear crimson-purple; a very good attempt at table wine with this variety; spicy, savoury nuances do not come over the top of the red fruits (cherry, strawberry and raspberry) at its core. Screwcap. 12.5% alc. **Rating** 90 **To** 2013 $23

Kirrihill Wines ★★★★☆

Wendouree Road, Clare, SA 5453 **Region** Clare Valley
T (08) 8842 4087 **www**.kirrihillwines.com.au **Open** 7 days 10–4
Winemaker Donna Stephens, Marnie Roberts **Est.** 1998 **Dozens** 35 000
A large development, with an 8000-tonne, $12 million winery making and marketing its own range of wines, also acting as a contract maker for several producers. Focused on the Clare Valley and Adelaide Hills, grapes are sourced from specially selected parcels of Kirribilly's 1300ha of managed vineyards, as well as the Edwards and Stanway families' properties in these regions. The quality of the wines is thus no surprise. The Companions range comprises blends of both regions, while the Single Vineyard Series aims to elicit a sense of place from the chosen vineyards. Exports to all major markets.

ŶŶŶŶŶ ✪ **Single Vineyard Series Tullymore Vineyard Clare Valley Cabernet Sauvignon 2010** Outstanding, intense crimson-purple; a full-bodied wine proclaiming its varietal base from the word go; blackcurrant, blackberry and hints of earth run through the bouquet and full-bodied palate, the tannins – as they should be – firm; a touch of mocha oak softens the farewell; the wine is exceptionally good value. Screwcap. 14.5% alc. **Rating** 94 **To** 2025 $20

ŶŶŶŶŶ ✪ **Clare Valley Shiraz 2010 Rating** 93 **To** 2020 $14
✪ **Single Vineyard Series Barton Springs Adelaide Hills Sauvignon Blanc 2011** Pale straw-green; a lively and expressive bouquet and palate provide plenty of kiwi fruit, snow pea and apple running through to the long, gently citrussy, finish. Screwcap. 12.5% alc. **Rating** 92 **To** 2013 $16
✪ **Clare Valley Cabernet Sauvignon 2010 Rating** 92 **To** 2016 $14

○ Single Vineyard Slate Creek Vineyard Clare Valley Riesling 2011
Rating 91 To 2014 $16

♀♀♀♀ Single Vineyard Serendipity Adelaide Hills Pinot Noir Rose Brut NV
○ Rating 87 To Now $17

KJB Wine Group   ★★★☆
82 Ridge Street, Northgate, Qld 4013 (postal) **Region** Various
T 0409 570 694 **F** (07) 3266 8552 **Open** Not
Winemaker Adam Hooper, Kurt Brill **Est.** 2008 **Dozens** 500
KJB Wine Group (formerly Oenotria Vintners) is the venture of Kurt Brill, who began
his involvement in the wine industry in 2003, largely through the encouragement of his
wife Gillian. He commenced the wine marketing course at the University of Adelaide, but
ultimately switched from that to the winemaking degree at CSU. His main business is the
distribution company Grace James Fine Wines, but he also runs a virtual winery operation,
purchasing chardonnay from the Yarra Valley and cabernet sauvignon from McLaren Vale.
Needless to say, he participates as far as possible in the winemaking process. Exports to the UK.

♀♀♀♀♀ Land of the Vines McLaren Vale Shiraz 2010 Healthy crimson-purple; there
is so much dark chocolate, blackberry, plum, licorice and vanilla oak here that the
alcohol is simply not obvious. Were it not for the modest-quality cork, it might
have had a long and distinguished future. 15% alc. **Rating** 90 **To** 2018 $23

Knappstein   ★★★★★
2 Pioneer Avenue, Clare, SA 5453 **Region** Clare Valley
T (08) 8841 2100 **www.**knappstein.com.au **Open** Mon–Fri 9–5, Sat 11–5, Sun &
public hols 11–4
Winemaker Glen Barry **Est.** 1969 **Dozens** 35 000 **Vyds** 114ha
Knappstein's full name is Knappstein Enterprise Winery & Brewery, reflecting its history
before being acquired by Petaluma, and since then part of Lion Nathan's stable. The substantial
mature estate vineyards in prime locations supply grapes both for the Knappstein brand and
for wider Petaluma use. Despite making seriously good wines, Knappstein can't seem to
regularly get across the line to greatness. Exports to all major markets.

♀♀♀♀♀ Enterprise Vineyard Clare Valley Cabernet Sauvignon 2009 Deep but
vibrant crimson-purple; from the single vineyard that has produced this wine
every vintage since 1974; a potent, full-bodied wine that retains balance and is not
extractive; blackcurrant and regional touches of earth and mint run in a seamless
line through the long palate, the tannins firm but balanced. Screwcap. 14.5% alc.
Rating 94 **To** 2029 $40
Yertabulti Vineyard Clare Valley Fortified Shiraz 2010 Dense, opaque
purple-crimson; made in the modern Australian style, significantly reducing the
baume to a level similar to that of Portuguese vintage port; that said, it is an
exceptionally rich style, and the history from prior decades suggests it will take
many years to reach its peak – and probably be drunk long before that eventuates.
Cork. 19% alc. **Rating** 94 **To** 2040 $22

♀♀♀♀♀ Ackland Vineyard Watervale Riesling 2011 **Rating** 93 **To** 2025 $30
The Insider Clare Valley Riesling 2010 **Rating** 93 **To** 2020 $24
✪ Clare Valley Shiraz 2010 Strong purple-crimson; the medium- to full-bodied
palate seems to have one foot in McLaren Vale, with its savoury dark chocolate
nuances, the other in the Clare Valley, with its ripe plum and blackberry fruit;
common to both are the firm tannins that provide both balance and length, with
oak in a support role. Screwcap. 14.5% alc. **Rating** 93 **To** 2020 $22
Hand Picked Clare Valley Riesling 2011 **Rating** 90 **To** 2017 $20

♀♀♀♀ Three Clare Valley Gewurztraminer Riesling Pinot Gris 2011 **Rating** 88
To 2013 $24
Clare Valley Cabernet Merlot 2009 **Rating** 88 **To** 2017 $19

Knee Deep Wines   ★★★★☆

160 Johnson Road, Wilyabrup, WA 6280 **Region** Margaret River
T (08) 9755 6776 **www**.kneedeepwines.com.au **Open** 7 days 10–5
Winemaker Cliff Royle (red), Bob Cartwright (white) **Est.** 2000 **Dozens** 8800 **Vyds** 20ha
Perth surgeon and veteran yachtsman Phil Childs and wife Sue acquired a 34ha property in
Wilyabrup in 2000. This was planted to chardonnay (3.2ha), sauvignon blanc (4.ha), semillon
(1.48ha), chenin blanc (4ha), cabernet sauvignon (6.34ha) and shiraz (1.24ha). The name, Knee
Deep Wines, was inspired by the passion and commitment needed to produce premium wine
and as a tongue-in-cheek acknowledgement of jumping in 'boots and all' during a testing time
in the wine industry, the grape glut building more or less in tune with the venture.

♀♀♀♀♀ **Margaret River Cabernet Sauvignon 2010** While the dominant pungent
herbal note will not be to everyone's taste, the concentration and purity of fruit
are undeniable; essency cassis fruit, with cedar and super fine-grained tannins draw
out the finish to a long, finely balanced and complex conclusion, with a hint of
bitterness that will resolve with some time in bottle. Screwcap. 14% alc. **Rating** 94
To 2025 $28 BE

♀♀♀♀♀ **Kelsea's Limited Release Margaret River Cabernet Sauvignon 2009**
Rating 93 **To** 2024 $45 BE
Margaret River Cabernet Merlot 2010 Rating 91 **To** 2018 $22 BE
Margaret River Sauvignon Blanc Semillon 2011 Rating 90 **To** 2014 $22 BE

♀♀♀♀ **Margaret River Sauvignon Blanc 2011 Rating** 88 **To** 2014 $22 BE
Margaret River Rose 2011 Rating 88 **To** 2013 $22 BE

Knots Wines   ★★★★

A8 Shurans Lane, Heathcote, Vic 3552 **Region** Heathcote
T (03) 5441 5429 **www**.thebridgevineyard.com.au **Open** Select w'ends, or by appt
Winemaker Lindsay Ross **Est.** 1997 **Dozens** 1000 **Vyds** 4.75ha
This venture of former Balgownie winemaker Lindsay Ross and wife Noeline is part of
a broader business known as Winedrops, which acts as a wine production and distribution
network for the Bendigo wine industry. The Knots wines are sourced from long-established
vineyards, providing shiraz (4ha), malbec (0.5ha) and viognier (0.25ha). The viticultural accent
is on low-cropping, with concentrated flavours, the winemaking emphasis on flavour, finesse
and varietal expression.

K1 by Geoff Hardy   ★★★★★

Tynan Road, Kuitpo, SA 5172 **Region** Adelaide Hills
T (08) 8388 3700 **www**.k1.com.au **Open** Fri–Sun & public hols 11–5
Winemaker Geoff Hardy, Shane Harris **Est.** 1980 **Dozens** 7000 **Vyds** 36.5ha
The ultra-cool Kuitpo vineyard in the Adelaide Hills was planted by Geoff Hardy in 1987
after searching the hills for an ideal location for premium wine production. As this was the
first significant vineyard planted in the region it became known as the K1 Vineyard. All fruit
for Geoff Hardy's K1 brand is sourced from this vineyard, perched on the southwestern
ridge of the Adelaide Hills above McLaren Vale. Exports to the US, Canada, the Netherlands,
Switzerland, Malaysia, Hong Kong and Singapore.

♀♀♀♀♀ **Gold Label Adelaide Hills Gruner Veltliner 2011** The third Gruner Veltliner
to be commercially released, its perfumed, peppery bouquet exactly as that of
Austrian federspiel (the lowest alcohol), the palate long and minerally. Full of
promise as the vines gain maturity. Screwcap. 11% alc. **Rating** 93 **To** 2015 $28
Silver Label Riesling Gewurztraminer 2011 Light straw-green; early picking
has paid a good dividend, for the wine is wonderfully juicy, fresh and mouth-
watering. I'm not sure the gewurztraminer component adds a great deal to the
blend, but that's by the by. The wine will cruise along for 10 years or more.
Screwcap. 10.5% alc. **Rating** 92 **To** 2021 $25

Gold Label Adelaide Hills Shiraz 2009 Crimson-purple; comes from a multi-clone vineyard situated on a warm site in the Adelaide Hills, leading to the plush richness of the wine, in turn augmented by positive oak inputs. Screwcap. 14.5% alc. **Rating** 92 **To** 2020 $35 BE

Gold Label Adelaide Hills Chardonnay 2010 An unusually pungent blend of grapefruit and menthol for the variety, with a savoury charcuterie backbone; the palate is tense and textured, with a lingering toasty oak note a feature. Screwcap. 13.5% alc. **Rating** 91 **To** 2016 $35

● **Silver Label Shiraz 2009 Rating** 91 **To** 2014 $20

Gold Label Adelaide Hills Cabernet Sauvignon 2009 Bright crimson-purple; reflects the warm part of the Adelaide Hills occupied by Geoff Hardy, for the wine is full-bodied with powerful tannins, a trifle beyond those needed for the variety; if and when those tannins soften, a very good wine will emerge. Screwcap. 14.5% alc. **Rating** 91 **To** 2020 $35

● **Silver Label Cabernet Tempranillo 2009 Rating** 91 **To** 2019 $20

✪ **Gold Label Adelaide Hills Arneis 2011** Pale quartz-green; everyone seems to have a different idea about what the varietal character of arneis is or should be; this has an almost savoury herbal note to the citrus juice and citrus pith flavours. Could be a surprise with the right food. Screwcap. 12.5% alc. **Rating** 90 **To** 2014 $22

✪ **Silver Label Rose 2011** Bright crimson-pink; a fragrant bouquet of small red fruits leads into a fresh, crisp palate, with good balance and length; pleasingly dry finish. Screwcap. 11.5% alc. **Rating** 90 **To** 2013 $20

ΨΨΨΨ   **Gold Label Adelaide Hills Pinot Noir 2010 Rating** 89 **To** 2016 $35
Gold Label Adelaide Hills Sauvignon Blanc 2011 Rating 87 **To** 2013 $20

Kominos Wines

27145 New England Highway, Severnlea, Qld 4352 **Region** Granite Belt
T (07) 4683 4311 **www.**kominoswines.com **Open** 7 days 9–5
Winemaker Tony Comino **Est.** 1976 **Dozens** NFP **Vyds** 12ha

Tony Comino, a dedicated viticulturist and winemaker, and wife Mary took over ownership of the winery from his parents on its 21st vintage. Tony is proud of the estate-grown, made and bottled heritage of the winery and is content to keep a relatively low profile, although the fine show record of the wines might suggest otherwise. In addition to the estate plantings, he manages another 7ha. The varieties planted are sauvignon blanc, chenin blanc, semillon, chardonnay, shiraz, merlot, cabernet franc and cabernet sauvignon. Another Qld producer to make good wines, capable of holding its own against all comers from the south (as Queenslanders refer to anyone not born in the state). Fifty per cent of production is exported to the US, Taiwan, South Korea, China and Singapore.

ΨΨΨΨ   **MS Cabernet Sauvignon 2009** Good colour; has a very considerable rustic personality, black fruits grappling strong tannins and an earthy undercurrent. Spit roasts the order of the day. Screwcap. 14.3% alc. **Rating** 89 **To** 2017 $25

Sauvignon Blanc 2011 Estate-grown, hand-picked and whole bunch grapes were cooled before whole bunch-pressing, giving the fruit maximum opportunity to express itself. Yet while it has texture, there isn't great deal of varietal fruit to be found. Screwcap. 12.3% alc. **Rating** 87 **To** 2013 $17

Chenin Blanc 2010 Full-on fruit salad with lots of sweet fruit, and the suspicion of some residual sweetness on the finish all of which will greatly appeal to cellar door customers. Screwcap. 12% alc. **Rating** 87 **To** 2013 $17

Nouvelle 2009 Light, bright crimson, a little deeper than rose; has very considerable sweetness, designed strictly for cellar door. An interesting closure: ProCork membrane over a Diam body. Belts and braces stuff. 13% alc. **Rating** 87 **To** 2013 $15

Koonara ★★★★☆

44 Main Street, Penola, SA 5277 **Region** Coonawarra
T (08) 8737 3222 **www**.koonara.com **Open** 7 days 10–6
Winemaker Peter Douglas **Est.** 1988 **Dozens** 8000 **Vyds** 9ha

Koonara is a sister, or, more appropriately, a brother company to Reschke Wines. The latter is run by Burke Reschke, Koonara by his brother Dru. Both are sons of Trevor Reschke, who planted the first vines on the Koonara property in 1988. The initial planting was of cabernet sauvignon, followed by shiraz in '93 and additional cabernet sauvignon in '98. Peter Douglas, formerly Wynns' chief winemaker before moving overseas for some years, has returned to the district and is consultant winemaker. The Bay of Apostles range was released in 2008, with four of the five wines under the label sourced from Vic. A Bay of Apostles cellar door has been opened in the main street of Apollo Bay on the Great Ocean Road. In 2010–11 organic management of the vineyard was initiated. Exports to Malaysia, Singapore and China.

🍷🍷🍷🍷 **Ezra's Gift Family Reserve Coonawarra Shiraz 2009** Deep garnet in colour, with a bouquet redolent of mulberry, eucalypt and licorice; the palate is warm and packed with gravelly tannins and toasty oak to conclude. Screwcap. 13.5% alc. **Rating** 90 **To** 2020 $30 BE

Ambriel's Gift Family Reserve Coonawarra Cabernet Sauvignon 2009 A bright and red-fruited bouquet, revealing glimpses of florals and eucalypt, is accompanied by a complex and savoury palate, with a lingering toasty oak note to conclude. Screwcap. 13.5% alc. **Rating** 90 **To** 2020 $35 BE

Koonowla Wines ★★★★★

PO Box 45, Auburn, SA 5451 **Region** Clare Valley
T (08) 8849 2080 **www**.koonowla.com **Open** Not
Winemaker O'Leary Walker Wines **Est.** 1997 **Dozens** 5000 **Vyds** 100ha

It's not often that a light as large as this can be hidden under a bushel. Koonowla is a historic Clare Valley property; situated just east of Auburn, it was first planted with vines in the 1890s, and by the early 1900s was producing 60 000 litres of wine annually. A disastrous fire in '26 destroyed the winery and wine stocks, and the property was converted to grain and wool production. Replanting of vines began in '85, and accelerated after Andrew and Booie Michael purchased the property in '91; there are now 40ha of cabernet sauvignon, 36ha riesling, 20ha of shiraz, and 2ha each of merlot and semillon. In an all-too-familiar story, the grapes were sold until falling prices forced a change in strategy; now a major part of the grapes are vinified by the infinitely experienced David O'Leary and Nick Walker, with the remainder sold. A cellar door is planned. Exports to the UK, the US, Scandinavia, Malaysia and NZ.

🍷🍷🍷🍷 ✪ **The Ringmaster Clare Valley Riesling 2011** Bright, pale green-straw; estate-grown, but made by O'Leary Walker, the wine has a fragrant, flowery bouquet with a classic lime/lemon mix, then a crisp, vibrant and long palate, guaranteeing its future. Exceptional value. Screwcap. 11.5% alc. **Rating** 94 **To** 2021 $16

Clare Valley Riesling 2011 Light, bright green-quartz; the floral bouquet is fresh and enlivened by a touch of spice, but it is the palate that takes the wine onto the top level, with penetrating purity and length to its citrus and green apple flavour, the finish crisp and dry. Screwcap. 11.5% alc. **Rating** 94 **To** 2021 $19

🍷🍷🍷🍷 ✪ **Clare Valley Cabernet Sauvignon 2008 Rating** 90 **To** 2023 $23

The Ringmaster Clare Valley Cabernet Sauvignon 2008 Lighter, fresher and more savoury than the principal Koonowla Cabernet; a touch of mint is one consequence, but doesn't upset me; good drinking over the next 5+ years. Screwcap. 14.5% alc. **Rating** 90 **To** 2017 $17

Kooyong ★★★★★

PO Box 153, Red Hill South, Vic 3937 **Region** Mornington Peninsula
T (03) 5989 4444 **www**.kooyong.com **Open** At Port Phillip Estate
Winemaker Sandro Mosele **Est.** 1996 **Dozens** 10 000 **Vyds** 33.4ha

Kooyong, owned by Giorgio and Dianne Gjergja, released its first wines in 2001.The vineyard is planted to pinot noir (20ha), chardonnay (10.4ha) and, more recently, pinot gris (3ha). Winemaker Sandro Mosele is a graduate of CSU, and has a deservedly high reputation. He also provides contract winemaking services for others.The Kooyong wines are made at the spectacular new winery of Port Phillip Estate, also owned by the Gjergjas. Exports to the UK, the US, Canada, Sweden, Singapore, Hong Kong, Japan and China.

ŶŶŶŶŶ **Single Vineyard Selection Haven Pinot Noir 2010** Deep crimson; pure dark fruits are abundant on the bouquet, with a delicate thread of Asian spices, and well-handled oak; the palate starts with a refreshing blend of red and dark fruits and tangy acidity, and then makes way for a rush of firm but fine tannins; long, lively and unevolved. Screwcap. 13% alc. **Rating** 96 **To** 2020 $70 BE

Single Vineyard Selection Farrago Chardonnay 2010 If you are looking for a rich, buttery chardonnay this is NOT the wine for you; tightly wound and full of citrus fruit and mineral complexity, the palate reveals a fine, elegant and complex wine, with tense acidity and evenly balanced fruit; long, savoury and thoroughly satisfying. Screwcap. 13.5% alc. **Rating** 95 **To** 2020 $60 BE

Single Vineyard Selection Meres Pinot Noir 2010 Deep garnet; the bouquet is a seductive melange of red fruits, spices, earthy notes and a touch of game; there is a suppleness and softness to the palate that makes this the most approachable of the three single vineyard wines, but there is plenty of depth, backbone and finesse to see it age with grace. Screwcap. 13% alc. **Rating** 95 **To** 2019 $70 BE

Clonale Mornington Peninsula Chardonnay 2011 The very embodiment of restraint and complexity, with tightly wound citrus fruit, charcuterie and quartz minerality in spades; the palate is racy and pure, linear, focused and long; ready to go and with a great deal of flexibility possible for food and wine matching. Screwcap. 13% alc. **Rating** 94 **To** 2018 $30 Be

Single Vineyard Selection Faultline Chardonnay 2010 The Faultline is a fuller and richer wine than the Farrago, offering grapefruit, cashews and mealy complexity; the palate is generously textured, fresh and focused, with ample weight and a long and sweet-fruited conclusion; truly two contrasting styles. Screwcap. 13% alc. **Rating** 94 **To** 2018 $60

Estate Mornington Peninsula Chardonnay 2010 Vivid green hue; the bouquet offers ripe melon, nectarine and lemon pith aromas; the palate is generous on entry, with mealy complexity coming to the fore, offset by fine acidity in harmony with the fruit. Screwcap. 13% alc. **Rating** 94 **To** 2018 $43 BE

Beurrot Mornington Peninsula Pinot Gris 2011 Pale colour, bright; a lean and restrained example of the variety, with pure fresh-cut pear flesh and a dollop of spice; the palate is racy and linear, fine and full of character, no mean feat for a variety notorious for its blandness; long and complex. Screwcap. 13% alc. **Rating** 94 **To** 2015 $30 BE

Single Vineyard Selection Ferrous Pinot Noir 2010 Deep garnet; dark and savoury and you cannot but help being struck by the strong sense of ironstone in the bouquet, coupled with dark fruits and sappy complexity; the palate is firm, taut and rugged, needing time to soften; the fine acidity, ample tannins and weighty fruit, not to mention the closure, should see this evolve into something special. Screwcap. 13.5% alc. **Rating** 94 **To** 2022 $70 BE

Estate Mornington Peninsula Pinot Noir 2010 Deep crimson, bright; a dark and sultry bouquet of black cherry, liqueur-soaked plums, Asian spices and a gentle lick of toasty oak; the palate is fleshy, fresh and focused on entry, with a fine line of acidity and tightly wound tannins providing length to the generous depth of fruit on offer. Screwcap. 13.5% alc. **Rating** 94 **To** 2018 $50 BE

ŶŶŶŶŸ **Clonale Mornington Peninsula Chardonnay 2010** **Rating** 92 **To** 2015 $28

Kooyonga Creek   ★★★

2369 Samaria Road, Moorngag, Vic 3673 **Region** North East Victoria Zone
T (03) 9629 5853 **www**.kooyongacreek.com.au **Open** W'ends & public hols 11–5 or by appt
Winemaker Barry Saunders **Est.** 2011 **Dozens** 5000 **Vyds** 8ha
When you read the name of this winery, you expect to find it somewhere on or near the
Mornington Peninsula. In fact it's a very long way to the North East Victoria Zone, where
Barry and Pam Saunders planted 8ha of vineyards on their farm and released the first wines
under the name Kooyonga Chapel in 2003. They planted a sensibly focused range of 1.6ha
each of shiraz, cabernet sauvignon, merlot, chardonnay and sauvignon blanc, and what started
as a hobby has now become a business. Family and friends help with the peak seasons (picking
and pruning). Having initially been sold locally under the Kooyonga Chapel brand, the name
has been changed and distribution into the Melbourne market has begun.

🍷🍷🍷🍷   **Chardonnay 2008** Attractive green–gold colour; has retained freshness as it has
built its peachy fruit flavour thanks to good acidity. A pleasant mature chardonnay.
Screwcap. 14.3% alc. **Rating** 88 **To** 2014 $18
Sauvignon Blanc 2011 Light straw-green; a well-made wine, particularly given
the vintage conditions in this neck of the woods, and even more given the price. It
is not flashy, but has unmistakable varietal character, and the finish is dry. Screwcap.
13.2% alc. **Rating** 87 **To** Now $12
Cabernet Sauvignon 2008 The colour is unconvincing, but the wine has a
respectable level of blackcurrant fruit, some oak, and soft tannins. Ready now.
Screwcap. 14.4% alc. **Rating** 87 **To** 2013 $17

Kopparossa Wines   ★★★☆

Stentiford Vineyard, Lot 95 Skinner Road, Coonawarra, SA 5263 **Region** Coonawarra
T (08) 8736 3268 **F** (08) 8736 3363 **Open** By appt
Winemaker Gavin Hogg **Est.** 1996 **Dozens** 10 000 **Vyds** 24ha
Of the many complicated stories, this is one of the most complicated of all. Founded by Gavin
Hogg and Mike Press in 1996 and based on an 80ha vineyard in the Wrattonbully region,
the Kopparossa label was born in 2000. The vineyard was sold in '02, and Mike retired to
pursue separate interests in his Adelaide Hills family vineyard. Various wine releases and events
occurred until '05, when a joint venture between Stentiford Pty Ltd (Kopparossa's parent
company) and Estate Licensing Pty Ltd (Olivia Newton-John's wine-naming rights company)
was entered into. Says Gavin's newsletter, 'Put simply, Stentiford produces and packages
wine for the Olivia Label, which is then marketed and sold by Estate Licensing.' Another
complication followed in '09, when Gavin purchased a 24ha vineyard on the Murray River at
Yelta, adjacent to his parents' vineyard; as from vintage '11 the majority of the fruit from the
24ha Hoggies Vineyard is being used for Hoggies Estate brand, and for various private labels.
Exports to the UK, the US, Canada, Vietnam, Hong Kong and China.

🍷🍷🍷🍷🍷   **Vintage Reserve Coonawarra Cabernet Sauvignon 2005** A rich and
warm-fruited cabernet, with essency cassis sitting neatly alongside leather, thyme
and tar; full-bodied and with gravelly tannins aplenty, there is plenty of time left in
this wine yet. Cork. 14% alc. **Rating** 91 **To** 2018 $60 BE
Vintage Reserve Coonawarra Shiraz 2004 Mid garnet; a spicy bouquet
of dark plum blackberry, sage and bacon bones; the palate is lively for its age,
with good acidity and a warm fruitful conclusion. Cork. 14% alc. **Rating** 90
To 2017 $60 BE

🍷🍷🍷🍷   **Coonawarra Shiraz 2002 Rating** 89 **To** 2014 $30 BE
✪   **Hoggies Estate Chardonnay 2011 Rating** 87 **To** 2014 $10 BE

Krinklewood Biodynamic Vineyard   ★★★★

712 Wollombi Road, Broke, NSW 2330 **Region** Hunter Valley
T (02) 6579 1322 **www**.krinklewood.com **Open** W'ends 10–5
Winemaker Liz Jackson, Rod Windrim **Est.** 1981 **Dozens** 6500 **Vyds** 19.9ha

A boutique, family-owned biodynamic vineyard, Krinklewood produces 100% estate-grown wines reflecting the terroir of the Broke Fordwich subregion of the Hunter Valley. The cellar door is set among Provençal-style gardens that overlook the vineyard, with the Wollombi Brook and Brokenback range providing a spectacular backdrop. In 2010 the winery was extended and upgraded, including the installation of a Vaslin Bucher basket press.

🍷🍷🍷🍷🍷 **Chardonnay 2010** A restrained bouquet of grapefruit, peach and grilled nuts; the palate is layered and subtle, with lemon pith and zesty acidity providing detail to conclude. Screwcap. 13% alc. **Rating** 90 **To** 2016 $28 BE

Kurrajong Downs   ★★★

Casino Road, Tenterfield, NSW 2372 **Region** New England
T (02) 6736 4590 **www.**kurrajongdownswines.com **Open** Thurs–Mon 9–4
Winemaker Ravens Croft Wines (Mark Ravenscroft), Symphony Hill (Mike Hayes)
Est. 2000 **Dozens** 2000 **Vyds** 4.4ha
Jonus Rhodes arrived at Tenterfield in 1858, lured by the gold he mined for the next 40 years, until his death in 1898. He was evidently successful, for the family now runs a 2800ha cattle-grazing property on which Lynton and Sue Rhodes began the development of their vineyard, at an altitude of 850m, in 1996. Plantings include pinot noir, shiraz, cabernet sauvignon, chardonnay, semillon, gewurztraminer and tempranillo. Lynton says the last few vintages have been difficult because of some frost damage and heavy rain near harvest.

🍷🍷🍷🍷 **Louisa Mary Tenterfield Semillon 2011** Pale straw-green; a cleverly made
✪ wine that circumvents the slight lack of intensity with low-level residual sugar; the palate does have varietal character in a grassy/fruit juice spectrum. Its best years are ahead of it. Screwcap. 10.7% alc. **Rating** 89 **To** 2018 $17
Timbarra Gold Tenterfield Chardonnay 2011 Pale straw-green; a light-bodied chardonnay with one foot in the citrus/grapefruit spectrum, the other (hesitantly) in the stone fruit/melon spectrum; sensitively made given the inherent delicacy of the fruit. Screwcap. 12.8% alc. **Rating** 88 **To** 2015 $18
Tenterfield Pinot Noir Chardonnay 2010 Traditional method; pale, bright salmon-pink; the red cherry and grapefruit flavours come as no surprise, but the wine really needed a longer time on lees to allow the sharp edges of those flavours to soften; that said, it's a respectable sparkling. Cork. 14.2% alc. **Rating** 88 **To** 2013 $25

Kurtz Family Vineyards   ★★★★★

PO Box 460, Nuriootpa, SA 5355 **Region** Barossa Valley
T 0418 810 982 **www.**kurtzfamilyvineyards.com.au **Open** At Barossa Collective, Tanunda
Winemaker Steve Kurtz **Est.** 1996 **Dozens** 3500 **Vyds** 15.04ha
The Kurtz family vineyard is at Light Pass, with 9ha of shiraz, the remainder planted to chardonnay, cabernet sauvignon, semillon, sauvignon blanc, petit verdot, grenache, mataro and malbec. Steve Kurtz has followed in the footsteps of his great- grandfather Ben Kurtz, who first grew grapes at Light Pass in the 1930s. During a career working first at Saltram and then Foster's, until 2006, Steve gained invaluable experience from Nigel Dolan, Caroline Dunn and John Glaetzer, among others. Exports to the US, Canada, Macau, Hong Kong and China.

🍷🍷🍷🍷🍷 **Schmick Barossa Shiraz 2008** Sold only in magnums, of which one assumes there are precious few. Obviously matured in new oak for an extended period, with an attractive savoury twist on the finish to balance the profusion of black fruits, mocha and multi-spice flavours of the mid palate. I'm not entirely convinced the oak will come back into balance, but given 20+ years you would hope so. Screwcap. 14% alc. **Rating** 94 **To** 2035 $125
Lunar Block Individual Vineyard Barossa Valley Shiraz 2008 The Kurtz family purchased the then-unplanted property on the day man first walked on the moon. Dense red-purple, it is stacked with a profusion of aromas and flavours, none of them overripe; blackberry, black cherry, plum cake, licorice, spices and dark chocolate all make their appearance at various points of the bouquet and palate; medium- to full-bodied, it will be very long lived. 36 dozen made. Screwcap. 14% alc. **Rating** 94 **To** 2030 $45

ŦŦŦŦŸ Boundary Row Barossa Valley Shiraz 2009 Rating 93 To 2030 $24
Boundary Row Barossa Valley Cabernet Sauvignon 2009 Rating 91
To 2019 $24

Kyneton Ridge Estate ★★★★

90 Blackhill School Road, Kyneton, Vic 3444 **Region** Macedon Ranges
T (03) 5422 7377 **www**.kynetonridge.com.au **Open** W'ends & public hols 10–5, or by appt
Winemaker John and Luke Boucher **Est.** 1997 **Dozens** 2000 **Vyds** 4ha
Established by John Boucher and partner Pauline Russell in the shadow of Black Mountain, an
ideal environment for pinot noir and chardonnay vines. With five generations of winemaking
behind them, John and Luke Boucher continue the quest for quality and refinement. Being
boutique winemakers, they maintain the traditional hand-making processes that complement
the character of the wines. New facilities have recently been introduced to enhance the
production process for all the sparkling wines. The additional production capacity gives the
opportunity to source additional suitable quality parcels of shiraz and cabernet sauvignon from
the Macedon and Heathcote regions.

ŦŦŦŦŸ Heathcote Shiraz 2010 Strong crimson-purple; a rich, multifaceted wine in
mainstream Heathcote style, the intensity of the black fruits carrying the alcohol
without demur, the finish long and supple. Trophy (Best Wine of Show) at
Daylesford Wine Show '11. Screwcap. 15% alc. **Rating** 93 **To** 2025 $45
Macedon Ranges Cabernet Sauvignon 2010 Good colour; shows the
warm year that Macedon thrives on; ripe but not the least jammy blackcurrant;
foresty/spicy nuances plus oak all play their role. Screwcap. 14.2% alc. **Rating** 92
To 2020 $28
Fortunate Land Macedon Ranges Chardonnay 2010 Light straw-green;
has a fragrant citrus and apple bouquet, the palate more intense and prolonged,
with more grapefruit and a touch of peach. Screwcap. 12.5% alc. **Rating** 90
To 2017 $25
Macedon Pinot Noir Chardonnay 2009 Light bronze, hint of pink; complex
traditional method wine, with mouth-filling flavours of peach, brioche and cashew,
the finish long and satisfying. Diam. 12.5% alc. **Rating** 90 **To** 2013 $30

La Curio ★★★★☆

Lot 90 Chalk Hill Road, McLaren Vale, SA 5171 **Region** McLaren Vale
T (08) 8323 8623 **www**.lacuriowines.com **Open** 7 days 10–4
Winemaker Adam Hooper **Est.** 2003 **Dozens** 2000
La Curio has been established by Adam Hooper, who purchases small parcels of grapes from
vineyards in McLaren Vale with an average age of 40 years, the oldest 80 years. The wines
are made at Redheads Studio, a boutique winery in McLaren Vale that caters for a number
of small producers. The manacles depicted on the striking label are those of Harry Houdini,
and the brand proposition is very cleverly worked through. Winemaking techniques, too, are
avant-garde, and highly successful. Exports to the UK, the US, Canada and Sweden.

ŦŦŦŦŦ The Original Zin McLaren Vale Primitivo 2010 Brilliantly bright and clear
✪ crimson; the palate is rich and full, while retaining freshness and elegance; cherry
and raspberry fruit is framed by fine tannins and subtle oak. It is, of course,
zinfandel (hence 'Zin') under its alternative name. A drop-dead bargain. Screwcap.
14.5% alc. **Rating** 94 **To** 2018 $21

ŦŦŦŦŸ Reserve McLaren Vale Shiraz 2010 Excellent, full purple-crimson; hand-
✪ plunged and basket-pressed, 'followed by grooming in oak for 18 months'. That's
a new concept, but this is a very good, medium-bodied wine, with black fruits, a
hint of dark chocolate, and of licorice, and high-quality tannins framing the finish.
Cork. 14.5% alc. **Rating** 93 **To** 2020 $21
Reserve Bush Vine McLaren Vale Grenache 2010 Rating 91 To 2018 $28
The Nubile McLaren Vale Grenache Shiraz 2010 Rating 90 To 2018 $21
New World Order McLaren Vale Sangiovese 2010 Rating 90 To 2017 $21

La Linea   ★★★★★

36 Shipsters Road, Kensington Park, SA 5068 (postal) **Region** Adelaide Hills
T (08) 8431 3556 www.lalinea.com.au **Open** Not
Winemaker Peter Leske **Est.** 2007 **Dozens** 2500 **Vyds** 9ha
La Linea is a partnership of experienced wine industry professionals, including Peter Leske
and David LeMire MW. Peter was among the first to recognise the potential of Tempranillo in
Australia, and his knowledge of it is reflected in the three wine styles made from the variety:
Tempranillo Rose, the Tempranillo blended from several Adelaide Hills vineyards, and Norteno,
from a single vineyard at the northern end of the Hills. Two Rieslings are produced under the
Vertigo label: TRKN (short for trocken), and the off-dry 25GR (25 g/l residual sugar).

ΨΨΨΨΨ Vertigo TRKN Adelaide Hills Riesling 2010 Bright straw-green; a very
       deliberately constructed wine, bone dry (hence the abbreviation for Trocken)
       and finely chiselled, its core of lime, lemon and green apple within a sheath of
       acidity that will open up fully sometime over the next 20 years. Screwcap. 12% alc.
       Rating 95 **To** 2030 $26
       Vertigo TRKN Adelaide Hills Riesling 2011 Pale straw; a flowery bouquet
       leads into a finely structured palate, lime and apple flavours bound together by
       bright acidity; the palate has great length and balance, and is uncompromisingly
       dry. Screwcap. 11.5% alc. **Rating** 94 **To** 2020 $26

ΨΨΨΨΨ **Adelaide Hills Tempranillo 2011 Rating** 92 **To** 2016 $27
✪   **Adelaide Hills Tempranillo Rose 2011** Pale pink; an uncompromisingly tangy
       and crisp red berry wine with potent acidity running through the length of the
       palate. Screwcap. 12% alc. **Rating** 90 **To** 2013 $20

Laanecoorie   ★★★★

4834 Bendigo/Maryborough Road, Betley, Vic 3472 **Region** Bendigo
T (03) 5468 7260 www.laanecoorievineyard.com **Open** W'ends & public hols 11–5,
Mon–Fri by appt
Winemaker Graeme Jukes, John Ellis (Contract) **Est.** 1982 **Dozens** 1000
John and Rosa McQuilten's vineyard (shiraz, cabernet franc, merlot and cabernet sauvignon)
produces grapes of high quality, and competent contract winemaking does the rest, the
vicissitudes of vintages in recent years permitting. Exports to China.

ΨΨΨΨΨ **McQuilten's Reserve Shiraz 2009** A dark and sweet-fruited bouquet,
       with essency blackberry pastille fruit and licorice character; the palate is fleshy
       and generous, with a soft, yet harmonious, finish. Diam. 14.6% alc. **Rating** 92
       To 2018 $40 BE
       Cabernet Sauvignon Cabernet Franc Merlot 2006 Bright crimson,
       exceptional for age; the bouquet and light- to medium-bodied palate have an array
       of redcurrant, red cherry and blackcurrant fruit; overall, the wine is as fresh as the
       colour suggests it should be. Screwcap. 13.5% alc. **Rating** 92 **To** 2016 $23

Lake Barrington Vineyard   ★★★★★

1133–1136 West Kentish Road, West Kentish, Tas 7306 **Region** Northern Tasmania
T (03) 6491 1249 www.lbv.com.au **Open** Wed–Sun 11–4 (Jan–Feb), w'ends 11–4
(Nov–Dec, Mar–Apr)
Winemaker Frogmore Creek (Alain Rousseau), White Rock, Julian Alcorso **Est.** 1986
Dozens 450 **Vyds** 1ha
Charles and Jill Macek purchased the vineyard from founder Maree Tayler in 2005. Charles
is a distinguished company director (Telstra, Wesfarmers). Lake Barrington's primary focus is
on high-quality sparkling wine, and it has won many trophies and gold medals over the years
at the Tasmanian Wine Show; it makes lesser quantities of high-quality chardonnay and pinot
noir. There are picnic facilities at the vineyard and, needless to say, the scenery is very beautiful.

ŶŶŶŶŶ Alexandra 2008 Pale straw-green; fresh lively citrus; excellent mousse; then a lively, long and balanced palate with finesse the key descriptor. Gold Tas Wine Show '12. Cork. 12.5% alc. **Rating** 94 **To** 2015 $40

Lake Breeze Wines ★★★★★

Step Road, Langhorne Creek, SA 5255 **Region** Langhorne Creek
T (08) 8537 3017 **www**.lakebreeze.com.au **Open** 7 days 10–5
Winemaker Greg Follett **Est.** 1987 **Dozens** 15 000 **Vyds** 90ha
The Folletts have been farmers at Langhorne Creek since 1880, and grapegrowers since the 1930s. Most of the grape production is sold, but the quality of the Lake Breeze wines has been exemplary, with the red wines particularly appealing. Lake Breeze also owns and makes the False Cape wines from Kangaroo Island. Exports to the US and other major markets.

ŶŶŶŶŶ Bullant Langhorne Creek Shiraz 2010 Deep colour; combines fresh black
✪ fruits in abundance with contrasting quartz-like mineral highlights; the palate is medium-bodied, unctuous and generous, fresh and focused. Outstanding value for the price. Screwcap. 14.5% alc. **Rating** 94 **To** 2020 $15 BE
Arthur's Reserve Cabernet Sauvignon Petit Verdot 2008 An 89/11 % blend; strong purple-crimson after almost four years in bottle; likewise, the palate has a bevy of dark fruit flavours and powerful, although balanced, tannins. An impressive example of a wine built for the long haul. Screwcap. 14.5% alc. **Rating** 94 **To** 2028 $32

ŶŶŶŶŶ Bullant Langhorne Creek Cabernet Merlot 2010 Deep crimson; a succulent
✪ combination of red and black fruits, sage and cinnamon; the palate is medium-bodied, fleshy and evenly balanced, offering plenty of complexity and depth for the price tag. Screwcap. 14.2% alc. **Rating** 93 **To** 2018 $15 BE
✪ **Langhorne Creek Cabernet Sauvignon 2009** Excellent purple-crimson; has an intense but well-balanced palate, with juicy cassis fruit, fine, ripe tannins and cedary French oak. Very good value. Screwcap. 14% alc. **Rating** 93 **To** 2019 $23
Section 54 Langhorne Creek Shiraz 2009 Rating 92 **To** 2024 $24
Bernoota Langhorne Creek Shiraz Cabernet 2009 Rating 91 **To** 2018 $22
✪ **Langhorne Creek Moscato 2011** A fresh and tangy example of the style, with a grapey note that is harmony with the sugar; well made and in keeping with the refreshing aspect of moscato from Piedmont. 500ml. Crown seal. 6.5% alc. **Rating** 90 **To** 2013 $17 BE

ŶŶŶŶ Reserve Langhorne Creek Chardonnay 2011 **Rating** 89 **To** 2014 $24
False Cape Ship's Graveyard Shiraz 2010 Rating 88 **To** 2015 $18 BE

Lake George Winery ★★★★☆

Old Federal Highway, Lake George, NSW 2581 **Region** Canberra District
T (02) 9948 4676 **www**.lakegeorgewinery.com.au **Open** 7 days 10–5
Winemaker Nick Spencer, Hamish Young **Est.** 1971 **Dozens** 3000 **Vyds** 20ha
Lake George Winery was established by legend-in-his-own-lifetime Dr Edgar Riek, who has contributed so much to the Canberra District and the Australian wine industry. It has now passed into good hands, and the plantings of 40-year-old chardonnay, pinot noir, cabernet sauvignon, semillon and merlot have been joined by shiraz and tempranillo, pinot gris, viognier, pinot noir and malbec. In March 2008 Lake George acquired the Madew vineyard, providing yet more grape resources. The winemaking techniques include basket-pressing and small-batch barrel maturation under the expert eyes of consultant winemaker Alex McKay, now retired, and replaced by the equally expert Nick Spencer. Exports to China.

ŶŶŶŶŶ Riesling 2011 Pale straw, green hue; a pure citrus, fennel and struck quartz bouquet; the palate tells the full story, completely dry and with mouth-watering acidity, which is certainly on the challenging side of pleasure; will be interesting to watch over time. Screwcap. 11% alc. **Rating** 91 **To** 2025 $28 BE

Reserve Pinot Noir 2009 Deep garnet; a dark and savoury wine, showing lifted black fruits and bracken on the bouquet; the palate is very firm, with densely packed tannins a dominant feature; licorice and tar linger on the big-boned finish. Cries out for more time. Screwcap. 14% alc. **Rating** 90 **To** 2016 $45 BE

Lake Moodemere Vineyards   ★★★

McDonalds Road, Rutherglen, Vic 3685 **Region** Rutherglen
T (02) 6032 9449 **www**.moodemerewines.com.au **Open** Mon, Thurs, Fri, Sun 10–4, Sat & public hols 10–5
Winemaker Michael Chambers **Est.** 1995 **Dozens** 2000 **Vyds** 20.74ha
Michael, Belinda, Peter and Helen Chambers are members of the famous Chambers family of Rutherglen. The vineyards (tended by Peter), include the Italian grape variety biancone, a vineyard specialty made in a light-bodied late-harvest style. The cellar door sits high above Lake Moodemere, and gourmet hampers can be arranged with 24 hours' notice.

🍷🍷🍷🍷 **Late Harvest Biancone 2006** Interesting wine; while it is described as late harvest, the alcohol of only 6.5% strongly suggests the sweetness in the wine comes from unfermented sugar, all of which is fine. But if the grapes were picked much riper (than, say 12° baume), there would be more sweetness. A nitpick, for the wine is remarkably fresh and youthful. Screwcap. 6.5% alc. **Rating** 89 **To** 2014 $16
Rutherglen Riesling 2010 The wine is estate-grown (and hasn't looked to the nearby King Valley); the flavours are generous, yet not bloated or tired; early picking and the retention of a hint of sugar have resulted in a very pleasing, drink-now style. Screwcap. 12.5% alc. **Rating** 88 **To** 2015 $16

Lake's Folly   ★★★★★

2416 Broke Road, Pokolbin, NSW 2320 **Region** Hunter Valley
T (02) 4998 7507 **www**.lakesfolly.com.au **Open** 7 days 10–4 while wine available
Winemaker Rodney Kempe **Est.** 1963 **Dozens** 5000 **Vyds** 12.2ha
The first of the weekend wineries to produce wines for commercial sale, long revered for its Cabernet Sauvignon and nowadays its Chardonnay. Very properly, terroir and climate produce a distinct regional influence and thereby a distinctive wine style. The winery continues to enjoy an incredibly loyal clientele, with much of each year's wine selling out quickly by mail order. Lake's Folly no longer has any connection with the Lake family, having been acquired some years ago by Perth businessman Peter Fogarty. Peter's family company previously established the Millbrook Winery in the Perth Hills, so is no stranger to the joys and agonies of running a small winery. Curiously, it is the Chardonnay that justifies the rating (and the historic nature of the winery). No wines were received for this edition; the rating is that of last year.

Lambert Estate   ★★★☆

Barossa Valley Way, Tanunda, SA 5352 **Region** Barossa Valley
T (08) 8563 3375 **www**.lambertestate.com.au **Open** 7 days 11–5
Winemaker Kirk Lambert, Vanessa Herrern **Est.** 1986 **Dozens** 15 000 **Vyds** 40ha
James (Jim) and Pamela Lambert are the owners of the recently renamed Lambert Estate Wines (previously Stanley Lambert Wines), with son Kirk now winemaker. Like his parents, Kirk was born in Wisconsin, and followed his parents' footsteps to the University of Wisconsin. Graduating as a mechanical engineer, he worked for several years for General Electric, but decided to move to Australia, and after working in the vineyard and winery for some years, obtained his Masters degree in oenology from the University of Adelaide. In 2003 Jim and Pamela purchased a 24ha vineyard planted in 1986, and subsequently expanded this to 40ha, with shiraz, riesling, chardonnay, cabernet sauvignon, zinfandel, tempranillo, grenache, mourvedre, merlot and viognier. Exports to the UK, the US and other major markets.

🍷🍷🍷🍷🍷 **Forgive Me Barossa Valley Zinfandel 2009** Bright, clear red; a well-made,
✪   fresh wine from this somewhat temperamental varietal, the picking decision being all important; a fresh, lively finish. Diam. 14% alc. **Rating** 91 **To** 2015 $20

TITT The Family Tree Barossa Valley Shiraz 2008 Rating 89 To 2018 $80
A Thousand Words Barossa Valley Chardonnay 2010 Rating 87
To 2013 $20
August Barossa Valley Shiraz 2008 Rating 87 To 2014 $30

Lambert Vineyards ★★★☆

810 Norton Road, Wamboin, NSW 2620 **Region** Canberra District
T (02) 6238 3866 **www**.lambertvineyards.com.au **Open** Thurs–Sun 10–5, or by appt
Winemaker Steve and Ruth Lambert **Est.** 1998 **Dozens** 4000 **Vyds** 10ha
Ruth and Steve Lambert have established riesling (2.5ha), pinot noir, pinot gris (2ha each), merlot (1.5ha), chardonnay (1ha), cabernet sauvignon and shiraz (0.5ha each). Steve makes the many wines onsite, and does so with skill and sensitivity. Definitely a winery to watch.

TITTT Canberra District Late Harvest Pinot Gris 2010 The wine does live up to the implications of 'late harvest', with the varietal fruit in a pear/spiced pear spectrum, supported by low level sweetness, in turn balanced by acidity. Surprise packet. Screwcap. 12% alc. **Rating** 90 **To** 2014 $22

TITT Canberra District Pinot Noir 2010 Rating 88 To 2015 $25

🍇 Lambloch Estate ★★★★★

2342 Broke Road, Pokolbin, NSW 2320 **Region** Hunter Valley
T 0416 922 030 **www**.lambloch.com **Open** Fri–Mon 10–5
Winemaker Scott Stephens **Est.** 2008 **Dozens** 2000 **Vyds** 8ha
Whether it be upmarket housing or mining tenements, the address is all important. When Jas Khara acquired the 8ha vineyard now known as Lambloch Estate, it adjoined Lake's Folly and is directly opposite McWilliam's Rosehill Vineyard. All three share the red volcanic soils not often found in the Hunter Valley. With a strong marketing background in brand creation, he has invested in a new cellar door on Broke Road (itself an all-important artery) with large open areas overlooking the vines and a backdrop of the Brokenback Range in the middle distance. Currently almost all of the production is sold in Belgium, Hong Kong, Macau, Singapore, Thailand and Malaysia.

TITTT The Loch 2010 Strong, deep purple-crimson is an introduction to a poised, powerful shiraz from 50-year-old vines planted on the prized red soil found in pockets here and there in the Hunter Valley; the intense blackberry and licorice fruit flavours are supported by ripe tannins and balanced oak. Will live for at least 50 years. Screwcap. 13.5% alc. **Rating** 96 **To** 2060 $75
The Loch 2009 The colour has slightly more purple to its hue, but is otherwise similar to the standard Shiraz; the intensity and character of the wine are remarkable, with a pure expression of full-bodied Hunter Valley shiraz, and the tannins to support a very long life. Screwcap. 14% alc. **Rating** 96 **To** 2039 $75
Hunter Valley Shiraz 2010 Ample purple-crimson; the expressive bouquet of spicy black fruits leads into a light- to medium-bodied palate that has a lovely open mouthfeel and structure, and a long finish and aftertaste. Screwcap. 13.5% alc. **Rating** 94 **To** 2025 $30

TITTT Classic Hunter Valley Semillon 2010 Rating 93 To 2025 $25
Hunter Valley Chardonnay 2010 Rating 93 To 2017 $25
Hunter Valley Shiraz 2009 Rating 92 To 2017 $30
✪ Flipside Hunter Valley Semillon 2010 Pale straw-green; the very low alcohol simply reflects the decision to arrest the fermentation with similar residual sugar to that of the '11, having been picked earlier in the first place, and the wine is similarly bracingly sweet, balanced by acidity on the long finish. Screwcap. 8.5% alc. **Rating** 91 **To** 2020 $22
Classic Hunter Valley Semillon 2011 Rating 90 To 2016 $25
Flipside Hunter Valley Riesling 2011 Rating 90 To 2015 $22

ΨΨΨΨ   **Hunter Valley Shiraz Rose 2010** Rating 89 To Now $22
Hunter Valley Verdelho 2010 Rating 87 To Now $22
Hunter Valley Shiraz Rose 2011 Rating 87 To Now $22

Lambrook Wines   ★★★
6 Coorara Avenue, Payneham South, SA 5070 **Region** Adelaide Hills
T 0437 672 651 **www**.lambrook.com.au **Open** By appt
Winemaker Adam Lampit, Michael Sykes **Est.** 2008 **Dozens** 2000
This is a virtual winery created by the husband and wife team of Adam and Brooke Lampit.
With almost two decades of industry experience between them, they began purchasing
sauvignon blanc, shiraz and pinot noir (for sparkling) in 2008, having the wine made by Sam
Scott. Adam's experience came through working with Stonehaven, Norfolk Rise and Bird in
Hand, while Brooke also worked at Norfolk Rise before moving to work for Wine Australia.

ΨΨΨΨ   **Adelaide Hills Shiraz 2009** Light red-purple; ripe black cherry, licorice
and plum fruit at the heart of the wine is appealing, but less oak would have
had resulted in an even better outcome. 350 dozen made. Screwcap. 14.5% alc.
Rating 89 **To** 2016 $18

Lamont's Winery   ★★★★☆
85 Bisdee Road, Millendon, WA 6056 **Region** Swan Valley
T (08) 9296 4485 **www**.lamonts.com.au **Open** Fri–Mon 10–5
Winemaker Digby Leddin **Est.** 1978 **Dozens** 7000 **Vyds** 2ha
Corin Lamont is the daughter of the late Jack Mann, and oversees the making of wines in
a style that would have pleased her father. Lamont's also boasts a superb restaurant run by
granddaughter Kate Lamont. The wines are going from strength to strength, utilising both
estate-grown and contract-grown (from southern regions) grapes. Lamont's restaurant in
Perth, open for lunch and dinner Wed–Sun, offers food of the highest quality, and is superbly
situated. The Margaret River cellar door is open Thurs–Mon 11–5 for wine tasting, sales and
lunch. Full details of Lamont's venues are available on the website.

ΨΨΨΨΨ   Margaret River Chardonnay 2010 Vivid green hue; a pure grapefruit and
nectarine fruit bouquet, complemented by a touch of cinnamon and spice;
the palate is taut and energetic, unevolved and super bright, focused and linear.
Screwcap. 13.5% alc. Rating 94 To 2018 $30 BE

ΨΨΨΨ♀   The Great Southern Riesling 2011 Rating 91 To 2017 $25 BE
Margaret River Cabernet Sauvignon 2008 Rating 90 To 2018 $35 BE

ΨΨΨΨ   Liqueur NV Rating 88 To 2018 $50 BE

Landhaus Estate   ★★★★★
PO Box 2135, Bethany SA 5352 **Region** Barossa Valley
T (08) 8353 8442 **www**.landhauswines.com **Open** Not
Winemaker Kane Jaunutis **Est.** 2002 **Dozens** 5000
The Jaunutis family (John, Barbara and son Kane) purchased Landhaus Estate in November
2002, and the following month bought 'The Landhaus' cottage and 1ha vineyard at Bethany.
Bethany is the oldest German-established town in the Barossa (1842) and the cottage was
one of the first to be built. Kane has worked vintages for Mitolo and Kellermeister, as well
as managing East End Cellars, one of Australia's leading fine wine retailers, while John brings
decades of owner/management experience and Barbara 20 years in sales and marketing.
Rehabilitation of the estate plantings and establishing a grower network has paid handsome
dividends. A cellar door is planned to open in late '12. Exports to Canada, Singapore and China.

ΨΨΨΨΨ   Classics Barossa Valley Shiraz 2010 Mid red-crimson; a fine and elegant
medium-bodied shiraz; the scented bouquet is of blackberry and bramble, the
palate bringing red fruits, spice and licorice into play as well; and the tannins are of
the highest quality, running the length of the palate, supporting, not threatening it.
Screwcap. 14.1% alc. Rating 95 To 2025 $45

Rare Barossa Valley Shiraz 2008 Has retained good hue, although the colour is not especially deep; it is almost certain the grapes were picked well before the heatwave commenced, for it is a fine an elegant wine, with very good mouthfeel thanks to gossamer-fine tannins; the only query is the amount of French oak, which I have accepted. Screwcap. 14.5% alc. Rating 95 To 2028 $100

Rare Barossa Valley Shiraz 2006 Strong red hue attests to the top vintage; this is a shiraz of exceptional intensity and richness, the grapes picked at optimum ripeness, and the wine matured in new French hogsheads; it is full of juicy plum and cherry fruit, the tannins polished, the finish long. Screwcap. 14% alc. Rating 95 To 2026 $100

✪ The Diva Savagnin 2010 The case for savagnin (initially thought to be albarino) grows ever stronger, for it is a wine with real character and substance, its relationship with gewurztraminer no surprise. The texture is rich, and the citrus/lychee flavours long and persistent. Given that all the plantings are recent, even more character should come once the vines are more than 10 years old. Screwcap. 12.7% alc. Rating 94 To 2013 $20

✪ The Saint 2010 Full purple-crimson; if depth and power of flavour are the sole criteria of quality, this shiraz would get 100 points; the flavours, too, are very good indeed; the only point of criticism is the somewhat thick texture. Will cellar very well, and is an outrageously priced bargain. Screwcap. 14% alc. Rating 94 To 2025 $20

Classics Barossa Valley Mourvedre Grenache Shiraz 2010 Good colour for the blend; from this point on, it soars above normal expectations, with a seamless union between the three varieties, and a similarly seamless balance between the fruit and tannins. It is only in exceptional years such as '10 that this level of perfection can be achieved. Screwcap. 13.8% alc. Rating 94 To 2020 $30

🍷🍷🍷🍷🍷 Classics Barossa Valley Shiraz Mourvedre 2010 Rating 93 To 2025 $35
Classics Barossa Valley Shiraz Cabernet Sauvignon 2010 Rating 93 To 2025 $35
Classics Barossa Valley Grenache 2010 Rating 90 To 2015 $25
The Sinner 2010 Rating 90 To 2015 $20

🍷🍷🍷🍷 Classics Savagnin 2011 Rating 87 To 2013 $30

Lane's End Vineyard ★★★★☆

885 Mount William Road, Lancefield, Vic 3435 Region Macedon Ranges
T (03) 5429 1760 www.lanesend.com.au Open By appt
Winemaker Howard Matthews Est. 1985 Dozens 400 Vyds 2ha
Pharmacist Howard Matthews and family purchased the former Woodend Winery in 2000, with 1.8ha of chardonnay and pinot noir (and a small amount of cabernet franc) dating back to the mid 1980s. Subsequently, the cabernet franc has been grafted over to pinot noir (with a mix of four clones), and the chardonnay now totals 1ha. After working with next-door neighbour Ken Murchison of Portree Wines for two years gaining winemaking experience, Howard has been making the wines since 2003.

🍷🍷🍷🍷🍷 Macedon Ranges Pinot Noir 2010 Vivid crimson colour; 30% whole bunches, 3–4 days cold soak, 7 days primary ferment, 2 days post-ferment, 50% new and 50% second-use French oak; sterile cross-flow filtered. This is a beautiful wine, with a seamless flow of red fruits, the oak both balanced and integrated. 100 dozen made. Screwcap. 13.5% alc. Rating 95 To 2018 $33

🍷🍷🍷🍷 Macedon Ranges Chardonnay 2010 Rating 89 To 2016 $28

Langmeil Winery ★★★★★

Cnr Para Road/Langmeil Road, Tanunda, SA 5352 Region Barossa Valley
T (08) 8563 2595 www.langmeilwinery.com.au Open 7 days 10.30–4.30
Winemaker Paul Lindner, Tyson Bitter Est. 1996 Dozens 35 000 Vyds 25.3ha

Vines were first planted at Langmeil (which possesses the oldest block in Australia) in the 1840s, and the first winery on the site, known as Paradale Wines, opened in 1932. In '96, cousins Carl and Richard Lindner with brother-in-law Chris Bitter formed a partnership to acquire and refurbish the winery and its 5ha vineyard (planted to shiraz, and including 2ha planted in 1843). Another vineyard was acquired in 1998, which included cabernet sauvignon and grenache. Exports to all major markets.

ΨΨΨΨΨ Hangin' Snakes Barossa Shiraz 2010 Bright colour; essency and pure
✪   blackberry, fruitcake, licorice and some tarry complexity on the bouquet; the
         palate is generous, super fresh and focused, leaving a trail of minerals and toast on
         the finish. Excellent value, vibrant Barossa shiraz. Screwcap. 14.5% alc. **Rating** 94
         To 2018 $22 BE
         Valley Floor Barossa Shiraz 2009 As always, there is a classic Barossa 'feel'
         to this wine, with the sweet perfume of fresh black fruits, fruitcake and a little
         oak-derived spice; the palate is juicy, generous, almost luscious, and there can be
         little doubt of the accessible nature of this wine; simply put, this is easy to enjoy.
         Screwcap. 14.5% alc. **Rating** 94 **To** 2018 $30 BE
         The Freedom 1843 Barossa Shiraz 2009 As is often the case with very
         old vines, elegance and restraint are the key; bright and fragrant red fruits are
         underpinned by a splash of mocha, licorice and olive; the palate is fine and silky,
         long and complex, with a fine core of acidity and minerals adding to the story.
         Screwcap. 14.5% alc. **Rating** 94 **To** 2025 $100 BE
         Barossa Old Vine Company Shiraz 2008 There is more of everything in this
         wine – red fruits, black fruits, toasty oak, mocha, tannins and even some florals, and
         yet the wine does not go too far, but remains in balance for its vintage and style.
         Cork. 14.5% alc. **Rating** 94 **To** 2020 $100 BE

ΨΨΨΨΨ Barossa Old Vine Company Shiraz 2007 **Rating** 92 **To** 2018 $100 BE
         The Long Mile Barossa Shiraz 2010 **Rating** 91 **To** 2018 $22 BE
✪   Three Gardens Barossa SGM 2010 Bright colour; fresh, lifted and fragrant
         spicy bouquet, with red and black fruits and sage thrown in for good measure;
         lively and refreshing, this is a young style of wine simply made to be enjoyed,
         and not necessarily in moderation. A 45/35/20% blend of shiraz, mourvedre and
         grenache. Screwcap. 14.5% alc. **Rating** 91 **To** 2016 $20 BE
         Dry Eden Valley Riesling 2011 **Rating** 90 **To** 2018 $25 BE
         Orphan Bank Barossa Shiraz 2009 **Rating** 90 **To** 2018 $50 BE
         Resurrection Barossa Mataro 2010 **Rating** 90 **To** 2016 $40 BE

ΨΨΨΨ   Blacksmith Barossa Cabernet Sauvignon 2009 **Rating** 89 **To** 2017 $29
         The Fifth Wave Barossa Grenache 2009 **Rating** 88 **To** 2015 $40 BE
         Jackaman's Barossa Valley Cabernet 2009 **Rating** 88 **To** 2016 $50 BE

Lansdowne Vineyard   ★★★★
180 Forreston Road, Forreston, SA 5233 **Region** Adelaide Hills
T 0402 505 763 **www**.lansdownevineyard.com **Open** Not
Winemaker Tim Smith, Simon Greenleaf **Est.** 2003 **Dozens** 500 **Vyds** 18.6ha
Lansdowne's vineyard was planted between 1996 and 2004, and takes its name from the
late Victorian house built at Forreston in 1896. Since the 1940s a 3m cedar hedge has been
trimmed with 'Lansdowne', creating a local landmark. Janet and Brendan Cameron purchased
the house and existing vineyard in 2002, and have since retrained or replanted the vineyard to
its current mix of viognier, chardonnay, semillon, pinot gris, pinot noir and sauvignon blanc.
Most of the grapes are sold, but since 2005 small quantities have been held for the Lansdowne
Vineyard label. The Camerons are moving to an organic regime for the vineyard.

ΨΨΨΨΨ Adelaide Hills Viognier 2011 Pale straw-gold; the bouquet has obvious
         musk and apricot varietal character; the palate does not build on the bouquet,
         and doesn't really need to do so, and certainly not if the consequence would be
         oily phenolics – which the wine does not have. Screwcap. 12.5% alc. **Rating** 90
         To 2014 $24

 # Lanz Vineyards ★★★★☆

Lot 1 Rosedale Scenic Road, Lyndoch, SA 5351 **Region** Barossa Valley
T 0417 858 967 **www**.lanzvineyards.com **Open** By appt
Winemaker Michael Paxton **Est.** 1998 **Dozens** 1750 **Vyds** 15ha
The major part of the grape production from the vineyards is sold to premium producers in
the Barossa Valley. However, Marianne and Thomas Lanz take enough of the grapes to make
their Shiraz and Grenache Shiraz Mourvedre. Their choice of Michael Paxton as winemaker is
no accident; he is a committed biodynamic grower (together with father David) and the Lanzs
are aiming at the three L wine style: Lower alcohol, Lower intervention, and Lower carbon
footprint. It seems to me they missed the opportunity of a fourth L, but that's by-the-by.

ŸŸŸŸŸ   **Scenic Road Barossa Valley Shiraz 2010** Vibrant purple-crimson; a full-
✪   bodied, powerful shiraz that will live for decades; the intensity and length of the
        palate are remarkable, with layers of black fruits, spice, licorice and taut tannins to
        hold the structure for years to come. Screwcap. 13.5% alc. **Rating** 94 **To** 2030 $25

ŸŸŸŸŸ   **The Club Barossa Valley Grenache Shiraz Mourvedre 2010** Light to
✪   medium red-purple; has more savoury grip to the 50/45/5% blend than most
        other Barossa Valley examples; the tannins on the finish are exemplary. Screwcap.
        13.5% alc. **Rating** 90 **To** 2016 $20

Lark Hill   ★★★★★

521 Bungendore Road, Bungendore, NSW 2621 **Region** Canberra District
T (02) 6238 1393 **www**.larkhillwine.com.au **Open** Wed–Mon 10–5
Winemaker Dr David, Sue and Chris Carpenter **Est.** 1978 **Dozens** 4000 **Vyds** 10.5ha
The Lark Hill vineyard is situated at an altitude of 860 m, level with the observation deck
on Black Mountain Tower, offering splendid views of the Lake George escarpment. The
Carpenters have made wines of real quality, style and elegance from the start, but have defied
all the odds (and conventional thinking) with the quality of their Pinot Noirs in favourable
vintages. Significant changes have come in the wake of son Christopher gaining three
degrees, including a double in wine science and viticulture through CSU, the progression
towards biodynamic certification of the vineyard and the opening of a restaurant in 2007.
They have also planted 1ha of gruner veltliner; it is hard to understand why there have
been so few plantings of this high-quality Austrian variety. In 2011 Lark Hill purchased one
of the two Ravensworth vineyards from Brian Martin, with plantings of sangiovese, shiraz,
viognier, roussanne and marsanne; they will also be converting it (renamed as Dark Horse) to
biodynamic farming. Exports to the UK.

ŸŸŸŸŸ   **Canberra District Riesling 2011** A good outcome for a biodynamic vineyard
        in a challenging (read wet and rainy) vintage; the bouquet is clean and crisp,
        the wine opening up in no uncertain fashion with a display of green apple and
        citrus flavours built on a platform of steely, minerally acidity. A long future ahead.
        Screwcap. 11.5% alc. **Rating** 94 **To** 2020 $30 BE
        Canberra District Chardonnay 2011 Vibrant green hue; a taut citrus and
        mineral-accented wine, with a linear and tightly wound palate; while there
        is plenty of acidity, the fruit is lying in wait as time will see it reveal a mealy
        and complex example; incredibly refreshing and precise. Screwcap. 12.5% alc.
        Rating 94 **To** 2018 $35

ŸŸŸŸŸ   **Canberra District Gruner Veltliner 2011** **Rating** 92 **To** 2015 $40
        Canberra District Shiraz Viognier 2010 **Rating** 92 **To** 2017 $40
        Canberra District Pinot Noir 2011 **Rating** 91 **To** 2015 $30 BE

ŸŸŸŸ   **Dark Horse Vineyard Canberra District Viognier 2011** **Rating** 89
        To 2013 $25
        Exaltation Cabernet Sauvignon Merlot Shiraz 2005 **Rating** 87
        To 2016 $45 BE

Larry Cherubino Wines ★★★★★

15 York Street, Subiaco, WA 6000 **Region** Western Australia
T (08) 9382 2379 **www**.larrycherubino.com **Open** Not
Winemaker Larry Cherubino, Imogen Dillon, Jake Bacchus **Est.** 2005 **Dozens** 10 000
Vyds 70ha

Larry Cherubino has had a particularly distinguished winemaking career, first at Hardys Tintara, then Houghton, and thereafter as consultant/Flying Winemaker in Australia, NZ, South Africa, the US and Italy. In 2005 he started Larry Cherubino Wines and has developed three ranges: at the top is Cherubino (Riesling, Sauvignon Blanc, Shiraz and Cabernet Sauvignon); next The Yard, five single vineyard wines from WA; and at the bottom the Ad Hoc label, all single-region wines. The range and quality of his wines is extraordinary, the prices irresistible. The runaway success of the business (owned by Larry and wife Edwina) has seen the accumulation of 70ha of vineyards, the appointment of two additional winemakers, and Larry's own appointment of Director of Winemaking at Robert Oatley Vineyards. The number of wines rated at 94 points and above (19) is far greater than those of any other producer in a single year since the inception of my annual review in 1986. Exports to the UK, the US, Canada, Ireland, Switzerland, Hong Kong and NZ.

🍷🍷🍷🍷🍷 **Cherubino Porongurup Riesling 2011** Pale quartz-green; has the blue blood Porongurup restraint on the gently floral bouquet, then the entrancingly delicate and supremely focused palate, principally lime-accented (juice and zest), but also with apple; the acidity is perfect, and the wine is bone dry, the finish exceptionally long. Screwcap. 12% alc. **Rating** 96 **To** 2031 $40

Cherubino Pemberton Sauvignon Blanc 2011 Bright straw-green; although The Yard gets a Burgundy bottle, this has a high-shouldered, dark green Claret bottle, and the flavours are more towards the tropical end, although more finely structured and focused than The Yard, with a touch of ripe citrus, and great overall intensity and length. Screwcap. 13% alc. **Rating** 96 **To** 2014 $35

Cherubino Frankland River Shiraz 2010 Deep crimson; the bouquet is loaded with dark, brooding and ripe black fruits, offset by a heady perfume of spice and roasted game; the palate is thickly textured, and displays opulence on the one hand, and a strict backbone of firm, fine-grained tannins on the other; destined for a long life. Screwcap. 14% alc. **Rating** 96 **To** 2030 $65 BE

Cherubino Margaret River Cabernet Sauvignon 2010 Full magenta-purple hue; a deep and compelling bouquet of cassis, florals, cedar, olive and subtle spice of herbaceous complexity; the palate is deliciously silky and generous on entry, with a fleshiness that is hedonistic, yet the strictness of the variety prevails with a long, poised and highly polished finish; elegance and power seamlessly interwoven. Screwcap. 13.5% alc. **Rating** 96 **To** 2030 $75 BE

✪ **Ad Hoc Wallflower Great Southern Riesling 2011** Quartz-green colour; the flowery, fragrant bouquet doesn't prepare you for the sunburst of ripe citrus fruits on the palate, held together by a fine, high-tensile wire of acidity. Excellent now, even better in the years to come. Screwcap. 11.5% alc. **Rating** 95 **To** 2021 $18

✪ **The Yard Riversdale Vineyard Riesling 2011** From the Frankland River, this wine has an intense lime blossom/lime leaf/spice bouquet, then an intense palate with supercharged lime flavours running through to the long, lingering finish that is bone dry. Screwcap. 12.5% alc. **Rating** 95 **To** 2026 $25

Cherubino Great Southern Riesling 2011 A 60/40% blend of Porongurup/ Frankland River grapes; it is precisely as it should be with that parentage, the overall elegance and restraint from Porongurup, the juicy lime fruit from the Frankland River, and an almost imperceptible touch of residual sugar. Screwcap. 11.5% alc. **Rating** 95 **To** 2026 $35

✪ **The Yard Pedestal Vineyard Margaret River Semillon Sauvignon Blanc 2011** A 60/40% blend, the grapes grown by Cherubino's partners in Pedestal, Greg and Kerilie Brindle, in prime Wilyabrup real estate. It is not your everyday Sauvignon Blanc Semillon, as much about texture and structure as flavour, although not reliant on oak to achieve this. Be brave and give it 5–10 years in the cellar. Screwcap. 13% alc. **Rating** 95 **To** 2020 $22

The Yard Riversdale Vineyard Shiraz 2010 Strong crimson-purple; like Ad Hoc, from Frankland River; a more elegant yet more intense wine, with spicy red and black fruits on the bouquet, moving to black cherry/blackberry on the medium- to full-bodied palate, quality tannins built in on the long, savoury, spicy finish. Screwcap. 13.9% alc. **Rating** 95 **To** 2025 $35

✪ **Ad Hoc Etcetera Margaret River Cabernet Merlot 2010** Noticeably deeper colour than most of its peers, but the hue on the rim is vibrant. The delphic back label says 'Cabernet merlot … and the rest', the 'rest' being 4% malbec and 2% petit verdot (added to the 65% cabernet sauvignon and 29% merlot). An altogether more powerful and layered wine, with fruit, not alcohol or excessive tannins, driving it. Any lack of finesse is easily forgiven at this price. Screwcap. 14% alc. **Rating** 95 **To** 2025 $21

✪ **Pedestal Margaret River Cabernet Merlot 2009** This is an estate-grown blend of 89% cabernet sauvignon and 11% merlot grown in the Wilyabrup area. The strong purple-red colour introduces a rich, highly textured medium- to full-bodied palate with black fruits and cassis wrapped in ripe tannins and mocha oak. Will be long lived. Screwcap. 14.5% alc. **Rating** 95 **To** 2025 $25

Cherubino Great Southern Cabernet Sauvignon 2010 Deep crimson; a heady blend of sweet black fruits, layered with complex aromas of cedar, violets, mulberry and spice; the palate is generous and soft-centred on entry, with a fine backbone of tannins providing a long and expansive ride to the savoury finish. Screwcap. 13% alc. **Rating** 95 **To** 2025 $75 BE

Pedestal Vineyard Elevation Margaret River Cabernet Sauvignon 2009 Medium red-purple; in the mainstream of Margaret River cabernet, perfectly ripened varietal fruit filling the bouquet and palate, with cassis, plum and a feathery bed of spice and gravel/earth; the tannins are fine, and the French oak positive, but not excessive. Screwcap. 13.8% alc. **Rating** 95 **To** 2025 $50

The Yard Channybearup Vineyard Sauvignon Blanc 2011 Rating 94 **To** 2013 $25

Cherubino Porongurup Sauvignon Blanc 2011 Rating 94 **To** 2014 $35

Cherubino Margaret River Chardonnay 2011 Rating 94 **To** 2022 $49

✪ **Ad Hoc Middle of Everywhere Frankland River Shiraz 2010 Rating** 94 **To** 2025 $21

Cherubino Cowaramup Cabernet Sauvignon 2010 Rating 94 **To** 2030 $75

Cherubino Laissez Faire Cabernet Sauvignon Shiraz 2010 Rating 94 **To** 2024 $49 BE

🍷🍷🍷🍷🍷 **Ad Hoc Straw Man Margaret River Sauvignon Blanc Semillon 2011** Pale
✪ quartz; Cherubino says (on the back label) 'the blend reminds me of dried straw and fresh-cut grass'. I'll buy that, but would like to add (for this wine at least) nuances of ripe citrus and guava. Screwcap. 12.5% alc. **Rating** 93 **To** 2013 $21

The Yard Acacia Vineyard Frankland River Shiraz 2010 Rating 93 **To** 2025 $35 BE

✪ **Mix Master Shiraz Grenache Mataro Viognier 2010** The blend is 64/16/12/8%, the origin (within WA) of the grenache and mataro (mourvedre) anyone's guess. The colour is bright, light crimson-purple, the bouquet with a truly extraordinary amalgam of garam masala and virtually every other spice you can think of, inevitably dictating the flavours of the long medium-bodied palate, and its savoury/spicy conclusion. A wild but riveting ride. Screwcap. 13.6% alc. **Rating** 93 **To** 2018 $18

Cherubino Wilyabrup Cabernet Sauvignon 2010 Rating 93 **To** 2028 $75 BE

The Yard Pusey Road Vineyard Margaret River Cabernet Sauvignon 2010 Rating 92 **To** 2022 $35 BE

The Yard Riversdale Vineyard Frankland River Cabernet Sauvignon 2010 Rating 92 **To** 2025 $35 BE

The Yard Orondo Vineyard Mourvedre Grenache Shiraz 2010 Rating 92 **To** 2016 $25

Cherubino Laissez Faire Porongurup Riesling 2011 Rating 91
To 2020 $29 BE
Ad Hoc Hen & Chicken Pemberton Chardonnay 2011 Rating 91 To 2016
$21 BE
Ad Hoc The Riddler Chardonnay Pinot Noir NV Rating 91 To Now $21
Ad Hoc Nitty Gritty Pemberton Pinot Grigio 2011 Rating 90 To 2014 $21

Lashmar   ★★★☆

c/- 24 Lindsay Terrace, Belair, SA 5052 **Region** Kangaroo Island
T (08) 8278 3669 **www**.lashmarwines.com **Open** Not
Winemaker Colin Cooter **Est.** 1996 **Dozens** 1000
Colin and Bronwyn Cooter (who are also part of the Lengs & Cooter business) are the
driving force behind Antechamber Bay Wines. The wines are in fact labelled and branded
Lashmar; the Kangaroo Island Cabernet Sauvignon comes from vines planted in 1991 on the
Lashmar family property, which is on the extreme eastern end of Kangaroo Island overlooking
Antechamber Bay. The Three Valleys and Sisters wines (from other regions, including McLaren
Vale and Adelaide Hills) give the business added volume. Exports to Singapore and Japan.

ΥΥΥΥ **Adelaide Hills Pinot Noir 2010** Purple-crimson; a full-bodied pinot noir with
lashings of dark plum fruit and supporting tannins; teeters on the edge of dry red
character. Time may help. Screwcap. 14% alc. **Rating** 89 **To** 2018 $22
Sister's Blend 2008 Named after the two daughters who have hand-pruned and
picked the grapes from this vineyard on the southern edge of suburban Adelaide
for over 30 years. While only light-bodied, two years in French oak have done it
no harm at all, providing another layer of flavour to the shiraz (70%) and cabernet
sauvignon (30%), which on their own might lack appeal, for despite the alcohol,
the flavours are tending lean. Screwcap. 14.5% alc. **Rating** 89 **To** 2016 $22
McLaren Vale Nebbiolo 2009 While light and clear, has held on to its red hue
very well; for those who can put up with the hard trappings of nebbiolo, this is
worth a look, particularly given the user-friendly price. It's not for me, but c'est la
vie. Screwcap. 13% alc. **Rating** 88 **To** 2015 $18

Laughing Jack   ★★★★★

Cnr Seppeltsfield Road/Stonewell Road, Marananga, SA 5355 **Region** Barossa Valley
T 0427 396 928 **www**.laughingjackwines.com.au **Open** By appt
Winemaker Shawn Kalleske **Est.** 1999 **Dozens** 3000 **Vyds** 38.88ha
The Kalleske family has many branches in the Barossa Valley. Laughing Jack is owned by
Shawn, Nathan, Ian and Carol Kalleske, and Linda Schroeter. The lion's share of the vineyard
is planted to shiraz, with lesser amounts of semillon, chardonnay, riesling and grenache. Vine
age varies considerably, with old dry-grown shiraz the jewel in the crown. A small part of the
production is taken for the Laughing Jack Shiraz. As any Australian knows, the kookaburra is
also called the laughing jackass, and there is a resident flock of kookaburras in the stands of
blue and red gums surrounding the vineyards. Exports to the UK and the US.

ΥΥΥΥΥ **Moppa Block Barossa Valley Shiraz 2008** From a single vineyard on the
slopes of Moppa Hills, it has excellent colour, with crimson–purple still in the
driver's seat; the flavour spectrum and structure have some points of difference,
but are overwhelmingly similar to the Limited Two; there is a juicy quality to the
finish that suggests this wine may be even longer lived. Cork. 14.5% alc. **Rating** 96
To 2030 $60
Limited Two Barossa Valley Shiraz 2008 Dry-grown, open-fermented,
basket-pressed and unfiltered, plus the massive bottle and long, high-quality cork,
all sing the same Stars and Stripes song. It is the product of the best two barrels of
the vintage, the colour still deep and strong, the flavours instantaneously flooding
the mouth from the first sip, essentially in a sombre dark fruit, licorice, bitter
chocolate and oak spectrum. Cork. 14.5% alc. **Rating** 96 **To** 2028 $95

✪ **Jack's Barossa Valley Shiraz 2010** Deep purple-crimson; while it has a proud
   record, it is also a reflection of the '10 vintage; open-fermented, basket-pressed and
   matured for 18 months in American and French hogsheads; it is full of black fruits,
   licorice and spice that build on the back-palate and finish, rather than fall away.
   Exceptional value. Screwcap. 14.5% alc. **Rating** 94 **To** 2025 $20
   Old Vine Moppa Barossa Valley Grenache 2008 Made from old, low-
   yielding estate vines, open-fermented and matured for 18 months in French
   oak hogsheads; packaged in the killer bottle and high-quality cork. The colour
   is still very deep for Barossa grenache, the flavours running through confit plum,
   prune, blackberry, spice and a touch of chocolate. Cork. 14.5% alc. **Rating** 94
   To 2018 $45

🍷🍷🍷🍷🍷 **Greenock Barossa Valley Shiraz 2009 Rating** 93 **To** 2024 $40

🍷🍷🍷🍷 **Jack's Barossa Valley Riesling 2009 Rating** 87 **To** 2014 $15

Laurance of Margaret River   ★★★★★
3518 Caves Road, Wilyabrup, WA 6280 **Region** Margaret River
T (08) 9755 6199 **www**.laurancewines.com **Open** 7 days 10–5
Winemaker Naturaliste Vintners (Bruce Dukes) **Est.** 2001 **Dozens** 8000 **Vyds** 23ha
Founder and chairwoman Dianne Laurance is the driving force behind this family-owned
and run business, with sons Brendon (Executive Director) and Danny (Special Events
Manager) representing the next generation. The 100ha property has vines (planted in 1996
to three clones of chardonnay, plus sauvignon blanc, shiraz, cabernet sauvignon, semillon and
merlot), beautiful gardens, artwork and sculptures. The quality of the wines can be lost behind
the oddly shaped bottles, reminiscent of Perrier-Jouët's Belle Epoque deluxe Champagne.
Exports to Singapore, Hong Kong, Malaysia, Thailand and China.

🍷🍷🍷🍷🍷 **Merlot 2007** Good crimson-purple given its age. This is an unambiguously high-
   quality merlot, its expressive bouquet strongly varietal with its mix of cassis, plum
   and a hint of forest, the medium-bodied palate with positive savoury nuances
   that swirl around the fruit, tannins and oak both adding to the appeal. Screwcap.
   13.5% alc. **Rating** 95 **To** 2015 $26

Laurel Bank   ★★★★☆
130 Black Snake Lane, Granton, Tas 7030 **Region** Southern Tasmania
T (03) 6263 5977 **www**.laurelbankwines.com.au **Open** By appt
Winemaker Winemaking Tasmania (Julian Alcorso) **Est.** 1987 **Dozens** 1100 **Vyds** 3.5ha
Laurel (hence Laurel Bank) and Kerry Carland began planting their vineyard in 1986 to
sauvignon blanc, riesling, pinot noir, cabernet sauvignon and merlot. They delayed the first
release of their wines for some years and (by virtue of the number of entries they were able
to make) won the trophy for Most Successful Exhibitor at the Hobart Wine Show '95. Things
have settled down since; wine quality is very reliable.

🍷🍷🍷🍷🍷 **Riesling 2011** Bright quartz-green; opens with a potent bouquet; powerful lime/
   herb/wild flower aromas that flow directly onto the long, lingering palate; great
   length. Gold Tas Wine Show '12. Screwcap. 11.9% alc. **Rating** 95 **To** 2021 $22

🍷🍷🍷🍷🍷 **Pinot Noir 2010 Rating** 90 **To** 2016 $33

🍷🍷🍷🍷 **Sauvignon Blanc 2011 Rating** 89 **To** 2014 $22

Lavina Wines   ★★★☆
263 Main Road, McLaren Vale, SA 5171 **Region** McLaren Vale
T (08) 8323 9646 **www**.lavinawines.com.au **Open** Mon–Fri 9–5,
Winemaker Tim Whitrow **Est.** 2004 **Dozens** 50 000
Lavina Wines is owned by Sam and Victoria Daw, who continue to rapidly build and expand
the Lavina brand along with its sub-brands and private label to both domestic and overseas
markets. Tim Whitrow is responsible for producing the new Grand Royale and existing Select
Series wines. Exports to Europe and Asia.

ŢŢŢŢႺ **Meritus McLaren Vale Shiraz 2008** Good colour; right in the mainstream of McLaren Vale style, with a strong, chocolate overlay to the ripe plum and blackberry fruit; tannins and oak well integrated. Blue-gold Sydney International Wine Competition '11. Screwcap. 14.5% alc. **Rating** 90 **To** 2016 $28

ŢŢŢŢ **Gold Series Barossa Valley Shiraz 2008 Rating** 89 **To** 2015 $25
Meritus McLaren Vale Shiraz Grenache 2008 Rating 87 **To** 2014 $28

Lazy Ballerina   ★★★☆

Lot 11 Brookman Road, Dingabledinga (Kuitpo), SA 5172 **Region** McLaren Vale
T (08) 8556 7085 **www**.lazyballerina.com **Open** Fri–Sun & public hols 11–5
Winemaker James Hook **Est.** 2004 **Dozens** 800
James Hook, a leading viticulturist, and father Paul have set up a small – perhaps very small is a better description – winery in a converted McLaren Vale garage. The equipment extends to shovels, buckets, open fermenters and a small basket press, and enough French and American oak barrels to allow 20 months' maturation. The grapes come from micro-selections from a number of vineyards in McLaren Vale, chosen with great skill. Exports to the UK, the US and Canada.

ŢŢŢŢႺ **McLaren Vale Shiraz Viognier 2009** Showing viognier on the front label means at least 5% must have been included; whether that is the 'few bunches' detailed on the back label I don't know; regardless, the similarities between the two light-bodied Shirazs far outweigh their differences. Screwcap. 14.5% alc. **Rating** 90 **To** 2019 $25

ŢŢŢŢ **McLaren Vale Shiraz 2009 Rating** 89 **To** 2019 $25

Leabrook Estate   ★★★★

Cnr Greenhill Road/Reserve Road, Balhannah, SA 5242 **Region** Adelaide Hills
T 0400 600 448 **www**.leabrookestate.com **Open** W'ends & public hols 11–5
Winemaker Michael Fogarty **Est.** 1998 **Dozens** 3000 **Vyds** 5ha
With a background as an engineer and having dabbled in home winemaking for 30 years, Colin (and Chris) Best took the plunge and moved into commercial winemaking in 1998. His wines are found in a who's who of restaurants, and in some of the best independent wine retailers on the east coast. Colin says, 'I consider that my success is primarily due to the quality of my grapes (2.25ha of pinot noir, 0.5ha of chardonnay), since they have been planted on a 1.2m × 1.2m spacing and very low yields.' The business continued to grow, with contract-grown grapes coming from here, there and everywhere. In 2008 the Bests took over the former Spur Creek winery, with a consequent move of cellar door. Michael Fogarty (together with partner Dr Diana Hodge and her brother David), with a track record as chief winemaker at Tamar Ridge ('01–'05), then Nepenthe ('06–'08) purchased Leabrook Estate from Colin and Chris Best in early 2011. Exports to the UK.

ŢŢŢŢႺ **Adelaide Hills Chardonnay 2010** Mid gold; nectarine and grapefruit with some spicy oak notes; the toasty oak is a prominent feature of the palate, but the zesty acidity provides freshness and vitality. Screwcap. 13.5% alc. **Rating** 90 **To** 2014 $30 BE

ŢŢŢŢ **Adelaide Hills Pinot Gris Savagnin 2010 Rating** 88 **To** 2014 $19 BE
Adelaide Hills Sauvignon Blanc 2011 Rating 87 **To** Now $22 BE

Leamon Estate   ★★★★☆

PO Box 487, Bendigo, Vic 3550 **Region** Bendigo
T 0419 896 622 **www**.chateauleamon.com.au **Open** Not
Winemaker Ian Leamon **Est.** 1973 **Dozens** 2000 **Vyds** 8ha
One of the longest-established wineries in the region, Ian Leamon is the second generation of the family to be involved, taking responsibility for winemaking in the 1980s. 'Chateau' has been dropped from the winery name because of export complications. The property was

sold in early 2012, but Ian Leamon will continue to make wine, buying shiraz and cabernet sauvignon from regional vineyards. Mail order is still available, but there will no longer be a cellar door. Exports to Singapore and China.

ŶŶŶŶŶ Isabella 2006 Made using traditional method from chardonnay and pinot noir grown in two Macedon vineyards, and spending five years on lees prior to its release. Bright straw-gold, it has developed yeasty, brioche complexity underneath the still-bright fruit flavours. A very commendable effort. Diam. 12% alc. Rating 94 To 2015 $38

ŶŶŶŶŶ Reserve Bendigo Shiraz 2010 Rating 93 To 2025 $45
Bendigo Shiraz 2009 Rating 92 To 2019 $25

ŶŶŶŶ Bendigo Cabernet Sauvignon Cabernet Franc Merlot 2009 Rating 88 To 2020 $25

Leaning Church Vineyard   ★★★★
76 Brooks Road, Lalla, Tas 7267 **Region** Northern Tasmania
T (03) 6395 4447 **www**.leaningchurch.com.au **Open** Thurs–Mon 10–5
Winemaker Guy Wagner **Est.** 1988 **Dozens** 3000 **Vyds** 6.8ha
In 2011 Mark and Sarah Hirst purchased the then 20-year-old Lalla Gully Vineyard from long-term owner Taltarni. Sarah has a background in journalism, media, event management and wine marketing; Mark has years of experience in agriculture, accounting and business management. It's difficult not to describe that as a match made in heaven. They appointed Guy Wagner as winemaker, and their '10 Sauvignon Blanc won the trophy for Best Other White Wine at the Tasmanian Wine Show '11, their first foray into the world of wine shows. Guy was prescient when he declared it one of the best Sauvignon Blancs he's ever made a week or two before the show was held.

ŶŶŶŶŶ Sauvignon Blanc 2011 Pale quartz-green; has a complex tropical-accented bouquet with a dash of spice, and a firm mineral background to the fruit of the palate; good length. Screwcap. 12.5% alc. Rating 93 To 2013 $28
Chardonnay 2010 Pale straw-green; starting to show its wares, especially on the palate, which has great focus and power, driven by grapefruit and crisp acidity; whether the Dolly Parton reference on the back label ('big melons') is justified is a matter of opinion. Screwcap. 12.7% alc. Rating 91 To 2017 $26

ŶŶŶŶ Vintage Sparkling 2009 Rating 89 To Now $33

Leasingham   ★★★★★
PO Box 57, Clare, SA 5453 **Region** Clare Valley
T 1800 088 711 **www**.leasingham-wines.com.au **Open** Not
Winemaker Charlie Seppelt **Est.** 1893 **Dozens** NFP
Leasingham has experienced death by a thousand cuts. First, its then owner CWA sold its Rogers Vineyard to Tim Adams in 2009, and unsuccessfully endeavoured to separately sell the winemaking equipment and cellar door, while retaining the winery. In January 2011 Tim Adams was able to buy the winery, cellar door and winemaking equipment, making the once-proud Leasingham a virtual winery. Exports to all major markets.

ŶŶŶŶŶ Classic Clare Riesling 2007 Vivid green-straw; five years has wrought its magic, the wine now filled with sweet lime juice and honey; has reached the early part of the plateau that it will hold for another 10 years, and worth every cent. Screwcap. 12.5% alc. Rating 96 To 2022 $40
Classic Clare Shiraz 2008 Good colour; in the time-honoured Classic Clare style, but with a particularly good structure and texture to what is a medium-bodied wine showing a mix of juicy red and black fruits and positive tannins. Screwcap. 14% alc. Rating 95 To 2033 $57

ŶŶŶŶŶ Bin 7 Clare Valley Riesling 2011 Rating 92 To 2021 $23
Bin 61 Clare Valley Shiraz 2009 Rating 90 To 2024 $23

Leconfield ★★★★★

Riddoch Highway, Coonawarra, SA 5263 **Region** Coonawarra
T (08) 8737 2326 **www**.leconfieldwines.com **Open** Mon–Fri 11–4.30, w'ends & public hols 11–4
Winemaker Paul Gordon, Tim Bailey **Est.** 1974 **Dozens** 26 000 **Vyds** 43.7ha
Sydney Hamilton purchased the unplanted property that was to become Leconfield in 1974, having worked in the family wine business for over 30 years until his retirement in the mid '50s. When he acquired the property and set about planting it, he was 76, and reluctantly bowed to family pressure to sell Leconfield to nephew Richard in '81. Richard has progressively increased the vineyards to their present level, over 75% to cabernet sauvignon, for long the winery's specialty. Exports to the UK, Canada, Denmark, Switzerland, Belgium, Japan, Malaysia, Hong Kong, Singapore, the Philippines, Vietnam, China and NZ.

🍷🍷🍷🍷🍷 ✪ **McLaren Vale Shiraz 2010** Full, bright crimson-purple; a high-quality shiraz, with great texture, structure and length, 20 months in French oak bringing its many qualities into high relief; intense peppery black fruits, fine tannins and a savoury finish. Screwcap. 14% alc. **Rating** 95 **To** 2030 $25

Coonawarra Petit Verdot 2010 Medium red-purple; petit verdot produces a far more elegant wine in cool climates than in warm to hot regions, which is handsomely demonstrated here; the red and black berry fruits are folded in a silky palate along with fine tannins and quality French oak. The first petit verdot bottled by Leconfield since 2002. Screwcap. 14% alc. **Rating** 95 **To** 2025 $25

Old Vines Coonawarra Riesling 2011 When the vines were planted in 1974, Coonawarra had vast plantings of riesling, but they are now down to a small level; the wine has the typical flowery Coonawarra aromas, and a delicate mix of lime and apple on the palate. It is a style I much enjoy. Screwcap. 12% alc. **Rating** 94 **To** 2020 $25

Coonawarra Merlot 2010 Bright red-crimson; an elegant, medium-bodied wine with an impressive pedigree added to by a deserved gold medal at Brisbane Wine Show '11; it has fresh redcurrant and mulberry fruit running throughout the bouquet and palate, supported by very fine, persistent tannins; a merlot that doesn't rely on plum. Screwcap. 14% alc. **Rating** 94 **To** 2020 $25

🍷🍷🍷🍷½ **Coonawarra Noble Riesling 2011** **Rating** 91 **To** 2015 $20

🍷🍷🍷🍷 **Coonawarra Chardonnay 2010** **Rating** 89 **To** 2014 $25

Leeuwin Estate ★★★★★

Stevens Road, Margaret River, WA 6285 **Region** Margaret River
T (08) 9759 0000 **www**.leeuwinestate.com.au **Open** 7 days 10–5
Winemaker Paul Atwood **Est.** 1974 **Dozens** 60 000 **Vyds** 121ha
This outstanding winery and vineyard is owned by the Horgan family, with parents Denis and Tricia at the helm, son Justin as general manager. The Art Series Chardonnay is, in my opinion, Australia's finest example, based on the wines of the last 29 vintages. The decision to move to screwcap brought a large smile to the faces of those who understand just how superbly the wine ages, unless sabotaged by sporadic oxidation (caused by cork). The large estate plantings, coupled with strategic purchases of grapes from other growers, provide the base for high-quality Art Series Cabernet Sauvignon and Shiraz; a hugely successful, quick-selling Art Series Riesling and Sauvignon Blanc; and lesser-priced wines such as Prelude Chardonnay and Siblings Sauvignon Blanc Semillon. Exports to all major markets.

🍷🍷🍷🍷🍷 **Art Series Margaret River Chardonnay 2009** Pale gold, vivid green hue; a deeply fruited and hedonistically adorned bouquet of grapefruit, nectarine, spices and pain grillee; the palate is deeply weighted and powerful on entry, with finesse taking over and purity of fruit remaining on the finish; a pure, long and precise edition of an Australian classic. Screwcap. 14.5% alc. **Rating** 97 **To** 2025 $85 BE

Art Series Margaret River Cabernet Sauvignon 2008 Vivid deep crimson; restrained and understated, the bouquet offers a tantalising glimpse of red and black fruits, cigar box and a little briary complexity; the palate is finely detailed, and while elegant, contains its inherent power and longevity with ease. Screwcap. 13% alc. **Rating** 95 **To** 2030 $60 BE

Prelude Vineyards Margaret River Chardonnay 2010 Light straw-green; the bouquet is fresh, but does not prepare the way for the palate, which has tremendous drive to its grapefruit-accented fruit; while 100% barrel-fermented and matured, it is driven by its fruit, not oak. Screwcap. 14% alc. **Rating** 94 **To** 2020 $33

ΨΨΨΨΨ **Prelude Vineyards Margaret River Cabernet Merlot 2008 Rating** 93 **To** 2018 $29 BE

Art Series Margaret River Riesling 2011 Rating 90 **To** 2017 $22 BE

Siblings Margaret River Sauvignon Blanc Semillon 2011 Rating 90 **To** 2013 $23 BE

ΨΨΨΨ **Art Series Margaret River Sauvignon Blanc 2011 Rating** 88 **To** 2013 $29 BE

Lengs & Cooter ★★★★☆

24 Lindsay Terrace, Belair, SA 5042 **Region** Adelaide Zone
T (08) 8278 3998 **www**.lengscooter.com.au **Open** Not
Winemaker Colin Cooter and Contract **Est.** 1993 **Dozens** 3000
Karel Lengs and Colin Cooter began making wine as a hobby in the early 1980s. Each had (and has) a full-time occupation outside the wine industry, so it was all strictly for fun. One thing led to another, and although they still possess neither vineyards nor what might truly be described as a winery, the wines have graduated to big-boy status, winning gold medals at national wine shows and receiving critical acclaim from writers across Australia. The wines come from McLaren Vale and the Clare Valley. Exports to the UK, Singapore and Japan.

ΨΨΨΨΨ **Watervale Riesling 2011** Light straw-green; the attractive bouquet and palate
✪ both feed off the lime, lemon and apple of the fruit; the acidity is well balanced, and freshens and lengthens the finish. Screwcap. 12% alc. **Rating** 92 **To** 2018 $19

Swinton McLaren Vale Cabernet Sauvignon 2009 Full crimson-purple; hand-picked, open-fermented, hand-plunged, basket-pressed, and spent almost three years in new French hogsheads. If a wine is to spend three years in barrel, it is far better that it be French than American, particularly if it's Cabernet. As at March '12, needed to shake off the oak manacles, and it is far too early to say whether it will or it won't; given its handling in the winery, I'm giving it the benefit of the doubt. Screwcap. 14.5% alc. **Rating** 90 **To** 2024 $25

ΨΨΨΨ **Reserve McLaren Vale Shiraz 2008 Rating** 87 **To** 2018 $45

Lenton Brae Wines ★★★★★

3887 Caves Road, Margaret River, WA 6285 **Region** Margaret River
T (08) 9755 6255 **www**.lentonbrae.com **Open** 7 days 10–6
Winemaker Edward Tomlinson **Est.** 1983 **Dozens** NFP **Vyds** 9ha
Former architect and town planner Bruce Tomlinson built a strikingly beautiful winery (now heritage listed by the Shire of Busselton), which is now in the hands of winemaker son Edward, who consistently makes elegant wines in classic Margaret River style. Exports to Vietnam, Hong Kong and China.

ΨΨΨΨΨ **Wilyabrup Chardonnay 2010** Vibrant green hue; a complex and enticing bouquet, displaying pure grapefruit, toast, charcuterie, spice and minerals; the palate is truly exciting, engaging and energetic, with rapier-like acidity, concentrated fruit and layers of flavour cascading down and across the palate; long, pristine and beautifully formed. Screwcap. 13% alc. **Rating** 96 **To** 2020 $55 BE

Wilyabrup Semillon Sauvignon Blanc 2011 The perfume on this wine can be described as nothing short of astonishing, with lavender, bath talc, citrus blossom and cut grass; the palate is racy on entry, with zesty acidity commencing the journey and then the almond expression of barrel work drawing out the generous finish; exotic and thoroughly engaging, this has complexity and freshness in spades. Screwcap. 13% alc. **Rating** 95 **To** 2015 $50 BE

✪ **Southside Margaret River Chardonnay 2011** Made from 26-year-old estate-grown vines, barrel-fermented and matured in French oak; the palate is exceptionally intense and incisive, the fruit having easily absorbed the oak and showing its potent grapefruit base, nectarine and white peach each playing second fiddle; the high natural acidity will see this wine through to the next decade without batting an eyelid. Exceptional value. Screwcap. 13.5% alc. **Rating** 95 **To** 2025 $25

Wilyabrup Cabernet Sauvignon 2010 Bright crimson; a 92/6/2% blend of cabernet sauvignon, merlot and petit verdot matured in French oak for 18 months; yet another example pointing to Wilyabrup as the epicentre of cabernet in the region; picked at precisely the right moment, it is lithe and long, the blackcurrant, cedar and briar flavours adding up to that autocratic character always especially prominent when the alcohol is controlled. Screwcap. 14% alc. **Rating** 95 **To** 2025 $60

Margaret River Semillon Sauvignon Blanc 2011 **Rating** 94 **To** 2014 $25
Margaret River Shiraz 2010 **Rating** 94 **To** 2020 $35

♟♟♟♟♟ **Margaret River Cabernet Merlot 2010** **Rating** 93 **To** 2020 $25 BE

Leo Buring   ★★★★★

Sturt Highway, Nuriootpa, SA 5355 **Region** Eden Valley/Clare Valley
T 1300 651 650 **www**.leoburing.com.au **Open** Not
Winemaker Peter Munro **Est.** 1931 **Dozens** NFP
Australia's foremost producer of rieslings over a 35-year period, with a rich legacy left by former winemaker John Vickery. After veering away from its core business with other varietal wines, it has now been refocused as a specialist Riesling producer. The top of the range are the Leopold Derwent Valley Riesling and the Leonay Eden Valley Riesling, under a changing DW bin no. (DWN for 2010, DWO for '11 etc), supported by Clare Valley Riesling and Eden Valley Riesling at significantly lower prices, and expanding its wings to Tasmania and WA.

♟♟♟♟♟ **Leopold Derwent Valley Riesling 2011** DWO 21. Leo Buring went to Tasmania for riesling some years ago, and hasn't looked back; very different from the Clare Valley, the natural acidity being considerable higher, and the fruit aromas and fragrance more intense. Has wonderful drive and length to the palate, the alcohol adding to the likelihood of there being some residual sugar, but it is simply not obvious. Screwcap. 11.5% alc. **Rating** 96 **To** 2020 $40

Leonay Riesling 2011 DWO 18. Bright straw-green; The aroma and palate are not the least dilute nor green; a delicious mix of lemon and lime fruit, with floral echoes from the bouquet; has all the length and persistence one could wish for. Screwcap. 11.5% alc. **Rating** 94 **To** 2021 $40

♟♟♟♟♟ **Medium Dry Eden Valley Riesling 2011** **Rating** 93 **To** 2026 $20
Medium Sweet Eden Valley Riesling 2011 **Rating** 92 **To** 2021 $20

✪ **Dry Clare Valley Riesling 2011** One of an increasing number of producers using the International Riesling Foundation scale to denote the degree of sweetness in Riesling, here at the dry end of the scale. The floral, citrus blossom aromas lead into a palate with excellent length and balance, the flavours such that there is no suggestion of any hard acidity. Delicious now, but with the usual Riesling future. Screwcap. 12% alc. **Rating** 92 **To** 2017 $20

Leogate Estate Wines   ★★★★★

1693 Broke Road, Pokolbin, NSW 2320 **Region** Hunter Valley
T (02) 4998 7499 **www**.leogate.com.au **Open** 7 days 10–5
Winemaker Mark Woods **Est.** 2009 **Dozens** 7000 **Vyds** 55.5ha

Since purchasing the substantial Brokenback Vineyard in 2009 (a key part of the original Rothbury Estate, with vines over 40 years old), Bill and Vicki Widin have wasted no time. Initially the Widins leased the Tempus Two winery, but by the 2013 vintage will have moved into a newly built winery on the Brokenback Vineyard property. Mark Woods will continue to make the wines.

🍷🍷🍷🍷🍷 **Reserve Hunter Valley Shiraz 2010** An impressive medium- to full-bodied wine, with the fruit intensity and richness many regions struggle to provide at this alcohol level; the black cherry and plum fruit is supported by silky tannins and quality oak on a medium-bodied palate that has great mouthfeel and length, and a future as long as you wish. Screwcap. 13.5% alc. **Rating** 95 **To** 2030 $35

✪ **Creek Bed Reserve Hunter Valley Semillon 2011** Pale quartz; a tight and compact Semillon on the bouquet and palate alike, welding lemon, apple and mineral acidity; has excellent length and balance, making it a top cellaring style, with honey and toast to come in 5+ years. Screwcap. 11% alc. **Rating** 94 **To** 2021 $19

H10 Block Reserve Hunter Valley Chardonnay 2010 Hand-picked, part wild yeast-fermented in new French oak, the other part fermented with cultured yeast in stainless steel. The result is a strikingly fresh palate with white and yellow peach, nectarine and citrussy acidity to close. Clever winemaking. Screwcap. 13% alc. **Rating** 94 **To** 2016 $28

🍷🍷🍷🍷🍷 **Brokenback Hunter Valley Shiraz 2010 Rating** 93 **To** 2020 $23

✪ **Hunter Valley Adelaide Hills Semillon Sauvignon Blanc 2011** Pale straw-quartz; a strange year to go to the Adelaide Hills for sauvignon blanc, but the decision worked well, semillon providing the base for a seamless wine, with an array of citrus flavour and length to the finish. Screwcap. 12% alc. **Rating** 91 **To** 2015 $18

✪ **Brokenback Hunter Valley Rose 2011** Bright puce-pink; exceptional colour for estate-grown shiraz picked ripe; has abundant red cherry and raspberry fruit flavours running through the palate and onto the aftertaste. Screwcap. 13% alc. **Rating** 91 **To** Now $18

🍷🍷🍷🍷 **Brokenback Hunter Valley Chardonnay 2010 Rating** 89 **To** 2013 $20

Brokenback Hunter Valley Verdelho 2011 Rating 89 **To** Now $18

Lerida Estate ★★★★★

The Vineyards, Old Federal Highway, Lake George, NSW 2581 **Region** Canberra District
T (02) 6295 6640 **F** (02) 6295 6676 **Open** 7 days 10-5
Winemaker Malcolm Burdett **Est.** 1999 **Dozens** 5000 **Vyds** 7.93 ha

Lerida Estate, owned by Jim Lumbers and Anne Caine, owes a great deal to the inspiration of Dr Edgar Riek, planted as it is immediately to the south of his former Lake George vineyard, and also planted mainly to pinot noir (there are also smaller plantings of pinot gris, chardonnay, shiraz, merlot, cabernet franc and viognier). The Glenn Murcutt–designed winery, barrel room, cellar door and café complex has spectacular views over Lake George which, after being empty for 10 years, is now filling with the recent rains. The Shiraz Viognier and Pinot Noir enjoy continuing wine show success. The '09s will continue to be available until 2013. Exports to China.

🍷🍷🍷🍷🍷 **Lake George Shiraz Viognier 2009** Bright colour; polished and poised black fruit, layered with spice, graphite and roasted game; medium-bodied and fleshy on entry, the latent power of the wine provides a long, savoury and thoroughly beguiling mixture of spicy shiraz to conclude. Screwcap. 14.9% alc. **Rating** 94 **To** 2020 $50 BE

Lake George Canberra District Botrytis Pinot Gris 2011 Yellow-gold; very rich and luscious, its citrus, mango and apricot flavours balanced by the type of acidity that only comes from botrytised wines. Pinot gris made thus is a rare beast. Screwcap. 11.8% alc. **Rating** 94 **To** 2016 $30

ΨΨΨΨ♀ Lake George Chardonnay 2010 Rating 92 To 2016 $32 BE
Canberra District Pinot Grigio 2011 Rating 91 To 2014 $25 BE

ΨΨΨΨ Lake George Canberra District Pinot Rose 2011 Rating 88 To Now $18

Lethbridge Wines   ★★★★★
74 Burrows Road, Lethbridge, Vic 3222 **Region** Geelong
T (03) 5281 7279 **www**.lethbridgewines.com **Open** Thurs–Sun & public hols 10.30–5,
or by appt
Winemaker Ray Nadeson, Maree Collis, Alexander Byrne **Est.** 1996 **Dozens** 3000
Vyds 7ha
Lethbridge was founded by scientists Ray Nadeson, Maree Collis and Adrian Thomas. In
Ray's words, 'Our belief is that the best wines express the unique character of special places.'
As well as understanding the importance of terroir, the partners have built a unique straw-bale
winery, designed for its ability to recreate the controlled environment of cellars and caves in
Europe. Winemaking is no less ecological: hand-picking, indigenous yeast fermentations, small
open fermenters, pigeage (foot-stamping) and minimal handling of the wines throughout the
maturation process are all part and parcel of the highly successful Lethbridge approach. Ray
also has a special touch with chardonnay, and has a successful contract winemaking limb to
the business. Exports to the UK.

ΨΨΨΨΨ Allegra Geelong Chardonnay 2009 A completely seductive and savoury
bouquet of charcuterie, grilled cashews, grapefruit and well-handled spicy oak;
the palate is a revelation of complexity and freshness, able to capture the ability of
this wonderful grape to produce simply scintillating wines. Screwcap. 13.5% alc.
Rating 96 To 2018 $65 BE
Geelong Pinot Gris 2011 This is pinot gris with personality, with an almost
explosive bouquet, finely tuned palate and a long and engaging finish; exotic on
the one hand and trim, taut and long on the other; the skills of Ray Nadeson
shine through in this wine. Screwcap. 12.5% alc. Rating 94 To 2014 $30 BE
Geelong Pinot Noir 2010 Deep colour; with charry oak and ripe dark
fruits on the bouquet; the palate is firm, densely fruited and needing time to
fully integrate, but the intense fruit and serious structure are undeniable; time is
essential for optimum pleasure. Screwcap. 13% alc. Rating 94 To 2018 $38 BE
Geelong Shiraz 2010 A spicy, gamey and complex example of shiraz, with
roasted meats, thyme and a combination of red and black fruits on display;
medium bodied, with ample silky tannins and zesty acidity drawing out the long
and savoury finish. Screwcap. 14% alc. Rating 94 To 2018 $38 BE

ΨΨΨΨ♀ Ooh la la Geelong Chardonnay 2010 Rating 93 To 2018 $25
Menage a Noir Geelong Pinot Noir 2010 Rating 93 To 2015 $25
Heathcote Shiraz 2010 Rating 93 To 2025 $38
Indra Geelong Shiraz 2009 Rating 92 To 2018 $65 BE
Geelong Chardonnay 2010 Rating 91 To 2016 $38 BE
Mietta Geelong Pinot Noir 2009 Rating 91 To 2018 $65 BE
Hugo George 2009 Rating 90 To 2015 $65 BE
Dr Nadeson Riesling 2011 Rating 90 To 2018 $30 BE

Leura Park Estate   ★★★★★
1400 Portarlington Road, Curlewis, Vic 3222 **Region** Geelong
T (03) 5253 3180 **www**.leuraparkestate.com.au **Open** W'ends & public hols 10.30–5,
7 days Jan, or by appt
Winemaker Ray Nadeson, Darren Burke **Est.** 1995 **Dozens** 8000 **Vyds** 15.94ha
Leura Park Estate's vineyard is planted to chardonnay (50%), pinot noir, pinot gris, sauvignon
blanc and shiraz. Owners David and Lyndsay Sharp are committed to maintaining minimal
interference in the vineyard, and have expanded the estate-grown wine range (Sauvignon
Blanc, Pinot Gris, Chardonnay, Pinot Noir and Shiraz) to include Vintage Grande Cuvee
(Pinot Noir Chardonnay). The next step was the erection of an onsite winery prior to the
2010 vintage, leading to increased production. Exports to South Korea and Singapore.

ΨΨΨΨΨ **Limited Release Block 1 Reserve Chardonnay 2010** Mid gold; a complex mealy bouquet of grapefruit, grilled cashews and charcuterie; rich and nutty on the palate, long and savoury, with a lively backbone of acidity; one could close one's eyes and think of Meursault, if one was of that mind. Screwcap. 14% alc. **Rating** 94 **To** 2015 $45 BE
Bellarine Peninsula Pinot Noir 2010 Dark in colour, and displaying abundant dark cherry fruits and barrel ferment aromas; the palate is generous and rich, with spicy notes and some whole bunch nuances; finishes with good acidity. Gold medal National Wine Show '11, in very good company. Screwcap. 13% alc. **Rating** 94 **To** 2015 $40

ΨΨΨΨ **25 d'Gris Bellarine Peninsula Pinot Gris 2010 Rating** 89 **To** 2013 $30 BE
Bellarine Peninsula Shiraz 2010 Rating 88 **To** 2015 $40 BE
Bellarine Peninsula Sauvignon Blanc 2011 Rating 87 **To** 2013 $30 BE

Light's View/Pure Vision Organic Wines ★★★

PO Box 258, Virginia, SA 5120 **Region** Adelaide Plains
T 0412 800 875 **www**.lightsviewwines.com.au **Open** Not
Winemaker David Norman, Jim Irvine, Ken Carypidis **Est.** 2001 **Dozens** 10 000
Vyds 55ha
The Carypidis family runs two brands: Pure Vision (15ha of certified organically grown grapes), and Light's View (with a much larger planting of conventionally grown grapes). Growing grapes under a certified organic regime is much easier if the region is warm to hot and dry, conditions unsuitable for botrytis and downy mildew. You are still left with weed growth (no herbicides are allowed) and powdery mildew (sulphur sprays are permitted) but the overall task is much simpler. The Adelaide Plains, where Pure Vision's vineyard is situated, is such a region, and owner Ken Carypidis has been clever enough to secure the services of Jim Irvine as co-winemaker. Exports to the US, Canada, Taiwan and China.

ΨΨΨΨ **Nature's Step Wild Ferment Organic Chardonnay 2011** It is only in years such as '11 (very cool and wet) that the Adelaide Plains could be expected to produce a wine such as this, particularly given its wild fermentation. The flavours are not deep, but they are varietal. Screwcap. 13.5% alc. **Rating** 87 **To** 2013 $10
Pure Vision Organic Cabernet Sauvignon 2010 Good colour; the wine has impressive structure, but shows the often talked about, less frequently encountered, dip in the mid palate fruit flavour, also known as the doughnut character. Good character for those willing to pay a premium for organic product. Screwcap. 13.5% alc. **Rating** 87 **To** 2014 $15

Lightfoot & Sons ★★★★☆

Myrtle Point Vineyard, 717 Calulu Road, Bairnsdale, Vic 3875 (postal) **Region** Gippsland
T (03) 5156 9205 **www**.lightfootwines.com **Open** Not
Winemaker Alastair Butt, Tom Lightfoot **Est.** 1995 **Dozens** 4000 **Vyds** 29.3ha
Brian and Helen Lightfoot have established pinot noir, shiraz, chardonnay, cabernet sauvignon and merlot, the lion's share to pinot noir and shiraz. The soil bears a striking resemblance to that of Coonawarra, with terra rossa over limestone. The vines are irrigated courtesy of a licence allowing the Lightfoots to pump water from the Mitchell River, and most of the grapes are sold (as originally planned) to other Vic winemakers. With the arrival of Alastair Butt (formerly of Brokenwood and Seville Estate), supported by son Tom, production has increased, and may well rise further. Second son Rob has also come on board, bringing 10 years' experience in sales and marketing.

ΨΨΨΨΨ **Myrtle Point Single Vineyard Pinot Noir 2010** Excellent clear crimson-purple; a fragrant red berry bouquet leads into a pure palate, red cherry to the fore, with a long, silky finish; pure pinot noir. Unlucky not to win more than a silver medal at the Gippsland Wine Show '11. Screwcap. 13.4% alc. **Rating** 93 **To** 2016 $25

Myrtle Point Single Vineyard Cabernet Sauvignon 2010 Good colour; the fruit has ripened to precisely the right point, giving the wine an extra level of blackcurrant fruit on the fragrant bouquet and palate; touches of dried herb join the ripe tannins on the long finish. Screwcap. 14% alc. **Rating** 92 **To** 2025 $22

Chardonnay Pinot Noir 2007 Extended time on tirage has given the wine complexity, but without in any way flattening the quite delicate fruit flavours. The dosage has been sensibly restrained, giving the wine a fresh, bright finish. Cork. 12.5% alc. **Rating** 92 **To** 2013 $35

Myrtle Point Single Vineyard Shiraz 2010 Good hue, although not especially deep; a smooth and supple light- to medium-bodied shiraz, built around black cherry, plum and warm spices, the tannins fine and integrated. Gold medal Gippsland Wine Show '11 Screwcap. 14.5% alc. **Rating** 91 **To** 2018 $22

Sparkling Shiraz 2008 The volume of oak in the wine strongly suggests it spent some years in barrel before being tiraged, which is in turn consistent with its colour. Has quite good balance, and is not overly sweet. Cork. 13.5% alc. **Rating** 91 **To** 2014 $30

Myrtle Point Single Vineyard Chardonnay 2010 Bright straw-green; super-juicy white peach, grapefruit and nectarine flavours have subtle, integrated oak from the barrel fermentation and subsequent lees contact. Has a come-hither stance that is hard to resist. Screwcap. 13% alc. **Rating** 90 **To** 2017 $22

ΨΨΨΨ
✪
Calulu Road Gippsland Lakes Shiraz Cabernet 2010 I'm not entirely sure the price does justice to the wine, but no one should look a gift horse in the mouth; a pleasantly spicy, medium-bodied wine with an attractive array of red and black fruits, with enough tannins to provide structure. Screwcap. 14% alc. **Rating** 89 **To** 2016 $15

Calulu Road Gippsland Lakes Unwooded Chardonnay 2011 Rating 87 To 2013 $15

Lillian ★★★★★

Box 174, Pemberton, WA 6260 **Region** Pemberton
T (08) 9776 0193 **F** (08) 9776 0193 **Open** Not
Winemaker John Brocksopp **Est.** 1993 **Dozens** 420 **Vyds** 3.2ha
Long-serving (and continuing consultant) viticulturist to Leeuwin Estate, John Brocksopp established 2.8ha of the Rhône trio of marsanne, roussanne and viognier, and 0.4ha of shiraz. The varietal mix may seem a la mode, but it in fact comes from John's early experience working for Seppelt at Barooga in NSW, and his years in the Barossa Valley. Exports to the UK.

ΨΨΨΨΨ
Lefroy Brook Pemberton Chardonnay 2010 Light, bright straw-green; a beautifully weighted and harmonious wine with delicate white peach, grapefruit and nectarine captured in a web of subtle French oak; perfect length and balance. Six weeks' barrel fermentation (25% new French, plus older barrels), partial mlf, then 18 months on lees, stirring fortnightly, minimal fining/filtration; 75 dozen made. Screwcap. 13.5% alc. **Rating** 94 **To** 2018 $28

Pemberton Marsanne Roussanne 2010 A 63/37% blend; pale straw-green; a perfectly weighted light-bodied palate with gentle honeysuckle, apple and citrus flavours; a died-in-the-wool stayer for at least 10 years; during that time, honeyed/toasty characters will emerge to give the wine another dimension. Screwcap. 13.5% alc. **Rating** 94 **To** 2020 $20

Lillydale Estate ★★★★

68 Anzac Street, Chullora, NSW 2190 (postal) **Region** Yarra Valley
T (02) 9722 1299 **www**.mcwilliamswinesgroup.com **Open** Not
Winemaker Adrian Sparks **Est.** 1975 **Dozens** NFP **Vyds** 13.4ha
Lillydale Estate was acquired by McWilliam's in 1994. The major part of the production comes from the two estate vineyards, Morning Light and Sunnyside, planted in 1976. The names have been given by McWilliam's: the former is that of the ship that brought Samuel McWilliam from Ireland to Melbourne in 1857, and Sunnyside is the name of the first winery

and vineyard he established, at Corowa in NSW in 1877. The estate production is bolstered by contract-grown fruit from other growers in the Valley. Exports to Fiji and Singapore.

♀♀♀♀♀ **Yarra Valley Chardonnay 2009** Pale green-straw; compared with the other McWilliam's regional wines at this price, a little disappointing; it has been nicely groomed, but the fruit lacks the intensity needed at this price point. Screwcap. 13.5% alc. **Rating** 90 **To** 2015 $27

♀♀♀♀ **Yarra Valley Pinot Noir 2010** **Rating** 88 **To** 2015 $27 BE

Lillypilly Estate ★★★★☆

Lillypilly Road, Leeton, NSW 2705 **Region** Riverina
T (02) 6953 4069 www.lillypilly.com **Open** Mon–Sat 10–5.30, Sun by appt
Winemaker Robert Fiumara **Est.** 1982 **Dozens** 12 000 **Vyds** 27.9ha
Botrytised white wines are by far the best offering from Lillypilly, with the Noble Muscat of Alexandria unique to the winery; these wines have both style and intensity of flavour and can age well. However, table wine quality is always steady. Exports to the UK, the US, Canada, South Korea and China.

♀♀♀♀♀ **Family Reserve Noble Blend 2010** Vibrant mid gold; the very essence of pure botrytis and complex peaches and cream; essency, lithe, long and showing savoury complexity that will see the wine age beautifully; pristine and pure, long and fragrant. 375ml. Screwcap. 11.5% alc. **Rating** 95 **To** 2020 $85 BE

♀♀♀♀♀ **Family Reserve Noble Blend 2008** **Rating** 92 **To** 2016 $39 BE
Noble Blend 2011 **Rating** 91 **To** 2018 $24 BE

♀♀♀♀ **Shiraz 2009** **Rating** 88 **To** 2014 $18 BE

Limbic ★★★★★

295 Morrison Road, Pakenham Upper, Vic 3810 **Region** Port Phillip Zone
T (03) 5942 7723 www.limbicwines.com.au **Open** By appt
Winemaker Michael Pullar **Est.** 1997 **Dozens** 600 **Vyds** 6.1ha
Jennifer and Michael Pullar have established a vineyard on the hills between the Yarra Valley and Gippsland, overlooking the Mornington Peninsula and Westernport Bay (thus entitled only to the Port Phillip Zone GI). They have planted pinot noir, chardonnay, sauvignon blanc and nebbiolo, increasingly using organic and thereafter biodynamic practices. 'Limbic' is the word for a network of neural pathways in the brain that link smell, taste and emotion.

♀♀♀♀♀ **Sauvignon Blanc 2011** Light straw-green; the barrel-fermented wine that threaded the eye of the needle in the '11 growing season, emerging triumphant, with intense lime and tropical flavours held together by racy acidity. Screwcap. 13% alc. **Rating** 95 **To** 2014 $20
Chardonnay 2010 A very attractive wine, with admirable varietal fruit expression in a white peach to grapefruit spectrum; the oak has been well handled, supporting the fruit, but not interfering with its message; has classic neo-Yarra length, and will cellar well. Screwcap. 13.5% alc. **Rating** 94 **To** 2017 $30

♀♀♀♀♀ **Pinot Noir 2010** **Rating** 90 **To** 2017 $30

Lindemans (Coonawarra) ★★★★★

Coonawarra Wine Gallery, Riddoch Highway, Coonawarra, SA 5263 **Region** Coonawarra
T (08) 8737 3250 www.lindemans.com **Open** 7 days 10–5
Winemaker Brett Sharpe **Est.** 1908 **Dozens** NFP
Lindemans' Limestone Coast vineyards are of increasing significance because of the move towards regional identity in the all-important export markets, which has led to the emergence of a range of regional/varietal labels. After a quiet period, the wines are on the march again. Exports to the UK, the US, Canada and NZ.

ŸŸŸŸŸ **St George Vineyard Cabernet Sauvignon 2009** Strong purple-crimson; from the 35-year-old vines on the 12ha estate-owned St George Vineyard. Has the blackcurrant/cassis, mint and mulberry cabernet profile of Coonawarra, augmented by 17 months in new and used French oak, that makes its mark on the wine; it is the texture of the tannins (and the fruit) that carries the wine through to an altogether superior finish. Screwcap. 14% alc. **Rating** 95 **To** 2030 $65
Limestone Ridge Vineyard Shiraz Cabernet 2009 Medium to full red-purple; a particularly supple and smooth Limestone Ridge with blackberry, mulberry and blackcurrant in a smooth embrace, hints of Coonawarra earth and mint validating the union, oak handling particularly good. Screwcap. 14.5% alc. **Rating** 94 **To** 2029 $65
Pyrus Cabernet Sauvignon Malbec Merlot 2009 A wine that came into existence when an experimental blend won the Jimmy Watson Trophy in the days when the wine did not have to be bottled; it is curious that these blends are not common in Coonawarra, for the result is a harmonious medium-bodied wine, fruit to the fore, with a long, balanced palate, the oak integrated. Screwcap. 14.5% alc. **Rating** 94 **To** 2024 $65

ŸŸŸŸ **Reserve Pinot Noir Chardonnay Pinot Meunier 2006** Rating 88 **To** Now $14

Lindemans (Hunter Valley)   ★★★★☆

McDonalds Road, Pokolbin, NSW 2320 **Region** Hunter Valley
T (02) 4998 7684 **www**.lindemans.com.au **Open** 7 days 10–5
Winemaker Brett Sharpe **Est.** 1843 **Dozens** NFP
Just when I expected it least, Lindemans has produced some seriously good wines from the Hunter Valley, and one half of the Lindeman winemaking or marketing side (without talking to the other half) has exhumed some of the Bin number systems that were used in the glory days of the 1960s, admittedly without total consistency. Thus for white wines, 50 or 55 were the last two digits used for what was named Riesling, 70 for what was named White Burgundy, and 75 for what was called Chablis; with the shiraz-based wines, the last two digits were either 00, 03 or 10. The most famous were the 1965 Claret and Burgundy releases Bin 3100 and Bin 3110, the most famous Chablis 1967 Bin 3475. Enquiries about the present system were, it seems, not understood. Exports to the UK, the US and other major markets.

ŸŸŸŸŸ **Limited Release Reserve Semillon 2011** Bin 1150. Vivid green hue; restrained lemon zest, lanolin, straw and ginger are tightly focused on the bouquet; the palate is generous on entry, with ample levels of fruit, yet the wine tightens and becomes minerally, focused and full of energy and verve on the finish; long and pure. Screwcap. 12.5% alc. **Rating** 95 **To** 2030 $40 BE

ŸŸŸŸŸ **Limited Release Hunter Valley Semillon 2011** Rating 93 **To** 2025 $30 BE
Limited Release Hunter Valley Shiraz 2010 Rating 93 **To** 2025 $30 BE

ŸŸŸŸ **Limited Release Hunter Valley Chardonnay 2011** Rating 89
To 2017 $30 BE
Reserve Hunter Valley Verdelho 2008 Rating 87 **To** Now $14

Lindemans (Karadoc)   ★★★

44 Johns Way, Karadoc, Vic 3496 **Region** Murray Darling
T (03) 5051 3285 **www**.lindemans.com.au **Open** 7 days 10–4.30
Winemaker Wayne Falkenberg **Est.** 1974 **Dozens** NFP
Now the production centre for all the Lindemans and Leo Buring wines, with the exception of special lines made in Coonawarra. The very large winery allows all-important economies of scale, and is the major processing centre for TWE's beverage wine sector (casks, flagons and low-priced bottles). Exports to all major markets.

ᵠᵠᵠᵠ **Bin 65 Chardonnay 2011** Has more green tinges to the colour than most of
✪   its peers, and likewise has more texture, possibly from lees contact in tank and/
      or its touch of oak. Ready now, and well priced. Screwcap. 12.5% alc. **Rating** 88
      To 2013 $10

✪   **Bin 85 Pinot Grigio 2011** Despite its low alcohol, and belying its price, this has
      remarkable flavour, with a mix of nashi pear, citrus and a hint of stone fruit – its
      RRP simply a starting point for the discounters. Screwcap. 10.5% alc. **Rating** 88
      To Now $10

✪   **Bin 95 Sauvignon Blanc 2011** A bright, clean and fresh bouquet, showing
      glimpses of tropical fruit; clean, zesty and fresh; for immediate consumption.
      Screwcap. 9.5% alc. **Rating** 87 **To** 2013 $10 BE

Lindenderry at Red Hill   ★★★★

142 Arthurs Seat Road, Red Hill, Vic 3937 **Region** Mornington Peninsula
T (03) 5989 2933 **www**.lindenderry.com.au **Open** W'ends 11–5
Winemaker Lindsay McCall, Sandro Mosele, Barnaby Flanders **Est.** 1999 **Dozens** 2000
Vyds 3.35ha
Lindenderry at Red Hill is a sister operation to Lancemore Hill in the Macedon Ranges and
Lindenwarrah at Milawa. It has a five-star country house hotel, conference facilities, a function
area, day spa and restaurant on 16ha of gardens, but also has a little over 3ha of immaculately
maintained vineyards, planted equally to pinot noir and chardonnay more than 15 years ago.

ᵠᵠᵠᵠᵠ **Mornington Peninsula Chardonnay 2010** Pale gold, green hue; tightly wound
      and focused lemon and blanched almond, spicy bouquet; the palate is zesty and
      shows traces of minerals and fine fruits that expand gracefully from start to finish.
      Screwcap. 13% alc. **Rating** 93 **To** 2016 $32 BE

ᵠᵠᵠᵠ **Mornington Peninsula Pinot Noir 2010 Rating** 89 **To** 2014 $35 BE

Linfield Road Wines   ★★★★★

65 Victoria Terrace, Williamstown, SA 5351 **Region** Barossa Valley
T (08) 8524 7355 **www**.linfieldroadwines.com **Open** 7 days 10–5
Winemaker Daniel Wilson, Natasha Mooney **Est.** 2002 **Dozens** 2500 **Vyds** 19ha
Linfield Road produces small batches of single vineyard wines from the Wilson family
vineyard at Williamstown. The story began in 1860 when Edmund Major Wilson planted the
first vines on the outskirts of Williamstown. Since Edmund's first plantings, the Wilson family
has fostered a viticulture tradition that now spans five generations; three generations of the
family currently live and work on the property. The vineyard is located at the very southern
edge of the Barossa. It is situated high above the valley floor, leading to cooler nights and
longer ripening periods. This results in elegant red and white wines with good structure.
Exports to the US, Canada, Hong Kong, South Korea, Singapore, Japan and China.

ᵠᵠᵠᵠᵠ **The Stubborn Patriarch Single Vineyard Barossa Shiraz 2010** Bright
✪   crimson-purple; the perfumed bouquet has the full offering of red and black fruits,
      spice and oak, the medium-bodied palate having no need to go beyond those
      characters, but having seriously good texture, and a long, balanced finish. Screwcap.
      14.5% alc. **Rating** 96 **To** 2025 $25

      The Black Hammer Single Vineyard Barossa Cabernet Sauvignon 2010
      Crimson-purple; the quality of this cabernet is partly due to the cool site, partly to
      the outstanding vintage; it all adds up to an elegant wine fettered neither by excess
      tannins nor oak. Screwcap. 14.4% alc. **Rating** 94 **To** 2025 $22

ᵠᵠᵠᵠ **Dear Nellie Single Vineyard Barossa Semillon 2011** Light colour; made
✪   in the modern Barossa Valley style, unoaked and relatively early picked, the focus
      intensified by the '11 vintage, however many challenges must have arisen in the
      vineyard for the thin-skinned semillon. Outstanding value. Screwcap. 12% alc.
      Rating 89 **To** 2016 $15

The Monarch Single Vineyard Barossa Merlot 2010 Rating 89
To 2015 $22
The Steam Maker Single Vineyard Barossa Riesling 2011 Rating 87
To 2015 $18

Lirralirra Estate   ★★★★

15 Paynes Road, Chirnside Park, Vic 3116 **Region** Yarra Valley
T (03) 9735 0224 **www**.lirralirraestate.com.au **Open** W'ends & hols 10–6 or by appt
Winemaker Alan Smith, Sean Crinion, Mike Warren **Est.** 1981 **Dozens** 300 **Vyds** 2.3ha
Alan and Jos Smith, stalwarts of the Yarra Valley for 30 years, had decided that the 2010 vintage
would be their last. The decision came in the wake of '07 (frost, no vintage); '08 (drought and
heat, only pinot noir made but sold in bulk); and '09 (drought, heat and smoke). The cellar
door will remain open for several years until the wines are sold, and then it will be closed, but
the Smiths will continue to live on the property 'with or without vines for as long as possible'.
In fact, Alan's personal swan song was with the '11 Pinot Noir, which at the time of writing
had not been bottled, let alone released. It is ironic that the last two pinots should be so good.

♀♀♀♀♀ **Pinot Noir 2010** Clear crimson; an attractive light-bodied pinot, with red
cherry kernel nuances to the bouquet, red and black cherry, spice and a hint of
forest floor all gently jostling for front position on the palate. Screwcap. 12.3% alc.
Rating 92 **To** 2016 $23
Pinot Noir 2008 Has held its hue remarkably well, likewise the fresh varietal
fruit on its bouquet; the palate lives up to the promise of the bouquet, with plum
fruit to the fore, and an attractive touch of savoury forest on the finish. Screwcap.
12.5% alc. **Rating** 92 **To** 2014 $23

Lithostylis   ★★★

17 Church Street, Leongatha, Vic 3953 (postal) **Region** Gippsland
T (03) 5662 2885 **www**.lithostylis.com **Open** Not
Winemaker Dean Roberts **Est.** 2006 **Dozens** 300 **Vyds** 2.25ha
Dean and Dayna Roberts purchased a vineyard in 2006, which had been planted in 1997
with very close spacing of 1m × 1m. They say 'organic and biodynamic practices are preferred,
but not dogmatically pursued. Winemaking is limited to essential interventions.' Dean began
his career with a viticulture diploma from Swinburne University, Lilydale, in 2002, becoming
vineyard manager for Diamond Valley Vineyards, simultaneously undertaking further winemaking studies. He then completed a vintage at Ponzi Wines in Oregon, and on returning
to Australia had a short, but intense, period of employment with Bass Phillip. He now works
as a vineyard management contractor, and on the winemaking front receives assistance from
Dayna, who has a biomedical science degree from Monash University.

♀♀♀♀ **South Gippsland Chardonnay Viognier 2010** It would seem chardonnay
was the dominant partner, for the peach and melon fruit is more obvious than any
apricot contribution. An elegant, albeit a touch simple, wine for early drinking.
Diam. 13.5% alc. **Rating** 88 **To** 2014 $26
Ironstone South Gippsland Pinot Noir 2010 Light, clear red-purple; a
fragrant bouquet leads into a very light-bodied palate, with a mix of red berry
and mint flavours, fine tannins its main virtue. Screwcap. 13.5% alc. **Rating** 87
To 2013 $28

Little Brampton Wines   ★★★☆

PO Box 61, Clare, SA 5453 **Region** Clare Valley
T (08) 8843 4201 **www**.littlebramptonwines.com.au **Open** By appt
Winemaker Contract **Est.** 2001 **Dozens** 800 **Vyds** 10ha
Little Brampton Wines is a boutique, family-owned business operated by Alan and Pamela
Schwarz. They purchased their 24ha property in the heart of the Clare Valley in the early
1990s (Alan had graduated from Roseworthy in 1981). The property had produced grapes

since the 1860s, but the vineyard had been removed during the Vine Pull Scheme of the 1980s. The Schwarzes have replanted riesling (2ha), shiraz and cabernet sauvignon (4ha each) on northwest slopes at 520 m; a small proportion of the production is vinified for the Little Brampton label. Exports to the UK and Singapore.

ΨΨΨΨ   **No Regrets Clare Valley Rose 2011** Vibrant pale pink; Turkish delight, red fruits and floral accents on the bouquet; fleshy and generous on entry, yet finishing dry and lively. Screwcap. 12% alc. **Rating** 89 **To** 2013 $20 BE

Little Bridge
106 Brooks Road, Bywong, NSW 2621 **Region** Canberra District
T (02) 6236 9620 **www**.littlebridgewines.com.au **Open** W'ends & public hols 11–4
Winemaker Canberra Winemakers, Lark Hill, Mallaluka Winemakers **Est.** 1996
Dozens 1000 **Vyds** 5.5ha
Little Bridge is a partnership between long-term friends John Leyshon, Rowland Clark, John Jefferey and Steve Dowton. There are 2ha of chardonnay, pinot noir, riesling and merlot planted at Folly Run; 2ha of shiraz, cabernet sauvignon, sangiovese, cabernet franc and malbec at Mallaluka; and 1.5ha of riesling, chardonnay and mourvedre at Brooks Creek. Canberra Winemakers makes the white wines, Lark Hill the Pinot Noir, and Mallaluka the other reds. Steve purchased Brooks Creek Vineyard in 2009 (largely derelict, and being rehabilitated), and it is here that the Little Bridge cellar door is situated. Exports to Singapore and China.

ΨΨΨΨ   **Canberra District Pinot Noir 2010** There is a lot going on in this wine, starting with the strong colour, then the foresty bouquet, and finishing with the multilayered, black cherry and bramble fruit; just a little too extractive for comfort. Screwcap. 13.1% alc. **Rating** 89 **To** 2014 $25

 # Little Cathedral
PO Box 1188, Thornbury, Vic 3071 **Region** Upper Goulburn
T (03) 9480 1511 **www**.littlecathedral.com.au **Open** Not
Winemaker Kilchurn Wines (David Cowburn) **Est.** 1996 **Dozens** 300 **Vyds** 3.25ha
The 4ha Little Cathedral vineyard was planted in 1996 under the lee of the striking Cathedral Ranges at Taggerty. It has been established on a gentle north-facing slope at an altitude of 280m, and should irrigation be required, it comes from the gin-clear Little River, a mountain stream that originates deep within the forest that the vineyard backs onto. Since Madge Alexandra and Anna Pickworth acquired the property in 2006, it has been a sharp learning curve. Drought and frost destroyed the '07 vintage, and when the surrounding forest was burnt in February '09, smoke taint destroyed the crop. 2008 and '10 have been the standouts, '11 confronted by the abnormally cool and wet growing season. Nonetheless, it is a truly beautiful vineyard and is capable of producing pinot noir of high quality.

ΨΨΨΨΨ   **Upper Goulburn Pinot Noir 2010** Bright, clear crimson-purple; a very lively and fresh pinot, with cherry and sour cherry fruit on the bouquet and palate. If only it had been picked a little later with a touch more flesh. Still, it's a very good wine. Hand-picked from a 3.25ha vineyard planted only to MV6 clone. 300 dozen made. Screwcap. 12.5% alc. **Rating** 92 **To** 2016 $25

Little River Estate   ★★★
c/- 147 Rankins Road, Kensington, Vic 3031 (postal) **Region** Upper Goulburn
T 0418 381 722 **Open** Not
Winemaker Philip Challen, Oscar Rosa, Nick Arena **Est.** 1986 **Dozens** 250
Philip (a chef and hotelier) and Christine Challen began the establishment of their vineyard in 1986 with the planting of 0.5ha of cabernet sauvignon. Several years later, 2ha of chardonnay (and a few vines of pinot noir) followed. Vineyard practice and soil management are based on organic principles; there are low yields, notwithstanding the age of the vines.

♟♟♟♟   **Forgotten Hero 2009** Petit verdot from Heathcote has been blended with
8% shiraz from the same region. An attractive wine, with an abundance of
predominantly black fruits, the savoury tannins just held at bay; no need to rush it,
just find the right hearty meal. Screwcap. 13.5% alc. **Rating** 89 **To** 2016 $27
Chardonnay 2008 Now fully developed, and just a touch broad on the finish;
the fruit and oak balance is up to the mark. Screwcap. 13% alc. **Rating** 87
To 2013 $20
Taggerty Sparkling Brut 2008 Full gold; a blend of pinot noir and chardonnay
made in the traditional manner, and certainly full-flavoured; the vanillin notes
suggest that part of the base wine might have spent some time in oak before being
put on tirage. Diam. 12.5% alc. **Rating** 87 **To** 2013 $33

Littles   ★★★

Cnr Palmers Lane/McDonalds Road, Pokolbin, NSW 2321 **Region** Hunter Valley
T (02) 4998 7626 **www**.littleswinery.com.au **Open** Fri–Mon 10–4.30
Winemaker Rhys Eather (Contract) **Est.** 1984 **Dozens** 2000 **Vyds** 21.6ha
Littles is managed by the Kindred family, the ownership involving a number of investors. The
winery has mature vineyards planted to shiraz (7.3ha), cabernet sauvignon (4.5ha), semillon
(4.3ha), pinot noir (3.4ha), chardonnay (1.3ha) and marsanne (0.8ha). Exports to Germany,
Taiwan and Japan.

♟♟♟♟   **Hunter Valley Sparkling Chardonnay 2011** A light and fresh lemon-accented
aperitif-style sparkling wine; clean, fresh and simple. Cork. 12.5% alc. **Rating** 87
To 2014 $18 BE

Lobethal Road Wines

Lot 1, Lobethal Road, Mount Torrens, SA 5244 **Region** Adelaide Hills
T (08) 8389 4595 **www**.lobethalroad.com **Open** W'ends & public hols 11–5
Winemaker Michael Sykes (Contract) **Est.** 1998 **Dozens** 1500 **Vyds** 5.1ha
Dave Neyle and Inga Lidums bring diverse but very relevant experience to the Lobethal
Road vineyard, the lion's share planted to shiraz (3.1ha), with smaller amounts of chardonnay,
tempranillo, sauvignon blanc and graciano. Dave has been in vineyard development and
management in SA and Tasmania since 1990. Inga brings 25 years' experience in marketing
and graphic design in Australia and overseas, with a focus on the wine and food industries. The
property is managed with minimal chemical input, and the use of solar power in the pursuit
of an environmentally sustainable product and lifestyle.

♟♟♟♟♟   **Bacchant Adelaide Hills Chardonnay 2010** Vibrant green hue; a pure-fruited
expression of chardonnay with melon and grapefruit, offset by a little spice;
the palate is unctuous and soft, with a layered and spicy grilled hazelnut finish.
Screwcap. 13.1% alc. **Rating** 93 **To** 2016 $42 BE
Adelaide Hills Shiraz 2010 Deep crimson; bright red and blue fruits are
offset by spice and thyme on the bouquet; the palate is medium-bodied, with
tangy acidity driving the palate to a moderately long finish. Screwcap. 14% alc.
Rating 91 **To** 2016 $22 BE

♟♟♟♟   **Adelaide Hills Pinot Gris 2011** **Rating** 88 **To** 2013 $22 BE

Lofty Valley Wines

PO Box 55, Summertown, SA 5141 **Region** Adelaide Hills
T 0400 930 818 **www**.loftyvalleywines.com.au **Open** Not
Winemaker Brendon Keys **Est.** 2004 **Dozens** 600 **Vyds** 3ha
Medical practitioner Brian Gilbert began collecting wine when he was 19, flirting with the
idea of becoming a winemaker before being headed firmly in the direction of medicine by his
parents. Thirty or so years later he purchased a blackberry- and gorse-infested 12ha property
in the Adelaide Hills, eventually obtaining permission to establish a vineyard. Chardonnay
(2ha) was planted in 2004, and 1ha of pinot noir in '07, both on steep slopes.

ŶŶŶŶŶ **Single Vineyard Adelaide Hills Chardonnay 2010** Bright, light green-gold; the bouquet shows the impact of barrel fermentation, but the focus changes entirely with the unexpectedly elegant palate, dominated by lively nectarine fruit, oak in the background; the finish is clean and fresh. Screwcap. 13.5% alc. Rating 94 To 2015 $35

ŶŶŶŶŶ **Single Vineyard Adelaide Hills Pinot Noir 2010** Rating 91 To 2016 $35

Logan Wines ★★★★★

Castlereagh Highway, Apple Tree Flat, Mudgee, NSW 2850 **Region** Mudgee
T (02) 6373 1333 **www.**loganwines.com.au **Open** 7 days 10–5
Winemaker Peter Logan **Est.** 1997 **Dozens** 50 000
Logan is a family-owned and operated business with emphasis on cool-climate wines from Orange and Mudgee. The business is run by husband and wife team Peter (winemaker) and Hannah (sales and marketing). Wines are released from three ranges: Logan (from Orange), Weemala and Apple Tree Flat. Exports to the UK, the US, Japan and other major markets.

ŶŶŶŶŶ **Orange Sauvignon Blanc 2011** Light straw-green; the quality of this wine comes through the excellent finish and lingering aftertaste, which bring together the passionfruit and grapefruit flavours of the palate promised by the bouquet. A delicious sauvignon blanc once again proving the terroir of Orange for the variety. Screwcap. 12% alc. Rating 94 To 2013 $22
Orange Shiraz 2009 Good hue, although not entirely clear; a complex bouquet of licorice, star anise, game and black fruits is followed by a medium- to full-bodied palate that has a near-identical range of flavours plus a savoury undertone. Screwcap. 14% alc. Rating 94 To 2020 $25

ŶŶŶŶŶ **Orange Chardonnay 2010** Rating 91 To 2018 $22
Hannah Orange Rose 2011 Rating 91 To 2013 $22
Weemala Central Ranges Merlot 2009 Rating 90 To 2014 $18
Orange Cabernet Merlot 2009 Rating 90 To 2018 $25

ŶŶŶŶ **Weemala Orange Gewurztraminer 2011** Rating 89 To 2014 $18
⊙ **Weemala Orange Gewurztraminer 2010** Rating 89 To 2014 $18
Orange Pinot Noir 2010 Rating 89 To 2016 $30
Weemala Orange Pinot Gris 2011 Rating 87 To Now $18

Lonely Vineyard ★★★★

61 Emmett Road, Crafers West, SA 5152 (postal) **Region** Eden Valley
T 0413 481 163 **www.**lonelyvineyard.com.au **Open** Not
Winemaker Michael Schreurs **Est.** 2008 **Dozens** 400 **Vyds** 1.5ha
This is the venture of winemaker Michael Schreurs and Karina Ouwens, a commercial lawyer from Adelaide. Daughter Amalia Schreurs can 'hoover a box of sultanas in record time' while Meesh, the family cat, 'treats Karina and Amalia well, and Michael with the contempt he deserves. As cats do.' One or other of the partners (perhaps both) has a great sense of humour. Michael's winemaking career in Australia began with Seppelt Great Western winery for three years, followed by six years at Henschke, and, more recently, The Lane Vineyard in the Adelaide Hills, backed up by stints in Burgundy, the Rhône, the US and Spain.

ŶŶŶŶŶ **Eden Valley Riesling 2011** Pale quartz; builds character at a hectic pace after a slow opening on the bouquet, climaxing on the finish and aftertaste with bracing minerally acidity, herbs and citrus peel. Will be long lived. Screwcap. 12% alc. Rating 91 To 2025 $28
Eden Valley Riesling 2010 Very pale straw-green; the riesling bottle, taller and heavier than any other on the Australian market I have come across, signals a Riesling with striking power and intensity, and needing five or so years to fully open up. Screwcap. 12% alc. Rating 91 To 2020 $28

Eden Valley Shiraz 2009 Youthful light, bright crimson-purple; the bouquet is particularly fragrant, with spicy notes from fruit rather than oak; the medium-bodied palate, too, is fresh and fruit-driven; the overall balance of tannin suggests it may live longer than one might expect. Screwcap. 14% alc. **Rating** 91 To 2018 $38

Long Gully Estate

Long Gully Road, Healesville, Vic 3777 **Region** Yarra Valley
T (03) 9510 5798 **www**.longgullyestate.com **Open** 7 days 11–5
Winemaker Han Tao Lau **Est.** 1982 **Dozens** 10 000 **Vyds** 21ha
Owned by Reiner and Irma Klapp, this is one of the larger Yarra Valley producers to have successfully established a number of export markets, doubtless due to its core of mature vineyards, which have grown from 2.2ha to over 20 ha, underlining its commercial success. There have been various winemaking changes over recent years, culminating with the appointment of Han Tao Lau as winemaker in Nov '10. Han came to Australia to study wine business at the University of Adelaide, intending to open a boutique wine store in his home city of Hong Kong. Instead, he fell in love with winemaking, and completed the graduate diploma in oenology. He has worked for wineries including the icon Château Valandraud in St Emilion and Weingut Okonomierat Rebholz in Pfalz, Germany; over the past six years he has been in the Yarra Valley, with vintages at Coldstream Hills, then Domaine Chandon, followed by two years as assistant winemaker at Yarra Yering. He has been joined by newly appointed viticulturist Aaron Bailey. Exports to the UK, Switzerland, Singapore and China.

ΨΨΨΨΨ **Yarra Valley Riesling 2011** A fine and fragrant example of Riesling, showing an elegant and restrained mineral fruit, with lovely purity and precision; very dry, almost austere, yet the laser-like acidity and strong mineral content continue pleasantly and unabated for an impressively long time. One of a handful of Yarra Rieslings. Screwcap. 12% alc. **Rating** 94 To 2020 $25 BE
Yarra Valley Chardonnay 2011 Made with the Penfolds 58 clone chardonnay, one of the best going in mature vines; barrel-fermented in French hogsheads and puncheons (18% new) and stirred fortnightly for five months. The bouquet is fragrant, but it is the exceptional length of the palate that immediately grabs hold of you; the flavours open with white and yellow peach, with a hint of cream, then break out into intense grapefruit notes. The Yarra Valley produced many outstanding chardonnays in '11. Screwcap. 13.2% alc. **Rating** 94 To 2017 $25

ΨΨΨΨ **Cheery Giant Pinot Noir 2011 Rating** 88 To 2014 $15 BE

Longview Creek Vineyard

150 Palmer Road, Sunbury, Vic 3429 **Region** Sunbury
T (03) 9740 2448 **www**.longviewcreek.com.au **Open** Sun 12–5, Sat by appt
Winemaker Bill Ashby **Est.** 1988 **Dozens** 400 **Vyds** 2.2ha
Bill and Karen Ashby purchased the Longview Creek Vineyard from founders Dr Ron and Joan Parker in 2003. It is situated on the brink of the spectacular Longview Gorge. The bulk of the chardonnay (0.9ha), pinot noir (0.6ha) and chenin blanc (0.3ha) was planted between 1988 and '90. Thereafter a little cabernet franc and riesling were planted.

ΨΨΨΨΨ **Pippin Pinot 2010** Clear crimson colour; this is the answer to those seeking a
✪ budget-priced pinot; estate-grown, open-fermented, and matured in barrel and tank for 15 months. Fragrant red and black cherry fruit drives the bouquet and the silky, soft palate. Exceptional value. Screwcap. 13% alc. **Rating** 90 To 2015 $15

ΨΨΨΨ **Unwooded Chardonnay 2011** Light green-straw; has ample varietal aroma and
✪ flavour, with grapefruit to the fore, stone fruit in the second row. Any time over the next few years. Screwcap. 13% alc. **Rating** 89 To 2014 $16
Chardonnay 2010 Rating 89 To 2013 $18
○ **Chenin Blanc 2011 Rating** 88 To 2014 $14

Longview Vineyard

Pound Road, Macclesfield, SA 5153 **Region** Adelaide Hills
T (08) 8388 9694 **www**.longviewvineyard.com.au **Open** 7 days 11–5
Winemaker Ben Glaetzer (Contract) **Est.** 1995 **Dozens** 20 000 **Vyds** 59.48ha
The Saturno family purchased Longview from founder Duncan MacGilvray in 2007, with members of the extended family now also involved in many aspects of the business. Shiraz and cabernet sauvignon are the major varieties, followed by chardonnay, and smaller plantings of alternative varieties of gruner veltliner (as part of the Adelaide Hills Vine Improvement Society). A significant investment has been made in upgrading the function facilities, and in rejuvenating the vineyard. Exports to the UK, the US, Ireland, Denmark, the Netherlands, Malaysia, Taiwan, Hong Kong and China.

ŸŸŸŸŸ **Yakka Adelaide Hills Shiraz 2009** A deep and concentrated wine, showing lifted sweet fruits, florals, licorice and loads of spice; medium-bodied yet rich and generous, with the ample sweet fruits being supported by fine-grained tannins and tangy acidity; long and fragrant. Screwcap. 14.5% alc. **Rating** 93 **To** 2025 $27 BE
Whippet Adelaide Hills Sauvignon Blanc 2011 Pale quartz; a lively, crisp and crunchy sauvignon, with vibrant citrus, apple, gooseberry and acidity all in play; very good length. Screwcap. 10.5% alc. **Rating** 92 **To** Now $18

ŸŸŸŸ **Devils Elbow Adelaide Hills Cabernet Sauvignon 2009** **Rating** 89 **To** 2025 $27 BE
Adelaide Shiraz Cabernet Sauvignon 2010 **Rating** 88 **To** 2016 $16 BE

Loom Wine ★★★

90 Chalk Hill Road, McLaren Vale, SA 5171 **Region** McLaren Vale
T (08) 8323 8623 **www**.loomwine.com **Open** 7 days 10–5
Winemaker Steve Grimley, Adam Hooper, Jess Hardy **Est.** 2005 **Dozens** 300 000
Loom Wine is a family-operated wine business located in McLaren Vale. It makes wines under two labels: the widely distributed Loom Wine range, now made by Jess Hardy, and the cellar door-only wines of Stamford & Clark, which are made by owner Steve Grimley. All wines are made onsite in a recently completed 'small batch' winery. In addition to managing the Loom Wine business, Steve consults to UK-based Direct Wines (the largest direct marketer of wine in the world) and is in charge of making and sourcing their Australian range. Exports to the UK, the US and other major markets.

ŸŸŸŸ **Long Yarn McLaren Vale Shiraz 2010** **Rating** 88 **To** 2014 $14
◯

Lost Lake ★★★★★

14591 Vasse Highway, Pemberton, WA 6260 **Region** Pemberton
T (08) 9776 1251 **www**.lostlake.com.au **Open** 7 days 10–4
Winemaker Katie Masters **Est.** 1990 **Dozens** 4500 **Vyds** 7.82ha
Previously known as Eastbrook Estate, Lost Lake's origins go back to 1990, to the acquisition of an 80ha farming property which was subdivided into three portions: 16 ha, now known as Picardy, were acquired by Dr Bill Pannell, 18ha became the base for Lost Lake, and the remainder was sold. The initial plantings in 1990 were of pinot noir and chardonnay, followed by shiraz, sauvignon blanc, merlot and cabernet sauvignon. A jarrah and cedar winery with a crush capacity of 150 tonnes was built in '95, together with a large restaurant. Steve and Karen Masters acquired the property in 2006 and moved from Perth to live there full-time.

ŸŸŸŸŸ **Single Vineyard Pemberton Sauvignon Blanc 2011** An extremely powerful
✿ and concentrated wine, that must surely have come from low-yielding vines; is more herbal than tropical, and has grainy acidity, all adding up to a wine with one foot (metaphorically) planted in white Bordeaux, the other in the Loire Valley. Points for distinction. Screwcap. 13.5% alc. **Rating** 94 **To** 2014 $20

Barrel Selection Pemberton Pinot Noir 2009 Good colour; there is undoubtedly oak influence here, but it is matched with the perfumed, ripe, strongly spiced, cherry fruit; the mouthfeel is likewise very good, the wine ready now, although will hold. Screwcap. 13.3% alc. **Rating** 94 **To** 2015 $35

ΨΨΨΨ   **Pemberton Sauvignon Blanc Semillon 2011** Pale straw-green; the bouquet
✪   is quite pungent, with strong herb and grass aromas; the complex palate brings in some element of sweet fruit; plenty of attitude. Screwcap. 12.7% alc. **Rating** 91 **To** 2014 $18
Single Vineyard Pemberton Shiraz 2010 Rating 91 **To** 2018 $25
Single Vineyard Pemberton Pinot Noir 2010 Rating 90 **To** 2015 $25

ΨΨΨΨ   **Barrel Selection Pemberton Pinot Noir 2010 Rating** 89 **To** 2015 $35
Pemberton Cabernet Sauvignon 2009 Rating 89 **To** 2017 $35
Pemberton Red 2010 Rating 89 **To** 2014 $18
Amici Pemberton Pinot Noir Chardonnay 2009 Rating 89 **To** Now $25
Barrel Selection Pemberton Chardonnay 2010 Rating 87 **To** 2013 $35

Lost Valley Winery   ★★★★
PO Box 4123, Wishart, Vic 3189 **Region** Upper Goulburn
T 0439 373 453 **www**.lostvalleywinery.com **Open** By appt
Winemaker Alex White (Contract) **Est.** 1995 **Dozens** 5000 **Vyds** 12ha
While ultimate ownership of Lost Valley has changed, with John Taaff Managing Director, Marco Shen Director of Operations and two Chinese directors, the team of Alex White (winemaker) and Paul Hilder (vineyard manager) remains in place. The plan is to increase production by 1500–2000 dozens per year, with export markets (especially China) increasing. Exports to the UK, the US, Canada, Hong Kong, Singapore, Indonesia and China.

ΨΨΨΨ   **Mornington Peninsula Sauvignon Blanc 2011** Vibrant green hue; the
presence of ripe guava and gun flint is undeniable on the bouquet; the palate is generous and textured, providing depth as well as freshness; an interesting interpretation of the variety. Screwcap. 13% alc. **Rating** 91 **To** 2013 $24 BE
Mountain Country Central Victoria Cortese 2011 Pale colour; this is pure citrus fruit and citrus blossom, with tangy acidity driving the palate and providing a fresh and satisfying journey for this very rare variety in Australia. Screwcap. 11.5% alc. **Rating** 90 **To** 2014 $25 BE
Mountain Country Central Victoria Merlot 2010 Lifted red fruits with herbs, toasty oak and a brambly, savoury edge; medium-bodied and toasty on the palate, the wine displays life and vitality, not to mention a little mint, but the freshness and drive are commendable. Diam. 13.5% alc. **Rating** 90 **To** 2018 $27 BE

ΨΨΨΨ   **Mountain Country Central Victoria Shiraz 2010 Rating** 87 **To** 2014 $27 BE

Lou Miranda Estate   ★★★★
Barossa Valley Way, Rowland Flat, SA 5352 **Region** Barossa Valley
T (08) 8524 4537 **www**.loumirandaestate.com.au **Open** Mon–Fri 10–4, w'ends 11–4
Winemaker Lou Miranda **Est.** 2005 **Dozens** 20 000 **Vyds** 23.29ha
Lou Miranda's daughters Lisa and Victoria are the driving force behind the estate, albeit with continuing hands-on involvement from Lou. The jewels in the crown of the estate plantings are 0.5ha of mourvedre planted in 1897 and 1.5ha of shiraz planted in 1907. The remaining vines have been planted gradually since '95, the varietal choice widened by cabernet sauvignon, merlot, chardonnay and pinot grigio. The cellar door works on the principle that there should be a wine for every conceivable taste. Exports to the UK and other major markets.

ΨΨΨΨ   **Leone Adelaide Hills Sauvignon Blanc 2011** Pale colour, bright; the bouquet
✪   offers ripe tropical notes and fresh-cut grass; the palate is generous and lively, with a lingering chalky dry finish. Screwcap. 11.5% alc. **Rating** 90 **To** 2013 $18 BE

Leone Riverina Botrytis Semillon 2009 Deep colour and heavily affected by botrytis with candied apricots, ginger and fresh citrus fruits; the palate is sweet, but not overly so, with toffee brittle providing freshness on the conclusion. Screwcap. 12% alc. **Rating** 90 **To** 2016 $26 BE

♀♀♀♀ **Individual Vineyard Old Vine Barossa Valley Shiraz 2009** Rating 87 **To** 2016 $33 BE
Leone Barossa Valley Cabernet Sauvignon 2010 Rating 87 **To** 2015 $18 BE

Lowe Wines   ★★★★★
Tinja Lane, Mudgee, NSW 2850 **Region** Mudgee
T (02) 6372 0800 **www.**lowewine.com.au **Open** 7 days 10–5
Winemaker David Lowe, Liam Heslop **Est.** 1987 **Dozens** 10 000 **Vyds** 21.8ha
Lowe Wines has undergone a number of changes in recent years, the most recent the acquisition of Louee and its two vineyards. The first is at Rylstone with 10 ha, led by shiraz, cabernet sauvignon, petit verdot and merlot, with chardonnay, cabernet franc, verdelho and viognier making up the balance. The second is on Nullo Mountain, bordered by the Wollemi National Park, at an altitude of 1100 m, high by any standards, and often the coolest location in Australia. Here 4.45ha of cool-climate varieties (riesling, sauvignon blanc, chardonnay, pinot noir, pinot gris and nebbiolo) have been planted. Lowe Wines continues with its organic profile, with just over 20ha of its own. With the increase in the size of the business, David Lowe is being assisted by Liam Heslop. Exports to the UK and Japan.

♀♀♀♀♀ **Organic Block 8 Mudgee Shiraz 2009** Excellent purple-crimson; a high-quality, medium- to full-bodied wine that spent 20 months in large, used American oak casks (4500 l), which imparted texture but (happily) little or no vanilla. The overall balance and mouthfeel are admirable. Screwcap. 13.5% alc. Rating 94 **To** 2020 $30
Mudgee Zinfandel 2009 After two vintages with no yield, this wine pays its own reward. The richly spiced plum cake bouquet loudly proclaims its varietal presence, and the palate positively ripples with ripe prune and plum flavours, backed by soft tannins. There is absolutely no issue with the alcohol, necessary to achieve fully ripe flavours, and not imparting any undue warmth on the finish. Cork. 15.3% alc. **Rating** 94 **To** 2017 $75

♀♀♀♀♀ **Louee Nullo Mountain Rylstone Riesling 2011** Rating 93 **To** 2021 $25
Louee Tongbong Rylstone Chardonnay 2005 Rating 92 **To** 2014 $30
Block 5 Reserve Mudgee Shiraz 2009 Rating 92 **To** 2016 $45
Mudgee Muscat NV Rating 91 **To** 2013 $45
Louee Nullo Mountain Rylstone Pinot Grigio 2011 Rating 90 **To** 2013 $25

♀♀♀♀ **Louee Nullo Mountain Rylstone Chardonnay 2010** Rating 89 **To** 2015 $25
Mudgee Vintage Port 2005 Rating 89 **To** 2015 $45
Louee Nullo Mountain Rylstone Chardonnay 2011 Rating 88 **To** 2015 $25
Tinja Preservative Free Mudgee Merlot Shiraz 2011 Rating 88 **To** 2013 $20

Luke Lambert Wines   ★★★★★
PO Box 1297, Healesville, Vic 3777 **Region** Yarra Valley
T 0448 349 323 **www.**lukelambertwines.com.au **Open** By appt
Winemaker Luke Lambert **Est.** 2003 **Dozens** 1500 **Vyds** 4.5ha
Luke Lambert graduated from CSU's wine science course in 2002, aged 23, cramming in winemaking experience at Mount Pleasant, Coldstream Hills, Mount Prior, Poet's Corner, Palliser Estate in Martinborough, and Badia di Morrona in Chianti. With this background he has established a virtual winery, purchasing grapes from quality-conscious growers in the Yarra Valley and Heathcote. After several trial vintages, the first wines were released from the 2005 vintage. He has now settled in the Yarra Valley, leasing slightly less than 1ha of Heathcote nebbiolo, and similar amounts of Yarra Valley shiraz and nebbiolo (newly grafted). The wines are wild yeast-fermented and bottled without fining or filtration. Exports to the UK and the US.

🍷🍷🍷🍷🍷 **Reserve Yarra Valley Syrah 2010** The ultimate in minimalist labels, 'Reserve' appearing in microscopic print as far away from the rest of the (admittedly few) words on the front label – hunt the thimble. Although the alcohol is lower, the colour has great depth and purple hue. The focus of the wine is like a fencer's épée, an extraordinary example of precision and ever so finely focused power, the black cherry fruits with a pot pourri of spices and bramble. Is strikingly good. Diam. 13% alc. **Rating** 96 **To** 2035 $70

Yarra Valley Syrah 2010 Clear crimson-red; the fragrant, almost perfumed, bouquet is full of red fruits and spices, and you don't expect the much fuller and more savoury flavours on the complex palate and textured finish. An impressive wine. Diam. 13.5% alc. **Rating** 94 **To** 2030 $40

Lyre Bird Hill   ★★★☆

370 Koonwarra-Inverloch Road, Koonwarra, Vic 3954 **Region** Gippsland
T (03) 5664 3204 **www**.lyrebirdhill.com.au **Open** Wed–Mon 10–5
Winemaker Owen Schmidt **Est.** 1986 **Dozens** 2000 **Vyds** 2.4ha
Former Melbourne professionals Owen and Robyn Schmidt make small quantities of estate-grown wine (the vineyard is 2.4ha). Various weather-related viticulture problems have seen the Schmidts supplement their estate-grown intake with grapes from contract growers in Gippsland and the Yarra Valley, and also provide contract winemaking services for others.

🍷🍷🍷🍷🍷 **South Gippsland Shiraz 2008** Light colour, but good hue for age; there is a
✪   gentle spice and pepper overlay to the red cherry fruit of the bouquet, the palate providing more of the same, the tannins fine and balanced. Drink sooner rather than later. Screwcap. 12.6% alc. **Rating** 92 **To** 2015 $20

🍷🍷🍷🍷 **South Gippsland Pinot Grigio 2011 Rating** 89 **To** Now $20
South Gippsland Pinot Noir 2009 Rating 89 **To** 2014 $20
Phantasy Pinot Noir Chardonnay 2010 Rating 87 **To** 2014 $25

M. Chapoutier Australia   ★★★★★

11 Nicholson Place, Melbourne, Vic 3000 **Region** Pyrenees
T (03) 9602 1570 **www**.mchapoutieraustralia.com **Open** By appt
Winemaker Michel Chapoutier, Mathieu Apffel **Est.** 1998 **Dozens** 20 000 **Vyds** 51.9ha
M. Chapoutier Australia is the eponymous offshoot of the famous Rhône Valley producer. Having disposed of its plantings in Mount Benson, the business now focuses on vineyards in the Pyrenees, Heathcote and Beechworth, with collaboration from Ron Laughton of Jasper Hill and Rick Kinzbrunner of Giaconda. After first establishing a vineyard in Heathcote adjacent to Jasper Hill (see La Pleiade), Chapoutier purchased the Malakoff Vineyard in the Pyrenees to create Domaine Terlato & Chapoutier (the Terlato & Chapoutier joint venture was established in 2000 with its first vintage in '04; Terlato still owns 50% of the Malakoff Vineyard). In '09 Michel Chapoutier purchased two neighbouring vineyards, Landsborough Valley and Shays Flat, all three sites within 5km of each other; all these are now fully owned by Domaine Tournon. (Domaine Tournon consists of Landsborough and Shays Flat estates in the Pyrenees and Lady's Lane estate in Heathcote.) No wines were received for this edition; the rating is that of last year. Exports to all major markets.

McAdams Lane   ★★★★

90 McAdams Lane, Bellarine, Vic 3223 (postal) **Region** Geelong
T 1300 651 485 **www**.mcadamslane.com.au **Open** Not
Winemaker Anthony Brain **Est.** 2003 **Dozens** 1000 **Vyds** 4.6ha
Retired quantity surveyor Peter Slattery bought the 48ha property in 2001, intending to plant the vineyard, make wine and develop a restaurant. He has achieved all of this (with help from others, of course), planting shiraz (0.5ha), pinot noir (1.8ha), pinot gris (1ha), picolit (0.6ha), chardonnay (0.4ha) and zinfandel (0.3ha). Picolit is most interesting: it is a highly regarded grape in northern Italy, where it makes small quantities of high-quality sweet wine. It has proved to be very temperamental here, as in Italy, with very unreliable fruitset.

♟♟♟♟♟ Terindah Estate Bellarine Peninsula Pinot Noir 2010 Strong, clear crimson;
✪   the aromas and flavours turn around red and dark plum, with good oak and ripe
               tannins exactly weighted for the volume of fruit. Good now, even better in a few
               years. Great value. Screwcap. 13.1% alc. **Rating** 93 **To** 2017 $20
✪   Terindah Estate Bellarine Peninsula Chardonnay 2010 Gleaming yellow-
               green; it has layers of white peach and nectarine fruit with a squeeze of grapefruit
               juice to provide some tension and balance the ripe stone fruit flavours, oak unseen.
               Screwcap. 13.4% alc. **Rating** 92 **To** 2016 $20
✪   Terindah Estate Bellarine Peninsula Shiraz 2010 Bright, clear crimson; the
               bouquet is very fragrant, with gently spiced red berry fruits, the palate opening
               with those characters, the spicy/savoury notes on the finish extending the length
               and interest of the wine. Screwcap. 14.1% alc. **Rating** 92 **To** 2025 $20

♟♟♟♟ Terindah Estate Bellarine Peninsula Pinot Gris 2010 **Rating** 87 **To** 2013 $20

Macaw Creek Wines   ★★★
Macaw Creek Road, Riverton, SA 5412 **Region** Mount Lofty Ranges Zone
T (08) 8847 2237 www.macawcreekwines.com.au **Open** By appt
Winemaker Rodney Hooper **Est.** 1992 **Dozens** 6000 **Vyds** 10ha
The property on which Macaw Creek Wines is established has been owned by the Hooper
family since the 1850s, but development of the estate vineyards did not begin until 1995.
The Macaw Creek brand was established in 1992 with wines made from grapes from other
regions, including the Preservative-Free Yoolang Cabernet Shiraz. Rodney Hooper is a highly
qualified and skilled winemaker with experience in many parts of Australia and in Germany,
France and the US. Macaw Creek is now the face of Cockatoo Wines, and will offer these
wines through its cellar door (open twice a year!). Exports to Canada and China.

♟♟♟♟ Em's Table Premium Organic Preservative Free Shiraz 2010 Bright
              purple-crimson; sweet and supple flavours on the medium-bodied palate; a touch
              of American oak and near-invisible tannins make this is an immediate drinking
              proposition, with obvious appeal to those allergic to SO_2. Screwcap. 14% alc.
              Rating 89 **To** 2014 $18
              Shiraz 2008 Mid purple-red; the bouquet has spicy nuances, partly fruit-
              derived, partly oak-derived; the medium-bodied palate brings blackberry, cherry
              and a touch of licorice into play, finishing with ripe tannins. Screwcap. 14% alc.
              Rating 89 **To** 2018 $17

McCrae Mist Wines   ★★★☆
21 Bass Street, McCrae, Vic 3938 (postal) **Region** Mornington Peninsula
T 0416 008 630 **F** (03) 5986 6973 **Open** Not
Winemaker Brien Cole **Est.** 2003 **Dozens** 1200 **Vyds** 18ha
The McCrae Mist vineyard was acquired by Dr Stephen Smith after the Kings Creek business
was broken up in 2003. He thus inherited over 15ha of pinot grigio, pinot noir, shiraz and
sangiovese, adding another 4ha of chardonnay in 2005.

♟♟♟♟♟ Reserve Mornington Peninsula Pinot Noir 2009 Good colour and clarity;
              the wine manages to combine varietal expression in a complex, full-bodied (for
              pinot) frame; the palate offers red and black fruits, strong forest floor underlay, and
              a long, savoury, finish. Screwcap. 13.9% alc. **Rating** 93 **To** 2015 $50

♟♟♟♟ Traditionale Pinot Grigio 2010 **Rating** 89 **To** 2014 $20
              Classico Sangiovese 2009 **Rating** 88 **To** 2015 $35

macforbes   ★★★★★
770 Healesville-Koo Wee Rup Road, Healesville, Vic 3777 **Region** Yarra Valley
T (03) 9818·8099 www.macforbes.com **Open** By appt
Winemaker Mac Forbes, Tony Fikkers **Est.** 2004 **Dozens** 2000

Mac Forbes cut his vinous teeth at Mount Mary, where he was winemaker for several years before heading overseas in 2002. He spent two years in London working for Southcorp in a marketing liaison role, then travelled to Portugal and Austria to gain further winemaking experience. He returned to the Yarra Valley prior to the '05 vintage, purchasing grapes for the two-tier portfolio: first, the Victorian range (employing unusual varieties or unusual winemaking techniques); and, second, the Yarra Valley range of multiple terroir-based offerings of Chardonnay and Pinot Noir. The business has grown steadily, with Tony Fikkers joining the winemaking team, and Dylan Grigg as viticulturist guiding the contract grapegrowers upon whom macforbes relies. Exports to the UK, the US, Dubai and Japan.

♟♟♟♟♟ **Yarra Junction Pinot Noir 2010** The extra degree of alcohol subtly adds to all its dimensions, most obviously its fruit flavour profile and its mouthfeel, and – ultimately and unexpectedly – to the clarity of its varietal fruit expression. A truly delicious pinot noir. Screwcap. 13.5% alc. **Rating** 95 **To** 2018 $46

Woori Yallock Pinot Noir 2010 Presumably, the price of these wines varies according to the cost of the grapes, and not the fame of the region; this wine does fill the mouth more completely with its fruit flavours, and in particular, the peacock's tail of its finish. Screwcap. 12.5% alc. **Rating** 95 **To** 2017 $56

Coldstream Pinot Noir 2010 Like all wines in the range, the colour is light but bell-clear; right in the mainstream of the macforbes style, although showing the benefit of the excellent vintage in no uncertain fashion; super elegant, it is nonetheless intense with red fruits and a pot pourri of spice. Screwcap. 12.5% alc. **Rating** 94 **To** 2016 $46

Gruyere Pinot Noir 2010 Has fractionally more ripe fruit and a hint of plum joining the red fruits of the Coldstream; comes into its own on the finish and lingering aftertaste. Screwcap. 12.5% alc. **Rating** 94 **To** 2016 $46

♟♟♟♟♟ **Yarra Glen Pinot Noir 2010 Rating** 93 **To** 2015 $38
Gruyere Syrah 2010 Rating 93 **To** 2025 $36
Yarra Valley Chardonnay 2010 Rating 92 **To** 2020 $30
Hoddles Creek Chardonnay 2010 Rating 92 **To** 2018 $38
Woori Yallock Chardonnay 2010 Rating 92 **To** 2019 $44
Yarra Valley Pinot Noir 2010 Rating 92 **To** 2015 $30
Hugh Cabernet Sauvignon Merlot Cabernet Franc Petit Verdot 2010 Rating 90 **To** 2017 $56
RS19 Strathbogie Ranges Riesling 2011 Rating 90 **To** 2014 $28

McGlashan's Wallington Estate   ★★★★☆

225 Swan Bay Road, Wallington, Vic 3221 **Region** Geelong
T (03) 5250 5760 **www.**mcglashans.com.au **Open** W'ends & public hols 11–5, 7 days in Jan, or by appt
Winemaker Robin Brockett (Contract) **Est.** 1996 **Dozens** 2000 **Vyds** 10ha
Russell and Jan McGlashan began the establishment of their vineyard in 1996. Chardonnay (6ha) and pinot noir (4ha) make up the bulk of the plantings, the remainder shiraz and pinot gris (1ha each); the wines are made by Robin Brockett, with his usual skill and attention to detail. Local restaurants around Geelong and the Bellarine Peninsula take much of the wine, although a newly opened cellar door offering food and music will see an increase in direct sales.

♟♟♟♟♟ **Bellarine Peninsula Shiraz 2010** Deep, dense purple-crimson; estate-grown, and French oak-matured, it is a luscious, velvety wine with great depth to the confit plum, black cherry and licorice flavours, tannins and oak lazing somewhere in the background. A cellaring special. Screwcap. 14.5% alc. **Rating** 94 **To** 2030 $34

♟♟♟♟♟ **Bellarine Peninsula Chardonnay 2010 Rating** 93 **To** 2016 $28
Bellarine Peninsula Pinot Noir 2010 Rating 92 **To** 2017 $30

♟♟♟♟ **Bellarine Peninsula Pinot Grigio 2011 Rating** 89 **To** 2013 $24
Bellarine Peninsula Shiraz Rose 2011 Rating 88 **To** 2013 $24

McGrath Wines

101 Burkes Lane, Brewongle via Bathurst, NSW 3795 **Region** Central Ranges Zone
T (02) 6337 5501 **www**.mcgrathwines.com.au **Open** By appt
Winemaker Peter McGrath **Est.** 1999 **Dozens** 1000 **Vyds** 3.5ha
Peter McGrath has endured all the hard knocks of establishing an isolated vineyard (no near vigneron neighbours to give friendly advice), which coincided with a drought and the failure of irrigation equipment to arrive when promised. This led to his enrolment in a viticulture course. His first attempt at winemaking produced what he describes as 'nondescript vinegar', which led to the decision to enrol in a winemaking course. All this transpired between 1999 and 2003, and thereafter he achieved modest show success in cool-climate and small winemaker wine shows. His estate-grown shiraz, cabernet and riesling is supplemented by purchased chardonnay from the Bathurst area.

ΤΤΤΤΤ **Riesling 2011** Cleverly made, using some residual sugar to balance the acidity and flesh out the lime-accented palate. Drinks well now, but will continue to do so well into the future. Screwcap. 12.5% alc. **Rating** 91 **To** 2016 $20
Shiraz 2008 It is not the least bit surprising that the wine has won a string of silver and bronze medals in cool-climate and small winemaker wine shows. Light- to medium-bodied, with a mix of spicy and juicy characters to its red cherry and plum fruit; most importantly, perhaps, is that there are no minty or green undertones. Probably close to its best now. Screwcap. 14% alc. **Rating** 90 **To** 2014 $25

ΤΤΤΤ **Chardonnay 2010 Rating** 88 **To** 2014 $15
Cabernet Sauvignon 2009 Rating 87 **To** 2014 $20

McGuigan Wines

Cnr Broke Road/McDonalds Road, Pokolbin, NSW 2321 **Region** Hunter Valley
T (02) 4998 7400 **www**.mcguiganwines.com.au **Open** 7 days 9.30–5
Winemaker Neil McGuigan, Peter Hall **Est.** 1992 **Dozens** 1.5 million
A publicly listed company – the ultimate logical expression of Brian McGuigan's marketing drive and vision, which is on a par with that of Wolf Blass in his heyday. The overall size of the company has been increased by the acquisition of Simeon Wines; Yaldara and Miranda, now also part of the business, made wine industry headlines in 2006 when they terminated a large number of grape purchase contracts. In '07 McGuigan Simeon acquired Nepenthe, a move that surprised many, and in '08 the group was renamed Australian Vintage Limited, a slightly curious moniker. In November '11, for the second time in three years, Neil McGuigan won the International Wine & Spirit Competition (London) International Winemaker of the Year award, and for good measure, Australian Producer of the Year. Exports to all major markets.

ΤΤΤΤΤ **Bin Series No. 9000 Hunter Valley Semillon 2006** Bright green–gold, illuminated from within; wafts of lemon and honey arise on the bouquet, the palate delivering exactly what the bouquet suggests; superb balance and length, the wine still cruising along. Trophy International Wine & Spirit Competition '11. Screwcap. 11% alc. **Rating** 97 **To** 2021 $35
Miranda Golden Botrytis 2008 Exceptional green–gold colour, still vibrant; the wine certainly has a serious level of sweetness, but its wonderful racy acidity rides over the top of that sweetness. 375ml. Cork. 9.5% alc. **Rating** 95 **To** 2013 $19

ΤΤΤΤΤ **The Shortlist Eden Valley Riesling 2005 Rating** 93 **To** 2020 $29
✪ **Bin Series No. 9000 Hunter Valley Semillon 2011** Pale quartz; the bouquet is more expressive in its youth than many other Semillons of the vintage, with lime/citrus blossom aromas; the palate is a vibrant replay of the bouquet, and history shows how well this chronically underrated wine develops over 5+ years in bottle. Screwcap. 11.5% alc. **Rating** 93 **To** 2020 $13
✪ **Bin Series No. 7000 Hunter Valley Chardonnay 2010** Green-gold, moderately developed; an enjoyable wine, as fresh and fragrant on the bouquet as it is on the palate, where white peach, melon and citrus coalesce on the finish. Oak not needed, wine best now. Screwcap. 13.5% alc. **Rating** 91 **To** 2013 $13

✪ **Bin Series No. 8000 Adelaide Sauvignon Blanc 2011** I'm far from convinced that three medals for Winemaker of the Year gained in 2009 deserve to be put on the front label, even if this is a good example of the Adelaide Hills Sauvignon Blanc, with strong tropical fruit aromas and flavours, sustained by good natural acidity on the palate. Screwcap. 11.5% alc. **Rating** 90 **To** Now $13

♗♗♗♗ **The Semillon Blanc 2011 Rating** 87 **To** 2013 $13
✪

McHenry Hohnen Vintners ★★★★★

McHenrys Farm Shop, 5962 Caves Road, Margaret River, WA 6285 **Region** Margaret River
T (08) 9757 7600 **www**.mchv.com.au **Open** Wed–Mon 10–5
Winemaker Ryan Walsh **Est.** 2004 **Dozens** 10 000 **Vyds** 56ha
McHenry Hohnen is owned by the McHenry and Hohnen families, sourcing grapes from four vineyards owned by various members of the families. Vines have been established on the McHenry, Calgardup Brook, Rocky Road and McLeod Creek properties. A significant part of the grape production is sold to others (including Cape Mentelle), but McHenry Hohnen has 12 varieties to choose from in fashioning its wines. The family members with direct executive responsibilities are leading Perth retailer Murray McHenry and Cape Mentelle founder and former long-term winemaker David Hohnen. In 2007 David received the inaugural Len Evans Award for Leadership. Exports to the UK, Ireland, Sweden, Indonesia, Japan, Singapore, Hong Kong and NZ.

♗♗♗♗♗ **Calgardup Brook Vineyard Margaret River Chardonnay 2011** Mid gold; a highly expressive and complex wine with grapefruit, grilled cashews and candle wax on display; the palate is medium-weighted with zesty acidity providing a long and even ride from start to finish; fine grilled nut flavours linger tantalisingly. Screwcap. 13.5% alc. **Rating** 94 **To** 2016 $37 BE
Burnside Margaret River Chardonnay 2010 Significant colour development; estate-grown on unusual black soils, the vineyard planted in the early 1980s, the wine wild yeast-fermented and given extended lees contact in French oak. Its intensity and elegance are slightly at odds with the colour development; citrus, stone fruit and fig are drivers of the flavour. Screwcap. 13.8% alc. **Rating** 94 **To** 2016 $37

♗♗♗♗♗ **Margaret River Semillon Sauvignon Blanc 2011 Rating** 92 **To** 2014 $22 BE
Rocky Road Vineyard Margaret River Chardonnay 2011 Rating 91 **To** 2016 $37 BE
Burnside Margaret River Chardonnay 2011 Rating 90 **To** 2014 $37 BE

♗♗♗♗ **Tiger Country 2008 Rating** 89 **To** 2015 $28
Rocky Road Margaret River Zinfandel 2010 Rating 87 **To** 2013 $37 BE

McIvor Estate ★★★★

80 Tooborac-Baynton Road, Tooborac, Vic 3522 **Region** Heathcote
T (03) 5433 5266 **www**.mcivorestate.com.au **Open** W'ends & public hols 10–5, or by appt
Winemaker Various contract **Est.** 1997 **Dozens** 2000
McIvor Estate is situated at the base of the Tooborac Hills, at the southern end of the Heathcote wine region, 5km southwest of Tooborac. Gary and Cynthia Harbour have planted 5.3ha of marsanne, roussanne, shiraz, cabernet sauvignon, merlot, nebbiolo and sangiovese.

♗♗♗♗♗ **Heathcote Sangiovese 2010** Bright, clear red colour; savoury tannins run through the length of the palate, but so do red cherry fruit and spice; Sangiovese is only really happy with food, and this wine would shine in that environment. Screwcap. 13.3% alc. **Rating** 92 **To** 2018 $28
Nebbiolo 2010 Typical very pale, although bright, red colour; tannins are part of the territory, but here do allow the spicy red berry/cherry fruits room to move on the long, fine palate. Not the best Nebbiolo in Australia, but certainly one of the better. Screwcap. 13.1% alc. **Rating** 92 **To** 2020 $35

Shiraz 2010 Mid crimson-purple; a medium-bodied palate has predominantly red berry fruit flavours lifted by spicy notes and a hint of licorice, then a crisp finish with Central Victorian nuances of mint. Screwcap. 13.8% alc. **Rating** 90 **To** 2017 $40

Cabernet Sauvignon 2010 Light to medium crimson; Central Victorian mint weaves a web around the blackcurrant fruit on the medium-bodied palate; the length and balance are good, yet the wine lacks the X factor needed for higher points. Screwcap. 13.9% alc. **Rating** 90 **To** 2018 $30

♥♥♥♥ **Mr Mundy Heathcote Shiraz 2010** **Rating** 87 **To** 2013 $20

McKellar Ridge Wines   ★★★★☆

Point of View Vineyard, 2 Euroka Avenue, Murrumbateman, NSW 2582
Region Canberra District
T (02) 6258 1556 **www**.mckellarridgewines.com.au **Open** Sun 12–5, by appt Sept–Jun
Winemaker Dr Brian Johnston **Est.** 2000 **Dozens** 600 **Vyds** 5.5ha

Dr Brian Johnston and his wife Janet are the partners in McKellar Ridge Wines. Brian has completed a postgraduate diploma in science at CSU, focusing on wine science and wine production techniques. The wines come from low-yielding mature vines (shiraz, cabernet sauvignon, chardonnay, merlot and viognier) and have had significant show success. They are made using a combination of traditional and new winemaking techniques, the emphasis being on fruit-driven styles.

♥♥♥♥♥ **Canberra District Riesling 2011** Pale straw-green; another Canberra District riesling from '11 to have a dramatically full-flavoured and very long palate, with lime juice and racy acidity combining to provide both intensity and length. Screwcap. 12% alc. **Rating** 94 **To** 2030 $22

♥♥♥♥♀ **Canberra District Merlot Cabernet Franc 2010** **Rating** 90 **To** 2015 $28

♥♥♥♥ **Canberra District Shiraz Viognier 2010** **Rating** 89 **To** 2019 $28
Trio Canberra District Cabernet Sauvignon Merlot Cabernet Franc 2010 **Rating** 89 **To** 2020 $28

McLaren Vale III Associates   ★★★★☆

130 Main Road, McLaren Vale, SA 5171 **Region** McLaren Vale
T 1800 501 513 **www**.associates.com.au **Open** Mon–Fri 9–5, w'ends 11–4
Winemaker Brian Light **Est.** 1999 **Dozens** 20 000 **Vyds** 34ha

McLaren Vale III Associates is a very successful boutique winery. Its signature wine is Squid Ink Shiraz. Mary Greer, Managing Director, Reg Wymond, Director and Brian Light, Winemaker have over 80 years' combined experience in the wine industry. An impressive portfolio of estate-grown wines allows them control over quality and consistency, thus enjoying success in Australian and International wine shows (in 2011 they won ten gold medals and a trophy). Exports to the US, Canada, Indonesia, Hong Kong, Singapore and China.

♥♥♥♥♥ **Giant Squid Ink Reserve Shiraz 2010** Deep, dense and dark; archetypal McLaren Vale, almost into a caricature, redolent of dark chocolate closing on 90% cocoa solids; has great length, and the alcohol is irrelevant in this highly structured wine. Left field, but very good. Screwcap. 14.5% alc. **Rating** 94 **To** 2025 $150

♥♥♥♥♀ **The Descendant of Squid Ink Shiraz 2010** **Rating** 90 **To** 2016 $35 BE

♥♥♥♥ **Squid Ink Reserve Shiraz 2010** **Rating** 88 **To** 2016 $55 BE

McLean's Farm

barr-Eden Vineyard, Menglers Hill Road, Tanunda, SA 5352 **Region** Eden Valley
T (08) 8564 3340 **www**.mcleansfarm.com **Open** W'ends 10–5 or by appt
Winemaker Bob and Wilma McLean **Est.** 2001 **Dozens** 6000 **Vyds** 5.3ha

The ever-convivial, bigger-than-life, Bob McLean has covered a lot of wine turf over the past 40 years. The farm shed on the home property produces 1000 dozens of red wine; the remainder of the production is contract-made by some very savvy winemakers. There are now three brands: barr-Eden from the dry-grown estate vineyard and sold only ex cellar for private buyers and some trade; McLean's Farmgate, made in lots of 250–300 dozen each when special parcels of grapes become available from 'a few old chums'; and McLean's Farm, 100% Barossa fruit and made through the Dorrien Estate facility. These wines are sold through Cellarmasters, but with some restaurant listings. The barr-Eden Vineyard, at an altitude of around 500m, is one of the highest in the Eden Valley, and the annual blend of some or all of its grenache, shiraz and mataro is strictly dependent on the quality and character of the components from year to year. Exports to the UK.

ㅇㅇㅇㅇㅇ **Eden Valley Shiraz Mataro Grenache 2010** A bright and fragrant red-fruited bouquet, showing a touch of brine and meaty complexity; medium-bodied with savoury tannins and a fresh, tangy finish. Screwcap. 14% alc. **Rating** 91 **To** 2016 $35 BE

Eden Valley Mataro Shiraz 2009 A blackberry pastille bouquet and palate, with a soft-centred palate, licorice and a splash of savoury tar thrown in for good measure. Screwcap. 15% alc. **Rating** 90 **To** 2016 $30 BE

McLeish Estate

462 De Beyers Road, Pokolbin, NSW 2320 **Region** Hunter Valley
T (02) 4998 7754 **www**.mcleishhunterwines.com.au **Open** 7 days 10–5, or by appt
Winemaker Andrew Thomas (Contract) **Est.** 1985 **Dozens** 8000 **Vyds** 17.3ha
Bob and Maryanne McLeish began planting their vineyard in 1985, and now have semillon, chardonnay, verdelho, shiraz, merlot and cabernet sauvignon. They have also opened their cellar door, having accumulated a number of gold medals for their wines, thanks in no small measure to the winemaking skills of Andrew Thomas. Exports to the UK, the US and Asia.

ㅇㅇㅇㅇㅇ **Hunter Valley Semillon 2011** Bright quartz-green; the bouquet has a touch of complexity, its source not obvious; the palate has superb intensity and length, the flavours moving beyond lemon into lime and a touch of grapefruit; the steel core of acidity is there to guide the wine into an indefinite future. Screwcap. 11.1% alc. Rating 96 To 2026 $23

✪ **Hunter Valley Chardonnay 2011** Glowing green-quartz; fermentation in used French oak has thrown the focus onto the delicious fruit, ranging through citrus to white peach, nectarine and a hint of melon; a great example of perfect varietal character coming from a hot climate, thus defying the prophets of gloom on climate change. Screwcap. 13% alc. Rating 94 To 2018 $20

ㅇㅇㅇㅇㅇ **Hunter Valley Semillon Chardonnay 2010** A 60/40% blend; 20% of the
✪ chardonnay was fermented in 1-year-old French oak, the remainder in stainless steel; the outcome is exceptionally synergistic, the flavour of both semillon and chardonnay intensified, but not at the expense of each other. The overall flavours are of stone fruit with a strong dressing of lemon juice on the long finish. Screwcap. 12.5% alc. **Rating** 93 **To** 2018 $18

✪ **Hunter Valley Adelaide Hills Semillon Sauvignon Blanc 2011** Hunter Valley semillon is the main driver, its influence running right through from the start of the palate to the sustained acidity on the finish, sauvignon blanc filling the mid palate; adroit winemaking. Screwcap. 11.7% alc. **Rating** 92 **To** 2015 $18

Reserve Hunter Valley Merlot 2010 Rating 92 To 2018 $35

✪ **Dwyer Hunter Valley Rose 2011** Vivid puce; aromatic red berry fruits from the shiraz base, the palate lively, and finishing with a nice twist of spice. Screwcap. 11.9% alc. **Rating** 91 **To** 2013 $18

Hunter Valley Shiraz 2010 Rating 91 To 2015 $22

Reserve Hunter Valley Cabernet Sauvignon 2010 Rating 90 To 2020 $35

Tri Moir 2011 Rating 90 To 2016 $22

ŶŶŶŶ   Hunter Valley Chardonnay 2010 Rating 89 To 2015 $20
Hunter Valley Cabernet Sauvignon 2011 Rating 88 To 2017 $22
Hunter Valley Merlot 2011 Rating 87 To 2013 $22

McPherson Wines   ★★★★

PO Box 767, Hawthorn, Vic 3122 **Region** Nagambie Lakes
T (03) 9832 1700 **www**.mcphersonwines.com.au **Open** Not
Winemaker Geoff Thompson, Joanne Nash **Est.** 1993 **Dozens** 400 000 **Vyds** 262ha
McPherson Wines is not well known in Australia but is, by any standards, a substantial business.
Its wines are largely produced for the export market, with some sales in Australia. Made at
various locations from the estate vineyards and supplemented with contract-grown grapes,
they represent very good value. For the record, McPherson Wines is a joint venture between
Andrew McPherson and Alister Purbrick (Tahbilk), both of whom have had a lifetime of
experience in the industry. Exports to all major markets.

ŶŶŶŶŶ   Chapter Three Cabernet Sauvignon 2009 Medium red-purple; the bouquet
has strong blackcurrant, plum, mint and cedar aromas enriched on the palate by
high-quality French oak; there is a sweetness to the wine that has nothing to do
with residual sugar, and has spicy/savoury offsets. Screwcap. 14.5% alc. **Rating** 93
To 2020 $30

◐   Basilisk Shiraz Mourvedre 2010 Rating 93 To 2016 $18
✪   Basilisk Marsanne Viognier 2008 Pale straw-gold; a remarkable wine given its
age, explicable if the marsanne is (say) 85% or more of the blend, for it is quite full
on the mid palate, but fresh and crisp on the finish. Screwcap. 14% alc. **Rating** 90
To 2013 $18

✪   Cabernet Merlot 2010 Light, bright purple-red; if you really wish to taste (and
drink) Cabernet Merlot, and are happy with a light-bodied wine, you can't miss
this. Its red berry fruit is the core, but there are slightly savoury foresty characters
to take the wine into light food territory. And you don't have to wait for it, let
alone cellar it. Screwcap. 14% alc. **Rating** 90 To 2013 $11

ŶŶŶŶ   Chapter Three Shiraz 2010 Rating 89 To 2018 $30
Basilisk Riesling 2011 Rating 88 To 2014 $18
✪   Aimee's Garden Moscato 2011 Packaged in a standard wine bottle, but does
have a quite obvious touch of spritz; this also helps balance the sweet, musky,
strawberry fruit; further assisted by balanced acidity. A good example of the style.
Screwcap. 5.5% alc. **Rating** 88 To Now $12

McWilliam's   ★★★★★

Jack McWilliam Road, Hanwood, NSW 2680 **Region** Riverina
T (02) 6963 3400 **www**.mcwilliamswinesgroup.com **Open** Mon–Fri 10–4, Sat 10–5
Winemaker Corey Ryan, Jim Brayne, Scott McWilliam, Russell Cody, Greg Halloran
Est. 1916 **Dozens** NFP **Vyds** 445ha
The best wines to emanate from the Hanwood winery are from other regions, notably the
Barwang Vineyard at Hilltops (see separate entry), Coonawarra (Brand's Laira), Yarra Valley,
Tumbarumba and Eden Valley. As McWilliam's viticultural resources have expanded, it has
been able to produce regional blends from across Australia of startlingly good value. The 2006
sale of McWilliam's Yenda winery to Casella has led to a major upgrade in both the size and
equipment at the Hanwood winery, now the nerve centre of the business. Exports to all major
markets via a major distribution joint venture with Gallo and PLB Group.

ŶŶŶŶŶ   1877 Cabernet Sauvignon Shiraz 2008 Vivid purple hue; the complex
bouquet is absolutely beguiling, crammed full with black fruits, fine spices, well-
handled oak and a suggestion of violets; the palate is densely packed and full-
bodied, yet there is a lightness and ethereal grace that belies the 15% alc/vol on
the bottle; this will age beautifully, but offers gorgeous drinking as a young wine.
Screwcap. 15% alc. **Rating** 96 To 2040 $95 BE

Morning Light Riverina Botrytis Semillon 2009 Full gold; the real deal, with cumquat marmalade, honey and spice kept together by good acidity on the finish. Screwcap. 11% alc. **Rating** 94 **To** 2015 $25

ooooo   Hanwood Estate Shiraz 2010 Light purple-red; a distinctly well-made wine,
✪   combining parcels of grapes from many regions; the bouquet and palate offer attractive plummy fruit with some bright berry highlights; the tannin support has been particularly well judged, oak likewise. Not for the first time, has upset the apple cart with a gold medal from the National Wine Show '11. Screwcap. 13.5% alc. **Rating** 93 **To** 2016 $13

✪   Catching Thieves Margaret River Chardonnay 2010 Pale straw-green; the wine has the expected flavours of grapefruit and white peach, but what is not expected is the structure and texture of the palate, with grainy acidity doing the heavy lifting, oak largely absent. An interesting alternative view. Screwcap. 13% alc. **Rating** 91 **To** 2016 $17

✪   Hanwood Estate Cabernet Sauvignon 2009 Light to medium red-purple; light-bodied, perhaps, but has an evenly balanced and long palate with gentle cassis fruit and fine tannins in support, oak barely visible. Gold medal Sydney Wine Show '11 reflects a desire to recognise wines with elegance. Drink now. Screwcap. 13.5% alc. **Rating** 90 **To** 2014 $13

oooo   Inheritance Riesling 2011 **Rating** 89 **To** 2015 $7
✪   Catching Thieves Margaret River Semillon Sauvignon Blanc 2011 **Rating** 89 **To** 2014 $17
✪   Inheritance Chardonnay 2010 **Rating** 89 **To** Now $8
✪   Hanwood Estate Cabernet Merlot 2009 **Rating** 89 **To** 2015 $13
✪   Hanwood Estate Semillon Sauvignon Blanc 2011 **Rating** 88 **To** 2013 $12
✪   Inheritance Cabernet Merlot 2010 **Rating** 88 **To** 2013 $7
✪   Hanwood Estate Muscat NV **Rating** 88 **To** Now $13
✪   Inheritance Semillon Sauvignon Blanc 2011 **Rating** 87 **To** 2013 $7
✪   Balance Semillon Sauvignon Blanc 2011 **Rating** 87 **To** 2013 $16
✪   Hanwood Estate Chardonnay 2010 **Rating** 87 **To** 2013 $12
✪   Hanwood Estate Pinot Noir 2010 **Rating** 87 **To** 2013 $12
✪   Inheritance Shiraz Cabernet 2010 **Rating** 87 **To** 2016 $7 BE

McWilliam's Mount Pleasant   ★★★★★

Marrowbone Road, Pokolbin, NSW 2320 **Region** Hunter Valley
T (02) 4998 7505 **www**.mcwilliamswinegroup.com **Open** 7 days 10–5
Winemaker Phillip Ryan, Scott McWilliam, Corey Ryan, Gwyn Olsen **Est.** 1921
Dozens NFP **Vyds** 119ha
McWilliam's Elizabeth and the glorious Lovedale Semillon are generally commercially available with four to five years of bottle age; they are undervalued treasures with a consistently superb show record. The individual vineyard wines, together with the Maurice O'Shea memorial wines, add to the lustre of this proud name. Exports to all major markets.

ooooo   Lovedale Limited Release Hunter Valley Semillon 2007 Still pale quartz-green when five years old; festooned with gold medals and a trophy (from Rutherglen), the wine is undoubtedly superb, coming as it does from a good vintage and a very great vineyard. The interesting part is the CO_2 prickle, deliberately introduced into the wine at bottling with a minimum five years' cellaring in mind. What it does is absolutely underwrite the longer term future of an already beautiful lemon and mineral-accented wine. Screwcap. 11.5% alc. **Rating** 96 **To** 2022 $60

Maurice O'Shea Shiraz 2010 Clear red-crimson; a classic in the making; at this early point in its life, the influence of place and of variety are equally balanced, appropriate given the balance struck between oak, tannins, fruit and acidity. It will change greatly as it ages, progressively taking on the character of three wines: initially resolutely youthful; then changing as it moves towards adulthood; and finally as a mature wine that has nothing left to prove. Screwcap. 14.5% alc. **Rating** 96 **To** 2040 $75

Original Vineyard OP&OH Hunter Valley Shiraz 2010 Deep crimson, vivid hue; a pure, complex and seductive bouquet of red and blue fruits, spices and liqueur-soaked plums; despite the elegance, the latent power and ample fine-grained tannins almost move this into the full-bodied spectrum, with the oak merely showing glimpses on the finish; beautifully detailed and polished, with an extremely long life ahead. Screwcap. 14.5% alc. **Rating** 95 **To** 2050 $50 BE

✪ **Elizabeth Semillon 2006** Cellar Aged. Mid gold, vibrant green hue; a lovely blend of youthful purity and aged complexity, with lemon curd, toast and ginger; the palate is fleshy, fragrant and ready to go, but will also maintain freshness, especially as it is under screwcap. Screwcap. 10.5% alc. **Rating** 94 **To** 2018 $23 BE

✪ **Florence Adelaide Hills Sauvignon Blanc 2011** Pale straw-green; a wine right in the mainstream of Adelaide Hills Sauvignon Blanc style, fusing tropical, citrus and herb aromas and flavours into a synergistic whole, with no single part dominating; has very good balance and length. Screwcap. 12.5% alc. **Rating** 94 **To** 2013 $19

Original Vineyard Rosehill Hunter Valley Shiraz 2010 Deep garnet; a dense and mocha-laden bouquet, showing lavish levels of black fruits, toasty oak and a glimpse of fresh leather; the palate is juicy, thickly textured and generous, and providing enough structure and muscle to appease the heartiest full-bodied shiraz lover. Screwcap. 14.5% alc. **Rating** 94 **To** 2030 $38 BE

Mount Henry Shiraz Pinot 2011 Clear, light purple-crimson; all of the Maurice O'Shea connotations are brought into focus here, including his predilection for shiraz/pinot blends, dominated by shiraz. This is a wine with the potential longevity that the O'Shea wines had, and it would be a crime to drink more than an exploratory bottle now; the tight structure around the cherry kernel core, and seemingly low acidity, will be the architects of its long future. Screwcap. 14% alc. **Rating** 94 **To** 2041 $40

✪ **Jack Coonawarra Cabernet Sauvignon 2010** Named in honour of Jack McWilliam, the eldest of the McWilliam brothers, long deceased. Its trophy at the National Wine Show '11, and its top-gold at the Hobart Wine Show '11, make its price unfathomable. There is no question this is an exemplary, medium-bodied Cabernet Sauvignon, with great fruit and oak balance, and a long, supple finish. Screwcap. 14% alc. **Rating** 94 **To** 2020 $18

🍷🍷🍷🍷🍷 **Elizabeth Semillon 2011** The days are long gone when this wine was first
✪ released, at 4–5 years of age. Pale quartz-green; it has classic young Hunter Semillon aromas and flavours, with bracing acidity and lemon flavours. Needs three of four years to start opening up and softening. Screwcap. 11% alc. **Rating** 93 **To** 2025 $18

Leontine Hunter Valley Chardonnay 2011 **Rating** 93 **To** 2018 $27
High Paddock Hunter Valley Shiraz 2009 **Rating** 93 **To** 2029 $27

🍷🍷🍷🍷 **Mothervine Hunter Valley Pinot Noir 2011** **Rating** 89 **To** 2021 $36
Philip Shiraz 2009 **Rating** 89 **To** 2015 $19

Mad Dog Wines ★★★☆

PO Box 166, Tanunda, SA 5352 **Region** Barossa Valley
T (08) 8563 2758 **www.**maddogwines.com **Open** Not
Winemaker Matthew Munzberg **Est.** 1999 **Dozens** 500 **Vyds** 35ha

Geoff (aka Mad Dog) Munzberg, a third-generation grapegrower, joined with Jeremy and Heidi Holmes, Aaron and Kirsty Brasher and son Matthew to create Mad Dog Wines. Management has now passed to Matthew (also carrying the 'mad dog' mantle) after a 25-year apprenticeship. The purchase of a neighbouring vineyard in 2006 has led to the inclusion of some 100-year-old vine fruit, and the range has been extended with small amounts of Sangiovese. Exports to the UK, Canada and Denmark.

ΨΨΨΨΨ **Barossa Valley Shiraz 2008** Has retained good brightness to its hue; this is in the mainstream of Barossa shiraz style, medium- to full-bodied, with an abundance of black fruits and balanced tannins; there are also oak-influenced nuances of fruit, oak and vanilla. Screwcap. 14.5% alc. **Rating** 90 **To** 2018 $25

ΨΨΨΨ **Barossa Valley Savagnin 2011** Pale straw-green; has a convincing mix of
✪ bright fruit flavours and an almost earthy acidity; at the right price for those prepared to experiment. Screwcap. 12.1% alc. **Rating** 89 **To** 2013 $15

Madeleines Wines   ★★★★★

Lot 7 Nangkita Road, Nangkita, SA 5210 **Region** Southern Fleurieu
T 0447 009 795 **www.**vincognita.com.au **Open** By appt
Winemaker Peter Belej, Chris Dix **Est.** 1999 **Dozens** 4000 **Vyds** 42.3ha
This is the former Vincognita, jointly owned by Peter Belej and Chris Dix. The business was in fact founded by Chris, who had been winemaker with Lindemans for six years, and chief winemaker at Fox Creek Wines for five years. In 2002 Peter joined the business, with primary responsibility for the vineyards, but also with an executive winemaking role. The estate plantings are substantial, and the wines have accumulated an extraordinary number of gold medals and other awards. No wines were received for this edition; the rating is that of last year. Exports to China.

Maglieri of McLaren Vale   ★★★

GPO Box 753, Melbourne, Vic 3001 **Region** McLaren Vale
T 1300 651 650 **Open** Not
Winemaker Kate Hongell **Est.** 1972 **Dozens** 10 000
One of the better-kept secrets among the wine cognoscenti, but not among the many customers who drink thousands of cases of white and red Lambrusco every year; an example of niche marketing at its profitable best. It was a formula that proved irresistible to Beringer Blass, which acquired Maglieri in 1999. Its dry red wines are generously proportioned and full of character, the Shiraz particularly so.

ΨΨΨΨ **Shiraz 2009** Deep colour; an abundantly ripe bouquet of blackberry confiture, chocolate and mocha; the palate is sweet and forward, lacking complexity, but for those with more of a sweet tooth than a savoury one, this could be for you. Screwcap. 14.5% alc. **Rating** 87 **To** 2014 $20 BE

Magpie Estate   ★★★★★

PO Box 126, Tanunda, SA 5352 **Region** Barossa Valley
T (08) 8562 3300 **F** (08) 8562 1177 **Open** Not
Winemaker Rolf Binder, Noel Young **Est.** 1993 **Dozens** 5000
This is a partnership between Rolf Binder and Cambridge (UK) wine merchant Noel Young. It came about in 1993 when there was limited demand for or understanding of Southern Rhône-style blends based on shiraz, grenache and mourvedre. Initially a small, export-only brand, the quality of the wines was such that it has grown over the years, although the intention is to limit production. The majority of the wines are reasonably priced, the super-premiums more expensive. Exports to the UK, the US, Canada, Austria, Finland, Belgium and the Bahamas.

🍷🍷🍷🍷🍷 **The Election Barossa Valley Shiraz 2009** Strong colour; a selection of the best vineyards, and of the best barrels of that wine; it has a wonderfully complex array of black cherry, spice and oak contributions, the finish featuring fine, persistent tannins. Screwcap. 14.5% alc. **Rating** 95 **To** 2034 $65
The Gomersal Barossa Valley Grenache 2009 Good purple-red hue; has a mix of spicy/savoury aromas and flavours set among the red berry fruits and well-balanced tannins; quality French oak and a dash of shiraz also contribute. At the upper quality end of Barossa Valley grenache, with little or no confection characters. Screwcap. 14% alc. **Rating** 94 **To** 2016 $65

🍷🍷🍷🍷🍷 **The Sack Barossa Valley Shiraz 2009 Rating** 93 **To** 2024 $33
✪ **The Schnell Barossa Valley Shiraz Grenache 2009** Strongly coloured; it would seem that shiraz is the dominant partner, with its blackberry and black cherry fruit, grenache providing a touch of red berry sweetness; well-judged American and French oak complete a convincing wine with a healthy future. Screwcap. 14% alc. **Rating** 93 **To** 2018 $18
The Call Bag Barossa Valley Mourvedre Grenache 2009 Rating 91 **To** 2016 $23
The Fakir Barossa Valley Grenache 2009 Rating 90 **To** 2017 $25
The Mixed Thing 2010 Rating 90 **To** 2016 $22

🍷🍷🍷🍷 **The Salvation Barossa Valley Gewurztraminer 2011 Rating** 89 **To** 2013 $18
The Salvation Barossa Valley Gewurztraminer 2010 Rating 89 **To** 2016 $24
The Mexican Dancer Barossa Valley Viognier 2010 Rating 89 **To** 2013 $20
The Malcolm Barossa Valley Shiraz 2009 Rating 89 **To** 2029 $150
The Wit & Shanker Barossa Valley Cabernet Sauvignon 2009 Rating 87 **To** 2017 $30

Main Ridge Estate ★★★★★

80 William Road, Red Hill, Vic 3937 **Region** Mornington Peninsula
T (03) 5989 2686 **www**.mre.com.au **Open** Mon–Fri 12–4, w'ends 12–5
Winemaker Nat White **Est.** 1975 **Dozens** 1200 **Vyds** 2.8ha
Quietly spoken and charming founder/owners Nat and Rosalie White preside over their immaculately maintained vineyard and equally meticulously run winery. Their site is a particularly cool one, and if global warming proves to be a permanent part of the landscape, they say they will not be complaining.

🍷🍷🍷🍷🍷 **Half Acre Mornington Peninsula Pinot Noir 2010** Bright mid garnet; red fruits, florals and spicy notes mingle with restraint on the bouquet; the palate is fresh, taut and generous, with vibrant acidity, silky tannins and an expansive peacock's tail of flavour on full display; time will reward patient cellaring, but there is much to like about this as a young wine. Screwcap. 13.5% alc. **Rating** 95 **To** 2020 $70 BE
The Acre Mornington Peninsula Pinot Noir 2010 Sweet cherry fruit, plum confiture and seductive Asian spice accent on the bouquet; the palate is soft, supple and fine-boned, with a dominant soft side belying the undercurrent of structure that is sure to see this wine evolve with grace. Screwcap. 13.5% alc. **Rating** 94 **To** 2017 $60 BE

🍷🍷🍷🍷🍷 **Mornington Peninsula Chardonnay 2010 Rating** 92 **To** 2015 $55 BE

Mainbreak Wines

199 McDonald Road, Karridale, WA 6288 (postal) **Region** Margaret River
T (08) 9758 6779 **www**.mainbreak.net.au **Open** Not
Winemaker Contract **Est.** 2009 **Dozens** 3000

This is a small side venture to Hamelin Bay, also owned by Mainbreak Wines proprietors Richard and Roslyn Drake-Brockman. The grapes are sourced from the southern end of the Margaret River and the business has grown under the direction of winemaker and keen surfer Julian Scott. The label underlines the association between the region and its outstanding surf beaches.

ŶŶŶŶŶ **Surfers Point Margaret River Sauvignon Blanc Semillon 2011** Bright, light
○   straw-green; the two varieties come together from the get-go; sauvignon blanc
            providing the gooseberry and gently tropical fruit, semillon the lemony acidity.
            Screwcap. 13% alc. **Rating** 90 **To** 2013 $19

ŶŶŶŶ **Surfers Point Margaret River Unoaked Chardonnay 2011** **Rating** 88
          To 2014 $19

Majella   ★★★★★

Lynn Road, Coonawarra, SA 5263 **Region** Coonawarra
T (08) 8736 3055 **www.**majellawines.com.au **Open** 7 days 10–4.30
Winemaker Bruce Gregory **Est.** 1969 **Dozens** 25 000 **Vyds** 55ha
Majella is one of the foremost grapegrowers in Coonawarra, with important vineyards, principally shiraz and cabernet sauvignon, with a little riesling and merlot. The Malleea is one of Coonawarra's greatest wines, The Musician one of Australia's most outstanding red wines selling for less than $20. Exports to the UK, the US and other major markets.

ŶŶŶŶŶ **Coonawarra Cabernet Sauvignon 2009** Purple-crimson; the fragrant
            bouquet tells you of the super-elegant wine that is to follow, with vibrant
            blackcurrant and redcurrant fruit set within fine, silky tannins and quality oak.
            Screwcap. 14.5% alc. **Rating** 95 **To** 2020 $33
○   **The Musician Coonawarra Cabernet Shiraz 2010** **Rating** 94 **To** 2020 $18
            The Malleea 2009 Bright red-purple; as usual, a blend of cabernet sauvignon
            and shiraz that has an expressive fruit bouquet, the layered palate ranging through
            plum, blackberry and blackcurrant with an undertone of Coonawarra mint, the
            tannins fine and ripe, oak doing its job well. ProCork. 14.5% alc. **Rating** 94
            To 2020 $80

ŶŶŶŶŶ **Coonawarra Shiraz 2009** **Rating** 93 **To** 2020 $28
○   **Coonawarra Riesling 2011** Straw-quartz colour; has an unexpectedly expressive
            apple/apple blossom bouquet, then a firm, layered, but not phenolic, palate with
            sparks of fruit (not necessarily sugar) sweetness. Attractive early-drinking style.
            Screwcap. 11% alc. **Rating** 91 **To** 2014 $18
            Coonawarra Merlot 2010 **Rating** 90 **To** 2015 $28 BE

ŶŶŶŶ **Melody Coonawarra Rose 2011** **Rating** 89 **To** Now $18
○

Majors Lane Wines   ★★★★☆

64 Majors Lane, Lovedale, NSW 2320 **Region** Hunter Valley
T (02) 4930 7328 **www.**majorslane.com **Open** 7 days 10–5
Winemaker Daniel Binet, Andrew Thomas, David Hook **Est.** 1987 **Dozens** 800
Vyds 9.4ha
Elizabeth and Elvis Metelovski acquired Majors Lane Wines in 2010, inheriting a fully mature vineyard planted to shiraz, chardonnay, semillon, chambourcin and pinot gris. They say they are seeking to differentiate the wines by having each variety made by a winemaker with a track record for the variety in question. Thus Andrew Thomas is making the Semillon, David Hook the Pinot Grigio and Daniel Binet the Shiraz.

ＹＹＹＹＹ **Elena's Pond Hunter Valley Semillon 2011** A touch of green to the colour is
✪ encouraging; a totally delicious young Semillon, with abundant lemongrass/lemon
flavours balanced by soft but persistent acidity. As good today as in 10 years' time,
or vice versa. Screwcap. 10.9% alc. **Rating** 94 **To** 2021 $19

ＹＹＹＹ **The First Pick Hunter Valley Pinot Grigio 2011** Rating 87 **To** Now $23

Malcolm Creek Vineyard

Bonython Road, Kersbrook, SA 5231 **Region** Adelaide Hills
T (08) 8389 3619 **www**.malcolmcreekwines.com.au **Open** By appt
Winemaker Peter Leske **Est.** 1982 **Dozens** 700 **Vyds** 2ha
Malcolm Creek was set up as the retirement venture of Reg Tolley, who decided to upgrade
his retirement by selling the venture to Bitten and Karsten Pedersen in 2007. They intend to
continue making the wines in the same age-worthy style. The wines are invariably well made
and develop gracefully; they are worth seeking out, and are usually available with some extra
bottle age at a very modest price. Exports to the UK, the US and Denmark.

ＹＹＹＹＹ **Ashwood Estate Adelaide Hills Cabernet Sauvignon 2008** The feat of
picking the fruit around 13° baume in the '08 vintage has paid dividends; the
savoury blackcurrant fruit is framed by a substantial amount of French oak, but the
perfectly inserted cork should allow time for the final stages of integration to take
place without mishap. 13.5% alc. **Rating** 91 **To** 2018 $25
Ashwood Estate Adelaide Hills Cabernet Sauvignon 2007 Good retention
of hue; the relatively sweet blackcurrant and plum fruit avoids the harshness
of the vintage and provides an attractive, berry-filled wine for relatively early
consumption. Cork. 13% alc. **Rating** 90 **To** 2015 $25

ＹＹＹＹ **Adelaide Hills Sauvignon Blanc 2011** Rating 89 **To** 2013 $17

Malone Wines

PMB 47, Naracoorte, SA 5271 **Region** Wrattonbully
T (08) 8764 6075 **www**.malonewines.com.au **Open** Not
Winemaker Paulett **Est.** 2005 **Dozens** 500 **Vyds** 23ha
The third and fourth generations of the Malone family continue to farm the Talinga property,
owned by the family since 1930. The planting of vines in '98 was a minor diversification from
the core businesses of producing prime lamb, hay and pasture seed. The decision was taken
to focus on shiraz and cabernet sauvignon, with most of the grapes being sold, and limited
amounts made under the Malone label. The results have been impressive, to say the least.

ＹＹＹＹＹ **Wrattonbully Shiraz 2009** Deep colour, with blackberry, licorice and bitter
chocolate on display; full-bodied, dense and brooding, with weight the central
theme, and the tannin to carry it off. Screwcap. 14.8% alc. **Rating** 90 **To** 2020
$25 BE

Mandala ★★★★★

1568 Melba Highway, Dixons Creek, Vic 3775 **Region** Yarra Valley
T (03) 5965 2016 **www**.mandalawines.com.au **Open** 7 days 10–5
Winemaker Scott McCarthy (Contract) **Est.** 2007 **Dozens** 8400 **Vyds** 29ha
Mandala was officially opened in July 2008 by owner Charles Smedley. The estate vineyard
has vines up to 20 years old, but the spectacular restaurant and cellar door complex is a more
recent addition. The vineyards are primarily at the home base, Dixons Creek, with chardonnay
(8ha), cabernet sauvignon (6ha), sauvignon blanc and pinot noir (4ha each), shiraz (2ha) and
merlot (1ha), and a separate 4ha vineyard planted entirely to pinot noir at Yarra Junction with
an impressive clonal mix. The restaurant has deservedly achieved considerable praise. Like
many Yarra Valley wineries, no wines were made in 2009 due to smoke taint from the Black
Saturday bushfires.

ŶŶŶŶŶ Yarra Valley Shiraz 2010 Full crimson-purple; this is shiraz at its best within the context of the Yarra Valley; it is fragrant and perfumed, the red and black cherry fruits having Côte Rôtie-like touches of licorice and earth, the tannins fine and precisely measured. Screwcap. 14% alc. **Rating** 95 **To** 2025 $28

Yarra Valley Chardonnay 2010 An attractive Yarra Valley Chardonnay, with a blend of white peach, melon, grapefruit and creamy/nutty nuances; the balance, mouthfeel and length are very good indeed. Screwcap. 12.5% alc. **Rating** 94 **To** 2019 $28

Prophet Yarra Valley Pinot Noir 2010 Deeper colour than the Black Lab, with black cherry and plum allowing the framework of foresty tannins to add to complexity without in any way threatening the fruit; has excellent focus and length. Screwcap. 13.5% alc. **Rating** 94 **To** 2018 $50

Yarra Valley Cabernet Sauvignon 2010 An almost fiercely varietal Cabernet, driven from the back by powerful tannins; on retasting, the fruit fights back and prevails, and given the courtesy of five years' bottle age, the true quality of the wine will be more obvious. Screwcap. 13% alc. **Rating** 94 **To** 2025 $28

ŶŶŶŶŶ Yarra Valley Pinot Noir 2010 **Rating** 93 **To** 2016 $28

ŶŶŶŶ Yarra Valley Blanc de Blancs 2010 **Rating** 89 **To** 2013 $30
The Black Lab Yarra Valley Pinot Noir 2010 **Rating** 87 **To** 2015 $28

Mandalay Estate ★★★

Mandalay Road, Glen Mervyn via Donnybrook, WA 6239 **Region** Geographe
T (08) 9732 2006 **www.**mandalayroad.com.au **Open** 7 days 11–5
Winemaker Fermoy Estate (Liz Dawson), Faber Vineyard (John Griffiths) **Est.** 1997
Dozens 300 **Vyds** 4.2ha

Tony and Bernice O'Connell left careers in science and education to establish plantings of shiraz, chardonnay, zinfandel and cabernet sauvignon on their property in 1997. What started off as a fun venture has quickly turned into serious grapegrowing and winemaking. A hands-on approach with low yields has brought out the best characteristics of the grape varieties and the region. Most of the grapes are sold to Fermoy Estate.

ŶŶŶŶŶ Bryan Q's Geographe Chardonnay 2011 Bright straw-green; while it would
✪ seem the wine is unoaked, it has marked texture and complexity to the structure; the flavours run through grapefruit to melon and white peach, all persisting on the long finish. Screwcap. 13.1% alc. **Rating** 90 **To** 2014 $16

ŶŶŶŶ Mandalay Road Geographe Moscato 2011 **Rating** 87 **To** 2013 $15

Mandurang Valley Wines ★★★★☆

77 Fadersons Lane, Mandurang, Vic 3551 **Region** Bendigo
T (03) 5439 5367 **www.**mandurangvalleywines.com.au **Open** W'ends & Public hols 11–5 or by appt
Winemaker Wes Vine, Steve Vine **Est.** 1994 **Dozens** 4000 **Vyds** 2.5ha

Wes and Pamela Vine planted their first vineyard at Mandurang in 1976 and started making wine as a hobby. Commercial production began in '93, and an additional vineyard was established in '97. Wes (a former school principal) became full-time winemaker in '99. Son Steve has progressively taken greater responsibility for the winemaking, while Wes is spending more time developing export markets. Pamela manages the cellar door café, established in 2001 and extended in '05. Expansive lawns and gardens provide the opportunity for visitors to enjoy wine and food outdoors. Exports to China.

ŶŶŶŶŶ Old Vine 2009 A robust estate-grown blend of shiraz, cabernet sauvignon and merlot, the old vines in question planted in 1976 and '78; the wine spent 12 months in new French oak barriques, and the ripe blackcurrant fruit, the oak, and the powerful tannins all point to a wine with a long future. Screwcap. 14.3% alc. **Rating** 93 **To** 2029 $35

Bendigo Chardonnay 2010 Bright yellow-green; barrel fermentation in used French oak has contributed to the texture and, to a minor degree, to the aroma; it was picked at the optimum time, and has come through with finesse. Screwcap. 13.6% alc. **Rating** 90 **To** 2015 $22

Bendigo Shiraz 2009 Strong colour; a potent, concentrated and powerful wine that is very different from an earlier release of '09 Bendigo Shiraz, but unfortunately not differentiated on the label. If you get the good one, it gets these points. Screwcap. 14.2% alc. **Rating** 90 **To** 2029 $28

♟♟♟♟ De Vine 2010 **Rating** 87 **To** 2013 $20

Mansfield Wines ★★★☆

201 Eurunderee Lane, Mudgee, NSW 2850 **Region** Mudgee
T (02) 6373 3871 **www**.mansfieldwines.com.au **Open** Thurs–Tues & public hols 10–5, or by appt
Winemaker Bob Heslop **Est.** 1975 **Dozens** 1000 **Vyds** 5.5ha
Ian McLellan and family purchased Mansfield Wines from his cousin Peter Mansfield in late 1997. Before and after that time, the original plantings, which included chardonnay, frontignac, sauvignon blanc, cabernet sauvignon, merlot and shiraz, were removed, to be replaced by a Joseph's coat patchwork of savagnin, vermentino, petit manseng, parellada, tempranillo, touriga, zinfandel and tinta cao, supported by grenache, mourvedre and pedro ximinez. Souzao and carignan are more recent arrivals. The wines offer excellent value.

♟♟♟♟♟ Touriga Nacional 2010 The light red colour always comes as a shock when the grapes are used to make a table wine; has some of the mouthfeel and structure of Sangiovese, but the flavours are in a different red fruit spectrum, more tangy and zesty. Diam. 13.5% alc. **Rating** 90 **To** 2017 $19

♟♟♟♟ Petit Manseng 2011 **Rating** 89 **To** 2015 $19
Savagnin 2011 **Rating** 88 **To** 2015 $17
Mudgee V.P. 2004 **Rating** 88 **To** 2013 $17

Marchand & Burch ★★★★★

PO Box 180, North Fremantle, WA 6159 **Region** Great Southern
T (08) 9336 9600 **www**.marchandburchwines.com.au **Open** At Howard Park
Winemaker Pascal Marchand, Jeff Burch **Est.** 2006 **Dozens** 1100
A joint venture between Canadian-born and Burgundian-trained Pascal Marchand and the Burch family, which owns Howard Park. The wines include Chardonnay and Pinot Noir sourced from the Porongurup and Mount Barker subregions of the Great Southern, and Shiraz from Frankland River/Margaret River. The Chardonnay, in particular, is outstanding. The venture has extended to wines made by Pascal Marchand in Burgundy (tasting notes are available on www.winecompanion.com.au). Exports to the UK, the US and other major markets.

♟♟♟♟♟ Porongurup Chardonnay 2010 Developed green-gold; hand-picked and whole bunch-pressed grapes from two of the highest vineyards in the Porongurup region are wild yeast-fermented in French barriques to produce a wine with utterly exceptional intensity and length. You can't put your finger precisely on it, but this shows the Burgundian training of Pascal Marchand. Screwcap. 13.5% alc. **Rating** 97 **To** 2024 $70

Porongurup Chardonnay 2011 Bright straw-green; it has exceptional drive and intensity to the long, lingering palate, fruit flavours in the nectarine, white peach and grapefruit spectrum; oak has played its part in creating a wine with great texture and structural complexity, its destiny far in the future. Screwcap. 13% alc. **Rating** 96 **To** 2021 $70

Mount Barrow Mount Barker Pinot Noir 2011 Has significantly more colour than Gibraltar Rock, the palate following suit; here there are red and black cherry, plum, spice and fine tannins all contributing to the overall flavour, mouthfeel and length of the wine. Screwcap. 14% alc. **Rating** 94 **To** 2017 $70

Margaret River Shiraz 2009 Strong red-purple; all about elegance and balance, the bouquet a fragrant array of spice, plum and quality oak, the medium- to full-bodied palate creating a web of ripe tannins to sustain and enhance the dark fruit flavours; it also has exemplary acidity. Screwcap. 13.5% alc. **Rating** 94 **To** 2034 $65

♥♥♥♥♡ **Gibraltar Rock Porongurup Pinot Noir 2011 Rating** 92 **To** 2015 $70

Marcus Hill Vineyard ★★★★

560 Banks Road, Marcus Hill, Vic 3222 (postal) **Region** Geelong
T (03) 5222 5764 **www**.marcushillvineyard.com.au **Open** Not
Winemaker Darren Burke (Contract), Richard Harrison **Est.** 2000 **Dozens** 1000 **Vyds** 3ha
In 2000, Richard and Margot Harrison, together with 'gang pressed friends', planted 2ha of pinot noir overlooking Port Lonsdale, Queenscliff and Ocean Grove, a few kilometres from Bass Strait and Port Phillip Bay. Since then chardonnay, shiraz and more pinot noir have been added. The vineyard is run with minimal sprays, and the aim is to produce elegant wines that truly express the maritime site.

♥♥♥♥♡ Bellarine Peninsula Chardonnay 2010 Developed straw-green; it has a complex bouquet of peach and oak with differing inputs ex barrel fermentation; the palate is likewise textured, partly reflecting 40% mlf; the one weakness of the wine is diminished intensity on the finish and aftertaste. Screwcap. 13.3% alc. **Rating** 91 **To** 2015 $25
Bellarine Peninsula Shiraz 2010 Mid red-crimson; while only light- to medium-bodied, fits a lot into the bouquet and palate, with sundry spices, plum and red cherry/berry fruits, and savoury tannins from some whole bunch inclusion. Screwcap. 13% alc. **Rating** 91 **To** 2020 $20
Bellarine Peninsula Pinot Gris 2011 Pale straw-green; barrel-fermented and then matured for six months in used French oak barriques; has all of the texture one would expect from this treatment, the cool vintage accentuating the underlying citrus, apple and pear fruit. Screwcap. 12.9% alc. **Rating** 90 **To** 2013 $20
People Madly Stomping Bellarine Peninsula Pinot Noir 2009 Light, clear red; a most attractive pinot at the price, with spicy red cherry aromas and flavours, the texture quite silky, the finish long. Screwcap. 13% alc. **Rating** 90 **To** 2015 $18

♥♥♥♥ Bellarine Peninsula Pinot Noir 2009 **Rating** 87 **To** 2016 $25

Margan Family ★★★★★

1238 Milbrodale Road, Broke, NSW 2330 **Region** Hunter Valley
T (02) 6579 1317 **www**.margan.com.au **Open** 7 days 10–5
Winemaker Andrew Margan **Est.** 1997 **Dozens** 25 000 **Vyds** 98ha
Andrew Margan, following in his father's footsteps, entered the wine industry over 20 years ago, and has covered a great deal of territory since, working as a Flying Winemaker in Europe, then for Tyrrell's. Andrew and wife Lisa now have almost 100ha of fully mature vines at their Ceres Hill property at Broke, and lease the nearby Vere Vineyard. Wine quality is consistently good. The rammed-earth cellar door and restaurant are highly recommended. Exports to the UK, the US and other major markets.

♥♥♥♥♥ Aged Release Semillon 2007 The colour is still remarkably pale, the bouquet with subtle beeswax and lanolin before the palate takes total control of proceedings with the citrus flavours running from the tip of the tongue through to the finish and aftertaste. Great wine. Screwcap. 11.5% alc. **Rating** 96 **To** 2022 $35
Aged Release Semillon 2006 Glowing green-gold; has developed exactly as it should over the first five years of its life, with utterly seductive honey and lemon cake nuances backed by precise acidity. Will go on from here. Screwcap. 11% alc. **Rating** 96 **To** 2020 $35
Limited Release Semillon 2010 Light straw-green; a high-quality semillon still in the early years of a distinguished life; it has great drive and intensity to its lemon, talc and citrus acidity, leaving the mouth fresh and asking for more. Screwcap. 11% alc. **Rating** 95 **To** 2020 $30

Limited Release Shiraz 2009 The moderately deep colour has a convincing purple hue; reflects the excellent vintage and the perfect alcohol that together provide the precise dark fruit flavours of the medium- to full-bodied palate; maturation in new French oak is another positive contributor to the spicy tannins. Will be very long lived. Screwcap. 13.5% alc. **Rating** 95 **To** 2040 $50

Aged Release Shiraz 2007 Holding purple-crimson hue very well; five years young, not five years old; is still at the dawn of its life, and will continue to gain complexity as it ages over the next decade, but the creative tension between the regional earth/leather and powerful black fruits will remain. Screwcap. 13.5% alc. **Rating** 95 **To** 2037 $65

O **Hunter Valley Shiraz 2009 Rating** 94 **To** 2020 $20

Special Reserve Ripasso 2009 Ripasso is an Italian technique, with the '09 shiraz in this bottle refermented by being momentarily blended with the skins of fermented red grapes from the '10 vintage. The consequences are not especially obvious, but there is a certain roundness to the black cherry and plum fruit, and the scent of the wine is also subtly different. It is a technique not to be tried by the inexperienced. Screwcap. 14% alc. **Rating** 94 **To** 2024 $35

Aged Release Shiraz 2006 Strikingly packaged in heavy-duty bottle and unusual label. It has very strong regional earthy/tarry/spicy notes to the berry fruit; French oak also contributes to the long palate. The 40-year-old vines yielded 1 tonne per acre and 30% of the juice was removed from the must, increasing the concentration further. Despite this, has overall elegance and attractive juicy flavours. Screwcap. 14.5% alc. **Rating** 94 **To** 2026 $65

ΨΨΨΨΨ **Limited Release Shiraz Mourvedre 2009 Rating** 93 **To** 2024 $35
Limited Release Cabernet Sauvignon 2009 Rating 93 **To** 2029 $30
Limited Release Chardonnay 2011 Rating 92 **To** 2017 $30
Limited Release Barbera 2009 Rating 92 **To** 2015 $30

✪ **Hunter Valley Semillon 2011** Positive green-quartz colour, but no oak used; simply 40-year-old vines and possibly some skin contact; the palate is generously endowed with flavour on the mid palate; from red volcanic soil. Screwcap. 12.5% alc. **Rating** 91 **To** 2018 $18
Limited Release Chardonnay 2010 Rating 91 **To** 2014 $30

ΨΨΨΨ **Hunter Valley Verdelho 2011 Rating** 89 **To** 2015 $18
✪ **Hunter Valley Shiraz Saignee Rose 2011 Rating** 89 **To** 2013 $17
Hunter Valley Merlot 2009 Rating 89 **To** 2016 $20
Limited Release Barbera 2010 Rating 89 **To** 2014 $30

Maritime Estate   ★★★★☆

65 Tucks Road, Red Hill, Vic 3937 **Region** Mornington Peninsula
T 0432 931 890 **www**.maritime-estate.com.au **Open** Not
Winemaker Sandro Mosele **Est.** 1988 **Dozens** 1000 **Vyds** 4.5ha
Maritime Estate is the venture of the Ruljancich family since brothers John and Kevin purchased the property in 1993. The first vines had been established by Dr Hugh Robinson, who continued to be involved with the vineyard for many years, until management passed to the present viticulturist, Matthew Frewer. Plantings were expanded in '95 to their present level of 2.7ha of MV6, 114, 115 and 777 clones of pinot noir, 1ha of chardonnay and 0.8ha of pinot gris. The family's involvement with wine dates back to the early 1800s, with vines on the tiny Dalmatian island of Vis, Croatia. The Ruljancichs migrated to Australia in 1946, but the vineyard on Vis was still being attended until the '80s by John and Kevin's uncle. John died in 2007, but the business continues on under the care of Kevin and John's children, Jane, Paul and Sally.

ΨΨΨΨΨ **Mornington Peninsula Chardonnay 2010** Pale straw-green; an elegant chardonnay, picked at the right moment to give crystal clear varietal expression, with white peach and nectarine tempered by citrussy acidity and subtle, nutty French oak. Screwcap. 13% alc. **Rating** 93 **To** 2017 $34

Mornington Peninsula Pinot Gris 2010 A wine that shows the extra depth that the Mornington Peninsula seems to attain with its pinot gris, perhaps reflecting the fact that it was one of the first out of the blocks with the variety (along with Tasmania) and the suitability of the climate. That said, the flavours are 100% mainstream. Screwcap. 14% alc. **Rating** 91 **To** 2013 $24

Mornington Peninsula Pinot Noir 2010 Light, bright crimson-magenta; a complex pinot, with spice and forest fruits to the fore on both bouquet and palate; has more length than depth, which is perhaps no bad thing. Screwcap. 13.5% alc. **Rating** 91 **To** 2015 $34

Marius Wines   ★★★★★

PO Box 545, Willunga, SA 5172 **Region** McLaren Vale
T 0402 344 340 **www**.mariuswines.com.au **Open** By appt
Winemaker Roger Pike, James Hastwell **Est.** 1994 **Dozens** 1000 **Vyds** 1.8ha

Roger Pike says he has loved wine for over 30 years; that for 15 years he has had the desire to add a little bit to the world of wine; and that over a decade ago he decided to do something about it, ripping the front paddock and planting shiraz in 1994. He sold the grapes from the 1997–99 vintages, but when the '98 vintage became a single vineyard wine (made by the purchaser of the grapes), selling in the US at $40, the temptation to make his own wine became irresistible. No wines were made in 2009 due to the impact of the short heatwave at a critical point in the middle of veraison. Rather than compromise with a second label, he decided to skip the vintage altogether, and was richly rewarded with an array of high-quality wines from 2010.

🍷🍷🍷🍷🍷 **Symphony Single Vineyard McLaren Vale Shiraz 2010** Similar colour to Simpatico; comes from a special part of the Home Block and is matured in new and used French oak, but otherwise made in identical fashion. A wine of extreme length, perfect balance and great texture, able to outlive most who taste it. Screwcap. 14.5% alc. **Rating** 96 **To** 2050 $40

Simpatico Single Vineyard McLaren Vale Shiraz 2010 Dense purple-crimson; a wine of exceptional concentration and power coming from the 1.8ha estate Home Block, open-fermented, basket-pressed, and spending 21 months in French and American oak. The array of black fruits, tannins and oak justify long-term cellaring. Screwcap. 14.5% alc. **Rating** 94 **To** 2030 $27

🍷🍷🍷🍷♀ **Matarius Single Vineyard McLaren Vale Mataro 2010** Rating 93 **To** 2030 $38

Symposium McLaren Vale Shiraz Mourvedre 2010 Rating 90 **To** 2020 $35

Marq Wines   ★★★★☆

2 Gibson Drive, Dunsborough, WA 6281 (postal) **Region** Margaret River
T 0411 122 662 **www**.marqwines.com.au **Open** Not
Winemaker Mark Warren **Est.** 2011 **Dozens** 1000

Mark Warren has a degree in wine science from CSU and a science degree from the University of WA; to complete the circle, he is currently lecturing in wine science and wine sensory processes at Curtin University, Margaret River – the last position held for the past eight years. He also has 22 years' experience in both the Swan Valley and Margaret River, and his current major commercial role is producing the extensive Happs range as well as wines under contract for several other Margaret River wine brands. When all of this is added up, he is responsible for 60 to 70 individual wines each year, now including six wines under his own Marq Wines label. A quick look at the list (Vermentino, Fiano, Wild Ferment Chardonnay, Gamay, Tempranillo and Malbec, with an Amarone Shiraz in the pipeline) points to the underlying philosophy: an exploration of the potential of alternative varieties and unusual winemaking methods by someone with an undoubted technical understanding of the processes involved. The wines are produced in very small amounts: 100–200 dozen of each.

ŶŶŶŶŶ Wild Ferment Margaret River Chardonnay 2010 Light straw-green; a fragrant and stylish bouquet is a prelude to the song of grapefruit, white peach and restrained mineral acidity on the palate, with some funky notes deliberately added for complexity. Screwcap. 13% alc. **Rating** 95 **To** 2018 $28

ŶŶŶŶŶ Margaret River Vermentino 2011 **Rating** 93 **To** 2014 $25
Margaret River Malbec 2009 **Rating** 91 **To** 2020 $28
Margaret River Tempranillo 2010 **Rating** 90 **To** 2018 $28

ŶŶŶŶ Margaret River Fiano 2011 **Rating** 89 **To** 2014 $25
Margaret River Gamay 2010 **Rating** 89 **To** 2013 $25

Marri Wood Park

Caves Road, Yallingup, WA 6282 **Region** Margaret River
T 0438 525 580 **www**.marriwoodpark.com.au **Open** 7 days 11–5
Winemaker Ian Bell, Bob Cartwright **Est.** 1993 **Dozens** 1500 **Vyds** 7ha
With plantings commencing in 1993, Marri Wood Park has 2.2ha of chenin blanc, 1.6ha of sauvignon blanc, 1.5ha of cabernet sauvignon, with semillon, malbec and merlot making up the total; part of the grape production is sold to other makers. The budget-priced Guinea Run range takes its name from the guinea fowl which are permanent vineyard residents, busily eating the grasshoppers, weevils and bugs that cluster around the base of the vines, thus reducing the need for pesticides. The vineyard is certified 'In Conversion Biodynamic' and since the 2009 vintage, the wines have been biodynamic.

Marsh Estate

Deasy's Road, Pokolbin, NSW 2321 **Region** Hunter Valley
T (02) 4998 7587 **www**.marshestate.com.au **Open** Mon–Fri 10–4.30, w'ends 10–5
Winemaker Andrew Marsh **Est.** 1971 **Dozens** 4000 **Vyds** 32ha
Through sheer consistency, value for money and unrelenting hard work, the Marsh family has built up a sufficiently loyal cellar door and mailing list clientele to allow all the production to be sold direct. Wine style is always straightforward, with oak playing a minimal role, and prolonged cellaring paying handsome dividends.

ŶŶŶŶŶ Holly's Block Hunter Valley Semillon 2011 Vibrant green hue; the bouquet is fine, pure and focused, exhibiting classic lemon and lime sherbet and straw; the palate is taut and racy, with enough generosity for early consumption, yet also trim enough to put on some weight over the coming years. Screwcap. 12% alc. **Rating** 94 **To** 2020 $30 BE

ŶŶŶŶŶ Vat N Hunter Valley Cabernet Sauvignon 2009 **Rating** 90 **To** 2016 $37 BE

ŶŶŶŶ Poppy's Maverick Hunter Valley Semillon 2011 **Rating** 89 **To** 2016 $27 BE
Private Bin Hunter Valley Shiraz 2010 **Rating** 88 **To** 2015 $49 BE
Vat R Hunter Valley Shiraz 2010 **Rating** 87 **To** 2015 $37 BE

Mason Wines ★★★☆

27850 New England Highway, Glen Aplin, Qld 4381 **Region** Granite Belt
T (07) 4684 1341 **www**.masonwines.com.au **Open** Wed–Sun 10–4
Winemaker Anthony Rametta **Est.** 1998 **Dozens** 3000 **Vyds** 30.5ha
Robert and Kim Mason set strict criteria when searching for land suited to viticulture: a long history of commercial stone fruit production with well-drained, deep soil. The first property was purchased in 1997, the vines planted thereafter. A second property was purchased in 2000, and a cellar door was constructed. They have planted cabernet sauvignon, chardonnay, shiraz, merlot, viognier, semillon, verdelho, sauvignon blanc and petit verdot. Yet another Queenslander on the ascent. Exports to Japan.

♟♟♟♟ **Cellar Collection Granite Belt Cabernet Merlot 2010** Deep crimson; the bouquet offers ripe red and black fruits, and a splash of licorice; the palate is medium-bodied and has moderate concentration and complexity; an easy-going wine. Screwcap. 13.5% alc. **Rating** 88 **To** 2016 $22 BE
Granite Belt Cabernet Sauvignon 2010 Bright mulberry fruit with a savoury accent of leather; the palate is medium-bodied with tangy acidity and fine tannins to conclude. Screwcap. 13.5% alc. **Rating** 88 **To** 2016 $20 BE

Massena Vineyards

PO Box 54, Tanunda, SA 5352 **Region** Barossa Valley
T (08) 8564 3037 **www**.massena.com.au **Open** At Artisans of Barossa
Winemaker Dan Standish, Jaysen Collins **Est.** 2000 **Dozens** 5000 **Vyds** 4ha
Massena Vineyards draws upon 1ha each of mataro (mourvedre), saperavi, petite syrah and tannat at Nuriootpa, also purchasing grapes from other growers. It is an export-oriented business, although the wines can be purchased by mail order, which, given both the quality and innovative nature of the wines, seems more than ordinarily worthwhile. Exports to the UK, the US and other major markets.

♟♟♟♟♟ **The Eleventh Hour 2009** Strong red-purple; the bouquet is full of promise, with dark fruits and quality oak both having their say, and the medium- to full-bodied palate does not disappoint; gently spicy blackberry fruit runs through to the back-palate, where fine, ripe yet savoury tannins come to the fore, investing the wine with class and balance. The cork is no doubt for the benefit of the US market. 14.5% alc. **Rating** 95 **To** 2029 $38
Barossa Valley Tannat 2010 Dense, deep, impenetrable purple; I thought I might need a mouth replacement as I went to taste the wine, but in fact the tannins are ripe, balanced and, indeed, subservient to the juicy black fruits of the palate. A fascinating wine, with the ability to long outlive its cork provided everything goes right, something that Murphy tries to guard against. 14.5% alc. **Rating** 94 **To** 2030 $25

♟♟♟♟♀ **Barossa Valley Barbera 2011 Rating** 90 **To** 2018 $25

♟♟♟♟ **The Moonlight Run 2009 Rating** 89 **To** 2016 $27

Massoni

30 Brasser Avenue, Dromana, Vic 3936 **Region** Pyrenees/Mornington Peninsula
T (03) 5981 0711 **www**.massoniwines.com **Open** Not
Winemaker Robert Paul **Est.** 1984 **Dozens** 9600 **Vyds** 277.5ha
Massoni is a substantial business owned by the Pellegrino and Ursini families, and is a venture with two completely distinct arms. In terms of vineyard and land size, by far the largest is the GlenKara vineyard in the Pyrenees (269ha). It endured years of drought, which finally broke in 2010, giving the venture much to look forward to. It also has 8.5ha on the Mornington Peninsula where Massoni started, and where it gained its reputation.

♟♟♟♟♟ **Mornington Peninsula Chardonnay 2010** Pale quartz-green; estate-grown,
✪ hand-picked grapes were pressed, fermented in and thereafter matured for 11 months in, French oak barriques. The strikingly juicy citrus and white peach fruit is the sole driver of the long palate and cleansing finish. Screwcap. 13.5% alc. **Rating** 94 **To** 2016 $25

♟♟♟♟♀ **Pyrenees Ranges Shiraz 2008** Deep purple-crimson; a very rich wine from
✪ drought-stressed vines, yet not harsh or extractive; blackcurrant and blackberry flavours are dominant, and the tannins are soft. Can be drunk now or much later. Screwcap. 14.5% alc. **Rating** 93 **To** 2018 $25
Mornington Peninsula Sauvignon Blanc 2010 Rating 92 **To** Now $25
Mornington Peninsula Pinot Noir 2010 Rating 92 **To** 2017 $30
Pyrenees Ranges Merlot 2008 Rating 90 **To** 2018 $25

Matilda's Estate ★★★★★

18 Hamilton Road, Denmark, WA 6333 **Region** Denmark
T (08) 9848 2622 **www**.matildasestate.com **Open** 7 days 11–5
Winemaker Coby Ladwig, Brenden Smith **Est.** 1990 **Dozens** 5000 **Vyds** 10ha
In 2003 the founders of Matilda's Meadow (as it was then known), Don Turnbull and Pamela Meldrum, sold the business to former citizen of the world Steve Hall. It is a thriving business based on the estate plantings of chardonnay, semillon, sauvignon blanc, pinot noir, cabernet sauvignon, cabernet franc, shiraz and merlot. The construction of an onsite winery in 2007 and the building of a substantial restaurant and event facility marked a significant change in the tempo of the business. Exports to Malaysia, Singapore and Hong Kong.

ŸŸŸŸŸ Chardonnay 2010 Full green-yellow-gold; an estate-grown wine that fully reflects the very cool climate of Denmark; it is driven by its nectarine, white peach and citrus fruit, oak all but incidental. Screwcap. 13% alc. **Rating** 94 **To** 2017 $35
Shiraz 2009 Bright purple-crimson; the aromatic red berry bouquet leads into a spicy medium-bodied palate with red and black cherry fruit drawn out on the long finish by fine, persistent tannins. From the Great Southern, and a very good example of cool-grown shiraz. Screwcap. 14% alc. **Rating** 94 **To** 2019 $25
Cabernet Merlot Cabernet Franc 2010 Clear, light red-purple; a blend of 55% cabernet sauvignon, 40% merlot and 5% cabernet franc grown in several subregions in Great Southern. The bouquet has fragrant cassis and red berry aromas that are also foremost on the palate, albeit joined by positive tannins and sweet, warm oak that extend the finish. Screwcap. 14% alc. **Rating** 94 **To** 2019 $25

ŸŸŸŸŸ Quarram Rocks Sauvignon Blanc Semillon 2010 Rating 92
O   To 2013 $14
O   Shiraz Cabernet 2009 Rating 91 To 2020 $18
O   Quarram Rocks Sauvignon Blanc Semillon 2011 Rating 90 To 2013 $14
O   Sauvignon Blanc Semillon Chenin Blanc 2011 Rating 90 To Now $18
O   Sauvignon Blanc Semillon Chenin Blanc 2010 Rating 90 To 2013 $18

ŸŸŸŸ Quarram Rocks Pinot Noir 2010 Rating 89
O   To Now $14
O   Quarram Rocks Cabernet Shiraz 2009 Rating 88 To 2013 $14

Maverick Wines ★★★★★

Lot 141 Light Pass Road, Vine Vale, Moorooroo, SA 5352 **Region** Barossa Valley
T (08) 8563 3551 **www**.maverickwines.com.au **Open** By appt
Winemaker Ronald Brown **Est.** 2004 **Dozens** 10 000 **Vyds** 35.82ha
This is the very successful venture of Ronald Brown, Jeremy Vogler and Adrian Bell. Taking advantage of excess grape production in Australia, the partners have acquired four vineyards in key areas of the Eden Valley and Barossa Valley, with vines ranging in age from 40 to over 140 years. The wines are made in small batches in tanks of 0.5–3-tonne capacity, and are then matured in French oak. Maverick has achieved listings in top restaurants and fine wine retailers in Australia and internationally. Exports to the UK, the US, Canada, France, Scandinavia, Russia, Cambodia, Malaysia, Thailand, Singapore, Hong Kong, Japan and China.

ŸŸŸŸŸ Old Ben Eden Valley Shiraz 2009 Intense purple-crimson; this estate vineyard has three small blocks (total 3.2ha) of 90-year-old shiraz; the wine is densely packed with spicy black fruits that expand progressively in the mouth; clever oak handling has added another layer in support of the fruit, and the gently savoury tannins have been precisely judged. Cork. 14.5% alc. **Rating** 96 **To** 2029 $50
Greenock Rise Barossa Valley Shiraz 2009 Healthy crimson-purple; while full-bodied like all of the '09 Maverick Shirazs, has a degree of elegance tracking the supple, rounded and very long palate, replete with black cherry, blackberry and spice. Cork. 14% alc. **Rating** 95 **To** 2029 $60

Trial Hill Eden Valley Shiraz 2008 From the 1.6ha estate vineyard high in the Eden Valley. The strong colour and very complex aromas and flavours are a tribute to the site; the fruit is predominantly in the black spectrum, leavened by quality oak, fine, savoury tannins and hints of spice and licorice. Cork. 14.5% alc. Rating 95 To 2028 $70

✪ Twins Barossa Grenache Shiraz Mourvedre 2010 Exceptional colour; the twins are the Greenock Rise and Trial Hill Vineyards, the source of the grenache; the wine has stunning drive and vigour, characters rarely encountered with this blend. The dark plum and black cherry flavours have a twist of licorice and spicy tannins to close. Exceptional value. Screwcap. 13.8% alc. Rating 95 To 2025 $25
Paraview Barossa Valley Shiraz 2008 Medium red-purple; from the Paraview Vineyard in the Stonewell area, this wine must surely have been picked before the heatwave; that said, it is full-bodied, with a panoply of red and black fruit flavours, the tannins and oak perfectly integrated. Cork. 14% alc. Rating 94 To 2023 $40

♟♟♟♟♀ Twins Barossa Shiraz 2009 Rating 93 To 2024 $25
✪ Twins Barossa Valley Cabernet Sauvignon Merlot Petit Verdot Cabernet Franc 2009 Good colour; the wine has better varietal fruit quality than the Barossa Valley should be able to provide, particularly in a year such as '09; obviously, attention to detail in the vineyard and in the winery is paying dividends; it is also an object lesson in controlling alcohol. All up, a very attractive wine. Screwcap. 13.5% alc. Rating 93 To 2019 $25
✪ Breechens 2009 Bright crimson-red; this Barossa-grown shiraz has marked red fruit fragrance leading into a lively, light- to medium-bodied palate with blackberry and red cherry supported by superfine, silky tannins and integrated oak. Screwcap. 14% alc. Rating 92 To 2019 $18

♟♟♟♟ Trial Hill Eden Valley Riesling 2011 Rating 89 To 2015 $25
Twins Eden Valley Chardonnay 2010 Rating 89 To 2014 $25
Breechens Blend Barossa White 2010 Rating 89 To 2014 $18

Maximus Wines   ★★★★☆

Cnr Foggo Road/Penny's Road, McLaren Vale, SA 5171 **Region** McLaren Vale
T (08) 8323 8777 **www**.maximuswinesaustralia.com.au **Open** W'ends & public hols 11–4
Winemaker Scott Rawlinson **Est.** 2007 **Dozens** NA **Vyds** 1.82ha
Sailing master Rowland Short, having run one of Australia's most successful sailing schools, decided (in his words) 'to brave the choppy waters of the Australian wine industry' by establishing Maximus Wines in partnership with wife Shelley. They purchased an already-planted shiraz vineyard, and built a cellar door using sandstone blocks, with western red cedar doors and windows. It is built into the side of a hill, and has a barrel store underneath for maturing cask and bottled wine. Grapes are purchased from other vineyards in McLaren Vale, and the wines are contract-made by local winemaker Scott Rawlinson.

♟♟♟♟♟ McLaren Vale Cabernet Sauvignon 2010 Dense crimson-purple; a potent black-fruited bouquet carries through to the full-bodied palate with layers of black fruits, licorice, dark chocolate and savoury notes from the small percentage of petit verdot included. Screwcap. 14.6% alc. Rating 94 To 2030 $25

♟♟♟♟♀ Old Vine McLaren Vale Grenache 2010 Rating 92 To 2018 $25
Adelaide Hills Chardonnay 2010 Rating 91 To 2015 $25

♟♟♟♟ McLaren Vale Grenache Tempranillo Rose 2011 Rating 89 To Now $20
McLaren Vale Cabernet Shiraz 2010 Rating 88 To 2015 $25
McLaren Vale Tempranillo 2010 Rating 87 To 2015 $25

Maxwell Wines

Olivers Road, McLaren Vale, SA 5171 **Region** McLaren Vale
T (08) 8323 8200 **www**.maxwellwines.com.au **Open** 7 days 10–5
Winemaker Alexia Roberts **Est.** 1979 **Dozens** 17 000 **Vyds** 28.5ha

Over the past 30 years Maxwell Wines has carved out a reputation as a premium producer in McLaren Vale. The brand has produced some excellent red wines in recent years, making the most of the solid limestone hill in the Seaview area on which the winery and vineyards are situated. The majority of the vines on the estate were planted in 1972, and include 19 rows of the highly regarded Reynella Selection cabernet sauvignon. The Ellen Street shiraz block in front of the winery was planted in '53. During vintage, visitors to the elevated cellar door can watch the gravity-flow operations in the winery as the winemaking team plunge and pump-over the red ferments. Owned and operated by Mark Maxwell. Exports to all major markets.

Eocene Ancient Earth McLaren Vale Shiraz 2009 Sourced from the oldest vines on the estate, planted on marine limestone created 34–56 million years ago. Here the wine has spent 22 months in French oak and is significantly better balanced than Ellen Street, the fruit having greater freedom of expression; the gently spicy/savoury palate has excellent length and balance. Screwcap. 14.5% alc. **Rating** 94 **To** 2029 $45

Minotaur Reserve McLaren Vale Shiraz 2009 Deep, dense purple-red; the wine is almost a caricature of McLaren Vale shiraz: full-bodied and filling every corner and crevice of the mouth with its sultry black fruits and bitter chocolate, the impact magnified by the strong, although ripe, tannins. For lovers of monster minotaurs. Another 10 years would have been added to the drink-to date if the wine had a screwcap. Cork. 14.5% alc. **Rating** 94 **To** 2030 $75

K.I. Kangaroo Island Shiraz 2010 Strong purple-crimson; the savoury, bramble, spicy overtones to the plum and black cherry fruit attest to the cool climate of Kangaroo Island, strongly influenced as it is by winds from the Southern Ocean; the finish has particular appeal. Screwcap. 14% alc. **Rating** 93 **To** 2025 $25

Silver Hammer McLaren Vale Shiraz 2010 Has ripe black fruits, elements of char and tar, and a fresh and vibrant personality, with lots of energy; unencumbered by heavy-handed winemaking, this is sure to please. Screwcap. 14.5% alc. **Rating** 92 **To** 2020 $20 BE

Ellen Street McLaren Vale Shiraz 2009 Rating 92 **To** 2024 $40
Four Roads McLaren Vale Shiraz Grenache 2010 Rating 90 **To** 2017 $20 BE

Little Demon McLaren Vale Cabernet Merlot 2010 Full red-purple; McLaren Vale may not be the most obvious region for this 75/25% blend, but the wine has considerable flavour and presence, 16 months in French oak adding to the parcel. Outstanding value. Screwcap. 14.5% alc. **Rating** 90 **To** 2018 $15

Adelaide Hills Chardonnay 2010 Rating 89 **To** 2014 $22
Lime Cave McLaren Vale Cabernet 2009 Rating 88 **To** 2020 $40

Mayer ★★★★★

66 Miller Road, Healesville, Vic 3777 **Region** Yarra Valley
T (03) 5967 3779 **www.**timomayer.com.au **Open** By appt
Winemaker Timo Mayer **Est.** 1999 **Dozens** 600

Timo Mayer, also winemaker at Gembrook Hill Vineyard, teamed with partner Rhonda Ferguson to establish Mayer Vineyard on the slopes of Mt Toolebewoong, 8km south of Healesville. The steepness of those slopes is presumably 'celebrated' in the name given to the wines (Bloody Hill). There is just under 2.5ha of vineyard, the lion's share to pinot noir and smaller amounts of shiraz and chardonnay – all high-density plantings. Mayer's winemaking credo is minimal interference and handling, and no filtration.

Close Planted Yarra Valley Pinot Noir 2010 Crystal clear crimson; a distinguished pinot almost living up to the cheeky label (inspired by that of Rousseau's Grand Cru Chambertin); it is very intense, with red and black cherry fruit, spice and perfectly judged savoury/earthy nuances to the fine tannins on the exceptionally long palate. Diam. 13.5% alc. **Rating** 97 **To** 2019 $60

Bloody Hill Yarra Valley Chardonnay 2010 Pale straw-green; a very elegant wine with perfectly ripened grapes providing a midpoint between white peach and nectarine on the one side, grapefruit and natural acidity on the other; the oak is suitably restrained, and the balance cannot be faulted. Diam. 13% alc. **Rating** 94 **To** 2018 $40

Big Betty Yarra Valley Shiraz 2010 Light crimson-purple; a fascinating bouquet with a cinnamon spice overlay, the medium-bodied palate with zesty red cherry fruit and fine but savoury tannins drawing out the finish. Diam. 13% alc. **Rating** 94 **To** 2020 $40

Mayfield Vineyard

Icely Road, Orange, NSW 2800 **Region** Orange
T (02) 6365 9292 **www.**mayfieldvineyard.com **Open** Wed–Sun 10–4
Winemaker Jon Reynolds **Est.** 1998 **Dozens** 11 000 **Vyds** 40.4ha
The property – including the house in which owners Richard and Kathy Thomas now live, and its surrounding arboretum – has a rich history as a leading Suffolk sheep stud, founded upon the vast fortune accumulated by the Crawford family via its biscuit business in the UK. The Thomases planted the vineyard in 1998, with merlot (12ha) leading the way, followed (in descending order) by cabernet sauvignon, sauvignon blanc, chardonnay, pinot noir, riesling and sangiovese. The wines are marketed under the Mayfield Vineyard and Icely Road brands. Exports to the UK and Asia.

♛♛♛♛♛
✪ **Icely Rd Orange Riesling 2011** Pale quartz-green; lime and apple blossom aromas fill the bouquet, the fresh, long and beautifully balanced palate capturing all the fruit promised by the bouquet. Screwcap. 13.5% alc. **Rating** 94 **To** 2021 $20

Single Vineyard Orange Riesling 2008 First tasted three years ago; the colour is still that of a 1- or 2-year-old wine, not 4-year-old; likewise the bouquet and palate are fragrant and full of zest, the flavours still focused on apple and citrus fruit. Screwcap. 12.5% alc. **Rating** 94 **To** 2018 $28

✪ **Icely Rd Sauvignon Blanc 2011** Estate-grown, and picked at different levels of ripeness; has that inherent balance of flavours that seems to be part and parcel of sauvignon blanc from Orange; tropical, gooseberry and sweet citrus fruits are welded together into an indivisible whole; the finish is supple and balanced. Quality wine at a mouth-watering price. Screwcap. 12% alc. **Rating** 94 **To** 2013 $20

Single Vineyard Orange Chardonnay 2011 Has significantly greater texture and structure than the Icely Rd, although the underlying fruit has many things in common. A wine that will flourish over the next 3–5 years. Screwcap. 13% alc. **Rating** 94 **To** 2018 $28

Single Vineyard Orange Cabernet Sauvignon 2009 Bright red-purple; an immediately attractive Cabernet that manages to combine positive varietal character with quite elegant fruit, fine tannins and good oak; fruit drives right through the palate beside more savoury notes. Screwcap. 14% alc. **Rating** 94 **To** 2024 $28

♛♛♛♛♕
✪ **Icely Rd Orange Chardonnay 2011** Bright straw-green; the fragrant and flowery bouquet is a precise introduction into the delicious nectarine and white peach flavours of the palate, oak in the background for those who look for it. Screwcap. 13% alc. **Rating** 93 **To** 2017 $20

✪ **Icely Rd Orange Merlot 2009** Good hue, although on the light side; the fragrant, red fruit bouquet comes through with total clarity on the palate, with a mix of red berry and plum flavours offset by notes of black olive and fine-grained tannins; as it should be, medium-bodied, but with overall length and intensity. Screwcap. 14% alc. **Rating** 93 **To** 2018 $20

Single Vineyard Orange Pinot Noir 2009 Rating 91 **To** 2015 $35

✪ **Icely Rd Orange Rose 2011** A blend of sangiovese, pinot noir and cabernet sauvignon, an eclectic assemblage that, one assumes, was dictated by the vintage; it has both flavour and textural complexity, with a long palate and a dry finish. Screwcap. 12.5% alc. **Rating** 90 **To** 2013 $20

Mayford Wines ★★★★★

6815 Great Alpine Road, Porepunkah, Vic 3740 **Region** Alpine Valleys
T (03) 5756 2528 **www**.mayfordwines.com **Open** By appt
Winemaker Eleana Anderson **Est.** 1995 **Dozens** 500 **Vyds** 3ha

The roots of Mayford go back to 1995, when forester Brian Nicholson planted a small amount of shiraz, since extended to its present level with 0.8ha. Chardonnay (1.6ha) and tempranillo (0.6ha). In the words of their backgrounder, 'in-house winemaking commenced shortly after he selected his seasoned winemaker bride [in '02], and the first Mayford wines were released in '07'. Wife and co-owner Eleana Anderson became a Flying Winemaker, working four vintages in Germany while completing her wine science degree at CSU (having much earlier obtained an arts degree). Vintages in Australia included one at Boynton's Feathertop (also at Porepunkah), where she met her husband-to-be. Initially, she was unenthusiastic about the potential of tempranillo, which Brian had planted after consultation with Mark Walpole, Brown Brothers' viticulturist, but since making the first vintage in '06 she has been thoroughly enamoured with the variety. The hillside plantings on hungry soils keep vigour and yields down, the three-tonne harvest fermented in six half-tonne batches. Eleana practises minimalist winemaking, declining to use enzymes, cultured yeasts, tannins and/or copper.

♟♟♟♟♟ **Porepunkah Shiraz 2009** Vivid crimson hue; the Alpine Valleys GI often produces wines with a savoury edge, and this is no exception; ripe black cherry, blackberry, fresh sap, spice and a mineral edge of struck quartz; medium-bodied with refreshing acidity and ripe, gravelly tannins providing a long and engaging conclusion. Cork. 14% alc. **Rating** 95 **To** 2020 $36 BE
Porepunkah Tempranillo 2010 This is benchmark Australian tempranillo, with a black fruit-laden bouquet offering cola, spice and charcuterie complexity; medium-bodied, luscious, refreshing and savoury, the tannins are in complete harmony with the fruit; if you have an itch to see how good Australian tempranillo can be, look no further. Cork. 14% alc. **Rating** 95 **To** 2015 $35 BE

♟♟♟♟ **Porepunkah Chardonnay 2010 Rating** 87 **To** 2014 $34 BE

Maygars Hill Winery ★★★★☆

53 Longwood-Mansfield Road, Longwood, Vic 3665 **Region** Strathbogie Ranges
T 0402 136 448 **www**.strathbogieboutiquewines.com **Open** By appt
Winemaker Contract **Est.** 1997 **Dozens** 1100 **Vyds** 3.2ha

Jenny Houghton purchased this 8ha property in 1994, planting shiraz (1.9ha) and cabernet sauvignon (1.3ha), and establishing a stylish B&B cottage. The name comes from Lieutenant Colonel Maygar, who fought with outstanding bravery in the Boer War in South Africa in 1901, and was awarded the Victoria Cross. In World War I he rose to command the 8th Light Horse Regiment, winning yet further medals for bravery. He died on 1 November 1917. Exports to Fiji.

♟♟♟♟♟
✪ **Reserve Shiraz 2010** Labelled Reserve and indeed is reserved in personality; · fine, fragrant and complex, and certainly not as concentrated as the 'normal'; the intriguing aspect of this medium-bodied and fragrant wine is the texture of the tannins, which are silky and fine, and the finish, which is long and lacy; a wine that relies on subtlety rather than brute force, and is all the better for it. Screwcap. 14.5% alc. **Rating** 94 **To** 2020 $36 BE

♟♟♟♟♟ **Shiraz 2010 Rating** 90 **To** 2017 $24 BE
Reserve Cabernet Sauvignon 2010 Rating 90 **To** 2015 $36 BE

♟♟♟♟ **Shiraz 2008 Rating** 89 **To** 2016 $20
Cabernet Sauvignon 2010 Rating 87 **To** 2014 $24 BE

Mayhem & Co

39 Sydney Road, Nairne, SA 5252 **Region** Adelaide Hills
T (08) 8188 0011 **www**.mayhemandcowine.com.au **Open** Not
Winemaker Brendon Keys **Est.** 2009 **Dozens** 3000 **Vyds** 2.5ha

This is the venture of farmer Andrew Taylor, with significant involvement of winemaker Brendon Keys. Andrew had long harboured an ambition to build a winery in the Adelaide Hills, and Brendon, having worked vintages in NZ, Australia, the US and Argentina, was only too happy to join the venture. The estate vineyard is planted to sauvignon blanc; the remaining wines are made from grapes purchased from various local growers. Exports to Singapore.

ŶŶŶŶŶ **Wicked Adelaide Hills Chardonnay 2010** Rating 93
○   To 2016 $19
       Newcomer Adelaide Hills Pinot Noir 2009 Light crimson; wild yeast-
       fermented with 30 days on skins, then aged in 10% new French oak; the fruit has
       stood up manfully, but you can see the edges lopped off, complexity not entirely
       compensating. Brave effort. Screwcap. 13.5% alc. **Rating** 92 **To** 2016 $24

ŶŶŶŶ **Very Adelaide Hills Viognier 2010** Rating 88 To Now $17

Mazza Wines   ★★★★
PO Box 480, Donnybrook, WA 6239 **Region** Geographe
T (08) 9201 1114 **www**.mazza.com.au **Open** Not
Winemaker Contract **Est.** 2002 **Dozens** 600 **Vyds** 4ha
The inspiration for this venture of David and Anne Mazza was the great wines of Rioja and the Douro Valley, as well as the opportunity to continue a long-standing family tradition of making wine. So they planted the key varieties of those two regions: tempranillo, graciano, bastardo, sousao, tinta cao and touriga nacional. As the tasting notes indicate, the quantities of each wine made are very small, but they do have successive vintages of some of the wines. They have entered small wine shows, their 2008 Tempranillo winning a gold medal and trophy for Best Spanish Varietal at the Australian Alternative Wine Show '10. They believe they are the only Australian vineyard to present this collection of varieties on a single site, and I am reasonably certain they are correct in this belief.

ŶŶŶŶŶ **Cinque 2010** A blend of sousao, graciano, touriga national, tinta cao and
       tempranillo: a blend to end all blends in this idiom. The clear, bright colour leads
       into the fragrant berry and spice aromas of the bouquet; the next step is the
       medium-bodied palate; most impressive is the way the silky tannins have been
       handled. Screwcap. 14.5% alc. **Rating** 93 **To** 2018 $25
       Touriga Nacional 2010 Full crimson-purple; a bouquet of gently spiced black
       fruits leads into a particularly well-structured palate with its dark berries finishing
       with fine, ripe tannins; 25 dozen made. Screwcap. 14% alc. **Rating** 93 **To** 2023 $25
       Graciano 2010 Mid crimson; unusual fresh tobacco character on the bouquet; an
       elegant medium-bodied palate with raspberry and red cherry fruit supported by
       fine tannins; 80 dozen made. Screwcap. 14.5% alc. **Rating** 92 **To** 2017 $25
       Tinta Cao 2010 Fresh crimson-purple; has a fresh raspberry bouquet, then a
       light palate with balanced acidity and persistent, but fine, tannins; 25 dozen made.
       Screwcap. 14.5% alc. **Rating** 92 **To** 2018 $25
       Bastardo Rose 2011 Pink, tinged with salmon; quite possibly the only rose
       made from bastardo anywhere in the world (the Portuguese plantings go to port);
       spice, rose petal, red cherry and strawberry provide the flavour, the mouthfeel
       from good texture, the finish dry; 40 dozen made. Screwcap. 13% alc. **Rating** 90
       To 2013 $18
       Tempranillo 2009 Light but bright hue, still purple; fine tannins run right
       through the length of the palate; cherry and plum fruit confronted by the tannins,
       the final outcome some years away. By far the largest varietal production for
       Mazza, with 370 dozen made. Screwcap. 14.3% alc. **Rating** 90 **To** 2024 $23

ŶŶŶŶ **Tempranillo 2010** Rating 89 To 2018 $23

Meadow Croft Wines
221 Woodlands Road, Mittagong, NSW 2575 **Region** Southern Highlands
T (02) 4878 5344 **Open** By appt
Winemaker Jonathan Holgate **Est.** 1998 **Dozens** 400 **Vyds** 1.2ha

Carl and Linda Bahls have 20ha of prime grazing country, but decided on a minor diversification by planting 0.6ha each of chardonnay and cabernet sauvignon. 'While chardonnay was a natural choice of fruit for a cool climate, cabernet sauvignon was a gamble, albeit a calculated one.' The gamble was fully justified when the 2007 Cabernet Sauvignon was placed first at the Southern Highlands Wine Show, the result of meticulous work in the vineyard, and the wine-making team of Jonathan Holgate at High Range Vintners (overseen by Nick Bulleid MW).

♀♀♀♀ **Southern Highlands Cabernet Sauvignon 2009** Yet another wine from Southern Highlands to show the importance of site selection and vintage conditions coming together well; redcurrant fruit, with a touch of green but low tannins, makes for an early-drinking cabernet. Well priced. Screwcap. 12.5% alc. **Rating** 87 **To** 2015 $17

Medhurst ★★★★★
24–26 Medhurst Road, Gruyere, Vic 3770 **Region** Yarra Valley
T (03) 5964 9022 **www.**medhurstwines.com.au **Open** Fri–Sun & public hols 11–5 or by appt
Winemaker Matt Steel **Est.** 2000 **Dozens** 5000 **Vyds** 15.2ha
The wheel has come full circle for Ross and Robyn Wilson. In the course of a very distinguished corporate career, Ross was CEO of Southcorp when it brought the Penfolds, Lindemans and Wynns businesses under the Southcorp banner. Robyn spent her childhood in the Yarra Valley, her parents living less than a kilometre away as the crow flies from Medhurst. Immaculately sited and tended vineyard blocks, most on steep, north-facing slopes, promise much for the future. The vineyard is planted to sauvignon blanc, chardonnay, pinot noir, cabernet sauvignon and shiraz, all running on a low-yield basis. Prior to the 2011 vintage a large winery was built; despite its size, it focuses on small-batch production. This means it will be able to not only handle the estate-grown Medhurst wines, but also to provide contract winemaking services to other wine producers. The visual impact of the winery has been minimised by recessing the building into the slope of land and locating the barrel room underground. Medhurst is also redesigning the cellar door to include 'Medhurst and More' which will offer high-quality food to match their wines.

♀♀♀♀♀ Yarra Valley Sauvignon Blanc 2011 Light straw-green; the wine has clear-cut varietal character throughout the bouquet and palate, with no hint of botrytis to take away from the purity of the flavours that seamlessly cover the full range from grassy to citrussy to tropical; the balance is very good, the length likewise. Screwcap. 11.9% alc. Rating 94 To 2013 $25
Yarra Valley Shiraz 2008 Good colour, deep and clear; the fragrant bouquet is followed by a medium- to full-bodied palate that brings many things to the table; a strong overlay of spice and pepper to the luscious black fruits, giving a distinctive and classy savoury base for the fruit, a touch of licorice joining in on the finish. Still calmly getting on with its business. Cork. 14.5% alc. Rating 94 To 2028 $28

♀♀♀♀♀ **Red Shed Yarra Valley Chardonnay 2011** Rating 92 To 2015 $22
Yarra Valley Rose 2011 Rating 90 To 2013 $25
Yarra Valley Cabernet Sauvignon 2008 Rating 90 To 2023 $28

♀♀♀♀ **Red Shed Yarra Valley Pinot Noir 2011** Rating 88 To 2014 $22
Whatever Spicy Red 2011 Rating 87 To 2013 $22

Meehan Vineyard ★★★☆
4536 McIvor Highway, Heathcote, Vic 3523 **Region** Heathcote
T 0407 058 432 **F** (03) 5433 2105 **Open** W'ends & public hols 10–5
Winemaker Phil Meehan **Est.** 2003 **Dozens** 600 **Vyds** 2ha
In 1999, after their children had left the nest, Phil and Judy Meehan decided to return to the country and grow grapes for sale to wineries. In that year they took the first step, planting a small pinot noir vineyard at Bannockburn. It then took until April 2003 to find a near-perfect site, just within the Heathcote town boundary, its northeast-facing gentle slope on the famous

Cambrian soil. Phil graduated with a Diploma of Winemaking and a Diploma of Viticulture in '05, saying, 'After a mere six years of study I only learned, after all that time, just how much more to winemaking there was to learn.' The planting stock was secured from nearby vineyards with similar soil, and planting is continuing. Exports to the UK.

ΥΥΥΥΥ **Heathcote Shiraz 2009** Excellent purple-crimson colour; an impressive wine, its two-year sojourn in 85% French oak obvious but not oppressive; the supple, medium-bodied palate has blackberry and spice fruit supported by fine tannins. Screwcap. 14.5% alc. **Rating** 93 **To** 2030 $28

Meerea Park ★★★★★

2198 Broke Road, Pokolbin, NSW 2320 **Region** Hunter Valley
T (02) 4998 7474 **F** (02) 4998 7974 **Open** 7 days 10–5
Winemaker Rhys Eather **Est.** 1991 **Dozens** 12 000
All the wines are produced from grapes purchased from growers primarily in the Pokolbin area, but also from the Upper Hunter, and as far afield as Young. It is the brainchild of Rhys Eather, a great-grandson of Alexander Munro, a leading vigneron in the mid 19th century; he makes the wine at the former Little's Winery at Palmers Lane in Pokolbin, which was purchased in 2007 and is now named Meerea Park. Exports to Germany, the Netherlands, Hong Kong and China.

ΥΥΥΥΥ **Alexander Munro Individual Vineyard Hunter Valley Semillon 2007** The colour is still pale, but with vivid green tinges; the bouquet foreshadows a totally delicious palate with ripe citrus, almost reaching into passionfruit, flavours, and a long finish tied together with gentle acidity. Screwcap. 11.5% alc. **Rating** 96 **To** 2020 $35
Terracotta Semillon 2007 Light green-straw; walks a slightly different path from the Alexander Munro, more focused on lime and lemon aromas and flavours, the finish long and crisp, with tingling acidity. Screwcap. 11.5% alc. **Rating** 95 **To** 2022 $30
Aged Release Alexander Munro Individual Vineyard Hunter Valley Shiraz 2003 From the Ivanhoe Vineyard planted over 50 years ago. Has started to show a strong spicy/earthy regional overlay to the fragrant black fruits at the heart of the wine, and to invest it with considerable complexity and length. Screwcap. 14.5% alc. **Rating** 94 **To** 2020 $100

ΥΥΥΥΥ **Hell Hole Individual Vineyard Hunter Valley Semillon 2010 Rating** 92 **To** 2015 $25

ΥΥΥΥ **Alexander Munro Individual Vineyard Hunter Valley Chardonnay 2011** **Rating** 89 **To** 2014 $35
XYZ Hunter Valley Chardonnay 2010 Rating 89 **To** 2015 $22
○ **Shiraz 2010 Rating** 89 **To** 2018 $15

Merilba Estate ★★★★

3611 Kingstown Road, Uralla, NSW 2358 **Region** New England
T (02) 6778 9145 **www**.merilbaestatewines.com.au **Open** W'ends 11–4
Winemaker Shaun Cassidy **Est.** 1998 **Dozens** 3000 **Vyds** 11ha
This impressive venture is owned and run by Shaun and Kassy Cassidy and John and Annette Cassidy. With the exception of Tempranillo and Gewurztraminer, all of the wines are estate-grown and made, all coming from the New England region. Sean also makes the wines for Thunder Ridge (see separate entry). The converted Cobb & Co. stables on the property provide the cellar door and a function and wedding venue.

ΥΥΥΥΥ **New England Chardonnay 2011** Deep straw, vibrant green hue; a fine and fragrant bouquet of melon, pear and a touch of spice; fleshy and accessible, with soft acidity, and enough texture to maintain interest from start to finish. Screwcap. 13.8% alc. **Rating** 90 **To** 2016 $25 BE

Mermerus Vineyard ★★★★☆

60 Soho Road, Drysdale, Vic 3222 **Region** Geelong
T (03) 5253 2718 **www**.mermerus.com.au **Open** Sun 11–4
Winemaker Paul Champion **Est.** 2000 **Dozens** 600 **Vyds** 2.5ha
Paul Champion has established pinot noir, chardonnay and riesling at Mermerus since 1996. The wines are made from the small but very neat winery on the property, with small-batch handling and wild yeast fermentation playing a major part in the winemaking, oak taking a back seat. Paul also acts as contract winemaker for small growers in the region.

ዋዋዋዋዋ Bellarine Peninsula Pinot Noir 2010 Mid garnet, bright; a pure-fruited expression of cranberry, liqueur-soaked plums and fresh sap; the palate is bright and fresh, juicy and direct, relying on purity rather than complexity for its character; there is firmness on the finish, but this works seamlessly with the fruit. Screwcap. 13.5% alc. **Rating** 94 **To** 2016 $28 BE

ዋዋዋዋዋ Bellarine Peninsula Chardonnay 2010 **Rating** 90 **To** 2016 $24 BE

ዋዋዋዋ Bellarine Peninsula Riesling 2011 **Rating** 87 **To** 2014 $19 BE

Merricks Creek Wines ★★★★★

44 Merricks Road, Merricks, Vic 3916 **Region** Mornington Peninsula
T (03) 5989 8868 **www**.pinot.com.au **Open** Not
Winemaker William Downie **Est.** 1998 **Dozens** 650 **Vyds** 2ha
The pinot noir vineyard established by Peter and Georgina Parker has consistently produced grapes of exceptional quality. It is planted to a sophisticated collection of pinot noir clones, and includes a small planting at an ultra-high density of 0.5m spacing, which produces the Close Planted Pinot Noir. Retaining William Downie as (part-time) winemaker will be seen by many as a coup, as his dedication to pinot noir is well known.

ዋዋዋዋዋ Mornington Peninsula Pinot Noir 2009 Mid garnet, bricking hue; while there are developed notes of leather and earth on the bouquet, there is life, energy and red fruits on the palate, with fine acidity, fine tannins and well-handled oak on the silky and very long finish. Screwcap. 13.5% alc. **Rating** 94 **To** 2016 $46 BE

ዋዋዋዋ Close Planted Mornington Peninsula Pinot Noir 2009 **Rating** 88 **To** 2016 $70 BE

Merricks Estate ★★★★★

Thompsons Lane, Merricks, Vic 3916 **Region** Mornington Peninsula
T (03) 5989 8416 **www**.merricksestate.com.au **Open** 1st w'end of month, daily 26–31 Dec, each w'end in Jan & public hol w'ends 12–5
Winemaker Paul Evans **Est.** 1977 **Dozens** 2500 **Vyds** 4ha
Melbourne solicitor George Kefford, with wife Jacky, runs Merricks Estate as a weekend and holiday enterprise. Right from the outset it has produced distinctive, spicy, cool-climate Shiraz, which has accumulated an impressive array of show trophies and gold medals.

ዋዋዋዋዋ Mornington Peninsula Shiraz 2007 Deep garnet; a dark and sweet-fruited offering with layers of spice and earthy complexity; the palate is unctuous on entry, with fresh acidity providing line and length on the finish; vibrant and fresh for its age. Diam. 14% alc. **Rating** 94 **To** 2022 $27 BE

○ Thompson's Lane Chardonnay 2010 **Rating** 94 **To** 2016 $18

○ Thompson's Lane Shiraz 2010 **Rating** 94 **To** 2020 $20

ዋዋዋዋዋ Thompson's Lane Pinot Noir 2010 **Rating** 91

○ **To** 2015 $20

✪ Thompson's Lane Chardonnay 2011 A ripe bouquet of quince, melon and lots of cinnamon and nutmeg form spicy oak; the palate is surprisingly soft and fleshy, with a fine backbone of acidity providing line and length. Screwcap. 13% alc. **Rating** 90 **To** 2017 $18 BE

○ Thompson's Lane Cabernet 2010 **Rating** 90 **To** 2016 $18

ዋዋዋዋ Thompson's Lane Pinot Noir 2011 **Rating** 87 **To** 2015 $20 BE

Merum Estate   ★★★★★

PO Box 840, Denmark, WA 6333 **Region** Pemberton
T (08) 9848 3443 **www**.merumestate.com.au **Open** Not
Winemaker Harewood Estate (James Kellie) **Est.** 1996 **Dozens** 3700 **Vyds** 10ha
Merum Estate stirred from slumber after morphing from grower and winemaker to pure
grapegrowing after the 2006 vintage. Mike Melsom is the link with the past, for it was he and
partner Julie Roberts who were responsible for the extremely good wines made in '05 and
'06. The wines are released at three levels: the entry point Curious Nature, then the Signature
range, and finally the Estate Premium Reserve range.

ᵧᵧᵧᵧᵧ **Premium Reserve Pemberton Chardonnay 2010** Light, gleaming straw-
green; has the elegance of its varietal sibling, and many of its flavours, but is
significantly more intense, with white peach, nectarine and nutty/toasty oak fused
together right through the length of the palate. Screwcap. 13.5% alc. **Rating** 95
To 2020 $35
Premium Reserve Pemberton Shiraz 2010 Strong purple-crimson, although
slightly turbid; an unusual but seductive wine, with a wonderful array of aromas
and flavours; spice, licorice, black pepper, black cherry, plum and blackberry all
flow backwards and forwards across the ever-enticing palate, the finish impeccable.
Screwcap. 14.5% alc. **Rating** 95 **To** 2030 $45
Pemberton Chardonnay 2011 Light straw-green; while the French oak is
sticking its head up at the moment, time will quickly pull it back into line with
the fruit, with its array of white peach, nectarine, cashew and fig. Screwcap.
14% alc. **Rating** 94 **To** 2018 $25

ᵧᵧᵧᵧᵧ **Pemberton Chardonnay 2010** **Rating** 93 **To** 2017 $25
Pemberton Semillon Sauvignon Blanc 2011 **Rating** 92 **To** 2015 $25
Pemberton Semillon Sauvignon Blanc 2010 **Rating** 92 **To** 2014 $25
Pemberton Shiraz Viognier 2010 **Rating** 92 **To** 2020 $25

✪ **Curious Nature Remarkable Red Shiraz Cabernet 2010** Full crimson;
a 71/29% blend of Pemberton and Great Southern fruit, with a highly spiced
bouquet of black fruits, black cherry and blackcurrant riding high on the palate,
licorice and cedary oak the stirrups. The extreme designs of the Merum labels
are full of interest, but I'm not sure they establish a consistent brand message. The
most remarkable thing about this wine is its price. Screwcap. 14.5% alc. **Rating** 92
To 2020 $15

✪ **Curious Nature Wondrous White 2010** A blend of semillon, chardonnay,
sauvignon blanc and viognier, a modern interpretation of classic dry white; I
haven't the faintest idea how this blend could be as synergistic as it is, the flavours
having some quasi-savoury overtones, the mouthfeel possibly contributed by the
viognier. All in all, has far more personality than the vast majority of these shotgun
blends. Screwcap. 13.5% alc. **Rating** 90 **To** 2013 $15

Miceli   ★★★★

60 Main Creek Road, Arthurs Seat, Vic 3936 **Region** Mornington Peninsula
T (03) 5989 2755 **www**.miceli.com.au **Open** W'ends 12–5, public hols by appt
Winemaker Anthony Miceli **Est.** 1991 **Dozens** 3500 **Vyds** 5.5ha
This may be a part-time labour of love for general practitioner Dr Anthony Miceli, but that
hasn't prevented him taking the whole venture very seriously. He acquired the property in
1989 specifically to establish a vineyard, planting 1.8ha in '91. Subsequent plantings have
brought it to its present size, with pinot gris, chardonnay and pinot noir the varieties grown.
Between '91 and '97 Dr Miceli completed the wine science course at CSU and now manages
both vineyard and winery. One of the top producers of sparkling wine on the Peninsula.

ᵧᵧᵧᵧᵧ **Olivia's Mornington Peninsula Chardonnay 2008** Medium straw-green;
still quite tight and firm in the mouth, stone fruit to the fore, but with some
creamy cashew touches starting to appear on the back-palate and finish. Screwcap.
13.5% alc. **Rating** 91 **To** 2015 $26

Lucy's Choice Mornington Peninsula Pinot Noir 2008 Light, developed colour, but still healthy; now as good as it will ever be, but with a couple more years under its belt before it begins its descent from the plateau; spice, cherry, plum and forest notes all run through the length of the palate; overall, there is good focus and balance. Screwcap. 13.5% alc. **Rating** 91 **To** 2015 $26

Iolanda Mornington Peninsula Pinot Grigio 2010 Pale green; a grigio with more character and flavour than most, nearly infringing on gris territory. Has built this flavour and texture with almost two years in bottle, and should continue in this vein for a further year or two. Screwcap. 13.5% alc. **Rating** 90 **To** 2013 $23

Michael Mornington Peninsula Brut 2006 A bright and fresh citrus bouquet, with a dry and chalky palate; an aperitif style, offering purity and freshness rather than depth and complexity. Crown seal. 12.5% alc. **Rating** 90 **To** 2015 $32 BE

Michael Hall Wines ★★★★★

10 George Street, Tanunda, SA 5352 (postal) **Region** Mount Lofty Ranges Zone
T 0419 126 290 **www**.michaelhallwines.com **Open** Not
Winemaker Michael Hall **Est.** 2008 **Dozens** 1200

For reasons no longer relevant (however interesting), Michael Hall was once a jewellery valuer for Sotheby's in Switzerland. He came to Australia in 2001 to pursue winemaking, a lifelong interest, and undertook the wine science degree at CSU, graduating as dux in '05. His vintage work in Australia and France is a veritable who's who: in Australia with Cullen, Giaconda, Henschke, Shaw & Smith, Coldstream Hills and Veritas; in France with Domaine Leflaive, Meo-Camuzet, Vieux Telegraphe and Trevallon. He is now involved full-time with his eponymous brand, except for some teaching at the Nuriootpa TAFE; the Adelaide Hills Sang de Pigeon Pinot Noir was made in '11, together with a Stonewell Valley Roussanne. The wines are as impressive as his CV suggests they should be. Exports to the UK.

♥♥♥♥♥ **Stonewell Valley Barossa Valley Shiraz 2009** The vineyard block is in conversion to biodynamic; hand-picked, destemmed, wild yeast-fermented, unfiltered. A vividly coloured, vibrant, black and red cherry-flavoured wine reflecting the great benefits of early picking. 225 dozen made. Diam. 13.8% alc. **Rating** 95 **To** 2024 $40

Barossa Valley Roussanne 2010 Wild yeast, barrel-fermented, but with only 10% new; 11 months in barrel, with monthly lees stirring. Hall says he sees honeysuckle, dried apricot, wildflowers, cut hay and tarragon in the wine, and try as much as I can, I can't better that description; 220 dozen made. Screwcap. 12.9% alc. **Rating** 94 **To** 2015 $35

Flaxman's Valley Eden Valley Syrah 2009 Self-described Syrah indicates an attempt to produce an elegant style of Shiraz, and in this instance has done so, with a lifted bouquet of dark plums, spice and floral notes; the palate is medium-bodied and vibrant, with fresh acidity and red fruits coming to the fore on the long, even and relatively elegant finish. Diam. 13.2% alc. **Rating** 94 **To** 2025 $40 BE

♥♥♥♥♡
✪ **Sang de Pigeon Barossa Shiraz Saignee 2011** Vibrant pink hue; a savoury and spicy bouquet with wild strawberry, red cherry, anise and clove; the palate is dry and refreshing, finishing with a chalky textured twist; very good saignee rose. Screwcap. 13.5% alc. **Rating** 93 **To** 2014 $21 BE

Sang de Pigeon Barossa Shiraz Saignee 2010 Rating 93 **To** 2013 $20

♥♥♥♥ **Piccadilly Adelaide Hills Chardonnay 2010 Rating** 89 **To** 2015 $40 BE

Michael Unwin Wines ★★★★★

2 Racecourse Road, on the Western Highway, Beaufort, Vic 3373
Region Western Victoria Zone
T (03) 5349 2021 **www**.michaelunwinwines.com.au **Open** Mon–Fri 8.30–5,
Sat 11–4.30, Sun 12–4.30
Winemaker Michael Unwin **Est.** 2000 **Dozens** 2500 **Vyds** 8ha

Michael Unwin, a veteran of 30 vintages, learned the art of winemaking around the world with some of the most influential and forward-thinking winemakers of the time. The winery location was chosen because it is the geographical centre of the best viticultural areas in Western Victoria. The grapes come from three vineyards in the Pyrenees, two in the Grampians and one in the Henty region. In all, approximately 2ha of shiraz and 1ha each of cabernet sauvignon, sangiovese, barbera, durif, riesling and chardonnay are grown or contracted.

♀♀♀♀♀ Acrobat Umbrella Man Barbera 2010 Clear crimson-purple; plum, raspberry and cherry fruit in a medium-bodied, supple palate; has good line, length and balance, and is as good as they come with this variety. Screwcap. 13.5% alc. Rating 94 To 2018 $26
Acrobat Umbrella Man Petit Verdot 2010 Deep, bright purple; a luscious confit array of blackberry, plum, prune and licorice flavours fill the mouth, yet there is no aggression; the finish is particularly enjoyable. Screwcap. 13.5% alc. Rating 94 To 2018 $26

♀♀♀♀♀ Acrobat Umbrella Man Pinot Gris 2011 Rating 93 To 2014 $26
Acrobat Umbrella Man Durif 2007 Rating 92 To 2017 $26
Acrobat Umbrella Man Riesling 2011 Rating 91 To 2016 $26
Acrobat Umbrella Man Late Harvest Riesling 2011 Rating 90 To 2016 $26

Michelini Wines   ★★★☆

Great Alpine Road, Myrtleford, Vic 3737 **Region** Alpine Valleys
T (03) 5751 1990 **www**.micheliniwines.com.au **Open** 7 days 10–5
Winemaker Greg O'Keefe **Est.** 1982 **Dozens** 10 000 **Vyds** 34.5ha
The Michelini family is among the best-known grapegrowers in the Buckland Valley of North East Victoria. Having migrated from Italy in 1949, they originally grew tobacco, diversifying into vineyards in '82. The main vineyard (16.74ha), on terra rossa soil, is at an altitude of 300m, mostly with frontage to the Buckland River. The Devils Creek Vineyard (17.69ha) was planted in '91 on grafted rootstocks, merlot and chardonnay taking the lion's share. The winery can handle 1000 tonnes of fruit, which eliminates the problem of moving grapes out of a declared phylloxera area. Exports to China.

♀♀♀♀♀ Alpine Valleys Pinot Grigio 2010 Pale straw; an unusually dependable producer of a true Italian-style Pinot Grigio, with pear, fennel, straw and citrus on the bouquet; the palate is lively on entry, leaving a trailing note of hazelnut and anise; an excellent wine for food. Screwcap. 13.5% alc. Rating 90 To 2013 $18 BE

Mihi Creek Vineyard   ★★★

1292 Enmore Road, Mihi via Uralla, NSW 2358 (postal) **Region** New England
T (02) 6778 2166 **Open** W'ends 1–4.30, Mon–Fri by appt
Winemaker Contract **Est.** 2003 **Dozens** 750 **Vyds** 2.2ha
Andrew and Belle Close purchased 180ha of what was part of the large Mihi Station sheep and cattle property in 2001. Situated at an elevation of 1000 m, the first plantings in '03 (sauvignon blanc, viognier, pinot noir, cabernet sauvignon and merlot) performed well, with the first vintage in '06. Since then, there have been further plantings of sauvignon blanc, with removal of the cabernet sauvignon making way for yet more sauvignon blanc. Further plantings of pinot noir and viognier are planned.

♀♀♀♀ New England Viognier 2011 Pale straw; a very fresh and crisp wine, with a hint of oak, but the varietal character has been compromised by the early picking. Screwcap. 11.5% alc. Rating 87 To 2014 $20

Mike Press Wines   ★★★★☆

PO Box 224, Lobethal, SA 5241 **Region** Adelaide Hills
T (08) 8389 5546 **www**.mikepresswines.com.au **Open** Not
Winemaker Mike Press **Est.** 1998 **Dozens** 12 000 **Vyds** 22.7ha

Mike and Judy Press established their Kenton Valley Vineyards in 1998, when they purchased 34ha of land in the Adelaide Hills at an elevation of 500m. Over the next two years they planted mainstream cool-climate varieties (merlot, shiraz, cabernet sauvignon, sauvignon blanc, chardonnay and pinot noir), intending to sell the grapes to other wine producers. Even an illustrious 42-year career in the wine industry did not prepare Mike for the downturn in grape prices that followed, and that led to the development of the Mike Press wine label. They produce high-quality Sauvignon Blanc, Chardonnay, Pinot Noir, Merlot, Shiraz, Cabernet Merlot and Cabernet Sauvignon, which are sold at mouth-wateringly low prices. Exports to Denmark.

ＴＴＴＴＴ Single Vineyard Adelaide Hills Cabernet Sauvignon 2010 Bright
❂   crimson; has the elegance that has marked the Mike Press wines since day one, and the irresistible price; fragrant blackcurrant fruit is the driver, cedary oak and fine tannins bring up the rear in fine style. From estate vines now 13 years old. Screwcap. 14% alc. **Rating** 94 **To** 2017 $14

ＴＴＴＴＴ Adelaide Hills Sauvignon Blanc 2011 **Rating** 93
❂   To Now $12
❂   Adelaide Hills Shiraz 2010 **Rating** 93 **To** 2015 $13
❂   Adelaide Hills Chardonnay 2011 **Rating** 92 **To** 2014 $12
❂   Single Vineyard Adelaide Hills Pinot Noir Rose 2011 Light, bright pink; perfumed red berry/cherry/strawberry aromas, the palate with marked acidity reflecting the early picking. Screwcap. 11% alc. **Rating** 90 **To** Now $12

Miles from Nowhere   ★★★★★

PO Box 197, Belmont, WA 6984 **Region** Margaret River
T (08) 9267 8555 **www**.milesfromnowhere.com.au **Open** Not
Winemaker Rory Clifton-Parks **Est.** 2007 **Dozens** 15 000 **Vyds** 46.9ha
Miles from Nowhere is the born-again business of Franklin (Frank) and Heather Tate; Frank was CEO of Evans & Tate for many years. The demise of Evans & Tate has been well chronicled, but has not prevented the Tates from doing what they know best. The plantings of petit verdot, chardonnay, shiraz, sauvignon blanc, semillon, viognier, cabernet sauvignon and merlot are scattered across the Margaret River region, miles from nowhere. Production has risen from 6000 dozen to its current level; the vineyards have also increased significantly (from 36ha), with excess grapes being sold. Exports to the UK, Canada, Sweden and Thailand.

ＴＴＴＴＴ Best Blocks Margaret River Semillon Sauvignon Blanc 2011 Pale straw-
             green; partial barrel fermentation and selection of the best parcels of fruit have paid dividends; the complex fruit is seamlessly fused with the oak, yet free to display snow pea, gooseberry, lemon and minerally acidity. Screwcap. 12.5% alc. **Rating** 94 **To** 2014 $27
             Best Blocks Margaret River Chardonnay 2010 Still pale in colour; a skilfully made Chardonnay combining focused elegance and harmonious fruit/oak balance and integration, melon and white peach fruit teamed with creamy, nutty oak. Screwcap. 13.5% alc. **Rating** 94 **To** 2016 $27

ＴＴＴＴＴ Margaret River Sauvignon Blanc Semillon 2011 Pale, bright straw-green;
❂   the aromatic, fragrant bouquet is faithfully reflected in the flavours of passionfruit, grapefruit, melon and citrussy acidity on the long palate; has good short-term cellaring prospects. Screwcap. 12.5% alc. **Rating** 93 **To** 2014 $21
             Best Blocks Margaret River Shiraz 2010 **Rating** 93 **To** 2020 $27
❂   Margaret River Cabernet Merlot 2010 Clear red-purple; has the hallmark freshness and energy of the winery, with cassis/blackcurrant aromas and flavours supported by precisely judged tannins and oak. Screwcap. 13.9% alc. **Rating** 93 **To** 2020 $21
❂   Margaret River Chardonnay 2011 Bright, light straw-green; a bracingly fresh and vibrant wine displaying white peach, nectarine and grapefruit; the only query is the amount of toasty/dusty oak. Screwcap. 13.5% alc. **Rating** 92 **To** 2016 $21

✪ **Margaret River Shiraz 2010** Like Best Blocks, has excellent crimson-purple colour; this wine has more depth, structure and fruit flavour than Best Blocks, but doesn't have the same elegance. Six of one, half a dozen of the other. Screwcap. 13.7% alc. **Rating** 92 **To** 2025 $21

🍷🍷🍷🍷 **Margaret River Sauvignon Blanc 2011** **Rating** 89 **To** Now $21
Margaret River Verdelho 2011 **Rating** 89 **To** 2013 $17

Milhinch Wines ★★★☆

PO Box 655, Greenock, SA 5360 **Region** Barossa Valley
T 0412 455 553 **www**.seizetheday.net.au **Open** At Bibu Barossa, Tanunda or by appt
Winemaker Contract **Est.** 2003 **Dozens** 1200 **Vyds** 4ha

Peter Milhinch and Sharyn Rogers have established 2ha each of shiraz and cabernet sauvignon near the Greenock Creek, which flows through their Seppeltsfield property. At the foot of their vineyard is Seppeltsfield Vineyard Cottage, a restored German settler's cottage offering luxury accommodation for one couple. The Cottage has won three successive SA Tourism Awards, two National Tourism Awards and was inducted into the SA Tourism Hall of Fame in 2007. The Cottage project and Peter and Sharyn's wine production began in 2003 when Peter was recovering from cancer. They gained inspiration and hope from legendary American cyclist Lance Armstrong's own cancer journey; so much so that the Seize the Day phrase on their wine labels has been borrowed from Lance's book, *It's Not About the Bike*.

🍷🍷🍷🍷½ **Seize the Day Single Vineyard Barossa Valley Shiraz 2009** Very good purple-red; despite its alcohol, the fruit of the bouquet and palate is essentially fresh and vibrant, with high-toned black cherry and blackberry flavours, oak and tannins following in due order. Screwcap. 15% alc. **Rating** 91 **To** 2024 $30

🍷🍷🍷🍷 **Seize the Day Single Vineyard Barossa Valley Shiraz 2008** **Rating** 89 **To** 2023 $30
Seize the Day Single Vineyard Barossa Valley Shiraz Cabernet 2009 **Rating** 89 **To** 2020 $30
Seize the Day Single Vineyard Barossa Valley Fortified Shiraz 2010 **Rating** 89 **To** 2020 $30
Seize the Day Single Vineyard Barossa Valley Cabernet Sauvignon 2009 **Rating** 87 **To** 2015 $30
Seize the Day Single Vineyard Barossa Valley Fortified Cabernet Sauvignon 2010 **Rating** 87 **To** 2015 $30

Millbrook Winery ★★★★★

Old Chestnut Lane, Jarrahdale, WA 6124 **Region** Perth Hills
T (08) 9525 5796 **www**.millbrookwinery.com.au **Open** 7 days 10–5
Winemaker Damian Hutton, Josh Uren **Est.** 1996 **Dozens** 20 000 **Vyds** 7.8ha

The strikingly situated Millbrook Winery is owned by highly successful Perth-based entrepreneur Peter Fogarty and wife Lee. They also own Lake's Folly in the Hunter Valley and Deep Woods Estate in Margaret River, and have made a major commitment to the quality end of Australian wine. Millbrook draws on vineyards in the Perth Hills planted to sauvignon blanc, semillon, chardonnay, viognier, cabernet sauvignon, merlot, shiraz and petit verdot. The wines (Millbrook and Barking Owl) are of consistently high quality. Exports to Belgium, Germany, Malaysia, Hong Kong, China and Japan.

🍷🍷🍷🍷🍷 ✪ **Margaret River Sauvignon Blanc 2011** Pale straw-green; the bouquet offers lifted passionfruit and tropical aromas, but is overshadowed by the notably intense palate, adding ripe citrus and grass/herb flavours; very good balance and length. Remarkable value for money. Screwcap. 12% alc. **Rating** 96 **To** 2013 $20

LR Chardonnay 2011 Made from a blend of Great Southern and Pemberton grapes, it has great intensity from layers of fruit, and integrated oak that largely hides itself until the finish of the long palate. A wolf in sheep's clothing. Screwcap. 13.5% alc. **Rating** 94 **To** 2014 $45

ттттт Pemberton Riesling 2011 Rating 93 To 2017 $20
PX Pedro Ximenes NV Rating 93 To 2013 $45
Margaret River Cabernet Sauvignon Malbec 2010 Rating 92 To 2020 $25

✪ Barking Owl Sauvignon Blanc Semillon 2011 From Geographe and
Margaret River; both regions have come together seamlessly and effortlessly to
produce a wine that requires no introspection, and will fit in anywhere, any time.
Screwcap. 12.5% alc. Rating 90 To 2014 $18

✪ Barking Owl Chardonnay 2010 Sourced from the Great Southern and
Geographe regions; stone fruit, grapefruit and cashew/vanilla aromas and flavours
are seamlessly interwoven from start to finish. Screwcap. 13% alc. Rating 90
To 2016 $18

тттт Barking Owl Shiraz Viognier 2010 Rating 89 To 2016 $18
LR Fogs Folly 2010 Rating 89 To 2030 $45

Milton Vineyard   ★★★★☆

14635 Tasman Highway, Cranbrook, Tas 7190 **Region** East Coast Tasmania
T (03) 6257 8298 **www**.miltonvineyard.com.au **Open** 7 days 10–5
Winemaker Winemaking Tasmania (Julian Alcorso) **Est.** 1992 **Dozens** 2840 **Vyds** 9ha
Michael and Kerry Dunbabin have one of the most historic properties in Tasmania, dating
back to 1826. The property is 1800 ha, meaning the vineyard (2.7ha of pinot noir, 1.4ha of
riesling, 1.2ha of pinot gris and 1ha of gewurztraminer) has plenty of room for expansion.
Michael says, 'I've planted some of the newer pinot clones in 2001, but have yet to plant what
I reckon will prove to be some of the best vineyard sites on the property.' Initially the grapes
were sold to Hardys, but since '05 most of the production has been retained for the Milton
Vineyard label. Exports to Japan.

ттттт Iced Riesling 2010 Bright straw-green; a striking wine with great intensity and
length to its citrus/mandarin flavours; perfect balance between its sugar and acidity.
Gold Tas Wine Show '12. Screwcap. 8.9% alc. Rating 94 To 2016 $30

ттттт Riesling 2011 Rating 90 To 2018 $24

тттт Laura Sparkling Rose NV Rating 89 To 2014 $30

Minko Wines   ★★★☆

13 High Street, Willunga, SA 5172 **Region** Southern Fleurieu
T (08) 8556 4987 **www**.minkowines.com **Open** Wed–Mon 11–5, Sat 9.30–5
Winemaker James Hastwell (red), Linda Domas (white) **Est.** 1997 **Dozens** 1500
Vyds 10.5ha
Mike Boerema (veterinarian) and Margo Kellet (ceramic artist) established the Minko
Vineyard on their cattle property at Mt Compass. The vineyard, which is in conversion to
biodynamic, is planted to pinot noir, merlot, cabernet sauvignon, chardonnay, pinot gris and
savagnin; 60ha of the 160ha property is heritage listed. Exports to the UK.

тттт Fleurieu Peninsula Merlot 2010 Strong colour; Asian spices and fruitcake
aromas are unusual, but the wine largely comes together on the palate. The one
criticism is the alcohol and its attendant very ripe fruit; surely the vintage would
have allowed less alcohol. Screwcap. 14.5% alc. Rating 89 To 2017 $20
Fleurieu Peninsula Unwooded Chardonnay 2011 Another of many low-
alcohol unwooded Chardonnays that emphasise the flavour links with Sauvignon
Blanc, particularly the grapefruit/citrus/passionfruit. Screwcap. 11.5% alc.
Rating 88 To 2013 $18
Fleurieu Peninsula Pinot Noir 2010 Good hue; a fragrant and pure bouquet
leads into a palate that opens confidently, but shows some signs of over-extraction
on the finish. A pity. Screwcap. 13.5% alc. Rating 88 To 2016 $25
Fleurieu Peninsula Cabernet Sauvignon 2010 Medium red-purple; a
number of disparate aromas and flavours, ranging from savoury black olive,
licorice, blackcurrant and eucalyptus, certainly contribute to complexity. Screwcap.
14.5% alc. Rating 88 To 2014 $20

Fleurieu Peninsula Pinot Grigio 2011 A pleasant grigio, with riper flavours, less acidity and less intensity than the vintage usually imposed, gaining balance and drinkability on the roundabouts. Screwcap. 11.7% alc. **Rating** 87 **To** 2014 $18

Minnow Creek   ★★★☆
5 Hillside Road, Blackwood, SA 5051 (postal) **Region** McLaren Vale
T 0404 288 108 **www**.minnowcreekwines.com.au **Open** Not
Winemaker Tony Walker **Est.** 2005 **Dozens** 1800
Former Fox Creek winemaker Tony Walker has set up Minnow Creek in partnership with William Neubauer; the grapes are grown by Don Lopresti at vineyards just west of Willunga. The name of the venture reflects the intention of the partners to keep the business focused on quality rather than quantity, and to self-distribute much of the wine through the large number of highly regarded Adelaide restaurants. Exports to the US, Canada and Germany.

♀♀♀♀   **McLaren Vale Shiraz 2010** Strong colour; a full-bodied shiraz with generous black fruits and good tannins; its Achilles heel is the 19 months it spent in American and French oak – an expensive way to knock a few points off its otherwise score. Screwcap. 14.5% alc. **Rating** 89 **To** 2020 $27
McLaren Vale Rose 2011 A barrel-fermented blend of 62% cabernet sauvignon and 38% sangiovese throws unexpected challenges to both the bouquet and palate, with some green-accented fruit notwithstanding its alcohol, and an edgy back-palate and finish. Screwcap. 13.5% alc. **Rating** 87 **To** Now $18

Mintaro Wines   ★★★☆
Leasingham Road, Mintaro, SA 5415 **Region** Clare Valley
T (08) 8843 9150 **www**.mintarowines.com.au **Open** 7 days 10–4.30
Winemaker Peter Houldsworth **Est.** 1984 **Dozens** 4000 **Vyds** 10ha
Mintaro Wines' vineyards were planted in 1962, and were incorporated into a functioning winery complex in '85 by the present owner and winemaker, Peter Houldsworth. There are five vineyards in the Mintaro and Polish Hill districts of the Clare Valley, one-third planted to riesling, the remainder divided equally between cabernet sauvignon and shiraz. Wines are released under the Mintaro and Monarch of Montaro labels. Exports to Singapore.

♀♀♀♀♀   **Clare Valley Riesling 2011** Pale straw-green; by Feb '12 had already gained a dimension of sweet citrus fruit on the palate, but not at the expense of good acidity. A 5-year, rather than a 10-year, wine. Screwcap. 11% alc. **Rating** 92 **To** 2016 $22

♀♀♀♀   **Leckie Window Clare Valley Cabernet Sauvignon 2010** Rating 89 **To** 2015 $28

Mistletoe Wines   ★★★★★
771 Hermitage Road, Pokolbin, NSW 2320 **Region** Hunter Valley
T (02) 4998 7770 **www**.mistletoewines.com **Open** 7 days 10–6
Winemaker Nick Paterson **Est.** 1989 **Dozens** 5000 **Vyds** 5.5ha
Mistletoe Wines, owned by Ken and Gwen Sloan, can trace its history back to 1909, when a vineyard was planted on what was then called Mistletoe Farm. The Mistletoe Farm brand made a brief appearance in the late '70s. The wines are made onsite by Nick Paterson, who has had significant experience in the Hunter Valley. The quality and consistency of these wines is irreproachable, as is their price. Mistletoe has also been steadily building museum stock for sale, with several years' bottle age.

♀♀♀♀♀   **Reserve Hunter Valley Semillon 2011** A classic bouquet of straw, lemongrass and fresh lemon juice; the palate is generous on entry, with zesty acidity and plenty of cut and line to finish; accessible as a young wine, with plenty of fuel in the tank for the years to come. Screwcap. 10.8% alc. **Rating** 94 **To** 2025 $25 BE

Hilltops Shiraz Viognier 2010 Purple-crimson; the highly aromatic bouquet leads into a palate bursting with energy and expression, black cherry, plum and spicy, savoury nuances running through to the long and well-balanced finish. Screwcap. 14.5% alc. Rating 94 To 2018 $25

○ Home Vineyard Hunter Valley Semillon 2011 Rating 94 To 2021 $20

♈♈♈♈♈ Home Vineyard Hunter Valley Shiraz 2010 Rating 93 To 2020 $30 BE
✪ Barrel Fermented Hunter Valley Rose 2010 A blend of cabernet sauvignon and shiraz, crushed and chilled with 24 hours soaking on skins before barrel fermentation in used French oak puncheons. Mouth-coating, with lots of flavour and good balance. Screwcap. 13% alc. Rating 92 To 2014 $20
Reserve Hunter Valley Chardonnay 2010 Rating 91 To 2017 $40 BE
Hilltops Shiraz 2010 Rating 90 To 2018 $30 BE
✪ Hunter Valley Petite Muscat 2009 Bright straw-green; uses the muscat de beaumes de venise, the muscat grape juice fortified with neutral spirit, fermentation irrelevant. It is tangy and intense rather than sweet, and should be drunk somewhere before or at the start of the meal, rather than with the dessert. Screwcap. 15.5% alc. Rating 90 To 2013 $20

Mitchell ★★★★★

Hughes Park Road, Sevenhill via Clare, SA 5453 **Region** Clare Valley
T (08) 8843 4258 **www**.mitchellwines.com **Open** 7 days 10–4
Winemaker Andrew Mitchell **Est.** 1975 **Dozens** 30 000 **Vyds** 75ha
One of the stalwarts of the Clare Valley, established by Jane and Andrew Mitchell, producing long-lived Rieslings and Cabernet Sauvignons in classic regional style. The range now includes very creditable Semillon, Grenache and Shiraz. A lovely old stone apple shed provides the cellar door and upper section of the upgraded winery. Children Angus and Edwina are now working in the business, heralding generational changes. Over the years the Mitchells have established or acquired 75 ha of vineyards on four excellent sites, some vines over 50 years old; all are managed organically, with the use of biodynamic composts for the past decade.

♈♈♈♈♈ McNicol Clare Valley Riesling 2008 Mid gold-green hue; coming out of its 'awkward' phase, the bouquet now reveals toast and lemon curd, ginger and wet slate; the palate is generous and sweet-fruited with vibrancy and complexity all playing key roles; long and luscious for the variety in the region. Screwcap. 13% alc. Rating 95 To 2025 $35 BE
Watervale Riesling 2011 Vibrant green hue; a perfumed and almost exotic bouquet of fresh lime, coriander and spice; the palate is linear and generous on entry, with grip entering the equation on the dry finish; long and fragrant. Screwcap. 13% alc. Rating 94 To 2022 $22 BE
Sevenhill Vineyard Clare Valley Cabernet Sauvignon 2008 Deep crimson; a bright and highly perfumed red-fruited bouquet, with a touch of licorice and sage; the palate is lively and linear, with super fine-grained tannins and plush fruit providing a long and detailed conclusion. Screwcap. 14.5% alc. Rating 94 To 2022 $26 BE

♈♈♈♈♈ McNicol Clare Valley Shiraz 2004 Rating 93 To 2020 $40 BE
Peppertree Vineyard Clare Valley Shiraz 2009 Rating 92 To 2022 $26 BE
Clare Valley Semillon 2009 Rating 91 To 2020 $26 BE

♈♈♈♈ GSM Clare Valley Grenache Sangiovese Mourvedre 2008 Rating 88 To 2015 $22 BE

Mitchell Harris Wines ★★★★★

38 Doveton Street, North Ballarat, Vic 3350 **Region** Pyrenees
T 0417 566 025 **www**.mitchellharris.com.au **Open** Not
Winemaker John Harris **Est.** 2008 **Dozens** 800

Mitchell Harris Wines is a partnership between Alicia and Craig Mitchell and Shannyn and John Harris, the latter winemaker for this eponymous producer. John began his career at Mount Avoca, then spent eight years as winemaker at Domaine Chandon in the Yarra Valley, cramming in northern hemisphere vintages in California and Oregon. The Mitchells grew up in the Ballarat area, and have an affinity for the Macedon and Pyrenees ranges districts. While the total make is not large, a lot of thought has gone into the creation of each of the wines. A new cellar door opened mid 2012.

ŸŸŸŸŸ **Sabre 2008** A blend of chardonnay and pinot noir sourced from the Macedon Ranges and the Pyrenees, made using the traditional method, spending a minimum of three years on lees. Bright, pale green-gold, fine mousse; a perfectly balanced wine showing John Harris's long time at Domaine Chandon; the flavours are delicate and show great finesse, yet the aftertaste lingers for a substantial time. Diam. 12.5% alc. **Rating** 95 **To** 2014 $40
Pyrenees Sauvignon Blanc Fume 2011 Fermented in a mixture of 5-year-old Hungarian oak hogsheads, new to 2-year-old French oak and partial wild yeast fermentation are the cornerstones of this wine, together with carefully handled fruit picked when it was flavour-ripe. It is at once structured and savoury, yet vibrantly fresh, with texture a high point. Screwcap. 12.5% alc. **Rating** 94 **To** 2014 $22

ŸŸŸŸŸ
✪ **Rose 2011** Light puce; early-picked pinot has been blended with sangiovese to make a very interesting rose, with strawberry, rose petals and red cherry intertwined on the palate, which is uncompromisingly dry and crisp on the finish. Screwcap. 12.5% alc. **Rating** 93 **To** 2013 $22
Pyrenees Cabernet Sauvignon 2010 Rating 93 **To** 2020 $25
Pyrenees Sangiovese 2010 Rating 90 **To** 2017 $25

Mitchelton ★★★★★

Mitchellstown via Nagambie, Vic 3608 **Region** Nagambie Lakes
T (03) 5736 2222 **www**.mitchelton.com.au **Open** 7 days 10–5
Winemaker Travis Clydesdale **Est.** 1969 **Dozens** 220 000
Acquired by Petaluma in 1994 (both now part of Lion Nathan), having already put the runs on the board in no uncertain fashion with gifted winemaker Don Lewis (who retired in 2004). Mitchelton, which celebrated its 40th birthday in '09, boasts an array of wines across a broad spectrum of style and price, each carefully aimed at a market niche. In '10 Travis Clydesdale returned to complete a circle that began when his father Mark was appointed Mitchelton's cellar manager 30 years or more ago. Travis recalls riding around catwalks and playing hide and seek between the tanks as a young boy. This is not the only link with Michelton: while recently he has been winemaker at Deep Woods Estate in Margaret River, he spent seven years at Tahbilk before moving to WA, and developed a deep understanding and appreciation of Nagambie regional wine styles. In June '11 Mitchelton changed hands, purchased by Nagambie Wine Corporation (a business owned by the Ryan family), which is no doubt the reason wines were not sent in time for this edition. Tasting notes appear on www.winecompanion.com.au. Exports to all major markets.

Mitolo Wines ★★★★★

PO Box 520, Virginia, SA 5120 **Region** McLaren Vale
T (08) 8282 9012 **www**.mitolowines.com.au **Open** Not
Winemaker Ben Glaetzer **Est.** 1999 **Dozens** 20 000
Mitolo has had a meteoric rise since Frank Mitolo decided to turn a winemaking hobby into a business. In 2000 he took the plunge into the commercial end of the business, inviting Ben Glaetzer to make the wines. Split between the Jester range and single vineyard wines, Mitolo began life as a red wine-dominant brand, but now also produces Rose and Vermentino. Exports to all major markets.

�Tᵀᵀᵀᵀ Savitar McLaren Vale Shiraz 2009 Excellent crimson-purple; spicy cedary
cigar box nuances to both the bouquet and the tapestried, full-bodied palate;
the use of oak and tannin management lengthens and complexes the finish and
aftertaste. Screwcap. 14.9% alc. **Rating** 95 **To** 2030 $80
G.A.M. McLaren Vale Shiraz 2009 Excellent deep crimson-purple; first and
last a demonstration of regional character, with lush black plum in a wrapping of
dark chocolate, anise and spice; pleasantly savoury tannins on the finish. Screwcap.
14.9% alc. **Rating** 94 **To** 2029 $58
Jester McLaren Vale Cabernet Sauvignon 2010 Deep crimson-purple;
uses the Amarone technique pioneered by Joe Grilli in Australia, with 20% of the
grapes air-dried for eight weeks before being crushed; it worked for him and it
works here, adding a dimension of richness to the blackcurrant fruit and creating a
velvety texture. Screwcap. 14.9% alc. **Rating** 94 **To** 2025 $28

ᵀᵀᵀᵀ♀ Jester McLaren Vale Sangiovese Rose 2011 **Rating** 91 **To** 2013 $24

ᵀᵀᵀᵀ Jester McLaren Vale Shiraz 2010 **Rating** 89 **To** 2018 $28
Reiver Barossa Valley Shiraz 2009 **Rating** 89 **To** 2018 $58
Serpico McLaren Vale Cabernet Sauvignon 2009 **Rating** 87 **To** 2014 $80

Momentum Wines   ★★★★

8 Canal Rocks Road, Yallingup, WA 6282 **Region** Margaret River
T (08) 9755 2028 **www**.winemomentum.com **Open** W'ends & hols 10–5
Winemaker Egidijus Rusilas, Todd Payne **Est.** 1978 **Dozens** 000 **Vyds** 3.5ha
The vineyard, planted to semillon, cabernet sauvignon (1.5ha each) and sauvignon blanc
(0.5ha), was established by David Hunt in 1978. Originally called Sienna Estate, it has now
passed into the ownership of the Rusilas family, which has significantly enhanced its legacy.
Exports to Lithuania.

ᵀᵀᵀᵀ♀ Momentum of Passion Margaret River Semillon Sauvignon Blanc 2011
✪   A totally delicious easy-access blend of cut grass, citrus, pineapple, guava and
passionfruit all flowing along a single line, the aftertaste fresh and clear. Screwcap.
13% alc. **Rating** 93 **To** 2015 $15

Mongrel Vineyard   ★★★★

571 Spring Flat Road, Mudgee, NSW 2850 **Region** Mudgee
T (02) 6372 2681 **www**.mongrelwine.com.au **Open** W'ends & public hols 10–4, or by appt
Winemaker Michael Slater, Jacob Stein, David Lowe **Est.** 1998 **Dozens** 700 **Vyds** 3.2ha
In 1986 Sue and David Fairlie-Cuninghame purchased a 50ha property on Spring Flat, 6km
east of the Mudgee township. It was a weekend retreat, and the main occupation was (and
remains) fattening steers. But wine was in their blood: both were founding members of The
Rothbury Estate, and Sue was Executive Editor Food & Wine at Vogue Entertaining for over
10 years, adding, 'I was influenced by many leading winemakers from all over the world, but
not one of them ever told me what bloody back-breaking work it is, the discipline required
and how dodgy the returns.' So it was in 1998 that they planted a shiraz vineyard on their
property, using six of the principal clones. The name was chosen because of the uncontrollable
vigour of the vines, itself a legacy of the time when a sheepyard had existed where the vines
were planted, providing the soil with an inexhaustible supply of nitrogen.

ᵀᵀᵀᵀ♀ Riesling 2009 Light straw-green; has developed slowly but well, reflecting the
retention of a small amount of residual sugar; while honeyed notes are already
joining the lime base, hints of toast are just around the corner. Good each way
drinking. Screwcap. 11.5% alc. **Rating** 90 **To** 2015 $22
The Blend Shiraz Barbera Tempranillo Viognier 2010 Bright hue, but
not deep; this multinational blend works surprisingly well, the overall effect
of sparkling bright red fruits very seductive. Screwcap. 13.3% alc. **Rating** 90
To 2016 $22

Barbera 2010 Bright red-purple; has an attractive mix of red cherry and darker, more savoury, characters on its well-balanced, medium-bodied palate. Well made. Screwcap. 13.5% alc. **Rating** 90 **To** 2016 $22

♥♥♥♥   Shiraz Viognier 2010 **Rating** 87 **To** 2014 $22

Monichino Wines   ★★★

70 Berrys Road, Katunga, Vic 3640 **Region** Goulburn Valley
T (03) 5864 6452 **www**.monichino.com.au **Open** Mon–Sat 9–5, Sun 10–5
Winemaker Carlo Monichino, Terry Monichino **Est.** 1962 **Dozens** 15 000 **Vyds** 25ha
Carlo Monichino arrived in Australia from Piedmont, northern Italy, in 1948, and, together with wife Margaret, founded Monichino Wines in '62. Son Terry became involved in the winery early in his life, subsequently obtaining his wine science degree at CSU. He gained added experience visiting wineries in Italy and France, and undertaking a vintage in the Napa Valley. He and his sister Anna now run the winery, although 81-year-old Carlo still makes the fortified wines, winning a trophy at Rutherglen in 2008 for Best Australian Vintage Fortified Red. The table wine range includes Chardonnay, Sauvignon Blanc, Riesling, Semillon, Pinot Grigio, Sangiovese, Barbera, Shiraz, Cabernet Sauvignon, Merlot and Durif. The winery has excellent catering facilities, holding many wine dinners and functions, and is a popular tourist destination for a wide range of events.

♥♥♥♥   **Cabernet Sauvignon 2009** Something of a surprise packet; oak, so often
✪   misused with wine that struggles to compete, has been used here to good effect. What is more, it is the American, not the French, component that is most obvious. The end result is a wine full of berry fruit, mocha, vanilla and cedar plus ripe tannins. Screwcap. 14.1% alc. **Rating** 89 **To** 2014 $16
Chardonnay 2011 A fresh, fault-free chardonnay, with some stone fruit aromas and flavours to accompany the citrus notes. Simple, and ready now. Screwcap. 13% alc. **Rating** 87 **To** 2013 $15

Montalto Vineyards   ★★★★★

33 Shoreham Road, Red Hill South, Vic 3937 **Region** Mornington Peninsula
T (03) 5989 8412 **www**.montalto.com.au **Open** 7 days 11–5
Winemaker Simon Black **Est.** 1998 **Dozens** 6000 **Vyds** 11ha
John Mitchell and family established Montalto Vineyards in 1998, but the core of the vineyard goes back to '86. There are 6ha of pinot noir, 3ha of chardonnay, 1ha of pinot gris, and 0.5ha each of semillon and riesling. Intensive vineyard work opens up the canopy, with yields ranging between 1.5 and 2.5 tonnes per acre. Wines are released under two labels, the flagship Montalto and Pennon, the latter a lower-priced second label. In 2010 Montalto opened its own winery in a converted coolstore in Merricks North, ending a long period of skilled contract winemaking by Robin Brockett of Scotchmans Hill.

♥♥♥♥♥   **Estate Mornington Peninsula Chardonnay 2010** A heady mix of stone fruits, grilled cashews, charcuterie and spices are all on show on the bouquet; the concentration and the level of complexity step up another notch on the palate, with tangy acidity and a long, fresh, even and pure finish; an excellent wine for drinking early, or for holding on to. Screwcap. 13.5% alc. **Rating** 96 **To** 2020 $39 BE
Single Vineyard The Eleven Mornington Peninsula Chardonnay 2009 This comes from the eleven oldest rows of chardonnay, hence the name. Bright quartz-green, the wine is an exercise in purity and elegance, tangy stone fruit dominant, the French oak now tightly fused with the fruit, the long finish dry and almost airy. Screwcap. 13.5% alc. **Rating** 96 **To** 2018 $55
Pennon Hill Mornington Peninsula Shiraz 2010 Deep crimson; a bright, fragrant and perfumed bouquet, showing complexity and purity in spades; red and black fruits, spices, florals and a fascinating thread of quartz minerality; medium-bodied and fleshy, with taut acidity and fine-grained tannins aplenty. Screwcap. 14% alc. **Rating** 95 **To** 2018 $30 BE

Estate Mornington Peninsula Riesling 2011 A fine lemon and mineral-accented bouquet, showing bath talc and a touch of thyme; the palate is fine, lacy and focused, fresh and zesty; accessible as a young wine, while also having plenty in reserve for cellaring. Screwcap. 13% alc. Rating 94 To 2020 $25

Single Vineyard Hawkins Hill Mornington Peninsula Chardonnay 2010 A fleshy and fresh bouquet, redolent of nectarine, clove, grilled cashews and a touch of fennel; the palate reveals a soft personality on entry, building with flavour seamlessly; restrained power. Screwcap. 13.5% alc. Rating 94 To 2017 $55 BE

Single Vineyard Lake Block Mornington Peninsula Pinot Noir 2010 Mid garnet; this single block wine displays an elegant, subtle and refined personality, full of red fruits, a splash of thyme and spicy oak; the palate is light-bodied and graceful, with silky tannins prevailing on the sweet oak, and a long and fragrant finish. Screwcap. 14.5% alc. Rating 94 To 2016 $65 BE

Single Vineyard Merricks Block Mornington Peninsula Pinot Noir 2010 Deep crimson in colour; the bouquet is redolent of dark fruits, hoi sin, Asian spices and traces of charry oak; the palate is generous and rich on entry, making way for savoury spice and fine tannins on the warm and engagingly generous finish. Screwcap. 14.5% alc. Rating 94 To 2017 $65 BE

Estate Mornington Peninsula Pinot Noir 2010 Mid garnet; a distinctly savoury, vibrant and mineral-accented bouquet, showing spice and plenty of perfume; the light to medium-bodied palate is succulent and attractive on entry, and builds in flavour; silky texture, with fine tannins lingering on the balanced, elegant and poised finish. Gold medal National Wine Show '11. Screwcap. 14.5% alc. Rating 94 To 2016 $48 BE

ΨΨΨΨΩ Single Vineyard The Eleven Mornington Peninsula Chardonnay 2010 Rating 93 To 2016 $55 BE
Estate Mornington Peninsula Cuvee One 2008 Rating 93 To 2016 $40 BE
Single Vineyard Main Ridge Block Mornington Peninsula Pinot Noir 2010 Rating 92 To 2017 $65 BE
Pennon Hill Mornington Peninsula Pinot Noir 2010 Rating 91 To 2015 $30 BE
Pennon Hill Mornington Peninsula Tempranillo 2010 Rating 90 To 2016 $30 BE

ΨΨΨΨ Pennon Hill Mornington Peninsula Sauvignon Blanc 2011 Rating 88 To 2014 $23 BE
Pennon Hill Mornington Peninsula Pinot Grigio 2011 Rating 88 To 2014 $23 BE
Pennon Hill Mornington Peninsula Rose 2011 Rating 88 To 2014 $23 BE

Montara ★★★★

76 Chalambar Road, Ararat, Vic 3377 **Region** Grampians
T (03) 5352 3868 **www.**montara.com.au **Open** Fri–Sun 11–4
Winemaker Leigh Clarnette **Est.** 1970 **Dozens** 3000 **Vyds** 19.2ha
Gained considerable attention for its Pinot Noirs during the 1980s, and continues to produce wines of distinctive style. One of the most engaging promotions in the entire wine industry is the annual Montara Scarecrow Competition held in the vineyard at the end of April, even Cirque du Soleil might gain inspiration. I hope the Stapleton family, who have purchased the winery from the founding McRae family, will not evict the scarecrows. Exports to the US, Ireland and China.

ΨΨΨΨΩ Grampians Pinot Noir 2010 Rating 93 To 2018 $25

ΨΨΨΨ Grampians Riesling 2010 Rating 87 To 2013 $17

Montgomery's Hill ★★★★★

South Coast Highway, Upper Kalgan, Albany, WA 6330 **Region** Albany
T (08) 9844 3715 **www**.montgomeryshill.com.au **Open** 7 days 11–5
Winemaker The Vintage Wineworx, Bill Crappsley (Consultant) **Est.** 1996 **Dozens** 6000
Montgomery's Hill is 16km northeast of Albany on a north-facing slope on the banks of the
Kalgan River. Previously used as an apple orchard, it is a diversification for the third generation
of the Montgomery family. Chardonnay, cabernet sauvignon, cabernet franc, sauvignon blanc,
shiraz and merlot were planted in 1996–97. The wines are made with a gentle touch.

🍷🍷🍷🍷🍷 **The Mulberry Block Reserve Albany Chardonnay 2010** This is a very good
Chardonnay by any standards, proclaiming its quality with the first whiff of the
bouquet, and even more with the first sip of the palate. Beautifully intense and
focused, its flavours centre around stone fruit and grapefruit, oak far from obvious.
It surges on the finish, leaving a tingling aftertaste. Screwcap. 12% alc. **Rating** 95
To 2017 $35

✪ **Albany Sauvignon Blanc 2010** Bright straw-green; the wine has exceptional
intensity to the bouquet of snow pea and citrus, and even more to the delicious
palate of pink grapefruit and tropical fruit salad, finishing with fresh, zesty acidity.
Screwcap. 12% alc. **Rating** 94 **To** Now $18

✪ **Albany Shiraz 2009** Vivid purple-crimson; an impressive cool-grown shiraz,
showing what Albany can achieve with this variety. Sultry spices, pepper and clove
are woven through the black cherry/blackberry fruit, the tannins firm but fine.
Screwcap. 13% alc. **Rating** 94 **To** 2020 $20

Moombaki Wines ★★★★★

341 Parker Road, Kentdale via Denmark, WA 6333 **Region** Denmark
T (08) 9840 8006 **www**.moombaki.com **Open** 7 days 11–5
Winemaker Harewood Estate (James Kellie) **Est.** 1997 **Dozens** 1000 **Vyds** 2.4ha
David Britten and Melissa Boughey (with three young sons in tow) established vines on
a north-facing gravel hillside, with picturesque Kent River frontage. Not content with
establishing the vineyard (cabernet sauvignon, shiraz, cabernet franc, malbec and chardonnay),
they put in significant mixed tree plantings to increase wildlife habitats. It is against this
background that they chose Moombaki as their vineyard name: it is a local Aboriginal word
meaning 'where the river meets the sky'. No wines were received for this edition; the rating
is that of last year. Exports to the UK, Switzerland, Malaysia and Singapore.

Moondah Brook ★★★★☆

Dale Road, Middle Swan, WA 6056 **Region** Swan Valley
T (08) 9274 9540 **www**.moondahbrook.com.au **Open** Not
Winemaker Courtney Treacher **Est.** 1968 **Dozens** NFP
Part of Accolade Wines, Moondah Brook has its own special character, as it draws part
of its fruit from the large Gingin vineyard, 70km north of the Swan Valley, and part from
the Margaret River and Great Southern. From time to time it has exceeded even its own
reputation for reliability with some quite lovely wines, in particular honeyed, aged Chenin
Blanc, generous Shiraz and finely structured Cabernet Sauvignon. Last year's rating is
maintained in the absence of a representative submission of its wines. Exports to Canada,
Pacific Islands and China.

🍷🍷🍷🍷 **Shiraz 2010** Bright and clear purple-crimson; light- to medium-bodied
with spicy red and black fruits, fine tannins and subtle oak. Screwcap. 14% alc.
Rating 88 **To** 2015 $16

Moondarra ★★★★☆

Browns Road, Moondarra via Erica, Vic 3825 (postal) **Region** Gippsland
T 0408 666 348 **www**.moondarra.com.au **Open** Not
Winemaker Neil Prentice **Est.** 1991 **Dozens** 3000 **Vyds** 10ha

In 1991 Neil Prentice and family established their Moondarra Vineyard in Gippsland, eventually focusing on the 2ha of low-yielding pinot noir. Subsequently, they began planting their Holly's Garden vineyard at Whitlands in the King Valley, where they have 8ha of pinot gris and pinot noir. It is from this vineyard that all but 200 dozen of their wines come, sold under the Holly's Garden label. Exports to the US, Singapore, Hong Kong, the Philippines, South Korea and Japan.

ŶŶŶŶŶ **Conception Gippsland Pinot Noir 2010** Slight bricking; the bouquet is a complex melange of cold tea, spiced plums, earth and a little struck match complexity; the palate is fine, fragrant and vibrant, with velvety tannins persisting on the expansive conclusion; lots of flavour at 13% alc/vol, bravo. Screwcap. 13% alc. **Rating** 94 **To** 2015 $60 BE

ŶŶŶŶ **Holly's Garden Pinot Gris 2011 Rating** 89 **To** 2015 $25
Samba Side Gippsland Pinot Noir 2010 Rating 89 **To** 2020 $80

Moorebank Vineyard   ★★★

150 Palmers Lane, Pokolbin, NSW 2320 **Region** Hunter Valley
T (02) 4998 7610 **www**.moorebankvineyard.com.au **Open** 7 days 10–5
Winemaker Gary Reed **Est.** 1977 **Dozens** 3000 **Vyds** 6ha
Ian Burgess and Debra Moore own a mature vineyard planted to chardonnay (3ha), semillon, gewurztraminer and merlot (1ha each), with a small cellar door operation offering immaculately packaged wines in avant-garde style. Exports to Singapore, China and Japan.

ŶŶŶŶ **The Press Room Classic S.C.M. Red 2009** Relatively light colour, the hue still good; blackberry and redcurrant fruit flavours drive the medium-bodied palate before oak comes into the picture on the finish, aided by fine tannins. Shiraz/ Cabernet Sauvignon/Merlot. Screwcap. 12.5% alc. **Rating** 89 **To** 2019 $38
The Press Room S.C.G. 2008 A blend of Semillon, Chardonnay and Gewurztraminer, the wine has a bright, green-straw colour, and plenty of ripe fruit flavours; most likely at its best over the next couple of years. Screwcap. 11.5% alc. **Rating** 88 **To** 2014 $38
Hunter Valley Shiraz Merlot 2007 Merlot is not expected to show well in the Hunter Valley, but this is a pleasant wine with gently sweet red berry fruits, soft tannins and a balanced finish. Screwcap. 13.5% alc. **Rating** 88 **To** 2015 $38

Moores Hill Estate   ★★★★☆

3343 West Tamar Highway, Sidmouth, Tas 7270 **Region** Northern Tasmania
T (03) 6394 7649 **www**.mooreshill.com.au **Open** 7 days 10–5
Winemaker Julian Allport **Est.** 1997 **Dozens** 3000 **Vyds** 4.5ha
Planting of the Moores Hill Estate vineyard (jointly owned by winemaker Julian Allport with Fiona and Lance Weller) began in 1997 and progressively expanded, and now consists of pinot noir, chardonnay and riesling, with a very small amount of cabernet sauvignon and merlot. The vines are located on a northeast-facing hillside, 5km from the Tamar River and 30km from the Bass Strait. The cellar door is built from timber found on the property.

ŶŶŶŶŶ **CGR Late Harvest Riesling 2010** Mid straw-green; the balance between the unctuous sweetness and Tasmanian acidity comes off well, and garnered the wine a gold medal at the International Sweet Wine Challenge '11. It has unusual texture for a wine in this category. 375ml. Screwcap. 9.2% alc. **Rating** 94 **To** 2015 $30

ŶŶŶŶŶ **Riesling 2011 Rating** 90 **To** 2020 $27

ŶŶŶŶ **Pinot Noir 2010 Rating** 89 **To** 2014 $31
Cabernet Merlot 2010 Rating 88 **To** 2015 $27

Moorilla Estate

655 Main Road, Berriedale, Tas 7011 **Region** Southern Tasmania
T (03) 6277 9900 **www**.moorilla.com.au **Open** 7 days 10–5
Winemaker Conor van der Reest **Est.** 1958 **Dozens** 9400 **Vyds** 14.3ha

Moorilla Estate was the second winery to be established in Tasmania in the 20th century, Jean Miguet's La Provence beating it to the punch by two years. However, through much of the history of Moorilla Estate, it was the most important winery in the state, if not in size but as the icon. Magnificently situated on a mini-isthmus reaching into the Derwent River, and a lazy 20-min drive from the Hobart CBD, it has always been a must-visit for wine lovers and tourists. A new winery, completed prior to the 2010 vintage, saw a decrease of 80% from peak production to around 90 tonnes per year sourced entirely from the vineyards around Moorilla, and its St Matthias Vineyard (Tamar Valley). It's almost incidental that the new winery is part of an overall development said by observers (not Moorilla) to cost upwards of $150 million. It also houses the boutique brewery Moo Brew, but its raison d'être is the establishment of an art gallery (MONA) that has the highest accreditation of any gallery in the Southern Hemisphere, housing both the extraordinary ancient and contemporary art collection assembled by Moorilla's owner, David Walson, and visiting exhibitions from major art museums around the world. The official opening of the Museum in Jan '11 was attended by 2000 guests from all corners of the globe.

ŶŶŶŶŶ **Muse Riesling 2009** Still remarkably pale colour; the flowery and fragrant bouquet has citrus and honeysuckle blossom nuances that join together on the long, fine palate; still in its infancy, and will repay extended cellaring. Screwcap. 13.3% alc. **Rating** 94 **To** 2025 $25
Muse Chardonnay 2009 The most (sexually) explicit label in the Muse series, and that's saying something. The wine has a shaft of purity driving through the length of the palate, the absence of mlf the reason; white peach fruit is shrouded by citrussy acidity, oak in the shadows; it all works surprisingly well. Screwcap. 14% alc. **Rating** 94 **To** 2020 $45
Muse Pinot Noir 2009 Good depth to the colour; a substantial pinot by any standards, full of spicy, ripe and rounded berry, plum and black cherry fruit; the tannins are ripe, and the wine will continue to develop well for years to come. Screwcap. 14% alc. **Rating** 94 **To** 2019 $45
Muse St Matthias Vineyard Syrah 2009 Good colour; an intensely spicy, savoury Shiraz with a palate of high-tensile energy signalling the very cool climate that has nonetheless allowed the grapes to fully ripen. Has considerable length and underlines the fact that Tasmanian Shiraz/Syrah is here to stay (in good vintages). Screwcap. 14.2% alc. **Rating** 94 **To** 2030 $60

ŶŶŶŶŶ **Praxis Riesling 2009** **Rating** 92
O To 2024 $20
Muse Gewurztraminer 2011 **Rating** 91 **To** 2015 $35
Muse Sauvignon 2010 **Rating** 91 **To** 2015 $29
Praxis Pinot Noir 2010 **Rating** 91 **To** 2016 $30
Muse Shiraz 2009 **Rating** 91 **To** 2018 $60
Praxis Sauvignon Blanc 2011 **Rating** 90 **To** 2014 $25

ŶŶŶŶ **Muse Pinot Gris 2010** **Rating** 89 **To** 2014 $35
Muse Merlot Cabernet 2009 **Rating** 89 **To** 2018 $35
Muse Vintage Brut 2007 **Rating** 89 **To** 2014 $49
Muse Methode Traditionelle Vintage Brut Rose 2007 **Rating** 89 **To** 2013 $49

Moorooduc Estate

501 Derril Road, Moorooduc, Vic 3936 **Region** Mornington Peninsula
T (03) 5971 8506 **www**.moorooducestate.com.au **Open** Thurs–Mon 11–5
Winemaker Dr Richard McIntyre **Est.** 1983 **Dozens** 5000 **Vyds** 6.5ha

Richard McIntyre has taken Moorooduc Estate to new heights, having completely mastered the difficult art of gaining maximum results from wild yeast fermentations. Starting with the 2010 vintage, there has been a complete revamp of grape sources, and hence changes to the tiered structure of the releases. These changes were driven by the simple fact of life that the estate vineyards had no possibility of providing the 5000–6000 dozen bottles of wine sold each year. The entry point wines under the Devil Bend Creek label remain, as before, principally sourced from the Osborn Vineyard. The mid priced Chardonnay and Pinot Noir are no longer single estate vineyard wines, and are now simply labelled by vintage and variety. At the top come the Robson Vineyard Pinot Noir and Chardonnay, elevated to reserve wine status, priced a little below the ultimate 'Ducs' (Moorooduc Vineyard). These have always been individual vineyards, and will remain so, but clearly declared as such on the front labels. Exports to the UK, the US, Hong Kong and Singapore.

ŢŢŢŢŢ **The Moorooduc McIntyre Chardonnay 2010** Richard McIntyre has pulled out the funky stick with this wine and held nothing back; the bouquet is full of ripe hedonistic stone fruit aromas, carried along by a wind of savoury charcuterie and spice; the palate is unctuous, deep and long, with generosity and a backbone of grip the central theme. Screwcap. 13.5% alc. **Rating** 95 **To** 2017 $65 BE
Robinson Pinot Noir 2010 Deep crimson; a dark and brooding combination of spice, game, star anise and seductive fruits all evident on the bouquet; the palate is almost luscious on entry, compelling and incredibly long, with ample silky tannins, linear acidity and true precision all present and accounted for. Screwcap. 14% alc. **Rating** 95 **To** 2018 $55 BE
Robinson Chardonnay 2010 A tightly wound and pure-fruited wine, showing pear and nectarine, lots of seductive spices and a lick of toasty oak; the palate is sweet-fruited and generous, silky and layered, with a fine backbone of acidity and a long, savoury and mealy conclusion. Screwcap. 12.5% alc. **Rating** 94 **To** 2016 $55 BE
Pinot Noir 2010 Mid crimson; the bouquet is loaded with seductive sweet red and black fruits, Asian spices and a little gamey complexity; the palate is silky and seductive on entry, the mid palate with a firm structure in harmony with the generous fruit; long, layered and expansive. Screwcap. 14% alc. **Rating** 94 **To** 2018 $35 BE
The Moorooduc McIntyre Pinot Noir 2010 Deep colour; this is a thought-provoking blend of aromas ranging from black cherry, liqueur-soaked plums, exotic spices and orange to a bracken complexity adding extra lift; the palate is long, rich and expressive, certain to create discussion around the table. Screwcap. 14% alc. **Rating** 94 **To** 2017 $65 BE
McIntyre Vineyard Shiraz 2009 Rhône-inspired savoury and medium-bodied Shiraz is a good fit for the Mornington Peninsula, and this wine is fragrant and finely detailed, showing red fruits, vine sap, fine tannins and a long and expansive finish; Shiraz for the Pinot lover. Screwcap. 13.5% alc. **Rating** 94 **To** 2018 $35 BE

ŢŢŢŢŢ **Chardonnay 2010 Rating** 91 **To** 2016 $35 BE
Devil Bend Creek Pinot Noir 2010 Rating 90 **To** 2016 $28 BE

ŢŢŢŢ **Devil Bend Creek Chardonnay 2010 Rating** 89 **To** 2013 $28 BE

Moorooroo Park Vineyards ★★★

Nitschke Road, Tanunda, SA 5352 **Region** Barossa Valley
T (08) 8563 0422 **www.**moorooroopark.com.au **Open** Fri–Mon 11–5
Winemaker Stephen Black, Wyndham House **Est.** 2000 **Dozens** 2000 **Vyds** 1.25ha
Moorooroo Park Vineyards is owned by Wyndham and Patricia House, who have had many years' experience in the catering business. It is part of a larger venture known as the Jacobs Creek Retreat, established in 1996 for accommodation, with ongoing restoration of the historic buildings set among lavish French-inspired gardens. It has nothing to do with the Pernod Ricard Jacob's Creek; place names cannot be trademarked, hence the ability to use the Jacob's Creek name. They have a little over 1ha of shiraz planted to clone 1654, and also purchase grapes from other growers.

ŶŶŶŶ **Dolce Far Niente Barossa Valley Late Harvest Semillon 2008** Curious name: Far Niente is the name of a highly distinguished Napa Valley winery. The wine has very good green-tinged colour, but late harvest semillon without botrytis has its limitations, catching on the finish. Diam. 12% alc. **Rating** 87 **To** 2013 $26

Moothi Estate   ★★★
85 Rocky Waterhole Road, Mudgee, NSW 2850 **Region** Mudgee
T (02) 6372 2925 **www**.moothiestate.com.au **Open** Fri–Mon 10–5
Winemaker Michael Slater **Est.** 1995 **Dozens** 2000 **Vyds** 17.5ha
Phil and Susan Moore purchased a property on the northwest-facing slopes of Mt Frome, at an elevation of 550 m, in 1995. The site has reddish-brown clay with limestone, quartz and ironstone gibber soil, well suited to the cabernet sauvignon, shiraz, merlot, chardonnay, semillon, riesling, viognier and pinot gris established on the property. The names of the wines are derived from the Koori name for Mudgee, which is Moothi; 'Moothi Mud' is said to be local slang for Mudgee's full-bodied reds.

ŶŶŶŶ **Rocky Waterhole Road Mudgee Riesling 2011** A fragrant blend of tropical fruits, rosehip and coriander; the palate is soft, forward and built in a user-friendly style. Screwcap. 11% alc. **Rating** 87 **To** 2015 $24 BE
Rocky Waterhole Road Mudgee Chardonnay 2011 Mid gold; a brassy and ripe bouquet of fig, melon and spice; the palate is soft, fleshy and with enough acidity to provide freshness and contrast; toasty on the finish. Screwcap. 13% alc. **Rating** 87 **To** 2013 $18 BE

Moppity Vineyards   ★★★★★
Moppity Road, Young, NSW 2594 (postal) **Region** Hilltops
T (02) 6382 6222 **www**.moppity.com.au **Open** Not
Winemaker Jason Brown **Est.** 1973 **Dozens** 30 000 **Vyds** 73ha
Jason Brown and wife Alecia, with backgrounds in fine wine retail and accounting, purchased Moppity Vineyards in 2004; it was then already 31 years old. Initially they were content to sell the grapes to other makers, but that changed with the release of the '06 Shiraz, which won top gold in its class at the London International Wine & Spirit Competition. In Nov '09 the '08 Eden Road Long Road Hilltops Shiraz, made from Moppity Vineyards grapes, won the Jimmy Watson Trophy. These awards are among a cascade of golds for its Shirazs, Riesling, Tumbarumba Chardonnay and Cabernet Sauvignon. The consequence has been that production (and sales) have soared, and all of the grapes from the estate are now used for the Moppity Vineyards brand. The Lock & Key range provides exceptional value for money. Exports to the UK and China.

ŶŶŶŶŶ **Reserve Hilltops Shiraz 2009** Good crimson-purple; the small percentage of co-fermented viognier may have helped this beautifully balanced and composed wine, made from very low-yielding, drought-affected vines, yet magically showing no signs of stress. The bouquet is beautifully fragrant and perfumed, the medium-bodied palate with black and red cherry, licorice, spice and high-quality oak flavours. Screwcap. 13.9% alc. **Rating** 97 **To** 2030 $60
Single Vineyard Hilltops Riesling 2011 Bright quartz-green; a distinguished Riesling, its fragrant lime aromas allied with a touch of spice, the palate with finely focused lime juice backed and lengthened by minerally acidity. Screwcap. 11.5% alc. **Rating** 94 **To** 2020 $25

ŶŶŶŶŶ **Lock & Key Single Vineyard Orange Sauvignon Blanc 2011** An interesting
✪   move from the estate-owned Hilltops vineyards, with contract-grown fruit still allowing Moppity to come in at the critical $15 price barrier. Orange is a remarkable region for sauvignon blanc and Nick Spencer is a top-class winemaker. The wine is intense and long, fusing citrus and tropical fruits into a coherent whole. Screwcap. 12% alc. **Rating** 93 **To** 2013 $15
Single Vineyard Orange Sauvignon Blanc 2011 Rating 93 **To** 2013 $5

✪ **Lock & Key Single Vineyard Hilltops Riesling 2011** Light straw-green; a deceptive wine, the bouquet with good varietal expression, but not hinting at the green grapefruit and lemon zest mid palate and on the finish; a wine with attitude, not entirely respectful, although time may teach it good manners. Screwcap. 11% alc. **Rating** 91 **To** 2019 $15

✪ **Lock & Key Single Vineyard Orange Chardonnay 2010** Bright straw-green; the bouquet has light aromas of melon and peach plus a hint of oak spice from partial barrel fermentation, the palate adding citrus that helps extend its intensity and length. Comes together very well. Screwcap. 13% alc. **Rating** 90 **To** 2014 $15

🍷🍷🍷🍷 **Lock & Key Single Vineyard Hilltops Shiraz 2010 Rating** 89 **To** 2015 $15

Morambro Creek Wines ★★★★
PMB 98, Naracoorte, SA 5271 (postal) **Region** Padthaway
T (08) 8765 6043 **www**.morambrocreek.com.au **Open** Not
Winemaker Ben Riggs **Est.** 1994 **Dozens** 30 000 **Vyds** 178.5ha
The Bryson family has been involved in agriculture for more than a century, moving to Padthaway in 1955 as farmers and graziers. Since the '90s, they have progressively established large plantings of shiraz (88.5ha), cabernet sauvignon (47.5ha), chardonnay (34.5ha) and sauvignon blanc (8ha). The Morambro Creek and Mt. Monster wines have been consistent winners of wine show medals. Exports to the UK, the US and other major markets.

🍷🍷🍷🍷🍷 **Padthaway Shiraz 2010** Impenetrable colour; deep and dark in fruit and structure, this is a more of everything style of wine, and while very concentrated, exhibits life and generosity; big-boned, charry and ripe. For lovers of big shiraz. Screwcap. 14.5% alc. **Rating** 91 **To** 2018 $30 BE

✪ **Jip Jip Rocks Padthaway Shiraz Cabernet 2010** Strong red-purple; a powerful, full-bodied 55/45% blend that has a large volume of mouth-filling black fruits, ripe tannins and background oak. Is tailor-made for charcoal-grilled meat. Screwcap. 14.5% alc. **Rating** 90 **To** 2020 $19

The Bryson Barrel Select 2009 Deep garnet; a dark and brooding bouquet of black fruits offset by a touch of eucalypt; the full-bodied palate is full of toasty oak, dark fruits and chewy tannins; big-boned and rich. Shiraz/Cabernet Sauvignon. Screwcap. 14.5% alc. **Rating** 90 **To** 2017 $55 BE

🍷🍷🍷🍷 **Jip Jip Rocks Padthaway Unoaked Chardonnay 2011 Rating** 89 **To** 2013 $19

✪ **Mt. Monster Shiraz 2010 Rating** 89 **To** 2015 $15
Jip Jip Rocks Padthaway Shiraz 2010 Rating 89 **To** 2020 $19

✪ **Mt. Monster Cabernet 2010 Rating** 89 **To** 2020 $15
Padthaway Cabernet Sauvignon 2010 Rating 89 **To** 2017 $30 BE
Jip Jip Rocks Padthaway Sauvignon Blanc 2011 Rating 87 **To** Now $19 BE
Jip Jip Rocks Sparkling Shiraz NV Rating 87 **To** Now $19

Morgan Simpson ★★★
PO Box 39, Kensington Park, SA 5068 **Region** McLaren Vale
T 0417 843 118 **www**.morgansimpson.com.au **Open** Not
Winemaker Richard Simpson **Est.** 1998 **Dozens** 1500
Morgan Simpson was founded by SA businessman George Morgan (since retired) and winemaker Richard Simpson, who is a graduate of CSU. The grapes are sourced from the Clos Robert Vineyard (where the wine is made), planted to shiraz (11.8ha), cabernet sauvignon (3.6ha), chardonnay (1.8ha), mourvedre (3.5ha), sauvignon blanc (2.5ha), semillon and chardonnay (1.8ha each), and established by Robert Allen Simpson in 1972. Most of the grapes are sold, the remainder used to provide the reasonably priced, drinkable wines for which Morgan Simpson has become well known.

🍷🍷🍷🍷 **Plan B McLaren Vale Mataro 2010** Bright colour; pencil lead, raspberry and Provençal herbs on the bouquet; the palate is zesty on entry, but tannic to conclude. Screwcap. 15.7% alc. **Rating** 88 **To** 2016 $18 BE

Endangered Species McLaren Vale Semillon 2011 Green fruit dominates the bouquet, with a pungency that is challenging; the palate is lively and fresh, so if you like wines that grab your attention, this may be a good one for you. Screwcap. 11.6% alc. **Rating** 87 **To** 2013 $18 BE

Morningside Vineyard ★★★★☆

711 Middle Tea Tree Road, Tea Tree, Tas 7017 **Region** Southern Tasmania
T (03) 6268 1748 **www**.morningsidevineyard.com.au **Open** By appt
Winemaker Peter Bosworth **Est.** 1980 **Dozens** 600 **Vyds** 2.8ha
The name Morningside was given to the old property on which the vineyard stands because it gets the morning sun first; the property on the other side of the valley was known as Eveningside. Consistent with the observation of the early settlers, the Morningside grapes achieve full maturity with good colour and varietal flavour. Production will increase as the vineyard matures, and as recent additions of clonally selected pinot noir (including 8104, 115 and 777) come into bearing. The Bosworth family, headed by Peter and wife Brenda, do all the vineyard and winery work, with conspicuous attention to detail.

♟♟♟♟♟ **Chardonnay 2009** The ideal slopes of the vineyard explain why this immaculately balanced wine has none of the searing acidity that can appear in Tasmanian Chardonnay; instead there is a delicious mix of stone fruit and melon with a cradle of subtle oak. Screwcap. 13% alc. **Rating** 94 **To** 2017 $25

♟♟♟♟♟ **Riesling 2011 Rating** 90 **To** 2018 $24 BE

Morris ★★★★★

Mia Mia Road, Rutherglen, Vic 3685 **Region** Rutherglen
T (02) 6026 7303 **www**.morriswines.com **Open** Mon–Sat 9–5, Sun 10–5
Winemaker David Morris **Est.** 1859 **Dozens** 100 000 **Vyds** 96ha
One of the greatest of the fortified winemakers, ranking with Chambers Rosewood. Morris has changed its labelling system for its sublime fortified wines, with a higher-than-average entry point with the (Classic) Liqueur Muscat; Tokay, and the ultra-premium wines are being released under the Old Premium Liqueur (Rare) label. The oldest components of the Old Premium are entered in a handful of shows, but the trophies and stratospheric gold medal points they receive are not claimed for the Old Premium wines. The art of these wines lies in the blending of very old and much younger material. They have no equivalent in any other part of the world.

♟♟♟♟♟ **Old Premium Liqueur Muscat NV** Deep olive-brown, coating the sides of the glass briefly when it is swirled; needless to say, is exceptionally rich and luscious, but – even more – complex, with a dense array of oriental sweet spices, dried raisins, and (for me) childhood memories of mother's Christmas pudding laced with brandy. And, yes, this really does go with dark, bitter chocolate in any form. 500ml. Cork. 17.5% alc. **Rating** 97 **To** 2013 $65

Old Premium Tawny NV Medium depth to the colour; a true tawny and not liqueur; a vibrant palate, with rich and luscious fruit, then extreme rancio providing perfect balance, the acidity neither biting nor volatile. Great texture. 500ml. Cork. 18% alc. **Rating** 96 **To** 2013 $45

Old Premium Liqueur Tokay NV Mahogany, with an olive rim; aromas of Christmas cake and tea; incredibly viscous and rich, with layer upon layer of flavours ranging through ginger snap, burnt butterscotch, and every imaginable spice, the length and depth of the palate is as extraordinary as is that of the aftertaste. Released in tiny quantities each year, which maintains the extreme average age of each release. 500ml. Screwcap. 18% alc. **Rating** 96 **To** 2013 $65

✪ **Cellar Reserve Rutherglen Tokay NV** So viscous, rich, concentrated and complex it is hard to imagine there is a level higher than the Grand, but the magnificent Old Premium (all but in name Rare) delivers it. 500ml Screwcap. 17% alc. **Rating** 95 **To** 2013 $35

CHM Rutherglen Durif 2007 Deeper colour than the '08 standard Durif; named in honour of Mick (Charles Henry) Morris, and made from the best parcels of the oldest vines on the vineyard. It has an excellent bouquet and mid palate, but I just wish the tannins weren't quite so dry. It's probable they will soften with age, and in every other respect the wine is excellent. Screwcap. 15% alc. Rating 94 To 2027 $50

Liqueur Tokay NV Golden brown; highly perfumed classic aromas of cold tea, rose petals and Christmas cake; excellent spirit and balance. 500ml. Screwcap. 17.5% alc. Rating 93 To 2013 $17

Liqueur Muscat NV More touches of red-brown than the Liqueur Tokay, precisely as it should be; fragrant raisin varietal fruit luring you into the second glass; perfect balance. 500ml. Screwcap. 17.5% alc. Rating 93 To 2013 $17

Rutherglen Durif 2008 Rating 92 To 2018 $25

Old Premium Amontillado Sherry NV Rating 87 To 2015 $45

Moss Brothers ★★★★★

3857 Caves Road, Wilyabrup, WA 6280 **Region** Margaret River
T (08) 9755 6270 **www**.mossbrothers.com.au **Open** 7 days 10–5
Winemaker Bernie Stanlake **Est.** 1984 **Dozens** 7000 **Vyds** 9.6ha
Patriarch Jeff Moss began his wine career in 1947, first with Mildara, then the Victorian Government, while simultaneously developing a 20ha vineyard, followed by a five-year stint with Seppelt. In 1978 he and his family moved to WA, where he became vineyard manager for Houghton, part of his job entailing the identification of worthwhile vineyards in the cooler south of the state. The family took its first step in 1984 when it purchased the Caves Road property, commencing planting the following year. With various children involved in differing roles over the years, Moss Brothers has grown, most significantly with the construction of a 400-tonne winery in '92, which processes both estate-grown and purchased grapes for the Moss Brothers label, and provides contract winemaking services. Exports to Germany and Singapore.

The Wilyabrup 2010 Strong colour; 50% cabernet sauvignon, 25% cabernet franc and 25% petit verdot, a highly fragrant bouquet foreshadowing the mix of cedar, cassis and black cherry on the fine-boned and long palate; a highly successful venture into left field. Screwcap. 14.5% alc. Rating 95 To 2020 $30

Margaret River Cabernet Sauvignon 2010 Good hue; the bouquet is complex, with focused cassis/blackcurrant fruit, as is the elegant palate with its finely drawn tannins and lingering finish. Screwcap. 14.5% alc. Rating 94 To 2020 $30

Moses Rock Margaret River Semillon Sauvignon Blanc 2011 Light straw-green; snow pea, cut grass and citrus drive the bouquet and palate alike, with some tropical nuances coming through towards the finish. Screwcap. 12.5% alc. Rating 89 To 2014 $19

Moses Rock Margaret River Cabernet Shiraz 2010 Medium red-purple; there is a profusion of aromas and flavours on the bouquet and palate alike: red cherry, mint, spice and blackberry, fruity more than savoury. Screwcap. 14.5% alc. Rating 89 To 2015 $19

Margaret River Shiraz 2010 Rating 88 To 2017 $30

Moss Wood ★★★★★

Metricup Road, Wilyabrup, WA 6284 **Region** Margaret River
T (08) 9755 6266 **www**.mosswood.com.au **Open** By appt
Winemaker Keith Mugford, Josh Bahen, Amanda Shepherdson **Est.** 1969 **Dozens** 15 000
Widely regarded as one of the best wineries in the region, capable of producing glorious Semillon in both oaked and unoaked forms, unctuous Chardonnay and elegant, gently herbaceous, superfine Cabernet Sauvignon which lives for many years. In 2000 Moss

Wood acquired the Ribbon Vale Estate; the Ribbon Vale wines are now treated as vineyard-designated within the Moss Wood umbrella. Exports to all major markets.

ΥΥΥΥΥ Margaret River Cabernet Sauvignon 2008 Strong, healthy red-purple; a distinguished vintage for this Margaret River blue-blood wine, medium-bodied but with innate complexity; fine savoury tannins run through the black fruits and cassis of the palate, putting structure in place so subtly you can barely notice it, or the length of the palate. Screwcap. 14.5% alc. **Rating** 96 **To** 2028 $115
Ribbon Vale Vineyard Margaret River Semillon Sauvignon Blanc 2011 There can be no doubting the synergy of Semillon Sauvignon Blancs from Margaret River, nor their fundamental difference from those of the Hunter Valley; here structural and textural factors drive the intense citrus, herb, snow pea and mineral flavours along a path with the precision of a railroad track, continuing into the far distance. Screwcap. 13% alc. **Rating** 95 **To** 2020 $29
Margaret River Chardonnay 2010 Full yellow-green; the rich and complex bouquet presages an intense, complex palate with strong barrel-ferment inputs to the white peach, melon, fig and cashew flavours; a tight strand of acidity stops any possibility of the palate wandering off on a frolic of its own. Screwcap. 14.5% alc. **Rating** 95 **To** 2018 $65
Margaret River Semillon 2011 Light straw-green; a clean and crisp bouquet with no hint of phenolics there or anywhere else in the wine; rather, it has an autocratic personality, with grass, herb, lemon peel and mineral flavours on the long palate and dry finish. Bred to stay. Screwcap. 13% alc. **Rating** 94 **To** 2021 $38
Margaret River Chardonnay 2009 Bright green-gold; a generous, complex and layered wine, with ripe stone fruit and melon woven with creamy cashew notes; the acidity is in a different line underneath the fruit, providing balance. Screwcap. 14% alc. **Rating** 94 **To** 2016 $65
Ribbon Vale Vineyard Margaret River Merlot 2009 Light, clear crimson-purple; a fragrant and fresh Merlot, with attractive red berry fruits on both bouquet and palate, French oak adding its influence, but respectfully so; the tannins are fine, ripe and in balance. True merlot varietal character on display. Screwcap. 14% alc. **Rating** 94 **To** 2019 $50
Ribbon Vale Vineyard Margaret River Cabernet Sauvignon Merlot 2009 Bright, clear crimson-purple; an elegant, medium-bodied wine with fragrant red berry/cassis to the fore, blackcurrant backstage; the tannins are superfine but help build the long palate, assisted by balanced and integrated French oak. Screwcap. 14% alc. **Rating** 94 **To** 2022 $50

ΥΥΥΥΥ Mornington Peninsula Pinot Noir 2009 Rating 93 **To** 2015 $50
Margaret River Pinot Noir 2008 Rating 90 **To** 2015 $60

Mount Alexander Winery ★★★★

410 Harcourt Road, Sutton Grange, Vic 3448 **Region** Bendigo
T (03) 5474 2567 **www**.mawine.com.au **Open** W'ends & public hols 10–5, or by appt
Winemaker Bill Blamires **Est.** 2001 **Dozens** 2000 **Vyds** 7.4ha
Bill and Sandra Blamires acquired their property after a two-year search of the southern Bendigo area for what they considered an ideal location. They have firmly planted their faith in shiraz (5.9ha), with merlot, cabernet sauvignon, chardonnay and viognier contributing 1.5ha. The winery was previously called Blamires Butterfly Crossing (because of the butterfly population on Axe Creek, which runs through the property), but has been changed due to confusion with Angove's Butterfly Ridge.

ΥΥΥΥΥ Reserve Wellington Flat Shiraz 2009 The grapes were deliberately allowed to ripen beyond the norm, yet retain some of the savoury, spicy characters achieved at lower alcohol levels; the flavours also manage to skirt dead fruit, and the impact of the alcohol is less than one might expect. Screwcap. 15.3% alc. **Rating** 90 **To** 2019 $30

Mount Avoca ★★★★★

Moates Lane, Avoca, Vic 3467 **Region** Pyrenees
T (03) 5465 3282 **www**.mountavoca.com **Open** 7 days 10–5
Winemaker William Talbot **Est.** 1970 **Dozens** 10 000 **Vyds** 23.72ha
A winery that has long been one of the stalwarts of the Pyrenees region, owned by Matthew and Lisa Barry. The estate vineyards (shiraz, sauvignon blanc, cabernet sauvignon, chardonnay, merlot, cabernet franc and semillon) are organically managed, and provide the total intake of the winery. Exports to China.

🍷🍷🍷🍷🍷
✪ **Pyrenees Viognier 2010** Vivid light green-straw; hand-picked, partial wild yeast barrel ferment and prolonged lees contact have cumulatively added very good texture, the bouquet also benefiting. Well above-average for this difficult variety. Only 150 dozen made. Screwcap. 13.5% alc. **Rating** 94 **To** 2015 $24
Reserve Pyrenees Shiraz 2009 Deep crimson, bright; a lively and highly polished wine, showing pure blackberry aromas and a touch of lilac; the medium-bodied palate is generous and lively with ample tannins and toasty oak to conclude. ProCork. 14.5% alc. **Rating** 94 **To** 2018 $66 BE

🍷🍷🍷🍷🍷
✪ **Pyrenees Sauvignon Blanc 2011** Vibrant green hue; the bouquet is full of fresh-cut grass, gooseberry and a little spice; the palate is lively and fresh, with zesty acidity, concentrated fruit and an even and finely balanced finish. Screwcap. 12.5% alc. **Rating** 91 **To** 2014 $20 BE
Pyrenees Cabernet Sauvignon 2010 **Rating** 91 **To** 2020 $28 BE
Pyrenees Fume Blanc 2010 **Rating** 90 **To** 2013 $24 BE
✪ **Pyrenees Chardonnay 2011** Pale colour; a juicy lemon-accented and fresh wine, showing quartz minerals at the core and fresh acidity drawing out the finish; clean and focused. Screwcap. 12% alc. **Rating** 90 **To** 2015 $20 BE
Pyrenees Merlot 2010 **Rating** 90 **To** 2015 $28 BE

🍷🍷🍷🍷 **Pyrenees Chardonnay 2010** **Rating** 89 **To** 2013 $20 BE

Mount Beckworth ★★★

46 Fraser Street, Clunes, Vic 3370 **Region** Ballarat
T (03) 5343 4207 **www**.mountbeckworthwines.com.au **Open** W'ends 11–5 or by appt
Winemaker Paul Lesock **Est.** 1984 **Dozens** 1000 **Vyds** 4ha
The Mount Beckworth vineyard was planted between 1984 and '85, but it was not until '95 that the full range of wines under the Mount Beckworth label appeared. Until that time much of the production was sold to Seppelt (Great Western) for sparkling wine use. It is owned and managed by Paul Lesock, who studied viticulture at CSU, and his wife Jane. The wines usually reflect the very cool climate.

🍷🍷🍷🍷 **Beckworth Chardonnay 2010** Pale, bright green-quartz; unwooded, and proclaims its cool climate with a strong citrus and steely acid make-up, the acidity a challenge, but not to seafood, perhaps. Screwcap. 13% alc. **Rating** 89 **To** 2014 $16
Beckworth Ballarat Shiraz 2009 Fresh crimson-purple; the spicy red fruits are fully ripe, vanillin oak emphasising that ripeness; the warm vintage has opened the door for Shiraz in Ballarat. Screwcap. 13.5% alc. **Rating** 89 **To** 2015 $20
Beckworth Cabernet Merlot 2009 A 70/30% blend, the colour relatively light, but the hue good. A vibrant and tangy, zesty, minty array of predominantly red fruits on a light- to medium-bodied palate; drink while it retains its youthfulness. Screwcap. 13.5% alc. **Rating** 89 **To** 2014 $18

Mt Bera Vineyards ★★★

PO Box 372, Gumeracha, SA 5233 **Region** Adelaide Hills
T (08) 8389 2433 **www**.mtberavineyards.com.au **Open** Not
Winemaker Jeanneret Wines **Est.** 1997 **Dozens** 900 **Vyds** 11.63ha

In 2008 Greg and Katrina Horner (plus four kids and a growing collection of animals) purchased Mt Bera from Louise Warner. Both Greg and Katrina grew up on farms, and the 75ha property, with its homestead built in the 1880s, was irresistible. The property is located in a sanctuary overlooking the Torrens Valley, looking out to Adelaide, 45 mins' drive away. For the time being, at least, most of the production is sold, but the intention is to increase the range and quantity of wines available. Exports to the UK.

3.13 Adelaide Hills Pinot Noir 2008 Good hue for age, still without any browning; attractive savoury/spicy/foresty nuances add complexity to the base of red cherry fruit; still developing. Screwcap. 13.5% alc. **Rating** 89 **To** 2015 $25
4.19 Adelaide Hills Cabernet Sauvignon 2007 Has survived a tough, mean vintage very well, its varietal virginity intact and unsullied; that said, expect no more miracles for this medium-bodied, gently savoury, Cabernet. Screwcap. 14.5% alc. **Rating** 89 **To** 2015 $25

Mt Billy   ★★★★★

58 Waterport Road, Port Elliott, SA 5212 **Region** Southern Fleurieu
T 0416 227 100 **www**.mtbillywines.com.au **Open** 7 days 10–5
Winemaker Dan Standish, Peter Schell, John Edwards **Est.** 2000 **Dozens** 2000 **Vyds** 2.4ha
Having been an avid wine collector and consumer since 1973, John Edwards (a dentist) and wife Pauline purchased a 3.75ha property on the hills behind Victor Harbor, planting chardonnay and pinot meunier. There have been various viticultural peregrinations since that time, involving the progressive grafting of all of the original plantings so that the vineyard (named 'No Secrets') now comprises 0.7ha each of shiraz and tempranillo, the balance to petite syrah, sangiovese and viognier, from which both varietal and blended wines are made, with the active involvement of John Edwards. Exports to the US, Canada, South Korea, Hong Kong, Japan and China.

Circe Southern Fleurieu Shiraz 2009 Strong crimson; the first question is why was such a high alcohol achieved in the moderate climate of the Southern Fleurieu? Second, how does the wine shrug off the manacles of alcohol until the very last second, and then only to a moderate degree? Diam. 15.5% alc. **Rating** 92 **To** 2020 $30
Soliloquy Southern Fleurieu Syrah 2010 Red-purple; notes of licorice, bramble and earth give this elegant, medium-bodied wine a distinctly savoury character; the length and balance are right on the money. Screwcap. 14.3% alc. **Rating** 91 **To** 2021 $35
Destiny Barossa Valley Shiraz 2008 Mid crimson-red; this is a full-flavoured, medium-bodied wine, fruit and vanillin oak woven together and a fleeting edge of mint, or is it spice? Diam. 14.5% alc. **Rating** 91 **To** 2018 $30
McLaren Vale Rose 2011 Bright pale pink; a cutting-edge blend of Spanish varieties tempranillo and garnacha (grenache); the bouquet is very fragrant, promising much, the palate delivering most of that promise, but not all; red cherry and strawberry flavours are nicely balanced with acidity. Screwcap. 13% alc. **Rating** 90 **To** 2014 $23
Winehead McLaren Vale Sangiovese 2011 Typical light Sangiovese colour, and equally typical red cherry fruits of different characters; for once the fruit does not have to grapple with the tannins (or vice versa). Screwcap. 13.3% alc. **Rating** 90 **To** 2016 $26
Winehead McLaren Vale Tempranillo 2011 Good colour; the bright red and black cherry fruits and fine but persistent tannins are as they should be; has some development potential. Screwcap. 14% alc. **Rating** 90 **To** 2017 $26

Adelaide Hills Arneis 2011 **Rating** 87 **To** 2013 $25

Mount Broke Wines   ★★★★

130 Adams Peak Road, Broke, NSW 2330 **Region** Hunter Valley
T (02) 6579 1314 **www**.mtbrokewines.com.au **Open** Fri–Sun 10–5
Winemaker Suzanne and Ian Little **Est.** 1997 **Dozens** 1000 **Vyds** 8ha

Phil McNamara began planting the vineyard to shiraz, barbera, chardonnay, tempranillo, semillon and verdelho in 1997 on the west side of Wollombi Brook. Over the years since coming into production, the wines have been prolific medal winners in regional and boutique wine shows. Most of the grapes are sold, with limited production under the Mount Broke label.

ΨΨΨΨΨ **Quince Tree Paddock Barbera 2010** Youthful hue, not entirely clear; the black cherry and plum of the bouquet are matched by the earthy/savoury palate, the tannins pronounced. Screwcap. 13.5% alc. **Rating** 90 **To** 2015 $25
Quince Tree Paddock Barbera 2009 Brilliantly clear and bright colour; as the bouquet suggests, light-bodied, and here the palate is more flavour-intense than the '10, the tannins less aggressive. Different styles, same quality. Screwcap. 13.5% alc. **Rating** 90 **To** 2014 $25

ΨΨΨΨ **River Bank Verdelho 2011** Has above-average weight and complexity to its
❂ fruit salad, half fresh, half poached. Good food style. Screwcap. 15% alc. **Rating** 89 **To** 2013 $18
River Bank Chardonnay 2009 Rating 88 **To** 2019 $25

Mount Burrumboot Estate ★★★★

3332 Heathcote-Rochester Road, Colbinabbin, Vic 3559 **Region** Heathcote
T (03) 5432 9238 **www.**burrumboot.com **Open** W'ends & public hols 11–5,
Mon–Fri 11–5 by appt
Winemaker Cathy Branson **Est.** 1999 **Dozens** 1500 **Vyds** 16.5ha
To quote: 'Mount Burrumboot Estate was born in 1999, when Andrew and Cathy Branson planted vines on the Home Block of the Branson family farm, Donore, on the slopes of Mt Burrumboot, on the Mt Camel Range, above Colbinabbin. Originally the vineyard was just another diversification of an already diverse farming enterprise. However, the wine bug soon bit, and so a winery was established. The first wine was contract-made in 2001 – however, '02 saw the first wine made by Cathy in the machinery shed, surrounded by headers and tractors. Very primitive, and the appearance of the new 50-tonne winery in '02 was greeted with great enthusiasm!' And then you taste the wines. Amazing. The original plantings of a little over 11ha of shiraz and merlot have since been expanded to take in lesser amounts of petit verdot, sangiovese, tempranillo, gamay, marsanne and viognier. There is no intention to expand the business further.

ΨΨΨΨΨ **Heathcote Merlot 2008** The colour is somewhat indifferent, but the wine has considerable presence and varietal character in a savoury/black olive spectrum; the tannins, too, are silky and pleasing. Diam. 14% alc. **Rating** 93 **To** 2017 $30
Heathcote Tempranillo 2008 There is some colour development, but the wine shrugs that off very quickly; there is a river of red cherry fruit, striking in its purity, neither tannins nor excess oak interfering with that expression. Delicious now or over the next few years. Screwcap. 13.4% alc. **Rating** 92 **To** 2015 $30
Heathcote Gamay 2008 Strong red-purple; one of a handful of Gamays being made in Australia, and this is a very attractive and full-flavoured wine. Whether it might be mistaken for a Beaujolais is highly doubtful, but it really does have considerable depth and length to the palate. Screwcap. 13.5% alc. **Rating** 91 **To** 2015 $30
Heathcote Shiraz 2008 The heavily crusted and stained Diam suggests the wine was stored upside down, but in less than ideal conditions, although the spicy, savoury fruit aromas and flavours of the medium-bodied palate show that so far the cork has done its job, and the wine still speaks with clarity. I recommend a shorter timeframe for drinking, before the savoury components become too pronounced. 14% alc. **Rating** 90 **To** 2015 $30

ΨΨΨΨ **Heathcote Petit Verdot 2008 Rating** 88 **To** 2015 $30
Heathcote Sangiovese 2008 Rating 87 **To** 2015 $30

Mount Charlie Winery   ★★★★

228 Mount Charlie Road, Riddells Creek, Vic 3431 **Region** Macedon Ranges
T (03) 5428 6946 **www.**mountcharlie.com.au **Open** Fri–Sun 10–4 or by appt
Winemaker Trefor Morgan **Est.** 1991 **Dozens** 800 **Vyds** 3ha

Mount Charlie's wines are sold principally by mail order and through selected restaurants. A futures program encourages mailing-list sales, with a substantial discount to the eventual release price. Owner/winemaker Trefor Morgan is perhaps better known as Professor of Physiology at Melbourne University. He also acts as a contract maker for others in the region. The vineyard is planted to 0.5ha each of chardonnay, sauvignon blanc, tempranillo, merlot, malbec and shiraz.

ΨΨΨΨΨ **Olivia Chardonnay 2010** Brassy-gold; a generous mouthful of ripe fruit flavours; backed by good acidity. Screwcap. 13.4% alc. **Rating** 93 **To** 2020 $20
Chardonnay 2010 Bright, pale straw–green; the grapes obviously fully ripened in the '10 vintage, giving this wine abundant mouthfeel, complexed by barrel ferment and, I would guess, some mlf. Screwcap. 13.4% alc. **Rating** 90 **To** 2015 $20

ΨΨΨΨ **Sauvignon Blanc 2011 Rating** 88 **To** 2013 $18

Mount Coghill Vineyard   ★★★☆

Cnr Pickfords Road/Coghills Creek Road, Coghills Creek, Vic 3364 **Region** Ballarat
T (03) 5343 4329 **F** (03) 5343 4329 **Open** W'ends 10–5
Winemaker Owen Latta **Est.** 1993 **Dozens** 200 **Vyds** 0.7ha

Ian and Margaret Pym began planting their tiny vineyard in 1995 with 1280 pinot noir rootlings, adding 450 chardonnay rootlings the next year. Since 2001 the wine has been made and released under the Mount Coghill Vineyard label. Ian is an award-winning photographer, and his photographs are on display at the cellar door.

ΨΨΨΨΨ **Ballarat Chardonnay 2011** Vibrant green hue; a mineral-laden bouquet with lemon, grilled nuts and honeycomb; the palate is driven by nervy lemony acidity, revealing plenty of mineral complexity and texture; not textbook by any means, but interesting and refreshing. Screwcap. 12.5% alc. **Rating** 90 **To** 2018 $25 BE

ΨΨΨΨ **Ballarat Pinot Noir 2010 Rating** 88 **To** 2015 $25 BE

Mount Cole Wineworks   ★★★★

6669 Western Highway, Buangor, Vic 3375 **Region** Grampians
T (03) 5352 2311 **www.**mountcolewineworks.com.au **Open** 7 days 10–5
Winemaker Dr Graeme Bertuch **Est.** 1998 **Dozens** 1000 **Vyds** 8.5ha

Dr Graeme Bertuch's involvement in grapegrowing and winemaking goes back far further than the establishment of Mount Cole Wineworks. In 1977 he established Cathcart Ridge, but found the time demands on a rural doctor-cum-vigneron were too much. He sold Cathcart Ridge in '93, but did not sell the itch to grow grapes and make wine. He now has 3.5ha of shiraz and 1ha of viognier planted since '98, and in 2007 purchased the somewhat neglected and rundown Mt Chalambar Vineyard previously owned by the late Trevor Mast; it had 2ha each of riesling and chardonnay, planted in the 1980s. Since that time there has been a systematic, albeit gradual, resurrection of the vineyard. Exports to China.

ΨΨΨΨΨ **Off the Beaten Track Collector's Edition Nebbiolo 2010** Crystal-clear red; the grapes fully ripen on this vineyard in only exceptional years, and this was one of those, even at this early stage showing why nebbiolo and pinot noir are often compared; the foresty/bramble nuances to the savoury cherry fruit are clearly varietal, and the wine has good length and balance. Screwcap. 14% alc. **Rating** 93 **To** 2020 $30

 Mast Hill Grampians Riesling 2011 Bright straw–green; already has a substantial volume of sweet citrus fruit; the balance is good, as are the length and aftertaste. The vines have recovered from a long period of drought. Screwcap. 14% alc. **Rating** 91 **To** 2017 $20

✪ **Mast Hill Grampians Chardonnay 2011** Light straw-green; a wine packed with flavour, hounded by its alcohol. Uncommon these days, but doubly so in '11; the flavours straddle citrus, stone fruit, rockmelon and fig, yet there is no obvious oak influence; lees contact may be a filler. Screwcap. 13.9% alc. **Rating** 90 **To** 2016 $20

Mount Eyre Vineyards   ★★★★★

173 Gillards Road, Pokolbin, NSW 2321 **Region** Hunter Valley
T 0438 683 973 **www**.mounteyre.com **Open** At Garden Cellars, Hunter Valley Gardens
Winemaker Rhys Eather **Est.** 1970 **Dozens** 5000 **Vyds** 33ha
This is the venture of two families whose involvement in wine extends in an unbroken line back several centuries: the Tsironis family in the Peleponnese, Greece, and the Iannuzzi family in Vallo della Lucania, Italy. Their vineyards are at Broke (the largest), with a smaller vineyard at Pokolbin. The three principal varieties planted are chardonnay, shiraz and semillon, with small amounts of merlot, viognier and chambourcin. Exports to the Maldives, Malaysia, China and Hong Kong.

♆♆♆♆♆ **Three Ponds Hunter Valley Semillon 2011** Light straw-green; a finely structured Semillon with lemongrass nuances to the bouquet, then an impressive palate bringing citrus, herbs and minerals to the party; has seriously good length. Screwcap. 11% alc. **Rating** 94 **To** 2021 $20
Heirloom Semillon 2005 Re-release. The cork has served this bottle well, and if the other bottles are all the same (they won't be), a very attractive example of aged Semillon from a top vintage, elegance and flavour combining with the even flow of citrus/lemon/mineral through to the long finish. 11.5% alc. **Rating** 94 **To** Now $30

♆♆♆♆♀ **Three Ponds Hunter Valley Semillon 2004 Rating** 93 **To** 2019 $40
Heirloom Semillon 2009 Rating 92 **To** 2017 $30
Holman Hunter Valley Shiraz 2009 Rating 92 **To** 2030 $45
Holman Hunter Valley Shiraz 2006 Rating 92 **To** 2016 $50
Three Ponds Hunter Valley Shiraz 2009 Rating 90 **To** 2024 $25

♆♆♆♆ **Heirloom Semillon 2011 Rating** 89 **To** 2014 $30
Three Ponds Hunter Valley Chardonnay 2010 Rating 89 **To** 2014 $23
Three Ponds Hunter Valley Verdelho 2011 Rating 88 **To** 2014 $20
Three Ponds Hunter Valley Verdelho 2009 Rating 87 **To** Now $20

Mt Franklin Estate   ★★★☆

2 Whybrow Street, Franklinford, Vic 3461 **Region** Macedon Ranges
T (03) 5476 4475 **www**.mtfranklinwines.com.au **Open** By appt
Winemaker Scott McGillivray, Colin Mitchell **Est.** 2000 **Dozens** 700 **Vyds** 4.04ha
Owner Lesley McGillivray was well ahead of her time when, in 1988, she planted two test rows of Italian varieties on rich volcanic soil near the foothills of Mt Franklin. The varieties to succeed best were dolcetto and pinot gris, and with family and friends she planted the first third of the vineyard with dolcetto and pinot gris in 2000. Since then, the vineyard has been completed, with more dolcetto, pinot gris and a little nebbiolo.

♆♆♆♆♀ **Dolcetto 2009** You would never expect a 75% crop loss due to sunburn and heat at Daylesford, but that is what happened in the record-breaking week of searing temperatures of '09. Amazingly, the wine has great colour, and good mouthfeel to its black cherry fruit and fine, juicy finish. Screwcap. 13% alc. **Rating** 90 **To** 2014 $20

♆♆♆♆ **Pinot Grigio 2010 Rating** 89 **To** Now $20

Mount Gisborne Wines   ★★★★☆

83 Waterson Road, Gisborne, Vic 3437 **Region** Macedon Ranges
T (03) 5428 2834 **www**.mountgisbornewines.com.au **Open** Wed–Sun 10–6
Winemaker David Ell, Stuart Anderson (Consultant) **Est.** 1985 **Dozens** 1200 **Vyds** 3ha

David and Mary Ell began the development of their vineyard on fractured granitic and volcanic soils in 1986. Planting of the pinot noir and chardonnay was completed in '90, but a small plot of clone 115 pinot noir has recently been added. Balgownie Estate founder Stuart Anderson moved to Macedon many years ago, and has added his immense knowledge to the crucible of learning on the job. The wines are made in the small winery on the property. Exports to Canada, Singapore and Malaysia.

99999 **Macedon Ranges Chardonnay 2011** Vivid green hue; this is a racy and minerally driven Chardonnay, with lemon pith and cashew also on display; taut, vibrant and linear on the palate, the concentration of fruit is undeniable, as is the length of flavour; this will be interesting to watch develop over time. Screwcap. 13.5% alc. **Rating** 94 **To** 2022 $27 BE

9999 **Macedon Ranges Pinot Noir 2010 Rating** 88 **To** 2015 $42 BE

Mount Horrocks ★★★★★
The Old Railway Station, Curling Street, Auburn, SA 5451 **Region** Clare Valley
T (08) 8849 2243 **www.**mounthorrocks.com **Open** W'ends & public hols 10–5
Winemaker Stephanie Toole **Est.** 1982 **Dozens** 4500 **Vyds** 9.4ha
Owner/winemaker Stephanie Toole has never deviated from the pursuit of excellence in the vineyard and winery. She has three vineyard sites in the Clare Valley, each managed using natural farming and organic practices. Stephanie has continuously built on the business since becoming sole owner in 1993, with the cellar door in the old, renovated, Auburn railway station. The attention to detail and refusal to cut corners is obvious in all of her wines. Exports to the UK, the US and other major markets.

99999 **Watervale Riesling 2011** Light straw-green; a complex bouquet, with spice and citrus, then a multilayered palate offering vibrant lime juice flavours backed by slatey minerality. Screwcap. 12.5% alc. **Rating** 94 **To** 2026 $30
Cordon Cut Clare Valley Riesling 2011 Has already developed a bright, full yellow-green colour; the flavours are, as usual, superrich and ripe, with lime, honey and vanilla balanced by acidity. Can handle rich desserts with ease. 375ml Screwcap. 12% alc. **Rating** 94 **To** 2015 $35

Mount Langi Ghiran Vineyards ★★★★★
Warrak Road, Buangor, Vic 3375 **Region** Grampians
T (03) 5354 3207 **www.**langi.com.au **Open** Mon–Fri 9–5, w'ends 10–5
Winemaker Dan Buckle, Kate Petering **Est.** 1969 **Dozens** 60 000
A maker of outstanding cool-climate peppery Shiraz, crammed with flavour and vinosity, and very good Cabernet Sauvignon. The Shiraz points the way for cool-climate examples of the variety. The business was acquired by the Rathbone family group in 2002, and the marketing integrated with the Yering Station, Parker Coonawarra and Xanadu Estate wines, a synergistic mix with no overlap. In '12 the Rathbone Group wine interests were placed on the market for sale either as a group or individually. Exports to all major markets.

99999 **Cliff Edge Grampians Shiraz 2009** Bright crimson; a fragrant bouquet
✪ encompasses spice, plum, black cherry and blackberry aromas that flow through to the medium-bodied palate, there picking up quality oak, and finishing with polished tannins. Great bargain. Screwcap. 14% alc. **Rating** 96 **To** 2029 $30
✪ **Moyston Hills Vineyard Shiraz 2008** Bright purple-crimson; has a fragrant bouquet with a mix of red and black cherry and the usual spice; the medium-bodied palate is beautifully balanced, all the focus on the pure fruit flavours until the very finish, when fine, savoury tannins click in. Screwcap. 14.5% alc. **Rating** 95 **To** 2023 $30
Nowhere Creek Vineyard Shiraz 2008 Strong crimson-purple; sweet and spicy plum and cherry fruit aromas fill the bouquet, the medium- to full-bodied palate complex but supple, with quality oak adding to the flavour matrix; while showing its cool origins, is slightly riper than Moyston Hills. Screwcap. 15% alc. **Rating** 95 **To** 2020 $30

Cliff Edge Grampians Shiraz 2010 Deep garnet; a dark and deeply black-fruited bouquet, showing heady levels of spice and exotic undergrowth complexity; has well-handled toasty oak, mocha and a succulent medium-bodied palate that slowly unveils itself on the long finish. Screwcap. 13.5% alc. **Rating** 94 **To** 2025 $30 BE

Kneebones Shiraz 2010 Mid crimson; a bright red-fruited and floral bouquet, with a splash of licorice and bracken; the palate is medium-bodied and reveals pure red fruits and lively acidity; the fine-grained tannins and toasty oak linger harmoniously on the finish. Screwcap. 13.5% alc. **Rating** 94 **To** 2025 $30 BE

Moyston Hills Vineyard Shiraz 2010 Deep crimson, bright; the lifted savoury perfume of bracken, spice and cold tea is complemented by red and black fruits; the palate reveals firm tannins that are in harmony with the succulent fruit; a savoury and interesting offering. Screwcap. 13% alc. **Rating** 94 **To** 2025 $30 BE

✪ **Billi Billi Shiraz 2009** Bright, clear red-purple; the scented and fragrant bouquet has a warm spice and pepper introduction to the fleshy red and black cherry fruit of the perfectly balanced medium-bodied palate; the quality of the wine comes through on the lingering finish and aftertaste. Drink whenever you like. Screwcap. 14% alc. **Rating** 94 **To** 2019 $18

Langi Cabernet Sauvignon 2006 Deep, bright crimson; a pure and essency bouquet of blue fruits and blackcurrant, offset by a splash of sage; the palate is full-bodied, with ample fine-grained tannins and a long, fresh conclusion the result; will certainly age with dignity. Screwcap. 14% alc. **Rating** 94 **To** 2025 $50 BE

Nut Tree Hill Sangiovese 2009 Very light, but has retained crimson hue; one of a few Sangioveses going around that have fragrant cherry and even raspberry bouquets, then a palate where the cherry fruit is juicy, spicy and savoury, and the tannins are fine, not dry or harsh. Screwcap. 14% alc. **Rating** 94 **To** 2016 $26

🍷🍷🍷🍷 **Bradach Vineyard Pinot Noir 2010 Rating** 93 **To** 2020 $38 BE
Langi Shiraz 2010 Rating 93 **To** 2020 $100

✪ **Billi Billi Shiraz 2010** Mid crimson; a restrained and elegant bouquet, offering black and blue fruits, spice, sage and struck quartz; the palate is medium-bodied and focused, showing lovely depth and a lightness of touch that belies the modest price tag; brilliant everyday drinking. Screwcap. 13.5% alc. **Rating** 93 **To** 2022 $18 BE
Langi Grampians Riesling 2011 Rating 90 **To** 2025 $25 BE
Blanc de Blancs 2009 Rating 90 **To** 2020 $45 BE

🍷🍷🍷🍷 **Cliff Edge Grampians Pinot Gris 2010 Rating** 87 **To** 2014 $25 BE

Mt Lofty Ranges Vineyard ★★★★★

Harris Road, Lenswood, SA 5240 **Region** Adelaide Hills
T (08) 8389 8339 **www.**mtloftyrangesvineyard.com.au **Open** W'ends & public hols 11–5 or by appt
Winemaker Peter Leske **Est.** 1992 **Dozens** 3000 **Vyds** 4.6ha
Mt Lofty Ranges is owned and operated by Sharon Pearson and Garry Sweeney. Nestled high in the Lenswood subregion of the Adelaide Hills at an altitude of 500 m, the very steep north-facing vineyard (pinot noir, sauvignon blanc, chardonnay and riesling) is hand-pruned and hand-picked. The soil is sandy clay loam with a rock base of white quartz and ironstone, and irrigation is kept to a minimum to allow the wines to display vintage characteristics.

🍷🍷🍷🍷 ✪ **Hand Picked Lenswood Riesling 2011** There is seldom any mention of clones with Riesling, so the five-clone mix on this single vineyard is very interesting. While, as befits its youth, it is fresh and crisp, there is a hidden well of complex flavours on the palate, lime and lemon first up, then a touch of spice, and on the aftertaste, a note of ginger. Screwcap. 11.5% alc. **Rating** 94 **To** 2020 $22

Lenswood Chardonnay 2010 Light straw-green; an aromatic and elegant wine with grapefruit, nectarine and white peach flavours all pursuing each other on the palate, notes of cashew coming from extended lees contact in the barrels in which the wine was fermented; a long and lingering finish. Screwcap. 13.5% alc. **Rating** 94 **To** 2018 $25

ŶŶŶŶŶ **Lenswood Sauvignon Blanc 2011** Light, bright straw-green; citrus, grass and
✪   herb aromas and flavours are given high relief by the lingering acidity; some may
        find that disconcerting, but it does not worry me. Screwcap. 12% alc. **Rating** 90
        To 2013 $20

ŶŶŶŶ   **Reserve Lenswood Pinot Noir 2010** Rating 88 To 2015 $55
        Old Pump Shed Lenswood Pinot Noir 2010 Rating 87 To 2014 $27

Mount Majura Vineyard   ★★★★★
RMB 314 Majura Road, Majura, ACT 2609 (postal) **Region** Canberra District
T (02) 6262 3070 **www**.mountmajura.com.au **Open** Thurs–Mon 10–5
Winemaker Dr Frank van de Loo **Est.** 1988 **Dozens** 4000 **Vyds** 9.31ha
The first vines were planted in 1988 by Dinny Killen on a site on her family property that
had been especially recommended by Dr Edgar Riek; its attractions were red soil of volcanic
origin over limestone, with reasonably steep east and northeast slopes providing an element
of frost protection. The tiny vineyard established in '88 has been significantly expanded since
it was purchased in '99. The pre-existing blocks of pinot noir, chardonnay and merlot have
all been increased, and have been joined by pinot gris, shiraz, tempranillo, riesling, graciano,
cabernet franc and touriga. In additional, there has been an active planting program for the
pinot noir, introducing Dijon clones 114, 155 and 777.

ŶŶŶŶŶ **TSG Canberra District Tempranillo Shiraz Graciano 2010** Bright, light
        crimson-red; an aromatic and fragrant bouquet of spice, pepper and red fruits
        is built on by the light- to medium-bodied palate, adding some black cherry
        fruit and fine-grained tannins to the long finish. Trophy Winewise '11. Screwcap.
        14% alc. **Rating** 95 **To** 2018 $28
        Canberra District Riesling 2011 While there is nothing remarkable about the
        colour or bouquet, the palate is a very different proposition, with intense lime
        juice and steely acidity wound around each other through to the finish – no
        surprise given that the wine has 11g/l acidity with no residual sugar to balance
        that acidity; the final surprise sprung by the wine is its balance. 141 dozen made.
        Screwcap. 12% alc. **Rating** 94 **To** 2021 $25
        Canberra District Tempranillo 2010 Clear, bright red-purple; a scented,
        fragrant bouquet with a swirl of exotic spices leads into a truly complex palate,
        the complexity from the cherry, spice and savoury leather flavours, and from the
        framework of ripe but firm tannins. Will surely flower further with time in bottle.
        Screwcap. 14.5% alc. **Rating** 94 **To** 2025 $40

ŶŶŶŶŶ **Canberra District Shiraz 2010** Rating 93 To 2025 $30
        Canberra District Pinot Gris 2011 Rating 92 To 2013 $25

ŶŶŶŶ   **Canberra District Pinot Noir 2010** Rating 89 To 2015 $25

Mount Mary   ★★★★★
Coldstream West Road, Lilydale, Vic 3140 **Region** Yarra Valley
T (03) 9739 1761 **www**.mountmary.com.au **Open** Not
Winemaker Sam Middleton **Est.** 1971 **Dozens** 4500 **Vyds** 9.6ha
Superbly refined, elegant and intense Cabernets and usually outstanding and long-lived Pinot
Noirs fully justify Mount Mary's exalted reputation. The Triolet blend is very good; more
recent vintages of Chardonnay are even better. Founder and long-term winemaker, the late
Dr John Middleton, was one of the great, and truly original, figures in the Australian wine
industry. He liked nothing more than to tilt at windmills, and would do so with passion. His
annual newsletter grew longer as each year passed, although the paper size did not. The only
change necessary was a reduction in font size, and ultimately very strong light or a magnifying
glass (or both) was needed to fully appreciate the barbed wit and incisive mind of this great
character. The determination of the family to continue the business is simply wonderful.
Limited quantities of the wines are sold through the wholesale/retail distribution system in
Vic, NSW, Qld and SA. No wines were received for this edition; the rating is that of last year.
Exports to the UK, the US, Denmark, Hong Kong, Singapore, South Korea and China.

Mount Monument Winery

1399 Romsey Road, Romsey, Vic 3434 **Region** Macedon Ranges
T 0407 291 449 **www**.mountmonumentwines.com **Open** By appt
Winemaker Keith Brien **Est.** 2008 **Dozens** 1000 **Vyds** 3.7ha
Prominent Melbourne architect Nonda Katsalidis and wife Jane acquired the pre-existing vineyard in 2008, and embarked on major trellis redesign for the existing chardonnay, pinot noir and riesling, while undertaking major terracing works on a new site on the north face of Mt Monument, where 1ha of nebbiolo (with three clones) will be planted. All of these changes, and the future winemaking, will be under the direction of Keith Brien.

♀♀♀♀♀ Riesling 2011 Vibrant green hue; an exotic candied lemon rind and green-edged bouquet, showing lots of spice and a fresh herbaceous note; off-dry with mouth-puckering acidity and a long tail of quartz minerals adding complexity. Diam. 11% alc. **Rating** 94 **To** 2020 $22 BE

♀♀♀♀♀ Winemakers Reserve Pinot Noir 2010 **Rating** 90 **To** 2015 $49 BE

Mt Moriac Estate/Waurn Ponds Estate ★★★

580 Hendy Main Road, Mt Moriac, Vic 3240 **Region** Geelong
T (03) 5266 1116 **www**.kurabana.com **Open** Not
Winemaker Lee Evans **Est.** 1987 **Dozens** 9600 **Vyds** 35.3ha
The development of the quite extensive Kurabana Vineyard, west of Geelong in the foothills of Mt Moriac, began in 1987. Pinot noir (7.8ha) is the largest portion, followed by (in descending order) shiraz, chardonnay, sauvignon blanc, pinot gris and viognier. In 2009 there were a number of major changes: the name of the business was changed, and it purchased the Waurn Ponds Estate label and all current wine from Deakin University. It also leased the Waurn Ponds vineyard from Deakin, lifting the aggregate area to 35.3ha. The two brands continue, but have a common headquarters and ownership.

♀♀♀♀ Mt Moriac Traditional Method Blanc de Noirs 2006 Bronzing colour; a big personality sparkling wine, with toasted hazelnuts shadowing a touch of citrus blossom; the palate is big in flavour, but a little short on length. Diam. 12.5% alc. **Rating** 87 **To** 2014 $35 BE

Mount Pierrepoint Estate

271 Pierrepoint Road, Tarrington, Vic 3301 **Region** Henty
T (03) 5572 5553 **F** (03) 5572 5553 **www**.mountpierrepoint.com **Open** By appt
Winemaker Scott Ireland (Contract) **Est.** 1998 **Dozens** 1200 **Vyds** 5ha
Mount Pierrepoint Estate was established by Andrew and Jennifer Lacey on the foothills of Mt Pierrepoint between Hamilton and Tarrington at an altitude of 200m. The predominantly red buckshot soils of the vineyard are derived from ancient volcanic basalt, rich in minerals and free-draining. Two hectares each of pinot noir and pinot gris, and 1ha of chardonnay are planted on an ideal north-facing slope.

♀♀♀♀♀ Pinot Noir 2010 Bright, clear crimson; from 2ha of estate plantings in 1998, typically yielding 1 tonne per acre and spending 12 months in French oak prior to bottling; the highly perfumed bouquet leads into a light-bodied but nonetheless complex palate with bright red fruits framed by fine but persistent savoury tannins. Screwcap. 13.5% alc. **Rating** 94 **To** 2019 $30

♀♀♀♀ Pinot Gris 2010 **Rating** 88 **To** 2013 $27

Mt Pilot Estate

208 Shannons Road, Byawatha, Vic 3678 **Region** North East Victoria Zone
T (03) 5726 5434 **www**.mtpilotestatewines.com.au **Open** By appt
Winemaker Bruce Holm **Est.** 1996 **Dozens** 1000 **Vyds** 13ha

Lachlan and Penny Campbell have planted shiraz (6ha), cabernet sauvignon (3ha), durif and viognier (2ha each). The vineyard has been planted on deep, well-drained granitic soils at an altitude of 250m near Eldorado, 20km from Wangaratta and 35km from Beechworth.

🍷🍷🍷🍷   **Viognier Chardonnay 2011** Glowing green-gold, amazing for age; the viognier certainly rules the flavour roost, and the phenolics on the finish, the chardonnay the otherwise absent mid palate. A striking wine to be consumed with roast turkey or pheasant. Screwcap. 13.4% alc. **Rating** 88 **To** 2013 $25

Mt Terrible   ★★★★★

289 Licola Road, Jamieson, Vic 3723 **Region** Central Victoria Zone
T (03) 5777 0703 **www**.mtterrible-pinot.com **Open** By appt
Winemaker Andy Browning, John Eason **Est.** 2001 **Dozens** 400 **Vyds** 2ha
John Eason and wife Janene Ridley began the long, slow (and at times very painful) business of establishing their vineyard in 1992, just north of Mt Terrible – hence the choice of name. The original plantings were trials, DIY home winemaking likewise, aided by an extensive library of how-to books. In 2001 they found the courage to plant 2ha of pinot noir (MV6, 115, 114 and 777 clones) on a gently sloping, north-facing river terrace adjacent to the Jamieson River. The DIY trials persuaded John to have the first commercial vintage in 2006 contract-made by Jane Donat, then Delatite winemaker. Construction has begun on an underground fireproof wine cellar, with a cellar door to be built above. The Central Victoria Zone is shown as the region, as the vineyard is 5km outside the boundary of the Upper Goulburn region. The '07 vintage was lost to frost and smoke taint, but '08 should put Mt Terrible back on track. No wines were received for this edition; the rating is that of last year. Exports to the UK.

Mt Toolleen   ★★★

Level 12, North Tower, 459 Collins Street, Melbourne, Vic 3000 (postal)
Region Barossa Valley/Heathcote
T (03) 9885 1367 **www**.mttoolleen.com.au **Open** Not
Winemaker Mark Jamieson (Contract) **Est.** 2000 **Dozens** 1500 **Vyds** 17.5ha
Mt Toolleen is owned by a group of Melbourne investors in a somewhat complicated joint venture scheme that gives Mt Toolleen access to 100ha of shiraz grown in Barossa Valley, and ownership of a 17.5ha vineyard in Heathcote. Exports to Canada, China, Taiwan, the United Arab Emirates and Hong Kong.

🍷🍷🍷🍷   **Premium Reserve Heathcote Shiraz 2006** Developed colour, as expected for its age; a complex wine with spice, earth, licorice, smoke and black fruits all contributing to the bouquet and palate, the latter with a degree of lift that doesn't help. Screwcap. 14.5% alc. **Rating** 88 **To** 2016 $27

Mount Torrens Vineyards   ★★★★★

PO Box 1679, Mt Torrens, SA 5244 **Region** Adelaide Hills
T 0418 822 509 **www**.solstice.com.au **Open** Not
Winemaker Torbreck (David Powell, Craig Isbel)1996 **Dozens** 1000
Mount Torrens Vineyards has 2.5ha of shiraz and viognier, and the distinguished team of Mark Whisson as viticulturist and David Powell as contract winemaker. The excellent wines are available by mail order and through selected retailers, but are chiefly exported to the UK, the US and other major markets. The marketing is handled by owner and founder David Thompson.

🍷🍷🍷🍷🍷   **Solstice Adelaide Hills Shiraz Viognier 2010** Deep colour, with a fragrant and lifted bouquet of blackberry, violet, fruitcake spices and tar; the palate is luscious and rich on entry, with freshness returning on the finish through zesty acidity and ample fine-grained tannins; silky and succulent. Screwcap. 13.2% alc. Rating 94 **To** 2020 $38 BE

🍷🍷🍷🍷   **Solstice Adelaide Hills Shiraz 2010 Rating** 88 **To** 2017 $40 BE

Mount Towrong   ★★★★

10 Taylors Road, Mount Macedon, Vic 3441 (postal) **Region** Macedon Ranges
T (03) 5426 3050 **www**.mounttowrong.com.au **Open** Not
Winemaker Kilchurn Wines **Est.** 1996 **Dozens** 600 **Vyds** 2ha
When George and Deirdre Cremasco commenced the establishment of their vineyard (chardonnay, nebbiolo and prosecco), they did so with the help of George's father and grandfather. Strongly influenced by their Italian heritage, the vineyard has been terraced, with Chardonnay the first wine in production, and some commendable Nebbiolo and Prosecco following in its footsteps.

♟♟♟♟♀ **Macedon Ranges Prosecco 2010** Fine mousse; crisp, clean and bracing, with subtle citrus nuances; a very good example of Prosecco. Crown seal. 11.5% alc. **Rating** 93 **To** 2013 $35
Macedon Ranges Nebbiolo 2009 Better hue and depth than Rosso; a very respectable Nebbiolo, especially given its low alcohol; crisp, sour cherry and spice flavours run the length of the palate, the tannins not the least green. Screwcap. 12% alc. **Rating** 91 **To** 2016 $30

♟♟♟♟ **Macedon Ranges Chardonnay 2009** **Rating** 88 **To** 2015 $20
Macedon Ranges Rosso 2009 **Rating** 87 **To** 2013 $25

Mount Trio Vineyard   ★★★★☆

2534 Porongurup Road, Mount Barker, WA 6324 **Region** Porongurup
T (08) 9853 1136 **www**.mounttriowines.com.au **Open** When sign is out or by appt
Winemaker Gavin Berry, Andrew Siddell **Est.** 1989 **Dozens** 5000 **Vyds** 7.8ha
Mount Trio was established by Gavin Berry and Gill Graham shortly after they moved to the Mount Barker area in late 1988. They have slowly built up the business, increasing estate plantings with shiraz (2.5ha), riesling (2.1ha), pinot noir (2ha) and sauvignon blanc (1.4ha). Exports to the UK, Denmark, Japan and Singapore.

♟♟♟♟♟ **Great Southern Riesling 2010** Quartz-green; made in typical Great Southern
✪ fashion, with a floral bouquet and touches of talc, the dry but long, finely boned, dry palate saying as much of the future as the present; absolutely guaranteed to burst into song over the next decade. Screwcap. 11.5% alc. **Rating** 94 **To** 2020 $19

♟♟♟♟♀ **Great Southern Pinot Noir 2009** Is holding hue well; the bouquet is attractive
✪ and expressive, and the palate lives up to its promise; there are spicy, gently savoury, red berry fruits with a silky web of tannins, the oak restrained. Screwcap. 13.8% alc. **Rating** 93 **To** 2015 $19
✪ **Great Southern Shiraz 2010** Bright purple-crimson; both the bouquet and the medium-bodied palate bring spice, licorice and black fruits onto the centre stage, dusty tannins and good oak providing a mouth-watering finish. Screwcap. 13.8% alc. **Rating** 93 **To** 2020 $19
✪ **Great Southern Cabernet Merlot 2010** Crimson-purple; fragrant and ripe cassis fruit leads the way on the bouquet and palate, backed up by blackcurrant and plum woven together with quality oak. Screwcap. 13.7% alc. **Rating** 91 **To** 2020 $16

♟♟♟♟ **Chardonnay 2011** **Rating** 89 **To** 2016 $16

Mount View Estate   ★★★★★

Mount View Road, Mount View, NSW 2325 **Region** Hunter Valley
T (02) 4990 3307 **www**.mtviewestate.com.au **Open** Mon–Sat 10–5, Sun 10–4
Winemaker Phillip Halverson **Est.** 1971 **Dozens** 3000 **Vyds** 16ha
John and Polly Burgess became the owners of Mount View Estate (8ha) in 2000, and in '04 purchased the adjoining Limestone Creek Vineyard (8ha); planted in 1982, it fits seamlessly into the Mount View Estate production.

ŦŦŦŦŦ Reserve Hunter Valley Semillon 2011 Quartz-white; while the bouquet is shy, the palate proclaims its intense juicy fruit flavours of lemon, lemongrass and lime juice, with a backbone of steely acidity. Screwcap. 11.5% alc. **Rating** 95 To 2021 $25

✪ Hunter Valley Chardonnay 2010 Light, bright straw-green; fermentation in new French oak has barely left a mark on the white peach and melon fruit, although it has a creamy cashew note to add complexity and length. Screwcap. 13.5% alc. **Rating** 94 To 2017 $19

ŦŦŦŦŦ Hunter Valley Verdelho 2011 Pale straw-green; a Verdelho with attitude and
✪ the option of cellaring; the intense fruit salad flavours are given this energy by lemon and lime acidity woven through the fruit, the finish long and balanced. Screwcap. 13% alc. **Rating** 92 To 2014 $19
Hunter Valley Shiraz 2010 **Rating** 92 To 2025 $25

✪ Hunter Valley Rose 2011 Brilliant, clear puce; partially fermented in used oak barrels, it has a fragrant small red berry bouquet with similar flavours on the light-bodied palate; a subliminal touch of sweetness fills in the gaps nicely. Screwcap. 13.5% alc. **Rating** 90 To 2013 $19

ŦŦŦŦ Flagship Hunter Valley Merlot 2007 **Rating** 87 To 2015 $55

Mount William Winery ★★★★★

890 Mount William Road, Tantaraboo, Vic 3764 **Region** Macedon Ranges
T (03) 5429 1595 www.mtwilliamwinery.com.au **Open** 7 days 11–5
Winemaker David Cowburn (Contract), Murray Cousins **Est.** 1985 **Dozens** 1500
Vyds 7.5ha
Adrienne and Murray Cousins purchased a 220ha grazing property in 1985; the sheep and Angus cattle remain the principal part of the general farming program, but between '87 and '99 they established pinot noir, chardonnay, cabernet franc and merlot. The quality of the wines has been consistently good, and they are sold through a stone cellar door, as well as at a number of fine wine retailers around Melbourne.

ŦŦŦŦŦ Macedon 2004 Still pale straw-green after six years on yeast lees in this bottle, a Blanc de Blancs (Chardonnay) that seems to have the Peter Pan secret to perpetual youth. Small wonder Mount William is disgorging small parcels over time. Aperitif style. Cork. 12% alc. **Rating** 95 To Now $45

ŦŦŦŦŦ Chardonnay 2004 **Rating** 93 To 2020 $30
Pinot Noir 2005 **Rating** 93 To 2013 $30
Louise Clare NV **Rating** 93 To 2015 $50

Mountadam ★★★★★

High Eden Road, Eden Valley, SA 5235 **Region** Eden Valley
T (08) 8564 1900 www.mountadam.com.au **Open** By appt
Winemaker Con Moshos **Est.** 1972 **Dozens** 35 000 **Vyds** 80ha
Founded by the late David Wynn for the benefit of winemaker son Adam, Mountadam was (somewhat surprisingly) purchased by Cape Mentelle (doubtless under the direction of Möet Hennessy Wine Estates) in 2000. Rather less surprising was its sale in '05 to Adelaide businessman David Brown, who has extensive interests in the Padthaway region. Con Moshos (long-serving senior winemaker at Petaluma) has made a significant impact in lifting the quality of the wines. One should hope so, because Con eats (well, almost), drinks and sleeps Mountadam. Exports to the UK, France, Switzerland, Poland and Hong Kong.

ŦŦŦŦŦ High Eden Estate Chardonnay 2010 Gleaming green-gold; a blend of four clones fermented in French barriques (50% new), with mlf and lees contact following for nine months in barrel; it has an intensely structured and textured palate, white peach, grilled cashew and some grapefruit on the farewell; the oak has simply disappeared into the wine, which has a long future. Placed first by Andrew Jefford in a major Chardonnay tasting in the UK for *The World of Fine Wine* magazine. Screwcap. 14% alc. **Rating** 95 To 2020 $35

Patriarch High Eden Shiraz 2009 Red-purple; the wine spent an astonishingly long seven-week fermentation and maceration on skins, yet shows no over-extraction characters; that said, it is a wine of marked complexity with an array of spices plus pepper to the patterned array of plum, blackberry and black cherry fruits; the finish is long and well balanced. Cork. 14.5% alc. **Rating** 95 **To** 2029 $40

The Red 2009 A blend of cabernet sauvignon, merlot and cabernet franc from the High Eden, matured for two years in new French oak; while obviously enough, the oak is a significant force, the rousing display of blackcurrant, redcurrant, plum and cassis fruit, together with fine tannins, emerges triumphant. Cork. 14.5% alc. **Rating** 95 **To** 2029 $40

ΨΨΨΨΨ **Eden Valley Pinot Gris 2011 Rating** 92 **To** 2014 $25 BE
Eden Valley Riesling 2011 Rating 91 **To** 2018 $25 BE

ΨΨΨΨ **Barossa Shiraz 2009 Rating** 88 **To** 2014 $20 BE
Barossa Cabernet Merlot 2009 Rating 88 **To** 2015 $20 BE
High Eden Pinot Noir Chardonnay NV Rating 88 **To** 2013 $30 BE

 Mr Mick ★★★★

7 Dominic Street, Clare, SA 5453 **Region** Clare Valley
T (08) 8842 2555 **www.**mrmick.com.au **Open** 7 days 10–5
Winemaker Tim Adams, Brett Schutz **Est.** 2011 **Dozens** 10 000
This is the venture of Tim Adams and wife Pam Goldsack, the name chosen to honour KH (Mick) Knappstein, a legend both in the Clare Valley and the broader Australian wine community. Adams worked at Leasingham Wines with Mick between 1975 and 1986, and knew him very well. When Tim and Pam acquired the Leasingham winery in January 2011, together with its historic buildings, it brought the wheel full circle. Various commentators (including myself) have used Mick's great one-liner 'There are only two types of people in the world: those who were born in Clare, and those who wished they had been.' This is a separate business from the eponymous Tim Adams Wines. Exports to China.

ΨΨΨΨΨ **Clare Valley Riesling 2011** Pale straw-green; the best of the Mr Mick releases,
✪ honouring the late Mick Knappstein, doyen of Clare winemakers; crisp lemon/lime flavours have a strong acid backbone, the palate ending firm and dry. Screwcap. 10.5% alc. **Rating** 93 **To** 2018 $15

✪ **Clare Valley Rose 2011** Bright, pale blush pink; interesting wine, with distinct citrus peachy notes on the back-palate and finish. Some clever winemaking here, especially if this wine is 85% pinot gris. Screwcap. 12% alc. **Rating** 90 **To** Now $15

ΨΨΨΨ **Late Harvest Riesling 2011** One of the better wines in the range, its fresh, juicy-sweet flavours running the length of the palate, the aftertaste tingling and dry. 500ml. Screwcap. 11% alc. **Rating** 89 **To** Now $15
Clare Valley Cabernet Shiraz 2009 Rating 87 **To** 2013 $15

Mr Riggs Wine Company ★★★★★

Main Road, McLaren Vale, SA 5171 **Region** McLaren Vale
T (08) 8557 0808 **www.**mrriggs.com.au **Open** At Penny's Hill 7 days 10–5
Winemaker Ben Riggs2001 **Dozens** 20 000 **Vyds** 7.5ha
After a quarter of a century of winemaking experience, Ben Riggs is well established under his own banner. Ben sources the best fruit from individual vineyards in McLaren Vale, Clare Valley, Adelaide Hills, Langhorne Creek, Coonawarra, and from his own Piebald Gully Vineyard (shiraz and viognier). Each wine is intended to express the essence of not only the vineyard, but also the region's terroir. The vision of the Mr Riggs brand is unpretentious and personal, 'to make the wines I love to drink'. Exports to the US, Canada, Denmark, Sweden, Germany, the Netherlands, Switzerland, China, Hong Kong, Singapore, Japan and NZ.

ɏɏɏɏɏ **McLaren Vale Shiraz 2010** Impenetrable colour, and dark and dense, with tar, black fruits and charry oak all on display; the palate is richly textured, chewy, with ripe tannins and charry oak and a long Christmas cake spice and fruit finish; a big, muscular wine in every respect. Diam. 14.5% alc. **Rating** 94 **To** 2025 $50 BE
Yacca Paddock Adelaide Hills Tempranillo 2005 Has retained remarkable hue, and developed well since last tasted four years ago, still meriting the same points, although steak would be a good idea. Screwcap. 15% alc. **Rating** 94 **To** 2013 $50

ɏɏɏɏɏ **Watervale Riesling 2011 Rating** 93 **To** 2020 $20
d'Adelaide Hills Montepulciano 2009 Rating 93 **To** 2015 $25
Piebald Adelaide Syrah 2010 Rating 92 **To** 2018 $25 BE
Outpost Coonawarra Cabernet 2010 Rating 92 **To** 2025 $25 BE
The Gaffer McLaren Vale Shiraz 2010 Rating 90 **To** 2016 $22 BE
Yacca Paddock Adelaide Hills Tempranillo 2010 Rating 90 **To** 2017 $25 BE

ɏɏɏɏ **Three Corner Jack McLaren Vale Shiraz Cabernet Merlot 2010**
✪ **Rating** 89 **To** 2015 $17 BE
Ein Riese Adelaide Hills Riesling 2011 Rating 89 **To** 2016 $22 BE
McLaren Vale Sticky End 2011 Rating 89 **To** 2014 $22 BE
The Truant McLaren Vale Shiraz 2010 Rating 87 **To** 2016 $17 BE

Mudgee Wines   ★★★★☆

Henry Lawson Drive, Mudgee, NSW 2850 **Region** Mudgee
T (02) 6372 2258 www.mudgeewines.com.au **Open** 7 days 10–5
Winemaker Luciano Lombardino **Est.** 1963 **Dozens** NA
Mudgee Wines has a long history, indirectly dating back to Andreas Kurtz's establishment of vineyards in 1856. Under the management of interim owner Jennifer Meek the vines were grown organically, and the wine was made naturally in the full sense of that term, ie no sulphur dioxide was used. With the acquisition of the business by the Conway family, conventional viticulture and winemaking practises have been resumed, winemaking in the hands of Italian-trained Luciano Lombardini, who circuitously found his way to Mudgee by working with the Lowe Family and thereafter Pieter van Gent. No less than 23 wines were submitted for this edition, including Cellar Reserve wines made before the arrival of Luciano.

ɏɏɏɏɏ **Chardonnay 2010** Bright straw-green; it was picked at the perfect point of ripeness, with abundant white peach and nectarine fruit sustained by citrussy acidity and precisely balanced French oak. Screwcap. 12.6% alc. **Rating** 93 **To** 2018 $27
William Reserve Durif 2009 Good, full purple; while immensely concentrated and powerful, it is more polished than the standard version, with notes of tar, earth and unsweetened espresso, the tannins balanced and likely to remain so in the years ahead. Diam. 14.5% alc. **Rating** 93 **To** 2020 $30
Linden Reserve Chardonnay 2011 Pale straw-green; adroit winemaking has captured as much fresh chardonnay fruit as the vineyard is capable of expressing; white peach, apricot and passionfruit on the bouquet flow through to the palate, there joined by a light touch of French oak and a sweet fruit finish. Screwcap. 12.6% alc. **Rating** 91 **To** 2016 $27
Grady Reserve Shiraz 2009 Impressive purple-crimson colour; blackberry and vanillin aromas on the bouquet lead into a medium- to full-bodied palate, showing the impact of maturation in new oak barrels (origin unspecified, but presumably American) to match the sultry black fruits of the palate, the tannins firm but not dry. Diam. 14.1% alc. **Rating** 91 **To** 2024 $30
Durif Shiraz 2010 Medium red-purple; an attractive wine with a range of red and black fruits moving from blackberry through to plum, then red cherry; the tannins are balanced, oak a bystander. Diam. 13.2% alc. **Rating** 90 **To** 2016 $25

ɏɏɏɏ **Unwooded Chardonnay 2011 Rating** 89 **To** 2014 $25
✪ **Clia Chardonnay 2005** Light straw-green; has hung on extraordinarily well given that all of the flavours are delicate, albeit varietally correct. The cork is also very youthful, ageing slowly. 12.9% alc. **Rating** 89 **To** 2014 $15

Verdelho 2011 Rating 89 To 2014 $25
Old Bush Vine Shiraz 2006 Rating 89 To 2016 $35
Durif 2011 Rating 89 To 2017 $20
Durif 2005 Rating 89 To 2015 $30
Shiraz 2005 Rating 88 To 2015 $18
Rose 2010 Rating 87 To 2013 $25
Old Bush Vine Shiraz 2011 Rating 87 To 2013 $20
Shiraz Durif Cabernet 2011 Rating 87 To 2014 $20
Cabernet Sauvignon 2011 Rating 87 To 2014 $20
Old Bush Vine Cabernet Sauvignon 2006 Rating 87 To 2014 $35
Golden Triangle Late Harvest 2010 Rating 87 To 2013 $20

Munari Wines

Ladys Creek Vineyard, 1129 Northern Highway, Heathcote, Vic 3523 **Region** Heathcote
T (03) 5433 3366 **www**.munariwines.com **Open** Tues–Sun 11–5
Winemaker Adrian Munari **Est.** 1993 **Dozens** 3000 **Vyds** 6.9ha
Established on one of the original Heathcote farming properties, Ladys Creek Vineyard is
situated on the narrow Cambrian strip 11km north of the town. Adrian Munari has harnessed
traditional winemaking practices with New World innovation to produce complex, fruit-
driven wines that marry concentration and elegance. They are produced from estate plantings
of shiraz, cabernet sauvignon, merlot, cabernet franc and malbec. Exports to France, Denmark,
Taiwan and China.

ﾔﾔﾔﾔﾔ Black Lady Shiraz 2009 This is a deluxe blend of Barossa wine made by
Richard Sheedy at his Glen Eldon vineyard under the Twisted Arm Reserve label,
and Adrian Munari's Lady's Pass Heathcote wine. It is an extremely complex
tapestry of predominantly black fruit flavours, dark spices, licorice and quality oak.
It is full-bodied, but not corpulent. Cork. 14.5% alc. **Rating** 96 To 2029 $110
Ladys Pass Heathcote Shiraz 2009 Intense and deep purple-crimson colour is
a signal for a high-quality, medium- to full-bodied wine, exemplifying Heathcote
at its best. Along with the usual range of flavours, there is a touch of chocolate and
fruitcake that adds to the appeal of the wine, and to its cellaring future. Screwcap.
14% alc. **Rating** 95 To 2029 $45

ﾔﾔﾔﾔﾔ Schoolhouse Red 2009 Rating 93 To 2024 $30
The Ridge Shiraz 2009 Rating 92 To 2020 $30

Murdoch Hill

Mappinga Road, Woodside, SA 5244 **Region** Adelaide Hills
T (08) 8389 7081 **www**.murdochhill.com.au **Open** By appt
Winemaker Brian Light (Contract), Michael Downer **Est.** 1998 **Dozens** 2350
Vyds 20.6ha
A little over 20ha of vines were established on the undulating, gum-studded countryside of
Charlie and Julie Downer's 60-year-old Erinka property, 4km east of Oakbank. In descending
order of importance, the varieties planted are sauvignon blanc, shiraz, cabernet sauvignon and
chardonnay. Son Michael, with a Bachelor of Oenology degree from Adelaide University, is
assistant winemaker. Exports to the UK and Canada.

ﾔﾔﾔﾔﾔ Adelaide Hills Sauvignon Blanc 2011 Hand-picking and selection has paid
✪ substantial dividends; both the bouquet and palate have a seductive array of gently
tropical fruit flavours, passionfruit to the fore, and just a twist of citrus on the
finish. Screwcap. 12% alc. **Rating** 94 To 2014 $20
✪ Adelaide Hills Chardonnay 2011 Bright, gleaming green-quartz; elegance and
finesse are the key descriptors for a wild-fermented, lees-stirred Chardonnay; the
flavours are in the grapefruit spectrum, not surprising given the alcohol, and some
may argue it crosses the line into Sauvignon Blanc territory. Screwcap. 12.5% alc.
Rating 94 To 2017 $25

The Cronberry Adelaide Hills Shiraz 2010 Crimson-purple; the bouquet and palate tell the same story, with delicious black fruits shot through with spice and pepper notes; medium-bodied and supple in the mouth, oak where it should be. Screwcap. 14% alc. **Rating** 94 **To** 2020 $25

ΨΨΨΨΩ Adelaide Hills Cabernet Sauvignon 2010 Bright crimson-purple; both the
✪ bouquet and palate have a core of cassis and spice, framed by carefully measured French oak; some black olive and savoury fine tannins give authority to the finish, and promise much for the future. Exceptional value. Screwcap. 14.5% alc. **Rating** 93 **To** 2025 $20

Murphy Wines   ★★★★
377 High Street, Nagambie, Vic 3608 **Region** Strathbogie Ranges
T (03) 5792 2074 **www**.arranmurphywines.com.au **Open** Not
Winemaker Arran Murphy **Est.** 2004 **Dozens** 400
The story of Arran Murphy has a fairytale ring to it. He began as an unqualified cellarhand at Tahbilk in 2000, and in '03 was offered the opportunity of a traineeship at Plunkett Wines. He began studying wine production, and in 2004 received a scholarship that enabled him to do a harvest in the Sonoma Valley. Since 2000 he had been making small batches of wine by collecting grapes from the end of rows picked by mechanical harvesters, using chicken wire as a destemmer, and using a three-generations-old basket press. In 2004 he decided to purchase a few tonnes of grapes and make his first commercial wine. With next to no capital, he was unable to afford any new oak, so experimented with inner staves, chips and oak cubes. This resulted in three batches of wine in '04, which he called Hazel Shiraz, honouring his late grandmother Hazel Murphy, who had encouraged him to aim high.

ΨΨΨΨΩ Hazel Shiraz 2008 Good colour; this is the most ambitious wine made to date by Arran Murphy, replete with lusciously ripe fruit and a handsome amount of new oak. A final blend prior to bottling. Screwcap. 14.5% alc. **Rating** 92 **To** 2020 $50

ΨΨΨΨ The Master Mason Goulburn Valley Shiraz Cabernet 2009 **Rating** 87 **To** 2019 $35

Murray Street Vineyard   ★★★★★
Murray Street, Greenock, SA 5360 **Region** Barossa Valley
T (08) 8562 8373 **www**.murraystreet.com.au **Open** 7 days 10–4.30
Winemaker Andrew Seppelt **Est.** 2001 **Dozens** 10 000 **Vyds** 46ha
Andrew Seppelt has moved with a degree of caution in setting up Murray Street Vineyard, possibly because of inherited wisdom and the business acumen of partner Bill Jahnke, a successful investment banker with Wells Fargo. Andrew is a direct descendant of Benno and Sophia Seppelt, who built Seppeltsfield and set the family company on its path to fame. The partnership has two vineyards, one block at Gomersal, the other at Greenock, with the lion's share going to shiraz, followed by grenache, mourvedre, viognier, marsanne, semillon and zinfandel. Most of the grapes are sold, with an increasing amount retained for the Murray Street Vineyard brand. Unusually good point of sale/propaganda material. Exports to the UK, the US, Canada, Denmark, Laos, Macau, Malaysia, Singapore and Hong Kong.

ΨΨΨΨΨ Black Label Barossa Shiraz 2009 Bright, full crimson-purple; a plush, lush but not jammy wine that has excellent texture and structure to its blackberry, licorice and black cherry fruit; the oak is integrated, and the tannins are fine. Impressive wine. Screwcap. 14.5% alc. **Rating** 95 **To** 2029 $25
Barossa Valley Shiraz VP 2008 Deep crimson-purple; a classy bouquet with black fruits, licorice, spice and clean spirit leads into an exceptionally good palate, much drier than the usual Australian style, and right in the centre of Portuguese VP. Great future, however striking it is now. Cork. 19.5% alc. **Rating** 95 **To** 2023 $40

Sophia 2009 A deep and brooding Shiraz with mocha, black fruits, tar and licorice all in abundance; the palate follows suit with more of everything punching through on the palate, yet not overstepping the mark, as there is freshness to provide contrast to the concentration. Screwcap. 14.5% alc. **Rating** 94 **To** 2030 $75 BE

ŶŶŶŶŶ **Black Label Barossa Cabernet Sauvignon 2010** **Rating** 93 **To** 2020 $25
O   **Barossa Valley Semillon 2010** **Rating** 92 **To** 2020 $20
    Benno 2009 **Rating** 90 **To** 2018 $75 BE
    Black Label Barossa Mataro 2010 **Rating** 90 **To** 2016 $25 BE

Murrindindi Vineyards ★★★★

30 Cummins Lane, Murrindindi, Vic 3717 **Region** Upper Goulburn
T (03) 9817 7330 **www**.murrindindivineyards.com **Open** Not
Winemaker Hugh Cuthbertson **Est.** 1979 **Dozens** 5000 **Vyds** 16ha
This small winery is owned and run by the Cuthbertson family, established by Alan and Jan as a minor diversification from their cattle property. Plantings began in 1978, increasing in '82 and '95 to their present level. Son Hugh, himself with a long and high-profile wine career, has overseen the marketing of the wines, including the Family Reserve and Don't Tell Dad brands. Exports to the UK, the US, Finland, Estonia and China.

ŶŶŶŶŶ **Family Reserve Yea Valley Cabernet Sauvignon 2010** Bright colour;
    a savoury-accented bouquet, with dark fruits, olive and ironstone; the palate
    is densely structured, with voluminous black fruits, then a firm, tannic finish.
    Screwcap. 14% alc. **Rating** 92 **To** 2016 $30 BE

Myola Vineyard ★★★☆

137 Griffins Road, Coghills Creek, Vic 3364 (postal) **Region** Ballarat
T (03) 5343 4368 **www**.myolavineyard.com.au **Open** Not
Winemaker Scott Ireland (Contract) **Est.** 1996 **Dozens** 100 **Vyds** 2.5ha
Cheryl Hines and Anthony Fergusson purchased Conihfer Park in 2003. It is part agistment farm and part vineyard, with 1.5ha of pinot noir and 1ha of chardonnay planted in 1996. The vines were in full bearing, and the grapes were sold to other wineries in the region. One tonne of pinot was retained and vinified for Myola Vineyard in 2005, followed by another small make in '07. The partners hope to eventually make some pinot each year, with chardonnay part of the mix. They made a sparkling wine for their daughter's wedding, and intend to follow this up with limited releases in the years to come.

ŶŶŶŶŶ **Sparkling Pinot Noir Blanc 2009** Plenty of colour, and the bouquet offers
    plenty of character, with wild strawberry, pain grillee and hints of florals; the palate
    is dry and chalky, tight and refined, with a long and fresh finish. Diam. 12% alc.
    Rating 90 **To** 2014 $25 BE

ŶŶŶŶ **Unwooded Chardonnay 2009** **Rating** 89 **To** 2015 $25 BE

Myrtaceae

53 Main Creek Road, Main Ridge, Vic 3928 **Region** Mornington Peninsula
T (03) 5989 2045 **www**.myrtaceae.com.au **Open** W'ends & public hols 12–5, 7 days
27 Dec to end Jan
Winemaker Julie Trueman **Est.** 1985 **Dozens** 300 **Vyds** 1ha
Owners John Trueman (viticulturist) and wife Julie (winemaker) began the planting of Myrtaceae in 1985, intending to make a Bordeaux-style red blend. It became evident that these late-ripening varieties were not well suited to the site, so the vineyard was converted to chardonnay (0.6ha) and pinot noir (0.4ha) in 1998. Part of the property is devoted to the Land for Wildlife Scheme; the integrated Australian garden is a particular feature.

🍷🍷🍷🍷🍷 **Mornington Peninsula Pinot Noir 2009** Unsurprisingly, starting to show some colour development; the vineyard is situated near the top of Red Hill, with cool growing conditions that do not, however, prevent full ripening, as this wine demonstrates. Spiced plum flavours are cosseted by a neat touch of French oak, making an altogether attractive wine. Screwcap. 14% alc. **Rating** 93 **To** 2016 $35
Mornington Peninsula Chardonnay 2009 Attractive green-gold; a rich palate that already has started to fill out with ripe, peachy stone fruit, hints of cashew and toasty oak, and a softly rounded – but not flabby – finish. Screwcap. 14% alc. **Rating** 92 **To** 2015 $35

Nalbra Estate Wines ★★★★☆

225 Whitcombes Road, Drysdale, Vic 3222 **Region** Geelong
T (03) 5253 2654 **F** (03) 5253 2414 **Open** By appt
Winemaker Ray Nadeson, Maree Collis (Contract) **Est.** 2001 **Dozens** NFP **Vyds** 2.5ha
Terri and Leigh Robinson began the establishment of their vineyard, perched on Mt Bellarine overlooking Port Phillip Bay, in 2001. Shiraz and pinot gris were planted in that year, followed by sauvignon blanc and viognier in '03. The quality of the grapes they are growing has resulted in gold and silver medals over '10 and '11.

🍷🍷🍷🍷🍷 **Territory Bellarine Peninsula Shiraz Viognier 2010** The colour is not as bright as one might expect, raising the question whether the varieties were co-fermented or simply blended; however, its flavour and textural complexity resulted in it winning a gold medal at the Geelong Wine Show '11; the spicy, foresty notes add interest to the palate, resulting in light and shade, and add energy to the finish. Screwcap. 13.5% alc. **Rating** 93 **To** 2018 $35

Nannup Ridge Estate ★★★★★

PO Box 2, Nannup, WA 6275 **Region** Blackwood Valley
T (08) 9756 2005 **www**.nannupridge.com.au **Open** Not
Winemaker Naturaliste Vintners (Bruce Dukes) **Est.** 1998 **Dozens** 3500 **Vyds** 31ha
The business is owned by the Blizard and Fitzgerald families, who purchased the then unplanted property from the family that had farmed it since the early 1900s. Mark and Alison Blizard had in fact moved to the region in the early 1990s and established a small vineyard on the banks of the beautiful Donnelly River. The '98 transition was from boutique to serious grapegrowing, as the partners established 31ha of mainstream varieties (and 1ha of tempranillo) backed by a (then) grape sale agreement with Constellation. They still regard themselves as grapegrowers, but since 2004 have had small amounts of wine contract-made with outstanding success. Exports to China.

🍷🍷🍷🍷🍷 **Cabernet Sauvignon 2010** Very strong purple-red; Bruce Duke's winemaking skills have produced four gold medals (including Perth and Adelaide) plus the trophy for Best Wine of Show at the Australian Cool Climate Show '11. Blackcurrant/cassis/bramble fruit flavours are perfectly balanced with French oak and firm, but fine, tannins. Screwcap. 14.1% alc. **Rating** 95 **To** 2025 $25

✪ **Sauvignon Blanc 2011** Light straw-green; an altogether snappy Sauvignon Blanc, with aromas and flavours of snow pea, citrus/lime and gooseberry filling the palate with nervosity (a French term for nervous energy) and echoing repeatedly on the finish and aftertaste. Screwcap. 12.5% alc. **Rating** 94 **To** 2013 $17
Merlot 2010 Medium purple-red; had already won four silver medals by the end of '11, and it's not hard to see why. The wine has the elegance and fine tannins of first-class merlot, and the fruit register is in the redcurrant spectrum, aided by cedary French oak. I am deliberately giving it gold medal points. Screwcap. 13.9% alc. **Rating** 94 **To** 2017 $24

🍷🍷🍷🍷🍷 **Shiraz 2010** **Rating** 93 **To** 2018 $24

✪ **Chardonnay 2011** Bright, light green-straw; made entirely from the Dijon clone 99 that has performed very well in many cool-climate regions; gentle grapefruit and apple aromas gain traction on the long, well-balanced palate. Screwcap. 12.5% alc. **Rating** 92 **To** 2016 $18

Nardone Baker Wines

PO Box 386, McLaren Vale, SA 5171 **Region** McLaren Vale
T (08) 8445 8100 **www**.nardonebaker.com **Open** Not
Winemaker Brian Light (Contract) **Est.** 1999 **Dozens** 70 000
Italian-born Joe Nardone and English-born John Baker were brought together by the marriage of Joe's daughter and John's son. Both were already in the wine industry, John studying at Roseworthy Agricultural College and establishing a vineyard. The second generation of Frank Nardone and Patrick Baker, the latter having also studied at Roseworthy, now run what is a significant virtual winery, sourcing grapes from all over SA, with contract winemaking by Brian Light at Boar's Rock. There are five ranges, headed by The Wara Manta Reserve, followed by Nardone Baker, Blaxland's Legacy, Treeview Selection and then Wara Manta (non-reserve). Exports to the UK, the US, Italy, Singapore, China and Japan.

ŸŸŸŸ **Cabernet Sauvignon 2010** Good colour; a well-made wine, with clear varietal character thanks to its blackcurrant fruit, and good structure ex tannins and oak. Cork. 14.5% alc. **Rating** 89 **To** 2017 $16
Moscato 2010 One of the few Moscatos to have real length, and some nice lime cordial flavours on the way through. Screwcap. 6% alc. **Rating** 87 **To** Now $14

Narkoojee   ★★★★★

170 Francis Road, Glengarry, Vic 3854 **Region** Gippsland
T (03) 5192 4257 **www**.narkoojee.com **Open** 7 days 10.30–4.30
Winemaker Harry and Axel Friend **Est.** 1981 **Dozens** 4000
Narkoojee Vineyard (originally a dairy farm owned by the Friend family) is near the old gold-mining town of Walhalla and looks out over the Strzelecki Ranges. The wines are produced from a little over 10ha of estate vineyards, with chardonnay accounting for half the total. Former lecturer in civil engineering and extremely successful amateur winemaker Harry Friend changed horses in 1994 to take joint control, with Axel Friend, of the family vineyard and winery, and hasn't missed a beat since; their skills show through with all the wines, none more so than the Chardonnay. Exports to Canada, Japan, Hong Kong, Singapore and China.

ŸŸŸŸŸ **Reserve Gippsland Pinot Noir 2010** Strong, clear ruby-red; the fragrant bouquet leads into a palate full of varietal cherry and plum fruit, with a healthy sprinkling of spice; the flavours make themselves known immediately the wine enters the mouth, and drive the very long palate through to a logical, and wholly satisfying, finish. Screwcap. 13.5% alc. **Rating** 94 **To** 2017 $34
Reserve Isaac Gippsland Shiraz 2009 Full red-purple; a complex wine, the only question being the amount of French oak, which operates to fill in the gaps, as it were, but sits on top of the fruit. On retasting several times, I came to the conclusion that the good parts of the wine significantly outweighed the oak issue, particularly given that the quality of the oak is high. Screwcap. 14% alc. **Rating** 94 **To** 2029 $34

ŸŸŸŸŸ **Myrtle Point Gippsland Shiraz 2009** **Rating** 93 **To** 2020 $24

ŸŸŸŸ **Lily Grace Gippsland Chardonnay 2011** **Rating** 89 **To** 2015 $24

Nashwauk

PO Box 852, Nuriootpa, SA 5355 **Region** McLaren Vale
T (08) 8562 4488 **F** (08) 8562 4499 **www**.nashwaukvineyards.com.au **Open** Not
Winemaker Reid Bosward, Stephen Dew **Est.** 2005 **Dozens** 5000 **Vyds** 20ha
This is an estate-based venture, with 17ha of shiraz, 2ha of cabernet sauvignon and 1ha of tempranillo, all except the tempranillo between 13 and 40+ years old. It is a stand-alone business of the Kaesler family, and the first time it has extended beyond the Barossa Valley. The striking label comes from satellite photos of the vineyard, showing the contour planting; the name Nashwauk comes from Canada's Algonquin indigenous language, meaning 'land between'. The property is situated in the (unofficial) Seaview subregion, with Kays, Chapel

Hill and Coriole as its neighbours; they all benefit from sea breezes and cooler nights. Exports to the US, Singapore, Malaysia and China.

🍷🍷🍷🍷🍷 **McLaren Vale Cabernet Sauvignon 2009** Bright colour; fragrant cassis and briar bouquet, with a medium-bodied and fleshy palate; shows ripe black fruit, richness and fruitcake spice to conclude. Cork. 14.2% alc. **Rating** 90 **To** 2015 $25 BE

Native Point Wines   ★★★★☆
718 Windermere Road, Windermere, Tas 7252 **Region** Northern Tasmania
T (03) 6328 1628 **www**.nativepoint.com **Open** 7 days 8–6
Winemaker Winemaking Tasmania **Est.** 1999 **Dozens** 1100 **Vyds** 5ha
The story of Tim and Sheena High's adventure might well have been written by Hans Christian Anderson, complete with happy ending. In 1993 they decided to establish a vineyard and start producing wine in Tasmania. What made that decision out of the ordinary was that they were living in Denmark at that time. Born in the UK, they had relocated to Melbourne in 1987 for Tim's work in the dairy industry, but drank more wine than milk. Tim's career took him and Sheena to Chicago, London, Minneapolis, Amsterdam and Auckland for extended periods. But the seed had been sown, and Sheena, with a degree in biology, began a four-year distance education applied science degree course in winemaking through CSU. It was a chance visit to Launceston for a dairy conference, and a drive along the eastern side of the Tamar Valley, that led to their ultimate '94 purchase of a 40ha cattle grazing property that had previously been an apple orchard. Tim has now retired from the dairy business, and the pair devote themselves to Native Point Wines and the local community, having planted pinot noir, riesling, pinot gris and sauvignon blanc. Exports to Sweden.

🍷🍷🍷🍷🍷 **Riesling 2010** Pale straw-green; a deliciously juicy wine by Tasmanian standards, lime-accented fruit and acidity already in an equal partnership, with the fruit to build over the next few years while the acidity remains constant. Screwcap. 11.5% alc. **Rating** 92 **To** 2018 $25
Pinot Noir 2004 Given the age, the bouquet is fresh and full of black cherry and spices, with a herbal note that is consistent across the vintages; the palate is lively and fine, with a long and even conclusion. Screwcap. 13.5% alc. **Rating** 91 **To** 2014 $55 BE
Sauvignon Blanc 2011 Vibrant green hue; a pungent and herbaceous example of the variety with pea pod and gun flint on display; fresh on the palate, a touch of sugar adds weight to the mid palate, and demands that the wine be enjoyed thoroughly chilled. Screwcap. 12.5% alc. **Rating** 90 **To** 2013 $25 BE
Pinot Noir 2010 Bright crimson; a lifted example of Northern Tasmanian Pinot Noir, with bramble, black cherry and a notable accent of mint; lively and fresh, with a bitter Amaro note lingering on the finish. Screwcap. 13.6% alc. **Rating** 90 **To** 2014 $35 BE

Nazaaray   ★★★★
266 Meakins Road, Flinders, Vic 3929 **Region** Mornington Peninsula
T (03) 5989 0126 **www**.nazaaray.com.au **Open** 1st weekend of month, or by appt
Winemaker Paramdeep Ghumman **Est.** 1996 **Dozens** 800 **Vyds** 2.28ha
Paramdeep Ghumman is, as far as I am aware, the only Indian-born winery proprietor in Australia. He and his wife migrated from India over 20 years ago, and purchased the Nazaaray vineyard property in 1991. An initial trial planting of 400 vines in 1996 was gradually expanded to the present level of 1.6ha of pinot noir, 0.44ha of pinot gris and 0.12ha each of sauvignon blanc and shiraz. Notwithstanding the micro size of the estate, all the wines are made and bottled onsite.

🍷🍷🍷🍷🍷 **Mornington Peninsula Sauvignon Blanc 2011** A ripe, pungent and fresh bouquet of gooseberry and nettle, also showing a fine thread of citrus; the palate is lively, with tangy acidity and a long, trailing mineral conclusion. Screwcap. 13.5% alc. **Rating** 92 **To** 2014 $30 BE

Mornington Peninsula Syrah 2010 A spicy, savoury and medium-bodied wine, showing red fruits, plums, licorice and charred meat; fine-boned and vibrant acidity; make no mistake, this is an all savoury experience. Screwcap. 13.4% alc. **Rating** 90 **To** 2018 $40 BE

♛♛♛♛ **Reserve Mornington Peninsula Pinot Noir 2010 Rating** 88 **To** 2016 $50 BE
Mornington Peninsula Pinot Gris 2011 Rating 87 **To** 2014 $30 BE

Nepenthe ★★★★★

Jones Road, Balhannah, SA 5242 **Region** Adelaide Hills
T (08) 8398 8888 **www.**nepenthe.com.au **Open** 7 days 10–4
Winemaker Andre Bondar **Est.** 1994 **Dozens** 70 000 **Vyds** 108.68ha
Nepenthe quickly established its reputation as a producer of high-quality wines, but when founder Ed Tweddell died unexpectedly in 2006, the business was purchased by McGuigan Simeon the following year. The winery was closed in '09, and winemaking operations transferred to Australian Vintage, McGuigan Simeon's principal SA winery. (The Nepenthe winery has since been purchased by Peter Leske and Mark Kozned, and provides contract winemaking services via their Revenir venture.) Nepenthe has over 100ha of close-planted vineyards spread over four vineyards in the Adelaide Hills, with an exotic array of varieties. Exports to the UK, the US and other major markets.

♛♛♛♛♛ **Adelaide Hills Tempranillo 2010** A simply excellent example of tasty young
✪ Tempranillo, with cola, spice and a little bacon bone complexity; the palate is lively and fine, zesty and long, and while easy drinking, has plenty of backbone and structure; trophy Riverina Wine Show. Screwcap. 14% alc. **Rating** 95 **To** 2015 $20 BE
  Ithaca Adelaide Hills Chardonnay 2010 Bright, light straw-green; the wine spent nine months on lees in a mix of new and 1-year-old French barrels; its early picking accentuates the grapefruit and citrus characters, but there is enough fruit sweetness to keep the wine out of the wannabe Sauvignon Blanc category; has a long and finely balanced finish. Screwcap. 12.5% alc. **Rating** 94 **To** 2017 $30
✪ **Adelaide Hills Shiraz 2010** Bright red fruit and spice on the bouquet, with a truly medium–bodied and crunchy red fruit personality; there is a splash of toasty oak on the finish. Outstanding value for money. Gold medal Adelaide Hills Wine Show. Screwcap. 14.5% alc. **Rating** 94 **To** 2018 $20 BE

♛♛♛♛♛ **Adelaide Hills Sauvignon Blanc 2011** Showing the gun flint sometimes
✪ found in dry Sauvignon, with crisp acidity and mineral complexity; there is real drive and interest in this wine, moving away from one-dimensional sauvignon to impart texture and complexity alongside fruit and generosity. Screwcap. 12.5% alc. **Rating** 93 **To** 2014 $20 BE
✪ **Adelaide Hills Pinot Noir 2010** A good dose of mint is evident on the bouquet, yet the palate reveals an almost luscious level of sweet black fruits; tannins come to the fore on the finish, almost rugged and certainly plentiful; big end of town Pinot. Screwcap. 14% alc. **Rating** 90 **To** 2016 $20 BE

♛♛♛♛ **Adelaide Hills Pinot Gris 2011 Rating** 89 **To** 2013 $20 BE

New Era Vineyards ★★★

PO Box 391, Woodside SA 5244 **Region** Adelaide Hills
T (08) 8389 7715 **www.**neweravineyards.com.au **Open** Not
Winemaker Robert Baxter, Reg Wilkinson **Est.** 1988 **Dozens** 500 **Vyds** 12.5ha
The New Era vineyard is situated over a gold reef that was mined for 60 years until all recoverable gold had been extracted (mining ceased in 1940). The vineyard was originally planted to chardonnay, shiraz, cabernet sauvignon, merlot and sauvignon, mostly contracted to Foster's. Recently 2ha of cabernet sauvignon and 1.1ha of merlot have been grafted over to sauvignon blanc. Much of the production is sold to other winemakers in the region. The small amount of wine made has been the subject of favourable reviews.

♥♥♥♥ **Adelaide Hills Cabernet Sauvignon 2004** The clear, bright colour foreshadows a wine that is lot fresher than the '04 Shiraz; while only medium-bodied at best, there are flavours of mint and cassis given substance by fine tannins. There is little or no point in cellaring it further, despite the protection afforded by the screwcap. Screwcap. 13.5% alc. **Rating** 87 **To** 2014 $22

Newtons Ridge

1170 Cooriemungle Road, Timboon, Vic 3268 **Region** Geelong
T (03) 5598 7394 www.newtonsridgeestate.com.au **Open** 7 days 11–5 Nov–Apr, or by appt
Winemaker David Newton **Est.** 1998 **Dozens** 1200 **Vyds** 4ha
David and Dot Newton say that after milking cows for 18 years, they decided to investigate the possibility of planting a northeast-facing block of land that they also owned. Their self-diagnosed mid life crisis also stemmed from a lifelong interest in wine. They planted 2ha of chardonnay and pinot noir in 1998, and another 2ha of pinot gris, pinot noir and sauvignon blanc the following year. Having done a short winemaking course at Melbourne University (Dookie Campus), the Newtons completed a small winery in 2003. Originally called Heytesbury Ridge, the winery had a speedy name change to Newtons Ridge after a large legal stick was waved in their direction. David and Carla Falk became owners in June '12.

♥♥♥♥♀ **Sauvignon Blanc 2011** Pale quartz; has an attractive passionfruit bouquet that feeds through on the lively palate, there joined by mineral notes that reinforce the passionfruit theme. Screwcap. 11.9% alc. **Rating** 93 **To** 2014 $18
Shiraz 2010 Strong colour; licorice, briar, plum, black cherry and earth all to be found, the palate well balanced and long. Screwcap. 13.3% alc. **Rating** 90 **To** 2018 $22

✪ **Taisha's Sparkling Trio 2008** Full-on pink colour; a blend of pinot noir, chardonnay and pinot meunier; quite fresh, with strawberry fruits to the fore, and touches of spice, and fruitcake; good length and acidity. Diam. 13.2% alc. **Rating** 90 **To** 2013 $20

♥♥♥♥ **Lila's Chardonnay 2010** **Rating** 88 **To** 2014 $29
Millie's Pinot Grigio 2011 **Rating** 87 **To** Now $15
Zara's Pinot Noir 2010 **Rating** 87 **To** 2015 $20

Ngeringa

119 Williams Road, Mount Barker, SA 5251 **Region** Adelaide Hills
T (08) 8398 2867 www.ngeringa.com **Open** Fri–Sun & public hols 11–5
Winemaker Erinn Klein **Est.** 2001 **Dozens** 2500 **Vyds** 5ha
Erinn and Janet Klein say, 'As fervent practitioners of biodynamic wine growing, we respect biodynamics as a sensitivity to the rhythms of nature, the health of the soil and the connection between plant, animal and cosmos. It is a pragmatic solution to farming without the use of chemicals and a necessary acknowledgement that the farm unit is part of a great whole.' It is not an easy solution, and the Kleins have increased the immensity of the challenge by using ultra-close vine spacing of 1.5m × 1 m, necessitating a large amount of hand training of the vines plus a tiny crawler tractor. Lest it be thought they have stumbled onto biodynamic growing without understanding wine science, they teamed up while studying at Adelaide University in 2000 (Erinn – oenology, Janet – viticulture/wine marketing), and then spent time looking at the great viticultural regions of the Old World, with a particular emphasis on biodynamics. The thick straw-bale walls of the winery result in a constant temperature throughout the year. The JE label is used for the basic wines, Ngeringa only for the very best. Exports to the UK, the US, Canada, Austria, Sweden and Japan.

♥♥♥♥♀ **JE Adelaide Hills Syrah 2009** Light crimson-purple; a very fresh and lively light-bodied wine with attractive red berry and spice fruit flavours; needs a touch more conviction to the fruit. Screwcap. 13.5% alc. **Rating** 93 **To** 2019 $25
Adelaide Hills Rose 2010 Pale salmon-pink; a mix of spice and strawberry aromas on the bouquet builds intensity on the palate and smooth, dry, gently savoury finish. Screwcap. 13% alc. **Rating** 90 **To** Now $28

JE Adelaide Hills Assemblage White 2009 Rating 89 To 2013 $25
Adelaide Hills Syrah 2009 Rating 89 To 2018 $50 BE
Adelaide Hills Chardonnay 2010 Rating 87 To 2015 $35 BE

Nicholson River   ★★★★

57 Liddells Road, Nicholson, Vic 3882 **Region** Gippsland
T (03) 5156 8241 **www**.nicholsonriverwinery.com.au **Open** 7 days 10–4 during hols
or by appt
Winemaker Ken Eckersley **Est.** 1978 **Dozens** 500 **Vyds** 8ha
Nicholson River's fierce commitment to quality in the face of the temperamental Gippsland
climate and frustratingly small production has been handsomely repaid by some massive
Chardonnays and impressive red wines (from estate plantings). Ken Eckersley refers to
his Chardonnays not as white wines but as gold wines, and lists them accordingly in his
newsletter.

 Pinot Noir 2009 Mid crimson; a bright and savoury bouquet, exhibiting red
fruits, fresh herbs and minerals; the palate is driven by tangy acidity and fine-
grained tannins, finishing with a long and expansive personality and focus.
Screwcap. 13.5% alc. **Rating** 91 **To** 2016 $30 BE
The Nicholson 2008 A 50/30/20% blend of merlot, cabernet sauvignon and
cabernet franc. Clear red, it has a fragrant bouquet leading into a supple, medium-
bodied palate, with redcurrant and blackcurrant fruit to the fore, tannins and oak
to the rear, giving it an overall juicy character. Screwcap. 13.5% alc. **Rating** 91
To 2018 $30

Nick O'Leary Wines   ★★★★★

129 Donnelly Lane, Bungendore, NSW 2621 **Region** Canberra District
T (02) 6161 8739 **www**.nickolearywines.com.au **Open** By appt
Winemaker Nick O'Leary **Est.** 2007 **Dozens** 3000
At the ripe old age of 28, Nick O'Leary had been involved in the wine industry for over a
decade, working variously in retail, wholesale, viticulture and winemaking. Two years earlier
he had laid the foundation for Nick O'Leary Wines, purchasing shiraz from local vignerons
(commencing in 2006) and riesling following in '08. His wines have had extraordinarily
consistent success in local wine shows and competitions since the first vintages. No wines
were received for this edition; the rating is that of last year.

Night Harvest   ★★★★★

PO Box 569, Dunsborough, WA 6280 **Region** Margaret River
T (08) 9756 7813 **www**.greenpiper.com.au **Open** Not
Winemaker Contract **Est.** 2005 **Dozens** NFP
This is the rags-to-riches story of Andy and Mandy Ferreira, who arrived in the Margaret
River in 1986 as newly married young migrants. They soon became involved in the
construction and establishment of the new vineyards of that time, as well as growing vegetables
for the local and export markets. Their vineyard-contracting business expanded quickly when
the region experienced its rapid growth in the late 1990s, so the vegetable business was
closed, and they put all their focus into wine. During this period they were involved in the
establishment of about 3000ha of Margaret River vineyards, many of which they continue
to manage today (Woodside Valley Estate and Chapman Grove are among the 16 estates
that fall into this category). As their fortunes grew, they purchased their own property and
produced the first wines in 2005, employing contract winemakers Kevin McKay and Bruce
Dukes. Harvesting is a key part of their contracting business, and currently they run seven
self-propelled harvesters and are responsible for harvesting the fruit from over 100 different
sites in the southwest. Hence the Night Harvest brand was born. Butler Crest was added as a
premium label, and more recently they have formed their own distribution service. Exports
to Thailand and China.

ΨΨΨΨΨ **Reserve Margaret River Chardonnay 2010** Light straw-green; takes off with
✪ excellent energy and drive the moment it enters the mouth, with an intense array
of grapefruit, stone fruit and melon flavours, yet retaining finesse. The oak is well
integrated, and the wine will undoubtedly develop well over the coming years.
Screwcap. 13% alc. **Rating** 94 **To** 2018 $22
Butler Crest Cabernet Sauvignon 2010 Light, bright crimson; the bouquet
is complex, with touches of cedar and spice; the medium- to full-bodied palate
moves quickly into cabernet stride, with abundant blackcurrant and redcurrant
fruit interspersed with savoury tannins; the length and balance are good. Uses the
first Colmated (white-coated) corks I have seen in Australia for years. 13.7% alc.
Rating 94 **To** 2020 $39

ΨΨΨΨΨ **John George Reserve Margaret River Cabernet Sauvignon 2010**
Rating 93 **To** 2020 $35
Butler Crest Semillon 2011 Rating 92 **To** 2020 $25
Butler Crest Sauvignon Blanc 2011 Rating 90 **To** 2014 $30
✪ **Margaret River Sauvignon Blanc Semillon 2011** Pale quartz-green; the
fragrant bouquet offers a mix of gently tropical and gooseberry aromas that flow
on into the light-bodied mid palate; somewhat unexpectedly, the back palate
picks up intensity, with an attractive acid grip. Screwcap. 13.8% alc. **Rating** 90
To 2014 $17
✪ **Margaret River Shiraz 2010** Deep crimson; may have bypassed the crusher/
destemmer on the way to fermentation. A medium- to full-bodied wine, with
black fruits and vanilla oak to the fore, trailing off ever so slightly on the finish, but
still offering much to enjoy. Diam. 14.7% alc. **Rating** 90 **To** 2017 $17

ΨΨΨΨ **Reserve Margaret River Vermentino 2011 Rating** 89 **To** 2015 $22
✪ **Margaret River Merlot 2010 Rating** 89 **To** 2015 $17

Nillumbik Estate   ★★★★☆

PO Box 24, Smiths Gully, Vic 3760 **Region** Yarra Valley
T (03) 9710 1773 **www**.nillumbikestate.com.au **Open** Not
Winemaker John Tregambe **Est.** 2001 **Dozens** 500 **Vyds** 1.6ha
In establishing Nillumbik Estate, John and Chanmali Tregambe drew on the multi-generational
winemaking experience of John's parents, Italian immigrants who arrived in Australia in the
1950s. The estate plantings of pinot noir are supplemented by cabernet sauvignon, chardonnay,
shiraz and nebbiolo purchased variously from Sunbury, Heathcote and the King Valley.

ΨΨΨΨΨ **Old Earth Heathcote Shiraz 2009** Dense, deep purple-crimson; this
full-bodied shiraz is stacked with blackberry, plum, licorice and earth on the
generously structured palate; will be very long lived. Screwcap. 14% alc. **Rating** 93
To 2034 $32

ΨΨΨΨ **Matteo King Valley Nebbiolo 2009 Rating** 89 **To** 2017 $28

Nine Fingers   ★★★

PO Box 212, Lobethal, SA 5241 **Region** Adelaide Hills
T (08) 8389 6049 **Open** By appt
Winemaker Contract **Est.** 1999 **Dozens** 200 **Vyds** 1ha
Simon and Penny Cox established their sauvignon blanc vineyard after encouragement from
local winemaker Robb Cootes of Leland Estate. The small vineyard has meant that they do
all the viticultural work, and meticulously tend the vines. They obviously have a sense of
humour, which may not be shared by their youngest daughter Olivia. In 2002, 2-year-old
Olivia's efforts to point out bunches that needed to be thinned resulted in Penny's secateurs
cutting off the end of Olivia's finger. A race to hospital and successful microsurgery resulted in
the full restoration of the finger; strangely, Olivia has shown little interest in viticulture since,
but will be reminded of the incident by the name of the business and the design of the label.
Exports to Singapore.

ΨΨΨΨ
✪
Adelaide Hills Sauvignon Blanc 2011 Pale straw-green; a juicy wine with a delicate array of citrus, snow pea and gooseberry flavours, the finish crisp and fresh. Screwcap. 12% alc. **Rating** 89 **To** 2013 $19

919 Wines

39 Hodges Road, Berri, SA 5343 **Region** Riverland
T (08) 8582 4436 **www**.919wines.com.au **Open** Wed–Sun & public hols 10–5
Winemaker Eric and Jenny Semmler **Est.** 2002 **Dozens** 2000 **Vyds** 17ha
Eric and Jenny Semmler have been involved in the wine industry since 1986, and have a special interest in fortified wines. Eric previously made fortified wines for Hardys at Berri Estates, and worked at Brown Brothers. Jenny has worked for Strathbogie Vineyards, Pennyweight Wines, St Huberts and Constellation. They have planted micro-quantities of varieties specifically for fortified wines: palomino, durif, tempranillo, muscat a petits grains, tinta cao, shiraz, tokay and touriga nacional. Notwithstanding their Riverland GI, they use minimal water application, deliberately reducing the crop levels, practising organic and biodynamic techniques. In 2011 they purchased the 12.3ha property at Loxton they now call 809 Vineyard, and have taken a further 2ha under management. The 919 vineyard is certified biodynamic; the 809 vineyard is in pre-certification.

ΨΨΨΨΨ
Tempranillo 2010 Exceptionally deep purple-red; the wine has not only voluminous aromas and layered flavours of red and black cherry, but also tannins not often seen in the Riverland; a lighter touch with those tannins might have made a very good wine indeed. Screwcap. 15% alc. **Rating** 90 **To** 2017 $40
Durif 2010 Dense, dark red; a massive wine in every respect: its alcohol, extract, body and tannins must set some sort of record for red table wine from the Riverland, but not all would agree this was a correct pursuit. Points for valour. Screwcap. 16% alc. **Rating** 90 **To** 2030 $50
Durif 2009 Good purple-crimson; a medium- to full-bodied wine, with abundant confit black fruits and spice; controlled extract and good length. Screwcap. 14.5% alc. **Rating** 90 **To** 2017 $38

ΨΨΨΨ
Pale Dry Apera NV Rating 87 **To** 2013 $28

Nintingbool

56 Wongerer Lane, Smythes Creek, Vic 3351 (postal) **Region** Ballarat
T (03) 5342 4393 **www**.nintingbool.com **Open** Not
Winemaker Peter Bothe **Est.** 1998 **Dozens** 350 **Vyds** 2ha
Peter and Jill Bothe purchased the Nintingbool property in 1982 and built the home in which they now live in '84, using old bluestone dating back to the goldrush period. They established an extensive Australian native garden and home orchard, but in '98 diversified with the planting of pinot noir, a further planting the following year lifting the total to 2 ha; a small amount of the property remains to be planted with pinot gris. This is one of the coolest mainland regions, and demands absolute attention to detail (and a warm growing season) for success. In 2002 and '03 the grapes were sold to Ian Watson, the wine made and released under the Tomboy Hill label but with the Nintingbool Vineyard shown on the label (the '02 was quite a beautiful wine). In '04 they decided to make the wines themselves, the opening vintage producing a tiny 44 cases.

ΨΨΨΨΨ
Ballarat Pinot Noir 2010 Deep crimson; the bouquet is loaded with essency red and black fruits; the palate is generous, and pushing the boundaries of pinosity, with assertive tannins dominating from start to finish; a big-boned and muscular Pinot Noir needing patience. Screwcap. 13.7% alc. **Rating** 90 **To** 2015 $35 BE

Nocton Park
★★★☆

373 Colebrook Road, Richmond, Tas 7025 **Region** Southern Tasmania
T (02) 9371 4952 **www**.noctonpark.com.au **Open** By appt
Winemaker Winemaking Tasmania (Julian Alcorso) **Est.** 1998 **Dozens** 8000 **Vyds** 33ha

Prior to the 2010 vintage, Nocton Park emerged from two years' administration following the financial demise of its founders. Jerry Adler and viticulturist Richard Meyman now run the business, the 100ha property planted to pinot noir, chardonnay, merlot and sauvignon blanc. The site was originally earmarked by Peter Althaus of Domaine A (see separate entry), who, back in 1995, described it as the best vineyard land in the Coal River Valley. A super-premium Pinot Noir and Chardonnay are due for release in 2012/13. Exports to China.

ŶŶŶŶŶ **Reserve Pinot Noir 2010** Deep garnet; a dark and savoury bouquet, loaded with spices and gamey complexity; the palate is densely packed with fine tannins and ample fruits, finishing with a long, savoury and fresh conclusion. Screwcap. 13.4% alc. **Rating** 92 **To** 2016 $38 BE

ŶŶŶŶ **Pinot Noir 2010 Rating** 89 **To** 2015 $25 BE
Sauvignon Blanc 2011 Rating 88 **To** 2013 $20 BE
Reserve Chardonnay 2010 Rating 88 **To** 2014 $30 BE
Chardonnay 2010 Rating 87 **To** 2014 $25 BE
Sparkling Rose 2009 Rating 87 **To** 2014 $30

Noonji Estate   ★★★★★

386 Wilderness Road, Lovedale, NSW 2321 **Region** Hunter Valley
T 0413 996 624 **www**.noonji.com.au **Open** W'ends & public hols 10–6, Mon–Fri by appt
Winemaker Nick Paterson2004 **Dozens** 250 **Vyds** 5.5ha
Self-described wine tragics Peter and Barbara Jensen chose to leave Sydney to pursue their dream of owning a small vineyard in an idyllic setting in the Hunter Valley. In 2004 they found a block of 40-year-old vines and began the long task of completely rejuvenating the vineyard, securing the services of Nick Paterson (Chateau Pâto) as contract winemaker. The 2.5ha of chardonnay included in the plantings are among the oldest in the Hunter Valley. No wines were received for this edition; the rating is that of last year.

Norfolk Rise Vineyard   ★★★☆

Limestone Coast Road, Mount Benson, SA 5265 **Region** Mount Benson
T (08) 8768 5080 **www**.norfolkrise.com.au **Open** Not
Winemaker Daniel Berrigan **Est.** 2000 **Dozens** 22 000 **Vyds** 130.3ha
This is by far the largest and most important development in the Mt Benson region. It is ultimately owned by a privately held Belgian company, G & C Kreglinger, established in 1797. In early 2002 Kreglinger acquired Pipers Brook Vineyard; it will maintain the separate brands of the two ventures. The Mt Benson development commenced in 2000, with a large vineyard and a 2000-tonne winery, primarily aimed at the export market. It has to be said that the large investment in the winery and vineyards has not been supported by the quality of the wines so far made. Exports to Europe and Asia.

ŶŶŶŶŶ **Mount Benson Sauvignon Blanc 2011** Pale quartz; one of the best wines to
✪   come from Norfolk Rise to date, yet another example of the cool season; it has gently fragrant tropical fruit aromas and a distinct touch of musk, unusual but not the least unpleasant, the palate long and focused, minerally acidity supporting, not dominating, the varietal fruit flavours. Screwcap. 12.5% alc. **Rating** 93 **To** 2013 $16

ŶŶŶŶ **Mount Benson Pinot Grigio 2011 Rating** 87 **To** 2013 $16 BE
Mount Benson Shiraz 2008 Rating 87 **To** 2013 $16

Norton Estate   ★★★★★

758 Plush Hannans Road, Lower Norton, Vic 3401 **Region** Western Victoria Zone
T (03) 5384 8235 **www**.nortonestate.com.au **Open** Fri–Sun 11–4 or by appt
Winemaker Best's Wines **Est.** 1997 **Dozens** 1300 **Vyds** 4.66ha
In 1996 the Spence family purchased a run-down farm at Lower Norton and, rather than farming the traditional wool, meat and wheat, trusted their instincts and planted vines on the elevated, frost-free, buckshot rises. The surprising vigour of the initial planting of shiraz

prompted further plantings of shiraz, cabernet sauvignon and sauvignon blanc. The vineyard is halfway between the Grampians and Mt Arapiles, 6km northwest of the Grampians region, and will have to be content with the Western Victoria Zone, but the wines show regional Grampians character and style. A traditional Wimmera ripple-iron barn has been converted into a cellar door.

🍷🍷🍷🍷🍷 **Wendy's Dedication Shiraz 2010** Dedicated to Wendy Spence, Norton's founder, who picked the grapes, but died before the wine was bottled (200 bottles). It is a full-bodied Shiraz, with great depth and savoury complexity, and will be a living reminder of her role for another two decades. Screwcap. 14.5% alc. **Rating** 95 **To** 2030 $100
Arapiles Run Shiraz 2010 Good hue, although slightly turbid; a complex, well-structured and balanced wine, with black fruits, spice and tannins running through the very long palate; seemingly more oak than in the varietal. Screwcap. 14.2% alc. **Rating** 94 **To** 2025 $37

🍷🍷🍷🍷 **Shiraz 2010 Rating** 89 **To** 2020 $23

Norton Summit Vineyards ★★★☆
59 Nicholls Road, Norton Summit, SA 5136 **Region** Adelaide Hills
T (08) 8390 1986 **www**.nsv.net.au **Open** By appt
Winemaker Kenn Fisher **Est.** 1998 **Dozens** 500 **Vyds** 1.5ha
Dr Kenn Fisher and partner Meredyth Taylor planted pinot noir and chardonnay in 1998. The vineyard has five blocks, each with its own mesoclimate, orientation and soil type. To add further complexity, four clones have been utilised. With additional vine age, the use of new French oak has been increased to 30%. Kenn makes the wines using traditional Burgundian methods of open fermenters and a basket press.

🍷🍷🍷🍷🍷 **Brut Sauvage Chardonnay Pinot Noir 2007** Straw-gold; despite the (slightly ambiguous) 'Brut Sauvage' which theoretically means the absence of any sweetness in the wine when it is topped up post-disgorgement, the wine is well balanced, with a creamy/nutty flavour along with dried fruits, and a pleasing finish. Diam. 13.5% alc. **Rating** 90 **To** 2014 $30

Nova Vita Wines ★★★★★
GPO Box 1352, Adelaide, SA 5001 **Region** Adelaide Hills
T (08) 8356 0454 **www**.novavitawines.com.au **Open** Not
Winemaker Peter Leske, Taras Ochota, Mark Kozned **Est.** 2005 **Dozens** 14 000 **Vyds** 46ha
Mark and Jo Kozned did months of painstaking research before locating the property on which they have now established their vineyard. Situated 4km outside of Gumeracha, it has gentle slopes, plenty of water and, importantly, moderately fertile soils. Here the 30ha Woodlands Ridge Vineyard is planted (in descending order of size) to chardonnay, sauvignon blanc, pinot gris and shiraz. They have subsequently established the Tunnel Hill Vineyard near Forreston, with 16ha planted to pinot noir, shiraz, cabernet sauvignon, sauvignon blanc, semillon, verdelho, merlot and sangiovese. The name Nova Vita reflects the beginning of the Kozneds' new life, the firebird on the label coming from their Russian ancestry. It is a Russian myth that only a happy or lucky person may see the bird or hear its song. The increased vineyard resources have led to the Mad Russian range, exclusive to Cellarmasters in Australia, but also exported. The Kozneds have joined forces with Peter Leske to form Revenir, a contract winemaking business that has purchased the former Nepenthe winery, and is where the Nova Vita wines are made. Exports to Singapore and China.

🍷🍷🍷🍷🍷 **Firebird Adelaide Hills Chardonnay 2010** Hand-picked and chilled before whole bunch pressing, fermentation with a mix of wild and cultured yeasts, then lees-aged for 12 months in French oak; a finely structured, intense and long wine is the result, with substantial natural acidity to the nectarine, apple and white peach fruit flavours. Screwcap. 13.5% alc. **Rating** 94 **To** 2017 $25

Firebird Adelaide Hills Pinot Noir 2010 Wild yeast, small-batch fermentation including some whole bunches and maturation in French oak embroider a multi-site, mutli-clone origin; full to the brim with red and black cherry fruit, it also has the texture and tannin structure to flourish with some years in bottle. Screwcap. 14% alc. **Rating** 94 **To** 2017 $25

Firebird Adelaide Hills Sauvignon Blanc 2011 The majority of grapes come from Nova Vita's Woodlands Ridge Vineyard, in its third year of conversion to biodynamic. There is no sign of rot or disease in the wine, just concentrated varietal and regional fruit flavours in that coherent Adelaide Hills style fusing herb and tropical fruits. Screwcap. 11.5% alc. **Rating** 92 **To** 2013 $20

Mad Russian Adelaide Hills Pinot Noir 2010 Clear, deep crimson colour; a powerful and complex wine with contrasting black cherry and savoury/foresty nuances; the strong mid palate falters fractionally on the finish. Screwcap. 14% alc. **Rating** 92 **To** 2016 $17

Firebird Adelaide Hills Pinot Gris 2010 Rating 90 **To** Now $25

Mad Russian Adelaide Hills Shiraz 2010 Medium red-purple; the medium-bodied, plum, licorice, fruitcake and cherry palate has good flavour and texture; it is, however, ironic that the back label should take a potshot at 'warmer, overripe shiraz', when this wine weighs in with 14.5% alcohol. Screwcap. 14.5% alc. **Rating** 90 **To** 2018 $17

Firebird Sparkling Pinot Noir NV Rating 87 **To** 2013 $23

Nugan Estate ★★★★★

Kidman Way, Wilbriggie, NSW 2680 **Region** Riverina
T (02) 9362 9993 **www.**nuganestate.com.au **Open** Mon–Fri 9–5
Winemaker Darren Owers **Est.** 1999 **Dozens** 400 000 **Vyds** 606ha
Nugan Estate arrived on the scene like a whirlwind. It is an offshoot of the Nugan Group headed by Michelle Nugan, inter alia the recipient of an Export Hero Award in 2000. In the mid 1990s the company began developing vineyards, and it is now a veritable giant, with five vineyards: Cookoothama (335ha), Talinga Park (115ha) and Manuka Grove (46ha) in the Riverina, Frasca's Lane (100ha) in the King Valley and McLaren Parish (10ha) in McLaren Vale. In addition, it has contracts in place to buy 1000 tonnes of grapes per year from Coonawarra. It sells part of the production as grapes, part as bulk wine and part under the Cookoothama and Nugan Estate labels. Both brands are having considerable success in wine shows, large and small. Today the wine business is in the energetic hands of Matthew and Tiffany Nugan, Michelle's children. Exports to the UK, the US and other major markets.

Alcira Vineyard Coonawarra Cabernet Sauvignon 2008 Excellent crimson-purple; the best release from this vineyard to date; the bouquet and palate sing the same song of cassis, sweet earth, mint and soft but persistent mocha/vanilla oak that allies itself with the equally persistent fine, ripe tannins. Screwcap. 14% alc. **Rating** 95 **To** 2020 $23

Frasca's Lane Vineyard King Valley Chardonnay 2009 Light straw-green; a most attractive wine that has totally absorbed the barrel fermentation and maturation for 15 months in new and seasoned French oak; the bouquet is delicate but very fragrant, the palate fine and long, with white peach and citrus to the fore. Screwcap. 13.5% alc. **Rating** 94 **To** 2016 $20

Cookoothama Darlington Point Botrytis Semillon 2008 Rating 92 **To** 2015 $21

Alfredo Frasca's Lane Vineyard King Valley Sangiovese 2009 Rating 90 **To** 2016 $23

Cookoothama Darlington Point Shiraz 2009 Rating 87 **To** 2013 $15

O'Leary Walker Wines ★★★★★

Main Road, Leasingham, SA 5452 **Region** Clare Valley
T (08) 8843 0022 **www**.olearywalkerwines.com **Open** Mon–Sat 10–4, Sun 11–4
Winemaker David O'Leary, Nick Walker, Keeda Zilm **Est.** 2001 **Dozens** 19000 **Vyds** 35ha
David O'Leary and Nick Walker together had more than 30 years' experience as winemakers
working for some of the biggest Australian wine groups when they took the plunge in 2001
and backed themselves to establish their own winery and brand. Initially the principal focus
was on the Clare Valley, with 10ha of riesling, shiraz, cabernet sauvignon and semillon the
main plantings; thereafter attention swung to the Adelaide Hills, where they now have 25ha
of chardonnay, cabernet sauvignon, pinot noir, shiraz, sauvignon blanc and merlot. Exports to
the UK, Ireland and Asia.

Polish Hill River Riesling 2011 Bright green-straw; the bouquet has lime,
apple blossom and talc aromas, the fresh and zesty palate driving through to the
finish on the back of lime and mineral flavours. Screwcap. 12.5% alc. **Rating** 94
To 2023 $22

Wyebo Adelaide Hills Shiraz 2010 Medium red-purple; the aromas of the
bouquet and the medium-bodied palate bring red fruits into display alongside
black fruits; has spicy nuances and a pleasing, lively lift to the finish and aftertaste.
Screwcap. 14% alc. **Rating** 94 **To** 2020 $35

Claire Reserve Shiraz 2008 The attention to detail in this wine is palpable, with
ample levels of red and black fruits, florals, fine toasty oak and sappy complexity;
medium-bodied and layered, a little time is needed for maximum integration of
all parts; the wait is sure to be worth the effort. Screwcap. 14.5% alc. **Rating** 94
To 2025 $90 BE

Clare Valley Cabernet Sauvignon 2010 Bright and essency redcurrant and
blackcurrant bouquet, with a lick of toasty oak and cedar; the palate is medium-
bodied, fresh and vibrant, with a seductive tannin profile that extends the finish
and will provide ageing potential; very good at the price. Screwcap. 14.5% alc.
Rating 94 **To** 2020 $22 BE

Clare Valley McLaren Vale Shiraz 2010 **Rating** 93 **To** 2018 $22 BE
Watervale Riesling 2011 **Rating** 92 **To** 2021 $20
Adelaide Hills Sauvignon Blanc 2011 Pale green-quartz; the cool (and wet)
growing season and early picking give the wine almost uncomfortable drive and
length on the palate, with its bundle of tropical, green grass and citrus flavours
wrapped in flinty, minerally acidity. Food recommended. Screwcap. 11% alc.
Rating 92 **To** 2013 $17

Wyatt Earp Vintage Shiraz 2010 **Rating** 90 **To** 2025 $35 BE

Blue Cutting Road Clare Valley Cabernet Merlot 2009 **Rating** 89
To 2015 $15

Adelaide Hills Pinot Noir 2009 **Rating** 88 **To** 2014 $22 BE

Hurtle Adelaide Hills Pinot Noir Chardonnay 2008 **Rating** 88 **To** 2014
$28 BE

Oak Works Wines

PO Box 1661, Renmark, SA 5341 **Region** Riverland
T 0420 975 692 **F** (08) 8595 1794 **Open** Not
Winemaker Peter Rogers **Est.** 2001 **Dozens** 100
Owner Peter Rogers has a full-time job with the CSIRO, Oak Works being a labour of
love for his evenings and weekends. He has a decidedly unusual approach to making his red
wines, eschewing the use of pumps and filters in the belief that they can oxidise the wine.
However, all are matured in oak (mainly American) for 16–18 months prior to bottling, with
obvious oak impact on the wines. All the grapes are purchased, each variety in very small
amounts, from local experimental plots. Over the years he has made and released Zinfandel,
Shiraz, Petit Verdot, Cabernet Merlot, Chambourcin, Durif, Tannat, Tinta Molle, Saperavi and
Montepulciano. Exports to Denmark and Singapore.

ỴỴỴỴ   Chambourcin 2008 Rating 88
O   To 2013 $18
O   Tinta Molle 2008 Rating 87 To 2014 $20

Oakdene Vineyards   ★★★★★

255 Grubb Road, Wallington, Vic 3221 **Region** Geelong
T (03) 5256 3886 **www**.oakdene.com.au **Open** Sun–Tues 10–4, Wed–Sat 10–late
Winemaker Ray Nadeson, Robin Brockett **Est.** 2001 **Dozens** 4000 **Vyds** 11.3ha
Bernard and Elizabeth Hooley purchased Oakdene in 2001. Bernard focused on planting the
vineyard (shiraz, pinot gris, sauvignon blanc, pinot noir, chardonnay, merlot, cabernet franc and
cabernet sauvignon), while Elizabeth worked to restore the 1920s homestead. Ray Nadeson
makes Chardonnay, Pinot Noir and Shiraz; Robin Brockett makes the Sauvignon Blanc.
Much of the wine is sold through the award-winning Oakdene Restaurant and cellar door.

ỴỴỴỴỴ   William Single Vineyard Bellarine Peninsula Shiraz 2010 Deep, dark
    crimson-purple; made using the same technique as the Pinot Noir, with the
    inclusion of some whole bunches; this is a flavour powerhouse, with saturated
    black fruits, licorice and spice; will age superbly. Screwcap. 14.5% alc. **Rating** 95
    To 2030 $28
    Peta's Single Vineyard Bellarine Peninsula Pinot Noir 2010 Good colour;
    the bouquet shows the influence of the small percentage of whole bunches
    included in the ferment, adding both flavour and texture to a Pinot full of dark
    cherry fruit wrapped around the savoury, spicy characters of the finish. Screwcap.
    13.5% alc. **Rating** 94 To 2020 $30

ỴỴỴỴỴ   Matilda Single Vineyard Macedon Ranges Blanc de Noirs 2008
    Rating 93 To 2014 $35
    Jessica Single Vineyard Bellarine Peninsula Sauvignon 2011 Rating 91
    To 2014 $28
    Elizabeth Single Vineyard Bellarine Peninsula Chardonnay 2010
    Rating 91 To 2017 $28
O   Chardonnay Pinot Noir NV Pale straw-green; a complex 80/20% blend
    from the Pyrenees (60%) and Geelong (40%) with white peach chardonnay the
    dominant player; the balance is good, as is the length. All-purpose bubbly. Cork.
    12% alc. **Rating** 91 To 2014 $21
O   Single Vineyard Bellarine Peninsula Sauvignon Blanc 2011 Light straw-
    green; the bouquet is fresh and clean, and it is left to the palate to express varietal
    character, which it does with a mix of citrus and gently tropical flavours that
    gain greatest impact on the finish and aftertaste. Screwcap. 12% alc. **Rating** 90
    To 2013 $21

ỴỴỴỴ   Bellarine Peninsula Pinot Grigio 2011 Rating 89 To 2013 $21

Oakridge Wines   ★★★★★

864 Maroondah Highway, Coldstream, Vic 3770 **Region** Yarra Valley
T (03) 9738 9900 **www**.oakridgewines.com.au **Open** 7 days 10–5
Winemaker David Bicknell **Est.** 1978 **Dozens** 23 000 **Vyds** 9.8ha
Winemaker and CEO David Bicknell has proved his worth time and again as an extremely
talented winemaker. At the top of the brand tier is 864, all Yarra Valley vineyard selections, and
only released in the best years (Chardonnay, Shiraz, Cabernet Sauvignon, Riesling); next is the
Oakridge core label (the Chardonnay, Pinot Noir and Sauvignon Blanc come from the cooler
Upper Yarra Valley; the Shiraz, Cabernet Sauvignon and Viognier from the Lower Yarra); and
the Over the Shoulder range, drawn from all of the sources available to Oakridge (Sauvignon
Blanc, Pinot Grigio, Pinot Noir, Shiraz Viognier, Cabernet Sauvignon). Exports to the UK,
Canada, Papua New Guinea, Indonesia, Singapore, Hong Kong, Japan and China.

ɪɪɪɪɪ 864 Single Block Release Charlie's Block J&J D'Aloisio Vineyard
Yarra Valley Chardonnay 2011 Bright straw-green; the spectacular power
and intensity of the fruit has completely absorbed the French oak derived from
50% of the wine barrel-fermented in new oak; the white peach and citrus fruit
persist in the mouth long after the wine has been swallowed. Screwcap. 13.2% alc.
Rating 96 To 2021 $72
864 Single Block Release Winery Block Yarra Valley Syrah 2010 Bright,
clear crimson-purple; supple and luscious, with vibrant red and black cherry
aromas, which flow through to the mouth-filling palate; the whole berry ferment
results in great purity of the fruit flavour, yet it has all of the texture one could
wish for. Screwcap. 13.3% alc. Rating 96 To 2020 $72
Limited Release Yarra Valley Riesling 2011 This glorious wine was made
from grapes harvested on 9 May at 18° baume; the juice, without any SO$_2$ or acid
addition, was 75% fermented in stainless steel and 25% in 6-year-old French oak
puncheons, before being stopped with 180 g/l of residual sugar. While there is a
multiplicity of nuances, the mainstream of the palate is exhilaratingly pure lime
juice varietal riesling flavours and balanced acidity. Screwcap. 8% alc. Rating 96
To 2016 $40
864 Single Block Release Drive Block Funder & Diamond Vineyard
Yarra Valley Chardonnay 2011 Like all 864 Chardonnays, whole bunch-
pressed direct to barrel for natural (wild yeast) fermentation, 14% of the oak new.
The riper fruit aromas come through strongly on the bouquet and nectarine,
white peach and melon flavours, grapefruit conspicuous by their absence.
Screwcap. 13.4% alc. Rating 95 To 2021 $72
Local Vineyard Series Guerin Vineyard Chardonnay 2011 Sourced from
the Ray Guerin Vineyard (Ray is long-term viticulturist for the largest vineyard
in the Upper Yarra, now owned by Accolade). Strongly structured and layered,
with white peach and nectarine joined by cashew. Screwcap. 13.3% alc. Rating 95
To 2021 $38
Local Vineyard Series Denton Vineyard Yarra Valley Chardonnay 2011
Sourced from the east-facing Denton Vineyard, sited on a degraded granite soil
plug near Yarra Glen. Despite the low alcohol, is the most delicate of the Local
Vineyard Series Chardonnays, with white peach fruit up front, steely acidity
coming on the finish. Screwcap. 12.6% alc. Rating 95 To 2021 $38
Local Vineyard Series Barkala Ridge Vineyard Yarra Valley Chardonnay
2011 Sourced from the east-facing Barkala Ridge Vineyard, sited on the red
volcanic soils of Wandin East. Identical winemaking for the Local Vineyard Series
wines, with whole bunches pressed directly to 500 l French oak puncheons for
natural fermentation and 10 months' maturation on lees; precisely framed and
pitched, with intense grapefruit leading the way. Screwcap. 13.2% alc. Rating 95
To 2021 $38
Local Vineyard Series Lusatia Park Vineyard Yarra Valley Chardonnay
2011 Sourced from the north-facing Lusatia Park Vineyard, sited on the red
volcanic soils of Woori Yallock. Has grapefruit and melon up front, its extreme
length revealing itself progressively. Screwcap. 13.1% alc. Rating 95 To 2021 $38
Local Vineyard Series Whitsend & Oakridge Vineyards Yarra Valley
Shiraz 2010 Deeper colour than the 864 Winery Block; this is a very different
proposition, with significantly more extract and darker fruit flavours; there is no
reason why this wine should not last for 15 years or more. Screwcap. 13.7% alc.
Rating 95 To 2025 $38
✪ Over the Shoulder Chardonnay 2011 Rating 94 To 2019 $22

ɪɪɪɪɪ Over the Shoulder Pinot Grigio 2011 Pale quartz; a juicy and vibrant
✪ wine enlivened by early picking that has highlighted the citrus and green apple
components, and lengthened the finish. All up, purity, not complexity, is the deal.
Screwcap. 11.1% alc. Rating 93 To Now $20
Limited Release Yarra Valley Fume 2011 Rating 93 To 2014 $32

✪   **Over the Shoulder Yarra Valley Cabernet Merlot 2008** Has retained very good hue; a 76/24% blend from three vineyards in the Coldstream area; it is medium- to full-bodied, with substantial but ripe tannins to support the wealth of red and blackcurrant fruit. Excellent cellaring potential. Screwcap. 13.5% alc. **Rating** 93 **To** 2020 $20

✪   **Over the Shoulder Pinot Noir 2011** Brilliant, light crimson; right in the heartland of Yarra Valley Pinot, with streams of small red fruits and savoury, foresty nuances woven together, the overall length and balance excellent. Screwcap. 12.5% alc. **Rating** 92 **To** 2016 $22

Over the Shoulder Yarra Valley Shiraz 2010 Rating 92 **To** 2013 $22
Local Vineyard Series Oakridge Vineyard Yarra Valley Cabernet Sauvignon 2010 Rating 92 **To** 2018 $38

Oakway Estate   ★★★☆

575 Farley Road, Donnybrook, WA 6239 **Region** Geographe
T (08) 9731 7141 **www**.oakwayestate.com.au **Open** W'ends & public hols 11–5
Winemaker Stuart Pierce **Est.** 1998 **Dozens** 1500 **Vyds** 2ha
Ria and Wayne Hammond run a vineyard, beef cattle and sustainable blue gum plantation in undulating country on the Capel River in the southwest of WA. The grapes are grown on light gravel and loam soils that provide good drainage, situated high above the river, giving even sun exposure to the fruit and minimising the effects of frost. The vineyard is planted to shiraz, merlot, cabernet sauvignon, muscat, sauvignon blanc and chardonnay, and the wines have won a number of medals at wine shows.

🍷🍷🍷🍷♀   **Reserve Cabernet Sauvignon 2010** Deep garnet; while a fair share of spicy oak dominates the bouquet, red fruits, sage and bramble are also evident; medium-bodied and fleshy, with toasty oak and chewy tannins persisting on the finish. Screwcap. 14.8% alc. **Rating** 90 **To** 2016 $25 BE

🍷🍷🍷🍷   **Reserve Merlot 2010 Rating** 87 **To** 2016 $25 BE

Observatory Hill Vineyard   ★★★☆

107 Centauri Drive, Mt Rumney, Tas 7170 **Region** Southern Tasmania
T (03) 6248 5380 **www**.observatoryhill.com.au **Open** By appt
Winemaker Frogmore Creek (Alain Rousseau, Nick Glaetzer) **Est.** 1991 **Dozens** 1000
Vyds 3.1ha
Glenn and Chris Richardson's Observatory Hill Vineyard began in 1991, when Glenn and his late father-in-law Jim Ramsey planted the first of the 8500 vines that now make up the estate. Together with the adjoining property, owned by Chris' brother Wayne and his wife Stephanie, the vineyard now covers just over 3 ha, new plantings having been made each year. The name 'Observatory Hill' comes from the state's oldest observatory, which is perched on the hill above the vineyard.

🍷🍷🍷🍷♀   **Cabernet Sauvignon 2009** Good colour; unequivocally cool grown, but well made, and has ripe cassis fruit filling its mid palate, the tannins fine. Silver Tas Wine Show '12. Screwcap. 14% alc. **Rating** 90 **To** 2017 $29

🍷🍷🍷🍷   **Riesling 2010 Rating** 89 **To** 2018 $26

Ocean Eight Vineyard & Winery   ★★★★★

271 Tucks Road, Shoreham, Vic 3916 **Region** Mornington Peninsula
T (03) 5989 6471 **www**.oceaneight.com **Open** 1st w'end each month
Winemaker Michael Aylward **Est.** 2004 **Dozens** 5000 **Vyds** 16ha
Chris, Gail and Michael Aylward were involved in the establishment of the Kooyong vineyard and winery, and after selling Kooyong in 2003, retained their 6ha pinot gris vineyard at Shoreham. After careful investigation, they purchased another property, where they have now planted 7ha of pinot noir and 3ha of chardonnay. A small winery has been set up, and the focus will always be on estate-grown grapes. Exports to the UK and Canada.

ŸŸŸŸŸ Verve Mornington Peninsula Chardonnay 2010 Striving to deliver a
Chablis-inspired experience, this tightly wound wine exhibits lemon pith, minerals
and a splash of talc on the bouquet; the palate is taut, linear and as fresh as a daisy,
with mouth-watering acidity in balance with the tight core of fruit; long and
harmonious. Screwcap. 12.2% alc. **Rating** 94 **To** 2018 $38 BE
Mornington Peninsula Pinot Noir 2010 2011 Young Gun of Wine Award
winner Mike Aylward is inspired by Burgundy, and unashamedly has no formal
training in winemaking; he has been able to make a tightly wound, focused
and pure red-fruited and spicy Pinot, with plenty of stuffing and backbone,
and scintillating acidity, successfully combining power with elegance. Screwcap.
13.2% alc. **Rating** 94 **To** 2018 $45 BE

ŸŸŸŸŸ Mornington Peninsula Pinot Gris 2011 **Rating** 93 **To** 2016 $33 BE

Ochota Barrels ★★★★☆

Merchants Road, Basket Range, SA 5138 **Region** Various SA
T 0400 798 818 **www**.ochotabarrels.com **Open** Not
Winemaker Taras Ochota **Est.** 2008 **Dozens** 600 **Vyds** 0.5ha
This is the venture of Taras and Amber Ochota, but don't let the tiny production fool you.
Taras has had an incredibly varied career as a winemaker after completing his oenology
degree at Adelaide University. He has not only made wine for top-end Australian producers,
but has had a Flying Winemaker role in many parts of the world, most recently as consultant
winemaker for one of Sweden's largest wine-importing companies, working on Italian wines
from Puglia and Sicily made specifically for Oenoforos. Amber has accompanied him to many
places, working in a multiplicity of technical and marketing roles. His day job now is working
for Peter Leske and Mark Kozned's new venture, Revenir, completing another circle, for part
of his early career was working with Peter at Nepenthe. The website explains how the Ochota
Barrels name came about, and underlines its artisan, low technical input approach. Exports to
the US, Sweden and Denmark.

ŸŸŸŸŸ The Shellac Vineyard Syrah 2010 Starts with alluring crimson-purple and
goes on from there; on the one hand there is an array of velvet and satin red
and black fruits, on the other hand, medium-bodied elegance, the two streams
joining on the long, supple palate. Bottle no. 612 of 1444 made. Screwcap. 13% alc.
Rating 96 **To** 2030 $50

ŸŸŸŸŸ The Slint Vineyard Chardonnay 2011 **Rating** 93 **To** 2018 $45
The Fugazi Vineyard Grenache 2010 **Rating** 92 **To** 2017 $35
Strange Little Girl Arneis 2011 **Rating** 90 **To** 2014 $35

ŸŸŸŸ Surfer Rosa Sangiovese 2011 **Rating** 87 **To** 2014 $25

Old Kent River ★★★☆

1114 Turpin Road, Rocky Gully, WA 6397 **Region** Frankland River
T (08) 9855 1589 **www**.oldkentriverwines.com.au **Open** At Kent River, Denmark
Winemaker Alkoomi (Andrew Cherry) **Est.** 1985 **Dozens** 1500 **Vyds** 17ha
Mark and Debbie Noack have earned much respect from their neighbours and from the other
producers to whom they sell more than half the production from the vineyard on their sheep
property. The quality of their wines has gone from strength to strength, Mark having worked
particularly hard with his Pinot Noir. The Noacks have added a 2ha vineyard at Denmark to
their much older 15ha vineyard at Rocky Gully; this has not prevented them from planting
60 000 native trees, numerous shrubs and acres of perennial grasses.

ŸŸŸŸŸ Special Release Burls Pinot Noir 2002 Exceptional colour for its age, holding
its crimson-red hue right to the edge; early picking, low alcohol and low pH
are both cause and consequence of a wine with near-perpetual youth; there is
an inescapable fine print admission of some mint and green leaf, but this is of
small consequence in the overall scheme of things. Left field, but succeeds. Cork.
11.5% alc. **Rating** 93 **To** 2017 $70

ΨΨΨΨ   **Frankland River Chardonnay 2010** Gleaming yellow-green; French oak barrel
✪   fermentation has been well handled, recognising the fact that the fruit is not
particularly intense; the flavours run through the right spectrum, but need more
conviction. Screwcap. 14% alc. **Rating** 89 **To** 2015 $20

✪   **Frankland River Shiraz 2009** Light, bright red; a light- to medium-bodied
shiraz, with spicy notes to its red berry fruits, and persistent, fine tannins. Screwcap.
13% alc. **Rating** 89 **To** 2015 $18

Old Plains   ★★★★

71 High Street, Grange, SA 5023 (postal) **Region** Adelaide Plains
T 0407 605 601 **www**.oldplains.com **Open** Not
Winemaker Domenic Torzi, Tim Freeland **Est.** 2003 **Dozens** 3000 **Vyds** 14ha
Old Plains is a partnership between Tim Freeland and Domenic Torzi, who have acquired
small parcels of old vine shiraz (3ha), grenache (1ha) and cabernet sauvignon (4ha) in the
Adelaide Plains region. A portion of the wines, sold under the Old Plains, Longhop and Raw
Power labels, is exported to the US, Denmark, Hong Kong. Singapore and China.

ΨΨΨΨΨ   **Longhop Mount Lofty Ranges Shiraz 2010 Rating** 93
○   **To** 2030 $16

Power of One Old Vine Shiraz 2009 Strong colour; a robust, full-flavoured,
full-bodied wine befitting the 50-year-old vines of the hot Adelaide Plains; open-
fermented and basket-pressed, it is neither alcoholic nor extractive. Diam. 14% alc.
Rating 91 **To** 2020 $30

○   **Longhop Mount Lofty Ranges Cabernet Sauvignon 2010 Rating** 91
To 2020 $16

Olivers Taranga Vineyards   ★★★★☆

246 Seaview Road, McLaren Vale, SA 5171 **Region** McLaren Vale
T (08) 8323 8498 **www**.oliverstaranga.com **Open** 7 days 10–4
Winemaker Corrina Wright **Est.** 1841 **Dozens** 7000 **Vyds** 85.42ha
William and Elizabeth Oliver arrived from Scotland in 1839 to settle at McLaren Vale. Six
generations later, members of the family are still living on the Whitehill and Taranga farms.
The Taranga property has 15 grape varieties planted (the lion's share shiraz and cabernet
sauvignon, with lesser quantities of chardonnay, chenin blanc, durif, fiano, grenache, mataro,
merlot, petit verdot, sagrantino, semillon, tempranillo, viognier and white frontignac); grapes
from the property have been sold, but since 1994 a portion has been made under the Olivers
Taranga label. Since 2000 the wine has been made by Corrina Wright (the Oliver family's
first winemaker and a sixth-generation family member), and in 2011 the family celebrated
170 years of grapegrowing. Exports to the US, Canada, Hong Kong and China.

ΨΨΨΨΨ   **DJ Reserve McLaren Vale Cabernet Sauvignon 2009** Dedicated to DJ
(Don) Oliver, the fifth-generation custodian of Olivers. Dense purple-crimson, it
is at once full-bodied and complex, yet avoids any suggestion of over-extraction
or overripe grapes. Blackcurrant fruit, regional dark chocolate notes, fine,
dusty tannins and integrated oak come together to provide an impressive wine.
Screwcap. 14.5% alc. **Rating** 94 **To** 2030 $50

ΨΨΨΨΨ   **Small Batch McLaren Vale Fiano 2011 Rating** 90 **To** Now $24

Olsen   ★★★☆

529 Osmington Road, Osmington, WA 6285 **Region** Margaret River
T (08) 9757 4536 **www**.olsen.com.au **Open** By appt
Winemaker Jarrad Olsen **Est.** 1986 **Dozens** 2000 **Vyds** 9.5ha
Steve and Ann Marie Olsen have planted cabernet sauvignon, chardonnay, semillon, verdelho
and shiraz, which they tend with the help of their four children. It was the desire to raise their
children in a healthy country environment that prompted the move to establish the vineyard,
coupled with a long-standing dream to make their own wine. Not to be confused with Olsen
Wines in Melbourne.

ŸŸŸŸŸ **Lucille Margaret River Chardonnay 2010** Vivid yellow-green; a very interesting wine, its suite of aromas and flavours riper and richer than one might expect from a wine with this low alcohol. Those flavours run through a conventional spectrum of white peach, nectarine and a dash of grapefruit, the oak balanced and integrated, and the finish fresh. Screwcap. 12.6% alc. **Rating** 91 **To** 2017 $30

Olsen Wines Victoria   ★★★★
21 Carinish Road, Oakleigh South, Vic 3167 **Region** Port Phillip Zone
T (03) 9544 4033 **F** (03) 9588 0189 **www.**vin888.com **Open** Mon–Fri 9.30–5
Winemaker Glenn Olsen **Est.** 1991 **Dozens** 55 000
Glenn Olsen, a science and engineering graduate of the University of Melbourne, has been involved in the wine industry since 1975, initially importing wines and spirits from Europe, then moving into retailing. In 1991, he and Angie Joso-Olsen started Olsen Wines, claiming to be Melbourne's first inner-suburban winery. Several others may dispute this claim, but that is perhaps neither here nor there. Most of the wines come either from grapes grown on the Murray River in Northeast Victoria (for the full-bodied Big Fella range), or from the Yarra Valley. Exports to the US, Canada, the Philippines, South Korea, Cambodia, Vietnam, Singapore, Hong Kong and China.

ŸŸŸŸŸ **Barrel Fermented Yarra Valley Sauvignon Blanc 2011** Full straw-green; a wine that is all about power, structure and texture, ripe kiwi and citrus fruit simply to fill in the spaces. An interesting wine given the vintage. Screwcap. 13.3% alc. **Rating** 90 **To** 2013 $26

✪ **Premium Sparkling Shiraz NV** There is clearly substantial age in the base wine; made from a number of vintages of shiraz, and is neither too oaky nor too sweet. Cork. 14.9% alc. **Rating** 90 **To** 2014 $20

ŸŸŸŸ **Yarra Valley Chardonnay 2007** **Rating** 89 **To** 2013 $24
Autumn Harvest Muscat Blanc 2008 **Rating** 88 **To** 2014 $17

Olssens of Watervale   ★★★★
Sollys Hill Road, Watervale, SA 5452 **Region** Clare Valley
T (08) 8843 0065 **F** (08) 8843 0065 **Open** At The Little Red Grape, Sevenhill
Winemaker Contract **Est.** 1994 **Dozens** 3000 **Vyds** 31.6ha
Kevin and Helen Olssen first visited the Clare Valley in 1986. Within two weeks they and their family decided to sell their Adelaide home and purchased a property in a small, isolated valley 3km north of the township of Watervale. As a result of the acquisition of the Bass Hill Vineyard, estate plantings have risen to almost 32 ha, including unusual varieties such as carmenere and primitivo di Gioia. The business is a joint venture involving Kevin and children David and Jane Olssen, Helen having passed away in 2010. Exports to Hong Kong and China.

ŸŸŸŸŸ **Clare Valley Riesling 2011** Flowery, blossom, tropical nuances to the bouquet build significantly on the fleshy palate, with ripe citrus and an echo of tropical notes ex the bouquet. Now or medium-term drinking. Screwcap. 12.5% alc. **Rating** 90 **To** 2015 $20

Onannon
PO Box 190, Flinders, Vic 3929 **Region** Port Phillip Zone
T 0448 900 229 **www.**onannon.com **Open** Not
Winemaker Sam Middleton, Kaspar Hermann, Will Byron **Est.** 2008 **Dozens** 200
Onannon is the venture of Sam Middleton, Kaspar Hermann and Will Byron, who donated the last two or three letters of their surnames to come up with Onannon. They have many things in common, not the least working vintages at Coldstream Hills, Will for six years, Sam for two (before ultimately returning to the family's winery, Mount Mary) and Kaspar for one. Since then they have bounced between vintages in Burgundy and Australia, Will accumulating the most frequent flyer points. Strictly speaking, I should disqualify myself from making any

comment about them or their wine, but you would have to go a long way to find three more open-hearted and utterly committed winemakers; the world is their oyster, their ambitions unlimited. No wines were received for this edition; the rating is that of last year.

Optimiste ★★★★

PO Box 4214, Castlecrag, NSW 2068 **Region** Mudgee
T (02) 9967 3294 **www**.optimiste.com.au **Open** Not
Winemaker Michael Slater, Jacob Stein **Est.** 1998 **Dozens** 2000 **Vyds** 11ha
Steven and Sharlene Dadd had been growing grapes for over a decade before realising a long-held dream to launch their own wines under the Optimiste label. The name is inspired by their son's struggle with deafness and a quote by Helen Keller: 'Optimism is the faith that leads to achievement. Nothing can be done without hope and confidence.' The first vines planted were cabernet sauvignon, petit verdot and merlot, with more recent plantings of viognier, semillon, tempranillo and pinot gris (chardonnay is purchased). A cellar door is planned. Exports to Singapore.

 Limited Release Mudgee Semillon 2011 You have to get to the palate, and indeed to the finish and aftertaste, to see what this wine has to offer; in the fullness of time, the range of flavours on the fore- and mid palate will increase exponentially. Screwcap. 11% alc. **Rating** 90 **To** 2021 $20

Mudgee Shiraz 2010 Light, clear red-purple; the bouquet is fragrant, the light- to medium-bodied palate quite savoury and showing little evidence of the touch of viognier included; on the other hand, the maturation in French and American oak has been well-judged. Screwcap. 13.5% alc. **Rating** 90 **To** 2020 $20

Mudgee Pinot Gris 2011 Rating 89 **To** 2013 $20
Paris in Spring Limited Release Mudgee Rose 2011 Rating 89 **To** Now $20

Orange Highland Wines ★★★

131 Nashdale Lane, Nashdale, NSW 2800 **Region** Orange
T (02) 6365 3002 **www**.orangehighland.com.au **Open** W'ends 10–5, Mon, Thu–Fri 10–1, 2–5
Winemaker Richard Parker, Marko Bernt (Contract) **Est.** 2004 **Dozens** 600 **Vyds** 4.5ha
The full name of this enterprise is Orange Highland Wines & Gardens, the gardens the lifelong passion of Helen Harrison, supported by former banker husband Ross. Having started in Sydney, they moved to the Adelaide Hills in 1979, Helen then teaching music in high school, and Ross continuing his career as a banker. Over the next 20 years Helen created a large garden, but a chance trip through the Central Ranges brought them to Orange, and their retirement vision took shape. They moved in 2004, buying a property that had a single native tree and a peculiar covenant that they could only build a house if they practised irrigated agriculture. So, in addition to the garden, they planted sauvignon blanc, pinot gris and pinot noir, recently adding sangiovese (the first vintage in '10). The 1.8ha of gardens established by Helen are designed in themed 'rooms', and were one of the 12 finalists in the ABC Gardener of the Year competition in '08. They are augmented by displays from time to time, including sculpture exhibitions.

 Pinot Gris 2011 Fruit salad bouquet, with bath talc and fresh acidity; lively, juicy and fresh. Screwcap. 13.2% alc. **Rating** 87 **To** 2013 $19 BE

Orange Mountain Wines ★★★★☆

Cnr Forbes Road/Radnedge Lane, Orange, NSW 2800 **Region** Orange
T (02) 6365 2626 **www**.orangemountain.com.au **Open** Wed–Fri 9–3, w'ends 9–5
Winemaker Terry Dolle **Est.** 1997 **Dozens** 2500
Terry Dolle has a total of 5.5ha of vineyards, part at Manildra (established 1997) and the remainder at Orange (in 2001). The Manildra climate is distinctly warmer than that of

Orange, and the plantings reflect the climatic difference, with pinot noir and sauvignon blanc at Orange, shiraz, cabernet sauvignon, merlot and viognier at Manildra. Exports to China.

🍷🍷🍷🍷🍷 **Riesling 2011** Pale straw-green; the bouquet is flowery and aromatic, but does not prepare you for the intensity and length of the lime juice-infused palate nor the cleansing minerally acidity of the finish. Screwcap. 11% alc. **Rating** 94 **To** 2026 $22

🍷🍷🍷🍷🍷 **Mountain Ice Viognier 2011 Rating** 93 **To** 2017 $25

🍷🍷🍷🍷 **Sauvignon Blanc 2011 Rating** 89 **To** 2014 $22
Chardonnay 2010 Rating 89 **To** 2014 $25

Oranje Tractor ★★★★★
198 Link Road, Albany, WA 6330 **Region** Albany
T (08) 9842 5175 **www.**oranjetractor.com **Open** Fri–Sun 11–5 (Tues–Sun during school hols)
Winemaker Rob Diletti, Mike Garland (Contract) **Est.** 1998 **Dozens** 1000 **Vyds** 2.9ha
The name celebrates the 1964 vintage, orange-coloured Fiat tractor, acquired when Murray Gomm and Pamela Lincoln began the establishment of the vineyard. Murray was born next door, but moved to Perth to work in physical education and health promotion. Here he met nutritionist Pamela, who completed the wine science degree at CSU in 2000, before being awarded a Churchill Fellowship to study organic grape and wine production in the US and Europe. When the partners established their vineyard, they went down the organic path.

🍷🍷🍷🍷🍷 **Albany Riesling 2011** Pale straw-green; a blossom-filled bouquet leads into a juicy palate, with a fruit intensity very different from any SA Riesling; lime juice is dominant, but there are also seductive notes of passionfruit on the long finish. Screwcap. 12% alc. **Rating** 95 **To** 2021 $24
Sauvignon Blanc 2011 Light straw-green; a power-packed Sauvignon Blanc that even the Adelaide Hills would strive to equal; while there are some minerally notes as the foundation for the wine, its extroverted passionfruit/tropical aromas and flavours steal centre stage. But don't think it's heavy or phenolic; it is delightfully fresh as well as flavoursome. Screwcap. 13% alc. **Rating** 94 **To** 2014 $25
Top Paddock Shiraz 2010 A hand-inserted, heavily stained cork may or may not mean a tank sample; deep crimson-red, it is an unusually intense and deeply flavoured wine, with luscious blackberry fruit interspersed with spice, licorice and red berry notes; given the benefit of the bottling doubt. 14% alc. **Rating** 94 **To** 2025 $28

Orlando ★★★★
Barossa Valley Way, Rowland Flat, SA 5352 **Region** Barossa Valley
T (08) 8521 3111 **www.**orlandowines.com **Open** Not
Winemaker Bernard Hickin **Est.** 1847 **Dozens** NFP **Vyds** 1600ha
Orlando is the parent who has been divorced by its child, Jacob's Creek (see separate entry). While Orlando is 165 years old, Jacob's Creek is little more than 39 years old. For what are doubtless sound marketing reasons, Orlando aided and abetted the divorce, but the average consumer is unlikely to understand the logic, and – if truth be known – will care about it even less. The vineyard holding is for all brands (notably Jacob's Creek) and for all regions across SA, Vic and NSW; it will likely be less in coming years.

🍷🍷🍷🍷🍷 **Gramp's Barossa Valley Shiraz 2009** Bright red-purple; fills the mouth with
✪ ripe plum and black cherry fruit, soft but persistent tannins, and more than a touch of oak. Drink now or much later. Screwcap. 14.5% alc. **Rating** 90 **To** 2019 $20
✪ **Gramp's Cabernet Merlot 2008** Good colour retention; not a natural blend for the Barossa, even though it can include Eden Valley. Clever winemaking and lavish oak have resulted in a flavoursome wine. Screwcap. 14.5% alc. **Rating** 90 **To** 2016 $20

Outlook Hill Vineyard

97 School Lane, Tarrawarra, Vic 3777 **Region** Yarra Valley
T (03) 5962 2890 **www.**outlookhill.com.au **Open** By appt
Winemaker Peter Snow, Al Fencaros **Est.** 2000 **Dozens** 1200 **Vyds** 5.4ha
After several years overseas, former Melbourne professionals Peter and Lydia Snow returned in 1997 planning to open a wine tourism business in the Hunter Valley. However, they had second thoughts, and in 2000 moved to the Yarra Valley, where they have now established five B&B cottages, a vineyard, and a cellar door outlet, backed by a constant temperature wine storage cool room. Exports to China.

ΨΨΨΨΨ **Yarra Valley Cabernet Merlot 2010** Mid garnet; an attractively perfumed bouquet of cranberry, cassis, sage and lavender; medium-bodied and elegant with fresh acidity and fine-grained tannins in balance with the fruit on display. Screwcap. 13.5% alc. **Rating** 90 **To** 2015 $29 BE

Oxford Landing Estate ★★★

Pipeline Road, Nuriootpa, SA 5355 **Region** Riverland
T (08) 8561 3200 **www.**oxfordlanding.com.au **Open** By appt
Winemaker Matthew Pick **Est.** 1958 **Dozens** NFP **Vyds** 250ha
Oxford Landing Estate is, so the website tells us, 'A real place, a real vineyard. A place distinguished by clear blue skies, rich red soil and an abundance of golden sunshine.' In the 50+ years since the vineyard was planted, the brand has grown to reach all corners of the world. Success has been due to over-delivery against expectations at its price points, and it has largely escaped the scorn of the UK wine press. In 2008 a five-year experiment began to determine whether a block of vines could survive and produce an annual crop with only 10% of the normal irrigation. This apart, there is now 1ha of native vegetation for every ha of vineyard. Outstanding new packaging with custom-made, branded bottles in '11. Exports to the UK, the US and NZ.

ΨΨΨΨ ✪ **Shiraz 2010** Light, bright purple-crimson; a light- to medium-bodied Shiraz made for immediate consumption, with juicy raspberry/red berry fruits, and a sprinkle of tannins just for luck. Ever reliable, especially in a vintage as good as '10. Screwcap. 13.5% alc. **Rating** 89 **To** 2014 $10

✪ **Shiraz 2011** Excellent colour; pulled from the jaws of the vintage without any scars; a light- to medium-bodied wine with abundant blackberry and black cherry fruit, the finish long and convincing. Screwcap. 13% alc. **Rating** 88 **To** 2014 $10

○ **Cabernet Sauvignon Shiraz 2010** **Rating** 88 **To** 2014 $9
○ **Sauvignon Blanc 2011** **Rating** 87 **To** Now $9
○ **Chardonnay 2011** **Rating** 87 **To** Now $9
○ **Pinot Grigio 2011** **Rating** 87 **To** Now $9

Pages Creek ★★★★

624 Middle Teatree Road, Teatree, Tas 7017 **Region** Southern Tasmania
T (03) 6260 2311 **www.**pagescreekwine.com.au **Open** By appt
Winemaker Winemaking Tasmania (Julian Alcorso) **Est.** 1999 **Dozens** 1500 **Vyds** 4.5ha
In 1999 Peter and Sue Lowrie planted a vineyard on their 20ha Pages Creek property, named after the creek that runs through it. They have cabernet sauvignon, pinot noir, chardonnay and merlot. The tiny first vintage (2002) was consumed at their wedding; the first full vintage was '03, and the Pages Creek label was launched in '04. Exports to the US.

ΨΨΨΨΨ **Chardonnay Pinot Noir NV** Light straw-green; has fine, persistent mousse; the palate is crisp, fine, long; youthful and well balanced, with bright citrus flavours and a hint of brioche. Silver Tas Wine Show '12. Diam. 12% alc. **Rating** 92 **To** 2014 $28
Merlot 2010 Good colour; some black olive and earth on the bouquet and palate underlying the classic cool-grown blackcurrant fruit character. Screwcap. 13% alc. **Rating** 90 **To** 2015 $28

ΨΨΨΨ **Pinot Noir 2010** **Rating** 89 **To** 2015 $28

Palmara

1314 Richmond Road, Richmond, Tas 7025 **Region** Southern Tasmania
T (03) 6260 2462 **www**.palmara.com.au **Open** Sept–May 7 days 12–6
Winemaker Allan Bird **Est.** 1985 **Dozens** 250 **Vyds** 0.9ha
Allan Bird makes the Palmara wines in tiny quantities (the vineyard is planted to pinot noir, chardonnay, cabernet sauvignon, ehrenfelser, siegerrebe and semillon). The Pinot Noir has performed consistently well since 1990. The Exotica Siegerrebe blend is unchallenged as Australia's most exotic and unusual wine, with pungent jujube/lanolin aromas and flavours.

Coal River Valley Pinot Noir 2006 Bright, light red tinged with tawny; the bouquet is aromatic, with spicy nuances, the palate fresh and full of life; only light-bodied, but has length and style sustained by balanced Tasmanian acidity. 12.5% alc. **Rating** 90 **To** 2016 $20

 # Palmarium

395B Belmore Road, Balwyn, Vic 3103 (postal) **Region** Various
T 0422 546 825 **www**.palmarium.com.au **Open** Not
Winemaker John Ellis, Walter Clappis, Kym Teusner **Est.** 2010 **Dozens** 1300
This virtual winery was established by Peter Mornement. His philosophy (and business plan) was simple: to develop a portfolio of high-quality, high-value shiraz from six premium Shiraz-producing regions. Each wine would be made by a winemaker in that region with an established reputation, and a simple instruction from Peter: buy the best fruit you can, and use the new oak of your choice. The quantity of each wine made will be 650 dozen bottles. He has joined forces with John Ellis (of Hanging Rock) for Heathcote; Walter Clappis and Kym Teusner (of their eponymous wineries) for McLaren Vale and Barossa Valley respectively. The wines are sold in a six-bottle case, the initial releases from Heathcote and McLaren Vale, only to subscribers. If all are as good as the first wine released, there is much to look forward to.

Exemplar McLaren Vale Shiraz 2010 Deep, dense purple-crimson; the blackberry, black cherry, licorice and bitter chocolate quadrella is as deep and intense as you might imagine; the palate is either velvety or thick, depending on one's viewpoint. The product of a great vintage that will live for decades. Screwcap. 14% alc. **Rating** 95 **To** 2035 $65

Palmer Wines

1271 Caves Road, Dunsborough, WA 6281 **Region** Margaret River
T (08) 9756 7024 **www**.palmerwines.com.au **Open** 7 days 10–5
Winemaker Mark Warren **Est.** 1977 **Dozens** 6000 **Vyds** 51.39ha
Stephen and Helen Palmer began the planting of their vineyard in 1977; with encouragement and direction from Dr Michael Peterkin of Pierro, the plantings have been increased over the years, and are now headed by cabernet sauvignon, sauvignon blanc, shiraz, merlot, chardonnay and semillon, with smaller amounts of malbec and cabernet franc. Recent vintages have had major success in WA wine shows, and won the WIAWA wine industry award for Most Outstanding Cellar Door/Wine Tourism Facility '11. Exports to Indonesia (Bali) and Hong Kong.

Margaret River Shiraz 2009 Full red-purple; the bouquet signals the display of black and red cherry, spice and quality oak that is to follow; the wine has considerable length, the finish with perfectly balanced, gently savoury tannins. Gold medal National Wine Show '11. Screwcap. 14.5% alc. **Rating** 94 **To** 2029 $37
Margaret River Merlot 2009 Light to medium red-purple; the variety performs better in Margaret River than the majority of regions in which it is grown; this wine brings plum, cassis and savoury black olive onto the table, finishing with firm but fine tannins. Screwcap. 14.5% alc. **Rating** 94 **To** 2019 $35

ŶŶŶŶ♀ Margaret River Cabernet Sauvignon 2009 Rating 92 To 2024 $37
Margaret River Semillon Sauvignon Blanc 2011 Rating 91 To 2015 $24

ŶŶŶŶ Margaret River Malbec 2009 Rating 89 To 2021 $28

Pankhurst

'Old Woodgrove', Woodgrove Road, Hall, NSW 2618 **Region** Canberra District
T (02) 6230 2592 **www**.pankhurstwines.com.au **Open** W'ends, public hols, or by appt
Winemaker Lark Hill, Brindabella Hills **Est.** 1986 **Dozens** 2000 **Vyds** 5ha
Agricultural scientist and consultant Allan Pankhurst and wife Christine (with a degree in
pharmaceutical science) have established a split-canopy vineyard (pinot noir, chardonnay,
cabernet sauvignon, merlot, sangiovese, tempranillo, semillon and sauvignon blanc). Pankhurst
has had success with Pinot Noir, Chardonnay and, most recently, with its Cabernet Sauvignon
and Sangiovese. Exports to China.

ŶŶŶŶ♀ Dorothy May Canberra District Cabernet Sauvignon 2010 Purple-
crimson; there is a fertile union between Canberra's cool climate and cabernet
sauvignon; it has an attractive black olive/savoury edge to the blackcurrant fruit,
plum and spice somewhere in the background. The tannins are fine and firm, as
befits the variety. Screwcap. 14% alc. **Rating** 93 **To** 2025 $30
Canberra District Cabernet Merlot 2010 Relatively light colour, but the hue
is correct; the wine is a 70/30% blend, matured in American oak for 12 months,
and topped its class at the National Wine Show '11 with a silver medal. The judges
must have been impressed with the overall weight and structure of the wine,
which is good, the choice of oak type not so impressive, although it may well be
the case that the oak is older rather than newer. Screwcap. 14% alc. **Rating** 90
To 2017 $20
Canberra District Sangiovese 2010 Bright colour for the variety; clearly
expressed varietal fruit with a range from red cherry through to sour cherry
flavours backed by fine tannins, which are almost, but not quite, silky. Screwcap.
13% alc. **Rating** 90 **To** 2016 $30

ŶŶŶŶ Canberra District Tempranillo 2010 Rating 89 To 2019 $30

Panorama

1848 Cygnet Coast Road, Cradoc, Tas 7109 **Region** Southern Tasmania
T (03) 6266 3409 **www**.panoramavineyard.com.au **Open** Wed–Mon 11–5
Winemaker Michael Vishacki **Est.** 1974 **Dozens** 500 **Vyds** 13ha
Michael and Sharon Vishacki purchased Panorama from Steve Ferencz in 1997, increasing the
vineyard (pinot noir, chardonnay and sauvignon blanc), and establishing an attractive cellar
door. They take advantage of the strong demand for Tasmanian wines both domestically and
in China. Exports to Denmark and China.

ŶŶŶŶ♀ Estate Chardonnay 2010 Gleaming straw-green; a fragrant, indeed white
flower-perfumed, bouquet, the palate exhilarating in its incisiveness and freshness,
Tasmanian acidity part of the parcel, oak somewhere in the background. Screwcap.
13.5% alc. **Rating** 93 **To** 2020 $35
Estate Pinot Noir 2010 Full purple-crimson; as ever, the wine has a great
volume and depth of red and black fruits, but seems to have achieved this simply
by the quality of the grapes, and not through over-extraction. Good now, but will
be better in three or four years. Screwcap. 13.5% alc. **Rating** 91 **To** 2017 $45

Panton Hill Winery

145 Manuka Road, Panton Hill, Vic 3759 **Region** Yarra Valley
T (03) 9719 7342 **www**.pantonhillwinery.com.au **Open** W'ends & public hols 11–5,
or by appt
Winemaker Dr Teunis AP Kwak **Est.** 1988 **Dozens** 1000 **Vyds** 4ha

Melbourne academic Dr Teunis Kwak and wife Dorothy have a 4ha fully mature vineyard, part planted in 1976, the remainder in '88. The deliberately low-yielding vineyard was established on a fairly steep, picturesque, undulating hillside. Over the years the Kwaks have built four major, and a couple of lesser, stone buildings on the property, all from sandstone sourced onsite or from their neighbour's paddocks. A number of left-field wines are made, including a Vintage Pinot Port, a Chardonnay Liqueur and a Sparkling Cabernet Franc, and the Kwaks cheerfully admit that even their table wines are calculated to please their cellar door customers rather than wine show judges. Exports to China.

ΨΨΨΨ **Yarra Valley Chardonnay 2006** Developed green-gold; a notably rich wine with layers of peach and rock melon; it was taken through mlf, thereby reducing the acidity and hastening the development, so the wine is ready now. If you are looking for lots of flavour from Yarra Chardonnay, this is a good place to start. Diam. 13.9% alc. **Rating** 88 **To** 2013 $25
Yarra Valley Sauvignon Blanc 2008 Light, bright straw-green; bottle age has not been kind to the bouquet, but the tropical fruit flavours of the mid palate are certainly pleasant; backs off on the finish, but on the whole has hung on tenaciously. Don't press it further. Screwcap. 12.5% alc. **Rating** 87 **To** Now $22
Yarra Valley Pinot Noir 2006 Much as though I wish it were otherwise, the wine is starting to come apart at the seams; at least part of this is due to the oak, which has imparted a vanilla/caramel flavour to the wine. If you can walk around that, there is plenty to enjoy. Diam. 13% alc. **Rating** 87 **To** 2014 $28

Paracombe Wines   ★★★★★

294b Paracombe Road, Paracombe, SA 5132 **Region** Adelaide Hills
T (08) 8380 5058 **www.**paracombewines.com **Open** By appt
Winemaker Paul Drogemuller, James Barry **Est.** 1983 **Dozens** 10 000 **Vyds** 17.7ha
Paul and Kathy Drogemuller established Paracombe following the devastating Ash Wednesday bushfires in 1983. It has become a successful business, producing a range of wines that are never less than good, often very good. The wines are made onsite in the 250-tonne winery, with every part of the production process through to distribution handled from there. Exports to the UK, Canada, Sweden, Switzerland, Poland, India, Singapore, Taiwan, Hong Kong, Malaysia and China.

ΨΨΨΨΨ **Adelaide Hills Sauvignon Blanc 2011** Light straw-green; distinctive tropical
❂ passionfruit and kiwi fruit aromas and flavours drive this wine from the first whiff of the bouquet through to the finish of the palate; citrussy acidity freshens the lingering aftertaste. Screwcap. 12.5% alc. **Rating** 94 **To** 2013 $21
❂ **The Reuben 2008** A complex blend of 43% merlot, 31% cabernet sauvignon, 9% cabernet franc, 9% malbec and 3% shiraz, part estate-, part contract-grown. The scented, perfumed bouquet has red fruits, French oak and distinct leatherwood aromas, with the silky palate driven by a complex array of sweet red fruits, the tannins fine and balanced. Screwcap. 14.5% alc. **Rating** 94 **To** 2018 $21

ΨΨΨΨ **Somerville Adelaide Hills Shiraz 2007** **Rating** 93 **To** 2017 $69
❂ **Adelaide Hills Cabernet Sauvignon 2008** Typical deep Paracombe colour; also has the heroic flavour concentration of Paracombe heat; it is dripping with cassis fruit, and less might have been better still. Screwcap. 14.5% alc. **Rating** 91 **To** 2018 $21
Holland Creek Adelaide Hills Riesling 2011 **Rating** 90 **To** 2016 $20
Adelaide Hills Cabernet Franc 2008 **Rating** 90 **To** 2015 $27

ΨΨΨΨ **Adelaide Hills Pinot Gris 2011** **Rating** 89 **To** Now $20
Adelaide Hills Shiraz Viognier 2009 **Rating** 89 **To** 2024 $21
❂ **Adelaide Hills Pinot Noir 2010** **Rating** 88 **To** 2013 $20
Adelaide Hills Shiraz 2008 **Rating** 88 **To** 2014 $21
Adelaide Hills Chardonnay 2011 **Rating** 87 **To** 2013 $21
Adelaide Hills Pinot Noir Chardonnay NV **Rating** 87 **To** 2013 $35

Paradigm Hill ★★★★★

26 Merricks Road, Merricks, Vic 3916 **Region** Mornington Peninsula
T (03) 5989 9000 **www**.paradigmhill.com.au **Open** 1st w'end of month
Winemaker Dr George Mihaly **Est.** 1999 **Dozens** 1500 **Vyds** 4.2ha
Dr George Mihaly (with a background in medical research, biotechnology and pharmaceutical
industries) and wife Ruth (a former chef and caterer) have realised a 30-year dream of
establishing their own vineyard and winery, abandoning their previous careers to do so.
George had all the necessary scientific qualifications, and built on those by making the 2001
Merricks Creek wines, moving to home base at Paradigm Hill in '02, all along receiving
guidance and advice from Nat White of Main Ridge Estate. The vineyard, under Ruth's
control with advice from Shane Strange, is planted to 2.1ha of pinot noir, 0.9ha of shiraz, 0.8ha
of riesling and 0.4ha of pinot gris. Exports to China and Singapore.

♟♟♟♟♟ **Col's Block Mornington Peninsula Shiraz 2010** Deep crimson; a highly
expressive and perfumed bouquet, with black cherry, spiced plums, violets and
intriguing game aromas; the palate is medium-bodied, generous and succulently
fleshy, with a long, complex and thoroughly satisfying finish; this is delicious and
will age with grace. Screwcap. 13.8% alc. **Rating** 96 **To** 2020 $40 BE
Mornington Peninsula Riesling 2011 George and Ruth Mihaly have been
making one of the most interesting and exciting Rieslings coming out of Victoria
for a few years now, and the 2011 is no exception; a savoury wine, tightly wound
and focused, driven by minerality and a crystalline presence of acidity; long,
focused and energetic. Screwcap. 13% alc. **Rating** 95 **To** 2020 $31 BE
Mornington Peninsula Pinot Gris 2011 The Mornington Peninsula is one
of the best performers with Pinot Gris, and this wine proves the point; the
bouquet offers an array of spiced fruits from pear to grapefruit, and the palate is
concentrated, lively and full of bath talc complexity; great persistence and energy
for the variety. Screwcap. 13.6% alc. **Rating** 95 **To** 2016 $45 BE
Les Cinq Mornington Peninsula Pinot Noir 2010 Mid crimson; a young
and unevolved bouquet of red fruits, Asian spices and an underlying fresh herb
complexity; the palate is finely textured, lacy and long, with a truly expansive
personality showing generosity and the backbone for cellaring potential. Screwcap.
13.8% alc. **Rating** 95 **To** 2020 $70 BE

♟♟♟♟♟ **L'Ami Sage Mornington Peninsula Pinot Noir 2010** **Rating** 93 **To** 2020
$55 BE
Transition Mornington Peninsula Rose 2011 **Rating** 90 **To** 2013 $34 BE

Paradise IV ★★★★★

45 Dog Rocks Road, Batesford, Vic 3221 (postal) **Region** Geelong
T (03) 5276 1536 **F** (03) 5276 1665 **Open** By appt
Winemaker Douglas Neal **Est.** 1988 **Dozens** 600 **Vyds** 3.1ha
The former Moorabool Estate has been renamed Paradise IV for the very good reason that it
is the site of the original Paradise IV Vineyard, planted in 1848 by Swiss vigneron Jean-Henri
Dardel. It is owned by Ruth and Graham Bonney in partnership with former schoolteacher
and wine lover Douglas Neal, who has the agency for various French barrel makers in
Australia and South Africa. Douglas is also a self-trained winemaker, and his role in the
partnership is to make and sell the wines, with Graham and Ruth responsible for the vineyard,
which is planted on decomposed granite over limestone, an ideal structure. In practice, the
functions overlap to a degree, as one would expect with a relatively small business. The winery
has an underground barrel room, and the winemaking turns around wild yeast fermentation,
natural mlf, gravity movement of the wine and so forth.

♟♟♟♟♟ **Moorabool Estate Dardel Geelong Shiraz 2010** Deep purple-crimson;
an opulent bouquet, with a precocious display of spiced plum and black cherry;
it is on the palate that winemaking skill comes into play: the exotic flavours are
retained, but the texture and structure are elegant, tannins and oak both restrained.
Screwcap. 13.5% alc. **Rating** 96 **To** 2025 $49

♟♟♟♟♟ **Chaumont 2010** **Rating** 90 **To** 2018 $40

Paramoor Wines ★★★★

439 Three Chain Road, Carlsruhe via Woodend, Vic 3442 **Region** Macedon Ranges
T (03) 5427 1057 **www**.paramoor.com.au **Open** Fri–Mon 10–5
Winemaker William Fraser **Est.** 2003 **Dozens** 1300 **Vyds** 1.6ha

Paramoor Wines is the retirement venture of Will Fraser, formerly Managing Director of Kodak Australasia. To be strictly correct, he is Dr William Fraser, armed with a PhD in chemistry from Adelaide University. Much later he added a diploma of wine technology from the University of Melbourne (Dookie Campus) to his qualifications. Paramoor's winery is set on 17ha of beautiful country not far from Hanging Rock; it was originally a working Clydesdale horse farm, with a magnificent heritage-style barn now used for cellar door sales and functions. Will has planted 0.8ha each of pinot noir and pinot gris, and leases 2.6ha of vines in the lower Goulburn Valley (1.3ha shiraz, 0.9ha cabernet sauvignon, 0.4ha merlot). He also receives regular supplies of pinot noir and chardonnay grapes from another Macedon Ranges vineyard owned by friends.

ŢŢŢŢŢ **Master Angus Cabernet Sauvignon Merlot 2009** Deep colour; intense blackcurrant pastille and black olive; deep and sweet-fruited, and while generous; needs more structure for higher points. Diam. 14.5% alc. **Rating** 90 **To** 2018 $25

ŢŢŢŢ **Rose 2011 Rating** 87 **To** 2013 $22 BE
The Fraser Shiraz Cabernet Sauvignon 2009 Rating 87 **To** 2024 $25 BE

Paringa Estate ★★★★★

44 Paringa Road, Red Hill South, Vic 3937 **Region** Mornington Peninsula
T (03) 5989 2669 **www**.paringaestate.com.au **Open** 7 days 11–5
Winemaker Lindsay McCall, Craig Thompson **Est.** 1985 **Dozens** 15 000 **Vyds** 24.7ha

Schoolteacher-turned-winemaker Lindsay McCall has shown an absolutely exceptional gift for winemaking across a range of styles, but with immensely complex Pinot Noir and Shiraz leading the way. The wines have an unmatched level of success in the wine shows and competitions Paringa Estate is able to enter, the limitation being the relatively small production of the top wines in the portfolio. His skills are no less evident in contract winemaking for others. The next releases are due towards the end of 2012. Exports to the UK, Denmark, South Korea, Singapore, Taiwan, Hong Kong, China and Japan.

ŢŢŢŢŢ **The Paringa Single Vineyard Pinot Noir 2009** A fraction of purple to the crimson colour; the super-fragrant bouquet leaps out of the glass, exuding black cherries and a dash of French oak; the palate has even greater elegance and length than the '10 Estate, oak very much part of the picture as an essential part of the future of a beautiful Pinot. Screwcap. 14% alc. **Rating** 97 **To** 2020 $90
Estate Pinot Noir 2010 Mid crimson, bright hue; a lifted bright and elegant perfume of red and black cherry, hoisin and Asian spices; the palate is racy and light on its feet, with lacy fine tannins and a long, expansive, elegant structure; a wine built on finesse rather than raw power. Screwcap. 14.5% alc. **Rating** 96 **To** 2020 $60 BE
The Paringa Single Vineyard Shiraz 2008 Deep, dark colour; the rich bouquet of blackberry, satsuma plum and pepper leads into an intense and long palate; the oak is perfectly balanced and integrated, the tannins likewise. From the estate vineyard, a wine inheriting a glittering show record. Screwcap. 14.5% alc. **Rating** 96 **To** 2023 $80
The Paringa Single Vineyard Chardonnay 2010 Vivid green hue; the bouquet offers a strong accent of spicy oak, with the pure pear and nectarine fruit lingering beneath; the palate is soft and generous on entry, showing great concentration and a long expansive rush of sweet fruit and charcuterie on the finish; big-boned and warm, done well. Screwcap. 14% alc. **Rating** 94 **To** 2018 $50 BE

ŢŢŢŢŢ ✪ **Estate Pinot Gris 2011** Pale colour, vibrant hue; a ripe bouquet of spiced pear and anise; the palate is fleshy on entry, with an energetic backbone of acidity and minerals; long, generous and with plenty of flavour for the naysayers of this variety. Screwcap. 13.5% alc. **Rating** 92 **To** 2015 $20 BE

✪   Estate Chardonnay 2010 Rating 91 To 2016 $35 BE
     Estate Riesling 2011 Vivid green hue; a lean and minerally bouquet, showing
     fresh-squeezed lemon, ginger and lime leaf; the palate is bone dry and linear, with
     tangy acidity the prominent feature, and a long tail of fresh fennel and bath talc.
     Screwcap. 13% alc. Rating 90 To 2018 $20 BE
     Peninsula Shiraz 2009 Rating 90 To 2018 $25 BE

♀♀♀♀   Peninsula Chardonnay 2010 Rating 88 To 2015 $22 BE
        Estate Rose 2011 Rating 88 To 2014 $18 BE

Parker Coonawarra Estate   ★★★★★

Riddoch Highway, Coonawarra, SA 5263 **Region** Coonawarra
T (08) 8737 3525 **www**.parkercoonawarraestate.com.au **Open** 7 days 10–4
Winemaker Peter Bissell (Contract) **Est.** 1985 **Dozens** 7000
Parker Coonawarra Estate is at the southern end of Coonawarra, on rich terra rossa soil over
limestone. Cabernet sauvignon is the predominant variety (17.45ha), with minor plantings
of merlot and petit verdot. In 2012 the Rathbone Group wine interests were placed on the
market for sale either as a group or individually. Exports to all major markets.

♀♀♀♀♀   Terra Rossa First Growth 2008 The colour is distinctly deeper than that of
         the Terra Rossa Cabernet Sauvignon, and the fruit is decidedly more intense and
         focused, with tannins sitting alongside the black fruits as they power through the
         palate to the long, savoury/earthy finish. I have often wondered whether Bordeaux
         has taken exception to the name, but if they were to do so for this vintage, it
         might be out of concern. A great name for the Chinese market, too. Screwcap.
         14.5% alc. Rating 95 To 2028 $110
         Favourite Son Chardonnay 2009 Bright straw-green; fastidious winemaking
         (whole bunch-pressing, etc) has kept the emphasis on the fresh fruit, encompassing
         grapefruit and white peach flavours not always found in Coonawarra; the barrel
         fermentation with some wild yeast has been important but subtle in impact.
         Screwcap. 12.5% alc. Rating 94 To 2019 $24
         Terra Rossa Cabernet Sauvignon 2008 Medium red-purple; what a
         difference a vintage makes. This wine has masses of rich blackcurrant, mint and
         earthy flavours, tannins made to measure, the oak integrated and in balance.
         Screwcap. 14.5% alc. Rating 94 To 2023 $40

♀♀♀♀♀   Terra Rossa Cabernet Sauvignon 2009 Rating 92 To 2022 $40 BE
         Favourite Son Chardonnay 2010 Rating 91 To 2017 $25 BE
         Favourite Son Cabernet Merlot 2008 Rating 90 To 2025 $24
         Terra Rossa First Growth 2009 Rating 90 To 2025 $110 BE

♀♀♀♀   Favourite Son Shiraz 2009 Rating 89 To 2020 $25 BE

Passing Clouds   ★★★★☆

30 Roddas Lane, Musk, Vic 3461 **Region** Macedon Ranges
T (03) 5348 5550 **www**.passingclouds.com.au **Open** 7 days 11–5
Winemaker Cameron and Graeme Leith **Est.** 1974 **Dozens** 3500 **Vyds** 12ha
Graeme Leith (and son Cameron) have undertaken a monumental vine change. This has
involved moving the entire operation that started way back in 1974 in Bendigo to its new
location at Daylesford. The vines at the original vineyard had been disabled by ongoing
drought and all manner of pestilence, and it was no longer feasible to continue the business
there. Sixteen semi-trailer loads later, all of their winemaking equipment and stock arrived at
Musk, and the emphasis has moved to elegant Pinot Noir and Chardonnay, with a foot still
in Bendigo courtesy of their friends, the Adams at Riola. Back vintages of the Bendigo wines
will be available for the foreseeable future. Exports to the UK, the US and Europe.

♀♀♀♀♀   Bendigo Shiraz 2010 Deep crimson; the bouquet offers a fresh and fragrant
         aroma of red and black fruits, sage and a splash of spice; medium-bodied and juicy,
         finishing with a savoury note of sage and licorice. Screwcap. 14% alc. Rating 91
         To 2018 $29 BE

The Angel Cabernet Sauvignon 2010 A soft and dark-fruited wine, tightly wound at the core, offering a fleshy palate of black fruits and gravelly tannins; unevolved and looking to stand the test of time with aplomb. Diam. 13.6% alc. **Rating** 91 **To** 2024 $40 BE

Graeme's Blend Shiraz Cabernet 2010 Deep crimson; sweet mulberry, sage and a dollop of licorice are evident on the bouquet; medium-bodied, soft and fleshy on the palate with an easygoing personality and vibrancy to conclude. Diam. 14% alc. **Rating** 90 **To** 2018 $30 BE

ꟼꟼꟼꟼ **Reserve Bendigo Shiraz 2010** Rating 87 To 2016 $40 BE

Patina ★★★★☆

109 Summerhill Lane, Orange, NSW 2800 **Region** Orange
T (02) 6362 8336 **www**.patinawines.com.au **Open** W'ends 11–5, or by appt
Winemaker Gerald Naef **Est.** 1999 **Dozens** 3000 **Vyds** 3ha
Gerald Naef's home in Woodbridge in the Central Valley of California was surrounded by the vast vineyard and winery operations of Gallo and Robert Mondavi. It would be hard to imagine a more different environment than that provided by Orange. Gerald and wife Angie left California in 1981, initially establishing an irrigation farm in the northwest of NSW; 20 years later they moved to Orange, and by 2006 Gerald was a final-year student of wine science at CSU. He set up a micro-winery at the Orange Cool Stores, and his first wine was a 2003 Chardonnay, made from vines he planted in '99. At its first show entry it won the trophy for Best White Wine of Show at the Orange Wine Show '06, of which I was Chairman. Dream starts seldom come better than this.

ꟼꟼꟼꟼꟼ **Orange Sauvignon Blanc Fume 2007** The bright, light quartz-green colour is extraordinary for a 5-year-old wine; the palate is no less surprising, with no hint of the vegetal breakup characters that can occur with bottle-aged Sauvignon, and the oak balance is nigh-on perfect. A great mystery why this wine has not been sold long since. Screwcap. 12.5% alc. **Rating** 94 **To** 2013 $27

ꟼꟼꟼꟼꟼ **Reserve Orange Chardonnay 2007** Rating 93 To 2017 $27

✪ **Scandalous Orange Riesling 2010** Given that the wine is only 9.7% alcohol, it must have been picked very early, because the sugar level is moderately low, giving the lime juice fruit free rein, the sweetness neatly balanced by acidity. Screwcap. **Rating** 91 **To** 2015 $19

✪ **Sticky Tea Orange Riesling 2011** Gleaming green-gold; the depth of colour comes from the fermentation on skins for some days; that colour might lead you to expect a very sweet style, but in fact it is moderately well balanced. What is more, there is a character that seems to stick to the front of the tongue and introduce some tea notes, which reappear on the finish and aftertaste. Avant-garde making that very nearly comes off. 375ml. Screwcap. 8.4% alc. **Rating** 90 **To** 2014 $22

ꟼꟼꟼꟼ **Orange Riesling 2009** Rating 87 To 2013 $19

Patrick of Coonawarra ★★★★★

Cnr Ravenswood Lane/Riddoch Highway, Coonawarra, SA 5263 **Region** Coonawarra
T (08) 8737 3687 **www**.patrickofcoonawarra.com.au **Open** 7 days 10–4.30
Winemaker Pat and Luke Toccaciu **Est.** 2004 **Dozens** 7000 **Vyds** 79.5ha
Patrick Tocaciu is a district veteran, with prior careers at Heathfield Ridge Winery and Hollick Wines. He and his partners have over 41ha of vines at Wrattonbully, and another 38.5ha in Coonawarra in Coonawarra. The Wrattonbully plantings cover all the major varieties, while the Coonawarra plantings give rise to the Home Block Cabernet Sauvignon. Also carries out contract winemaking for others. Pat has been joined by son Luke in the winery. Exports to Chile, South Korea and NZ.

ꟼꟼꟼꟼꟼ **Wrattonbully Riesling 2011** Pale straw-green; has a delicious blossom-filled bouquet, translating into an even more delicious palate, the sweet lime juice and apple flavours precisely corralled by fresh acidity. The price comes as no surprise. Screwcap. 11% alc. **Rating** 95 **To** 2020 $32

Aged Riesling 2006 Glowing, light green–yellow; the lime, toast and lemon butter aromas of the bouquet are precisely replicated by the strongly built palate; still for the long haul, although easy to enjoy now. Screwcap. 11% alc. **Rating** 94 To 2021 $45

ҬҬҬҬҬ **Estate Grown Wrattonbully Cabernet Sauvignon 2008 Rating** 93 To 2030 $32

✪ **Mother of Pearl Sauvignon Blanc 2011** A very well-made wine, coaxing the maximum flavour from Wrattonbully and Coonawarra-grown grapes; the aromas and flavours range from citrus to gooseberry to tropical, wrapped in a swathe of lemony acidity. Screwcap. 11% alc. **Rating** 92 **To** 2013 $19

Home Block Coonawarra Cabernet Sauvignon 2008 Rating 92 To 2018 $45

✪ **Toccas Deuce Sauvignon Blanc 2010** An altogether friendly wine, with soft tropical fruits on both the bouquet and palate making it ideal for present drinking as an aperitif or with summer salads. Screwcap. 11.5% alc. **Rating** 90 **To** Now $14

Estate Grown Wrattonbully Merlot 2009 Rating 90 To 2016 $32

ҬҬҬҬ **Mother of Pearl Limestone Coast Shiraz 2009 Rating** 89 To 2016 $19

Mother of Pearl Cabernet Merlot 2009 Rating 89 To 2014 $19

Mother of Pearl Coonawarra Chardonnay Pinot Noir NV Rating 89 To 2013 $19

Toccas Oaks Cabernet Rose 2010 Rating 88 To Now $14

Botrytis Riesling 2010 Rating 88 To 2014 $50 BE

Toccas Game Shiraz Cabernet Merlot 2008 Rating 87 To 2014 $14

Roosters Run Cabernet Sauvignon 2010 Rating 87 To 2015 $18 BE

Patritti Wines ★★★★★

13–23 Clacton Road, Dover Gardens, SA 5048 **Region** Adelaide Zone
T (08) 8296 8261 **www.**patritti.com.au **Open** Mon–Sat 9–5
Winemaker James Mungall, Ben Heide **Est.** 1926 **Dozens** 200 000
A traditional, family-owned business offering wines at modest prices, but with impressive vineyard holdings of 10ha of shiraz in Blewitt Springs and 6ha of grenache at Aldinga North. The surging production points to success in export markets, and also to the utilisation of contract-grown grapes as well as estate-grown. Quite how this has come about I don't know, but Patritti is currently releasing wines of very high quality at enticing prices, and a range of lesser quality wines at unfathomably low prices. The JPB Single Vineyard celebrates the arrival of Giovanni Patritti in Australia in 1925; he sold his wines under the 'John Patritti Brighton' label. Exports to the US and other major markets.

ҬҬҬҬҬ **JPB Single Vineyard Shiraz 2010** This is an awesome wine, so full of flavour that it burst out of my mouth, not once, but twice, on a shirt that is unlikely to ever be the same again. This is liquid blackberry, dark chocolate and licorice, oak and tannins mere support players. The cork in both wines is of high quality, and correctly inserted. 14.5% alc. **Rating** 96 **To** 2030 $45

Single Vineyard Lot 3 McLaren Vale Shiraz 2010 Dense, deep purple; it's a remarkable achievement for a wine to have such depth and density of flavour, yet not overstay its welcome in the mouth, and certainly showing no sign of overripe fruit; rather, it is a voluptuous, fleshy tribute to McLaren Vale, with all of the dark fruits and dark chocolate one expects from the region, but without a tannin burden to carry. Cork. 14% alc. **Rating** 95 **To** 2030 $28

ҬҬҬҬҬ **Old Gate McLaren Vale Shire Shiraz 2009** Good crimson-purple; like the
✪ '10 Single Vineyard Shirazs, comes from Patritti's Blewitt Springs vineyard, hand-picked, and matured in 100% new French and American oak puncheons for two years, black fruits, chocolate and fruitcake doing battle with the oak. It is a mystery how this wine could possibly sell for $18 or less. Cork. 14.5% alc. **Rating** 93 To 2024 $18

✪ **Marion Vineyard Adelaide Grenache Shiraz 2009** This 100-year-old vineyard was compulsorily acquired when the city suburb was given over to housing, but is leased to its former owner, Patritti. The colour is good, the flavours a mix of red and black fruits, and a surprising array of tannins in support. The deluxe bottle is at odds with its very short cork, and, even more with the price. 13.5% alc. **Rating** 92 **To** 2015 $18

ŸŸŸŸ **Adelaide Hills Barbera 2010** **Rating** 89
✪ **To** 2018 $16
✪ **Barossa Valley Saperavi 2010** **Rating** 89 **To** 2020 $16

Paul Bettio Wines ★★★★

145 Upper King River Road, Cheshunt, Vic 3678 **Region** King Valley
T (03) 5729 8101 **www.paulbettiowines.com.au Open** Fri–Mon 10–5, or by appt
Winemaker Paul Bettio **Est.** 1995 **Dozens** 12 000 **Vyds** 25ha
The Bettio family settled in the King Valley during the 1950s. Paul and Helen Bettio have been growing cabernet sauvignon, merlot and sauvignon blanc in the region since '88 beside the King River. Paul's father Joe has the winery's second vineyard at Cheshunt, with chardonnay, merlot, barbera and pinot grigio.

ŸŸŸŸŸ **King Valley Barbera 2010** **Rating** 90 **To** 2014 $18
◉

ŸŸŸŸ **King Valley Cabernet Sauvignon 2010** **Rating** 87 **To** 2013 $18
◉

Paul Conti Wines ★★★★☆

529 Wanneroo Road, Woodvale, WA 6026 **Region** Greater Perth Zone
T (08) 9409 9160 **www.paulcontiwines.com.au Open** Mon–Sat 10–5, Sun by appt
Winemaker Paul and Jason Conti **Est.** 1948 **Dozens** 5000 **Vyds** 12ha
Third-generation winemaker Jason Conti has assumed control of winemaking, although father Paul (who succeeded his own father in 1968) remains involved in the business. Over the years Paul challenged and redefined industry perceptions and standards; the challenge for Jason is to achieve the same degree of success in a relentlessly and increasingly competitive market environment, and he is doing just that. Plantings at the Carabooda Vineyard have been expanded with tempranillo, petit verdot and viognier, and pinot noir and chardonnay are purchased from Manjimup. In a further extension, a property has been acquired at Cowaramup in Margaret River, with sauvignon blanc, shiraz, cabernet sauvignon and semillon; muscat and malbec are yet to come into full production. Jason Conti is a firm believer in organics, and the Swan Valley and Manjimup vineyards will soon join the family's Cowaramup organic vineyard. The original 2ha vineyard (shiraz) of the Mariginiup Vineyard remains the cornerstone. Exports to the UK, Malaysia, China and Japan.

ŸŸŸŸŸ **Mariginiup Shiraz 2010** An estate-grown wine from old, low-yielding vines on the unique Tuart soils of the western end of the Greater Perth Zone; the fragrant, spicy bouquet leads into a lively and vibrant palate, with spice, dark chocolate and red cherry fruit framed by fine, harmonious tannins. A wine that deserves a wider audience. Screwcap. 14.5% alc. **Rating** 94 **To** 2025 $28

ŸŸŸŸŸ **Margaret River Cabernet Sauvignon 2010** Light crimson-purple; the
✪ fragrant bouquet brings into play a touch of merlot and 12 months in French oak, along with a distinct touch of mint to the ripe red and blackcurrant fruit; savoury/ dusty tannins are in perfect balance. Screwcap. 14.5% alc. **Rating** 93 **To** 2020 $20
◉ **Organic Vines Margaret River Sauvignon Blanc 2011** **Rating** 90
To Now $16
✪ **Medici Ridge Chardonnay 2011** Hand-picked grapes from South West Australian vineyards. Straw-green; partial fermentation and ageing in French oak has worked very well, allowing the white peach and grapefruit flavours to express themselves; good length and balance. Screwcap. 13.5% alc. **Rating** 90 **To** 2017 $20

✪   **Roccella Grenache Shiraz 2011** Light but vivid crimson-purple; the fragrant red fruits of the bouquet are followed by an unexpectedly tightly focused palate; here delicious cherry and red berry flavours have good tannin structure, giving the wine authority and length. Excellent value. Screwcap. 14.5% alc. **Rating** 90 **To** 2017 $16

♟♟♟♟   **Late Harvest Fronti 2011 Rating** 89
◐   **To** Now $16
Tuart Vineyards Chenin Blanc 2011 Rating 88 **To** 2017 $16
Medici Ridge Pinot Noir 2011 Rating 87 **To** 2014 $25

Paul Nelson Wines   ★★★☆

11 Kemsley Place, Denmark, WA 6333 (postal) **Region** Mount Barker
T 0406 495 066 **www**.paulnelsonwines.com.au **Open** Not
Winemaker Paul Nelson **Est.** 2009 **Dozens** 600
Paul Nelson has a remarkably youthful face for someone who started making wine with one foot in the Swan Valley, the other in the Great Southern region of Denmark, while completing a bachelor's degree in viticulture and oenology at Curtin University. He then worked successively at Houghton in the Swan Valley, Goundrey in Mount Barker, Santa Ynez in California, South Africa (for four vintages), hemisphere hopping to the Rheinhessen, three vintages in Cyprus, then moving to a large Indian winemaker in Mumbai before returning to work for Houghton at Nannup. He has since moved on from Houghton to employment elsewhere, but (in partnership with wife Bianca Swart) makes small quantities of table wines.

♟♟♟♟♟   **Maison Madeleine 2011** Made from a blend of grenache and mourvedre, its pale but vivid pink colour leading into a fragrant, gently spicy bouquet; the palate is light-bodied, but pure and long, with good balance. Screwcap. 13.7% alc. **Rating** 91 **To** 2014 $34

♟♟♟♟   **Mount Barker Fume Blanc 2011 Rating** 89 **To** 2015 $32

Paul Osicka   ★★★★★

39 Osickas Lane, Graytown, Vic 3608 **Region** Heathcote
T (03) 5794 9235 **F** (03) 5794 9288 **Open** By appt
Winemaker Paul and Simon Osicka **Est.** 1955 **Dozens** NFP **Vyds** 13ha
The Osicka family arrived in Australia from Czechoslovakia in the early 1950s. Vignerons in their own country, they settled at Graytown and commenced planting vines in '55. Their vineyard was the first new venture in Central and Southern Victoria for over half a century. With the return of Simon Osicka to the family business, there have been substantial changes. Prior to joining the family business full-time in 2010, Simon had senior winemaking positions at Houghton, Leasingham and as group red winemaker for Constellation Wines Australia, interleaved with vintages in Italy, Canada, Germany and France, working at the prestigious Domaine J.L. Chave in Hermitage for the '10 vintage. The fermentation of the red wines has been changed from static to open fermenters, and French oak has replaced American oak.

♟♟♟♟♟   **Moormbool Reserve Shiraz 2010** This is a selection of only two barrels of wine made from some of the oldest vines on the property; a fascinating wine, for you know the spice, oak and tannins evident in the 'normal' Shiraz are all there, but the intensity of the fruit drives the wine; the further paradox is that it remains medium-bodied, and beautifully balanced. Diam. 14.5% alc. **Rating** 96 **To** 2030 $45
Majors Creek Vineyard Heathcote Shiraz 2010 Good colour depth and hue; the penetrating aromas of the bouquet are based on a foundation of black fruits, warm spices and cedary oak; the palate takes the baton with ease, unfurling a complex array of flavours shot through with fine but persistent tannins. A died-in-the-wool stayer. Diam. 14.2% alc. **Rating** 95 **To** 2025 $35

Majors Creek Vineyard Heathcote Cabernet Sauvignon 2010 Crimson-purple; a very pure and stylish example of cool-grown cabernet sauvignon picked at precisely the right moment; the bouquet and palate have pristine blackcurrant and redcurrant fruit, the palate with almost silky, and certainly very fine, tannins; medium-bodied at best, but with all of the ingredients for a long life. Diam. 13.7% alc. **Rating** 95 **To** 2025 $35

Paulett ★★★★★

Polish Hill Road, Polish Hill River, SA 5453 **Region** Clare Valley
T (08) 8843 4328 **www**.paulettwines.com.au **Open** 7 days 10–5
Winemaker Neil Paulett, Kelvin Budarick **Est.** 1983 **Dozens** 14 000 **Vyds** 174ha
The Paulett story is a saga of Australian perseverance, commencing with the 1982 purchase of a property with 1ha of vines and a house, promptly destroyed by the terrible Ash Wednesday bushfires of the following year. Son Matthew has joined Neil and Alison Paulett as a partner in the business, responsible for viticulture on a much-expanded property holding, following the recent purchase of a large vineyard at Watervale. The winery and cellar door have wonderful views over the Polish Hill River region, the memories of the bushfires long gone. Exports to the UK, the US, Denmark, China and NZ.

♈♈♈♈♈ **Polish Hill River Riesling 2011** Vibrant colour and personality, pure lime
✪ juice, slate and talc bouquet; searingly high levels of acidity will make this wine a challenge early on, but the pleasure will be in the future, as the fruit unwinds and reveals its inner beauty. Screwcap. 11% alc. **Rating** 94 **To** 2025 $22
Polish Hill River Aged Release Riesling 2007 Mid gold, green hue; fresh toast and lemon curd bouquet, with ginger and spice; generous, soft and toasty, the palate reveals a fully developed wine; as an aged release, no more time is needed. Screwcap. 12.5% alc. **Rating** 94 **To** 2015 $45 BE

♈♈♈♈♈ **Polish Hill River Late Harvest Riesling 2011** Green apple bouquet, laced
✪ with scents of bath talc and violets; off-dry, focused and linear and certainly not recommended for desserts, but definitely for starters. Screwcap. 9.5% alc. **Rating** 92 **To** 2018 $20

♈♈♈♈ **Andreas Polish Hill River Shiraz 2008 Rating** 89 **To** 2018 $50 BE
Polish Hill River Shiraz 2008 Rating 88 **To** 2015 $24 BE

Paulmara Estates ★★★☆

47 Park Avenue, Rosslyn Park, SA 5072 (postal) **Region** Barossa Valley
T 0417 895 138 **www**.paulmara.com.au **Open** Not
Winemaker Paul Georgiadis, Neil Pike **Est.** 1999 **Dozens** 300 **Vyds** 11.8ha
Born to an immigrant Greek family, Paul Georgiadis grew up in Waikerie, where his family had vineyards and orchards. His parents worked sufficiently hard to send him first to St Peters College in Adelaide and then to do a marketing degree at Adelaide University. He became the whirlwind grower-relations manager for Southcorp, and one of the best-known faces in the Barossa Valley. Paul and wife Mara established a vineyard in 1995, planted to semillon, shiraz, sangiovese, merlot and cabernet sauvignon. Part of the production is sold, and the best shiraz makes the Syna Shiraz ('syna' being Greek for together).

♈♈♈♈ **The Melee Barossa Valley Cabernet Lagrein Shiraz Touriga 2010**
Melee by name and by nature, as the blend is bound to bring a cacophony of personalities together in this wine; dark-fruited with prunes, blackberry, cola and spice; the palate is warm, rich and thickly textured, with bitter tannins lingering on the finish; interesting at best. Screwcap. 13.5% alc. **Rating** 88 **To** 2016 $18 BE

Paxton ★★★★★

68 Wheaton Road, McLaren Vale, SA 5171 **Region** McLaren Vale
T (08) 8323 9131 **www**.paxtonvineyards.com **Open** 7 days 10–5
Winemaker Michael Paxton **Est.** 1979 **Dozens** 20 000 **Vyds** 74.5ha

David Paxton is one of Australia's best-known viticulturists and consultants. He founded Paxton Vineyards in McLaren Vale with his family in 1979, and has since been involved in various capacities in the establishment and management of vineyards in several leading regions across the country. Son Michael, a former Flying Winemaker (with experience in Spain, South America, France and Australia), is responsible for making the wines. There are five vineyards in the family holdings: the Thomas Block (28ha), the Jones Block (22ha), Quandong Farm (19ha), Landcross Farm (2ha) and Maslin Vineyard (3.5ha). By 2006 all of the vineyards were managed using full biodynamic principles. Paxton has become one of the first members of 1% For the Planet (www.onepercentfortheplanet.org). An underground barrel store has been completed and a cellar door opened in the original shearing shed. Exports to the UK, the US, Canada, Denmark, Sweden, Germany, Taiwan and China.

ŸŸŸŸŸ **AAA McLaren Vale Shiraz Grenache 2010** Bright crimson-purple; this
✪ is where modern McLaren Vale should be, gloriously fresh and inviting, with controlled alcohol and subtle oak. The varieties are so seamlessly joined all you register is a cascade of red berry fruits and fine-grained tannins. Outstanding value. Screwcap. 14% alc. **Rating** 95 **To** 2020 $23
Quandong Farm Single Vineyard McLaren Vale Shiraz 2010 Full purple-red; a complex, dense, full-bodied wine, with a complex regional palate bringing blackberry, plum cake and dark chocolate into play on the palate, oak and tannins nicely balanced. Screwcap. 13.5% alc. **Rating** 94 **To** 2025 $30
MV McLaren Vale Shiraz 2010 A beguiling combination of freshness and concentrated dark fruits, with bramble and spice providing added interest; the palate reveals depth and generosity, ample fine-grained tannins and a very long finish that belies the modest price. Screwcap. 14% alc. **Rating** 94 **To** 2016 $23 BE
Jones Block Single Vineyard McLaren Vale Shiraz 2009 A ripe and inviting array of red and black fruits, spice, fruitcake, mocha and sea salt; the palate is bright and fresh, with generous lashings of sweet fruit and a trailing accent of choc mint that weaves through seamlessly; a warm and easygoing wine, with plenty of time ahead. Screwcap. 14% alc. **Rating** 94 **To** 2018 $39 BE

ŸŸŸŸ♀ **Thomas Block Single Vineyard McLaren Vale Chardonnay 2010**
Rating 91 **To** 2014 $29

ŸŸŸŸ **Pinot Gris 2011 Rating** 87 **To** 2013 $23 BE
McLaren Vale Shiraz Rose 2011 Rating 87 **To** Now $20 BE

Payne's Rise   ★★★★☆
10 Paynes Road, Seville, Vic 3139 **Region** Yarra Valley
T (03) 5964 2504 **www.**paynesrise.com.au **Open** Thurs–Sun 11–5, or by appt
Winemaker Franco D'Anna (Contract) **Est.** 1998 **Dozens** 600 **Vyds** 4ha
Tim and Narelle Cullen have progressively established 1ha each of cabernet sauvignon, shiraz, chardonnay and sauvignon blanc since 1998, supplemented by grapes purchased from local growers. They carry out all the vineyard work; Tim is also a viticulturist for a local agribusiness, and Narelle is responsible for sales and marketing. The contract-made wines have won several awards at the Victorian Wines Show.

ŸŸŸŸŸ **Yarra Valley Chardonnay 2010 Rating** 94 **To** 2018 $20
✪

ŸŸŸŸ♀ **Yarra Valley Cabernet Sauvignon 2010** Bright purple; a beautifully made
✪ wine balancing blackcurrant fruit with more earthy/black olive notes on the fine, medium-bodied palate. Screwcap. 13.5% alc. **Rating** 93 **To** 2019 $22
Redlands Yarra Valley Shiraz 2010 Rating 90 **To** 2020 $26

ŸŸŸŸ **Yarra Valley Sauvignon Blanc 2011** Pale straw-green; barrel fermentation in
✪ used oak has not modified the flavour, leaving a crisp, fresh, citrus-driven wine, but has added to the texture; the only question is the high level of acidity on the finish. Screwcap. 12% alc. **Rating** 89 **To** 2014 $18

Peccavi Wines   ★★★★★

1121 WIldwood Road, Yallingup Siding, WA 6282 **Region** Margaret River
T 0404 873 093 **www.**peccavi-wines.com **Open** By appt
Winemaker Various contract **Est.** 1996 **Dozens** 5000 **Vyds** 16ha
Owner Jeremy Muller was introduced to the great wines of the world by his father when
he was young, and says he spent many years searching New and Old World wine regions
(even looking at the sites of ancient Roman vineyards in England), but did not find what he
was looking for until one holiday in Margaret River. There he found a vineyard in Yallingup
that was available for sale, and he did not hesitate. He quickly put together a very impressive
contract winemaking team, and appointed Colin Bell as chief viticulturist. The wines are
released under two labels: Peccavi, for 100% estate-grown fruit (all hand-picked) and No
Regrets, for wines that include contract-grown grapes and estate material. The quality of the
wines is very good, reflecting the skills and experience of Brian Fletcher, Amanda Kraemer
and Bruce Dukes as contract/consultant winemakers. Exports to the UK, Germany, Malaysia,
Singapore and Dubai.

ŸŸŸŸŸ   Margaret River Shiraz 2009 Mid garnet; restrained and savoury in style,
with black fruits, struck quartz minerals and anise; the palate is medium-bodied
and fresh, almost fine-boned, with silky tannins and a long and expansive finish;
understated complexity. WAK screwcap. 13.5% alc. **Rating** 94 **To** 2020 $40 BE
Margaret River Cabernet Sauvignon 2009 Deep colour; a complex and
concentrated bouquet full of black fruits, olive and a little crushed leaf complexity;
the palate tells the full story, with layers of fruit, fine tannins and a long and
expansive finish. WAK screwcap. 13.5% alc..Rating 94 **To** 2018 $45 BE

ŸŸŸŸŸ   No Regrets Margaret River Sauvignon Blanc Semillon 2011 A restrained
✪   and pleasant bouquet of nectarine, cut grass and blanched almond; the palate is
fine, fresh and fragrant, balanced and user friendly. Screwcap. 12.5% alc. **Rating** 93
To 2013 $20 BE
Margaret River Sauvignon Blanc Semillon 2010 **Rating** 93 **To** 2014 $34 BE
Margaret River Chardonnay 2010 **Rating** 90 **To** 2014 $45 BE

ŸŸŸŸ   No Regrets Margaret River Cabernet Merlot 2009 **Rating** 89 **To** 2014
$24 BE

Pedestal Vineyard Wines   ★★★★★

PO Box 871, Canning Bridge, WA 6153 **Region** Margaret River
T (08) 6364 4862 **www.**pedestalwines.com.au **Open** Not
Winemaker Larry Cherubino **Est.** 2008 **Dozens** 1500 **Vyds** 14ha
This was a joint venture between land (and vineyard) owners Greg and Kerilee Brindle,
and winemaker Larry Cherubino and wife Edwina. Now fully-owned by the latter, the
vineyard (cabernet sauvignon, merlot, sauvignon blanc and semillon) was planted in 1998, the
grapes being sold over the ensuing years to other winemakers in the region. Distribution by
Bibendum on the eastern seaboard is testimony to the skills of Larry Cherubino, leading to
increased sales. This is a venture worth watching.

ŸŸŸŸŸ   Elevation Margaret River Cabernet Sauvignon 2010 Comes from
individual rows in the vineyard, hand-picked and berry-sorted before fermentation,
thereafter spending 12 months in oak and 12 months thereafter in bottle prior
to release. Somewhat surprisingly, is more elegant and supple than the Cabernet
Merlot, flavours of blackcurrant, mulberry and cedary oak all coming effortlessly
together, the tannins so fine you barely notice them. Screwcap. 14% alc. **Rating** 96
To 2035 $49
Margaret River Cabernet Merlot 2010 Strong colour; an 89/11% blend, this
is a medium- to full-bodied wine that has an almost limitless future; cassis and
blackcurrant flavours are coupled with quality French oak and a powerful tannin
structure to underwrite the future development of a classic Margaret River style.
Screwcap. **Rating** 95 **To** 2040 $25

Margaret River Sauvignon Blanc Semillon 2011 Pale straw-green; a 60/40% blend with all the focus on the synergy between the two varieties, and the seemingly effortless creation of the texture on the palate, most likely stemming from use of the lees post ferment, and particular attention to the pH and acidity. Screwcap. 13% alc. **Rating** 94 **To** 2015 $20

Peel Estate

290 Fletcher Road, Karnup, WA 6176 **Region** Peel
T (08) 9524 1221 **www.**peelwine.com.au **Open** 7 days 10–5
Winemaker Will Nairn, Mark Morton **Est.** 1974 **Dozens** 4000 **Vyds** 16ha
Peel's icon wine is the Shiraz, a wine of considerable finesse and with a remarkably consistent track record. Every year Will Nairn holds a Great Shiraz Tasting for six-year-old Australian shirazs, and pits Peel Estate (in a blind tasting attended by 100 or so people) against Australia's best. It is never disgraced. The wood-matured Chenin Blanc is another winery specialty, although not achieving the excellence of the Shiraz. Exports to the UK, Ireland, China and Japan.

🍷🍷🍷🍷🍷 **Old Vine Shiraz 2005** Excellent colour given its age, although it would seem this wine had a leisurely journey before being bottled; the palate has quite delicious spiced plum flavours, the tannins fine, and the overall impact is mouth-watering. One of the best Shirazs in a long history. Cork. 14% alc. **Rating** 94 **To** 2018 $35

🍷🍷🍷🍷🍷 **Cabernet Sauvignon 2006 Rating** 92 **To** 2016 $30
Chardonnay 2011 Rating 90 **To** 2016 $25
Wood Matured Chenin Blanc 2010 Rating 90 **To** 2017 $25

Penfolds

Tanunda Road, Nuriootpa, SA 5355 **Region** Barossa Valley
T (08) 8568 9408 **www.**penfolds.com **Open** 7 days 10–5
Winemaker Peter Gago **Est.** 1844 **Dozens** NFP
Senior among the numerous wine companies or stand-alone brands of TWE, and undoubtedly one of the top wine companies in the world in terms of quality, product range and exports. The consistency of the quality of the red wines and their value for money have long been recognised worldwide; the white wines, headed by the ultra-premium Yattarna Chardonnay, are now on a par with the red wines. Exports to all major markets.

🍷🍷🍷🍷🍷 **Bin 620 Coonawarra Cabernet Shiraz 2008** Excellent purple-crimson colour; the seamless bouquet is already showing elegance, complex cedar, cigar box aromas entwined with perfect ripe fruit characters. The palate has great drive, length and line; outstanding tannins give the wine great balance, texture and a certain authority; this is not a fruit bomb style. By far the best 3-year-old Penfolds red wine I have tasted. Screwcap. 14.5% alc. **Rating** 98 **To** 2040 $1000
RWT Barossa Valley Shiraz 2009 Saturated purple hue; the Red Winemaking Trial of Penfold's continues unabated, and this 100% Barossa Valley Shiraz (it always is) is certainly built for the long haul; incredibly dense and concentrated lively and fresh black fruits, with layers of roasted meat, spice, licorice and more; massively proportioned, but beautifully constructed and staggeringly long. Big, bold and beautiful. Screwcap. 14.5% alc. **Rating** 97 **To** 2050 $175 BE
Bin 169 Coonawarra Cabernet Sauvignon 2008 The wine spent 18 months in new French oak, and is fundamentally different from Bin 707 Cabernet Sauvignon. Deep purple-crimson, it has exceptional focus, intensity and length, cedary notes of French oak precisely woven through the vibrant blackcurrant fruit, reaching a crescendo on the finish. It follows in the footsteps of a one-off Coonawarra Cabernet from the 1973 vintage, also given the Bin 169 tag. Screwcap. 14.5% alc. **Rating** 97 **To** 2038 $250
Grandfather Fine Old Liqueur Tawny NV Fully aged but bright tawny; the very complex Christmas cake bouquet has all manner of Asian spices asking to he heard; the palate is very luscious yet magically made elegant by its burnt sugar acidity. Cork. 20% alc. **Rating** 97 **To** Now $100

Great Grandfather Limited Release Rare Tawny NV Light golden brown; bottle no. 454 of 4200 from the Series 12 selection. Arguably the best of all Australian tawnies, with more luscious fruit than Seppelt DP90 (the other contender); luscious it may be, but it is also wonderfully elegant, with rancio and Christmas cake and toffee flavours on the mid palate, moving to a spicy, dry and ultimately fresh finish. Cork. 19.5% alc. **Rating** 97 **To** 2013 $350

Bin 311 Henty Chardonnay 2011 Bin 311 has previously come from Tumbarumba, but it was never the intention to tie it to any particular region. This year the vineyard established by Seppelt in the 1960s produced outstanding grapes, hence the move. Fermented and matured for seven months in 18% new French oak; the bouquet is exuberantly aromatic, with grapefruit blossom and the merest whisper of oak; the palate has intense grapefruit and white peach flavours, tensioned and lengthened by lingering minerally acidity. Screwcap. 12% alc. **Rating** 96 **To** 2022 $40

Reserve Bin A Chardonnay 2010 Pure and understated, with savoury complexity running neatly alongside fragrant grapefruit, charcuterie and mineral aromas; the palate is taut, racy, linear and polished, with a long and expansive finish. If you feel the need to age your Chardonnay, then look no further. Screwcap. 13.3% alc. **Rating** 96 **To** 2018 $95 BE

Yattarna Chardonnay 2009 Yattarna is almost the antithesis of Grange, as it is so tightly wound, understated, reserved and shy that it is hard to believe they are relatives; the true depth and potential are revealed on the palate, which is unevolved, minerally, layered and pure, simply demanding time before appreciation can truly begin. Screwcap. 12.9% alc. **Rating** 96 **To** 2025 $130 BE

Grange 2007 Full crimson, with a purple rim; a 98/2% blen of shiraz and cabernet sauvignon that exudes power and authority; the bouquet is already complex, the American oak making an impact as it always does when Grange is in its youth, the palate with multiple layers of predominantly black fruits; the tannins, like the oak, need to soften, and should do so well before the fruit starts to fade. Follows the Grange pattern, with 21 months in the 100% new American oak in which it finished its fermentation. A good Grange, but not a very good/great one. Cork. 14.5% alc. **Rating** 95 **To** 2030 $625 BE

Bin 389 Cabernet Shiraz 2009 There is true depth of aroma and flavour in this wine, ranging from fragrant florals to menacing black fruits, all offset by sweet spices and well-handled oak; full-bodied, with full-throttle tannins, bright acid and an exceedingly long finish. This will cellar brilliantly, but is not likely to get the chance. Screwcap. 14.5% alc. **Rating** 95 **To** 2030 $70 BE

Bin 51 Eden Valley Riesling 2011 **Rating** 94 **To** 2026 $30
Bin 128 Coonawarra Shiraz 2010 **Rating** 94 **To** 2020 $35 BE
Bin 28 Kalimna Shiraz 2009 **Rating** 94 **To** 2029 $35
Bin 150 Marananga Barossa Valley Shiraz 2009 **Rating** 94 **To** 2035 $70 BE
St Henri 2008 **Rating** 94 **To** 2025 $95 BE
Bin 138 Barossa Valley Grenache Shiraz Mourvedre 2010 **Rating** 94 **To** 2018 $35 BE

ΨΨΨΨΨ **Thomas Hyland Cool Climate Adelaide Chardonnay 2011** **Rating** 93 **To** 2016 $23 BE
Cellar Reserve Adelaide Chardonnay 2010 **Rating** 93 **To** 2016 $34 BE
✪ **Thomas Hyland Adelaide Shiraz 2009** Deep, vivid crimson–purple; as one would expect and hope, has the Penfolds red wine stamp all over it, from the blackberry, plum and plum cake fruit, to the positive integrated oak and soft tannins. A treat in store for those keeping it for a decade at least. Screwcap. 14.5% alc. **Rating** 93 **To** 2030 $23
Bin 2 Shiraz Mourvedre 2010 **Rating** 93 **To** 2020 $38 BE
✪ **Koonunga Hill Seventy Six Shiraz Cabernet 2010** Bright crimson–purple; the retro label is a nostalgic look back to the first vintage of Koonunga Hill, made in '76, and still the best ever. This medium- to full-bodied blend is a cut above the standard Koonunga Hill of today, and is very much in the mould of that first vintage. A special on-premise wine. Screwcap. 14.5% alc. **Rating** 92 **To** 2018 $20

Thomas Hyland Cabernet Sauvignon 2009 Rating 92 To 2019 $23
Cellar Reserve Woodbury Vineyard Eden Valley Traminer 2010
Rating 91 To 2014 $34 BE
Bin 23 Adelaide Hills Pinot Noir 2011 Rating 91 To 2016 $40 BE
Bin 407 Cabernet Sauvignon 2009 Rating 90 To 2018 $60 BE
Bin 8 Cabernet Shiraz 2010 Rating 90 To 2018 $38 BE

Penfolds Magill Estate ★★★★★

78 Penfold Road, Magill, SA 5072 **Region** Adelaide Zone
T (08) 8301 5569 **www**.penfolds.com **Open** 7 days 10.30–5
Winemaker Peter Gago **Est.** 1844 **Dozens** NFP **Vyds** 5.2ha
This is the birthplace of Penfolds, established by Dr Christopher Rawson Penfold in 1844;
his house is still part of the immaculately maintained property. It includes 5.2ha of precious
shiraz used to make Magill Estate; the original and subsequent winery buildings, most still
in operation or in museum condition; and the much-acclaimed Magill Restaurant, with
panoramic views of the city, a great wine list and fine dining. All this is a 20 min drive from
Adelaide's CBD. Exports to the UK, the US and other major markets.

🍷🍷🍷🍷🍷 Shiraz 2009 This edition of Magill Estate Shiraz, like so many before, offers
a generous personality of spiced plums, fruitcake and succulent sweet oak, in
harmony with its fruit; medium-bodied and lively, the tannins are ample, ripe
succulent and long. Cork. 14.5% alc. **Rating** 95 To 2030 $130 BE

Penley Estate ★★★★★

McLeans Road, Coonawarra, SA 5263 **Region** Coonawarra
T (08) 8736 3211 **www**.penley.com.au **Open** 7 days 10–4
Winemaker Kym Tolley, Greg Foster **Est.** 1988 **Dozens** 45 000 **Vyds** 111ha
Owner Kym Tolley describes himself as a fifth-generation winemaker, the family tree
involving both the Penfolds and the Tolleys. He worked in the industry for 17 years before
establishing Penley Estate and has made every post a winner since, producing a succession of
rich, complex, full-bodied red wines and stylish Chardonnays. These are made from precious
estate plantings. Exports to all major markets.

🍷🍷🍷🍷🍷 Special Select Coonawarra Shiraz 2009 Deep colour and loaded with
focused dark fruits, char and spice; the palate is medium-bodied and unctuous,
revealing a long, even and harmonious wine, power held in check, and ready for
the long haul. Cork. 14.5% alc. **Rating** 94 To 2024 $51 BE
Tolmer Limited Release Coonawarra Cabernet Sauvignon 2009
Deep garnet; an expressive and savoury bouquet exhibiting cedar, cassis, olive and
sage; the full-bodied palate has firm tannins, in balance with the generous fruit on
offer, and with a fine and fragrant finish. Screwcap. 14.5% alc. **Rating** 94 To 2020
$32 BE

🍷🍷🍷🍷🍷 Phoenix Coonawarra Cabernet Sauvignon 2010 Vibrant deep crimson; a
✪ punchy and expressive cabernet bouquet with redcurrant, cassis, clove and olive on
display; the palate is medium- to full-bodied, fleshy, and manages to create a long
and even finish; designed for early consumption, but will stand the test of time in
the medium term. Screwcap. 14.5% alc. **Rating** 93 To 2020 $20 BE
Reserve Coonawarra Cabernet Sauvignon 2009 **Rating** 90 To 2018 $51 BE
✪ Condor Coonawarra Cabernet Shiraz 2010 Bright colour, with fresh red
and black fruits, black olive and a gentle lift of thyme; the palate is medium-
bodied, fleshy and succulent, with a long, juicy and approachable conclusion; enjoy
in the full flush of youth. Screwcap. 14.5% alc. **Rating** 90 To 2016 $20 BE

🍷🍷🍷🍷 Chertsey 2009 **Rating** 89 To 2016 $51 BE
Aradia Coonawarra Chardonnay 2010 **Rating** 88 To 2014 $20
Hyland Coonawarra Shiraz 2010 **Rating** 88 To 2016 $20 BE
Gryphon Coonawarra Merlot 2010 **Rating** 88 To 2014 $20 BE
○ Over the Moon Coonawarra Rose 2011 **Rating** 87 To Now $15

Penmara

Unit 8, 28 Barcoo St, Roseville, NSW 2069 (postal) **Region** Hunter Valley/Orange
T (02) 9417 7088 **www**.penmarawines.com.au **Open** Not
Winemaker Hunter Wine Services (John Hordern) **Est.** 2000 **Dozens** 25 000 **Vyds** 120ha
Penmara was formed with the banner 'Five Families: One Vision', pooling most of their
grapes, with a central processing facility, and marketing focused exclusively on exports. The
sites are Lilyvale Vineyards in New England; Tangaratta Vineyards at Tamworth; Birnam Wood
and Martindale Vineyards in the Hunter Valley; and Highland Heritage at Orange. In all, these
vineyards give Penmara access to 120ha of shiraz, chardonnay, cabernet sauvignon, semillon,
verdelho and merlot, mainly from the Hunter Valley and Orange. Exports to South Korea,
Malaysia, Singapore and China.

ℙℙℙℙℙ **Reserve Hunter Valley Chardonnay 2010** Bright straw-green; an altogether
impressive Chardonnay, with an intense and tightly focused display of grapefruit,
stone fruit and melon fruit, the oak subtle, the finish long. Screwcap. 13.5% alc.
Rating 94 **To** 2017 $22

ℙℙℙℙℙ **Five Families Orange Riesling 2011** Pale, bright straw-green; while the
✪ bouquet is as yet restrained, the palate surges with a mix of lime juice and
pineapple; classic now or later style, possibly assisted by a touch of botrytis.
Screwcap. 12.5% alc. **Rating** 93 **To** 2016 $16

Penna Lane Wines

Lot 51, Penna Lane, Penwortham via Clare, SA 5453 **Region** Clare Valley
T (08) 8843 4033 **www**.pennalanewines.com.au **Open** Thurs–Sun 11–5, or by appt
Winemaker Peter Treloar, Paulett Wines **Est.** 1998 **Dozens** 5000 **Vyds** 4.37ha
Peter Treloar acquired Penna Lane Wines from its founders, the Klavins and Stafford-Brookes
families, in 2009. Peter is no stranger to wine, having established Heritage Wines in 1984
in partnership with Steve Hoff. His return to the Clare Valley was preceded by his ancestor
Francis Treloar, who in 1870 established a vineyard and winery that became known as
Springvale. Peter has no intention of making major changes, and is keen to produce Riesling
that reflects the distinct subregions within the Clare Valley, sourcing additional parcels of grapes
from the Skilly Valley and Watervale. Exports to Hong Kong, South Korea, Fiji, Vietnam,
Thailand, China and Japan.

ℙℙℙℙℙ **Clare Valley Shiraz 2009** Bright colour; dark fruits and a little charcuterie
complexity combine with grace on the bouquet; the palate is dark and savoury,
with vibrant acidity and pure fruit remaining on the long and even finish.
Screwcap. 14.2% alc. **Rating** 94 **To** 2025 $28 BE

ℙℙℙℙℙ **Skilly Clare Valley Riesling 2011 Rating** 92 **To** 2020 $25 BE

ℙℙℙℙ **Clare Valley Cabernet Sauvignon 2009 Rating** 88 **To** 2016 $28 BE

Penny's Hill

281 Main Road, McLaren Vale, SA 5171 **Region** McLaren Vale
T (08) 8557 0888 **www**.pennyshill.com.au **Open** 7 days 10–5
Winemaker Ben Riggs **Est.** 1988 **Dozens** 15 000 **Vyds** 44ha
Founded in 1988 by Tony and Susie Parkinson, Penny's Hill produces high-quality Shiraz
(Footprint and The Skeleton Key) from its 18.4ha estate vineyard that, unusually for McLaren
Vale, is close-planted with a thin vertical trellis/thin vertical canopy. Malpas Road Vineyard
(15ha of shiraz, cabernet sauvignon and merlot) and Goss Corner Vineyard (10.6ha of viognier,
shiraz and merlot) complete the estate holdings, and provide the fruit for the Cracking Black
Shiraz. Penny's Hill also produces estate-grown Grenache, Cabernet Sauvignon and Merlot
(the Sauvignon Blanc and Chardonnay come from 'estates of mates' vineyards in the Adelaide
Hills), all wines with a distinctive 'red dot', inspired by red dot 'sold' stickers on works of art
in commercial galleries. Exports to the UK, the US, Canada, Sweden, Denmark, Germany,
Switzerland, Singapore, China and NZ.

ŸŸŸŸŸ **Cracking Black McLaren Vale Shiraz 2010** Crimson-purple; an enticing
✪   bouquet full of fruit and hints of spice and oak draws you into a juicy, textured
          palate with dark plum, blackberry, licorice and bitter chocolate all having their
          say on the long palate, the extract well managed. Screwcap. 14.5% alc. **Rating** 95
          To 2025 $22

          Footprint McLaren Vale Shiraz 2010 While dark in colour, the essency
          bouquet reveals a luscious and almost exotic array of sweet black fruits, offset
          by a mere suggestion of anise; full-bodied and very tannic, despite the generous
          lashings of fruit, this is a 'take no prisoners' example of McLaren Vale Shiraz; big,
          rugged, dense and for lovers of wine with plenty of flavour and stuffing. Screwcap.
          14.5% alc. **Rating** 94 **To** 2025 $65 BE

          Skeleton Key McLaren Vale Shiraz 2010 A rich, ripe, warm and inviting
          bouquet of dark fruits, licorice, fruitcake and clove; the palate is fleshy and
          generous, with a backbone of acidity that brings the fruit to life; ready to go as
          a young wine, yet with the stuffing to hang around for a while yet. Screwcap.
          14.5% alc. **Rating** 94 **To** 2023 $35 BE

          Footprint McLaren Vale Shiraz 2009 Medium to full red-purple, not clear;
          like the Skeleton Key, after two years in barrel a rich and complex wine, fruit and
          oak both to the fore; the extra 0.5% alcohol is worth the trade-off for this 'best
          barrels' selection; rich plum and blackberry fruit carry the oak; traditional generous
          McLaren Vale style. Screwcap. 15% alc. **Rating** 94 **To** 2024 $65

✪   **Edwards Road McLaren Vale Cabernet Sauvignon 2010** Deep purple-
          crimson; open-fermented and matured in French and American oak for 15
          months, this is a luscious wine with Cherry Ripe, cassis, chocolate and spice
          flavours, some oak-derived, but mainly ex fruit. It's no crime to drink it today, but
          do save some for tomorrow. Screwcap. 14.5% alc. **Rating** 94 **To** 2015 $24

ŸŸŸŸŸ **The Agreement Adelaide Hills Sauvignon Blanc 2011** Pale quartz; an
✪   elegant, well-balanced and structured wine, with a fragrant bouquet and precisely
          framed palate, bringing grass/herb, green pea/asparagus and tropical nuances into
          play, backed by bright, crisp acidity. Screwcap. 12% alc. **Rating** 93 **To** 2013 $19

✪   **Thomas Goss McLaren Vale Shiraz 2010** Deep crimson-purple; an archetypal
          McLaren Vale Shiraz, stacked to the rafters with juicy blackberry fruit, dark
          chocolate, licorice and well-balanced and integrated ripe tannins, oak submerged
          in the fruit. Classy packaging a plus. Drink or cellar. Screwcap. 14.5% alc.
          Rating 93 **To** 2020 $16

          The Experiment McLaren Vale Grenache 2010 **Rating** 93 **To** 2018 $30 BE
          Skeleton Key McLaren Vale Shiraz 2009 **Rating** 91 **To** 2020 $35

✪   **Thomas Goss McLaren Vale Cabernet Sauvignon 2010** Bright red-purple;
          in traditional McLaren Vale style, ripe, luscious and full-bodied, but not obviously
          alcoholic, nor with dead fruit; dark chocolate, plum cake, vanillin oak and plush
          tannins fill the mouth. Screwcap. 14.5% alc. **Rating** 91 **To** 2020 $16

⦿   **The Black Chook McLaren Vale Shiraz 2010** **Rating** 90 **To** 2018 $17
✪   **Malpas Road McLaren Vale Merlot 2010** Medium red-purple; there are
          two faces of Merlot in Australia; the first is soft and plummy (New World), the
          second distinctly more savoury and black olive-influenced (traditional Old World).
          This wine is an appealing example of the latter. Screwcap. 14.5% alc. **Rating** 90
          To 2015 $19

ŸŸŸŸ   **Thomas Goss Adelaide Hills Chardonnay 2011** **Rating** 89 **To** 2014
✪ $16 BE

          The Specialized McLaren Vale Shiraz Cabernet Merlot 2010 **Rating** 89
          To 2020 $22

          Thomas Goss Adelaide Hills Riesling 2011 **Rating** 88 **To** 2016 $15
⦿   **Red Dot McLaren Vale Shiraz 2010** **Rating** 88 **To** 2014 $15
⦿   **Woop Woop Shiraz 2010** **Rating** 88 **To** 2014 $15
          The Black Chook Sparkling Shiraz NV **Rating** 88 **To** Now $17
          The Black Chook Adelaide Hills Sauvignon Blanc 2011 **Rating** 87
          To Now $17

Pennyweight Winery ★★★

Pennyweight Lane, Beechworth, Vic 3747 **Region** Beechworth
T (03) 5728 1747 **F** (03) 5728 1704 **www.**pennyweight.com.au **Open** 7 days 10–5
Winemaker Stephen Newton Morris, Stephen MG Morris, Frederick Morris **Est.** 1982
Dozens 1500 **Vyds** 8ha
Pennyweight was established by Stephen Newton Morris, great-grandson of GF Morris,
founder of Morris Wines. The 4ha each of vines at Beechworth and Rutherglen are not
irrigated and are biodynamically grown. The business is run by Stephen, together with his
wife Elizabeth and assisted by their three sons; Elizabeth says, 'It's a perfect world', suggesting
that Pennyweight is more than happy with its lot in life.

🍷🍷🍷🍷 **Beechworth Gamay 2010** The low alcohol was a deliberate choice, not one
forced by nature. The wine is open-fermented and hand-plunged, but taken
to barrel prior to the end of fermentation; the light strawberry and red cherry
flavours are well balanced, the wine ready for immediate consumption. Cork.
10.9% alc. **Rating** 89 **To** 2013 $26
Beechworth Shiraz 2009 The colour is not deep, and is faintly hazy/turbid; the
plum and blackberry fruit has some tannin structure; finishes with good acidity.
Cork. 12.9% alc. **Rating** 87 **To** 2014 $35

Pepper Tree Wines ★★★★★

Halls Road, Pokolbin, NSW 2321 **Region** Hunter Valley
T (02) 4998 7539 **F** (02) 4998 7746 **www.**peppertreewines.com.au **Open** Mon–Fri 9–5,
w'ends 9.30–5
Winemaker Jim Chatto **Est.** 1991 **Dozens** 50 000 **Vyds** 172.1ha
The Pepper Tree winery is part of a complex that also contains The Convent guest house
and Roberts Restaurant. In 2002 it was acquired by a company controlled by Dr John Davis,
who owns 50% of Briar Ridge. The appointment of Jim Chatto as chief winemaker in '07
brought the expertise of the best young wine judge on the Australian wine show circuit, with
winemaking talents to match, and should bring further improvement (vintage conditions
accepted). It sources the majority of its Hunter Valley fruit from its Tallavera Grove vineyard
at Mt View, but also has premium vineyards at Orange, Coonawarra and Wrattonbully, which
provide its Grand Reserve and Reserve (single-region) wines. Self-evidently, the wines are
exceptional value for money. Exports to the US, Canada, Singapore, China and NZ.

🍷🍷🍷🍷🍷 **Alluvius Single Vineyard Reserve Hunter Valley Semillon 2011** Bright
quartz-green; the bouquet is striking and notably complex, with nuances of grass,
herb and citrus zest, the palate at once mouth-filling yet elegant, the flavours
running through with drive and energy; has the balance, line and length of a
true champion. From the Braemar Vineyard. Screwcap. 10.8% alc. **Rating** 97
To 2026 $32
Random Acts of Winemaking Hunter Valley Grampians Shiraz 2010
The result of a 007 licence to kill, this was the brainchild of close friends Jim
Chatto and Dan Buckle at Mount Langi Ghiran; a blend of two estate vineyards,
the Hunter providing the depth and savoury elements, the Grampians the very
obvious spice and floral lift. A high class, long-lived wine. Screwcap. 13.8% alc.
Rating 97 **To** 2030 $55
Tallawanta Limited Release Hunter Valley Semillon 2011 Bright quartz;
an altogether seamless and perfectly balanced Semillon, with a deceptive youthful
delicacy to the classic flavours of lemongrass and lemon citrus, minerality and
acidity providing the life line into a very long future. Screwcap. 11.5% alc.
Rating 96 **To** 2026 $28
Single Vineyard Reserve Coquun Hunter Valley Shiraz 2010 Bright
crimson-purple; a young, exuberant and lively bouquet, with red fruits, spices, fine
toasty oak and fresh leather all on display; the medium-bodied palate reveals a silky
texture, fresh acidity and fine-grained tannins, all in harmony and cohesion. A wine
for drinking and for cellaring. Screwcap. 14.5% alc. **Rating** 96 **To** 2030 $55 BE

✪ **Single Vineyard Limited Release Hunter Valley Semillon 2011** Pale straw-green; has the lemongrass aroma unique to Semillon, with a hint of spice hiding in the background; the palate has great intensity, drive and length, drawing saliva from the mouth as the acidity clicks in. Has a certain 20-year future. Screwcap. 11.3% alc. **Rating** 95 **To** 2031 $22

Tallavera Limited Release Hunter Valley Shiraz 2010 Crimson-purple; the complex bouquet has plum, mulberry and a hint of sweet earth, the soft, supple medium-bodied palate with great line, length and balance, the tannins silky, oak restrained. Screwcap. 14.5% alc. **Rating** 95 **To** 2030 $45

Single Vineyard Strandlines Grand Reserve Wrattonbully Cabernet Shiraz 2010 Has a whirl of blackcurrant, blackberry, black cherry and plum interleaved with spicy notes; the tannins are fine, the oak doing its job, but both leaving the focus on the fruit. Screwcap. 14.5% alc. **Rating** 95 **To** 2025 $55

✪ **Hunter Valley Marlborough Semillon Sauvignon Blanc 2011** **Rating** 94 **To** 2014 $18

Single Vineyard Reserve Venus Block Orange Chardonnay 2011 **Rating** 94 **To** 2018 $30 BE

Single Vineyard Limited Release Hunter Valley Shiraz 2010 **Rating** 94 **To** 2025 $35

Single Vineyard Reserve The Gravels Wrattonbully Shiraz Viognier 2010 **Rating** 94 **To** 2023 $42 BE

Single Vineyard Reserve Calcare Coonawarra Cabernet Sauvignon 2010 **Rating** 94 **To** 2030 $42 BE

♟♟♟♟♟ **Single Vineyard Limited Release Hunter Valley Chardonnay 2011**
✪ Vivid green hue; a taut, tight and linear wine showing lime, lemon, quartz and a light dusting of toasty oak; the palate is racy and fine, with a bath talc minerality lingering on the finish. Screwcap. 13.5% alc. **Rating** 92 **To** 2018 $22 BE

Single Vineyard Reserve 14 Shores Wrattonbully Merlot 2010 **Rating** 91 **To** 2019 $35 BE

✪ **Wrattonbully Coonawarra Cabernet Sauvignon 2010** An easy wine to enjoy, with the ripe black fruit flavours buffered by quality French oak, and the soft tannins that are usually the mark of Wrattonbully; has good length and is balanced. Screwcap. 14.5% alc. **Rating** 90 **To** 2018 $18

Single Vineyard Reserve Elderslee Road Wrattonbully Cabernet Sauvignon 2010 **Rating** 90 **To** 2020 $42 BE

♟♟♟♟ **Wrattonbully Shiraz 2010** **Rating** 87 **To** 2015 $18 BE

Pepperilly Estate Wines ★★★☆

Suite 16, 18 Stirling Highway, Nedlands, WA 6009 (postal) **Region** Geographe
T 0401 860 891 **www**.pepperilly.com **Open** Not
Winemaker Damian Hutton **Est.** 1999 **Dozens** 2500 **Vyds** 10ha

Partners Geoff and Karyn Cross, and Warwick Lavis, planted their vineyard in 1991 with 2ha each of cabernet sauvignon and shiraz, and 1ha each of semillon, sauvignon blanc, viognier, chardonnay, mourvedre and grenache. The vineyard has views across the Ferguson Valley to the ocean, with sea breezes providing good ventilation.

♟♟♟♟♟ **Ferguson Valley Chardonnay 2010** Estate-grown, with four clones, probably
✪ with one or two of the Dijon clones; the fragrant, almost flowery bouquet and intense fruit-focused palate confirms that judgement. Top-class value. Screwcap. 14.5% alc. **Rating** 92 **To** 2016 $15

♟♟♟♟ **Ferguson Valley Shiraz 2010** **Rating** 89 **To** 2025 $18
Purple Patch 2010 **Rating** 89 **To** 2014 $18
Ferguson Valley Sauvignon Blanc Semillon 2011 **Rating** 88 **To** 2014 $15
Ferguson Valley Rose 2011 **Rating** 87 **To** Now $15

Peregrine Ridge

19 Carlyle Street, Moonee Ponds, Vic 3039 (postal) **Region** Heathcote
T 0411 741 772 **www**.peregrineridge.com.au **Open** Not
Winemaker Graeme Quigley, Sue Kerrison **Est.** 2001 **Dozens** 1000 **Vyds** 5.5ha
Graeme Quigley and Sue Kerrison were wine lovers and consumers before they came to growing and making their own wine. Having purchased a property high on the Mt Camel Range (the name comes from the peregrine falcons that co-habit the vineyard and the ridgeline that forms the western boundary of the property), they progressively planted their vineyard solely to shiraz. Irrigation is used sparingly, with the yields restricted to 2.5 to 3.5 tonnes per ha; the grapes are hand-picked into small baskets, transported direct to small open fermenters and made in small batches. A new cellar door is planned for late 2012.

ȲȲȲȲȲ **Winemaker's Reserve Heathcote Shiraz 2007** The bright garnet-red colour is outstanding given the age of the wine, and the bouquet and medium-bodied palate do not disappoint; intense black cherry, licorice, spice and French oak come through in an unbroken streak, silky tannins joining the harmonious, lingering finish. Finding that all of this has been achieved with sky-high alcohol from a drought is a huge surprise. Screwcap. 15.8% alc. **Rating** 94 **To** 2022 $65

ȲȲȲȲȲ **Shearstone Heathcote Shiraz 2009 Rating** 92 **To** 2024 $28
Heathcote Sparkling Shiraz NV Rating 91 **To** 2015 $28

Pertaringa

Cnr Hunt Road/Rifle Range Road, McLaren Vale, SA 5171 **Region** McLaren Vale
T (08) 8323 8125 **www**.pertaringa.com.au **Open** Mon–Fri 10–5, w'ends & public hols 11–5
Winemaker Shane Harris, Geoff Hardy **Est.** 1980 **Dozens** 10 000 **Vyds** 64ha
The name Pertaringa means 'belonging to the hills' and originates from the local Kaurna indigenous language. Tucked away in the cooler eastern foothills of McLaren Vale, Pertaringa was founded in 1980 by highly respected viticulturists Geoff Hardy and Ian Leask. In December 2011, Geoff and his family acquired the Leask interest in Pertaringa to become the sole custodians of the brand. Winemaker Shane Harris, also a chef by trade, oversees all winemaking along with Geoff. Geoff's commitment to industry innovation through clonal and varietal trials has seen, in recent times, the traditional range of Pertaringa wines complimented by the arrival of Tannat, Aglianico and the 'Tin Man' Spanish blend. Exports to the UK, the US and other major markets.

ȲȲȲȲȲ **Over The Top McLaren Vale Shiraz 2009** Vivid deep purple-crimson; a multi-block selection with separate fermentations and a choice of French and American oak works very well indeed; the dark berry fruits have energy and drive, with fresh acidity still apparent after 20 months in oak; excellent balance and length. ProCork. 14.5% alc. **Rating** 95 **To** 2024 $39
GSM McLaren Vale Grenache Shiraz Mourvedre 2009 Light to medium red-purple; the first GSM from Pertaringa, one of a trio of newly packaged wines; this is an impressive medium-bodied wine, with a flourish of red and black fruits, a dash of spice and oak, and fine tannins running through the long finish. Screwcap. 14% alc. **Rating** 94 **To** 2019 $30
Rifle & Hunt Adelaide Cabernet Sauvignon 2009 Purple-crimson; a striking blackcurrant and earth bouquet, then a vibrant palate with almost juicy fruit flavours, quality oak and fine, savoury tannins in harmonious fusion; very good line and length. ProCork. 14% alc. **Rating** 94 **To** 2020 $35

ȲȲȲȲȲ ✪ **Undercover McLaren Vale Shiraz 2009** Deep purple-crimson; stacked to the rafters with blackberry, plum, dark chocolate and earth, but not the least overripe or extractive; has a complex, savoury, medium- to full-bodied palate bringing all the characters of the bouquet into play; fine tannins underwrite the future. Screwcap. 14.5% alc. **Rating** 93 **To** 2030 $22

✪   **Bonfire Block McLaren Vale Semillon 2010** Bright green-quartz; part barrel fermentation in new French oak, plus the combined alcohol and acidity, give this wine an Adelaide Hills feel; there is a range of citrus fruit flavours that will fill out with more time in bottle. Screwcap. 13% alc. **Rating** 91 **To** 2015 $18

✪   **Tin Man Adelaide Tempranillo Graciano Garnacha 2010** Light colour; a mix of spicy and savoury characters runs through the length of the light- to medium-bodied palate; red cherry and forest strawberries also come into play on a thoroughly interesting wine. Screwcap. 13% alc. **Rating** 91 **To** 2016 $20

✪   **McLaren Vale Autumn Harvest 2010** Full gold-green; terms such as late harvest and autumn harvest have no particular meaning; here the wine is lusciously sweet, albeit with good balance; complex peach, cumquat and lime marmalade are all at work on the palate. 375ml. Screwcap. 10.5% alc. **Rating** 91 **To** 2013 $18
McLaren Vale Vintage Fortified 2010 Rating 90 **To** 2025 $29

♟♟♟♟   **Single Vineyard McLaren Vale Aglianico 2010 Rating** 89 To 2015 $30
Understudy McLaren Vale Cabernet Petit Verdot 2009 Rating 88 To 2014 $20
Single Vineyard McLaren Vale Tannat 2009 Rating 88 To 2019 $30
Scarecrow Adelaide Sauvignon Blanc 2011 Rating 87 To 2013 $18
Stage Left Adelaide Merlot 2009 Rating 87 To 2014 $20

Petaluma   ★★★★★

Spring Gully Road, Piccadilly, SA 5151 **Region** Adelaide Hills
T (08) 8339 9300 **www**.petaluma.com.au **Open** At Bridgewater Mill, 7 days 10–5
Winemaker Andrew Hardy, Mike Mudge, Penny Jones **Est.** 1976 **Dozens** 60 000
Vyds 240ha
The Lion Nathan group (owned by Kirin of Japan) comprises Petaluma, Knappstein, Mitchelton, Stonier and Smithbrook. The Petaluma range has been expanded beyond the core group of Croser Sparkling, Clare Valley Riesling, Piccadilly Chardonnay and Coonawarra (Cabernet Sauvignon/Merlot). Newer arrivals of note include Adelaide Hills Viognier and Adelaide Hills Shiraz. Bridgewater Mill is the second label, which consistently provides wines most makers would love to have as their top label. The SA plantings in the Clare Valley, Coonawarra and Adelaide Hills provide a more than sufficient source of estate-grown grapes for the wines. Exports to all major markets.

♟♟♟♟   **Tiers Piccadilly Valley Chardonnay 2009** The Tiers site includes soils derived from rock 1.8 billion years old, and the vines themselves are now mature; the aromas and flavours are particularly intense, ripe stone fruit, fig and melon lanced by a steel spike of perfectly balanced acidity. A wine of quality in every respect, protected by the screwcap. 14% alc. **Rating** 96 **To** 2020 $115
Hanlin Hill Clare Valley Riesling 2011 How you can write a War and Peace back label for a Riesling I don't know, as I quickly gave up trying to read it, lacking a microscope and a lazy five minutes or so. Pale straw-green, it has considerable depth to its juicy fruit, ranging from lime/citrus to a hint of red apple; admirable length and balance. Screwcap. 12.5% alc. **Rating** 94 **To** 2021 $25

✪   **Bridgewater Mill Adelaide Hills Chardonnay 2010** Straw-green; the fragrant bouquet introduces an immaculately structured and balanced wine, with nectarine, white peach and citrus/grapefruit seamlessly welded with subtle French oak and minerally acidity, the finish long and fresh. Screwcap. 14% alc. **Rating** 94 **To** 2018 $20
Project Co. Piccadilly Valley Chardonnay 2010 Pale, bright straw-green; another take on Petaluma's first permanent home and vineyard; impeccably balanced, with nectarine, fig and hints of creamy cashew. Screwcap. 14% alc. **Rating** 94 **To** 2016 $35
Adelaide Hills Shiraz 2010 Medium red-purple; a War and Peace back label rivals d'Arenberg; the wine spent 18 months in 75% new French oak, and the spicy black cherry and blackberry fruit has managed to maintain its integrity in the oak forest; good now, but with even better things in store. Screwcap. 14% alc. **Rating** 94 **To** 2030 $45

Coonawarra Merlot 2007 Light to medium red-purple; marries elegance and intensity, the cassis aromas and flavours tempered by 19 months in new and one-year-old French barriques that play a significant role in shaping both the flavour and texture of the wine. It emerges as a Merlot demanding respect. Screwcap. 14% alc. **Rating** 94 **To** 2022 $50

Croser Piccadilly Valley Rose 2008 Sports the most ghastly remake of what was once a very elegant label, the virulent puce colour to blame. A 100% pinot noir, tiraged into this bottle Nov '08. Pale salmon, it is well-balanced, with complex spice, brioche and cake flavours intermingling with red berry fruit in the background; good balance, mouthfeel and length. Cork. 13% alc. **Rating** 94 **To** Now $34

ŢŢŢŢŢ **Project Co. Adelaide Hills Riesling 2009 Rating** 93 **To** 2019 $25
Croser Piccadilly Valley Pinot Noir Chardonnay 2009 Rating 93 **To** 2015 $34
Project Co. Adelaide Hills Riesling 2009 Rating 92 **To** 2020 $25

✪ **Bridgewater Mill Adelaide Hills Pinot Gris 2011** Light straw-green; a decision was taken to let the fruit do all the talking, and not elaborate the wine in any way, notwithstanding the gris rather than grigio name. The decision was exactly correct: it is overflowing with pear, apple and citrus flavours, and might even cause lunchtime conversation to momentarily halt. Screwcap. 12.5% alc. **Rating** 91 **To** 2013 $20
Bridgewater Mill Adelaide Hills Shiraz 2010 Rating 91 **To** 2018 $25
Bridgewater Mill Adelaide Hills Shiraz 2009 Rating 90 **To** 2019 $25

ŢŢŢŢ **The Hundred Line Coonawarra Cabernet Sauvignon 2009 Rating** 87 **To** 2015 $27

Peter Lehmann ★★★★★

Para Road, Tanunda, SA 5352 **Region** Barossa Valley
T (08) 8565 9555 **www.**peterlehmannwines.com **Open** Mon–Fri 9.30–5, w'ends & public hols 10.30–4.30
Winemaker Andrew Wigan, Ian Hongell, Kerry Morrison, Peter Kelly **Est.** 1979
Dozens 750 000
Under the benevolent ownership of the Swiss/Californian Hess Group, Peter Lehmann has continued to flourish, making wines from all the major varieties at multiple price points, the common link being over-delivery against expectations. Its record with its Reserve Eden Valley Riesling (usually released when five years old) is second to none, and it has refined its Semillons to the point where it can take on the Hunter Valley at its own game with five-year-old releases, exemplified by the recent wines. At the base level, the Semillon is the largest seller in that category in the country (albeit significantly diminished by Marlborough Sauvignon Blanc sales). Yet it is as a red winemaker that Peter Lehmann is best known in both domestic and export markets, with some outstanding wines leading the charge. Grapes are purchased from 150 growers in the Barossa and Eden valleys, and the quality of the wines has seen production soar. Chief winemaker Andrew Wigan notched up his 30th vintage in 2012. Exports to all major markets.

ŢŢŢŢŢ **Stonewell Barossa Shiraz 2008** Impenetrable colour; a flagship wine without excessive baggage and window dressing; pure, ripe and fragrant Barossa fruit, layered, perfumed and attractive in every regard; the palate is densely structured, but far removed from overbearing, with a fine thread of tannins and a long and expansive finish; a lovely fresh wine from a challenging vintage. Screwcap. 14% alc. **Rating** 96 **To** 2030 $90 BE

VSV Orrock Shiraz 2009 A homage to the hard work done by the growers this 'very special vineyard' wine displays rich and ripe mulberry, mocha and spice on the bouquet; the palate shows great concentration, yet a lightness of touch, despite the depth of fruit on offer; seamless, long and engaging from start to finish. Screwcap. 14.5% alc. **Rating** 95 **To** 2025 $60 BE

Mentor Cabernet 2008 Bright medium red-purple; a brand that has reinvented itself over its lifetime, originally matured in American oak, then a mix of French and American, the primary fermentation finished in that oak followed by 18 months' maturation. It is a Cabernet with real authority to its fruit, suggesting some comes from old vines in the Eden Valley as well as the Barossa Valley; it has length aplenty, and good balance. Screwcap. 14.5% alc. **Rating** 95 **To** 2023 $43

EVS Eden Valley Shiraz 2010 The bouquet on this wine is highly fragrant and expressive, showing mulberry, blackberry, clove and violet; the palate is juicy and forward on entry, yet reveals a backbone of tannin and acid that freshens things up, and provides a long and harmonious finish. Screwcap. 14.5% alc. **Rating** 94 **To** 2020 $25

VSV 1885 Shiraz 2009 VSV denotes a very special vintage from a special vineyard. This is a 4-acre block (1.8ha) planted in 1885 by the Schrapel family (now six generations of residence), matured for 18 months in French oak hogsheads; 700 dozen bottles produced, which (mathematically) equals 7.95 tonnes per acre. Hmmm. It has very good colour, and delicious dark berry and plum fruit, fine tannins and obvious oak; the last will soon integrate. Screwcap. 14.5% alc. **Rating** 94 **To** 2034 $60

Eight Songs Barossa Shiraz 2008 Deep and succulently fruited, with mulberry, fruitcake, licorice and a fine seasoning of toasty oak; the palate is richly textured and warm, but maintains freshness and complexity for a big-impact, big-boned style. Screwcap. 14% alc. **Rating** 94 **To** 2020 $40 BE

Eight Songs Barossa Shiraz 2007 Medium red-purple; a complex wine that has surmounted the challenge of the dry vintage, the spicy/cedary bouquet leading into a long, medium-bodied palate with black fruits accompanied by the spice and cedar of the bouquet, the tannins fine. Screwcap. 14.5% alc. **Rating** 94 **To** 2022 $43

Black Queen Sparkling Shiraz 2007 Purpose built for seriousness in a category that is not often taken seriously, this dark and savoury wine exhibits sweet black fruits, leather, spice and cinnamon in spades; long and tightly packed fruits and well-handled sugar on the palate combine to make a complete wine. Cork. 14% alc. **Rating** 94 **To** 2015 $40 BE

EVC Eden Valley Chardonnay 2010 Rating 93 **To** 2018 $25 BE

Layers Red 2010 A Mediterranean blend in every respect, with the fresh Provençal herb character palpable; a juicy, medium-bodied wine that is pleasant, fleshy and savoury all at the same time; a drink to enjoy without pretence. Shiraz/Tempranillo/Mourvedre/Grenache. Screwcap. 14.5% alc. **Rating** 90 **To** 2016 $16 BE

Shiraz Cabernet 2010 Light to medium red-purple; a more than adequate mouthful of flavour, homage to the '10 vintage, and to the first class handling in the winery of some pretty impressive grapes. There is nothing to be gained from cellaring it, although it won't fall over any time soon. Screwcap. 14.5% alc. **Rating** 90 **To** 2013 $12

Pewsey Vale ★★★★★

Eden Valley Road, Eden Valley, SA 5353 **Region** Eden Valley
T (08) 8561 3200 **www**.pewseyvale.com **Open** By appt
Winemaker Louisa Rose **Est.** 1847 **Dozens** 20 000 **Vyds** 50ha
Pewsey Vale was a famous vineyard established in 1847 by Joseph Gilbert, and it was appropriate that when the Hill-Smith family began the renaissance of the Adelaide Hills plantings in 1961, it should do so by purchasing Pewsey Vale and establishing 40ha of riesling and 4ha each of gewurztraminer and pinot gris. The Riesling has also finally benefited from being the first wine to be bottled with a Stelvin screwcap in 1977. While public reaction forced the abandonment of the initiative for almost 20 years, Pewsey Vale never lost faith in the technical advantages of the closure. A quick taste (or better, a share of a bottle) of five- to seven-year-old Contours Riesling will tell you why. Exports to all major markets.

♟♟♟♟♟ **Prima 24GR Individual Vineyard Selection Eden Valley Riesling 2011** Light straw-green; the 24 g/l of residual sugar is perfectly balanced by acidity, and together they lift the flavour profile dramatically. There is no rule of any kind about when you should drink the wine between now and 2025, nor is there any rule about when not to drink it. Vino-Lok. 9.5% alc. **Rating** 96 **To** 2025 $27
The Contours Museum Reserve Eden Valley Riesling 2006 Mid gold, vibrant green hue; a classic museum release from an icon of the Eden Valley, and this wine is ready to go; lemon curd, toast and mineral complexity in spades; the palate is generously textured and toasty to finish, and for those lovers of Riesling with a little age, this is sure to please. Screwcap. 12.5% alc. **Rating** 94 **To** 2018 $30 BE

♟♟♟♟♀ **The Contours Museum Reserve Eden Valley Riesling 2007 Rating** 93 **To** 2017 $30
Eden Valley Riesling 2011 Rating 90 **To** 2015 $23

Pfeiffer Wines   ★★★★★

167 Distillery Road, Wahgunyah, Vic 3687 **Region** Rutherglen
T (02) 6033 2805 **www.**pfeifferwines.com.au **Open** Mon–Sat 9–5, Sun 10–5
Winemaker Chris and Jen Pfeiffer **Est.** 1984 **Dozens** 20 000 **Vyds** 32ha
Family-owned and run, Pfeiffer Wines occupies one of the historic wineries (built in 1880) that abound in Northeast Victoria, and which is worth a visit on this score alone. Both hitherto and into the future, Pfeiffer's Muscats, Topaques and other fortified wines are a key part of the business. The arrival of daughter Jen, by a somewhat circuitous and initially unplanned route, has dramatically lifted the quality of the table wines, led by the reds. The results at the Victorian Wine Show '11 were unprecedented: trophies for the 2010 Merlot and Shiraz, and top-gold medals for the '10 Cabernet Sauvignon, NV Topaque and Classic Topaque. Watch this space. Exports to the UK, Canada, Belgium, Malaysia, Taiwan and China.

♟♟♟♟♟ **Rare Rutherglen Muscat NV** Significantly deeper and darker than the Grand, and voluptuously smooth and velvety, the first-up flavours a celestial smoothie of raisins, chocolate and coffee, thereafter opening up to allow the rancio to enter and freshen the mouth, and begin building the prodigiously long finish. A mere sip of a wine such as this will stay in your taste buds for literally minutes. 500ml. Screwcap. 17.5% alc. **Rating** 98 **To** 2013 $123
Rare Rutherglen Topaque NV Light, clear burnt amber, distinctly lighter than other Rutherglen Rare Topaques; consistent with the colour, it is very fine and detailed, yet displays the full array of toffee, cake, tea leaf and rich spices. Screwcap. 17.5% alc. **Rating** 97 **To** 2013 $123
Grand Rutherglen Muscat NV Deep brown grading to olive on the rim; exceptionally viscous for the Grand category, with layers of raisined fruit, dried fruits, Christmas cake and coffee; the rancio cuts in quite early, thus preventing any suggestion of cloying sweetness, the back-palate and finish drawing out so effortlessly that there is no alcohol hit or full-on sweetness. 500ml. Screwcap. 17.5% alc. **Rating** 97 **To** 2013 $84
Shiraz 2010 Bright, clear crimson; particularly notable for its elegance and fragrance; light- to medium-bodied, but very long; fresh red and black cherry fruit; controlled oak and tannins. Screwcap. 14.5% alc. **Rating** 95 **To** 2025 $24
✪ **Cabernet Sauvignon 2010** Excellent crimson-purple; has an expressive, varietal bouquet with blackcurrant/cassis to the fore; the medium-bodied palate is long, silky and very well balanced, new oak making a contribution, the tannins fine-grained. Screwcap. 14.5% alc. **Rating** 95 **To** 2020 $24
Merlot 2010 Bright, light crimson-purple; the fragrant cassis and red cherry bouquet is a welcome start, the medium-bodied palate fresh and long, with sweet cassis red berry fruit sprinkled with savoury nuances. Trophy Best Merlot Victorian Wines Show '11. Screwcap. 14% alc. **Rating** 94 **To** 2019 $25
Seriously Fine Pale Dry Apera NV Bright light green-gold; a very good example of a flor fino style, fine, intense and bone dry, the finish and aftertaste lingering for a very long time. Screwcap. 17% alc. **Rating** 94 **To** 2013 $29

Seriously Nutty Medium Dry Apera NV Golden-orange; it has an average age of 25 years, with some of the components twice that age. It is no longer possible to use any of the classic Sherry names, but if it were permitted, this would be a dry Amontillado; it has wonderful nutty flavours on the mid palate, with rancio evident but not overwhelming, and miraculously finishes dry; an elegant and convincing older brother for the Pale Dry Apera. Screwcap. 21.5% alc. Rating 94 To 2013 $50

Christopher's VP 2008 Deep colour; very much in the modern style of what used to be vintage port; the sweetness is controlled, leaving the black fruits and spices free rein, the finish balanced and clean. Screwcap. 18% alc. Rating 93 To 2020 $30

Rutherglen Topaque NV Bright golden amber; not dissimilar to the Cambells Rutherglen Topaque, with bright honey and candied fruit, and a backing of tea leaf, warm spices and vanilla cake. 500ml. Screwcap. 17.5% alc. Rating 93 To 2013 $20

Riesling 2011 Pale quartz; certainly imbued with the steely citrus bite of acidity that is the mark of the cool vintage, and convincing fruit flavours spun around the cool core of the wine. Screwcap. 11.5% alc. Rating 92 To 2021 $19

Rutherglen Muscat NV A rich and luscious style with abundant raisin, burnt toffee and Christmas pudding flavours, the finish lifted by a cut of rancio. 500ml. Screwcap. 17.5% alc. Rating 92 To 2013 $20

Gamay 2011 Rating 90 To Now $18

Carlyle Shiraz 2010 Rating 89 To 2015 $19
Marsanne 2011 Rating 89 To 2019 $19
Carlyle Chardonnay Marsanne 2011 Rating 89 To Now $17

Phaedrus Estate ★★★★

220 Mornington-Tyabb Road, Moorooduc, Vic 3933 **Region** Mornington Peninsula
T (03) 5978 8134 **www**.phaedrus.com.au **Open** W'ends & public hols 11–5
Winemaker Ewan Campbell, Maitena Zantvoort **Est.** 1997 **Dozens** 3500 **Vyds** 2.5ha
Since Maitena Zantvoort and Ewan Campbell established Phaedrus Estate, they have gained a reputation for producing premium cool-climate wines. Their winemaking philosophy brings art and science together to produce wines showing regional and varietal character with minimal winemaking interference. Exports to Hong Kong.

Mornington Peninsula Shiraz 2010 Strong crimson-purple; the Phaedrus style is extraordinarily consistent, with a depth of flavour and structure that puts it apart from the other Peninsula makers. Tasted blind, you would have no idea where the wine came from. All of that said, it's a mouth-filling wine with varietal character and time to go. Screwcap. 13.8% alc. Rating 91 To 2025 $24

Mornington Peninsula Chardonnay 2010 Bright straw-green; an elegant wine with nicely ripened stone fruit flavours ex wild yeast fermentation and extended lees stirring and contact. Screwcap. 13.4% alc. Rating 90 To 2015 $22

Mornington Peninsula Pinot Gris 2011 Fully deserves the gris label, and has achieved its complexity and mouthfeel without obvious effort; good pear and apple flavours are backed by balanced acidity. Screwcap. 13.8% alc. Rating 90 To 2014 $22

Reserve Mornington Peninsula Pinot Noir 2009 Some colour development, and not absolutely brilliant, despite 20 months in French oak. As always with Phaedrus, there is no shortage of flavour, whether it be ripe fruit, tannins or oak, but they are in balance. This was bottle 154 of 400 made, one new French hogshead containing the entire production. Screwcap. 13.8% alc. Rating 90 To 2015 $45

PHI ★★★★★

Lusatia Park Vineyard, Owens Road, Woori Yallock, Vic 3139 **Region** Yarra Valley
T (03) 5964 6070 **www**.phiwines.com **Open** By appt
Winemaker Steve Webber **Est.** 2005 **Dozens** 1700 **Vyds** 7.5ha

This is a joint venture between two very influential wine families: De Bortoli and Shelmerdine. The key executives are Stephen Shelmerdine and Steve Webber (and their respective wives). It rests upon the selection and management of specific blocks of vines without regard to cost. Until 2010 the wines all came from the Lusatia Park Vineyard in the Yarra Valley, but in that year a Heathcote Syrah Grenache was made, and, if the opportunity arises, other wines will be added to the portfolio. The name, incidentally, is derived from the 21st letter of the ancient Greek alphabet, symbolising perfect balance and harmony. It's courageous pricing for a new kid on the block, but reflects the confidence the families have in the wines. Exports to the UK and China.

ㅜㅜㅜㅜㅜ **Single Vineyard Yarra Valley Pinot Noir 2010** Clear red-purple; a complex wine from start to finish, doubtless why it walked away with multiple trophies (including Best Wine of Show) at the National Wine Show '11. Despite the depth and savoury complexity the wine has, its dark berry fruits also have purity and length. Screwcap. 13% alc. **Rating** 96 **To** 2019 $60
Single Vineyard Heathcote Syrah Grenache 2010 Light, clear red-purple; from the first whiff of the bouquet through to the aftertaste of the palate, the message is the same: the pursuit of finesse and elegance to allow the origin of the wine (the Willoughby Bridge Vineyard) maximum opportunity to express itself; the spiced red and black cherry fruits of the finish and aftertaste are totally delicious. Screwcap. 14% alc. **Rating** 95 **To** 2020 $35
Single Vineyard Yarra Valley Chardonnay 2010 From 26-year-old estate vines, hand-picked, whole bunch-pressed direct to used barrels for wild yeast fermentation and 100% mlf; has retained good acidity to balance the nutty brioche notes, and melon and citrus fruit. Elegant wine. Screwcap. 13% alc. **Rating** 94 **To** 2017 $44
ESTE 2006 Fermented in this bottle, with 54% pinot noir, 46% chardonnay; hand-riddled and disgorged after four years on yeast lees, the dosage only 2 g/l; a fine-boned and structured wine, brioche, crème brulée and honey intermingling with the crisp citrussy fruit. Diam. 12.5% alc. **Rating** 94 **To** 2014 $40

ㅜㅜㅜㅜㅜ **Single Vineyard Yarra Valley Sauvignon 2010 Rating** 93 **To** 2014 $40

Philip Lobley Wines ★★★★☆

1084 Eucalyptus Road, Glenburn, Vic 3717 (postal) **Region** Upper Goulburn
T (03) 5797 8433 **F** (03) 5797 8433 **Open** Not
Winemaker Philip Lobley **Est.** 2008 **Dozens** 450 **Vyds** 2.82ha

The micro, patchwork-quilt vineyard was first planted by Philip Lobley in 1995 with pinot noir, merlot and cabernet sauvignon. In 2008 nebbiolo, semillon, sauvignon blanc and moscato giallo (or gold muskateller, thought to be a version of muscat a petits grains) were added. These are high-density plantings and, with shoot and crop thinning, yield is kept to 600–800 g per vine. The red wines are wild yeast-fermented and neither filtered nor fined; the Yarra Valley Sauvignon Blanc (purchased) is whole bunch-pressed and wild yeast-fermented. The 2008 plantings were destroyed by the Black Saturday bushfires, and nebbiolo and moscato giallo have been replanted; 80% of the older wines recovered thanks to the good spring/summer rainfall of '10.

ㅜㅜㅜㅜㅜ **Pinot Noir 2010** A blend of grapes from Yea (grown on red soil at 550 m) and Yarra Valley (grown on grey sandstone-derived soils), with a total production of four barrels. The colour is good, the bouquet perfumed, and the palate has basically been left to look after itself; in best Burgundian tradition, it works. Diam. 12.5% alc. **Rating** 94 **To** 2017 $36

ㅜㅜㅜㅜㅜ **Nebbiolo 2010 Rating** 91 **To** 2018 $35
○ **Sauvignon 2010 Rating** 91 **To** 2013 $20
The Gauntlet 2010 Rating 90 **To** 2013 $32

Philip Murphy Estate

484 Purves Road, Main Ridge, Vic 3928 (postal) **Region** Mornington Peninsula
T (03) 5989 6609 **www**.philipmurphyestate.com.au **Open** Not
Winemaker Philip Murphy **Est.** 2004 **Dozens** 200 **Vyds** 1ha

Few would know the challenges facing small, start-up wineries better than Philip Murphy. After the sale of his very substantial retail wine business to Coles, he and wife Jennifer decided to have a seachange and move down to the Mornington Peninsula. He then happened to meet Kevin Bell of Hurley Vineyard, who gave him the confidence to enrol in wine science at CSU in 2003. The Murphys built a new house, incorporating a winery and cellar door underneath. They planted chardonnay and pinot noir (the latter French clones and MV6), and the first experimental vintage followed in '07; the '08 was 'a big step forward' says Philip, and he's not wrong. And, of course, he has completely circumvented the sale challenges with the tiny make (although it may be expanded) by selling most of the wine through the mailing list and small amounts through the Pinot Shop in Launceston, the Prince Wine Store and Como Wines & Spirits in Melbourne.

🍷🍷🍷🍷🍷 Mornington Peninsula Pinot Noir 2010 As you would expect from a man with such an intimate knowledge of Burgundy, this wine has a savoury personality full of dark cherry, sap and cold tea; the palate is youthful and bright, with the ample level of silky tannins providing a long and complex finish; will be interesting to watch over time. Diam. 13.5% alc. **Rating** 94 **To** 2016 $45 BE

🍷🍷🍷🍷🍷 Jennifer's Mornington Peninsula Chardonnay 2010 **Rating** 90 **To** 2014 $45 BE

Philip Shaw Wines

Koomooloo Vineyard, Caldwell Lane, Orange, NSW 2800 **Region** Orange
T (02) 6365 2334 **www**.philipshaw.com.au **Open** W'ends 12–5, or by appt
Winemaker Philip Shaw, Daniel Shaw **Est.** 1989 **Dozens** 15 000 **Vyds** 47ha

Philip Shaw, former chief winemaker of Rosemount Estate and then Southcorp, first became interested in the Orange region in 1985. In '88 he purchased the Koomooloo Vineyard and began extensive plantings, the varieties including shiraz, merlot, pinot noir, sauvignon blanc, cabernet franc, cabernet sauvignon and viognier. Son Daniel has joined Philip in the winery, at a time when the quality of the portfolio of wines goes from strength to strength. Exports to the UK, the US and other major markets.

🍷🍷🍷🍷🍷 No. 11 Orange Chardonnay 2010 Light green-straw; a very elegant and refined Chardonnay, the focus on citrus and mineral, not on fig, melon or ripe stone fruit; the oak is subtle, and the overall flinty character bows to Chablis. The question is whether the bow is a little obsequious. Time will tell. Screwcap. 12.3% alc. **Rating** 94 **To** 2017 $35

The Idiot Orange Shiraz 2011 Vibrant crimson; the bouquet offers a very attractive black cherry, pepper and charcuterie perfume; the palate is medium-bodied, incredibly fresh and succulent, with tangy acidity, fruit and fine tannins working in complete harmony; excellent value and should be enjoyed in the full flush of youth. Screwcap. 13% alc. **Rating** 94 **To** 2016 $20 BE

No. 5 Orange Cabernet Sauvignon 2009 Clear purple-red; a fragrant red fruit bouquet with cassis and a touch of cherry leads into a stylish medium-bodied palate, the positive fruit supported by balanced and integrated oak and polished tannins. Screwcap. 13.5% alc. **Rating** 94 **To** 2024 $75

🍷🍷🍷🍷🍷 The Architect Orange Chardonnay 2010 Light straw-green; the complex
✪ bouquet has interlocking stone fruit and cashew aromas that flow into the long and polished palate, reflecting precisely judged ripeness. I am smitten with the label, part of a continuing design pattern. Screwcap. 13.3% alc. **Rating** 93 **To** 2017 $20

No. 89 Orange Shiraz 2009 **Rating** 90 **To** 2020 $50 BE

🍷🍷🍷🍷 Pink Billy Orange Saignee 2011 **Rating** 89 **To** 2013 $25 BE
Edinburgh NV **Rating** 88 **To** 2013 $35

Pierro ★★★★★

Caves Road, Wilyabrup via Cowaramup, WA 6284 **Region** Margaret River
T (08) 9755 6220 **www**.pierro.com.au **Open** 7 days 10–5
Winemaker Dr Michael Peterkin **Est.** 1979 **Dozens** 10 000 **Vyds** 7.85ha
Dr Michael Peterkin is another of the legion of Margaret River medical practitioners; for good measure, he married into the Cullen family. Pierro is renowned for its stylish white wines, which often exhibit tremendous complexity; the Chardonnay can be monumental in its weight and texture. That said, its red wines from good vintages can be every bit as good. Exports to the UK, Denmark, Belgium, Russia, Malaysia, Indonesia, Hong Kong, Singapore and Japan.

🍷🍷🍷🍷🍷 **LTC Margaret River Semillon Sauvignon Blanc 2011** Gleaming light straw-green; in the usual richly flavoured and layered style of Pierro, LTC denoting a little touch of chardonnay; in the middle of all the opulent tropical richness, a stainless steel rod of iron from the semillon provides balance and ability to age. Screwcap. 13.5% alc. **Rating** 95 **To** 2017 $31
Margaret River Chardonnay 2010 Vibrant green hue; almost exotic in its appeal, this stalwart of Margaret River delivers a heady blend of grapefruit, pain grillee and cashews, not to mention a sprinkling of toasty oak; thickly textured yet light on its feet, there is a lot to like in this wine. Screwcap. 14% alc. **Rating** 95 **To** 2016 $78 BE

🍷🍷🍷🍷 **Margaret River Cabernet Sauvignon Merlot LTCf 2009 Rating** 87 **To** 2014 $38 BE

Pike & Joyce ★★★★★

PO Box 54, Sevenhill, SA 5453 **Region** Adelaide Hills
T (08) 8843 4370 **www**.pikeandjoyce.com.au **Open** Not
Winemaker Neil Pike, John Trotter, Steve Baraglia **Est.** 1998 **Dozens** 5000 **Vyds** 18.5ha
This is a partnership between the Pike family (of Clare Valley fame) and the Joyce family, related to Andrew Pike's wife, Cathy. The Joyce family have been orchardists at Lenswood for over 100 years, but also have extensive operations in the Riverland. Together with Andrew they have established a vineyard planted to sauvignon blanc (5.9ha), pinot noir (5.73ha), pinot gris (3.22ha), chardonnay (3.18ha) and semillon (0.47ha). The wines are made at Pikes Clare Valley winery. Exports to the UK, Canada, the Netherlands, Taiwan, Singapore, Hong Kong, and Japan.

🍷🍷🍷🍷🍷 **Adelaide Hills Chardonnay 2010** From the estate Lenswood vineyard; a complex bouquet with notes of cashew and smoky bacon, the palate with excellent focus, intensity and drive; verges on mouth-watering, so intense is it. Screwcap. 13.5% alc. **Rating** 95 **To** 2020 $30
Adelaide Hills Sauvignon Blanc 2011 Bright, pale straw-green; stacked full of generous varietal fruit on the bouquet and palate; the flavours range through herb and snow pea at one end, gooseberry, passionfruit and guava at the other; any more would be too much. Screwcap. 13% alc. **Rating** 94 **To** 2014 $20

🍷🍷🍷🍷 **The Bleedings Adelaide Hills Pinot Noir Rose 2011 Rating** 89 **To** 2013 $20
Adelaide Hills Pinot Noir 2010 Rating 89 **To** 2015 $30
Adelaide Hills Pinot Gris 2011 Rating 88 **To** 2013 $20

Pikes ★★★★★

Polish Hill River Road, Sevenhill, SA 5453 **Region** Clare Valley
T (08) 8843 4370 **www**.pikeswines.com.au **Open** 7 days 10–4
Winemaker Neil Pike, John Trotter, Steve Baraglia **Est.** 1984 **Dozens** 35 000 **Vyds** 69.41ha
Owned by the Pike brothers: Andrew was for many years the senior viticulturist with Southcorp, Neil was a winemaker at Mitchell. Pikes now has its own winery, with Neil presiding. In most vintages its white wines, led by Riesling, are the most impressive. Planting of the vineyards has been an ongoing affair, with a panoply of varietals, new and traditional,

reflected in the 2007 plantings of an additional 4.3ha of riesling (26ha in total), 3.5ha of shiraz and a first-up planting of 1.24ha of savagnin. The Merle is Pikes' limited production, flagship Riesling. Exports to the US, Canada, the Netherlands, Switzerland, Poland, Cyprus, Singapore, Malaysia, Hong Kong, Taiwan, Japan and China.

ΤΤΤΤΤ **The Merle Clare Valley Riesling 2011** Brilliant pale lemon colour; the bouquet here is textbook age-worthy Clare, showing fresh lime juice, bath talc minerals and a suggestion of floral complexity; the palate is linear, racy, long and pure, with precise acidity and tightly wound fruit providing considerable line and length. Screwcap. 12% alc. **Rating** 95 **To** 2025 $38 BE

The EWP Reserve Clare Valley Shiraz 2009 A pure and ripe expression of essency blackberry pastille, ironstone and charcuterie complexity; medium-bodied and refined, with silky tannins, and polished red and black fruits, mixed with florals, that linger elegantly for a very long time. Screwcap. 14.5% alc. **Rating** 95 **To** 2025 $70 BE

Eastside Clare Valley Shiraz 2009 Bright, clear crimson-purple; a remarkably elegant wine in the context of the Clare Valley, brimming with fresh red berry fruits, finely drawn tannins and fresh acidity, oak incidental to the main play, alcohol totally irrelevant. Screwcap. 14.5% alc. **Rating** 94 **To** 2020 $26

The Assemblage Clare Valley Shiraz Mourvedre Grenache 2009 Mid garnet; a pristine and attractive bouquet offering spicy red fruits, plums and dried Provençal herbs; medium-bodied and pure-fruited, with life and energy aplenty; excellent value and a lovely example of elegance in this particular blend. Screwcap. 14.5% alc. **Rating** 94 **To** 2020 $22 BE

ΤΤΤΤ♀ **Gill's Farm Clare Valley Viognier 2010** Rating 93 **To** 2015 $23 BE
Traditionale Clare Valley Riesling 2011 Rating 91 **To** 2018 $23 BE
Damside Clare Valley Chardonnay 2010 Rating 90 **To** 2016 $23 BE

✪ **Impostores Clare Valley Savignan 2011** A very eurocentric personality, with little to observe on the bouquet, yet with a palate that has a real kick of acidity to grab your attention; the depth is not really there, but the freshness is enervating and to be enjoyed in the right context; outdoors on a hot day with seafood. Screwcap. 10.5% alc. **Rating** 90 **To** 2014 $20 BE

ΤΤΤΤ **Gill's Farm Clare Valley Mourvedre 2009** Rating 89 **To** 2016 $22 BE
⊙ **Clare Hills Shiraz Cabernet 2009** Rating 89 **To** Now $15
✪ **Luccio Clare Valley Pinot Grigio 2011** Rating 89 **To** 2014 $18 BE
⊙ **The Red Mullet 2009** Rating 88 **To** 2014 $15
The Dogwalk Clare Valley Cabernet Merlot 2009 Rating 88 **To** 2016 $20 BE
Valley's End Clare Valley Sauvignon Blanc Semillon 2011 Rating 87 **To** 2014 $20 BE
Luccio Clare Valley Sangiovese Carmenere Rose 2011 Rating 87 **To** 2013 $18 BE

Pimpernel Vineyards   ★★★★★

6 Hill Road, Coldstream, Vic 3770 **Region** Yarra Valley
T 0457 326 436 **www.**pimpernelvineyards.com.au **Open** W'ends & public hols 11–5, or by appt
Winemaker Mark Horrigan, Damien Archibald **Est.** 2001 **Dozens** 2000 **Vyds** 6ha
Lilydale-based cardiologist Mark Horrigan's love affair with wine started long before he had heard about either the Yarra Valley or his family's links, centuries ago, to Condrieu, France. He is a direct descendant of the Chapuis family, his ultimate ancestors first buried in the Church of St Etienne in 1377. In a cosmopolitan twist, his father came from a Welsh mining village, but made his way to university and found many things to enjoy, not the least wine. When the family moved to Australia in 1959, wine remained part of everyday life and, as Mark grew up in the '70s, the obsession passed from father to son. In '97, while working at Prince Alfred Hospital (Sydney), Mark was offered a job in Melbourne, and within weeks of arriving had

started looking for a likely spot in the Yarra Valley. In 2001 he and wife Fiona purchased the property on which they have built a (second) house, planted a vineyard, and erected a capacious winery designed by WA architect Peter Moran. In the course of doing so they became good friends of near-neighbour the late Bailey Carrodus. A cellar door is planned.

ΨΨΨΨΨ Viognier 2010 Glowing yellow-green; this is a seriously difficult grape to grow and wine to make, but this wine makes light of that; it has a perfumed bouquet, and a palate that treads the treacherous path between the bland anonymity on the one hand and heavy phenolics on the other, with a skill of a ballet dancer. It does indeed have opulent mouthfeel, and the stone fruit flavours are, for me at least, those of apricot, often found more on back labels than in bottle. Diam. 14.4% alc. Rating 94 To 2014 $36

Pinot Noir Two 2010 Near identical to Pinot Noir One; this has greater complexity and fruit depth, with some savoury crosscuts to the flow of dark cherry fruit; will repay longer cellaring than Pinot Noir One, but individual choice is purely a question of style, not quality. Diam. 13.5% alc. Rating 94 To 2023 $38

Pinot Noir One 2010 A fragrant, scented bouquet of cherry and a dab of spice introduces a supple, silky palate with a range of red fruit flavours backed up by appreciable but balanced tannins; achieves the aim of elegance and purity. Diam. 13.5% alc. Rating 94 To 2019 $38

Grouch 2010 Very different from the '10 Syrah; everything about this single vineyard shiraz is amplified: the colour, the alcohol, the depth of flavour, and the tannins. There is a veritable labyrinth of aromas and flavours, black fruits, licorice and spice the drivers, oak somewhere caught up in the bowels of the wine. Diam. 15% alc. Rating 94 To 2030 $55

ΨΨΨΨΨ Syrah 2010 Rating 93 To 2020 $42
Chardonnay 2010 Rating 92 To 2016 $36

Pipers Brook Vineyard ★★★★★

1216 Pipers Brook Road, Pipers Brook, Tas 7254 **Region** Northern Tasmania
T (03) 6382 7527 **www.**pipersbrook.com.au **Open** 7 days 10–5
Winemaker René Bezemer **Est.** 1974 **Dozens** 80 000 **Vyds** 185ha
The Pipers Brook Tasmanian empire has 185ha of vineyard supporting the Pipers Brook and Ninth Island labels, with the major focus, of course, being on Pipers Brook. Fastidious viticulture and winemaking, immaculate packaging and enterprising marketing create a potent and effective blend. Pipers Brook operates two cellar door outlets, one at headquarters, the other at Strathlyn. In 2001 it was acquired by Belgian-owned sheepskin business Kreglinger, which has also established a large winery and vineyard (Norfolk Rise, see separate entry) at Mount Benson in SA. Exports to the UK, the US and other major markets.

ΨΨΨΨΨ Estate Pinot Gris 2010 Pale, bright straw; adventurous winemaking, with a period of skin contact and barrel fermentation that has worked well, for the fruit flavours of citrus, apple and pear are all clearly defined, with drive from the acidity, and texture from the handling. Screwcap. 13.5% alc. Rating 94 To 2014 $30

Kreglinger Vintage Brut 2005 A blend of Pinot Noir/Chardonnay from a single estate vineyard block with an east/southeast slope, the base wine fermented in a mix of old oak and stainless steel tanks. The wine spent five years on lees prior to disgorgement in early '11. It is very fresh and pure, with great length, and will gain substantially if kept in bottle for another 3+ years. Cork. 12.5% alc. Rating 94 To 2015 $50

ΨΨΨΨΨ Estate Pinot Gris 2009 Rating 92 To 2013 $28
Estate Pinot Noir 2009 Rating 92 To 2016 $42 BE
Pipers Sparkling 2008 Rating 92 To 2014 $37
Ninth Island Sparkling NV Rating 90 To Now $27

ΨΨΨΨ Ninth Island Sauvignon Blanc 2011 Rating 88 To 2013 $22 BE
Ninth Island Pinot Grigio 2011 Rating 88 To 2013 $23 BE

Pirramimma

Johnston Road, McLaren Vale, SA 5171 **Region** McLaren Vale
T (08) 8323 8205 **www.**pirramimma.com.au **Open** Mon–Fri 10–4.30, w'ends & public
hols 10.30–5
Winemaker Geoff Johnston **Est.** 1892 **Dozens** 40 000 **Vyds** 76.51ha
A long-established family-owned company with outstanding vineyard resources. It is using
those resources to full effect, with a series of intense old-vine varietals including Semillon,
Sauvignon Blanc, Chardonnay, Shiraz, Grenache, Cabernet Sauvignon and Petit Verdot, all
fashioned without over-embellishment. Wines are released under several ranges: Pirra, Stock's
Hill, White Label, ACJ, Katunga and Eight Carat. Exports to the UK, the US and other
major markets.

♥♥♥♥♥ **McLaren Vale Shiraz 2009** Deep red-purple; both the bouquet and palate are
an object lesson in the characters stemming from the terroir of McLaren Vale; the
flavour and mouthfeel are rich but not jammy, with blackberry, plum, spice and
dark chocolate; the ripe tannins on the finish are balanced and integrated, oak
barely raising its hand. Screwcap. 14.5% alc. **Rating** 94 **To** 2024 $25

♥♥♥♥♀ **Katunga GTS 2008** A 54/24/22% blend of grenache, tannat and shiraz. Even
✪ deeper colour than the Eight Carat Grenache '08, the fruits moving into a more
savoury profile contributed by the tannat and shiraz; the unusual blend works well,
providing a neatly balanced, full-bodied wine; the finish is long and well balanced.
Screwcap. 14.5% alc. **Rating** 93 **To** 2018 $20

✪ **Eight Carat Old Bush Vine McLaren Vale Grenache 2008** Even at this age,
the colour is still youthful and deep, a mark of the special character of grenache
from McLaren Vale; the medium-bodied palate has an exotic array of flavours,
with spicy cherry jam matched by even spicier quickly poached raspberry; there
is ample structure, although the tannins are not the least bit assertive. Screwcap.
14.5% alc. **Rating** 92 **To** 2015 $20

✪ **Eight Carat McLaren Vale Liqueur Port NV** Blended from shiraz and
grenache, the youngest wine in the blend is 12 years old; the abundant rancio
gives the wine great complexity, and a cut that prevents the palate from cloying,
notwithstanding its richness. One from left field. Cork. 18.5% alc. **Rating** 92
To 2013 $20

✪ **Stock's Hill McLaren Vale Chardonnay 2011** Fresh and lively, with a
particularly enjoyable finish and aftertaste harking back to the bouquet and mid
palate; it is equally balanced between peach and nectarine on the one hand,
and grapefruit/citrus on the other; there is also a breath of French oak. Should
be drunk while it retains its youthful freshness. Screwcap. 13% alc. **Rating** 91
To 2014 $16

✪ **Stock's Hill McLaren Vale Shiraz 2008** Medium red-purple; the complex
bouquet and medium-bodied palate offer black cherry, blackberry, plum, licorice
and regional chocolate; balanced tannins and integrated oak constitute the farewell
of a basement bargain wine. Screwcap. 14.5% alc. **Rating** 91 **To** 2020 $16
Marina Bay Sands McLaren Vale Cabernet Petit Verdot 2007 **Rating** 90
To 2015 $25

♥♥♥♥ **Eight Carat McLaren Vale Shiraz 2007** **Rating** 89 **To** 2014 $20
✪ **Eight Carat Moscato 2010** **Rating** 89 **To** 2013 $16
McLaren Vale Cabernet Sauvignon 2008 **Rating** 88 **To** 2018 $25
✪ **Eight Carat Chardonnay Pinot Noir NV** **Rating** 88 **To** 2014 $16
Stock's Hill McLaren Vale Adelaide Hills Sauvignon Blanc Semillon 2011
Rating 87 **To** 2013 $16
French Oak McLaren Vale Adelaide Hills Chardonnay 2011 **Rating** 87
To 2013 $20
Stock's Hill Cachet Blanc 2011 **Rating** 87 **To** 2019 $16
McLaren Vale Petit Verdot 2008 **Rating** 87 **To** 2014 $25

Pizzini   ★★★★

175 King Valley Road, Whitfield, Vic 3768 **Region** King Valley
T (03) 5729 8278 **F** (03) 5729 8495 **Open** 7 days 10-5
Winemaker Joel and Alfred Pizzini **Est.** 1980 **Dozens** 29 000 **Vyds** 48.7ha
Fred and Katrina Pizzini have been grapegrowers in the King Valley for over 30 years, with
a substantial vineyard. Originally much of the grape production was sold, but today 80% is
retained for the Pizzini brand, and the focus is on winemaking, which has been particularly
successful. Their wines rank high among the many King Valley producers. It is not surprising
that their wines should span both Italian and traditional varieties, and I can personally vouch
for their Italian cooking skills. Katrina's A tavola! cooking school opened in 2010 with lessons
in antipasti, gnocchi, ravioli, cakes and desserts, and of course, pasta. Exports to Japan.

ᵧᵧᵧᵧᵧ **King Valley Shiraz 2010** Bright colour; pungent and savoury on the bouquet,
with black plums and cherries, laced with cinnamon and sage; medium-bodied,
fleshy and generous, with silky tannins providing length and interest. Screwcap.
13.8% alc. **Rating** 91 **To** 2016 $20 BE
King Valley Sangiovese 2010 Light, bright hue, typical of the variety; has a
distinct rose petal and cherry pip bouquet, then a fine, savoury palate ideally suited
to Italian food, especially cold platters, pasta, osso bucco – you name it. Screwcap.
13.1% alc. **Rating** 91 **To** 2014 $25
King Valley Arneis 2011 Rating 90 **To** 2013 $20
King Valley Verduzzo 2010 Light straw-green; a striking and unusual palate
of poached pears, nutmeg and a touch of cream, acidity freshening the finish. The
variety is rare in Italy, confined to Veneto, but has also been grown by Bianchet in
the Yarra Valley for decades. Screwcap. 13.2% alc. **Rating** 90 **To** 2014 $20
King Valley Nebbiolo 2008 Light colour; fragrant cedar cigar box aromas are
followed by a sweet and sour palate – but in the best sense. For aficionados – and
food. Cork. 14.1% alc. **Rating** 90 **To** 2016 $45

ᵧᵧᵧᵧ **King Valley Pinot Grigio 2011 Rating** 89 **To** 2013 $19
Il Barone 2006 Rating 89 **To** 2015 $43 BE
King Valley Prosecco 2011 Right in the middle of prosecco style, the palate
fresh, dry and well-balanced, with some notes of fruit pips and river stones. Crown
seal. 10.5% alc. **Rating** 89 **To** 2013 $20
King Valley Merlot 2010 Rating 88 **To** 2017 $18

Plan B   ★★★★

679 Calgardup Road, Forest Grove, WA 6286 **Region** Great Southern
T 0413 759 030 **www.**planbwines.com **Open** Not
Winemaker Bill Crappsley **Est.** 2005 **Dozens** 16 000 **Vyds** 20ha
This is a joint venture between Bill Crappsley, a 44-year veteran winemaker/consultant;
Martin Miles, who has a wine distribution business in the southwestern part of the state;
Gary Gosatti, of Arlewood Estate; and Terry Chellappah, wine consultant and now also in
partnership with Gary. The Shiraz is sourced from Bill's Calgardup Vineyard, the remaining
wines from Arlewood, and all are single vineyard releases. It has been a notably successful Plan
B, the estate vineyards increasing from 8 ha, and production up from 7000 dozens. Exports to
the UK, Canada, Sweden, Norway, Finland, Switzerland, Singapore, Hong Kong and China.

ᵧᵧᵧᵧᵧ **Frankland River Shiraz 2009** A pungent and lifted bouquet of charcuterie,
black fruit, bracken and spice; the palate is rustic and rugged, yet not entirely
lacking charm; fresh acidity provides line and interest on the finish. Screwcap.
14% alc. **Rating** 91 **To** 2020 $20 BE
OD Frankland River Riesling 2011 This is an off-dry style, showing the
minerality of the region with lively lime accents and racy acidity; a good
alternative as an aperitif. Screwcap. 11% alc. **Rating** 90 **To** 2015 $17 BE

Plantagenet ★★★★★

Albany Highway, Mount Barker, WA 6324 **Region** Mount Barker
T (08) 9851 3111 **www.**plantagenetwines.com **Open** 7 days 10–4.30
Winemaker John Durham (former) **Est.** 1974 **Dozens** 60 000 **Vyds** 130ha

Plantagenet was established by Tony Smith, who continues to be involved in its management 35 years later, notwithstanding that it has been owned by Lionel Samson & Son for many years. He established five vineyards: Bouverie in 1968, Wyjup in '71, Rocky Horror I in '88, Rocky Horror 2 in '97 and Rosetta in '99 and these vineyards are the cornerstone of the substantial production of the consistently high-quality wines that have always been the mark of Plantagenet: highly aromatic Riesling, tangy citrus-tinged Chardonnay, glorious Rhône-style Shiraz and ultra-stylish Cabernet Sauvignon. Exports to all major markets.

🍷🍷🍷🍷🍷 **Mount Barker Riesling 2011** Vivid, pale green–straw; classic Mt Barker Riesling, with a spine of steely acidity around which the wine is built, the flavours of lime and lemon; its long-term development is as much a certainty as Black Caviar. Screwcap. 12.5% alc. **Rating** 94 **To** 2026 $25

Great Southern Chardonnay 2010 Bright straw-green; a lively and penetrating wine, with classic regional varietal expression to its grapefruit and white peach fruit, oak barely evident. Scores for its finesse. Screwcap. 13.9% alc. **Rating** 94 **To** 2020 $28

Mount Barker Pinot Noir 2010 Clear red-purple; in some vintages Mt Barker can produce Pinot with marked varietal character, and '10 was one of these; it has obvious bramble/forest floor/spice characters, but a deep well of cherry and plum fruit to meet the challenge. Complex and enjoyable now, and should remain so through the rest of this decade. Screwcap. 13% alc. **Rating** 94 **To** 2019 $45

Mount Barker Shiraz 2009 Good crimson colour; brings to the table all the things expected of medium–bodied Mt Barker shiraz: spice and a touch of licorice, ripe red and black berry fruits, and fine tannins; oak too, is where it should be. Screwcap. 13.9% alc. **Rating** 94 **To** 2024 $45

Wyjup Vineyard Ringbark Riesling 2010 Bright, light green-gold; made by cordon cutting (ringbarking was the old term), and is a particularly fine example of the style; beautifully precise lime juice fruit has its intense sweetness perfectly balanced by acidity. Small wonder it received a gold medal at the Canberra International Riesling Challenge '11. Screwcap. 10% alc. **Rating** 94 **To** 2016 $25

🍷🍷🍷🍷 **Wild Mount Barker Riesling 2010 Rating** 92 **To** 2020 $25
Mount Barker Cabernet Sauvignon 2009 Rating 91 **To** 2024 $44

✪ **Omrah Great Southern Chardonnay 2011** Bright, light straw-green; Plantagenet was one of the pioneers with quality unoaked Chardonnay; this is a deliciously juicy mix of grapefruit and passionfruit, the finish long and clean. Screwcap. 13.5% alc. **Rating** 90 **To** 2014 $18

✪ **Omrah Great Southern Shiraz 2009** Clear, light red-purple; spice and pepper perfectly season the red cherry/berry fruit of the bouquet and light- to medium-bodied palate alike; fine tannins lend structural support and complexity. Ready now for whatever food (not fish) you choose. Screwcap. 14.5% alc. **Rating** 90 **To** 2015 $18

🍷🍷🍷 **Omrah Great Southern Sauvignon Blanc 2011 Rating** 89
✪ **To** 2013 $18
✪ **Omrah Great Southern Chardonnay 2010 Rating** 89 **To** 2014 $18
Omrah Cabernet Merlot 2009 Rating 87 **To** 2013 $18

Poacher's Ridge Vineyard ★★★★★

1630 Spencer Road, Narrikup, WA 6326 **Region** Mount Barker
T (08) 9857 6066 **www.**prv.com.au **Open** Fri–Sun 10–4, or by appt
Winemaker Robert Diletti (Contract) **Est.** 2000 **Dozens** 1000 **Vyds** 6.9ha

Alex and Janet Taylor purchased the Poacher's Ridge property in 1999; before then it had been used for cattle grazing. The vineyard includes shiraz, cabernet sauvignon, merlot, riesling, marsanne and viognier. The first small crop came in 2003, a larger one in '04, together making an auspicious debut. However, winning the Tri Nations '07 merlot class against the might of Australia, NZ and South Africa with its '05 Louis' Block Great Southern Merlot was a dream come true.

ΨΨΨΨΨ Sophie's Yard Great Southern Shiraz 2010 Mid crimson; a bright, fresh and floral-accented bouquet with redcurrant, blackberry and sage on display; a splash of toasty oak is revealed on the medium-bodied palate, with tangy acidity and graphite tannins to conclude; needs food, but in the right way. Screwcap. 13.5% alc. **Rating** 94 **To** 2018 $24 BE
Louis' Block Great Southern Cabernet Sauvignon 2010 Deep crimson; cassis, violet and cedary oak are all evident on the bouquet; the palate is generous and dark-fruited, and the tannins are fine and lingering; an even and approachable Cabernet. Screwcap. 13.2% alc. **Rating** 94 **To** 2018 $24 BE

ΨΨΨΨΨ
✪ Great Southern Riesling 2011 Vibrant hue; the bouquet is austere, providing glimpses of fresh lemon and minerals; the palate is tightly wound, high in acid and mineral-driven, finishing with a savoury fennel character; a very refreshing style, requiring a little thought. Screwcap. 12.3% alc. **Rating** 91 **To** 2018 $19 BE

ΨΨΨΨ Limited Release Great Southern Viognier 2011 **Rating** 88 **To** 2013 $24 BE

Point Leo Road Vineyard ★★★★

214 Point Leo Road, Red Hill South, Vic 3937 **Region** Mornington Peninsula
T 0406 610 815 **www**.pointleoroad.com.au **Open** By appt
Winemaker Simon Black, Andrew Thomson, David Cowburn **Est.** 1996 **Dozens** 1000
Vyds 3.6ha
John Law and family planted 1.9ha of pinot noir and 1.5ha of chardonnay in 1996 as contract growers for several leading Mornington Peninsula wineries. Plantings have been progressively expanded, now including small amounts of pinot gris, lagrein and gewurztraminer. Some of the grapes are now contract-made, and they have two labels: Point Leo Road for premium wines, and Point Break the second label.

ΨΨΨΨΨ Mornington Peninsula Chardonnay 2010 Mid gold, green hue; deep and concentrated, showing a great deal of richness and complexity, yet maintaining a light touch of acidity and texture for freshness; nice line and flesh in harmony. Screwcap. 13.5% alc. **Rating** 91 **To** 2016 $28 BE
Mornington Peninsula Pinot Noir 2010 Light garnet; a fragrant and forward, red-fruited and spice-laden bouquet, showing a soft, silky and generous palate; ready for drinking early, but with a fine backbone of acidity and tannin that will provide pleasant drinking for a few years to come. Screwcap. 13.8% alc. **Rating** 91 **To** 2016 $29 BE

Pokolbin Estate

McDonalds Road, Pokolbin, NSW 2321 **Region** Hunter Valley
T (02) 4998 7524 **www**.pokolbinestate.com.au **Open** 7 days 9–5
Winemaker Andrew Thomas (Contract) **Est.** 1980 **Dozens** 4000 **Vyds** 15.5ha
Pokolbin Estate has a very unusual, but very good, multi-varietal, multi-vintage array of wines available for sale at any one time. The Riesling is true Riesling, not misnamed Semillon, the latter being one of their best wines, and wines under screwcap going back six or seven vintages, and single vineyard offerings to boot, are available. Also look for bargains such as the 2003 Shiraz, and some of the best Tempranillos in the Valley. Part of the cellar door (and office) were damaged by fire in '11, but the Olive Centre is fully functional and covering wine tastings.

ΨΨΨΨΨ Ken Bray Hunter Valley Semillon 2011 Bright, light quartz colour; a precisely delineated Semillon with the perfect line, length and balance promised by the fragrant bouquet; the mouth-watering mix of lemon and lemongrass flavours are highlighted by the crisp, lingering acidity, all befitting this great vineyard. Screwcap. 11.6% alc. **Rating** 95 **To** 2026 $25

Limited Release Reserve Hunter Valley Shiraz 2009 Bright, clear red-purple; the fragrant bouquet of black cherry and plum leads into an intense, focused and long palate, with fruit to the fore, the tannins superfine, the oak obvious but balanced, and a regional earthy/savoury twist to conclude. Screwcap. 13.5% alc. **Rating** 95 **To** 2030 $50

Phil Swannell Hunter Valley Semillon 2011 Bright, light quartz; an expressive wine, with lime and lemon sherbet flavours wreathed by slatey acidity that lengthens the finish. Will develop very well. Screwcap. 11.5% alc. **Rating** 94 **To** 2021 $25

♀♀♀♀♀ Hunter Valley Riesling 2011 **Rating** 93 **To** 2020 $28
Belebula Hunter Valley Tempranillo 2009 **Rating** 90 **To** 2018 $28

Polleters   ★★★★

80 Polleters Road, Moonambel, Vic 3478 **Region** Pyrenees
T (03) 9569 5030 **www**.polleters.com **Open** 2nd & 4th w'end each month & long w'ends 10–5
Winemaker Contract **Est.** 1994 **Dozens** 1200 **Vyds** 8.5ha
Pauline and Peter Bicknell purchased the 60ha property on which their vineyard now stands in 1993, at which time it was part of a larger grazing property. The first vines were planted in '94, and include shiraz, cabernet sauvignon, cabernet franc and merlot. In the first few years the grapes were sold, but since 2001 part of the production has been used to make the impressively rich and powerful wines. The grapes are hand-picked, fermented in open vats with hand-plunging, and matured for 18 months in American oak. Exports to Canada, Singapore and China.

♀♀♀♀♀ Moonambel Shiraz 2008 Dark crimson-purple; the aromas and flavours seem incredibly fresh until you see the alcohol, only a fraction above 14%; the elegant, spiced red and black cherry fruits have not been blanketed with alcohol, oak or tannins. Screwcap. 14.1% alc. **Rating** 93 **To** 2023 $25

Y@ Shiraz 2008 Good retention of hue and depth; an attractive medium-bodied shiraz that completely ignores its alcohol, only a smidgeon under 16%; instead of heat on the finish, there is lingering spice, adding texture to the range of medium-bodied red and black fruits. Screwcap. 15.9% alc. **Rating** 91 **To** 2018 $25

♀♀♀♀ Morgan's Choice 2008 **Rating** 89 **To** 2017 $25
Moonambel Cabernet Franc 2009 **Rating** 88 **To** 2014 $25 BE
Moonambel Shiraz 2009 **Rating** 87 **To** 2015 $25 BE

Polperro/Even Keel   ★★★★☆

76 Arthurs Seat Road, Red Hill, Vic 3937 **Region** Mornington Peninsula
T 0405 155 882 **www**.evenkeelwines.com **Open** Not
Winemaker Samuel Coverdale **Est.** 2006 **Dozens** 1500
Sam Coverdale lives on the Mornington Peninsula, makes wine there full-time and surfs part-time. Before taking up residence on the Peninsula, he obtained his degree in oenology from CSU, and accumulated 10 years of winemaking experience in Australia, France, Spain and Italy. Polperro is his single vineyard Mornington Peninsula range, and includes Pinot Noir, Chardonnay and Pinot Gris. Second label Even Keel uses grape varieties that best represent their region. Exports to Hong Kong.

♀♀♀♀♀ Polperro Mill Hill Single Vineyard Mornington Peninsula Chardonnay 2010 Brilliant straw-green; a long and intense palate, with white peach and grapefruit flavours; the acid balance is immaculate, leaving the mouth fresh and thirsting for the next mouthful. A light year away from Even Keel. Diam. 12.9% alc. **Rating** 95 **To** 2018 $45

♀♀♀♀♀ Polperro Mornington Peninsula Pinot Gris 2011 **Rating** 92 **To** 2014 $35
Polperro Mill Hill Single Vineyard Mornington Peninsula Pinot Noir 2010 **Rating** 91 **To** 2015 $48

Polperro Landividdy Lane Single Vineyard Mornington Peninsula Pinot Noir 2010 Rating 90 To 2015 $48

ϤϤϤϤ Even Keel Mornington Peninsula Pinot Noir 2010 Rating 88 To 2014 $33

Ponda Estate ★★★★☆

150 Rhinds Road, Wallington, Vic 3221 **Region** Geelong
T 0438 845 696 **Open** W'ends & public hols 10–5, or by appt
Winemaker Lethbridge Wines (Ray Nadeson) **Est.** 2000 **Dozens** 300
This small family-owned vineyard is situated on the Bellarine Taste Trail, 15 minutes from Geelong and five minutes from Ocean Grove. The low-yielding vines are managed by owners Peter Congdon and Tracey Frigo, who are committed to using sustainable and organic viticultural practices. Babydoll sheep and chooks work the block to sort out weeds/bugs and provide fertilisation for the vines, and each year family and friends gather to help pick the grapes and celebrate harvest. Peter and Tracey also source a small amount of chardonnay from local growers.

ϤϤϤϤϤ **Bellarine Peninsula Chardonnay 2010** Bright yellow-green; a generous wine, with a wide spectrum of varietal fruit flavours running through citrus, melon and fig, the oak flavours in harmony with those of the fruit. Definitely to be enjoyed sooner rather rather than later. Screwcap. 14% alc. **Rating** 93 **To** 2015 $33
Bellarine Peninsula Pinot Noir 2010 From a micro, hand-managed vineyard, and contract-made by local star Ray Nadeson, winning the trophy for Best Pinot Noir at the Geelong Wine Show '11. In typical Nadeson fashion, it is rich and generous, full of black cherry and blood plum fruit. A tiny chink in its armour is that it does not accelerate on the finish. Screwcap. 13.5% alc. **Rating** 93 **To** 2017 $33

Pondalowie Vineyards ★★★★★

123 View Street, Bendigo, Vic 3550 **Region** Bendigo
T (03) 5444 4842 **www.**pondalowie.com.au **Open** W'ends 12–5, or by appt
Winemaker Dominic Morris, Krystina Morris **Est.** 1997 **Dozens** 2500 **Vyds** 10ha
Dominic and Krystina Morris both have strong winemaking backgrounds gained from working in Australia, Portugal and France. Dominic has worked alternate vintages in Australia and Portugal since 1995, and Krystina has also worked at St Hallett and Boar's Rock. They have established 5.5ha of shiraz, 2ha each of tempranillo and cabernet sauvignon, and a little malbec. Incidentally, the illustration on the Pondalowie label is not a piece of barbed wire, but a very abstract representation of the winery kelpie dog. Further wines were received after this issue went to print; tasting notes appear on www.winecompanion.com.au. Exports to the UK, Singapore, Macau, Hong Kong and Japan.

ϤϤϤϤϤ **Vineyard Blend 2008** Dense, almost impenetrable colour; the bouquet has an
✪ exotic array of spice, cassis and black fruits, the full-bodied palate no surprise after the lead up. Licorice and dark chocolate join the band, along with appropriately powerful tannins and oak. Full of individuality, great for lovers of big reds for long ageing, and all this for next to nothing. Screwcap. 14% alc. **Rating** 94 **To** 2030 $20

ϤϤϤϤϤ **Special Release Sparkling Shiraz NV** Rating 90 To 2013 $40

Poole's Rock ★★★★☆

DeBeyers Road, Pokolbin, NSW 2321 **Region** Hunter Valley
T (02) 4993 3688 **www.**poolesrock.com.au **Open** 7 days 10–5
Winemaker Usher Tinkler, Mike Wells **Est.** 1988 **Dozens** 35 000 **Vyds** 15ha
Ever the professional, David Clarke had made steps for the sale of Poole's Rock prior to his death in April 2012. Discussions with neighbour Brian Agnew, owner of Audrey Wilkinson, led to an agreement between the Clarke and Agnew families for Poole's Rock to be acquired by the Agnew interests. The two wineries will keep their separate identities, and winemakers

Jeff Byrne and Ushker Tinker will continue in their roles at Audrey Wilkinson and Poole's Rock respectively. James Agnew, general manager of Audrey Wilkinson, will also become general manager of Poole's Rock. The original vineyard, in the Broke Fordwich subregion, was controversially sold to AGL, currently exploring for coal seam gas in the area. Exports to the UK, the US and other major markets.

ŶŶŶŶŶ **Hunter Valley Shiraz 2009** Vivid purple hue; highly perfumed with blueberry, violets and pencilly oak on display; medium-bodied with graphite tannins, tightly wound fruit and linear acidity; very tannic at this early stage, but with all the ingredients for a long future. Screwcap. 13.2% alc. Rating 95 To 2025 $40 BE

ŶŶŶŶŶ **Regional Selection Tasmania Pinot Noir 2009** Rating 93 To 2015 $40 BE
Cockfighter's Ghost Premium Reserve McLaren Vale Shiraz 2009 Rating 91 To 2016 $25 BE

ŶŶŶŶ **Cockfighter's Ghost Premium Reserve Hunter Valley Chardonnay 2009** Rating 88 To 2014 $25 BE
Cockfighter's Ghost Victoria Pinot Gris 2010 Rating 88 To 2013 $20 BE

Pooley Wines   ★★★★★
Belmont Vineyard, 1431 Richmond Road, Richmond, Tas 7025 **Region** Southern Tasmania
T (03) 6260 2895 **www.pooleywines.com.au Open** 7 days 10–5
Winemaker Matt Pooley **Est.** 1985 **Dozens** 4000 **Vyds** 12.2ha
Three generations of the Pooley family have been involved in the development of Pooley Wines, although the winery was previously known as Cooinda Vale. Plantings have now reached over 12ha in a region that is warmer and drier than most people realise. In 2003 the family planted pinot noir and pinot grigio (with more recent plantings of pinot noir and chardonnay) at Belmont Vineyard, a heritage property with an 1830s Georgian home and a second cellar door in the old sandstone barn and stables.

ŶŶŶŶŶ **Coal River Pinot Noir 2010** Strong, clear colour; has layers of black and red cherry fruit with a filigree of fine tannins; excellent line, length and balance. Gold Tas Wine Show '12. Screwcap. 13.7% alc. Rating 94 To 2018 $40
Butchers Hill Pinot Noir 2009 Medium purple-red; a fragrant bouquet, then a lively, intense, focused and long palate; some stemmy/foresty complexity. Gold Tas Wine Show '12. Screwcap. 13.8% alc. Rating 94 To 2016 $60
Matilda Pinot Noir Chardonnay 2008 Elegant, lively and fresh; considerable length (and balance); juicy citrus and stone fruit flavours drive the palate, allied with some bready/yeasty notes. Silver Tas Wine Show '12. Cork. 12.8% alc. Rating 94 To 2013 $40
Late Harvest Riesling 2011 Pale straw-green; has great elegance and intensity, yet is light of foot and still to fully evolve; the purity of the lime juice flavours borders on the painful. Screwcap. 9.6% alc. Rating 94 To 2021 $35

ŶŶŶŶŶ **Margaret Pooley Tribute Riesling 2011** Rating 91 To 2021 $40
Coal River Riesling 2010 Rating 90 To 2018 $27
Pinot Noir Cuvee 2007 Rating 90 To 2014 $35

ŶŶŶŶ **Family Reserve Cabernet Merlot 2009** Rating 89 To 2016 $45
Family Reserve Cabernet Merlot 2008 Rating 88 To 2015 $40

Poonawatta Estate   ★★★★★
Angaston Road, Eden Valley, SA 5235 **Region** Eden Valley
T (08) 8565 3248 **www.poonawatta.com Open** By appt
Winemaker Reid Bosward, Andrew Holt **Est.** 1880 **Dozens** 1200 **Vyds** 1.6ha
The Poonawatta Estate story is complex, stemming from 1.8ha of shiraz planted in 1880. When Andrew Holt's parents purchased the Poonawatta property, the vineyard had suffered decades of neglect, and a slow process of restoration began. While that was underway, the strongest canes available from the winter pruning of the 1880s block were slowly and progressively dug

into the stony soil of the site. It took seven years to establish the matching 1.8 ha, and the yield is even lower than that of the 1880s block. In 2004 Andrew and wife Michelle were greeted with the same high yields that were obtained right across South Eastern Australia, and this led to declassification of part of the production, giving rise to a second label, Monties Block, which sits underneath The Cuttings (from the 'new' vines) and, at the top, The 1880. The Riesling is produced from a single vineyard of 2ha hand-planted by the Holt family in the 1970s. Exports to France, Denmark and China.

🍷🍷🍷🍷 **The Eden Riesling 2011** Bright quartz-green; the wine has an electric intensity to the flavours and acidity of the palate, mouthpuckering and mouthwatering at the same time, and carrying the lime and mineral flavours through to a lingering finish. Screwcap. 11.6% alc. **Rating** 95 **To** 2026 $26
The 1880 Eden Valley Shiraz 2009 Deep and dark in colour and personality, this wine is laden with black fruits, quartz minerality and a streak of brambly complexity; the palate is warm, thickly textured and unctuous, revealing a long finish of mocha and toast. Cork. 14.9% alc. **Rating** 94 **To** 2020 $85 BE

Port Phillip Estate ★★★★★
263 Red Hill Road, Red Hill, Vic 3937 **Region** Mornington Peninsula
T (03) 5989 4444 **www**.portphillipestate.com.au **Open** 7 days 11–5
Winemaker Sandro Mosele **Est.** 1987 **Dozens** 4000 **Vyds** 9.3ha
Port Phillip Estate has been owned by Giorgio and Dianne Gjergja since 2000. The ability of the site (enhanced, it is true, by the skills of Sandro Mosele) to produce outstanding Syrah, Pinot Noir and Chardonnay, and very good Sauvignon Blanc, is something special. Whence climate change? Quite possibly the estate may have answers for decades to come. A futuristic, multimillion-dollar restaurant, cellar door and winery complex was opened prior to the 2010 vintage. Exports to the UK, Canada and Singapore.

🍷🍷🍷🍷 **Mornington Peninsula Chardonnay 2010** This wine always displays a thrilling backbone of acidity, and the nervous tension carries through from the citrus blossom, mealy bouquet to the taut, savoury and thoroughly engaging palate; long and minerally to conclude. Screwcap. 12.5% alc. **Rating** 95 **To** 2020 $32 BE
Mornington Peninsula Pinot Noir 2010 Light, clear crimson; the wine has to be tasted several times before it displays what it has locked up in the system; its bouquet is fresh and delicate, the palate very different, savoury tannins to the fore, small red berry fruits in the vanguard. Patience needed. Screwcap. 13.5% alc. **Rating** 94 **To** 2018 $38
Single Vineyard Selection Morillon Pinot Noir 2010 Mid crimson, bright; lively and essency red and black cherry on the bouquet, with a lifted herbaceous note an attractive subtext; the palate is nothing short of racy, with plenty of drive, length and silky tannins lingering on the finish; elegance and power combined. Screwcap. 14% alc. **Rating** 94 **To** 2020 $50 BE
Single Vineyard Selection Serenne Mornington Peninsula Shiraz 2010 Deep crimson; the bouquet is full of pastille blackberry aromas, with a spicy and floral accent that is both charming and intriguing; the palate is medium-bodied, pure-fruited and has a savoury charcuterie character that offsets the sweet fruit on offer; long, fine and focused, with silky tannins in complete harmony. Screwcap. 13.5% alc. **Rating** 94 **To** 2023 $50 BE

🍷🍷🍷🍷 **Quartier Arneis 2011 Rating** 93 **To** 2015 $30 BE
Mornington Peninsula Sauvignon 2011 Rating 92 **To** 2016 $25 BE
Quartier Pinot Gris 2011 Rating 90 **To** 2014 $30 BE

🍷🍷🍷🍷 **Salasso Mornington Peninsula Rose 2011 Rating** 88 **To** 2014 $22 BE

Portsea Estate ★★★★☆
PO Box 3148, Bellevue Hill, NSW 2023 **Region** Mornington Peninsula
T (02) 9328 6359 **www**.portseaestate.com **Open** By appt
Winemaker Tim Elphick, Chris Catlow **Est.** 2000 **Dozens** 1400 **Vyds** 3.14ha

Noted film maker Warwick Ross and sister (and silent partner) Caron Wilson-Hawley have moved fast and successfully since the first vintage in 2004. Having had the luxury of having their first seven vintages made at Paringa Estate by Lyndsay McCall and his team, they have built an onsite winery, and hired not one, but two, winemakers with impeccable pedigrees. Amongst other things, Tim Elphick spent five years at Paringa Estate, while Chris Catlow started at Sorrenberg, then moved on to Paringa, and later still, under Sandro Mosele at Port Phillip Estate. By the time of publication, Warwick's film 'Red Obsession', with Andrew Caillard MW playing a leading role, will have been completed and distributed through Village Road Show. It takes an inside look at Bordeaux, and will no doubt be devoured by audiences stretching from Shanghai to New York.

ਊਊਊਊਊ **Mornington Peninsula Pinot Noir 2009** Excellent colour and clarity; maturation in 50% new French oak has not thrown the bouquet or palate out of balance, simply because of the intensity of the fruit; the foresty nuances play an important part of the long and satisfying palate. Screwcap. 13.6% alc. **Rating** 94 **To** 2016 $38

ਊਊਊਊਊ **Mornington Peninsula Pinot Noir 2010 Rating** 93 **To** 2017 $36
Mornington Peninsula Pinot Gris 2011 Rating 91 **To** 2014 $27

Possums Vineyard ★★★★

88 Adams Road, Blewitt Springs, SA 5171 **Region** McLaren Vale
T (08) 8272 3406 **www**.possumswines.com.au **Open** By appt
Winemaker Pieter Breugem **Est.** 2000 **Dozens** 10 000 **Vyds** 52ha
Possums Vineyard is owned by Dr John Possingham and Carol Summers. They have two vineyards in McLaren Vale — one at Blewitt Springs, the other at Willunga — covering shiraz (23ha), cabernet sauvignon (17ha), chardonnay (6.5ha), viognier, malbec (1.3ha each), pinot gris (1.2 h), sauvignon blanc (0.9ha), and grenache (0.5ha). In 2007 they completed construction of a 500-tonne winery at Blewitt Springs and sell both bottled and bulk wine. Winemaker Pieter Breugem has come from South Africa via the US and Constellation Wines. Wines were received after this issue went to print, tasting notes appear on www.winecompanion.com.au. Exports to the UK, Denmark, Germany, Poland, Singapore, Hong Kong and China.

Postcode Wines ★★★☆

PO Box 769, Cessnock, NSW 2325 **Region** Various NSW
T (02) 4998 7474 **www**.postcodewines.com.au **Open** At Meerea Park
Winemaker Rhys Eather **Est.** 2004 **Dozens** 900
This is a new and separate venture for Rhys and Garth Eather (of Meerea Park), taking as its raison d'être wines that clearly show their postcode by exhibiting true regional character. The initial releases were two Shirazs from the Hunter Valley (2320) with a Cabernet Sauvignon from Hilltops (2587), and with several white wines in the future mix. After a slow and opaque start there is now clarity to the focus. Exports to China.

ਊਊਊਊਊ **2320 Hunter Valley Marsanne 2010** Has quickly developed a green sheen to
✪ its colour; this is not an aromatic variety, but it has presence with its mix of lemon and honeysuckle, finishing with good acidity. Impressive first-up effort. Screwcap. 13% alc. **Rating** 93 **To** 2014 $20

ਊਊਊਊ **2587 Kingsvale Shiraz 2010 Rating** 89 **To** 2016 $20
2587 Hilltops Cabernet Sauvignon 2010 Rating 88 **To** 2015 $20

Poverty Hill Wines ★★★★

PO Box 76, Springton, SA 5235 **Region** Eden Valley
T (08) 8568 2220 **www**.povertyhillwines.com.au **Open** Fri–Mon 10–5
Winemaker John Eckert **Est.** 2002 **Dozens** 5000 **Vyds** 29ha
I'm not sure whether there is a slight note of irony in the name, but Poverty Hill Wines brings together men who have had a long connection with the Eden Valley. Robert Buck owns a

small vineyard on the ancient volcanic soils east of Springton, producing both shiraz and cabernet sauvignon. Next is Stuart Woodman, who owns the vineyard with the riesling that produced glorious wines in the early 1990s, and also has high-quality, mature-vine cabernet sauvignon. Finally, there is John Eckert, who once worked at Saltram. He not only works as winemaker at Poverty Hill, but manages Rob Buck's vineyard and his own small block of young riesling in the highlands of Springton. Prolonged drought to 2009, with extreme black frosts down to −14°C at night, gave way to incessant rain that devastated the 2011 vintage. Poverty Hill indeed. (We await the '10 vintage, which should restore Poverty Hill's rating.) Exports to the US, Hong Kong and NZ.

ꢰꢰꢰꢰꢰ **Eden Valley Merlot 2009** Clear red-purple; red fruits drive both the bouquet and light- to medium-bodied palate; here the texture is of slightly fluffy and fine tannins that work well in the overall context of the wine; the elevated alcohol is blessing and bane, blessing because it has eliminated any green or hard elements, bane the signal it will send to those who don't like high-alcohol wines. Here the impact is in fact minimal. Screwcap. 15% alc. **Rating** 90 **To** 2020 $24

ꢰꢰꢰꢰ **Eden Valley Cabernet Sauvignon 2008** **Rating** 89 **To** 2020 $24

Prancing Horse Estate ★★★★★

39 Paringa Road, Red Hill South, Vic 3937 **Region** Mornington Peninsula
T (03) 5989 2602 **www**.prancinghorseestate.com **Open** By appt
Winemaker Sergio Carlei, Pascal Marchand, Patrick Piuze **Est.** 1990 **Dozens** 1500
Vyds 6ha
Anthony and Catherine Hancy acquired the Lavender Bay Vineyard in early 2002, renaming it Prancing Horse Estate and embarking on increasing the estate vineyards, with 2ha each of chardonnay and pinot noir, and 0.5ha of pinot gris. The vineyard moved to organic farming in '03, progressing to biodynamic in '07. They appointed Sergio Carlei as winemaker, and the following year became joint owners with Sergio in Carlei Wines. An additional property 150m west of the existing vineyard has been purchased, and 2ha of vines was planted there in the spring of '10. Prancing Horse has become has become one of a small group of Australian wineries having wines specifically made for them in Burgundy. Pascal Marchand makes an annual release of Morey-St-Denis Clos des Ormes Premier Cru and Meursault Premier Cru Blagny, while Patrick Piuze makes four Chablis appellation wines. Tasting notes for these wines appear on www.winecompanion.com.au. Exports to the UK, the US, France and Sweden.

ꢰꢰꢰꢰꢰ **Mornington Peninsula Pinot Noir 2010** Mid garnet; a fragrant bouquet of cherry, bramble and fresh-cut sage; the palate reveals fine acidity, fine tannins with a strong savoury aspect providing complexity on the long finish. Screwcap. 12% alc. **Rating** 94 **To** 2020 $70 BE

Pressing Matters ★★★★★

665 Middle Tea Tree Road, Tea Tree, Tas 7017 **Region** Southern Tasmania
T (03) 6268 1947 **www**.pressingmatters.com.au **Open** By appt 0414 980 798
Winemaker Winemaking Tasmania (Julian Alcorso), Paul Smart **Est.** 2002 **Dozens** 1350
Vyds 7.1ha
Greg Melick simultaneously wears more hats than most people manage in a lifetime. He is a top-level barrister (Senior Counsel), a Major General (the highest rank in the Australian Army Reserve) and has presided over a number of headline special commissions and enquiries into subjects as diverse as cricket match-fixing allegations against Mark Waugh and others, to the Beaconsfield mine collapse. Yet, if asked, he would probably nominate wine as his major focus in life. Having built up an exceptional cellar of the great wines of Europe, he has turned his attention to grapegrowing and winemaking, planting riesling (2.9ha) at his vineyard on Middle Tea Tree Road in the Coal River Valley. It is a perfect north-facing slope, the Mosel-style Rieslings sweeping all before them. It is moderately certain that Greg is waiting impatiently for his multi-clone pinot noir block to perform in a similar manner. Exports to Singapore.

ŶŶŶŶŶ **R9 Riesling 2006** This wine was the top gold medal at the '11 Tas Wine Show in the '08 and Older Riesling class, prompting the judges to observe, 'These are world class rieslings', with 17 of the 19 entries winning medals. In a unique trifecta, the younger '07 and '08 R9s (all $29 ex cellar door) also won gold medals, and it was fitting that the '06 should also win the Trophy for Best Wine of Show. It still has brilliant lime green colour, the sugar and acid balance perfect, the finish of prodigious length. Screwcap. 13.5% alc. **Rating** 97 **To** 2026 $29
R9 Riesling 2010 Having previously published tasting notes for this and most other Pressing Matters Rieslings, I will content myself with saying that these wines have a wholly remarkable consistency of purity, line and length, whether dry, off-dry or sweet. At the Tasmanian Wine Show '12, they were awarded three trophies, three top gold medals, one gold and six silver medals. It is clearly an exceptional site, with a highly skilled contract winemaker. Screwcap. 10% alc. **Rating** 96 **To** 2015 $29
R69 Riesling 2011 Pale straw-green; a truly lovely young wine; near perfect balance of all its components, despite the (deliberately) high residual sugar; all up, elegant but intense; the '10 gives a glimpse of its future. Screwcap. 9.8% alc. **Rating** 95 **To** 2021 $29
R69 Riesling 2010 Pale green-gold; a stunningly rich and complex wine, with exceptional balance, line and length; fresh lime juice is a diamond-cut expression of the variety, its key word 'elegance'. Gold Tas Wine Show '12. Screwcap. 10% alc. **Rating** 95 **To** 2025 $29
Pinot Noir 2010 Deep colour; multilayered richness to dark fruits; I think the wine manages to carry its load of lots of charry oak, and will come into its own over the next two to three years. Gold Tas Wine Show '12. Screwcap. 13.5% alc. **Rating** 94 **To** 2018 $49

ŶŶŶŶŶ **Block B Pinot Noir 2010 Rating** 90 **To** 2016 $49
Block C Pinot Noir 2010 Rating 90 **To** 2016 $49

Preveli Wines   ★★★★☆

Bessell Road, Rosa Brook, Margaret River, WA 6285 **Region** Margaret River
T (08) 9757 2374 **www.**preveliwines.com.au **Open** At Prevelly General Store, 7 days 10–8
Winemaker Fraser Gallop Estate (Clive Otto, Kate Morgan) **Est.** 1998 **Dozens** 4000
Vyds 7.5ha
While Preveli Wines is a relative newcomer, its owners, the Home family, have lived on the property for three generations. Vince and Greg Home also operate the Prevelly Park Beach Resort and Prevelly Liquor Store, where the wines are available for tasting. Fruit from the vineyard at Rosa Brook (3.5ha of semillon and 1ha each of pinot noir, merlot, cabernet sauvignon and sauvignon blanc) is supplemented by contracts with local growers. The wines are of impressive quality.

ŶŶŶŶŶ **Margaret River Cabernet Merlot 2010** Clear crimson; fragrant red berry fruits on the bouquet have a distinct overlay of mulberry, the palate picking up all of the calling cards of the bouquet, setting them in a medium- to full-bodied framework, juicy notes offset by quality French oak and fine tannins. Has a great future. Screwcap. 13.5% alc. **Rating** 94 **To** 2025 $26

ŶŶŶŶŶ
✪ **Margaret River Semillon Sauvignon Blanc 2011** Has straw-green colour, explained by the barrel fermentation of part of each of the varieties, with the remainder fermented in small stainless steel barrels; has complex texture and flavour, the aromas and flavours ranging through passionfruit at one extreme, lemon curd and cashew at the other. Top value and cellaring capacity. Screwcap. 13% alc. **Rating** 93 **To** 2015 $19
Margaret River Chardonnay 2010 Rating 93 **To** 2017 $24

Primo Estate ★★★★★

McMurtrie Road, McLaren Vale, SA 5171 **Region** McLaren Vale
T (08) 8323 6800 **www.**primoestate.com.au **Open** 7 days 11–4
Winemaker Joseph Grilli, Daniel Zuzolo **Est.** 1979 **Dozens** 30 000 **Vyds** 34ha
One time Roseworthy dux Joe Grilli has always produced innovative and excellent wines.
The biennial release of the Joseph Sparkling Red (in its tall Italian glass bottle) is eagerly
awaited, the wine immediately selling out. Also unusual and highly regarded are the vintage-
dated extra-virgin olive oils. However, the core lies with the La Biondina, the Il Briccone
Shiraz Sangiovese and the Joseph Cabernet Merlot. The business has expanded to take in
both McLaren Vale and Clarendon, with plantings of colombard, shiraz, cabernet sauvignon,
riesling, merlot, sauvignon blanc, chardonnay, pinot gris, sangiovese, nebbiolo and merlot.
Exports to all major markets.

ŸŸŸŸŸ **Joseph Moda McLaren Vale Cabernet Sauvignon Merlot 2009** A hand-
picked 80/20% blend, whole bunches air-dried under cover for one week, then
crushed into open fermenters before spending 20 months in oak. The bouquet
has an immediate touch of dark chocolate along with red and black fruits, then
a superbly rich and balanced palate weaving black fruits, mocha and cedar into a
sinuous stream of flavour. Screwcap. 15% alc. **Rating** 96 **To** 2024 $75
Joseph Angel Gully Clarendon Shiraz 2009 Good colour; a powerful
wine that clearly reflects the cool Clarendon growing conditions with fragrant
spice, pepper and licorice all adding to the complexity of the black cherry and
plum fruit; the medium- to full-bodied structure is excellent, as are the tannins.
Screwcap. 14.5% alc. **Rating** 95 **To** 2030 $75
Joseph Sparkling Red NV The base wine is a traditional method blend of
Australian reds from the 1960s and '70s, the amount bottled each year (30 dozen)
replaced by the same amount of current vintage Joseph Moda Cabernet Merlot;
the liqueur for topping up the bottle after disgorgement is old Australian fortified.
This is a very complex wine that invites the second glass as the multi-spice
flavours run across the palate. Cork. 13.5% alc. **Rating** 95 **To** Now $70
Shale Stone McLaren Vale Shiraz 2009 Part comes from the Clarendon
Vineyard, part from the floor of McLaren Vale, the former calling the tune and
adding elegance to the mix; certainly there is a chocolate/vanilla overtone, but
the mid palate freshness and fine tannin finish are exemplary. Screwcap. 14.5% alc.
Rating 94 **To** 2024 $32
✪ **Il Briccone McLaren Vale Shiraz Sangiovese 2010** Youthful purple-red; an
elegant medium-bodied blend largely driven by the shiraz component until the
finish, where the savoury, sour cherry tannins give the wine its personality and
length. Screwcap. 14% alc. **Rating** 94 **To** 2020 $25
Zamberlan McLaren Vale Cabernet Sauvignon Sangiovese 2009 An
85/15% blend, matured for 20 months in 40% new French and American oak;
despite its alcohol, the wine has a coat of dark chocolate and savoury tannins
around the luscious black cherry and blackcurrant at its centre. Screwcap. 15% alc.
Rating 94 **To** 2025 $35

ŸŸŸŸŸ **Joseph Adelaide Pinot Grigio d'Elena 2011 Rating** 92 **To** Now $28
○ **La Biondina Colombard 2011 Rating** 90 **To** 2013 $16
Joseph McLaren Vale Nebbiolo 2009 Rating 90 **To** 2020 $75

ŸŸŸŸ **Merlesco McLaren Vale Merlot 2011 Rating** 88 **To** Now $16
○ **Primo Secco NV Rating** 89 **To** Now $20

Principia ★★★★

139 Main Creek Road, Red Hill, Vic 3937 (postal) **Region** Mornington Peninsula
T (03) 5931 0010 **www.**principiawines.com.au **Open** By appt
Winemaker Darrin Gaffy **Est.** 1995 **Dozens** 500 **Vyds** 3.5ha
Darrin and Rebecca Gaffy parted company in 2007 after bring Principia to maturity. Darrin
Gaffy has been winemaker and general manager since, and is more than happy with his lot.

The guiding philosophy for Principia is minimal interference, thus the vines (2.7ha of pinot noir and 0.8ha of chardonnay) are not irrigated, and yields are restricted to 1.5–2 tonnes per acre (3.75 tonnes perha) or less, and all wine movements are by gravity or by gas pressure, which in turn means there is no filtration, and both primary and secondary fermentation are by indigenous yeasts. Principia comes from the word 'beginnings' in Latin: 'The Principia' was Sir Isaac Newton's famous scientific work that incorporated his theory of gravitation and the laws of motion.

ŸŸŸŸ♀ **Mornington Peninsula Pinot Noir 2010** A savoury blend of dark cherry, bramble, charcuterie and spice; the palate is fresh, despite the advanced colour, with red fruits coming to the fore and the ample tannins drawing out the finish; still in the elegant mould, but with a little more muscle than the Altior. Diam. 13.8% alc. **Rating** 92 **To** 2016 $39 BE
Mornington Peninsula Chardonnay 2010 Deep colour and showing a rounded assemblage of melons and pears; the palate is slow to build in flavour, but the tight core of fruit and fine acidity draw out the finish, making it surprisingly long; truly a sleeper. Diam. 13.9% alc. **Rating** 90 **To** 2016 $39 BE
Altior Mornington Peninsula Pinot Noir 2010 While showing some bricking in the colour; the bouquet is expressive, elegant and complex, with cherry, cold tea, Asian spices and bramble; there is stuffing on the light-bodied palate in the form of silky fine tannins; a shy, reserved and almost ethereal style. Diam. 13.9% alc. **Rating** 90 **To** 2016 $50 BE

Printhie Wines   ★★★★★
489 Yuranigh Road, Molong, NSW 2866 **Region** Orange
T (02) 6366 8422 **www.**printhiewines.com.au **Open** Mon–Sat 10–4, or by appt
Winemaker Drew Tuckwell **Est.** 1996 **Dozens** 25 000 **Vyds** 33.1ha
Owned by the Swift family, Printhie has established itself at the forefront of quality viticulture and winemaking in Orange. The estate vineyards have matured and fruit intake is supplemented by contract growers, avoiding the fruit salad vineyard approach by sourcing fruit from the best growers in the best sites with the best varietal match. The new generation at Printhie continues to make its mark with Ed Swift, former President of the Orange Region Vignerons Association and a participant of the Future Leaders Program. Winemaker Drew Tuckwell is a Len Evans Tutorial scholar and participant in the Wine Communicators of Australia Young Guns and Gurus program (as a young gun). The wine portfolio has been consolidated: the entry-level Mountain Range now comprises just six wines (three white, three red), the Mount Canobolas Collection (MCC) range is a quasi-reserve range, and the Swift Family Heritage flagship range has been trimmed to just one red wine (a Cabernet Sauvignon/Shiraz blend). Exports to the US, Denmark, Ivory Coast and China.

ŸŸŸŸŸ **MCC Orange Shiraz 2010** Bright crimson-purple; a beguiling bouquet of black cherry, plum, spice and French oak is not a false dawn, for it is followed by a medium-bodied palate with outstanding mouthfeel and balance, all the flavours in a seamless bond with fine, ripe tannins. Screwcap. 14% alc. **Rating** 96 **To** 2025 $35
MCC Orange Chardonnay 2010 Pale, bright straw-green; despite Drew Tuckwell's comment 'has all the winemaking tricks and 35% new oak', the wine is strikingly fragrant and pure, grapefruit/citrus to the fore on the long and intense palate. Screwcap. 13% alc. **Rating** 94 **To** 2018 $35
Swift Family Heritage 2006 A Merlot/Cabernet Sauvignon blend that has retained good hue; if you wish to glean any information from the back label, a magnifying glass in good light, or a microscope at the dining table, will be required. It is intense, concentrated and long, the medium- to full-bodied palate showing fully ripe, gently sweet, fruit. Printhie's flagship wine. Screwcap. 14.5% alc. **Rating** 94 **To** 2020 $45

ŸŸŸŸ♀ **MCC Orange Chardonnay 2009 Rating** 93 **To** 2019 $35
MCC Orange Riesling 2011 Rating 90 **To** 2016 $25

✪   **Orange Sauvignon Blanc 2011** Light straw-green; a wine with plenty of impact provided by the mix of herb, citrus and mineral characters hinted at by the bouquet and delivered on the firm, dry palate. Screwcap. 12.5% alc. **Rating** 90 **To** 2013 $18

🍷🍷🍷🍷   **Mountain Range Orange Shiraz 2009** Rating 89
✪   **To** 2015 $18
Mountain Range Orange Chardonnay 2011 Rating 88 **To** 2013 $18
Mountain Range Orange Pinot Gris 2011 Rating 87 **To** Now $18

Provenance Wines   ★★★★★

870 Steiglitz Road, Sutherlands Creek, Vic 3331 **Region** Geelong
T (03) 5281 2230 **www.**provenancewines.com.au **Open** By appt
Winemaker Scott Ireland, Sam Vogel **Est.** 1995 **Dozens** 1800 **Vyds** 5ha
Scott Ireland and partner Jen Lilburn established Provenance Wines in 1997 as a natural extension of Scott's years of winemaking experience, both here and abroad. Located in the Moorabool Valley, the winery team focuses on the classics in a cool-climate sense – Pinot Gris, Chardonnay and Pinot Noir in particular, as well as Shiraz. Fruit is sourced both and within the Geelong region and further afield (when the fruit warrants selection). They are also major players in contract making for the Geelong region.

🍷🍷🍷🍷🍷   **Tarrington Pinot Gris 2010** Full straw; ginger is often attributed to pinot gris by winemakers, but not easy to see: here it is obvious, as are some unexpected honeysuckle flavours, and a textural richness to the palate. From a seriously cool climate, and is most impressive, as is its cellaring potential. Screwcap. 13% alc. Rating 94 **To** 2015 $26
Golden Plains Pinot Noir 2010 Vivid, clear crimson-purple; a fragrant burst of red berry fruit arises from the glass as it is swirled, the palate building layers of red cherry, plum and a touch of forest floor. Lovely wine. Screwcap. 13.3% alc. Rating 94 **To** 2016 $32
Regional Selection Geelong Pinot Noir 2010 Deep garnet; a deep, dark and rugged wine showing glimpses of the muscular black fruit on the bouquet that certainly follows on the palate; dense fruit and ample forceful tannins are surprisingly held in check by the tightly wound core of sweet black fruits, spicy oak and ironstone minerality; long and expansive and needing a little time to reveal all. Diam. 13.4% alc. **Rating** 94 **To** 2018 $47 BE
Geelong Shiraz 2010 Deep crimson; a spicy melange of red and black fruits, sage and lots of mixed pepper; the palate is medium-bodied and shows fine-grained tannins and fresh acidity to full effect; surprisingly soft and supple to conclude; the possibilities for food and wine matching are a mouth-watering prospect. Screwcap. 13.2% alc. **Rating** 94 **To** 2020 $32 BE

🍷🍷🍷🍷🍷   **Geelong Chardonnay 2010** Rating 93 **To** 2017
Regional Selection Ballarat Pinot Noir 2010 Rating 93 **To** 2018 $47 BE
Regional Selection Henty Pinot Noir 2010 Rating 92 **To** 2017 $47 BE
Barrel Selection Turas Pinot Noir 2010 Rating 91 **To** 2018 $65 BE

Pulpit Rock   ★★★☆

PO Box 271 Mittagong, NSW 2575 **Region** Southern Highlands
T 0418 242 045 **www.**pulpitrockestate.com.au **Open** Not
Winemaker Rhys Eather (Contract) **Est.** 1998 **Dozens** 600 **Vyds** 4ha
Pulpit Rock brings together a team of professionals covering the field from grape to glass. Dr Richard Smart was the consultant viticulturist to give the venture his blessing; the wine is made by well-known Hunter Valley winemaker Rhys Eather; it is distributed by co-owner Carol-Ann Martin, with more than 20 years' experience as owner of a fine wine distribution business; and the wine is consumed wherever possible by her architect husband Philip Martin. The 2ha each of chardonnay and pinot noir are managed on a minimal intervention basis, never easy in the Southern Highlands climate, but with obvious success.

ŸŸŸŸ **Southern Highlands Chardonnay 2010** Deep, glowing gold-green; you have to wonder whether there has been some de facto skin contact in the trip to the Hunter Valley for crushing and pressing. An erratic texture results, although the flavours are ok. Screwcap. 12.5% alc. **Rating** 88 **To** 2014 $28

Southern Highlands Pinot Noir 2009 Good colour. with some development; notwithstanding the modest alcohol, both the bouquet and palate show some cooked fruit characters and an element of vanilla bean. Not unpleasant, but not mainstream. Screwcap. 13% alc. **Rating** 87 **To** 2014 $40

Punch ★★★★★

2130 Kinglake Road, St Andrews, Vic 3761 (postal) **Region** Yarra Valley
T (03) 9710 1155 **www.**punched.com.au **Open** Not
Winemaker James Lance **Est.** 2004 **Dozens** 570 **Vyds** 3.45ha
In the wake of Graeme Rathbone taking over the brand (but not the real estate) of Diamond Valley, the Lances' son James and his wife Claire leased the vineyard and winery from David and Catherine Lance, including the 0.25ha block of close-planted pinot noir. In all, Punch has 2.25ha of pinot noir (including the close-planted), 0.8ha of chardonnay and 0.4ha of cabernet sauvignon. When the 2009 Black Saturday bushfires destroyed the crop, various grapegrowers wrote offering assistance, which led to the purchase of the grapes used for that dire year, and the beginning of the 'Friends of Punch' wines.

ŸŸŸŸŸ **Lance's Vineyard Close Planted Yarra Valley Pinot Noir 2010** Only 25 dozen of this wine was produced, after the devastation of the 2009 fires; the vines have been able to produce a dark and exotic blend of spice, roast meat and dark fruits; the palate is young, fresh, poised and precise, and while time will see this evolve into a thing of beauty, as a young wine it is already set to beguile. Screwcap. 13% alc. **Rating** 96 **To** 2020 $110 BE

Lance's Vineyard Yarra Valley Chardonnay 2010 A very concentrated and expressive bouquet, with pure grapefruit and nashi pear, combined with a little sizzling bacon fat; the palate is taut, linear, deeply fruited and long, combining power with effortless precision; extraordinarily tasty Yarra Valley chardonnay. Screwcap. 13% alc. **Rating** 95 **To** 2018 $45 BE

Lance's Vineyard Yarra Valley Pinot Noir 2010 While deeply fruited and expressive, there is an elegance and spicy complexity that is enchanting; fragrant spiced plums and a lick of star anise; the palate is silky and unctuous, showing the sex appeal of the variety at an early stage of development. Screwcap. 13.5% alc. **Rating** 94 **To** 2017 $55 BE

ŸŸŸŸ♀ **Friends of Punch Quartz Reef Vineyard Central Otago Pinot Noir 2010** **Rating** 91 **To** 2016 $55 BE

Friends of Punch Mallani Vineyard Gippsland Chardonnay 2010 **Rating** 90 **To** 2018 $31 BE

ŸŸŸŸ **Friends of Punch Bannockburn Vineyards Geelong Syrah 2010** **Rating** 87 **To** 2015 $31 BE

Punt Road ★★★★★

10 St Huberts Road, Coldstream, Vic 3770 **Region** Yarra Valley
T (03) 9739 0666 **www.**puntroadwines.com.au **Open** 7 days 10–5
Winemaker Kate Goodman **Est.** 2000 **Dozens** 20 000 **Vyds** 63.5ha
Punt Road has been producing wine for over a decade, and is now under the sole ownership of the Napoleone family. The emphasis is firmly on wines produced from vineyards owned by the family; this has resulted in the introduction of the Airlie Bank range, a sub-$20 Yarra Valley range made in a fruit-driven, lightly oaked style to complement the successful Punt Road range at the premium end of their offerings. There will also be more focus on small-production single vineyard wines in the coming vintages, especially under the Punt Road label. Exports to the UK, the US, Canada, Japan, China and other major markets.

🍷🍷🍷🍷🍷 **Napoleone Vineyard Yarra Valley Shiraz 2010** Good hue, although not deep; produced from the 21-year-old vineyard running down to the Maroondah Highway, and the epitome of elegance, with fragrant, aromatic red berry/cherry fruits, very fine tannins and equally good length. Barely medium-bodied, but that only adds to its appeal. Screwcap. 13% alc. **Rating** 94 **To** 2020 $29
Napoleone Vineyard Yarra Valley Merlot 2010 Bright, clear crimson-red; a distinguished example of this elusive variety, with the cherry and plum fruit of the medium-bodied palate supported by fine-grained tannins and judicious oak. Screwcap. 12.5% alc. **Rating** 94 **To** 2018 $29

🍷🍷🍷🍷🍷 **Chemin Yarra Valley Pinot Noir 2010 Rating** 93 **To** 2015 $39
Coldstream Vineyards Yarra Valley Cabernet Sauvignon 2010 Rating 93 **To** 2023 $29
✪ **Yarra Valley Chardonnay Pinot Noir NV** A 93/7% blend pinot noir and chardonnay 67% from '08 and 33% from '07; traditional method used, and spent three years on lees prior to disgorgement. Pale straw-gold, it has considerable intensity and length to the fruit, the citrus and white peach flavours of the chardonnay forming the base, with yeasty brioche notes from the time on lees. Is elegant, and very good value. Diam. 13% alc. **Rating** 93 **To** 2014 $29
Nehme Vineyard Yenda Botrytis Semillon 2010 Rating 93 **To** 2015 $32
✪ **Airlie Bank Yarra Valley Chardonnay 2010** Bright, light straw-green; an attractive example of Yarra Valley Chardonnay, with a long, elegant palate picking up nectarine, white peach and grapefruit flavours, and a subliminal touch of cashew from the subtle oak influence. Screwcap. 12.5% alc. **Rating** 92 **To** 2016 $18
✪ **Airlie Bank Yarra Valley Pinot Grigio 2011** Bright straw-green; the fragrant, flowery bouquet has clear-cut apple, pear and citrus flavours that flow into the palate; has zest and lift, and is a particularly good example of Grigio. Screwcap. 12.5% alc. **Rating** 92 **To** 2013 $18
Napoleone Vineyard Yarra Valley Pinot Noir 2010 Rating 92 **To** 2017 $29
Chemin Yarra Valley Syrah 2010 Rating 92 **To** 2020 $39
Emperor's Prize Vineyard Yarra Valley Viognier 2010 Rating 91 **To** 2013 $25
Emperor's Prize Vineyard Yarra Valley Pinot Gris 2011 Rating 90 **To** 2014 $25

🍷🍷🍷🍷 **Napoleone Vineyard Yarra Valley Rose 2011 Rating** 89 **To** 2013 $22

Punters Corner ★★★★★

Cnr Riddoch Highway/Racecourse Road, Coonawarra, SA 5263 **Region** Coonawarra
T (08) 8737 2007 **www**.punterscorner.com.au **Open** Mon–Fri 10–4, w'ends & public hols 12–4
Winemaker Balnaves (Peter Bissell) **Est.** 1988 **Dozens** 7000 **Vyds** 25.43ha
In 1988 David Muir and Robert Hance (and their wives) purchased a property on V&A Lane and planted 16ha of vines. Since then the vineyard area has expanded considerably with the development of a further three vineyards, including the cellar door block that is situated on the Riddoch Highway. In 1996 a winery designed by Peter Bissell was built, and in late '99 the Punters Corner Retreat accommodation centre was opened. While judging the Limestone Coast Wine Show, I frequently had occasion to eat at the Retreat; it has won various architectural and tourism awards. Punters Corner had a moment of glory when its 1999 Spartacus Reserve Shiraz won the Jimmy Watson Trophy in 2000. Exports to Canada, the Netherlands, Malaysia, Singapore, Japan and China.

🍷🍷🍷🍷🍷 **Single Vineyard Coonawarra Chardonnay 2010** Excellent green-gold; vibrant grapefruit and white peach; very good length and drive. Top gold medal Winewise '11. Screwcap. 13.5% alc. **Rating** 95 **To** 2017 $26
Spartacus Reserve Shiraz 2009 The extended maturation of this wine in new oak, for 21 months, has produced a wine with strong charry roasted meat, spice, sage and juniper; the full-bodied palate is a take no prisoners approach, with dense fruit, zesty acidity and a mouthful of chewy tannins lingering on the finish; big-boned, not shy on oak, and done well. ProCork. 14% alc. **Rating** 94 **To** 2030 $60 BE

ŶŶŶŶŶ Coonawarra Shiraz 2009 Rating 90 To 2020 $20 BE
Coonawarra Cabernet Sauvignon 2009 Rating 90 To 2018 $30 BE

ŶŶŶŶ Sovereign Reserve Cabernet Sauvignon 2009 Rating 89 To 2020 $60 BE

Purple Hands Wines ★★★★★

PO Box 11, Williamstown, SA 5351 **Region** Barossa Valley
T 0401 988 185 **www**.purplehandswines.com.au **Open** Not
Winemaker Craig Stansborough **Est.** 2006 **Dozens** 1100 **Vyds** 8ha
This is a remarkable new (well, only six years old) venture, a partnership between Craig
Stansborough, who provides the winemaking know-how and an 8ha vineyard of shiraz,
northwest of Williamstown in a cooler corner of the southern Barossa, and Mark Slade,
who provides the passion. Don't ask me how this works – I don't know, but I do know they
are producing outstanding single vineyard wines (the grenache is contract-grown) of quite
remarkable elegance. The wines are made at Grant Burge, where Craig is chief winemaker.

ŶŶŶŶŶ Barossa Valley Shiraz 2009 Has excellent bright crimson colour, not always
achieved in the Barossa. The bouquet speaks of the 18 months the wine spent in
French oak (including 12 months on lees) and of fresh, dark berry fruit; this classy
wines has ripe, fine-grained tannins through the long palate and contributing to
the lipsmacking finish. Screwcap. 14% alc. **Rating** 95 To 2023 $28
Barossa Valley Shiraz 2008 Exceptional colour for an '08. The wine heralds
a new voice in the Barossa, with an almost austere flavour and structure, usually
confined to cool-climate regions; the black fruits have tannins seamlessly woven
through the length of the palate. Gold medal Barossa Wine Show '10. Screwcap.
14% alc. **Rating** 94 To 2021 $28
Old Vine Barossa Valley Grenache 2009 Given the best possible chance:
hand-picked bush vines, old concrete fermenters, wild yeast, hand-plunged, hot
ferment, basket-pressed, 10 months on lees in old puncheons. Abundant fleshy,
raspberry-accented notes to the fruit, the texture, structure and length admirable.
Indeed, one of the best Barossa grenaches going around, a conclusion reached
before finding it had won a trophy at the Barossa Wine Show '10. Screwcap.
14% alc. **Rating** 94 To 2015 $28

ŶŶŶŶŶ Old Vine Barossa Valley Grenache 2010 Rating 93 To 2016 $28
Barossa Valley Mataro Shiraz Grenache 2011 Rating 92 To 2017 $28
Old Vine Barossa Valley Grenache 2011 Rating 91 To 2015 $28

ŶŶŶŶ Barossa Valley Shiraz 2010 Rating 88 To 2020 $28

Pyren Vineyard ★★★★★

22 Errard Street North, Ballarat, Vic 3350 (postal) **Region** Pyrenees
T (03) 5467 2352 **www**.pyrenvineyard.com **Open** By appt
Winemaker Andrew Davey **Est.** 1999 **Dozens** 5000 **Vyds** 34ha
Brian and Kevyn Joy have planted 23ha of shiraz, 5ha of cabernet sauvignon and 1ha split
between malbec, cabernet franc and petit verdot on the slopes of the Warrenmang Valley near
Moonambel. Yield is restricted to between 1.5 and 2.5 tonnes per acre. Five hectares of their
vineyard is currently being redeveloped. Exports to Vietnam and China.

ŶŶŶŶŶ Yardbird Union 2010 A crimson-purple 50/25/25% blend of cabernet
sauvignon, malbec and petit verdot; any thought of premature picking is
immediately dispelled by the juicy fruit aromas and, even more, flavours of the
wine, with joyous red cherry, cassis and mulberry fruit, the tannins fine and ripe.
Screwcap. 12.8% alc. **Rating** 95 To 2020 $30
● Broken Quartz Pyrenees Shiraz 2010 Rating 94 To 2020 $20
Studio Ink 2009 Made from estate-grown shiraz/cabernet sauvignon. Deep
colour, and the bouquet has smoky bacon/char overtones to the black fruits,
the palate reinforcing those characters with its interesting tannin structure, more
powerful on the mid palate than the finish. There is nothing mundane about this
wine, nor its future. Screwcap. 14.2% alc. **Rating** 94 To 2024 $30

○ Broken Quartz Pyrenees Cabernet Sauvignon 2010 Rating 94 To 2010 $20

♏♏♏♏♏ Block E Pyrenees Shiraz 2010 Rating 93 To 2025 $30
○ Broken Quartz Pyrenees Shiraz 2009 Rating 93 To 2019 $20

Pyrenees Ridge Winery ★★★★★

532 Caralulup Road, Lamplough via Avoca, Vic 3467 **Region** Pyrenees
T (03) 5465 3320 **www.**pyreneesridge.com.au **Open** Thurs–Mon & public hols 11–5
Winemaker Graeme Jukes **Est.** 1998 **Dozens** 5000 **Vyds** 15.3ha
Notwithstanding the quite extensive winemaking experience (and formal training) of Graeme Jukes, this started life as small-scale winemaking in the raw version of the French garagiste approach. Graeme and his wife Sally-Ann now have 10ha of shiraz and 3ha cabernet sauvignon, with lesser amounts of chardonnay, merlot and a hatful of viognier. There are plans to plant a further 3–4ha of shiraz. After a fire in 2007 destroyed the winery and cellar door, the facility has been rebuilt, bigger and better than before. Further wines were received after this issue went to print; tasting notes appear on www.winecompanion.com.au. Exports to Canada, Germany, Denmark, South Korea, Hong Kong, China and Japan.

♏♏♏♏♏ Cabernet Sauvignon 2010 Good crimson-purple; the bouquet is a very complex mix of mocha, cassis and regional mint, the textured and layered palate with a superabundance of predominantly red fruits and French oak, the tannins ripe, but still partly submerged. Needs time to slim down. Screwcap. 13.5% alc. Rating 94 To 2025 $28

♏♏♏♏♏ Chardonnay 2011 A lifted bouquet of nectarine, melon and a distinct pine resin
✪ edge; the palate is taut and racy, with quartz minerals and citrus notes lingering on the finish. Screwcap. 13.5% alc. **Rating** 90 **To** 2015 $20 BE
○ **Ridge Red 2010 Rating** 90 **To** 2019 $16

Quarisa Wines ★★★☆

743 Slopes Road, Tharbogang, NSW 2680 (postal) **Region** South Australia
T (02) 6963 6222 **www.**quarisa.com.au **Open** Not
Winemaker John Quarisa **Est.** 2005 **Dozens** 50 000
Quarisa Wines was established by John and Josephine Quarisa (and their three children). John has had a distinguished career as a winemaker spanning over 20 years, working for some of Australia's largest wineries, including McWilliam's, Casella and Nugan Estate. He was also chiefly responsible in 2004 for winning the Jimmy Watson Trophy (Melbourne) and the Stodart Trophy (Adelaide). In a busman's holiday venture, the Quarisas set up a very successful family business using grapes from various parts of NSW and SA, made in leased space. Production has risen from 20 000 dozen in a tough economic environment, value for money part of the success. It is no surprise that leading national distributor Domaine Wine Shippers has taken on the brand. Exports to the UK, Canada, Sweden, Switzerland, Poland, Israel, Indonesia, Malaysia, China, Hong Kong, South Korea, Thailand, Singapore, Japan and NZ.

♏♏♏♏♏ Johnny Q Chardonnay Viognier 2010 A blend that I seldom find synergistic,
✪ but works very well here, adding fruit flesh without a phenolic payday. Exceptional value. Screwcap. 13% alc. **Rating** 90 **To** 2013 $12

♏♏♏♏ Johnny Q Adelaide Hills Semillon Sauvignon Blanc 2011 Pale straw-green;
✪ there is a surprising volume of varietal fruit in the wine, with a mix of lemon/ citrus and tropical flavours; good length and balance. Outstanding value. Screwcap. 13% alc. **Rating** 89 **To** 2013 $12
✪ **Treasures Coonawarra Merlot 2010** Good colour; continues the pattern of excellent value for money, with the merlot flavours that are clearly enjoyed by many consumers, centring on plum rather than black olive, and fleshed out with just a touch of oak. Screwcap. 14% alc. **Rating** 89 **To** 2014 $15
Treasures Padthaway Chardonnay 2010 Rating 88 **To** Now $15

Quartz Hill Vineyard ★★★★★

65 Lillicur West Road, Lamplough, Vic 3352 (postal) **Region** Pyrenees
T (03) 5465 3670 **www**.quartzhillwines.com.au **Open** Not
Winemaker Darrin Gaffy **Est.** 1995 **Dozens** 400 **Vyds** 3.6ha
Shane and Michelle Mead say they have wine in their blood. Michelle's brother is Darrin
Gaffy of Principia Wines on the Mornington Peninsula, and uncle Brian Gaffy has Clair de
Lune in South Gippsland. Shane came onboard with his first memorable tasting of a Langi
Ghiran Shiraz; it was this that led to the search for a suitable vineyard site in the Pyrenees.
Plantings began in 1995, and Shane and Michelle moved up from Melbourne with their very
young family in '99, expanding the plantings of shiraz and also planting viognier. The standard
of the labelling and packaging matches the high quality of the wines.

🍷🍷🍷🍷🍷 Pyrenees Viognier 2010 Pale, bright straw-green; you would have little or no
    hope of recognising that this wine had spent 18 months in French oak barrels; it
    is intense, focused and has no oily phenolic characters whatsoever on the finish;
    whether it has sufficient varietal character is another question altogether, but it gets
    the benefit of the doubt. Diam. 13.5% alc. **Rating** 94 **To** 2016 $32
    Pyrenees Syrah 2010 Light, clear red-purple; the bouquet is very fragrant, with
    an array of spice and pepper notes woven through the predominantly red berry
    fruits; those fruit flavours take hold of the elegant, medium-bodied palate, the
    outcome of 18 months in French oak most evident on the back-palate and finish.
    It's quite a journey for a relatively light-bodied wine. Diam. 13.5% alc. **Rating** 94
    To 2025 $32

Quattro Mano ★★★★

PO Box 189, Hahndorf, SA 5245 **Region** Barossa Valley
T 0430 647 470 **www**.quattromano.com.au **Open** By appt
Winemaker Anthony Carapetis, Christopher Taylor, Philippe Morin **Est.** 2006
Dozens 3000 **Vyds** 3.8ha
Anthony Carapetis, Philippe Morin and Chris Taylor have collective experience of over
50 years working in various facets of the wine industry, Morin as a leading sommelier for over
25 years, and presently as Director of French Oak Cooperage, Carapetis and Taylor as long-
serving winemakers. The dream of Quattro Mano began in the mid 1990s, but only became a
reality in 2006 (I'm still not sure how three equals four). They now have an eclectic range of
wines, Tempranillo the cornerstone, extending at one extreme to the multi-Iberian Peninsula
Duende, and to La Deft Pinot Noir and La Hada Barossa Valley Mourvedre at the other. It's
an impressive, albeit small, business. Exports to Japan.

🍷🍷🍷🍷♀ La Morada Barossa Valley Touriga Tinta Amarela Tinta Cao 2010 A juicy
    and fresh, slightly savoury wine, with a light- to medium-bodied personality; fine
    tannins and lively acidity provide length and interest on the moderately long finish.
    Screwcap. 13% alc. **Rating** 90 **To** 2013 $26 BE

Quealy Balnarring Vineyard ★★★★☆

62 Bittern-Dromana Road, Balnarring, Vic 3926 **Region** Mornington Peninsula
T (03) 5983 2483 **www**.quealy.com.au **Open** 7 days 11–5
Winemaker Kathleen Quealy **Est.** 1982 **Dozens** 5000 **Vyds** 8ha
Kathleen Quealy and husband Kevin McCarthy lost no time after T'Gallant was purchased
from them by Foster's in 2003. As they were fully entitled to do, they already had their ducks
set up in a row, and in short order acquired Balnarring Estate winery (being significantly
upgraded) and leased Earl's Ridge Vineyard near Flinders. In a move reminiscent of Janice
McDonald at Stella Bella/Suckfizzle in the Margaret River, they launched their business with
Pobblebonk (a white blend) and Rageous (a red blend), plus a Pinot Noir and a Pinot Gris
as a passing nod to convention. The estate plantings are 2ha each of pinot noir, tocai friulano
and pinot gris, and 1ha each of chardonnay and muscat giallo. Kathleen (with five children) is
a human dynamo. Wines are also available at Merricks General Wine Store.

🍷🍷🍷🍷 **Seventeen Rows Pinot Noir 2010** Excellent colour; the ultra-complex bouquet has fragrances of exotic spices coupled with dark berry fruits; the palate has great focus, length and intensity, with finely textured tannins on the finish. One tonne per acre yield, vines planted 1982, MV6 clone. Screwcap. 13% alc. Rating 95 To 2018 $50

🍷🍷🍷🍷 **Musk Creek Pinot Gris 2011** Rating 92 To 2015 $30
Rageous Sangiovese Shiraz Pinot Noir 2009 Rating 92 To 2014 $30
Pinot Grigio 2011 Rating 90 To 2014 $25

🍷🍷🍷🍷 **Balnarring Vineyard Pinot Grigio Friulano 2010** Gold-bronze; if there is
✪ such a thing as a full-bodied pinot gris – essentially an oxymoron – this is it; true, after a full mid palate it does slip away a little on the finish. Screwcap. 13% alc. Rating 89 To Now $20
Musk Creek Pinot Noir 2010 Rating 89 To 2014 $25
Pyrenees Nebbiolo 2010 Rating 89 To 2016 $40
Moscato 2009 Rating 89 To Now $25

Quilty Wines ★★★★★
16 Inglis Street, Mudgee, NSW 2850 (postal) **Region** Mudgee
T 0419 936 233 **www.**quiltywines.com.au **Open** Not
Winemaker Des Quilty, Andrew Ewart **Est.** 2008 **Dozens** 450
Owner Des Quilty grew up in the Hunter Valley and studied agriculture at the University of New England, Armidale. To support himself while at university, he drifted into viticulture, his first job after graduation at Tyrrell's as assistant vineyard manager. He was soon promoted and formed part of the Tyrrell's management team in the first half of the 1990s. Over the latter half of the '90s he worked for a rural outlet supplying products to Hunter Valley grape and wine producers, before moving to Mudgee as a viticulturist around 2000. While his focus remains on that region, he has also been involved in vineyards in Orange and Young. With a wife and two young children, he ventured into small-scale winemaking in '08, relying on the depth of his experience to secure small parcels of top-quality grapes to make top-quality wines.

🍷🍷🍷🍷 **Running Stitch Single Vineyard Rylstone Mudgee Cabernet Sauvignon 2010** Bright colour; an impressive cabernet from a tiny planting (98 dozen made) high in the Cudgegong Valley, blackcurrant, cassis, cedar and spice welded together with fine tannins. Screwcap. 13.5% alc. Rating 94 To 2025 $28

Racecourse Lane Wines ★★★☆
28 Racecourse Lane, Pokolbin, NSW 2320 **Region** Hunter Valley
T 0408 242 490 **www.**racecourselane.com.au **Open** By appt
Winemaker David Fatches (Contract) **Est.** 1998 **Dozens** 500 **Vyds** 4.7ha
Mike and Helen McGorman purchased their 15ha property in 1998. They have established shiraz, sangiovese, semillon, verdelho and viognier. Consultancy viticultural advice from Brian Hubbard, and winemaking by David Fatches (a long-term Hunter Valley winemaker, who also makes wine in France each year), has paid dividends. Exports to the UK.

🍷🍷🍷🍷 **Hunter Valley Verdelho 2005** Bright, light green-straw; six years since last tasted, and has barely developed; nutty/toasty characters a la Semillon, also braced by Semillon-like acidity. Screwcap. 13% alc. Rating 90 To 2015 $19

Radford Wines ★★★★★
RSD 355, Eden Valley, SA 5235 (postal) **Region** Eden Valley
T (08) 8565 3256 **F** (08) 8565 3244 **www.**radfordwines.com **Open** Not
Winemaker Gill and Ben Radford **Est.** 2003 **Dozens** 2000 **Vyds** 4.2ha
I first met Ben Radford when he was working as a head winemaker at the Longridge/ Winecorp group in Stellenbosch, South Africa. A bevy of international journalists grilled Ben, a French winemaker and a South African about the wines they were producing for the

group. The others refused to admit there were any shortcomings in the wines they had made (there were), while Ben took the opposite tack, criticising his own wines even though they were clearly the best. He and wife Gill are now the proud owners of a vineyard in the Eden Valley, with 1.2ha of riesling planted in 1930, another 1.1ha planted in '70, 1.7ha of shiraz planted in 2000 and 0.2ha of mataro planted '10. Following Ben's appointment as winemaker at Rockford in '07, executive winemaking responsibilities are now Gill's. Exports to the UK, the US, Canada, Denmark and South Africa.

♟♟♟♟♟ **Bio-Dynamically Grown Eden Valley Shiraz 2010** Impenetrable colour, and a dark and savoury personality; while this is big end of town stuff in terms of concentration, the savoury complexity and ample black fruits are offset by a lifted floral accent that is beguiling; the palate is warm and thickly textured, with a refreshing touch of tannin cleaning up the finish; long and very complex. Screwcap. 14.5% alc. **Rating** 95 **To** 2025 $43 BE
Spice Bush Eden Valley Shiraz 2008 Deep crimson; a bright and fragrant shiraz, showing fresh blackberry and a strap of licorice and roasted game; the palate is lively, medium-bodied, fresh and fine; ready for consumption at any time. Screwcap. 14.5% alc. **Rating** 94 **To** 2018 $38 BE

♟♟♟♟♟ **Bio-Dynamically Grown Eden Valley Riesling 2011 Rating** 93 **To** 2020 $39 BE
Quartz Garden Eden Valley Riesling 2011 Rating 90 **To** 2018 $25 BE
✪ **Dame Nellie Eden Valley Rose 2011** Made entirely from shiraz, this pale pink rose offers a restrained bouquet, showing spice and lifted red fruits; the palate is dry and savoury, finishing with warmth and generosity; surprisingly long for the style. Screwcap. 13% alc. **Rating** 90 **To** 2013 $18 BE

Raidis Estate   ★★★
147 Church Street, Penola, SA 5277 **Region** Coonawarra
T (08) 8737 2966 **www**.raidis.com.au **Open** Thurs–Sun 12–6, or by appt
Winemaker Amelia Anderson **Est.** 2006 **Dozens** 1600 **Vyds** 24.29ha
The Raidis family has lived and worked in Coonawarra for over 40 years. Chris Raidis was only three years old when he arrived in Australia with his parents, who were market gardeners in Greece before coming here. In 1994 he planted just under 5ha of cabernet sauvignon; son Steven significantly expanded the vineyard in 2003 with sauvignon blanc, riesling, pinot gris, merlot and shiraz. The cellar door was opened by then Deputy Prime Minister Julia Gillard in Nov '09, an impressive example of pulling power.

♟♟♟♟ **The Kid Coonawarra Riesling 2011** Deep colour; the bouquet shows a distinct menthol edge to the fruit, offset by attractive orange zest aromas; the palate is firm and very dry, with tart lemons providing cut on the finish. Screwcap. 12.3% alc. **Rating** 87 **To** 2016 $19 BE

Ravens Croft Wines   ★★★★
274 Spring Creek Road, Stanthorpe, Qld 4380 **Region** Granite Belt
T (07) 4683 3252 **www**.ravenscroftwines.com.au **Open** Fri–Sun
Winemaker Mark Ravenscroft **Est.** 2002 **Dozens** 800 **Vyds** 1.20ha
Mark Ravenscroft was born in South Africa, and studied oenology there. He moved to Australia in the early 1990s, and in '94 became an Australian citizen. His wines come from estate plantings of verdelho and pinotage, supplemented by contract-grown grapes from other vineyards in the region. A new winery has recently been completed. The rating has been retained, having regard for some very difficult vintages, especially 2011. Exports to Japan.

♟♟♟♟♟ **Granite Belt Chardonnay 2011** Partially barrel-fermented in a mix of American and French oak, part wild-fermented and part taken through mlf; of undoubted complexity, the question being whether that complexity has been achieved at the expense of varietal fruit expression – a question likely to result in split votes. Screwcap. 13% alc. **Rating** 90 **To** 2014 $35

♟♟♟♟ Granite Belt Cabernet Sauvignon 2010 Rating 89 To 2016 $30
Gewurztraminer 2010 Rating 88 To 2014 $25
Granite Belt Pinotage 2011 Rating 88 To 2014 $35

Red Earth Estate

18L Camp Road, Dubbo, NSW 2830 **Region** Western Plains Zone
T (02) 6885 6676 **www.**redearthestate.com.au **Open** Thurs–Tues 10–5
Winemaker Ken Borchardt **Est.** 2000 **Dozens** 2500 **Vyds** 6.2ha
Red Earth Estate, owned by Ken and Christine Borchardt, is the focal point of grapegrowing and winemaking in the Western Plains Zone. They have planted riesling, verdelho, frontignac, grenache, shiraz, cabernet sauvignon and a small amount of torrentes (supplemented by purchased grapes). The winery has a capacity of 14 000 dozens, and the Borchardts also offer contract winemaking facilities for others in the region. Exports to China.

♟♟♟♟♟ **Verdelho 2011** How you get so much flavour and mouthfeel at this alcohol level from verdelho grown in Orange I don't know. Oak may be part of the answer, although it is subtle, and the layers of fruit salad have a layer of citrus embedded in the wine. Screwcap. 11.6% alc. **Rating** 90 To 2014 $28

♟♟♟♟ **Shiraz + C 2010** Rating 89 To 2014 $22
Borchardt Sauvignon Blanc 2011 Rating 87 To 2013 $22

Red Edge

Golden Gully Road, Heathcote, Vic 3523 **Region** Heathcote
T 0407 422 067 **www.**rededgewine.com.au **Open** By appt
Winemaker Peter Dredge **Est.** 1971 **Dozens** 1500 **Vyds** 14ha
Red Edge's vineyard dates back to 1971 and the renaissance of the Victorian wine industry. In the early 1980s it produced the wonderful wines of Flynn & Williams, and was rehabilitated by Peter and Judy Dredge, producing two quite lovely wines in their inaugural vintage and continuing that form in succeeding years. Exports to the US, Canada and China.

♟♟♟♟♟ **Heathcote Shiraz 2009** Like the Degree Shiraz, follows prior years' approach with 25% whole bunch-pressed by foot-stomping, the remainder crushed and destemmed; after a wild yeast fermentation, spent 21 months in new French barriques. Shows the yield of less than a tonne per acre in its densely packed, full-bodied palate, with spice, French oak, red and black cherry and lingering but ripe tannins. Screwcap. 14.8% alc. **Rating** 95 To 2034 $45

✪ **Degree Heathcote Shiraz 2009** Compelling deep purple-crimson; follows the unique but tried and true (for Red Edge) co-fermentation of 6% mourvedre and 3% riesling; luscious and rich licorice, satsuma plum and blackberry fruit fill the medium- to full-bodied palate, paradoxically lightened by the fine-grained tannins. Drink any time over the next decade or two. Screwcap. 14.7% alc. **Rating** 95 To 2030 $25

Heathcote Cabernet Sauvignon 2009 Like the Shiraz, 25% of the bunches foot-stamped, the remaining 75% crushed and destemmed but co-fermented. It has not blinked an eyelid at two years in oak, and is a triumph for cabernet grown in a hot drought year, the cassis/blackcurrant fruit illuminating the back-palate and finish in rosy glow. Screwcap. 14.5% alc. **Rating** 95 To 2025 $40

Heathcote Tempranillo Monastrell 2009 A 50/50% blend, the wine has excellent purple-crimson colour, and after 18 months in used French oak brings together the spicy cherry fruit of the tempranillo with the more savoury/plummy flavour of the monastrell very well, the finish a highlight. Screwcap. 14.6% alc. Rating 94 To 2023 $28

Limited Edition Heathcote Mataro 2009 What's in a name? Peter Dredge uses monastrell in one instance, mataro in this instance, leaving mourvedre to the French. Three barrels were so outstanding he decided not to blend any of them with other reds, and it's not hard to see why. The wine has the correct firm structure, but also has light-footed and bright fruit flavours filling in the palate. Screwcap. 14.3% alc. **Rating** 94 To 2024 $35

🍇 Red Gully Wines   ★★★★☆

PO Box 263, Nannup, WA 6275 **Region** Blackwood Valley
T (08) 9385 9568 **www**.redgully.com.au **Open** Not
Winemaker Contract **Est.** 1997 **Dozens** 1000 **Vyds** 3ha
Garth, Ken and Rae Walter established their vineyard in 1997, with the primary purpose of growing red grapes for sale to other producers. They planted shiraz and cabernet sauvignon, with small blocks of pinot noir, merlot, chardonnay and semillon. That part of each year's grape production which is kept for the Red Gully label is contract-made, although with direct involvement of Garth and Ken. A nice, and not common, touch is that customers may buy grapes to make their own wine, or have wines tailor-made for them by Red Gully. An impressive debut.

🍷🍷🍷🍷🍷 **Reserve Nannup Cabernet Sauvignon 2008** Holding hue well; the more
✪   times I tasted the wine, the more impressed I was with its intensity, complexity
     and length. The cassis fruit is built on a foundation of fine, savoury tannins and
     controlled oak, and is built to live, however appealing the wine may be now.
     Screwcap. 13.8% alc. **Rating** 94 **To** 2018 $20

🍷🍷🍷🍷♀ **Reserve Nannup Shiraz 2007 Rating** 93 **To** 2017 $30
✪   **Nannup Cabernet Shiraz 2006** Good colour; now nearing its optimum
     development, with complex, gently spicy/savoury fruit, balanced tannins, and –
     even better – balanced oak; the moderate alcohol also contributes to its freshness.
     Screwcap. 13.8% alc. **Rating** 90 **To** 2016 $15

🍷🍷🍷🍷 **Reserve Nannup Shiraz 2008 Rating** 89 **To** 2016 $20
✪   **Chardonnay 2009 Rating** 88 **To** 2015 $8
     Nannup Cabernet Shiraz 2007 Rating 88 **To** 2014 $20

Red Hill Estate   ★★★★★

53 Shoreham Road, Red Hill South, Vic 3937 **Region** Mornington Peninsula
T (03) 5989 2838 **www**.redhillestate.com.au **Open** 7 days 11–5
Winemaker Barry Kooij **Est.** 1989 **Dozens** 25 000 **Vyds** 72.2ha
Red Hill Estate was established by Sir Peter Derham and family, and has three vineyard sites: Range Road, Red Hill Estate (the home vineyard), and The Briars. Taken together, the three vineyards make Red Hill Estate one of the larger producers of Mornington Peninsula wines. The tasting room and ever-busy restaurant have a superb view across the vineyard to Westernport Bay and Phillip Island. In 2007 it (surprisingly) merged with Arrowfield Estate in the Hunter Valley, both companies thereafter owned by the InWine Group until October '10, when InWine was acquired by Cheviot Bridge. Further wines were received after this issue went to print; tasting notes appear on www.winecompanion.com.au. Exports to the US, Canada, Ireland, Poland, Sweden, Singapore, Japan and Hong Kong.

🍷🍷🍷🍷♀ **Reserve Mornington Peninsula Pinot Noir 2009** Some colour development
     as expected; a mix of spicy, savoury, stalky characters with plum-accented fruit;
     has its work cut out competing with the beautiful '10s. Screwcap. 13.5% alc.
     Rating 92 **To** 2014 $35

Redbank Alpine Valleys Estates   ★★★★☆

Whitfield Road, King Valley, Vic 3678 **Region** King Valley
T 0411 404 296 **www**.redbankwines.com **Open** Not
Winemaker Nick Dry **Est.** 2005 **Dozens** 33 000 **Vyds** 15ha
The Redbank brand was for decades the umbrella for Neill and Sally Robb's Sally's Paddock. In 2005 Hill-Smith Family Vineyards acquired the Redbank brand from the Robbs, leaving them with the Redbank winery and Sally's Paddock label. Redbank Alpine Valley purchases grapes from the King Valley, Whitlands, Beechworth and the Ovens Valley (among other vineyards sources). Exports to all major markets.

ＹＹＹＹＹ The Anvil Beechworth Shiraz 2009 The fragrant bouquet leads into a juicy, medium-bodied palate with red and black cherry to the fore; fine tannins and quality oak are the final cadenza in a quality wine. Cork. 13.5% alc. Rating 94 To 2019 $52

ＹＹＹＹＹ The Long Paddock Sauvignon Blanc 2011 Straw-green; the bouquet and
✪ palate are flush with gooseberry and tropical fruits, and sufficient acidity to give both length and balance. A singular achievement for the vintage, ready to go right now. Screwcap. 11% alc. Rating 90 To 2013 $13
King Valley Garganega 2010 Rating 90 To 2013 $25
Fighting Flat King Valley Shiraz 2009 Rating 90 To 2015 $25

ＹＹＹＹ The Long Paddock Pinot Gris 2011 Rating 89
✪ To 2013 $13
✪ The Long Paddock Shiraz 2009 Rating 88 To 2015 $13
✪ The Long Paddock Merlot 2010 Rating 88 To 2014 $13
The Long Paddock Chardonnay 2011 Rating 87 To 2013 $13
Sunday Morning King Valley Pinot Gris 2011 Rating 87 To 2013 $25

Redbox Vineyard & Winery ★★★★☆

2 Ness Lane, Kangaroo Ground, Vic 3097 **Region** Yarra Valley
T (03) 9712 0440 **www**.redboxvineyard.com.au **Open** W'ends & public hols 11–6, or by appt
Winemaker Contract **Est.** 2004 **Dozens** 2000 **Vyds** 4ha
Colin and Clayton Spencer have moved quickly since establishing their business in 2004. Initially using grapes from several regions, they now only use Yarra Valley fruit, and likewise only use the Redbox label. The estate plantings are of 2ha of cabernet sauvignon, 0.8ha of chardonnay and 0.4ha of riesling, with an additional 0.8ha of cabernet sauvignon offsite.

ＹＹＹＹＹ Private Reserve Yarra Valley Cabernet Sauvignon 2010 Clear, full red-purple; has significantly greater weight and concentration than the Reserve, with some Bordeaux-like nuances; has excellent length, with cedar nuances to its core of blackcurrant fruit and firm tannins. Diam. 13.5% alc. Rating 95 To 2025 $48

ＹＹＹＹＹ Reserve Yarra Valley Cabernet Sauvignon 2010 Rating 91 To 2020 $24
✪ Chardonnay 2011 Quartz-green; a crisp, tight wine with a distinctly figgy bouquet, and a palate moving more to citrus and stone fruit; has good length and persistence. Screwcap. 12.5% alc. Rating 90 To 2014 $18

Redgate ★★★★★

659 Boodjidup Road, Margaret River, WA 6285 **Region** Margaret River
T (08) 9757 6488 **www**.redgatewines.com.au **Open** 7 days 10–5
Winemaker Joel Page **Est.** 1977 **Dozens** 6500 **Vyds** 18.98ha
Founder and owner of Redgate, the late Bill Ullinger, chose the name not simply because of the nearby eponymous beach, but also because – so it is said – a local farmer (with a prominent red gate at his property) had run an illegal spirit-still 100 or so years ago, and its patrons would come to the property and ask whether there was any 'red gate' available. True or not, Redgate was one of the early movers in the Margaret River, now with close to 20ha of mature estate plantings (the majority to sauvignon blanc, semillon, cabernet sauvignon, cabernet franc, shiraz and chardonnay, with smaller plantings of chenin blanc and merlot). Exports to the US, Switzerland, Denmark, Japan and Singapore.

ＹＹＹＹＹ Margaret River Chardonnay 2010 Full green-yellow; hand-picked, whole bunch-pressed and barrel-fermented; the wine has crisp, citrussy acidity on one side, white peach, nectarine and creamy cashew on the other. The tension they create is very good, drawing out the length of the palate and the finish. Screwcap. 14% alc. Rating 94 To 2016 $35

Margaret River Shiraz 2009 Holding on to purple notes well; an elegant, medium-bodied wine with delicious mouthfeel; plum, black cherry and blackberry fill the mid palate, withdrawing gracefully towards the finish, allowing very fine, savoury tannins (and oak) to provide complexity and length. Screwcap. 13.5% alc. **Rating** 94 **To** 2020 $33

ɛɛɛɛɛ OFS Margaret River Semillon 2011 **Rating** 90 **To** 2015 $25
Reserve Oak Matured Margaret River Sauvignon Blanc 2010 **Rating** 90 **To** 2014 $29

ɛɛɛɛ Margaret River Sauvignon Blanc Semillon 2011 **Rating** 87 **To** 2014 $23

Redman   ★★★★

Main Road, Coonawarra, SA 5263 **Region** Coonawarra
T (08) 8736 3331 **www**.redman.com.au **Open** Mon–Fri 9–5, w'ends 10–4
Winemaker Bruce, Malcolm and Daniel Redman **Est.** 1966 **Dozens** 18 000 **Vyds** 34ha
In March 2008 the Redman family celebrated 100 years of winemaking in Coonawarra. The 2008 vintage also marked the arrival of Daniel as the fourth-generation Redman winemaker. Daniel gained winemaking experience in Central Victoria, the Barossa Valley and the US before taking up his new position. It was felicitous timing, for the 2004 Cabernet Sauvignon and '04 Cabernet Merlot were each awarded a gold medal from the national wine show circuit in '07, the first such accolades for a considerable time. The quality has stabilised at a level in keeping with the long-term history of the winery and its mature vines.

ɛɛɛɛɛ Coonawarra Shiraz 2009 Deep colour, and essency in character, with blackberry pastille, thyme and toasty oak; medium- to full-bodied with tangy acidity and a fine, dry and even finish; follows on from the '08, which won a gold medal at the National Wine Show '11. Cork. 14.8% alc. **Rating** 91 **To** 2018 $23 BE
Coonawarra Cabernet Sauvignon 2009 Another success for Redman, with its generous blackcurrant and mint bouquet and palate; ripe tannins give structure. Strong silver medal National Wine Show '11. Cork. 14% alc. **Rating** 91 **To** 2016 $33
Coonawarra Cabernet Sauvignon Merlot 2008 Deep garnet; a savoury bouquet reminiscent of the Old World, showing slightly developed leather and cedar notes, underpinned by fresh mulberry fruit; full-bodied, yet succulent and direct; not one for the cellar, but a decent drink. Cork. 15% alc. **Rating** 90 **To** 2016 $36 BE

Reillys Wines   ★★★★☆

Cnr Leasingham Road/Hill Street, Mintaro, SA 5415 **Region** Clare Valley
T (08) 8843 9013 **F** (08) 8843 9275 **www**.reillyswines.com.au **Open** 7 days 10–4
Winemaker Justin Ardill **Est.** 1994 **Dozens** 15 000 **Vyds** 85ha
This has been a very successful venture for Adelaide cardiologist Justin Aardill and wife Julie, beginning as a hobby in 1994, but growing significantly over the intervening years. They now have vineyards at Watervale, Leasingham and Mintaro, growing riesling, cabernet sauvignon, shiraz, grenache, tempranillo and merlot. Justin is also a partner in another Clare Valley venture (Rockridge, see separate entry). The cellar door and restaurant were built between 1856 and 1866 by Irish immigrant Hugh Reilly; 140 years later they were restored by the Ardills, distant relatives of Reilly. Exports to the US, Canada, Ireland, Malaysia, China and Singapore.

ɛɛɛɛɛ Dry Land Clare Valley Fortified Shiraz 2008 Dense blackish colour; a well-made and well-balanced vintage port style; the fruit is spicy and deep with black cherry flavours together with spice and licorice; the spirit used to fortify the wine is clean, and the overall balance very good. 500ml WAK screwcap. 18% alc. Rating 94 To 2018 $25

ɛɛɛɛɛ Barking Mad Clare Valley Cabernet Sauvignon 2009 Good colour; spent
✪   18 months in French oak, and has very good varietal character, with blackcurrant fruit leading the way on the long, well-balanced palate. It's taken a little while for Reillys to come to terms with its St Clare vineyard, but it has now done so, making this wine a notable bargain. Screwcap. 14.5% alc. **Rating** 92 **To** 2024 $15

○ Dry Land Clare Valley Cabernet Sauvignon 2006 Rating 92 To 2021 $29
Watervale Riesling 2011 Bright green-quartz; the bouquet offers a mix of
spice and citrus, with some overtones of gruner veltliner, and the palate has layers
of sweet citrus fruit, the acidity quite soft, rewarding early drinking. Screwcap.
13% alc. Rating 91 To 2015 $18

ŶŶŶŶ Dry Land Clare Valley Shiraz 2009 Rating 89 To 2019 $21
○ Barking Mad Clare Valley Shiraz 2009 Rating 89 To 2019 $15
Dry Land Clare Valley Tempranillo 2010 Rating 89 To 2015 $25
○ Barking Mad Watervale Riesling 2011 Rating 89 To 2017 $15
Barking Mad Clare Valley Rose 2011 Rating 87 To 2013 $15
Clare Valley Cabernet Sauvignon 2009 Rating 87 To 2015 $18
Dry Land Clare Valley Cabernet Sauvignon 2009 Rating 87 To 2015 $29

Renards Folly   ★★★★

PO Box 499, McLaren Vale, SA 5171 **Region** McLaren Vale
T (08) 8556 2404 **www**.renardsfolly.com.au **Open** Not
Winemaker Tony Walker **Est.** 2005 **Dozens** 2000
The dancing foxes on the label, one with a red tail, give a subliminal hint that this is a
virtual winery, owned by Linda Kemp (who looks after the marketing and sales) and Mark
Dimberline, who has spent 17 years in the wine industry. Aided by friend and winemaker
Tony Walker, they source grapes from McLaren Vale, and allow the Vale to express itself
without too much elaboration, the alcohol nicely controlled. Exports to the US, Canada,
Germany an Singapore.

ŶŶŶŶŶ McLaren Vale Shiraz 2010 Good colour; black cherry and plum, a touch of
dark chocolate and subtle spicy oak aromas lead into a medium- to full-bodied
palate underpinned by firm tannins. Good cellaring prospect. Screwcap. 14% alc.
Rating 92 To 2025 $24
○ McLaren Vale Sauvignon Blanc Semillon 2011 Rating 90 To 2013 $16

Repertoire   ★★★☆

PO Box 293, Cowaramup, WA 6284 **Region** Margaret River
T 0404 987 417 **www**.repertoirewines.com.au **Open** Not
Winemaker Richard Tattam, Mark Warren **Est.** 2008 **Dozens** 800
Repertoire is the virtual winery venture of Richard Tattam, who has turned his attention from
sculpting bronze artworks to winemaking. He learnt to craft wines by working three vintages
at Cullen Wines, two at Happs Three Hills winery, and two in France. The influence of Vanya
Cullen has no doubt played a role in the decision of the business to be carbon neutral, while
Richard's artistic credentials come through in the highly unusual labels and background stories
of each of the wines to be found on the website. It is, indeed, the website that constitutes the
retail sales outlet, apart from the numerous Margaret River restaurants and wine shops that
list or stock the wines.

ŶŶŶŶŶ Shim Margaret River Chardonnay 2010 Bright mid gold; a fragrant and
ripe bouquet of peach, grapefruit and oak-derived spice; the palate is fleshy and
vibrant, revealing a trail of cashews and fine acidity on the moderately long finish.
Screwcap. 12.9% alc. Rating 91 To 2018 $26 BE

ŶŶŶŶ Skimpy But Buxom Margaret River Sauvignon Blanc Semillon 2010
Rating 88 To 2013 $25 BE

Reschke Wines   ★★★☆

Level 1, 183 Melbourne Street, North Adelaide, SA 5006 (postal) **Region** Coonawarra
T (08) 8239 0500 **www**.reschke.com.au **Open** Not
Winemaker Peter Douglas (Contract) **Est.** 1998 **Dozens** 15 000 **Vyds** 161.87ha
It's not often that the first release from a new winery is priced at $100 per bottle, but that was
precisely what Reschke Wines achieved with its 1998 Cabernet Sauvignon. The family has

been a landholder in Coonawarra for 100 years, with a large holding that is part terra rossa, part woodland. Cabernet sauvignon (with over 100ha) takes the lion's share of the plantings, with merlot, shiraz and petit verdot making up the balance. Exports to the UK, Canada, Germany, Hong Kong and Japan.

ᵀᵀᵀᵀᵀ **Botrytis Late Picked Sauvignon Blanc 2010** From Mount Gambier, part botrytis-infected, some just dried fruit, and matured in 60% new Allier (French) oak. Full golden-yellow, it is rich and toffee-like, with some apricot fruit. Best enjoyed sooner rather than later. Screwcap. 11.8% alc. **Rating** 93 **To** 2014 $25

ᵀᵀᵀᵀ **Vitulus Coonawarra Cabernet Sauvignon 2008 Rating** 87 **To** 2014 $26

Resolution Vineyard ★★★★★
4 Glen Street, South Hobart, Tas 7004 (postal) **Region** Southern Tasmania
T (03) 6224 9497 **www.**theresolutionvineyard.com **Open** Not
Winemaker Frogmore Creek **Est.** 2003 **Dozens** 150 **Vyds** 0.8ha
Owners Charles and Alison Hewitt live in England and entrust the care of the property and vineyard to Alison's father Peter Brown, with support from former Parks & Wildlife ranger Val Dell. A love of red burgundy and fishing was sufficient for Charles to establish the vineyard planted to three clones of pinot noir in Tasmania, where Alison had spent most of her formative years. The vineyard is on a north-facing slope overlooking the D'Entrecasteaux Channel. Exports to the UK.

ᵀᵀᵀᵀᵀ **Pinot Noir 2010** Deep garnet, bright; a hedonistic blend of liqueur-soaked dark fruits, spices and charcuterie jump out of the glass; the palate is rich, generous and sweet-fruited, with silky tannins and finishing long and fresh; should stand the test of time. Gold medal Hobart Wine Show '11. Screwcap. 13.8% alc. **Rating** 94 **To** 2018 $25 BE

Reynella ★★★★★
Reynell Road, Reynella, SA 5161 **Region** McLaren Vale/Fleurieu Peninsula
T (08) 8392 2300 **F** (08) 8392 2202 **Open** Mon–Sat 10–4
Winemaker Charlie Seppelt **Est.** 1838 **Dozens** NFP
John Reynell laid the foundations for Chateau Reynella in 1838; over the next 100 years the stone buildings and cellars, with patches of lawn and leafy gardens were constructed. Thomas Hardy's first job in SA was with Reynella, noting in his diary that he would be able to better himself soon. He did just that, becoming by far the largest producer in SA by the end of the 19th century; 150 or so years after Chateau Reynella's foundation CWA (now Accolade Wines) completed the circle by acquiring it and making it corporate headquarters, while preserving the integrity of the Reynella brand in no uncertain fashion. In a sign of the times, 'Chateau' has been dropped from its name. Exports to Canada, Europe and China.

ᵀᵀᵀᵀᵀ **Cellar No. One Reserve McLaren Vale Shiraz 2005** Very good colour for a 7-year-old red; it comes from 80-year-old vines that, together with 20 months in French oak, invest the wine with exceptional intensity and length; spices of every description; black fruits, licorice, fruitcake and cedary oak are all part of the picture. High-quality cork. 14% alc. **Rating** 96 **To** 2025 $87
Basket Pressed McLaren Vale Shiraz 2009 Deep purple-crimson; a faultless evocation of all things McLaren Vale, with a dark chocolate coat surrounding the wonderfully supple red and black fruits of the palate and its velvety tannins. Screwcap. 14% alc. **Rating** 95 **To** 2034 $54

Rhythm Stick Wines ★★★★★
PO Box 270, Clare, SA 5453 **Region** Clare Valley
T (08) 8843 4325 **www.**rhythmstickwines.com.au **Open** Not
Winemaker Tim Adams **Est.** 2007 **Dozens** 1000 **Vyds** 1.62ha
Rhythm Stick has come a long way in a short time, and with a small vineyard. It is owned by Ron and Jeanette Ely, who in 1997 purchased a 3.2ha property at Penwortham. The couple

had already decided that in the future they would plant a vineyard, and simply to obtain experience they planted 135 cabernet sauvignon cuttings from Waninga Vineyards in four short rows. Since 2006 they have produced 26 dozen bottles of Cabernet a year, making the wine and sharing it with friends. In '02 they planted riesling, and the first harvest followed in '06, the grapes from this and the ensuing two vintages sold to Clare Valley winemakers. Prior to the '09 harvest they were advised that due to the GFC no grapes would be required, which simply operated to advance Richard's planned retirement after 40 years in electrical engineering consulting and management. The '09 vintage produced 20 tonnes of fruit, and the wines had what can only be described as spectacular success for a first-time producer. The high yield for a young, dry-grown vineyard comes about because of the ideal combination of rich, red-brown loam over sandstone reef structures with limestone and slate components, including areas of perched water. This has resulted in full canopy cover in drought conditions.

ΨΨΨΨΨ **Red Robin Clare Valley Riesling 2011** Quartz-green; the fragrant, blossom
✪   and spice-filled bouquet leads into a mouth-watering palate with lemon and lime jousting for supremacy, lemon with its nose (just) in front. No need to wait, but 5+ years won't challenge it. Screwcap. 11.2% alc. **Rating** 94 **To** 2016 $18
          Red Robin Reserve Clare Valley Riesling 2011 Quartz-green; a high-quality wine, less overt than the standard wine, but with a purity and precision and underlying minerality that makes it certain this will emerge as the better wine in a few years' time. So drink the standard, and cellar this. Screwcap. 11.2% alc. **Rating** 94 **To** 2021 $23

Richard Hamilton   ★★★★★

Cnr Main Road/Johnston Road, McLaren Vale, SA 5171 **Region** McLaren Vale
T (08) 8323 8830 **www**.leconfieldwines.com **Open** Mon–Fri 10–5, w'ends & public hols 11–5
Winemaker Paul Gordon, Tim Bailey **Est.** 1972 **Dozens** 28 000 **Vyds** 73.09ha
Richard Hamilton has outstanding estate vineyards, some of great age, all fully mature. An experienced and skilled winemaking team has allowed the full potential of those vineyards to be realised. The quality, style and consistency of both red and white wines has reached a new level; being able to keep only the best parcels for the Richard Hamilton brand is an enormous advantage. Exports to the UK, the US, Canada, Denmark, Sweden, Germany, Belgium, Malaysia, Hong Kong, Singapore, Japan, China, Vietnam and NZ.

ΨΨΨΨΨ **Centurion Old Vine McLaren Vale Shiraz 2010** Deep red-purple; the
          potential of a top vintage and superb grapes has been effortlessly captured; everything about the wine is in harmonious balance, with dark plum, spice and a whisper of regional chocolate encased in a fine web of ripe tannins and quality oak. Screwcap. 14% alc. **Rating** 96 **To** 2040 $65
✪   **Hut Block McLaren Vale Cabernet Sauvignon 2010** Bright, clear purple-crimson; the lower alcohol pays dividends with the more elegant and intense profile of the fruit flavours and the persistent high-quality tannins of the kind you find in Bordeaux in a good vintage. Especially impressive for ancient mariners such as myself. Screwcap. 14% alc. **Rating** 94 **To** 2025 $19

ΨΨΨΨ♀ **McLaren Vale Shiraz 2010** Good colour; classic McLaren Vale shiraz, with
✪   plum, blackberry, spice and dark chocolate on the bouquet replayed on the medium-bodied palate, where well-balanced but positive tannins come into play. Can be enjoyed now, but will repay cellaring. Screwcap. 14% alc. **Rating** 93 **To** 2020 $19
          Burton's Vineyard Old Bush Vine McLaren Vale Grenache 2010 **Rating** 92 **To** 2015 $45

ΨΨΨΨ **Lot 148 McLaren Vale Merlot 2010** **Rating** 89
✪   **To** 2014 $19
          Gida's McLaren Vale Rose 2011 **Rating** 88 **To** Now $16
          McLaren Vale Sauvignon Blanc Semillon 2011 **Rating** 87 **To** Now $16

Richard Meyman Wines

PO Box 173, Franklin, Tas 7113 **Region** Southern Tasmania
T 0417 492 835 **www**.richardmeymanwines.com.au **Open** Not
Winemaker Frogmore Creek (Alain Rousseau), Winemaking Tasmania (Julian Alcorso,
John Schuts) **Est.** 2010 **Dozens** 350
Richard Meyman had accumulated many years in the wine trade as grower, owner and
manager before returning to Tasmania to run and resurrect the important Nocton Park
vineyard in the Richmond/Coal River area. Few would dispute the primacy of pinot noir as
Tasmania's finest grape variety, and its multifaceted riesling is in the same quality league. So it
is that Richard has chosen those two varieties, and put them in the hands of Tasmania's most
highly skilled contract winemakers.

ŶŶŶŶŶ Waseca Riesling 2011 Pale straw-green; given its youth and Tasmanian origin,
the wine already has fragrant citrus aromas, and a soft and accessible palate, the
balance provided by a subliminal hint of sweetness. Very clever. Trophy Best
Riesling National Cool Climate Wine Show '11. Screwcap. 12.5% alc. **Rating** 94
To 2018 $25

Bersenbrück Pinot Noir 2010 Good hue; has the texture and structure and
elegance missing from so many of these '10 Tasmanian Pinots; plum and black
cherry fruit aromas and flavours are backed by fine tannins and forest floor notes
on the palate. Screwcap. 13.8% alc. **Rating** 94 **To** 2017 $32

ŶŶŶŶ Colebrook Road Pinot Noir 2010 **Rating** 89 **To** 2015 $30

Richmond Grove

Para Road, Tanunda, SA 5352 **Region** Barossa Valley
T (08) 8563 7303 **www**.richmondgrovewines.com **Open** 7 days 10.30–4.30
Winemaker Steve Clarkson **Est.** 1983 **Dozens** NFP
Owned by Orlando Wyndham, Richmond Grove draws its grapes from diverse sources.
The Richmond Grove Barossa Valley and Watervale Rieslings, a legacy of master winemaker
John Vickery, represent excellent value for money year in, year out. The Coonawarra
Cabernet Sauvignon is not as incongruous as it may seem, for John Vickery was transferred
to Coonawarra for a couple of years in the latter stages of his career at Leo Buring, until
sanity prevailed and he returned to the Barossa Valley to continue making Riesling, thereafter
moving to Richmond Grove.

ŶŶŶŶŶ Limited Release Coonawarra Vineyards Cabernet Sauvignon 2008
Medium red-purple; a well-made upper-level commercial wine, with plenty of
cassis and mulberry/blackberry flavour, a dusting of regional mint and earth, and
fine tannins. Screwcap. 14.5% alc. **Rating** 90 **To** 2016 $22

Ridgemill Estate

218 Donges Road, Severnlea, Qld 4352 **Region** Granite Belt
T (07) 4683 5211 **www**.ridgemillestate.com **Open** Fri–Mon 10–5, Sun 10–4
Winemaker Martin Cooper, Peter McGlashan **Est.** 1998 **Dozens** 900 **Vyds** 2.1ha
Martin Cooper and Dianne Maddison acquired what was then known as Emerald Hill
Winery in 2004. In '05 they reshaped the vineyards, which now have plantings of chardonnay,
tempranillo, shiraz, merlot and cabernet sauvignon, saperavi, shiraz, verdelho and viognier,
setting a course down the alternative variety road. The 2005 Chardonnay was the first Qld
wine to win an international gold medal (at the International Chardonnay Challenge '05 in
Gisborne, NZ).

ŶŶŶŶ Verdelho 2011 A sweet-fruited and sweet example of the style; juicy, with plenty
of sugar, best served very cold. 72 dozen made. Screwcap. 13.1% alc. **Rating** 87
To Now $20 BE

RidgeView Wines

273 Sweetwater Road, Pokolbin, NSW 2320 **Region** Hunter Valley
T (02) 6574 7332 **F** (02) 6574 7041 **www**.ridgeview.com.au **Open** 7 days 10–5
Winemaker Darren Scott, Gary MacLean, Mark Woods **Est.** 2000 **Dozens** 3000 **Vyds** 9ha
Darren and Tracey Scott (plus their four children and extended family) have transformed
a 40ha timbered farm into a vineyard, together with self-contained accommodation and
cellar door. The lion's share of the plantings are 4.5ha of shiraz, with cabernet sauvignon,
chambourcin, merlot, pinot gris, viognier and traminer making up a somewhat eclectic
selection of varieties. In 2010 the family celebrated 10 years in business by opening a cellar
door and restaurant. Exports to Japan.

ΥΥΥΥΥ **Aged Release Generations Reserve Hunter Valley Semillon 2007** Bright
green-gold; this wine is so fresh it might have come down in the last shower; the
lemon and lime fruit is still in a primary phase, and the acidity is as high as one
would hope; it really needs another five years, and will likely still be going strong
another 10 years thereafter. Screwcap. 10.5% alc. **Rating** 94 **To** 2027 $30

ΥΥΥΥΥ **Generations Reserve Hunter Valley Semillon 2011 Rating** 93 **To** 2026 $25
Impressions Hunter Valley Shiraz 2010 Rating 92 **To** 2020 $30
Hunter Valley Shiraz 2010 Rating 90 **To** 2020 $25

ΥΥΥΥ **Impressions Hunter Valley Chardonnay 2011 Rating** 89 **To** 2017 $25
Hunter Valley Chardonnay 2011 Rating 88 **To** 2017 $20

Rieslingfreak

8 Roenfeldt Drive, Tanunda, SA 5352 (postal) **Region** Clare Valley
T (08) 8563 3963 **www**.rieslingfreak.com **Open** Not
Winemaker John Hughes **Est.** 2009 **Dozens** 450 **Vyds** 20ha
The name of John Hughes' winery leaves no doubt about his long-term ambition: to explore
every avenue of Riesling, whether bone-dry or quite sweet, coming from regions across the
wine world, albeit with a strong focus on Australia. The first two wines come from his Clare
Valley vineyard, and offer No. 3 (dry) and No. 5 (off-dry), and bin numbers that will be
maintained for future vintages, supplemented by other styles.

ΥΥΥΥ **No. 5 Off Dry Riesling 2011** The wine is fairly phenolic, but the overall
balance of sugar and acidity is good, as is the length. Will definitely benefit from
cellaring. Screwcap. 11.5% alc. **Rating** 89 **To** 2018 $20
No. 3 Riesling 2011 Light straw-green; the faintly floral bouquet will build with
time, but the somewhat phenolic palate needs more drive to the fruit; it has some
development potential. Screwcap. 11.5% alc. **Rating** 87 **To** 2015 $20

Riposte

PO Box 256, Lobethal, SA 5241 **Region** Adelaide Hills
T (08) 8389 8149 **www**.timknappstein.com.au **Open** Not
Winemaker Tim Knappstein **Est.** 2006 **Dozens** 10 000
It's never too late to teach an old dog new tricks when the old dog in question is Tim
Knappstein. With 40 years of winemaking and more than 500 wine show awards under his belt,
Tim started yet another new wine life with Riposte, a subtle response to the various vicissitudes
he has suffered in recent years. While having no continuing financial interest in Lenswood
Vineyards, established many years ago, Tim is able to source grapes from it and also from other
prime sites in surrounding areas. Exports to the UK, Canada, Singapore, Indonesia and China.

ΥΥΥΥΥ **The Stiletto Adelaide Hills Pinot Gris 2011** Pale quartz-green; the bouquet
✿ is far more expressive than most, with pear, orange zest and lime pith, and the
zesty palate fulfils all the promise of the bouquet and then some. A rare beast is a
pinot gris with the degree of varietal expression coming from the vineyard, not
the winery, where Tim Knappstein's role has been that of quality control officer.
Screwcap. 12% alc. **Rating** 95 **To** 2013 $19

Reserve Pinot Noir 2010 Similar colour to The Sabre; the aromas and flavours introduce plum to join the cherry; the quality of the wine is revealed on the finish and aftertaste, with a web of silky tannins adding an extra dimension to the texture and length. Screwcap. 14% alc. **Rating** 94 **To** 2018 $45

Reserve Noble Traminer 2011 The clouds and rain of '11 had a silver lining for Tim Knappstein when botrytis descended, and he was able to make this marvellously opulent and rich (and very sweet) wine. On the German scale, it would be headed towards Trockenbeerenauslese level. 375ml. Screwcap. 11% alc. **Rating** 94 **To** 2015 $25

The Sabre Adelaide Hills Pinot Noir 2010 **Rating** 93 **To** 2017 $29
The Cutlass Adelaide Hills Shiraz 2010 **Rating** 93 **To** 2020 $26
The Foil Adelaide Hills Sauvignon Blanc 2011 Just a tinge of green to the colour; the bouquet has some appealing flowery notes, the palate with gooseberry, passionfruit and strong lemony/steely acidity on the finish. Screwcap. 12% alc. **Rating** 92 **To** 2014 $20
The Dagger Adelaide Hills Pinot Noir 2011 Good colour; because of the vintage conditions, no Sabre Pinot Noir was produced, leaving this with the best available fruit; has red and black cherry flavours and good length. Screwcap. 13.5% alc. **Rating** 90 **To** 2015 $20

Riversdale Estate   ★★★★★

222 Denholms Road, Cambridge, Tas 7170 **Region** Southern Tasmania
T (03) 6248 5666 **www**.riversdaleestate.com.au **Open** At Zero Cafe, Hobart
Winemaker Nick Badrice **Est.** 1991 **Dozens** 10 000 **Vyds** 23ha
Ian Roberts purchased the Riversdale property in 1980 while a university student, and says he paid a record price for the district. The unique feature of the property is its frontage to the Pittwater waterfront, which acts as a buffer against frost, and also moderates the climate during the ripening phase. The vines are planted on a gentle, easterly facing slope. It is a large property, with over 20ha of vines, and one of the largest olive groves in Tasmania, producing 50 olive-based products. Five families live permanently on the estate, providing all the labour for the various operations, which also include four 5-star French Provincial cottages overlooking the vines. Wine quality is consistently good.

Coal River Valley Riesling 2011 Vibrant green hue; a restrained and complex bouquet of lime, green apple, washed river stones and jasmine; the palate shows purity of fruit and a linear personality that provides a tremendous level of punch and energy across the palate; this will age beautifully. Screwcap. 12% alc. **Rating** 95 **To** 2025 $23 BE

Crater Coal River Valley Chardonnay 2010 Pale colour, bright; the essence of taut and linear Chardonnay, all lemon, mineral and bath talc; the palate is racy, and the acidity will challenge some, however the freshness and drive, not to mention the age-worthiness, will see this wine have a long and perhaps even majestic future. Screwcap. 13.5% alc. **Rating** 95 **To** 2018 $50 BE

Coal River Valley Pinot Noir 2010 **Rating** 92 **To** 2016 $25 BE

Crux Sparkling NV **Rating** 89 **To** 2014 $44 BE
Coal River Valley Sauvignon Blanc 2011 **Rating** 88 **To** 2013 $23 BE

Robert Channon Wines

32 Bradley Lane, Stanthorpe, Qld 4380 **Region** Granite Belt
T (07) 4683 3260 **www**.robertchannonwines.com **Open** Mon–Fri 11–4, w'ends & public hols 10–5
Winemaker Stephen Oliver **Est.** 1998 **Dozens** 3000 **Vyds** 8ha
Peggy and Robert Channon have established verdelho, chardonnay, pinot gris, shiraz, cabernet sauvignon and pinot noir under permanent bird protection netting. The initial cost of installing permanent netting is high, but in the long term it is well worth it: it excludes birds and protects the grapes against hail damage. Also, there is no pressure to pick the grapes

before they are fully ripe. The winery has established a particular reputation for its Verdelho. Exports to China.

ⅤⅤⅤⅤⅤ **Reserve Chardonnay 2009** A well-made wine, barrel-fermented in French oak, followed by nine months' maturation. It has developed at an impressively leisurely pace, and is well balanced, its only shortcoming a slightly short finish. Screwcap. 13.5% alc. **Rating** 90 **To** 2013 $35

Pinot Noir 2009 Strong purple-red; takes no prisoners with its powerful bouquet and a palate that is still decidedly youthful; against the odds, it does allow some pinot characters to shine through, although in a far-from-classic style. Its development may be equally surprising. Screwcap. 13.5% alc. **Rating** 90 **To** 2019 $35

ⅤⅤⅤⅤ **Chardonnay 2011 Rating** 89 **To** 2014 $19
Verdelho 2011 Rating 89 **To** 2013 $28

✪ **Singing Lake Rose 2011** Light, bright puce-pink; lively, fresh and crisp, with small red fruit flavours, and zesty acidity to prolong the finish. Screwcap. 12.5% alc. **Rating** 89 **To** Now $18

Pinot Gris 2011 Rating 87 **To** Now $19

Robert Johnson Vineyards ★★★☆

Old Woollen Mill, Lobethal, SA 5241 **Region** Eden Valley
T (08) 8359 2600 **www**.robertjohnsonvineyards.com.au **Open** Fri–Sun 11–4
Winemaker Robert Johnson **Est.** 1997 **Dozens** 3000 **Vyds** 3.86ha
The home base for Robert Johnson is a 12ha vineyard and olive grove purchased in 1996, with 0.4ha of merlot and 5ha of olive trees. The olive grove has been rehabilitated, and 2.1ha of shiraz, 1.2ha of merlot and a small patch of viognier have been established. Wines made from estate-grown grapes are released under the Robert Johnson label; these are supplemented by Alan & Veitch wines made from grapes purchased from the Sam Virgara vineyard in the Adelaide Hills, and named after Robert Johnson's parents. Exports to the UK and the US.

ⅤⅤⅤⅤⅤ **Alan & Veitch Adelaide Hills Sauvignon Blanc 2010** Still pale quartz-green; the major portion was cool-fermented in stainless steel, the remainder barrel-fermented in oak; the combination has worked well, helping build the citrus, gooseberry and kiwi fruit flavours, the finish neatly tied up with a bow by the barrel-ferment inputs. Screwcap. 12.5% alc. **Rating** 92 **To** 2013 $22

ⅤⅤⅤⅤ **Alan & Veitch Adelaide Hills Merlot 2009 Rating** 87 **To** 2014 $28
Alan & Veitch Adelaide Hills Merlot 2008 Rating 87 **To** 2014 $28

Robert Oatley Vineyards ★★★★★

Craigmoor Road, Mudgee, NSW 2850 **Region** Mudgee
T (02) 6372 2208 **www**.robertoatley.com.au **Open** 7 days 10–4
Winemaker Chris Hancock, Larry Cherubino, Derek Fitzgerald, Robert Merrick
Est. 2006 **Dozens** NFP **Vyds** 440ha
Robert Oatley Vineyards is the venture of the Oatley family, previously best known as the owners of Rosemount Estate until it was sold to Southcorp. The chairman is Bob Oatley; the new venture is run by son Sandy, with considerable hitting power added by deputy executive chairman Chris Hancock. Wild Oats, as anyone with the remotest interest in yachting and the Sydney–Hobart Yacht Race will know, has been the name of Bob's racing yachts. The family has long owned vineyards in Mudgee, but the new business has been rapidly expanded by the acquisition of the Montrose winery, and the Craigmoor cellar door and restaurant. The family has completed a $10 million upgrade of the Montrose winery. The recruitment of Larry Cherubino as a winemaker has been a major factor in the radical reshaping of the overall business, with all of the best wines now coming coming from WA. While there is a plethora of wines, stripped to its essentials the portfolio is easy to understand: at the bottom, James Oatley Tic Tok; next Wild Oats; then Robert Oatley; and at the top, Robert Oatley limited releases. Exports to the UK, the US and other major markets.

ŸŸŸŸŸ **Robert Oatley Finisterre Margaret River Chardonnay 2010** Full, bright yellow-green; the complex bouquet has an attractive touch of Burgundian funk before the vibrant and lively palate comes into play; here there are grapefruit, white peach and subtle French oak inputs. The length of the wine is excellent, and it will have a long cellaring future. Screwcap. 13.5% alc. **Rating** 96 **To** 2022 $38

Robert Oatley Finisterre Margaret River Cabernet Sauvignon 2009 The purity of this wine comes through with the utmost clarity on the bouquet with fragrant blackcurrant/cassis aromas; the medium- to full-bodied palate is a great example of Margaret River Cabernet, the focused fruit supported by tannins that, while firm, are in no way out of balance. Screwcap. 14.2% alc. **Rating** 96 **To** 2029 $42

Robert Oatley Finisterre Great Southern Shiraz 2011 Brilliant, youthful purple-crimson; the wine is flush with blackberry, black cherry, licorice and spice flavours, the oak positive but balanced, the tannins fine. Screwcap. 14.1% alc. **Rating** 95 **To** 2026 $42

Robert Oatley Finisterre Margaret River Cabernet Sauvignon 2010 Alluring colour grading to crimson on the rim; this is a potent, full-bodied, no holds barred Cabernet, the blackcurrant fruit armour-plated with ripe tannins that help draw out the length of the palate and the lingering finish that follows. Will absolutely need five years to throw open its arms in welcome. Screwcap. 14% alc. **Rating** 95 **To** 2040 $42

Robert Oatley Great Southern Riesling 2011 Pale quartz-green; has the purity of varietal expression peculiar to the Great Southern; the fruit flavours of lime and lemon are delicate, yet run through the long palate and finish, sustained by perfectly balanced acidity. Has a great future. Screwcap. 12.5% alc. **Rating** 94 **To** 2021 $24

Robert Oatley Margaret River Sauvignon Blanc 2011 Pale straw-green; a lively, zesty, mouth watering combination of freshly mown grass, mineral, citrus and a dab of passionfruit create an abundance of flavour, yet leaves the mouth fresh and thirsting for more. Screwcap. 12.5% alc. **Rating** 94 **To** 2014 $24

Robert Oatley McLaren Vale Shiraz 2010 Deep purple-crimson; both the bouquet and palate have a clarion call of regional character, black fruits, bitter chocolate and spice in a medium- to full-bodied framework; French oak has contributed, but it is the quality of the grapes, and the controlled alcohol, that make the wine what it is. Screwcap. 14% alc. **Rating** 94 **To** 2025 $24

Robert Oatley Margaret River Cabernet Sauvignon 2010 Crimson-purple; a wine that exudes its class and character, with blackcurrant fruit leading the way on the bouquet and palate, and supported by ripe, rounded tannins plus quality French oak. Screwcap. 14% alc. **Rating** 94 **To** 2025 $24

ŸŸŸŸ♀ **Robert Oatley Margaret River Chardonnay 2011 Rating** 92 **To** 2017 $24
Robert Oatley Craigmoor AC1 Mudgee Chardonnay 2010 Rating 92 **To** 2014 $29

✪ **Wild Oats Shiraz 2010** Sourced from various Victorian regions, this medium-bodied wine has distinct style, with plum and black cherry fruit on the medium-bodied palate, moving to a more savoury, spicy finish, Screwcap. 14% alc. **Rating** 91 **To** 2017 $19

✪ **James Oatley Tic Tok Cabernet Sauvignon 2010** Crimson-purple; highly fragrant and very expressive, with a display of redcurrant and other red fruits, slightly darker fruit flavours lurking in the background; the faultless balance means the wine can be fully enjoyed right now. Excellent value. Screwcap. 13.8% alc. **Rating** 91 **To** 2018 $18

✪ **Wild Oats Sauvignon Blanc 2011** An interesting wine that has things in common with Tic Tok, but has more texture, if not structure; there's little point in cellaring the wine, but it won't collapse any time soon. Screwcap. 13.2% alc. **Rating** 90 **To** 2014 $19

Robert Stein Vineyard ★★★★★

Pipeclay Lane, Mudgee, NSW 2850 **Region** Mudgee
T (02) 6373 3991 **www**.robertstein.com.au **Open** 7 days 10–4.30
Winemaker Andrew and Jacob Stein **Est.** 1976 **Dozens** 20 000 **Vyds** 18.67ha
While three generations of the family have been involved since Robert (Bob) Stein began
the establishment of the vineyard, the chain stretches even further back, going to Bob's great-
great-grandfather, Johann Stein, who was brought to Australia by the Macarthur family to
supervise the planting of the Camden Park vineyard. Bob's son Drew and grandson Jacob
have now taken over winemaking responsibilities. Jacob worked vintages in Italy, Canada,
Margaret River and Avoca, and, more particularly, in the Rheingau and Rheinhessen regions
of Germany. Since Jacob's return to the winery, one success has followed another, with a
deluge of trophies, culminating in six trophies at the Mudgee Wine Show '10. Exports to
Germany, Hong Kong, Singapore and China.

♀♀♀♀♀ Reserve Shiraz 2010 Deep crimson; complex, spicy, fragrant and floral, with
a finely textured and almost ethereal grace from well-handled stems, fine oak
and super silky tannins; the finish is long, harmonious and beautifully balanced.
Screwcap. 13.5% alc. **Rating** 95 **To** 2020 $50 BE
Half Dry Mudgee Riesling 2011 Light straw-green; the bouquet has citrus,
apple and a whisker of spice, the palate with gently sweet lime juice offset by crisp
acidity; particularly well made, and can be enjoyed now or later. 15g/l residual
sugar. Screwcap. 10% alc. **Rating** 94 **To** 2018 $25
Mudgee Riesling 2011 Light straw-green; the bouquet is similar to that of the
Half Dry, but not bone dry; elegant palate with lime and apple sharing the space;
impressive winemaking. Screwcap. 11% alc. **Rating** 94 **To** 2021 $30

♀♀♀♀♀ Reserve Mudgee Cabernet Sauvignon 2009 **Rating** 93 **To** 2024 $45
Mudgee Shiraz 2010 **Rating** 92 **To** 2018 $25 BE
Reserve Cabernet Sauvignon Shiraz 2009 **Rating** 90 **To** 2017 $55 BE

♀♀♀♀ Mudgee Rose 2011 **Rating** 89 **To** Now $15
Mudgee Shiraz Viognier 2010 **Rating** 89 **To** 2015 $25 BE
Third Generation Mudgee Chardonnay 2011 **Rating** 88 **To** 2014 $20 BE

Robertson of Clare ★★★★☆

PO Box 149, Killara, NSW 2071 **Region** Clare Valley
T (02) 9499 6002 **www**.rocwines.com.au **Open** Not
Winemaker Simon Gilbert, Leigh Eldredge, Biagio Famularo **Est.** 2004 **Dozens** NFP
This is a venture of Simon Gilbert, established after he ceased to have an executive position
with Simon Gilbert Wines in Mudgee. He has joined with Clare Valley vigneron Leigh
Eldredge to produce limited quantities of Clare Valley wines. Lavish oak is the hallmark of
MAX V, a Bordeaux style sourced from three growers in the Clare Valley. Exports to the UK,
the US, Denmark, the Netherlands, the Maldives, Singapore, Hong Kong and China.

♀♀♀♀♀ MAX V 2008 Strong purple-crimson; a blend of cabernet sauvignon, malbec,
cabernet franc, merlot and petit verdot, one-third fermented in special 400-litre
French oak vessels, the remainder in slate fermenters; 30 months with 19 different
parcels in 100% new oak; lives up to the description, not unlike Vega Sicilia. At this
price you will either think it's a great bargain or an expensive curiosity. Screwcap.
14.5% alc. **Rating** 93 **To** 2038 $75

Robyn Drayton Wines ★★★★

Cnr McDonalds Road/Pokolbin Mountain Road, Pokolbin, NSW 2321
Region Hunter Valley
T (02) 4998 7523 **www**.robyndraytonwines.com.au **Open** 7 days 10–5
Winemaker Robyn Drayton, Andrew Spanazi **Est.** 1989 **Dozens** 5000 **Vyds** 14ha
Robyn Drayton inherited the business started by her parents following their death in a plane
crash in 1994. Together with her sons, Justin, Liam and Taylor, she has grown the business

exponentially. The cellar door has been expanded twice, a new café and function centre opened, and an additional 6ha of vines planted. Robyn is a fifth-generation Drayton, and continues the proud tradition of over 150 years of Drayton winemaking in the Hunter Valley.

ＴＴＴＴ **Reginald Reserve Hunter Valley Semillon 2010** Pale, gleaming green-quartz; a Hunter Semillon bred to stay; the extra degree of alcohol builds the lemony fruit flavours, but is inherently balanced by the acidity; much of it will be drunk before its best. Screwcap. 11.8% alc. **Rating** 93 **To** 2025 $30

Three Sons Reserve Hunter Valley Shiraz 2010 Bright crimson; has all of the indicia of Hunter Shiraz that make it so appealing: restrained alcohol, supple mouthfeel, medium body, and refined, faintly earthy, tannins; the one jarring note is the white glass bottle, but I suppose you can't have everything. Screwcap. 14% alc. **Rating** 92 **To** 2025 $28

Liam Reserve Hunter Valley Verdelho 2009 Bright, light green-straw is a promising start for a wine that very nearly makes it over 90 points thanks to bottle-developed complexity. Screwcap. 13.4% alc. **Rating** 90 **To** 2013 $25

ＴＴＴＴ **Pamela Reserve Hunter Valley Rose 2009** **Rating** 87 **To** 2013 $25

Rochford Wines

Cnr Maroondah Highway/Hill Road, Coldstream, Vic 3770 **Region** Yarra Valley
T (03) 5962 2119 **www**.rochfordwines.com **Open** 7 days 10–5
Winemaker Andrew Leitch **Est.** 1988 **Dozens** 20 000 **Vyds** 45.26ha
Following the acquisition of the former Eyton-on-Yarra by Helmut Konecsny, major changes occurred. Most obvious is the renaming of the winery and brand, slightly less so the move of the winemaking operations of Rochford from the Macedon Ranges to the Yarra Valley. Rochford has 30.55ha of vineyards in the Macedon Ranges, and just under 15ha in the Yarra Valley, with a heavy focus on chardonnay and pinot noir. The large restaurant is open seven days for lunch and Rochford is well known for the numerous concerts it stages in its lakeside amphitheatre. No wines were received for this edition; the rating is that of last year. Exports to the UK, the US, Canada, Sweden, Philippines, Singapore, Hong Kong and China.

RockBare

102 Main St, Hahndorf, SA 5245 **Region** McLaren Vale
T (08) 8388 7155 **www**.rockbare.com.au **Open** 7 days 10.30–5
Winemaker Marty O'Flaherty **Est.** 2000 **Dozens** 50 000 **Vyds** 47ha
A native of WA, Tim Burvill moved to SA in 1993 to do the winemaking course at the Adelaide University Roseworthy campus. Having completed an honours degree in oenology, he was recruited by Southcorp and quickly found himself in a senior winemaking position, responsible for super-premium whites including Penfolds Yattarna. He oversees the team that makes the RockBare wines under lend-lease arrangements with other wineries. Has moved to a new cellar door in the centre of Hahndorf. Exports to all major markets.

ＴＴＴＴＴ **McLaren Vale Chardonnay 2010** Some early colour development; the wine
✪ makes a substantial impact on entering the palate with its mix of grapefruit and stone fruit, but drops off a little on the finish before coming again on the aftertaste. Screwcap. 13% alc. **Rating** 91 **To** 2016 $18

✪ **Mojo Sauvignon Blanc 2011** Light straw-green; a solidly constructed Sauvignon Blanc, with good depth and varietal character from its range of grass, herb and tropical nuances. Screwcap. 12.5% alc. **Rating** 90 **To** 2013 $18

✪ **McLaren Vale Chardonnay 2011** A savoury bouquet of struck match and nectarine is on display; the palate is fresh and lively, well constructed, with tangy acidity and a soft finish; enjoy this in the full flush of youth. Screwcap. 13% alc. **Rating** 90 **To** 2014 $18 BE

✪ **Mojo Barossa Valley Shiraz 2011** Vibrant purple hue; a juicy, young fresh and accessible Shiraz, unencumbered by oak, and made for immediate appeal and drinkability; blue and black fruits, sea salt and a dash of licorice all make for an easygoing drink. Screwcap. 14.5% alc. **Rating** 90 **To** 2015 $18 BE

McLaren Vale Shiraz 2010 Impenetrable colour; the choc-mint bouquet is strongly regional, the palate thickly textured, rich and complex, with oak coming through on the finish. Screwcap. 14.5% alc. **Rating** 90 **To** 2020 $22 BE

Barossa Babe Shiraz 2007 Medium red-purple; better than many Barossa Valley Shirazs from this vintage; while the wine is distinctly savoury, it is not tough; oak has made a positive contribution without going over the top, and the overall structure is good. Cork. 15% alc. **Rating** 90 **To** 2017 $40

🍷🍷🍷🍷 **Mojo Fizz Brut Cuvee Adelaide Hills Chardonnay Pinot Noir NV** **Rating** 89 **To** 2013 $20

Barossa Babe Shiraz 2008 **Rating** 88 **To** 2014 $40 BE

Rockfield Estate

687-721 Rosa Glen Road, Margaret River, WA 6285 **Region** Margaret River
T (08) 9757 5006 **www**.rockfield.com.au **Open** 7 days 11–5, or by appt
Winemaker James Kalleske, Andrew Garman **Est.** 1997 **Dozens** 5000 **Vyds** 11ha
Rockfield Estate Vineyard is very much a family affair. Dr Andrew Gaman wears the hats of chief executive officer and co-marketing manager, wife Anne is a director, son Alex is the viticulturist, and Anna Walter (née Gaman) helps with the marketing. Chapman Brook meanders through the property, the vines running from its banks up to the wooded slopes above the valley floor. No wines were received for this edition; the rating is that of last year. Exports to the UK and China.

Rockford

Krondorf Road, Tanunda, SA 5352 **Region** Barossa Valley
T (08) 8563 2720 **www**.rockfordwines.com.au **Open** 7 days 11–5
Winemaker Robert O'Callaghan, Ben Radford **Est.** 1984 **Dozens** NFP
Rockford can only be described as an icon, no matter how overused that word may be. It has a devoted band of customers who buy most of the wine through the cellar door or mail order (Rocky O'Callaghan's entrancing annual newsletter is like no other). Some wine is sold through restaurants, and there are two retailers in Sydney, and one each in Melbourne, Brisbane and Perth. Whether they will have the Basket Press Shiraz available is another matter; it is as scarce as Henschke Hill of Grace (and less expensive). Ben Radford, whom I first met in South Africa some years ago, has been entrenched as Rocky's right-hand man, and is destined to take over responsibility for winemaking when the time comes for Rocky to step back from an active role. Exports to the UK, Canada, Switzerland, South Korea, Singapore, Japan, Hong Kong, China and NZ.

🍷🍷🍷🍷🍷 **Basket Press Barossa Shiraz 2009** Medium red-purple; this is in the heartland of Barossa Shiraz style, the custom-made bottle a throwback to the 1940s; the bouquet is fragrant, and hides no secrets: silky, ripe tannins, abundant blackberry and spice fruit, and oak in perfect unison. Cork. 14.5% alc. **Rating** 95 **To** 2029 $54

Black Shiraz NV Rockford uses a unique approach, maturing the base wine for three years in large oak, then starting the process on tirage, leaving the wine on lees for one year, then returning it to the Rockford cellar after disgorgement for further ageing. This is a particularly well-balanced release, with delicious red fruits and a balanced finish. Cork. 13.5% alc. **Rating** 95 **To** 2020 $57

Rod & Spur Barossa Shiraz Cabernet 2008 Good colour and clarity; another Rockford wine honoured by its long history; a 53/47% blend, the accent on the blackberry and blackcurrant fruit, oak and tannins playing no more than support roles. Cork. 14.5% alc. **Rating** 94 **To** 2022 $30

🍷🍷🍷🍷🍷 **Rifle Range Barossa Valley Cabernet Sauvignon 2009** **Rating** 93 **To** 2019 $37

✪ **Barossa Valley White Frontignac 2011** Classic Rockford Frontignac, conceived years before moscato and other low-alcohol wines came onto the market, giving a true expression of the grape, in this vintage with lovely acidity. Screwcap. 9% alc. **Rating** 92 **To** Now $17

Moppa Springs Barossa Valley Grenache Mataro Shiraz 2007 Rating 92
To 2017 $24

✪ Local Growers Barossa Valley Semillon 2007 Deep glowing green colour;
the utterly unpredictable results of ageing on cork makes the whole exercise
fraught with difficulty. This bottle has travelled well, although at a helter-skelter
pace. Cork. 12.2% alc. Rating 90 To 2014 $19
PS Marion Tawny NV Rating 90 To 2013 $34

♛♛♛♛ Barossa Valley Alicante Bouchet 2011 Rating 89 To Now $18
✪

 # Rockridge Estate ★★★☆

PO Box 374, Kent Town, SA 5071 **Region** Clare Valley
T (08) 8376 9563 **www**.rockridgewines.com.au **Open** Not
Winemaker Justin Ardill (red), Peter Leske (white) **Est.** 2007 **Dozens** 7500 **Vyds** 40ha
In the Vine Pull Scheme of the 1980s, the 120ha Leasingham Wines vineyard in the hills
immediately above the hamlet of Leasingham was removed. Partially replanted in 1999, this
precious block of terra rossa over deep limestone is producing outstanding grapes, sold to Tim
Adams, Kilikanoon, Reilly's, Claymore, Old Station, Foster's and Yalumba. In 2007 owners
Andrew Miller, Richard Yeend and Justin Ardill decided to retain a significant part of the
crop to produce Riesling, Shiraz and Sparkling Riesling, purchasing sauvignon blanc from
premium cool-climate regions. Rockridge Estate is a custom label exclusively sold through
Cellarbrations, The Bottle-O and IGA plus Liquor.

♛♛♛♛ Watervale Riesling 2011 Rating 89
○ To 2014 $15
○ Watervale Riesling 2010 Rating 89 To 2015 $13
○ Adelaide Hills Sauvignon Blanc 2010 Rating 88 To Now $15
○ Clare Valley Shiraz 2009 Rating 88 To 2019 $15
Sauvignon Blanc 2011 Pale straw-green; a blend of estate-grown grapes, together
with grapes from 'other cool climate regions'. This is not a great Sauvignon Blanc
(yes, I know that's an oxymoron), but has a range of unmistakably varietal flavours,
and a soft, not minerally, finish. Screwcap. 12.5% alc. Rating 87 To 2013 $15

Rocky Passes Estate ★★★★★

1590 Highlands Road, Whiteheads Creek, Vic 3660 **Region** Upper Goulburn
T (03) 5796 9366 **www**.rockypasses.com.au **Open** Sun 11–5, or by appt
Winemaker Vitto Oles **Est.** 2000 **Dozens** 500 **Vyds** 2ha
Vitto Oles and Candi Westney run this tiny, cool-climate vineyard situated at the southern
end of the Strathbogie Ranges, which in fact falls in the Upper Goulburn region. They have
planted 1.6ha of shiraz and 0.4ha of viognier, growing the vines with minimal irrigation and
preferring organic and biodynamic soil treatments. Vitto is also a fine furniture designer and
maker, with a studio at Rocky Passes.

♛♛♛♛♛ Syrah 2010 Good colour; a wine that builds on the promise of the '09, with a
✪ complex bouquet of leather, spice and licorice over black fruits, the medium- to
full-bodied palate providing a replay of the bouquet, but with greater intensity;
excellent cellaring potential, and outstanding value. Diam. 14.5% alc. Rating 94
To 2025 $18

Rocland Estate ★★★★

PO Box 679, Nuriootpa, SA 5355 **Region** Barossa Valley
T (08) 8562 2142 **www**.roclandestate.com **Open** By appt
Winemaker Sarah Siddons **Est.** 2000 **Dozens** 21 000 **Vyds** 6ha
Rocland Estate is primarily a bulk winemaking facility for contract work, but Frank Rocca
does have 6ha of shiraz to make the Rocland wines, supplemented by contract-grown grapes.
Largely destined for export markets but with retail distribution in Adelaide. Rocland releases
wines under the Lot 147, Kilroy Was Here, Duck Duck Goose, Chocolate Box, and the
charmingly named Ass Kisser labels Exports to the UK, the US, Singapore, China and NZ.

ŢŢŢŢŢ Duck Duck Goose Barossa Valley Shiraz 2010 Impenetrable colour; dark
✪   fruits, mocha, olive and eucalypt bouquet; full-bodied, with lashings of fruit and
      muscle; power over elegance, but in the slot for lovers of big-boned and bold
      Shiraz. Screwcap. 14.5% alc. **Rating** 90 **To** 2014 $17 BE
      Barossa Valley Shiraz 2009 Extremely ripe and sweet-fruited, with blackberry
      jam, mocha and licorice; warm and unctuous on the palate, richness and sweet
      fruit are the order of the day. Screwcap. 14.5% alc. **Rating** 90 **To** 2014 $33 BE
      Lot 147 Single Vineyard Barossa Valley Shiraz 2009 Deep colour; very ripe
      aromas of blackberry, raspberry and fruitcake spice; the palate is warm and forward,
      showing generous sweet fruit, and is ultimately easygoing and accessible. Screwcap.
      14.5% alc. **Rating** 90 **To** 2016 $40 BE

ŢŢŢŢ Chocolate Box Cherry Chocolate GSM 2009 **Rating** 88 **To** 2014 $20 BE
      Chocolate Box Dark Chocolate Shiraz 2009 **Rating** 87 **To** 2014 $20 BE
      Barossa Valley Grenache 2009 **Rating** 87 **To** 2014 $33 BE

Rohrlach Family Wines   ★★★★☆

PO Box 864, Nuriootpa, SA 5355 **Region** Barossa Valley
T (08) 8562 4121 **www.**rohrlachfamilywines.com.au **Open** Not
Winemaker Peter Schell (Contract) **Est.** 2000 **Dozens** 1000 **Vyds** 160.6ha
Brothers Kevin, Graham and Wayne Rohrlach, with wives Lyn, Lynette and Kaylene, are
third-generation owners of prime vineyard land, the first plantings made back in 1930 by their
paternal grandfather. Until 2000 the grapes were sold to two leading Barossa wineries, but (in
a common story) in that year some of the grapes were retained to make the first vintage of
what became Rohrlach Family Wines. In '03 the family received the ultimate local accolade
when the Barons of the Barossa gave them the title of 'Vignerons of the Year'.

ŢŢŢŢŢ Family Reserve Barossa Valley Shiraz 2010 Deep but bright crimson-purple;
✪   from the family estate vineyards, the wine displays all the many attributes of the
      vintage, with a seamless union of black fruits, plum and spice backed by high-
      quality tannins; 10 months in new American oak has barely impacted on the wine.
      Screwcap. 14.5% alc. **Rating** 94 **To** 2030 $26

ŢŢŢŢŢ Mum's Block Barossa Valley Shiraz 2009 **Rating** 91 **To** 2029 $43
      Family Reserve Barossa Valley Merlot 2010 **Rating** 90 **To** 2018 $26

ŢŢŢŢ Barossa Shiraz 2009 **Rating** 89 **To** 2017 $20

Rolf Binder Veritas Winery   ★★★★★

Cnr Seppeltsfield Road/Stelzer Road, Tanunda, SA 5352 **Region** Barossa Valley
T (08) 8562 3300 **www.**rolfbinder.com **Open** Mon–Sat 10–4.30
Winemaker Rolf Binder, Christa Deans **Est.** 1955 **Dozens** 30 000 **Vyds** 36ha
The change of accent from Veritas to Rolf Binder came with the 50th anniversary of the
winery, established by the parents of Rolf and sister Christa Deans. The growth in production
and sales is due to the quality of the wines rather than the (hitherto) rather laid-back approach
to marketing. The winery produces a full range of all the main white and red wines sourced
from the Barossa and Eden valleys. It has had conspicuous success with Semillon at the Barossa
Valley Wine Show, but the red wines are equally commendable. Exports to all major markets.

ŢŢŢŢŢ Eden Valley Riesling 2011 Bright, pale straw-green; the evocative, fragrant
✪   bouquet does not prepare you for the exceptional power and mouth-gripping
      intensity of the palate and its equally exceptional length. Wow, this is great
      Riesling. Screwcap. 12% alc. **Rating** 96 **To** 2025 $18
      Rolf Binder's Bull's Blood Shiraz Mataro Pressings 2008 The Bull's Blood
      name has been used for many years by Veritas, and once was descriptive of the
      wine. Times have changed, and this is a fragrant, elegant and medium-bodied wine
      with almost juicy fruit flavours and fine tannins to finish. A triumph for the '08
      vintage. Cork. 14% alc. **Rating** 94 **To** 2025 $50

Heinrich Barossa Valley Shiraz Mataro Grenache 2008 Bright and clear red-purple, another remarkable escape from the clutches of the heatwave; it is possible to deconstruct the blend and look at the contribution of each component: suffice it to say they all contribute to the spicy and savoury aspects of a refreshing medium-bodied wine, both the modest alcohol and abstemious use of oak the final touches. Screwcap. 14% alc. **Rating** 94 **To** 2020 $35

ŢŢŢŢ♀ Barossa Valley Shiraz 2010 Bright crimson; if only more winemakers in the
✪   Barossa would look carefully at wines such as this, and realise high alcohol is not a
       universal panacea. Here there is a lovely blend of red and black cherry fruit, with
       fine spicy/savoury tannins; a bargain at the price. Screwcap. 13.5% alc. **Rating** 93
       To 2018 $18
✪   Barossa Valley Cabernet Sauvignon Merlot 2010 Deep purple-crimson;
       a somewhat left field, very enjoyable, medium-bodied wine with the degree of
       dark chocolate you would expect to find in McLaren Vale, not the Barossa; there
       is an overall opulence on the palate, aided and abetted by the oak that has been
       sensitively used. Screwcap. 13.5% alc. **Rating** 93 **To** 2025 $18
       Veritas Petit Syrah 2009 **Rating** 91 **To** 2029 $25

ŢŢŢŢ   Christa Rolf Barossa Valley Semillon 2011 **Rating** 87 **To** 2016 $17
       Veritas Cabernet Mataro 2009 **Rating** 87 **To** 2017 $25

Romney Park Wines   ★★★★★

Lot 100, Johnson Road, Balhannah, SA 5242 **Region** Adelaide Hills
T (08) 8398 0698 **www**.romneyparkwines.com.au **Open** By appt
Winemaker Rod and Rachel Short **Est.** 1997 **Dozens** 800 **Vyds** 3ha
Rod and Rachel Short began the planting of chardonnay, shiraz and pinot noir in 1997. The first vintage was in 2002, made from 100% estate-grown grapes. Yields are limited to 3.7–5 tonnes per hectare for the red wines, and 2–3 tonnes for the Chardonnay. The vineyard is managed organically, with guinea fowl cleaning up the insects, all vines hand-picked and hand-pruned. In every way (including the wines) has the beauty of a hand-painted miniature. Exports to China.

ŢŢŢŢŢ Adelaide Hills Blanc de Blancs 2009 Second disgorgement, Aug '11. Bright
       gold-green; barrel-fermented with full mlf, it was tiraged in Aug '09. Attractive
       biscuity yeast characters, and the benefit of mlf, have resulted in a generous
       and rounded palate, the white peach fruit with a touch of cream. Crown seal.
       12.5% alc. **Rating** 95 **To** Now $42
       Adelaide Hills Shiraz 2005 Mature Release. Wonderful colour, still in the red-
       purple spectrum, with no hint of browning; it spent 18 months in 50% new and
       second-use French oak, and 50% in older American oak; oak makes an indelible
       mark on the aromas and flavour, but the length of the red and black fruits on the
       finish and aftertaste is sufficient to give balance to what is structurally an elegant,
       medium-bodied wine. Diam. 14.5% alc. **Rating** 94 **To** 2020 $50

ŢŢŢŢ♀ Adelaide Hills Blanc de Blancs 2010 **Rating** 93 **To** 2015 $42

ŢŢŢŢ   Adelaide Hills Sparkling Shiraz 2008 **Rating** 89 **To** 2015 $45

Rookery Wines   ★★★

PO Box 132, Kingscote, Kangaroo Island, SA 5223 **Region** Kangaroo Island
T (08) 8553 9099 **www**.rookerywines.com.au **Open** By appt
Winemaker Garry Lovering **Est.** 1999 **Dozens** 800 **Vyds** 8ha
Garry and Gael Lovering have established 3.2ha of cabernet sauvignon and 1.6ha of shiraz, with smaller plantings of sauvignon blanc, tempranillo, saperavi, sangiovese, chardonnay, merlot, petit verdot, riesling and zinfandel. Kangaroo Island is one of SA's best-kept secrets, a place of genuine magic with its aquatic life, amazing coastline sculpture, wild flowers and prolific native fauna.

ȲȲȲȲ **Kangaroo Island Sangiovese 2010** Remarkably full colour for the variety; the full-bodied palate is likewise most unusual, its accent mostly on red and black cherry fruit, and little attention drawn to the normally snappy tannins. I have no idea where this will head in the future, but it might be interesting to watch its development. Screwcap. 14.5% alc. **Rating** 89 **To** 2020 $18
Kangaroo Island Saperavi 2010 If ever a wine was designed to reflect its variety, it is this one; saperavi is a Russian variety noted for the depth of its colour, here so dense there is no hope of seeing through it. There is lots of structure in the palate, rather like a Meccano set, but with nothing to fill in the spaces; that said, the potential is obvious, and in the short term the wine will certainly create interest. Screwcap. 14.5% alc. **Rating** 88 **To** 2015 $18

Ros Ritchie Wines

52 Crosby's Lane, Mansfield, Vic 3722 **Region** Upper Goulburn
T 0448 900 541 **www**.rosritchiewines.com **Open** By appt
Winemaker Ros Ritchie **Est.** 2008 **Dozens** 2000 **Vyds** 5ha
This is the new venture for Ros Ritchie and husband John. Ros was winemaker at the Ritchie family's Delatite winery from 1981 to 2006, but moved on to establish her own winery with John in '08. They lease a vineyard planted to merlot and cabernet sauvignon on a northeastern slope close to Mansfield. They source their white wines from growers who work in tandem with them to provide high-quality grapes. Foremost are Gumbleton's Vineyard, Retief's Vineyard and Baxendale's Vineyard, the last planted by the very experienced viticulturist Jim Baxendale (and wife Ruth) high on the Woodfield Plateau above the King River Valley. All the vineyards are managed with minimal spray regimes.

ȲȲȲȲȲ **Dead Man's Hill Vineyard Gewurztraminer 2010** Bright colour, with rosewater, pot pourri, lemon pith and ginger on the bouquet; the palate is richly textured and fresh, and the freshness is commendable in a variety that can so easily become hard work. Screwcap. 12.5% alc. **Rating** 94 **To** 2016 $26 BE

ȲȲȲȲȲ **Barwite Vineyard Riesling 2011 Rating** 93 **To** 2017 $26 BE
Baxendale's Vineyard Cabernet Sauvignon 2009 Rating 93 **To** 2022 $27 BE
Dead Man's Hill & Whitegate Vineyards Gewurztraminer 2011 Rating 92 **To** 2015 $26 BE
Gumbleton's & Baxendale's Vineyards Sauvignon Blanc 2010 Rating 90 **To** 2014 $21 BE
Retief's & Whitegate Vineyards Pinot Gris 2011 Rating 90 **To** 2014 $26 BE
Retief's Vineyard Pinot Gris 2010 Rating 90 **To** 2013 $26 BE

ȲȲȲȲ **Barwite Vineyard Late Harvest Riesling 2011 Rating** 89 **To** 2014 $26 BE

Rosabrook Margaret River Wine

Yungarra Estate, Lot 68 Yungarra Drive, Quedjinup, WA 6281 **Region** Margaret River
T (08) 9368 4555 **www**.rosabrook.com.au **Open** Mon–Fri 8.30–5
Winemaker Brian Fletcher **Est.** 1980 **Dozens** 8000 **Vyds** 10ha
Mike and Sally Calneggia have been at the forefront of vineyard development in the Margaret River over the past decade, but also have various winemaking interests. The original Rosabrook Estate vineyards were established progressively between 1984 and '96. In 2007 Rosabrook relocated its estate vineyard to the northwestern end of the Margaret River wine region, overlooking Geographe Bay and the Indian Ocean. The warm days and cool nights, influenced by the ocean, result in slow, mild-ripening conditions. The cellar door is housed in what was Margaret River's first commercial abattoir, built in the early 1930s, hence the icon red is named Slaughterhouse Block. Exports to Dubai, Hong Kong, China and Japan.

ȲȲȲȲȲ **Cabernet Sauvignon 2010** A lifted, fragrant and violet-accented cabernet bouquet, with purity and precision the order of the day; the palate is finely textured, with lacy tannins, ample fruits and a long and expansive finish; excellent quality for the price. Screwcap. 14.5% alc. **Rating** 94 **To** 2018 $25 BE

Single Vineyard Estate Cabernet Sauvignon 2010 Clear purple-crimson; a cabernet that ticks each and every box: fragrant blackcurrant fruit, gently savoury tannins providing a crosscut of complexity, and cedary oak all in harmonious balance on the long, sinuous palate. Screwcap. 14% alc. **Rating** 94 **To** 2025 $35

ΨΨΨΨΨ Sauvignon Blanc Semillon 2011 **Rating** 93 **To** 2013 $22 BE
Single Vineyard Estate Cabernet Sauvignon 2009 **Rating** 93 **To** 2019 $35
Chardonnay 2010 **Rating** 92 **To** 2016 $25
○ Classic White 2010 **Rating** 91 **To** 2013 $17
Chenin Blanc 2011 **Rating** 91 **To** 2015 $20
○ Cabernet Merlot 2010 **Rating** 91 **To** 2017 $17

Rosby ★★★

122 Strikes Lane, Mudgee, NSW 2850 **Region** Mudgee
T (02) 6373 3856 **www**.rosby.com.au **Open** By appt
Winemaker Tim Stevens **Est.** 1996 **Dozens** 1000 **Vyds** 6ha
Gerald and Kaye Norton-Knight have 4ha of shiraz and 2ha of cabernet sauvignon established on what is truly a unique site in Mudgee. Many vignerons like to think that their vineyard has special qualities, but in this instance the belief is well based. It is situated in a small valley, with unusual red basalt over a quartz gravel structure, encouraging deep root growth, and making the use of water far less critical than normal. Tim Stevens of Huntington Estate has purchased some of the ample production, as well as making the Rosby wines.

ΨΨΨΨ Mudgee Shiraz 2009 Some colour development; a generously flavoured wine with plummy fruit and a superfluity of American oak, 25% of the barrels being new. Screwcap. 14.2% alc. **Rating** 88 **To** 2013 $20

Rosemount Estate ★★★★★

114 Chaffeys Road, McLaren Vale, SA 5171 **Region** McLaren Vale
T (08) 8323 6220 **www**.rosemountestate.com.au **Open** Mon–Sat & public hols 10–5, Sun 11–5
Winemaker Matt Koch, Andrew Locke, Randall Cummins **Dozens** 3 million
Rosemount Estate has vineyards in McLaren Vale, Fleurieu, Coonawarra and Robe that are the anchor for its top-of-the-range wines. It also has access to other TWE estate-grown grapes, but the major part of its intake for the Diamond Label wines is supplied by contract growers across SA, NSW, Vic and WA. As the tasting notes show, the quality and range of the wines has greatly improved over the past few years as Rosemount Estate endeavours to undo the damage done to the brand around the new millennium. Abandoning the diamond-shaped bottle is but one tangible signpost of the future. Exports to all major markets.

ΨΨΨΨΨ Nursery Project Langhorne Creek Fiano 2011 Pale green-quartz; this is an emerging variety, albeit with other producers in Australia; there is an immediate burst of creamy fruit – derived from five months on full lees – underpinning the primary ripe pear fruit. Screwcap. 12% alc. **Rating** 94 **To** 2015 $25
 District Release McLaren Vale Shiraz 2010 Medium purple-crimson; a liquid portrait of the region, with lush blackberry/plum fruit, dark chocolate and soft tannins all filling the mouth, but without any aggression. Classic now or later – even much later – style. Screwcap. 14.5% alc. **Rating** 94 **To** 2020 $20
Balmoral McLaren Vale Syrah 2010 Impenetrable colour; deep and dark-fruited, with lashings of oak, black fruits and a splash of dark chocolate; the palate is unctuous, rich, dense and thickly textured, with high levels of tannin and toast dominant; more is certainly more in this example, but the quality of the fruit cannot be denied. Screwcap. 14.5% alc. **Rating** 94 **To** 2020 $75 BE
G.S.M. McLaren Vale Grenache Syrah Mourvedre 2010 A fresh blueberry, black cherry, spice and roasted meat bouquet; fleshy and dense in one regard, yet shows lightness and a fresh fruit aspect that is attractive and pure; an excellent example of this once groundbreaking wine again in full flight. Screwcap. 14.5% alc. **Rating** 94 **To** 2018 $35 BE

Nursery Project McLaren Vale Graciano Mataro Grenache 2011 Bright crimson, some purple; graciano is the magic ingredient, with its almost floral lift and finely boned mouthfeel, but it makes light work of the mataro and grenache, although the sweet fruit of the latter is also at play. Lively wine. Screwcap. 13% alc. Rating 94 To 2020 $30

ΨΨΨΨΨ Diamond Label Shiraz 2010 Light red-purple; a neatly composed wine, with an array of red and black fruits, soft tannins and oak. Part of the quality resurgence of Rosemount's wines across the board, winning a gold medal at the National Wine Show '11. Screwcap. 13.5% alc. Rating 93 To 2015 $16

Nursery Project McLaren Vale Grenache 2010 Rating 93 To 2020 $30

Regional Showcase Coonawarra Cabernet Sauvignon 2010 Better colour than that of the District Release; attractive cassis and spice aromas introduce a well-balanced, medium-bodied palate with blackcurrant fruit to the fore, backed by fine tannins and cedary oak. Screwcap. 13.5% alc. Rating 92 To 2020 $20

Diamond Label Cabernet Sauvignon 2010 Light but bright colour; attractive cassis/blackcurrant/blueberry fruit set in a wreath of fine tannins, bright acidity and a touch of oak. So well balanced, drink now or whenever the occasion arises. Screwcap. 13.5% alc. Rating 91 To 2018 $16

District Release Robe Chardonnay 2011 One of two Rosemount Chardonnays sourced from Robe, with radically different packaging, but the same price. There is far more similarity to the wine in each bottle than there is difference, but it is arguable that this wine has greater purity of line and focus on its mix of grapefruit and white peach. Length, too, is a virtue. Screwcap. 12% alc. Rating 90 To 2014 $20

Regional Showcase Robe Chardonnay 2011 Here the trade-off seems to be with more complexity and texture to the mouthfeel, however similar the underlying fruit flavours may be. Each wine goes through a separate supermarket chain. Screwcap. 12.5% alc. Rating 90 To 2014 $20

ΨΨΨΨ Diamond Label Chardonnay 2011 Rating 89 To 2013 $16

Diamond Label Chardonnay 2010 Rating 89 To 2014 $16

District Release Coonawarra Cabernet Sauvignon 2010 Rating 88 To 2017 $20

Diamond Label Sauvignon Blanc 2011 Rating 87 To 2013 $16

Diamond Label Pinot Noir 2010 Rating 87 To 2013 $16

Diamond Cellars Grenache Shiraz 2010 Rating 87 To 2014 $12

Rosenthal Wines ★★★★☆

PO Box 1458, South Perth, WA 6951 Region Blackwood Valley
T 0407 773 966 www.rosenthalwines.com.au Open Not
Winemaker Matilda's Estate (Toby Ladwig) Est. 2001 Dozens 1000 Vyds 4ha
Perth medical specialist Dr John Rosenthal heads Rosenthal Wines, which is a small part of the much larger 180ha Springfield Park cattle stud situated between Bridgetown and Manjimup. He acquired the property from Gerald and Marjorie Richings, who in 1997 had planted a small vineyard as a minor diversification. The Rosenthals extended the vineyard, which is equally divided between shiraz and cabernet sauvignon. The wines have had significant show success, chiefly in WA-based shows.

ΨΨΨΨΨ Richings Shiraz 2010 Bright medium red-purple; an elegant, medium-bodied shiraz fully deserving the Richings label, denoting an exceptional release, the last in '05; it is full of very attractive cherry and plum fruit, with fine, ripe tannins and good oak in the background. The modest alcohol is another plus. Screwcap. 13.6% alc. Rating 94 To 2023 $25

ΨΨΨΨΨ The Naomi Cabernet Shiraz 2010 Rating 90 To 2020 $25

Rosenvale Wines

Lot 385 Railway Terrace, Nuriootpa, SA 5355 **Region** Barossa Valley
T 0407 390 788 **www**.rosenvale.com.au **Open** By appt
Winemaker James Rosenzweig, Chris Taylor **Est.** 1999 **Dozens** 4000 **Vyds** 105ha
The Rosenzweig family vineyards, some old and some new, are planted to riesling, semillon, chardonnay, grenache, shiraz, merlot and cabernet sauvignon. Most of the grapes are sold to other producers, but since 2000 some have been retained and vinified for release under the Rosenvale label. A cellar door opened in 2012. Exports to the UK and other major markets.

🍷🍷🍷🍷🍷 **Old Vines Reserve Barossa Valley Semillon 2011** An exceptionally intense and focused Semillon, taking all of the characters of the variety to another level – quite amazing given the vintage, and would be remarkable in a good vintage. The amount of flavour already present makes it enjoyable right from the word go. Screwcap. 12.5% alc. **Rating** 94 **To** 2016 $39
Old Vines Reserve Barossa Valley Shiraz 2009 Made from 50-year-old vines, and matured in French oak; the bouquet and palate are full of rich black fruit, the palate quite luscious and velvety, its dark berry flavours borrowing a touch of chocolate from McLaren Vale. Diam. 15.2% alc. **Rating** 94 **To** 2034 $39

🍷🍷🍷🍷🍷 **Estate Barossa Semillon 2011** Gleaming straw-green; a very impressive
✪ Semillon with intense lemongrass and lemon juice flavours; its quality is derived from the texture and structure, which fill the mouth and lengthen the finish. Screwcap. 12.5% alc. **Rating** 93 **To** 2021 $24
Vine Vale Sands Barossa Cabernet Sauvignon 2009 **Rating** 92 **To** 2019 $30

Rosily Vineyard

871 Yelverton Road, Wilyabrup, WA 6284 **Region** Margaret River
T (08) 9755 6336 **www**.rosily.com.au **Open** 7 days Dec–Jan 11–5
Winemaker Mike Lemmes **Est.** 1994 **Dozens** 7500 **Vyds** 12.28ha
The partnership of Mike and Barb Scott, and Ken and Dot Allan acquired the Rosily Vineyard site in 1994, and the vineyard was planted over three years to sauvignon blanc, semillon, chardonnay, cabernet sauvignon, merlot, shiraz, grenache and cabernet franc. The first crops were sold to other makers in the region, but by '99 Rosily had built a 120-tonne capacity winery. Since then it has gone from strength to strength, all of its estate-grown grapes being vinified under the Rosily Vineyard label. Exports to the UK, the Maldives and China.

🍷🍷🍷🍷🍷 **Margaret River Sauvignon Blanc 2011** Pale quartz; a cleverly made wine,
✪ with a touch of oak perfectly integrated into the seamless palate spanning notes of herb and grass at one end, juicy citrus/tropical at the other; overall excellent line, length and balance. Screwcap. 13% alc. **Rating** 94 **To** 2013 $18

🍷🍷🍷🍷🍷 **Margaret River Chardonnay 2010** **Rating** 93 **To** 2018 $23
Margaret River Shiraz 2007 **Rating** 92 **To** 2017 $23
The Cartographer 2008 **Rating** 92 **To** 2018 $23
◐ **The Other Side of the Moon Margaret River Classic 2009** **Rating** 90 **To** 2013 $17

🍷🍷🍷🍷 **Margaret River Semillon Sauvignon Blanc 2011** **Rating** 88 **To** 2014 $20

Ross Estate Wines

Barossa Valley Way, Lyndoch, SA 5351 **Region** Barossa Valley
T (08) 8524 4033 **www**.rosswines.com **Open** 7 days 10–4
Winemaker Alex Peel **Est.** 1999 **Dozens** 15 000 **Vyds** 44ha
Darius and Pauline Ross laid the foundation for Ross Estate Wines when they purchased a vineyard that included two blocks of 75- and 90-year-old grenache. Also included were blocks of 30-year-old riesling and semillon, and 14-year-old merlot; plantings of chardonnay,

sauvignon blanc, cabernet sauvignon, cabernet franc, shiraz and tempranillo have followed. Exports to the UK, the US, Canada, Denmark, Germany, Hong Kong and China.

ΨΨΨΨΨ JDR Barossa Shiraz 2008 Deep purple-crimson, exceptional for the vintage; small batch-fermented and matured in predominantly new American and French oak for two years; the intense blackberry and plum fruit has soaked up the oak, leaving it (the fruit) in pole position. This is a wine of striking elegance and power. Screwcap. 14.5% alc. **Rating** 96 **To** 2038 $70
Single Vineyard Barossa Shiraz 2008 Very good colour for vintage; the bouquet is an aromatic mix of blackberry, spice and oak, the palate taking up the theme, and adding firm tannins to give the wine length and longevity. Screwcap. 14.5% alc. **Rating** 94 **To** 2023 $35

ΨΨΨΨΨ Single Vineyard Old Vine Barossa Grenache 2008 Rating 90 **To** 2014 $25
Limited Release Barossa Sparkling Shiraz 2008 Rating 90 **To** 2016 $45

ΨΨΨΨ Limited Release Barossa Cabernet Franc 2010 Rating 89 **To** 2018 $30
The Beekeeper 2011 Rating 88 **To** 2014 $15

Ross Hill Wines

134 Wallace Lane, Orange, NSW 2800 **Region** Orange
T (02) 6365 3223 **www**.rosshillwines.com.au **Open** W'ends & public hols 10–4, or by appt
Winemaker Phil Kerney **Est.** 1994 **Dozens** 15 000 **Vyds** 18.2ha
Owned by the Robson and Jones families. Chardonnay, merlot, sauvignon blanc, cabernet franc, shiraz and pinot noir have been established on north-facing, gentle slopes at an elevation of 800m. No insecticides are used in the vineyard, the grapes are hand-picked and the vines are hand-pruned. The arrival of Phil Kerney from the Mornington Peninsula is significant, as is the increase from 12ha to just over 18ha of estate vineyards, production increasing from 300 dozen to its present level. Ross Hill also has an olive grove with Italian and Spanish varieties. The onsite winery, opened in time for the 2009 vintage, has also had a major impact. Exports to Singapore, the Maldives, Sri Lanka, Hong Kong and China.

ΨΨΨΨΨ Pinnacle Series Orange Sauvignon Blanc 2011 Light, bright straw-green; picked later than Jessica & Lily, and wild yeast-fermented, but has a more precisely focused palate and finish; here citrussy acidity makes itself felt as a dressing for the tropical fruit flavours, adding significant length. Screwcap. 13.5% alc. **Rating** 94 **To** 2013 $28
Pinnacle Series Orange Chardonnay 2011 Bright straw-green; the grapes were whole bunch-pressed, and the juice run straight to barrel for wild fermentation; the texture and balance are nigh on perfect, and provide a perfect backdrop to the white peach, nectarine and pear fruit. Screwcap. 12.7% alc. **Rating** 94 **To** 2018 $32
Pinnacle Series Orange Chardonnay 2010 Hand-picked and whole bunch-pressed straight to barrel, fermentation initiated by wild yeast; despite its relatively low alcohol, this is a wine of significant concentration and power, white peach cut by grapefruit zest and grilled cashew coming from the barrel fermentation; long in the mouth due to the backbone of natural acidity. Screwcap. 12.7% alc. **Rating** 94 **To** 2020 $35
Pinnacle Series Orange Cabernet Sauvignon 2010 Bright colour; hand-picked, wild-fermented and matured in French oak barriques for 18 months; this is an intense and potent Cabernet, imposing its will with the carrot of blackcurrant and cassis fruit, and the stick of savoury tannins. The combination works well. Screwcap. 14.5% alc. **Rating** 94 **To** 2020 $40

ΨΨΨΨΨ ✪ Jessica & Lily Orange Sauvignon Blanc 2011 The bouquet and palate are flooded with a full range of tropical fruits, with peach and passionfruit to the fore; the finish is long and even, fruit the driver. Screwcap. 12.2% alc. **Rating** 92 **To** 2013 $20
Pinnacle Series Orange Pinot Gris 2011 Rating 91 **To** 2014 $30
Pinnacle Series Orange Shiraz 2010 Rating 91 **To** 2020 $36

Isabelle & Jack Orange Cabernet Franc Merlot 2010 Rating 90
To 2018 $25
Pinnacle Series Orange Cabernet Franc 2010 Rating 90 To 2017 $40
ỹỹỹỹ   Tom & Harry Orange Cabernet Sauvignon 2010 Rating 87 To 2014 $25 BE

Rowanston on the Track   ★★★☆

2710 Burke & Wills Track, Glenhope, Vic 3444 **Region** Macedon Ranges
T (03) 5425 5492 **www**.rowanston.com **Open** 7 days 9–5
Winemaker John Frederiksen, Laura Sparrow **Est.** 2003 **Dozens** 3000 **Vyds** 9.3ha
John (a social worker) and Marilyn (a former teacher turned viticulturist) Frederiksen are no
strangers to grapegrowing and winemaking in the Macedon Ranges. They founded Metcalfe
Valley Vineyard in 1995, planting 5.6ha of shiraz, going on to win gold medals at local wine
shows. They sold the vineyard in early 2003 and moved to their new property, which now has
over 9ha of vines (shiraz, riesling, sauvignon blanc, merlot and pinot noir) in the same year.
The heavy red soils and basalt ridges hold moisture, which allows watering requirements to
be kept to a minimum. Exports to the US.

Rowsley Fault Vineyards   ★★★★

PO Box 1665, Geelong, Vic 3220 **Region** Geelong
T (03) 5281 1811 **www**.rowsleyfaultwines.com **Open** By appt
Winemaker Brett Snelson **Est.** 2000 **Dozens** 6000 **Vyds** 42ha
Rowsley Fault is the new name for what was previously known as Sutherlands Creek. Its
five investor-owners bring a range of business backgrounds to the venture, spanning the UK,
Hong Kong, Asia and Australia. The total investment in the venture was $12 million; there are
two separate vineyard properties and an onsite winery, together planted to pinot noir, viognier,
shiraz, zinfandel, sauvignon blanc, pinot gris and semillon. In addition there is a 2.4ha planting
of 42 varietals, rootstocks and clones at the Russells Bridge Vineyard, including varieties such
as gamay, nebbiolo, mourvedre and roussanne. The reduction in production from 12 500 to
6000 cases, and the re-branding of the business, suggests the marketing business plan hasn't so
far achieved the desired goals. Exports to the UK, China and Hong Kong.

ỹỹỹỹỹ   Questa CB115 Clone Geelong Pinot Noir 2010 An earlier clone selection
by Professor Bernard than 777, that has stood up to the later selections. There is
sweet plum and stewed cherry fruit, the slash of acidity less than that of the rose,
and less than the 777, but still evident. There is enough varietal fruit to get it over
the line. Diam. 12.5% alc. **Rating** 90 To 2015 $38
Geelong Graciano 2010 Light but bright colour; the bouquet and palate have a
mix of small red berry fruits, spice and pepper; good length and balance. Screwcap.
13% alc. **Rating** 90 To 2015 $28
ỹỹỹỹ   Questa B777 Clone Geelong Pinot Noir 2010 Rating 89 To 2015 $38

Russell Wines   ★★★☆

45 Murray Street, Angaston, SA 5353 **Region** Barossa Valley
T (08) 8564 2511 **www**.russellwines.com.au **Open** By appt
Winemaker Tim Smith **Est.** 2001 **Dozens** 4000 **Vyds** 32.47ha
John Russell (and wife Rosalind) came to the Barossa in 1990 to create the Barossa Music
Festival. The winemaking bug soon bit, and in '94 they planted vines at Krondorf (expanded
over the years) and on three vineyards – at St Vincent, Augusta and Greenock Farm – which
in turn give rise to the three labels. The cellar door is in the old Angaston Court House, where
wine, food, music and art exhibitions are all on offer. Part of the grape production is sold to
other Barossa wineries. Exports to Switzerland., Finland and China.

ỹỹỹỹỹ   Greenock Farm The Fenceline 2006 A quixotic blend of grenache, shiraz,
mourvedre, semillon, riesling, red frontignac, white frontignac and tokay.
Interestingly, the high quality corks in both vintages have only been in the bottles
for a short time (maximum two years), so the wines have been held in old wood
or tank. 15.3% alc. **Rating** 90 To 2020 $85

🍷🍷🍷🍷 **St Vincent Barossa Valley Chardonnay 2008** Something of a wolf in sheep's
✪ clothing, with a shaft of vibrant citrussy acidity running through the stone fruit
and melon heart of the wine. Screwcap. 13.5% alc. **Rating** 89 **To** 2014 $20
Greenock Farm The Amegilla 2008 Rating 88 To 2013 $40
Greenock Farm The Fenceline 2008 Rating 88 To 2018 $85

Rusticana ★★★☆
Lake Plains Road, Langhorne Creek, SA 5255 **Region** Langhorne Creek
T (08) 8537 3086 **www**.rusticanawines.com.au **Open** 7 days 10–5
Winemaker John Glaetzer (Consultant) **Est.** 1998 **Dozens** 1500 **Vyds** 9.8ha
Brian and Anne Meakins are also owners of Newman's Horseradish, which has been on the
SA market for over 80 years. Increasing demand for the horseradish forced a move from Tea
Tree Gully to Langhorne Creek in 1985. It wasn't until 1997 that they succumbed to the
urging of neighbours and planted shiraz (4.2ha) and cabernet sauvignon (4.6ha), adding 0.5ha
each of durif and zinfandel several years later.

🍷🍷🍷🍷🍷 **Langhorne Creek Zinfandel 2009** The light colour is common in Napa Valley
zinfandel, and it does not mean there is insufficient flavour. It is simply strange that
you say a 15.4% alcohol wine is light-bodied, for that is what it is, its red berry/
cherry fruit pleasantly incisive. Screwcap. 15.3% alc. **Rating** 90 **To** 2015 $25

🍷🍷🍷🍷 **Langhorne Creek Durif 2009** Rating 88 To 2015 $30

Rutherglen Estates ★★★★
Cnr Great Northern Road/Murray Valley Highway, Rutherglen, Vic 3685 **Region** Rutherglen
T (02) 6032 7999 **www**.rutherglenestates.com.au **Open** At Tuileries Complex,
Rutherglen 7 days 10–6
Winemaker Marc Scalzo **Est.** 1997 **Dozens** 20 000 **Vyds** 26.5ha
Rutherglen Estates is one of the larger growers in the region. The focus of the business has
changed in recent times by slightly reducing its own fruit intake while maintaining its contract
processing. Production has turned to table wine made from parcels of fruit hand-selected from
the five Rutherglen vineyard sites. Rhône and Mediterranean varieties such as durif, viognier,
shiraz and sangiovese are a move away from traditional varieties, as are alternative varieties
including zinfandel, fiano and savagnin. At the time of going to press, Rutherglen Estates was
being offered for sale. Exports to the UK, the US and other major markets.

🍷🍷🍷🍷🍷 **Rutherglen Muscat NV** A medium-bodied muscat, but with the full panoply
of flavours ranging from raisin to toffee to butterscotch and a fresh, nutty finish.
375 ml. Screwcap. 17% alc. **Rating** 91 **To** 2013 $21
Renaissance Viognier Roussanne Marsanne 2009 Deep gold, green hue;
a toasty bouquet of straw, oak and lemon curd; the palate is fleshy and full of
lemon fruit alongside grilled hazelnuts on the finish; big on flavour and personality.
Screwcap. 13.5% alc. **Rating** 90 **To** 2014 $31 BE

🍷🍷🍷🍷 **Single Vineyard Savagnin 2011** Pale colour; fleshy and savoury, with fennel,
✪ citrus blossom and a little sea salt; the palate is vibrant, fresh and shows an
intriguing mineral edge. Screwcap. 12.5% alc. **Rating** 89 **To** 2013 $17 BE
Single Vineyard Tempranillo 2010 Rating 89 To 2013 $21 BE
✪ **Red 2009** Bright colour; juicy and generous with redcurrant and black cherry
fruit the central theme; savoury in nature, with high acidity and gentle tannins, this
wine is a luncheon proposition, and best consumed young. An 85/15% blend of
shiraz and durif. Screwcap. 13.5% alc. **Rating** 88 **To** 2013 $14BE
Single Vineyard Fiano 2011 Rating 88 To 2013 $23 BE
Sparkling Shiraz Durif 2009 Rating 88 To 2014 $28 BE
Single Vineyard Arneis 2011 Rating 87 To 2013 $17 BE

Rymill Coonawarra

Riddoch Highway, Coonawarra, SA 5263 **Region** Coonawarra
T (08) 8736 5001 **www**.rymill.com.au **Open** 7 days 10–5
Winemaker Sandrine Gimon **Est.** 1974 **Dozens** 35 000 **Vyds** 137ha
The Rymills are descendants of John Riddoch and have long owned some of the finest
Coonawarra soil, upon which they have grown grapes since 1970. The promotion of
Champagne-trained Sandrine Gimon to chief winemaker (after three years as winemaker
at Rymill) is interesting. Sandrine is a European version of a Flying Winemaker, having
managed a winery in Bordeaux, and made wine in Champagne, Languedoc, Romania and
WA. Sandrine became an Australian citizen in 2011. The winery building also houses the
cellar door and art exhibitions, which, together with viewing platforms of the winery, make
it a must-see destination for tourists. Exports to all major markets.

TTTTT   **GT Coonawarra Gewurztraminer 2011** Straw-green; a rare beast indeed,
✪   a gewurz with clear-cut varietal character immediately leaping out of the glass;
           heady spice, lychee and rosewater characters all inhabit the bouquet and are
           maintained on the refreshingly dry palate, which has none of the oily phenolics
           which often mar such wines. Screwcap. 12.5% alc. **Rating** 95 **To** 2016 $20
✪   **June Traminer 2008** Glowing golden-orange; botrytised traminer was picked
           in June, a very successful move. The wine has intense apricot, spice and lychee
           fruit, balanced by good acidity. A bargain, ready now. 375ml. Screwcap. 12.5% alc.
           Rating 95 **To** 2016 $18
           Shiraz 2006 Medium red-purple, still bright and healthy; an elegant shiraz, with
           seductive, mulberry and cherry fruit that harmoniously blends with the oak and
           fine, ripe tannins; the wine glides along the mouth, with a long, balanced finish,
           every component in perfect balance. Diam. 14% alc. **Rating** 94 **To** 2026 $27

TTTTT   **Single Vineyard No. 8 Chardonnay 2010** **Rating** 93 **To** 2018 $27
○   **The Yearling Shiraz 2010** **Rating** 92 **To** 2016 $15
           Cabernet Sauvignon 2009 **Rating** 91 **To** 2024 $29
✪   **MC² Cabernet Sauvignon Merlot Cabernet Franc 2010** A bright and fresh,
           varietal and savoury wine, combining savoury complexity with up-front appeal;
           fleshy and seamlessly constructed; best enjoyed in the short to medium term.
           Screwcap. 14% alc. **Rating** 91 **To** 2017 $20 BE
           Brut Chardonnay Pinot Noir Pinot Meunier 2010 **Rating** 91 **To** 2014 $25
○   **The Yearling Sauvignon Blanc 2011** **Rating** 90 **To** Now $15
           Shiraz 2009 **Rating** 90 **To** 2020 $27
○   **MC² Cabernet Sauvignon Merlot Cabernet Franc 2009** **Rating** 90
           To 2015 $20

TTTT   **SBS Sauvignon Blanc Semillon 2011** **Rating** 88 **To** 2013 $20 BE
           The Yearling Cabernet Sauvignon 2010 **Rating** 88 **To** 2014 $15

Saddler's Creek

Marrowbone Road, Pokolbin, NSW 2320 **Region** Hunter Valley
T (02) 4991 1770 **www**.saddlerscreek.com **Open** 7 days 10–5
Winemaker Nick Flanagan **Est.** 1989 **Dozens** 6000 **Vyds** 10ha
Saddler's Creek is a boutique winery that is little known outside of the Hunter Valley but has
built a loyal following of dedicated supporters. Came onto the scene over 20 years ago with
some rich, bold wines, and maintains this style today. Fruit is sourced from the Hunter Valley
and Langhorne Creek, with occasional forays into McLaren Vale, Wrattonbully and other
premium fruit-growing regions. Exports to Sweden and China.

TTTTT   **Saddler's Chardonnay 2011** Oddly enough, this entry-level chardonnay is in
           a stupendously heavy and impressive bottle; this aside, the wine shows the elegant
           side of Hunter Chardonnay, with melon, nectarine and citrus blossom; fairly
           light-weighted, with fine acidity and subtle oak all evenly balanced with the fruit.
           Screwcap. 12.5% alc. **Rating** 94 **To** 2017 $24 BE

Reserve Semillon 2007 **Rating** 93 **To** 2015 $38 BE
Reserve Chardonnay 2011 **Rating** 92 **To** 2017 $32 BE
Saddler's Langhorne Creek Shiraz Viognier 2010 **Rating** 90 **To** 2020 $36

Bluegrass Shiraz 2009 **Rating** 88 **To** 2019 $35
Bluegrass The Blend 2010 **Rating** 88 **To** 2014 $35 BE
Reserve Riesling 2011 **Rating** 87 **To** 2014 $28 BE

 St Brioc Wines ★★★★

PO Box 867, McLaren Vale, SA 5171 **Region** McLaren Vale
T 0423 777 088 **www**.stbriocwines.com.au **Open** Not
Winemaker Contract **Est.** 2008 **Dozens** 250
St Brioc Wines is a collaboration between sisters Jo Madigan and Trish Wenk and their families. The name comes from the property where the girls spent their early years, further supported by the Celtic symbol dedicated to St Brioc, the Inchbrayok Cross that provided the inspiration for the logo and label.

The Cure McLaren Vale Shiraz 2008 Good colour for vintage; plum cake, dark chocolate and savoury characters are interwoven on the bouquet and full-bodied palate alike; curiously – and happily – the alcohol does not overwhelm the palate. Screwcap. 15.4% alc. **Rating** 92 **To** 2023 $22
The Fraternity McLaren Vale Shiraz 2008 Deep colour; an interesting comparison, with family ties, this wine having greater intensity and power through a greater fruit and tannin impact, yet finishing slightly shorter than its junior brother. Given these achievements, the '09 and '10 (especially) should be very good indeed. Screwcap. 15.4% alc. **Rating** 92 **To** 2025 $45

St Hallett ★★★★★

St Hallett Road, Tanunda, SA 5352 **Region** Barossa Valley
T (08) 8563 7000 **www**.sthallett.com.au **Open** 7 days 10–5
Winemaker Stuart Blackwell, Toby Barlow **Est.** 1944 **Dozens** 100 000
Nothing succeeds like success. St Hallett merged with Tatachilla to form Banksia Wines, which was then acquired by NZ's thirsty Lion Nathan. St Hallett understandably continues to ride the shiraz fashion wave, with Old Block the ultra-premium leader of the band (using grapes from Lyndoch and the Eden Valley) supported by Blackwell (taking its grapes from Greenock, Ebenezer and Seppeltsfield). It has also had conspicuous success with its Eden Valley Rieslings, and its large-volume Poacher's range. Exports to all major markets.

Old Block Barossa Shiraz 2009 Fresh crimson-purple; the quality of the fruit filling the bouquet transposes directly to the medium- to full-bodied palate, in turn brimming to overflowing with luscious but not overripe fruit. The finish is the high point of the wine, bringing all the best characters together. WAK screwcap. 14.5% alc. **Rating** 96 **To** 2034 $100
Single Vineyard Release Materne Barossa Valley Shiraz 2010 Deep, dense purple-crimson, the best of the three Single Vineyard Release Shirazs; from the Greenock area, the grapes grown by the fourth generation of the Materne family; a full-bodied, densely packed palate with blackberry, blackcurrant, licorice and a hint of spice is supported by firm tannins running through to a long, lingering finish. WAK screwcap. 14% alc. **Rating** 95 **To** 2035 $40
Single Vineyard Release Mattschoss Eden Valley Shiraz 2010 Medium crimson, the lightest colour of the three Single Vineyard Shirazs; the vineyard high in the Eden Valley produces a wine of great elegance, with perfumed red fruits punctuated by spicy notes on the palate, the tannins fine and long. In a category all of its own. WAK screwcap. 13.5% alc. **Rating** 95 **To** 2025 $50
Single Vineyard Release Scholz Estate Barossa Valley Shiraz 2010 The extended Scholz family is well known throughout the Valley for the care they lavish on their vines. Strong crimson-purple, the wine is flooded with blackberry, black cherry and licorice fruit flavours; despite this, it is only just medium- to full-bodied, balance being a key word. It has just taken the first few steps of what will be a long life. WAK screwcap. 14.5% alc. **Rating** 95 **To** 2035 $40

Garden of Eden Barossa Shiraz 2010 Bright crimson, the wine has remarkable depth and complexity while retaining finesse and elegance; the flavours encompass all the small berry fruits you care to think of, embraced by gentle, ripe tannins and quality oak. The saints be praised for flavour at this alcohol level. Screwcap. 13.5% alc. **Rating** 95 **To** 2030 $25

Single Vineyard Release Dawkins Eden Valley Shiraz 2010 Bright crimson-purple; an impressive marriage of elegance and power, the bouquet of red berries and menthol; the medium-bodied palate cruises along, as fresh as a daisy, revelling in its (relatively) low alcohol. A glimpse of the future. WAK screwcap. 13% alc. **Rating** 95 **To** 2025 $40

Blackwell Barossa Shiraz 2010 **Rating** 94 **To** 2025 $38 BE
Barossa GST Grenache Shiraz Touriga 2010 **Rating** 94 **To** 2025 $30

ΨΨΨΨΨ **Eden Valley Riesling 2011** The citrus blossom bouquet leads into a palate with
✪   an interplay between lime, lemon and spice, balanced acidity drawing out the long finish, without introducing any green flavours. Screwcap. 11.5% alc. **Rating** 93 **To** 2018 $19

✪   **Faith Barossa Shiraz 2010** Deep purple-crimson; a medium- to full-bodied wine awash with red and black fruit, principally cherry, abundant ripe tannins and enough oak; has balance and length. Screwcap. 14.5% alc. **Rating** 93 **To** 2025 $19

✪   **Faith Barossa Shiraz 2009** Good depth to red-purple colour; attractive wine; exuberant red and black cherry fruit aromas on the bouquet lead into a juicy, spicy, medium-bodied palate; fine tannins and oak are in carefully measured support. Screwcap. 14.5% alc. **Rating** 93 **To** 2020 $20

        Old Vine Barossa Valley Grenache 2010 **Rating** 93 **To** 2018 $40

ΨΨΨΨ **Gamekeeper's Barossa Shiraz Grenache 2010** **Rating** 89 **To** 2013 $14
✪

St Huberts

Cnr Maroondah Highway/St Huberts Road, Coldstream, Vic 3770 **Region** Yarra Valley
T (03) 9739 1118 **www.**sthuberts.com.au **Open** Mon–Fri 9.30–5, w'ends 10.30–5.30
Winemaker Greg Jarratt **Est.** 1966 **Dozens** NFP
A once-famous winery (in the context of the Yarra Valley) that is now part of TWE. The wines are now made at Coldstream Hills, and on an upwards trajectory. (I have no part in their making.)

ΨΨΨΨΨ **Yarra Valley Cabernet Merlot 2010** Vibrant deep crimson; the bouquet is like a textbook of ripe Yarra cabernet, showing an amalgam of redcurrant, cassis, cedar and a light touch of herbaceous complexity; the palate is juicy and accessible on entry, yet tightens up with fine-grained tannins, lively acidity and a succulent conclusion; ready to go, but will cellar gracefully. Screwcap. 13.5% alc. **Rating** 94 **To** 2022 $27 BE

ΨΨΨΨΨ **Hubert the Stag Yarra Valley Pinot Noir 2011** **Rating** 93 **To** 2017 $24 BE
        Yarra Valley Cabernet Sauvignon 2010 **Rating** 93 **To** 2025 $27 BE
        Yarra Valley Chardonnay 2011 **Rating** 92 **To** 2018 $27

St John's Road

PO Box 311, Greenock, SA 5360 **Region** Barossa Valley
T (08) 8423 0272 **www.**stjohnsroad.com **Open** Not
Winemaker Kim Jackson **Est.** 2002 **Dozens** 6000
Following the tragic death of founder Martin Rawlinson from motor neurone disease, there was a period of inactivity before Adelaide wine identity Alister Mibus purchased the St John's Road label. The policy of selecting the best possible parcels of fruit from the Barossa and Eden valleys continues. Exports to Canada and China.

ΨΨΨΨ **Peace of Eden Riesling 2011** A toasty and lightly developed mineral-accented bouquet is followed by a moderately rich and forward palate; best enjoyed early. Screwcap. 13% alc. **Rating** 87 **To** 2014 $20 BE

Blood & Courage Barossa Valley Shiraz 2010 A combination of prunes, chocolate and a sweet-fruited and fleshy palate; soft-centred and finishing with a long mocha note. Screwcap. 14.5% alc. **Rating** 87 **To** 2017 $22 BE

St Leonards Vineyard ★★★★

St Leonards Road, Wahgunyah, Vic 3687 **Region** Rutherglen
T 1800 021 621 **www**.stleonardswine.com.au **Open** Thurs–Sun 10–5
Winemaker Dan Crane **Est.** 1860 **Dozens** 5200 **Vyds** 8ha
An old favourite, relaunched in late 1997 with a range of premium wines cleverly marketed through an attractive cellar door and bistro at the historic winery on the banks of the Murray. It is essentially a satellite operation of All Saints, under the same ownership and management.

♀♀♀♀♀ **Wahgunyah Chardonnay 2008** Gleaming yellow-green; remarkably youthful thanks to the backbone of acidity, but the peach and grapefruit flavours are also fresh, the French oak in which it was fermented totally integrated. Screwcap. 13.8% alc. **Rating** 93 **To** 2015 $30
Durif 2010 Open-fermented with wild yeast and spent three weeks in the fermenter before going to the 130-year-old wooden press; ultimately bottled without being fined. The colour is good, and the rounded fruit flavours have a delicious lift of plum, raspberry and cherry fruit. Screwcap. 14.2% alc. **Rating** 91 **To** 2020 $28

♀♀♀♀ **Classic Rutherglen Muscat NV Rating** 89 **To** 2013 $35
Shiraz 2009 Rating 88 **To** 2015 $25
Chardonnay 2011 Rating 87 **To** 2015 $22
Cabernet Franc 2011 Rating 87 **To** 2014 $28

St Regis ★★★★

35 Princes Highway, Waurn Ponds, Vic 3216 **Region** Geelong
T (03) 5241 8406 **www**.stregis.com.au **Open** 7 days 11–5
Winemaker Peter Nicol **Est.** 1997 **Dozens** 500 **Vyds** 1ha
St Regis is a family-run boutique winery focusing on estate-grown shiraz, and locally sourced chardonnay and pinot noir. Each year the harvest is hand-picked by members of the family and friends, with Peter Nicol (assisted by wife Viv) the executive onsite winemaker. While Peter has a technical background in horticulture, he is a self-taught winemaker, and has taught himself well, also making wines for others.

♀♀♀♀♀ **The Reg Geelong Shiraz 2010** Has received the works: wild yeast, 25% whole bunches; 30% new oak, a massive eight weeks post-fermentation maceration. The colour is good, and the bouquet and palate are as complex as one would expect, with a strong spice and pepper component to the red and black berry fruits; the tannins are fine and in total balance, and the wine did not need to be fined. Screwcap. 14.5% alc. **Rating** 93 **To** 2025 $25
Geelong Pinot Noir 2010 One-third wild yeast-fermented; 25% whole bunch; 15% new oak; not fined or filtered; a spicy, tangy Pinot clearly showing whole bunch characters; needed a bit more substance to the fruit in the first instance. Screwcap. 12.9% alc. **Rating** 90 **To** 2015 $20

♀♀♀♀ **Geelong Chardonnay 2010 Rating** 88 **To** 2014 $20

Salena Estate ★★★

Bookpurnong Road, Loxton, SA 5333 **Region** Riverland
T (08) 8584 1333 **www**.salenaestate.com.au **Open** Mon–Fri 9–4
Winemaker Melanie Kargas, David Smallacombe **Est.** 1998 **Dozens** 200 000 **Vyds** 208ha
This business encapsulates the once hectic rate of growth across the entire Australian wine industry. Its 1998 crush was 300 tonnes, and by '01 it was processing around 7000 tonnes. It is the venture of Bob and Sylvia Franchitto; the estate named after their daughter. Exports to Canada, Sweden, Indonesia, Taiwan, Singapore, South Korea, Hong Kong, Japan and China.

ττττ **Ink Series Viognier 2011** Positive green-straw; while the alcohol is theoretically too low for viognier to express itself, here the bouquet has quite marked pear, both dried and fresh, along with a pinch of baker's spices, the palate with some echoes of the bouquet, but basically citrus-driven and fresh. Screwcap. 11.5% alc. **Rating** 89 **To** 2013 $20

✪ **Shiraz 2010** Clear crimson-purple; another notch up the quality marker, with predominantly cherry and plum fruit on the mid palate, then a gently savoury finish. Screwcap. 14.5% alc. **Rating** 89 **To** 2015 $15

Ink Series Sangiovese 2011 Light, clear crimson-purple; the floral, spiced cherry aromas lead into a fresh and brisk red berry palate, typical tannins with a wisp of oak bringing up the rear. Screwcap. 12% alc. **Rating** 89 **To** 2015 $20

Ink Series Petit Verdot 2009 The colour is not exceptional, although it is adequate and befits this remarkable variety that is so amenable to the Riverland and relatively high yields, its dark berry flavours round and juicy. Screwcap. 14.5% alc. **Rating** 89 **To** 2014 $20

✪ **Chardonnay 2011** Bright straw-green; has more intensity and length than most Chardonnays at $15 or less; white peach, melon and a touch of cashew are the drivers, with some prospect of short-term cellaring. Screwcap. 13.5% alc. **Rating** 88 **To** 2014 $15

Ink Series Vermentino 2011 There are aromas of tea tree blossom and spice, the palate with more shape than many similar wines from '11 (similar in the sense that they are aromatic and unwooded); the palate gains traction and intensity to its ripe citrus fruits running through to the finish, leaving the aftertaste fresh and breezy. Screwcap. 11% alc. **Rating** 88 **To** 2013 $20

Ink Series Pinot Grigio 2011 Quartz-white, with the faintest hint of pink; the palate is brisk and minerally, with a touch of citrus; is in Grigio style. Screwcap. 11% alc. **Rating** 87 **To** 2013 $20

Ink Series Bianco d'Alessano 2011 The voluminous bouquet has a strong musk overlay and some loquat; the zesty acidity and absence of any sugar suggests the grapes were picked before they were fully ripe, had they been left to ripen further, one wonders what the bouquet could have morphed into. Screwcap. 10.5% alc. **Rating** 87 **To** 2013 $20

✪ **Legacy Shiraz 2010** Light, bright crimson; a wine that is an exemplary example of what the Riverland can achieve, with a light- to medium-bodied palate of red fruits and a hint of cigar box, possibly from the use of chips or oak staves. Whatever, it all works. Screwcap. 13.5% alc. **Rating** 87 **To** 2013 $12

Salitage   ★★★☆

Vasse Highway, Pemberton, WA 6260 **Region** Pemberton
T (08) 9776 1771 **www**.salitage.com.au **Open** 7 days 10–4
Winemaker Patrick Coutts **Est.** 1989 **Dozens** 10 000 **Vyds** 21.4ha
Owned and operated by John and Jenny Horgan, Salitage is a showpiece of Pemberton. John had worked and studied under the guidance of Robert Mondavi in California, and also acquired a share in the famous Burgundy winery, La Pousse D'or (with other Aussie investors, all of whom have since sold out). Together with Bill and Sandra Pannell's Picardy, it is a bellwether for the reputation of the region. Further wines were received after this issue went to print; tasting notes appear on www.winecompanion.com.au. Exports to Europe, Indonesia, South Korea, Singapore, Taiwan and China.

ττττ **Pemberton Pinot Noir 2009** Light colour; a light savoury/stemmy style, with forest floor characters dominating, but some persistent red berry notes just making their presence felt. Screwcap. 13% alc. **Rating** 89 **To** 2016 $44

Pemberton Chardonnay 2009 The developed green-gold colour sets the scene: the wine is full and nutty, with some contrasting citrus notes, but is loosely framed, and is made for early consumption. Screwcap. 13.5% alc. **Rating** 88 **To** 2015 $37

Salo Wines

28 Dorothy Street, Healesville, Vic 3777 (postal) **Region** Yarra Valley
T (03) 5962 5331 **www**.salowines.com.au **Open** Not
Winemaker Steve Flamsteed, Dave Mackintosh **Est.** 2008 **Dozens** 250

Business partners Steve Flamsteed and Dave Mackintosh say that Salo means dirty and a little uncouth, which with the Australian sense of humour, can be used as a term of endearment. They wish to keep their wines a little dirty by using hands–off, minimal winemaking except for a few strange techniques to make more gritty, textured wines. Thus the 2010 Chardonnay, using grapes grown on the Gladysdale Vineyard in the Upper Yarra Valley, was made using 85% whole bunch-pressed grapes, the juice going direct to barrel with full solids for a wild yeast fermentation in puncheons, but the remaining 15% was fermented on skins and stems. The whacky 'orange' ferment was stirred a few times and both portions were blended in early September, the mlf prevented. Then they looked across the ditch to Hawke's Bay, NZ, and found some outstanding shiraz. Quantities are unfortunately minuscule, with 150 dozen bottles of Chardonnay and 100 cases of Syrah, both wonderful wines.

ΨΨΨΨΨ Hawke's Bay Syrah 2010 Vivid crimson-purple; distinctive and very intense; the complex bouquet has echoes of Côte Rôtie, with strong spice and pepper characters, yet retaining an almost juicy vinosity. Great length to a very classy wine. Screwcap. 14% alc. **Rating** 95 **To** 2025 $40

Yarra Valley Chardonnay 2011 There is no over-elaboration, rather simply attention to detail, and some clever decisions on the journey through to bottle. The result is a wine of purity and the length typical of Yarra Valley Chardonnay. Screwcap. 13% alc. **Rating** 94 **To** 2017 $40

Yarra Valley Chardonnay 2010 Light, bright straw-green; while there is very little colour change, the extra year and the warmer vintage have resulted in significantly more texture and structure, although the fruit expression is similar to the '11. Screwcap. 13% alc. **Rating** 94 **To** 2018 $40

Yarra Valley Chardonnay 2009 A little deeper in colour, although still with the green flashes to the fore; many high-quality Chardonnays were made in the Yarra Valley off the back of a vintage that was 95% excellent, the remainder lethal for red wines, but largely irrelevant for white wines. This is in the mainstream of the Salo style, with a juicy grapefruit cut to the flavour and texture of the palate. Screwcap. 13.5% alc. **Rating** 94 **To** 2018 $40

Yarra Valley Chardonnay 2008 Barely perceptible colour change, still bright and predominantly green; not the easiest vintage for Chardonnay, but this wine has a very attractive touch of funk to its complexity, possibly bottle-developed, but probably always part of the wine since the outset. The characters of all four Salo Chardonnays are still in a formative stage, leaving a 10- or 15-year vertical tasting to really sort out the difference. Rather than force the issue now, I have elected to give each wine the same points and (conservative) eight-year best-by drinking span. Screwcap. 13.5% alc. **Rating** 94 **To** 2018 $40

Salomon Estate

PO Box 829, McLaren Vale, SA 5171 **Region** Southern Fleurieu
T 0417 470 590 **www**.salomonwines.com **Open** Not
Winemaker Bert Salomon, Mike Farmilo **Est.** 1997 **Dozens** 6500 **Vyds** 12.1ha

Bert Salomon is an Austrian winemaker with a long-established family winery in the Kremstal region, not far from Vienna. He became acquainted with Australia during his time with import company Schlumberger in Vienna; he was the first to import Australian wines (Penfolds) into Austria in the mid 1980s, and later became head of the Austrian Wine Bureau. He was so taken by Adelaide that he moved his family there for the first few months each year, sending his young children to school and setting in place an Australian red winemaking venture. He retired from the Bureau and is now a full-time travelling winemaker, running the family winery in the northern hemisphere vintage, and overseeing the making of the Salomon Estate wines at Boar's Rock in the first half of the year. The circle closes as Mike Farmilo, former Penfolds chief red winemaker, now makes Salomon Estate wines at Boar's Rock. Exports to the UK, the US, and other major markets.

♥♥♥♥♥ **Finniss River Shiraz 2009** Deep red-purple; has greater richness and depth than prior vintages, flush with blackberry, spicy plum and Christmas cake flavours, tannins playing an important role. Cork. 14.5% alc. **Rating** 94 **To** 2024 $35

Fleurieu Peninsula Syrah Viognier 2010 Strong, bright red-purple; the scented red and black fruits of the bouquet are amplified by the energy and drive of the medium- to full-bodied palate, and its lively finish. The screwcap guarantees its future. Screwcap. 14.5% alc. **Rating** 94 **To** 2025 $26

Norwood Shiraz Cabernet 2010 Very good crimson-purple colour; a wine that has massively benefited from the '10 vintage; the mid palate is awash with plum and blackberry fruit, but is eclipsed by the drive and energy of the back-palate and finish; fruit, oak and tannins are all on the same page. Screwcap. 14.5% alc. **Rating** 94 **To** 2030 $21

Aestatis Grenache Shiraz Mourvedre 2009 Clear medium red-purple; the aromatic bouquet offers red and black fruits, spices ranging from nutmeg to pepper, the delicious palate fruity and fresh, fine tannins providing the structure. Screwcap. 14.5% alc. **Rating** 94 **To** 2019 $43

Finniss River Cabernet Sauvignon 2009 Medium red-purple; a very well made Cabernet with excellent varietal expression, and similarly structured and balanced; the cassis fruit reflects perfect ripening in the vineyard, the tannins likewise. The '10 should be a great wine. Cork. 14.5% alc. **Rating** 94 **To** 2029 $32

♥♥♥♥♡ **Baan Shiraz & Company 2010 Rating** 90 **To** 2016 $16
○

Saltram   ★★★★★

Nuriootpa Road, Angaston, SA 5353 **Region** Barossa Valley
T (08) 8561 0200 **www**.saltramwines.com.au **Open** 7 days 10–5
Winemaker Shavaughn Wells, Richard Mattner **Est.** 1859 **Dozens** 150 000
There is no doubt that Saltram has taken strides towards regaining the reputation it held 30 or so years ago. Grape sourcing has come back to the Barossa Valley for the flagship wines. The red wines, in particular, have enjoyed great show success over the past few years, with No. 1 Shiraz, Mamre Brook and Metala leading the charge. Further wines were received after this issue went to print; tasting notes appear on www.winecompanion.com.au. Exports to the UK, the US and other major markets.

♥♥♥♥♥ **Mr Pickwick's Limited Release Particular Tawny NV** The very soul of Australian tawny, this wine straddles the boundary of rancio nuttiness and exotic dried fruit sweetness with aplomb; long, refreshing, deep, compelling and exotic. Cork. 18.5% alc. **Rating** 95 **To** 2018 $72 BE

♥♥♥♥ **Mamre Brook Eden Valley Riesling 2011 Rating** 88 **To** 2014 $23

Sam Miranda of King Valley   ★★★★

1019 Snow Road, Oxley, Vic 3678 **Region** King Valley
T (03) 5727 3888 **www**.sammiranda.com.au **Open** 7 days 10–5
Winemaker Sam Miranda **Est.** 2004 **Dozens** 15 000 **Vyds** 15ha
Sam Miranda, grandson of Francesco Miranda, joined the family business in 1991, striking out on his own in 2004 after Miranda Wines was purchased by McGuigan Simeon. The High Plains Vineyard is in the Upper King Valley at an altitude of 450m; estate plantings are supplemented by some purchased grapes. In '05 Sam purchased Symphonia Wines, and has kept its identity intact and separate from the Sam Miranda brand. Exports to China.

♥♥♥♥♡ **Cellar Door Release Chardonnay 2010** Clearly showing its cool-climate origins, with citrus and fennel on the bouquet; the palate is lively and mineral-accented, showing an extra dimension of perfume on the grilled nut finish. Screwcap. 12.4% alc. **Rating** 90 **To** 2016 $30 BE

Etiquette Jaune Special Release Pinot Noir 2010 A savoury and spicy bouquet, showing damsel plums and a generous dollop of toasty oak; the palate is soft and silky, with fresh-cut herb complexity and firm tannins lingering. Distinctly highlands Pinot, done well. Screwcap. 13.5% alc. **Rating** 90 **To** 2014 $40 BE

Girls Block Single Vineyard Cabernet Sauvignon Petit Verdot Merlot 2010 Good colour; a juicy medium-bodied wine with cassis interlaced by mint; the tannins are fine, and the oak well integrated. Screwcap. 13.5% alc. **Rating** 90 **To** 2020 $40

Limited Release Trial 4 Botrytis Semillon 2010 Full gold; has developed very quickly, but still has good balance; rich cumquat and mandarin skin. 375ml. Screwcap. 13.8% alc. **Rating** 90 **To** 2013 $25

ŶŶŶŶ **Cellar Door Release Sauvignon Blanc 2011** **Rating** 89 **To** 2013 $20
Cellar Door Release Semillon 2010 **Rating** 87 **To** 2014 $20 BE
Cellar Door Release Barbera Shiraz 2010 **Rating** 87 **To** 2014 $30 BE

Samuel's Gorge ★★★★★

Lot 10 Chaffeys Road, McLaren, SA 5171 **Region** McLaren Vale
T (08) 8323 8651 **F** (08) 8323 8673 **www**.gorge.com.au **Open** 7 days 11–5
Winemaker Justin McNamee **Est.** 2003 **Dozens** 3000 **Vyds** 10ha
After a wandering winemaking career in various parts of the world, Justin McNamee became a winemaker at Tatachilla in 1996, where he remained until 2003, leaving to found Samuel's Gorge. He has established his winery in a barn built in 1853, part of the old Seaview Homestead. The historic property was owned by Sir Samuel Way, variously Chief Justice of the South Australian Supreme Court and Lieutenant Governor of the state. The grapes come from small contract growers spread across the ever-changing (unofficial) subregions of McLaren Vale, and are basket-pressed and fermented in old open slate fermenters lined with beeswax – with impressive results. Exports to the UK, the US, Canada and Hong Kong.

ŶŶŶŶŶ **McLaren Vale Shiraz 2010** Deep, dense purple-crimson; has amazing depth of flavour on its multilayered full-bodied palate, redolent with blackberry, stewed plum, licorice, spice and dark chocolate, with a nice touch of oak just making itself heard. Potentially very long lived, so let's pray for the cork. 14.5% alc. **Rating** 95 **To** 2025 $40

McLaren Vale Shiraz 2009 Deep crimson-purple; a brooding full-bodied wine, with black fruits, tar, licorice and dark chocolate dominating proceedings; however, it is well balanced and has good line. The tree bark (cork) is of good quality, and has been professionally inserted, giving the wine a chance to reach full maturity in 20 years' time. 14.5% alc. **Rating** 94 **To** 2029 $40

Cadenzia McLaren Vale Grenache 2009 Has all the attributes McLaren Vale can confer on the variety that the Barossa Valley can't: good colour, firm dark berry fruit tinged with spice, and fine tannins in support. Cork. 14.5% alc. **Rating** 94 **To** 2016 $35

Grenache Mourvedre Shiraz 2009 A 43/43/14% blend; a lengthy sojourn in oak has welded the varieties together, the blackberry, plum, spice and dark chocolate running in a continuous stream across the palate; the length is very good, the balance likewise. Cork. 14.2% alc. **Rating** 94 **To** 2024 $75

Tempranillo Graciano Grenache 2009 A 61/23/16% blend in a massive, dreadnought bottle, which turns out to be wholly appropriate for the full-bodied, stentorian palate; having got over the original shock of the tannins, the full array of black cherry, sour cherry, red cherry, spice and licorice all become apparent. Blends of this kind are not always suited to cellaring, but this most certainly is, provided prayers for the cork are answered. 14% alc. **Rating** 94 **To** 2029 $75

Mourvedre 2010 Dense purple-crimson; it has an enormous volume of flavour and structure compared with the usual run of mourvedre, presumably coming from low-yielding old vines; what is more, this flavour and colour has been achieved without excessive maceration, for the tannins, while substantial, are ripe and essentially balanced. Cork. 15% alc. **Rating** 94 **To** 2025 $35

ŶŶŶŶŶ **McLaren Vale Tempranillo 2010** **Rating** 90 **To** 2015 $40

Sandalford

3210 West Swan Road, Caversham, WA 6055 **Region** Margaret River
T (08) 9374 9374 **www**.sandalford.com **Open** 7 days 9–5
Winemaker Paul Boulden, Hope Metcalf **Est.** 1840 **Dozens** 60 000 **Vyds** 105ha
Sandalford is one of Australia's oldest and largest privately owned wineries. In 1970 it moved beyond its original Swan Valley base, purchasing a substantial property in Margaret River that is now the main source of its premium grapes. With most of the vines now 40 years old, and with the highly experienced former Flying Winemaker Paul Boulden in charge, it is no surprise that the quality of the wines is consistently excellent. Exports to all major markets.

Estate Reserve Margaret River Sauvignon Blanc Semillon 2011 Pale quartz; the bouquet is fragrant and expressive, speaking of the intense mix of citrus, kiwi fruit, snow pea and passionfruit (not always in that order) on the lively, fresh palate. While the semillon will provide stability over the next few years, I would drink it sooner rather than later. Screwcap. 13% alc. **Rating** 95 **To** 2014 $23
Prendiville Reserve Margaret River Chardonnay 2011 Hand-picked and whole bunch-pressed to a mix of new and used French oak for fermentation using different yeasts. The full straw-green colour is a little more developed than I would expect, but the palate is brilliantly fresh and lively, with pink grapefruit and white peach the main flavour contributors; cashew nuances from the oak are among the complexing factors, factors that will continue to influence the wine as it develops in bottle. Screwcap. 13.5% alc. **Rating** 95 **To** 2018 $60
Margaret River Rose 2011 Made from 100% cabernet sauvignon purpose-picked on the first days of vintage. Bright puce-pink; has the balance lacking in many eastern states' roses in '11, its raspberry and cherry fruit aromas and flavours finishing dry, acidity providing a framework for the sweet fruit on the back-palate and perfectly balanced, lingering finish. Screwcap. 12.5% alc. **Rating** 94 **To** Now $19
Estate Reserve Margaret River Shiraz 2009 Bright, clear crimson; estate-grown and finished its primary fermentation in new and 1-year-old tight-grained barrels, followed by 18 months' maturation in those barrels. The oak integration achieved by this method has worked well, for the wine is no more than medium-bodied, the fruit vulnerable to any attempt to over-extract it. Elegance gets the wine over the line. Screwcap. 14% alc. **Rating** 94 **To** 2024 $35

Classic Dry White Margaret River Semillon Sauvignon Blanc 2011 Light straw-green; the bouquet has the tropical fruit component missing from most eastern Australian Sauvignon Blanc or Sauvignon Blanc Semillon wines; it carries on to the fore-palate, whereafter lemon zest and herb semillon fill in the picture. Screwcap. 12.5% alc. **Rating** 92 **To** 2013 $20
Estate Reserve Margaret River Chenin Blanc 2011 Rating 92 **To** 2021 $25
Estate Reserve Margaret River Cabernet Sauvignon 2009 Rating 92 **To** 2025 $45 BE
Margaret River Chardonnay 2011 Bright straw-green; a massive contrast to the Prendiville, for this wine has been entirely fermented in stainless steel, seeing no oak at any stage during its journey to bottle. Flavour development is exactly as it should be, with a mix of citrus and stone fruit flavours, and no cross-dressing with Sauvignon Blanc. Screwcap. 13.5% alc. **Rating** 91 **To** 2016 $20
Margaret River Cabernet Merlot 2010 Deep crimson; the bouquet exhibits cassis, tar and a little leafy complexity; medium- to full-bodied with plenty of stuffing and freshness; a little time will see a lot more delivered. Screwcap. 14.5% alc. **Rating** 90 **To** 2018 $20 BE

Margaret River Shiraz 2010 Rating 89 **To** 2015 $19
Element Late Harvest 2011 Rating 88 **To** 2013 $14

Sandhurst Ridge ★★★★

156 Forest Drive, Marong, Vic 3515 **Region** Bendigo
T (03) 5435 2534 **www**.sandhurstridge.com.au **Open** 7 days 11–5
Winemaker Paul Greblo **Est.** 1990 **Dozens** 3000 **Vyds** 7.3ha

The Greblo brothers (Paul is the winemaker, George the viticulturist), with combined experience in business, agriculture, science and construction and development, began the establishment of Sandhurst Ridge in 1990, planting the first 2ha of shiraz and cabernet sauvignon. Plantings have increased to over 7 ha, principally cabernet and shiraz, but also a little merlot, nebbiolo and sauvignon blanc. As the business has grown, the Greblos have supplemented their crush with grapes grown in the region. Exports to Canada, Norway, Taiwan, Hong Kong, Japan and China.

🍷🍷🍷🍷½ **Bendigo Shiraz 2010** Parts of Bendigo were affected by rain and cool weather; the hue is good, although without the usual depth of Sandhurst Ridge. Hand-picked, open-fermented in small vats, followed by over 18 months in American and French oak barriques. The result is a pleasant medium-bodied shiraz with clear varietal expression, but only just able to carry the oak flavours. Screwcap. 13% alc. **Rating** 90 **To** 2017 **$30**

Fringe Bendigo Shiraz Classic Blend 2010 A 70/30% blend of shiraz and cabernet sauvignon, made in the same way as the Shirazs. Vintage conditions have resulted in an uncharacteristically light- to medium-bodied wine, but it is arguable that it is none the worse for that, with its lively cassis and red berry flavours, supported by fine tannins. Screwcap. 13% alc. **Rating** 90 **To** 2018 **$24**

🍷🍷🍷🍷 **Fringe Bendigo Shiraz 2010** **Rating** 89 **To** 2016 **$24**
Bendigo Nebbiolo 2010 **Rating** 88 **To** 2016 **$30**
Bendigo Sauvignon Blanc 2011 **Rating** 87 **To** 2014 **$22**

Sanguine Estate ★★★★★

77 Shurans Lane, Heathcote, Vic 3523 **Region** Heathcote
T (03) 5433 3111 **www**.sanguinewines.com.au **Open** By appt
Winemaker Mark Hunter **Est.** 1997 **Dozens** 3500 **Vyds** 21.57ha

The Hunter family – parents Linda and Tony at the head, and their children Mark and Jodi, with their respective partners Melissa and Brett – began establishing the vineyard in 1997. It has grown to 20.16ha of shiraz, with smaller plantings of chardonnay, viognier, merlot, tempranillo, petit verdot, cabernet sauvignon and cabernet franc. Low-yielding vines and the magic of the Heathcote region have produced Shiraz of exceptional intensity, which has received rave reviews in the US, and led to the 'sold out' sign being posted almost immediately upon release. With the ever-expanding vineyard, Mark has become full-time vigneron, and Jodi part-time marketer and business developer. Exports to Denmark and Singapore.

🍷🍷🍷🍷🍷 **Heathcote Shiraz 2010** Deep garnet, purple hue; loaded with sweet dark fruits, liqueur kirsch, bay and thyme; full-bodied, unctuously textured, with toasty oak a mere seasoning to the huge volume of fruit on offer; plenty of backbone, with ample fine-grained tannins and a long sweet-fruited finish. Screwcap. 14.8% alc. **Rating** 94 **To** 2018 **$40** BE

Music Festival Heathcote Shiraz 2009 A veritable orchestra of flavours that are sufficiently varied in their complexity and impact to avoid any hot/high alcohol concerns. The flavours range from bitter chocolate and earth at one extreme, through to plum, blackberry and blackcurrant at the other; oak and tannins play their part, but do so sotto voce. Screwcap. 14.8% alc. **Rating** 94 **To** 2029 **$30**

🍷🍷🍷🍷½ **D'Orsa Heathcote Shiraz 2009** **Rating** 93 **To** 2020 **$60** BE

✪ **Progeny Heathcote Shiraz 2010** Vivid deep crimson; highly expressive on the bouquet with blueberry, blackberry sage and cinnamon on display; the palate is generous and sweet-fruited on entry with a racy subtext of acidity providing line and length; certainly the junior wine of the stable, but the wine to drink while the big brothers mature. Screwcap. 14.8% alc. **Rating** 92 **To** 2016 **$20** BE

🍷🍷🍷🍷 **Heathcote Chardonnay 2010** **Rating** 88 **To** 2014 **$20** BE

Saracen Estates

3517 Caves Road, Wilyabrup, WA 6280 **Region** Margaret River
T (08) 9755 6000 **www**.saracenestates.com.au **Open** 7 days 11–5
Winemaker Bob Cartwright (Consultant) **Est.** 1998 **Dozens** 6000 **Vyds** 16.94ha
Luke and Maree Saraceni's first foray into the wine industry came via a small import business.
The next step was the establishment of Saracen Estates; today they have almost 17ha of vines
on their 80ha property, with a striking restaurant and cellar door (opened in 2007). This was
followed by a visitor facility in '08, incorporating a wine education centre, craft brewery, beer
garden and restaurant. Won Most Successful Exhibitor Margaret River Wine Show '10.

♀♀♀♀♀ Margaret River Sauvignon Blanc Semillon 2011 Pale colour, vibrant green
hue; a ripe and generous bouquet of straw, tropical fruit and bath talc; the palate
is taut and energetic, with good concentration, lively acidity and a finely balanced
finish. Screwcap. 12.3% alc. **Rating** 94 **To** 2015 $22 BE

♀♀♀♀♀ Reserve Margaret River Cabernet Sauvignon 2009 **Rating** 93
To 2022 $85 BE
Reserve Margaret River Shiraz 2009 **Rating** 90 **To** 2022 $50
Maree 2009 **Rating** 90 **To** 2015 $38 BE

♀♀♀♀ Margaret River Cabernet Sauvignon 2009 **Rating** 87 **To** 2017 $40 BE

Sarsfield Estate ★★★★

345 Duncan Road, Sarsfield, Vic 3875 **Region** Gippsland
T (03) 5156 8962 **www**.sarsfieldestate.com.au **Open** By appt
Winemaker Dr Suzanne Rutschmann **Est.** 1995 **Dozens** 1200 **Vyds** 2 ha
Owned by Suzanne Rutschmann, who has a PhD in Chemistry, a Diploma in Horticulture
and a BSc (Wine Science) from CSU, and Swiss-born Peter Albrecht, a civil and structural
engineer who has also undertaken various courses in agriculture and viticulture. For a part-
time occupation, these are exceptionally impressive credentials. Their vineyard (pinot noir,
cabernet, shiraz, cabernet franc and merlot) was planted between 1991 and '98. Sarsfield Pinot
Noir has enjoyed success in both domestic and international wine shows. No insecticides
are used in the vineyard, the winery runs on solar and wind energy and relies entirely on
rain water. Wines were received after this issue went to print, tasting notes appear on www.
winecompanion.com.au.

SC Pannell

Box 1159, Unley BC, SA 5061 **Region** McLaren Vale
T (08) 8271 7118 **www**.scpannell.com.au **Open** Not
Winemaker Stephen Pannell **Est.** 2004 **Dozens** 3000
The only surprising piece of background is that it took (an admittedly still reasonably
youthful) Stephen Pannell (and wife Fiona) so long to cut the painter from Constellation/
Hardys and establish their own winemaking and consulting business. Steve radiates intensity,
and extended experience, backed by equally long experimentation and thought, has resulted
in wines of the highest quality right from the first vintage. At present the focus of their virtual
winery (they own neither vineyards nor winery) is grenache and shiraz grown in McLaren
Vale. This is a label well on its way to icon status. Exports to the UK, the US and Singapore.

♀♀♀♀♀ Adelaide Hills Sauvignon Blanc 2011 Pale straw-green; this is a very tightly
✪   focused and intense wine, with grapefruit, kiwi fruit and ripe citrus welded
together; the finish and aftertaste of astonishing length and purity. Screwcap.
12.5% alc. **Rating** 96 **To** 2014 $27
McLaren Vale Shiraz 2008 Strong red-purple; open-fermented in small
concrete vats and matured in French puncheons for 18 months. While the flavours
are in typical McLaren Vale mode, the texture is distinctly finer, black fruits, dark
chocolate and oak seamlessly woven together, fine-grained tannins the ribbon that
ties up the parcel. Screwcap. 14.5% alc. **Rating** 96 **To** 2020 $60

McLaren Vale Shiraz Grenache 2008 A 76/24% blend of shiraz from 42-year-old vines and grenache from 68-year-old dry-grown vines open-fermented and matured in used French oak puncheons for 18 months. It is very elegant, but also intense and focused, with dark berry and red berry fruits, and an earthy edge to the tannins that really works. Screwcap. 14.5% alc. **Rating** 95 **To** 2023 $40
Fleurieu Touriga Tempranillo 2009 Has retained strong, deep colour; this is a red wine with real attitude, the smoky charred black fruits/plum pudding of the touriga in pride of place, cherry and a hint of herb/citrus diffidently contributed by the tempranillo. Screwcap. 14% alc. **Rating** 94 **To** 2016 $27

♀♀♀♀♀ **Pronto Tinto 2009 Rating** 93 **To** 2018 $27

Scaffidi Wines

Talunga Cellars, 198 Torrens Valley Road, Gumeracha, SA 5233 **Region** Adelaide Zone
T (08) 8389 1222 **www.**talunga.com.au **Open** Wed–Sun & public hols 10.30–4.30
Winemaker Vince Scaffidi **Est.** 1994 **Dozens** 2000 **Vyds** 101.2ha
Owners Vince and Tina Scaffidi have sold their interest in the 80ha Gumeracha Vineyards, but have retained 2.2ha of sauvignon blanc and chardonnay at their Gumeracha house property. They also have 99ha on their One Tree Hill Vineyard, planted to shiraz, cabernet sauvignon, merlot, sangiovese, nebbiolo, petit verdot and chardonnay, the majority of the grape production being sold. The cellar door and restaurant is named Talunga Cellars. The wines are exceptionally well priced.

♀♀♀♀♀ **Adelaide Hills Shiraz 2010** Crimson-purple; a full-bodied Adelaide Hills Shiraz,
✪ with a framework of savoury tannins for the relatively rich blackcurrant fruits; the alcohol is no issue, and the wine has not been over-extracted. Ludicrously good (cleanskin) value. Screwcap. 15% alc. **Rating** 91 **To** 2020 $9

♀♀♀♀ **One Tree Hill Sangiovese Blend 2010** Good colour for Sangiovese; the
✪ savoury red cherry fruit and equally savoury tannins are varietal, and, in its cleanskin guise the wine is exceptional value. Screwcap. 14.5% alc. **Rating** 88 **To** 2015 $8

✪ **Di Cesare Adelaide Hills Semillon 2010** Clean, fresh and still very youthful; could quite well develop over the next few years and take on greater character. Any criticism is superfluous at this price. Available in cleanskin from the cellar door. Screwcap. 12.7% alc. **Rating** 87 **To** 2013 $7

Scarborough Wine Co

179 Gillards Road, Pokolbin, NSW 2320 **Region** Hunter Valley
T (02) 4998 7563 **www.**scarboroughwine.com.au **Open** 7 days 9–5
Winemaker Ian and Jerome Scarborough **Est.** 1985 **Dozens** 25 000 **Vyds** 14ha
Ian Scarborough honed his white winemaking skills during his years as a consultant, and has brought all those skills to his own label. He makes three different styles of Chardonnay: the Blue Label is a light, elegant, Chablis style for the export market; a richer barrel-fermented wine (Yellow Label) is primarily directed to the Australian market; the third is the White Label, a cellar door-only wine made in the best vintages. The Scarborough family also acquired a portion of the old Lindemans Sunshine Vineyard (after it lay fallow for 30 years) and planted it with semillon and (quixotically) pinot noir. Scarborough has recently opened a second cellar door 'Scarborough on Hermitage' at 972 Hermitage Rd, Pokolbin NSW 2320 (open Thurs-Mon 10–5). Exports to the UK and the US.

♀♀♀♀♀ **Green Label Semillon 2011** Straw-green; hints of grass, citrus and lanolin on
✪ the bouquet are very expressive and varietal, the palate framed by strong mineral notes, amplified by acidity. Excellent balance and sure to flourish mightily with time in bottle. Screwcap. 11% alc. **Rating** 94 **To** 2025 $19

♀♀♀♀♀ **White Label Hunter Valley Chardonnay 2010 Rating** 92 **To** 2016 $30
Shiraz 2009 Rating 92 **To** 2019 $27
Yellow Label Chardonnay 2009 Rating 91 **To** 2017 $22

♟♟♟♟   **Blue Label Chardonnay 2010** Rating 89 To 2014 $20
Late Harvest Semillon 2011 Rating 89 To 2014 $20

Schild Estate Wines ★★★★

Cnr Barossa Valley Way/Lyndoch Valley Road, Lyndoch, SA 5351 **Region** Barossa Valley
T (08) 8524 5560 **www.**schildestate.com.au **Open** 7 days 10–5
Winemaker Scott Hazeldine **Est.** 1998 **Dozens** 45 000 **Vyds** 162.95ha
Ed Schild is a Barossa Valley grapegrower who first planted a small vineyard at Rowland Flat
in 1952, steadily increasing his vineyard holdings over the next 50 years to their present level.
The flagship wine is made from 150-year-old shiraz vines on the Moorooroo Block. The
cellar door is in the old ANZ Bank at Lyndoch, and provides the sort of ambience that can
only be found in the Barossa Valley. A $4 million winery was constructed and opened in time
for the 2010 vintage. Schild Estate was caught up in a PR storm in early '11 after its '08 Shiraz
was ranked no. 8 in the Top 100 Wines of the *Wine Spectator*. All of its stock had to be sent to
the US, and a separate blend was made for Australian distribution with a slip label stating it was
blend no. 2. The event has not stopped production increasing from 20 000 to 45 000 dozen.
Exports to all major markets.

♟♟♟♟♟   **Ben Schild Reserve Barossa Shiraz 2007** Bright crimson–purple, impressive
for age and vintage; open-fermented, then spent 17 months in American and
Hungarian oak; all in all, a pretty snappy wine from the tough '07 vintage, with
good balance and freshness. Screwcap. 15% alc. **Rating** 91 **To** 2017 $30

✪   **Barossa Riesling 2011** Light green-straw; apple, spice and citrus all drive the
bouquet and palate, although the wine in the mouth has some talc adding texture.
Screwcap. 12% alc. **Rating** 90 **To** 2016 $16

♟♟♟♟   **Barossa Shiraz 2009** Rating 89 To 2014 $19
Barossa Sparkling Shiraz 2008 Rating 87 To 2013 $26

Schubert Estate ★★★★★

Roennfeldt Road, Marananga, SA 5355 **Region** Barossa Valley
T (08) 8562 3375 **www.**schubertestate.com **Open** By appt
Winemaker Steve Schubert **Est.** 2000 **Dozens** 1100 **Vyds** 14ha
Steve and Cecilia Schubert are primarily grapegrowers, with 12ha of shiraz and 2ha of
viognier. They purchased the 25ha property in 1986, when it was in such a derelict state
that there was no point trying to save the old vines. Both were working in other areas, so
it was some years before they began replanting, at a little under 2ha per year. Almost all
the production is sold to Torbreck. In 2000 they decided to keep enough grapes to make a
barrique of wine for their own (and friends') consumption. They were sufficiently encouraged
by the outcome to venture into the dizzy heights of two hogsheads a year (since increased to
four or so). The wine is made with wild yeast, open fermentation, basket-pressing and bottling
without filtration. Exports to the UK, Canada, Germany, Hong Kong and China.

♟♟♟♟♟   **Goose-yard Block Barossa Valley Shiraz 2009** Dense, inky purple-red; open-
fermented, basket-pressed and matured in oak for 18 months; a very potent wine
with prune, poached plum and licorice fruit supported by ripe tannins and oak.
Just escapes the alcohol trap; 135 dozen made, 50% with screwcap, 50% with cork.
15% alc. **Rating** 94 **To** 2020 $55

✪   **The Sentinel Barossa Valley Shiraz 2007** Utterly exceptional purple-crimson
colour given the age and the nature of the '07 vintage; the bouquet and medium-
bodied palate have a mix of black cherry and blackberry, the tannins fine, the oak
integrated and balanced. 98 dozen produced from the Goose-yard Block vineyard.
Screwcap. 14.5% alc. **Rating** 94 **To** 2017 $25

♟♟♟♟♟   **Le Jars Blanc Barossa Valley Viognier 2010** Rating 92
✪   **To** 2014 $18
✪   **The Gosling Barossa Valley Shiraz 2009** Rating 91 To 2020 $20

Schulz Vignerons

★★★★

PO Box 121, Nuriootpa, SA 5355 **Region** Barossa Valley
T (08) 8565 6257 **F** (08) 8565 6257 **Open** By appt
Winemaker David Powell (Contract) **Est.** 2003 **Dozens** 450 **Vyds** 58.5ha
Marcus and Roslyn Schulz are the fifth generation of one of the best known wine families
(or, rather, extended families) in the Barossa Valley. Four generations of grapegrowing and
winemaking precede them, but they went down a new path by initiating biological farming
in 2002. They have moved from irrigation and extensive spraying to the situation where the
vines are now virtually dry-grown, producing generous yields of high-quality grapes, using
natural nitrogen created by the active soil biology, and minimal chemical input. The vineyard is
planted to 12 varieties, shiraz, mourvedre, grenache and cabernet sauvignon leading the band.
They are also actively involved in a local co-operative campaign to protect blocks of native
vegetation to encourage biodiversity. As might be imagined, the lion's share of the grapes is
sold to other producers (some finding its way to Torbreck).

 Johann Barossa Valley Zinfandel 2007 Expected colour development; floods
the mouth with spicy, dark fruits, ground coffee, Christmas cake and vanillin oak; it
comes as no surprise to find the winemaker is David Powell of Torbreck. Screwcap.
Anthony Barossa Valley Cabernet Sauvignon 2009 Full red-purple; has
power and flavour, and will stand tall among its regional peers; however, when
set against (say) Margaret River, it has to yield to superior fruit quality. Screwcap.
14% alc. **Rating** 90 **To** 2019 $20

ΨΨΨΨ **Julius Barossa Valley Merlot 2009 Rating** 88 **To** 2019 $20

Schwarz Wine Company

★★★★☆

Biscay Road, Tanunda, SA 5352 **Region** Barossa Valley
T 0417 881 923 **www.**schwarzwineco.com.au **Open** At Artisans of Barossa
Winemaker Jason Schwarz **Est.** 2001 **Dozens** 2000
The economical name is appropriate for a business that started with 1 tonne of grapes
making two hogsheads of wine in 2001. The shiraz was purchased from Jason Schwarz's
parents' vineyard in Bethany, the vines planted 60 years ago; the following year half a tonne
of grenache was added, once again purchased from the parents. Production remained static
until '05, when the grape sale agreements to another (larger) winery were terminated, freeing
up 1.8ha of shiraz and 0.8ha of grenache. From this point on things moved more quickly: in
'06 Jason, while working with Peter Schell of Spinifex, formed a partnership (Biscay Road
Vintners) with Peter giving each total control over production. Using grapes purchased from
other growers, Jason hopes to eventually increase production to 3000–4000 dozen. Exports to
the UK, the US, Canada, France, Denmark, Singapore, Hong Kong and China.

 The Schiller Barossa Valley Shiraz 2009 Deep crimson; a perfumed and
appealing blend of red and black fruits, spices, bitter chocolate and florals on the
bouquet; the palate is medium-bodied, fresh and focused, with ample fine-grained
tannins, finishing with an even, long and harmonious conclusion; belies the 15%
alcohol on the label with ease. Screwcap. 15% alc. **Rating** 95 **To** 2030 $65 BE

ΨΨΨΨ **Nitschke Block Barossa Valley Shiraz 2009 Rating** 89 **To** 2017 $35 BE
Thiele Road Barossa Valley Grenache 2009 Rating 87 **To** 2014 $30 BE

Scorpiiion

★★★★★

575 Royal Esplanade, Manly, Qld 4179 **Region** Barossa
T 0409 551 110 **www.**scorpiiionwines.com.au **Open** Not
Winemaker Pete Schell **Est.** 2002 **Dozens** 800
Scorpiiion Wines is the concept of Mark Herbertt, who decided to buy a small quantity of
McLaren Vale and Barossa grapes in 2002 and have the wine made for himself, friends and
family. In '04 Paddy Phillips and Michael Szwarcbord – with Mark Herbertt, they share the
Scorpio birth sign – joined the partnership. It is a virtual winery, with the grapes purchased,
and the wines contract-made by the brilliant Peter Schell. They say, 'We share a number of
likes and dislikes in relation to Australian red wines – apart from that, we don't really agree

on anything … We aim for a fruit-driven style with elegant oak, rather than a big, oak-driven style.' Oh, and they are united in their insistence on using screwcaps rather than corks.

🍷🍷🍷🍷🍷 **The Scorpiiion Single Vineyard Barossa Valley Shiraz 2008** Deep colour; a voluptuously, velvety rich palate ranges through blackberry, licorice, chocolate, plum cake, spice and tar – what more do you want? – yet retains balance and line. Impressive wine from '08 from a single vineyard, surely picked before the heat. Screwcap. 14.5% alc. **Rating** 95 **To** 2028 $67

Barossa Valley Shiraz 2010 The inky purple colour is a sure sign of the full-bodied wine that follows, with layer upon layer of black fruits; however, it is not the least attractive nor alcoholic; the tannins are ripe but soft, the French oak barely evident. Screwcap. 14.5% alc. **Rating** 94 **To** 2030 $28

🍷🍷🍷🍷 ✪ **Barossa Valley Rose 2011** A blend of 52% grenache and 48% mataro. Pale, bright pink; a relatively delicate and reserved wine until the end of the palate, when it opens up and delivers a shaft of red fruits and lemony acidity. Screwcap. 13.7% alc. **Rating** 90 **To** Now $20

Scorpo Wines ★★★★★

23 Old Bittern-Dromana Road, Merricks North, Vic 3926 **Region** Mornington Peninsula
T (03) 5989 7697 **www**.scorpowines.com.au **Open** By appt
Winemaker Paul Scorpo, Sandro Mosele (Contract) **Est.** 1997 **Dozens** 3500 **Vyds** 9.64ha

Paul Scorpo has a background as a horticulturist/landscape architect, working on major projects ranging from private gardens to golf courses in Australia, Europe and Asia. His family has a love of food, wine and gardens, all of which led to them buying a derelict apple and cherry orchard on gentle rolling hills between Port Phillip and Westernport bays. Part of a ridge system that climbs up to Red Hill, it offers north and northeast-facing slopes on red-brown, clay loam soils. They have established pinot gris (4.84ha), pinot noir (2.8ha), chardonnay (1ha) and shiraz (1ha). Exports to Singapore and Hong Kong.

🍷🍷🍷🍷🍷 **Mornington Peninsula Pinot Noir 2010** Deep, bright crimson; an exciting and enervating blend of red cherry, vine sap, spices and a suggestion of oak; the palate is simply electric, carving a long and direct path of precise flavours, while revealing layers of complexity and texture across the staggeringly long and attractive finish; world class in every sense. Screwcap. 13.5% alc. **Rating** 97 **To** 2020 $44 BE

Mornington Peninsula Pinot Gris 2011 In 2011 the conditions seemed to encourage complex sulphide aromas in Pinot Gris on the Peninsula, and this wine is no exception; struck match, bacon fat, candied lemon and lots of spice; the palate is racy on the one hand and richly textured on the other; simply outstanding pinot gris, regardless of origin. Screwcap. 13.5% alc. **Rating** 95 **To** 2015 $35 BE

🍷🍷🍷🍷 **Mornington Peninsula Shiraz 2008** **Rating** 90 **To** 2016 $32 BE

🍷🍷🍷🍷 **Mornington Peninsula Rose 2011** **Rating** 88 **To** 2013 $29 BE

Scotchmans Hill ★★★★★

190 Scotchmans Road, Drysdale, Vic 3222 **Region** Geelong
T (03) 5251 3176 **www**.scotchmanshill.com.au **Open** 7 days 10.30–5
Winemaker Robin Brockett, Marcus Holt **Est.** 1982 **Dozens** 70 000

Situated on the Bellarine Peninsula, southeast of Geelong, with a well-equipped winery and first-class vineyards. It is a consistent performer with its Pinot Noir and has a strong following in Melbourne and Sydney for its astutely priced, competently made wines. The second label, Swan Bay, has been joined at the other end of the spectrum with top-end individual vineyard wines. The Ferryman brand was added in 2009, using contract-grown grapes from the Mornington Peninsula, later joined by the Henry Frost and Estella labels from SA regions. The more recent establishment of the Charlotte Sound and Pebble Bay labels, both using 100% Marlborough, NZ grapes, lifts the number of wines on the current mail order form to a cool 45. Exports to Asia and other major markets.

𝟻𝟻𝟻𝟻𝟻 **Bellarine Peninsula Pinot Noir 2010** Clear crimson; hand-picked, destemmed, five-day cold soak small fermenters, wild ferment to 28°C, mlf in barrel, bottled July '11. A richly robed, full-flavoured Pinot Noir that has not lost any varietal expression or otherwise gone over the top, as only 4-year-old Troncais oak was used. Will have a long (Pinot) life. Screwcap. 14% alc. **Rating** 95 **To** 2020 $30
Bellarine Peninsula Chardonnay 2010 Barrel-fermented in new to 4-year-old Vosges oak. Has livewire intensity and energy, white peach, nectarine and grapefruit reaching every corner of the mouth, the oak barely obvious. Screwcap. 13.5% alc. **Rating** 94 **To** 2020 $25
Cornelius Single Vineyard Bellarine Peninsula Syrah 2009 A fragrant and red-fruited bouquet, with lots of spice, toasty oak and a splash of sea salt; the palate is medium-bodied, fragrant and fresh, with fine-grained tannins providing a seamless and harmonious finish. Screwcap. 15% alc. **Rating** 94 **To** 2020 $65 BE

𝟻𝟻𝟻𝟻𝟿 **Cornelius Single Vineyard Bellarine Peninsula Sauvignon 2010 Rating** 93 **To** 2015 $40 BE
Bellarine Peninsula Shiraz 2009 Rating 93 **To** 2024 $25

✪ **Swan Bay Sauvignon Blanc Semillon 2011** Sourced entirely from vineyards in Geelong, the wine has exceptional drive and intensity on the palate, lemon, gooseberry and tropical flavours all in a single embrace, the finish fresh and zesty. Great value. Screwcap. 12.5% alc. **Rating** 92 **To** 2013 $15
Sutton Vineyard Bellarine Peninsula Chardonnay 2008 Rating 92 **To** 2016 $55 BE

✪ **Swan Bay Shiraz 2010** Curious labelling, the front prominently stating Bellarine Peninsula, the back label saying the grapes are from premium Victorian regions. Swan Bay itself is on the Bellarine Peninsula, but that is not enough. This should not distract attention from the wine in the glass, with rich cherry, plum, licorice and spice flavours welded together with the aid of ripe tannins. Screwcap. 14.5% alc. **Rating** 92 **To** 2025 $15

✪ **Estella McLaren Vale Shiraz 2010** Deep purple-crimson; this wine delivers infinitely more than its price suggests; it is full of fragrant plum and blackberry fruit shot through with licorice and bitter chocolate; the tannins are fine, the French and American oak not the least obvious. Drinker sooner or later. Screwcap. 14.5% alc. **Rating** 92 **To** 2020 $15
Ferryman The Courier Mornington Peninsula Pinot Noir 2008 Rating 91 **To** 2017 $55 BE

✪ **Bellarine Peninsula Sauvignon Blanc 2011 Rating** 90 **To** 2013 $19
Cornelius Single Vineyard Bellarine Peninsula Chardonnay 2009 Rating 90 **To** 2016 $55 BE

⬤ **Swan Bay Pinot Noir 2010 Rating** 90 **To** 2014 $16
Cornelius Single Vineyard Bellarine Peninsula Pinot Noir 2009 Rating 90 **To** 2018 $55 BE
Norfolk Vineyard Bellarine Peninsula Pinot Noir 2008 Rating 90 **To** 2015 $55 BE

⬤ **Estella McLaren Vale Shiraz Cabernet Sauvignon 2010 Rating** 90 **To** 2015 $16

⬤ **The Hill Merlot 2009 Rating** 90 **To** 2013 $12

Scott ★★★★★

Building 3C, Old Woollen Mill, Main Street, Lobethal, SA 5241 **Region** Adelaide Hills
T 0439 553 228 **www.**scottwinemaking.com.au **Open** W'ends & most public hols 11–5
Winemaker Sam Scott **Est.** 2009 **Dozens** 2000
When Sam Scott established his winemaking business in 2009, it was the result of water dropping on stone over a long period. His story began with his great-grandfather working in the cellar for Max Schubert, and who passed his knowledge to Sam's grandfather. It was he who gave Scott his early education. Even then, he enrolled in business at university, continuing the casual retailing he had started while at school with Booze Brothers, picking up the trail with Baily & Baily. Next came wine wholesale experience with David Ridge,

selling iconic Australian and Italian wines to the trade. This then led to a job with Michael Fragos at Tatachilla in '00, and since then he has been the 'I've been everywhere man' model, working all over Australia, and in California. He moved to Bird in Hand winery at the end of '06, where Andrew Nugent indicated that it was about time he took the plunge on his own account, and this he has done. Like many, he was hard hit by the '11 vintage. Scott is a star in the making.

🍷🍷🍷🍷🍷 **Adelaide Hills Shiraz 2009** Bright purple-crimson; it takes a millisecond for the wine to proclaim its class as you taste it: finely woven spice, pepper and oak run through the river of black plum fruit. Great now, or in 20 years. Screwcap. 14.5% alc. **Rating** 96 **To** 2030 $40

Adelaide Hills Fiano 2011 This wine won two trophies at the Alternative Wines Show '11, including Best White Wine of Show. It offers a delicious combination of juicy citrus fruit with a subtle crosscut of spice on the long, refreshing palate. Screwcap. 13.5% alc. **Rating** 94 **To** 2013 $26

Adelaide Hills Shiraz Sangiovese 2010 An 88/12% blend, the colour bright; an altogether balanced wine, in terms of flavour, texture, structure and weight; the sangiovese adds its sour cherry and lingering tannins to the shiraz, which retains its structural integrity. Screwcap. 14% alc. **Rating** 94 **To** 2020 $26

Seabrook Wines   ★★★★★

Lot 350 Light Pass Road, Tanunda, SA 5352 **Region** Barossa Valley
T 0427 224 353 **www**.seabrookwines.com.au **Open** At Simpatico Wines
Winemaker Hamish Seabrook **Est.** 2004 **Dozens** 1500 **Vyds** 2ha
Hamish Seabrook is the youngest generation of a proud Melbourne wine family once involved in wholesale and retail distribution, and as leading show judges of their respective generations. Hamish, too, is a wine show judge, but was the first to venture into winemaking, working with Best's and Brown Brothers in Vic before moving to SA with wife Joanne. Here they have a small planting of shiraz (recently joined by viognier) but also continue to source small amounts of shiraz from the Barossa and Pyrenees. In 2008 Hamish set up his own winery, on the family property in Vine Vale, having previously made the wines at Dorrien Estate and elsewhere. Exports to the UK and Hong Kong.

🍷🍷🍷🍷🍷 **The Chairman Great Western Shiraz 2009** Deep crimson; fresh blackberry on the bouquet offset by the presence of regional eucalypt; the palate is fleshy and densely packed with tangy acidity providing freshness on the full-bodied finish. Screwcap. 14.5% alc. **Rating** 94 **To** 2018 $28 BE

The Merchant Barossa Valley Shiraz 2009 Deep colour, and while brooding and dark, there are layers of light and shade as well; black fruits, licorice, tar and quartz-like minerals; full-bodied on the palate, with densely packed fruit and ample tannins; long and muscular, but well proportioned. Screwcap. 14.5% alc. **Rating** 94 **To** 2025 $35 BE

Sedona Estate   ★★★★

182 Shannons Road, Murrindindi, Vic 3717 **Region** Upper Goulburn
T (03) 9730 2883 **www**.sedonaestate.com.au **Open** 7 days 11–5
Winemaker Paul Evans **Est.** 1998 **Dozens** 2000 **Vyds** 4ha
Sedona Estate, established by Paul Evans and Sonja Herges, is located in the picturesque Yea Valley, gateway to Victoria's high country. The unique combination of abundant sunshine, cool nights and low rainfall in this elevated wine region provides a true cool climate for growing premium-quality fruit. January 2011 saw the completion of the new winery, which is Paul's winemaking home for the future growth of the Sedona Estate brand.

🍷🍷🍷🍷🍷 **Yea Valley Shiraz 2010** Deep crimson colour; a lifted bouquet of red fruits, sage and mocha notes; the palate is fleshy and finely detailed, with fresh acidity and a lingering savoury/mineral aspect to the finish. Screwcap. 13.5% alc. **Rating** 90 **To** 2020 $22 BE

Yea Valley Auslese Shiraz 2010 'Auslese' conjours up images of the sweet Rieslings of Germany, yet here it improbably stands for a quite powerful and dry red wine of a 'select harvest'; the bouquet is full of mocha, black fruits and dense chewy tannins; broad-shouldered and focused, with a notable charcuterie note lingering on the finish. Screwcap. 13.5% alc. **Rating** 90 **To** 2022 $30

♥♥♥♥ **Yea Valley Sauvignon Blanc 2011** A ripe bouquet of guava, tomato leaf and
✪ smoky gun flint; the palate is soft on entry, with vibrant acidity providing contrast to the sweet fruit on offer; fresh and fragrant. Screwcap. 12% alc. **Rating** 89 **To** 2014 $18 BE

Yea Valley Auslese Merlot 2010 Rating 89 **To** 2016 $30 BE

See Saw ★★★

PO Box 611, Manly, NSW 1655 **Region** Hunter Valley
T (02) 8966 9020 **www**.seesawwine.com **Open** Not
Winemaker Hamish MacGowan, Andrew Margan **Est.** 2006 **Dozens** 8000
This is another venture of Hamish MacGowan, the winemaker-cum-marketer who is responsible for Angus the Bull (see separate entry). Prior to setting out on his own, Hamish worked for Andrew Margan, who now has his own substantial winery and business in the Hunter Valley. The wine they make for the See Saw label is a blend of semillon from the Hunter Valley and sauvignon blanc from high-altitude vineyards in the Central Ranges. Exports to the UK and the US.

♥♥♥♥ **Hunter Valley Central Ranges Semillon Sauvignon Blanc 2011** A well-
made wine, but when tasted along with Margaret River blends of '11, you come back to earth with a thud; here you rely on structure and balance, accepting the low profile of the fruit flavours as a positive, not a negative. Screwcap. 12% alc.
Rating 88 **To** 2014 $18

Semprevino ★★★★

1 Waverly Drive, Willunga, SA 5171 **Region** McLaren Vale
T 0417 142 110 **www**.semprevino.com.au **Open** Not
Winemaker Russell Schroder **Est.** 2006 **Dozens** 400
Semprevino is the venture of three men who became close friends while studying at Monash University in early 1990s – Russell Schroder (mechanical engineering), Simon Doak and David Bruce (both science) – although all three branched in different directions after graduating in 1993. The prime mover is Russell who, after working for CRA/Rio Tinto for five years, left on a four-month trip to Western Europe and became captivated with the life of a vigneron. Returning to Australia, he enrolled in part-time wine science at CSU, spending the next six years working for Bluescope Steel at Hastings on the Mornington Peninsula, obtaining his wine science degree in 2005. Between '03 and '06 he worked vintages in Italy and Vic, coming under the wing of Stephen Pannell at Tinlins, where the Semprevino wines are made, in '06.

♥♥♥♥♀ **McLaren Vale Cabernet Merlot 2010** An 85/25% blend with admirably deep
✪ purple-crimson colour; a wine to please everyone with its rich cassis fruit, quality oak and fine tannins. Screwcap. 14.3% alc. **Rating** 93 **To** 2020 $24

GSM McLaren Vale Grenache Shiraz Mourvedre 2010 Good purple-crimson hue; a 73/18/9% blend; the fruit flavours are lively and intense, they carry the alcohol with ease, instead imposing their array of plum, raspberry, spice and dark chocolate on the finish. Screwcap. 14.8% alc. **Rating** 91 **To** 2018 $24

Adelaide Hills Nebbiolo 2009 Typical light, clear colour; the fragrant, gently spicy aromas are 100% varietal, and don't prepare you for the strong, spicy/savoury tannins of the palate – but that is Nebbiolo, after all. Screwcap. 14.8% alc.
Rating 90 **To** 2018 $35

Seppelt ★★★★★

Moyston Road, Great Western, Vic 3377 **Region** Grampians
T (03) 5361 2239 **www**.seppelt.com.au **Open** 7 days 10–5
Winemaker Adam Wadewitz, Adam Curnaby **Est.** 1865 **Dozens** NFP
Australia's best-known producer of sparkling wine, always immaculate in its given price range
but also producing excellent Great Western-sourced table wines, especially long-lived Shiraz
and Australia's best Sparkling Shirazs. The glitzy labels of the past have rightly been consigned
to the rubbish bin, and the product range has been significantly rationalised and improved.
Following the sale of Seppeltsfield to Kilikanoon, this is the sole operating arm of Seppelt
under TWE ownership Exports to the UK, the US and other major markets.

ŸŸŸŸŸ **Drumborg Vineyard Riesling 2011** Take any Seppelt Drumborg Riesling (or
✪   nearby Crawford River) over 10 years old and you will have a glimpse of where
       this gloriously intense wine is headed, its lime juice, mineral and acid all perfectly
       balanced on the very long palate. Screwcap. 11% alc. **Rating** 97 **To** 2031 $35
       Salinger Vintage Cuvee 2008 A similar blend to the Select Cuvee, and
       likewise no bottle fermentation claimed. However, this is more complex, finer and
       more elegant; the brioche on the mid palate and finish sets it apart. Cork. 12% alc.
       Rating 94 **To** 2015 $30

ŸŸŸŸŸ **Salinger Select Cuvee NV Rating** 93 **To** 2013 $25
       Original Sparkling Shiraz 2007 Rating 91 **To** 2016 $25

ŸŸŸŸ **Fleur de Lys Pinot Noir Chardonnay 2008 Rating** 89 **To** 2014 $24

Seppeltsfield ★★★★★

1 Seppeltsfield Road, Seppeltsfield via Nuriootpa, SA 5355 **Region** Barossa Valley
T (08) 8568 6200 **www**.seppeltsfield.com.au **Open** 7 days 10.30–5
Winemaker Fiona Donald **Est.** 1851 **Dozens** 10 000 **Vyds** 100ha
In August 2007 this historic property and its treasure trove of great fortified wines dating
back to 1878 was purchased by the Kilikanoon group. A series of complicated lease-back
arrangements and supply agreements were entered into between Kilikanoon and vendor
Foster's, further complicated by Foster's (now Treasury Wine Estates) keeping the Seppelt
brand for table and sparkling wines (mostly produced at Great Western, Vic; see separate entry),
but the Seppelt brand for fortified wines vesting in purchaser Kilikanoon. The winery has
been recommissioned, including the gravity

ŸŸŸŸŸ **100 Year Old Para Liqueur 1912** Dark burnt umber; the wine paints the
✪   sides of the glass when swirled, the bouquet rearing out of the glass like a dragon
       from the bowels of the earth; exceptionally viscous and thick, it also paints the
       interior of the mouth, liberating its rainbow of aromas and flavours in a merry-go-
       round that will continue for as long as you have a few precious drops in the glass.
       Thereafter, the bouquet will seem equally potent in the empty glass. The points of
       100 have been given for several vintages now, and will be so in the future, simply
       because this wine is utterly unique in the world as an annual 100% 100-year-old
       commercial release, and while there may be some genuine single vintage, very old
       tawny ports in Portugal, they will be few and far between. Superbly packaged and
       presented. 100ml. Cork. 22.7% alc. **Rating** 100 **To** 2013 $349
✪   **Eden Valley Riesling 2011** Bright green-straw; intensive work in the vineyard
       and a relatively light hand in the winery have resulted in a very high-quality wine
       that won the Hugo Gramp Memorial Trophy at the Barossa Wine Show '11.
       What makes the wine special is its mouthfeel and flavour, which take it out of the
       light-bodied, albeit crisp, pattern of SA Riesling in '11. This is a perfectly balanced
       wine for consumption now, or in a decade or more. Screwcap. 12% alc. **Rating** 96
       To 2026 $19
       SGC Shiraz Grenache Carignan 2010 Deep purple-crimson; a fragrant
       bouquet leads into an outstanding palate with a very complex mix of black and
       red fruits, fine tannins and an airbrush of oak. Screwcap. 12.5% alc. **Rating** 95
       To 2030 $39

GST Grenache Shiraz Touriga 2010 Full, but bright and clear crimson; it uses the grapes from very old vines that traditionally went into the fortified wine stream; not only are they liberated here, but the alcohol is exemplary, heightening the spicy red fruits of the grenache, the shiraz and touriga providing the anchor for a potentially long-lived wine. Trophy Barossa Valley Wine Show '11. Screwcap. 14% alc. **Rating** 95 **To** 2020 $29

Para Liqueur 1981 In the same family as the 1991 Para, the major difference being the greater intensity and cut to the flavours, reflecting the higher level of rancio that has developed with greater age in barrel; burnt toffee is also very much in evidence. The cleansing aftertaste has to be experienced to be believed. Cork. 19% alc. **Rating** 95 **To** 2013 $95

Para 1991 In case you miss the vintage on the neck label, the main label says '21 years old'. Light tawny, tending to light green on the rim; an immensely rich tawny style quite different from the tawny ports of Portugal; the strong rancio character serves to highlight the brandy snap, cumquat, Christmas pudding, spice and many other flavours embodied in the luscious palate. Screwcap. 21% alc. **Rating** 94 **To** 2013 $80

ŸŸŸŸŸ Ubër Shiraz 2010 **Rating** 92 **To** 2030 $149

Serafino Wines ★★★★★

Kangarilla Road, McLaren Vale, SA 5171 **Region** McLaren Vale
T (08) 8323 0157 **www.**serafinowines.com.au **Open** Mon–Fri 10–4.30, w'ends & public hols 10–4.30
Winemaker Charles Whish **Est.** 2000 **Dozens** 30 000 **Vyds** 100ha
After the sale of Maglieri Wines to Beringer Blass in 1998, Maglieri founder Serafino (Steve) Maglieri acquired the McLarens on the Lake complex originally established by Andrew Garrett. The operation draws upon 40ha each of shiraz and cabernet sauvignon, 7ha of chardonnay, 2ha each of merlot, semillon, barbera, nebbiolo and sangiovese, and 1ha of grenache. Part of the grape production is sold. Between 1997 and 2007, Serafino Wines won a succession of major trophies in Australia and the UK. The Cabernet Sauvignon has been particularly successful. Exports to the UK, the US, Canada, Hong Kong, Malaysia and NZ.

ŸŸŸŸŸ Sharktooth Wild Ferment McLaren Vale Chardonnay 2010 Many of the characteristics of the Reserve are present, but with greater intensity on the length of the palate; the Chablis-like mouthfeel and flavour continues, but the back-palate and finish do not dip or shorten. Sophisticated winemaking. Screwcap. 13.5% alc. **Rating** 94 **To** 2017 $50

✪ Bellissimo Pinot Grigio 2011 Pale quartz; vibrant and fresh, one of several pinot gris from 2011 that revelled in the cool, damp conditions to provide wines of interest and intensity, with citrus/citrus blossom/citrus pith all contributing. It would be unkind to suggest that something came of nothing here, but McLaren Vale is not a natural home for Grigio of this character and quality. Screwcap. 12% alc. **Rating** 94 **To** 2013 $18

Terremoto Single Vineyard McLaren Vale Syrah 2009 Vivid purple hue; a concentrated and almost essency bouquet of blackberry pastille, cinnamon and clove; there is great life and energy on the palate, with zesty acidity, toasty oak and ample fine-grained tannins combining seamlessly. Diam. 14.5% alc. **Rating** 94 **To** 2030 $110 BE

ŸŸŸŸŸ Reserve McLaren Vale Chardonnay 2010 The light straw-green colour is
✪ a reflection of the low alcohol, one assumes; it's a strategy that has largely, if not entirely, worked, for the flavours are on all fours with cooler grown chardonnay; here grapefruit and white peach; barrel fermentation, 11 months' lees contact and – surprisingly – full mlf have all been employed. Is there enough flavour left in the glass? Screwcap. 12.8% alc. **Rating** 93 **To** 2015 $22

Sharktooth McLaren Vale Shiraz 2009 **Rating** 93 **To** 2020 $60 BE
⦿ Bellissimo Primitivo 2010 **Rating** 92 **To** 2015 $18

GSM McLaren Vale Grenache Shiraz Mourvedre 2010 Rating 91
To 2015 $26 BE

✪ The Goose Island Adelaide Semillon Sauvignon Blanc 2011 Pale straw-green; a blend of McLaren Vale Semillon (from Willunga) and Adelaide Hills Sauvignon Blanc that works particularly well, giving a vibrantly juicy lemon and lime spray of flavours running through to a long, fresh finish. Screwcap. 12% alc. Rating 90 To 2013 $13

McLaren Vale Shiraz 2010 Rating 90 To 2016 $26 BE

🍷🍷🍷🍷 BDX McLaren Vale Cabernet Sauvignon Cabernet Franc Carmanere Merlot 2010 Rating 89 To 2016 $26 BE

⬤ Bellissimo Vermentino 2011 Rating 88 To 2013 $18
⬤ Goose Island McLaren Vale Shiraz 2009 Rating 88 To Now $13
⬤ Goose Island McLaren Vale Cabernet Merlot 2009 Rating 87 To Now $13

McLaren Vale Cabernet Sauvignon 2010 Rating 87 To 2018 $26 BE

Serrat

PO Box 478, Yarra Glen, Vic 3775 **Region** Yarra Valley
T (03) 9730 1439 **www**.serrat.com.au **Open** Not
Winemaker Tom Carson **Est.** 2001 **Dozens** 150 **Vyds** 2.04ha

Serrat is the family business of Tom Carson (after a 12-year reign at Yering Station, now running Yabby Lake and Heathcote Estate for the Kirby family) and partner Nadege Suné. They have close-planted (at 8800 vines per ha) 0.8ha each of pinot noir and chardonnay, 0.42ha of shiraz, and a sprinkling of viognier. Serrat was devastated by the Black Saturday bushfires in February 2009, the entire vintage destroyed. The 2009 Chardonnay and Pinot Noir are made from grapes donated by friends John and Anthea Ellis from Bellvale Vineyard (a close-planted vineyard in Gippsland) and David Griffiths of Wombat Creek (a 20-year-old vineyard in the Upper Valley Valley).

🍷🍷🍷🍷🍷 Yarra Valley Pinot Noir 2010 Only 120 dozen bottles made, the vines still recovering from the '09 bushfires. It is 100% MV6 clone, and had 20% whole bunch inclusion in the ferment. It is extremely fragrant, with ethereal floral aromas, and the palate lives up to the promise of the bouquet, with a presence like that of Chambolle Musigny; it has a silky, juicy mouthfeel, and a fine tannin conclusion; all the components are immaculately balanced. Screwcap. 13.5% alc. Rating 96 To 2018 $36

Yarra Valley Shiraz Viognier 2010 An exercise in miniature, only 50 dozen bottles produced in the aftermath of the '09 bushfires. Five to six per cent of viognier was co-fermented, with 20% whole bunches of the shiraz. Intensely coloured, it has spicy black fruit aromas with touches of violets and tar in the background; the palate is driven by warm spices, black fruits, touches of licorice and earth, and supported by ample fine-grained tannins. It has the authority of top Côte-Rôtie. Screwcap. 13.5% alc. Rating 95 To 2025 $36

Setanta Wines

Glen Ewin Estate, Lower Hermitage Road, SA 5131 **Region** Adelaide Hills
T 0419 850 932 **www**.setantawines.com.au **Open** Tues–Sun 11–4
Winemaker Briony Hoare **Est.** 1997 **Dozens** 5000 **Vyds** 26ha

Setanta is a family-owned operation involving Sheilagh Sullivan, her husband Tony, and brother Bernard; the latter is the viticulturist, while Tony and Sheilagh manage marketing, administration and so forth. Of Irish parentage (they are first-generation Australians), they chose Setanta, Ireland's most famous mythological hero, as the brand name. The beautiful and striking labels tell the individual stories that give rise to the names of the wines. Exports to Ireland, of course; also to the UK, Singapore, Hong Kong and Japan.

🍷🍷🍷🍷 **Emer Adelaide Hills Chardonnay 2010** Full straw-green; this is a tightly textured and complex wine with layers of fruit flavour bringing white and yellow peach, melon and grapefruit together; fermentation and maturation in French hogsheads add to, but in no way obscure, the fruit flavours of the palate. Screwcap. 13.5% alc. **Rating** 94 **To** 2017 $24

Cuchulain Adelaide Hills Shiraz 2009 Good colour; has the tension and inherent structure of cool-grown shiraz, the inclusion of a small percentage of viognier adding a further twist; the palate builds on the fragrant bouquet, providing an array of blackberry, black cherry and multi-spice flavours, 12 months in French hogsheads adding the final touches. Screwcap. 14.5% alc. **Rating** 94 **To** 2020 $29

🍷🍷🍷🍷 **Emer Adelaide Hills Chardonnay 2009 Rating** 93 **To** 2020 $25
Talunga Ridge Shiraz 2008 Rating 93 **To** 2028 $25
Black Sanglain Adelaide Hills Cabernet Sauvignon 2009 Rating 92 **To** 2017 $29

Seven Ochres Vineyard

PO Box 202, Dunsborough, WA 6281 **Region** Margaret River
T (08) 9755 2030 **www**.sevenochres.com.au **Open** Not
Winemaker Chris Harding **Est.** 1998 **Dozens** 1000 **Vyds** 4ha
Chris and Alice Harding have taken a circuitous route to the Margaret River, Chris' interest in wine blossoming while working at the Royal Sydney Yacht Squadron in the late 1970s, before moving to Scotland. He and wife Alice returned to Australia in 1994, settling in the Margaret River region with their young family. They established the Viticlone Supplies Grapevine Nursery, and now have 60 varieties and over 120 clones available. Some of the more exotic varieties in propagation are vermentino, fiano, mondeuse, lagrein, sagrantino, cilliegiolo and sangiovese brunello di montalcino. They have established 1ha of viognier, encouraged by the early results from this variety. They have also purchased cabernet sauvignon, petit verdot and merlot from a single vineyard site in the northern part of the Margaret River.

🍷🍷🍷🍷 **Margaret River Petit Verdot 2009** Solid colour; there is a fleeting moment of sweetness as the wine enters the mouth, but it disappears once the powerful, savoury tannins take over. It's an interesting wine, and attractively priced, but a work in progress for Seven Ochres. Diam. 14% alc. **Rating** 89 **To** 2016 $18

Glyn's Block Margaret River Fiano 2009 The level of residual sugar will no doubt appeal to cellar door visitors, but makes it very difficult to properly evaluate the potential of this interesting variety, normally grown in normal climates. Diam. 11.9% alc. **Rating** 87 **To** 2013 $15

Sevenhill Cellars

College Road, Sevenhill, SA 5453 **Region** Clare Valley
T (08) 8843 4222 **www**.sevenhill.com.au **Open** Mon–Fri 9–5, w'ends & public hols 10–5
Winemaker Liz Heidenreich, Brother John May **Est.** 1851 **Dozens** 26 000 **Vyds** 104.26ha
One of the historical treasures of Australia; the oft-photographed stone wine cellars are the oldest in the Clare Valley, and winemaking is still carried out under the direction of the Jesuitical Manresa Society. Value for money is excellent, particularly for the powerful Shiraz and Riesling; all the wines reflect the estate-grown grapes from old vines. Notwithstanding the difficult economic times, Sevenhill Cellars has increased its vineyard holdings from 74 to 104 ha, and production has risen by 4000 dozen. Exports to the US, Switzerland, Indonesia, South Korea, Japan, Vietnam and China.

🍷🍷🍷🍷 **Inigo Clare Valley Riesling 2011** Light straw-green; the flowery aromatic
✪ bouquet leads logically into a very focused and balanced palate, with lime and lemon citrus fruit offset by immaculately judged acidity. Screwcap. 11.5% alc. **Rating** 93 **To** 2021 $19

✪ **Inigo Clare Valley Merlot 2010** A savoury example of the variety, showing black fruits, black olive and a little vine sap complexity; medium- to full-bodied, with chewy fresh tannins and vibrant acidity; an excellent and affordable example of the true personality of merlot. Screwcap. 14.5% alc. **Rating** 92 **To** 2016 $19 BE

✪ **Inigo Clare Valley Shiraz 2010** Estate-grown, with some of the vines over 100 years old. Strong colour, and with a decidedly full-bodied palate, black fruits with an emphatic finish deriving partly from the warmth of the alcohol; at this price, these are carping criticisms. Screwcap. 15% alc. **Rating** 90 **To** 2022 $19

○ **Inigo Clare Valley Cabernet Sauvignon 2009 Rating** 90 **To** 2020 $19
St Ignatius 2009 A blend of estate-grown cabernet sauvignon, merlot, cabernet franc and malbec, with a riotous mixture of black fruits, preserves and spicy jams plus ripe tannins. Will appeal more to some than others. Screwcap. 15.5% alc. **Rating** 90 **To** 2017 $29

♥♥♥♥ **St Aloysius 2009 Rating** 89 **To** 2016 $29 BE
Brother John May Reserve Shiraz 2008 Rating 88 **To** 2018 $75 BE
Vintage Touriga 2008 Rating 88 **To** 2020 $45

Seville Estate   ★★★★★
65 Linwood Road, Seville, Vic 3139 **Region** Yarra Valley
T (03) 5964 2622 **www**.sevilleestate.com.au **Open** 7 days 10–5
Winemaker Dylan McMahon **Est.** 1970 **Dozens** 6000 **Vyds** 8.08ha
Dr Peter McMahon and wife Margaret commenced planting Seville Estate in 1972, part of the resurgence of the Yarra Valley. Peter and Margaret retired in '97, selling to Brokenwood. Graham and Margaret Van Der Meulen acquired the property in 2005, bringing it back into family ownership. Graham and Margaret are hands-on in the vineyard and winery, working closely with winemaker Dylan McMahon, who is the grandson of Peter and Margaret. The philosophy is to capture the fruit expression of the vineyard in styles that reflect the cool climate. Exports to Fiji, Taiwan, South Korea, Hong Kong, Singapore and China.

♥♥♥♥♥ **Dr McMahon Yarra Valley Shiraz 2010** Judging by the back label this could be renamed '100%', as everything has been done at full throttle to celebrate an icon of the Yarra Valley, Dr Peter McMahon. The colour is as vibrant as the spicy, whole bunch and new oak bouquet, and clearly the quality of fruit from the 1972 plantings is able to handle plenty of winemaking in good years, as the palate is scintillating in its precision and depth. A little patience will be rewarded as all of the complex parts fully integrate, but what a pleasure to have so much complexity at 13% alcohol. Screwcap. 13% alc. **Rating** 97 **To** 2030 $100 BE

✪ **Yarra Valley Chardonnay 2010** This is a highly expressive and savoury wine, showing charcuterie, pear, citrus blossom and a touch of spicy oak; the palate is linear, pure, racy and enthralling, leaving a trail of broken-hearted taste buds in its wake; truly expansive and expressive, if you need to be convinced of the Yarra's suitability for Chardonnay, this may be the wine you simply have to try. Screwcap. 13% alc. **Rating** 96 **To** 2020 $30
Reserve Yarra Valley Chardonnay 2010 Vibrant green hue; while the hand of the winemaker is evident, the concentration of the fruit requires such attention; rich, ripe, opulent and oaky at this early stage, but wait a little while and the parts will come together, as the savoury complexity comes to the fore; enjoy the estate wine as the Reserve matures. Screwcap. 13% alc. **Rating** 96 **To** 2022 $60 BE
Old Vine Reserve Yarra Valley Shiraz 2010 Deep crimson, vibrant purple hue; it is hard to dispute the influence of 'old vine' quality when the bouquet offers so much depth of fruit and complexity of character; the palate fulfils promises of the bouquet, with layers of dark fruits, spices, roasted meat and tightly wound acidity, drawing out the finish to a harmonious and almost luxurious conclusion; will certainly stand the test of time. Screwcap. 13% alc. **Rating** 96 **To** 2030 $60 BE
Yarra Valley Shiraz 2010 Rating 94 **To** 2022 $30 BE

♥♥♥♥♡ **Old Vine Morgan's Vineyard Yarra Valley Cabernet Sauvignon 2010 Rating** 93 **To** 2025 $40 BE
Yarra Valley Riesling 2011 Rating 92 **To** 2024 $30 BE
The Barber Yarra Valley Chardonnay 2011 Rating 92 **To** 2020 $20 BE

Old Vine Reserve Yarra Valley Cabernet Sauvignon 2010 Rating 92 To 2025 $60 BE

Yarra Valley Pinot Noir 2011 Rating 90 To 2017 $30 BE

ŸŸŸŸ **The Barber Yarra Valley Pinot Noir 2011** Rating 88 To 2015 $22 BE

Seville Hill ★★★★

8 Paynes Road, Seville, Vic 3139 **Region** Yarra Valley
T (03) 5964 3284 **www.**sevillehill.com.au **Open** 7 days 10–6
Winemaker Dominic Bucci, John D'Aloisio **Est.** 1991 **Dozens** 3000
John and Josie D'Aloisio have had a long-term involvement in the agricultural industry, which ultimately led to the establishment of the Seville Hill vineyard in 1991. There they have 2.4ha of cabernet sauvignon and 1.3ha each of merlot, shiraz and chardonnay. John makes the wines with Dominic Bucci, a long-time Yarra resident and winemaker.

ŸŸŸŸŸ **Reserve Yarra Valley Shiraz 2008** Striking bright purple-magenta colour; the bouquet is very fragrant and fresh, remarkably so for an '08; both it and the palate have spicy red cherry to the fore, oak positive but balanced. The tannins are superfine and almost sweet, disappearing into the wine. Early-drinking style. Diam. 14.5% alc. **Rating** 92 **To** 2015 $30
Methode Champenoise Yarra Valley Chardonnay Pinot Noir 2008 Pale blush pink colour suggests a significant percentage of pinot noir (or a dash of red table wine); the wine has a pleasing combination of complexity and delicacy, the finish long, crisp and bright. Diam. 12.5% alc. **Rating** 92 **To** 2014 $35
Yarra Valley Sauvignon Blanc 2010 An interesting style of Sauvignon Blanc, with snow pea and lemon/citrus flavours driving an intense and long palate, tropical characters all but hidden. Screwcap. 13.5% alc. **Rating** 90 **To** 2013 $22
Yarra Valley Merlot 2006 Described as medium brick-red on the label; the colour in my bottle was light crimson, with no hint of brown anywhere to be seen. The palate is juicy and fresh, with small red berry fruits. One possibility is that this was a second bottling, kept in tank for some years before being bottled. Whatever, an attractive light- to medium-bodied wine. Diam. 14.7% alc. **Rating** 90 **To** 2016 $25
Yarra Valley Cabernet Sauvignon 2005 The colour development is normal for the wine's age; pleasantly ripe red and black fruits have a foundation of typical cabernet tannins on the medium-bodied palate; the Diam cork seems to be doing its job well. 14.2% alc. **Rating** 90 **To** 2015 $25
Yarra Valley Tempranillo 2008 Light, bright and clear crimson-purple; if you are to find maraschino cherry in a Seville Hill wine, forget looking for it in the Cabernet Sauvignon (despite the label insistence) and instead find it here, together with the distinctive citrus-like tang to the tannins on the finish. Diam. 14.2% alc. **Rating** 90 **To** 2015 $45
Yarra Valley Late Harvest Sauvignon Blanc 2010 Late harvest, then the fermentation stopped by cooling and filtration; lovely crisp citrus acidity, although the variety is not particularly obvious. 375ml Screwcap. 10% alc. **Rating** 90 **To** 2014 $35
Yarra Valley Vintage Port 2005 Expected colour development, but no more; bright and clear; has come together well since '08, the dark berry/cherry fruit with distinct spicy notes, the spirit well integrated. Diam. 19.5% alc. **Rating** 90 **To** 2015 $30

ŸŸŸŸ **Yarra Valley Rose 2010** Rating 88 **To** Now $18

Shadowfax ★★★★★

K Road, Werribee, Vic 3030 **Region** Geelong
T (03) 9731 4420 **www.**shadowfax.com.au **Open** 7 days 11–5
Winemaker Matt Harrop **Est.** 2000 **Dozens** 15 000
Shadowfax is part of an awesome development at Werribee Park, a mere 20 mins from Melbourne. The truly striking winery, designed by Wood Marsh Architects and built in 2000,

is adjacent to the extraordinary private home built in the 1880s by the Chirnside family and known as The Mansion. It was then the centrepiece of a 40 000ha pastoral empire, and the appropriately magnificent gardens were part of the reason for the property being acquired by Parks Victoria in the early 1970s. The Mansion is now The Mansion Hotel, with 92 rooms and suites. Exports to the UK, Japan, NZ and Singapore.

ΨΨΨΨΨ **Pink Cliffs Heathcote Shiraz 2010** Clear purple-crimson; while retaining a medium-bodied structure, this wine has even greater intensity than One Eye; the bouquet is fragrant and fruit-driven, the palate with layers of blackberry, black cherry and red cherry fruit sewn together by fine tannins and French oak. Will gain yet more complexity as it ages. Screwcap. 13.5% alc. **Rating** 95 **To** 2030 $65

Chardonnay 2010 A complex and intriguing array of nectarine, citrus blossom, almond meal and spicy oak; the palate is lively and linear, with taut acidity, quartz and charcuterie lingering harmoniously with cashews on the very long finish. Macedon Ranges/Geelong. Screwcap. 13% alc. **Rating** 94 **To** 2020 $30 BE

Geelong Pinot Noir 2011 Very impressive colour given the vintage; the bouquet and palate are driven by red and black cherry fruit that pushes through the long and even palate, and onto the finish and aftertaste; well balanced in every way, and deserves its price. Screwcap. 12.8% alc. **Rating** 94 **To** 2018 $45

One Eye Heathcote Shiraz 2010 Light, clear red-purple; the elegant palate reveals more than the colour might suggest, with a mix of juicy red and black fruits; the tannins are fine, the oak well balanced and integrated; all-up elegance. Screwcap. 13.5% alc. **Rating** 94 **To** 2020 $45

ΨΨΨΨΨ **Shiraz 2010** A blend of grapes from estate-grown Heathcote fruit and from
✪ southern Victorian vineyards, matured in new and used French oak. An even more compelling example of full flavour achieved at modest alcohol levels than the other Shadowfax reds from '10. Its luscious, spicy red and black fruits have a subtext of persistent, fine tannins, augmented by French oak, and it all comes together with conviction. Screwcap. 13.5% alc. **Rating** 93 **To** 2020 $20

Geelong Semillon 2011 Rating 90 **To** 2017 $22 BE
✪ **Adelaide Hills Sauvignon Blanc 2011** A subtle and savoury rendition of Adelaide Hills Sauvignon from Matt Harrop, with texture and depth sought and found; pea pod, capsicum and a mere suggestion of tropical fruit, offset by a soft, evenly balanced and persistent finish. Screwcap. 12.5% alc. **Rating** 90 **To** 2014 $20

Macedon Ranges Chardonnay 2010 Rating 90 **To** 2018 $45 BE

ΨΨΨΨ **Geelong Riesling 2011 Rating** 89 **To** 2025 $20 BE
Minnow 2011 Rating 88 **To** 2013 $28

Sharmans ★★★☆

Glenbothy, 175 Glenwood Road, Relbia, Tas 7258 **Region** Northern Tasmania
T (03) 6343 0773 **F** (03) 6343 5338 **www**.sharmanswines.com **Open** W'ends 10–5
Winemaker Josef Chromy Wines (Jeremy Dineen), Bass Fine Wines (Guy Wagner)
Est. 1987 **Dozens** 1000 **Vyds** 4.6ha
Mike Sharman pioneered one of the more interesting wine regions of Tasmania, not far south of Launceston but with a distinctly warmer climate than (say) Pipers Brook. Ideal north-facing slopes are home to the vineyard (planted to pinot noir, chardonnay, riesling, sauvignon blanc, cabernet sauvignon, merlot and malbec). This additional warmth gives the red wines greater body than most Tasmanian counterparts.

ΨΨΨΨΨ **Barrel Fermented Pinot Noir 2011** I'm not entirely sure what the name means – the complete fermentation (unusual) or the end of fermentation (less unusual). However, the wine has very good colour; the bouquet is fragrant, oak by no means swamping the black cherry fruit, and the elegant palate has good balance and length. Screwcap. 13.5% alc. **Rating** 91 **To** 2016 $30

ΨΨΨΨ **Barrel Fermented Chardonnay 2010 Rating** 89 **To** 2015 $25
Shaman 2008 Rating 87 **To** 2014 $28

Sharpe Wines of Orange ★★★★

789 Icely Road, Emu Swamp, Orange, NSW 2800 **Region** Orange
T (02) 6361 9046 **www**.sharpewinesoforange.com.au **Open** By appt
Winemaker Margot Sharpe **Est.** 1998 **Dozens** 800 **Vyds** 4ha

When Tony and Margot Sharpe planted their vineyard in 1998, the wheel of fortune turned a sharp 180 degrees. Their ancestors, strict Methodists, established Sharpe Bros cordials in 1868 to provide the working man with an alternative to the demon alcohol at the end of his working day. The vicissitudes of this life of wine are reflected in the names of their wines: Shattered Margot, Battered Sauv, Gentleman's Claret (a nod to the forebears), Lazy Rosy, Redemption Chardonnay and Just Franc (cabernet franc).

🍷🍷🍷🍷🍷 **Lazy Rosy 2009** Bright pink-red; both the bouquet and palate have above-average texture and complexity; wild strawberry rather than cultivated, and power on the finish. All-purpose rose. Screwcap. 13.5% alc. **Rating** 90 **To** Now **$13**
Shattered Margot Merlot 2009 A wine for classicists, with its tightly woven mix of black olive, earth, plum and cassis; has length and drive, but be warned, this may not enthral all. Screwcap. 14% alc. **Rating** 90 **To** 2016 **$18**

🍷🍷🍷🍷 **The Battered Sauv 2009** **Rating** 87 **To** 2015 **$18**

Shaw & Smith ★★★★★

136 Jones Road, Balhannah, SA 5242 **Region** Adelaide Hills
T (08) 8398 0500 **www**.shawandsmith.com **Open** 7 days 11–5
Winemaker Martin Shaw, Darryl Catlin **Est.** 1989 **Dozens** NFP **Vyds** 62.9ha

Cousins Martin Shaw and Michael Hill-Smith MW already had unbeatable experience when they founded Shaw & Smith as a virtual winery in 1989. The brand was firmly established as a leading producer of Sauvignon Blanc by the time they acquired a 42ha property at Woodside known as the M3 Vineyard, as it is owned by Michael and Matthew Hill-Smith and Martin Shaw. It produces the grapes for the M3 Chardonnay, and the most important part of the Sauvignon Blanc. In '99 Martin and Michael purchased the 36ha Balhannah property, building the superbly designed winery in 2000 and planting more sauvignon blanc, shiraz, pinot noir and riesling. It is here that visitors can taste the wines in appropriately beautiful surroundings. Exports to all major markets.

🍷🍷🍷🍷🍷 **Adelaide Hills Sauvignon Blanc 2011** Pale straw-green; the perfumed bouquet offers passionfruit, kiwi fruit and citrus aromas that set the scene for the palate, with a feline grace that would capture the most ardent disciple of Sauvignon Blanc. Screwcap. 12.5% alc. **Rating** 96 **To** 2014 **$25**
M3 Adelaide Hills Chardonnay 2010 The formula is tried and true: hand-picked, whole bunch-pressed in a cool environment; wild yeast barrel fermentation in a refrigerated cuverie, lees contact and partial mlf with a neutral innoculant; stone fruit, citrus, cashew and fig all combine seamlessly on the long and flawless palate. Screwcap. 13% alc. **Rating** 96 **To** 2018 **$40**
Adelaide Hills Shiraz 2010 Vivid crimson hue; a complex bouquet, with a wealth of red and black fruits, spice and ironstone complexity; the medium- to full-bodied palate is fleshy, silky, rich and almost hedonistic in its appeal; long, languid and beautifully detailed from start to finish; excellent viticulture and winemaking in total harmony. Screwcap. 14% alc. **Rating** 96 **To** 2025 **$44** BE
Aged Release Adelaide Hills Riesling 2005 Bright green hue; lime oil and buttered brioche notes merge on the bouquet; the palate is developed and generous, with sweet fruit in abundance, and the finish is long and languid; a pleasant and well-rounded aged example. Screwcap. 13% alc. **Rating** 94 **To** 2018 **$35** BE

🍷🍷🍷🍷🍷 **Adelaide Hills Pinot Noir 2010** **Rating** 92 **To** 2016 **$48** BE

Shaw Vineyard Estate   ★★★★☆

34 Isabel Drive, Murrumbateman, NSW 2582 **Region** Canberra District
T (02) 6227 5827 **www**.shawvineyards.com.au **Open** Wed–Sun & public hols 10–5
Winemaker Bryan Currie, Graeme Shaw **Est.** 1999 **Dozens** 14 000 **Vyds** 33ha

Graeme and Ann Shaw established their vineyard (cabernet sauvignon, merlot, shiraz, semillon and riesling) in 1998 on a 280ha fine wool-producing property established in the mid 1800s and known as Olleyville. It is one of the largest privately owned vineyard holdings in the Canberra area, and one of the few to produce 100% estate-grown wines. Their children are fully employed in the family business, Michael as viticulturist and Tanya as cellar door manager. The cellar door offers a wide range of local produce, as well as handmade ceramics from Deruta in Italy. Fifty dollars from each dozen sale from the Laughter Series range is donated to Camp Quality. Exports to the Netherlands, Vietnam, China and Singapore.

♈♈♈♈♈ **Premium Canberra Cabernet Sauvignon 2009** Deep crimson-purple;
✪   redcurrant and blackcurrant fruit make their mark instantly, but it is on the second and third tastings that the quality of the balance, texture and structure become apparent. This is a seriously good Cabernet at a great price. Screwcap. 14% alc. **Rating** 94 **To** 2029 $22

♈♈♈♈♀ **Premium Canberra Riesling 2011** Light straw-green; has a range of aromas
✪   and flavours with lime juice grading to more tropical notes; really shines on the back-palate and aftertaste. Screwcap. 11.5% alc. **Rating** 92 **To** 2018 $22
       Premium Canberra Shiraz 2009 Rating 91 **To** 2019 $22
       Premium Canberra Cabernet Shiraz 2009 Rating 91 **To** 2020 $22
✪   **Winemakers Selection Shiraz 2008** A restrained wine that accurately reflects the normally cool growing conditions of the Canberra District; the red and black cherry fruit has fine tannins and good oak in support, providing length and balance. Screwcap. 14.5% alc. **Rating** 90 **To** 2016 $16

♈♈♈♈ **Premium Canberra Semillon Sauvignon Blanc 2011 Rating** 89
       To 2013 $22
       Premium Canberra Merlot 2009 Rating 89 **To** 2015 $22
       Winemakers Selection Merlot 2008 Rating 89 **To** 2014 $16

 # Shedleys   ★★★★

275 Dalmore Road, Winnejup, WA 6255 **Region** Blackwood Valley
T (08) 9761 7512 **www**.shedleywines.com **Open** By appt
Winemaker Chris Shedley **Est.** 1992 **Dozens** 1000 **Vyds** 4ha

Chris and Erica Shedley may only have 4ha of vines (three-quarters devoted to 1ha each of cabernet sauvignon, shiraz and sauvignon blanc, the remainder a mix of mainstream and alternative varieties) but their story is a rich one, the website an object lesson in design and content. The vineyard and winemaking enterprise occupies 1% of the family's mixed farming property, which includes running sheep, harvest crops, blue gum plantation and (as from 1992) grapegrowing and winemaking. I particularly like their one-line summary, 'Good wines, made by real people in a beautiful place. Come and get involved.' Chris and Erica have four adult children, the youngest two (Anthea and Alan) environmental scientists. I read all too many stories of wineries with organic and biodynamic symbols emblazoned everywhere that leave me with a big question mark: are these feel-good aspirations or are they real achievements (as here) that come about as a result of total commitment at all levels? The mouth-watering prices of the wines speak for themselves.

♈♈♈♈♀ **Blackwood Valley Cabernet Sauvignon 2007** Good colour and hue; made
✪   in the usual Shedley fashion (with French oak), which has worked very well here. Has an attractive mix of cassis and bramble, oak and tannins making positive but balanced contributions. Screwcap. 14.1% alc. **Rating** 92 **To** 2017 $14
✪   **Blackwood Valley Shiraz 2007** Has good colour for its age; the warmer vintage and riper grapes (and possibly 5% cabernet) have given greater fruit depth, better able to deal with two years in American oak than the '08, although less would have been better. Screwcap. 14.2% alc. **Rating** 90 **To** 2016 $14

Blackwood Valley Cabernet Sauvignon 2008 Medium purple-red; estate-grown grapes, hand-picked, open-fermented with two years in French oak have provided a medium-bodied Cabernet with good cassis/blackcurrant fruit and fine tannins; the oak is obvious. Screwcap. 13.2% alc. **Rating** 90 **To** 2016 $15

🍷🍷🍷🍷 **Blackwood Valley Shiraz 2008 Rating** 89 **To** 2015 $15

Shelmerdine Vineyards ★★★★★

Merindoc Vineyard, Lancefield Road, Tooborac, Vic 3522 **Region** Heathcote
T (03) 5433 5188 **www**.shelmerdine.com.au **Open** 7 days 10–5
Winemaker De Bortoli (Yarra Valley) **Est.** 1989 **Dozens** 6500 **Vyds** 62ha
Stephen Shelmerdine has been a major figure in the wine industry for over 25 years, like his family (who founded Mitchelton Winery) before him, and has been honoured for his many services to the industry. The venture has vineyards spread over three sites: Lusatia Park in the Yarra Valley, and Merindoc Vineyard and Willoughby Bridge in the Heathcote region. Substantial quantities of the grapes produced are sold to others; a small amount of high-quality wine is contract-made.

🍷🍷🍷🍷🍷 **Yarra Valley Chardonnay 2010** The Lusatia Park Vineyard is in the transition to the Upper Yarra Valley, and the style of the wine certainly supports this; overall the white peach and pink grapefruit flavours are left largely unmarked (in terms of flavour) by barrel fermentation in used French oak, which was a decision of choice, not economics. A class act. Screwcap. 13% alc. **Rating** 95 **To** 2017 $29
Lusatia Park Yarra Valley Chardonnay 2010 Vibrant green hue; this is the epitome of a gentle, soft, sophisticated and poised Yarra Valley Chardonnay, not unlike Stephen Shelmerdine himself; the bouquet offers pear, nectarine and spice, while the palate is understated and finely textured, with a notable mineral presence and tangy acidity to conclude. Screwcap. 13% alc. **Rating** 94 **To** 2020 $48 BE
Heathcote Viognier 2010 Gleaming straw-green; fully ripe grapes whole bunch-pressed and barrel-fermented in used oak give rise to a strong almond blossom/almond meal bouquet, and a supple palate that carries its alcohol with ease; a powerful, driving finish. Screwcap. 15% alc. **Rating** 94 **To** 2015 $26
Yarra Valley Pinot Noir 2010 Bright, clear crimson; an elegant, fine Pinot that nonetheless has considerable underlying complexity to its black cherry, spice and forest notes, oak in restraint; the finish is long and persistent. Screwcap. 13% alc. **Rating** 94 **To** 2016 $34
Heathcote Shiraz 2010 Deep garnet; the bouquet is a spicy melange of black fruits, bay, licorice and tar; the palate is soft and approachable on entry, yet follows through with both firmness and finesse on the finish; evenly balanced, poised and generous. Screwcap. 13.5% alc. **Rating** 94 **To** 2020 $33 BE
Yarra Valley Blanc de Noirs 2006 Bright, light straw-green, with no hint of pink or bronze; despite its 100% pinot noir base (Upper Yarra Valley), bottle-fermented, with four years on yeast lees, disgorged Feb '11. It is still tight and unyielding, but will develop very attractively as it softens in bottle. Cork. 12.9% alc. **Rating** 94 **To** Now $40

🍷🍷🍷🍷🍷 **Merindoc Single Vineyard Heathcote Shiraz 2010 Rating** 92 **To** 2025 $68 BE
Lusatia Park Yarra Valley Pinot Noir 2010 Rating 90 **To** 2020 $60 BE

🍷🍷🍷🍷 **Yarra Valley Pinot Noir Rose 2011 Rating** 89 **To** 2014 $24 BE

Shenton Ridge

PO Box 37, Margaret River, WA 6285 **Region** Margaret River
T (08) 9726 1284 **www**.shentonridge.com.au **Open** Not
Winemaker Dave Johnson **Est.** 2002 **Dozens** 3000 **Vyds** 6.5ha
The Catalano family purchased the Shenton Ridge property in the Jindong area of Margaret River in 2002. The choice lay between extracting the gravel-rich soils or planting a vineyard; the coin came down on the side of a vineyard, and vines (predominantly shiraz, chardonnay and merlot) were planted. Andrea Catalano is now the sole owner and manager of the vineyard.

🍷🍷🍷🍷 ✪ **Margaret River Semillon Sauvignon Blanc 2011** Pale green-quartz; pleasant, gently tropical fruits come to the fore of the bouquet and palate alike, passionfruit and citrus neatly balanced. Screwcap. 12.6% alc. **Rating** 89 **To** 2014 $18

Margaret River Shiraz Merlot 2008 Light, bright crimson-purple; the fragrant red fruits of the bouquet lead into a light- to medium-bodied palate, with dusty tannins ex fruit and oak; no need for patience. Screwcap. 13.6% alc. **Rating** 88 **To** 2014 $18

Shepherd's Hut ★★★★☆

PO Box 194, Darlington, WA 6070 **Region** Porongurup
T (08) 9299 6700 **www**.shepherdshutwines.com **Open** Not
Winemaker Rob Diletti **Est.** 1996 **Dozens** 2000 **Vyds** 18ha

The shepherd's hut that appears on the wine label was one of four stone huts used in the 1850s to house shepherds tending large flocks of sheep. When WA pathologist Dr Michael Wishart (and family) purchased the property in 1996, the hut was in a state of extreme disrepair. It has since been restored, still featuring the honey-coloured Mt Barker stone. Riesling, chardonnay, sauvignon blanc, shiraz and cabernet sauvignon have been established. The business is now owned by son Philip and wife Cathy, who also run a large farm of mainly cattle. Most of the grapes are sold to other makers in the region.

🍷🍷🍷🍷🍷 **Porongurup Shiraz 2008** Bright and clear colour; a spicy and fragrant example of cool-climate shiraz; medium-bodied and very well balanced, with spicy black and red cherry fruits supported by superfine tannins and a touch of cedary French oak. Screwcap. 14% alc. **Rating** 94 **To** 2020 $22 BE

🍷🍷🍷🍷 ✪ **Porongurup Sauvignon Blanc 2011** Light straw-green; in typical Porongurup fashion, a wine that leaves it until the last moment to express its varietal personality, with a mix of herbaceous and gently tropical fruits surge on the finish and lingering aftertaste. Screwcap. 13.8% alc. **Rating** 92 **To** 2014 $20

Shingleback ★★★★★

Cnr Main Road/Stump Hill Road, McLaren Vale, SA 5171 **Region** McLaren Vale
T (08) 8323 7388 **www**.shingleback.com.au **Open** 7 days 10–5
Winemaker John Davey, Dan Hills **Est.** 1995 **Dozens** 100 000 **Vyds** 100ha

Shingleback has been a success story since its establishment in 1995. Originally focused on export, as times have changed, so has its focus. Its 100ha of estate vineyards are one of the keys to that success, winning the Jimmy Watson Trophy '06 for its '05 D Block Cabernet Sauvignon another. The well-made wines are rich and full-flavoured, but not overripe (and, hence, not excessively alcoholic). Exports to the UK, the US, Canada, Switzerland, Germany, Indonesia, China and NZ.

🍷🍷🍷🍷🍷 **D Block Reserve McLaren Vale Shiraz 2010** Full purple-crimson; the bouquet is expressive and complex, with a mix of herb and spice, the medium- to full-bodied palate with singular intensity and length to its array of blackberry, licorice, bitter chocolate and earth flavours. The combination may seem odd, but comes together very well. Cork. 14.5% alc. **Rating** 95 **To** 2035 $60

⭘ **Red Knot McLaren Vale Shiraz 2010** **Rating** 94 **To** 2020 $15

Unedited McLaren Vale Shiraz 2010 Impenetrable colour and a whopping 15.5% alcohol, this is McLaren Vale in its concentrated form, expressing sweet black fruits, mocha, chocolate and fruitcake; rich and unctuous, with hedonistic levels of fruit and a long and surprisingly even and fragrant finish, considering the concentration on display. Diam. **Rating** 94 **To** 2030 $70 BE

D Block Reserve McLaren Vale Shiraz 2009 Has six gold and three silver medals, the majority awarded by international wine shows. Deep purple-crimson; it is a massive, full-bodied wine filled to the brim with black fruits of every description, with a coat of dark chocolate plus oak. Has to be respected for its regional and varietal integrity. Diam. 14.5% alc. **Rating** 94 **To** 2030 $60

⭘ **Red Knot McLaren Vale Grenache Shiraz Mourvedre 2010** **Rating** 94 **To** 2025 $15

The Davey Estate McLaren Vale Cabernet Sauvignon 2010 Good colour; in the very intense and tightly focused style of the Shingleback red wines, delivering shimmering mouthfuls of blackcurrant complexed by touches of earth, olive and savoury tannins; all these come together on the long finish, leaving nothing more to say. Screwcap. 14.5% alc. **Rating** 94 **To** 2030 $25

D Block Reserve McLaren Vale Cabernet Sauvignon 2010 Deep crimson, vibrant hue; a fragrant and concentrated bouquet of red and black fruits, mocha, nutmeg and cedar; the palate is medium-bodied and fleshy, with a backbone of fine-grained tannins and fresh acidity; accessible as a young wine, with plenty in the tank for the future; a question mark remains over the heavy bottle and closure. Diam. 14.5% alc. **Rating** 94 **To** 2025 $60 BE

ഇഇഇഇ   The Davey Estate McLaren Vale Shiraz 2010 **Rating** 93 **To** 2025 $25
The Gate McLaren Vale Shiraz 2010 **Rating** 92 **To** 2023 $35 BE
Red Knot McLaren Vale Cabernet Sauvignon 2010 **Rating** 92 **To** 2020 $15
Haycutters McLaren Vale Shiraz 2010 The quality of the vintage, the inclusion of a small percentage of co-fermented viognier, and well-directed winemaking decisions all add up to a wine that is significantly better than its price would suggest; it brings together varietal character, regional character, balance and length. Screwcap. 14.5% alc. **Rating** 91 **To** 2018 $17
Haycutters McLaren Vale Shiraz 2009 **Rating** 91 **To** 2015 $17
Red Knot McLaren Vale Shiraz 2011 Deep colour, exhibiting plump dark fruits of essency blackberry and spicy oak on the bouquet; the palate is generous and fresh, with tangy acidity providing a spine of freshness that accents the accessibility of the wine; a drink-early style. Screwcap. 14% alc. **Rating** 90 **To** 2014 $15 BE

ഇഇഇഇ   McLaren Vale Chardonnay 2011 **Rating** 89 **To** 2016 $19
Black Bubbles McLaren Vale Sparkling Shiraz NV **Rating** 89 **To** Now $23
Red Knot McLaren Vale Cabernet Sauvignon 2011 **Rating** 87 **To** 2014 $15 BE

Shottesbrooke   ★★★★★

Bagshaws Road, McLaren Flat, SA 5171 **Region** McLaren Vale
T (08) 8383 0002 **www**.shottesbrooke.com.au **Open** Mon–Fri 10–4.30, w'ends & public hols 11–5
Winemaker Hamish Maguire **Est.** 1984 **Dozens** 12 000 **Vyds** 30.64ha
Founded by Nick Holmes, who has since passed the winemaking baton on to stepson Hamish Maguire, Shottesbrooke these days is a very different business from that of the 1980s and '90s. As well as the great advantage of over 30ha of mature vines in McLaren Vale, it has ongoing access to sauvignon blanc from the Adelaide Hills. Exports to all major markets.

ഇഇഇഇഇ   The Proprietor Reserve 2009 Good colour; a blend of Merlot/Cabernet Sauvignon/Malbec matured in French and America oak for 14 months; the bouquet has a distinctly aromatic array of red and black berry fruits that continue on the very elegant palate, supported by fine-grained tannins and cedary oak. An altogether classy wine. Screwcap. 14.5% alc. **Rating** 94 **To** 2020 $38
McLaren Vale Shiraz 2010 **Rating** 94 **To** 2020 $20
McLaren Vale Cabernet Sauvignon 2010 **Rating** 94 **To** 2025 $20

ഇഇഇഇഇ   Adelaide Hills Sauvignon Blanc 2011 **Rating** 90 **To** Now $20

ഇഇഇഇ   Engine Room Sparkling Shiraz NV **Rating** 89 **To** Now $20
Engine Room Sauvignon Blanc 2011 **Rating** 87 **To** Now $19

Sidewood Estate   ★★★★☆

2 Hunt Road, Hahndorf, SA 5245 (postal) **Region** Adelaide Hills
T (08) 8388 7084 **www**.sidewood.com.au **Open** Not
Winemaker Natasha Mooney **Est.** 2000 **Dozens** 15 000 **Vyds** 62.7ha

Sidewood Estate is part-vineyard and part-horse stables and racehorse training. Owned by Owne and Cassandra Inglis since 2004, both aspects of the business are flourishing. Sidewood Estage lies in the Onkaparinga Valley, with the westerly vines weathering the coldest climate in the Adelaide Hills. In recent times Sidewood Estate has undergone a substantial planting regeneration program, the vineyard growing to over 60 ha, and extensive investment in modern viticulture equipment has resulted in improved yields. Wines are released under the Sidewood Estate, Stable Hill and Mappinga labels, Mappinga is the new premier range, named after the road on which Sidewood resides. A cellar door is planned. Exports to the UK, the US, Canada, Belgium, Malaysia, Hong Kong, Singapore, Thailand and China.

ȲȲȲȲȲ **Adelaide Hills Pinot Gris 2011** Although no mention is made of it, and probably it's an illusion, there are some faint echoes of oak on the bouquet and palate. However, it's the intensity of the pear, citrus and apple fruit on the palate that lifts the wine out of the ruck. Screwcap. 12% alc. **Rating** 93 **To** 2013 $24
Mappinga Adelaide Hills Shiraz 2010 Full crimson-purple; a densely packed, full-bodied palate with a flood of black fruits meeting a wall of oak; which force will prove stronger is irrelevant at this stage, for the wine demands to be cellared. Screwcap. 14% alc. **Rating** 92 **To** 2030 $34
Adelaide Hills Sauvignon Blanc 2011 The bouquet is a floral mix of apple and citrus blossom, the palate with very good mouthfeel moving into a tropical spectrum, with passionfruit and a hint of kiwi fruit. Screwcap. 12% alc. **Rating** 91 **To** 2013 $24
Mappinga Adelaide Hills Sauvignon Blanc 2011 Pale straw-green; flush with ripe but tangy varietal fruit aromas and flavours; right from the outset on the palate there is an impression of sweetness, but it seems to be coming from the fruit, rather than residual sugar per se. Not what you would expect from the year, some botrytis being the other possible contributor. Screwcap. 12% alc. **Rating** 90 **To** 2013 $34
Adelaide Hills Shiraz 2009 Mid crimson; a lifted and eucalypt-accented bouquet also offers red fruits, plum and a touch of spice; medium-bodied with a surprising amount of tannin rolling around on the finish. Screwcap. 14% alc. **Rating** 90 **To** 2020 $24 BE

ȲȲȲȲ   **Stable Hill Adelaide Hills Shiraz 2010 Rating** 88 **To** 2014 $18 BE
Stable Hill Adelaide Hills Chardonnay 2011 Rating 87 **To** 2015 $18 BE

Sieber Road Wines   ★★★★

Sieber Road, Tanunda, SA 5352 **Region** Barossa Valley
T (08) 8562 8038 **www**.sieberwines.com **Open** 7 days 11–4
Winemaker Tony Carapetis **Est.** 1999 **Dozens** 4500 **Vyds** 18ha

Richard and Val Sieber are the third generation to run Redlands, the family property, traditionally a cropping/grazing farm. They have diversified into viticulture with shiraz (14ha) the lion's share, the remainder viognier, grenache and mourvedre. Son Ben Sieber is a viticulturist. Exports to Canada and China.

ȲȲȲȲȲ **Barossa Valley Shiraz Mataro 2009** An estate-grown 75/25% blend; the
✪   bouquet and medium-bodied palate have the full range of blackberry, plum, licorice and bitter chocolate aromas and flavours; it carries its alcohol with ease, the palate long and fresh. Screwcap. 14.9% alc. **Rating** 93 **To** 2019 $20
✪   **Barossa Valley Grenache Shiraz Mourvedre 2009** A 50/32/18% blend that has a vivid personality, offering a range of spiced red and black fruits in a light- to medium-bodied frame, with no hint whatsoever of its alcohol. Screwcap. 14.4% alc. **Rating** 93 **To** 2019 $18

Silkwood Wines ★★★★★

5204/9649 Channybearup Road, Pemberton, WA 6260 **Region** Pemberton
T (08) 9776 1584 **www**.silkwoodwines.com.au **Open** Fri–Mon & public hols 10–4
Winemaker Blair Meiklejohn **Est.** 1998 **Dozens** 8000 **Vyds** 23.5ha

Peter Bowman purchased Silkwood Wines from Pam and John Allen in 2004, followed by the purchase of Phillips Estate Vineyard in '05. The vineyard is patrolled by a large flock of guinea fowl, eliminating most insect pests and reducing the use of chemicals. A modern winery was built in time for the '06 vintage, and in '05 Phillips Estate was purchased, lifting estate vineyard holdings to 23.5ha. Plantings include shiraz (5.4ha), cabernet sauvignon (4.3ha), merlot (3.5ha), sauvignon blanc (2.8ha), chardonnay (2.5ha), pinot noir and riesling (2ha each) and zinfandel (1ha). The new cellar door overlooks a large lake on the property. The wines offer outstanding value for money.

🍷🍷🍷🍷🍷 ✪ **Pemberton Sauvignon Blanc 2010** A very well-crafted wine that reaffirms the ability of the Pemberton region to respond well to the variety; the flavours are generous, tropical fruits being neatly trimmed by a touch of herb, and punchy acidity. Trophy Perth Wine Show '11. Screwcap. 12.8% alc. **Rating** 94 **To** 2014 **$**18

✪ **Pemberton Pinot Noir 2010** Light, clear crimson-purple; a delicious, highly fragrant bouquet and perfectly balanced palate; while essentially light-bodied, it holds the attention right through the palate with its red cherry fruit, subtle French oak and nuances of spice. Trophy Qantas Wine Show WA '11. Screwcap. 14.2% alc. **Rating** 94 **To** 2015 **$**20

🍷🍷🍷🍷½ ✪ **Pemberton Shiraz 2010** Bright, clear crimson; the fragrant bouquet accurately foreshadows a lively, light- to medium-bodied palate, with red cherry fruit at its core and a gentle seasoning of spice. Will live, but arguably never be better than it is right now. Screwcap. 14% alc. **Rating** 92 **To** 2015 **$**16

✪ **Pemberton Zinfandel 2010** By chance, tasted between the two massive pillars of the '09 and '10 Cape Mentelle Zinfandel, an unfair field. Lighter in body; despite its high alcohol, it does keep its varietal shape, cherry, spice and chocolate to the fore. Screwcap. 15.5% alc. **Rating** 91 **To** 2015 **$**15

✪ **Pemberton Cabernet Merlot 2010** As close to perfection as one could wish for a wine at this price point designed to be at its best for up to six years, but no more; the light- to medium-bodied palate has juicy red berry fruits supported by fine, but persistent, tannins. Screwcap. 14% alc. **Rating** 90 **To** 2016 **$**15

Little Bitch Blanc de Blanc NV **Rating** 90 **To** 2014 **$**25

🍷🍷🍷🍷 ✪ **Pemberton Riesling 2010** Light straw-green; the floral bouquet has an unusual but clear scent of roses, the palate filled with very sweet citrus fruit that continues through to the finish. Ready now with almost any Asian dish you choose to match it with. Screwcap. 10.5% alc. **Rating** 89 **To** 2013 **$**15

Pemberton Verdelho 2011 **Rating** 88 **To** 2014 **$**15
Pemberton Rose 2011 **Rating** 88 **To** 2013 **$**15
Premium Red NV **Rating** 87 **To** 2013 **$**15

Silverstream Wines ★★★☆

2365 Scotsdale Road, Denmark, WA 6333 **Region** Denmark
T (08) 9840 9119 **www**.silverstreamwines.com **Open** By appt
Winemaker Harewood Estate (James Kellie), Mt Shadforth Contract Crush (Michael Garland) **Est.** 1997 **Dozens** 2500 **Vyds** 9ha

Tony and Felicity Ruse have 9ha of chardonnay, merlot, cabernet franc, pinot noir, riesling and viognier in their vineyard 23km from Denmark. The wines are contract-made, and after some hesitation, the Ruses decided their very pretty garden and orchard more than justified opening a cellar door, a decision supported by the quality on offer at very reasonable prices.

🍷🍷🍷🍷 **Denmark Sparkling Chardonnay 2009** No mention of the traditional method being used, although this is the second disgorgement. It is bracingly fresh and crisp, and if later disgorgement wines aren't available, this could well profit from time on cork. 12.1% alc. **Rating** 89 **To** 2015 **$**32

Four Vines White 2011 A blend of chardonnay, sauvignon blanc, semillon and riesling. While the aromas and primary flavours are still to fully express themselves, there is enough overall flavour and mouthfeel to suggest short-term cellaring may be rewarding. Screwcap. 13.5% alc. **Rating** 87 **To** 2015 $18

Single Vineyard Denmark Cabernet Franc 2010 Bright red-crimson; the wine spent 15 months in French oak, 30% new, and has an unexpectedly powerful palate, with tannins closing in on the mid palate and thereafter, and even more on the aftertaste. Screwcap. 14.5% alc. **Rating** 87 **To** 2015 $27

 # Simon Lang Wines

Level 30, 91 King William Street, Adelaide, SA 5000 (postal) **Region** Adelaide Zone
T (08) 7129 8183 **www.**simonlangwines.com.au **Open** Not
Winemaker Joanne Irvine **Est.** 2008 **Dozens** NFP

Simon Lang practised as a corporate, commercial and tax lawyer before becoming fascinated by the wine industry. His first step was obtaining a masters degree in wine business, and then establishing a virtual winery. With Joanne Irvine as winemaker and mentor, sauvignon blanc was purchased from the Limestone Coast, and shiraz from the Barossa Valley.

ΨΨΨΨΩ **Barossa Shiraz 2008** Made from grapes grown in the Gomersal and Tanunda areas, with the distinctive Irvine touch from finishing the fermentation in French and American oak barrels perfectly integrating the fruit, oak and tannin flavours. Seductive style pioneered in 1951 by Max Schubert. Carries its alcohol well, likewise its fresh colour. Screwcap. 14.5% alc. **Rating** 93 **To** 2020 $25

ΨΨΨΨ **Limestone Coast Sauvignon Blanc 2009 Rating** 89 **To** 2013 $25

Simon Whitlam & Co

PO Box 1108, Woollahra, NSW 1350 **Region** Hunter Valley Zone
T (02) 9007 5331 **F** (02) 9328 0499 **Open** Not
Winemaker Graeme Scott (Contract) **Est.** 1979 **Dozens** 2000

My association with the owners of Simon Whitlam – Andrew and Hady Simon, Nicholas and Judy Whitlam, and Grant Breen – dates back to the late 1970s, at which time I was a consultant to the Simons' leading wine retail shop in Sydney, Camperdown Cellars. The association continued for a time after I moved to Melbourne in '83, but ceased altogether in '87 when Camperdown Cellars was sold, thereafter being merged with Arrowfield Wines. The Simon Whitlam label was part of the deal, and it passed through a number of corporate owners until 20 years later, when the original partners regained control of the business. It is a virtual winery, the grapes purchased and the wine contract-made. This reflects the combined marketing and financial expertise of the partners. Exports to New Caledonia and China.

ΨΨΨΨΩ **Hunter Valley Shiraz 2009** Attractive bright red-purple; the product of a partnership between the Simon and Whitlam families that is a graphic illustration of the 'not broken, don't fix' euphemism; the palate is laden with rich shiraz fruit that will guarantee a long life for the wine; the 'not broken' approach is evidenced by maturation in American oak. Screwcap. 13.5% alc. **Rating** 93 **To** 2030 $22

Reserve Hunter Valley Chardonnay 2010 Light straw-green; a very well-made wine with abundant varietal fruit and complexity ex barrel fermentation; flavours are of ripe stone fruit and cashew, all these characters showing that the grapes were picked at precisely the right time. Screwcap. 13% alc. **Rating** 92 **To** 2017 $22

ΨΨΨΨ **McLaren Vale Cabernet Sauvignon 2010 Rating** 89 **To** 2018 $22
Hunter Valley Cabernet Sauvignon 2009 Rating 88 **To** 2016 $22

Simpatico Wines

Cnr Barossa Valley Way/Vine Vale Road, Tananuda, SA 5352 **Region** Barossa Valley
T (08) 8561 1222 **www.**simpaticowines.com.au **Open** 7 days 10.30–5
Winemaker Hamish Seabrook (Contract) **Est.** 2008 **Dozens** 10 000 **Vyds** 13ha

As I read the background material to this venture of Steve and Rebecca Hay, I realised that 'simpatico' was a term often used by my parents and elder brother and sister in my youth, but one I had almost forgotten about. I like the Hays' explanation that it is a word applied to people being like-minded and on the same wavelength. The Hays extend it to being open-minded, agreeable and approachable. In the prime of their lives, Steve (a carpenter and builder) and Rebecca (banking and HR) uprooted themselves from Melbourne to live in the Barossa Valley in 2007. While wine drinkers with a special affinity for Barossa red wines, neither had any winemaking background, but they had the good sense to buy the Vinecrest Wines cellar door, and a vineyard with shiraz and cabernet sauvignon the major plantings, and to secure the highly talented Hamish Seabrook as contract winemaker. Exports to China.

ŢŢŢŢ♀ **Sunrise Block Barossa Valley Shiraz 2009** Good colour; the bouquet offers an array of black fruits, with a touch of licorice and oak; the medium- to full-bodied palate has blackberry and fruitcake flavours running through to the fine, ripe tannins of the finish. Good outcome a year that had its challenges. Screwcap. 14.5% alc. **Rating** 93 **To** 2020 $35

✪ **Secret Vale Barossa Valley Cabernet Sauvignon 2010** Dense, deep purple-red; a singularly potent, intense Cabernet Sauvignon that stays within varietal bounds, showing what the Barossa Valley can sometimes deliver with the variety; has lashings of blackcurrant, blackberry and bitter chocolate on the full-bodied palate; despite the appropriate presence of ripe tannins, has an almost juicy lift to the finish. Exceptional value. Screwcap. 14.5% alc. **Rating** 93 **To** 2025 $18

The C.P. Barossa Valley Vintage Port 2010 Dense crimson; an impressively rich and complex wine, with good balance and depth; the black fruits easily balance the spirit, and the finish is particularly appealing, with its spicy notes and fine tannins. Cork. 19% alc. **Rating** 92 **To** 2016 $23

Max's 3 Lost Barrels Barossa Valley Muscat NV Mahogany-brown, with rich luscious, layered plum pudding flavours and notes of marmalade. Screwcap. 17% alc. **Rating** 91 **To** 2013 $60

ŢŢŢŢ **Pandora's Gold Barossa Valley Rose 2011** **Rating** 89 **To** 2013 $18
Secret Vale Barossa Valley Shiraz 2010 **Rating** 89 **To** 2015 $18
Sunset Block Barossa Valley Cabernet Sauvignon 2009 **Rating** 89 **To** 2019 $35
Barossa Valley Viognier 2011 **Rating** 88 **To** 2013 $23
Secret Vale Barossa Valley Merlot 2010 **Rating** 87 **To** 2015 $18

Sinclair of Scotsburn   ★★★★

256 Wiggins Road, Scotsburn, Vic 3352 **Region** Ballarat
T (03) 5341 3936 **www.**sinclairofscotsburn.com.au **Open** W'ends 11–4, Mon–Fri by appt
Winemaker Scott Ireland **Est.** 1997 **Dozens** 260 **Vyds** 2ha
David and (the late) Barbara Sinclair purchased their property in 2001. At that time 1.2ha of chardonnay and 0.8ha of pinot noir had been planted, but had struggled, the pinot noir yielding less than 0.25 tonnes in '02. With the aid of limited drip irrigation, cane pruning, low crop levels and bird netting, limited quantities of high-quality chardonnay and pinot have since been produced. Two-thirds of the annual production is sold to Tomboy Hill and Provenance Wines, the remaining third made for the Sinclair of Scotsburn label.

ŢŢŢŢ♀ **Manor House Pinot Noir 2009** Mid garnet; a fragrant and savoury bouquet, showing glimpses of tea, cherry and game; the palate is fine and focused, with silky tannins persisting on the elegantly structured conclusion. Screwcap. 13.5% alc. **Rating** 90 **To** 2014 $21 BE

Sinclair's Gully   ★★★★☆

288 Colonial Drive, Norton Summit, SA 5136 **Region** Adelaide Hills
T (08) 8390 1995 **www.**sinclairsgully.com **Open** W'ends & public hols 12–4 (Aug–June), Fri 5–9 (Nov–Mar), or by appt
Winemaker Contract **Est.** 1998 **Dozens** 1000 **Vyds** 1ha

Sue and Sean Delaney purchased their property at Norton Summit in 1997. The property had a significant stand of remnant native vegetation, with a State Conservation Rating, and much energy has been spent in restoring 8ha of pristine bushland, home to 130 species of native plants and 66 species of native birds, some recorded as threatened or rare. The vineyard has been a DIY venture for the Delaneys, with Sue hand-pruning the 0.4ha each of chardonnay and sauvignon blanc planted in '98. The adoption of biodynamic viticulture has coincided with numerous awards for the protection of the natural environment and, more recently, eco-tourism; they operate the only eco-certified cellar door in the Adelaide Hills, and have won innumerable ecological and general tourism awards. Sparkling wine disgorgement demonstrations are a particular attraction.

♀♀♀♀♀ **Rubida 2008** Disgorged Jan '12; golden-bronze, faintly tinged with pink; an elegant pinot noir chardonnay blend that has built complexity from its extended time on lees, but is still fine and fresh on the well-balanced finish. Diam. 13% alc. Rating 94 To 2014 $55

♀♀♀♀♀ **Kyle 2009** Rating 92 To 2015 $40
Rubida 2010 Rating 91 To 2014 $40
Talia 2009 Rating 91 To 2014 $40

Singlefile Wines   ★★★★☆
90 Walter Road, Denmark, WA 6333 **Region** Denmark
T 1300 885 807 **www**.singlefilewines.com **Open** 7 days 10–5
Winemaker Mike Garland, Coby Ladwig (Contract) **Est.** 2007 **Dozens** 3500 **Vyds** 3.75ha
Reading the background to Singlefile, and its marketing and mission statements, might lead one to think that this is a 50 000-dozen venture, not a 3500-dozen business based on 2.5ha of 25-year-old estate chardonnay and 1.25ha of shiraz. Recognising that Denmark is best-suited to chardonnay and pinot noir, Singlefile decided to purchase riesling from Porongurup, cabernet sauvignon from Margaret River, shiraz from both Frankland River and Barossa Valley, and produces a Semillon Sauvignon Blanc from Margaret River. Owners Phil and Viv Snowden took a circuitous path to the Denmark subregion, exiting Zimbabwe to join academia in South Africa (with a mining focus) before migrating to Australia in the late 1980s to start an Australian mining consultancy. When they sold the business in 2004 for just under $15 million, it had 200 employees and was one of the leaders in its field in WA. This is downsizing on a grand scale. Exports to China.

♀♀♀♀♀ **Family Reserve Denmark Chardonnay 2010** Vibrant green hue; a ripe, vibrant and lively wine, with pure grapefruit supported by well-handled toasty oak; the palate is zesty and direct, long and fragrant, finishing with a pleasant chalky grip in keeping with the fruit. Screwcap. 13.8% alc. Rating 94 To 2018 $45 BE

♀♀♀♀♀ **Frankland River Shiraz 2010** Rating 93 To 2016 $38 BE
Margaret River Cabernet Merlot 2010 Rating 92 To 2020 $37 BE
Porongurup Riesling 2011 Rating 90 To 2018 $25 BE
Denmark Semillon Sauvignon Blanc 2011 Rating 90 To 2014 $25 BE

♀♀♀♀ **Family Reserve Margaret River Fume Blanc 2011** Rating 88 To 2014 $30 BE
Mount Barker Syrah 2010 Rating 87 To 2016 $35 BE

Sir Paz Estate   ★★★☆
384 George Street, Fitzroy, Vic 3065 (postal) **Region** Yarra Valley
T (03) 9417 9337 **www**.sirpaz.com **Open** Not
Winemaker Gary Mills, John Zapris **Est.** 1997 **Dozens** 4500 **Vyds** 22ha
The Zapris family established Sir Paz Estate in 1997, planting just under 6ha of shiraz; the first release of '01 scored an emphatic gold medal at the Victorian Wines Show '03 as the highest scored entry. The success led to the planting of additional merlot, chardonnay and sauvignon blanc. It is not hard to see the anagrammatic derivation of the name. Exports to the US, Canada, Brazil, Germany, the United Arab Emirates and China.

ȚȚȚȚȚ   **Bee Hive Yarra Valley Chardonnay 2010** Full straw-green; sometimes winemakers' descriptions seem to have little to do with reality, other times they can be illuminating; here the suggestion of oatmeal is right on the money, albeit in second place to the grapefruit and green apple fruit flavours; the wine has typical Yarra Valley length. Screwcap. 13.9% alc. **Rating** 91 **To** 2017 $28

ȚȚȚȚ   **Yarra Valley Shiraz 2009 Rating** 88 **To** 2016 $34

Sirromet Wines

850–938 Mount Cotton Road, Mount Cotton, Qld 4165 **Region** Queensland Coastal
T (07) 3206 2999 **www**.sirromet.com **Open** 7 days 9–4.30
Winemaker Adam Chapman, Jessica Ferguson **Est.** 1998 **Dozens** 35 000 **Vyds** 85.6ha
This was an ambitious venture, which has succeeded in its aim of creating Qld's premier winery. The founding Morris family retained a leading architect to design the striking state-of-the-art winery; the state's foremost viticultural consultant to plant three major vineyards (in the Granite Belt); and the most skilled winemaker practising in Qld, Adam Chapman, to make the wine. It has a 200-seat restaurant, a wine club, and is firmly aimed at the tourist market, taking advantage of its situation, halfway between Brisbane and the Gold Coast. In 2009 it mothballed part of its Granite Belt vineyards, thus reducing production in the face of the GFC. The blocks so treated were then flooded in 2011, leaving the blocks in commission unharmed. Exports to Sweden, South Korea, Papua New Guinea, Hong Kong, China and Japan.

ȚȚȚȚȚ   **Seven Scenes Signature Collection Granite Belt Merlot 2010** Good, clear colour; a wine that says many things, cigar box on the bouquet, although with plenty of fruit, a bracing medium-bodied palate, and a skein of almost citrussy acidity on the back-palate and finish. Screwcap. 14% alc. **Rating** 90 **To** 2016 $25
   Seven Scenes Signature Collection Granite Belt Cabernet Sauvignon 2009 Deep garnet; a deep and dark-fruited bouquet offering cassis, black olive and brine; the palate is firmly textured, with ample gravelly tannins and a long chewy finish; rustic indeed, but not without charm. Screwcap. 13.6% alc. **Rating** 90 **To** 2016 $28 BE

ȚȚȚȚ   **Seven Scenes Signature Collection Granite Belt Viognier 2009** Rating 89 To 2013 $25
   Seven Scenes Signature Collection Granite Belt Shiraz Viognier 2010 Rating 89 To 2016 $25
o   **820 Above Vineyard Selection Granite Belt Verdelho 2011** Rating 88 To Now $18
   Saint Jude's Road Vineyard Grand Reserve Monopole Shiraz 2010 Rating 88 To 2015 $300 BE
   Saint Jude's Road Vineyard Grand Reserve Monopole Merlot 2010 Rating 88 To 2014 $300 BE
   Wild Granite Belt Chardonnay 2010 Rating 87 To 2014 $55 BE
   Seven Scenes Signature Collection Granite Belt Pinot Noir Chardonnay 2008 Rating 87 To 2013 $30 BE

Six Gates

Lot 294 Barossa Valley Highway, Lyndoch, SA 5351 (postal) **Region** Barossa Valley
T 0422 030 303 **www**.6gates.com.au **Open** Not
Winemaker Mark Jamieson (Contract) **Est.** 1998 **Dozens** 4000 **Vyds** 12ha
Six Gates originates from the six entries to the ancient city of Shiraz, and it is thus appropriate that this organically managed vineyard should be predominantly planted to that variety (4ha of cabernet sauvignon make up the balance). While there is a long history of viticulture on the property, the present plantings were established in 1998 on highly suitable soil, with 25cm of loam on 60cm of red clay over well-decayed limestone, providing good drainage and water-holding capacity. Every one of the 18 000 vines is pruned by the vineyard manager, Bruce Wutke, who has spent a long time as a grapegrower. Exports to China.

🍷🍷🍷🍷 **The Majnun Barossa Valley Shiraz 2010** Bright crimson; while the alcohol is less than that of '09, the concentration and in-your-face attitude of the wine are similar, the bouquet with an odd oak character; brawny and muscular, it will always be what it is today. Cork. 14.5% alc. **Rating** 88 **To** 2020 $27
The Leyli Barossa Valley Cabernet Sauvignon 2010 Strong purple-crimson; a full-bodied Cabernet Sauvignon, big on flavour, not on finesse; the fruit is ripe, the tannins formidable, and if the wine achieves balance, it will be a long way down the track. Cork. 14.5% alc. **Rating** 87 **To** 2018 $27

Skillogalee   ★★★★★

Trevarrick Road, Sevenhill via Clare, SA 5453 **Region** Clare Valley
T (08) 8843 4311 **www**.skillogalee.com.au **Open** 7 days 10–5
Winemaker Dan Palmer **Est.** 1970 **Dozens** 15 000 **Vyds** 50.3ha
David and Diana Palmer purchased the small hillside stone winery from the George family at the end of the 1980s and have fully capitalised on the exceptional fruit quality of the Skillogalee vineyards. All the wines are generous and full-flavoured, particularly the reds. In 2002 the Palmers purchased next-door neighbour Waninga Vineyards, with 30ha of 30-year-old vines, allowing an increase in production without any change in quality or style. Exports to the UK, Canada, Switzerland, Hong Kong, Malaysia, Singapore and NZ.

🍷🍷🍷🍷🍷 **Clare Valley Riesling 2011** Green-straw colour, green dominant; hand-picked from the highest part of the estate vineyards, each block fermented separately, the wine has that extra dimension of fruit the vintage bestowed, with lime/lemon flavours to the fore; good length and balance, especially with its impressive acidity. Screwcap. 12% alc. **Rating** 94 **To** 2021 $24
Trevarrick Single Contour Clare Valley Riesling 2010 From 40-year-old vines planted along the highest contour in the vineyard. It is intense and tightly focused, with considerable texture to the palate and pleasingly dry finish. Vino-Lok. 12.5% alc. **Rating** 94 **To** 2030 $45
Basket Pressed Clare Valley Shiraz 2008 Deep but clear red-purple; hand-picked, open-fermented, basket-pressed and oak-matured for two years; good bloodlines for what is a very good wine, with great line and balance. Dark fruits and totally integrated oak fill the supple, medium-bodied palate, the tannins round and ripe. Screwcap. 14.5% alc. **Rating** 94 **To** 2023 $30
Trevarrick Single Contour Clare Valley Cabernet Shiraz 2007 It's not clear whether a single contour means a single row within a contour block, or the contour block itself. It really doesn't matter very much; this is a blend of the two best parcels of the varieties in '07, and has soared effortlessly above the limitations of that year. It is remarkably intense and focused, yet not the least heavy in the mouth; the black fruits are held neatly in place by balanced tannins and quality oak. Screwcap. 14% alc. **Rating** 94 **To** 2027 $70

🍷🍷🍷🍷🍷 **Take Two Basket Pressed Clare Valley Shiraz Cabernet 2009** Rating 90 **To** 2017 $22
Basket Pressed Clare Valley The Cabernets 2009 Rating 90 **To** 2024 $28

🍷🍷🍷🍷 **Clare Valley Gewurztraminer 2011** Rating 89 **To** 2015 $24
Lees Stirred Clare Valley Chardonnay 2009 Rating 88 **To** 2013 $24
Cabernet Malbec Rose 2011 Rating 87 **To** Now $22

Skimstone   ★★★★

1307 Castlereagh Highway, Apple Tree Flat, Mudgee, NSW 2850 **Region** Mudgee
T (02) 6373 1220 **www**.skimstone.com.au **Open** Thurs–Fri 11–3, w'ends & public hols 10–4
Winemaker Joshua Clementson **Est.** 2009 **Dozens** 500 **Vyds** 15ha
This is a joint venture between Josh and Kate Clementson and Michael and Anne-Marie Horton; the Clementsons live on and run the estate and cellar door. Josh had previously worked for Orlando (one year), then Peter Logan (five years), and has been vineyard manager

at Huntington Estate for the past three vintages. The partners were thus able to assess the potential of the rundown Apple Tree Flat vineyard in 2007, and have since worked hard to bring the vineyard back to full health. They have particular faith in sangiovese and barbera (5ha) as varieties for the future. Almost all the fruit is sold under contract, but they keep small amounts of grapes to make the Skimstone wines.

ŶŶŶŶ♀ **Mudgee Chardonnay 2011** Whole bunch pressed and no mlf; this is a very well-made wine, with most attractive grapefruit and some white peach supported by subtle oak. Great outcome for a difficult vintage, and a major step forward for Skimstone. Screwcap. 12% alc. **Rating** 92 **To** 2015 $25
Mudgee Sangiovese Rose 2011 Pale but vivid pink; light, fresh cherry blossom aromas lead into a fresh, crisp and dry palate; perfect now as an aperitif or as an accompaniment to cold dishes. Screwcap. 12.5% alc. **Rating** 90 **To** Now $25
Mudgee Barbera 2011 Deliberately picked as late as possible to maximise fruit flavour; the colour is excellent, and the wine shows no overripe characters whatsoever. Seems as if it bypassed oak, but there are no hard tannins. Screwcap. 15% alc. **Rating** 90 **To** 2015 $30

ŶŶŶŶ **Mudgee Sangiovese 2011 Rating** 88 **To** 2014 $30

Smallfry Wines ★★★★★

13 Murray Street, Angaston, SA 5353 **Region** Barossa Valley
T (08) 8564 2182 **www.**smallfrywines.com.au **Open** By appt, 0412 153 243
Winemaker Wayne Ahrens **Est.** 2005 **Dozens** 1600 **Vyds** 27ha
The engagingly named Smallfry Wines is the venture of Wayne Ahrens and partner Suzi Hilder. Wayne is from a fifth-generation Barossa family; Suzi is the daughter of well-known Upper Hunter viticulturist Richard Hilder and wife Del, partners in Pyramid Hill Wines. Both have degrees from CSU, and both have extensive experience – Suzi as a senior viticulturist for TWE, and Wayne's track record includes seven vintages as a cellar hand at Orlando Wyndham and other smaller Barossa wineries. They have a 10ha vineyard in the Eden Valley (led by cabernet sauvignon and riesling), and a long-established 17ha vineyard in the Vine Vale subregion of the Barossa Valley, which has no less than 16 varieties, led by shiraz, grenache, semillon, mourvedre, cabernet sauvignon and riesling. Most of the grapes are sold to other Barossa wineries, with enough retained from each vineyard to meet Smallfry Wines' needs. Exports to the Philippines, Singapore, Indonesia and Hong Kong.

ŶŶŶŶŶ **Eden Valley Cabernet Sauvignon 2010** Strong purple-crimson; a wine that seduces from the first sip; the bouquet is full of blackcurrant fruit, but it is the supple density of the wine in the mouth that is so striking, with layer upon layer of flavour, perfectly balanced tannins giving structure but not obscuring the delicious fruit on the farewell. 136 dozen made. Screwcap. 14.5% alc. **Rating** 95 **To** 2035 $28

ŶŶŶŶ♀ **Eden Valley Riesling 2011 Rating** 90 **To** 2021 $18

ŶŶŶŶ **Eden Valley Pinot Noir 2011 Rating** 87 **To** 2014 $28
Barossa Riesling 2011 Rating 87 **To** 2017 $18

Smidge Wines

62 Austral Terrace, Malvern, SA 5061 (postal) **Region** South Eastern Australia
T (08) 8272 0369 **www.**smidgewines.com **Open** Not
Winemaker Matt Wenk **Est.** 2004 **Dozens** 1000
Matt Wenk and Trish Callaghan have many things in common: joint ownership of Smidge Wines, marriage, and their real day jobs. Matt has a distinguished record as a Flying Winemaker and, in Australia, working with Tim Knappstein and then Peter Leske at Nepenthe. These days he is the winemaker for Two Hands Wines (and Sandow's End). Trish holds a senior position in one of the world's largest IT services companies, and was a finalist in the Australian Young Business Woman of the Year '03. The Houdini label provides entry-level wines, followed by the white label varietal wines: (The Cellar-pod Viognier, Adam Shiraz, The Tardy Zinfandel,

The Donald Zinfandel and Le Grenouille Merlot, with flagship S Smitch Shiraz at the top. All the Magic Dirt wines are made in precisely the same way, and each is a best barrel selection (French oak) from selected areas of the Barossa Valley. Exports to the UK and the US.

ŸŸŸŸŸ Magic Dirt Stonewell Barossa Valley Shiraz 2010 Medium- to full-bodied, with sultry black fruits at the core of the wine; balanced and integrated oak and tannins. Cork. 14.5% alc. **Rating** 96 **To** 2020 $65
Magic Dirt Greenock Barossa Valley Shiraz 2009 Full crimson-purple; the fragrant bouquet introduces an elegant medium-bodied palate, with spicy red berry fruits and fine tannins; harmonious and long in the mouth. Cork. 14.5% alc. **Rating** 96 **To** 2030 $65
Magic Dirt Moppa Barossa Valley Shiraz 2009 Full purple-crimson; dark/black fruits on the bouquet and medium- to full-bodied palate; highly structured fruit and tannin towards the finish, but does not lose line or balance. Cork. 14.5% alc. **Rating** 95 **To** 2030 $65

❂ Houdini McLaren Vale Shiraz 2010 Dense, deep purple; laden with deep, essency black fruits, licorice and plum, yet displays no dead fruit characters. The tannins and oak inputs are balanced, and this is a wine that I would cellar for many years with absolute confidence about the outcome. Outstanding value. Screwcap. 13.6% alc. **Rating** 94 **To** 2035 $18
Adamo Barossa Valley Shiraz 2009 Full crimson; the fragrant red and black fruit bouquet leads into a palate with black fruits, licorice and quality oak; the tannin texture and weight cannot be faulted. Screwcap. 14.5% alc. **Rating** 94 **To** 2025 $25

ŸŸŸŸŸ Houdini Barossa Valley Shiraz Zinfandel 2009 Light crimson-purple;
❂ the sweet berry bouquet leads into an array of spicy red and black fruits on a medium-bodied palate, the tannins fine; one assumes the zinfandel is responsible for the elevated alcohol, which doesn't spoil the wine. Screwcap. 15% alc. **Rating** 90 **To** 2016 $18

ŸŸŸŸ Houdini Adelaide Hills Sauvignon Blanc 2011 **Rating** 88 **To** 2013 $18
Houdini McLaren Vale Cabernet Sauvignon 2010 **Rating** 87 **To** 2015 $18

Smith & Hooper of Wrattonbully   ★★★★☆

Caves Edward Road, Naracoorte, SA 5271 **Region** Wrattonbully
T 0412 847 383 **www**.smithandhooper.com **Open** By appt
Winemaker Peter Gambetta **Est.** 1994 **Dozens** 13 000
On one view of the matter, Smith & Hooper is simply one of many brands within various of the Hill-Smith family financial/corporate structures. However, it is estate-based, with cabernet sauvignon (21ha) and merlot (13ha) planted on the Hooper Vineyard in 1994, and cabernet sauvignon (15ha) and merlot (9ha) planted on the Smith Vineyard in '98. Spread across both vineyards are 15ha of shiraz and 9ha of trial varieties. Exports to all major markets.

ŸŸŸŸŸ Reserve Merlot 2008 Medium red-purple; given some prior vintages, it is no surprise that this should be a delicious Merlot with clear-cut varietal flowing from cassis fruit complexed by spice and gently savoury tannins; impeccable length and balance. Cork. 13.5% alc. **Rating** 94 **To** 2016 $40

ŸŸŸŸŸ Sauvignon Blanc Semillon 2011 Bright straw-green; a wine of considerable
❂ depth of flavour and personality with juicy tropical fruits welded to more minerally/herbaceous nuances from the semillon, the tropical easily the winning side. Screwcap. 11.5% alc. **Rating** 93 **To** 2014 $22

ŸŸŸŸ Merlot 2009 **Rating** 89 **To** 2015 $22

Smiths Vineyard   ★★★★★

27 Croom Lane, Beechworth, Vic 3747 **Region** Beechworth
T 0412 475 328 **www**.smithsvineyard.com.au **Open** W'ends & public hols 10–5, or by appt
Winemaker Will Flamsteed **Est.** 1978 **Dozens** 1000 **Vyds** 3.3ha

Pete and Di Smith established the first vineyard in Beechworth in 1978, with the encouragement of John Brown Jr of Brown Brothers. In 2003 the winery and vineyard were taken over by their daughter Sarah and husband Will Flamsteed. At 550 m, the vineyard is predominantly chardonnay (1.8ha), with some cabernet sauvignon (1ha) and merlot (0.5ha), which make the estate wines. Will and Sarah made their first Beechworth Shiraz in 2006. The Heathcote Shiraz was a response to the smoke taint and frost damage in 2007. No wines were received for this edition; the rating is that of last year.

 # Snake + Herring   ★★★★★

PO Box 918, Dunsborough, WA 6281 **Region** South West Australia Zone
T 0419 487 427 **www**.snakeandherring.com.au **Open** Not
Winemaker Tony Davis **Est.** 2010 **Dozens** 3000 **Vyds** 5ha
This is the venture of Tony Davis (Snake) and Redmond Sweeny (Herring). Both started university degrees before finding they were utterly unsuited to their respective courses. Having stumbled across Margaret River, Tony's life changed forever; he enrolled at Adelaide University's Roseworthy Campus, thereafter doing vintages in the Eden Valley, Oregon, Beaujolais and Tasmania, before three years at Plantagenet, next Brown Brothers, then a senior winemaking role at Yalumba, then a six-year stint designing Millbrook winery in the Perth Hills, and finally four years with Howard Park in Margaret River. Redmond's circuitous course included a chartered accounting degree and employment with an international accounting firm in Busselton, and the subsequent establishment of Forester Estate in 2001 in partnership with Kevin McKay. Back on home turf he is the marketing and financial controller of Snake + Herring.

ŶŶŶŶŶ **Teardrop Mt Barker Great Southern Riesling 2011** Like the High and Dry, pale quartz-green; a lovely wine that at this stage has expressive lime juice fruit flavours running through the length of the palate; great aftertaste. Screwcap. 12% alc. **Rating** 95 **To** 2020 $28

High and Dry Porongurup Great Southern Riesling 2011 Typical Porongurup finesse and delicacy; a spotlessly clean, floral bouquet leads into a perfectly balanced palate that progressively builds lime-accented flavour through to the finish and aftertaste. Screwcap. 12% alc. **Rating** 94 **To** 2021 $28

✪ **Perfect Day Margaret River Sauvignon Blanc Semillon 2011** The snake and herring meet each other on the striking label; both the bouquet and palate have an extra degree of varietal fruit fused together so tightly you can't decide where the sauvignon blanc ends and the semillon kicks in. That said, cut grass and herb notes do claim equal billing with melon and tropical notes. Screwcap. 12.5% alc. **Rating** 94 **To** 2014 $23

✪ **Tough Love Karridale Margaret River Chardonnay 2011** Bright quartz-green; a youthful Chardonnay already showing its class, with nectarine, white peach and grapefruit woven together by very subtle oak; the texture and mouthfeel are excellent. Screwcap. 12.5% alc. **Rating** 94 **To** 2017 $23

Cannonball Margaret River Cabernet Sauvignon Merlot Petit Verdot 2010 Bright, light crimson-purple; the fragrant bouquet has an array of red berry fruits, the juicy medium-bodied palate building on that promise; savoury tannins and quality oak are woven through the very attractive cassis and berry flavours. Screwcap. 14% alc. **Rating** 94 **To** 2020 $35

Calypso Margaret River Cabernet Franc Merlot 2010 Light, clear crimson-purple; a fragrant and juicy display of red berry fruits of every description, complexed by fine-grained tannins and French oak. Probably best over the next four years. Screwcap. 14% alc. **Rating** 94 **To** 2015 $35

ŶŶŶŶŶ **Dirty Boots Margaret River Cabernet Sauvignon 2010** Rating 91 **To** 2020 $23

Somerled   ★★★★☆

89 Main Street, Hahndorf, SA 5245 **Region** Adelaide Hills
T (08) 8388 7478 **www**.somerled.com.au **Open** Thurs–Sun 10–6
Winemaker Rob Moody **Est.** 2001 **Dozens** 2500

This is the venture of Robin and Heather Moody, and daughters Emma and Lucinda. The quietly spoken Robin (with a degree in oenology) joined Penfolds in 1969, and remained with Penfolds/Southcorp until 2001. In that year the Moodys commenced establishing a range of wines using contract-grown grapes, and now produce a sparkling wine, Sauvignon Blanc, Chardonnay, Fume Blanc and Picnic Races Red and Shiraz (from Kangaroo Island). The wines are selected by Robin from parcels of young wine, during or after fermentation and are blended and matured at Boar's Rock at McLaren Vale. The name comes from the bay gelding that Robin's grandfather raced to victory in the amateur steeplechase at the Oakbank Picnic Races in 1908, and which took its name from the Scottish king who defeated the Vikings in 1156. The other names, obviously enough, follow in the footsteps of Somerled. Exports to Hong Kong and China.

♀♀♀♀♀ **Steeplechase Adelaide Hills Chardonnay 2010** Mid gold; ripe nectarine, spice, fig and toasty oak are evident on the bouquet; the palate is fresh and lively, travelling along a single plane and finishing moderately long. Screwcap. 12.5% alc. **Rating** 90 **To** 2016 $26 BE
Picnic Races Red Cabernet Sauvignon Cabernet Franc 2010 A fragrant and soft-centred wine, showing leafy complexity and a forward, fleshy palate; best enjoyed in the full flush of youth. Screwcap. 13% alc. **Rating** 90 **To** 2016 $26 BE

♀♀♀♀ **Reserve Fume Blanc 2010 Rating** 87 **To** 2013 $33 BE

Somerset Hill Wines   ★★★★

540 McLeod Road, Denmark, WA 6333 **Region** Denmark
T (08) 9840 9388 **www.**somersethillwines.com.au **Open** 7 days 11–5 summer, winter 11–4
Winemaker Contract **Est.** 1995 **Dozens** 3500 **Vyds** 10.7ha
Graham Upson commenced planting pinot noir, chardonnay, semillon, merlot, pinot meunier and sauvignon blanc in 1995 on one of the coolest and latest-ripening sites in WA. The limestone cellar door area has sweeping views out over the ocean and to the Stirling Ranges, and also sells Belgian chocolates. Graham makes the red wines, James Kellie (Harewood Estate) the whites. Exports to the UK, Denmark, Russia, Poland and Japan.

♀♀♀♀♀ **Sauvignon Blanc Semillon 2011** Certainly in the family style of the Somerset
✪ Hills' trio of Semillon, Sauvignon Blanc and Semillon Sauvignon Blanc; an aromatic bouquet of grass, lemongrass and citrus leads into a firmly weighted and structured palate with obvious staying power. Screwcap. 13.7% alc. **Rating** 93 **To** 2015 $19
Constellation Pinot Noir Chardonnay 2006 Burnished gold; while no less fully developed, there are no unusual characters in this wine, although it would not benefit from any longer on lees prior to disgorgement (Nov '11); toast, brioche and honey join with the citrus and apricot fruit. Cork. 12.5% alc. **Rating** 90 **To** 2013 $65

♀♀♀♀ **Semillon 2011 Rating** 89 **To** 2015 $21
● **Sauvignon Blanc 2011 Rating** 89 **To** Now $19
● **Chardonnay 2011 Rating** 89 **To** 2013 $19
Constellation Traditional Method Blanc de Blanc 2006 Rating 89 **To** 2013 $65
Pinot Noir 2010 Rating 88 **To** 2014 $30
Constellation Traditional Method Blanc de Blanc 2009 Rating 88 **To** 2015 $39
Merlot 2010 Rating 87 **To** 2015 $35

Sons & Brothers Vineyard   ★★★★

Spring Terrace Road, Millthorpe, NSW 2798 **Region** Orange
T (02) 6366 5117 **www.**sonsandbrothers.com.au **Open** Not
Winemaker Dr Chris Bourke **Est.** 1978 **Dozens** 300 **Vyds** 2ha

Chris and Kathryn Bourke do not pull their punches when they say, 'Our vineyard has had a chequered history because in 1978 we were trying to establish ourselves in a non-existent wine region with no local knowledge and limited personal knowledge of grapegrowing and winemaking. It took us about 15 years of hit and miss before we started producing regular supplies of appropriate grape varieties at appropriate ripeness levels for sales to other NSW wineries.' Chris has published two fascinating papers on the origins of savagnin in Europe, and also traced its movements in Australia after it was one of the varieties collected by James Busby – and moved just in time to save the last plantings in NSW of Busby's importation. The idea is that a percentage will be co-fermented with the Cabernet Shiraz blend which is the mainstay of the winery.

Cabernet Shiraz 2008 Good hue, although not especially deep; a generous, well-balanced wine, with a mix of red and black fruits and sundry spices, the tannins soft, the oak nuanced. A blend of Cabernet Sauvignon (66%)/Shiraz (33%)/Savagnin (1% from Australia's oldest planting, but less than the normal 5%). Crown seal. 13.5% alc. **Rating** 90 **To** 2018 $25

Sons of Eden   ★★★★★

Penrice Road, Angaston, SA 5353 **Region** Barossa Valley
T (08) 8564 2363 **www**.sonsofeden.com **Open** 7 days 10–6
Winemaker Corey Ryan, Simon Cowham **Est.** 2000 **Dozens** 6750 **Vyds** 60ha
Sons of Eden is the venture of winemaker Corey Ryan and viticulturist Simon Cowham, who both learnt and refined their skills in the vineyards and cellars of Eden Valley. Corey is a trained oenologist with over 20 vintages under his belt, having cut his teeth as a winemaker at Henschke. Thereafter he worked for Rouge Homme and Penfolds in Coonawarra, backed up with winemaking stints in the Rhône Valley, and in 2002 took the opportunity to work in NZ for Villa Maria Estates. In '07 he won the Institute of Masters of Wine scholarship. Simon has a similarly international career, covering such diverse organisations as Oddbins, UK and the Winemakers' Federation of Australia. Switching from the business side to grapegrowing when he qualified as a viticulturist, he worked for Yalumba as technical manager of the Heggies and Pewsey Vale vineyards. With this background, it comes as no surprise to find the estate-grown wines are of outstanding quality. Exports to the US, Hong Kong, the Philippines, Taiwan and China.

Remus Old Vine Eden Valley Shiraz 2009 From two low-yielding vineyards with vines over 50 years old. Deep but vivid purple-crimson; given Rolls Royce treatment in the winery, including 22 months in predominantly new French oak hogsheads. A perfectly balanced medium- to full-bodied wine, with delicious dark cherry and spice aromas and flavours, the palate finishing with fine, lingering tannins. 250 dozen made. Cork. 14.5% alc. **Rating** 96 **To** 2029 $65
Zephyrus Barossa Valley Shiraz 2009 Bright crimson-purple; the lively and fresh perfume of the bouquet and red and black berry fruits of the medium-bodied palate may have been helped by the 2% co-fermented viognier; the mouthfeel is fine and supple, the finish long and balanced. A very well-conceived and executed wine. Screwcap. 14.5% alc. **Rating** 94 **To** 2024 $32
Romulus Old Vine Barossa Valley Shiraz 2009 From two very low-yielding vineyards over 80 years old. Deep purple-crimson; both the bouquet and palate walk along a very different path from that of Remus, the fruit flavours darker, but with lots of vanilla, coffee bean and spice highlighted by 20 months in new American oak hogsheads; despite all this flavour, the medium-bodied palate has elegance. 250 dozen made. Cork. 14.5% alc. **Rating** 94 **To** 2024 $65
Stauros Old Vine Barossa Valley Mourvedre 2008 Only 100 dozen made, yet has a one-off ceramic baked label (front and back); the wine comes from a single 80-year-old vineyard yielding less than 1 tonne per acre. I've never heard of a rotating oak barrel fermenter, but it was used here, before a conventional 20-month maturation in a single cask. Worth it? Absolutely, for this is a mourvedre with fine structure, ripe but not overripe flavour, and a long, almost silky, finish. Vino-Lok. 14.5% alc. **Rating** 94 **To** 2030 $130

ΨΨΨΨ♀ Kennedy Barossa Valley Grenache Shiraz Mourvedre 2010 Rating 93
To 2020 $22
Freya Eden Valley Riesling 2011 Rating 92 To 2018 $25
Cahoots Tempranillo 2010 Rating 90 To 2015 $20

Sorrenberg   ★★★★☆

Alma Road, Beechworth, Vic 3747 **Region** Beechworth
T (03) 5728 2278 **www**.sorrenberg.com **Open** By appt
Winemaker Barry and Jan Morey **Est.** 1986 **Dozens** 1600 **Vyds** 4.8ha
Barry and Jan Morey keep a low profile, but the wines from their vineyard at Beechworth
have a cult following not far removed from that of Giaconda; chardonnay, sauvignon blanc,
semillon, pinot noir, merlot, cabernet franc, cabernet sauvignon and gamay are the principal
varieties planted on the north-facing, granitic slopes. Gamay and Chardonnay are the winery
specialties. Exports to Japan.

ΨΨΨΨ♀ **Chardonnay 2010** Developed colour; undergoes 100% mlf and maturation in
30% new oak; complex from the word go, it progressively reveals more and more
in the glass, with some intentional funk and nutty overtones to the ripe stone
fruits. **Rating** 93 To 2015 $42
Sauvignon Blanc Semillon 2011 Tasted with six other vintages dating back
to the first in '89; despite the vintage conditions, showed minimal botrytis, and
no dilution; it has plenty of weight and structure and exemplary mouthfeel.
Rating 90 To 2014 $29

ΨΨΨΨ **Gamay 2010 Rating** 89 To 2014 $39

Soul Growers   ★★★★☆

PO Box 805, Tanunda, SA 5352 (postal) **Region** Barossa Valley
T 0439 026 727 **www**.soulgrowers.com **Open** By appt
Winemaker James Lindner, Paul Lindner, David Cruickshank, Paul Heinicke **Est.** 1998
Dozens 5000 **Vyds** 6.8ha
Soul Growers is owned by its four winemaker partners, headed by James Lindner. Its estate
vineyards are mainly on hillside country in the Seppeltsfield region, with shiraz, cabernet
sauvignon, grenache and chardonnay the most important, and lesser plantings of mataro
and black muscat; there are then pocket-handkerchief blocks of shiraz at Tanunda, mataro
at Nuriootpa and a 1.2ha planting of grenache at Krondorf. Exports to the US, Canada,
Singapore, Hong Kong and China.

ΨΨΨΨ♀ **Single Vineyard Eden Valley Riesling 2011** Sourced from a single vineyard
 on the outskirts of the Eden township, and is a major success for Soul Growers'
first foray into Riesling. Light straw-green; the lime flavours are focused and
long, with a distinct shaft of mineral providing backbone and length. Screwcap.
12.5% alc. **Rating** 92 To 2021 $20
Slow Grown Barossa Shiraz 2009 Deep, healthy crimson-purple, very good
given the alcohol level; a wine made without compromise and in the full-bodied
style the partners seek. If you must use cork, that chosen by Soul Growers should
be the aim. 15.5% alc. **Rating** 92 To 2024 $50
✪ **Solace 2008** A thoroughly intriguing 48/23/22/7% blend of grenache, shiraz,
mourvedre and cabernet sauvignon; the flavours are of raspberry, cherry and a
basket of spices, and it is not until the aftertaste that the alcohol hits. Drink with
food; it may not be so noticeable. Screwcap. 15.5% alc. **Rating** 91 To 2015 $20
Resurgence Barossa Valley Cabernet Sauvignon Shiraz 2009 Crimson-
purple; this is a 58/42% blend made, as are all the Soul Growers' red wines, with
open fermenters, basket presses and minimal winery adjustments; it is in fact a very
attractive wine that underlines the synergy that exists between cabernet sauvignon
and shiraz in the Barossa Valley, and makes light work of its alcohol. There's no
particular need for patience, but its best years are in front of it. Screwcap. 15% alc.
Rating 90 To 2020 $25

Defiant Barossa Valley Mataro 2009 Deep colour and dark and savoury, indeed meaty, in character; chewy tannins, charry oak and lively acidity combine to draw the finish out to a big-boned, but balanced, conclusion. Cork. 15% alc. **Rating** 90 **To** 2020 $50 BE

ꢸꢸꢸꢸ **Wild Iris Barossa Valley Chardonnay 2011 Rating** 89 **To** 2016 $20 BE
Equilibrium Barossa Valley Shiraz Grenache Mourvedre 2009 Rating 89 **To** 2014 $25
Cellar Dweller Barossa Cabernet Sauvignon 2009 Rating 89 **To** 2015 $50
Esperanza 2009 Rating 88 **To** 2018 $100 BE
106 Vines Barossa Valley Mourvedre 2010 Rating 87 **To** 2018 $100 BE

 # Souled Out

Level 1, 151 Greville Street, Prahran, Vic 3181 (postal) **Region** Various Vic
T 0418 856 669 **www**.souledoutwines.com **Open** Not
Winemaker Jason Searle, William Downie **Est.** 2009 **Dozens** 3000
This cleverly named business is owned by winemakers Jason Searle and William Downie. After many years of friendship they decided to make wines from suitable Vic regions at affordable prices, and which kept a sense of place more than convention. The Fulcrum label, with Pinot Noir and Chardonnay, is the outcome of their desire to see some of their wines available at a national retailer, in this instance Dan Murphy, usually cast in the role of villain when it comes to small winemaking enterprises.

ꢸꢸꢸꢸꢸ **Fulcrum Mornington Peninsula Pinot Noir 2011** Light, clear red-purple;
✪ the red cherry and plum fruit of the bouquet leads straight into the palate, which changes gear as you get to the back-palate; here savoury tannins add texture and structure. Good result for a difficult red wine vintage. Screwcap. 13.5% alc. **Rating** 90 **To** 2015 $19

ꢸꢸꢸꢸ **Fulcrum Mornington Peninsula Chardonnay 2011 Rating** 87 **To** 2014 $19

Soumah

18 Hexham Road, Gruyere, Vic 3770 **Region** Yarra Valley
T (03) 5962 4716 **www**.soumah.com.au **Open** Mon, Thurs–Fri 11–4, w'ends & public hols 10–5
Winemaker Scott McCarthy **Est.** 1997 **Dozens** 4000 **Vyds** 21ha
Unravelling the story behind the exotically named Soumah, and its strikingly labelled Savarro (reminiscent of 19th-century baroque design) was a voyage of discovery up and down a series of minor dead-end roads. This despite the fact that Soumah is within walking distance of my house at Coldstream Hills. Soumah is in fact an acronym meaning South of Maroondah (Highway), while Savarro is an alternative name for savagnin. It is a venture of the Butcher family, headed by patriarch Frank Wynyard Butcher, who was a horticultural scientist with the Victorian Department of Primary Industry for more than 30 years. Two of his sons, Greg and Brett, together with their families, own the Soumah project; Greg a retired electrical engineer, is revelling in the day-to-day management of Soumah, while non-executive director Brett has international experience in the hospitality industry as CEO of the Langham Group, and a long involvement in retailing wines to restaurants in many countries. Tim Brown is viticultural director, Scott McCarthy is winemaker and Steven Worley looks after marketing and branding. All of the many varieties planted have been clonally selected and grafted onto rootstock, with the long-term future in mind, although some of the sauvignon blanc is already being grafted over to bracchetto. Exports to Canada, Hong Kong and Japan.

ꢸꢸꢸꢸꢸ **Single Vineyard Yarra Valley Chardonnay 2010** Bright colour, especially given the low alcohol. Picked at 11.9° baume, reflected by the lean bouquet, but not by the elegant and supple palate with nectarine and white peach dominant, grapefruit in the back seat. If you have a spare 10 minutes, absorb the massive amount of information crammed onto the sky blue and maroon front and back labels. Screwcap. 12% alc. **Rating** 93 **To** 2016 $32

Single Vineyard Yarra Valley Savarro 2011 Very pale quartz-white; the bouquet is pungently fragrant, with spice, pear, apple and lychee all surging up the glass; the palate is more restrained, but certainly stays on the same page as the bouquet, providing a wine with real personality. Screwcap. 12% alc. **Rating** 92 **To** 2013 $26

Single Vineyard Yarra Valley Shiraz 2010 Lifted and spicy on the bouquet, with violets, blackberry and briary notes on show; the palate is surprisingly muscular, with oak and tannins coming to the fore; needs plenty of time to fully integrate, but the journey should be an interesting one. Screwcap. 13.5% alc. **Rating** 91 **To** 2018 $34 BE

♈♈♈♈ Single Vineyard Yarra Valley Pinot Grigio 2011 **Rating** 87 **To** Now $23

Spence   ★★★★☆
760 Burnside Road, Murgheboluc, Vic 3221 **Region** Geelong
T (03) 5265 1181 **www**.spencewines.com.au **Open** 1st Sun each month
Winemaker Peter Spence **Est.** 1997 **Dozens** 500 **Vyds** 3.2ha
Peter and Anne Spence were sufficiently inspired by an extended European holiday, which included living on a family vineyard in Provence, to purchase a small property specifically for the purpose of establishing a vineyard and winery. It remains a part-time occupation; Peter is an engineering manager at the Ford product development plant in Geelong, Anne a teacher. They have planted 3.2ha on a north-facing slope in a valley 7km south of Bannockburn; the lion's share to three clones of shiraz (1.83ha), the remainder to chardonnay, pinot noir and fast-diminishing cabernet sauvignon (it is being grafted over to viognier for use in the Shiraz). The vineyard attained full organic status in 2008 and is moving to biodynamic. The well-priced wines have been made with the sure hand of the fast-learning Peter.

♈♈♈♈♈ Chardonnay 2010 Mid gold; a fine combination of fresh nectarine, grapefruit, charcuterie and grilled cashews, offset by a touch of lemon zest; the palate is lively, fresh and focused, with a lingering trail of quartz and chalky texture; the grip adds gravitas and the length is impressive; a deserved trophy winner at the Geelong Wine Show '11. Screwcap. 13.5% alc. **Rating** 95 **To** 2018 $28 BE

Spinifex   ★★★★★
PO Box 511, Nuriootpa, SA 5355 **Region** Barossa Valley
T (08) 8564 2059 **www**.spinifexwines.com.au **Open** At Artisans of Barossa
Winemaker Peter Schell **Est.** 2001 **Dozens** 4000
Peter Schell and Magali Gely are a husband and wife team from NZ who came to Australia in the early 1990s to study oenology and marketing at Roseworthy College. They have spent four vintages making wine in France, mainly in the south, where Magali's family were vignerons for generations near Montpellier. The focus at Spinifex is the red varieties that dominate in the south of France: mataro (more correctly mourvedre), grenache, shiraz and cinsaut. The wine is made in open fermenters, basket-pressed, partial wild (indigenous) fermentations, and relatively long post-ferment maceration. This is a very old approach, but nowadays a la mode. The wines are made at Spinifex's winery in Vine Vale, where Peter also makes wines for a number of clients to whom he consults. As far as I am concerned Spinifex out-Torbrecks Torbreck. A representative submission of wines was not received for this edition. Exports to the UK, the US, Canada, Belgium, Taiwan, Singapore, Hong Kong and NZ.

♈♈♈♈♈ Barossa Valley Rose 2011 A 47/36/12/5% blend of grenache, cinsaut, mataro
✪   and shiraz. Bright salmon-pink; its scented bouquet is outgunned by the tinkling piano keys of the palate, skipping from one variety to the next and then back again. Roses seldom have fruit-derived mouthfeel, but this one does in spades, and is a bargain by any standards. Screwcap. 13% alc. **Rating** 94 **To** 2014 $20

♈♈♈♈♀ Fleur Roussanne 2011 **Rating** 90 **To** 2017 $23

♈♈♈♈ Lola 2011 **Rating** 89 **To** 2015 $20
✪

Spook Hill Wines

PO Box 335, Cadell, SA 5321 **Region** Riverland
T 0428 403 235 **www.**spookhillwines.com **Open** Not
Winemaker Jock Gordon **Est.** 1999 **Dozens** 1000 **Vyds** 10ha

Owner and winemaker Jock Gordon Jr's family have been grapegrowers for three generations, but in 1999 Jock took the plunge into commercial winemaking after a successful career as an amateur winemaker. He has 8ha of shiraz, 1ha of alicante bouschet and 1ha split between mourvedre and durif, supplemented by grapes from local growers. The Spook Hill vineyard is situated in the Cadell Valley, a former oxbow of the Murray River now bypassed by the river channel; silt soil deposited in the ancient river valley is especially suited to viticulture. All of the wines are open-fermented, basket-pressed and matured in the onsite winery.

Silent Partner Shiraz 2006 Remarkably fresh red crimson colour for a wine of this age and provenance; likewise, while only light- to medium-bodied, has fresh red and black cherry fruit in abundance, the tannins fine, oak relegated to the bleachers. Screwcap. 14% alc. **Rating** 90 **To** 2016 $18

The Apparition Cabernet Sauvignon 2008 Rating 88 **To** 2013 $18

Spring Vale Vineyards ★★★★☆

130 Spring Vale Road, Cranbrook, Tas 7190 **Region** East Coast Tasmania
T (03) 6257 8208 **www.**springvalewines.com **Open** 7 days 10–4
Winemaker Kristen and David Cush **Est.** 1986 **Dozens** 10 000 **Vyds** 12.1ha

Rodney Lyne has progressively established pinot noir (6.5ha), chardonnay (2ha), gewurztraminer (1.6ha), pinot gris and sauvignon blanc (1ha each). In 2007 Spring Vale purchased the Melrose Vineyard from Bishops Rock (not the Bishops Rock brand or stock), planted to pinot noir (3ha), sauvignon blanc and riesling (1ha each) and chardonnay (0.5ha). Exports to Singapore.

Reserve Chardonnay 2010 Light straw-green; very much in the Spring Vale Vineyards family style, with impeccable balance across the entire fabric of the wine, and will age with grace. Screwcap. 13.6% alc. **Rating** 94 **To** 2017 $40

Chardonnay 2011 Rating 92 **To** 2017 $22
Melrose Pinot Noir 2011 Bright and clear crimson-purple; a fragrant cherry blossom bouquet with a hint of spice, then a firm, crisp palate; has a splash of pinot meunier that may be responsible for the savoury/spice nuance on the finish. Screwcap. 13.4% alc. **Rating** 92 **To** 2015 $22
Pinot Noir 2009 Rating 92 **To** 2017 $40
Salute 2009 Rating 91 **To** 2015 $28

Pinot Gris 2011 Rating 87 **To** 2013 $28

Springs Hill Vineyard

Schuller Road, Blewitt Springs, SA 5171 **Region** McLaren Vale
T (08) 8383 7001 **www.**springshill.com.au **Open** Sun & public hols
Winemaker Anthony and Gary Whaite **Est.** 1998 **Dozens** 1000 **Vyds** 17.1ha

Anthony and Gary Whaite began the planting of their vineyard in 1975 with cabernet sauvignon and shiraz and have slowly expanded it over the following years with merlot, mourvedre and grenache. The vines are dry-grown, and the whole operation from vine to wine is carried out by the pair. They use traditional small-batch winemaking techniques of open fermenters, which are hand-plunged, basket-pressed, etc.

Blewitt Springs Shiraz 2009 Open-fermented, basket-pressed, aged in older French and American oak barriques for 20 months. Deep crimson-purple; archetypal, full-bodied McLaren Vale shiraz, although slightly fuller than one normally finds from the Blewitt Springs area; late picking may have played its part in leading to that full-body. Screwcap. 15% alc. **Rating** 92 **To** 2024 $29

Blewitt Springs Mourvedre 2009 Rating 88 **To** 2020 $29

Squitchy Lane Vineyard   ★★★★★

Medhurst Road, Coldstream, Vic 3770 **Region** Yarra Valley
T (03) 5964 9114 **www**.squitchylane.com.au **Open** W'ends 11–4
Winemaker Robert Paul **Est.** 1982 **Dozens** 2000 **Vyds** 5.75ha

Owner Mike Fitzpatrick acquired his taste for fine wine while a Rhodes scholar at Oxford University in the 1970s. Returning to Australia he guided Carlton Football Club to two premierships as captain, then established Melbourne-based finance company Squitchy Lane Holdings. The wines of Mount Mary inspired him to look for his own vineyard, and in 1996 he found a vineyard of sauvignon blanc, chardonnay, pinot noir, merlot, cabernet franc and cabernet sauvignon planted in '82 just around the corner from Coldstream Hills and Yarra Yering. Between then and 2003 the grapes were sold to well-known local wineries, but in '04 he began to put in place a team to take the venture through to the next stage, with wines under the Squitchy Lane label, commencing with the '05 vintage, launched in '07. Since '09 the wines have been made at Sticks.

♀♀♀♀♀ **Yarra Valley Pinot Noir 2010** Clear, bright garnet-red; has a fragrant, sweet fruit bouquet that is immediately appealing, and the palate carries the theme onwards, with silky red fruits and gossamer tannins running throughout. Clones MV6 and 114; 700 dozen made. Screwcap. 13% alc. **Rating** 94 **To** 2016 $35
Yarra Valley Cabernet Sauvignon 2010 Deep crimson, bright; a bright, fragrant and floral red-fruited bouquet, showing cedary complexity; medium-bodied with fine tannins and refreshing acidity; good line and drive, and the finish is even and long. Screwcap. 13% alc. **Rating** 94 **To** 2020 $32 BE

♀♀♀♀♀ **Yarra Valley Fume Blanc 2011 Rating** 91 **To** 2014 $26 BE

♀♀♀♀ **SQL Yarra Valley Pinot Noir 2010 Rating** 88 **To** 2015 $22 BE

Staindl Wines   ★★★★☆

63 Shoreham Road, Red Hill South, Vic 3937 (postal) **Region** Mornington Peninsula
T (03) 9813 1111 **www**.staindlwines.com.au **Open** By appt
Winemaker Rollo Crittenden (Contract) **Est.** 1982 **Dozens** 400 **Vyds** 3.1ha

As often happens, the establishment date for a wine producer can mean many things. In this instance it harks back to the planting of the vineyard by the Ayton family, and the establishment of what was thereafter called St Neots. Juliet and Paul Staindl acquired the property in 2002, and, with the guidance of Phillip Jones, have extended the plantings to 2.2ha of pinot noir, 0.6ha of chardonnay and 0.3ha of riesling. The vineyard is run on a low chemical regime, heading towards biodynamic viticulture. Paul says, 'It's all good fun and lots of learning.' I would add it's also more than slightly demanding.

♀♀♀♀ **Mornington Peninsula Riesling 2011** Reductive aromas on opening mingle with sea salt and Meyer lemon; the palate delivers prominent acidity, and a pleasant savoury ginger and fennel character lingers on the finish. Screwcap. 11.5% alc. **Rating** 88 **To** 2016 $25 BE

Staniford Wine Co   ★★★★★

20 Jackson Street, Mount Barker, WA 6324 **Region** Great Southern
T 0405 157 687 **www**.stanifordwineco.com.au **Open** Not
Winemaker Michael Staniford **Est.** 2010 **Dozens** 500

Michael Staniford has been making wine in the Great Southern region since 1995 principally as senior winemaker for Alkoomi at Frankland River, with additional experience as a contract maker for other wineries. The business will be built around single vineyard wines; the first two releases are a Chardonnay (Mendoza clone) from a 20-year-old vineyard in Albany, and a Cabernet Sauvignon from a 15-year-old vineyard at Denbarker in Mount Barker. The quality of these two wines is every bit as one would expect. In 2012 Michael plans to introduce a Riesling and Shiraz with a similar individual vineyard origin.

ΥΥΥΥΥ **Great Southern Reserve Chardonnay 2010** Medium straw-green; Michael Staniford's experience shines through in this beautifully crafted wine, with fruit and oak seamlessly interwoven; the fruit is in the grapefruit/white stone fruit spectrum, and although the French oak used was new, it never threatens to dominate. Screwcap. 13% alc. **Rating** 95 **To** 2017 $36

Great Southern Reserve Cabernet Sauvignon 2010 Bright, light crimson; while only medium-bodied, has great intensity and drive to its finely detailed palate, with cassis woven through cedar and savoury spice notes; has great length and overall balance. Screwcap. 13% alc. **Rating** 95 **To** 2025 $36

Stanton & Killeen Wines ★★★★★

440 Jacks Road, Murray Valley Highway, Rutherglen, Vic 3685 **Region** Rutherglen
T (02) 6032 9457 **www**.stantonandkilleenwines.com.au **Open** Mon–Sat 9–5, Sun 10–5
Winemaker Brendan Heath **Est.** 1875 **Dozens** 20 000 **Vyds** 40ha
Stanton & Killeen is a family-owned winery with over 100 years and seven generations of winemaking experience. Following on the tragic death of Chris Killeen some years earlier, 2011 saw the return of Simon (ex wine science tertiary studies), Natasha (likewise with university studies) and mother Wendy Killeen. Simon and Natasha are working in various roles, including vineyard management and marketing, while Wendy has taken on the role of CEO. Brendan Heath continues his role as long-term winemaker. Exports to the UK and Denmark.

ΥΥΥΥΥ **Grand Rutherglen Topaque NV** Bright and clear orange-brown; a total contrast to Buller, Morris, Chambers et al. with all the emphasis is on the fresh tea leaf, butterscotch and Christmas cake varietal fruit. Screwcap. 18.5% alc. **Rating** 96 **To Now** $80

Rutherglen Vintage Fortified 2006 A blend of shiraz, touriga, tinta barroca, tinta cao, tinta roriz and durif. The driest, most Portuguese and most elegant vintage port style in Australia; it is delicious now, but will cruise through the next 20 years, changing as it does so, and always giving pleasure. Cork. 18.2% alc. **Rating** 96 **To** 2026 $32

Classic Rutherglen Muscat NV The striking bouquet has a highly aromatic and perfumed array of spices, honey and butterscotch, the palate with greater depth and richness than many of the other classic Muscats. Average age 12 years. 500ml. Cork. 18% alc. **Rating** 94 **To** 2013 $40

ΥΥΥΥΥ **Jack's Block Rutherglen Shiraz 2008 Rating** 93 **To** 2020 $32
Rutherglen Durif 2009 Rating 92 **To** 2019 $32
Rutherglen Shiraz Durif 2009 Rating 90 **To** 2016 $20

Steels Creek Estate ★★★★★

1 Sewell Road, Steels Creek, Vic 3775 **Region** Yarra Valley
T (03) 5965 2448 **www**.steelsckestate.com.au **Open** W'ends & public hols 10–6, or by appt
Winemaker Simon Peirce **Est.** 1981 **Dozens** 400 **Vyds** 1.7ha
The Steels Creek vineyard (chardonnay, shiraz, cabernet sauvignon, cabernet franc and colombard), family-operated since 1981, is located in the picturesque Steels Creek Valley with views towards the Kinglake National Park. Red wines are made onsite, white wines with the assistance of consultants. Visitors can view the winemaking operations from the cellar door. Almost no wine was produced in the wake of the Black Saturday bushfires of 2009, which damaged the vineyard – and subsequent smoke taint affected all wineries in the Yarra Valley – but it bounced back in great style in '10.

ΥΥΥΥΥ **Yarra Valley Shiraz 2010** Crimson-purple; a vibrantly spicy, medium-bodied palate, with black cherry and blackberry fruit to underpin those spicy notes; good control of oak and tannins, and a great example of cool-grown shiraz picked at the right point. The only concern is a stained Diam. 12.5% alc. **Rating** 94 **To** 2020 $25

Yarra Valley Cabernet Sauvignon 2010 Light- to medium crimson-purple; despite its low alcohol, the wine shows no overt green or minty characters, just fresh cassis fruit, fine tannins and good acidity. This was a great vintage in the Yarra across all varieties. Diam. 12.5% alc. **Rating** 94 **To** 2020 $25

Steels Gate   ★★★★☆

227 Greenwoods Lane, Steels Creek, Vic 3775 **Region** Yarra Valley
T (03) 5988 6662 **www**.steelsgate.com.au **Open** Not
Winemaker Han Lau **Est.** 2010 **Dozens** 160 **Vyds** 2ha

Brad Atkins and Matthew Davis acquired a 2ha vineyard of 25–30-year-old dry-grown chardonnay and pinot noir in 2009. There is another 14+ha of natural bushland that backs on to the national park. For reasons unexplained, the owners have a particular love of gates, and as the property is at the end of Steels Creek, the choice of Steels Gate was obvious. The next step was to engage French designer Cecile Darcy to create what is known today as the Steels Gate logo. The 2010 Chardonnay makes up in quality what it lacks in quantity.

Yarra Valley Chardonnay 2010 From a single, dry-grown, estate vineyard; barrel-fermented and matured in French oak, 20% new; the palate has exhilarating drive and intensity to its grapefruit and white peach flavours, underpinned by lingering, cleansing acidity. Screwcap. 13.6% alc. **Rating** 94 **To** 2018 $25

Yarra Valley Pinot Noir Rose 2011 Pale orange-salmon; fermented in old barriques; spiced strawberry on the bouquet leads into a fresh palate, the red berry fruits expanding their base and driving the wine through to a long finish; if there is any sweetness present, it is balanced by acidity. Screwcap. 11.6% alc. **Rating** 91 **To** 2013 $20
Yarra Valley Pinot Noir 2010 Rating 90 **To** 2016 $25

Stefani Estate   ★★★★☆

389 Heathcote-Rochester Road, Heathcote, Vic 3523 **Region** Heathcote
T (03) 9570 8750 **www**.stefaniestatewines.com.au **Open** By appt
Winemaker Mario Marson **Est.** 2002 **Dozens** 3200 **Vyds** 27.6ha

Stefano Stefani came to Australia in 1985. Business success has allowed Stefano and wife Rina to follow in the footsteps of Stefano's grandfather, who had a vineyard and was an avid wine collector. The first property they acquired was at Long Gully Road in the Yarra Valley, planted to pinot grigio, cabernet sauvignon, chardonnay and pinot noir. The next was in Heathcote, where they acquired a property adjoining that of Mario Marson (ex Mount Mary), built a winery and established 14.4ha of vineyard, planted to shiraz, cabernet sauvignon, merlot, cabernet franc, malbec and petit verdot. In 2003 a second Yarra Valley property, named The View, reflecting its high altitude, was acquired and Dijon clones of chardonnay and pinot noir were planted. In addition, 1.6ha of sangiovese, mammolo bianco, malvasia, aleatico, trebbiano and crepolino bianco have been established, using scion material from the original Stefani vineyard in Tuscany. Mario Marson oversees the operation of all the vineyards and is also the winemaker. He is also able to use the winery to make his own brand wines, completing the business link. Exports to Italy and China.

Reserve Heathcote Shiraz 2008 Deep colour, bricking hue; showing developed leathery notes combined with black fruits and tar; full-bodied and rich, unctuous and deep, the leathery character remains on the finish; a good wine if you like aged characteristics, but is it premature? Diam. 14.5% alc. **Rating** 90 **To** 2016 $80 BE

Stefano de Pieri   ★★★★

27 Deakin Avenue, Mildura, Vic 3502 **Region** Murray Darling
T (03) 5021 3627 **www**.stefano.com.au **Open** Mon–Fri 8–6, w'ends 8–2
Winemaker Sally Blackwell, Stefano de Pieri **Est.** 2005 **Dozens** 29 000

Stefano de Pieri decided to have his own range of wines that reflect his Italian spirit and the region he lives in. Mostly hand-picked, the fruit comes from a variety of Mildura vineyards, including the highly respected Chalmers Nursery vineyard. They are intended to be fresh and zesty, deliberately aiming at lower alcohol, to retain as much natural acidity as possible, designed to go with food, and inexpensive and easy to enjoy, reflecting Stefano's philosophy of generosity and warmth. The emphasis is on the Italian varieties, from arneis to aglianico, including a frizzante pinot grigio and the innovative blend of moscato gialla, garganega and greco, while retaining some of the local workhorses like cabernet and chardonnay.

Tre Viti 2011 Fresh and fruity is the aim of the label – mission accomplished; perfumed fruit salad and musk aromas from the moscato combine with the cut and thrust of vermentino; serve cold to achieve optimum balance. Moscato Giallo/Vermentino/Pinot Gris. Screwcap. 10% alc. **Rating** 90 **To** 2013 $18 BE

Pinot Grigio 2011 A clean, fresh and fruitful wine, with musk accenting the fresh-cut lemon on the bouquet and palate; enjoy cold and as young as possible. Screwcap. 12% alc. **Rating** 89 **To** Now $17 BE
Fiano 2011 Rating 88 **To** 2013 $21 BE
Primitivo 2010 Rating 88 **To** 2014 $21 BE
Prosecco NV Rating 88 **To** 2013 $24 BE

Stefano Lubiana   ★★★★★

60 Rowbottoms Road, Granton, Tas 7030 **Region** Southern Tasmania
T (03) 6263 7457 **www.**slw.com.au **Open** Sun–Thurs 11–3 (closed some public hols)
Winemaker Steve Lubiana **Est.** 1990 **Dozens** NFP **Vyds** 25ha
Monique and Steve Lubiana left Riverland grapegrowing and winemaking in 1990, and purchased a greenfield site at Granton. In '91 they planted the first 2.5ha of their current 25ha vineyard. The first Pinot Chardonnay sparkling and Pinot Noir and Chardonnay table wines were made in '93. Five years later they began total organic vineyard management, evolving into a program of biodynamic management. The first steps were taken in 2011 for a new cellar door and vineyard café. Exports to the UK, Singapore, Japan, Hong Kong, Indonesia and China.

Riesling 2011 Twelve per cent of the wine was given extended skin contact, barrel fermentation, lees stirring and oak maturation, and blended with the conventionally made proportion. Bright straw-green; the extra palate weight and texture are instantly obvious as you taste the wine, with its overtones of Alscace Riesling, the one crucial difference being the higher acidity in this wine, which was the last to be bottled of the three '11 white wines reviewed in this edition. Seeing it develop will be well worth the journey. Screwcap. 12.5% alc. **Rating** 96 **To** 2026 $24
Collina Chardonnay 2008 The light, bright straw-green colour heralds a fragrantly elegant wine, with perfectly ripened fruit in a white peach, pear and melon spectrum; oak, and even Tasmanian acidity, are in perfect balance. This will be a prodigiously long-lived wine. Screwcap. 14% alc. **Rating** 96 **To** 2028 $75
Estate Pinot Noir 2010 Open-fermented, indigenous yeasts in a mix of stainless steel and oak vat fermenters, all hand-plunged; pre- and post-ferment skin contact for 16 days, 5% whole bunch fermentation; oak maturation 14 months, 26% new French. Lovely clear crimson, with a fragrant and expressive bouquet, then a beautiful palate with perfect line, length and balance, the flavours of gently spicy red and black cherry rising to a crescendo on the finish, the aftertaste revealing just a hint of forest floor. Screwcap. 14% alc. **Rating** 95 **To** 2020 $45
Vintage Brut 2004 It was sparkling wine that first drew Steve Lubiana to Tasmania, his business in the early days substantially built around contract sparkling winemaking; those days are long gone, but not the crafting of wines such as this. Golden-green, it speaks of many years on yeast lees, giving profound complexity and richness; there are layers of stone fruit, red berries and citrus interleaved with brioche yeast characters; this carnival of flavours is held tightly bound by firm acidity running through the wine. Cork. 12.5% alc. **Rating** 94 **To** 2016 $53

ℙℙℙℙℙ **Sauvignon Blanc 2011** Rating 93 To 2014 $28
Pinot Grigio 2011 Rating 93 To 2014 $28
Primavera Pinot Noir 2010 Rating 90 To 2014 $28

Steinborner Family Vineyards   ★★★★

91 Siegersdorf Road, Tanunda, SA 5352 **Region** Barossa Valley
T 0414 474 708 **www.**sfvineyards.com.au **Open** By appt
Winemaker David Reynolds **Est.** 2003 **Dozens** 1800 **Vyds** 9ha
Steinborner Family Vineyards is owned and operated by David and Rebecca Reynolds and
Rebecca's parents, Michael and Heather Steinborner. Their Ancestry Vineyards are located on
the floor of the Barossa Valley in Vine Vale. Shiraz (some 80 years old) accounts for two-thirds
of the total plantings, with equal quantities of marsanne, viognier, durif and semillon making
up the rest. Exports to Switzerland, Indonesia, Hong Kong, Singapore, China and Japan.

ℙℙℙℙℙ **Caroliene Marsanne 2010** Aged on lees for six months, but no oak involved,
allowing the 'dry' characteristic of one face of marsanne to show itself, along with
crisp acidity. The incipient almond and honeysuckle will slowly evolve over the
years ahead. Screwcap. 12.8% alc. **Rating** 90 **To** 2017 $18

Stella Bella Wines   ★★★★★

205 Rosabrook Road, Margaret River, WA 6285 **Region** Margaret River
T (08) 9757 6377 **www.**stellabella.com.au **Open** 7 days 10–5
Winemaker Stuart Pym, Luke Jolliffe **Est.** 1997 **Dozens** 50 000 **Vyds** 88ha
This enormously successful privately owned winemaking business produces wines of true
regional expression, with fruit sourced from the central and southern parts of Margaret River.
The company operates almost 90ha of vineyard and has its own winery in Karridale. Serie
Luminosa Cabernet Sauvignon is an outstanding flagship for Stella Bella. Exports of Stella
Bella, Suckfizzle and Skuttlebutt labels to the UK, the US and other major markets.

ℙℙℙℙℙ **Serie Luminosa Margaret River Cabernet Sauvignon 2008** A selection of
the best barrels from the best blocks of the estate vineyards. The colour is deep,
and the wine proclaims its quality from the first whiff of the bouquet, building
progressively through the blackcurrant, cedar and earth of the full-bodied palate;
15% merlot has been absorbed, as has the foundation of tannins. Great wine.
Screwcap. 14% alc. **Rating** 97 **To** 2030 $75
Suckfizzle Margaret River Sauvignon Blanc Semillon 2008 A blend that
'has a long maturation' over 18 months in French oak, all with a nod to White
Bordeaux. Light straw-green, this is one of the best blends of this type in the
Margaret River, and hence, Australia; it is long, intense and distinctly savoury,
powerful on the way in, and elegant on the way out. Screwcap. 13% alc. **Rating** 96
To 2020 $45
Suckfizzle Margaret River Sauvignon Blanc Semillon 2007 This is a
59.5/40.5% blend, whole bunch-pressed, briefly settled, then fermented in 100%
new French oak. At the conclusion of fermentation, 50% is transferred to older
oak. Deep green-gold, it is exceptionally complex, with multiple layers of toasty
oak and ripe fruit, yet with a magical spine of citrussy acidity that gives the wine
great length. Screwcap. 13% alc. **Rating** 96 **To** 2017 $48
Serie Luminosa Margaret River Chardonnay 2010 Bright straw-green; there
is no quiet entry into this wine, its grip on the mouth immediate and unrestrained;
despite this unbridled power, the line, the length and the balance are all exemplary,
the pure expression of varietal character needing no comment. Screwcap.
13.4% alc. **Rating** 96 **To** 2022 $65
Serie Luminosa Margaret River Cabernet Sauvignon 2009 The hue is not
as youthful as that of Suckfizzle despite the lower alcohol; that said, the bouquet
and palate are an exercise in varietal purity and precision, the medium-bodied
but very long palate with perfectly balanced tannins and integrated oak. Screwcap.
13.7% alc. **Rating** 96 **To** 2025 $80

Suckfizzle Margaret River Cabernet Sauvignon 2009 A classic Margaret River Cabernet in the style of Voyager Estate, with intense black fruit flavours and persistent tannins, all built for the long haul. Screwcap. 14% alc. **Rating** 95 To 2029 $55

✪ Margaret River Sauvignon Blanc 2011 Rating 94 To 2014 $24
✪ Margaret River Semillon Sauvignon Blanc 2010 Rating 94 To 2013 $21
Margaret River Chardonnay 2010 Rating 94 To 2020 $32
Margaret River Cabernet Sauvignon Merlot 2009 Rating 94 To 2024 $32

♟♟♟♟♟ Margaret River Viognier 2010 Rating 93 To 2014 $28
✪ **Skuttlebutt Margaret River Sauvignon Blanc Semillon 2011** A blend of 53% sauvignon blanc, 44% semillon and 3% chardonnay; straw-green, it has a vibrant mix of nettle and citrus on the bouquet introducing gooseberry and white peach on the palate. The balance and length are admirable. Screwcap. 13.5% alc. **Rating** 92 **To** 2015 $18

✪ **Margaret River Semillon Sauvignon Blanc 2011** In typical Stella Bella fashion, has more complexity and weight than many of its peers, the somewhat riper fruit allowing it to present characters such as custard apple and stone fruits as well as the more frequently encountered citrus and gooseberry; all this comes about thanks to slightly riper fruit, but without the loss of cleansing acidity on the finish. Screwcap. 13.5% alc. **Rating** 92 **To** 2015 $21

○ **Skuttlebutt Rose 2011** Rating 91 To 2013 $18
Margaret River Shiraz 2009 Rating 91 To 2019 $27
Margaret River Blanc de Blancs 2009 Rating 91 To 2014 $35
Margaret River Sangiovese Cabernet Sauvignon 2009 Rating 90 To 2015 $30
Margaret River Tempranillo 2009 Rating 90 To 2018 $30

Step Rd Winery/Beresford Wines ★★★

Davidson Road, Langhorne Creek, SA 5255 **Region** Langhorne Creek
T (08) 8300 0900 **www**.steprd.com **Open** Not
Winemaker Justin Coates **Est.** 1985 **Dozens** 200 000
Step Rd is home to both the Step Rd and Beresford ranges of wines. Fruit is primarily sourced from Adelaide Hills, Langhorne Creek, McLaren Vale and the Riverland. In a sign of the times, it is an environmentally aware winery: all liquid waste is stored in plastic-lined dams, treated to remove chemicals and salinity and then recycled as irrigation for the vineyard. All solid waste from the grapes (skins, stalks and seeds) is mulched and returned to the vineyards, reducing irrigation requirements by 25%. In December 2011, Step Rd went into receivership with several million dollars owed to creditors, and the 5000-tonne capacity winery, brands (including Step Rd, Beresford and Trig Point), and bulk and bottled wine stock were put on the market, and in April 2012 were acquired by VOK Beverages.

♟♟♟♟ **Beresford Reserve McLaren Vale Shiraz 2004** Spent 12–18 months in 'specialised' barrels which have certainly made their mark; however, there is also plenty of chocolate and plum cake fruit to provide a full-bodied palate. Cork. 14.5% alc. **Rating** 89 **To** 2015 $30
Step Road Langhorne Creek Cabernet Sauvignon 2007 The recently inserted cork and (for its age) the youthful colour suggest the wine may have spent several years in tank as well as 12 months in oak prior to bottling. Be that as it may, it has unexpected poise to its black fruits on its medium-bodied palate. 14.5% alc. **Rating** 89 **To** 2014 $22
Beresford McLaren Vale Cabernet Sauvignon 2009 Medium red-purple, not 100% bright; the wine spent 18 months in French oak, which was too long for the fruit – perhaps because it was too ripe to begin with. The outcome is a full-flavoured wine ideal for bbqs. Cork. 15.5% alc. **Rating** 88 **To** 2014 $20
Beresford McLaren Vale Shiraz 2008 The flawless high-quality cork looks very new, yet the wine spent only '12–14' months in oak, suggesting an extended spell in tank. The colour is good, and there is a surfeit of flavour at any price; less extract would have been better. 15.5% alc. **Rating** 87 **To** 2014 $20

Stephen John Wines

Sollys Hill Road, Watervale, SA 5452 **Region** Clare Valley
T (08) 8843 0105 **www**.stephenjohnwines.com **Open** 7 days 11–5
Winemaker Stephen John **Est.** 1994 **Dozens** 10 000 **Vyds** 5ha
The John family is one of the best known in the Barossa Valley, with branches running
Australia's best cooperage (AP John & Sons) and providing the former chief winemaker
of Lindemans (Philip John) and the former chief winemaker of Quelltaler (Stephen John).
Stephen and Rita John have now formed their own family business in the Clare Valley, based
on a vineyard (riesling and shiraz) overlooking Watervale, and supplemented by grapes from
local growers. The cellar door is a renovated 80-year-old stable full of rustic charm. Exports
to Canada, Malaysia, Thailand, the Maldives and Singapore.

ΨΨΨΨΨ **Dry Grown Clare Valley Shiraz 2010** Deep colour, and full of dark fruits, with
the lavish attention of toasty oak providing a charry smoked meat personality; the
palate is thickly textured, with a fresh spine of acidity providing lift on the run
home to the full-bodied finish. Screwcap. 14.5% alc. **Rating** 90 **To** 2020 $25 BE

Sticks Yarra Valley

179 Glenview Road, Yarra Glen, Vic 3775 **Region** Yarra Valley
T (03) 9730 1022 **www**.sticks.com.au **Open** 7 days 10–5
Winemaker Travis Bush **Est.** 2000 **Dozens** 60 000 **Vyds** 24ha
In 2005 the former Yarra Ridge winery, with a 3000-tonne capacity and over 20ha of
vineyards planted mainly in 1983, was acquired by a partnership headed by Rob 'Sticks'
Dolan. The estate production is significantly supplemented by contract-grown grapes sourced
elsewhere in the Yarra Valley and surrounding regions. Sticks also provides substantial contract-
making facilities for wineries throughout the Yarra Valley. While remaining a shareholder, Rob
has ceased to have any management or winemaking role at Sticks. Exports to the UK, the US,
Hong Kong and China.

ΨΨΨΨΨ **No. 29 Cabernet Sauvignon 2010** A vibrant, elegant and restrained bouquet
of pure cassis, redcurrant, toasty oak and nutmeg; the medium-bodied palate is
lined with ample and quite silky fine-grained tannins, lingering harmoniously for a
long time on the finish; elegance and power blended seamlessly. Screwcap. 13% alc.
Rating 95 **To** 2025 $40 BE

✪ **Cabernet Sauvignon 2010** Deep crimson; a fragrant and perfumed bouquet
showing mulberry and violet; the medium-bodied palate is soft, fleshy, elegant and
accessible with fine-grained tannins and lively acidity providing a plush ride to the
finish. Screwcap. 13% alc. **Rating** 94 **To** 2020 $20 BE

ΨΨΨΨΨ **Block A4 Sauvignon Blanc 2011 Rating** 92 **To** 2016 $25 BE
No. 29 Pinot Noir 2011 Rating 91 **To** 2016 $45

✪ **Pinot Grigio 2011** Vibrant hue; a fresh combination of pear, anise and a little
blanched almond complexity; the palate is fresh and fragrant, with a zesty lemony
acid cut to the finish. Screwcap. 12% alc. **Rating** 90 **To** 2014 $18 BE

Stomp Wine

1273 Milbrodale Road, Broke, NSW 2330 **Region** Hunter Valley
T (02) 6579 1400 **www**.stompwine.com.au **Open** W'ends 10.30–5.30
Winemaker Michael McManus **Est.** 2004 **Dozens** 500
After a lifetime in the food and beverage industry, Michael and Meredith McManus have
finally made a decisive move to full-time occupation in all aspects of winemaking. They have
set up Stomp Winemaking, a contract winemaker designed to keep small and larger parcels
of grapes separate through the fermentation and maturation process, thus meeting the needs
of boutique wine producers in the Hunter Valley. The addition of their own label, Stomp, is
a small but important part of their business; the Chardonnay, Verdelho and Shiraz are made
from purchased grapes.

🍷🍷🍷🍷 **Hunter Valley Verdelho 2011** A juicy, vibrant and refreshing blend of lime juice and nectarine; zesty, linear and fresh; ideal for consumption very cool and in the full flush of youth. Screwcap. 13.5% alc. **Rating** 88 **To** 2014 $18 BE

Stone Bridge Wines   ★★★★

Section 113 Gillentown Road, Clare, SA 5453 **Region** Clare Valley
T (08) 8843 4143 **www**.stonebridgewines.com.au **Open** Thurs–Mon 10–4
Winemaker Craig Thomson, Angela Meaney **Est.** 2005 **Dozens** 4000 **Vyds** 15.4ha
Stone Bridge Wines started out as a hobby but has turned into a commercial enterprise for its owners, Craig and Lisa Thomson. They say that Craig's 16 years as a baker have assisted in the art of winemaking: 'It's all about the mix.' Their own patch of shiraz provides only a small part of the annual crush; riesling, pinot gris, cabernet sauvignon and malbec are purchased from local growers. The cellar door is a rammed-earth and iron building with picturesque surrounds, where on Sundays Sept–May (weather permitting), visitors can relax and enjoy a gourmet wood-oven pizza.

🍷🍷🍷🍷🍷 **Clare Valley Cabernet Malbec 2010** Good colour; a rich and generous bouquet leads into a medium- to full-bodied palate, the cabernet and malbec flavours wielding similar synergy to Wendouree, filling in all the notes in the line of the palate. Screwcap. 14.5% alc. **Rating** 92 **To** 2025 $20

🍷🍷🍷🍷 **Clare Valley Riesling 2011 Rating** 89 **To** 2015 $18
Clare Valley Shiraz 2009 Rating 87 **To** 2014 $20

 Stonefish   ★★★★

Unit 5, 12 Clerke Place, Kurnell, NSW 2231 (postal) **Region** Various
T (02) 9668 9930 **www**.stonefishwines.com.au **Open** Not
Winemaker Contract, Peter Papanikitas **Est.** 2000 **Dozens** 20 000
Founder and owner Peter Papanikitas has been involved in various facets of the wine industry for the past 30 years. Initially his contact was with companies that included Penfolds, Lindemans and Leo Buring, then he spent five years working for Cinzano, gaining experience in worldwide sales and marketing. In 2000 he established Stonefish, a virtual winery operation, with a de facto partnership between Peter and the various grapegrowers and winemakers who supply him with the finished wines. The wines include Brut Cuvee, Sauvignon Blanc, Chardonnay, Verdelho, Shiraz, Merlot and Cabernet Sauvignon, all at $15, with a Reserve Shiraz at $20. Exports to China, Thailand, Vietnam, Hong Kong, Indonesia, Singapore and Fiji.

🍷🍷🍷🍷🍷 **Reserve Shiraz 2010** Deep crimson-purple; the wine has layer upon layer
✪   upon layer of blackberry, blood plum, spice and licorice flavours; oak barely rates a mention, and the tannins are full, round and soft. Exceptional value from the '10 vintage. Cork. 14% alc. **Rating** 93 **To** 2017 $20

✪ **Shiraz 2010** Light, clear crimson; from several vineyards in the Great Southern region, it has aromas of red and black cherries, licorice and multi-spice that flow on to the light- to medium-bodied palate; a deceptive wine, because the length of the palate and the lingering flavours on the aftertaste come as a pleasant surprise. Great value. Screwcap. 13.7% alc. **Rating** 91 **To** 2016 $15

✪ **Merlot 2010** Bright, clear crimson-purple; grown in the Great Southern, one of the few places in Australia able to produce Merlot with distinctive varietal fruit; the wine is light-bodied, but does have the savoury black olive nuances to the core of cassis fruit; the tannins are fine-grained, the oak subtle. Screwcap. 13.1% alc. **Rating** 91 **To** 2017 $15

✪ **Cabernet Sauvignon 2009** Once again shows that McLaren Vale can do with Cabernet Sauvignon, even at this low price point. The bouquet has strong savoury/earthy varietal aromas, the medium-bodied palate following suit on the savoury front, but also picking up plenty of blackcurrant and a modicum of regional chocolate. Screwcap. 13.8% alc. **Rating** 90 **To** 2017 $15

Verdelho 2011 Here the telescope swings to the Hunter Valley; once again, there is clear varietal character that has been carefully preserved in the winery; there is a fleeting hint of spice on the bouquet, half-suggesting some oak (there is none) and adding to the interest; the fruit is luscious and sweet within the usual fruit salad spectrum, but with pineapple more obvious than most. Screwcap. 13.5% alc. **Rating** 89 **To** 2014 $15

Chardonnay 2011 The light, vivid crystal-green colour of itself suggests the wine has not been barrel-fermented or otherwise exposed to oak, and the palate confirms this. It's at the riper end of the spectrum, with peach, nectarine and pear to the fore, and its generosity means there is no need to wait. Screwcap. 14% alc. **Rating** 88 **To** 2014 $15

Stonehaven

7089 Riddoch Highway, Padthaway, SA 5271 **Region** Padthaway
T (08) 8765 6140 **www.**stonehavenwines.com.au **Open** 7 days 10–5
Winemaker Grant Semmens, Leisha Slattery, Sean Carney **Est.** 1998 **Dozens** 500 000
Vyds 400ha
In 2011 the winery, built in 1998 at a cost of more than $33 million, was in mothballs. But it was then acquired by 'a family consortium from Melbourne' and rapidly brought back into production, processing 8000 tonnes in the '11 vintage (notwithstanding the problems of that year), destined for sale in both Australia and China initially. A local winemaking team has been put in charge, and the business is apparently linked to a major liquor producer and distributor in Australia providing a range of fruit-flavoured ciders. Exports to all major markets.

Artan Mount Benson Sauvignon Blanc 2011 Pale straw-green; the aromas and flavours are precisely positioned between the herbal snow pea side and the guava tropical side; the juxtaposition works well. An audacious price, but if you don't ask, you don't get. Screwcap. 13% alc. **Rating** 92 **To** 2013 $35

Artan Padthaway Chardonnay 2011 Light, bright straw-green; a highly fragrant, fruit-driven bouquet leads into a fine, long palate, with the grapefruit flavours that have always been the calling card of Padthaway, oak in balanced support. Screwcap. 13% alc. **Rating** 91 **To** 2017 $35

Stoney Rise

Hendersons Lane, Gravelly Beach, Tas 7276 **Region** Northern Tasmania
T (03) 6394 3678 **www.**stoneyrise.com **Open** Thurs–Mon 11–5
Winemaker Joe Holyman **Est.** 2000 **Dozens** 1500
This is the venture of Joe and Lou Holyman. The Holyman family has been involved in vineyards in Tasmania for 20 years, but Joe's career in the wine industry, first as a sales rep, then as a wine buyer, and more recently working in wineries in NZ, Portugal, France, Mt Benson and Coonawarra, gave him an exceptionally broad-based understanding of wine. In 2004 Joe and Lou purchased the former Rotherhythe vineyard, which had been established in 1986 but was in a somewhat rundown state, and set about restoring the vineyard to its former glory, with 3ha of pinot noir and 1ha of chardonnay. There are two ranges: the Stoney Rise wines, focusing on fruit and early drinkability, the Holyman wines with more structure, more new oak and the best grapes, here the focus on length and potential longevity. Exports to the UK.

Holyman Pinot Noir 2010 Vibrant crimson hue; quite beautiful red and black cherry pinot varietal character; has great length and balance, the finish bolstered by superfine tannins. Gold Tas Wine Show '12. Screwcap. 14% alc. **Rating** 96 **To** 2018 $45

Pinot Noir 2010 Clear crimson-red; the bouquet of dark cherries and plum is attractive, but in no way prepares you for the remarkable intensity of the palate, which brings foresty, stemmy tannins and French oak into play, but without losing the fruit. Screwcap. 14% alc. **Rating** 95 **To** 2016 $29

Holyman Chardonnay 2010 **Rating** 93 **To** 2016 $45 BE
Holyman Project X Pinot Noir 2010 **Rating** 93 **To** 2016 $90 BE

Tamar Valley Gruner Veltliner 2011 **Rating** 88 **To** 2013 $29 BE

Stonier Wines ★★★★★

Cnr Thompson's Lane/Frankston–Flinders Road, Merricks, Vic 3916
Region Mornington Peninsula
T (03) 5989 8300 **www**.stonier.com.au **Open** 7 days 11–5
Winemaker Michael Symons **Est.** 1978 **Dozens** 25 000 **Vyds** 6.25ha
This may be one of the most senior wineries on the Mornington Peninsula, but that does not stop it moving with the times. It has embarked on a serious sustainability program that touches on all aspects of its operations. It is one of the few wineries in Australia to measure its carbon footprint in detail, using the officially recognised system of WFA; it is steadily reducing its consumption of electricity; it uses rainwater, collected from the winery roof, for rinsing and washing in the winery, as well as supplying the winery in general; it has created a balanced ecosystem in the vineyard by strategic planting of cover crops and reduction of sprays; and has reduced its need to irrigate. None of this has in any way affected (other than beneficially) the quality of its wines. Exports to Europe, Canada, Malaysia, Vietnam, Hong Kong and China.

🍷🍷🍷🍷🍷 KBS Vineyard Mornington Peninsula Chardonnay 2009 Bright yellow-green; the vines were planted in 1988, and are thus fully mature, a factor in the complexity, bordering on outright richness, of the wine; it has layers of stone fruit, fig, melon and creamy cashew running through the length of the palate. Screwcap. 14% alc. **Rating** 95 **To** 2017 $55
KBS Vineyard Mornington Peninsula Chardonnay 2010 Full, but bright straw-green; effectively the missing piece from the other two Stonier chardonnays, an exercise in harmony, the fruit flavours balanced between citrus and stone fruit, leaning towards the latter, along with quality oak and a hint of cashew. Screwcap. 14.5% alc. **Rating** 94 **To** 2017 $55
Mornington Peninsula Pinot Noir 2010 Light, clear red; a fragrant strawberry-accented bouquet leads into a fine, elegant palate with strawberries, wild and cultivated, to the fore, then a juicy finish. The wine benefits from the low level of tannins because the fruit is so delicate and pure. Drink sooner rather than later. Screwcap. 13.5% alc. **Rating** 94 **To** 2015 $28
Windmill Vineyard Mornington Peninsula Pinot Noir 2010 Light colour with a hint of purple; the complex bouquet and palate successively reveal an array of flavours from dark red fruits through to notes of bramble and forest; the length of the palate is very good, as are the overall balance and mouthfeel. Screwcap. 14% alc. **Rating** 94 **To** 2018 $60
Windmill Vineyard Mornington Peninsula Pinot Noir 2009 Brilliantly bright and clear colour led into a complex bouquet of red fruits and integrated new oak, then a palate with powerful drive, texture and weight. Screwcap. 13.5% alc. **Rating** 94 **To** 2016 $65
KBS Vineyard Mornington Peninsula Pinot Noir 2009 Dramatically deeper in colour than its siblings; the distinction is equally dramatic on the palate, here with black cherry and blood plum, together with substantial tannins. Remarkable that this has the lowest alcohol of the three Stonier Pinots. Cellar it and drink the others. Screwcap. 13.5% alc. **Rating** 94 **To** 2020 $75

🍷🍷🍷🍷 Mornington Peninsula Chardonnay 2010 **Rating** 93 **To** 2017 $25
Reserve Mornington Peninsula Pinot Noir 2010 **Rating** 93 **To** 2017 $55
Reserve Mornington Peninsula Chardonnay 2010 **Rating** 91 **To** 2015 $45

Streicker

412 Abbeys Farm Road, Yallingup, WA 6282 (postal) **Region** Margaret River
T (08) 9755 2108 **www**.streickerwines.com.au **Open** Not
Winemaker Naturaliste Vintners (Bruce Dukes) **Est.** 2002 **Dozens** 2000 **Vyds** 146.09ha
This multifaceted business owned by New York resident John Streicker. It began in 2002 when he purchased the Yallingup Protea Farm and Vineyards, and was followed by the purchase of the Ironstone Vineyard in '03, and finally the Bridgeland Vineyard, which has one of the largest dams in the region; 1km long and covering 18ha. The Ironstone Vineyard is one

of the oldest vineyards in the Wilyabrup area, and required significant rehabilitation after its acquisition. Virtually all the grapes from the three vineyards are sold, and the proteas (from 12ha) are exported to the US and Hong Kong.

ҬҬҬҬҬ **Ironstone Block Old Vine Margaret River Chardonnay 2010** Hand-picked, whole bunch-pressed and aged on lees in French oak barriques. Light but bright green-straw; the sheer intensity of the flavour of the wine puts it in a category all of its own, the foundation of grapefruit flavours supported by strong minerality, in turn making the oak a lesser player. Screwcap. 13% alc. **Rating** 96 **To** 2020 $35
Bridgeland Block Margaret River Sauvignon Semillon 2010 Bright straw-green; a distinguished blend, barrel-fermented and matured in French oak; the intensity of the fruit has in no way been compromised, its union with the oak synergistic, taking one to white Bordeaux. Will have considerable longevity. Screwcap. 12.5% alc. **Rating** 94 **To** 2017 $33
Bridgeland Block Margaret River Syrah 2009 Crimson; a marriage of elegance and power, with brightly defined black cherry and plum fruit, the tannins fine, ripe and balanced, giving a slightly savoury note on the finish. Screwcap. 14% alc. **Rating** 94 **To** 2024 $39

ҬҬҬҬҬ **Ironstone Block Old Vine Margaret River Cabernet Sauvignon 2009** **Rating** 90 **To** 2020 $39

Stuart Wines

105 Killara Road, Gruyere, Vic 3770 (postal) **Region** Yarra Valley
T (03) 5964 9000 www.stuartwinesco.com.au **Open** Not
Winemaker Peter Wilson, Stephen Phillips **Est.** 1999 **Dozens** 95 000 **Vyds** 128.9ha
Hendra Widjaja came to Australia from Indonesia to establish a vineyard and winery, and he initially chose the Yarra Valley for the first vineyard, thereafter establishing a larger one in Heathcote. The Yarra Valley vineyard has 62.4ha (pinot noir, shiraz, cabernet sauvignon, merlot, chardonnay, sangiovese, pinot gris, mataro, petit verdot and viognier), the Heathcote vineyard 66.5ha (shiraz, nebbiolo, tempranillo, merlot, viognier and cabernet sauvignon). The wines are made at Heathcote winery. Wines are released under the Cahillton, White Box and Huma labels. The major part of production exports to Germany, the Netherlands, Indonesia, Malaysia, Macau, Taiwan, Hong Kong, China and NZ.

ҬҬҬҬҬ **Whitebox Yarra Valley Premium Cuvee Brut 2004** A blend of pinot noir,
✪   pinot meunier and chardonnay, all estate-grown; still vibrantly fresh after over six years on yeast lees, disgorged in Dec '11; the balance and length are both good, the dosage correct. Crown seal. 12.5% alc. **Rating** 92 **To** 2015 $50
Whitebox Yarra Valley Premium Cuvee Rose 2004 Bright salmon-pink; also an estate-grown blend of pinot noir, pinot meunier and chardonnay, and likewise disgorged in Dec '11. Here, too, the wine is remarkably fresh and crisp after such a long time on yeast lees, and will benefit from further time on cork, allowing the strawberry characters to develop in the company of the brioche already present. Crown seal. 12% alc. **Rating** 91 **To** 2015 $30
✪   **Whitebox Yarra Valley Shiraz 2010** Clear, bright purple-red; nicely ripened cherry and plum fruit are woven through French oak, or is it the other way around? Certainly neither yields to the other on the palate, and there's no universal rule about such things. Screwcap. 13.5% alc. **Rating** 90 **To** 2018 $20
Cellar Release Whitebox Heathcote Shiraz Viognier 2005 While developed, the colour is good for a 6-year-old wine, perhaps a legacy of the viognier; a pleasant medium-bodied wine with a complex array of spice, mint, berry and earth, the tannins now resolved but adding some savoury characters. Screwcap. 14.8% alc. **Rating** 90 **To** 2015 $23

ҬҬҬҬ **Whitebox Heathcote Shiraz 2009 Rating** 88 **To** 2017 $20
Whitebox Yarra Valley Sauvignon Blanc 2011 Rating 87 **To** 2013 $15

Stumpy Gully

1247 Stumpy Gully Road, Moorooduc, Vic 3933 **Region** Mornington Peninsula
T (03) 5978 8429 **www**.stumpygully.com.au **Open** W'ends 11–5
Winemaker Wendy, Frank and Michael Zantvoort **Est.** 1988 **Dozens** 9700 **Vyds** 40ha
Frank and Wendy Zantvoort began planting their first vineyard in 1988; Wendy, having enrolled in the oenology course at CSU, subsequently graduated with B. App.Sc (Oenology). Together with son Michael, the Zantvoorts look after all aspects of grapegrowing and winemaking. In addition to the original vineyard, they have deliberately gone against prevailing thinking with their Moorooduc vineyard, planting it solely to red varieties, predominantly cabernet sauvignon, merlot and shiraz. They believe they have one of the warmest sites on the Peninsula, and that ripening will present no problems. (Peninsula Panorama is their second label.) Exports to all major markets.

ΨΨΨΨ **Mornington Peninsula Cabernet Sauvignon 2009** Mid garnet; a fragrant and savoury bouquet of cassis, bramble and black olive; the palate is medium-bodied, fresh and focused, with lively acidity to conclude. Screwcap. 13.5% alc. **Rating** 90 **To** 2016 $25 BE

ΨΨΨΨ **Encore Mornington Peninsula Chardonnay 2010** **Rating** 87 **To** 2014 $48 BE

Sugarloaf Ridge

336 Sugarloaf Road, Carlton River, Tas 7173 **Region** Southern Tasmania
T (03) 6265 7175 **www**.sugarloafridge.com **Open** Fri–Mon 10–5 Oct–May
Winemaker Winemaking Tasmania (Julian Alcorso) **Est.** 1999 **Dozens** 5000 **Vyds** 5ha
Founders Dr Simon Stanley and wife Isobel were both microbiologists, but with thoroughly unlikely specialties: he in low-temperature microbiology, taking him to the Antarctic, and she in a worldwide environmental geosciences company. Daughter Kristen and husband Julian Colvile were partners in the original venture, but took over full ownership of Sugarloaf Ridge in 2007, continuing with an uncompromising approach to sustainable viticulture. Multiple clones of pinot noir, sauvignon blanc, pinot gris, viognier and lagrein have been planted, and 1580 native trees, 210 olive trees and 270 cherry trees have also helped transform the property. One of the few Tasmanian producers to export to Singapore, Hong Kong, China and Japan.

ΨΨΨΨ **Pinot Noir 2008** Good colour; has a fragrant bouquet with some spicy notes starting to develop; the palate is rich, supple and smooth; very good plum varietal character; overall, velvety mouthfeel. Screwcap. 13.6% alc. **Rating** 93 **To** 2015 $32
Chardonnay 2008 Bright green-straw; the bold nectarine, white peach and melon aromas and flavours are slightly at odds with the more citrus/grapefruit-driven palate and its umbilical cord of acidity. Interesting wine, possibly made without the use of oak, or certainly not new oak. Screwcap. 13.2% alc. **Rating** 91 **To** 2016 $26

ΨΨΨΨ **Chardonnay 2010** **Rating** 87 **To** 2013 $26

Summerfield

5967 Stawell-Avoca Road, Moonambel, Vic 3478 **Region** Pyrenees
T (03) 5467 2264 **www**.summerfieldwines.com **Open** 7 days 10–5
Winemaker Mark Summerfield **Est.** 1979 **Dozens** 10 000 **Vyds** 13.49ha
Founder Ian Summerfield has now handed over the winemaking reins to son Mark, who produces consistently outstanding and awesomely concentrated Shiraz and Cabernet Sauvignon, both in varietal and Reserve forms. The red wines are built for the long haul, for lovers of full-bodied styles, and will richly repay cellaring. Exports are now directed solely to China.

ΨΨΨΨ **Reserve Shiraz 2010** Deep, clear purple-crimson; a rich and voluptuous display of spicy cherries and licorice, the alcohol held in check by the savoury tannins that define the finish. From the original planting in 1970. Screwcap. 15% alc. **Rating** 95 **To** 2025 $50

Jo Shiraz 2009 Deep crimson; made from the best parcels of the '09 Reserve Shiraz, which in turn came from the 42-year-old vines; an incredibly rich and powerful wine flooding the mouth, then blackberry/black fruit flavours, with a distinct spicy/savoury twist on the finish. One of those wines that has to be taken at face value. Screwcap. 15.5% alc. **Rating** 95 **To** 2034 $80

Jo Shiraz 2010 Follows the pattern of prior releases, coming from a single block within a single estate vineyard. Deep, dense colour; a massive full-bodied shiraz that is not to my personal taste, but has to be respected for the balance it manages to achieve, fruit, alcohol, oak and savoury tannins welded together in a single stream. Screwcap. 15.6% alc. **Rating** 94 **To** 2035 $80

Saieh Shiraz 2010 Bright red-purple; has good structure, definition and presence to its array of blackberry and black cherry fruit on the medium-bodied palate. Altogether more fragrant and elegant than basic Shiraz, the finish long and balanced. Screwcap. 14% alc. **Rating** 94 **To** 2025 $50

Tradition 2010 A 80/9/9/2% blend of shiraz, cabernet franc, cabernet sauvignon and merlot. The colour is deep but bright; the fruit flavours are (happily) led by the black fruits of the shiraz, with a touch of red berries on the finish courtesy of the other varieties; oak and tannins are at the upper limit, and the wine will repay long-term cellaring. Screwcap. 14.5% alc. **Rating** 94 **To** 2030 $27

ŶŶŶŶŶ **R2 Shiraz 2010 Rating** 93 **To** 2025 $50
Reserve Cabernet 2010 Rating 90 **To** 2025 $50

ŶŶŶŶ **Cabernet 2010 Rating** 89 **To** 2018 $25
Shiraz 2010 Rating 87 **To** 2015 $25
Merlot 2010 Rating 87 **To** 2015 $27

Summit Estate ★★★★

291 Granite Belt Drive, Thulimbah, Qld 4377 **Region** Granite Belt
T (07) 4683 2011 **www**.summitestate.com.au **Open** 7 days 10–4.30
Winemaker Paola Cabezas Rhymer **Est.** 1997 **Dozens** 2800 **Vyds** 4.01ha
Summit Estate is the public face of the Stanthorpe Wine Co., owned by a syndicate of 10 professionals who work in Brisbane, and share a love of wine. They operate the Stanthorpe Wine Centre, which offers wine education as well as selling wines from other makers in the region (and, of course, from Summit Estate). The vineyard is planted to chardonnay, marsanne, viognier, verdelho, muscat of Alexandria, pinot noir, shiraz, merlot, tempranillo, monastrell, garnacha, malbec, petit verdot and cabernet sauvignon, and they have set up a small, specialised contract winemaking facility. The wines have improved out of all recognition under the direction of Argentine-born and Spanish-trained Paola Cabezas Rhymer. Exports to the UK.

ŶŶŶŶŶ **Limited Release Pinot Noir Shiraz 2010** No regional claim on the label, and the pinot noir looks like it came from somewhere south of the Granite Belt. Whatever the truth may be, a pleasant light- to medium-bodied wine with bright red cherry fruit, and fine tannins. Screwcap. 13.5% alc. **Rating** 90 **To** 2016 $35

○ **Premium Verdelho 2010 Rating** 90 **To** 2013 $20

ŶŶŶŶ **Premium Verdelho 2011 Rating** 89 **To** 2013 $20
○ **The Pinnacle Premium Red 2009 Rating** 89 **To** 2015 $19
Classic Dry White 2011 Rating 87 **To** 2013 $20
The Finest Acre Reserve Shiraz 2010 Rating 87 **To** 2018 $28

Sunset Winery ★★★★☆

4564 Hog Bay Road, Penneshaw, SA 5222 **Region** Kangaroo Island
T (08) 8553 1378 **www**.sunset-wines.com.au **Open** 7 days 11–5
Winemaker Colin Hopkins **Est.** 2003 **Dozens** 2600
This boutique winery is owned and run by friends and business partners Colin Hopkins and Athalie and David Martin. Construction of the winery and cellar door, with elevated sea views

overlooking Eastern Cove and beyond, was completed in 2003. It is otherwise surrounded by 14ha of native bushland, with a profusion of wildlife. Sunset Winery was the first dedicated cellar door on Kangaroo Island, and offers a range of products to accompany the Chardonnay, Cabernet Sauvignon, Shiraz and Sparkling Shiraz sourced from local growers.

ΨΨΨΨΨ **Kangaroo Island Sauvignon Blanc 2011** A delicious and very expressive ✪ Sauvignon Blanc that won a well-deserved gold medal at the Small Winemakers Show '11. Its strengths are its display of fine tropical fruit characters, led by passionfruit and guava, in turn backed up by citrussy acidity. Screwcap. 12.6% alc. Rating 94 To 2013 $19

ΨΨΨΨΨ **Shadow Kangaroo Island Shiraz 2010** Rating 92 To 2020 $25 ✪ **Kangaroo Island Sparkling Shiraz 2009** There are a lot more sparkling reds around, including sparkling shiraz, selling for higher prices and having less authenticity than this wine; the degree of sweetness will please most consumers, and is an authentic part of all sparkling reds. Further time on cork will benefit, rather than tire, the wine. 13.6% alc. Rating 90 To 2015 $18

ΨΨΨΨ **Kangaroo Island Cabernet Sauvignon 2010** Rating 89 ✪ To 2018 $19

Surveyor's Hill Vineyards ★★★★

215 Brooklands Road, Wallaroo, NSW 2618 **Region** Canberra District
T (02) 6230 2046 **www.**survhill.com.au **Open** W'ends & public hols, or by appt
Winemaker Brindabella Hills (Dr Roger Harris), Greg Gallagher (sparkling) **Est.** 1986
Dozens 1000 **Vyds** 10ha
Surveyor's Hill vineyard is on the slopes of the eponymous hill, at 550–680m above sea level. It is an ancient volcano, producing granite-derived, coarse-structured (and hence well- drained) sandy soils of low fertility. This has to be the ultimate patchwork-quilt winery, with 1ha each of chardonnay, shiraz and viognier; 0.5ha each of roussanne, marsanne; aglianico, nero d'alpha, mourvedre, grenache, muscadelle, moscato giallo, cabernet franc and riesling; and lesser amounts of semillon, sauvignon blanc, touriga nacional and cabernet sauvignon.

ΨΨΨΨΨ **Hills of Hall Cabernet Franc Rose 2011** Light, bright crimson-pink; the ✪ bouquet is full of fragrant small berry red fruits, and the palate delivers on the promise of the bouquet; the mouthfeel is good, as is the length, the finish dry, yet with echoes of strawberry. Screwcap. 12.5% alc. Rating 91 To 2013 $18
Hills of Hall Rouge 2010 A blend of shiraz, cabernet sauvignon, cabernet franc and merlot. Light, clear red-purple; it has a fragrant bouquet in the red fruit spectrum that leads directly to the palate, which has a similar range of flavours; spicy, savoury tannins come through on the finish, but are not overblown. Screwcap. 14% alc. Rating 90 To 2017 $25

ΨΨΨΨ **Hills of Hall Blanc 2011** Rating 87 To 2013 $20

Sutherland Estate ★★★★☆

2010 Melba Highway, Dixons Creek, Vic 3775 **Region** Yarra Valley
T 0402 052 287 **www.**sutherlandestate.com.au **Open** W'ends & public hols 10–5
Winemaker Phil Kelly (Contract), Cathy Phelan, Angus Ridley **Est.** 2000 **Dozens** 1500
Vyds 4ha
The Phelan family established Sutherland Estate in 2000 when they purchased a mature 2ha vineyard at Dixons Creek. Further plantings followed: the plantings now consist of 1ha each of chardonnay and pinot noir, and 0.5ha each of gewurztraminer, cabernet sauvignon, tempranillo and shiraz. Ron Phelan designed and built the cellar door, which enjoys stunning views over the Yarra Valley, while daughter Cathy studied Wine Science at CSU. The sparkling and white wines are made by Phil Kelly, the reds by Cathy and partner Angus Ridley (who has been at Coldstream Hills for the last eight years, and is the winemaker of the Tollana Mornington Pinot Noir).

❦❦❦❦❦ **Daniel's Hill Vineyards Yarra Valley Shiraz 2010** Wild yeast-fermented, and no acid additions; 12 months in French barriques, 33% new; unfined and unfiltered. Medium purple-red; the potent bouquet has a distinctly savoury/spicy twist to the black fruits, the palate picking up those characters in layers of complexity that extend its length to an impressive degree. Screwcap. 14.1% alc. Rating 94 To 2030 $28

❦❦❦❦❦ **Daniel's Hill Vineyards Yarra Valley Tempranillo 2010** Rating 93 To 2020 $28

Swan Valley Wines

261 Haddrill Road, Baskerville, WA 6065 **Region** Swan Valley
T (08) 9296 1501 **www.**swanvalleywines.com.au **Open** Fri–Sun & public hols 10–5
Winemaker Paul Hoffman, Karen Holper **Est.** 1999 **Dozens** 5500 **Vyds** 6ha
Peter and Paula Hoffman, with sons Paul and Thomas, acquired their property in 1989. It had a long history of grapegrowing, and the prior owner had registered the name Swan Valley Wines back in '83. In '99 the family built a winery to handle the estate-grown chenin blanc, grenache, semillon and cabernet sauvignon. The decision to release three Chenin Blancs from 2010 labelled Sec, Demi Sec and Moelleux respectively, is a precise (completely legitimate) copy of some of the best Loire Valley producers of Chenin Blanc, the most notable being Marc Bredif. Those wines have cellaring capacity of 70 years or more if kept in the cool chalk caves on the banks of the Loire Valley. The Australian climate will not permit that, but it will be interesting to see how the three wines develop.

❦❦❦❦❦ **Shiraz 2010** Bright and clear crimson; an 85/15% blend of Swan Valley and
✪ Mt Barker shiraz, the latter responsible for the oriental spice aromas that accompany the blackberry fruit on the bouquet; the medium-bodied palate is long and well balanced, with some licorice nuances most likely to come from Mt Barker, although the Swan Valley provides the flesh needed for balance. Sensitive, skilled winemaking at work. Screwcap. 13.2% alc. Rating 93 To 2018 $18

❦❦❦❦ **Sec Chenin Blanc 2011** Sec is French for 'dry', and over the years Swan Valley
✪ has sought to make Chenins with ascending levels of sweetness corresponding with the Chenin Blanc producers of the Loire Valley. Though it may be dry, the wine is full of ripe fruit salad flavours, while retaining good acidity. How long it will prosper in bottle remains to be seen; my estimate may prove conservative. Screwcap. 12.5% alc. Rating 89 To 2017 $17
Clarum Grenache 2011 Rating 88 To 2015 $18
Extent Sauvignon Blanc Semillon 2011 Rating 87 To 2013 $17

Swinging Bridge

33 Gaskill Street, Canowindra, NSW 2804 **Region** Central Ranges Zone
T 0409 246 609 **www.**swingingbridge.com.au **Open** Fri–Sun 11–6
Winemaker Tom Ward **Est.** 1995 **Dozens** 4000 **Vyds** 14ha
Swinging Bridge was founded by Mark Ward, who immigrated to Australia in 1965 from the UK with an honours degree in agricultural science from Cambridge University. He has been succeeded by Tom and Georgie Ward. The vineyard is part of a farming property, Gayton, 10km from Canowindra. The name comes from a suspension walking bridge that crosses the Belubula River at the foot of the vineyard. Since the first wines were made in 1997, Swinging Bridge has had considerable wine show success.

❦❦❦❦❦ **Orange Sauvignon Blanc 2011** Lees contact and a small portion barrel-
✪ fermented has made a subtle but positive contribution to this crisp wine, welding the mix of herbal and tropical fruits into a seamless whole. Screwcap. 11.8% alc. Rating 94 To 2013 $19

❦❦❦❦❦ **Orange Merlot 2010** Rating 91
O To 2020 $20
Reserve Chardonnay 2011 Rating 90 To 2017 $32 BE

○   **Orange Pinot Gris 2011** Pale straw-quartz; an interesting bouquet, with jasmine and pear floral notes; the palate has good balance and structure, making for a convincing expression of the variety. Screwcap. 13.3% alc. **Rating** 90 **To** 2013 $19
Reserve Canowindra Shiraz 2010 Rating 90 **To** 2019 $45 BE

♀♀♀♀   **Orange Cabernet Sauvignon 2010 Rating** 89 **To** 2018 $23 BE

Swings & Roundabouts   ★★★★☆

2807 Caves Road, Yallingup, WA 6232 **Region** Margaret River
T (08) 9756 6640 **www**.swings.com.au **Open** 7 days 10–5
Winemaker Brian Fletcher **Est.** 2004 **Dozens** 25 000 **Vyds** 5.86ha
The Swings & Roundabouts name comes from the expression used to encapsulate the eternal balancing act between the various aspects of grape and wine production. Swings aims to balance the serious side with a touch of fun. There are now four ranges: Kiss Chasey, Life of Riley, Swings & Roundabouts and the Backyard Stories. Exports to the US and China.

♀♀♀♀♀   **Backyard Stories Margaret River Chardonnay 2011** Has had a label, vineyard and winery upgrade, with barrel fermentation in French oak and extended lees contact. Bright yellow-green; it is a beautifully balanced and constructed wine, fruit and oak going hand in (a lace) glove with white peach, nectarine and cashew nuances, acidity giving extra length to the palate. Screwcap. 13.5% alc. **Rating** 94 **To** 2018 $29

♀♀♀♀♀   **Margaret River Chenin Blanc 2011** Light straw-green; has an unusually
○   fragrant and evocative bouquet of tropical fruit and lemon rind, leading into a fresh and juicy palate. Top-class example. Screwcap. 12.5% alc. **Rating** 93 **To** 2015 $18

○   **Margaret River Shiraz 2010** Moderately strong purple-crimson; has an expressive bouquet with warm spices and licorice, then an attractive medium-bodied palate with blackberry fruit and a powerful reprise of the bouquet's spice and licorice to the fore. Screwcap. 14% alc. **Rating** 93 **To** 2020 $20

○   **Margaret River Sauvignon Blanc Semillon 2011** Light straw-green; the bouquet of mixed herbaceous and citrus/gooseberry fruits is replicated on a palate that builds intensity through to the finish. Screwcap. 12.5% alc. **Rating** 92 **To** 2013 $20
Backyard Stories Margaret River Cabernet Sauvignon 2010 Rating 91 **To** 2020 $39 BE
Margaret River Chardonnay 2011 Rating 90 **To** 2016 $22 BE
○   **Margaret River Cabernet Merlot 2010** Light to medium red-purple; the red and blackcurrant fruit aromas and flavours hold together well, with vibrant mouthfeel and good length. Screwcap. 14% alc. **Rating** 90 **To** 2018 $20

Swooping Magpie   ★★★

860 Commonage Road, Yallingup, WA 6282 **Region** Margaret River
T (08) 9756 6227 **www**.swoopingmagpie.com.au **Open** 7 days 11–5
Winemaker Kevin McKay, Julian Langworthy (Contract) **Est.** 1998 **Dozens** 2000
Vyds 4.5ha
Neil and Leann Tuffield's vineyard is situated in the hills behind the coastal town of Yallingup. The name 'was inspired by a family of magpies who consider the property part of their territory'. Vineyard plantings (shiraz, semillon, chenin blanc, verdelho, cabernet franc, cabernet sauvignon and muscat a petit grains) are supplemented by purchased sauvignon blanc, chenin blanc, shiraz, cabernet sauvignon and merlot. Exports to Vietnam, Singapore and Thailand.

♀♀♀♀   **Margaret River Verdelho 2011** Pale, bright straw-green; it fills the mouth with ripe, tropical fruit salad flavours, rounded off nicely on the finish with lemon/citrus acidity. Screwcap. 12.5% alc. **Rating** 89 **To** 2014 $18

Margaret River Sauvignon Blanc Semillon 2011 Light straw-green; leaves it until the last moment on the back-palate and finish to really make its presence felt, and even then in a somewhat amorphous fashion in terms of fruit flavour, the texture and length the redeeming feature. Screwcap. 13.7% alc. **Rating** 87 To 2013 $18

Sylvan Springs ★★★

40 Blythmans Road, Blewitt Springs, SA 5171 (postal) **Region** McLaren Vale
T (08) 8383 0500 **www**.sylvansprings.com.au **Open** Not
Winemaker Brian Light (Consultant) **Est.** 1974 **Dozens** 4200 **Vyds** 35.34ha
The Pridmore family has been involved in grapegrowing and winemaking in McLaren Vale for four generations, spanning over 100 years. The pioneer was Cyril Pridmore, who established The Wattles Winery in 1896, and purchased Sylvan Park, one of the original homesteads in the area, in 1901. The original family land in the township of McLaren Vale was sold in '78, but not before third-generation Digby Pridmore had established vineyards (in '74) near Blewitt Springs. When he retired in '90, his son David purchased the vineyard (planted to nine different varieties) and, with sister Sally, is involved in all aspects of the business. Exports to the US, Canada, Denmark and China.

🍷🍷🍷🍷 **McLaren Vale Semillon Sauvignon Blanc 2011** Quartz-white; somewhat
✪ unexpectedly, makes an intense and lingering impact on the palate, citrus to the fore, tropical notes behind. Bang for the buck. Screwcap. 11% alc. **Rating** 89 To 2013 $13
Bell Rd McLaren Vale Cabernet Sauvignon 2009 Medium red-purple; a bright and lively wine with strong cassis fruit and lifted acidity on the finish; pH control may have been zealous. Diam. 14% alc. **Rating** 88 **To** 2017 $20
Hard Yards McLaren Vale Shiraz 2010 Good hue; a well-balanced medium-bodied shiraz, with plum, blackberry and dark chocolate, the vanillin American oak well integrated. Screwcap. 14.5% alc. **Rating** 87 **To** 2015 $15

Symphony Hill Wines ★★★★★

2017 Eukey Road, Ballandean, Qld 4382 **Region** Granite Belt
T (07) 4684 1388 **www**.symphonyhill.com.au **Open** 7 days 10–4
Winemaker Mike Hayes **Est.** 1999 **Dozens** 6000 **Vyds** 3.5ha
Ewen and Elissa Macpherson purchased what was then an old table grape and orchard property in 1996. In partnership with Ewen's parents, Bob and Jill Macpherson, they developed the vineyard, while Ewen completed his Bachelor of Applied Science in viticulture (2003). The vineyard (now much expanded) has been established using state-of-the-art technology; vineyard manager and winemaker Mike Hayes has a degree in viticulture and is a third-generation viticulturist in the Granite Belt region. Symphony Hill is planted to verdelho, viognier, pinot noir, shiraz and cabernet sauvignon. It has firmly established its reputation as one of the Granite Belt's foremost wineries. Exports to China and Japan.

🍷🍷🍷🍷🍷 **Semillon 2011** Light, bright straw-green; a very attractive, well-made wine, with lemongrass and citrus nuances running through the long, evenly balanced palate, finishing with cleansing acidity. Thoroughly impressive. Screwcap. 12.2% alc. Rating 94 To 2018 $25
Wild Child Viognier 2010 Gleaming straw-green; if you really like the varietal flavour of viognier, coupled with its weight and viscosity, this will hit the spot with considerable force. It is full to overflowing with varietal fruit expression, but finishes pleasantly bitter rather than with phenolic heaviness. Right up there with the best. Screwcap. 13.5% alc. Rating 94 To 2015 $30

🍷🍷🍷🍷🍷 **Gewurztraminer 2010** Rating 93 To 2016 $25
Reserve Granite Belt Sauvignon Blanc 2011 Rating 92 To 2014 $25
Granite Belt Shiraz 2009 Rating 92 To 2019 $25
Granite Belt Pinot Gris 2011 Rating 91 To 2014 $30
Danying Cabernet Sauvignon 2009 Rating 90 To 2019 $25

🍷🍷🍷🍷 **Reserve Granite Belt Verdelho 2011** Rating 89 To 2013 $25

Syrahmi
★★★★☆

PO Box 438, Heathcote, Vic 3523 **Region** Heathcote
T 0407 057 471 **www**.syrahmi.com.au **Open** Not
Winemaker Adam Foster **Est.** 2004 **Dozens** 1000
Adam Foster worked as a chef in Vic and London before moving to the front of house and becoming increasingly interested in wine. He then worked as a cellar hand with a who's who in Australia and France, including Torbreck, Chapoutier, Mitchelton, Domaine Ogier, Heathcote Winery, Jasper Hill and Domaine Pierre Gaillard. He became convinced that the Cambrian soils of Heathcote could produce the best possible Shiraz, and since 2004 has purchased grapes from the region, using the full bag of open-ferment techniques, with whole bunches, extended cold-soak, wild yeast and mlf and hand-plunging, then 13 months in French oak, bottled unfined and unfiltered. Exports to the US and Japan.

ΨΨΨΨΨ **La La Shiraz Viognier 2008** Has retained bright crimson-red colour; an
extremely fragrant bouquet with both fruit and French oak having their say, some of the spicy characters emanating from whole bunch inclusion; it is an interesting decision to hold back the release of the wine, for it was, is and always will be a Shiraz of finesse and elegance, notwithstanding the intensity and length of the fruit. Its character fully reflects Adam Foster's stellar winemaking career. Screwcap. 13.8% alc. **Rating** 96 **To** 2028 $120

ΨΨΨΨΨ **Heathcote Mourvedre 2010 Rating** 92 **To** 2018

T'Gallant

1385 Mornington-Flinders Road, Main Ridge, Vic 3928 **Region** Mornington Peninsula
T (03) 5989 6565 **www**.tgallant.com.au **Open** 7 days 10–5
Winemaker Kevin McCarthy **Est.** 1990 **Dozens** NFP
Husband-and-wife consultant winemakers Kevin McCarthy and Kathleen Quealy carved out such an important niche market for the T'Gallant label that in 2003, after protracted negotiations, it was acquired by Beringer Blass (now part of TWE). The acquisition of a 15ha property and the planting of 10ha of pinot gris gives the business a firm geographic base, as well as providing increased resources for its signature wine. La Baracca Trattoria is open seven days for lunch and for specially booked evening events.

ΨΨΨΨΨ **Grace Pinot Grigio 2011** The trying conditions of '11 have made for some
interesting savoury wines from the Mornington Peninsula, especially with Pinot Gris/Grigio. This example has great concentration, lots of lemony fruits and acidity, while also showing a strong and very attractive thread of sizzling bacon fat; lots of interest, and lots of fun. Screwcap. 12.5% alc. **Rating** 94 **To** 2016 $25 BE
Tribute Pinot Gris 2010 The pinot gris spectrum on the back label suggests this to be at the luscious end, and I must agree; candied pear, spices and bath talc are on the bouquet, with an unctuous texture that is commanding at the very least; a style set to polarise opinion. Screwcap. 14.5% alc. **Rating** 94 **To** 2015 $34 BE
Odysseus 2010 Bright crimson-purple; T'Gallant has never been afraid to venture into the unknown, and has certainly done so here, succeeding to an extraordinary degree; the black fruit of Bendigo shiraz has found a natural bedmate with the cherry fruit of the Pyrenees nebbiolo, and the bogeyman of mouth-ripping tannins has not appeared, perhaps scared by the single eye staring from the label. Screwcap. 14.5% alc. **Rating** 94 **To** 2030 $49

ΨΨΨΨΨ **Cyrano Pinot Noir 2010 Rating** 93 **To** 2016 $30
Imogen Pinot Gris 2011 Rating 90 **To** 2014 $25 BE
Tribute Pinot Noir 2010 Rating 90 **To** 2015 $40

Tahbilk

Goulburn Valley Highway, Tabilk, Vic 3608 **Region** Nagambie Lakes
T (03) 5794 2555 **www**.tahbilk.com.au **Open** Mon–Sat 9–5, Sun 11–5
Winemaker Alister Purbrick, Neil Larson, Alan George **Est.** 1860 **Dozens** 100 000
Vyds 221.50ha

A winery steeped in tradition (with National Trust classification), which should be visited at least once by every wine-conscious Australian, and which makes wines – particularly red wines – utterly in keeping with that tradition. The essence of that heritage comes in the form of the tiny quantities of Shiraz made entirely from vines planted in 1860. Tahbilk has a wetlands project, with walks connected by short journeys on a small punt. Serendipitous, perhaps, but the current release wines are absolutely outstanding. Exports to all major markets.

♥♥♥♥♥ **1860 Vines Shiraz 2006** Exceptionally bright, clear crimson with no hint of colour change; this is one of the best 1860s Vines ever made. It has effortless power that invests the palate with extreme length, the red and black cherry fruit responsible for all the aroma and flavour, oak merely a vehicle, the tannins superfine. The number of these vines killed by frost in 2007 is a tragedy of monumental proportions. Screwcap. 13.5% alc. **Rating** 97 **To** 2030 $212

1927 Vines Marsanne 2002 Deep gold; a delicious mixture of ripe stone fruit, pear and honey riding on a magic carpet of natural acidity. If you are prepared to gamble with the cork gods, go to it. 12.5% alc. **Rating** 96 **To** 2020 $45

Eric Stevens Purbrick Shiraz 2006 Bright crimson; in true Tahbilk style, and this is a particularly good example, blackberry, plum and cherry all present on the medium- to full-bodied palate; the tannins are distinct, but finer than in some years. A classy wine with a very long future. Screwcap. 13.5% alc. **Rating** 96 **To** 2036 $70

Eric Stevens Purbrick Cabernet Sauvignon 2006 Has retained good hue, although not especially deep. Medium-bodied, and more than usually elegant for Tahbilk's overall style; there are also attractive cassis/red berry varietal fruit flavours supported by fine tannins on the long palate. Screwcap. 14% alc. **Rating** 96 **To** 2026 $70

♥♥♥♥♀ **Marsanne 2011** Comes as part of a long and distinguished series of wines, the ✪ screwcap guaranteeing the development of honeyed, toasty flavours and aromas over the coming decade. Pale green-straw; at the start of a long life, already expressive and juicy, with a mix of lime and honeysuckle on the impressively long palate; has the acidity for long ageing. 11.5% alc. **Rating** 93 **To** 2021 $17

✪ **Shiraz 2008** Lively crimson-red colour; it is open-fermented and spends 18 months in a mix of French oak of various sizes and ages. It has a delicious, albeit unexpected, edge of red cherry fruit on the medium-bodied palate; the core is black cherry and plum, and the tannins are particularly good. A very appealing wine. Screwcap. 14.5% alc. **Rating** 93 **To** 2025 $20

✪ **Cabernet Sauvignon 2008** Good hue; a complex blend of six vineyard blocks planted between 1949 and 2001; its flavours are lively and juicy, with cassis obvious along with fine, ripe tannins; oak, as always, adds more to texture than to flavour. A really enjoyable wine, good now or in 10 years. Screwcap. 14.5% alc. **Rating** 93 **To** 2020 $20

Viognier 2011 Rating 91 **To** 2014 $22

Talisman Wines   ★★★★☆

PO Box 354, Cottesloe, WA 6911 **Region** Geographe
T 0401 559 266 **www**.talismanwines.com.au **Open** Not
Winemaker Peter Stanlake **Est.** 2009 **Dozens** 1700 **Vyds** 9ha

Kim Robinson (and wife Jenny) began the development of their vineyard in 2000, and now have cabernet, shiraz, malbec, zinfandel, chardonnay, riesling and sauvignon blanc. Kim says that 'after eight frustrating years of selling grapes to Evans & Tate and Wolf Blass, we decided to optimise the vineyard and attempt to make quality wines'. The measure of their success was the award of at least one gold medal for each of the wines submitted up to and including the Geographe Wine Show '10. They say this could not have been achieved without the assistance of vineyard manager Victor Bertola, and winemaker Peter Stanlake.

♥♥♥♥♥ **Ferguson Valley Riesling 2011** Pale straw-green; has excellent varietal character on both bouquet and palate, with ripe citrus balanced by perfect acidity; the finish is long and crystal bright. Ferguson Valley, incidentally, is in the Geographe region of WA. Screwcap. 13% alc. **Rating** 94 **To** 2019 $20

ȲȲȲȲȲ Ferguson Valley Riesling 2010 Rating 93
⭘   To 2020 $20
⭘   Ferguson Valley Riesling 2009 Rating 92 To 2019 $20
         Ferguson Valley Shiraz 2009 Rating 92 To 2024 $30

ȲȲȲȲ Ferguson Valley Sauvignon Blanc 2011 Rating 89 To Now $15
⭘   Ferguson Valley Sauvignon Blanc 2010 Rating 89 To Now $15
        Gabrielle Ferguson Valley Chardonnay 2010 Rating 89 To 2014 $25

Tallavera Grove Vineyard & Winery ★★★★★

749 Mount View Road, Mount View, NSW 2325 **Region** Hunter Valley
T (02) 4990 7535 **www.**tallaveragrove.com.au **Open** Thurs–Mon 10–5
Winemaker Luke Watson, Jim Chatto **Est.** 2000 **Dozens** 2500 **Vyds** 40ha
Tallavera Grove is one of the many wine interests of Dr John Davis and family. The family is a
50% owner of Briar Ridge, a 12ha vineyard in Coonawarra, a 100ha vineyard at Wrattonbully
(Stonefields Vineyard) and a 36ha vineyard at Orange (the Carillion wines are sourced from
this vineyard). The 40ha Hunter Valley vineyards are planted to chardonnay, shiraz, semillon,
verdelho, cabernet sauvignon and viognier. The Mount View winery will eventually be
equipped to handle 200–300 tonnes of fruit.

ȲȲȲȲȲ Fenestella Hunter Valley Shiraz 2010 Bright purple-crimson; a fragrant
        red and black cherry and plum bouquet is logically followed by a fruit-sweet
        palate with polished tannins and quality French oak. Fenestella is a tiny marine
        arnimal that long ago formed the limestone found in the red soils of the vineyard.
        Screwcap. 14.5% alc. **Rating** 95 **To** 2025 $42
        Carillion The Feldspars Orange Shiraz 2010 Deep purple-crimson; has a
        most impressive medium- to full-bodied palate, blackberry fruit interwoven with
        spicy/peppery nuances, licorice, and high-quality oak. Has a long and assured
        future. Screwcap. 14.5% alc. **Rating** 95 **To** 2025 $42
        Hunter Valley Semillon 2011 Pale quartz-green; full of flavour and personality,
        young Semillon with exuberant citrus and lemongrass flavours running through
        the length of the palate, finishing with crisp, cleansing acidity. Screwcap. 11.5% alc.
        Rating 94 **To** 2021 $22
        Carillion Orange Cabernet Sauvignon 2010 Full crimson-purple; perfectly
        ripened cabernet sauvignon fruit dovetailing with 15 months in French oak; the
        gently savoury tannins lend the palate the authority that top-quality Cabernet
        should show, yet this wine is no more than medium-bodied. Screwcap. 14% alc.
        Rating 94 **To** 2025 $28

ȲȲȲȲȲ Carillion Orange Chardonnay 2011 Rating 93 To 2018 $26
✪   Carillion Orange Cabernet Merlot 2010 Crimson-purple; a very attractive
        bouquet, with black and red currant fruit flavours that are precisely repeated
        on the medium- to full-bodied palate; deft oak handling throughout. Screwcap.
        14% alc. **Rating** 92 **To** 2020 $22
        Stonefields Vineyard Wrattonbully Arbitrage 2010 Rating 92 To 2022
        $35 BE
        Stonefields Vineyard Wrattonbully Arbitrage 2009 Rating 92 To 2025
        $35 BE

ȲȲȲȲ Hunter Valley Vermentino 2011 Rating 89 To 2013 $22
✪   Carillion Orange Sauvignon Blanc 2011 Rating 89 To 2013 $19
✪   Carillion Orange Verduzzo 2010 Rating 89 To 2015 $19

Tallis Wine ★★★☆

Major Plains Road, Dookie, Vic 3646 **Region** Central Victoria Zone
T (03) 5823 5383 **www.**talliswine.com.au **Open** W'ends 10–5 or by appt
Winemaker Richard Tallis, Tanya Blackmore **Est.** 2000 **Dozens** 2000 **Vyds** 24.75ha
Fourth-generation farmers Richard and Alice Tallis planted their vineyard on the red volcanic
loam soils of their traditional farming property, bringing back viticulture to the Dookie area

after its absence for almost 100 years. In the late 1800s Dookie flourished with expansive vineyards, and at its peak produced one-third of Victoria's wine. Annual wine balls were held on the Tallis property in a vast, and still undiscovered, cellar buried beneath the Dookie Hills. Tallis uses a 'tread lightly' approach in the vineyard, avoiding sprays and using mulching and composting, with minimum intervention in the winery. An eco-sensitive cellar door constructed from straw bales grown on the property, plus recycled and sustainable building materials, and with an energy-sensitive layout, opened in 2012. Exports to Fiji and China.

ΨΨΨΨϙ **The Silent Showman Shiraz 2010** Deeper colour than the Dookie Hills; a significantly deeper and more intense wine, although it shares the complex savoury/earthy undertones to its perfectly ripened blackberry and plum fruit; 20 months in new and used French oak precisely judged. Screwcap. 14% alc. **Rating** 93 **To** 2025 $35

ΨΨΨΨ **Dookie Hills Shiraz 2010** Medium red-purple; even here, the vintage has
❂　　worked its magic: savoury/spicy notes run through the bouquet and medium-bodied palate alike, and the wine has good balance and length. Screwcap. 14.6% alc. **Rating** 89 **To** 2017 $18
The Silent Showman Shiraz Viognier 2008 Rating 89 **To** 2018 $25

Taltarni
★★★★☆

339 Taltarni Road, Moonambel, Vic 3478 **Region** Pyrenees
T (03) 5459 7900 **www**.taltarni.com.au **Open** 7 days 10–5
Winemaker Loïc Le Calvez (former) **Est.** 1972 **Dozens** 80 000 **Vyds** 97ha
In 2009 the American owner and founder of Clos du Val (Napa Valley), Taltarni and Clover Hill (see separate entry) brought the management of these three businesses and Domaine de Nizas (Languedoc) under the one roof. The group is known as Goelet Wine Estates. Taltarni is the largest of the Australian ventures, its estate vineyards of great value and underpinning the substantial annual production. There is no question it makes good red wines, but given its region, the climate/terroir of its very large estate vineyards and the age of the vines, one has the constantly nagging feeling it ought to do better. Exports to all major markets.

ΨΨΨΨΨ **Estate Pyrenees Shiraz 2009** Deep magenta, vivid purple hue; a pure, expressive and ripe black-fruited bouquet, showing roasted meats, quartz and a dash of eucalypt; the palate is juicy, generous and fresh, with the concentration and structure to stand the test of time. Cork. 14% alc. **Rating** 94 **To** 2020 $40 BE

ΨΨΨΨϙ **Estate Pyrenees Cabernet Sauvignon 2009 Rating** 90 **To** 2018 $40 BE

ΨΨΨΨ **Three Monks Fume Blanc 2011 Rating** 89 **To** 2014 $25 BE
❂　　**T Series Sauvignon Blanc Semillon 2010 Rating** 89 **To** Now $17
Heathcote Shiraz 2008 Rating 89 **To** 2018 $40
❂　　**T Series Chardonnay Pinot Noir NV Rating** 89 **To** 2014 $17 BE
T Series Sauvignon Blanc Semillon 2011 Rating 88 **To** 2013 $17 BE
T Series Shiraz 2009 Rating 87 **To** 2015 $17 BE
Three Monks Shiraz Mourvedre Grenache 2005 Rating 87 **To** 2014 $25 BE
Tache Chardonnay Pinot Noir Pinot Meunier 2010 Rating 87 **To** 2013 $26

Tamburlaine

358 McDonalds Road, Pokolbin, NSW 2321 **Region** Hunter Valley
T (02) 4998 4200 **www**.mywinery.com **Open** 7 days 9.30–5
Winemaker Mark Davidson, Ashley Horner **Est.** 1966 **Dozens** 80 000
A thriving business that until exports started to grow significantly sold over 90% of its wine through the cellar door and by mailing list (with an active tasting club members' cellar program offering wines held and matured at Tamburlaine). The maturing of the estate-owned Orange vineyard has led to a dramatic rise in quality across the range. Both the Hunter Valley and Orange vineyards are now certified organic. Exports to the UK, the US and other major markets.

ΨΨΨΨΨ Reserve Orange Riesling 2011 A ripe, exotic and highly perfumed bouquet offering candied orange, spices and bath talc; the palate is fresh, textured and long, with a distinct Alsatian feel, finishing with washed river stone minerality and fine-boned acidity. Screwcap. 11.7% alc. **Rating** 94 **To** 2018 $30 BE
Reserve Orange Sauvignon Blanc 2011 A wine that can only add to the reputation of Orange as a natural producer of high-quality Sauvignon Blanc, with its exuberant display of passionfruit, green pineapple, passionfruit – and a strong streak of citrussy acidity to conclude. Screwcap. 11.3% alc. **Rating** 94 **To** 2013 $30
Reserve Orange Syrah 2010 Deep crimson; a fragrant combination of red fruits, nutmeg and cinnamon, with a little charcuterie complexity; medium-bodied and fleshy on entry, the fine tannins provide contrast and vibrancy on the balanced finish. Screwcap. 13.9% alc. **Rating** 94 **To** 2020 $44 BE

ΨΨΨΨΨ Reserve Hunter Valley Chardonnay 2011 **Rating** 91 **To** 2017 $30 BE

ΨΨΨΨ Reserve Orange Cabernet Sauvignon 2010 **Rating** 89 **To** 2020 $44 BE
Reserve Hunter Valley Semillon 2011 **Rating** 88 **To** 2017 $30 BE
Reserve Hunter Valley Syrah 2010 **Rating** 88 **To** 2018 $44 BE
Reserve Orange Chardonnay 2011 **Rating** 87 **To** 2015 $30 BE

Tanglewood Vines   ★★★★

RMB 383, Bridgetown, WA 6255 (postal) **Region** Blackwood Valley
T (08) 9764 4051 **www.**tanglewood-wines.com **Open** Not
Winemaker Hamish Hume, Bernie Stanlake **Est.** 1999 **Dozens** 500 **Vyds** 6.2ha
Hamish and Caroline Hume have established cabernet sauvignon (2.2ha), merlot and viognier (2ha each). While they have hitherto been content to keep a low profile and have not sent wines for appraisal, their recent wine show success has led them to take the plunge. Exports to the Philippines.

ΨΨΨΨΨ Blackwood Valley Merlot 2010 Good colour; an elegant and lively Merlot
✪ with cassis, black olive and spice aromas and flavours, the tannins fine and persistent. Has what I regard as traditional/correct merlot varietal character. Screwcap. 14% alc. **Rating** 90 **To** 2014 $15
✪ Blackwood Valley Cabernet Sauvignon 2010 Has many things in common with the '10 Merlot; no more than medium-bodied, but with good intensity and structure to the mix of blackcurrant and savoury/earthy nuances. Certainly very good value. Screwcap. 13.5% alc. **Rating** 90 **To** 2017 $15

ΨΨΨΨ Blackwood Valley Viognier 2011 **Rating** 87 **To** 2013 $16

Tanjil Wines   ★★★☆

1171 Moe Road, Willow Grove, Vic 3825 (postal) **Region** Gippsland
T 0409 773 037 **www.**tanjilwines.com **Open** Not
Winemaker Robert Hewet, Olga Garot **Est.** 2001 **Dozens** 2000 **Vyds** 3ha
Robert Hewet and Olga Garot have planted 1ha each of pinot noir, pinot grigio and savagnin on a north-facing slope at an altitude of 200m between the Latrobe and Tanjil valleys. The cool climate allows the vines to grow without irrigation; yields are kept low and the wines are made onsite.

ΨΨΨΨ Cabernet Shiraz 2010 Some early signs of colour development; consistently with the colour, the tannins and fruit profile are soft and ripe; that said, it has an attractive mix of black fruits, licorice, spice and some distinctly savoury components. Screwcap. 14.6% alc. **Rating** 89 **To** 2017 $20
Gippsland Sparkling Pinot Gris 2007 In one sense you have to wonder why anyone would go to the trouble of making Sparkling Pinot Gris, let alone giving it almost four years on tirage. This wine does provide some sort of answer, for it does have a nicely balanced palate with good fruit weight and length. Diam. 12.8% alc.
Rating 89 **To** 2014 $25

Tapanappa ★★★★★

PO Box 174, Crafers, SA 5152 **Region** South Australia
T 0419 843 751 **www**.tapanappawines.com.au **Open** Not
Winemaker Brian Croser **Est.** 2002 **Dozens** 2500 **Vyds** 16.7ha
The Tapanappa partners are Brian Croser (formerly of Petaluma), Jean-Charles Cazes of Chateau Lynch-Bages in Pauillac, and Société Jacques Bollinger, the parent company of Champagne Bollinger. The partnership has three vineyard sites in Australia: the Whalebone Vineyard at Wrattonbully (planted to cabernet sauvignon, shiraz and merlot over 30 years ago); the Tiers Vineyard (chardonnay) at Piccadilly in the Adelaide Hills (the remainder of the Tiers Vineyard chardonnay continues to be sold to Petaluma); and the Foggy Hill Vineyard on the southern tip of the Fleurieu Peninsula (pinot noir). Exports to all major markets.

🍷🍷🍷🍷🍷 Wrattonbully Shiraz 2009 Medium red-purple; an elegant, complex wine bringing spice, mint and quality oak aromas and flavours into line with the ripe mulberry/plum fruit of the medium-bodied palate, the tannins soft and balanced. Screwcap. 14.5% alc. **Rating** 94 **To** 2024 $47

Tapestry ★★★★☆

Olivers Road, McLaren Vale, SA 5171 **Region** McLaren Vale
T (08) 8323 9196 **www**.tapestrywines.com.au **Open** 7 days 11–5
Winemaker Jon Ketley **Est.** 1971 **Dozens** 10 000 **Vyds** 37.3ha
After a brief period of ownership by Brian Light, the former Merrivale Winery was acquired in 1997 by the Gerard family, previously owners of Chapel Hill. It has 30-year-old vineyards in McLaren Vale and in the distinctly different Bakers Gully location. Less than half the grapes are used for the Tapestry label. Exports to Singapore, Hong Kong, India, Indonesia and China.

🍷🍷🍷🍷🍷 The Vincent McLaren Vale Shiraz 2009 Medium purple-red; from Tapestry's Bakers Gully Vineyard planted in the early '70s; matured for 18 months in French oak; full-bodied, yet supple and rounded, with black fruits, spice and licorice reflecting the cool site. Why condemn this wine to cork and give its cheaper sibling the advantage of screwcap? 14.5% alc. **Rating** 94 **To** 2019 $50

🍷🍷🍷🍷 McLaren Vale Cabernet Sauvignon 2010 **Rating** 90 **To** 2020 $28

🍷🍷🍷🍷 McLaren Vale Shiraz 2009 **Rating** 89 **To** 2019 $28

Tar & Roses/Trust ★★★★☆

61 Vickers Lane, Nagambie, Vic 3608 (postal) **Region** Central Victoria Zone
T (03) 5794 1811 **www**.tarandroses.com.au **Open** Not
Winemaker Don Lewis, Narelle King **Est.** 2004 **Dozens** 15 000 **Vyds** 5ha
Tar & Roses is one of the more interesting new arrivals on the Australian winemaking scene, even though the partners, Don Lewis and Narelle King, have been making wine together for many years at Mitchelton and – for the past three years – Priorat, Spain. Don came from a grapegrowing family in Red Cliffs, near Mildura, and in his youth was press-ganged into working in the vineyard. When he left home he swore never to be involved in vineyards again, but in 1973 found himself accepting the position of assistant winemaker to Colin Preece at Mitchelton, where he remained until his retirement 32 years later. Narelle, having qualified as a chartered accountant, set off to travel, and while in South America met a young Australian winemaker who had just completed vintage in Argentina, and who lived in France. The lifestyle appealed greatly, so on her return to Australia she obtained her winemaking degree from CSU and was offered work by Mitchelton as a bookkeeper and cellar hand. Together they are making wines that are a mosaic of Australia, Italy and Spain in their inspiration.

🍷🍷🍷🍷🍷 Tar & Roses Alpine Valleys Heathcote Tempranillo 2010 Bright crimson-red; as pure an expression of tempranillo as you are likely to find, with a silky swirl of red cherry blossom and fruit that seems to have no end on the palate. No need to wait, although will not lose its charm any time soon. Screwcap. 14.5% alc. **Rating** 94 **To** 2018 $24

ΨΨΨΨΩ **Tar & Roses Central Victoria Pinot Grigio 2011** Pale pink; has a rose petal
✪ fragrance over and above the pear, verging on nougat; these nuances all reappear
with more impact on the back-palate of a Pinot Grigio with distinct attitude.
Screwcap. 13% alc. **Rating** 92 **To** Now $18
✪ **Tar & Roses Heathcote Shiraz 2010** A fragrant bouquet of fresh blackberry,
sage, violets and a lick of charry oak are on display; the medium to full-bodied
palate is fleshy, and the zesty acidity reveals red fruit highlights alongside some
fairly serious drying tannins; food in the form of protein is a necessity here.
Screwcap. 14.5% alc. **Rating** 92 **To** 2019 $20 BE
Tar & Roses Alpine Valleys Heathcote Tempranillo 2011 Rating 92
To 2015 $24 BE

Tarrawarra Estate ★★★★★

311 Healesville-Yarra Glen Road, Yarra Glen, Vic 3775 **Region** Yarra Valley
T (03) 5962 3311 **www**.tarrawarra.com.au **Open** Tues–Sun 11–5
Winemaker Clare Halloran **Est.** 1983 **Dozens** 14 000 **Vyds** 28.98ha
Tarrawarra is, and always has been, one of the top-tier wineries in the Yarra Valley. Founded
by Marc Besen AO and wife Eva, it has operated on the basis that quality is paramount, cost
a secondary concern. The creation of the Tarrawarra Museum of Art (twma.com.au) in a
purpose-built building constitutes another reason to visit the winery; indeed, many visitors
come specifically to look at the ever-changing displays in the Museum. On the wine front,
Clare Halloran adopts a low profile while nonetheless being actively engaged in numerous
winemaking events, be they Yarra Valley or Victorian (as in the case of the annual Pinot Noir
Workshop). Changes in the vineyard include the planting of shiraz and merlot, and in the
winery, the creation of a four-tier range: a deluxe MDB label made in tiny quantities and
only when the vintage permits; a single vineyard duo (J-Block Shiraz and K-Block Merlot);
a Reserve range of Chardonnay and Pinot Noir; and the 100% estate-grown varietal range.
Exports to the UK, the US, France, the Maldives and Singapore.

ΨΨΨΨΨ **Reserve Yarra Valley Chardonnay 2010** A reserved wine by name and nature,
with subdued citrus, stone fruits and spice on the bouquet; the palate is lively and
shows grip and texture, with the finish ultimately being long, generous, fresh and
expansive. Screwcap. 13% alc. **Rating** 94 **To** 2018 $50 BE
MDB Yarra Valley Chardonnay 2010 A special barrel selection to pay homage
to Marc and Daniel Besen, there is both power and finesse in this wine; nectarine,
pear, spice and toasty oak are on display, with the palate providing a fine entry
of citrus and then building to a long and nutty conclusion, with fine acidity
providing a neat foil to the generous fruit on offer. Screwcap. 13% alc. **Rating** 94
To 2018 $100 BE
J-Block Yarra Valley Shiraz 2010 Mid crimson; a spice-laden red and black-
fruited bouquet with an appealing mineral core; the palate is medium-bodied, fine
and pure-fruited, with silky tannins drawing out the even conclusion for a Pinot-
like and elegant experience. Screwcap. 14.5% alc. **Rating** 94 **To** 2016 $35 BE

ΨΨΨΨΩ **Reserve Yarra Valley Pinot Noir 2010** Rating 93 **To** 2018 $60 BE
K-Block Yarra Valley Merlot 2010 Rating 93 **To** 2016 $35 BE
K-Block Yarra Valley Merlot 2009 Rating 93 **To** 2017 $35
Yarra Valley Viognier Marsanne Roussanne 2010 Rating 92 **To** 2014 $30
Yarra Valley Pinot Noir 2010 Rating 90 **To** 2015 $22 BE
J-Block Yarra Valley Shiraz 2009 Rating 90 **To** 2016 $35

ΨΨΨΨ **Yarra Valley Chardonnay 2010** Rating 89 **To** 2014 $22 BE

Tasmanian Estates ★★★★★

653 Auburn Road, Kayena, Tas 7270 **Region** Northern Tasmania
T (03) 6394 1111 **www**.tamarridge.com.au **Open** 7 days 10–5
Winemaker Tom Ravech **Est.** 1994 **Dozens** 75 000 **Vyds** 134.6ha

In August 2010 Brown Brothers purchased Tamar Ridge from Gunns Limited for $32.5 million. While Dr Andrew Pirie has retired from his former position of CEO and chief winemaker, he has been at pains to point out that the end of his five-year tenure happened to coincide with the acquisition. Tasmania is the one region of Australia with demand for grapes and wine exceeding supply. Moreover, Tamar Ridge has been very well managed during the seven years it was owned by Gunns. In November '11 Tamar Ridge and Pirie Tasmania were joined under the banner of Tasmanian Estates; this will not affect the continuation of the brands. Exports to the UK, the US and other major markets.

🍷🍷🍷🍷🍷 **Pirie Pinot Noir 2009** Clear ruby; the bouquet is particularly fragrant, with plum and black cherry fruit aromas plus balanced oak; an elegant and restrained wine on the palate, then bursts into song as you take your first breath after swallowing the wine, with a delicious spray of red fruits. Screwcap. 13.3% alc. **Rating** 95 **To** 2017 $38
Tamar Ridge Kayena Vineyard Chardonnay 2010 Brilliant straw-green; river pebbles and Chablis; apple and citrus; long, zesty finish. Gold Tas Wine Show '12. Screwcap. 12.5% alc. **Rating** 94 **To** 2017 $28

🍷🍷🍷🍷 **Tamar Ridge Kayena Vineyard Riesling 2010 Rating** 93 **To** 2020 $26
Tamar Ridge Kayena Vineyard Pinot Noir 2010 Rating 93 **To** 2016 $33
Pirie Non Vintage NV Rating 93 **To** 2014 $35
Devil's Corner Non Vintage Cuvee NV Rating 92 **To** 2015 $23
Pirie Vintage Sparkling 2006 Rating 90 **To** 2015 $50
Kayena Vineyard Limited Release Botrytis Riesling 2010 Rating 90 **To** 2016 $28

🍷🍷🍷 **Tamar Ridge Kayena Vineyard Sauvignon Blanc 2010 Rating** 87 **To** 2013 $26

Tatachilla   ★★★
151 Main Road, McLaren Vale, SA 5171 **Region** McLaren Vale
T (08) 8323 8656 **www**.tatachillawines.com.au **Open** Not
Winemaker Fanchon Ferrandi **Est.** 1903 **Dozens** 50 000 **Vyds** 12.4ha
Tatachilla was reborn in 1995 but has had a tumultuous history going back to 1903. Between 1903 and '61 the winery was owned by Penfolds; it was closed in '61 and reopened in '65 as the Southern Vales Co-operative. In the late 1980s it was purchased and renamed The Vales but did not flourish; in '93 it was purchased by local grower Vic Zerella and former Kaiser Stuhl chief executive Keith Smith. After extensive renovations, the winery was officially reopened in 1995 and won a number of tourist awards and accolades. It became part of Banksia Wines in 2001, in turn acquired by Lion Nathan in '02. Exports to all major markets.

🍷🍷🍷🍷 **Foundation McLaren Vale Shiraz 2006** Showing expected development, the tarry black fruits and leathery characters melded together by a generous, medium-bodied palate. Best enjoyed over the next five years. Cork. 14.5% alc. **Rating** 92 **To** 2017 $55

🍷🍷🍷 **McLaren Vale Cabernet Sauvignon 2009 Rating** 89 **To** 2018 $23 BE
McLaren Vale Shiraz 2009 Rating 88 **To** 2016 $23 BE
✪ **Partners Cabernet Shiraz 2010** A brightly coloured, juicy, fresh and youthful wine that is medium-bodied and ready for early consumption; no tricks here, just juicy fruit. Screwcap. 14% alc. **Rating** 88 **To** 2015 $12 BE

Tatler Wines   ★★★★☆
477 Lovedale Road, Lovedale, NSW 2321 **Region** Hunter Valley
T (02) 4930 9139 **www**.tatlerwines.com **Open** 7 days 10–5
Winemaker Daniel Binet **Est.** 1998 **Dozens** 6000 **Vyds** 15ha
Tatler Wines is a family-owned company headed by Sydney hoteliers, brothers Theo and Spiro Isak (Isakidis). The name comes from the Tatler Hotel on George Street, Sydney, which was purchased by father James (Dimitri) Isak in 1974 and operated by the family until its closure in '86. In '98 the Tatler name was reborn with the purchase of a 40ha property in Lovedale.

The vineyard is planted to 7ha of chardonnay and 4ha each of semillon and shiraz, the wines are made onsite in the recently renovated winery. Exports to the US.

ΨΨΨΨΨ **Museum Release Nigel's Hunter Valley Semillon 2006** Vibrant green hue; a heady combination of lemon curd and freshly toasted brioche; the toastiness is prominent on the palate, with the lemony acidity providing cut and thrust; a generous, rich and certainly ready aged release. Screwcap. 10% alc. **Rating** 92 **To** 2018 $30 BE

The Filibuster Canberra Shiraz 2010 Mid crimson; a savoury and spicy bouquet of tar, red fruits and a little brambly complexity; the palate is light- to medium-bodied, full of silky tannins and fragrant fruits; elegantly constructed, with a lingering spicy note to conclude. Screwcap. 14% alc. **Rating** 92 **To** 2020 $35 BE

Archie's Paddock Hunter Valley Shiraz 2010 Deep crimson, bright; a perfumed and spicy bouquet of cinnamon, red fruits and fresh leather; the palate is lively, forward, fleshy and accessible, ready for early consumption. Screwcap. 13.8% alc. **Rating** 91 **To** 2018 $25 BE

The Nonpareil Hunter Valley McLaren Vale Shiraz 2010 Deep crimson; while oak is the dominant feature of the bouquet, there is a lot of sweet, ripe black fruit loitering beneath; the palate is toasty, thickly textured and full of gravelly tannins, with a little fruitcake warmth noticeable on the finish. Screwcap. 14% alc. **Rating** 91 **To** 2022 $45 BE

ΨΨΨΨ **Nigel's Hunter Valley Semillon 2011 Rating** 89 **To** 2016 $25 BE
Rita's Hunter Valley Rose 2011 Rating 88 **To** 2014 $25 BE

Taylor Ferguson   ★★★★

Level 1, 62 Albert Street, Preston, Vic 3072 (postal) **Region** South Eastern Australia
T (03) 9487 2599 **www**.alepat.com.au **Open** Not
Winemaker Norman Lever **Est.** 1996 **Dozens** 40 000

Taylor Ferguson is the much-altered descendant of a business of that name established in Melbourne in 1898. A connecting web joins it with Alexander & Paterson (1892) and the much more recent distribution business of Alepat Taylor. The development of the Taylor Ferguson wine label under the direction of winemaker Norman Lever, using grapes and wines purchased mainly from Coonawarra, Langhorne Creek and the Riverina, is yet another strand, leading to a significant increase in the size of the negociant business. Exports to Germany, Iraq, Singapore, Malaysia, Taiwan, Vietnam and China.

ΨΨΨΨΨ **Fernando The First Shiraz 2008** Full purple-red; excellent for its age and vintage; a blend of Padthaway and McLaren Vale fruit, it has full-flavoured black cherry, plum and spice notes leading the way, the oak balanced and integrated. Overall there is surprising elegance, perhaps due to the controlled alcohol and fine-grained tannins. Cork. 14.2% alc. **Rating** 93 **To** 2020 $40

✪ **Directors Reserve Limited Release McLaren Vale Shiraz 2010** Deep crimson-purple; the wine was matured in both French and American oak, now largely integrated into the palate; here typical McLaren Vale plum and chocolate flavours abound, with savoury tannins to conclude. Diam. 14.9% alc. **Rating** 92 **To** 2020 $20

ΨΨΨΨ
✪ **Willbriggie Estate Durif 2008** Still deep in colour, although losing some of its brightness; a massive, full-bodied wine with sombre black fruits, bitter chocolate and earth, the tannins likewise massive, but in fact in balance with the wine, which is a drop-dead bbq special. Screwcap. 15% alc. **Rating** 89 **To** 2018 $12

Premium Selection Langhorne Creek Shiraz 2010 Rating 88 **To** 2014 $15
Fernando The First Cabernet Sauvignon 2008 Rating 88 **To** 2015 $40

Tayloroo Farm Wines   ★★★☆

215 Tranter Road, Toolleen, Vic 3551 **Region** Central Victoria Zone
T (03) 9010 5598 **Open** By appt
Winemaker Nick Taylor **Est.** 2005 **Dozens** 50 **Vyds** 1ha

Michelle and Nick Taylor purchased a 32ha property from a very traditional Italian family; it was mostly used for grazing and cropping, but with a 2ha oasis of ancient olive trees, fruit trees of every description and almond trees surrounding 0.8ha of shiraz and interplanted riesling and chardonnay (with a few more interplants of table grapes and unknown varieties). The entire property is run organically, with no chemical sprays whatsoever.

ΨΨΨΨ♀ **Heathcote Shiraz 2009** Has retained bright hue and good depth; has greater purity and finesse than the '10, suggesting that all the latter needs is more time in bottle; the superfine tannins on the finish draw out the bright cherry fruit at the heart of the wine. Diam. 14% alc. **Rating** 91 **To** 2019 $25

ΨΨΨΨ **Heathcote Shiraz 2010 Rating** 88 **To** 2017 $30

Taylors

Taylors Road, Auburn, SA 5451 **Region** Clare Valley
T (08) 8849 1111 **www.**taylorswines.com.au **Open** Mon–Fri 9–5, Sat & public hols 10–5, Sun 10–4
Winemaker Adam Eggins, Ryan Waples **Est.** 1969 **Dozens** 500 000 **Vyds** 340ha
The family-founded and owned Taylors continues to flourish and expand – its vineyards now total over 300ha, by far the largest holding in the Clare Valley. There have also been changes in terms of both the winemaking team and the wine style and quality, particularly through the outstanding St Andrews range. With each passing vintage, Taylors is managing to do the same for the Clare Valley as Peter Lehmann is doing for the Barossa Valley. Taylors celebrated its 40th vintage in fine style with the much anticipated 2012 vintage. Exports (under the Wakefield brand, for trademark reasons) to all major markets.

ΨΨΨΨΨ **St Andrews Bottle Aged Clare Valley Riesling 2001** Bright green-gold; thanks to the screwcap, has aged exactly as one would wish, lime, toast and honey driving the bouquet and palate, with acidity playing a key role in the wine as it is now, and will be through the remainder of the decade. 13% alc. **Rating** 96 **To** 2021 $35
St Andrews Old Block Clare Valley Shiraz 2010 Deep crimson, vibrant; a surprisingly elegant and understated bouquet of red and black fruits, thyme and licorice; the medium-bodied palate is focused and fresh, with ample fine-grained tannins and a very long and even finish; beautifully balanced and showing the pedigree of old vine material. Screwcap. 14% alc. **Rating** 95 **To** 2025 $120 BE
St Andrews Old Block Clare Valley Cabernet Sauvignon 2009 Deep colour; a complex and layered wine with pure cassis, violets and cedar on display; the palate is generous on the one hand, yet fine-boned and almost lacy on the other; very long and destined for a long life. Screwcap. 14% alc. **Rating** 95 **To** 2025 $120 BE
Jaraman Clare Valley Eden Valley Riesling 2011 Bright, light green-straw; the gently floral, pristine bouquet leads into a finely tensioned palate, lemon/lime/apple fruit riding on top of a minerally base ex the Eden Valley. Dead set stayer. Screwcap. 12% alc. **Rating** 94 **To** 2026 $25
St Andrews Single Vineyard Release Clare Valley Shiraz 2006 Very good colour for age, still 100% red; the power and complexity of the varietal black fruits and balanced tannins have garnered a trophy and gold medals from various quarters, including the US, Luxembourg (I think this is in fact Belgium) and Australia. Screwcap. 14.5% alc. **Rating** 94 **To** 2021 $65
TWP Taylors Winemaker's Project Clare Valley GSM 2010 Good hue, bright and clear; a 49/38/13% blend of grenache, shiraz and mataro inspired by winemaker Helen McCarthy's experiences judging at Barossa Valley wine shows. It has more depth of flavour and texture than all but a small handful of Clare Valley blends of these grapes. It is built to stay, its array of red and black fruits sustained by precisely weighted tannins. Screwcap. 14.5% alc. **Rating** 94 **To** 2025 $34

Jaraman Clare Valley Coonawarra Cabernet Sauvignon 2009 A 64/36% blend that has good colour and an aromatic fruit-driven bouquet with a mix of juicy and more savoury black and red fruits on the medium-bodied palate; the tannins are fine and ripe, and sustain the finish. Screwcap. 14.5% alc. **Rating** 94 **To** 2020 $30

St Andrews Single Vineyard Release Clare Valley Cabernet Sauvignon 2006 Medium red-purple, good for age; very obviously, a special selection from estate vineyards; has blackcurrant and black olive fruit complexed by quite warm earthy notes and vanillin oak, the tannins fine and ripe. Screwcap. 14.5% alc. **Rating** 94 **To** 2020 $65

ŶŶŶŶŶ St Andrews Single Vineyard Release Clare Valley Chardonnay 2010 **Rating** 93 **To** 2017 $35 BE

Jaraman Clare Valley McLaren Vale Shiraz 2010 **Rating** 93 **To** 2025 $30
Jaraman Clare Valley McLaren Vale Shiraz 2009 **Rating** 93 **To** 2017 $30

✪ Clare Valley Riesling 2011 Bright straw-green; picked later than most from '11, with greater depth and strength, but less aromatics and flowery notes; will likely reach an impressive peak around 2016, but go on long thereafter. Screwcap. 13% alc. **Rating** 92 **To** 2021 $19

St Andrews Single Vineyard Release Clare Valley Riesling 2009 **Rating** 92 **To** 2020 $35 BE

◉ Clare Valley Shiraz 2009 **Rating** 92 **To** 2024 $19

St Andrews Single Vineyard Release Clare Valley Cabernet Sauvignon 2009 **Rating** 92 **To** 2025 $60 BE

✪ Tempranillo 2011 A blend of Wrattonbully and Clare Valley grapes given Rolls Royce treatment in the winery. Light, bright crimson; the red cherry aromas of the bouquet are amplified on the totally delicious medium-bodied palate, with its exuberant display of red fruits, including red and black cherries, and superfine tannins. Screwcap. 14% alc. **Rating** 92 **To** 2016 $19

✪ Clare Valley Chardonnay 2010 Vibrant green hue; pure nectarine and spice are evident on the bouquet; the palate is fine and fresh, with pure fruit and complex savoury notes of cashew and spice seamlessly in play. Screwcap. 13.5% alc. **Rating** 91 **To** 2015 $19

✪ TWP Taylors Winemaker's Project Riverland Vermentino 2011 Bright, pale straw-green; a totally arresting wine, with a rapier-like palate of ripe pear and apple skins offset by piercing, freshening acidity, the finish breezy and dry. Screwcap. 10.5% alc. **Rating** 91 **To** 2013 $18

◉ Adelaide Hills Pinot Noir 2010 **Rating** 91 **To** 2016 $19

Jaraman Margaret River Adelaide Hills Sauvignon Blanc 2011 **Rating** 90 **To** 2013 $25 BE

St Andrews Single Vineyard Release Clare Valley Shiraz 2009 **Rating** 90 **To** 2020 $60 BE

✪ Clare Valley Cabernet Sauvignon 2009 Medium red-purple; the expressive blackcurrant/cassis bouquet introduces a medium-bodied wine with distinct elegance, fruit and oak playing off each other to good effect, the result an enjoyable Cabernet for drinking soon. Screwcap. 14% alc. **Rating** 90 **To** 2016 $18

Tellurian   ★★★★★

408 Tranter Road, Toolleen, Vic 3551 **Region** Heathcote
T 0431 004 766 **www.**tellurianwines.com.au **Open** By appt
Winemaker Tobias Ansted **Est.** 2003 **Dozens** 2500 **Vyds** 21.87ha
The vineyard is situated on the western side of Mt Camel at Toolleen, on the red Cambrian soil that has made Heathcote one of the foremost regions in Australia for the production of Shiraz (Tellurian means 'of the earth'). Planning is underway for the construction of a winery on the Toolleen vineyard site, and viticultural consultant Tim Brown not only supervises the Tellurian estate plantings, but also works closely with the growers of grapes purchased under contract for Tellurian. Further Rhône red and white varieties have been planted on the Tellurian property in 2011.

ŢŢŢŢŢ Pastiche Shiraz 2010 Somewhat brighter crimson that the Tranter; the bouquet and medium- to full-bodied palate are essentially fruit-driven by plum and blackberry flavours, with a nice savoury twist to the long finish. Screwcap. 13.7% alc. **Rating** 94 **To** 2022 $27

Tranter Heathcote Shiraz 2010 Good, strong and clear colour; a medium- to full-bodied palate, with French oak (50% new) and 15 months in barrel, and texture from ripe tannins all contributing complexity to the array of black fruits. Screwcap. 14.5% alc. **Rating** 94 **To** 2025 $40

ŢŢŢŢŢ Heathcote Marsanne 2011 **Rating** 90 **To** 2018 $27

Temple Bruer ★★★

Milang Road, Strathalbyn, SA 5255 **Region** Langhorne Creek
T (08) 8537 0203 **www**.templebruer.com.au **Open** Mon–Fri 9.30–4.30
Winemaker David Bruer, Vanessa Altmann **Est.** 1980 **Dozens** 10 000 **Vyds** 19.2ha
Temple Bruer was in the vanguard of the organic movement in Australia and was the focal point for the formation of Organic Vignerons Australia. Part of the production from its estate vineyards is used for its own label, part sold. Winemaker-owner David Bruer also has a vine propagation nursery, likewise run on an organic basis. Exports to the US and Japan.

ŢŢŢŢ Organic Riverland Vermentino 2011 Bright colour; a fresh and crunchy wine; slightly short on concentration and length; interesting fruit character though. Screwcap. 10.5% alc. **Rating** 87 **To** 2013 $19 BE

Tempus Two Wines ★★★★☆

Broke Road, Pokolbin, NSW 2321 **Region** Hunter Valley
T (02) 4993 3999 **www**.tempustwo.com.au **Open** 7 days 9–5
Winemaker Scott Comyns **Est.** 1997 **Dozens** 80 000
Tempus Two is the name for what was once Hermitage Road Wines. It is a mix of Latin (Tempus means time) and English; the change was forced on the winery by the EU Wine Agreement and the prohibition of the use of 'hermitage' on Australian wine labels. It has been a major success story, production growing from 6000 dozen in 1997 to 80 000 dozen today. Its cellar door, restaurant complex (including the Oishii Japanese restaurant) and small convention facilities are situated in a striking building. The design polarises opinion; I like it. Exports to all major markets.

ŢŢŢŢŢ Pewter Semillon 2011 Pale quartz; yet another '11 Hunter Valley Semillon with the freshness of raindrops on a spring day, yet with no shortage of lemon and lime aromas and juicy flavours on the lively palate. Diam. 10.5% alc. **Rating** 94 **To** 2024 $30

ŢŢŢŢŢ Copper Series Sauvignon Blanc 2011 From warmer sites on the Adelaide
✪ Hills, barrel-fermented in French oak 'and experienced yeast lees stirring during fermentation', a breathless disclosure by a marketer who has no idea what happens with all white wines. It's full of verve, with intense tangy fruit driving through the long and vibrant palate. Screwcap. 12.5% alc. **Rating** 93 **To** Now $20

✪ Copper Series Wilde Chardonnay 2010 A blend of Hunter Valley/Adelaide Hills grapes that has unexpected zest and drive, with nectarine and grapefruit flavours woven through subtle oak; finishes with balanced and fresh acidity. Screwcap. 13% alc. **Rating** 92 **To** 2015 $20

✪ Copper Series Grenache Shiraz Mourvedre 2010 Light, clear red; a 40/40/20% blend that comes together with conviction, offering a range of small red fruit flavours on a juicy light- to medium-bodied palate, tannins and oak well into the background. Screwcap. 14% alc. **Rating** 90 **To** 2015 $20

Pewter Coonawarra Cabernet Sauvignon 2010 **Rating** 90 **To** 2018 $30

ŢŢŢŢ Pewter Pinot Gris 2011 **Rating** 88 **To** 2013 $30
Verdelho 2011 **Rating** 88 **To** Now $15
Cabernet Merlot 2010 **Rating** 87 **To** 2014 $15
Blanc de Blanc 2011 **Rating** 87 **To** 2013 $15

Ten Men

870 Maroondah Highway, Coldstream, Vic 3770 (postal) **Region** Yarra Valley
T 0409 767 838 **www.**tenmenwines.com **Open** Not
Winemaker Ben Portet **Est.** 2009 **Dozens** 250
Owner Ben Portet is the 10th-generation winemaker in the Portet family, father Dominique (for many years in charge of Taltarni) and uncle Bernard (long-serving winemaker at Clos Duval in the Napa Valley) members of the ninth generation. Ben has a winemaking background second to none, building on his degree in oenology from Adelaide University with four vintages at Petaluma (while completing his university studies), thereafter Bordeaux (Chateau Beychevelle), Champagne (Louis Roederer), the Rhône Valley (M. Chapoutier), Stellenbosch (Warwick Estate), and the Napa Valley (Vineyard 29). His 'day job' is assisting his father at Dominique Portet (see separate entry).

Yarra Valley Shiraz 2010 Crimson-purple hue; a seamless fusion of black cherry and spice fruit, quality oak and fine, ripe tannins has resulted in an elegant, medium-bodied wine of considerable length; assured winemaking. Screwcap. 14% alc. **Rating** 94 **To** 2025 $40

Yarra Valley Sauvignon Blanc 2011 Rating 91 **To** 2013 $30

Ten Minutes by Tractor

1333 Mornington-Flinders Road, Main Ridge, Vic 3928 **Region** Mornington Peninsula
T (03) 5989 6455 **www.**tenminutesbytractor.com.au **Open** 7 days 11–5
Winemaker Richard McIntyre, Martin Spedding **Est.** 1999 **Dozens** 6500 **Vyds** 34.4ha
The energy, drive and vision of Martin Spedding have transformed Ten Minutes by Tractor since he acquired the business in early 2004. In mid 2006 Ten Minutes By Tractor purchased the McCutcheon Vineyard; it also has long-term leases on the other two original home vineyards (Judd and Wallis), thus having complete control over grape production. Three new vineyards have been added in recent years: the one at the cellar door and restaurant site is organically certified and is used to trial organic viticultural practices that are progressively being employed across all the vineyards; the others are in the north of the Peninsula. There are now three labels: the first is Single Vineyard, from the home Judd, McCutcheon and Wallace Vineyards; next is Estate, the best blend of Pinot and of Chardonnay from the home vineyards; and, finally, 10X from the other estate-owned Mornington Peninsula vineyards. The winemaking partnership between Rick McIntyre and Martin continues to evolve, with a focus on traditional Burgundian and natural winemaking techniques. The restaurant has one of the best wine lists to be found at any winery. Exports to the UK, Canada and Sweden.

10X Mornington Peninsula Pinot Noir 2009 Excellent depth of colour; the bouquet has that X factor of top Pinot, with complex plum, spice and calibrated oak, the palate picking up precisely where it should, reinforcing the complexity and generosity of a truly delicious Pinot, retaining finesse and elegance in the midst of the candy store of flavours. Screwcap. 14% alc. **Rating** 97 **To** 2020 $36
McCutcheon Mornington Peninsula Pinot Noir 2010 Fermented for 20 days with indigenous yeasts, then aged for 14 months in new and used French oak barriques. The bouquet is highly fragrant, with a mix of red and black fruits running through a beautifully silky palate, operating at a very different level from the Estate. Screwcap. 13.5% alc. **Rating** 96 **To** 2018 $75
Judd Vineyard Mornington Peninsula Pinot Noir 2010 Good colour; the wine spent an unusually long 20 days on skins before spending 14 months in new and used French oak; a complex wine with fruit and oak in an inseparable embrace, and has impeccable mouthfeel, the flavours ranging across the full pinot spectrum, Lovely now, but undoubted development potential. Screwcap. 13.5% alc. **Rating** 96 **To** 2018 $75
Wallis Mornington Peninsula Chardonnay 2010 Slightly deeper colour than the Estate Chardonnay; an unashamedly complex Chardonnay, with citrus, stone fruit, fig and cashew notes all tightly woven together; it is almost on·the aftertaste that the benison of natural acidity makes its presence felt. Screwcap. 13.5% alc. **Rating** 95 **To** 2017 $55

McCutcheon Mornington Peninsula Chardonnay 2010 Like its siblings, hand-picked, whole bunch-pressed and wild-fermented in a mix of new and used French barriques, and matured therein for 10 months. Bright green-gold; an immaculately balanced and textured palate, with white peach, nectarine and creamy cashew notes running through to a long and distinguished finish and aftertaste. Screwcap. 13% alc. **Rating** 95 **To** 2019 $55

Wallis Vineyard Mornington Peninsula Pinot Noir 2010 Bright colour, made in the same way as the McCutcheon, both reflecting the outstanding vintage. The flavours here are deeper, with more dark berry fruits, heading back to the Estate rather than the McCutcheon. That said, the wine has very good length, and carries its foresty bramble overtones. Screwcap. 13.5% alc. **Rating** 95 **To** 2017 $75

10X Mornington Peninsula Sauvignon Blanc 2010 Rating 94 To Now $28
Estate Mornington Peninsula Chardonnay 2010 Rating 94 To 2016 $42
10X Mornington Peninsula Pinot Noir 2010 Rating 94 To 2017 $32
Estate Mornington Peninsula Pinot Noir 2010 Rating 94 To 2016 $46

ŶŶŶŶŶ **10X Mornington Peninsula Chardonnay 2010** Rating 92 To 2015 $30
10X Mornington Peninsula Pinot Gris 2010 Rating 90 To Now $28

Tenafeate Creek Wines   ★★★★

Lot 2 Gawler-One Tree Hill Road, One Tree Hill, SA 5114 **Region** Adelaide Zone
T (08) 8280 7715 **www**.tenafeatecreekwines.com **Open** Fri–Sun 11–5
Winemaker Larry and Michael Costa **Est.** 2002 **Dozens** 3000 **Vyds** 1ha
Long-term friends Larry Costa, a former hairdresser, and Dominic Rinaldi, an accountant, embarked on winemaking as a hobby in 2002. The property, with its 1ha of shiraz, cabernet sauvignon and merlot, is situated on the rolling countryside of One Tree Hill in the Mount Lofty Ranges. From a small beginning, the business has grown rapidly, with grenache, nebbiolo, sangiovese, petit verdot, chardonnay, semillon and sauvignon blanc purchased to supplement the estate-grown grapes. Despite Larry's eye illness (macular degeneration), which forced his retirement from hairdressing, he is the hands-on winemaker at Tenafeate Creek. Both Larry and Dominic have Italian family winemaking traditions, and Larry learnt much from his late father. The red wines have won many medals over the years, none more impressive than the trophy for the '04 Shiraz at the Great Australian Shiraz Challenge '09, for Best Wine Under $25. Back vintages of Shiraz and Cabernet Sauvignon are available from the cellar door.

ŶŶŶŶŶ **Basket Press Merlot 2009** Deeply coloured, the wine has abundant plum and blackcurrant fruit meshed with superfine tannins; never prejudge what Tenafeate may come up with; here it's an unqualified success. Screwcap. 14.5% alc. **Rating** 93 **To** 2019 $25

Basket Press Shiraz 2009 Strong colour; a very concentrated, full-bodied Shiraz that just manages to escape dead fruit notes through its firm, fresh tannins. I simply can't guess where it will end up. Screwcap. 14.5% alc. **Rating** 92 **To** 2020 $25

✪ **Limestone Coast Sauvignon Blanc 2011** Still devoid of colour when six months old, the gently flowery bouquet leads into a fresh and vibrant palate, with nuances of passionfruit and citrus; the finish is long and clean. Screwcap. 12% alc. **Rating** 91 **To** Now $20

Basket Press Shiraz 2003 Good colour for age; fully ripe grapes provide layers of aromas and flavours, with a mix of spice, bitter chocolate and savoury tannins threaded through the blackberry fruit; the palate has good length. Screwcap. 14.5% alc. **Rating** 90 **To** 2018 $25

ŶŶŶŶ **Basket Press Black Top Blend 2009** Rating 89 To 2016 $30
Barossa Pinot Grigio 2011 Rating 87 To Now $20
Basket Press Cabernet Sauvignon 2004 Rating 87 To 2013 $20
Basket Press Sangiovese 2005 Rating 87 To Now $20
Barossa Moscato Style 2011 Rating 87 To Now $20

Terra Felix

PO Box 2029, Wattletree Road, Malvern East, Vic 3134 **Region** Central Victoria
T 0419 539 108 **www**.terrafelix.com.au **Open** Not
Winemaker Robert Paul **Est.** 2001 **Dozens** 14 000

Terra Felix was for many years a brand of Tallarook Wines, jointly owned by the Riebl family and by Peter Simon, Stan Olszewski and John Nicholson. In 2005 it was decided to separate the businesses, with Luis Riebl now solely concerned with the production of the Tallarook wines. Peter and Stan had run the Stanley Wine Company in Clare over 20 years ago, leaving it in the early 1980s, but always harboured a desire to be involved in the industry as owners. Grapes continue to be sourced from Tallarook and are supplemented by other local growers. They have worked hard to establish export markets as well as on-premise distribution in Australia, with one-third of the production exported to India and China.

Prosecco NV Has more aroma and flavour than the vast majority of Proseccos, but has the all-important dry finish; there are flavours of citrus and stone fruit on the way through that linger in the mouth well after the wine is finished. Cork. 11.5% alc. **Rating** 90 **To** Now $20

La Vie En Rose 2010 Rating 89 **To** Now $18

Terramore Wines

Box 1, Coonawarra, SA 5263 **Region** Coonawarra
T 0427 809 518 **www**.terramorewines.com.au **Open** Not
Winemaker Keith Wilkens **Est.** 2010 **Dozens** 3000 **Vyds** 31ha

The Gartner family (parents Phil and Mandy, and three children, Taylor, Abbi and Cooper) has been involved in grapegrowing in Coonawarra for 20 or so years, and also runs a company managing 300ha of vineyards in Coonawarra and Padthaway. With the downwards pressure on grape prices, in 2009 they decided to keep part of the crop from their 31ha of owned vineyards (20ha of cabernet sauvignon, 3ha merlot, 3.5 sauvignon blanc, 4.5 shiraz) and venture into the wine market. They chose Barbara Harkness, the Adelaide designer famous for creating the yellow tail label, to come up with a name and a label design. The name is doggerel Italian, 'terra' for earth and 'amore' for love, thus for the love of wine.

Coonawarra Cabernet Sauvignon 2009 Good hue, although not particularly deep; the bouquet has a good regional/varietal thumbprint; the palate opens with bright cassis fruit, but has to contend with the impact of French oak and frisky tannins. Needs time to settle down. WAK screwcap. 14.5% alc. **Rating** 90 **To** 2020 $19

Coonawarra Sauvignon Blanc 2010 Light straw-green; well made, bringing out the ripe tropical fruit of the bouquet and palate, backed up by attractive grainy acidity. Screwcap. 13.4% alc. **Rating** 89 **To** Now $13

Terre à Terre

PO Box 3128, Unley, SA 5061 **Region** Wrattonbully
T 0400 700 447 **www**.terroir-selections.com.au **Open** Not
Winemaker Xavier Bizot **Est.** 2008 **Dozens** 2000 **Vyds** 7ha

It would be hard to imagine two better-credentialled owners than Xavier Bizot (son of the late Christian Bizot of Bollinger fame) and wife Lucy Croser (daughter of Brian and Ann Croser). 'Terre à terre', incidentally, is a French expression meaning down-to-earth. The wines are available through independent retailers and leading restaurants, but also direct from the winery. The close-planted vineyard is on a limestone ridge, adjacent to Tapanappa's Whalebone Vineyard. The vineyard area has increased (3ha of cabernet sauvignon, 2ha of sauvignon blanc and 1ha each of cabernet franc and shiraz), with an additional 0.5ha pinot noir leased. This has led to a doubling of production. Exports to Hong Kong.

ΤΤΤΤΤ **Wrattonbully Botrytis 2011** Pale straw-bronze; a very classy wine; the grapes were fully ripe at the end of March with only 20% showing any botrytis; harvest took place on 28 April, with half the grapes still uninfected, 30% shrivelled and 20% fully botrytised. The fermentation was stopped at the right moment. Screwcap. 10.4% alc. **Rating** 95 **To** 2021 $26

Wrattonbully Cabernet Sauvignon 2009 Light but bright crimson; a vibrantly fresh, light- to medium-bodied wine with a very particular juicy, tactile character to the palate, at least in part due to the sophisticated fermentation and oak maturation (for two years) techniques employed. Vive la différence. Screwcap. 13.9% alc. **Rating** 94 **To** 2020 $35

Tertini Wines

Kells Creek Road, Mittagong, NSW 2575 **Region** Southern Highlands
T (02) 4878 5213 **www.**tertiniwines.com.au **Open** Thurs–Mon 10–5, or by appt
Winemaker Jonathan Holgate **Est.** 2000 **Dozens** 4000 **Vyds** 7.9ha
When Julian Tertini began the development of Tertini Wines in 2000, he followed in the footsteps of Joseph Vogt 145 years earlier. History does not relate the degree of success that Joseph had, but the site he chose then was, as it is now, a good one. Tertini has pinot noir and riesling (1.8ha each), cabernet sauvignon and chardonnay (1ha each), arneis (0.9ha), pinot gris (0.8ha), merlot (0.4ha) and lagrein (0.2ha). Winemaker Jonathan Holgate, who is responsible for the outstanding results achieved at Tertini, presides over High Range Vintners, a contract winemaking business also owned by Julian Tertini. Exports to Asia.

ΤΤΤΤΤ **Southern Highlands Pinot Noir 2009** Won three trophies at the South Coast Wine Show '12 for Best Pinot Noir, Best Red Wine of Show and Best Wine from Southern Highlands Region (this followed a gold medal at the National Wine Show '11). It has a complex forest floor backing to the pinot fruit, balanced by fresh acidity and fine tannins. At its best now. Screwcap. 13.5% alc. **Rating** 94 **To** 2014 $55

Reserve Southern Highlands Noble Riesling 2009 Deep colour and loaded with botrytis and peanut brittle; very sweet, with caramel and honeyed fig also present on the finish. Gold medal South Coast Wine Show '12, at which only six gold medals were awarded, three to Tertini. 375ml. Screwcap. 12.5% alc. **Rating** 94 **To** 2014 $26 BE

ΤΤΤΤΤ **Reserve Southern Highlands Riesling 2009 Rating** 93 **To** 2020 $35 BE

ΤΤΤΤ **Southern Highlands Riesling 2009 Rating** 88 **To** 2018 $30 BE

Teusner

29 Jane Place, Tanunda, SA 5352 (postal) **Region** Barossa Valley
T (08) 8562 4147 **www.**teusner.com.au **Open** At Artisans of Barossa
Winemaker Kym Teusner, Phil Lehmann **Est.** 2001 **Dozens** 15 000
Teusner is a partnership between former Torbreck winemaker Kym Teusner and brother-in-law Michael Page, and is typical of the new wave of winemakers determined to protect very old, low-yielding, dry-grown Barossa vines. The winery approach is based on lees ageing, little racking, no fining or filtration, and no new American oak. As each year passes, the consistency, quality (and range) of the wines increases; there must be an end point, but it's not easy to guess when, or even if, it will be reached. Eden Valley Cabernet Sauvignon has (just) ended the monopoly of Shiraz and the Rhône Valley varietals. Exports to the UK, the US and other major markets.

ΤΤΤΤΤ **The Riebke Northern Barossa Shiraz 2010** Crimson-purple; the fragrant
✪   bouquet exudes plum and blackberry fruit, promptly picked up by the stylish medium-bodied palate; here those flavours are joined by perfect tannins, oak purring along in the background. So great is the balance that the wine will live forever, however enjoyable it is now. Screwcap. 14.5% alc. **Rating** 96 **To** 2030 $19

Righteous FG Barossa Valley Shiraz 2008 Dense crimson with a magenta edge; a single vineyard wine in a heavy bottle; loaded to the gills with opulent and supple black fruits, velvety tannins and quality oak. Alcohol is simply a part of the style, and in no sense detracts from it. Cork. 15% alc. **Rating** 96 **To** 2040 $130

Albert 2009 Strong, deep crimson-purple; rich and profound dark berry aromas of the bouquet are a template for the palate, with its plum, dark chocolate and cedar flavours, the tannins round, soft and integrated. While easy to drink now, will thrive for several decades. Shiraz. Screwcap. 14.5% alc. **Rating** 95 **To** 2030 $48

Joshua 2010 Excellent purple-crimson colour; a blend of grenache, mataro and shiraz from ancient vines. It is a Barossa blend that seldom rings my bell, but this one certainly does. Not only is it packed with vibrant fruit; it also has the structure to age for 20 or more years. Screwcap. 14.5% alc. **Rating** 95 **To** 2030 $27

Avatar 2009 Released at the same time as Joshua, spending an extra year or so in oak. It is a richer version (grenache/mataro/shiraz), part vintage, part barrel selection, with considerable drive to the medium-bodied palate, starting its journey at a different point, but with the same destination Screwcap. 14.5% alc. **Rating** 94 **To** 2024 $32

Avatar 2010 A blend of grenache, mataro and shiraz. The colour is good, and the wine has a rich bouquet, like the palate, with as much dark fruit in a plum spectrum rather than the more traditional raspberry; works very well indeed, with very good mouthfeel and balance. Screwcap. 14.5% alc. **Rating** 94 **To** 2023 $32

Eden Valley Cabernet Sauvignon 2009 Medium red-purple; a wine full of character, with cassis leading the way, but joined by spice, earth and vanilla oak on both the bouquet and the medium- to full-bodied palate. Apropos of nothing, I wonder why a sole leaf with a virus pattern is featured on the label. Screwcap. 14.5% alc. **Rating** 94 **To** 2024 $49

MC Barossa Valley Sparkling Shiraz 2006 Has clearly been in oak or tirage for upwards of five years judging by its colour and fine mousse; inspired by the challenge of matching Linke's famous smoky bacon for breakfast, Teusner's skills have prevailed, with a complex wine reflecting spice, mocha and tobacco box. Crown seal. 14% alc. **Rating** 94 **To** 2016 $50

ΨΨΨΨΨ **The Empress Eden Valley Riesling 2011 Rating** 93 **To** 2021 $22
Righteous FG Barossa Valley Shiraz 2009 Rating 93 **To** 2029 $130

✪ **The Independent Shiraz Mataro 2010** A 50/50% bend, with bright crimson colour; the bouquet is a fragrant mix of red fruits and spices, the latter part fruit-, part oak-derived; the elegant medium-bodied palate continues the theme, without even a hint of alcohol, the bright fruits meshed with fine, ripe tannins. Great early-drinking style. Screwcap. 14.5% alc. **Rating** 93 **To** 2015 $19

✪ **The Gentleman Eden Valley Cabernet Sauvignon 2010** Bright crimson-purple; elegant and incisive, the product of one of the highest vineyards in the Eden Valley plus the skills of Kim Teusner. Hints of wild flowers and spice on the bouquet are followed by a red red berry-fruited palate that seems to have distinctly lower alcohol than it in fact has. Screwcap. 14.5% alc. **Rating** 93 **To** 2020 $19

The Dog Strangler 2010 Rating 93 **To** 2020 $27
The Playground Durif 2009 Rating 92 **To** 2016 $28
100 Flowers Botrytis Riesling 2011 Rating 92 **To** 2015 $22

✪ **The Hungry Goat Barossa Valley Shiraz 2010** Go to the website for the full inspiration of this wine, but shortly put, all the profits are being donated to (unspecified) charities. The colour is strong, and the wine has real presence, the dark fruits within a cocoon of spice and licorice oak and tannins. Screwcap. 14.5% alc. **Rating** 91 **To** 2020 $25

ΨΨΨΨ **Woodside Adelaide Hills Sauvignon Blanc 2011 Rating** 89 **To** 2013 $19
Adelaide Hills Pinot Noir Chardonnay NV Rating 89 **To** Now $19
Salsa Barossa Valley Rose 2011 Rating 88 **To** Now $19

The Carriages Vineyard   ★★★☆

549 Kotta Road, Echuca, Vic 3564 **Region** Goulburn Valley
T (03) 5483 7767 **www**.thecarriagesvineyard.com.au **Open** By appt
Winemaker Greg Dedman, Australian Vintage Services **Est.** 1996 **Dozens** 800 **Vyds** 6ha
David and Lyndall Johnson began the development of The Carriages in 1996, and now have
cabernet sauvignon (2.5ha), merlot (2ha), chardonnay (1ha) and semillon (0.5ha). The name
and the innovative packaging stems from four old railway carriages which the Johnsons have
painstakingly rehabilitated, and now live in. Each bottle is identified with a cardboard rail
ticket that is strikingly similar to the tickets of bygone years. The ticket shows the brand name,
the vintage, the variety, the number of standard drinks, the alcohol and the bottle number
(which is in fact the ticket number, or vice versa). The ticket is fixed to the label with fine
twine, so it can be removed either as a memento or used for further orders.

♀♀♀♀♀ **Reserve Echuca Cabernet Sauvignon 2009** Deep colour; a ripe and essency,
warm-fruited wine, with fruitcake, mocha and toast on display; the palate is
unctuous and generous with depth and structure, finishing with a long mocha
note, befitting of its warm climate origins. Diam. 14% alc. **Rating** 90 **To** 2015
$38 BE

♀♀♀♀ **Echuca Merlot 2009 Rating** 87 **To** 2013 $18 BE

The Grapes of Ross   ★★★☆

PO Box 14, Lyndoch, SA 5351 **Region** Barossa Valley
T (08) 8524 4214 **www**.grapesofross.com.au **Open** Not
Winemaker Ross Virgara **Est.** 2006 **Dozens** 2000
Ross Virgara spent much of his life in the broader food and wine industry, taking the plunge
into commercial winemaking in 2006. The grapes come from a fourth-generation family
property in the Lyndoch Valley, and the aim is to make fruit-driven styles of quality wine. His
fondness for frontignac led to the first release of Moscato, followed in due course by Rose,
Merlot Cabernet and Old Bush Vine Grenache. Exports to China.

♀♀♀♀♀ **Black Rose Barossa Valley Shiraz 2009** Dense red-purple; a resounding full-
bodied Shiraz, awash with black fruits, tannins and French and American oak.
It does need to slim down somewhat, but has the necessary balance to do so.
Screwcap. 14.5% alc. **Rating** 90 **To** 2030 $30

♀♀♀♀ **Ruby Tuesday Barossa Valley Rose 2011 Rating** 87 **To** 2013 $18

The Growers   ★★★

1071 Wildwood Road, Yallingup, WA 6282 **Region** Margaret River
T (08) 9755 2121 **www**.thegrowers.com **Open** 7 days 10–5
Winemaker Philip May **Est.** 2002 **Dozens** 40 000
The Growers (once Abbey Vale) has had a turbulent history since it was founded in 2002,
with legal disputes between various partners making life complicated. In February '06 all that
was put behind it, and it is now a syndicate of 17 growers with vineyards spread across all six
regions in South West Australia, and 400ha planted to all the major varieties. Five shareholders
have key vineyards in the Margaret River region, where it is based. The modestly priced wines
are released under the Niche, Legs, Peppermint Grove, Jack Star, Reward and Dedication
labels. Significant exports into the US and Asia.

♀♀♀♀ **Shag on a Rock Semillon Sauvignon Blanc 2011** Light green-straw; a bold,
✪ flavourful style based on generous alcohol with ripe citrus and tropical fruit over a
grassy/minerally bed. Screwcap. 13.1% alc. **Rating** 89 **To** 2014 $15
Shag on a Rock Margaret River Chardonnay 2010 While not particularly
complex, the wine has exceptional intensity and length. Why this ghastly label (of
a vermin-ridden, fish-stealing bird) is chosen for the top tier, Peppermint Grove
for the top, I have no idea. Screwcap. 14% alc. **Rating** 89 **To** 2014 $20
✪ **Peppermint Grove Unwooded Chardonnay 2010** Ticks all the boxes: clear-
cut varietal character, freshness, balance, length and price. Screwcap. 13.5% alc.
Rating 88 **To** 2013 $10

Shag on a Rock Great Southern Riesling 2009 Glowing pale green-straw; the bouquet is not particularly expressive, but the palate has varietal fruit in a mineral/lime spectrum. Screwcap. 12% alc. **Rating** 87 **To** 2014 $15

Shag on a Rock Margaret River Rose 2011 Pale puce-pink; the Merlot base wine was briefly fermented on skins prior to pressing; nice wine, the touch of sweetness barely perceptible; good length and balance. Screwcap. 13% alc. **Rating** 87 **To** 2013 $15

Reward Margaret River Merlot 2004 Light- to medium-bodied; pleasantly aged, with savoury varietal character and fine tannins; said to have been matured in new French oak. Curious price. Screwcap. 14% alc. **Rating** 87 **To** 2014 $15

✪ **Peppermint Grove Cabernet Merlot 2010** Bright crimson-purple; Peppermint Grove is the second label of The Growers, in a classically simple, uncluttered typeface. Perhaps this is why I am taken by the expressive cassis/red fruit simplicity of the wine. Screwcap. 14% alc. **Rating** 87 **To** 2015 $10

Shag on a Rock Margaret River Cabernet Sauvignon 2009 Crimson colour; the wine has good fruit expression on the bouquet, but then runs into troubled waters on the palate, where herbal and olive characters are not softened by 18 months in French oak. Screwcap. 13.5% alc. **Rating** 87 **To** 2019 $20

The Hairy Arm ★★★★★

18 Plant Street, Northcote, Vic 3070 (postal) **Region** Sunbury
T 0409 110 462 **www.**hairyarm.com **Open** Not
Winemaker Steven Worley **Est.** 2004 **Dozens** 500
The Hairy Arm is a name and label not easy to forget, so marketing experts will surely applaud. Steven and Natalie Worley's business may be small, but it certainly meets a marketing mantra. Steven graduated as an exploration geologist with a Master of Geology degree, followed by a postgraduate Diploma in Oenology and Viticulture. Until December 2009 he was general manager of Galli Estate Winery, The Hairy Arm Wine Company having started as a university project in '04. It has grown from a labour of love to a semi-commercial undertaking, focusing exclusively on shiraz grown variously in the Heathcote, Sunbury, Upper Goulburn Valley and Yarra Valley regions. The hairy arm, incidentally, is Steven's.

🍷🍷🍷🍷🍷 **Sunbury Shiraz 2010** Light red-purple; the bouquet is fragrant, and the light- to medium-bodied palate has excellent intensity and length to its array of predominantly small red fruits; wild fermentation and 12 months in Burgundian oak, plus another year in bottle, have all paid dividends. Screwcap. 14% alc. **Rating** 94 **To** 2020 $30

The Islander Estate Vineyards ★★★★★

PO Box 868, Kingscote, SA 5223 **Region** Kangaroo Island
T (08) 8553 9008 **www.**iev.com.au **Open** By appt
Winemaker Jacques Lurton **Est.** 2000 **Dozens** 5000 **Vyds** 11ha
Established by one of the most famous Flying Winemakers in the world, Bordeaux-born and trained and part-time Australian resident Jacques Lurton. He has established a close-planted vineyard; the principal varieties are cabernet franc, shiraz and sangiovese, with lesser amounts of grenache, malbec, semillon and viognier. The wines are made and bottled at the onsite winery, in true estate style. The flagship wine (Yakka Jack) is an esoteric blend of Sangiovese/Cabernet Franc. Exports to the UK, Canada, France, Denmark, the Netherlands, the Finland, the United Arab Emirates, Hong Kong, Macau and China.

🍷🍷🍷🍷🍷 **The Red 2008** A blend of malbec, cabernet franc, shiraz, viognier and grenache,
✪ the colour light, clear purple-red; the bouquet is aromatic, verging on flowery, the supple medium-bodied palate bringing any number of fruit flavours into play, ranging from red to black, but all seamlessly held together, the oak has been well handled, and the tannins are fine, ripe and soft. Screwcap. 14% alc. **Rating** 94 **To** 2018 $20

🍷🍷🍷🍷🍷 **The White 2011 Rating** 90 **To** 2015 $20

The Lake House Denmark

106 Turner Road, Denmark, WA 6333 **Region** Denmark
T (08) 9848 2444 **www**.lakehousedenmark.com.au **Open** 7 days 11–5
Winemaker Harewood Estate (James Kellie) **Est.** 1995 **Dozens** 6000 **Vyds** 5.2ha
Garry Capelli and Leanne Rogers purchased the property in 2005 and have since created
the Lake House Denmark. They have restructured the vineyard to grow varieties suited to
the climate: chardonnay, pinot noir, semillon and sauvignon blanc, incorporating biodynamic
principles. They also control a couple of small family-owned vineyards in Frankland River
and Mount Barker, with a similar ethos. Wines are released in three tiers: the flagship Premium
Reserve range, the Postcard Series and the quirky He Said, She Said easy-drinking wines.
The combined cellar door, restaurant and gourmet food emporium is a popular destination.

ΨΨΨΨΨ **Single Vineyard Selection Semillon Sauvignon Blanc 2011** A fresh wine
showing vibrant tropical fruits in abundance; the palate is soft, juicy and ready
to go notwithstanding the Semillon dominance. Screwcap. 13% alc. **Rating** 90
To 2016 $25 BE
Premium Reserve Single Vineyard Chardonnay 2010 Pale gold, green hue;
a rich and complex wine with French oak woven through abundant nectarine
and white peach fruit; finishes with a seductive warm buttered brioche flavour.
Screwcap. 13.5% alc. **Rating** 90 **To** 2016 $35

ΨΨΨΨ **Single Vineyard Selection Unwooded Chardonnay 2011 Rating** 88
To 2013 $19 BE

The Lane Vineyard

Ravenswood Lane, Hahndorf, SA 5245 **Region** Adelaide Hills
T (08) 8388 1250 **www**.thelane.com.au **Open** 7 days 10–4.30
Winemaker Michael Schreurs, Hugh Guthrie **Est.** 1993 **Dozens** 30 000 **Vyds** 55ha
After 15 years at The Lane Vineyard, Helen and John Edwards, and sons Marty and Ben, took
an important step towards realising their long-held dream – to grow, make and sell estate-based
wines that have a true sense of place. In 2005, at the end of the (now discontinued) Starvedog
Lane joint venture with Hardys, they commissioned a state-of-the-art 500-tonne winery,
bistro and cellar door overlooking their vineyards on picturesque Ravenswood Lane. Having
previously invested in Delatite, and much earlier established Coombe Farm in the Yarra Valley,
the Vestey Group (UK), headed by Lord Samuel Vestey and the Right Honourable Mark
Vestey, have acquired a significant shareholding in the Lane Vineyard. Exports to all the UK,
the US, Belgium, Hong Kong and China.

ΨΨΨΨΨ **Reunion Single Vineyard Adelaide Hills Shiraz 2009** Bright red-purple; the
fragrant, gently spiced red and black cherry bouquet foretells an elegant, unforced
palate showcasing cool-climate shiraz picked at optimum ripeness. A wine to
drink, not sip. Screwcap. 13.5% alc. **Rating** 95 **To** 2020 $65

ΨΨΨΨΨ **Gathering Single Vineyard Adelaide Hills Sauvignon Blanc Semillon
2010 Rating** 92 **To** 2013 $35

The Little Wine Company ★★★★

Small Winemakers Centre, 426 McDonalds Road, Pokolbin, NSW 2320
Region Hunter Valley
T (02) 4998 7668 **www**.thelittlewinecompany.com.au **Open** 7 days 10–5
Winemaker Ian and Suzanne Little **Est.** 2000 **Dozens** 8000
Having sold their previous winery, Ian and Suzanne Little moved in stages to their new
winery at Broke. The Little Wine Company is part-owner of the 20ha Lochleven Vineyard
in Pokolbin, and contracts three vineyards in the Broke Fordwich area (where the winery
is situated). It also has access to the Talga Vineyard in the Gundaroo Valley near Canberra.
Exports to Hong Kong, Taiwan, China and Japan.

ΥΥΥΥΩ **Little Gem Hunter Valley Shiraz 2009** Relatively light colour, but the hue is good; the fragrant bouquet is a logical forerunner of the bright and intensely juicy palate; black and red cherry fruit is at the core of the medium-bodied palate, touches of spice and earth giving the wine regional authenticity. Has the balance necessary for a long life. Screwcap. 13.7% alc. **Rating** 93 **To** 2029 $35
Tempranillo 2010 Good crimson colour; a most attractive example of the variety, the aromatic bouquet leading into a palate filled with varietal cherry fruit, the tannins only a whisper, the aftertaste fresh. Screwcap. 13.5% alc. **Rating** 92 **To** 2017 $24

ΥΥΥΥ **Olivine Gewurz 2011 Rating** 87 **To** 2015 $20

 # The Ninth Mile
PO Box 254, Beechworth, Vic 3747 **Region** Beechworth
T (03) 5728 3052 **www**.theninthmile.com **Open** Not
Winemaker Adrian Kearton **Est.** 2003 **Dozens** 150 **Vyds** 1ha
Adrian and Conna Kearton have established their vineyard in part on what was once the Mayday Hills 'lunatic asylum' vegetable garden, and part in the township of Stanley, 9km southeast of Beechworth and at an elevation of 750m. It is hardly surprising that the Keartons say their wines are handmade.

ΥΥΥΥ **Riesling 2009** Developed, albeit bright, colour, doubtless derived from the fact that the wine was barrel-fermented; the palate has a mix of citrus and tropical fruits, honey and toast around the corner. To be enjoyed sooner rather than later. Diam. 12.1% alc. **Rating** 88 **To** 2013 $30
Pinot Noir 2009 Deep purple-hued colour; in typical Beechworth style, the flavours are generous, but are not clearly defined, as those of first-class Pinot must be. I doubt that development will change the outcome much. Diam. 13.5% alc. **Rating** 87 **To** 2015 $30

The Old Faithful Estate
Grants Gully Road, Clarendon, SA 5157 **Region** McLaren Vale
T 0419 383 907 **www**.adelaidewinemakers.com.au **Open** By appt
Winemaker Nick Haselgrove, Warren Randall **Est.** 2005 **Dozens** 1500 **Vyds** 5ha
This is a 50/50 joint venture between American John Larchet and Adelaide Winemakers (see separate entry). Larchet has long had a leading role as a specialist importer of Australian wines into the US, and guarantees the business whatever sales it needs there. Its shiraz, grenache and mourvedre come from old, single-site blocks in McLaren Vale. Wines were received after this issue went to print; tasting notes appear on www.winecompanion.com.au. Exports to the US, Canada, EU, South Korea, Hong Kong and China.

The Pawn Wine Co.
PO Box 139, Langhorne Creek, SA 5255 **Region** Adelaide Hills
T 0438 373 247 **www**.thepawn.com.au **Open** Not
Winemaker Tom Keelan **Est.** 2002 **Dozens** 5000 **Vyds** 53ha
This is a partnership between Tom and Rebecca Keelan and David and Vanessa Blows. Tom was for some time manager of Longview Vineyards at Macclesfield in the Adelaide Hills, and consulted to the neighbouring vineyard, owned by David and Vanessa. In 2004 Tom and David decided to make some small batches of Petit Verdot and Tempranillo at the Bremerton winery, where Tom is now vineyard manager. The wines are sourced from grapes grown on their Macclesfield vineyards; the remainder of the grapes supply brands such as Shaw & Smith, Penfolds and Orlando.

ΥΥΥΥΩ **Jeu de Fin Reserve Release Adelaide Hills Sauvignon Blanc 2011** Light straw-green; fermented part in stainless steel, part in French oak; the bouquet and palate share gooseberry, spice and citrus, the last softened by the neatly balanced barrel-ferment component. While fresh and crisp, there are some passionfruit notes that add to the overall interest and appeal. Screwcap. 12% alc. **Rating** 92 **To** 2013 $24

Jeu de Fin Reserve Release Adelaide Hills Shiraz 2010 Good colour; a very complex and ripe Shiraz from the Adelaide Hills, with blackberry and black cherry fruit given marked complexity by spice, black pepper and oak. The savoury notes on the finish partly deal with the alcohol, but you are left to wonder why, in such a vintage, that need should arise in the first place Screwcap. 15% alc. **Rating** 90 **To** 2018 $35

ŶŶŶŶ
✪ **El Desperado 2011** Very pale salmon; the sangiovese grapes grown in the Adelaide Hills were intended to make a red table wine; when the rain hit, and didn't go away, El Desperado was born. In this rose manifestation, it has pronounced flavour and good length, savoury red cherry fruit to the fore. Screwcap. 13% alc. **Rating** 89 **To** 2015 $19
En Passant Adelaide Hills Tempranillo 2010 Rating 89 To 2017 $24

The Poplars Wines ★★★

Riddoch Highway, Coonawarra, SA 5263 **Region** Coonawarra
T 0417 832 003 **www**.goldwinesales.com.au **Open** Not
Winemaker James Yates **Est.** 2004 **Dozens** 7000 **Vyds** 4ha
It all looked too good to be true, and so it proved for this new name in Coonawarra. It is part of Coonawarra Developments Pty Ltd, which is in turn the owner of Chardonnay Lodge, the only large-scale (and ever-growing) accommodation complex in the heart of Coonawarra. Founded by the Yates family over 20 years ago, it now offers 38 large suites and a deservedly popular restaurant. Most recently, and in a way most significantly, Coonawarra Developments also purchased the former Jamiesons Run Winery from Foster's. Financial problems led to the sale of the winery on 30 June '11; it is now known as Coonawarra Jack Winery. In a separate transaction, Gold Wine Sales purchased The Poplars bulk and bottled wine stock, labels and trademarks. Most of the wines are now being made for export, with smaller quantities available on the Australian market. Gold Wine Sales has shareholder links with Taiwan, leading to increased sales there. Exports to China and Taiwan.

ŶŶŶŶ **Reserve Release Limestone Coast Shiraz 2006** Specifically held back for late release, but it's not obvious why, for it is relatively light-bodied and significantly developed, French oak providing much of the flavour. Cork. 14.7% alc. **Rating** 87 **To** 2015 $28
Sundown Pinot Noir Chardonnay NV Pale orange-onion skin; the wine is full-flavoured, with strong strawberry characters throughout the palate; the packaging does not do it justice. Cork. 10.5% alc. **Rating** 87 **To** 2013 $18

The Roy Kidman Wine Co. ★★★★

Comaum School Road, Coonawarra, SA 5263 **Region** Coonawarra
T 0417 878 933 **www**.roykidman.com.au **Open** Not
Winemaker Peter Douglas (Contract) **Est.** 2003 **Dozens** 5000 **Vyds** 55.9ha
Branches of the Kidman family have been part of Coonawarra viticulture since 1970, and long before that one of the great names in the Australian cattle industry. Tim, Philip and Mardi Kidman (brothers and sister) run a separate business from that of cousin Sid Kidman, with 40.2ha of cabernet sauvignon and 15.7ha of shiraz, planting the first 2ha of shiraz in 1970, and moving into wine production in 2003, albeit still selling the major part of the grape production. Roy the Cattleman (Cabernet Sauvignon) is a tribute to their paternal grandfather, who worked as a stockman for his uncle Sir Sidney Kidman. Exports to Sweden, Hong Kong and China.

ŶŶŶŶŶ
✪ **Bar Over Box Coonawarra Shiraz 2008** Full crimson; an outstanding bargain, with the blackberry, plum and spice fruit of a much more expensive wine; medium-bodied, but has balance from tannins and oak to support the fruit, the spicy aftertaste particularly appealing. Screwcap. 14.5% alc. **Rating** 92 **To** 2018 $15
✪ **Bar Over Box Coonawarra Sauvignon Blanc 2011** Pale quartz-green; aromas of gooseberry and passionfruit on the bouquet continue on into the palate, there joined by juicy citrus, finishing with minerally acidity. Outstanding bargain. Screwcap. 11.5% alc. **Rating** 90 **To** 2013 $15

The Story Wines   ★★★★★

3/88 Grosvenor Street, Balaclava, Vic 3183 (postal) **Region** Grampians
T 0411 697 912 **www**.thestory.com.au **Open** Not
Winemaker Rory Lane **Est.** 2004 **Dozens** 1200
Over the years I have come across winemakers with degrees in atomic science, doctors with specialties spanning every human condition, town planners, sculptors, painters, and Rory Lane adds yet another to the list: a degree in ancient Greek literature. He says that after completing his degree, and 'desperately wanting to delay an entry into the real world, I stumbled across and enrolled in a postgraduate wine technology and marketing course at Monash University, where I soon became hooked on ... the wondrous connection between land, human and liquid'. Vintages in Australia and Oregon germinated the seed, and he zeroed in on the Grampians, where he purchases small parcels of high-quality grapes for his Shirazs, making the wines in a small factory where he has assembled a basket press, a few open fermenters, a mono pump and some decent French oak. Exports to Singapore.

🍷🍷🍷🍷🍷 Henty Estate Vineyard Shiraz 2010 Deep purple, with great concentration and power; spicy black fruits have a very appealing savoury underlay, the aromas and flavours all circling in a black fruit spectrum. One tonne of fruit was fermented with 100% whole bunches, and another destemmed and fermented in four open puncheons. The two parcels were blended and spent 12 months in 25% new barriques. The texture and length of the finish are simply outstanding. Screwcap. 13.5% alc. **Rating** 96 **To** 2030 $45
Rice's Vineyard Grampians Shiraz 2010 Deep purple-crimson; both the bouquet and palate tell a very different story, with a warmer infusion giving the bouquet and palate softer, more open flavours, the colour also deeper. Made using similar techniques to the other Story Shirazs, with micro-ferments and thereafter 12 months in barriques, here 25% new. The texture is rounder, the finish riper, but don't think this is going to go away any time soon. Screwcap. 13.5% alc. **Rating** 95 **To** 2025 $45
Garden Gully Vineyard Grampians Shiraz 2010 Bright, clear crimson-purple; the fragrant red and black fruit bouquet leads into a multi-flavoured, silky and supple palate with blackberry, plum, cedar and spice to the fore. Fermented with 50% whole bunches, then 12 months in French oak barriques hogsheads, 35% new; neither fined nor filtered; 120 dozen made from century-old vines. Screwcap. 13.5% alc. **Rating** 95 **To** 2025 $45

🍷🍷🍷🍷🍷 Henty Riesling 2011 Light green-quartz; a cleverly made wine balancing low
✪ alcohol, substantial acidity and barely detectable residual sugar. The aromas and flavours are predominantly citrus, but with some apple joining the party; its overall delicacy and balance guarantee a 10-year future. Screwcap. 11% alc. **Rating** 93 **To** 2021 $24
Westgate Vineyard Grampians Blanc Marsanne Roussane Viognier 2011 **Rating** 92 **To** 2016 $28

The Trades   ★★★

13/30 Peel Road, O'Connor, WA 6163 (postal) **Region** Margaret River
T (08) 9331 2188 **www**.terrawines.com.au **Open** Not
Winemaker Brad Wehr (Contract) **Est.** 2006 **Dozens** 1200
Thierry Ruault and Rachel Taylor have run a wholesale wine business in Perth since 1993, representing a group of top-end Australian and foreign producers. By definition, the wines they offered to their clientele were well above $20 per bottle, and they decided to fill the gap with a contract-made Shiraz from the Adelaide Hills, and a Sauvignon Blanc from Margaret River.

🍷🍷🍷🍷 Butcher's Margaret River Shiraz 2010 Brightly coloured and lively, with red fruits, licorice and mineral on display; medium-bodied, fresh and forward, constructed for early consumption. Screwcap. 13.9% alc. **Rating** 88 **To** 2014 $18 BE

The Wanderer ★★★★★

2850 Launching Place Road, Gembrook, Vic 3783 **Region** Yarra Valley
T 0415 529 639 **www**.wandererwines.com **Open** By appt
Winemaker Andrew Marks **Est.** 2005 **Dozens** 500

Andrew Marks is the son of Ian and June Marks, owners of Gembrook Hill, and after graduating from Adelaide University with a degree in oenology he joined Southcorp, working for six years at Penfolds (Barossa Valley) and Seppelt (Great Western), as well as undertaking vintages in Coonawarra and France. He has since worked in the Hunter Valley, Great Southern, Sonoma County in the US and Costa Brava in Spain – hence the name of his business.

🍷🍷🍷🍷🍷 **Upper Yarra Valley Pinot Noir 2010** The use of whole bunches creates a pungent sap, cold tea and Asian spice bouquet, with delicate red fruits lurking timidly beneath; the palate is super-fresh and inviting, with silky tannins and fine fruits cascading from start to finish; extremely long, focused and, while made in a style that is sure to polarise opinion, done exceedingly well. Diam. 13% alc. **Rating** 96 **To** 2018 $55 BE

Yarra Valley Shiraz 2010 Andrew Marks is not shy in using whole bunches for added complexity in his wines, and this Shiraz is full of bracken undergrowth, dried herbs, spices and succulent sweet red fruits as a result; the palate is silky and focused, with a savoury and dry finish in balance with the fruit on offer; interesting at the very least, incredibly exciting if you are so inclined. Screwcap. 13% alc. **Rating** 95 **To** 2018 $35 BE

Yarra Valley Pinot Noir 2010 The very essence of black cherry, subtle spices and a gentle seasoning of toasty oak on the bouquet; the palate is fresh and lively, pure and inviting, and while very good drinking as a young wine, has the stuffing to stick around for some time. Screwcap. 13.5% alc. **Rating** 94 **To** 2018 $35 BE

The Willow Lane Vineyard ★★★★☆

Eurunderee Lane, Mudgee, NSW 2850 **Region** Mudgee
T (02) 6373 3131 **www**.thewillowlane.com.au **Open** Fri, Sun & public hols 11–4, Sat 10.30–5.30
Winemaker Peter Wormald **Est.** 1995 **Dozens** 1200 **Vyds** 8.4ha

Peter and Ann Wormald's dream of owning a vineyard in Mudgee came true when they purchased a property in Eurunderee Lane which had an 1870s house and soil that seemed suited to viticulture. But it also involved Peter spending six years part-time studying for his degree in viticulture (while working full-time) and Ann going back into a pharmacy shop after many years in the pharmaceutical industry. Perseverance has seen the successful establishment of 4.4ha of chardonnay and 4ha of shiraz on the estate. The cellar door, which opened in 2004, was made in part from the sections of the old house removed for the extension.

🍷🍷🍷🍷🍷 **Mudgee Viognier 2010** Bright green-straw; a good expression of this difficult variety; it spent some time in old French oak, and that has contributed to its texture, but it is the combination of apricot, musk and peach on the mid palate, in turn cleansed by citrussy acidity on the finish, that makes this wine what it is. A real discovery. Screwcap. 13% alc. **Rating** 94 **To** 2016 $23

🍷🍷🍷🍷♀ **Premium Blend Mudgee Shiraz Cabernet 2009** **Rating** 90 **To** 2019 $25

🍷🍷🍷🍷 **Sweet Grace Mudgee Botrytis Semillon 2011** **Rating** 88 **To** 2013 $28

The Willows Vineyard ★★★★

Light Pass Road, Light Pass, Barossa Valley, SA 5355 **Region** Barossa Valley
T (08) 8562 1080 **www**.thewillowsvineyard.com.au **Open** Wed–Mon 10.30–4.30, Tues by appt
Winemaker Peter and Michael Scholz **Est.** 1989 **Dozens** 6500 **Vyds** 42.74ha

The Scholz family have been grapegrowers for generations and have over 40ha of vineyards, selling part and retaining the remainder of the crop. Current-generation winemakers Peter and Michael Scholz make smooth, well-balanced and flavoursome wines under their own label, some marketed with some bottle age. Exports to the UK, Switzerland, China and NZ.

ŤŤŤŤŢ **Single Vineyard Barossa Valley Semillon 2011** Rating 93
◐   To 2020 $17
✪   **Barossa Valley Riesling 2011** Vivid green hue; a classic bouquet blending lime, lemon, anise and candle wax; the palate is forward and fleshy, yet delivers a refreshing backbone of acidity and good line, finishing with a pleasant level of grip. Screwcap. 11.8% alc. **Rating** 90 **To** 2016 $17 BE

ŤŤŤŤ   **Bonesetter Barossa Shiraz 2009** Rating 88 To 2015 $56 BE

Thick as Thieves Wines   ★★★★★
1 Symons Street, Healesville, Vic 3777 (postal) **Region** Yarra Valley
T 0417 184 690 **F** (03) 5962 5319 **www**.tatwines.com.au **Open** Not
Winemaker Syd Bradford **Est.** 2009 **Dozens** 800
Syd Bradford is living proof that small can be beautiful, and, equally, that an old dog can learn new tricks. A growing interest in good food and wine might have come to nothing had it not been for Pfeiffer Wines giving him a vintage job in '03. In that year he enrolled in the wine science course at CSU, moving to the Yarra Valley in '05. He gained experience at Coldstream Hills (vintage cellar hand), Rochford (assistant winemaker), Domaine Chandon (cellar hand) and Giant Steps/Innocent Bystander (assistant winemaker). In '06 Syd achieved the Dean's Award of Academic Excellence at CSU and in '07 was the sole recipient of the A&G Engineering Scholarship. Aged 35, he was desperate to have a go at crafting his own 'babies', and in '09 came across a small parcel of arneis from the Hoddles Creek area, and Thick as Thieves was born. In '10 he purchased small parcels of arneis, chardonnay, pinot noir and nebbiolo, making his wine in a home-away-from-home. The techniques used to make his babies could only come from someone who has spent a long time observing and thinking about what he might do.

ŤŤŤŤŤ **The Show Pony Yarra Valley Sauvignon Blanc 2011** Hand-picked and whole bunch-pressed, cold-settled and clear juice barrel-fermented in used French oak barriques, half with cultured yeast, half wild-fermented; lees-stirred until July bottling. Bright straw-green, the wine has outstanding structure and texture to its display of grapefruit, guava and gooseberry fruits, all speaking sotto voce. Screwcap. 12.7% alc. **Rating** 94 **To** 2014 $25
         Another Bloody Yarra Valley Chardonnay 2011 Whole bunch-pressed direct to barrel, half left on full solids in a mix of new and used French oak; 15% mlf and no lees stirring. Its low baume, together with the making techniques, delivers a wine with energy and concentration, driving through emphatically to the finish and aftertaste, riding on the back of grapefruit and white peach. Screwcap. 12.5% alc. **Rating** 94 **To** 2017 $35

ŤŤŤŤŢ **Plump Yarra Valley Pinot Noir 2011** Rating 93 To 2016 $35

ŤŤŤŤ   **The Love Letter King Valley Sylvaner 2011** Rating 89 To 2014 $25

Third Child   ★★★★☆
134 Mt Rumney Road, Mt Rumney, Tas 7170 (postal) **Region** Southern Tasmania
T 0419 132 184 **www**.thirdchildvineyard.com.au **Open** Not
Winemaker John Skinner, Rob Drew **Est.** 2000 **Dozens** 275 **Vyds** 3ha
John and Marcia Skinner planted 2.5ha of pinot noir and 0.5ha of riesling in 2000. It is very much a hands-on operation, the only concession being the enlistment of Rob Drew (from an adjoining property) to help John with the winemaking. When the first vintage (2004) was reaching the stage of being bottled and labelled, the Skinners could not come up with a name and asked their daughter Claire. 'Easy,' she said. 'You've got two kids already; considering the care taken and time spent at the farm, it's your third child.'

ŢŢŢŢŢ   **Ella Mae Riesling 2011** Quartz-white; the flowery bouquet has many facets,
☼   but it is the explosive intensity of the palate, and its extreme length that takes you
        by storm – Tasmanian acidity, of course, is part of the picture. Screwcap. 11% alc.
        Rating 96 To 2026 $20

ŢŢŢŢŢ   **Benjamin Daniel Pinot Noir 2010** Rating 91 To 2017 $25

Thistle Hill
74 McDonalds Road, Mudgee, NSW 2850 **Region** Mudgee
T (02) 6373 3546 **www**.thistlehill.com.au **Open** Thurs–Fri 10–4.30, Sun & public hols 10–4
Winemaker Michael Slater **Est.** 1976 **Dozens** 12 000 **Vyds** 33ha
In 2009 Rob and Mary Loughan, owners of the adjoining Erudgere since '04, acquired
Thistle Hill from Lesley Robertson. Thistle Hill was already certified organic (by the National
Association for Sustainable Agriculture Australia [NASAA], which means no weedicides,
insecticides or synthetic fertilisers), and Erudgere became certified organic in July '10. From
the '11 vintage, all of the Erudgere and Thistle Hill wines will be sold under the Thistle
Hill label. The appointment of Michael Slater as winemaker paid immediate dividends, the
'09 Riesling winning multiple trophies. It is fascinating that, at a time of global warming,
Thistle Hill and Robert Stein should be producing Rieslings of the highest quality. Exports
to Mongolia and China.

ŢŢŢŢŢ   **Organic Riesling 2011** Pale quartz-green; the perfumed bouquet, with some
        talc nuances, leads into a palate with good focus and intensity to its citrus
        and apple flavours, accelerating on the finish. Fully priced. Screwcap. 12% alc.
        Rating 93 To 2021 $40
        Estate Reserve Mudgee Cabernet Sauvignon 2009 Infuriatingly hard-to-
        read printing discloses that the organic grapes, when fermented, spent two years
        in 100% new French hogsheads, and asserts that the wine will live for 25 years or
        more. Whether the impact of oak will diminish in that time is the first question;
        the second is whether the wine will go the distance. The cork is of good quality
        and has been properly inserted in the dreadnought bottle, so you may be lucky.
        14.5% alc. Rating 92 To 2019 $50
        Botrytis Semillon 2010 Intensely luscious; a very high level of botrytis leaves
        the palate flooded with honeyed cumquat and lemon tart fruit balanced by good
        acidity. Screwcap. 9% alc. Rating 92 To 2015 $22
        Organic Cabernet Sauvignon 2009 This wine also spent two years in oak, but
        clearly it was not new, and the cabernet has had greater opportunity of varietal
        expression; the black fruits have good tannins in support and a clarity that is
        commendable. Screwcap. 14% alc. Rating 91 To 2019 $32
☼   **Nine Bunches Riesling 2011** Pale quartz-green; the bouquet is perfumed with
        floral and talc aromas, the palate already showing generosity; the variety has always
        been a sleeper in Mudgee, and deserves to be better recognised. Screwcap. 12% alc.
        Rating 90 To 2014 $18
☼   **Nine Bunches Organic Central Ranges Shiraz 2010** Light to medium red-
        purple; covers most of the bases, with minimal SO$_2$ additions, certified organic
        grapes and suitable for vegetarians and vegans. Spicy red and black fruits run
        through the medium-bodied palate with an appealing savoury twist of tannins on
        the finish. Screwcap. 14% alc. Rating 90 To 2016 $18

ŢŢŢŢ   **Organic Chardonnay 2011** Rating 89 To Now $24
        Preservative Free Shiraz 2011 Rating 89 To Now $20

Thomas New England Estate
Delungra, NSW 2403 **Region** New England
T (02) 6724 8508 **www**.newenglandestatewines.com.au **Open** 7 days 10–5
Winemaker John Cassegrain (Contract), Jon Reynolds (Consultant) **Est.** 1996
Dozens NA **Vyds** 33ha
John Henry Thomas, great-grandfather of the present owners of the property arrived in the
New England area in 1860, and made the first beer in 1870; the old brewery still stands in

Brewery Street, Inverell. Ross and wife Rae Thomas inherited a mixed farming property of over 1200 ha, and in 1996 (after decades of ownership) decided to diversify by planting a vineyard. The first plantings were of chardonnay, cabernet sauvignon, merlot and shiraz, with durif, tannat and viognier following. The future of the family tradition is assured, with daughter Leigh and granddaughter Anita Johnson involved as sales and marketing manager.

PPPP **Cabernet Sauvignon 2007** Has held on to its crimson hue very well; a complex bouquet and palate with savoury bitter chocolate characters coming through on the finish and aftertaste, virtually defining the wine. Gold medal New England Wine Show '09, bronze at Cowra '10 probably nearer the mark. Screwcap. 13.5% alc. **Rating** 89 **To** 2017 $40

✪ **Chardonnay 2010** A well-made wine that fully deserved its bronze medal at the New England Wine Show '11. Peachy fruit is sustained by lemony acidity and a hint of oak; made to be drunk young, and is wellpriced. Screwcap. 13.2% alc. **Rating** 88 **To** 2013 $14

Reserve Shiraz 2010 Light red-purple; open-fermented and matured in a mix of oak barriques, the medium-bodied palate with a savoury, oaky sheen; one hopes the fruit will express itself over time, but there is a worrying lack of balance. Screwcap. 14.5% alc. **Rating** 87 **To** 2017 $22

Thomas Wines   ★★★★★

c/- The Small Winemakers Centre, McDonalds Road, Pokolbin, NSW 2321
Region Hunter Valley
T (02) 6574 7371 **www**.thomaswines.com.au **Open** 7 days 10–5
Winemaker Andrew Thomas, Phil Le Messurier **Est.** 1997 **Dozens** 7000 **Vyds** 3ha
Andrew Thomas came to the Hunter Valley from McLaren Vale to join the winemaking team at Tyrrell's. After 13 years, he left to undertake contract work and to continue the development of his own label. He makes individual vineyard wines, underlining the subtle differences between the various subregions of the Hunter. Plans for the construction of an estate winery have been abandoned for the time being, and for the foreseeable future he will continue to lease the James Estate winery on Hermitage Road, while the cellar door will continue at the Small Winemakers Centre. The major part of the production comes from long-term arrangements with growers of semillon (15ha) and shiraz (25ha); an additional 3ha of shiraz is leased. The quality of the wines and the reputation of Andrew Thomas have never been higher. Exports to Canada and Japan.

PPPPP **Cellar Reserve Braemore Individual Vineyard Hunter Valley Semillon 2002** Gleaming green and light gold; a re-release of 100 six-bottle packs, 25% having been destroyed by random oxidation; here a touch of honey has joined the lemon citrus and mineral foundation of a totally glorious wine, the loss heartbreaking, but no surprise. Emphatic drink now, unless you want to play continuing Russian roulette with the corks. Due for release end '12. 10.2% alc. **Rating** 97 **To** 2013 $60

Cellar Reserve Braemore Individual Vineyard Hunter Valley Semillon 2007 Glorious bright green-quartz; a perfect example of a wonderfully elegant Hunter Semillon that even now is at the start of its life, its lemon/lemongrass flavours woven around racy acidity. Screwcap. 10.5% alc. **Rating** 96 **To** 2020 $45

Kiss Limited Release Hunter Valley Shiraz 2010 Deep crimson; a complex and heady blend of red and black fruits, sage, hoisin and well-handled spicy oak; the palate is fleshy, silky and full of fine-grained tannins, vibrant acidity and a long finish that slowly unravels to reveal the beauty of the wine within; while lovely now, will truly stand the test of time and reward patient cellaring. Screwcap. 13.5% alc. **Rating** 95 **To** 2030 $60 BE

DJV Vineyard Selection Hunter Valley Shiraz 2010 Mid crimson, bright; a spicy and red-fruited bouquet with cinnamon, roasted meats and licorice on display; the palate is fleshy and forward on entry, immediately accessible, yet with backbone and a medium-bodied structure of silky fine tannins providing an expansive and harmonious conclusion. Screwcap. 13.5% alc. **Rating** 94 **To** 2022 $30 BE

Motel Block Individual Vineyard Hunter Valley Shiraz 2010 A ripe and sweet black-fruited example of Hunter Shiraz, with the bouquet also offering licorice, bramble and sea salt; the palate is juicy and generous on entry, with gravelly tannins playing a foil to the sweet fruit on offer; an expressive wine with much to say. Screwcap. 13.8% alc. **Rating** 94 **To** 2025 $50 BE

PPPPP Sweetwater Individual Vineyard Hunter Valley Shiraz 2010 Rating 93 To 2030 $35 BE
Braemore Individual Vineyard Hunter Valley Semillon 2011 Rating 92 To 2018 $28 BE

PPPP The O.C. Individual Vineyard Hunter Valley Semillon 2011 Rating 89 To 2016 $22 BE
Six Degrees Vineyard Selection Hunter Valley Semillon 2011 Rating 88 To 2016 $22 BE

Thompson Estate ★★★★★

299 Tom Cullity Drive, Wilyabrup, WA 6284 **Region** Margaret River
T (08) 9386 1751 **www**.thompsonestate.com **Open** 7 days 11–5
Winemaker Bob Cartwright **Est.** 1994 **Dozens** 6500 **Vyds** 28ha
Cardiologist Peter Thompson planted the first vines at Thompson Estate in 1997, inspired by his and his family's shareholdings in the Pierro and Fire Gully vineyards, and by visits to many of the world's premium wine regions. The vineyard is planted to cabernet sauvignon, cabernet franc, merlot, chardonnay, sauvignon blanc, semillon and pinot noir. Thompson Estate wines have been made solely by Bob Cartwright (former Leeuwin Estate winemaker) since 2006 at its state-of-the-art winery. Exports to the UK, the US, Canada, India and Hong Kong.

PPPPP Margaret River Semillon Sauvignon Blanc 2011 Even though semillon is the dominant partner in terms of percentage, there is a wider range of ripe/tropical fruits here than in the '11 Locum SBS; guava, passionfruit and gooseberry are corralled on the finish by lemony semillon and its attendant acidity. Screwcap. 12.6% alc. **Rating** 94 **To** 2014 $30
Locum Margaret River Cabernet Merlot 2010 Bright crimson-purple; the wine surges with juicy redcurrant, blackcurrant and plum fruit flavours, adding balanced tannins and an airbrush of oak. Delicious Margaret River example of the blend to be enjoyed whenever the mood takes you. Screwcap. 13.5% alc. Rating 94 **To** 2020 $25

PPPPP Locum Margaret River Sauvignon Blanc Semillon 2011 Pale quartz-
✪ green; an intense bouquet, and even more intense palate, with citrussy acidity driving through its length, the flavours ranging from green capsicum and snow pea through to grapefruit pith and lingering citrus flavours. Outstanding value. Screwcap. 12.5% alc. **Rating** 93 **To** 2014 $20
✪ Locum Margaret River Chardonnay 2011 Pale, bright quartz-green; the bouquet is complex, with some funky notes, and the palate has both precision and length to its perfectly pitched varietal fruit. Screwcap. 13.5% alc. **Rating** 93 **To** 2019 $25
Margaret River Chardonnay Pinot Noir 2008 Rating 93 **To** 2014 $45

Thorn-Clarke Wines ★★★★★

Milton Park, Gawler Park Road, Angaston, SA 5353 **Region** Barossa Valley
T (08) 8564 3036 **www**.thornclarkewines.com.au **Open** Mon–Fri 9–5, w'ends 11–4
Winemaker Helen McCarthy **Est.** 1987 **Dozens** 80 000 **Vyds** 268ha
Established by David and Cheryl Clarke (née Thorn), and son Sam, Thorn-Clarke is one of the largest family-owned estate-based businesses in the Barossa. Their winery is close to the border between the Barossa and Eden valleys, and three of their four vineyards in the Eden Valley: the Mt Crawford Vineyard is at the southern end of the Eden Valley, while the Milton Park and Sandpiper vineyards are further north in the Eden Valley. The fourth vineyard is at St Kitts, in the northern end of the Barossa Ranges, established when no other vignerons had ventured

onto what was hitherto considered unsuitable soil. In all four vineyards careful soil mapping has resulted in matching of variety and site, with all of the major varieties represented. The quality of grapes retained for the Thorn-Clarke label has resulted in a succession of trophy and gold medal-winning wines at very competitive prices. The arrival of the highly credentialled Helen McCarthy as winemaker in 2011 means wine quality continues in safe hands. Exports to all major markets.

Shotfire Quartage 2009 Rating 95
To 2024 $20
St Kitts Vineyard on Cambrian Greywacke Soils Northern Barossa Shiraz 2008 Deep healthy colour; potent plum, spice and some licorice aromas and flavours are unified by 20 months in new French oak and powerful tannins. Will be very long-lived. Screwcap. 14.5% alc. **Rating** 94 **To** 2038 $35
St Kitts Vineyard on Heatherdale Shale Northern Barossa Cabernet Sauvignon 2008 Very good colour, full crimson-purple; hand-plunged, open-fermented and matured for 20 months in new and French and American hogsheads; a remarkable achievement for the vintage, although the presence of some green olive notes suggests that the fruit may have not been 100% ripe; the flavours are intense, the tannins appropriately firm, and the oak not overly intrusive. Screwcap. 14% alc. **Rating** 94 **To** 2028 $35

Shotfire Barossa Shiraz 2010 There is a lot of wine here for the price, with blackberry, licorice, bitter chocolate and well-balanced spicy oak; the palate is firm and focused, revealing tension between its components; good now and with plenty of fuel in the tank for the future. Screwcap. 14.5% alc. **Rating** 92 **To** 2018 $20 BE
Kabininge Vineyard on Bay of Biscay Soil Barossa Valley Floor Shiraz 2008 Rating 92 To 2023 $35
St Kitts Vineyard on Truro Volcanic Soil Northern Barossa Malbec 2008 Rating 92 To 2018 $35
Sandpiper Barossa Merlot 2010 Rating 91 To 2018 $15
Angaston Vineyard on Melt Water Sand Eden Valley Petit Verdot Shiraz 2008 Rating 91 To 2020 $35
Sandpiper Barossa Shiraz 2010 Strong purple-crimson; the sheer consistency of the Thorn-Clarke wines is remarkable; this medium-bodied wine brings together gently ripe blackberry and plum fruit, fine-grained tannins and a wisp of oak. Great over the next five years. Screwcap. 14.5% alc. **Rating** 90 **To** 2016 $15

Sandpiper Eden Valley Riesling 2011 Rating 89 To 2016 $16 BE
Morello Barossa Valley Nebbiolo 2009 Rating 89 To 2019 $20
Sandpiper Barossa Cabernet Sauvignon 2011 Rating 88 To 2014 $16 BE
Sandpiper Barossa Cabernet Sauvignon 2010 Rating 88 To 2015 $16 BE

3 Drops   ★★★★★

PO Box 1828, Applecross, WA 6953 **Region** Mount Barker
T (08) 9315 4721 **www.3drops.com Open** Not
Winemaker Robert Diletti (Contract) **Est.** 1998 **Dozens** 5000 **Vyds** 21.5ha
The three drops are not the three founders (John Bradbury, Joanne Bradbury and, formerly, Nicola Wallich), but wine, olive oil and water, all of which come from the substantial property at Mt Barker. The plantings are riesling, sauvignon blanc, semillon, chardonnay, cabernet sauvignon, merlot, shiraz and cabernet franc, irrigated — like the olive trees — by a large wetland on the property. The business expanded significantly in 2007 with the purchase of the 14.7ha Patterson's Vineyard. Celebrated its 10th vintage in '10 in fine style. Exports to the UK, Canada, Hong Kong and China.

Mount Barker Riesling 2011 Pale straw-green; a wine with almost startling rectitude, with a tightly wound bundle of lime and lime zest, green apple, and unsweetened lemon built on a scaffold of minerally acidity. Patience will bring further rewards. Screwcap. 12.5% alc. **Rating** 94 **To** 2021 $22

✪   **Mount Barker Chardonnay 2010** Bright, light green-straw; a harmonious fusion of nectarine, white peach and grapefruit defines bouquet and palate alike, with just a hint of French oak to add depth. Very attractive wine. Screwcap. 13.5% alc. **Rating** 94 **To** 2017 $24

✪   **Mount Barker Chardonnay 2009** Bright, light green-straw, excellent for age; as the colour suggests, this is an elegant wine with aromas and flavours of grapefruit, white peach and melon offset by touches of vanillin oak. Screwcap. 13.5% alc. **Rating** 94 **To** 2016 $24

Mount Barker Shiraz 2008 Holding hue very well; a delicious medium-bodied cool-climate Shiraz that has pushed the ripeness envelope and got away with it scot-free, with perfectly ripened sweet red cherry fruit, fine dusty tannins and balanced oak. Screwcap. 14.5% alc. **Rating** 94 **To** 2020 $24

♟♟♟♟♟   **Mount Barker Cabernets 2010** A blend of cabernet sauvignon and cabernet
✪   franc, with excellent bright crimson-purple colour and a fragrant cassis/blackcurrant/cedar bouquet; the medium-bodied palate has good structure, needing a year or two for the tannins to fully knit. Screwcap. 14% alc. **Rating** 93 **To** 2020 $22

Mount Barker Merlot 2010 **Rating** 91 **To** 2016 $24

♟♟♟♟   **Mount Barker Sauvignon Blanc 2011** **Rating** 89 **To** Now $22

Three Willows Vineyard   ★★★☆

46 Montana Road, Red Hills, Tas 7304 **Region** Northern Tasmania
T 0438 507 069 **www.**threewillowsvineyard.com.au **Open** Most days 10–5 (summer), 11–4 (winter)
Winemaker Philip Parés **Est.** 2002 **Dozens** 200 **Vyds** 1.8ha
Philip Parés and Lyn Prove have planted a micro-vineyard with pinot noir, pinot gris and baco noir (a hybrid). It is 50km west of Launceston, near Deloraine, on a gentle north-facing slope at an elevation of 220–250m. The present tiny production will peak at around 250 dozen.

♟♟♟♟♟   **Pinot Rose 2008** Salmon-pink; despite the closure, this is emphatically not a Moscato style; it is in the opposite universe, a savoury/spicy rendition of barrel-fermented (old oak) Pinot Noir. Crown seal. 14% alc. **Rating** 90 **To** Now $20

♟♟♟♟   **Pinot Gris 2010** **Rating** 87 **To** 2013 $25
Home Block Pinot Noir 2009 **Rating** 87 **To** 2014 $26

Tidswell Wines   ★★★

14 Sydenham Road, Norwood, SA 5067 **Region** Limestone Coast Zone
T (08) 8363 5800 **F** (08) 8363 5888 **www.**tidswellwines.com.au **Open** By appt
Winemaker Ben Tidswell, Wine Wise Consultancy **Est.** 1997 **Dozens** 5000 **Vyds** 136.4ha
The Tidswell family (now in the shape of Andrea and Ben Tidswell) has two large vineyards in the Limestone Coast Zone near Bool Lagoon; the lion's share is planted to cabernet sauvignon and shiraz, with smaller plantings of merlot, sauvignon blanc, petit verdot, vermentino and pinot gris. Fifty per cent of the vineyards are organically certified, and more will be converted in due course. Wines are released under the Jennifer, Heathfield Ridge and Caves Road labels. Exports to Canada, Denmark, Germany, Singapore, Japan and China.

♟♟♟♟   **Caves Road Shiraz 2010** Ripe black fruits, with mulberry, blackberry and sage; the palate is medium-bodied, fleshy and forward, with a savoury leather note to conclude. Screwcap. 14.5% alc. **Rating** 87 **To** 2014 $16 BE

Tilbrook Estate

17/1 Adelaide-Lobethal Road, Lobethal, SA 5241 **Region** Adelaide Hills
T (08) 8389 5318 **F** (08) 8389 5315 **www.**tilbrookestate.com.au **Open** Fri–Sun 11–5 & public hols, or by appt
Winemaker James Tilbrook **Est.** 2001 **Dozens** 2000 **Vyds** 4.98ha

James and Annabelle Tilbrook have almost 5ha of multi-clone chardonnay and pinot noir, plus sauvignon blanc and pinot gris, at Lenswood. The winery and cellar door are in the old Onkaparinga Woollen Mills building in Lobethal; this not only provides an atmospheric home, but also helps meet the very strict environmental requirements of the Adelaide Hills in dealing with winery waste water. English-born James came to Australia in 1986, aged 22, but a car accident led to his return to England. Working for Oddbins and passing the WSET diploma set his future course. He returned to Australia, met Annabelle, purchased the vineyard and began planting it in '99. Finding the best combination of variety and site has proved frustrating; there are plans to graft part of one block to shiraz, and another (possibly) to riesling. The close-planted pinot noir block, with a row width of 1.25m, is being converted to 2.5m by the simple expedient of pulling out every second row.

ΨΨΨΨΨ **Reserve Adelaide Hills Syrah 2010** Full red-purple; a strong black shoe leather overtone to the dark berry fruits of the bouquet largely disappears into the wine on the medium- to full-bodied palate with its savoury black fruits and firm tannins, French oak coming through on the finish. Diam. 14% alc. **Rating** 93 **To** 2024 $35
Reserve Adelaide Hills Botrytis Pinot Gris 2010 Full glowing gold; a major surprise; has intensity and complexity, and the sweetness is balanced by acidity. The grapes must have been heavily botrytised for the wine to have 12.9% alcohol; 40 dozen made. 375ml. Diam. 12.9% alc. **Rating** 92 **To** 2016 $35

ΨΨΨΨ **Adelaide Hills Methode Traditionelle 2010 Rating** 89 **To** 2014 $25 BE
Adelaide Hills Pinot Gris 2010 Rating 88 **To** Now $20

Tim Adams   ★★★★★

Warenda Road, Clare, SA 5453 **Region** Clare Valley
T (08) 8842 2429 **www.**timadamswines.com.au **Open** Mon–Fri 10.30–5, w'ends 11–5
Winemaker Tim Adams **Est.** 1986 **Dozens** 50 000 **Vyds** 145ha
After almost 20 years slowly and carefully building the business, based on the classic Clare Valley varieties of riesling, semillon, grenache, shiraz and cabernet sauvignon, Tim Adams and Pam Goldsack decided to increase their production from 35 000 to 50 000 dozen. Like their move to a total reliance on screwcaps, there is nothing unexpected in that. However, the make-up of the new plantings is anything but usual: they will give Adams more than 10ha of tempranillo and pinot gris, and about 3.5ha of viognier, in each case with a very clear idea about the style of wine to be produced. In 2009 the business took a giant step forward with the acquisition of the 80ha Leasingham Rogers Vineyard from CWA for a reported price of $850 000, followed in '11 by the purchase of the Leasingham winery and winemaking equipment (for less than replacement cost). The only asset retained by Accolade Wines (the new owner of CWA) is the Leasingham brand name. The winery will become a major contract winemaking facility for the region. Exports to all major markets.

ΨΨΨΨΨ **Clare Valley Riesling 2011** Pale quartz-green; the gently floral bouquet flows through to the bright, fresh palate, where flavours of lime juice, lemon and apple are all on stage; the finish is crisp and clean. Using only the free-run juice – 500 litres from 700+ litres per tonne – invests the wine with elegance. Screwcap. 11% alc. **Rating** 94 **To** 2025 $22
Clare Valley Shiraz 2008 The grapes come from no less than seven vineyards; the wine spent two years in 1- and 2-year-old American oak. Given the challenge of this heatwave vintage, an impressive result, with pleasing black cherry, plum and blackberry fruit driving the medium-bodied palate, then a cleansing savoury finish. Screwcap. 14.5% alc. **Rating** 94 **To** 2020 $29

Tim Gramp   ★★★★☆

Mintaro/Leasingham Road, Watervale, SA 5452 **Region** Clare Valley
T (08) 8344 4079 **www.**timgrampwines.com.au **Open** W'ends & hols 12–4
Winemaker Tim Gramp **Est.** 1990 **Dozens** 6000 **Vyds** 16ha

Tim Gramp has quietly built up a very successful business, and by keeping overheads to a minimum provides good wines at modest prices. Over the years the estate vineyards (shiraz, riesling, cabernet sauvignon and grenache) have been expanded significantly. Exports to the UK, Taiwan and Malaysia.

🍷🍷🍷🍷🍷 ✪ **Gilbert Valley Mt Lofty Ranges Shiraz 2008** Still holding good colour, with little change from primary red-purple; the bouquet is very rich, with plum, spice and quality oak all in play; the palate is equally rich, but not overblown, finishing with fine tannins. Cellaring special. Screwcap. 14.5% alc. **Rating** 94 **To** 2023 $22

🍷🍷🍷🍷 ✪ **Watervale Riesling 2011** The citrus and apple blossom aromas are reflected in the intensely juicy palate, the extra cut of acidity courtesy of the cool vintage. Screwcap. 12% alc. **Rating** 93 **To** 2020 $20

✪ **Watervale Cabernet Sauvignon 2009** A savoury/earthy expression of Cabernet, the bouquet and medium-bodied palate both delivering the same message; its strengths lie in its structure and length, both of prime importance for the variety. Screwcap. 14.5% alc. **Rating** 90 **To** 2017 $21

🍷🍷🍷🍷 **McLaren Vale Grenache 2010** **Rating** 88 **To** 2014 $19 BE

Tim McNeil Wines ★★★★

PO Box 1088, Clare, SA 5453 **Region** Clare Valley
T (08) 8843 0040 **www**.timmcneilwines.com.au **Open** Not
Winemaker Tim McNeil **Est.** 2004 **Dozens** 1000 **Vyds** 2ha

When Tim and Cass McNeil established Tim McNeil Wines, Tim had long since given up his teaching career, graduating with a degree in oenology from Adelaide University in 1999. During his university years he worked at Yalumba, then moved with Cass to the Clare Valley in 2001, spending four years as a winemaker at Jim Barry Wines before moving to Kilikanoon in '05, where he currently works as a winemaker alongside Kevin Mitchell. The McNeils' 16ha property at Watervale includes mature, dry-grown riesling, and they intend to plant shiraz, currently purchasing that variety from the Barossa Valley. A cellar door facility is planned.

🍷🍷🍷🍷 **Reserve Watervale Riesling 2011** Like the standard wine, from dry-grown estate vines, but this is where the similarity ends. Here there is a fragrant citrus blossom bouquet, and perfectly poised and intense lime juice flavours, finishing with racy acidity. Screwcap. 12.5% alc. **Rating** 93 **To** 2021 $29

Clare Valley Shiraz 2009 Deep crimson with a bright rim; a very different wine to the Barossa version; while medium- to full-bodied, the sheer quality of the fruit fully justifies the 24 months' maturation in French hogsheads, 40% new; there are luscious black fruits with warm spices and licorice, the tannins well-balanced in the context of the wine. Screwcap. 14.5% alc. **Rating** 93 **To** 2029 $29

🍷🍷🍷🍷 **Barossa Shiraz 2009** **Rating** 89 **To** 2017 $27
Watervale Riesling 2011 **Rating** 88 **To** 2014 $21

Tim Smith Wines ★★★★★

PO Box 446, Tanunda, SA 5352 **Region** Barossa Valley
T (08) 8563 0939 **www**.timsmithwines.com.au **Open** Not
Winemaker Tim Smith **Est.** 2002 **Dozens** 3000 **Vyds** 1ha

With a talent for sourcing exceptional old vine fruit from the Barossa floor, Tim Smith has created a small but credible portfolio of wines, currently including Mataro, Grenache, Shiraz, Viognier, and more recently Eden Valley Riesling. Tim left his full-time winemaking role with a large Barossa brand in 2011, allowing him to concentrate 100% of his energy on his own brand. In '12 Tim joined forces with the team from First Drop (see separate entry), and has moved winemaking operations to a brand-new winery fondly named 'Home of the Brave' in Nuriootpa. Exports to the UK, Denmark, Taiwan and Singapore.

♀♀♀♀♀ Eden Valley Riesling 2011 Pale quartz-green; made from a single vineyard planted in the 1920s and packaged in a smart custom-made bottle branded 'Eden Valley'. This is a wine of outstanding quality, with wonderful intensity and focus to its bone-dry citrus/mineral palate, the lingering finish underlining its quality. Screwcap. 11.5% alc. **Rating** 96 **To** 2036 $25

Barossa Shiraz 2009 Bright red-purple; an elegant and refined wine bringing together parcels from six old vine vineyards in the Eden and Barossa valleys; it has outstanding length and precision to its red and black fruits, the tannins and oak perfectly weighted. Aged on lees in French and American oak; neither fined or filtered. Screwcap. 14.5% alc. **Rating** 96 **To** 2025 $32

Barossa Shiraz 2010 Vivid deep crimson; an attractive and pure liqueur kirsch and blackberry bouquet, with a dark edge of tar and ironstone; the palate is dense and dark, yet remains light on its feet, with the fruit providing silk to the firm tannins on offer; long, luscious and beautifully poised. Screwcap. 14.5% alc. **Rating** 95 **To** 2025 $36 BE

Barossa Mataro Grenache Shiraz 2010 Has excellent depth to the colour, and likewise to the display of black and red cherry, plum and plum cake fruit on the bouquet and medium- to full-bodied palate. Here is a wine to challenge the Rhône Valley. Whole bunch, barrel ageing on lees, no fining or filtration. Screwcap. 14.5% alc. **Rating** 94 **To** 2018 $28

Barossa Mataro 2010 This is a lovely and quite serious Mataro made in an elegant fashion, with high levels of sweet black fruits, spice and minerally complexity in abundance; the palate is lively, firm and long. Diam. 14.5% alc. **Rating** 94 **To** 2018 $32 BE

Tinklers Vineyard   ★★★★

Pokolbin Mountains Road, Pokolbin, NSW 2320 **Region** Hunter Valley
T (02) 4998 7435 **www.**tinklers.com.au **Open** 7 days 10–5
Winemaker Usher John Tinkler **Est.** 1997 **Dozens** 1500 **Vyds** 41ha
Three generations of the Tinkler family have been involved with the property since 1942. Originally a beef and dairy farm, vines have been both pulled out and replanted at various stages, and part of the adjoining 80-year-old Ben Ean Vineyard has been acquired. Plantings include semillon (14ha), shiraz (11.5ha), chardonnay (6.5ha) and smaller areas of merlot, muscat and viognier. In 2008 a new winery, adjoining the cellar door, was completed; all Tinklers wines are now vinified here (distinguished by a gold strip at the bottom of the label). The majority of the grape production continues to be sold to McWilliam's.

♀♀♀♀♀ U and I Hunter Valley Shiraz 2010 Bright purple hue; fragrant red and blue fruits offset by a touch of fresh leather and spice; the palate is firm and tannic, with plenty of fruit and vibrant acidity suggesting a long and healthy future; time is needed for optimum enjoyment. Screwcap. 14.5% alc. **Rating** 92 **To** 2020 $32 BE

✪ Hunter Valley Viognier 2011 Estate-grown, hand-picked, whole bunch-pressed and fermented in French barriques. Bright straw-green; while varietal character is not overly obvious, this is a beautifully made wine, the oak providing texture, and merely caressing the fruit flavours. There are some nutty apricot nuances, and the wine should be at its best over the next couple of years. Screwcap. 12.8% alc. **Rating** 91 **To** 2014 $18

Hunter Valley Shiraz Viognier 2010 Mid crimson; an attractively perfumed bouquet of red fruits, florals and spice; medium-bodied, and with fresh acidity, fine tannins and a juicy and generous finish. Screwcap. 14% alc. **Rating** 90 **To** 2015 $25 BE

♀♀♀♀ Hunter Valley Viognier 2009 **Rating** 89
❍ **To** 2013 $18
School Block Hunter Valley Semillon 2010 **Rating** 88 **To** 2015 $18 BE

Tintara
★★★★☆

202 Main Road, McLaren Vale, SA 5171 **Region** McLaren Vale
T (08) 8329 4124 **www**.tintara.com.au **Open** 7 days 10–4.30
Winemaker Neville Rowe **Est.** 1863 **Dozens** NFP
Tintara was the third of the three substantial winery and vineyard enterprises in the early days
of McLaren Vale. It was established by Dr Alexander Kelly, who purchased 280ha of land in
1861 and planted the first vines in 1863. It grew rapidly – indeed too rapidly, because it ran
into financial difficulties and was acquired by Thomas Hardy in 1876. He in turn recovered
his purchase price by wine sales over the following year. It has been a proud label for almost
150 years, but gained additional vigour with the 2008 release of the Single Vineyard wines,
which in the years prior to their release collected a swag of trophies and accolades. Exports to
the US, Canada, Europe and the Pacific Islands.

McLaren Vale Shiraz 2008 Strong crimson-red; the label does not show the
Hardy (now Accolade) ownership, but this is a classic Hardy McLaren Vale style,
the bouquet promising a seamless mix of juicy black fruits and quality oak on
a medium- to full-bodied palate, and that is precisely what you get, with extra
nuances of cedar and spice carried in the orbit of fine tannins. Great value.
Screwcap. 14% alc. **Rating** 96 **To** 2035 $27

McLaren Vale Cabernet Sauvignon 2009 Rating 93 **To** 2029 $25
McLaren Vale Shiraz 2009 Rating 91 **To** 2019 $25

Tintilla Wines
★★★★★

725 Hermitage Road, Pokolbin, NSW 2320 **Region** Hunter Valley
T (02) 6574 7093 **www**.tintilla.com.au **Open** 7 days 10.30–6
Winemaker James and Robert Lusby **Est.** 1993 **Dozens** 4000 **Vyds** 6.52ha
The Lusby family has established shiraz (2.2ha), sangiovese (1.6ha), merlot (1.32ha), semillon
(1.2ha) and cabernet sauvignon (0.2ha) on a northeast-facing slope with red clay and
limestone soil. Tintilla was the first winery to plant sangiovese in the Hunter Valley (1995).
The family has also planted an olive grove producing four different types of olives, which are
cured and sold from the estate.

Museum Release Hunter Valley Semillon 2003 Extraordinarily youthful but
brilliant green-straw colour; the palate is Chablis-like (25 years ago it would have
been labelled thus), crisp and vibrant, with lemon, apple and wonderful acidity;
another 10 years won't tire it. Screwcap. 10% alc. **Rating** 95 **To** 2023 $35
Angus Hunter Semillon 2011 A powerful, structured Semillon, with a
grapefruit zest and mineral character laying the foundation for a long future;
distinctly different from the majority of Hunter Valley Semillons, although very
much a member of the family. Screwcap. 10.9% alc. **Rating** 94 **To** 2026 $26

Patriarch Hunter Valley Syrah 2010 Rating 93 **To** 2025 $60
Reserve Hunter Valley Shiraz 2010 Rating 92 **To** 2020 $30
Pebbles Brief Hunter Valley Chardonnay 2011 Rating 90 **To** 2016 $30
Tarantella NV Rating 90 **To** 2015 $30

Four Marys Hunter Valley Pinot Noir 2010 Rating 87 **To** 2016 $30

Tizzana Winery
★★★☆

518 Tizzana Road, Ebenezer, NSW 2756 **Region** South Coast Zone
T (02) 4579 1150 **www**.tizzana.com.au **Open** W'ends, hols 12–6, or by appt
Winemaker Peter Auld **Est.** 1887 **Dozens** 2500 **Vyds** 3.4ha
Tizzana has been a weekend and holiday occupation for Peter Auld for many years now. It
operates in one of the great historic wineries, built (in 1887) by Australia's true renaissance
man, Dr Thomas Fiaschi. The wines may not be great, but the ambience is. Moreover, vines
have been replanted on the same vineyard as that first planted by Fiaschi in 1885 (shiraz,
cabernet sauvignon, aleatico, tannat and petit verdot). Peter has also developed Tizzana as a
wine education centre.

ΨΨΨΨ **Clarissa Shiraz Petit Verdot 2011** A 75/35% blend at the very start of its life, but has been well made and has all the requisites to age well. It was a cabernet petit verdot blend (made in 1930) that set Max Lake on the road to Lake's Folly. Screwcap. 12% alc. **Rating** 90 **To** 2021 $25

ΨΨΨΨ **Kirwan's Retreat Petit Verdot 2011 Rating** 88 **To** 2014 $30
Waterloo Shiraz 2011 Rating 87 **To** 2018 $25

Tobin Wines ★★★★
34 Ricca Road, Ballandean, Qld 4382 **Region** Granite Belt
T (07) 4684 1235 **www**.tobinwines.com.au **Open** 7 days 10–5
Winemaker Adrian Tobin **Est.** 1964 **Dozens** 6500 **Vyds** 5.9ha
In the early 1960s the Ricca family planted table grapes, followed by shiraz and semillon in '64–66, which are said to be the oldest vinifera vines in the Granite Belt region. The Tobin family (headed by Adrian and Frances) purchased the vineyard in 2000 and has increased plantings, which now consist of shiraz, cabernet sauvignon, merlot, tempranillo, semillon, verdelho, chardonnay, muscat sauvignon blanc, with some remaining rows of table grapes. The emphasis has changed towards quality bottled wines, with some success.

ΨΨΨΨΨ **Jacob Tempranillo 2011** Bright colour; a lusty bouquet of cherry cola and spice; the palate is racy and fresh, with an intriguing savoury bent that is sure to satisfy lovers of Spanish food and wine; is Tempranillo the great red hope of the Granite Belt? Screwcap. 13% alc. **Rating** 92 **To** 2015 $35 BE
Max Shiraz 2010 Mid crimson; a spicy and pure red-fruited bouquet with a medium-bodied and slightly savoury dried herb note on the palate; fresh and precise to conclude. Screwcap. 14.3% alc. **Rating** 91 **To** 2016 $35 BE

ΨΨΨΨ **Kate Sauvignon Blanc 2011 Rating** 89 **To** 2013 $28 BE
Lily Chardonnay 2011 Rating 87 **To** 2014 $28 BE
Maisie Verdelho 2011 Rating 87 **To** 2013 $28 BE

Tokar Estate ★★★★☆
6 Maddens Lane, Coldstream, Vic 3770 **Region** Yarra Valley
T (03) 5964 9585 **www**.tokarestate.com.au **Open** 7 days 10.30–5
Winemaker Martin Siebert **Est.** 1996 **Dozens** 4000 **Vyds** 14ha
Leon Tokar established 14ha of now mature chardonnay, pinot noir, shiraz, cabernet sauvignon and tempranillo at Tokar Estate, one of many vineyards on Maddens Lane. All the wines are from the estate, badged Single Vineyard (which they are), and have performed well in regional shows, with early success for the Tempranillo.

ΨΨΨΨΨ **The Aria 2008** A blend of tempranillo, cabernet sauvignon and shiraz; it takes a while, and several retastes, for the fruit to achieve ascendancy over the oak; all three varieties have a different red fruit character to contribute to the blend, and the result is both complex and satisfying. The colour, too, gives assurance for the long-term future of the wine. Screwcap. 14% alc. **Rating** 94 **To** 2023 $75

ΨΨΨΨΨ **Yarra Valley Pinot Noir 2010** Good colour; a well-made Pinot with a red
✪ cherry and spice bouquet; the palate has good texture and structure to the supple cherry and plum fruit. Screwcap. 13.5% alc. **Rating** 93 **To** 2018 $25
Yarra Valley Chardonnay 2009 Rating 90 **To** 2016 $25

Tomboy Hill ★★★★★
204 Sim Street, Ballarat, Vic 3350 (postal) **Region** Ballarat
T (03) 5331 3785 **Open** Not
Winemaker Scott Ireland (Contract) **Est.** 1984 **Dozens** 1000 **Vyds** 3.6ha
Former schoolteacher Ian Watson seems to be following the same path as Lindsay McCall of Paringa Estate (also a former schoolteacher) in extracting greater quality and style than any other winemaker in his region, in this case Ballarat. Since 1984 Ian has slowly and patiently

built up a patchwork quilt of small plantings of chardonnay and pinot noir. In the better years, single vineyard Chardonnay and/or Pinot Noir are released; Rebellion Chardonnay and Pinot Noir are multi-vineyard blends, but all 100% Ballarat. I have a particular fondness for the style.

♀♀♀♀♀ **Ruby's Picking Ballarat Goldfields Chardonnay 2009** Light to medium straw-green; held back for an extra year before release, an inspired decision by Ian Watson, as this is a beautiful Chardonnay; silky is not a word often used for white wines, but it certainly applies here, the fruit flavours running between white peach and grapefruit, taking the best from each. Screwcap. 13% alc. **Rating** 96 **To** 2017 $45

The Tomboy Ballarat Goldfields Pinot Noir 2010 This wine is entirely estate-grown on Ian Watson's own vineyard; the colour and overall texture are similar to The Rebel, the difference lying with the ultra-silky red and black cherry flavours of the fruit. Screwcap. 13.2% alc. **Rating** 96 **To** 2019 $75

The Tomboy Ballarat Goldfields Chardonnay 2010 Similar to Rebellion in its overall character, but with slightly more white flesh stone fruit flavours on the palate, and a supple, well-balanced finish, acidity spot on. Screwcap. 12.8% alc. **Rating** 94 **To** 2018 $45

The Rebel Ballarat Goldfields Pinot Noir 2010 This is a new addition to the range, a barrel selection of the wines normally included in Rebellion, with a major component from the Scotsburn Vineyard. Very good colour; it is an elegant and beautifully balanced Pinot, with utmost clarity and precision to the distinctive fruit flavours of Ballarat, always with some hints of forest floor in the background that add to complexity and length. Screwcap. 13.2% alc. **Rating** 94 **To** 2017 $45

♀♀♀♀♀ **Rebellion Ballarat Goldfields Chardonnay 2010 Rating** 93 **To** 2020 $25
Rebellion Ballarat Goldfields Pinot Noir 2010 Rating 92 **To** 2016 $35

Tomich Wines   ★★★★

87 King William Road, Unley, SA 5061 **Region** Adelaide Hills
T (08) 8272 9388 **www**.tomichwines.com **Open** Mon–Fri 10–4, w'ends 11–4.30
Winemaker John and Randal Tomich, Peter Leske (Contract) **Est.** 2002 **Dozens** 15 000
Vyds 80ha
There is an element of irony in this family venture. Patriarch John Tomich was born on a vineyard near Mildura, where he learnt first-hand the skills and knowledge required for premium grapegrowing. He went on to become a well-known Adelaide ear, nose and throat specialist. Taking the wheel full circle, he completed postgraduate studies in winemaking at the University of Adelaide in 2002, and embarked on to the Master of Wine revision course from the Institute of Masters of Wine. His son Randal is a cutting from the old vine (metaphorically speaking), having invented new equipment and techniques for tending the family's vineyard in the Adelaide Hills near Woodside, resulting in a 60% saving in time and fuel costs. Most of the grapes are sold, but the amount of wine made under the Tomich brand makes it far from a hobby. Exports to China, Hong Kong and Singapore.

♀♀♀♀♀ **Tomich Hill Family Reserve SIngle Vineyard Adelaide Hills Pinot Chardonnay NV** Would not appear to be fermented in this bottle, but does have some nutty complexity missing from the Chardonnay Pinot NV; pinot, too, is obvious. Cork. 12.5% alc. **Rating** 91 **To** 2014 $30

Tomich Hill Family Reserve Single Vineyard Adelaide Hills Pinot Gris 2010 Hand-picked ripe, crushed (more likely pressed) into old French barriques, wild yeast lees-stirred for six months; has lots of texture, but lacks drive on the finish. A massive contrast to the Pinot Grigio. Screwcap. 12.8% alc. **Rating** 90 **To** 2013 $30

♀♀♀♀ **Tomich Hill Single Vineyard Adelaide Hills Pinot Grigio 2010 Rating** 89
○ **To** Now $20
○ **Tomich Hill Shiraz 2008 Rating** 89 **To** 2016 $20
◐ **Adelaide Hills Chardonnay Pinot NV Rating** 89 **To** 2014 $20

Tomich Hill Family Reserve Single Vineyard Adelaide Hills Pinot Noir 2010 **Rating** 88 **To** 2015 $45

○ **Tomich Hill Adelaide Hills Late Harvest Gewurztraminer 2009** **Rating** 88 **To** 2016 $20

Toolangi Vineyards ★★★★★

PO Box 9431, South Yarra, Vic 3141 **Region** Yarra Valley
T (03) 9827 9977 **www**.toolangi.com **Open** By appt
Winemaker Various contract **Est.** 1995 **Dozens** 8000 **Vyds** 12.2ha

Garry and Julie Hounsell acquired their property in the Dixons Creek area of the Yarra Valley, adjoining the Toolangi State Forest, in 1995. The primary accent is on pinot noir and chardonnay, accounting for all but 2.7 ha, which is predominantly shiraz and a little viognier. Winemaking is by Yering Station (Willy Lunn), Giaconda (Rick Kinzbrunner), Hoddles Creek Estate (Franco D'Anna) and Oakridge (David Bicknell), as impressive a quartet of winemakers as one could wish for. Exports to the UK, Hong Kong and Singapore.

🍷🍷🍷🍷🍷 **Estate Yarra Valley Chardonnay 2010** Vibrant green hue; a beguiling combination of fresh grapefruit and pear, mixed with savoury notes of charcuterie, spicy oak and grilled nuts; the palate is electric on entry, with a fine balance of acidity and fruit weight seamlessly working towards a long, energetic and expansive conclusion. Screwcap. 13% alc. **Rating** 96 **To** 2018 $50 BE

Reserve Yarra Valley Chardonnay 2008 Deep gold, green hue; the concentration and depth of fruit in this wine are compelling, showing a savoury grilled nut and charcuterie-driven personality; rich, unctuous and mouth coating, the backbone of acidity plays a merely supporting role to such hedonistic offerings; long, toasty, tasty and complex. Screwcap. 14% alc. **Rating** 94 **To** 2015 $75 BE

🍷🍷🍷🍷½ **Estate Yarra Valley Shiraz 2010** **Rating** 92 **To** 2020 $50 BE
Yarra Valley Chardonnay 2010 **Rating** 90 **To** 2015 $25 BE
Yarra Valley Pinot Noir 2010 **Rating** 90 **To** 2016 $25 BE

Toorak Winery ★★★

Vineyard 279 Toorak Road, Leeton, NSW 2705 **Region** Riverina
T (02) 6953 2333 **www**.toorakwines.com.au **Open** Mon–Fri 10–5, Sat by appt
Winemaker Robert Bruno **Est.** 1965 **Dozens** 200 000 **Vyds** 145ha

A traditional, long-established Riverina producer with a strong Italian-based clientele around Australia. Production has increased significantly, utilising substantial estate plantings and grapes purchased from other growers in the Riverina and elsewhere. Wines are released under the Toorak Estate, Willandra Estate and Amesbury Estate labels. While, in absolute terms, the quality is not great, the low-priced wines in fact over-deliver in many instances. Exports to the US, Norway, Russia, Nigeria, India, Singapore and China.

🍷🍷🍷🍷 **Willandra Estate Premium Langhorne Creek Shiraz 2008** **Rating** 87
○ **To** 2013 $15
Frank Senior 8 Years Old Fine Old Tawny NV Has some of the rancio signs of age as per the label. Cork. 18.5% alc. **Rating** 87 **To** 2013 $14

Topper's Mountain Wines ★★★★☆

5km Guyra Road, Tingha, NSW 2369 **Region** New England
T 0411 880 580 **www**.toppers.com.au **Open** By appt
Winemaker Symphony Hill (Mike Hayes) **Est.** 2000 **Dozens** 1000 **Vyds** 9.79ha

Following a partnership dissolution, Topper's Mountain is now solely owned by Mark Kirkby. Planting began in the spring of 2000, with the ultimate fruit salad trial of 15 rows each of innumerable varieties and clones. The total area planted was made up of 28 separate plantings, many of these with only 200 vines in a block. As varieties proved unsuited, they were grafted to those that held the most promise. Thus far, Gewurztraminer and Sauvignon Blanc hold most promise among the white wines, the Mediterranean reds doing better than their French cousins. The original 28 varieties are now down to 16; chardonnay, gewurztraminer, sauvignon blanc, tempranillo, shiraz and merlot are the commercial varieties, the remainder in the fruit salad block still under evaluation. Integrated Pest Management has been successfully adopted throughout the vineyard. Champion Winery of Show, New England Wine Show '11.

🍷🍷🍷🍷🍷 New England Nebbiolo 2009 This is one of the most attractive and easy to drink Australian-made Nebbiolos. It has that tight black cherry fruit before moving into its savoury mode, but the tannins are remarkably fine, long and balanced. If only more were like this. Two trophies (including Best Wine of Show) New England Wine Show '11. Screwcap. 13.5% alc. **Rating** 94 **To** 2024 $38

🍷🍷🍷🍷🍷 **Single Estate New England Barbera 2010** Rating 91 To 2018 $34
New England Sauvignon Blanc 2011 Rating 90 To 2014 $30
Wild Ferment New England Viognier 2010 Rating 90 To 2017 $32
Barrel Ferment New England Petit Manseng 2011 Rating 90 To 2015 $32
Red Earth Child 2009 Rating 90 To 2024 $32
Single Estate New England Tannat 2010 Rating 90 To 2017 $34

Torbreck Vintners ★★★★★

Roennfeldt Road, Marananga, SA 5352 **Region** Barossa Valley
T (08) 8562 4155 **www**.torbreck.com **Open** 7 days 10–6
Winemaker David Powell **Est.** 1994 **Dozens** 55 000 **Vyds** 75ha
Of all the Barossa Valley wineries to grab the headlines in the US, with demand pulling prices up to undreamt-of levels, Torbreck stands supreme. David Powell has not let success go to his head, or subvert the individuality and sheer quality of his wines, all created around very old, dry-grown, bush-pruned vineyards. The top quartet is led by The Laird (single vineyard Shiraz), RunRig (Shiraz/Viognier), The Factor (Shiraz) and Descendant (Shiraz/Viognier); next The Struie (Shiraz) and The Steading (Grenache/Mataro/Shiraz). Notwithstanding the depth and richness of the wines, they have a remarkable degree of finesse. In 2008 the ownership was restructured, Californian vintner Peter Kight (of Quivira Vineyards) acquiring shares. The Laird is a cool $700 a bottle. Exports to all major markets.

🍷🍷🍷🍷🍷 The Laird 2006 Prior to the arrival of The Laird, RunRig was Torbreck's top wine, at $235 a bottle. It comes from a remarkable single vineyard that David Powell had coveted for 15 years. Apart from a high level of vigilance, normal open fermentation and basket pressing; following Guigal's 'La La's', it spent three years in new and hideously expensive Tardieu Laurent French barriques with staves 45 mm thick (normally 22–27 mm), the oak becoming embedded in the fruit, supporting not overwhelming it, with layer upon layer of gloriously complex flavours, the tannins superbly weighted. A magnificent wine from a great vintage. Cork. 14.8% alc. **Rating** 97 **To** 2036 $700

The Gask 2010 Impenetrable colour; a highly aromatic and perfumed shiraz bouquet with dark fruits aplenty, offset by violets and a wide array of spices; the palate is dense, as you would expect of Torbreck, yet there is freshness and a struck quartz minerality that thrills through the wine's spine; long, luscious and hedonistic. Screwcap. 15% alc. **Rating** 96 **To** 2025 $75 BE

RunRig 2009 This is larger than life, super-concentrated, black-fruited, dark and essency shiraz, befitting of maker David Powell; while the concentration is staggering, the underlying tannins and freshness provides length, complexity and interest. Make no mistake, this is big end of town, take no prisoners old-vine shiraz pushed to the limit. Screwcap. 15% alc. **Rating** 95 **To** 2025 $225 BE

The Struie 2009 Strong, deep red-purple; a blend of Barossa and Eden valleys; the complex bouquet and layered palate are driven by fruit, not by oak, although there is no shortage of the latter; spice, blackberry and black cherry join in the long palate that is sustained by ripe tannins. There is no time not to drink the wine. Shiraz. Cork. 15% alc. **Rating** 94 **To** 2029 $53

The Loon 2010 Deep purple and impenetrable in colour, this is fresh, young unencumbered and pure Barossa Shiraz (with a small percentage of Roussanne added); liqueur-soaked black fruits, sage, spices and a rugged aspect to the palate is offset by a generous and richly textured finish, without the least sign of heaviness. Screwcap. 16% alc. **Rating** 94 **To** 2025 $30 BE

The Loon 2009 A new arrival on the scene for Torbreck, 'Loon' the name of a young, boisterous Scottish boy, which is how David Powell describes this shiraz/roussanne blend. The bouquet is complex, with some tanned leather notes that also come through on the palate, which has lifted, energetic character to the black fruits and Asian spices also present. Interesting. Screwcap. 14.5% alc. **Rating** 94 **To** 2029 $33

Les Amis 2009 Deep garnet; the bouquet is savoury, dark, brooding and spicy, with lots of charry oak on display; the palate reveals a rich, hedonistic and spicy grenache, with layers of spice, black fruit, fruitcake and prunes; there is life and energy on the finish, with the new oak a mere seasoning for such concentration. Cork. 14.5% alc. **Rating** 94 **To** 2020 $188 BE

ŸŸŸŸŸ **The Factor 2008 Rating** 93 **To** 2023 $125
The Steading 2009 Rating 93 **To** 2016 $38 BE
The Struie 2010 Rating 92 **To** 2018 $49 BE
Woodcutter's Barossa Valley Shiraz 2010 Rating 90 **To** 2017 $22

ŸŸŸŸ **The Bothie Shiraz 2011 Rating** 89 **To** 2013 $20
The Bothie 2011 Rating 87 **To** 2014 $19 BE

Torzi Matthews Vintners   ★★★★

Cnr Eden Valley Road/Sugarloaf Hill Road, Mount McKenzie, SA 5353 **Region** Eden Valley
T 0412 323 486 **www**.torzimatthews.com.au **Open** At Taste Eden Valley, Angaston
Winemaker Domenic Torzi **Est.** 1996 **Dozens** 4000 **Vyds** 13ha
Domenic Torzi and Tracy Matthews, former Adelaide Plains residents, searched for a number of years before finding a block at Mt McKenzie in the Eden Valley. The block they chose is in a hollow; the soil is meagre, and they were in no way deterred by the knowledge that it would be frost-prone. The result is predictably low yields, concentrated further by drying the grapes on racks and reducing the weight by around 30% (the Appassimento method is used in Italy to produce Amarone-style wines). Four wines are made: Riesling and Shiraz under both the Frost Dodger and Schist Rock labels, the Shiraz wild yeast–fermented and neither fined nor filtered. Newer plantings of sangiovese and negroamaro, and an extension of the original plantings of shiraz and riesling, is likely to see the wine range increase in the future. Exports to the US, Denmark, Singapore and Hong Kong.

ŸŸŸŸŸ **Schist Rock Eden Valley Shiraz 2010 Rating** 91
⦿   **To** 2030 $18

ŸŸŸŸ **Frost Dodger Eden Valley Shiraz 2009 Rating** 87 **To** 2015 $30 BE

Tower Estate   ★★★★★

Cnr Broke Road/Hall Road, Pokolbin, NSW 2320 **Region** Hunter Valley
T (02) 4998 7989 **www**.towerestatewines.com.au **Open** 7 days 10–5
Winemaker Samantha Connew **Est.** 1999 **Dozens** 10 000 **Vyds** 3.32ha
Tower Estate was founded by the late Len Evans, with the award-winning 5-star Tower Lodge accommodation and convention centre a part of the development. There has been little day-to-day change in either part of the business since Len's passing. Tower Estate will continue to draw upon varieties and regions that have a particular synergy, the aim being to make the best possible wines in the top sector of the wine market. The appointment of Samantha (Sam) Connew as winemaker in December 2009 – she has had a long career as chief winemaker at Wirra Wirra – added icing to the cake. Exports to the UK.

🍷🍷🍷🍷🍷 **Coombe Rise Vineyard Hunter Valley Semillon 2011** Light green-straw; the Coombe Rise Vineyard is situated on sandy alluvial soils adjacent to some of the greatest Hunter vineyards, investing the wine with its seamless mix of lemon/lime citrus and intense minerality on a palate of prodigious length. Screwcap. 11.5% alc. **Rating** 96 **To** 2026 $38

Panorama Vineyard Tasmania Pinot Noir 2010 Excellent hue and brightness; marries elegance and intensity, with red and black cherry fruit, balanced oak and fine tannins. Even in the context of the 71 wines in the 2010 Pinot Noir class, it was notable for its freshness. It was my top gold, and emerged as such in the results. Screwcap. 14% alc. **Rating** 96 **To** 2017 $55

Horse Paddock Vineyard Barossa Valley Shiraz 2009 Deep red-purple; sure, the wine has blackberry, plum, chocolate and vanilla aromas and flavours that instantly appeal, but it is the polished and elegant mouthfeel that lifts the wine out of the ruck. The Hunter pays homage to the Barossa indeed. Screwcap. 13.5% alc. **Rating** 96 **To** 2030 $35

Meadowbank Vineyard Tasmania Riesling 2011 Bright quartz-green; the high-toned lime blossom and pine cone aromas are followed by an intense lime juice palate, the high acidity balanced by residual sugar in a Mosel Kabinett style, the finish long and clear. Screwcap. 8% alc. **Rating** 95 **To** 2026 $28

Hunter Valley Semillon 2011 Light straw-green; more generous and accessible than Coombe Rise, even though the alcohol is lower and closer to Hunter norms, but picks up energy and drive on the back-palate, finish and aftertaste. Screwcap. 11% alc. **Rating** 94 **To** 2020 $22

Bowyer Ridge Adelaide Hills Chardonnay 2010 Bright straw-gold; wild yeast, barrel-fermented, with very good mouthfeel to the nectarine and white peach fruit, oak contributing to the texture as much as to the flavour of the very long and well-balanced palate. Screwcap. 13% alc. **Rating** 94 **To** 2017 $38

Meadowbank Vineyard Tasmania Pinot Noir 2010 Light, bright crimson-purple; has a mix of sweet plum, cherry and forest floor on the bouquet and palate; the flavours are supported by fine but firm tannins. Screwcap. 13% alc. **Rating** 94 **To** 2017 $45

🍷🍷🍷🍷🍷 **Windmill Vineyard Clare Valley Riesling 2011** **Rating** 93 **To** 2021 $28
Hunter Valley Shiraz 2010 **Rating** 93 **To** 2025 $35
Bowyer Ridge Adelaide Hills Pinot Gris 2011 **Rating** 92 **To** 2014 $25

Treasury Wine Estates   ★★★★★

77 Southbank Boulevard, Southbank, Vic 3006 **Region** Various
T 1300 651 650 **www**.treasurywineestates.com **Open** Not
Winemaker Mark Robertson **Est.** 2005 **Dozens** NFP **Vyds** 11,01ha
Treasury Wine Estates (TWE), the renamed wine division of Foster's Group Limited, was fully separated from Foster's via a separate listing on the Australian Securities Exchange in May 2011. It has the full range of wine businesses: from those with a dedicated winery or wineries, household brand names and long-term grape supply from owned vineyards or contract arrangements, through to brands that have been stripped of their wineries and vineyards, but continue to have a significant brand presence in the marketplace. Those who fall into the dedicated winery/estate vineyards pattern are Penfolds, Wynns Coonawarra Estate, Seppelt, Baileys of Glenrowan, Devil's Lair, St Huberts and Coldstream Hills. Other brands include Annie's Lane, Heemskerk, Ingoldby, Jamiesons Run, Leo Buring, Lindemans, Rosemount Estate, Saltram, T'Gallant, Tollana, Wolf Blass and Yellowglen. Exports to all major markets.

🍷🍷🍷🍷🍷
✪ **Abel's Tempest Chardonnay 2010** Light green-gold; the fragrant and floral bouquet leads into a fine, intense palate with an enticing mix of citrus and white peach complexed by some nutty/creamy notes before acidity checks in to lengthen and refresh the pate. Screwcap. 13% alc. **Rating** 95 **To** 2017 $25

🍷🍷🍷🍷🍷 **Abel's Tempest Pinot Noir 2010** **Rating** 93 **To** 2015 $32
Abel's Tempest Traminer 2011 **Rating** 91 **To** 2016 $25
Abel's Tempest Traminer 2010 **Rating** 91 **To** 2015 $25
Abel's Tempest Sauvignon Blanc 2010 **Rating** 91 **To** 2013 $25

Treeton Estate

163 North Treeton Road, Cowaramup, WA 6284 **Region** Margaret River
T (08) 9755 5481 **www**.treetonestate.com.au **Open** 7 days 10–6
Winemaker David McGowan **Est.** 1982 **Dozens** 3500 **Vyds** 7.5ha
In 1982 David McGowan and wife Corinne purchased the 30ha property upon which
Treeton Estate is established, planting the vineyard two years later (shiraz, sauvignon blanc,
chenin blanc, cabernet sauvignon and chardonnay). David has tried his hand at a lot of things
in his life, and in the early years was working in Perth, which led to various setbacks for the
vineyard. The wines are light and fresh, sometimes rather too much so. Exports to South East
Asia and China.

ΤΤΤΤ   **Margaret River Sauvignon Blanc Semillon 2011** Grass and herb characters
lead the way, lemon/citrus bringing up the rear. Drink sooner rather than later,
while the subtle fruit flavours are still present. Screwcap. 13.5% alc. **Rating** 88
To 2013 $20
Park Block Margaret River Shiraz 2009 Light, clear crimson; an
unambiguously light-bodied wine with fresh, spicy red berry fruit flavours and fine
tannins to close. Screwcap. 14.8% alc. **Rating** 88 **To** 2016 $20
Margaret River Chardonnay 2011 Very much at the heart of the Treeton
Estate style, with delicate fruit that would not stand up to the full box of
winemaking tricks; simply a pleasant, fresh Chardonnay to be enjoyed rather than
analysed. Screwcap. 13% alc. **Rating** 87 **To** 2014 $20

Trellis

Valley Farm Road, Healesville, Vic 3777 **Region** Yarra Valley
T (03) 5962 5723 **www**.trelliswines.com.au **Open** By appt
Winemaker Luke Houlihan **Est.** 2007 **Dozens** 535 **Vyds** 3.2ha
This is the venture of winemaker Luke Houlihan and viticulturist Greg Dunnett. Luke was
formerly winemaker at Yarra Ridge and Long Gully Estate, and Greg owns Valley Farm
Vineyard. The pinot noir has had several distinguished purchasers over the years, and there has
never been any doubt about the quality of the fruit, which is from the dry-grown vines. The
partners have put the problems of the 2007 and '09 vintages behind them, with lovely '08s
and '10s from the Yarra Valley neatly stitched in with an '07 and '09 Syrah from Heathcote.

ΤΤΤΤΤ   **Yarra Valley Chardonnay 2010** Light straw-gold; a decidedly complex and
slightly funky bouquet leads into a textured palate, with layers of stone fruit,
creamy nuances and grilled nuts, tied together by good acidity. Screwcap. 13% alc.
Rating 94 **To** 2017 $32
Yarra Valley Pinot Noir 2010 Bright crimson; another lovely wine from a
great vintage, notable for its purity and elegance, red berry fruits cosseted by a
fine filigree of tannins. Screwcap. 12.5% alc. **Rating** 94 **To** 2017 $32

ΤΤΤΤ   **Yarra Valley Pinot Noir Rose 2011** **Rating** 89 **To** 2013 $20

Trentham Estate ★★★★

Sturt Highway, Trentham Cliffs, NSW 2738 **Region** Murray Darling
T (03) 5024 8888 **www**.trenthamestate.com.au **Open** 7 days 9.30–5
Winemaker Anthony Murphy, Shane Kerr, Kirk McDonald **Est.** 1988 **Dozens** 60 000
Vyds 50.65ha
Remarkably consistent tasting notes across all wine styles from all vintages attest to the
expertise of ex-Mildara winemaker Tony Murphy, a well-known and highly regarded
producer, with estate vineyards on the Murray Darling. With an eye to the future, but also to
broadening the range of the wines on offer, Trentham Estate is selectively buying grapes from
other regions with a track record for the chosen varieties. The value for money is unfailingly
excellent. Exports to the UK and other major markets.

ΥΥΥΥΩ   **Noble Taminga 2008** Glowing green-gold; extremely rich and complex, with
✪   cumquat, apricot and pineapple flavours set against lively acidity; has not blown
     out as some Australian botrytis wines do. 375ml Screwcap. 11% alc. **Rating** 92
     To 2014 $16
○   **Chardonnay 2010 Rating** 90 **To** 2013 $16

ΥΥΥΥ   **Estate Viognier 2010 Rating** 89 **To** Now $16
○   **Estate Merlot 2010 Rating** 89 **To** 2013 $16
○   **Cabernet Sauvignon Merlot 2009 Rating** 89 **To** 2014 $14
     La Famiglia Moscato 2011 Rating 89 **To** Now $14
○   **Sauvignon Blanc 2011 Rating** 88 **To** Now $14
     La Famiglia Vermentino 2010 Rating 88 **To** Now $16
     Two Thirds Semillon Sauvignon Blanc 2011 Rating 87 **To** Now $14
     Estate Chardonnay 2011 Rating 87 **To** 2013 $16 BE
○   **Pinot Noir 2010 Rating** 87 **To** 2013 $14

Trevelen Farm   ★★★★★

506 Weir Road, Cranbrook, WA 6321 **Region** Great Southern
T (08) 9826 1052 **www**.trevelenfarm.com.au **Open** Fri–Mon 10.30–4.30, or by appt
Winemaker Harewood Estate (James Kellie, Luke Hipper) **Est.** 1993 **Dozens** 3500
Vyds 6.5ha
In 2008 John and Katie Sprigg decided to pass ownership of their 1300ha wool, meat and
grain-producing farm to son Ben and wife Louise. However, they have kept control of the
6.5ha of sauvignon blanc, riesling, chardonnay, cabernet sauvignon and merlot planted in
1993. Each wine is made as a 100% varietal, and when demand requires, they will increase
production by purchasing grapes from growers in the Frankland River region. Riesling will
remain the centrepiece of the range. Exports to Denmark, China, Macau and Japan.

ΥΥΥΥΥ   **Riesling 2011** Pale straw-quartz; an expressive, if unusual bouquet, with
     nuances of mineral, rock and spice, then an intense, long and beautifully balanced
     palate with lemon and lime the flavour drivers, minerally acidity providing the
     framework for a long life ahead. Screwcap. 12% alc. **Rating** 94 **To** 2021 $25
     Frankland Reserve Shiraz 2009 Clear crimson-purple of moderate depth; a
     prime example of Frankland River terroir, with a profusion of spice, pepper, red
     cherry and blackberry aromas on the bouquet, the palate adding hints of bitter
     dark chocolate allied with fine-grained, persistent tannins, oak a continuous
     backdrop. Screwcap. 14.5% alc. **Rating** 94 **To** 2025 $25

ΥΥΥΥΩ   **Sauvignon Blanc Fume Reserve 2011** Bright, light green-straw; an elegant
✪   wine with subtle barrel-ferment inputs hiding behind the perfectly ripened fruit
     that provides the blossom aromas of the bouquet and the range of tropical notes
     on the palate. Screwcap. 13.5% alc. **Rating** 93 **To** 2013 $18
     The Tunney Cabernet Sauvignon 2009 Rating 92 **To** 2020 $23
✪   **Katie's Kiss Sweet Riesling 2011** In the low end of off-dry, delicate, crisp and
     flowery, the sweetness largely obscured by the acidity. Drink it now if you wish,
     but it will have far more to say in another five years' time. Screwcap. 11.5% alc.
     Rating 90 **To** 2018 $14

Trevor Jones Fine Wines   ★★★★★

Lot 292 Jollytown Road, Lyndoch, SA 5351 **Region** Barossa Valley
T 0417 869 981 **www**.trevorjonesfinewines.com.au **Open** By appt
Winemaker Trevor Jones **Est.** 1998 **Dozens** 2500 **Vyds** 5ha
The Trevor Jones and Kellermeister brands were for many years linked by family ties. Up to
2010 Trevor Jones (the person) was winemaker and production manager for Kellermeister,
but has left to concentrate on the eponymous business owned by himself and wife Mandy.
He now makes his wines at Torbreck, but plans to have his own winery operational in time
for the 2014 vintage. With 34 years' winemaking experience, he is also providing consultancy
advice to wineries in the Barossa. Exports to the US, Switzerland and Japan.

♥♥♥♥♥ Belle-Terroir Shiraz 2005 Excellent colour for age, still crimson; a fragrant bouquet with black fruits, warm spices and good oak; full-bodied, but has impeccable balance and texture, the tannins ripe, the black fruits still driving the wine with energy and conviction; 100 dozen made. High-quality cork. 14% alc. Rating 96 To 2030 $60

Belle-Terroir Shiraz 2004 Similar (excellent) colour to the '05; the bouquet has a complex array of predominantly black fruits, with touches of spice and polished leather; the full-bodied palate is likewise very complex, oak part of the picture; more elegant than the '05, but not quite so profound. Six of one … Wine travel down the sides of the long cork. 14.5% alc. Rating 95 To 2029 $70

Belle-Terroir Shiraz 2002 Dense, deep crimson-purple; intense, potent black fruit bouquet leads into a full-bodied palate overflowing with black fruits, licorice, spice and oak – so much so that the high alcohol doesn't dominate proceedings. The high quality cork fiercely resisted attempts to remove it. 15.5% alc. Rating 95 To 2027 $75

Cobbler Creek Riesling 2011 Bright green-straw; the flowery bouquet has unmistakable jasmine aromas, but these yield to focused lime and lemon flavours on the intense, energetic palate. From the Mount Lofty Ranges, the grapes chilled, then whole bunch-pressed. Screwcap. 12.5% alc. Rating 94 To 2021 $18

♥♥♥♥♡ Belle-Terroir Shiraz 2003 Rating 93 To 2020 $70

Tscharke Wines   ★★★★☆

Seppeltsfield Road, Marananga, SA 5360 **Region** Barossa Valley
T 0438 628 178 **www**.tscharke.com.au **Open** Thurs–Mon 10–5
Winemaker Damien Tscharke **Est.** 2001 **Dozens** 5000 **Vyds** 25.25ha
Damien Tscharke grew up in the Barossa Valley among the vineyards at Seppeltsfield and Marananga. In 2001 he began the production of Glaymond, four estate-grown wines based on what he calls the classic varieties (following the trend of having catchy, snappy names), followed by wines under the Tscharke brand using the alternative varieties of tempranillo, graciano, zinfandel, montepulciano and savagnin. Like the Glaymond wines, these are estate-grown, albeit in very limited quantities. Exports to the US, Canada, Denmark, Belgium, Germany, Israel, Indonesia, Singapore and China.

♥♥♥♥♥ Tscharke Girl Talk Marananga Savagnin 2011 Pale straw-green; has the extra
✪   layer of varietal character and texture that the best Savagnins have, with its mix of pear skin, apple, citrus and spice; the finish is full, but dry and not phenolic. Top Gold Winewise '11. Screwcap. 12.5% alc. Rating 94 To 2014 $20

♥♥♥♥♡ Tscharke The Master Marananga Montepulciano 2010 Rating 93
        To 2015 $34
        Tscharke Only Son Barossa Valley Tempranillo 2010 Rating 92
        To 2017 $25
        Tscharke Matching Socks Barossa Valley Touriga Nacional 2010
        Rating 90 To 2015 $22

♥♥♥♥ Tscharke [600 x 106] Marananga Syrah 2010 Rating 89 To 2018 $24
        Tscharke BGC Gnadenfrei Unfiltered Grenache 2010 Rating 88
        To 2016 $32
        Tscharke The Potter Barossa Valley Garnacha 2011 Rating 88
        To 2014 $24
✪   Eva Barossa Valley Savagnin Frizzante 2011 The screwcap has allowed the wine to be made in a fully sparkling style (in terms of gas in the mouth when the wine is swirled). It's an eclectic style, but succeeds, arguably in spite of itself. Screwcap. 7% alc. Rating 88 To 2013 $15
        Glaymond Asif Barossa Valley Cabernet Sauvignon 2009 Rating 87
        To 2015 $32

Tuck's Ridge ★★★★★

37 Shoreham Road, Red Hill South, Vic 3937 **Region** Mornington Peninsula
T (03) 5989 8660 **www**.tucksridge.com.au **Open** 7 days 11–6
Winemaker Michael Kyberd **Est.** 1985 **Dozens** 4500 **Vyds** 3.04ha
Tuck's Ridge has changed focus significantly since selling its large Red Hill vineyard. It has retained the Buckle Vineyards of chardonnay and pinot noir that consistently provide outstanding grapes (and wine). The major part of the production is purchased from the Turramurra Vineyard. Exports to the US and Hong Kong.

ΨΨΨΨΨ **Buckle Pinot Noir 2010** Bright crimson-purple; as ever, an aristocratic wine of great purity from a 25-year-old, low-yielding vineyard allowed free rein to express is sense of place; plum and cherry intermingle on the bouquet and intense, lively palate, French oak totally integrated. Should have a very long life ahead. Screwcap. 13.7% alc. **Rating** 97 **To** 2022 $100
Buckle Chardonnay 2010 The wine effortlessly establishes its range of fig, melon and white peach on a long and controlled palate, all the components of fruit, oak and acidity seamlessly woven together. Screwcap. 13.2% alc. **Rating** 95 **To** 2018 $50
Turramurra Chardonnay 2010 Light straw-green; the wine has an extra dimension of flavour and mouthfeel from the higher alcohol, but is in no way hot or clumsy, grapefruit and white peach in the driving seat, the oak perfectly integrated. Screwcap. 14.1% alc. **Rating** 95 **To** 2015 $35

✪ **Mornington Peninsula Pinot Rose 2011** Pale salmon-pink; the bouquet is perfumed and fragrant, with an ascendance of spice, rose petal and strawberry aromas; the palate is every bit as expressive, with a lifted finish. Some volatile acidity can be accepted. Screwcap. 13.9% alc. **Rating** 94 **To** Now $20
Mornington Peninsula Pinot Noir 2010 Light, bright crimson; fragrant red fruits are woven through a background of savoury/foresty notes, the palate with a mix of strawberry and sour cherry fruit; a delicate wine of presence and precision. Screwcap. 13.5% alc. **Rating** 94 **To** 2018 $39

ΨΨΨΨΩ **Mornington Peninsula Chardonnay 2010 Rating** 93 **To** 2017 $25
✪ **Mornington Peninsula Savagnin 2011** Straw-green; there is no question this is a variety with real potential, and able to perform well in a range of climates; here the emphasis is on citrus skin and pith, with grip from the fruit, not from phenolics. Screwcap. 12.9% alc. **Rating** 92 **To** 2014 $20
Mornington Peninsula Shiraz 2010 Rating 92 **To** 2017 $35
Mornington Peninsula Sauvignon Blanc 2011 Rating 91 **To** 2013 $20
Mornington Peninsula Pinot Gris 2011 Rating 91 **To** 2013 $29

ΨΨΨΨ **Unoaked Chardonnay 2010 Rating** 87 **To** 2013 $15

Tulloch ★★★★★

'Glen Elgin', 638 De Beyers Road, Pokolbin, NSW 2321 **Region** Hunter Valley
T (02) 4998 7580 **www**.tulloch.com.au **Open** 7 days 10–5
Winemaker Jay Tulloch, First Creek Winemaking Services (Liz Jackson, Damien Stevens)
Est. 1895 **Dozens** 35 000 **Vyds** 80ha
The Tulloch brand continues to build success on success. Its primary grape source is estate vines owned by part shareholder Inglewood Vineyard in the Upper Hunter Valley. It also owns the JYT Vineyard established by Jay Tulloch in the mid 1980s at the foot of the Brokenback Range in the heart of Pokolbin. The third source is contract-grown fruit from other growers in the Hunter Valley and further afield. Skilled winemaking by First Creek Winemaking Services has put the icing on the winemaking cake, and Christina Tulloch is a livewire marketer. Exports to Belgium, Canada, the Philippines, Singapore, Hong Kong, Malaysia, Thailand, Japan and China.

ŶŶŶŶŶ JYT Selection Semillon 2011 Pale quartz; the bouquet is bright, fresh and zesty, the undertones of unsweetened citrus fruit coming through clearly on the mid palate and the long and emphatic finish. Drink now or later style. Screwcap. 10.5% alc. **Rating** 94 **To** 2020 $25

Julia Limited Release Semillon 2011 Pale quartz; has a strongly varietal personality from the flowery apple blossom and acacia bouquet to the more citrussy palate, finishing with bright acidity. From a single vineyard of 0.7ha producing a maximum of 350 dozen a year. Screwcap. 11.5% alc. **Rating** 94 **To** 2021 $28

Private Bin Pokolbin Dry Red Shiraz 2010 Despite the lower alcohol than the standard wine, has brighter colour and a very different palate; here the red and black fruits are intense and focused, and drive the long palate in conjunction with acidity; oak is a minor player in the band. Screwcap. 12.9% alc. **Rating** 94 **To** 2030 $50

ŶŶŶŶŶ Hector of Glen Elgin Limited Release Shiraz 2009 **Rating** 93 **To** 2025 $60 BE

✪ Vineyard Selection Hunter Valley Verdelho 2011 Fragrant, tangy, zesty and lively, an altogether superior example of Verdelho, with citrus and pineapple contributing equally. Short-term cellaring possible, but will you gain more on the swings than the roundabouts? Screwcap. 12.5% alc. **Rating** 92 **To** 2013 $20

✪ Cellar Door Release Hunter Valley Viognier 2011 Pale straw-green; a major surprise packet, full of life and varietal fruit in an unbroken stream from the start of the palate to the finish, and no hint of phenolics. Screwcap. 12.1% alc. **Rating** 91 **To** 2014 $20

✪ Hunter Valley Semillon 2011 **Rating** 90 **To** 2015 $16
EM Limited Release Chardonnay 2011 **Rating** 90 **To** 2016 $28

✪ Cellar Door Release Orange Pinot Gris 2011 Bright colour, with fresh pear, bath talc and a touch of citrus; the palate is soft and refreshing, with vibrant acidity and fine texture to finish. Screwcap. 13.3% alc. **Rating** 90 **To** 2013 $20 BE

Cellar Door Release Hilltops Cabernet Sauvignon 2010 **Rating** 90 **To** 2018 $25 BE

Cellar Door Release Hilltops Barbera 2010 **Rating** 90 **To** 2015 $25

ŶŶŶŶ Cellar Door Release Beechworth Pinot Noir 2010 **Rating** 89 **To** 2015 $25
Pokolbin Dry Red Shiraz 2010 **Rating** 89 **To** 2016 $25
Cellar Door Release Hilltops Sangiovese 2010 **Rating** 89 **To** 2014 $25
Cellar Door Release Rylstone Petit Verdot 2010 **Rating** 89 **To** 2016 $25
Cellar Door Release Hunter Valley Marsanne 2011 **Rating** 88 **To** 2015 $20

✪ Hunter Valley Verdelho 2011 **Rating** 88 **To** Now $16
Hunter Valley Chardonnay 2011 **Rating** 87 **To** 2014 $16 BE

Turkey Flat ★★★★★

Bethany Road, Tanunda, SA 5352 **Region** Barossa Valley
T (08) 8563 2851 **www.turkeyflat.com.au Open** 7 days 11–5
Winemaker Mark Bulman **Est.** 1990 **Dozens** 20 000 **Vyds** 47.83ha

The establishment date of Turkey Flat is given as 1990 but it might equally well have been 1870 (or thereabouts), when the Schulz family purchased the Turkey Flat vineyard, or 1847, when the vineyard was first planted to the very old shiraz that still grows there today alongside 8ha of equally old grenache. Plantings have since expanded significantly, now comprising shiraz (24.04ha), grenache (10.5ha), cabernet sauvignon (5.89ha), mourvedre (3.7ha), and smaller plantings of marsanne, viognier and dolcetto. In late 2009 a long-term goal was realised with the installation of a new bottling line, replacing the use of outside contractors and/or a mobile bottling plant. Exports to the UK, the US and other major markets.

ŶŶŶŶŶ Barossa Valley Shiraz 2010 Strong crimson-purple; one of the best Turkey
✪ Flat Shirazs to date; the palate is exceedingly complex, and very intense, yet ends with a burst of red and black fruits to accompany all that has gone before. It could be mistaken for a wine from a cooler climate, such is its length and balance. Screwcap. 14.5% alc. **Rating** 97 **To** 2030 $42

Single Vineyard The Conqueror Barossa Valley Shiraz 2008 From the estate-owned Stonewell Road vineyard that crops at less than 2.4 tonnes per hectare. It spends 22 months in French oak hogsheads, 60% new. Has excellent colour, a cedary bouquet, then a gloriously elegant palate with black cherry and plum wrapped in a fine skein of French oak and gossamer tannins. Held in bottle for 18 months prior to release. Screwcap. 14% alc. **Rating** 96 **To** 2028 $80

Single Vineyard The Twist Barossa Valley Shiraz 2009 Named after third son Oliver; produced from the estate Koonunga Vineyard, it has a very distinctive bouquet, with cedar, mint and dark berry fruits; the powerful and strongly structured palate weighs in with more dark fruits and tannins than the other two Single Vineyard Shirazs, although it retains the medium-bodied elegance shared by all three wines. Screwcap. 14.5% alc. **Rating** 96 **To** 2039 $80

Single Vineyard The Conqueror Barossa Valley Shiraz 2009 Named after son William, this comes from the estate Stonewell Vineyard; offers a mix of savoury and dark chocolate nuances to the underlying blackberry and plum fruit, oak obvious but not overdone. Screwcap. 14.5% alc. **Rating** 96 **To** 2034 $80

Single Vineyard The Great Barossa Valley Shiraz 2009 Named after son Alexander, and sourced from a single Bethany vineyard; medium-bodied; it has a lively bouquet and palate, with notes of spice, the fruit more in the red than black spectrum, and has a particularly enjoyable finish and aftertaste. Screwcap. 14.5% alc. **Rating** 95 **To** 2029 $80

Single Vineyard The Great Barossa Valley Shiraz 2008 The colour is again excellent, as is the overall elegance. Here red and black fruits play chase with dark spices and a hint of bitter chocolate, the tannins firm but meticulously controlled. Screwcap. 14% alc. **Rating** 95 **To** 2028 $80

○ **Barossa Valley Rose 2011** **Rating** 94 **To** Now $18

✪ **Butchers Block Barossa Valley Shiraz Grenache Mourvedre 2010** **Rating** 94 **To** 2025 $20

Barossa Valley Cabernet Sauvignon 2010 **Rating** 94 **To** 2030 $40

Barossa Valley Sparkling Shiraz NV **Rating** 94 **To** 2016 $40

ΨΨΨΨΦ **Butchers Block Barossa Valley Marsanne Viognier Roussanne 2011**
✪ Estate-grown on Turkey Flat's Stonewell and Bethany vineyards, and has already established a reputation; fermented and aged in French oak, it is a wine that is all about structure, and not about aromas. While it may well seem to go to sleep after a couple of years, another 10 years thereafter might see a wine of great authority and quality emerge. Screwcap. 13% alc. **Rating** 93 **To** 2021 $20

Single Vineyard The Twist Barossa Valley Shiraz 2008 **Rating** 93 **To** 2020 $80

Barossa Valley Grenache 2010 **Rating** 93 **To** 2020 $25

Barossa Valley Mourvedre 2010 **Rating** 93 **To** 2020 $32

Turner's Crossing Vineyard   ★★★★★

747 Old Bridgewater-Serpentine Road, Serpentine, Vic 3517 **Region** Bendigo
T 0427 843 528 **www.**turnerscrossing.com **Open** Not
Winemaker Sergio Carlei **Est.** 1998 **Dozens** 6000 **Vyds** 42ha
The name of this outstanding vineyard comes from local farmers crossing the Loddon River in the mid to late 1800s on their way to the nearest town. The vineyard was planted in 1999 by former corporate executive and lecturer in the business school at La Trobe University, Paul Jenkins. However, Paul's experience as a self-taught viticulturist dates back to '85, when he established his first vineyard at Prospect Hill, planting all the vines himself. The grapes from both vineyards have gone to a who's who of winemakers in Central Victoria, but an increasing amount is being made under the Turner's Crossing label, not surprising given the exceptional quality of the wines. Phil Bennett and winemaker Sergio Carlei have joined Paul as co-owners of the vineyard, with Sergio putting his money where his winemaking mouth is. Exports to the UK, the US, Canada, Taiwan, Singapore and China.

ŸŸŸŸ Bendigo Shiraz Viognier 2010 Vivid, deep colour coming from the co-fermentation of 5% viognier, matured for 16 months in old French oak barriques. Everything about this wine is impressive, from its vibrant cherry and plum fruit through to the fine, spicy tannins that run through much of the palate, and the impressive finish and aftertaste. Diam. 14.5% alc. **Rating** 95 **To** 2020 $30
Bendigo Shiraz Viognier 2009 Deep crimson-purple; the outstanding bouquet, with black fruits at its core, leads into a full-bodied palate with black fruits, spice, licorice and oak all adding to the appeal. Diam. 14.5% alc. **Rating** 94 **To** 2034 $30

ŸŸŸŸ Bendigo Cabernet Sauvignon 2007 **Rating** 89 **To** 2017 $30

Two Bud Spur   ★★★

1033 Woodbridge Hill Road, Gardners Bay, Tas 7112 **Region** Southern Tasmania
T (03) 6234 4252 **www.**twobudspur.com.au **Open** Not
Winemaker Winstead (Neil Snare) **Est.** 1996 **Dozens** 300 **Vyds** 2.2ha
Marine scientists Craig Mundy and Karen Miller purchased Two Bud Spur vineyard in 2006 as a stress release from their day jobs (they still work full-time, managing the vineyard in their spare time). Their viticultural expertise came from voracious reading of books and scientific literature, and the management of a nearby 0.5 pinot vineyard in the lead-up to the '06 vintage, an experience that led directly to their purchase of Two Bud Spur. This vineyard has had a chequered history, with its present name between 1996 and '03, then Grandview Vineyard '04 to '06, and from '07 onwards back to its original name. The vineyard had been run organically, but with disastrous results: disease, weeds, nutrients, canopy management and pruning issues all required attention, as did the boundary fences and not-quite-complete trellis. Craig and Karen were emboldened by the fact that, as they say, 'it couldn't get much worse, so there was not much risk of ruining anything'. They depict a two-bud spur on their label, the base architecture for all spur-pruned vineyards.

ŸŸŸŸ Barrel Fermented Sauvignon Blanc 2010 Tropical fruit aromas and flavours; has good oak balance. Screwcap. 14% alc. **Rating** 88 **To** 2013 $30

Two Dorks Estate   ★★★★

PO Box 24032, Melbourne, Vic 3001 **Region** Heathcote
T 0409 134 332 **Open** Not
Winemaker Mark Bladon **Est.** 2001 **Dozens** 50 **Vyds** 2ha
Owners Mark Bladon and Nektaria Achimastos (described by Mark as 'Vineyard Goddess') have an exceptionally keen sense of humour. Having chosen a site in the southern end of Heathcote off the Cambrian soil ('In truth, the land in the area is not the best,' Mark admits), they planted 2ha of dry-grown vines in 2001. The ensuing seven years of drought meant that development of the vines has been painstakingly slow, and simultaneously demanding of much TLC and that sense of humour. The vineyard is predominantly shiraz, with a patch of viognier and 0.5ha of cabernet sauvignon and merlot. The frost, drought, fire and brimstone of '09 meant no estate-grown wine from that year, and all replacement vines in the future will be shiraz. Mark has given the Vineyard Goddess a yellow card, but acknowledges that 'to be fair, even Jesus – an acknowledged miracle worker, wine-wise – needed water to make the stuff!'

ŸŸŸŸŸ Shiraz Blend 2009 An 85/15% shiraz, and cabernet sauvignon and merlot blend; bright crimson-purple; a fresh and lively palate that has spicy, cool-grown spicy berry characters amplified by persistent, but fine and ripe tannins. Screwcap. 13.4% alc. **Rating** 92 **To** 2019 $28

Two Hands Wines   ★★★★★

Neldner Road, Marananga, SA 5355 **Region** Barossa Valley
T (08) 8562 4566 **www.**twohandswines.com **Open** 7 days 10–5
Winemaker Matthew Wenk **Est.** 2000 **Dozens** 50 000 **Vyds** 15ha

The 'hands' in question are those of SA businessmen Michael Twelftree and Richard Mintz, Michael in particular having extensive experience in marketing Australian wine in the US (for other producers). On the principle that if big is good, bigger is better, the style of the wines has been aimed squarely at the palate of Robert Parker Jr and *Wine Spectator's* Harvey Steiman. Grapes are sourced from the Barossa Valley (where the business has 15ha of shiraz), McLaren Vale, Clare Valley, Langhorne Creek and Padthaway. The retention of cork closures, the emphasis on sweet fruit, and the soft tannin structure all signify the precise marketing strategy of what is a very successful business. Exports to the US and other major markets.

ттттт **Barney's Block Single Vineyard McLaren Vale Shiraz 2009** Deep colour, and loaded with fragrant black fruits, floral notes, licorice and a whole lot of mocha; the palate is full-bodied and fresh, with focus and energy being maintained from start to finish, with the little prickle of heat in fact working with the fruit on offer. Cork. 15.2% alc. **Rating** 94 **To** 2025 $100 BE

Windmill Block Single Vineyard Seppeltsfield Barossa Valley Shiraz 2009 A lifted and fragrant melange of red and black fruits, florals, fruitcake and a splash of savoury earthy nuance; the palate is lively and fresh, with the red fruit highlights and fresh acidity really driving the palate; long, fresh and poised, while providing a hedonistic mouthful of wine. Cork. 13.5% alc. **Rating** 94 **To** 2025 $100 BE

Brave Faces Barossa Valley Grenache Shiraz Mataro 2010 Youthful purple-crimson; the bouquet is aromatic, with a display of predominantly red fruits, but plum and spice also make their mark; the delicious palate is fresh and lively, with perfectly ripe fruit flavours; why is it that so many of these blends are 15.5%? Screwcap. 14.3% alc. **Rating** 94 **To** 2017 $27

ттттт **Sexy Beast McLaren Vale Cabernet Sauvignon 2010** Rating 93 **To** 2025 $27

Aphrodite Barossa Valley Cabernet Sauvignon 2009 Rating 93 **To** 2030 $165 BE

Yesterday's Hero Barossa Valley Grenache 2010 Rating 92 **To** 2014 $35

The Bull and the Bear Barossa Valley Clare Valley Cabernet Sauvignon Malbec 2010 Rating 92 **To** 2020 $45 BE

Angels' Share McLaren Vale Shiraz 2010 Rating 91 **To** 2020 $27

Coach House Block Single Vineyard Barossa Valley Shiraz 2009 Rating 91 **To** 2023 $100 BE

Gnarly Dudes Barossa Valley Shiraz 2010 Rating 90 **To** 2019 $27

тттт **Ares Barossa Valley McLaren Vale Shiraz 2009** Rating 89 **To** 2020 $165 BE

Aerope Barossa Valley Grenache 2009 Rating 87 **To** 2016 $120 BE

Brilliant Disguise Barossa Valley Moscato 2011 Rating 87 **To** 2013 $18

201

★★★★

PO Box 731, Caringbah, NSW 1495 **Region** Hunter Valley
T 0420 905 608 **www**.201.com.au **Open** Not
Winemaker Scott Stephens **Est.** 1998 **Dozens** 750 **Vyds** 4ha

Yet another winery with a numeric name giving book indexers and sommeliers nightmares, but better than the unpronounceable GPS co-ordinates used by another winery. Owners and partners Barbara Smith and Geoff Schippers purchased the 4ha former Rothbury Ridge vineyard in 2006. At that stage it had a quixotic planting of 1.6ha of durif and 1.2ha of chambourcin dating back to the early 1990s, when both varieties were uncommon, and the new owners sensibly decided to plant an additional 0.6ha each of semillon and barbera. It is a weekend retreat for Barbara and Geoff, who have busy lives in Sydney.

ттттт **Hunter Valley Semillon 2011** Pale, bright straw-green; has all the hallmarks of high-quality young Semillon, with a bouquet that is already expressive, the palate likewise; the flavours are in the meyer lemon spectrum, gaining depth from lemongrass at one extreme, grapefruit at the other. The slightly higher than usual alcohol does help fill out the flavour. Screwcap. 12% alc. **Rating** 93 **To** 2021 $18

тттт **Hunter Valley Chambourcin 2011** Rating 87 **To** 2013 $20

2 Mates

Cnr Mangarilla Road/Foggo Road, McLaren Vale, SA 5171 **Region** McLaren Vale
T 0411 111 198 **www**.2mates.com.au **Open** 7 days 11–5
Winemaker Matt Rechner, Mark Venable, David Minear **Est.** 2003 **Dozens** 500
The two mates are Mark Venable and David Minear, who say, 'Over a big drink in a small bar
in Italy a few years back, we talked about making "our perfect Australian Shiraz". When we
got back, we decided to have a go.' The wine ('05) was duly made, and won a silver medal at
the Decanter Magazine World Wine Awards in London, in some exalted company.

🍷🍷🍷🍷🍷 McLaren Vale Shiraz 2010 Deep purple-crimson; part of the grapes came from
140-year-old vines, the other from much younger vines; the wine is an undeniably
full-bodied and powerful blend of black fruits, regional dark chocolate, savoury
tannins and oak – but is not alcoholic. Screwcap. 15% alc. **Rating** 94 **To** 2025 $30

Two Rivers ★★★★☆

2 Yarrawa Road, Denman, NSW 2328 (postal) **Region** Hunter Valley
T (02) 6547 2556 **www**.tworiverswines.com.au **Open** 7 days 11–4
Winemaker First Creek Winemaking Services **Est.** 1988 **Dozens** 10 000 **Vyds** 75.62ha
A significant part of the viticultural scene in the Upper Hunter Valley, with over 75ha of
vineyards, involving a total investment of around $7 million. Part of the fruit is sold under
long-term contracts, and part is made for the expanding winemaking and marketing operations
of Two Rivers, the chief brand of Inglewood Vineyards. The emphasis is on Chardonnay and
Semillon, and the wines have been medal winners at the Hunter Valley Wine Show. It is also
a partner in the Tulloch business, together with the Tulloch and Angove families, and supplies
much of the grapes for the Tulloch label. A contemporary cellar door adds significantly to the
appeal of the Upper Hunter Valley as a wine-tourist destination.

🍷🍷🍷🍷🍷 Stones Throw Hunter Valley Semillon 2011 A trophy and five gold medals,
✪ including medals at the Hunter Valley Wine and National Wine Show, the
trophy from the NSW Wine Awards '11, is the sort of success that even Tyrrell's
would proclaim as exceptional. What takes this wine out of the ordinary is the
supple mouthfeel achieved without compromising the purity of the varietal fruit
expression. The flavours run through zesty lemon and lime, and maybe a touch of
grapefruit, all built around a core of racy acidity. Screwcap. 11.8% alc. **Rating** 96
To 2026 $16

🍷🍷🍷🍷🍷 Reserve Hunter Valley Chardonnay 2011 **Rating** 91 **To** 2016 $24
✪ Lightning Strike Hunter Valley Chardonnay 2011 Bright, light straw-green;
an elegant wine with clear varietal fruit with white and yellow peach to the fore, a
hint of oak and citrussy acidity running through to the finish alongside the peachy
fruit. Enjoy now, while it keeps its zesty freshness. Screwcap. 13% alc. **Rating** 90
To 2015 $16

🍷🍷🍷🍷 Semillon Sauvignon Blanc 2011 **Rating** 89
○ To 2014 $16
○ Lightning Strike Hunter Valley Chardonnay 2010 **Rating** 88 **To** Now $16
Hidden Hive Hunter Valley Verdelho 2011 **Rating** 88 **To** 2013 $16

Two Way Range

PO Box 7, Tanunda, SA 5352 **Region** Barossa Valley
T (08) 8563 0245 **www**.twowayrange.com **Open** Not
Winemaker Iain Seabrook **Est.** 2001 **Dozens** 200 **Vyds** 30ha
Two Way Range is owned by Seabrook & Clancy Wine Co., and is a joint venture between
the Seabrook and Clancy families. Ian and Wendy Seabrook are part of the celebrated
Melbourne Seabrook wine family, while Paul and Fran Clancy are retired wine industry
book publishers who have run a historic vineyard on the upper reaches of Jacob's Creek
at Krondorf for nearly 20 years. The vineyard has a gilt-edged list of purchasers, including

Rockford, John Duval, Spinifex, Charlie Melton and Massena Wines. The exceptionally high quality of the grapes is thought to be due to the very young soils (200 000 years) originating high on Kaiser Stuhl hill, and the cold gully winds from the adjacent Eden Valley. Ian and Paul are both Vietnam veterans, and 'two way range' was an expression of black humour when Australians went out on patrol: akin to a rifle range where the targets shoot back. The wine is matured in a mix of new and used French oak for 18 months. Exports to Singapore, Hong Kong and China.

ΨΨΨΨΨ **Barossa Valley Shiraz 2009** Bright hue of medium depth; has a greater volume of red and black cherry, plum and cedar than the colour suggests; 18 months in French oak has added texture as well as flavour to this very elegant, old-vine wine. Screwcap. 14.5% alc. **Rating** 94 **To** 2029 $45

Twofold   ★★★★★

142 Beulah Road, Norwood, SA 5067 (postal) **Region** Various
T (02) 9572 7285 **F** (02) 9572 7742 **Open** Not
Winemaker Tim Stock, Nick Stock, Neil Pike (Contract) **Est.** 2002 **Dozens** 800
This is the venture of brothers Nick and Tim Stock, both of whom have had a varied background in the wine industry (primarily at the marketing end, whether as sommeliers or in wholesale) and both of whom have excellent palates. Their contacts have allowed them to source single vineyard Rieslings from Sevenhill in the Clare and Eden valleys, a single vineyard Shiraz from Heathcote, and an Eden Vineyard Riesling. As one might expect, the quality of the wines is excellent.

ΨΨΨΨΨ **Irene Lily Eden Valley Riesling 2010** A decidedly richer and more exotic expression of the Eden from the two Stock boys, with candied orange zest, coriander and bath talc; the soft and textured palate is almost luscious on entry, with the fresh acidity and trailing mineral content providing freshness and length; a generous wine. Screwcap. 12.5% alc. **Rating** 95 **To** 2020 $30 BE
Clare Valley Riesling 2011 A tightly wound and distinctly nervous bouquet of lime pith, lavender, talc and spice; the palate is dry and textured, long and refreshing, offering a bit of grip that will enhance a wide variety of foods; delicacy and power combined. Screwcap. 12% alc. **Rating** 94 **To** 2018 $25 BE
Clare Valley Riesling 2010 Showing a modicum of development in the form of fresh brioche, the lemon-accented bouquet is laden with mineral complexity; the palate is taut, dry and textured, leaving a trail of minerals and fine acidity on the long finish. Screwcap. 12% alc. **Rating** 94 **To** 2020 $25 BE
Aged Release Clare Valley Riesling 2005 This wine is in its prime, showing lemon curd, brioche and fennel; the palate provides plenty of depth on the one hand and freshness on the other, each playing a delightful foil to the other; long and harmonious. Screwcap. 12.5% alc. **Rating** 94 **To** 2018 $35 BE

ΨΨΨΨ **Perdu Heathcote Shiraz 2007 Rating** 88 **To** 2016 $26 BE

Tyrone Estate   ★★★

PO Box 2187, Berri, SA 5343 **Region** Riverland
T (08) 8584 1333 **www**.tyroneestate.com.au **Open** At Salena Estate
Winemaker Melanie Kargas, David Smallacombe **Est.** 2008 **Dozens** 120 000 **Vyds** 208ha
While this is the venture of Bob and Sylvia Franchitto, it has been set up for the benefit of their son Tyrone. When Bob began his various horticultural and farming activities, he applied a holistic view, preferring the use of selected cover crops and mulching instead of chemicals for weed control and soil conditioning. Care for the environment also extends to the winemaking process: the winery is fully undercover, eliminating stormwater run off and allowing the collection of rainwater for further use. The water used in winery wash-down procedures is processed before being recycled for supplementary irrigation of the vineyards. All the marc and grape skins are taken offsite and distilled to recover alcohol and tartaric acid before being combined with other ingredients for organic fertilisers. This is a sister winery to

that of Salena Estate. Exports to Canada, Sweden, Singapore, Taiwan, South Korea, Indonesia, Hong Kong and China.

ŦŦŦŦ **Chardonnay 2011** Light straw-green; has more nectarine and citrus varietal fruit on the palate than expected; good value at this price, but the Ides of March underline the need for early consumption. Screwcap. 13.5% alc. **Rating** 87 To Now $12

Home Block Chardonnay 2011 Light straw-green; evidently much less grape concentrate was used with this wine than with its siblings; the palate has a tangy, lemony core; is pushing the envelope hard with its RRP. Screwcap. 12% alc. **Rating** 87 **To** 2013 $20

Tyrrell's ★★★★★

Broke Road, Pokolbin, NSW 2321 **Region** Hunter Valley
T (02) 4993 7000 **www.**tyrrells.com.au **Open** Mon–Sat 8.30–5, Sun 10–4
Winemaker Andrew Spinaze, Mark Richardson **Est.** 1858 **Dozens** 450 000 **Vyds** 288.34ha
One of the most successful family wineries, a humble operation for the first 110 years of its life that has grown out of all recognition over the past 40 years. In 2003 it cleared the decks by selling its Long Flat range of wines for an eight-figure sum, allowing it to focus on its premium, super-premium and ultra-premium wines: Vat 1 Semillon is one of the most dominant wines in the Australian show system, and Vat 47 Chardonnay is one of the pacesetters for this variety. It has an awesome portfolio of single vineyard Semillons released when 5–6 years old. Its estate plantings are over 200ha in the Hunter Valley, 34ha in McLaren Vale, 26ha in the Limestone Coast and 26ha in Heathcote A percentage from sales of the Good Paw wine range is donated to Guide Dogs Queensland. Exports to all major markets.

ŦŦŦŦŦ **Vat 9 Hunter Shiraz 2010** Light, clear crimson-purple; the deliberately gentle touch in the winery is exemplified by the 2700-litre new and used French casks (10 times the capacity of a barrique) in which the wine is matured, and the resultant fragrance of the bouquet and the delicious light- to medium-bodied palate with its vibrant fruit and silky tannins. Has fantastic length. Screwcap. 13% alc. **Rating** 97 **To** 2030 $70

Johnno's Basket Pressed Semillon 2011 The vines were planted in 1908 on sandy flats; the hand-picked grapes were basket-pressed, reducing the volume of juice; and the bottle and label are a throwback to the '60s and '70s. It has all the vivid flavour of great young Semillon, with minerally acidity the turbo-charged energy that will drive the palate for decades to come. Screwcap. 11.4% alc. **Rating** 96 **To** 2036 $45

Vat 1 Hunter Semillon 2011 Vat 1 can always be relied upon to deliver a pure, focused and linear wine, year in, year out; as a young wine, there is just enough flesh for a little pleasure, with lemon sherbet, lime leaf and straw; the structure indicates a long future ahead, and real pleasure will come at least five years down the track. Certainly worth investing both time and money to watch it truly come together. Screwcap. 11.5% alc. **Rating** 96 **To** 2035 $36 BE

Futures Selection Hunter Semillon 2007 Bright green-straw, the green very marked; on the one hand, as fresh as a daisy, on the other, overflowing with a mix of lime and honey, toasty notes still to come. Glorious each-way bet. Screwcap. 11% alc. **Rating** 96 **To** 2022 $34

Museum Release Vat 1 Hunter Semillon 2006 It is hard to believe this wine is six years of age, as it is still restrained, youthful and backward, as lemon sherbet and mere suggestions of straw and coriander appear; beautiful line and length, and with much time ahead, this is a worthy investment indeed. Screwcap. 10.7% alc. **Rating** 96 **To** 2040 $69 BE

Single Vineyard Old Patch 1867 Hunter Shiraz 2010 Deep crimson; there is a lot to like in this wine, layered with pure red fruits, florals, fresh leather, fine spicy oak and some thyme thrown in for good measure; medium-bodied, the tannins are silky and refined, offsetting the pure fruit, and pulling the finish out to a stupendously long and generous conclusion; the essence of power and purity. Screwcap. 13.4% alc. **Rating** 96 **To** 2025 $70 BE

Johnno's Shiraz 2010 Mid crimson; elegance is the name of the game, and there is a feel of old-fashioned born anew; fragrant and lifted red fruit, leather and vine sap are evident on the bouquet, with a delicate seasoning of oak from a large barrel; the light- to medium-bodied palate is elegant, almost ethereal on entry, yet the length of flavour are outstanding; pure, pretty and extremely long. Screwcap. 12.5% alc. **Rating** 96 **To** 2025 $70 BE

Single Vineyard Stevens Hunter Semillon 2008 A classic and wonderfully expressive Hunter bouquet, with lemon curd, toast and straw; the palate is very lively, and while at face value this appears forward, the tension on the finish provides length and complexity, pointing to a healthy future. Screwcap. 11.5% alc. **Rating** 95 **To** 2020 $34 BE

Vat 8 Hunter Valley Hilltops Shiraz Cabernet 2010 A pristine and polished wine that seems to transcend varieties and instead embraces origin and producer; medium-bodied and simply silky in texture, the red fruit, fresh leather and fine spices of the two regions marry seamlessly, culminating in a long and expansive, beautifully balanced finish. Screwcap. 13.5% alc. **Rating** 95 **To** 2025 $91 BE

Belford Reserve Semillon 2007 Rating 94 **To** 2020 $34 BE

Single Vineyard HVD Hunter Chardonnay 2011 Rating 94 **To** 2017 $60

Vat 47 Hunter Chardonnay 2009 Rating 94 **To** 2015 $69

Old Vines Chardonnay 2009 Rating 94 **To** 2016 $60 BE

Lunatiq Heathcote Shiraz 2009 Rating 94 **To** 2019 $45

ㅇㅇㅇㅇㅇ **Rufus Stone Heathcote Shiraz 2009 Rating** 93 **To** 2020 $32

Rufus Stone McLaren Vale Shiraz 2009 Rating 92 **To** 2024 $32

✪ **Brookdale Hunter Valley Semillon 2011** Has more colour than most others when seven months old, but not alarmingly so. A single vineyard wine that has been made for consumption over the next five years, already with plenty of ripe lemon/lime aromas and flavours, the acidity restrained. Screwcap. 11.2% alc. **Rating** 91 **To** 2016 $19

Rufus Stone McLaren Vale Cabernet Sauvignon Malbec 2009 Rating 91 **To** 2029 $32

Single Vineyard Stevens Hunter Shiraz 2010 Rating 90 **To** 2018 $38 BE

Uleybury Wines ★★★

Uley Road, Uleybury, SA 5114 **Region** Adelaide Zone
T (08) 8280 7335 www.uleybury.com **Open** Tues–Sun 10–5
Winemaker Tony Pipicella **Est.** 1995 **Dozens** 20 000
The Pipicella family – headed by Italian-born Tony – has established nearly 45ha of vineyard near One Tree Hill in the Mount Lofty Ranges; 10 varieties have been planted, with more planned. Daughter Natalie Pipicella, who has completed the wine marketing course at the University of SA, was responsible for overseeing the design of labels, the promotion and advertising, and the creation of the website. Exports to the UK, Canada, Denmark, China, Singapore and Japan.

ㅇㅇㅇㅇ **Basket Press S.P.S. 2010** An eclectic blend of shiraz, petit verdot and
✪ sangiovese; the wine, too, is in two different parts: tannins from the petit verdot and sangiovese, fruit from the shiraz. The price is encouragement to see what happens over the next few years. Screwcap. 15% alc. **Rating** 89 **To** 2015 $16

Semillon 2011 Obvious colour pickup for a wine less than a year old is a fact, not a fault, although the wine does show the thumbprint of the winemaker; a powerful texture and structure, and some inevitable phenolics. Screwcap. 13% alc. **Rating** 88 **To** 2015 $16

Maritimo Semillon 2008 Bright straw-green; has the same focus and concentration as the '11; it seems skin contact has been used with both wines. Screwcap. 12.5% alc. **Rating** 88 **To** 2013 $20

Chardonnay 2011 At the other (pale) extreme; however, the grapefruit has let some white peach have a brief moment on stage, and the wine does end up with enough varietal character. Screwcap. 11.7% alc. **Rating** 88 **To** 2016 $16

Uley Chapel Shiraz 2008 Strong colour; the alcohol is the Achilles heel of the '08 vintage, with ripening taking place at a frightening speed; that said, does have some chocolate/confit/prune flavours that are not unpleasant. Screwcap. 15.5% alc. **Rating** 87 **To** 2014 $20

Moscatino NV Within the constraints of a very wide definition of what Moscato ought to be, a pleasant wine, with fruit sweetness offset by acidity, the finish quite firm. Screwcap. 10.5% alc. **Rating** 87 **To** Now $18

Ulithorne

The Mill at Middleton, 29 Mill Terrace, Middleton, SA 5213 **Region** McLaren Vale
T (08) 8554 2411 **www.**ulithorne.com.au **Open** W'ends & public hols 10–4
Winemaker Rose Kentish, Brian Light, Natasha Mooney (Contract) **Est.** 1971
Dozens 1800

Ulithorne produces small quantities of red wines from selected parcels of grapes from a vineyard in McLaren Vale planted by Rose Kentish's father-in-law Frank Harrison over 40 years ago. Rose's dream of making small-batch, high-quality wines from exceptional grapegrowing regions around the world has taken her to France, where she has made a Vermentinu on the island of Corsica and a Rose in Provence under the Ulithorne label. The cellar door is located in a converted flour mill in Middleton. Exports to the UK, the US, the Netherlands, Malaysia and South Korea.

🍷🍷🍷🍷🍷 **Frux Frugis McLaren Vale Shiraz 2004** Exceptional retention of crimson colour; still rich and complex, with supple and bright black berry fruits and regional chocolate; good oak and tannin balance. Tasted Mar '06 with the same points. Cork. 14.5% alc. **Rating** 94 **To** 2020 $60

Umamu Estate

PO Box 1269, Margaret River, WA 6285 **Region** Margaret River
T (08) 9757 5058 **www.**umamuestate.com **Open** Not
Winemaker Bruce Dukes (Contract) **Est.** 2005 **Dozens** 5000 **Vyds** 16.3ha

Chief executive Charmaine Saw explains, 'My life has been a journey towards Umamu. An upbringing in both eastern and western cultures, graduating in natural science, training as a chef, combined with a passion for the arts and experience as a management consultant have all contributed to my building the business creatively yet professionally.' The palindrome Umamu, says Charmaine, is inspired by balance and contentment. In practical terms this means an organic approach to viticulture and a deep respect for the terroir. In 1997, Charmaine's parents fell in love with the property and its plantings, dating back to 1978, of cabernet sauvignon (6ha), chardonnay (3.5ha), shiraz (1.7ha), semillon (2.2.ha), sauvignon blanc (1.5ha), merlot (0.9ha) and cabernet franc (0.7ha); the maiden vintage under the Umamu label followed in '05. Exports to the UK, the US, Hong Kong and Malaysia.

🍷🍷🍷🍷🍷 **Margaret River Cabernet Sauvignon 2009** Deep garnet, purple hue; lifted and perfumed bouquet showing florals, red fruits and some leafy complexity; the palate is fine and detailed, with ample fine-grained tannins and polished fruit a feature; lovely balance and very long. Screwcap. 13.5% alc. **Rating** 95 **To** 2020 $57 BE

Margaret River Shiraz 2009 Deep crimson; expressive and complex Shiraz, relying on savoury nuances for intrigue; medium-bodied with red fruits, fine-grained and plentiful tannins and a long and fragrant finish; demands protein for maximum enjoyment. Screwcap. 13.5% alc. **Rating** 94 **To** 2018 $30 BE

🍷🍷🍷🍷🍷 **Margaret River Sauvignon Blanc Semillon 2009** **Rating** 92 **To** 2014 $23 BE
Margaret River Chardonnay 2009 **Rating** 90 **To** 2016 $50 BE

🍷🍷🍷🍷 **Margaret River Cabernet Merlot 2009** **Rating** 88 **To** 2016 $30 BE

Underground Winemakers ★★★★

1282 Nepean Highway, Mt Eliza, Vic 3931 **Region** Mornington Peninsula
T (03) 9775 4185 **www**.ugwine.com.au **Open** 7 days 10–5
Winemaker Adrian Hennessy, Peter Stebbing, Jonathon Stephens **Est.** 2004
Dozens 10 000 **Vyds** 12ha

Underground winemakers indeed: Adrian Hennessy, Jonathon Stevens and Peter Stebbing started the business seven years ago, but have only now surfaced in the *Wine Companion* database. Each has made wine in Alsace, Burgundy, Northern Italy and Swan Hill. Each has extensive experience in the vineyards and wineries of the Mornington Peninsula. And each has either been laid off or dismissed by Foster's. Their first step in 2004 was to lease a small winery at Mt Eliza that had closed years earlier, but still had a vineyard with some of the oldest plantings of pinot noir, pinot gris and chardonnay on the Peninsula. A 1 tonne basket press and a tiny crusher processed 100–150 tonnes of grapes in each of the first four vintages. Their portfolio is nothing if not eclectic: Pinot Gris, Pinot Noir and Chardonnay from the Mornington Peninsula, and Durif, Moscato, Cabernet Merlot and Shiraz from Northern and Central Victoria. Exports to Guyana.

🍷🍷🍷🍷🍷 **Dr Durif 2008** Deep colour; a mix of spice, earth and licorice is wrapped around the black fruits of the bouquet, with an instant replay on the palate. The tannin and overall management of extract are very good. The only fly in the ointment is a stained Diam. 14.5% alc. **Rating** 93 **To** 2015 $29

✪ **Ms Thug Chardonnay 2008** Bright green-gold; this is certainly a wine that takes no prisoners, with a savoury, lemon rind edge to the intense chardonnay fruit that runs from the start to the finish of a notably long and challenging wine. Screwcap. 13.5% alc. **Rating** 92 **To** 2014 $19

✪ **San Pietro Pinot Noir 2010** Despite (or due to?) its lower alcohol, the colour is deeper, with more purple tints; here, too, the fruit aromas and flavours are in the plum spectrum, the tannins more pronounced; a complex wine at an attractive price. Screwcap. 12.5% alc. **Rating** 91 **To** 2018 $22

Mr T Shiraz 2010 Relatively light colour, albeit with good hue; the bouquet is fragrant, but it is on the light- to medium-bodied palate that the wine begins to assert itself; here predominantly red fruits have a garland of spice, white pepper and cedary oak, the balance, line and length in sync. Screwcap. 13.5% alc. **Rating** 91 **To** 2018 $25

Thug Pinot Noir 2008 Strong, clear purple-crimson; has the greatest depth of flavour and richness among the Pinots, with a distinct confit character; makes light of the age gap with the '10 wines; slightly extractive and very ripe. Will appeal to some for this reason. Screwcap. 14% alc. **Rating** 90 **To** 2016 $29

🍷🍷🍷🍷 **Mornington Peninsula Pinot Grigio 2010** Pale straw; there are notes of
✪ yesterday's mown grass and brown pear skin to the bouquet that settle down on the palate, with pear/poached pear to the fore. Screwcap. 13% alc. **Rating** 89 **To** 2013 $16

✪ **Mornington Peninsula Pinot Noir 2010** Clear, bright crimson-purple hue; a fragrant, plum-accented bouquet, then a potent palate with a few sharp edges, although not from tannins nor oak; the juicy character appeals. Great value. Screwcap. 13.5% alc. **Rating** 89 **To** 2015 $16

Cab Merl Oh! Cabernet Merlot 2010 Rating 89 **To** 2015 $18
Offspring Pinot Gris 2008 Rating 88 **To** Now $19

Upper Reach ★★★★☆

77 Memorial Avenue, Baskerville, WA 6056 **Region** Swan Valley
T (08) 9296 0078 **www**.upperreach.com.au **Open** 7 days 11–5
Winemaker Derek Pearse **Est.** 1996 **Dozens** 4000 **Vyds** 8.45ha

This 10ha property on the banks of the upper reaches of the Swan River was purchased by Laura Rowe and Derek Pearse in 1996. The original 4ha vineyard has been expanded, and plantings now include chardonnay, shiraz, cabernet sauvignon, verdelho, semillon, merlot, petit verdot and muscat. All wines are estate-grown. The fish on the label, incidentally, is black bream, which can be found in the pools of the Swan River during the summer months. Upper Reach had a golden wine show year in 2010, winning the trophy for Most Successful Exhibitor at the Swan Valley Wine Show, where every one of its 13 entries won a medal, backed up by gold, silver and bronze medal success at the Perth Wine Show.

ΨΨΨΨΨ **The Gig Shiraz 2010** Good depth and hue; a full-bodied Shiraz with a full sail
✪   of flavours that are as potent as they are enjoyable. Plum, black cherry, licorice and
       spice are built on fine, cedary/savoury tannins; great overall mouthfeel, length and
       balance. Has a great future. Screwcap. 14% alc. **Rating** 94 **To** 2030 $22

ΨΨΨΨΨ **Reserve Swan Valley Chardonnay 2010 Rating** 91 **To** 2016 $28
       Verdelho 2011 Rating 90 **To** 2014 $20

ΨΨΨΨ **Swan Valley Cabernet Sauvignon 2010 Rating** 89 **To** 2020 $30

Valhalla Wines

163 All Saints Road, Wahgunyah, Vic 3687 **Region** Rutherglen
T (02) 6033 1438 **www.**valhallawines.com.au **Open** 7 days 10–4
Winemaker Anton Therkildsen **Est.** 2001 **Dozens** 1400 **Vyds** 2.5ha
This is the venture of Anton Therkildsen and wife Antoinette Del Popolo. They acquired the property in 2001, and in '02 began the planting of shiraz (1.6ha) and durif (0.9ha). They intend to expand the vineyard with marsanne, viognier, grenache, mourvedre and riesling, reflecting their primary interest in the wines of the Rhône Valley. For the time being, they are relying on contract-grown grapes to develop these wine styles. The straw-bale winery was built in '07, underlining their desire for sustainable viticulture and biodiversity, with minimal use of sprays and annual planting of cover crops between the rows. A worm farm and the composting of grape skins and stalks complete the picture.

ΨΨΨΨ **The Ranga 2010 Rating** 88 **To** 2014 $18
○

Valley View Vineyard ★★★☆

21 Boundary Road, Coldstream, Vic 3770 (postal) **Region** Yarra Valley
T (03) 9739 1692 **www.**valleyviewvineyard.com.au **Open** Not
Winemaker Contract **Est.** 2000 **Dozens** 200 **Vyds** 2.2ha
Judy and John Thompson purchased their property in 1998, and on the unanimous advice of various contacts in the wine industry they planted 2.2ha of pinot noir on a north and northwest-facing rocky slope (the Chardonnay is made from purchased grapes).

ΨΨΨΨΨ **Yarra Valley Chardonnay 2010** Bright straw-green; the bouquet has hints of
       nut and toasty oak; the palate is more potent than the alcohol would suggest, with
       white and yellow peach, some cashew and a backbone of minerally/citrussy acidity.
       Screwcap. 12.5% alc. **Rating** 90 **To** 2016 $30

ΨΨΨΨ **Yarra Valley Chardonnay 2008 Rating** 89 **To** 2015 $25
       Yarra Valley Pinot Noir 2010 Rating 87 **To** 2014 $30
       Yarra Valley Pinot Noir 2008 Rating 87 **To** Now $25

Vasarelli Wines

164 Main Road, McLaren Vale, SA 5171 **Region** McLaren Vale
T (08) 8323 7980 **Open** 7 days 8–5
Winemaker Hamish Seabrook (Contract) **Est.** 1995 **Dozens** 25 000 **Vyds** 33ha
Pasquale (Pat) and Vittoria (Vicky) Vasarelli moved with their parents from Melbourne to McLaren Vale in 1976. They began the establishment of their vineyard, and over the succeeding years increased the area under vine to its present size, planted to semillon, sauvignon blanc, chardonnay, pinot gris, vermentino, shiraz, cabernet sauvignon and merlot. Until '95 the grapes were sold to other producers, but in that year they joined Cellarmaster

Wines and the Vasarelli label was born. In a reverse play to the usual pattern, they opened a cellar door in 2009 on a small property they had purchased in '92.

ỵỵỵỵ **Currency Creek Sangiovese 2010** Light red, quite turbid; good varietal
✪   character: cherry (red, black, morello, sour) is the dominant play on the bouquet and palate; the tannins are exactly as one would wish them to be. Screwcap. 13.5% alc. **Rating** 92 **To** 2014 $18
          McLaren Vale Shiraz 2010 Healthy red-purple colour; an unashamedly full-bodied wine filling the mouth with spicy blackberry fruit that is fleetingly sweet on entry to the palate before lengthening and drying out on the long finish. Screwcap. 14% alc. **Rating** 90 **To** 2025 $22

ỵỵỵỵ **Currency Creek Vermentino 2011** Has appealing flavours ranging from citrus
✪   to peach and nectarine, and thence onto tropical fruits, finishing with soft acidity. Screwcap. 11.5% alc. **Rating** 89 **To** 2015 $17

Vasse Felix   ★★★★★

Cnr Caves Road/Harmans Road South, Cowaramup, WA 6284 **Region** Margaret River
T (08) 9756 5000 **www.**vassefelix.com.au **Open** 7 days 10–5
Winemaker Virginia Willcock **Est.** 1967 **Dozens** 150 000 **Vyds** 232ha
Vasse Felix was the first winery to be built in the Margaret River. Owned and operated by the Holmes à Court family since 1987, Vasse Felix has undergone extensive changes and expansion. In recent years chief winemaker Virginia Willcock has energised the winemaking and viticultural team with her no-nonsense and fierce commitment to quality. The estate vineyards contribute all but a small part of the annual production, and are scrupulously managed, quality the sole driver. There are four ranges of wines: Heytesbury (a Cabernet blend) and Heytesbury Chardonnay; the Estate range of varietal wines; Classic Dry White and Dry Red; then Theatre White and Red. Limited quantities of specialty wines include Cane Cut Semillon, Viognier, Tempranillo and Silver Knight. Exports to all major markets.

ỵỵỵỵỵ **Margaret River Sauvignon Blanc Semillon 2011** An estate-grown blend, part-fermented in new French oak barriques; recent prior vintages have enjoyed outstanding show success. It not only has a greater degree of dazzling fruit flavours, but also the attention to detail and uncompromising attitude to quality that Virginia Willcock brings to her winemaking. Gold medal Perth Wine Show '11. Screwcap. 12.5% alc. **Rating** 96 **To** 2015 $25
           Margaret River Chardonnay 2010 Pale, bright green-straw; a fragrant bouquet flows from wild yeast fermentation of cloudy juice and nine months in new and used French oak barriques; the perfectly pitched palate has tangy stone fruit flavours interwoven with subtle oak and balanced acidity. Screwcap. 12.5% alc. **Rating** 95 **To** 2016 $27
           Margaret River Classic Dry White Semillon Sauvignon Blanc 2011 Light straw-green; the fragrant bouquet has some passionfruit and wild flower nuances, but it is the electric drive of the palate, with its citrus and mineral framework, that captures attention, and holds it for some time after the wine is swallowed. Screwcap. 12.5% alc. **Rating** 94 **To** 2015 $20
           Margaret River Cabernet Sauvignon 2009 The hue is good, although on the light side; the bouquet is fragrant, yet not especially powerful; it is on the palate that the intensity and length of the fruit takes no prisoners, blackcurrant/cassis, squeaky tannins and a spicy/savoury edge all adding interest and impact. Screwcap. 14.5% alc. **Rating** 94 **To** 2029 $40

Velo Wines   ★★★☆

755 West Tamar Highway, Legana, Tas 7277 **Region** Northern Tasmania
T (03) 6330 3677 **www.**velowines.com.au **Open** 7 days 10–5
Winemaker Micheal Wilson, Winemaking Tasmania (Julian Alcorso) **Est.** 1966 **Dozens** 3000

The story behind Velo Wines is fascinating, wheels within wheels. The 0.9ha of cabernet sauvignon and 0.5ha of pinot noir of the Legana Vineyard were planted in 1966 by Graham Wiltshire, legitimately described as one of the three great pioneers of the Tasmanian wine industry. Micheal and Mary Wilson returned to Tasmania in '91 after living in Italy and France for a decade. Micheal had been an Olympic cyclist and joined the professional ranks, racing in all of the major European events. Imbued with a love of wine and food, they spent 'seven long hard years in the restaurant game'. Somehow, Micheal found time to become a qualified viticulturist, and was vineyard manager for Moorilla Estate based at St Matthias; Mary spent five years working in wine wholesaling for leading distributors. In 2001 they purchased the Legana Vineyard, planted so long ago, and they have since painstakingly rehabilitated the 40-year-old vines. They have also built a small winery where Micheal makes the red wines, and Julian Alcorso makes the white wines.

♀♀♀♀♀ **Dominique Brut 2006** Slight bronze ex pinot noir; a fine-boned and taut wine, precise and long in the mouth, its natural acidity giving free rein with a relatively low dosage. Silver Tas Wine Show '12. Cork. 12% alc. **Rating** 90 **To** 2015 $40

♀♀♀♀ **Willo's Reserve Chardonnay 2010 Rating** 89 **To** 2014 $45

Verdun Park Wines ★★★★
PO Box 41, Verdun, SA 5245 **Region** Adelaide Hills
T (08) 8388 7357 **www**.verdunparkwines.com.au **Open** Not
Winemaker Michael Sykes **Est.** 2009 **Dozens** 700 **Vyds** 2ha
Verdun Park is owned by Sandy and Bob Voumard (with backgrounds in education and accountancy) and run with the assistance of their daughter Danielle and son-in-law Shaun (viticulturist). The initial release, 2009 Lyla Sauvignon Blanc, was made from specifically selected contract-grown grapes, and went on to win a gold medal at the fiercely contested (for sauvignon blanc) Adelaide Hills Wine Show '09; the '10 shows this was no fluke.

♀♀♀♀♀ **Albert Arthur Adelaide Hills Shiraz 2009** Good colour; the cool-climate fingerprint of the Adelaide Hills is very obvious here, with licorice, spice and pepper among the savoury characters of the black fruits; should be long-lived. Screwcap. 13.5% alc. **Rating** 92 **To** 2029 $37

♀♀♀♀ **Lyla Adelaide Hills Sauvignon Blanc 2011 Rating** 87 **To** 2013 $22

Veronique ★★★
PO Box 599, Angaston, SA 5353 **Region** Barossa Valley
T (08) 8565 3214 **www**.veroniquewines.com.au **Open** Not
Winemaker Domenic Torzi, Peter Manning **Est.** 2004 **Dozens** 1500
Peter Manning, general manager of Angas Park Fruits, and wife Vicki moved to Mt McKenzie in the 1990s. His wine consumption soon focused on Barossa Shiraz, and he quickly became a close drinking partner with Domenic Torzi of all things shiraz. By 2004 the Mannings decided it was high time to produce a Barossa Shiraz of their own, and, with the help of Torzi, sourced grapes from three outstanding blocks. The vineyards also include mataro and grenache (thoroughly excusable in the context) and sauvignon blanc.

♀♀♀♀ **Barossa Grenache Shiraz Mataro 2009** A blend sourced from vines dating back to 1960 in the Nuriootpa, Greenock and Angaston areas. A medium-bodied wine with obvious oak and some of the low-sulphur signs encountered with other Veronique wines, but escapes – with that qualification – in this instance. Screwcap. 14.8% alc. **Rating** 87 **To** 2014 $20

Victory Point Wines
4 Holben Road, Cowaramup, WA 6284 **Region** Margaret River
T 0417 954 6555 **www**.victorypointwines.com **Open** By appt
Winemaker Ian Bell (red), Mark Messenger (white) (Contract) **Est.** 1997 **Dozens** 2000
Vyds 14.8ha

Judith and Gary Berson (the latter a partner in the Perth office of a national law firm) have set their aims high. They have established their vineyard without irrigation, emulating those of the Margaret River pioneers (including Moss Wood). The plantings comprise 2ha chardonnay, the remainder the Bordeaux varieties, with cabernet sauvignon (6ha), merlot (2ha), cabernet franc (1.5ha), malbec (0.3ha) and petit verdot (0.3ha). In some vintages, a Petit Verdot and Malbec Cabernet Franc are made in limited quantities.

🍷🍷🍷🍷🍷 **Margaret River Chardonnay 2009** Gleaming, bright green-straw; made using Burgundian clones 76, 95, 96 and 277, plus the Mendoza clone, a distinguished assemblage that has duly produced a distinguished, finely drawn and structured wine of great length and intensity; will be long-lived. Screwcap. 13.5% alc. Rating 96 To 2020 $40

🍷🍷🍷🍷🍷 **Margaret River Rose 2011** Rating 90 To 2013 $23

🍷🍷🍷🍷 **Margaret River Cabernet Sauvignon 2008** Rating 88 To 2015 $35

Vinaceous   ★★★★

49 Bennett Street, East Perth, WA 6004 (postal) **Region** Various
T (08) 9221 4666 **www**.vinaceous.com.au **Open** Not
Winemaker Gavin Berry, Michael Kerrigan, Elena Brooks (Contract) **Est.** 2007
Dozens 16 000
This is the somewhat quirky venture of wine marketer Nick Stacy (West Cape Howe), Michael Kerrigan (winemaker/partner Hay Shed Hill) and Gavin Berry (winemaker/partner West Cape Howe). The brand is primarily directed at the US market, which took 90% of the four wines in the first release, the remaining 10% shared among all other markets. The wines are not primarily sourced from WA, as one might expect, but variously from McLaren Vale, Barossa Valley and the Limestone Coast, with a Verdelho, and the possibility of a Reserve Shiraz, from WA. Divine Light Verdelho, Snake Charmer Shiraz, Red Right Hand Shiraz Grenache Tempranillo and Raconteur Cabernet Sauvignon, coupled with ornate, turn-of-the-19th-century label, give the flavour of the wines and their export focus. Exports to the US, Canada, Denmark, the Philippines, Thailand, Singapore and Hong Kong.

🍷🍷🍷🍷🍷 **Red Right Hand McLaren Vale Shiraz Grenache Tempranillo 2010** Bright colour; raspberry, blackberry, spice and a little roasted meat complexity on the bouquet; the palate is taut, refreshing and well balanced, with Provençal garrigue providing added depth to the finish. Screwcap. 14.5% alc. **Rating** 91 To 2016 $25 BE
Snake Charmer McLaren Vale Shiraz 2009 Bright colour; blackberry and a touch of fruitcake spice; the palate is warm, generous and fleshy, with a refreshing backbone of acidity and tannin. Screwcap. 14% alc. **Rating** 90 To 2018 $25 BE

🍷🍷🍷🍷 **Salome Tempranillo Rose 2011** Rating 87 To 2013 $21 BE
Burlesque Resplendent Rose NV Rating 87 To Now $28 BE

Vinden Estate   ★★★☆

17 Gillards Road, Pokolbin, NSW 2320 **Region** Hunter Valley
T (02) 4998 7410 **www**.vindenestate.com.au **Open** 7 days 10–5
Winemaker Guy Vinden, John Baruzzi (Consultant) **Est.** 1998 **Dozens** 4200 **Vyds** 6.5ha
Sandra and Guy Vinden have a beautiful home and cellar door, landscaped gardens and a vineyard that includes shiraz (2.5ha), merlot and alicante bouschet (2ha each), with the Brokenback mountain range in the distance. The winemaking is done onsite, using estate-grown red grapes; semillon and chardonnay are purchased from other growers. The reds are open-fermented, hand-plunged and basket-pressed.

🍷🍷🍷🍷🍷 **Late Harvest Semillon 2007** Last tasted three years ago, and given 89 points. The usual progression of these wines tends to go down after a few years, but this is quite different because of its low alcohol and relatively high acidity, the last perfectly balanced by the moderate honeyed fruit. Tailor-made for a platter of fresh fruit. Screwcap. 10% alc. **Rating** 90 To 2014 $23

🍷🍷🍷🍷 Adelaide Hills Semillon Sauvignon Blanc 2011 Rating 88 To 2014 $23
Estate Reserve Hunter Valley Verdelho 2011 Rating 87 To 2013 $23
Basket Press Hunter Valley Shiraz 2010 Rating 87 To 2016 $30

Vinifera Wines   ★★★☆

194 Henry Lawson Drive, Mudgee, NSW 2850 **Region** Mudgee
T (02) 6372 2461 **www**.viniferawines.com.au **Open** Mon–Sat 10–5, Sun 10–4
Winemaker Frank Newman **Est.** 1997 **Dozens** 1200 **Vyds** 11.6ha
Having lived in Mudgee for 15 years, Tony McKendry (a regional medical superintendent)
and wife Debbie succumbed to the lure; they planted their small (1.5ha) vineyard in 1995.
In Debbie's words, 'Tony, in his spare two minutes per day, also decided to start Wine Science
at CSU in 1992.' She continues, 'His trying to live 27 hours per day (plus our four kids!) fell
to pieces when he was involved in a severe car smash in 1997. Two months in hospital stopped
full-time medical work, and the winery dreams became inevitable.' Financial compensation
finally came through and the small winery was built. The vineyard includes chardonnay,
cabernet sauvignon (3ha each), semillon, tempranillo, grenache and graciano (1ha each).

🍷🍷🍷🍷🍷 Easter Semillon 2008 Deep gold; the only possibility of the wine coming
from Mudgee is that it was cane-cut, the grapes being allowed to desiccate over
a number of weeks; it is lusciously sweet, with honey, cumquat and brandysnap
biscuit to the fore. 375ml. Screwcap. 13% alc. Rating 91 To 2013 $28

🍷🍷🍷🍷 Gran Tinto 2008 Rating 89 To 2018 $23
Mudgee Graciano 2009 Rating 88 To 2015 $32

Vinrock   ★★★★

23 George Street, Thebarton, SA 5031 (postal) **Region** McLaren Vale
T (08) 8408 8900 **www**.vinrock.com **Open** Not
Winemaker Contract **Est.** 1998 **Dozens** 10 000 **Vyds** 30ha
Owners Don Luca, Marco Iannetti and Anthony De Pizzol all have backgrounds in the wine
industry, none more than Don, a former board member of Tatachilla. He also planted the Luca
Vineyard in 1998 (20ha of shiraz, 5ha each of grenache and cabernet sauvignon). The majority
of the grapes are sold, but since 2004 steadily increasing quantities of wine have been made
from the best blocks in the vineyard. Exports to Canada, Malaysia and NZ.

🍷🍷🍷🍷🍷 Terra Mia McLaren Vale Cabernet Sauvignon 2010 Rating 93
⊙ To 2020 $15
Scarce Earth McLaren Vale Shiraz 2010 Bright colour; a rich and inviting
melange of sweet black fruits, spicy oak, bitter chocolate and fruitcake; the palate is
generous, ripe and juicy, with an even and abundantly fruit-dominant conclusion.
Screwcap. 14.8% alc. Rating 92 To 2018 $35 BE
⊙ McLaren Vale Grenache 2010 Rating 92 To 2016 $20
✪ Bayliss Road McLaren Vale Shiraz Grenache 2010 Deep crimson-purple;
an interesting 85/10/5% blend of shiraz, grenache and durif produces a rich,
medium- to full-bodied wine that has blackberry, spice and blueberry fruit and
tannins lined up in balanced support. Screwcap. 14.8% alc. Rating 91 To 2017 $17
⊙ Terra Mia McLaren Vale Shiraz 2009 Rating 90 To 2019 $15
🍷🍷🍷🍷 Terra Mia McLaren Vale Shiraz 2010 Rating 89
⊙ To 2016 $15
McLaren Vale Shiraz 2010 Rating 88 To 2016 $20 BE
Bayliss Road McLaren Vale Shiraz 2010 Rating 87 To 2015 $16 BE

Vintara   ★★★

Fraser Road, Rutherglen, Vic 3685 **Region** Rutherglen
T 0447 327 517 **www**.vintara.com.au **Open** 7 days 10–5
Winemaker Michael Murtagh **Est.** 2005 **Dozens** 1200 **Vyds** 17.6ha

Michael Murtagh (and wife Lisa) are long-term industry professionals, Michael adding 150 years of family ownership in Rutherglen for good measure. His great-grandfather arrived from Ireland 150 years ago and named his property Tara, after a mystical hill in Ireland which was the meeting place of kings. The view from the 47ha property owned by Michael and Lisa prompted the name Vintara for the vineyard, which has a veritable patchwork quilt of 10 varieties. Most of the grapes are sold, but Vintara makes Riesling, Viognier, Sangiovese, Tempranillo, Shiraz, Petit Verdot, Merlot and Durif.

ŸŸŸŸ **Durif 2009** Very ripe, sarsaparilla and cola bouquet with a cold tea, savoury edge to the fruit; as extreme an example of ripe fruit as you would expect of the variety, but generous, without doubt. Screwcap. 14.8% alc. **Rating** 88 **To** 2015 $27 BE
Viognier 2011 Deep colour; musk and rosewater with grapefruit freshness on the bouquet; the palate is generous, varietal and lively, holding back from the precipice of hedonistic exoticism. Screwcap. 13.9% alc. **Rating** 87 **To** 2013 $18 BE

Vinteloper Wines   ★★★★
PO Box 2601, Kent Town, SA 5071 **Region** Various
T 0415 297 787 **www**.vinteloper.com.au **Open** Not
Winemaker David Bowley **Est.** 2008 **Dozens** 1500
Raised in the Adelaide foothills, vineyards and wineries had permeated his David Bowley's mind before he left school. It was inevitable that he would obtain his agricultural science (oenology) degree at Adelaide University (in 2002); he worked at wineries and overseas over the next two years. A career in basketball meant a conventional day job was needed, and he worked for the Australian Wine & Brandy Corporation for six years, squeezing in a single vineyard McLaren Vale Shiraz during the last two years. He then took the plunge, and moved into full-time winemaking, seeking to match variety and region. He has also experimented with art versus science, making Watervale Riesling in two very different ways.

ŸŸŸŸŸ **Adelaide Hills Pinot Noir 2010** Light to medium red–purple; hand-picked by 15 friends named on the back label; stemmy, savoury whole bunch notes help to invest the wine with energy and drive; wild yeast-fermented in small open tanks, and a long, lingering finish. 70 dozen made. Screwcap. 14% alc. **Rating** 92 **To** 2016 $38
McLaren Vale Shiraz 2009 Medium to full red–purple; 180 dozen bottles produced from a single vineyard in the southeastern section of McLaren Vale; it certainly is strongly regional, with a juicy dark chocolate core and a cedary/spicy edge from the tannins. Screwcap. 14% alc. **Rating** 92 **To** 2029 $38
Adelo 2010 Youthful purple-crimson; as weird a blend as you could even come across: touriga, shiraz and pinot noir; a fresh medium-bodied wine with both red and black fruits and controlled tannins. Points for audacity. Screwcap. 14% alc. **Rating** 90 **To** 2016 $27

ŸŸŸŸ **Watervale Riesling 2011 Rating** 88 **To** 2018 $27
Odeon Watervale Riesling 2011 Rating 88 **To** 2017 $55

Vintners Ridge Estate   ★★★
Lot 18 Veraison Place, Yallingup, Margaret River, WA 6285 **Region** Margaret River
T 0417 956 943 **www**.vintnersridge.com.au **Open** By appt
Winemaker Flying Fish Cove (Simon Ding) **Est.** 2001 **Dozens** 750 **Vyds** 2.1ha
When Maree and Robin Adair purchased the Vintners Ridge vineyard in 2006 (cabernet sauvignon), it had already produced three crops, having been planted in Nov '01 (which is a perfectly permissible establishment date). Small acorns, great oaks. The vineyard overlooks the picturesque Geographe Bay.

ŸŸŸŸ **Margaret River Cabernet Sauvignon 2010** The depth of colour is less impressive than the '09, although the hue is good; oak plays a major role on the bouquet and palate alike, where blackcurrant fruit has a savoury tannin twist on the finish. Screwcap. 14.9% alc. **Rating** 89 **To** 2017 $30

Virgara Wines

Lot 11 Heaslip Road, Angle Vale, SA 5117 **Region** Adelaide Plains
T (08) 8284 7688 **www.**virgarawines.com.au **Open** Mon–Fri 9–5, w'ends & public hols 11–4
Winemaker Tony Carapetis **Est.** 2001 **Dozens** 30 000 **Vyds** 68.84ha

In 1962 the Virgara family – father Michael, mother Maria and 10 children ranging from one to 18 years old – migrated to Australia from southern Italy. Through the hard work so typical of many such families, in due course they became market gardeners on land purchased at Angle Vale (1967), and in the early '90s acquired an existing vineyard in Angle Vale. The plantings have since expanded to almost 70ha of shiraz, cabernet sauvignon, grenache, malbec, merlot, riesling, sangiovese, sauvignon blanc, pinot grigio and alicante, with a further 22ha currently under a replanting project. In 2001 the Virgara brothers purchased the former Barossa Valley Estates winery, but used it only for storage and maturation, as the first wine was made (in '02 from 40-year-old shiraz) by the Glaetzer family. The death of Domenic Virgara in a road accident led to the employment of former Palandri winemaker (and, before that, Tahbilk) Tony Carapetis, and the full commissioning of the winery. Exports to the US, Canada, China, Thailand, Malaysia and Japan.

Super Premium Shiraz 2010 Significantly deeper colour than the Adelaide Shiraz; it is bigger in every way, with higher alcohol, riper fruit, more tannins and more oak; that said, all of these inputs are largely balanced, and all the wine needs is time to gather its wits. Has that ever-frustrating use of cork with the more expensive wine, screwcap with the lesser. 14.2% alc. **Rating** 91 **To** 2020 $25

Adelaide Shiraz 2010 Red-purple; while no region is claimed, the wine is full-flavoured and ripe; ripe, balanced tannins add texture and interest to the finish, aided by the moderate alcohol. Screwcap. 13.6% alc. **Rating** 89 **To** 2017 $18

Adelaide Merlot 2010 Clear red-purple; appropriate body, texture and structure for the variety, the flavours between plum and savoury black olive. A very, very good example of the variety at this price point. Screwcap. 13.1% alc. **Rating** 89 **To** 2015 $15

Adelaide Plains Sauvignon Blanc 2011 Bright straw-green; a major beneficiary of the cool vintage; while the palate is not deep, the flavours are unmistakably varietal, with a mix of grassy/herbal characters on the one hand, tropical/stone fruit on the other. The value for money is bleedingly obvious. Screwcap. 11.6% alc. **Rating** 88 **To** 2013 $14

Voyager Estate

Lot 1 Stevens Road, Margaret River, WA 6285 **Region** Margaret River
T (08) 9757 6354 **www.**voyagerestate.com.au **Open** 7 days 10–5
Winemaker Steve James, Travis Lemm **Est.** 1978 **Dozens** 40 000 **Vyds** 118ha

Michael Wright, son of Peter Wright, who was a founding member of the Hancock & Wright Group at the forefront of mining in WA, pursued several avenues of business and agriculture before setting his sights on owning a vineyard and winery. It was thus an easy decision when he was able to buy what was then called Freycinet Estate from founder and leading viticulturist Peter Gherardi in 1991. Peter had established the vineyard in '78, and it has been significantly expanded by Michael over the ensuing years. Apart from the Cape Dutch-style tasting room and vast rose garden, the signpost for the estate is the massive Australian flag pole – after Parliament House in Canberra, the second largest flag pole in Australia. Michael has never done things by halves, and has had the financial resources to turn Voyager Estate into one of the best vineyards and wineries in the region. Exports to the UK, Asia and other major markets.

Margaret River Chardonnay 2009 Vivid green hue; a restrained and completely unevolved bouquet, laden with grapefruit, spice, grilled cashew, charcuterie and citrus blossom; the palate is taut and lively, showing great depth, freshness and finesse; will stand the test of time, yet offer glorious drinking as a young wine. Screwcap. 12.8% alc. **Rating** 96 **To** 2020 $42 BE

Margaret River Shiraz 2010 Vivid purple hue; a restrained and highly perfumed, almost exotic bouquet of cranberry, plum, spice, violets and roasted meat; the palate is super fine, lacy, almost ethereal, yet opens up with power and precision in an almost Pinot-like sensuality; long, precise and destined to go the distance. Screwcap. 13.5% alc. **Rating** 96 **To** 2025 $38 BE

Margaret River Cabernet Sauvignon Merlot 2008 Deep garnet; a complex array of aromas from cedar, cassis, cigar box and a touch of leafy interest; the palate is full-bodied, fine and poised, with polished tannins and fruit working seamlessly together; the length of flavour is nothing short of staggering, and while a joy to drink as a young wine, patient cellaring will be well rewarded. Screwcap. 13.6% alc. **Rating** 96 **To** 2030 $60 BE

♥♥♥♥♀ ✪ **Girt by Sea Margaret River Cabernet Merlot 2010** Deep magenta; leafy notes offset the pure cassis aromas of the bouquet; on the palate the complexity continues to unravel, with olive, cedar and red and black fruits on display; a very high level of quality for the price. Screwcap. 13.8% alc. **Rating** 93 **To** 2016 $24 BE

✪ **Margaret River Sauvignon Blanc Semillon 2011** Consistency is the key to Voyager and this wine provides freshness and texture, showing the ripe nature of the '11 vintage; fresh and vibrant on the one hand and fleshy and textural on the other. Screwcap. 13.1% alc. **Rating** 91 **To** 2014 $25 BE

✪ **Margaret River Chenin Blanc 2011** Fresh-cut green apple bouquet, with spice and talc; the palate is fleshy and shows just a hint of sweetness that will appear dry with food; serve chilled and will be excellent with Asian dishes. Screwcap. 13.4% alc. **Rating** 90 **To** 2016 $20 BE

Walter Clappis Wine Co.   ★★★★★

Rifle Range Road, McLaren Vale, SA 5171 **Region** McLaren Vale
T (08) 8323 8818 **www**.hedonistwines.com.au **Open** Not
Winemaker Walter Clappis, Kimberly Clappis **Est.** 1982 **Dozens** 15 000 **Vyds** 35ha
Walter Clappis (once known as Bill) has been a stalwart of the McLaren Vale wine scene for decades. The estate plantings of shiraz (14ha), cabernet sauvignon (10ha), merlot (9ha) and tempranillo (2ha) are the cornerstone of his new business, which also provides the home for the separately owned Amicus business (see separate entry). Exports to the UK, the US, Canada, Belgium, the Netherlands, Malaysia, Singapore, China and Japan.

♥♥♥♥♥ ✪ **The Hedonist McLaren Vale Sangiovese Rose 2011** Trophy McLaren Vale Wine Show '11 for Best Rose a handy introduction. Pale salmon-pink; the bouquet is of wild flowers and spice, the palate following on seamlessly, the lingering spiced cherry flavours needing no sweetness. Classy wine. Screwcap. 13.5% alc. **Rating** 94 **To** 2014 $17

✪ **The Hedonist McLaren Vale Shiraz 2009** Dense McLaren Vale Shiraz, 100% new American oak and that regional dark chocolate do make a hedonistic style. Its alcohol of (only) 14% is a major plus, but its award of the George Mackey Memorial Trophy '11 for the best Australian wine exported that year was controversial, but then consider the price! Screwcap. 14% alc. **Rating** 94 **To** 2029 $20

🍃 Walter Wines   ★★★★

179 Tinja Lane, Mudgee, NSW 2850 **Region** Mudgee
T (02) 6372 9143 **www**.walterwines.com.au **Open** Thurs–Tues 10.30–4.30
Winemaker David Lowe, Frank Newman (Contract) **Est.** 2005 **Dozens** 1000 **Vyds** 17ha
Lynn and Paul Walter had been keen observers of Mudgee and its wines for 15 years before deciding to take the plunge and plant a 17ha vineyard. It was the mid 1990s, and all the portents were good. As competition increased, and prices for grapes decreased, they realised that their original business plan of simply being growers for local producers was not going to be financially viable, even though they thought the downturn would prove to be a temporary one. In 2005 they had an opportunity to export bulk wine to Germany, and this triggered a

decision to also have wine contract-made for sale under their own label. The quality of the wine they have produced thoroughly justifies that decision.

🍷🍷🍷🍷♀ **Federation Hill Mudgee Shiraz 2009** Medium purple-red; open fermentation was followed by a reverse pattern (from normal) of maturation first in 4-year-old oak, then six months in new French hogsheads. It is a substantial medium- to full-bodied wine, with black fruits, oak and firm tannins all contributing to a wine with a long future. Screwcap. 14.7% alc. **Rating** 92 **To** 2024 $38

✪ **Federation Hill Mudgee Chardonnay 2006** Bright, glowing green-straw; has matured impressively, and already past the back label suggestion of cellaring to '10; grapefruit pith, stone fruit, and some French oak all contribute to the flavour. Screwcap. 13.5% alc. **Rating** 90 **To** 2014 $20

Federation Hill Mudgee Cabernet Sauvignon 2006 While relatively light, has retained crimson-purple hues; the palate is commensurately lively and juicy, the fine, savoury tannins providing a good contrast and balance for those juicy characters. Drink soon. Screwcap. 14.2% alc. **Rating** 90 **To** 2013 $28

🍷🍷🍷🍷 **Federation Hill Orange Mudgee Sauvignon Blanc Semillon 2011** **Rating** 89 **To** 2014 $18

Federation Hill Mudgee Chardonnay 2011 **Rating** 87 **To** 2013 $20

Federation Hill Mudgee Shiraz 2006 **Rating** 87 **To** 2013 $28

Wandin Hunter Valley ★★★★★

12 Wilderness Road, Lovedale, NSW 2320 **Region** Hunter Valley
T (02) 4930 9888 **www**.wandinhuntervalley.com.au **Open** 7 days 10–5
Winemaker Daniel Binet **Est.** 1973 **Dozens** 5000 **Vyds** 8ha
After some uncertainty, and changes of heart, Wandin Hunter Valley is now owned by Warraroong Estate (which in turn was formerly known as Swish Wine), and is part of an impressive portfolio of vineyards and brands. The cards have been thoroughly shuffled, and it will be interesting to see how they play out.

🍷🍷🍷🍷🍷 **Reserve Hunter Valley Semillon 2011** Pale, bright quartz-green; this is, as they say, the real deal; the bouquet is lively and expressive, the palate taking matters one step further with its finely drawn, precise varietal flavours; the drive through to the finish points to a long and prosperous future. Screwcap. 11% alc. **Rating** 94 **To** 2025 $25

Reserve Hunter Valley Semillon 2006 Still pale, although bright, straw-green; given 90 points in July '06, doubtless because it was relatively subdued; it is still as crisp and fresh as a daisy, with herb, mineral and lemon citrus flavours; the length and balance are impeccable, and the wine still has its best years in front of it. Screwcap. 10.5% alc. **Rating** 94 **To** 2020 $25

🍷🍷🍷🍷♀ **Wild Reserve Hunter Valley Chardonnay 2011** **Rating** 92 **To** 2018 $25

✪ **Pavilion Hunter Valley Rose 2011** Brilliant, bright crimson, made from a blend of cabernet sauvignon and shiraz; black and red cherry fruits drive the well-structured palate, which finishes dry; a rose for all seasons. Screwcap. 13% alc. **Rating** 91 **To** 2014 $18

🍷🍷🍷🍷 **Members Block Hunter Valley Ruby Cabernet 2009** **Rating** 87 **To** 2013 $25

Wangolina Station

Cnr Southern Ports Highway/Limestone Coast Road, Kingston SE, SA 5275
Region Mount Benson
T (08) 8768 6187 **www**.wangolina.com.au **Open** 7 days 10–5
Winemaker Anita Goode **Est.** 2001 **Dozens** 5000 **Vyds** 11ha
Four generations of the Goode family have been graziers at Wangolina Station, but now Anita Goode has broken with tradition by becoming a vigneron. She has planted sauvignon blanc, shiraz, cabernet sauvignon, semillon and pinot gris. Exports to the UK.

ŸŸŸŸ   Section 67 Mt Benson Cabernet Sauvignon 2010 Full red-purple; in the robust, full-bodied style of Wangolina; blackcurrant fruit and somewhat aggressive tannins are locked in combat, the outcome uncertain. Screwcap. 14.5% alc. **Rating** 88 **To** 2017 $24

Wantirna Estate   ★★★★★

10 Bushy Park Lane, Wantirna South, Vic 3152 **Region** Yarra Valley
T (03) 9801 2367 **www.**wantirnaestate.com.au **Open** Not
Winemaker Maryann and Reg Egan **Est.** 1963 **Dozens** 830 **Vyds** 4.2ha
Reg and Bertina (Tina) Egan were among the early movers in the rebirth of the Yarra Valley. The vineyard surrounds the house in which they live, which also incorporates the winery. These days Reg describes himself as the interfering winemaker, but in the early years he did everything, dashing from his legal practice to the winery to check on the ferments. Today much of the winemaking responsibility has been transferred to daughter Maryann, who has a degree in wine science from CSU. Both have honed their practical skills among the small domaines and châteaux of Burgundy and Bordeaux, where the single vineyard, terroir-driven wines have inspired them. Maryann was also a winemaker for many years in Domaine Chandon's infancy. Tina keeps the mailing list and accounts under control, as well as having that all-important role of looking after the pickers during vintage. Like all small wineries, it is a family affair, with everyone involved in some way. Exports to Hong Kong, Singapore and Japan.

ŸŸŸŸŸ   Lily Yarra Valley Pinot Noir 2010 Good colour; produced from vines with an average age of around 40 years, reflected in the structural strength of the palate and chewy tannin finish; the density of the fruit carries this extract well, but it should be given three or four years to soften and open up. Diam. 13.8% alc. **Rating** 94 **To** 2020 $65
Amelia Yarra Valley Cabernet Sauvignon Merlot 2009 Bright crimson-purple; richly robed and mouth-filling, with a precocious display of blackcurrant, redcurrant and subtle oak; the tannins are fine and well balanced, and sustain the finish. Diam. 12.7% alc. **Rating** 94 **To** 2020 $65

ŸŸŸŸŸ   Isabella Yarra Valley Chardonnay 2010 **Rating** 93 **To** 2015 $60

Waratah Hills Vineyard   ★★★★

20 Cottmans Road, Fish Creek, Vic 3959 **Region** Gippsland
T (03) 5683 2441 **www.**waratahhills.com.au **Open** W'ends & public hols 11–4
Winemaker Marcus Satchell **Est.** 1997 **Dozens** 800 **Vyds** 4ha
Peter and Liz Rushen acquired Waratah Hills Vineyard in 2001; it had been established with advice from Phillip Jones (of Bass Phillip) on a northeast slope in a beautifully domed valley formed by Battery Creek. The vines (2.8ha of pinot noir and 1.2ha of chardonnay) have developed slowly, the first vintage coming in '04, but Phillip Jones has had no involvement in the winemaking since the Rushens purchased the vineyard. There was yet another change of ownership, with Neil and Judy Travers the purchasers in '11.

ŸŸŸŸŸ   South Gippsland Chardonnay 2010 Closely spaced vines at 9000 vines per
✪   hectare; whole bunch-pressed to French oak barriques for 10 months, lees contact and ageing; the wine has intensity and drive, with the basket of fruit flavours based around a core of steely acidity providing length and focus; the flavours are of stone fruits, melon and grapefruit, oak carefully controlled. Screwcap. 13% alc. **Rating** 93 **To** 2020 $22
✪   Prom Road South Gippsland Chardonnay 2011 An unwooded Chardonnay that was picked at the precise moment to invest with an attractive mix of white peach, nectarine and gentle grapefruit flavours; seven months on lees in tank was also beneficial. Screwcap. 13.7% alc. **Rating** 90 **To** 2015 $17

ŸŸŸŸ   Prom Road South Gippsland Rose 2011 **Rating** 87 **To** 2013 $17
South Gippsland Pinot Noir 2010 **Rating** 87 **To** 2013 $24

Warner Glen Estate

PO Box 218, Melville, WA 6956 **Region** Margaret River
T (08) 9337 4601 **www**.warnerglenestate.com.au **Open** Not
Winemaker Bruce Dukes, Amanda Kramer (Contract) **Est.** 1993 **Dozens** 15 000
Vyds 30.8ha

Father John and son Travis French purchased a 100ha property abutting the Chapman Brook and Blackwood National Park in the southern part of Margaret River in 1992. Says Travis, 'We then realised that we had to do something with it, so the thing at the time to be done with rural land was to plant vines, and so we did.' Sauvignon blanc and semillon constitute the lion's share, but there are significant plantings of chardonnay, cabernet sauvignon, shiraz and merlot. Until 2006 they were content to sell their grapes to Cape Mentelle, but in that year decided to have wine contract-made by the highly experienced Bruce Dukes and Amanda Kramer. Given the maturity of the vineyards, it is not surprising that the wines are of such high quality. Warner Glen and Frog Belly are the main labels, Smokin' Gun and The Pick outliers; all are good value. Exports to China.

ㅇㅇㅇㅇㅇ **Margaret River Chardonnay 2010** Bright straw-green; has a striking bouquet, with pronounced hazelnut and nougat characters allied with a touch of figgy funk; the palate switches the point of attack to layers of white peach and nectarine typical of Margaret River at its best, cleansing the finish with poised acidity. Screwcap. 13% alc. **Rating** 95 **To** 2020 $30

P.B.F. Margaret River Sauvignon Blanc Semillon 2010 An estate-grown 75/25% blend that has been partially barrel-fermented, hence the name; it all adds up to a genuinely complex wine, its range of tropical and white flesh fruits fused with the vanilla oak. Screwcap. 12.8% alc. **Rating** 94 **To** 2014 $25

Margaret River Cabernet Sauvignon 2010 Slightly more purple notes to the crimson than the Frog Belly; there the similarity ends, for this has far more of the autocratic austerity of cabernet grown in the right place, tannins and blackcurrant fruit locked in an endless embrace, the oak integrated and balanced. Screwcap. 13.5% alc. **Rating** 94 **To** 2025 $30

ㅇㅇㅇㅇㅇ **Frog Belly Margaret River Sauvignon Blanc 2011** Light straw-green; a
✪ vibrantly fresh and crisp wine with distinct citrus/grapefruit tang emphasising the line of acidity that carries the wine through to its long finish. Screwcap. 12.7% alc. **Rating** 93 **To** 2013 $18

◐ **Frog Belly Semillon Sauvignon Blanc 2011 Rating** 92 **To** 2015 $18
✪ **Frog Belly Margaret River Rose of Syrah 2011** Vivid, light magenta; the fragrant, flowery bouquet sets the scene for the array of sweet and supple strawberry, cherry and raspberry fruits running across the palate; very seductive. Screwcap. 12.9% alc. **Rating** 92 **To** 2013 $18

◐ **Smokin' Gun Margaret River Semillon Sauvignon Blanc 2011 Rating** 91 **To** 2016 $15

Margaret River Cabernet Merlot 2009 Rating 91 **To** 2019 $25
✪ **Frog Belly Margaret River Cabernet Sauvignon 2010** Bright, clear crimson; a fresh and lively Cabernet, with cassis and oak intertwined on both bouquet and palate; the overall juicy character makes it a drink now or whenever proposition. Screwcap. 14% alc. **Rating** 91 **To** 2016 $18

✪ **Smokin' Gun Margaret River Shiraz Cabernet Merlot 2011** The hue is bright, light crimson-purple; Warner Glen says the (low) price for this estate-grown blend is criminal, and it's hard to disagree; there are abundant red fruit flavours, and obvious oak, not necessarily entirely from barrels. Screwcap. 14.1% alc. **Rating** 90 **To** 2015 $15

✪ **Frog Belly Margaret River Shiraz Cabernet 2010** Light, bright hue; bright red berry aromas lead into a relatively fleshy palate, with fine tannins and oak running through its entire length. Easy-access, drink-me-quick style. Screwcap. 14.5% alc. **Rating** 90 **To** 2017 $18

Warrabilla

6152 Murray Valley Highway, Rutherglen, Vic 3685 **Region** Rutherglen
T (02) 6035 7242 **www**.warrabillawines.com.au **Open** 7 days 10–5
Winemaker Andrew Sutherland Smith **Est.** 1990 **Dozens** 10 000 **Vyds** 21ha
Andrew Sutherland Smith and wife Carol have built a formidable reputation for their wines, headed by the Reserve trio of Durif, Cabernet Sauvignon and Shiraz, quintessential examples of Rutherglen red table wine at its most opulent. Their vineyard has been extended with the planting of riesling and zinfandel. Andrew spent 15 years with All Saints, McWilliam's, Yellowglen, Fairfield and Chambers before setting up Warrabilla, and his accumulated experience shines through in the wines. No wines will be released from the 2011 vintage.

🍷🍷🍷🍷🍷 Parola's Limited Release Shiraz 2005 Black fruits and vanilla oak; these wines have few parallels anywhere in the world. You have to look at the alcohol in the context of food in the same way you look at tannins in Italian red wines. Diam. 16.5% alc. **Rating** 94 **To** 2020 $30
Reserve Durif 2010 Dense, deep crimson, magenta rim; a Durif from Warrabilla is always going to be a massive wine, and this is no exception. However, it is not the least tannic or over-extracted, and can be enjoyed with roasted ox any time. Diam. 15% alc. **Rating** 94 **To** 2020 $25

🍷🍷🍷🍷🍷 Parola's Limited Release Durif 2009 **Rating** 90 **To** 2029 $33

Warramate ★★★★☆

27 Maddens Lane, Gruyere, Vic 3770 **Region** Yarra Valley
T (03) 5964 9219 **www**.warramatewines.com.au **Open** 7 days 10–5
Winemaker Paul Bridgeman **Est.** 1970 **Dozens** 2000 **Vyds** 6.6ha
A long-established and perfectly situated winery reaping the full benefits of its 40-year-old vines; recent plantings have increased production. All the wines are well made, the Shiraz providing further proof (if such be needed) of the suitability of the variety to the region. In 2011 was purchased by the Ed Peter partnership, owner of the adjoining Yarra Yering Winery; the intention is to keep the Warramate Vineyard and brand as a separate entity.

🍷🍷🍷🍷🍷 White Label Yarra Valley Riesling 2010 A fine and expressive bouquet of green apple, bath talc and anise; the palate is taut and racy on entry, expanding to a long, generous and evenly balanced finish; lots of fun to be had with food matching here. Screwcap. 13% alc. **Rating** 92 **To** 2018 $25 BE

🍷🍷🍷🍷 White Label Yarra Valley Pinot Noir 2010 **Rating** 89 **To** 2014 $25 BE

Warraroong Estate

247 Wilderness Road, Lovedale, NSW 2320 **Region** Hunter Valley
T (02) 4930 7594 **www**.warraroongestate.com.au **Open** 7 days 10–5
Winemaker Daniel Binet **Est.** 2008 **Dozens** 2000 **Vyds** 7.4ha
The Warraroong vineyard was planted in 1978, the name an Aboriginal word for 'hillside', reflecting the southwesterly aspect of the property, which looks back towards the Brokenback Range and Watagan Mountains. In 2007 Katrina and Russell Leslie moved to the Hunter Valley, buying existing wineries and/or brands, with the early stages under the Swish Wine umbrella. Tin Solider came and went, and after protracted discussions, Wandin Estate also became part of the group. Warraroong Estate is now at the head of the businesses, with the highly talented and very experienced Daniel Binet chief winemaker.

🍷🍷🍷🍷🍷 Hunter Valley Semillon 2005 The highly regarded Andrew Thomas wrote at the time of its release that it 'will last 10 years or more' and it indeed has a wonderful array of intense flavours, but so balanced that they could be partially overlooked. This is a great Hunter Semillon still with a use-by date far in the future. Screwcap. 11.3% alc. **Rating** 97 **To** 2025 $60

Hunter Valley Semillon 2006 Glowing gold, tinged with green; an intense and powerful Semillon, given 96 points as a young wine; it brings together that extra dimension of acidity from the low alcohol, surrounded on all sides by fleshy lime, honey and spice flavours. It will never be better than it is now, but can still be cellared with confidence. Screwcap. 9.6% alc. **Rating** 96 **To** 2016 $50

Hunter Valley Semillon 2007 Glowing, mid green-gold; received 94 points when tasted at the end of '08, and since then has developed the anticipated honey and lime/lemon characteristics of mature Semillon, toasty notes still to appear. Screwcap. 11.8% alc. **Rating** 95 **To** 2020 $40

Warrenmang Vineyard & Resort ★★★★★

Mountain Creek Road, Moonambel, Vic 3478 **Region** Pyrenees
T (03) 5467 2233 **www**.warrenmang.com.au **Open** 7 days 10–5
Winemaker Sean Schwager **Est.** 1974 **Dozens** 9000 **Vyds** 32.1ha

Luigi and Athelie Bazzani continue to watch over Warrenmang; a new, partially underground barrel room with earthen walls has been completed, wine quality remains high, and the accommodation for over 80 guests plus a restaurant underpin the business. Over the 34 years that Luigi and Athelie have been at Warrenmang, a very loyal clientele has been built up. But if a fair offer were made, it would be accepted. The restaurant at Warrenmang will surely bring rave reviews, with the appointment of head chef Bruno Rocca, and executive chef Sam Pinzoni; between them they have worked with Neil Perry, Jacques Reymond, at the Sydney Opera House, the Botanical (Melbourne) and at the Steer Bar & Grill with both Stacey Thompson and Sean Neilson. Exports to Denmark, the Netherlands, Poland, Taiwan, Singapore, Malaysia and China.

🍷🍷🍷🍷🍷 Black Puma Pyrenees Shiraz 2008 Deep, dense but bright purple-crimson; the wine is open-fermented, hand-plunged, basket-pressed and matured for over 30 months in French oak. The bouquet is redolent of blackberry, anise and black cherry fruits, together with cedary notes from the oak; the full-bodied palate is crammed with black fruit flavours following in the footsteps of the bouquet; it has won numerous accolades from wine shows and various people's choice events, attesting to its appeal in the eyes of the public. Thoroughly wine-stained cork. 15.5% alc. **Rating** 94 **To** 2030 $80

The Miracle 2008 A 70/15/10% blend of shiraz, cabernet franc, cabernet sauvignon and merlot. Deep, dark crimson-purple; the miracle was the arrival of rain after years of drought had brought the vineyard to its knees, allowing the vines to produce small crops of deeply coloured and intensely flavoured grapes, and hence wine. The full-bodied palate circles around black fruits and substantial, albeit ripe and balanced, tannins. The good-quality cork may allow the wine to develop to its optimum, decades hence. 15% alc. **Rating** 94 **To** 2035 $75

Grand Pyrenees 2007 Holding its colour well; a blend of cabernet sauvignon, cabernet franc, merlot and shiraz; fragrant cassis, blackcurrant and blackberry aromas lead into a supple medium–bodied palate, the tannins fine, soft and in balance; despite the drought, there is no sign of the toughness that marred many of the otherwise good wines of the vintage; is idling along, with a long future in front of it. Screwcap. 14.5% alc. **Rating** 94 **To** 2022 $35

🍷🍷🍷🍷🍸 Pyrenees Sauvignon Blanc 2010 **Rating** 91 **To** 2014 $25

🍷🍷🍷🍷 Bazzani Pyrenees Shiraz Cabernet 2009 Good crimson-purple; generous,
✪ full-bodied and complex, with an interplay between the shiraz and cabernet, oak and tannins. For more than just interested observers, bbq rump steak would be the perfect match. Screwcap. 15% alc. **Rating** 89 **To** 2024 $15

Vinello by Bazzani Nebbiolo Barbera Dolcetto Brunello 2008 **Rating** 87 **To** 2014 $20

 # Warwick Billings

c/- Post Office, Lenswood, SA 5240 (postal) **Region** Adelaide Hills
T 0405 437 864 **www**.wowique.com.au **Open** Not
Winemaker Warwick Billings **Est.** 2009 **Dozens** 250
This is the venture of Warwick Billings and partner Rose Kemp. Warwick was a cider
maker in the UK who came to study at Roseworthy, and got diverted into the wine world.
He completed postgraduate oenology at Adelaide University in 1995, and worked for
Miranda Wine, Orlando and Angove Family Winemakers from 2002 to '08, along the way
moonlighting in France and Spain for 12 vintages. Warwick's approach to his eponymous label
is self-deprecating, beginning with the name Wowique, and saying, 'Occasionally a vineyard
sings to the winemaker. [We] have taken one of these songs and out it into a bottle.' The
vineyard in question is an unusual clone of chardonnay nurtured on a sloping hilltop site in
Mt Torrens. The self-deprecation continues with the wine simply being labelled Wowique
Blanc, which presumably sells because it is so good, not because of the name. Warwick's final
word on all of this is, 'The winemaking is unashamedly inspired by Burgundy, but care is take
to acknowledge that the soil is different, the clones are often different, the climate is definitely
different, and the end consumer is usually different.'

ΨΨΨΨΨ Wowique Blanc 2010 Bright straw-green; barrel-fermented in oak from
    Dargaud & Jaegle, a Burgundian cooper of note; this Chardonnay is focused,
    intense and very well-balanced, with nectarine, white peach and grapefruit
    providing the drive through to the long, zesty finish. Screwcap. 12.8% alc.
    Rating 94 To 2017 $24

Water Wheel   ★★★

Bridgewater-on-Loddon, Bridgewater, Vic 3516 **Region** Bendigo
T (03) 5437 3060 **www**.waterwheelwine.com **Open** Mon–Fri 9–5, w'ends & public
hols 12–4
Winemaker Peter Cumming, Bill Trevaskis **Est.** 1972 **Dozens** 35 000 **Vyds** 136ha
Peter Cumming, with more than two decades of winemaking under his belt, has quietly built
on the reputation of Water Wheel year by year. The winery is owned by the Cumming family,
which has farmed in the Bendigo region for 50+ years, with horticulture and viticulture
special areas of interest. Over half the vineyard area is planted to shiraz (75ha), followed by
chardonnay, sauvignon blanc (15ha each), cabernet sauvignon, malbec (10ha each), and smaller
plantings of petit verdot, semillon, roussanne and grenache. The wines are of remarkably
consistent quality and modest prices. Exports to the UK, the US, Canada, Switzerland,
Denmark, Singapore, Thailand, China and NZ.

ΨΨΨΨΨ **Bendigo Shiraz 2010** Bright colour, deep; red fruits and thyme, with bay leaf
✪   lift, offset by liqueur-soaked blackberry; the palate is lively and direct, with fleshy
        black fruits and chewy tannins in abundance. Screwcap. 14.5% alc. **Rating** 90
        To 2016 $18 BE

ΨΨΨΨ **Memsie Homestead Shiraz 2010** Good hue, although light; the light- to
✪   medium-bodied palate has red and black cherry fruit with a generous – too
       generous – helping of oak; nonetheless, an enjoyable wine at its giveaway price.
       Screwcap. 14.5% alc. **Rating** 87 **To** 2013 $10
       Bendigo Cabernet Sauvignon 2010 Rating 87 **To** 2015 $18 BE

Waterton Vineyards   ★★★★★

PO Box 125, Beaconsfield, Tas 7270 **Region** Northern Tasmania
T (03) 6394 7214 **www**.watertonhall.com.au **Open** Not
Winemaker Winemaking Tasmania (Julian Alcorso) **Est.** 2006 **Dozens** 400 **Vyds** 2ha
Jennifer Baird and Peter Cameron purchased this remarkable property in 2002. Waterton
Hall was built in the 1850s and modified extensively by well-known neo-gothic architect
Alexander North in 1910. The property was owned by the Catholic church from 1949–96,

variously used as a school, a boys' home and a retreat. Following its sale the new owners planted 1ha of riesling at the end of the '90s. Jennifer and Peter extended the vineyard with 1ha of shiraz, electing to sell the riesling until 2006, when part was first made under the Waterton label. The plans are to use the existing buildings to provide a restaurant, accommodation and function facilities. Last year's rating is maintained in the absence of a representative submission of its wines (one wine tasted at the Tasmanian Wine Show).

ŸŸŸŸ **Half Dry Riesling 2011** Pale straw-green; has all the markers of a young wine, fresh, with some spritz; the flavours are a cross between citrus fruit and crushed lemon leaves. Screwcap. 12% alc. **Rating** 89 **To** 2015 $28

Watson Wine Group   ★★★★☆

PO Box 167, Fullarton, SA 5063 **Region** Coonawarra
T (08) 8338 3200 **www.**rexwatsonwines.com **Open** Not
Winemaker Greg Tilbrook **Est.** 1997 **Dozens** 100 000 **Vyds** 347ha
Rex Watson started in the Australian wine industry in 1991 and began growing wine grapes in Coonawarra in '97. In '99 he began planting the most significant modern vineyard development in Coonawarra. In less than five years, this was built into a venture that now controls and manages almost 350ha over three vineyards, all close to the historic township of Coonawarra and well within the Coonawarra GI. Production under the Rex Watson and Coonawarra Premium Vineyards brands continues to rise. Exports to the UK, the US, Canada, Sweden, Russia, China and NZ.

ŸŸŸŸŸ Coonawarra Premium Vineyards Cabernet Sauvignon 2010 Intense, youthful purple; classic young Coonawarra Cabernet in every respect; precise and focused on its red and blackcurrant fruit, admirably balanced tannins and good acidity. Enjoy soon or later. Screwcap. 13.5% alc. Rating 95 To 2030 $27

ŸŸŸŸŸ Coonawarra Premium Vineyards Reserve Cabernet Sauvignon 2010 Rating 93 To 2025 $27

ŸŸŸŸ **Rex Watson Coonawarra Cabernet Sauvignon 2010** Rating 89
✪ To 2020 $12

WayWood Wines   ★★★★

PO Box 746, Willunga, SA 5172 **Region** McLaren Vale
T (08) 8556 4536 **www.**waywoodwines.com **Open** By appt
Winemaker Andrew Wood **Est.** 2005 **Dozens** 1200
This is the venture of Andrew Wood and Lisa Robertson, the culmination of their wayward odyssey. Andrew left his career as a sommelier in London, and retrained as a winemaker, working in Portugal, the UK, Italy and the Granite Belt (an eclectic selection if ever there was one), and settling in McLaren Vale in early 2004. Working with Kangarilla Road winery for the next six years, while making small quantities of Shiraz, Cabernets and Tempranillo from purchased grapes, led them to Nebbiolo and shiraz, the first vintage of those varieties in '12. The wines are made in small batches, utilising cold soaking and extended maceration.

ŸŸŸŸŸ McLaren Vale Shiraz 2009 Purple-red; the palate is like a slow-burning fuse,
✪ the flavours building continuously as the wine travels along the palate, and even into the aftertaste; initially it seems oaky, but black fruits, licorice, spice and deliciously bitter chocolate progressively come into play, leaving the oak where it started. Screwcap. 14.8% alc. Rating 90 To 2020 $19
McLaren Vale Shiraz Cabernet 2007 Good colour; a major surprise, showing none of the toughness of the year; indeed, the palate is positively juicy, with plum, blackberry, mocha and dark chocolate fruit flavours. Screwcap. 14.5% alc. Rating 90 To 2014 $25

ŸŸŸŸ **McLaren Vale Tempranillo 2010** Rating 89 To 2017 $24
Quattro Vini 2010 Rating 87 To 2020 $24

Wedgetail Estate

40 Hildebrand Road, Cottles Bridge, Vic 3099 **Region** Yarra Valley
T (03) 9714 8661 **www**.wedgetailestate.com.au **Open** W'ends & public hols 12–5, or
by appt, closed from 25 Dec, reopens Australia Day w'end
Winemaker Guy Lamothe **Est.** 1994 **Dozens** 1500 **Vyds** 5.5ha
Canadian-born photographer Guy Lamothe and partner Dena Ashbolt started making wine
in the basement of their Carlton home in the 1980s. The idea of their own vineyard started
to take hold, and the search for a property began. Then, in their words, 'one Sunday, when we
were "just out for a drive", we drove past our current home. The slopes are amazing, true goat
terrain, and it is on these steep slopes that in 1994 we planted our first block of pinot noir.'
While the vines were growing Lamothe enrolled in the winegrowing course at CSU, having
already gained practical experience working in the Yarra Valley (Tarrawarra), the Mornington
Peninsula and Meursault (Burgundy). 2008 marked the 10th vintage for Wedgetail Estate
which, like many others in the Yarra Valley, suffered significant damage from frost and smoke in
'07, and smoke and fire in '09. Exports to the UK, Canada, Singapore, Hong Kong and China.

ŸŸŸŸŸ **Single Vineyard Yarra Valley Shiraz 2010** Mid crimson; the bouquet is
     redolent of dark cherry, black pepper and suggestions of florals; medium-bodied
     with nervy acidity and ample fine-grained tannins; a savoury and refreshing
     example of the variety. Screwcap. 14.5% alc. **Rating** 92 **To** 2018 $38 BE
     Single Vineyard Yarra Valley Chardonnay 2010 Mid gold, green hue;
     restrained and savoury on the bouquet with cashews, meyer lemon and pear on
     display; the palate is lively and fresh, focused and expansive, with a lingering clove
     note to conclude. Screwcap. 13% alc. **Rating** 91 **To** 2016 $36 BE

ŸŸŸŸ **Single Vineyard Yarra Valley Pinot Noir 2010 Rating** 88 **To** 2014 $40 BE
     Reserve Pinot Noir 2010 Rating 88 **To** 2014 $60 BE

Wehl's Mount Benson Vineyards

Wrights Bay Road, Mount Benson, SA 5275 **Region** Mount Benson
T (08) 8768 6251 **www**.wehlsmtbensonvineyards.com.au **Open** 7 days 10–4
Winemaker Contract **Est.** 1989 **Dozens** 2500 **Vyds** 24.2ha
Peter and Leah Wehl were the first to plant vines in the Mount Benson region, beginning the
establishment of their vineyard (shiraz, cabernet sauvignon, merlot and sauvignon blanc), in
1989. While primarily grapegrowers, they have moved into winemaking via contract makers,
and have increased the range of wines available.

ŸŸŸŸŸ Shiraz 2009 Light to medium red-purple; a lively, indeed vigorous, cool-grown
     Shiraz with sunbeams of spice and pepper illuminating the sustained black fruits
     of the long, medium-bodied palate. The vineyard is now mature; the lingering
     aftertaste adds stature to the wine. Screwcap. 14.4% alc. Rating 94 To 2020 $24

ŸŸŸŸŸ **Cabernet Sauvignon 2009 Rating** 92 **To** 2020 $24
✪   **Cabernet Sauvignon Merlot 2009** Crimson-purple; a medium- to full-bodied
     wine with abundant red and black berry fruits on the bouquet and palate alike;
     French oak plays a major role, for while it is obvious, it is well integrated and
     introduces both spicy notes and good texture. Screwcap. 14.7% alc. **Rating** 91
     To 2015 $19
✪   **Shiraz Cabernet 2009** Crimson-purple; the aromas and flavours range through
     blackcurrant, blackberry and plum, and are held in a fine web of savoury tannins
     and integrated oak; intended for early consumption, but has considerable merit.
     Screwcap. 14.5% alc. **Rating** 90 **To** 2017 $19

ŸŸŸŸ **Sauvignon Blanc 2011 Rating** 89 **To** 2013 $19
✪

Wellbush Vineyard

659 Huntly-Fosterville Road, Huntly, Vic 3551 **Region** Bendigo
T (03) 5448 8515 **Open** W'ends 11–4, Mon–Fri by appt
Winemaker Wes Vine, Greg Dedman **Est.** 2006 **Dozens** 550 **Vyds** 1.44ha
David and Lynn Wallace purchased the 10ha property in 2006; it brought with it a long history. In the early years of the last century it was a Chinese market garden, the hand-built ponds remaining today. In 1975 the first chardonnay, shiraz, cabernet sauvignon and merlot vines were planted, with further plantings of shiraz in '98; an addition to the cabernet sauvignon the following year brought the vineyard to its present level. The Wallaces (David having studied for his Bachelor of Applied Science (wine science) at CSU) have been progressively rehabilitating and retrellising the vineyard, building a 50-megalitre dam to provide reliable water in the seemingly endless drought years. They say 'our aims and aspirations are to produce the best-quality grapes we possibly can and eventually produce our own handcrafted wines, give up our day jobs and grow old ungracefully in our beautiful vineyard'.

Handpicked Bendigo Shiraz 2009 Medium to full red-purple; a rich wine, crammed with flavour in a similar way to prior vintages; while the red and black fruit has ample tannins, there is a fleeting touch of contrasting sweetness leading to a velvety mouthfeel. Screwcap. 14% alc. **Rating** 89 **To** 2019 $22

Wendouree

Wendouree Road, Clare, SA 5453 **Region** Clare Valley
T (08) 8842 2896 **Open** Not
Winemaker Tony Brady **Est.** 1895 **Dozens** 1800 **Vyds** 12ha
An iron fist in a velvet glove best describes these extraordinary wines. They are fashioned with passion and precision from the very old vineyard (shiraz, cabernet sauvignon, malbec, mataro and muscat of alexandria), with its unique terroir, by Tony and Lita Brady, who rightly see themselves as custodians of a priceless treasure. The 100-year-old stone winery is virtually unchanged from the day it was built; this is in every sense a treasure beyond price. I should explain, I buy three wines from Wendouree every year, always including the Shiraz. This is the only way I am able to provide tasting notes, and it's almost inevitably a last-minute exercise as I suddenly realise there are no notes in place. Moreover, Wendouree has never made any comment about its wines, and I realise that the change in style away from full-bodied to medium-bodied seems a permanent fixture of the landscape, not a one-off result of a given vintage. The best news of all is that I may actually get to drink some of the Wendourees I have bought over the past 10 years before I die, and not have to rely on my few remaining bottles from the 1970s (and rather more from the '80s and '90s). The Lord moves in mysterious ways. No wines were received for this edition; the rating is that of last year.

Were Estate

Cnr Wildberry Road/Johnson Road, Wilyabrup, WA 6280 **Region** Margaret River
T (08) 9755 6273 **www**.wereestate.com.au **Open** Not
Winemaker Clive Otto (Contract) **Est.** 1998 **Dozens** 4000 **Vyds** 9.72ha
Owners Diane and Gordon Davies say, 'We are different. We're original, we're bold, we're innovative.' This is all reflected in the design of the unusual back labels (incorporating pictures of the innumerable pairs of braces that real estate agent Gordon wears at work in Perth), in the early move to screwcaps for both white and red wine, and, for that matter, in the underground trickle irrigation system (plus a move towards organic methods) in their Margaret River vineyard that can be controlled from Perth. Exports to Hong Kong, China and Singapore.

The Moorabbin 2008 A curious name, that of the house JB Were built in Brighton, Melbourne in 1842, and now a suburb name. This winery started life as We're Wines, with no link to the Were family claimed. Regardless, this is a classy Shiraz, rich and juicy berry fruit seamlessly folded in quality oak and tannins. Screwcap. 14.5% alc. **Rating** 95 **To** 2023 $35

Single Vineyard Reserve Margaret River Chardonnay 2010 Straw-green; a complex, structured wine barrel-fermented and matured in new French oak for eight months; both bouquet and palate give multiple messages, with creamy/nutty melon, white peach and pink grapefruit woven together with oak and bound by a skein of acidity. Screwcap. 13.8% alc. **Rating** 94 **To** 2017 $30

The Griffith 2009 Strong red-purple; has a fragrant, perfumed bouquet of cassis and a distinct touch of bay leaf that reappears faintly on the finish; the palate is elegant, medium-bodied and has an appealing overall slightly herbal savoury nuance. Cabernet Sauvignon. Screwcap. 14.7% alc. **Rating** 94 **To** 2019 $35

ŸŸŸŸŸ The Griffith 2008 **Rating** 91 **To** 2017 $35

West Cape Howe Wines ★★★★★

Lot 14923 Muir Highway, Mount Barker, WA 6324 **Region** Mount Barker
T (08) 99892 1444 **ww**.westcapehowewines.com.au **Open** 7 days 10–5
Winemaker Gavin Berry, Dave Cleary, Andrew Siddell **Est.** 1997 **Dozens** 75 000
After a highly successful seven years, West Cape Howe founders Brenden and Kylie Smith moved on, selling the business to a partnership including Gavin Berry (until 2004, senior winemaker at Plantagenet) and viticulturist Rob Quenby. As well as existing fruit sources, West Cape Howe now has the 80ha Lansdale Vineyard, planted in 1989, as its primary fruit source. In March '09 it purchased the 7700 tonne capacity Goundrey winery and 237ha Goundrey estate vineyards from CWA; the grapes from these plantings will be purchased by Accolade Wines (the new owner of CWA) for years to come. The move vastly increases West Cape Howe's business base, and facilitates contract winemaking to generate cash flow. So should the exemplary quality and very modest prices of the wines. Exports to the UK, the US, Denmark, Germany, Singapore and Hong Kong.

ŸŸŸŸŸ Two Steps Great Southern Shiraz 2009 Bright but deep crimson-purple;
✪   this is a ripper red at its price, or indeed any price. The best shiraz of the vintage was co-fermented on the skins of viognier, producing a blaze of juicy, spicy red and black berry flavours, anchored by fine tannins and 18 months in French oak. Screwcap. 14.5% alc. **Rating** 95 **To** 2024 $24

✪   Book Ends Great Southern Cabernet Sauvignon 2009 Deep, vivid crimson-purple; a distinguished Cabernet, with pristine blackcurrant fruit on the bouquet, joined by some plum on the palate; 18 months in French oak has added cedary complexity, and the overall structure and balance is admirable. Screwcap. 14% alc. **Rating** 95 **To** 2024 $24

Styx Gully Great Southern Chardonnay 2010 Light straw-green; a particularly fine and restrained wine, the delicate melon and citrus fruit not overwhelmed by barrel fermentation in predominantly used French oak; a gently minerally finish enhances this modern Australian interpretation of Chablis. Screwcap. 12.5% alc. **Rating** 94 **To** 2018 $24

ŸŸŸŸŸ Great Southern Riesling 2011 Pale quartz-green; the flowery, aromatic
✪   bouquet has abundant citrus blossom notes, the fore-palate with more of the same before firm, minerally acidity provides the structure. Will cellar well. Screwcap. 12% alc. **Rating** 92 **To** 2019 $19

✪   Shiraz 2010 Bright crimson-purple; an elegant, medium-bodied wine that has regional spice and licorice overtones to its black fruits, French oak evident but not over the top, and will join with the tannins as the two soften over time. Screwcap. 14.5% alc. **Rating** 92 **To** 2025 $16

✪   Semillon Sauvignon Blanc 2011 Light straw-green; a blend with attitude, especially with the acidity and pleasing bite of the palate, which ranges between cut grass and green capsicum then on to gooseberry; has very good length and focus. Screwcap. 12.5% alc. **Rating** 91 **To** 2014 $16

✪   Cabernet Merlot 2010 Deep colour; essency blackcurrant pastille bouquet, very concentrated; the palate follows suit, with depth and generosity; sweet-fruited, with fine-grained tannins on the finish. Screwcap. 14% alc. **Rating** 90 **To** 2017 $16 BE

▼▼▼▼ Tempranillo 2010 Rating 89 To 2013 $19
Great Southern Sauvignon Blanc 2011 Rating 88 To Now $19

Westend Estate Wines ★★★★☆

1283 Brayne Road, Griffith, NSW 2680 **Region** Riverina
T (02) 6969 0800 **www**.westendestate.com **Open** Mon–Fri 8.30–5, w'ends 10–4
Winemaker William Calabria, Bryan Currie, Emma Norbiato, Tony Steffania **Est**. 1945
Dozens 300 000 **Vyds** 52ha

Along with a number of Riverina producers, Westend Estate has successfully lifted both the quality and the packaging of its wines. Its leading 3 Bridges range, which has an impressive array of gold medals to its credit, is anchored in part on estate vineyards. Bill Calabria has been involved in the Australian wine industry for more than 40 years, and is understandably proud of the achievements of both Westend and the Riverina wine industry as a whole. Westend is moving with the times, increasing its plantings of durif, and introducing aglianico, nero d'Avola, and st macaire (a problematic variety not recognised by the ultimate authority of such matters, Jancis Robinson, who says it is a small town in the Bordeaux region). These new plantings have paralleled an increase in wine production. Equally importantly, it is casting its net over the Canberra District, Hilltops and King Valley, premium regions. A producer that consistently delivers exceptional value for money across the entire range. Exports to the UK, the US, Canada, Russia, China and Japan.

▼▼▼▼▼ 3 Bridges Golden Mist Botrytis 2010 Deep gold, green hue; a pure-fruited,
✪ ripe and exotic wine, showing great concentration of apricot, marmalade, brittle and spice; the palate is unctuous and hedonistic, with a long, luscious and pure finish; wonderful value at the price. Screwcap. 10.5% alc. **Rating** 95 **To** 2020 $20 BE

▼▼▼▼▽ Coonawarra Cabernet Sauvignon 2010 Rating 93 To 2020 $27 BE
✪ 3 Bridges Winemakers Selection Durif 2010 Vivid purple hue; a dark and concentrated bouquet, showing elements of tar and licorice alongside essency black fruits; the palate is warm and generous on the one hand, yet firm and full of savoury interest on the other; very good warm–climate Durif. Screwcap. 14.5% alc. **Rating** 93 **To** 2018 $20 BE
◐ 3 Bridges Winemakers Selection Durif 2009 Rating 93 To 2020 $20
Francesco Show Reserve Grand Liqueur Muscat NV Rating 93
To 2025 $35 BE
✪ Cool Climate Series Hilltops Shiraz 2010 Deep crimson; a poised and fragrant bouquet of fresh blackberry, Asian spices and a splash of ironstone minerality; the palate is medium-bodied and finely detailed, with the tannins being plush and silky, finishing with a generous and warm touch of hoi sin; excellent value for the price. Screwcap. 14% alc. **Rating** 92 **To** 2020 $15 BE
✪ Cool Climate Series Hilltops Tempranillo 2010 A fragrant, lifted and varietal expression of tempranillo, with cola, charcuterie and lots of spice on display; the palate is fleshy and vibrant, with a succulent note to the acidity and added freshness from the Amaro bitterness of the tannins. A friendly, savoury wine for just about any occasion. Screwcap. 14% alc. **Rating** 92 **To** 2016 $15 BE
Grand Tawny Port NV Rating 92 To 2025 $35 BE
◐ Cool Climate Series Tumbarumba Pinot Noir 2010 Rating 91 To 2017 $15
✪ 3 Bridges Winemakers Selection Shiraz 2010 Deep colour, with pure black fruits and a high level of mocha and fruitcake on display; the palate is fleshy and generous, with good concentration, plenty of tannin backbone and an expansive and savoury finish. Screwcap. 14.5% alc. **Rating** 91 **To** 2020 $20 BE
✪ 3 Bridges Winemakers Selection Cabernet Sauvignon 2009 A densely concentrated and essency blackcurrant and black olive bouquet is on display; the palate reveals more light and shade, with vibrant acidity and firm gravelly tannins gelling harmoniously on the finish. A big-boned Cabernet done well. Screwcap. 14.5% alc. **Rating** 91 **To** 2020 $20 BE

✪ **Richland Shiraz 2010** Deep crimson; a bright, fragrant and expressive bouquet offering a juicy array of red and black fruits; pure, uncomplicated and constructed with precision and drinkability in mind; this wine offers significantly more than the price tag demands. Screwcap. 14% alc. **Rating** 90 **To** 2017 $11 BE
Calabria Bros. Barossa Shiraz 2010 **Rating** 90 **To** 2022 $27 BE

✪ **3 Bridges Winemakers Selection Shiraz 2009** Good colour; has an uncommon depth of flavour and richness to the fruit for a Riverina wine, but does not stray into the dead fruit zone; positive American oak and ripe tannins all contribute to an honest medium- to full-bodied red in traditional Australian style. Screwcap. 14.5% alc. **Rating** 90 **To** 2017 $20
3 Bridges Golden Mist Botrytis 2009 **Rating** 90 **To** Now $20

🍷🍷🍷🍷 **3 Bridges Winemakers Selection Chardonnay 2010** **Rating** 89 **To** 2015 $20 BE
✪ **Richland Pinot Grigio 2011** **Rating** 89 **To** 2014 $11 BE
✪ **Richland Cabernet Merlot 2010** **Rating** 89 **To** 2016 $11 BE
✪ **Calabria Private Bin Aglianico 2009** **Rating** 89 **To** 2016 $15
✪ **Calabria Private Bin Saint Macaire 2009** **Rating** 89 **To** 2015 $15 BE
✪ **Poker Face Semillon Sauvignon Blanc 2011** **Rating** 88 **To** 2014 $8 BE
✪ **Richland Chardonnay 2011** **Rating** 88 **To** 2015 $11 BE
✪ **Richland Pinot Grigio 2010** **Rating** 88 **To** Now $11
Cool Climate Hilltops Riesling 2009 **Rating** 87 **To** 2014 $15
Poker Face Rose 2011 **Rating** 87 **To** 2014 $8 BE
Eternity Cuvee NV **Rating** 87 **To** 2013 $11
Eternity Sparkling Dolcetto NV **Rating** 87 **To** 2013 $11

Western Range Wines ★★★☆

1995 Chittering Road, Lower Chittering, WA 6084 **Region** Perth Hills
T (08) 9571 8800 **www**.westernrangewines.com.au **Open** 7 days 10–5
Winemaker Israel De Brito **Est.** 2001 **Dozens** 25 000 **Vyds** 125ha

Between the mid 1990s and 2001, several prominent West Australians, including Marilyn Corderory, Malcolm McCusker, and Terry and Kevin Prindiville, established 125ha of vines (under separate ownerships) in the Perth Hills, planting a kaleidoscopic range of varieties. The next step was to join forces to build a substantial winery. This is a separate venture, but takes the grapes from the individual vineyards and markets the wine under the Western Range brand. The wines are made and sold at four levels: Lot 88, Goyamin Pool, Julimar and Julimar Organic. Exports to Canada, Poland, Russia, China and Japan.

🍷🍷🍷🍷 **Julimar Perth Hills Verdelho 2011** Pale colour; nectarine and lime oil bouquet; fresh, lively and fragrant, with balanced acidity and good flavour. Screwcap. 13% alc. **Rating** 88 **To** 2014 $20 BE

Westlake Vineyards ★★★★★

Diagonal Road, Koonunga, SA 5355 **Region** Barossa Valley
T 0428 656 208 **F** (08) 8565 6208 **Open** By appt
Winemaker Darren Westlake **Est.** 1999 **Dozens** 400 **Vyds** 36.2ha

Darren and Suzanne Westlake tend 22ha of shiraz, 6.5ha of cabernet sauvignon, 2ha of viognier, and smaller plantings of petit verdot, durif, mataro, grenache and graciano planted on two properties in the Koonunga area of the Barossa Valley. They do all the vineyard work personally, and have a long list of high-profile winemakers queued up to buy the grapes, leaving only a small amount for production under the Westlake label. Suzanne is a sixth-generation descendant of Johann George Kalleske, who came to SA from Prussia in 1838, while the 717 Convicts label draws on the history of Darren's ancestor Edward Westlake, who was transported to Australia in 1788.

ŢŢŢŢŢ **Eleazar Barossa Valley Shiraz 2009** Deep, healthy colour; only 70 dozen bottles of this wine were made, and spent 20 months in new French and American oak; while that input is obvious, the density of the dark berry fruit pulls the oak into balance. A sumptuous full-bodied wine with a peacock's display of flavours, and immaculate balance and length. Cork. 15% alc. **Rating** 96 **To** 2040 $44

717 Convicts The Warden Barossa Valley Shiraz 2009 Strong red-purple; the bouquet immediately sets the scene, with multifaceted fruit and generous vanillan oak to the fore; the palate has very good texture and structure to its blackberry fruit, licorice, spice and plum cake flavours, and the tannins are ripe and balanced. Cork. 15.1% alc. **Rating** 95 **To** 2029 $35

Albert's Block Barossa Valley Shiraz 2009 Good colour and depth; a complex, medium- to full-bodied wine, estate-grown shiraz with a voluminous array of spice, tar, licorice and black fruits allied with American and French oak inputs; neither fined nor filtered, like all the Westlake red wines. 250 dozen made. Cork. 14.6% alc. **Rating** 94 **To** 2024 $28

ŢŢŢŢŢ **717 Convicts The Felon Barossa Valley Shiraz Cabernet Sauvignon 2009** **Rating** 92 **To** 2020 $28

Whinstone Estate

295 Dunns Creek Road, Red Hill, Vic 3937 **Region** Mornington Peninsula
T (03) 5989 7487 **www**.whinstone.com.au **Open** W'ends & public hols 11–5, 7 days Jan
Winemaker Phaedrus Estate **Est.** 1994 **Dozens** 500 **Vyds** 2.88ha
Ken and Leon Wood began the development of their vineyard in 1994, planting 1.01ha of chardonnay, 0.81ha of pinot gris, 0.6ha of pinot noir, 0.4ha of sauvignon blanc and a few rows of melon (a grape of Muscadet, France). Initially the grapes were sold to other makers in the region, with a small amount made under the Whinstone label for friends and family. Demand has grown and, with it, production. The business was sold in July 2011, the as yet unnamed new owners indicating that they intend to continue the Whinstone brand.

ŢŢŢŢŢ **Mornington Peninsula Pinot Noir 2010** Light crimson-purple; fragrant red cherry, strawberry and spice aromas track directly through to the light- to medium-bodied palate; a pretty wine. Screwcap. 13.5% alc. **Rating** 90 **To** 2015 $25

ŢŢŢŢ **Mornington Peninsula Pinot Gris 2010** **Rating** 88 **To** Now $23

Whispering Hills

580 Warburton Highway, Seville, Vic 3139 **Region** Yarra Valley
T (03) 5964 2822 **www**.whisperinghills.com.au **Open** 7 days 10–6
Winemaker Murray and Darcy Lyons **Est.** 1985 **Dozens** 1500 **Vyds** 5ha
Whispering Hills is owned and operated by the Lyons family (Audrey and Darcy Lyons). Darcy is responsible for the winemaking, while Audrey takes care of the cellar door and distribution. The vineyard was established in 1985 with further plantings in '96 and some grafting in 2003, and now consists of cabernet sauvignon (2ha), riesling, chardonnay and pinot noir (1ha each). Exports to Japan and China.

ŢŢŢŢŢ **Hoddles Creek Yarra Valley Barbera 2010** An unexpected arrival in the Yarra Valley, but its colour, aroma and flavour all suggest it is quite comfortable with its new home; the flavours are centred on red cherry, but with a silky mouthfeel that accentuates the fruit. Screwcap. 13% alc. **Rating** 90 **To** 2017 $40

❂ **Hoddles Creek Yarra Valley Nebbiolo 2010** Good colour; has mouth-watering cherry, herb, spice and tannins all running in different directions in the mouth, but adding up to a wine with considerable presence, and a more than interesting partner for the Barbera. Screwcap. 12.5% alc. **Rating** 90 **To** 2016 $20

ŢŢŢŢ **Yarra Valley Premium Cuvee NV** **Rating** 89 **To** 2013 $30

Whistler Wines ★★★★

Seppeltsfield Road, Marananga, SA 5355 **Region** Barossa Valley
T (08) 8562 4942 **www**.whistlerwines.com **Open** 7 days 10.30–5
Winemaker Troy Kalleske, Christa Deans **Est.** 1999 **Dozens** 7500 **Vyds** 14ha
Brothers Martin and Chris Pfeiffer and their families have created one of the Barossa's hidden secrets: the vines and the cellar door tucked away from the view of those travelling along Seppeltsfield Road. Martin has over 25 years' viticultural experience with Southcorp, and Chris brings marketing skills from many years as a publisher. The wines are from estate-grown shiraz (6ha), merlot (2ha), cabernet sauvignon, riesling (1.3ha each), mourvedre, grenache (1.2ha each) and semillon (1ha). Exports to Canada, Denmark, Taiwan, Hong Kong and China.

ꙮꙮꙮꙮꙮ **Barossa Riesling 2011** I don't catch the 'fresh pear and apricot aromas', but do fall into step with the back label's description of 'bold lime and citrus flavours', however tautological that may be; crisp acidity completes the package. Screwcap. 12% alc. **Rating** 91 **To** 2019 $22

Barossa Shiraz 2009 Has a slightly weak rim to the colour, but there is nothing weak about the flavour – indeed, the contrary, for this is a full-bodied, boots and all Barossa Valley Shiraz from Whistler's Heysen Vineyard; luscious blackberry fruits and a warm finish. Screwcap. 15% alc. **Rating** 90 **To** 2024 $35

Barossa Grenache 2010 Light, clear red; an appealing Barossa Valley Grenache, light- to medium-bodied, fresh and well balanced; its pageant of red fruits expresses itself without confection characters; ready right now. Screwcap. 14.5% alc. **Rating** 90 **To** 2015 $26

Barossa Merlot 2009 Good colour; has far more good aspects than bad; a full range of red fruits runs through the length of the palate and into the aftertaste; 20 months in oak wasn't too long; the tannins are in balance. Screwcap. 14.5% alc. **Rating** 90 **To** 2014 $26

ꙮꙮꙮꙮ **Barossa Cabernet Sauvignon 2009 Rating** 89 **To** 2019 $26

Whitfield Estate ★★★☆

198 McIntyre Road, Scotsdale, Denmark, WA 6333 **Region** Great Southern
T (08) 9840 9016 **www**.whitfieldestate.com.au **Open** Thurs–Mon 10–5, 7 days during school hols
Winemaker Dave Cleary **Est.** 1994 **Dozens** 1000 **Vyds** 4.8ha
Graham and Kelly Howard acquired the Whitfield Estate vineyard (planted in 1994) in 2005. The estate is planted to chardonnay (2.5ha) and shiraz (2.3ha), the majority of which is sold to West Cape Howe, who contract-make the remaining grapes for Whitfield Estate. Other varieties are also purchased from growers in the region. The Picnic in the Paddock café opened in '08.

ꙮꙮꙮꙮꙮ **Tempranillo 2010** Bright, clear crimson; a fresh and vibrant palate, with pure red cherry and a drizzle of lemon juice running through to the lingering finish. Drink any time the fancy takes you. Screwcap. 14% alc. **Rating** 93 **To** 2016 $24

ꙮꙮꙮꙮ **Cabernet Merlot 2010 Rating** 89 **To** 2020 $24
Picnic Red Shiraz 2009 Rating 88 **To** 2014 $17
Semillon Sauvignon Blanc 2011 Rating 87 **To** 2014 $18

Wicks Estate Wines ★★★★

21 Franklin Street, Adelaide, SA 5000 (postal) **Region** Adelaide Hills
T (08) 8212 0004 **www**.wicksestate.com.au **Open** Not
Winemaker Tim Knappstein, Leigh Ratzmer **Est.** 2000 **Dozens** 15 000 **Vyds** 38.3ha
Tim and Simon Wicks had a long-term involvement with orchard and nursery operations at Highbury in the Adelaide Hills prior to purchasing the 54ha property at Woodside in 1999. They planted fractionally less than 40ha of chardonnay, riesling, sauvignon blanc, shiraz, merlot and cabernet sauvignon, following this with the construction of a winery in 2004. Wicks Estate has won more than its fair share of wine show medals over the years, winning the

top-gold medal for its Chardonnay Pinot Noir '09 and a gold medal for its Shiraz '10 at the Adelaide Wine Show '11. Exports to the UK, the US, the Netherlands, and China.

🍷🍷🍷🍷🍷 **Adelaide Hills Cabernet Sauvignon 2010** Deep colour, with pure cassis and
✪   cigar box on display; ample levels of sweet black fruits are given light and life, through lively acidity and well-handled toasty oak; long and fragrant to conclude. Screwcap. 14.5% alc. **Rating** 91 **To** 2019 $20 BE

✪   **Adelaide Hills Shiraz 2010** Deep crimson, purple hue; densely concentrated and full of fruitcake spice and essency blackberry fruit; the palate is dense and dark, finishing with a long tail of mocha and chewy tannins. Screwcap. 14.5% alc. **Rating** 90 **To** 2018 $20 BE

🍷🍷🍷🍷 **Eminence Adelaide Hills Shiraz Cabernet 2009** Rating 89 **To** 2018 $60 BE
Adelaide Hills Sauvignon Blanc 2011 Rating 88 **To** Now $20

wightwick   ★★★★
323 Slatey Creek Road North, Invermay, Vic 3352 **Region** Ballarat
T (03) 5332 4443 **www**.wightwick.com.au **Open** By appt
Winemaker Simon Wightwick **Est.** 1996 **Dozens** 180 **Vyds** 3ha
wightwick might be described as an angel on a pinhead exercise. Keith and Ann Wightwick planted the tiny estate vineyard to 0.12ha of chardonnay and 0.29ha of pinot noir in 1996. Son Simon works as a viticulturist and winemaker in the Yarra Valley, and looks after the vineyards on weekends (using organic principles) and the micro-winemaking during vintage.

🍷🍷🍷🍷🍷 **Ballarat Chardonnay 2010** Bright straw-green; the complex bouquet shows some barrel-ferment characters, the palate starting off with some hard edges to the grapefruit flavours; then the wine stands on its head on the back-palate and finish, with harmonious white peach and melon flavours. Should age well. Screwcap. 12.9% alc. **Rating** 93 **To** 2016 $29

Yarra Valley Cabernet Sauvignon 2008 Produced entirely from the estate Cottles Bridge Vineyard, from 25-year-old vines, producing a tiny crop and 49 dozen bottles. The colour is still fresh, but the palate has some savoury, minty characters that marginally detract from the lead play of blackcurrant fruit. Screwcap. 13.6% alc. **Rating** 90 **To** 2018 $28

🍷🍷🍷🍷 **Ballarat Pinot Noir 2009** Rating 89 **To** 2015 $33

Wignalls Wines   ★★★★
448 Chester Pass Road (Highway 1), Albany, WA 6330 **Region** Albany
T (08) 9841 2848 **www**.wignallswines.com.au **Open** 7 days 11–4
Winemaker Michael Perkins, Rob Wignall **Est.** 1982 **Dozens** 10 000 **Vyds** 18.5ha
While the estate vineyards have a diverse range of sauvignon blanc, semillon, chardonnay, pinot noir, merlot, shiraz, cabernet franc and cabernet sauvignon, founder Bill Wignall was one of the early movers with pinot noir, producing wines that, by the standards of their time, were well in front of anything else coming out of WA (and up with the then limited amounts being made in Vic and Tas). The star dimmed, problems in the vineyard and with contract winemaking both playing a role. The establishment of an onsite winery in 1998, and the assumption of the winemaking role by son Rob, with significant input by Michael Perkins, has seen the range of wines increase. Exports to Denmark, Japan, Taiwan, Singapore and China.

🍷🍷🍷🍷🍷 **Albany Pinot Noir 2010** Clear and enticing red; a curate's egg, with everything good except for one dark spot: the high alcohol that lies in wait until the finish and aftertaste. Before that point, the wine is full of pinot character expressed in complex layers of red and black fruits. Be sure to taste the wine with duck or similar at a Chinese restaurant, when the alcohol issue can be safely ignored. Screwcap. 15% alc. **Rating** 92 **To** 2016 $32

✪   **Albany Unwooded Chardonnay 2011** Pale straw-green; an elegant wine with pure, refined fruit expression in a grapefruit and white peach spectrum, crisp acidity tying the knot on the finish. Screwcap. 14% alc. **Rating** 90 **To** 2013 $17

Great Southern Cabernet Merlot 2010 Clear crimson; the bouquet has fragrant, almost floral, red fruits, and just a hint of forest; the light- to medium-bodied palate has crisp red berry fruits, a touch of mint, and fresh acidity. There is some question whether, despite its alcohol, it is fully ripe, and it is best enjoyed now for its freshness. Screwcap. 14% alc. **Rating** 89 **To** 2014 $17

Wild Dog Winery ★★★★☆

Warragul-Korrumburra Road, Warragul, Vic 3820 **Region** Gippsland
T (03) 5623 1117 **www**.wilddogwinery.com **Open** 7 days 11–5
Winemaker Folkert Janssen **Est.** 1982 **Dozens** 3000 **Vyds** 10.1ha
Wild Dog is a family-owned business operated by Gary and Judy Surman. Since acquiring the business in 2005 much work has been done in the vineyard (planted in 1982) with grafting, replanting and retrellising; winery expansion (all wines are now made onsite); they have also built a restaurant overlooking the vineyard. Now one of the larger wineries in Gippsland, having won four trophies at the Gippsland Wine Show '08 and Most Successful Exhibitor in '09, it would seem there is much to be confident about. Exports to China and Japan.

Gippsland Riesling 2011 While the wine has a quiet bouquet, it comes alive on the palate with crunchy acidity adding texture to the lime and apple flavours that accelerate past the finish and into the aftertaste. Superior to any Wild Dog Riesling so far produced. Screwcap. 11.2% alc. **Rating** 94 **To** 2021 $21

Gippsland Cabernet Sauvignon 2010 Rating 93 **To** 2025 $25
Wild Ice Gippsland Ice Riesling 2011 Rating 93 **To** 2014 $25
Gippsland Sauvignon Blanc 2011 Rating 92 **To** 2014 $23
Gippsland Shiraz 2010 Rating 92 **To** 2020 $27
Gippsland Pinot Noir 2009 Rating 91 **To** 2016 $24
Gippsland Sparkling 2008 Rating 90 **To** 2014 $27

Gippsland Pinot Gris 2011 Rating 87 **To** 2013 $23
Gippsland Cabernet Franc 2010 Rating 87 **To** 2014 $23

Wild Orchid Wines ★★★

PO Box 165, Boyup Brook, WA 6244 **Region** Blackwood Valley
T (08) 9767 3058 **www**.wildorchidwines.com.au **Open** Not
Winemaker James Kellie (Contract) **Est.** 1997 **Dozens** 1500 **Vyds** 17.7ha
Orest and Robyn Skraha, along with son Brad and his wife Kirsten, have established over 17ha of chardonnay, semillon, shiraz, merlot, cabernet sauvignon and tempranillo. Most of the grapes are sold, with small premium parcels contract-made for the Wild Orchid brand. Brad completed his Bachelor of Science in viticulture and oenology at Curtin University, then gained experience at Howard Park (Margaret River) and Chappellet winery in the Napa Valley.

Reserve Blackwood Valley Cabernet Sauvignon 2010 Purple-crimson; a medium-bodied wine with a jumble sale mix of aromas and flavours from mint to blackcurrant to vanilla, and various breaks along the line. A work in progress. Screwcap. 14% alc. **Rating** 87 **To** 2016 $28

Wildwood ★★★

154 Buckley Street, Essendon, 3040 (postal) **Region** Sunbury
T 0415 645 562 **www**.wildwoodvineyards.com.au **Open** Not
Winemaker Dr Wayne Stott **Est.** 1982 **Dozens** 2000 **Vyds** 9.4ha
Wildwood is just 4km past Melbourne's Tullamarine Airport, at an altitude of 130m in the Oaklands Valley, which provides unexpected views back to Port Phillip Bay and the Melbourne skyline. Ill health sadly led to Dr Wayne Stott closing the winery in 2012.

Petit Verdot 2010 A fragrant and lifted perfume of redcurrant, blackberry and violet; medium-bodied and showing high levels of acidity, with a strong saline character prevalent on the finish. Screwcap. 11% alc. **Rating** 87 **To** 2014 $40 BE

Will Taylor Wines

1B Victoria Avenue, Unley Park, SA 5061 **Region** South Eastern Australia
T (08) 8271 6122 **www**.willtaylor.com.au **Open** By appt
Winemaker Various contract **Est.** 1997 **Dozens** 1500
Will Taylor is a partner in the leading Adelaide law firm Finlaysons, and specialises in wine law. He and Suzanne Taylor have established a classic negociant wine business, having wines contract-made to their specifications. Moreover, they choose what they consider the best regions for each variety; thus Clare Valley Riesling, Adelaide Hills Sauvignon Blanc, Hunter Valley Semillon and Yarra Valley Pinot Noir. No wines were made in 2011 due to adverse vintage conditions, but there are high hopes for the '12s. Exports to Canada and China.

Willespie ★★★

555 Harmans Mill Road, Wilyabrup via Cowaramup, WA 6284 **Region** Margaret River
T (08) 9755 6248 **www**.willespie.com.au **Open** 7 days 10.30–5
Winemaker Anthony Neilson **Est.** 1976 **Dozens** 10 000 **Vyds** 25.9ha
Willespie has produced many attractive white wines over the years, typically in brisk, herbaceous Margaret River style; all are fruit- rather than oak-driven. The Squance family (which founded and owns Willespie) has increased winery capacity, drawing upon estate vineyards. Exports to the UK, Japan and Singapore.

 Margaret River Verdelho 2009 Bright green-yellow; interesting wine; while dry, has developed complex stone fruit flavours backed by good acidity; it will continue along this path for several years yet. Screwcap. 14% alc. **Rating** 89
To 2015 $20
Margaret River White 2011 A good example of the various multi-varietal blends made for decades in the Margaret River. Screwcap. 13% alc. **Rating** 87
To 2014 $17
Margaret River Red NV Some adroit blending ('03 Cabernet Sauvignon with Merlot and Cabernet Franc, the vintages not stated) has produced a full-flavoured wine, the younger components a major help. Screwcap. 14.5% alc. **Rating** 87
To 2014 $20

William Downie ★★★★★

121 Yarragon South Road, Yarragon, Vic 3823 (postal) **Region** Yarra Valley
T (03) 5634 2216 **www**.williamdownie.com.au **Open** Not
Winemaker William Downie **Est.** 2003 **Dozens** 500
William (Bill) Downie spends six months each year making wine in Burgundy, the other six based in the Yarra Valley with De Bortoli. He uses purchased grapes from older vines to make his own wines, avoiding the use of pumps, filtration and fining. The striking label, designed by artist Reg Mombassa, has helped obtain listings at The Prince Wine Store and elsewhere. In the 2006 Gourmet Traveller Winemaker of the Year Awards, Bill was awarded the Kemeny's Medal for the Best Young Winemaker. His boss at De Bortoli, Stephen Webber, goes a little further when he says, 'Downie is the best winemaker in Australia.' No wines were received for this edition; the rating is that of last year.

Willoughby Park ★★★★★

678 South Coast Highway, Denmark, WA 6333 **Region** Great Southern
T (08) 9848 1555 **www**.willoughbypark.com.au **Open** 7 days 10–5
Winemaker Andries Mostert **Est.** 2010 **Dozens** 18 000 **Vyds** 22ha
Bob Fowler, who comes from a rural background and has always hankered after a farming life, stumbled across the opportunity to achieve this in early 2010. Together with wife Marilyn, he purchased the former West Cape Howe winery and surrounding vineyard that had become available when West Cape Howe moved into the far larger Goundrey winery. In '11 Willoughby Park purchased the Kalgan River vineyard and business name, and winemaking operations have been transferred to Willoughby Park. There are now three labels: Willoughby Park, the Great Southern premium brand for estate and purchased grapes; Kalgan River, a single vineyard range; and Jami & Charli, a sub $20 Great Southern range of wines.

ŤŤŤŤŤ Great Southern Sauvignon Blanc 2011 Pale straw-green; a fresh and lively
wine, with a mix of cut grass, snow pea and — at the other extreme — tropical fruit,
the contrasting characters in fact coming together very well in an elegant wine.
Screwcap. 13% alc. **Rating** 95 **To** 2013 $28
Denmark Riesling 2011 Deep straw, vibrant hue; a ripe and exotic bouquet of
candied orange, florals and bath talc; juicy and generous, with softness a feature
on the long finish; an interesting departure from the dominant austere style of the
region. Screwcap. 12.5% alc. **Rating** 94 **To** 2020 $25 BE
Kalgan River Great Southern Syrah 2010 Deep magenta, crimson hue; the
bouquet is understated and shows glimpses of red and black fruits, tar, cinnamon
and charcuterie; the palate is taut, fresh and layered, with a solid core of fruit lying
in wait for the firm tannin to release its hold, and to ultimately reveal the true
beauty within. Screwcap. 13% alc. **Rating** 94 **To** 2022 $45 BE

ŤŤŤŤŸ Merlot 2010 **Rating** 93 **To** 2018 $52 BE
Kalgan River Great Southern Cabernet Sauvignon 2010 **Rating** 91
To 2023 $45 BE
Kalgan River Lower Great Southern Riesling 2011 **Rating** 90 **To** 2017 $30
Jamie & Charli Denmark Sauvignon Blanc 2011 All I can tell you about the
accuseds' mug shots on the front label is that the names are not of the new owners
of the former West Cape Howe vineyard, nor winemaker Michael Goundrey. The
wine is very potent, strictly within herb, asparagus and capsicum borders, with no
sweetness. Good food style. Screwcap. 13% alc. **Rating** 90 **To** 2013 $18

ŤŤŤŤ   Jamie & Charli Denmark Riesling 2011 **Rating** 89 **To** 2015
✪ $18 BE
Denmark Cabernet Sauvignon 2010 **Rating** 88 **To** 2016 $24 BE
Kalgan River Liquid Gold Great Southern Botrytis Riesling 2010
Rating 88 **To** 2014 $30 BE

Willow Bridge Estate   ★★★★★

Gardin Court Drive, Dardanup, WA 6236 **Region** Geographe
T (08) 9728 0055 **www**.willowbridge.com.au **Open** 7 days 11–5
Winemaker Simon Burnell, Jane Dunkley **Est.** 1997 **Dozens** 25 000 **Vyds** 59ha
Jeff and Vicky Dewar have followed a fast track in developing Willow Bridge Estate since
acquiring the spectacular 180ha hillside property in the Ferguson Valley: chardonnay, semillon,
sauvignon blanc, shiraz and cabernet sauvignon were planted, with merlot, tempranillo, chenin
blanc and viognier following. The winery is capable of handling the 300–500 tonnes from
the estate plantings. Willow Bridge won the trophy for Most Successful Western Australian
Exhibitor processing under 300 tonnes at the Perth Wine Show '11. Exports to the UK, the
US and other major markets.

ŤŤŤŤŤ Chardonnay 2010 Light straw-green; has had the full winemaking box of
tricks employed: hand-picked, whole bunch-pressed, wild yeast barrel-fermented,
partial mlf and 9 months on lees. The citrus/grapefruit and nectarine/white
peach flavours come through strongly on the long and intense palate, with acidity
likewise uncompromised. Screwcap. 12.5% alc. **Rating** 96 **To** 2018 $30
Black Dog Geographe Shiraz 2010 Bright purple-crimson; low yield
shiraz is open-fermented, hand-plunged and matured in French oak barriques
for 18 months. The bouquet positively sings of red and black fruits, with some
floral overtones, while the medium-bodied palate provides an interplay between
juicy, freshly squeezed red and black fruits, spice, cedar and fine-grained tannins.
A seriously lovely wine. Screwcap. 13.5% alc. **Rating** 96 **To** 2030 $65
Black Dog Geographe Shiraz 2009 Bright, clear crimson; as the name
suggests, this is not a wine to be trifled with or taken lightly. It is tightly packed
with black fruits — black, not just dark — and considerable acidity; it doesn't simply
move through the palate, it powers through. It is at the dawn of its life and will
only get better. Screwcap. 13.5% alc. **Rating** 95 **To** 2030 $60

✪ **Madam Dragonfly Rose 2011** An unusual bright pink blend of tempranillo, merlot and sangiovese with a fragrant bouquet of rose petals and warm spices, then an intense but very well-balanced palate with nougat/Turkish delight/red berry fruit flavours; the dry finish has a twist of citrussy acidity. Screwcap. 13% alc. **Rating** 95 **To** Now $18

✪ **Dragonfly Cabernet Merlot 2010** Bright red-purple; a classic example of the blend, with blackcurrant, redcurrant, dried herbs and black olive balanced by a nice touch of cedary oak, the tannins fine and ripe. Trophy Best Dry Red Blend, Perth Wine Show '11. Screwcap. 13.5% alc. **Rating** 94 **To** 2016 $18

✪ **Dragonfly Sauvignon Blanc Semillon 2011** Pale straw-green; the bouquet is driven by cut grass and snow pea aromas, the intense palate adding citrus to the suite of flavours running through to the long finish. Screwcap. 12.5% alc. **Rating** 94 **To** 2013 $18

Gravel Pit Geographe Shiraz 2010 Strong crimson-purple; co-fermentation with a small percentage of viognier may well have increased the juicy part of this wine, but it has not blunted the incisive edge to the structure of red and black fruit flavours (from the gravelly soils). Screwcap. 13.5% alc. **Rating** 94 **To** 2020 $30

Solana Geographe Tempranillo 2010 Light crimson; a fragrant bouquet with spicy cherry aromas, then a vibrant dark cherry palate, with the varietal twist of crushed citrus leaves on the finish; the tannins and oak have been well managed. Screwcap. 13.5% alc. **Rating** 94 **To** 2016 $25

🍷🍷🍷🍷🍷 **Dragonfly Shiraz 2010** Medium purple-red; the voluminous bouquet accurately
✪ tells of the tapestry of plum, blackberry, spice and French oak that follows; fine ripe tannins add to the texture of this medium-bodied wine, its juicy fruit the last impression on the palate. Screwcap. 14% alc. **Rating** 92 **To** 2019 $18

Pemberton Pinot Chardonnay 2009 Rating 91 **To** Now $28

🍷🍷🍷🍷 **Dragonfly Chardonnay 2011 Rating** 89 **To** 2014 $18

Willow Creek Vineyard ★★★★★

166 Balnarring Road, Merricks North, Vic 3926 **Region** Mornington Peninsula
T (03) 5989 7448 **www**.willow-creek.com.au **Open** 7 days 11–5
Winemaker Geraldine McFaul **Est.** 1989 **Dozens** 4000 **Vyds** 11.15ha
Willow Creek Vineyard is a significant presence in the Mornington Peninsula, with the mature vineyard planted to pinot noir, chardonnay, cabernet sauvignon, sauvignon blanc and pinot gris. The grape intake is supplemented by purchasing small, quality parcels from local growers. The Willow Creek wines rank with the best from the Peninsula, the arrival of Geraldine McFaul as winemaker promising a continuation in the quality of the wines.

🍷🍷🍷🍷🍷 **Mornington Peninsula Pinot Noir 2010** Light garnet; a fragrant bouquet revealing red fruits, game, cold tea, red pepper and a light touch of fine French oak; the elegant palate reveals a lithe, lively and finely textured wine, tightly wound and pure; expansive and beautifully detailed. Screwcap. 13.5% alc. **Rating** 95 **To** 2018 $40 BE

🍷🍷🍷🍷🍷 **Mornington Peninsula Sauvignon Blanc 2011 Rating** 92 **To** 2013 $35 BE
Mornington Peninsula Rose 2011 Rating 91 **To** 2013 $25 BE

🍷🍷🍷🍷 **Mornington Peninsula Pinot Gris 2011 Rating** 89 **To** 2014 $35 BE
Mornington Peninsula Brut 2007 Rating 87 **To** 2014 $40 BE

Wills Domain ★★★★★

Cnr Brash Road/Abbey Farm Road, Yallingup, WA 6281 **Region** Margaret River
T (08) 9755 2327 **www**.willsdomain.com.au **Open** 7 days 10–5
Winemaker Naturaliste Vintners (Bruce Dukes) **Est.** 1985 **Dozens** 12 500 **Vyds** 20.8ha
When the Haunold family purchased the original Wills Domain vineyard in 2000, they were adding another chapter to a family history of winemaking stretching back to 1383 in what is now Austria. Remarkable though that may be, more remarkable is that 36-year-old Darren,

who lost the use of his legs in an accident in 1989, runs the estate (including part of the pruning) from his wheelchair. Prior to the Haunolds' purchase of the property, the grapes were all sold to local winemakers, but since '01 they have been made for the Wills Domain label, and the vineyard holdings (shiraz, semillon, cabernet sauvignon, sauvignon blanc, chardonnay, merlot, petit verdot, malbec, cabernet franc and viognier) have been expanded. Exports to the UK, the US, Singapore, Malaysia, Indonesia, South Korea and Hong Kong.

ŸŸŸŸŸ **Margaret River Semillon 2011** Pale straw-quartz; has more vibrancy and minerality than many Margaret River Semillons, due to earlier picking; it has a range of citrus flavours, from juice to marmalade, and a powerful stream of acidity. Screwcap. 13% alc. **Rating** 94 **To** 2021 $25

Margaret River Chardonnay 2010 Vibrant green hue; a big, bold and brassy bouquet of grapefruit, peach, toasty oak and straw; the palate is fresh, showing tangy acidity and tightly wound fruit; there is volume here, as well as finesse. Screwcap. 14% alc. **Rating** 94 **To** 2018 $45 BE

Margaret River Cabernet Merlot 2009 A pure cassis and black olive personality, showing a little leafy complexity, but mostly pure black fruits; full-bodied and full throttle, with densely packed tannins and fruit both running through to the finish. Screwcap. 14.5% alc. **Rating** 94 **To** 2018 $28 BE

ŸŸŸŸŸ **Margaret River Semillon Sauvignon Blanc 2011** Light straw-green; the ✪ wine has a complete suite of kiwi fruit, passionfruit and citrus aromas and flavours supported by minerally acidity and a wild herb nuance on the aftertaste. Screwcap. 13% alc. **Rating** 93 **To** 2015 $20

✪ **Margaret River Rose 2011** Pale, but vivid, pink; the fragrant bouquet and palate both offer red cherry, raspberry and strawberry fruit at various points along the way, supported by balanced acidity. Quality rose. Screwcap. 13% alc. **Rating** 93 **To** Now $20

Margaret River Cabernet Merlot 2010 **Rating** 93 **To** 2020 $28

Margaret River Semillon 2010 **Rating** 90 **To** 2013 $25 BE

Reserve Margaret River Shiraz 2008 **Rating** 90 **To** 2018 $45 BE

ŸŸŸŸ **Reserve Margaret River Cabernet Sauvignon 2009** **Rating** 88 **To** 2015 $45 BE

Margaret River Reserve Bitza 2009 **Rating** 88 **To** 2014 $40 BE

Willunga 100 Wines   ★★★★★

c/-Haselgrove, Sand Road, McLaren Vale, SA 5171 **Region** McLaren Vale
T 0427 271 280 **www**.willunga100.com **Open** By appt
Winemaker Tim James, Kate Day **Est.** 2005 **Dozens** 20 000
This venture is now solely owned by Liberty Wines UK, sourcing its grapes from McLaren Vale and from Adelaide Hills (pinot gris and a portion of its viognier). Tim James has come on board as consultant winemaker, Kate Day continuing in the executive role. The business has export links to many parts of the world in addition to the UK.

ŸŸŸŸŸ **McLaren Vale Grenache 2010** Bright deep crimson; dark and exotic on the bouquet, with liqueur-soaked plums, clove and sage; the palate is warm and inviting, direct and expansive, showing the true class of grenache in McLaren Vale; moreover, the quality of the vintage shines through. Top gold Melbourne Wine Show '11. Screwcap. 14.5% alc. **Rating** 95 **To** 2016 $25 BE

McLaren Vale Shiraz Viognier 2009 A pretty and effusive, bright-fruited bouquet of blackberry, sage and licorice; the palate is direct and refreshing, offering a lively core of tannins, acidity and savoury interest; a sanguine wine worth seeking out. Screwcap. 14% alc. **Rating** 94 **To** 2020 $25 BE

ŸŸŸŸŸ **McLaren Vale Tempranillo 2010** **Rating** 92 **To** 2015 $25 BE

McLaren Vale Cabernet Shiraz 2010 **Rating** 90 **To** 2015 $25 BE

ŸŸŸŸ **The Tithing Grenache 2009** **Rating** 89 **To** 2014 $45 BE

Adelaide Hills Pinot Gris 2011 **Rating** 88 **To** 2013 $25 BE

Wilson Vineyard

Polish Hill River, Sevenhill via Clare, SA 5453 **Region** Clare Valley
T (08) 8843 4310 **www**.wilsonvineyard.com.au **Open** W'ends 10–4
Winemaker Daniel Wilson **Est.** 1974 **Dozens** 3000 **Vyds** 11.9ha
In 2009 the winery and general operations were passed on to son Daniel Wilson, the second generation. Daniel, a graduate of CSU, spent three years in the Barossa with some of Australia's largest winemakers before returning to Clare in 2003. Parents John and Pat Wilson still contribute in a limited capacity, content to watch developments in the business they created. Daniel continues to follow John's beliefs about keeping quality high, often at the expense of volume, and rather than talk about it, believes the proof is in the bottle. At Daniel's side are wife Tamara and daughters Poppy and Isabelle, who help keep the wheels turning behind the scenes. No wines were received for this edition; the rating is that of last year.

Wily Trout ★★★☆

Marakei-Nanima Road, via Hall, NSW 2618 **Region** Canberra District
T (02) 6230 2487 **F** (02) 6230 2211 **www**.poacherspantry.com.au **Open** 7 days 10–5
Winemaker Dr Roger Harris, Nick Spencer (Contract) **Est.** 1998 **Dozens** 8000 **Vyds** 20ha
The Wily Trout vineyard, owned by Robert and Susan Bruce, shares its home with the Poachers Pantry, a renowned gourmet smokehouse. The quality of the wines is very good, and a testament to the skills of the contract winemakers. The northeast-facing slopes, at an elevation of 720 m, provide some air drainage and hence protection against spring frosts. The production increase (from 3000 dozen) speaks for itself.

🍷🍷🍷🍷 **Methode Champenoise Sparkling Red Pinot Shiraz 2006** Strong red colour, the mousse still very much present; there are good blackcurrant flavours running through the palate; best of all, it avoids oak and the usual excessive dosage. Crown seal. 12.5% alc. **Rating** 91 **To** 2015 $28

🍷🍷🍷🍷 **Canberra District Sauvignon Blanc 2010** Pale straw-green; the extra year in
✪ bottle has benefited the development of aromas and flavours, with gooseberry and tropical fruit offset by a slightly rough mineral and zest finish. Screwcap. 13.6% alc. **Rating** 89 **To** Now $17

✪ **Canberra District Chardonnay 2007** Still remarkably pale green-straw; the palate (and bouquet) are similarly remarkably fresh and youthful, with gentle stone fruit and citrus flavours, and minimal oak. Screwcap. 12.5% alc. **Rating** 89 **To** 2014 $17
Canberra District Sparkling Salmon 2009 **Rating** 89 **To** Now $21

Wimbaliri Wines

3180 Barton Highway, Murrumbateman, NSW 2582 **Region** Canberra District
T (02) 6227 5921 **www**.wimbaliri.com.au **Open** W'ends 10–5, or by appt
Winemaker John Andersen, Scott Gledhill **Est.** 1988 **Dozens** 800 **Vyds** 2.2ha
John and Margaret Andersen moved to the Canberra District in 1987 and began establishing their vineyard at Murrumbateman in '88; the property borders highly regarded Canberra producer Clonakilla. The vineyard is close-planted with chardonnay, pinot noir, shiraz, cabernet sauvignon and merlot (plus a few vines of cabernet franc). Prior to the 2009 vintage the winery was purchased by Scott and Sarah Gledhill. Scott, born in Wallsend (NSW), is a sixth-generation descendant of German vine dressers who emigrated to the Hunter Valley in the 1850s; Sarah draws upon her science background to assist in the vineyard and winemaking.

🍷🍷🍷🍷 **The Gravel Block Murrumbateman Shiraz 2010** Healthy red-purple; a well-made wine, neatly balancing fruit, oak and tannins; it peaks on the finish and aftertaste, where all of the spicy elements of the wine combine with red fruits and fine-grained tannins. Diam. 13% alc. **Rating** 93 **To** 2020 $40
Close Planted Murrumbateman Pinot Noir 2010 A single barrel made, the first since the end of the drought; 20% whole bunch inclusion, the result a very complex, foresty pinot with ripe, black cherry and plum fruit. Unfiltered. Diam. 14% alc. **Rating** 91 **To** 2017 $40

Winbirra Vineyard

173 Point Leo Road, Red Hill South, Vic 3937 **Region** Mornington Peninsula
T (03) 5989 2109 **www.**winbirra.com.au **Open** First w'end month (every w'end Jan) &
public hols 11–5, or by appt
Winemaker Sandro Mosele, George Mihaly, Paramdeep Ghurman (Contract) **Est.** 1990
Dozens 1500 **Vyds** 4.1ha
Winbirra is a family-owned and run vineyard that has been producing grapes since 1990,
between then and '97 selling the grapes to local winemakers. Since '97 the wine has been
made and sold under the Winbirra label. The close-planted vineyard includes pinot noir (1ha),
pinot gris and viognier (1.3ha each), and shiraz and pinot meunier (0.25ha each).

ㅜㅜㅜㅜㅜ **The Brigadier Mornington Peninsula Pinot Noir 2010** Clear, light crimson-
red; the fragrant bouquet and the palate have a mix of cherry, plum and spice
aromas and flavours; the oak and tannin levels are where they should be. 150
dozen made. Diam. 14% alc. **Rating** 92 **To** 2017 $30
Mingary Vineyard Mornington Peninsula Pinot Gris 2011 Quartz-white;
stacked full of unusually powerful varietal fruit, especially given its youth and
the cool vintage; a slight touch of residual sugar will be seen by most as simply
generous fruit; 165 dozen made. Screwcap. 13.6% alc. **Rating** 90 **To** 2013 $28
Mingary Vineyard Mornington Peninsula Viognier 2010 Light straw-green;
has good texture and structure, and there is some peachy apricot varietal fruit;
the finish is free of excess phenolics. Screwcap. 14% alc. **Rating** 90 **To** 2013 $28
Shiraz Viognier 2010 Light, bright crimson; the co-fermentation of viognier
has given the fragrance and freshness to the red fruits as one would expect. The
medium-bodied palate is silky and well balanced, and ready whenever you are.
Screwcap. 13.5% alc. **Rating** 90 **To** 2016 $30

ㅜㅜㅜㅜ **The Brigadier's Daughter Mornington Peninsula Brut Cuvee 2007**
Rating 89 **To** 2013 $30

Winburndale

116 Saint Anthony's Creek Road, Bathurst, NSW 2795 **Region** Central Ranges Zone
T (02) 6337 3134 **www.**winburndalewines.com.au **Open** Mon–Fri 10–4, w'ends 11–4
Winemaker David Lowe (Consultant), Mike Burleigh **Est.** 1998 **Dozens** 3000 **Vyds** 10.4ha
Michael and Helen Burleigh acquired the 200ha Winburndale property in 1998: 160ha is
forest, to be kept as a nature reserve; three separate vineyards have been planted under the
direction of ASWS award-winning viticulturist Mark Renzaglia. The winery paddock has
shiraz facing due west at an altitude of 800–820 m; the south paddock, with north and
northwest aspects, varying from 790–810 m, has chardonnay, riesling, shiraz and cabernet
sauvignon. The home paddock is the most level, with a slight north aspect, and has riesling
and shiraz. The name derives from Lachlan Macquarie's exploration of the Blue Mountains in
1815. Winburndale's tally of three trophies and five gold medals (all at respected wine shows)
in 2010 was very impressive (achieved with wines other than those submitted for this edition).
Exports to the US and Denmark.

ㅜㅜㅜㅜ **Solitary Shiraz 2010** Deep crimson; a lifted and eucalypt-accented bouquet of
mulberry, prune and nutmeg; medium-bodied, with a charry oak note to finish.
Screwcap. 14% alc. **Rating** 87 **To** 2017 $30 BE

Windance Wines

2764 Caves Road, Yallingup, WA 6282 **Region** Margaret River
T (08) 9755 2293 **www.**windance.com.au **Open** 7 days 10–5
Winemaker Damon Eastaugh, Simon Ding, Melia Brent-White Consultant) **Est.** 1998
Dozens 4000 **Vyds** 7.25ha
Drew and Rosemary Brent-White own this family business, situated 5km south of Yallingup.
Cabernet sauvignon, shiraz, sauvignon blanc, semillon and merlot have been established,
incorporating sustainable land management and organic farming practices where possible. The
wines are exclusively estate-grown.

ŸŸŸŸȲ **Reserve Margaret River Shiraz 2010** Bright purple-crimson; a much more conventional wine than the standard Shiraz, with plum, blackberry and black cherry in fruitcake mode, 100% American oak for 14 months playing a key role, the tannins balanced. Screwcap. 14.2% alc. **Rating** 93 **To** 2025 $40
Reserve Margaret River Cabernet Sauvignon 2010 Full red-purple; a concentrated, full-bodied Cabernet with blackcurrant, chewy tannins and French oak all interwoven from the moment the wine enters the mouth, reflecting extended maceration; should surely repay a decade in the cellar. Screwcap. 14.5% alc. **Rating** 92 **To** 2025 $40

✪ **Margaret River Sauvignon Blanc Semillon 2011** Pale straw-green; an intense and zesty style from start to finish, with a battalion of tropical fruits opposed by a brigade of citrus, herb and mineral characters. Screwcap. 12% alc. **Rating** 91 **To** 2013 $18

ŸŸŸŸ **Margaret River Shiraz 2010 Rating** 89 **To** 2020 $22
Margaret River Cabernet Merlot 2010 Rating 89 **To** 2018 $22
Margaret River Chenin Blanc 2011 Rating 87 **To** 2016 $18

Windowrie Estate ★★★★

Windowrie Road, Canowindra, NSW 2804 **Region** Cowra
T (02) 6344 3234 **www**.windowrie.com.au **Open** At The Mill, Cowra
Winemaker Antonio D'Onise **Est.** 1988 **Dozens** 25 000 **Vyds** 240ha
Windowrie Estate was established by the O'Dea family in 1988 on a substantial grazing property at Canowindra, 30km north of Cowra and in the same viticultural region. A portion of the grapes from the substantial vineyard is sold to other makers, but increasing quantities are being made for the Windowrie Estate and The Mill labels; the Chardonnays have enjoyed show success. The cellar door is in a flour mill built in 1861 from local granite. It ceased operations in 1905 and lay unoccupied for 91 years until restored by the O'Dea family. Exports to China, Japan and Singapore.

ŸŸŸŸȲ **The Mill Hilltops Cabernet Merlot 2010 Rating** 91
✪   **To** 2020 $17
✪   **The Mill Central Ranges Merlot 2010 Rating** 90 **To** 2015 $17

ŸŸŸŸ **Family Reserve Shiraz 2010 Rating** 89 **To** 2016 $22
Family Reserve Chardonnay 2011 Rating 87 **To** 2014 $22
The Mill Central Ranges Shiraz 2010 Rating 87 **To** 2015 $15

Windows Estate ★★★★★

4 Quininup Road, Yallingup, WA 6282 **Region** Margaret River
T (08) 9755 2719 **www**.windowsestate.com **Open** 7 days 10–5
Winemaker Mick Scott **Est.** 1996 **Dozens** 4500 **Vyds** 6.3ha
Len and Barbara Davies progressively established their vineyard (cabernet sauvignon, shiraz, chenin blanc, chardonnay, semillon, sauvignon blanc and merlot), initially selling the grapes. In 2006 the decision was taken to move to winemaking. It has been rewarded with considerable show success for its consistently good, enticingly priced wines. Exports to the UK, Germany, Malaysia, Singapore and China.

ŸŸŸŸŸ **Margaret River Semillon Sauvignon Blanc 2011** Pale straw-green; while the
✪   wine is delicate and fine-boned, it has a full array of aromas and flavours ranging through passionfruit, stone fruit and citrus; the finish is clean and fresh. Screwcap. 12.5% alc. **Rating** 94 **To** 2013 $23
Single Vineyard Margaret River Chardonnay 2010 Sixty-six per cent Gingin clone, 34% Burgundian clones 76, 95, 96 and 277; 40% mlf, and 100% barrel-fermented, half new, half 1-year-old, for 11 months. An intense and stylish wine, which definitely needed the 40% mlf; it has the classic grapefruit, stone fruit and cashew mix that flows seamlessly along the palate and into the long finish. Screwcap. 13.5% alc. **Rating** 94 **To** 2019 $35

Basket Pressed Margaret River Cabernet Merlot 2010 Good crimson colour; the fragrant bouquet offers a savoury mix of blackcurrant and cassis fruit supported by fine, but ripe, tannins and quality oak; the savoury finish, defined by the cabernet sauvignon, is exemplary in its length and finesse. Screwcap. 14.5% alc. Rating 94 To 2023 $28

ΨΨΨΨΨ
✪ **Single Vineyard Margaret River Sauvignon Blanc 2011** Light straw-green; the expressive bouquet of tropical fruits leads directly into a palate with a display of gooseberry and passionfruit to the fore, brisk acidity bringing up the rear. Screwcap. 12.5% alc. Rating 93 To 2013 $23
Basket Pressed Margaret River Shiraz 2009 Rating 93 To 2019 $28
Basket Pressed Margaret River Cabernet Sauvignon 2010 Rating 93 To 2030 $35

WindshakeR Ridge ★★★☆
PO Box 106, Karrinyup, WA 6921 **Region** Swan District
T (08) 6162 2521 **www**.windshaker.com.au **Open** Not
Winemaker Ryan Sudano **Est.** 2003 **Dozens** NFP **Vyds** 20ha
The Moltoni family has owned a 2000ha farming property for three generations. Robert Moltoni is the driving force, establishing WindshakeR Ridge in 2003. The vineyard (5ha each of carnelian, semillon, shiraz and verdelho) is 9km north of Gingin, and looks out over the hills to the sea. Moltoni is an accomplished poet, and I cannot help but quote one of his poems: 'Easterlies whistle through the gums/Crashing over silent ridges/Bathing vines in Namatjira Crimson/WindshakeR, WindshakeR, WindshakeR/The ghost winds whisper down/Off the red plains to the sea.' Exports to the US and China.

ΨΨΨΨΨ
✪ **Reserve Shiraz 2009** Good hue and clarity; a particularly harmonious palate follows the equally pleasing bouquet, with gently spicy plum and cherry fruit, fine tannins and integrated oak. Drink right now, or cellar for five years. Screwcap. 14% alc. Rating 91 To 2016 $20

ΨΨΨΨ **Carnelian 2009** Rating 89 To 2015 $20

wine by brad ★★★★★
PO Box 475, Margaret River, WA 6285 **Region** Margaret River
T 0409 572 957 **www**.winebybrad.com.au **Open** Not
Winemaker Brad Wehr, Contract **Est.** 2003 **Dozens** 5000
Brad Wehr says that wine by brad 'is the result of a couple of influential winemakers and shadowy ruffians deciding there was something to be gained by putting together some pretty neat parcels of wine from the region, creating their own label, and releasing it with minimal fuss'. The premium Mantra range is made from separately sourced grapes. Exports to Ireland, Canada, South Korea and Singapore.

ΨΨΨΨΨ
○
○ **Mantra Revelation Margaret River Sauvignon Blanc 2011** Rating 94 To 2013 $20
Margaret River Semillon Sauvignon Blanc 2011 Rating 94 To 2015 $18
Mantra Muse Reserve Margaret River Cabernet Sauvignon 2009 Highly polished and fragrant bouquet of pure cassis, cedary, fine French oak and a little highlight of violet; the palate is soft and amply fruited on entry, with fine-grained tannins taking the fruit on a long and full-blooded ride to the finish line. Screwcap. 13.5% alc. Rating 94 To 2020 $35 BE

ΨΨΨΨΨ **Mantra Abundance Margaret River Cabernet Sauvignon 2009** Rating 91 To 2016 $25 BE
Mantra Journey Margaret River Shiraz 2009 Rating 90 To 2016 $25 BE
✪ **Margaret River Cabernet Merlot 2009** A bright and fragrant red fruit bouquet exhibiting redcurrant, cedar and rolled leaf; medium-bodied, fresh and direct, this is a perfect introduction to the real flavours of merlot; will perform best in the short to medium term. Screwcap. 13.5% alc. Rating 90 To 2016 $18 BE

🍷🍷🍷🍷 **Mantra Affirmation Margaret River Semillon Sauvignon Blanc 2011**
Rating 88 To 2013 $20 BE

Wines by KT   ★★★★★

Main North Road, Watervale, SA 5452 **Region** Clare Valley
T 0419 855 500 **www**.winesbykt.com **Open** By appt
Winemaker Kerri Thompson **Est.** 2006 **Dozens** 1400
KT is winemaker Kerri Thompson. Kerri graduated with a degree in oenology from
Roseworthy Agricultural College in 1993, and thereafter made wine in McLaren Vale, Tuscany,
Beaujolais and the Clare Valley, becoming well known as the Leasingham winemaker in the
Clare Valley. She resigned from Leasingham in 2006 after seven years at the helm, and after
a short break became winemaker at Crabtree. Here she is also able to make Wines by KT,
sourcing the grapes from two local vineyards, one biodynamic, the other farmed with sulphur
and copper sprays only. Exports to the UK.

🍷🍷🍷🍷🍷 **Melva Wild Fermented Riesling 2011** Kerri Thompson has Riesling in her
blood, and only a winemaker with her experience would be brave enough to
wild-ferment cloudy juice in used oak and leave it on lees for up to four months.
The result? A stunning wine; a fragrant and flowery bouquet leads into a palate
with a slippery texture, delicate acidity tying in the finish, perfectly balancing the
9 g/l residual sugar. Screwcap. 12.5% alc. **Rating** 97 **To** 2021 $28

WineSA   ★★★★★

PO Box 13, Walkerville, SA 5081 **Region** Various SA
T (08) 8234 5161 **www**.winesa.net **Open** Not
Winemaker Neil Pike **Est.** 2009 **Dozens** 2000
This is a separate venture from Australian Domaine Wines (solely owned by Mario and Ben
Barletta), owned by the Barlettas and Mike Backhouse. The Barlettas have great experience
in all aspects of the wine trade, and Mike brings a different professional business experience
career to the venture. The focal point of the business is the production of single vineyard/
single varietal wines, predominantly from McLaren Vale, Barossa Valley and Clare Valley. It has
two labels: Singular, which meets the main criteria; and D.O.V., standing for dried on vine.
These wines go in a separate directions, presumably with Italian Amarone wines somewhere
in the background. Exports to the US, Germany, Switzerland and Japan.

🍷🍷🍷🍷🍷 **Singular Kalimna Barossa Valley Shiraz 2009** Medium red-purple; well-made
and constructed medium-bodied Shiraz; supple mouthfeel to the red and black
fruits; very good tannins and oak management. Seriously nice wine. From the
Marschall Groom vineyards. Screwcap. 14.5% alc. **Rating** 95 **To** 2029 $50
Singular Marananga Barossa Valley Shiraz 2009 Medium red-purple; richer,
riper and denser than Kalimna; some licorice, plenty of fruit cake along with
some more tarry nuances; again, well handled in the winery. From the Paulmara
vineyard. Screwcap. 14.5% alc. **Rating** 94 **To** 2030 $85

🍷🍷🍷🍷🍷 **Singular Onkaparinga Hills McLaren Vale Shiraz 2009** Rating 93
To 2029 $50

🍷🍷🍷🍷 **The Contradiction Barossa Valley Rose 2011** Rating 87 **To** 2014 $20 BE

Winetrust Estates   ★★★★

PO Box 541, Balgowlah, NSW 2093 **Region** South Eastern Australia
T (02) 9949 9250 **www**.winetrustestates.com **Open** Not
Winemaker Rob Moody and various consultants **Est.** 1999 **Dozens** 57 000 **Vyds** 88.9ha
Mark Arnold is the man behind Winetrust Estates, drawing on a lifetime of experience in
wine marketing. It is a virtual winery operation, drawing grapes from three states and five
regions using contract winemakers according to the origin of the grapes (either contract-
grown or produced under a joint venture). The top-of-the-range Picarus red wines come
from the Limestone Coast; the other ranges are Ocean Grove and Firebox, covering all
the major varietal wines plus a few newcomers. Exports to the US, Canada, China, Japan,
Singapore, Hong Kong and Thailand.

ƳƳƳƳƳ **Picarus Clare Valley Riesling 2011** Quartz-white; a wine that marries power
✪   with precision, citrus with slatey/minerally acidity, and is great value, particularly
if you can also afford to cellar some for at least five years, preferably 10. Screwcap.
11.5% alc. **Rating** 93 **To** 2021 $16

✪   **Picarus Clare Valley Riesling 2009** The colour is still bright and pale, both the
bouquet and palate locked in some time warp; fine and fresh apple and citrus fruit
is backed by a shaft of acidity, but retains balance. Screwcap. 12% alc. **Rating** 91
To 2019 $18

Picarus Wrattonbully Cabernet Sauvignon 2008 Has retained excellent
colour, still full crimson; an elegant, medium-bodied wine with blackcurrant fruit,
touches of spice and earth, positive oak and balanced tannins all in play. Screwcap.
14% alc. **Rating** 91 **To** 2018 $23

✪   **Firebox Ridge Vineyard Selection Swan Hill Tempranillo 2009** Good
retention of colour; has good varietal character courtesy of red cherry fruit that
carries the savoury tannins on the finish. Trophy Inland Rivers Wine Show '10.
Screwcap. 14% alc. **Rating** 90 **To** 2014 $18

ƳƳƳƳ **Picarus Wrattonbully Cabernet Sauvignon 2009** Rating 89 To 2020 $24
Picarus Wrattonbully Pinot Gris 2010 Rating 88 To Now $18
Firebox Ridge Vineyard Selection Barossa Valley Shiraz 2010 Rating 87
To 2016 $20

✪   **Ocean Grove Merlot 2010** Good colour; has a pleasing depth to its red fruits
that are allied with balanced tannins and a touch of vanilla oak. Surprise packet.
Drink now. Screwcap. 14% alc. **Rating** 87 **To** 2013 $11

✪   **Ocean Grove Cabernet Sauvignon 2010** Light hue; offers more than the
colour would suggest, with a savoury, earthy cast to the blackcurrant fruit and
tannins. Screwcap. 14% alc. **Rating** 87 **To** 2013 $11

Winstead ★★★★

75 Winstead Road, Bagdad, Tas 7030 **Region** Southern Tasmania
T (03) 6268 6417 **Open** By appt
Winemaker Neil Snare **Est.** 1989 **Dozens** 350
The good news about Winstead is the outstanding quality of its extremely generous and rich
Pinot Noirs, rivalling those of Freycinet for the abundance of their fruit flavour without any
sacrifice of varietal character. The bad news is that production is so limited, with only 0.8ha
of pinot noir and 0.4ha riesling being tended by fly fishing devotee Neil Snare and wife
Julieanne. Last year's rating is maintained in the absence of a representative submission of its
wines (one wine was tasted at the Tasmanian Wine Show).

ƳƳƳƳ **Merlot 2010** Good colour; soft plum cake aromas and flavours and oak; a
pleasant, easy drinking style. **Rating** 89 **To** 2014

Winter Creek Wine ★★★★

Barossa Junction, Barossa Valley Way, Tanunda, SA 5352 **Region** Barossa Valley
T (08) 8524 6382 **www.**wintercreekwine.com.au **Open** Fri–Mon 10–5
Winemaker Pam Cross, Michael Sawyer **Est.** 2000 **Dozens** 2000 **Vyds** 3ha
The Cross family established their small vineyard at Williamstown in the cooler foothills of
the southern Barossa Valley in 1993. There is 2ha of Smart Dyson trellised shiraz, and 1ha of
88-year-old grenache which was acquired in 2001. They also produce a Sauvignon Blanc
and Pinot Gris from grapes purchased from the Adelaide Hills, and Riesling and Chardonnay
Pinot Noir from the Eden Valley.

ƳƳƳƳƳ **Single Vineyard Southern Barossa Shiraz 2008** Good colour; the overall
structure and mouthfeel of this wine, while powerful, don't not have the
ponderous character of the standard wine. Certainly, French oak has had a
significant impact on both the bouquet and palate, and less might have been
better, but you can't gainsay the depth of flavour and character. Screwcap. 14% alc.
Rating 93 **To** 2028 $40

Adelaide Hills Sauvignon Blanc 2011 Light straw-green; has achieved a strong tropical fruit spectrum of flavours belied by its low alcohol; if there is a touch of botrytis present, it doesn't mar the wine; balanced acidity on the finish is another plus. Screwcap. 11.5% alc. **Rating** 90 **To** 2013 $20

Southern Barossa Shiraz 2008 Strong colour; the sheer mass and density of the palate, with its multiple layers of flavour, come as a surprise given the 14% alcohol; 18 months in French oak has not slimmed the wine down much; that will only be achieved with substantial time in bottle. Screwcap. 14% alc. **Rating** 90 **To** 2028 $30

♀♀♀♀   The Old Barossa Blend Grenache Shiraz 2010 **Rating** 88 **To** 2015 $25

Wirra Wirra

McMurtrie Road, McLaren Vale, SA 5171 **Region** McLaren Vale
T (08) 8323 8414 **www**.wirrawirra.com **Open** Mon–Sat 10–5, Sun & public hols 11–5
Winemaker Paul Smith, Paul Carpenter **Est.** 1894 **Dozens** 180 000 **Vyds** 51.31ha
Long respected for the consistency of its white wines, Wirra Wirra has now established an equally formidable reputation for its reds. The wines are of exemplary character, quality and style, The Angelus Cabernet Sauvignon and RSW Shiraz battling with each other for supremacy. Long may the battle continue under the direction of new managing director Andrew Kay (following the retirement of highly respected Tim James), particularly in the wake of the death of the universally loved co-founder/owner Greg Trott in early 2005. In Dec '07 Wirra Wirra purchased the 20ha Rayner Vineyard (with blocks dating back to the 1950s), which had hitherto supplied Brokenwood with the grapes for its eponymous icon Shiraz. There has been a smooth transition since long-serving winemaker Samantha Connew decided to take a break before moving to Tower Estate in the Hunter Valley. Exports to all major markets.

♀♀♀♀♀   RSW McLaren Vale Shiraz 2010 Both the bouquet and palate command immediate attention, exhibiting a near-perfect paradigm for McLaren Vale Shiraz. Medium- to full-bodied, but without any obvious alcohol warmth, it has an unbroken stream of black fruits, licorice, dark chocolate, cedary oak and fine, ripe tannins; the balance, line and length reflect the very good vintage and equally good winemaking. Screwcap. 14.5% alc. **Rating** 96 **To** 2030 $65

The Angelus McLaren Vale Cabernet Sauvignon 2010 Deep purple-crimson; a reaffirmation of the ability of McLaren Vale to produce Cabernet Sauvignon of great authority and power; black fruits are the order of the day, the tannins skilfully moulded, the oak integrated. Screwcap. 14.5% alc. **Rating** 96 **To** 2030 $65

The Absconder McLaren Vale Grenache 2010 Super-deluxe packaging for an icon wine made from one of the oldest blocks of grenache in McLaren Vale, planted in the 1920s. This wine was open-fermented, hand-plunged and pressed in the ancient basket press at Wirra Wirra. The colour is bright, the flavours of the juicy red berries with excellent acidity and tannins, and the benison of 10 months in French oak Screwcap. 14.5% alc. **Rating** 95 **To** 2020 $65

✪   The Lost Watch Adelaide Hills Riesling 2011 The winemaking team at Wirra Wirra are polished practitioners, seemingly effortlessly producing polished wines such as this; the varietal fruit, line, length and – above all – balance all coalesce on the lime and honey back-palate, the acidity of the vintage not the least aggressive. Will develop beautifully in bottle. Screwcap. 12% alc. **Rating** 94 **To** 2020 $19

✪   Hiding Champion Adelaide Hills Sauvignon Blanc 2011 Light straw-green; a contrasting bouquet of grass, kiwi fruit, guava and passionfruit is replayed on the lively palate, ending with a flourish of citrussy acidity. Screwcap. 13% alc. **Rating** 94 **To** 2013 $23

The 12th Man Adelaide Hills Chardonnay 2011 Wild yeast-fermented in fine French oak; a super-elegant wine that, despite the cool vintage, has perfectly ripened white peach and melon fruit, oak contributing as much to the texture and structure of the wine as to the flavour. The tight structure guarantees that the wine will develop well over the next four or five years. Screwcap. 12.5% alc. **Rating** 94 **To** 2016 $32

ဝဝဝဝ္ The 12th Man Adelaide Hills Chardonnay 2010 Rating 93 To 2017 $32
✪ Original Blend McLaren Vale Grenache Shiraz 2010 Clear, bright colour; a 70/30% blend with a fragrant bouquet of red berries that continues on into the medium-bodied palate; the wine has excellent structure and striking purity, the tannins slightly savoury, and adding contrast. Screwcap. 14.5% alc. Rating 93 To 2018 $24
Woodhenge McLaren Vale Shiraz 2010 Rating 92 To 2020 $35 BE
Church Block McLaren Vale Cabernet Sauvignon Shiraz Merlot 2010 Rating 92 To 2018 $24
Catapult McLaren Vale Shiraz 2010 Rating 90 To 2020 $24

ဝဝဝဝ Scrubby Rise Sauvignon Blanc Semillon Viognier 2011 Rating 89
✪ To 2013 $17
Mrs Wigley McLaren Vale Grenache Rose 2011 Rating 89 To Now $19
Scrubby Rise Unwooded Chardonnay 2011 Rating 88 To Now $15
Mrs Wigley McLaren Vale Moscato 2011 Rating 87 To Now $19

Wise Wine   ★★★★★

Lot 4 Eagle Bay Road, Eagle Bay, WA 6281 **Region** Margaret River
T (08) 9756 8627 **www**.wisewine.com.au **Open** 7 days 10–5
Winemaker Jake Bacchus, Imogen Casely, Larry Cherubino (Consultant) **Est.** 1986
Dozens 15 000 **Vyds** 6ha
Wise Wine, headed by Perth entrepreneur Ron Wise, has been a remarkably consistent producer of high-quality wine. The vineyard adjacent to the winery in the Margaret River is supplemented by contract-grown grapes from Pemberton, Manjimup and Frankland River. The estate plantings are (in descending order of size) cabernet sauvignon, shiraz and zinfandel. The value for money of many of the wines is extraordinarily good. Exports to Sri Lanka, Vietnam, Malaysia, Hong Kong and Singapore.

ဝဝဝဝဝ Frankland River Riesling 2011 Pale straw-green; a very distinctive and totally
✪ delicious Riesling, with lime and orange blossom aromas, and a harmonious palate adding touches of pear and apple to the citrus foundation; light-bodied, yet intense. Screwcap. 13% alc. Rating 95 To 2021 $18
✪ Margaret River Pemberton Sauvignon Blanc Semillon 2011 A very attractive and elegant example of the blend, with snow pea, passionfruit and citrus on the bouquet, amplified on the long and beautifully balanced palate; the finish, too, is crisp and clean. Screwcap. 13% alc. Rating 95 To 2014 $18
Eagle Bay Single Vineyard Margaret River Chardonnay 2011 While oak is a prominent feature on the bouquet, the grapefruit, fennel and cashew notes are thoroughly beguiling; the palate is focused and lively, long and fragrant, with toasty oak managing to gently reassert itself on the finish. Screwcap. 13% alc. Rating 94 To 2016 $35 BE
✪ Margaret River Shiraz 2010 Strong purple-crimson; the fragrant bouquet leads into a palate that is medium-bodied but complex, thanks to pre-fermentation maceration then the fermentation finished in barrel; the dark berry fruits are enhanced by the oak and savoury, faintly earthy, tannins. A wine with personality and attitude. Screwcap. 13.5% alc. Rating 94 To 2020 $18

ဝဝဝဝ္ Pemberton Sauvignon Blanc 2010 The 10 lines of print on the back label are
✪ remarkable, as they could be used for any variety, white or red, grown anywhere. This wine in fact speaks volumes on its intense, citrus and herb palate, the dry finish long and lingering. Screwcap. 13.5% alc. Rating 93 To Now $18
◉ Margaret River Chardonnay 2011 Rating 93 To 2014 $18
Lot 80 Margaret River Cabernet Sauvignon 2010 Rating 93 To 2020 $28 BE
Eagle Bay Single Vineyard Margaret River Cabernet Sauvignon 2009 Rating 93 To 2030 $50
Reserve Pemberton Chardonnay 2010 Rating 92 To 2018 $28

✪ **Margaret River Cabernet Rose 2010** Very pale, bright crimson; an interesting wine that has been picked late enough to allow the development of some cassis fruit on both bouquet and palate, yet retaining a refreshing crispness. Screwcap. 12.5% alc. **Rating** 92 **To** Now $18

○ **Margaret River Shiraz 2009 Rating** 92 **To** 2015 $18

✪ **Margaret River Verdelho 2011** Very different from Hunter Valley Verdelho; lemon and orange blossom introduce a wine with a backbone of minerally acidity, and a lingering, cleansing finish. Screwcap. 13% alc. **Rating** 91 **To** 2013 $18

Eagle Bay Single Vineyard Margaret River Cabernet Sauvignon 2010 Rating 90 **To** 2015 $50 BE

♟♟♟♟ **Eagle Bay Single Vineyard Margaret River Shiraz 2010 Rating** 88 **To** 2014 $35 BE

Witches Falls Winery ★★★★

79 Main Western Road, North Tamborine, Qld 4272 **Region** Granite Belt
T (07) 5545 2609 **www**.witchesfalls.com.au **Open** Mon–Fri 10–4, w'ends 10–5
Winemaker Jon Heslop **Est.** 2004 **Dozens** 8000 **Vyds** 0.4ha
Witches Falls is the venture of Jon and Kim Heslop. Jon has a deep interest in experimenting with progressive vinification methods in order to achieve exceptional and interesting results. He has a degree in applied science (oenology) from CSU, and experience working in the Barossa and Hunter valleys as well as at Domaine Chantel Lescure, Burgundy, and a Napa-based wine grower in California. Witches Falls has a small estate planting of durif, with the majority of wines being made from contract-grown grapes sourced predominantly from the Granite Belt. One of the most consistently good producers in the Granite Belt. Exports to the UK, Malaysia and China.

♟♟♟♟♟ **Wild Ferment Granite Belt Chardonnay 2010** A complex and well-made wine reflecting wild yeast fermentation on cloudy juice in a mix of new and used French oak barrels; it has supple white peach and citrus fruit flavours, together with spicy, toasty characters from the barrel ferment; good acidity lengthens the finish. Screwcap. 13.2% alc. **Rating** 92 **To** 2018 $30

Wild Ferment Viognier 2010 Full straw-green; the wine was barrel-fermented, but not bottled until Jan '12 – how long it spent in barrel, I don't know, but the barrel ferment is certainly a colour contributor; the wine has considerable amounts of apricot and peach characters on the bouquet, and even a touch of fresh ginger on the palate; the mouthfeel is good, as is the balance. Screwcap. 13.6% alc. **Rating** 92 **To** 2014 $30

Co-Inoculated Granite Belt Sauvignon Blanc 2011 Straw-green; the co-inoculated name stems from research by the AWRI showing that the use of two cultured yeasts could enhance varietal fruit flavours; this is a striking wine with pronounced flavours all in the herbal end of the spectrum, including green capsicum, asparagus and hay. Screwcap. 12.8% alc. **Rating** 90 **To** 2014 $22

Co-Inoculated Granite Belt Verdelho 2011 The co-inoculation technique seems to work across a number of white varieties, here adding a layered, textured character to the complex fruit flavours running from citrus to tropical. Screwcap. 13.4% alc. **Rating** 90 **To** 2013 $22

Wild Ferment Fiano 2010 The grapes for this wine and for the Viognier were grown at a vineyard just to the west of Tamborine Mountain. The wild yeast, cloudy juice and barrel fermentation have all added to the pre-existing structure of fiano; the bouquet has a mix of fruit, honeysuckle and a hint of spice, the rich palate bringing further cashew/almond characters into play, reaffirming the complexity of the bouquet. How much the barrel fermentation has added to the wine is an open question. Screwcap. 13.3% alc. **Rating** 90 **To** 2014 $30

♟♟♟♟ **Co-Inoculated Granite Belt Unwooded Chardonnay 2011 Rating** 89 **To** 2015 $22

Wild Ferment Granite Belt Grenache 2009 Rating 88 **To** 2013 $30

Wild Ferment Granite Belt Pinot Noir 2010 Rating 87 **To** 2013 $30

Wobbly Tom Wines ★★★☆

PO Boz 48, Stirling North, SA 5710 **Region** Southern Flinders Ranges
T 0427 442 634 **www.**bundaleercottage.com.au **Open** Not
Winemaker Angela Meaney **Est.** 2005 **Dozens** 450 **Vyds** 2.5ha
Justin and Donna Burman purchased their property in the beautiful Bundaleer Forest, in the
Southern Flinders Ranges region. A second reason for purchasing the property was a 'tree
change' for their young family in a renovated cottage on the site. They planted shiraz in 2000,
and also 1700 olive trees. The name came from their young son Tom's vigilance when he saw
a wallaby sheltering in the shade, and called out, 'There's a wobbly in the vines.'

ŸŸŸŸ̨ **Southern Flinders Ranges Shiraz 2009** Full red-purple; the complex bouquet
✪ has hints of spice, hay and earth, which perfectly set the scene for the medium-
bodied palate, which has good length and balance. Screwcap. 14% alc. **Rating** 90
To 2024 $17

Wolf Blass

Bilyara Vineyards, 97 Sturt Highway, Nuriootpa, SA 5355 **Region** Barossa Valley
T (08) 8568 7311 **www.**wolfblasswines.com.au **Open** Mon–Fri 9–5, w'ends & public
hols 10–5
Winemaker Chris Hatcher (Chief), Matt O'Leary, Marie Clay, Caroline Dunn,
Steven Frost, Clare Schneider, Stuart Rusted **Est.** 1966 **Dozens** NFP
Although merged with Mildara and now under the giant umbrella of TWE, the brands (as
expected) have been left largely intact. The wines are made at all price points, ranging through
Red Label, Yellow Label, Gold Label, Brown Label, Grey Label, Black Label and Platinum
Label, at one price point or another covering every one of the main varietals. The pre-eminent
quality of the red wines has reasserted itself over the white wines, but without in any way
diminishing the attraction the latter have. All of this has occurred under the leadership of Chris
Hatcher, who has harnessed the talents of the winemaking team and encouraged the changes
in style. Exports to all major markets.

ŸŸŸŸŸ **Platinum Label Barossa Shiraz 2009** Inky purple-crimson; has used the time-
honoured approach of top-quality fruit with no pre-set vineyard contribution, the
warm fermentation finished in French oak; has layer upon layer of juicy black and
red fruits, supple tannins and balanced oak. Genuine Australian icon. Screwcap.
14% alc. **Rating** 96 **To** 2040 $170
White Label Specially Aged Release Adelaide Hills Chardonnay 2007
Won three trophies at the Adelaide Wine Show '09. Glowing green-yellow; it has
an uncommon combination of lightness of touch and a stream of mouth-watering
white peach and grapefruit flavours, all of which are far more important than
winemaker artefact. Screwcap. 12.5% alc. **Rating** 95 **To** 2015 $34
Black Label Cabernet Sauvignon Shiraz Malbec 2008 Deep purple colour;
a cascade of black fruits ranging through blackcurrant, blackberry, mulberry, plum
and licorice; firm tannins are in balance with the fruit; all the fruit and tannins are
wrapped in a thick coating of French oak. Drink now if you are likely to take a
$130 bottle to a bbq; failing this, it needs up to 10 years in the cellar to calm down
and learn some manners. Screwcap. 15% alc. **Rating** 95 **To** 2030
Gold Label Barossa Shiraz 2010 Deep, dense purple-crimson; the palate is as
luscious as the colour suggests, with waves of predominantly black fruits rolling
through new and used French oak, and ripe tannins. Carries its alcohol with ease,
and has line, length and balance. Screwcap. 14.5% alc. **Rating** 94 **To** 2025 $25
Grey Label McLaren Vale Shiraz 2010 Deep, vivid crimson-purple;
immediately fills every corner and crevice of the mouth when first tasted, and
doesn't back off on subsequent sips; the flavours are bang slap in the middle of
the mainstream for McLaren Vale (at its top end), with blackberry, licorice, dark
chocolate and oak intertwined with the aid of a cushion of soft, fine tannins.
Screwcap. 15% alc. **Rating** 94 **To** 2025 $43

❂ Red Label Shiraz Grenache 2010 What an amazing wine, winning two trophies at the Adelaide Wine Show '11, backed up by a gold medal at the Melbourne Wine Show '11 (class 47, Rhône styles). It is vibrant purple-crimson, with totally delicious red berry and spice flavours, at its best now or over the next three years. Screwcap. 13.5% alc. **Rating** 94 **To** 2014 $14

Grey Label Langhorne Creek Cabernet Shiraz 2010 Deep, bright purple-crimson; the naturally succulent nature of Langhorne Creek's red wines is heightened here by the traditional Blass method of finishing the fermentation in oak; the wine abounds with blackcurrant, blackberry and black cherry fruit; so intense is the fruit that you don't pay any attention to the alcohol. It's a good example of the Wolf Blass style, love it or hate it. Screwcap. 15% alc. **Rating** 94 **To** 2030 $43

♟♟♟♟♟ Gold Label Adelaide Hills Shiraz Viognier 2009 **Rating** 92 **To** 2019 $25
Gold Label Adelaide Hills Pinot Noir Chardonnay 2008 **Rating** 91 **To** 2013 $25
Gold Label Clare Valley Eden Valley Riesling 2011 **Rating** 90 **To** 2015 $25
Gold Label Adelaide Hills Sauvignon Blanc 2011 **Rating** 90 **To** 2013 $25
◉ Yellow Label Shiraz 2010 **Rating** 90 **To** 2015 $18
❂ Yellow Label Cabernet Sauvignon 2010 Good hue; comprehensively over-delivers against its price point, with its strong varietal signature, fine tannins and integrated oak. Has the balance to age well, although this is not its mission in life. Screwcap. 13.5% alc. **Rating** 90 **To** 2015 $18
❂ Yellow Label Moscato 2011 I embark on tasting these wines with a marked degree of reluctance, but this is actually enjoyable, its vivid Bickford's lime juice matched by lots of spritz and largely hidden acidity. Screwcap. 5% alc. **Rating** 90 **To** Now $18

Wombat Lodge ★★★

PO Box 460, Cowaramup, WA 6284 **Region** Margaret River
T 0418 948 125 **www**.wombatlodgewines.com.au **Open** Not
Winemaker Ian McIntosh, Ian Bell **Est.** 1997 **Dozens** 500 **Vyds** 4ha
It pays to have a keenly developed sense of humour if you are a small winemaker committed to producing the very best possible wine regardless of cost and market constraints. The short version (and I quote) is: 'Warick (sic) Gerrard, owner/consumer; Jan McIntosh, winemaker and life partner; Danny Edwards, viticulture and adopted son; 60ha of central Wilyabrup land, two houses and 60 cows; 4ha of spoilt vines and 600 dozen of red wine.' There is a much longer version, underlining Danny's freedom to organically grow the vines with limited irrigation limiting yield and maximising quality, and Jan's freedom to buy as much French oak as she wishes. The outcome is four clones of cabernet sauvignon, merlot, cabernet franc, malbec, petit verdot and semillon in the 500-dozen make-up, selling for the ludicrously low price of $120 per dozen plus postage. Verging on surreal is the fact that the red wines mature for 14–16 months in 30% new and 70% used French oak barriques.

♟♟♟♟ Margaret River Cabernet Sauvignon Merlot 2010 Slightly turbid red-
❂ purple; the ultimate bbq wine; it is stacked full of ripe blackcurrant fruit, and has a generous helping of savoury tannins on the finish. It is almost perversely rustic, but there is upside in both the price and that rusticity. Screwcap. 13.5% alc. **Rating** 88 **To** 2017 $10

Wood Park

263 Kneebones Gap Road, Markwood, Vic 3678 **Region** King Valley
T (03) 5727 3778 **www**.woodparkwines.com.au **Open** At Milawa Cheese Factory, 7 days 10–5
Winemaker John Stokes **Est.** 1989 **Dozens** 7000 **Vyds** 16ha
John Stokes planted the first vines at Wood Park in 1989 as part of a diversification program for his property at Bobinawarrah, in the hills of the Lower King Valley, east of Milawa. The vineyard is managed with minimal chemical use, winemaking a mix of modern and traditional

techniques. Some impressive wines have been made over the years. Exports to the US, Hong Kong and China.

ŶŶŶŶŶ Premium Reserve King Valley Shiraz 2009 The heavy-duty bottle (and price) signal something special, but the message is thoroughly mixed by a cork stained on all sides; this concern to one side, this is an unusually rich and complex Shiraz from the King Valley, with layer upon layer of blackberry and plum fruit, the oak integrated and balanced, as are the tannins. The points ignore the cork issue. 14% alc. **Rating** 94 **To** 2019 $80

ŶŶŶŶŶ Whitlands King Valley Pinot Noir 2010 Light, clear purple-red; the fragrant
✪ bouquet immediately proclaims its pinot noir parentage, the savoury and plum palate underscoring its varietal base. While not overtly fruity, will cellar well, and is a top food style. Exceptional value. Screwcap. 14% alc. **Rating** 92 **To** 2018 $25
The Kilnhouses Alpine Valleys Semillon 2010 Rating 91 **To** 2017 $25
Reserve King Valley Cabernet Sauvignon 2010 Rating 91 **To** 2020 $40
Meadow Creek Alpine Valleys Chardonnay 2010 Rating 90 **To** 2017 $28

ŶŶŶŶ Reserve King Valley Shiraz 2010 Rating 89 **To** 2017 $40
✪ **Forgotten Patch King Valley Sangiovese 2010** Conventional light, developed red colour; a fragrant, savoury palate with pronounced tannins and dried herb flavours is in accordance with normal expectations for the variety. Screwcap. 13% alc. **Rating** 89 **To** 2015 $20
Wild's Gully King Valley Sauvignon Blanc Semillon 2011 Rating 87 **To** 2013 $15

Woodlands   ★★★★★

3948 Caves Road, Wilyabrup, WA 6284 **Region** Margaret River
T (08) 9755 6226 **www.**woodlandswines.com **Open** 7 days 10–5
Winemaker Stuart and Andrew Watson **Est.** 1973 **Dozens** 9000 **Vyds** 18.87ha
Founder David Watson had spectacular success with the Cabernets he made in 1979 and the early '80s. Commuting from Perth on weekends and holidays, as well as raising a family, became all too much, and for some years the grapes from Woodlands were sold to other Margaret River producers. With the advent of sons Stuart and Andrew (Stuart primarily responsible for winemaking), the estate has bounced back to pre-eminence. The wines come in four price bands, the bulk of the production under the Chardonnay and Cabernet Merlot varietals, then a series of Reserve and Special Réserves, then Reserve de la Cave, and finally Robert Cabernet Sauvignon. The top-end wines primarily come from the original Woodlands Vineyard, where the vines are almost 40 years old. Exports to the UK, Denmark, Indonesia, Malaysia, South Korea, Singapore and Japan.

ŶŶŶŶŶ Alma May Margaret River Cabernet Sauvignon 2009 This is the essence of elegant Cabernet; the wine an essay in redcurrant, cassis, cedar, violets and fine oak; medium-bodied with abundant and super-fine tannins, crunchy acidity and a long, fragrant and expansive conclusion; this will stand the test of time, while also being good to drink now. Screwcap. 13.5% alc. **Rating** 96 **To** 2025 $130 BE
Chloe Reserve Margaret River Chardonnay 2010 The vivid green hue and slight green note on the bouquet suggest early picking here, but the energy and life that are captured as a result are tantalising; fresh grapefruit, spice, hazelnut and charcuterie are on show, with mouth-watering acidity providing a long, almost luscious, ride to the finish. Screwcap. 13.5% alc. **Rating** 95 **To** 2020 $60 BE
✪ **Margaret River Chardonnay 2011** Incredibly tightly wound as a young wine, showing a multilayered personality of pure grapefruit juice, bacon bones and grilled cashews; the palate is lively, focused and layered, unevolved and lying in wait to reveal its true depth; time is essential here, but the wait will be worth it. Screwcap. 13.5% alc. **Rating** 94 **To** 2020 $23 BE
Margaret 2010 Deep crimson; a vibrant and juicy bouquet offering red and black fruits, layers of spice and leafy complexity; the medium-bodied palate is lively and vivacious, finding harmony between succulent fruit and fine-grained tannin structure; a simply charming and elegant wine in every respect. Cabernet Sauvignon/Merlot/Malbec. Screwcap. 13.5% alc. **Rating** 94 **To** 2018 $45 BE

Reserve de la Cave Margaret River Cabernet Franc 2010 Only 300 bottles made; the concentration and generosity of fruit are undeniable; cassis and violets are offset by fine-grained tannins, and a long and savoury finish; accessible now, and showing enough stuffing and complexity to be enjoyed as it matures over the medium term. Screwcap. 13.5% alc. **Rating** 94 **To** 2020 $65 BE

♆♆♆♆♀ Reserve de la Cave Margaret River Malbec 2010 **Rating** 92 **To** 2018 $65 BE

✪   Margaret River Cabernet Merlot 2010 Bright colour; if structure is anything to go by, then this is a serious cabernet blend for the price; young, unevolved and a little hard-edged at this early stage, the tightly wound core of black fruits, black olive and cedar is hard to dismiss; protein is essential for enjoyment, and ageing is going to prove fruitful. Screwcap. 13.5% alc. **Rating** 91 **To** 2020 $23 BE Emily 2010 **Rating** 90 **To** 2020 $39 BE

Woodside Valley Estate   ★★★★★

PO Box 332, Greenwood, WA 6924 **Region** Margaret River
T (08) 9345 4065 **www**.woodsidevalleyestate.com.au **Open** Not
Winemaker Kevin McKay, Tod Payne **Est.** 1998 **Dozens** 1800 **Vyds** 19.4ha
Woodside Valley Estate has been developed by a small syndicate of investors headed by Peter Woods. In 1998 they acquired 67ha of land at Yallingup, and have now established chardonnay, sauvignon blanc, cabernet sauvignon, shiraz, malbec and merlot. The experienced Albert Haak is consultant viticulturist, and together with Peter took the unusual step of planting south-facing in preference to north-facing slopes. In doing so they indirectly followed in the footsteps of the French explorer Nicolas-Thomas Baudin, who mounted a major scientific expedition to Australia on his ship *Le Geographe*, and defied established views and tradition of the time in (correctly) asserting that the best passage for sailing ships travelling between Cape Leeuwin and Bass Strait was from west to east. Exports to the UK, the US, Singapore, China and Japan.

♆♆♆♆♆ Baudin Margaret River Cabernet Sauvignon 2009 Deep colour, with pure cassis, toasty oak, black olive complexity and a little briary edge to the fruit; the palate is full-bodied, tightly wound, very fresh and focused, with a long and silky fine-grained tannin conclusion; built for the long haul, provided the closure can get it there. Diam. 14.1% alc. **Rating** 95 **To** 2030 $58 BE
Bonnefoy Margaret River Shiraz 2009 Bright colour; while the level of toasty new oak makes getting to the fruit a little difficult, once navigated, the freshness of cranberry, blackberry, anise and toast is there to see; the palate is generous, and while time is needed to see the oak subside, the quality of the fruit will make the journey ahead a positive one. Diam. 13.8% alc. **Rating** 94 **To** 2025 $55 BE

♆♆♆♆♀ Le Bas Margaret River Chardonnay 2010 **Rating** 91 **To** 2016 $48 BE
Bissy Margaret River Merlot 2009 **Rating** 91 **To** 2017 $50 BE

Woodstock   ★★★★★

215 Douglas Gully Road, McLaren Flat, SA 5171 **Region** McLaren Vale
T (08) 8383 0156 **www**.woodstockwine.com.au **Open** 7 days 10–5
Winemaker Scott Collett, Ben Glaetzer **Est.** 1973 **Dozens** 25 000 **Vyds** 19.6ha
One of the stalwarts of McLaren Vale, owned by Scott Collett, who produces archetypal and invariably reliable full-bodied red wines, spectacular botrytis sweet whites and high-quality (25-year-old) Tawny Port. Also offers a totally charming reception-cum-restaurant, which does a roaring trade with wedding receptions. Exports to most major markets.

♆♆♆♆♆ The Stocks Single Vineyard McLaren Vale Shiraz 2009 Crimson-purple; produced from 31 rows of low-yielding vines planted circa 1900; the wine has that perfumed polish that comes from very old vines, the fruit flavours deep and dark, yet the tannins and extract fine. Astute winemaking has largely left the grapes to speak for themselves. Screwcap. 14.9% alc. **Rating** 95 **To** 2035 $60

Pilot's View McLaren Vale Shiraz 2010 Strong red-purple; the bouquet and palate are more intense and complex than the standard wine; spice, black fruits and fine, persistent tannins join with oak to make a medium- to full-bodied wine with good overall balance and length. Screwcap. 14.9% alc. **Rating** 94 **To** 2025 $38

ŸŸŸŸŸ McLaren Vale Cabernet Sauvignon 2010 Strong purple-crimson; a generous,
✪ medium-bodied wine with bitter chocolate characters signalling the region, the black and redcurrant fruit even more enthusiastic with its message. Very attractive wine. Exceptional value. Screwcap. 14.5% alc. **Rating** 93 **To** 2020 $22

✪ McLaren Vale Shiraz 2010 Crimson-purple; a generously proportioned wine telegraphed by the aromatic bouquet, which commences the seam of intertwined fruit and oak; McLaren Vale chocolate is the lynchpin for the black fruit flavours, in turn framed by balanced oak and tannins. Screwcap. 14.9% alc. **Rating** 92 **To** 2020 $22

✪ McLaren Vale Shiraz Cabernet Sauvignon 2010 Faintly turbid red-purple; the percentage contribution of the two varieties is not disclosed – shiraz must be in the lead, contributing its blackberry to the blackcurrant of the cabernet, and the savoury, dark chocolate notes of the region. Plenty to chew on at this price. Screwcap. 14.9% alc. **Rating** 90 **To** 2020 $18

ŸŸŸŸ McLaren Vale Semillon Sauvignon Blanc 2011 **Rating** 88 **To** 2014 $18

Woody Nook   ★★★★

506 Metricup Road, Wilyabrup, WA 6280 **Region** Margaret River
T (08) 9755 7547 **www**.woodynook.com.au **Open** 7 days 10–4.30
Winemaker Neil Gallagher, Michael Brophy **Est.** 1982 **Dozens** 7500 **Vyds** 14.23ha
Woody Nook, with a backdrop of 18ha of majestic marri and jarrah forest, does not have the high profile of the biggest names in Margaret River, but has had major success in wine shows over the years. It was purchased by Peter and Jane Bailey in 2000, and major renovations and expansions in '02 and '04 transformed Woody Nook, with a new winery, a gallery tasting room for larger groups and an alfresco dining area by the pond. A link with the past is Neil Gallagher's continuing role as winemaker, viticulturist and minority shareholder. Exports to the UK, the US, Canada, Bermuda, Hong Kong and China.

ŸŸŸŸŸ Gallagher's Choice Margaret River Cabernet Sauvignon 2010 A deep and essency cassis-fruited bouquet, with violets and cedary oak all in play; the palate is densely structured and deeply fruited, long and luscious; the essence of black fruits is promised and delivered. Diam. 14% alc. **Rating** 92 **To** 2018 $45 BE

✪ Killdog Creek Margaret River Tempranillo 2010 An ebullient blend of bright dark cherry, cola, spice and charcuterie; medium-bodied and very fleshy, with taut acidity providing freshness, line and length; plenty of fun in this wine. Screwcap. 14% alc. **Rating** 91 **To** 2015 $22 BE

Single Vineyard Margaret River Cabernet Merlot 2010 Deep crimson, bright; ripe and essency blackcurrant bouquet, offset by a splash of black olive complexity; unctuous and sweet-fruited on the palate, with vibrant acidity providing contrast on the finish. Diam. 14.5% alc. **Rating** 90 **To** 2016 $32 BE

Gallagher's Choice Margaret River Cabernet Sauvignon 2009 Leafy green and herbal aromas sit comfortably alongside red fruits and olive; the palate is medium-bodied, with savoury tannins and ironstone minerality prevailing on the finish. Diam. 13.5% alc. **Rating** 90 **To** 2016 $40 BE

ŸŸŸŸ Single Vineyard Margaret River Chardonnay 2011 **Rating** 88 **To** 2015 $32 BE

Margaret River Shiraz 2009 **Rating** 87 **To** 2014 $35 BE

Word of Mouth Wines ★★★☆

Campbell's Corner, 790 Pinnacle Road, Orange, NSW 2800 **Region** Orange
T (02) 6362 3509 **www**.wordofmouthwines.com.au **Open** Wed–Fri & Sun–Mon 10.30–3, Sat 10.30–5, or by appt (0429 653 316)
Winemaker David Lowe (Contract), Liam Heslop **Est.** 1991 **Dozens** 2500 **Vyds** 9ha

The 1991 plantings (made by the former Donnington Vineyard) have changed over the years, and, in particular, since the business was acquired by Word of Mouth Wines in 2003. Pinot gris, riesling, chardonnay, sauvignon blanc, merlot, pinot noir and cabernet sauvignon are all in bearing, and were joined by plantings of petit manseng in the winter of '08. Word of Mouth is the venture of Peter Gibson, Deborah Upjohn, Jamie Gordon and Sharyn Pussell.

🍷🍷🍷🍷🍷 **Orange Sauvignon Blanc 2011** A pleasant combination of ripe guava, fresh-cut grass and pea pod on the bouquet; the palate is lively, with a generous streak and a long savoury finish. Screwcap. 12% alc. **Rating** 90 **To** 2014 $30 BE

🍷🍷🍷🍷 **Orange Riesling 2011** **Rating** 89 **To** 2016 $30 BE

✪ **The Very Cool Red 2011** Inspired by Beaujolais, perhaps due to the challenges of the vintage, this wine exhibits bight red fruits with a floral accent; fresh, juicy, forward and made for early consumption, it would appear that the mission objective was achieved. Pinot Noir/Merlot. Screwcap. 12.5% alc. **Rating** 89 **To** 2013 $20 BE

Orange Chardonnay 2011 **Rating** 88 **To** 2014 $30 BE

Sweet Milli 2010 **Rating** 87 **To** 2015 $15 BE

Wykari Wines ★★★☆

PO Box 905, Clare, SA 5453 **Region** Clare Valley
T (08) 8842 1841 **www**.wykariwines.com.au **Open** Not
Winemaker Neil Paulett **Est.** 2006 **Dozens** 1200 **Vyds** 20ha

This is the venture of two local Clare families, Rob and Mandy Knight, and Peter and Robyn Shearer. Together they own two vineyards, one to the north, and the other to the south of Clare. The vineyards were first planted in 1974, and are dry-grown and hand-pruned. In all there is shiraz, riesling, cabernet sauvignon and chardonnay. Until 2009 much of the riesling and shiraz was sold to Leasingham Wines, but since '06 Wykari has steadily increased its production from 600 dozen, in partnership with Neil Paulett. Excess grapes continue to be sold.

🍷🍷🍷🍷🍷 ✪ **Clare Valley Riesling 2011** Pale green-straw; opens quietly on the bouquet, but changes gear immediately it enters the mouth, with lime juice and some tropical notes making a forceful statement; the long finish underlines the great value the wine offers. Screwcap. 12.1% alc. **Rating** 93 **To** 2019 $17

🍷🍷🍷🍷 **Clare Valley Cabernet Sauvignon 2009** **Rating** 88 **To** 2019 $19

Wyndham Estate ★★★★

700 Dalwood Road, Dalwood, NSW 2335 **Region** Hunter Valley
T (02) 4938 3444 **www**.wyndhamestate.com **Open** 7 days 9.30–4.30 except public hols
Winemaker Ben Bryant **Est.** 1828 **Dozens** 800 000 **Vyds** 55ha

This historic property is now merely a shop front for the Wyndham Estate label. The Bin wines often surprise with their quality, representing excellent value; the Show Reserve wines, likewise, can be very good. The wines come from various parts of South Eastern Australia, sometimes specified, sometimes not. It's easy to dismiss these wines with faint praise, which does no justice whatsoever to their quality and their value for money. Exports to Canada, Europe and Asia.

🍷🍷🍷🍷🍷 **George Wyndham Founder's Reserve Shiraz Cabernet 2009** Crimson-purple; the Limestone Coast origin makes its mark on the wine, which is elegant and bright-fruited, tannins playing a minimal role in a light- to medium-bodied palate with bright red berry fruits. Screwcap. 14.5% alc. **Rating** 92 **To** 2017 $22

George Wyndham Founder's Reserve Shiraz 2009 Vivid deep crimson; the bouquet is bright and fresh with black cherry, tar and a splash of mint on display; the palate is juicy, generous and vibrant, with ripe tannins and fruit working seamlessly together. Screwcap. 14.5% alc. **Rating** 91 **To** 2018 $22 BE

George Wyndham Founder's Reserve Shiraz 2008 This Langhorne Creek Shiraz has retained a youthful hue, and the medium-bodied palate reflects that freshness, with supple berry fruits, vanilla oak and soft, ripe tannins all coming together well. Screwcap. 14% alc. **Rating** 90 **To** 2018 $22

George Wyndham Founder's Reserve Cabernet Merlot 2007 A combination of varieties and regions with the end result delivering a plump and plummy blend of black fruits, spice and herb complexity; medium-bodied and moderately long. Screwcap. 14.3% alc. **Rating** 90 **To** 2015 $22 BE

ŸŸŸŸ
○   **Bin 444 Cabernet Sauvignon 2008** **Rating** 89 **To** 2015 $16

○   **Bin 444 Cabernet Sauvignon 2009** **Rating** 88 **To** 2014 $16
Bin 222 Chardonnay 2010 **Rating** 87 **To** Now $16

Wynns Coonawarra Estate   ★★★★★

Memorial Drive, Coonawarra, SA 5263 **Region** Coonawarra
T (08) 8736 2225 **www**.wynns.com.au **Open** 7 days 10–5
Winemaker Sue Hodder, Luke Skeer **Est.** 1897 **Dozens** NFP
Large-scale production has not prevented Wynns from producing excellent wines covering the full price spectrum, from the bargain-basement Riesling and Shiraz through to the deluxe John Riddoch Cabernet Sauvignon and Michael Shiraz. Even with steady price increases, Wynns offers extraordinary value for money. The large investments since 2000 in rejuvenating and replanting key blocks under the direction of Allen Jenkins, and skilled winemaking by Sue Hodder, have resulted in wines of far greater finesse and elegance than most of their predecessors. Exports to the UK, the US and Canada.

ŸŸŸŸŸ   **Michael Limited Release Shiraz 2009** Good purple-crimson; the excellent bouquet is a classy opening, but this wine is all about structure, mouthfeel and length; the blackberry, plum, spice and mulberry flavours are folded in quality French oak. Will be a classic. Screwcap. 14% alc. **Rating** 96 **To** 2040 $130

Cabernet Sauvignon 2009 Deep colour; it spent 15 months in a mix of old and new French and American oak barriques, giving rise to a fragrant and expressive bouquet of black fruits, spice and cedar nuances. The palate really sings with dark berry fruit, oak and tannins the supporting orchestra. Right up there with the best Black Labels. Screwcap. 14% alc. **Rating** 96 **To** 2024 $35

John Riddoch Cabernet Sauvignon 2009 Strong colour; a very potent, deeply layered, full-bodied wine in which all of the expected Coonawarra cabernet characters coalesce: blackcurrant, blackberry, mulberry, earth and mint, and that's before you start talking about the classy oak or fine, ripe tannins. Screwcap. 14% alc. **Rating** 96 **To** 2040 $130

V&A Lane Selected Vineyards Shiraz 2010 Deep purple-crimson; this is a beautifully weighted and constructed Shiraz; the medium-bodied palate effortlessly displays blackberry, sweet earth and classy oak, with fine tannins running through the very long finish and aftertaste. Screwcap. 13.5% alc. **Rating** 95 **To** 2035 $59

V&A Lane Selected Vineyards Shiraz 2009 The Wynns vineyards were planted along V&A (Victoria and Albert) Lane 40 years ago, and produce both shiraz and cabernet sauvignon of distinctive richness. This deep crimson wine has a very fragrant bouquet, then a truly lovely medium-bodied palate, its supple texture caressing the mouth, the blackberry fruit verging on juicy, the palate very long and fine. Screwcap. 13.5% alc. **Rating** 95 **To** 2024 $50

Limited Release The Gables Cabernet Shiraz 2010 Strong, deep crimson-purple; a delicious wine showcasing the synergy available with cabernet and shiraz; there are layers of blackcurrant and blackberry fruit, touches of mint and earth, and fine tannins all presenting themselves in a coherent whole. Screwcap. 14% alc. **Rating** 94 **To** 2025 $25

V&A Lane Selected Vineyards Cabernet Shiraz 2010 The colour is very good, although that of the Shiraz is better still; a full-bodied wine screaming out to be given as much time as possible in the cellar, for the brilliant, luscious blackcurrant, blackberry and plum fruits are needing to deal with the positive tannins that are trying to usurp the place of the fruit; their failure to do so is inevitable. Screwcap. 13.5% alc. **Rating** 94 **To** 2035 $59

ΤΤΤΤΩ **Shiraz 2010** The bouquet is driven by red and black cherry fruit, a sprinkle of
✪   spice and some oak, but it is the medium-bodied palate that defines the wine, effortlessly conveying its range of black fruits, savoury tannins and refreshing acidity. It is, I suppose, useless to suggest cellaring long into the future, but do keep some bottles as long as you can. Is often heavily discounted. Screwcap. 14% alc. **Rating** 93 **To** 2025 $23

✪   **Chardonnay 2011** Pale bright green-quartz; while quite delicate, the wine does have many-faceted aromas and flavours of stone fruit, grapefruit, melon and barrel-ferment oak. A commendable outcome for the vintage. Screwcap. 12.5% alc. **Rating** 91 **To** 2015 $23
Cabernet Sauvignon 2010 **Rating** 91 **To** 2025 $40 BE
The Siding Cabernet Sauvignon 2010 **Rating** 91 **To** 2020 $25

ΤΤΤΤ   **Riesling 2011** **Rating** 89 **To** 2013 $23
Cabernet Shiraz Merlot 2010 **Rating** 89 **To** 2025 $25

Xabregas   ★★★★★

1683 Porongurup Road, Porongurup, WA 6324 **Region** Mount Barker
T (08) 9321 2366 **www**.xabregas.com.au **Open** Not
Winemaker Martin Cooper **Est.** 1996 **Dozens** 10 000 **Vyds** 118ha
Owners of Xabregas, the Hogan family, have five generations of WA history and family interests in sheep grazing and forestry in the Great Southern, dating back to the 1860s. Terry Hogan, founding chairman, felt the Mount Barker region was 'far too good dirt to waste on blue gums', and vines were planted in 1996. The Hogan family concentrates on the region's strengths – Shiraz and Riesling. Exports to the US, Singapore, Japan, China and NZ.

ΤΤΤΤΤ **Artisan Sauvignon 2010** It is good to see Sauvignon with attitude in the marketplace, this style with exotic guava notes, minerals and added texture from work in the winery, brings a range of foods into play, which is great news for the consumer; texture, length and complexity all come to the fore, and if you want Sauvignon pushed to the limits, this wine may be the place to start. Screwcap. 12.3% alc. **Rating** 94 **To** 2014 $31 BE
Mount Barker Shiraz 2010 Deep magenta, vivid purple hue; a bright and fragrant bouquet of fresh blackberry, violets, sage and a fine underpinning of toasty oak; the palate is lively and fresh, with ample gravelly tannins and an expansive layering of fruit slowly unravelling on the savoury finish. Screwcap. 13.9% alc. **Rating** 94 **To** 2022 $23 BE
Artisan Syrah 2009 Here is a wine that jumps out of the glass with a pongy, reductive opening, but a good swirl of the glass reveals layers of black fruits spice and mineral complexity; the palate is lively and savoury, with tar, earth, spice and game on display, and the tannins, while plentiful, are ripe and fine; long and intriguing savoury Syrah. Screwcap. 13.6% alc. **Rating** 94 **To** 2020 $35 BE

ΤΤΤΤΩ **Artisan Riesling 2010** **Rating** 93 **To** 2020 $31 BE

Xanadu Wines   ★★★★★

Boodjidup Road, Margaret River, WA 6285 **Region** Margaret River
T (08) 9758 9500 **www**.xanaduwines.com **Open** 7 days 10–5
Winemaker Glenn Goodall **Est.** 1977 **Dozens** 70 000 **Vyds** 109.5ha
Xanadu fell prey to over-ambitious expansion and to the increasingly tight trading conditions in 2005 as wine surpluses hit hard. The assets were acquired by the Rathbone Group, completing

the Yering Station/Mount Langi Ghiran/Parker Coonawarra Estate/Xanadu group. The prime assets were (and are) the 110ha of vineyards and winery. The increasing production has been matched by a major lift in quality. In '12 the Rathbone Group wine interests were placed on the market for sale either as a group or individually. exports to most major markets.

ŸŸŸŸŸ **Reserve Margaret River Chardonnay 2010** Takes the elegance of its sister wine, Stevens Road, onto another level with its accompanying intensity and utterly exceptional length. There is a seamless union between the pink grapefruit and white peach fruit, quality French oak and supporting acidity. Screwcap. 13.5% alc. **Rating** 97 **To** 2020 $85

Stevens Road Margaret River Chardonnay 2010 Bright, pale quartz-green; an elegant wine with a seamless union of white-fleshed stone fruit, oak and acidity that provides lovely mouthfeel and length. Stylish and refined. Screwcap. 13% alc. **Rating** 95 **To** 2016 $60

Margaret River Shiraz 2009 Deep magenta; a restrained and complex bouquet of dark fruits, ironstone, wild thyme and licorice; the palate is medium- to full-bodied, precise and full of punchy tannins and lively acidity. Excellent value, and with a lot of time in the tank. Screwcap. 14% alc. **Rating** 95 **To** 2025 $26 BE

Stevens Road Cabernet Sauvignon 2009 A touch more purple in the colour than the standard wine, and lifts the overall intensity significantly, without, however, investing the wine with more extract, especially tannins. There is a strong chord of black and redcurrant fruit, firm cedary oak and a long, lingering finish. Screwcap. 14.5% alc. **Rating** 95 **To** 2034 $60

Reserve Margaret River Cabernet Sauvignon 2009 Crimson-purple; includes 4% petit verdot, matured in French oak (65% new) for 16 months; a wine that combines elegance and intensity, vibrant fruit with tannins and oak all in an overall medium-bodied framework. Will be very long-lived. Screwcap. 14.5% alc. **Rating** 95 **To** 2039 $85

Margaret River Cabernet Sauvignon 2009 Fermented in a mix of small-batch open and static fermenters, 35% given extended post-ferment maceration before the batches were blended and matured in French oak (40% new) for 14 months. This has given the wine excellent structure without diminishing the delicious cassis/blackcurrant fruit. Screwcap. 14% alc. **Rating** 95 **To** 2029 $35

Reserve Margaret River Cabernet Sauvignon 2008 **Rating** 94 **To** 2030 $85

Margaret River Graciano 2009 **Rating** 94 **To** 2020 $49

ŸŸŸŸŸ **Margaret River Chardonnay 2010** **Rating** 93 **To** 2022 $30 BE

✪ **Next of Kin Margaret River Shiraz 2010** Strong colour; both the bouquet and palate are powerful and complex, with red fruits backed by firm tannins and tangy acidity on the long finish. Gold medal at the National Wine Show '11. Screwcap. 14.5% alc. **Rating** 93 **To** 2018 $18

Margaret River Semillon 2011 **Rating** 92 **To** 2014 $26 BE

Margaret River Sauvignon Blanc Semillon 2011 **Rating** 92 **To** 2015 $26 BE

Margaret River Cabernet Merlot 2009 **Rating** 92 **To** 2020 $30

✪ **Next of Kin Margaret River Sauvignon Blanc Semillon 2011** Bright colour; a classic blend of tropical fruit, nettle, straw and a little citrus lift on the bouquet; the palate is fresh, accessible and lively, with just enough complexity to hold interest, but not so much as to challenge; certainly made in a drink early and drink often mould. Screwcap. 12.5% alc. **Rating** 90 **To** 2014 $18 BE

✪ **Next of Kin Margaret River Chardonnay 2010** A bright and fresh nectarine and spiced fruit bouquet, with a touch of lanolin also on display; the light- to medium-weighted palate is fleshy and fresh, open-knit and accessible; built for early consumption. Screwcap. 13.5% alc. **Rating** 90 **To** 2014 $18 BE

ŸŸŸŸ **Next of Kin Margaret River Cabernet Sauvignon 2009** **Rating** 89 **To** 2016 $18

Margaret River Viognier 2011 **Rating** 87 **To** 2014 $26 BE

Yabby Lake Vineyard   ★★★★★

86–112 Tuerong Road, Tuerong, Vic 3937 **Region** Mornington Peninsula
T (03) 9667 6541 **www**.yabbylake.com **Open** 7 days 10–5
Winemaker Tom Carson, Chris Forge **Est.** 1998 **Dozens** 3350 **Vyds** 50.8ha

This high-profile wine business was established by Robert and Mem Kirby (of Village Roadshow), who had been landowners in the Mornington Peninsula for decades. In 1998 they established Yabby Lake Vineyard, under the direction of vineyard manager Keith Harris; the vineyard is on a north-facing slope, capturing maximum sunshine while also receiving sea breezes. The main focus is the 25.4ha of pinot noir, 14ha of chardonnay and 7.7ha of pinot gris; shiraz, merlot and sauvignon blanc take a back seat. The arrival of the hugely talented Tom Carson as Group Winemaker has added lustre to the winery and its wines. The initiative of opening cellar doors in five cities in China is without parallel, facilitated by the involvement of a Chinese partner. The Yabby Lake, Heathcote Estate, Cooralook and Red Claw wines are all part of this arrangement. On the home front, after 10 years of planning, Robert and Mem handed control of the family's vineyards and brands to their children, Nina and Clark, in 2008. Exports to the US, the UK, Canada, Sweden, Singapore, Hong Kong and China.

🍷🍷🍷🍷🍷 **Single Block Release Block 2 Mornington Peninsula Pinot Noir 2010** Block 2 is a sensational pinot; the sole clone is MV6; 20% whole bunch; 20% new French oak puncheons; on lees until bottled in Feb '11. It has a rich fruit profile, more black cherry and plum clafouti flavours backed by outstanding tannins that nail the structure. It is also intensely perfumed, with rose petals and spices that will build further with time. Screwcap. 13.7% alc. **Rating** 97 **To** 2019 $75

Block 6 Pinot Noir 2010 Crimson-purple; made from 75% Pommard clone, 25% MV6, with 37% whole bunch inclusion. Has a super-fragrant floral bouquet with exotic spices, almost into forest floor; tight, intense and quite savoury, it has perfect balance and superb tannins, yet it is the length that is the key to this wine. 250 dozen made. Screwcap. 14% alc. **Rating** 97 **To** 2025 $80

Single Vineyard Mornington Peninsula Chardonnay 2010 A roughly equal blend of P58 and Mendoza clones, wild yeast-fermented, cloudy juice in French oak puncheons, 15% new. The wine has exceptional mouthfeel, drive and length, with white flesh peach on the mid palate, and marked minerality on the finish and aftertaste. Screwcap. 12.8% alc. **Rating** 96 **To** 2017 $44

Block 6 Chardonnay 2010 Bright, pale green-quartz, with no yellow yet appearing; a beautifully made wine, with a fragrant bouquet, and a palate that magically combines intensity with finesse, linearity and intensity; fruit, oak and acidity are so tightly woven together, it is pointless picking out one or other, except to say that the purity of the Chablis-like fruit is exceptional. Screwcap. 12.9% alc. **Rating** 96 **To** 2020 $80

Single Vineyard Mornington Peninsula Pinot Noir 2010 A blend of clones MV6 (80%), the remainder Pommard, G5V15, and 115; 20% whole bunch; 15% to 20% new French oak puncheons. Strong, deep and clear colour, with a mix of dark cherry, plum and spice in the core of the palate, and fine tannins running throughout giving texture, structure and flavour; glorious drive and length. Screwcap. 13.8% alc. **Rating** 96 **To** 2018 $58

Mornington Peninsula Pinot Gris 2011 Pale quartz; not only a single vineyard, but a single block; whole bunch-pressed, the wine undergoes some barrel fermentation and gentle lees stirring to gain mouthfeel and complexity. That complexity is evident the moment you take the wine into your mouth, with a veritable chorus of flavours enhanced by the texture. Up among the very best Pinot Gris. Screwcap. 12.5% alc. **Rating** 95 **To** 2014 $30

🍷🍷🍷🍷🍷 **Red Claw Mornington Peninsula Sauvignon Blanc 2011** Light straw-
✪ green; another wine to show just how much varietal flavour was achievable in '11 from all the white varieties. The palate flows sinuously, citrus and tropical fruits alternating, but always backed by good acidity. Definitely to be enjoyed while it retains its youthful zest. Screwcap. 12% alc. **Rating** 93 **To** 2013 $23

✪   **Red Claw Mornington Peninsula Chardonnay 2010** Light straw-green; while on the bottom tier of the Yabby Lake Chardonnays, has a complex, faintly funky (in the best sense) bouquet, and all the ripe white-fleshed stone fruit and melon you could wish for despite the low alcohol; oak plays a minor role. Good value. Screwcap. 12.5% alc. **Rating** 93 **To** 2016 $23

✪   **Red Claw Mornington Peninsula Pinot Noir 2010** Bright, clear crimson-purple; intense blood plum and dark berry fruit aromas with a waft of French oak flow through to the palate, where they back off a little on the mid palate before coming through strongly on the finish. Screwcap. 14% alc. **Rating** 93 **To** 2016 $25
Red Claw Mornington Peninsula Pinot Gris 2011 Rating 91 **To** 2013 $23
Pink Claw Mornington Peninsula Pinot Noir Rose 2011 Rating 90 **To** 2014 $23

Yal Yal Estate   ★★★★

2 Boyanda Road, Glen Iris, Vic 3146 (postal) **Region** Mornington Peninsula
T 0416 112 703 **www**.yalyal.com.au **Open** Not
Winemaker Sandro Mosele **Est.** 1997 **Dozens** 950 **Vyds** 2.63ha
In 2008 Liz and Simon Gillies acquired a vineyard planted in 1997 to 1.6ha of chardonnay and a little over 1ha of pinot noir. In '09 the grapes were sold to local winemakers, but since 2000 the wines have been made by Sandro Mosele (under the watchful eyes of the Gillies). The wines are available through mail order and specialist retail stores.

 Yal Yal Rd Mornington Peninsula Chardonnay 2010 Bright, light straw-green; I'm not entirely convinced by the oak contribution to the bouquet, but there are no quibbles about the palate, with beautifully focused and fine white peach and citrus flavours running through to the long and zesty finish. Screwcap. 13.5% alc. **Rating** 93 **To** 2017 $30
Yal Yal Rd Mornington Peninsula Pinot Noir 2010 Light, bright crimson-purple; the bouquet has fragrance and perfume, the light-bodied palate with unexpected tenacity to its mix of cherry, plum and forest flavours. To be carefully matched with food that doesn't overwhelm it. Screwcap. 13.5% alc. **Rating** 91 **To** 2016 $35

Yalumba   ★★★★★

Eden Valley Road, Angaston, SA 5353 **Region** Eden Valley
T (08) 8561 3200 **www**.yalumba.com **Open** 7 days 10–5
Winemaker Louisa Rose (chief), Peter Gambetta, Kevin Glastonbury, Andrew La Nauze, Teresa Heuzenroeder **Est.** 1849 **Dozens** 930 000 **Vyds** 150ha
Family-owned and run by Robert Hill-Smith, Yalumba has a long commitment to quality and great vision in its selection of vineyard sites, new varieties and brands. It has always been a serious player at the top end of full-bodied (and full-blooded) Australian reds, and was a pioneer in the use of screwcaps. While its estate vineyards are largely planted to mainstream varieties, it has taken marketing ownership of viognier. However, these days its own brands revolve around the Y Series and a number of stand-alone brands across the length and breadth of SA. Yalumba has been very successful in building its export base. Exports to all major markets.

 The Virgilius Eden Valley Viognier 2010 Bright straw-green; the bouquet is extremely complex, with both wood and fruit aromas, the palate with layers of complexity far beyond that obtained by any other Australian producer; exceptional length and great balance to all the components. Screwcap. 13.5% alc. **Rating** 96 **To** 2018 $50
FDW[7c] Adelaide Hills Chardonnay 2009 Produced from the outstanding Bernard Dijon clones 76 and 95 grown on special sites in the Adelaide Hills. Straw-green; has an exceptionally intense, tight and long palate that has devoured the oak in which it was fermented (or should I say I assume it was fermented thus); the flavours linger long in the mouth after it is swallowed. Screwcap. 13.5% alc. **Rating** 96 **To** 2019 $33

FDR1A Barossa Cabernet Sauvignon Shiraz 2009 Medium crimson-purple; a wine with a long and proud history dating back to the 1970s; a totally harmonious blend of the two varieties, blackcurrant, blackberry, plum and black cherry woven together with fine tannins and quality oak. A perfect example of a medium-bodied red wine. Cork. 14% alc. **Rating** 96 **To** 2029 $43

Single Site Craneford Shiraz 2007 The colour is still bright and fresh; a medium- to full-bodied wine with shafts of spice and licorice driving through the blackberry fruit; the tannins are on the cusp, not surprising given the vintage. Significantly stained cork. 13.5% alc. **Rating** 95 **To** 2027 $60

Single Site Spring Gully Shiraz 2007 Good colour retention, similar to all three Single Site Shirazs, partly the benefit of the near-perfect alcohol levels; an elegant, well-balanced palate with a seamless blend of berry fruits, oak and tannins, all immaculately balanced. Cork. 13.5% alc. **Rating** 95 **To** 2027 $60

The Signature Barossa Cabernet Shiraz 2008 Good colour for age; Yalumba moved before the heatwave in picking its best grapes; this is a powerful, full-bodied wine with black fruits, licorice and tannins (plus oak) all clamouring to be heard. A different vintage, to be sure, but doesn't have the finesse of the FDR1A. Both wines deserved better-quality corks. 13.5% alc. **Rating** 95 **To** 2030 $53

Eden Valley Viognier 2010 Rating 94 **To** 2016 $25

Single Site Kalimna Shiraz 2007 Rating 94 **To** 2022 $60

✪ **Bush Vine Barossa Grenache 2010 Rating** 94 **To** 2020 $22

The Scribbler Cabernet Sauvignon Shiraz 2009 Rating 94 **To** 2017 $23

🍷🍷🍷🍷🍷 **Hand Picked Eden Valley Shiraz + Viognier 2009 Rating** 93 **To** 2030 $37

◐ **Running With Bulls Barossa Tempranillo 2010 Rating** 93 **To** 2018 $19

✪ **Wild Ferment Eden Valley Chardonnay 2009** Bright, light green-straw; the wine has a particular textural character that Yalumba would attribute to the wild ferment – it also invests the wine with a special sense of place. A thoroughly interesting wine, with the varietal fruit markers of far less importance than the texture and structure. Screwcap. 12.5% alc. **Rating** 92 **To** 2019 $22

✪ **Y Series Sauvignon Blanc 2011** Bright, pale green; cleverly marries citrus and tropical fruits on the bouquet and palate, the latter with good mouthfeel in a lighter-bodied spectrum. Will have broad appeal, and is great value. Screwcap. 11% alc. **Rating** 91 **To** 2014 $15

◐ **Running With Bulls Wrattonbully Tempranillo 2010 Rating** 91 **To** 2020 $19

✪ **Y Series Vermentino 2011** Pale quartz; has a fragrant and flowery bouquet leading into a deliciously fresh lemon sherbet/lemon zest plate, and a bright finish. An amazing achievement to keep the yields under control in '11. Screwcap. 11.5% alc. **Rating** 90 **To** Now $15

✪ **Y Series Sangiovese Rose 2011** While dry, has more mouthfeel and fruit weight than many of its peers; cherry and berry flavours are neatly balanced by acidity, the profile assisted by the moderate alcohol. Screwcap. 11.5% alc. **Rating** 90 **To** 2013 $15

✪ **Galway Vintage Traditional Shiraz 2010** Yet more money spent on new label design, etc (in the footsteps of Oxford Landing) by the profligate CEO. The wine has a bright crimson colour, and a fresh, zesty palate with a politically correct modest alcohol; just when you think the red and black cherry and plum fruit is about to tail away on the finish, it goes in precisely the opposite direction, picked up by fine, spicy, savoury tannins. Screwcap. 13.5% alc. **Rating** 90 **To** 2015 $16

✪ **Y Series Shiraz 2010** You really can't ask for more than you get from this wine at this price point; there is excellent balance between fruit, oak and tannins, the fruit freshness amplified by the moderate alcohol. Screwcap. 14% alc. **Rating** 90 **To** 2015 $15

The Strapper Barossa Grenache Shiraz Mataro 2010 Rating 90 **To** 2016 $22

✪ **Y Series Merlot 2010** Light, bright crimson; the red berry bouquet leads into a light- to medium-bodied palate with distinctive varietal character, cassis – black olive, plum and spice all to be found – and the tannins fine. Screwcap. 13.5% alc. **Rating** 90 **To** 2015 $15

Yangarra Estate Vineyard ★★★★★

Kangarilla Road, McLaren Vale, SA 5171 **Region** McLaren Vale
T (08) 8383 7459 **www**.yangarra.com **Open** 7 days 10–5
Winemaker Peter Fraser, Shelley Thompson **Est.** 2000 **Dozens** 12 000 **Vyds** 89.3ha
This is the Australian operation of Kendall-Jackson, one of the leading premium wine producers in California. In 2000 Kendall-Jackson acquired the 172ha Eringa Park vineyard from Normans Wines (the oldest vines dated back to 1923). The renamed Yangarra Estate Vineyard is the estate base for the operation, which built a state-of-the-art premium red wine facility in '10, and is moving to certified organic status with its vineyards. In '12 it purchased the historic Clarendon Vineyard from the estate of the late Alan Hickinbotham – it had been on the market for $10 million, but the actual price paid was not disclosed. Whatever it may have been, it represents a major endorsement of the prospects for top-quality Australian wines. Exports to the UK, the US and other major markets.

🍷🍷🍷🍷🍷 **Ironheart McLaren Vale Shiraz 2008** Particularly good colour for age; how this wine retains its vibrant colour but, even more, its lively red and black fruit flavours in the face of its alcohol, is one of life's sweet mysteries. Ditto for the depiction of a vine on the front label, surely provided by someone who has never seen a grapevine in the flesh. The fruit flavours are truly seductive. Screwcap. 15.5% alc. **Rating** 94 **To** 2030 $80
Old Vine McLaren Vale Grenache 2010 Bright crimson-purple; the bouquet is fragrant and expressive, red fruits to the fore, the palate with excellent structure from spicy tannins ex vines planted in '46, open-fermented with wild yeast and basket-pressed. Screwcap. 14.5% alc. **Rating** 94 **To** 2017 $28
McLaren Vale Mourvedre 2010 Deep crimson-purple; a powerful wine, skilfully made to allow the red berry fruit of the mourvedre full expression while keeping the tannins under control; has very good length and balance. Screwcap. 14% alc. **Rating** 94 **To** 2020 $32

🍷🍷🍷🍷🍷 **Small Pot Whole Bunch McLaren Vale Shiraz 2009 Rating** 93 **To** 2029 $45
Small Pot Rose 2011 Rating 92 **To** Now $25
McLaren Vale Shiraz 2009 Rating 92 **To** 2029 $25
Cadenzia McLaren Vale Grenache Shiraz Mourvedre 2010 Rating 92 **To** 2019 $28
McLaren Vale Viognier 2010 Rating 91 **To** 2013 $25
McLaren Vale Roussanne 2010 Rating 90 **To** 2015 $25

🍷🍷🍷🍷 **Cadenzia McLaren Vale Grenache Shiraz Mourvedre 2008 Rating** 89 **To** 2014 $28
McLaren Vale Mourvedre 2009 Rating 89 **To** 2019 $32

Yarra Burn ★★★

10 Beenak Road, Hoddles Creek, Vic 3139 **Region** Yarra Valley
T 1800 088 711 **www**.yarraburn.com.au **Open** Not
Winemaker Ed Carr **Est.** 1975 **Dozens** NFP **Vyds** 88ha
At least in terms of name, this is the focal point of Accolade's Yarra Valley operations. However, the winery has effectively been closed, and the wines are now made elsewhere. The 88ha of Upper Yarra vineyard remain. The lack of interest in the brand and its quality is as sad as it is obvious. Exports to the US, Indonesia, Malaysia, the Pacific Islands, China and Japan.

🍷🍷🍷🍷 **Premium Cuvee Rose NV** Salmon-pink; the back label is a paradigm of obfuscation, announcing that Yarra Burn selects classic sparkling grape varieties from premium cool regions throughout Victoria, which says precisely nothing. Even if the flavours are slightly dilute, the balance is as dry as one could wish for. Cork. 12.5% alc. **Rating** 88 **To** 2014 $16

Yarra Yarra ★★★★★

239 Hunts Lane, Steels Creek, Vic 3775 **Region** Yarra Valley
T (03) 5965 2380 **www**.yarrayarravineyard.com.au **Open** By appt
Winemaker Ian Maclean **Est.** 1979 **Dozens** NFP **Vyds** 9.3ha

Despite its small production, the wines of Yarra Yarra have found their way into a veritable who's who of Melbourne's best restaurants, encouraging Ian Maclean to increase the estate plantings from 2ha to over 7ha in 1996 and '97. Demand for the beautifully crafted wines continued to exceed supply, so the Macleans planted yet more vines and increased winery capacity. All this seemed to go up in flames as the terrible 2009 Black Saturday bushfires consumed the winery, irreplaceable museum stock from '83 to 2000, the then yet-to-be-bottled '08 Syrah and '06 and '08 Sauvignon Blanc Semillon (the '07 vintage had been destroyed by frost), and scorched or burnt 50% of the estate vineyards. Friends rallied to the cause, and Ian has embarked on the long job of repairing/replacing the vineyard trellis system, methodically replanting the half of the vineyard destroyed by fire and introducing the use of organic/biodynamic sprays. The new winery was finished at the end of April '10, too late for the vintage, which was made in one of the farm buildings not destroyed. When friends asked why he should do all this, having turned 65, his answer was simple: 'My greatest wines have yet to be made.' June '12 saw wines from the '11 vintage made in the new winery. Exports to Singapore, Malaysia, Taiwan and Hong Kong.

🍷🍷🍷🍷 **The Phoenix Sauvignon Blanc Semillon 2009** The name is a poignant reminder of the destruction of the Yarra Yarra vineyard and various buildings; it is very full-bodied and rich, and I would prefer that people purchased it for what it is: a phoenix arising. Made from sauvignon blanc purchased from a nearby vineyard and semillon donated by De Bortoli. Diam. 13% alc. **Rating** 90 **To** 2016 **$40**

Yarra Yering ★★★★★

Briarty Road, Coldstream, Vic 3770 **Region** Yarra Valley
T (03) 5964 9267 **www**.yarrayering.com **Open** 7 days 10–5
Winemaker Paul Bridgeman **Est.** 1969 **Dozens** 5000 **Vyds** 26.37ha

In September 2008, founder Bailey Carrodus died, and in April '09 Yarra Yering was on the market. It was Bailey Carrodus' clear wish and expectation that any purchaser would continue to manage the vineyard and winery, and hence the wine style, in much the same way as he had done for the previous 40 years. Its acquisition in June '09 by a partnership headed by Swiss-born, Singapore-based Edward (Ed) Peters seems certain to fulfil that wish. The low-yielding, unirrigated vineyards have always produced wines of extraordinary depth and intensity, and there is every reason to suppose that there will be no change in the years ahead. Dry Red No. 1 is a cabernet blend; Dry Red No. 2 is a shiraz blend; Dry Red No. 3 is a blend of touriga, tinta cao, tinta amarela, roriz and sousao; Pinot Noir and Chardonnay are not hidden behind delphic numbers; Underhill Shiraz is from an adjacent vineyard purchased by Yarra Yering over a decade ago; and Potsorts is an extraordinary vintage port style made from the same varieties as Dry Red No. 3. Exports to the UK, the US, Singapore and Hong Kong.

🍷🍷🍷🍷🍷 **Dry Red No. 3 2009** This is the eclectic dry red made from the same varieties as Bailey Carrodus used with his Potsorts (drolly amended from Portsorts at the behest of officialdom), and is a silky tapestry of an amazingly harmonious red and black fruits, all in a medium-bodied frame. Cork. 13% alc. **Rating** 96 **To** 2030 **$70**

Potsorts 2009 Inky purple-crimson; a blend of touriga nacional, tinta cao and alvarelhao; exceptionally potent and concentrated, with a fearsome degree of alcohol, but avoids sweet fruit. Ten years minimum. Cork. 21% alc. **Rating** 95 **To** 2020 **$79**

Carrodus Viognier 2009 Glowing yellow-green; the flagship of the winery, made from a unique clone of viognier rising 40 years old. It has achieved the ever-so-difficult balance between positive varietal character (peach and apricot) and controlled phenolics on the finish. Will not appeal to all palates. Cork. 14% alc. **Rating** 94 **To** 2018 **$158**

Pinot Noir 2009 Strong red-purple; an extremely concentrated, powerful and densely packed Pinot Noir, with abundant black cherry and plum fruit that has soaked up the new oak. Prior vintages back to the '80s have proved their longevity. Cork. 13.5% alc. **Rating** 94 **To** 2019 $79

Dry Red No. 2 2009 Purple-crimson; the Shiraz/Viognier co-fermentation has worked its usual magic; the wine is wonderfully lively, yet complex, with elegance and intensity to its mix of spice, red and black fruits, fine tannins and quality oak. All this and more at 13.5% alcohol. Cork. **Rating** 94 **To** 2030 $82

♀♀♀♀♀ **Dry Red No. 1 2009 Rating** 93 **To** 2029 $82
Chardonnay 2009 Rating 90 **To** 2014 $79
Underhill Shiraz 2009 Rating 90 **To** 2020 $70

Yarrabank   ★★★★★

38 Melba Highway, Yarra Glen, Vic 3775 **Region** Yarra Valley
T (03) 9730 0100 **www**.yering.com **Open** 7 days 10–5
Winemaker Michel Parisot, Willy Lunn, Darren Rathbone **Est.** 1993 **Dozens** 5000
Vyds 4ha

Yarrabank is a highly successful joint venture between the French Champagne house Devaux and Yering Station, established in 1993. Until '97 the Yarrabank Cuvee Brut was made under Claude Thibaut's direction at Domaine Chandon, but thereafter the entire operation has been conducted at Yarrabank. There are 4ha of dedicated 'estate' vineyards at Yering Station (planted to pinot noir and chardonnay); the balance of the intake comes from other growers in the Yarra Valley and southern Vic. Wine quality has consistently been outstanding, frequently with an unmatched finesse and delicacy. In '12 the Rathbone Group wine interests were placed on the market for sale either as a group or individually. Exports to all major markets.

♀♀♀♀♀ **Late Disgorged 2004** Vibrant straw-gold; still wonderfully youthful after more
than seven years on lees, citrus and nectarine flavours more powerful and focused
than the bready/yeast characters that have slowly built during the time on lees; the
length of the palate is most impressive. Cork. 13% alc. **Rating** 96 **To** 2014 $55
Cuvee 2008 Bright colour, and good mousse; the palate is rich and complex,
with bready/brioche characters running through the fruit flavours of white peach
and nectarine. The finish is as substantial as it is long. Cork. 13% alc. **Rating** 95
To Now $38
Cuvee 2007 Pale straw; a complex blend of multi-regional pinot noir and
chardonnay fermented in this bottle and given four years on yeast lees; pale bright
straw, it is a very elegant and harmonious wine, with white peach and spice
flavours and a hint of cashew on the very long palate, the aftertaste clean and fresh.
Cork. 13% alc. **Rating** 95 **To** Now $38

YarraLoch   ★★★★★

Studio 308, 15-87 Gladstone Street, South Melbourne, Vic 3205 **Region** Yarra Valley
T (03) 9696 1604 **www**.yarraloch.com.au **Open** By appt
Winemaker David Bicknell **Est.** 1998 **Dozens** 3000 **Vyds** 12ha

This is the ambitious project of successful investment banker Stephen Wood. He has taken the best possible advice, and has not hesitated to provide appropriate financial resources to a venture that has no exact parallel in the Yarra Valley or anywhere else in Australia. Twelve hectares of vineyards may not seem so unusual, but in fact he has assembled three entirely different sites, 70km apart, each matched to the needs of the variety/varieties planted on that site. Pinot noir (4.4ha) is planted on the Steep Hill Vineyard, with a northeast orientation, and a shaley rock and ironstone soil. Cabernet sauvignon (4ha) has been planted at Kangaroo Ground, with a dry, steep northwest-facing site and abundant sun exposure in the warmest part of the day, ensuring full ripeness. Just over 3.5ha of merlot, shiraz, chardonnay and viognier are planted at the Upper Plenty Vineyard, 50km from Kangaroo Ground. This has an average temperature 2°C cooler and a ripening period 2–3 weeks later than the warmest parts of the Yarra Valley. Add skilled winemaking and some sophisticated (and beautiful) packaging, and you have a 5-star recipe for success. Exports to China.

🍷🍷🍷🍷🍷 **Chardonnay 2011** Bright straw-green; a wine that sings the praises of the '11 vintage for Yarra chardonnay; marries intensity with finesse, precision with flavour, the last given by white peach, nectarine and grapefruit flavours undimmed by French oak, and driving the brilliantly long finish. Screwcap. 12.5% alc. **Rating** 96 **To** 2018 $32

Stephanie's Dream Pinot Noir 2010 Light crystal-clear crimson-purple; a super-fragant red berry/cherry bouquet leads into a palate with strong spicy savoury tannins; needs time, so leave it alone until you've finished the standard Yarra Valley wine. Screwcap. 13.5% alc. **Rating** 94 **To** 2017 $50

🍷🍷🍷🍷 **Pinot Noir 2010** **Rating** 93 **To** 2014 $30

Arneis 2011 **Rating** 90 **To** 2016 $25

Yarran Wines ★★★★☆

178 Myall Park Road, Yenda, NSW 2681 **Region** Riverina
T (02) 6968 1125 **www**.yarranwines.com.au **Open** Wed–Mon 10–5
Winemaker Sam Brewer **Est.** 2000 **Dozens** 5000 **Vyds** 30ha

John and Lorraine Brewer have been grapegrowers for over 30 years, but when son Sam went to CSU to complete a degree in wine science, they celebrated his graduation by crushing 1 tonne of shiraz, fermenting the grapes in a milk vat. The majority of the grapes from the estate plantings are sold, but each year a little more has been made under the Yarran banner; along the way a winery with a crush capacity of 150 tonnes has been built. Sam worked for Southcorp and De Bortoli in Australia, and overseas (in the US and China), but after 10 years decided in 2009 to take the plunge and concentrate on the family winery, together with his parents. The majority of the grapes come from the family vineyard, but some parcels are sourced from growers, including Lake Cooper Estate in the Heathcote region. It is intended that the portfolio of regions will be gradually increased, and Sam has demonstrated his ability to make silk purses out of sow's ears. Exports to China.

🍷🍷🍷🍷🍷 ✪ **Leopardwood Heathcote Shiraz 2010** Medium to full red-purple; the highly expressive bouquet of ripe plum, berry and spice flows into a textured medium-bodied palate, where rounded tannins and oak provide a framework for the luscious, but not the least jammy, fruit. Screwcap. 14% alc. **Rating** 94 **To** 2025 $18

🍷🍷🍷🍷 ✪ **Leopardwood Yenda Petit Verdot 2010** Strong colour; petit verdot is a chameleon, able to adapt to warmer climates than its cool birthplace of France's Loire Valley and Bordeaux. It doesn't achieve the elegance it has there (or in cool parts of Australia) but shows here all the generous berry fruit one could wish for, plus ripe tannins. Screwcap. 14% alc. **Rating** 91 **To** 2020 $18

⚙ **Sauvignon Blanc Semillon 2011** **Rating** 90 **To** Now $10

✪ **Chardonnay 2011** A ridiculously low price for such a well-made wine, with white and yellow peach balanced by a gentle touch of citrus acidity and even more gentle toasty French oak. Small-batch winemaking and attention to detail have shone through in '11. Screwcap. 12.5% alc. **Rating** 90 **To** 2014 $10

🍷🍷🍷🍷 ✪ **Chenin Blanc 2011** **Rating** 89 **To** 2014 $10

⚙ **Pinot Grigio 2011** **Rating** 87 **To** Now $10

⚙ **Merlot 2010** **Rating** 87 **To** Now $13

Yarrawood Estate ★★★★

1275 Melba Highway, Yarra Glen, Vic 3775 **Region** Yarra Valley
T (03) 9730 2003 **www**.yarrawood.com.au **Open** 7 days 10–5
Winemaker Contract **Est.** 1997 **Dozens** 28 000 **Vyds** 40.6ha

Yarrawood Estate has pinot noir (10.6ha), cabernet sauvignon (7.9ha), chardonnay (7.2ha), merlot (5.3ha), shiraz (4.5ha) and lesser amounts of sauvignon blanc, riesling and verdelho. The major part of the grape production is sold, and the Yarrawood Tall Tales wines are contract-made. It does, however, have a café and cellar door on the Melba Highway, 3km north of Yarra Glen. Further wines were received after this issue went to print, tasting notes appear on www.winecompanion.com.au. Exports to Papua New Guinea, Japan, Singapore and China.

🍷🍷🍷🍷 **Tall Tales Chardonnay 2010** Light straw-green; a pleasant, well-made wine, with nectarine, melon and a touch of oak; not particularly intense, but well balanced. Screwcap. 13.5% alc. **Rating** 89 **To** 2015 $22

Yaxley Estate ★★★★

31 Dransfield Road, Copping, Tas 7174 **Region** Southern Tasmania
T (03) 6253 5222 **www**.yaxleyestate.com **Open** At Copping Museum, Arthur Highway
Winemaker Frogmore Creek, Kilbowie Wines (Peter Shields) **Est.** 1991 **Dozens** 100
Vyds 2.5ha
While Yaxley Estate was established back in 1991, it was not until '98 that it offered each of the four wines from its vineyard plantings. Once again, it is the small batch-handling skills (and patience) of Frogmore Creek that have made the venture possible. The vineyard (pinot gris, sauvignon blanc, pinot noir and chardonnay) was certified organic in 2010.

🍷🍷🍷🍷🍷 **Pinot Gris 2011** A remarkably focused and intense wine, with mineral acid, pear, apple and citrus pith and skin all vitamised together; considerable length. Screwcap. 12% alc. **Rating** 93 **To** 2014 $35
Pinot Noir 2010 Bright purple-crimson; there are some unusual, but attractive, nuances on the bouquet: fern, briar and sea shells as well as the cherry mainframe; the texture and structure of the palate are admirable. Screwcap. 13.2% alc. **Rating** 93 **To** 2018 $32

🍷🍷🍷🍷 **Pinot Gris 2010** **Rating** 89 **To** Now $35

Yelland & Papps ★★★★★

Lot 501 Nuraip Road, Nuriootpa, SA 5355 **Region** Barossa Valley
T (08) 8562 3510 **www**.yellandandpapps.com **Open** Mon, Wed–Sat 10–4, Tues & Sun by appt
Winemaker Michael Papps **Est.** 2005 **Dozens** 3000 **Vyds** 1ha
Michael and Susan Papps (née Yelland) set up this venture after their marriage in 2005. Susan decided she did not want to give up her surname entirely, and thus has been able to keep her family name in the business. Michael has the technical background, having lived in the Barossa Valley for more than 20 years, working at local wineries, bottling facilities and wine technology businesses. Susan, who grew up on the Yorke Peninsula, headed to New York for a year, working and studying at the Windows of the World Wine School. The quantity of wine made is limited by the scarcity of the high-quality grapes they manage to secure from the Greenock area for their wines. Exports to China.

🍷🍷🍷🍷🍷 **Divine Barossa Valley Grenache 2009** Another heavy bottle, and a price tag to match, yet the offering is serious and well executed; ripe raspberry liqueur, violets and thyme are on display, with a fleshy mid palate and the structure to match; surprisingly long, and there can be little doubt old-vine characters come through in the end. Screwcap. 14.5% alc. **Rating** 95 **To** 2020 $75 BE
Devote Greenock Barossa Valley Shiraz 2010 Deep crimson-purple; an immaculately balanced wine that has been open-fermented, basket-pressed, and matured in a mix of new and French oak barrels; a tribute to the '10 vintage and to the winemaking, allowing the quality of the fruit to dominate the medium-bodied palate with its black cherry and blackberry fruit; the tannins are fine, the oak integrated. Screwcap. 14.5% alc. **Rating** 94 **To** 2025 $35
Divine Barossa Valley Shiraz 2009 Impenetrable colour; dark-fruited, with lashings of oak-derived spices, mocha and licorice; the palate is dense and full-bodied, with power taking charge over finesse; big-boned and unashamed of its brutish personality and incredibly heavy bottle. Screwcap. 14.5% alc. **Rating** 94 **To** 2020 $75 BE
✪ **Delight Barossa Valley Grenache Shiraz 2010** Bright, light crimson; 71% 50-year-old grenache and 29% 25-year-old shiraz, both from Greenock, basket-pressed and spending 16 months in oak. It is a delicious, left-field take on Grenache, with bright red fruit that is tangy and lively, no Turkish delight characters, and a long finish. Screwcap. 14.5% alc. **Rating** 94 **To** 2018 $20

ϼϼϼϼϼ Devote Barossa Valley Roussanne 2011 Rating 93 To 2020 $35
     Devote Old Vine Barossa Valley Grenache 2010 Rating 93 To 2022 $32
✪   Delight Barossa Valley Shiraz 2010 Strong purple-red; made using the old/
     new tricks of hand picking, open fermentation, basket pressing and 15 months in
     a full mix of oak. The result is a luscious medium- to full-bodied wine, crammed
     with plum and blackberry jam, licorice, spice and oak, the tannins plush and soft.
     Screwcap. 14.5% alc. Rating 92 To 2025 $20

ϼϼϼϼ Devote Barossa Valley Cabernet Sauvignon 2010 Rating 89 To 2020 $32
     Divine Barossa Valley Mataro 2009 Rating 89 To 2018 $102 BE
     Delight Barossa Valley Grenache Rose 2011 Rating 87 To Now $20

Yellowglen   ★★★★

77 Southbank Boulevard, Southbank, Vic 3006 **Region** South Eastern Australia
T 1300 651 650 **www.**yellowglen.com **Open** Not
Winemaker Charles Hargrave, Trina Smith **Est.** 1975 **Dozens** NFP
It may come as a surprise to some (it certainly did to me) that Yellowglen is the clear leader
in the value share of the sparkling wine category in Australia, with over 20%, way in front of
Jacob's Creek at just under 9%. It is this dominant position (and a spread of RRP prices from
$14 for Yellow up to $30 for Vintage Perle) that underpins its separate listing. Exports to the
UK, the US and NZ.

ϼϼϼϼϼ Vintage Perle 2008 Bright straw-green; a blend of pinot noir and chardonnay
     that has spent an extended time on lees (not surprising given the age of the wine)
     but makes no claim of bottle fermentation. One can see why this is a widely liked
     wine, sold in large volumes. Cork. 12% alc. Rating 92 To 2014 $30
     Perle Non Vintage NV A blend of vintages of pinot noir and chardonnay, bottle-
     fermented but then taken to tank for final blending and bottling. An easygoing style
     with good balance and length. Cork. 12% alc. Rating 90 To 2013 $20

ϼϼϼϼ Vintage Cremant 2009 Rating 87 To 2013 $20

Yering Station   ★★★★★

38 Melba Highway, Yarra Glen, Vic 3775 **Region** Yarra Valley
T (03) 9730 0100 **www.**yering.com **Open** 7 days 10–5
Winemaker Willy Lunn, Darren Rathbone **Est.** 1988 **Dozens** 60 000 **Vyds** 112ha
The historic Yering Station (or at least the portion of the property on which the cellar door
sales and vineyard are established) was purchased by the Rathbone family in 1996 and is also
the site of the Yarrabank joint venture with French Champagne house Devaux (see separate
entry). A spectacular and very large winery has been erected, handling the Yarrabank sparkling
wines and the Yering Station table wines. It immediately became one of the focal points of the
Yarra Valley, particularly as the historic Chateau Yering, where luxury accommodation and fine
dining are available, is next door. Yering Station's own restaurant is open every day for lunch,
providing the best lunchtime cuisine in the Valley. In 2008 Tom Carson moved on and was
replaced by William (Willy) Lunn, a graduate of Adelaide University with more than 24 years'
cool-climate winemaking experience around the world, including at Petaluma, Shaw & Smith
and Argyle Winery (Oregon). In '12 the Rathbone Group wine interests were placed on the
market for sale either as a group or individually. Exports to all major markets.

ϼϼϼϼϼ Reserve Yarra Valley Chardonnay 2010 Bright, pale straw-green; an
     extremely impressive Chardonnay, the barrel-ferment characters adding
     considerable complexity, yet in no way diminishing the intensity and purity of
     grapefruit and white peach fruit flavours that linger on the finish and aftertaste of
     the very long palate. Screwcap. 13% alc. Rating 96 To 2020 $90
     Reserve Yarra Valley Pinot Noir 2010 Light crimson; the red berry aromas
     lead into an intense, elegant and very long palate, juicy fruit interwoven with satin
     tannins. Seriously lovely Pinot. Screwcap. 13.8% alc. Rating 96 To 2018 $90

Yarra Valley Shiraz Viognier 2010 Light, bright hue; the bouquet is highly fragrant, clearly a function of the viognier; the medium-bodied palate is full to the brim with vibrant black and red cherry fruit, leaving just enough space for the French oak and fine-grained tannins to add their contribution. Screwcap. 14.5% alc. **Rating** 96 **To** 2020 $38

Yarra Valley Cabernet Sauvignon 2010 Strong but clear purple-crimson; a distinguished Cabernet with deep and satisfying blackcurrant/cassis fruit aromas and flavours; the medium- to full-bodied palate has exemplary balance and structure, both ripe tannins and quality oak adding complexity. A minimum 20-year life ahead. Screwcap. 14% alc. **Rating** 96 **To** 2030 $38

Single Vineyard Old Beenak Road Shiraz 2010 Bright, clear crimson; a vibrant, fresh, red berry and spice wine reflecting its cool, red soil origins; it is medium-bodied, the palate with considerable length, and deepened by quality French oak. Screwcap. 14.5% alc. **Rating** 95 **To** 2022 $38

Reserve Yarra Valley Shiraz Viognier 2010 Strong crimson-red; the perfumed bouquet is a slightly deceptive introduction to dense and powerful, full-bodied palate, oak playing a much greater role. The trademark influence of viognier is there, of course, but at a lesser level. This wine demands, and will repay, time in bottle. Screwcap. 14.5% alc. **Rating** 95 **To** 2030 $90

Yarra Valley Chardonnay 2010 **Rating** 94 **To** 2018 $38
Yarra Valley Chardonnay 2009 **Rating** 94 **To** 2019 $30
Village Yarra Valley Pinot Noir 2010 **Rating** 94 **To** 2016 $24

♟♟♟♟♟ **Village Yarra Valley Chardonnay 2010** **Rating** 93 **To** 2015 $24
MVR Yarra Valley Marsanne Viognier Roussanne 2009 **Rating** 93 **To** 2013 $26
ED Yarra Valley Pinot Noir Rose 2011 **Rating** 93 **To** 2013 $24
Village Yarra Valley Shiraz Viognier 2010 **Rating** 93 **To** 2020 $24

✪ **Little Yering Cabernet Shiraz 2009** Light, bright red-purple; an uncommon blend in the Yarra Valley, snatched from the jaws of smoke and fire in Feb '09; is distinctly rich and concentrated, French oak a contributor to the blackberry and blackcurrant fruit; if there is any smoke taint, it's so far hidden by the exuberance of the fruit. However, best drunk earlier rather than later. Screwcap. 14% alc. **Rating** 93 **To** 2014 $18

✪ **Little Yering Yarra Valley Pinot Noir 2010** Light but clear colour; attractive early-drinking style, with purity and freshness to its red and black cherry fruit; the tannins are fine and supple, and 12 months in French oak has mainly contributed to the mouthfeel. Screwcap. 13.5% alc. **Rating** 92 **To** 2014 $18

Village Yarra Valley Fume Blanc 2011 **Rating** 91 **To** 2015 $25

✪ **Little Yering Yarra Valley Chardonnay 2010** Light straw-green; a complex wine with more or less equal contributions from lively fruit and quality French oak; the result is a layered wine, enjoyable now or in a few years, and made for generous food. Screwcap. 13.5% alc. **Rating** 90 **To** 2014 $18

Yarra Valley Pinot Noir 2010 **Rating** 90 **To** 2016 $38

Yeringberg   ★★★★★

Maroondah Highway, Coldstream, Vic 3770 **Region** Yarra Valley
T (03) 9739 1453 **www**.yeringberg.com **Open** By appt
Winemaker Guill and Sandra de Pury **Est.** 1863 **Dozens** 1200 **Vyds** 2.65ha
Guill de Pury and daughter Sandra, with Guill's wife Katherine in the background, make wines for the new millennium from the low-yielding vines re-established in the heart of what was one of the most famous (and infinitely larger) vineyards of the 19th century. In the riper years, the red wines have a velvety generosity of flavour rarely encountered, yet never lose varietal character, while the long-lived Marsanne Roussanne takes students of history back to Yeringberg's fame in the 19th century. Exports to the US, Switzerland, Singapore, Japan, Hong Kong and China.

♟♟♟♟♟ Yarra Valley Chardonnay 2010 Medium straw-green; a distinguished wine with a proud history, which it does not in any way let down; the intense fruit has considerable structure, part from the well-integrated oak, and part from the crisp acidity that prolongs the palate. Will mature gracefully over the next 5–10 years. Diam. 12.5% alc. **Rating** 94 **To** 2020 $50

Yarra Valley Viognier 2010 Light straw-green; a high-class grower and maker of Viognier, able to invest the wine with clear-cut peach and apricot varietal fruit without any heat or weight on the finish. What's more, it will have time in the cellar without protest if you decide this is the way to go. Diam. 13.5% alc. **Rating** 94 **To** 2015 $30

Yarra Valley Marsanne Roussanne 2010 Pale straw; a wine that, time and time again, has proved its ability to develop superbly given five years or more in the cellar; part of this is due to the fine, almost skeletal, structure and its moderate alcohol leaving good levels of natural acidity, particularly from the roussanne. Diam. 12% alc. **Rating** 94 **To** 2020 $50

♟♟♟♟
✪ Yeringberg Declassified 2009 Bright, clear red-purple; declassified is printed in large red letters across the front of the label so there is no possibility of anyone missing the message; it, like so many Yarra red wines in the '09 vintage, was affected by smoke taint, but I have to say there are others that have been released with even more taint, but without the warning or the massively reduced price. The one further warning is drink it asap, because the taint becomes progressively more obvious as the wine ages. The points are nominal. Screwcap. 13.5% alc. **Rating** 89 **To** 2013 $15

Yilgarnia   ★★★★☆

1847 Redmond West Road, Redmond, WA 6327 **Region** Denmark
T (08) 9845 3031 **www**.yilgarnia.com.au **Open** Fri–Mon, school & public hols 11–5 (closed May–Sept)
Winemaker Harewood Estate (James Kellie) **Est.** 1997 **Dozens** 3000 **Vyds** 12.5ha
Melbourne-educated Peter Buxton travelled across the Nullarbor over 40 years ago and settled on a bush block of 405 acres on the Hay River, 6km north of Wilson Inlet. For the first 10 years Peter worked for the Department of Agriculture in Albany, surveying several of the early vineyards in WA, and recognised the potential of his family's property. The vineyard (chardonnay, sauvignon blanc, shiraz, cabernet sauvignon, shiraz and semillon) is planted on north-facing blocks, the geological history of which stretches back 2 billion years.

♟♟♟♟♟ Denmark Semillon Sauvignon Blanc 2011 A 54/46% blend; there is some synergy at work here, the bouquet with plenty of presence, ranging between citrus, herb and tropical, the palate so complex and full-bodied it suggests barrel fermentation, although there is none; thus the flavours come down to a layered combination of tropical and stone fruit flavours, circumscribed on the finish by good acidity. Screwcap. 13% alc. **Rating** 94 **To** 2014 $17

♟♟♟♟♟
✪ Denmark Semillon 2011 A complex wine showing crossover characters with Riesling in much the same way as they can occur in the Hunter; the confounding addition here is a touch of passionfruit, often regarded as a marker for Sauvignon Blanc. Don't be confused, just enjoy the wine for the array of aromas and flavours it provides. Screwcap. 12% alc. **Rating** 91 **To** 2018 $19
✪ Denmark Chardonnay 2011 **Rating** 90 **To** 2014 $19
Denmark Shiraz 2009 **Rating** 90 **To** 2019 $24

♟♟♟♟
✪ Denmark Sauvignon Blanc 2011 **Rating** 89 **To** 2013 $19
Denmark Merlot 2009 **Rating** 89 **To** 2015 $24

Z Wine

PO Box 135, Lyndoch, SA 5351 **Region** Barossa Valley
T 0411 447 986 **www**.zwine.com.au **Open** At Bibu Barossa, Tanunda
Winemaker Janelle Zerk **Est.** 1999 **Dozens** 800 **Vyds** 60ha
Sisters Janelle and Kristen Zerk are the dynamic duo behind Z Wine. The Zerk family has been growing grapes in the Barossa Valley since 1846, but fifth-generation Janelle is the first family member to pursue a winemaking career, and has made wine in Tuscany, Burgundy (Puligny Montrachet) and Sonoma, California. Kirsten has a wine marketing degree from Adelaide University. Grapes are sourced from the family's Lyndoch vineyard.

ŶŶŶŶŶ **Barossa Valley Grenache Shiraz Mataro 2010** Bright colour, with a fragrant bouquet of red and black fruits, sage and spice; the palate is medium-bodied, fresh and fragrant, with a long tail of licorice and tannins working seamlessly together. Screwcap. 14.5% alc. **Rating** 91 **To** 2018 $25 BE

ŶŶŶŶ **Barossa Valley Shiraz 2010 Rating** 89 **To** 2018 $45 BE
Barossa Valley Rose 2011 Rating 88 **To** 2013 $15 BE

Zarephath Wines

424 Moorialup Road, East Porongurup, WA 6324 **Region** Porongurup
T (08) 9853 1152 **www**.zarephathwines.com **Open** Mon–Sat 10–5, Sun 12–4
Winemaker Robert Diletti **Est.** 1994 **Dozens** 1500 **Vyds** 8.9ha
The Zarephath vineyard is owned and operated by Brothers and Sisters of The Christ Circle, a Benedictine community. They say the most outstanding feature of the location is the feeling of peace and tranquillity that permeates the site, something I can well believe on the basis of numerous visits to the Porongurups. Plantings include chardonnay, cabernet sauvignon, pinot noir, shiraz, riesling and merlot.

ŶŶŶŶŶ **Porongurup Riesling 2011** Pale straw, vibrant hue; a complex bouquet of struck match, lemon pith and bath talc; the bouquet is energetic, generous and long, adding texture to the savoury finish for good measure. Screwcap. 13% alc. **Rating** 93 **To** 2017 $25 BE
Porongurup Shiraz 2008 A bright and fragrant bouquet with red fruits and an attractive mineral component; medium-bodied, defined and racy on the palate, this is ready to go now and should be enjoyed as such. Screwcap. 14% alc. **Rating** 92 **To** 2016 $30 BE
Porongurup Petit Chardonnay 2011 Mid gold, vibrant green hue; ripe nectarine, spice and bath talc are on display; the palate is taut and racy, relying on freshness and drive for its personality; moderately long, finishing with a dry mineral edge. Screwcap. 13% alc. **Rating** 90 **To** 2016 $25 BE
Porongurup Shiraz 2005 Showing a nice level of development, with fresh cranberry and blackberry supporting leather and spice; good depth and freshness for its age, and would be fun to match food with. Screwcap. 14% alc. **Rating** 90 **To** 2014 $30 BE

ŶŶŶŶ **Porongurup Cabernet Sauvignon 2008 Rating** 87 **To** 2015 $30 BE

Zema Estate ★★★★★

Riddoch Highway, Coonawarra, SA 5263 **Region** Coonawarra
T (08) 8736 3219 **www**.zema.com.au **Open** 7 days 9–5
Winemaker Greg Clayfield **Est.** 1982 **Dozens** 20 000 **Vyds** 61ha
Zema is one of the last outposts of hand-pruning in Coonawarra, with members of the Zema family tending the vineyard that has been progressively planted since 1982 in the heart of Coonawarra's terra rossa soil. Winemaking practices are straightforward; if ever there was an example of great wines being made in the vineyard, this is it. The extremely popular and equally talented former Lindemans winemaker Greg Clayfield has joined the team, replacing long-term winemaker Tom Simons. Exports to the UK, Vietnam, Hong Kong, Japan and Singapore.

ŦŦŦŦŦ Family Selection Coonawarra Cabernet Sauvignon 2008 Deep crimson, bright; a dark, compelling and concentrated black fruit offering, with cassis and violets the theme; the palate is juicy on entry, laden with sweet fruit, and then the structure comes along to draw out the long, full-bodied and harmonious finish. Screwcap. 14.5% alc. **Rating** 95 **To** 2025 $45 BE
Family Selection Coonawarra Shiraz 2008 Deep garnet, bright; a fresh and vibrant spice-laden bouquet with mulberry, fine oak and black olive on display; the palate is focused and lively with firm tannins and zesty acidity in equal proportion to the dark fruits on offer; long and layered, with a healthy future ahead. Screwcap. 14.5% alc. **Rating** 94 **To** 2025 $45 BE

ŦŦŦŦŦ Coonawarra Cabernet Sauvignon 2009 **Rating** 93 **To** 2020 $28 BE
Coonawarra Shiraz 2009 **Rating** 92 **To** 2018 $25 BE

ŦŦŦŦ Cluny Coonawarra Cabernet Merlot 2009 **Rating** 87 **To** 2015 $25 BE

Z4 Wines ★★★

PO Box 57, Campbell, ACT 2612 **Region** Canberra District
T (02) 6248 6445 **www**.Z4wines.com.au **Open** Not
Winemaker Canberra Winemakers **Est.** 2007 **Dozens** 1200
Z4 Wines is the venture of the very energetic Bill Mason and wife Maria. The name derives from the Masons' four children, each having a Christian name starting with 'Z'. Bill has been distributing wine in Canberra since 2004, with a small but distinguished list of wineries, which he represents with considerable marketing flair. The Z4 wines are listed on many Canberra restaurant wine lists, and are stocked by leading independent wine retailers. Exports to China.

ŦŦŦŦ Zachary Canberra District Cabernet Merlot 2010 Clear red-purple; a 51/49% blend with soft blackcurrant, black cherry and plum flavours on the medium-bodied palate; the tannins are soft and the oak discreet. Screwcap. 14.2% alc. **Rating** 88 **To** 2015 $20

Zig Zag Road ★★★★

201 Zig Zag Road, Drummond, Vic 3446 **Region** Macedon Ranges
T (03) 5423 9390 **www**.zigzagwines.com.au **Open** Thurs–Mon 10–6
Winemaker Eric Bellchambers, Llew Knight **Est.** 1972 **Dozens** 500 **Vyds** 3.8ha
Zig Zag Road's dry-grown vines produce relatively low yields, and until 1996 the grapes were sold to Hanging Rock Winery. In 1996 the decision was taken to manage the property on a full-time basis, and to make the wine onsite. In 2002 Eric and Anne Bellchambers became the third owners of this vineyard, planted by Roger Aldridge in 1972. The Bellchambers have extended the plantings with riesling and merlot, supplementing the older plantings of shiraz, cabernet sauvignon and pinot noir.

ŦŦŦŦŦ Macedon Ranges Shiraz 2008 Light but very youthful crimson-purple; the fragrant bouquet and lively palate, abounding with red fruits, seems more like a 1-year-old than a 4-year-old wine; however, this has not been achieved by a low pH, acidic base. Screwcap. 14% alc. **Rating** 93 **To** 2016 $22
Macedon Ranges Cabernet Rose 2011 Bright, light purple-crimson; the fruity, small red berry bouquet leads into a juicy palate, cassis flavours coming through strongly and lingering on the largely dry finish. Attractive wine. Screwcap. 12.5% alc. **Rating** 92 **To** 2013 $20
Macedon Ranges Cabernet Sauvignon 2008 Fresh, clear crimson-purple; has an attractive blend of quite juicy cassis fruit with earthy/savoury tannins that have declined to go to war with each other. Another interesting wine from what has to be a relatively warm site in the Macedon Ranges. Screwcap. 14% alc. **Rating** 92 **To** 2016 $22

Macedon Ranges Sparkling Shiraz 2009 Bright colour; as yet, still to develop complexity, but there is some really good base material here. If there are bottles still awaiting disgorgement down the track, watch out for them. This wine is no slouch, the dosage exactly correct. Diam. 14% alc. **Rating** 90 **To** 2015 $27

ΨΨΨΨ   **Macedon Ranges Pinot Noir 2010** Rating 87 **To** 2014 $22

Zilzie Wines   ★★★★

544 Kulkyne Way, Karadoc, Vic 3496 **Region** Murray Darling
T (03) 5025 8100 **www**.zilziewines.com **Open** Not
Winemaker Mark Zeppel **Est.** 1999 **Dozens** 110 000 **Vyds** 572ha
The Forbes family has been farming Zilzie Estate since the early 1990s; it is currently run by Ian and Ros Forbes, with sons Steven and Andrew. A diverse range of farming activities now includes grapegrowing from substantial vineyards. Having established a position as a dominant supplier of grapes to Southcorp, Zilzie formed a wine company in '99, and built a winery in 2000, expanding it in '06 to its current capacity of 35 000 tonnes. The wines consistently far exceed expectations, given their prices. The business includes contract processing, winemaking and storage. Exports to the UK, Canada, Hong Kong and China.

ΨΨΨΨΨ   **Regional Collection Wrattonbully Merlot 2010** Mid garnet; concentrated
✪   black cherry, olive and plum bouquet; the palate shows the seriousness of its intent, and provides depth and complexity in an accessible format. Screwcap. 13% alc. **Rating** 91 **To** 2015 $16 BE
✪   **Regional Collection Barossa Shiraz 2010** Deep colour; the bouquet is loaded with sweet black fruits, offering a notable pastille-like edge; the palate is dense, juicy and generous, with fruitcake, chocolate and chewy tannins. Screwcap. 14.5% alc. **Rating** 90 **To** 2016 $16 BE

ΨΨΨΨ   **Merlot 2010** Mid garnet; a fresh and fragrant red fruit, clove and cedar bouquet;
✪   medium-bodied, direct and lively; excellent value. Screwcap. 13% alc. **Rating** 89 **To** 2014 $11 BE
           MCMXI Cabernet Sauvignon 2009 Rating 89 **To** 2017 $33
✪   **Pinot Grigio 2011** Fresh, fragrant and floral, with citrus, pear and spice; the palate is lively and generous, well balanced and clean; well made. Screwcap. 12% alc. **Rating** 88 **To** 2013 $11 BE
           Selection 23 Shiraz 2010 Rating 87 **To** 2014 $10 BE
           Bulloak Moscato 2011 Rating 87 **To** Now $8 BE

Zitta Wines   ★★★★

3 Union Street, Dulwich, SA 5065 (postal) **Region** Barossa Valley
T 0419 819 414 **www**.zitta.com.au **Open** Not
Winemaker Angelo De Fazio **Est.** 2004 **Dozens** 1600 **Vyds** 26.3ha
Owner Angelo De Fazio says that all he knows about viticulture and winemaking came from his father (and generations before him). It is partly this influence that has shaped the label and brand name: Zitta is Italian for 'quiet' and the seeming reflection of the letters of the name Zitta is in fact nothing of the kind; turn the bottle upside down, and you will see it is the word Quiet. The Zitta vineyard dates back to 1864, with a few vines remaining from that time, and a block planted with cuttings taken from those vines. Shiraz dominates the plantings (22ha), the balance made up of chardonnay, grenache and a few mourvedre vines; only a small amount of the production is retained for the Zitta label. The property has two branches of the Greenock Creek running through it, and the soils reflect the ancient geological history of the site, in part with a subsoil of river pebbles reflecting the course of a long-gone river. Tradition there may be, but there is also some highly sophisticated writing and marketing in the background material and the website. Exports to China.

𝟗𝟗𝟗𝟗𝟘 **Single Vineyard Greenock Barossa Valley Shiraz 2009** The label indicates 15.5% alc/vol, and the density of colour and ripeness of fruit carries this with conviction; impenetrable colour and a dark as night palate lies in waiting, with prunes, licorice, tar, mocha and fruitcake spice; big-boned and over the top, more is certainly more in this wine. Screwcap. 15.5% alc. **Rating** 90 **To** 2019 $40 BE

𝟗𝟗𝟗𝟗 **Single Vineyard Bernardo Barossa Valley Shiraz 2009** Rating 89 **To** 2018 $28 BE

Zonte's Footstep ★★★★★

Main Road, McLaren Vale, SA 5171 **Region** McLaren Vale
T (08) 8556 2457 **www**.zontesfootstep.com.au **Open** Not
Winemaker Ben Riggs **Est.** 1997 **Dozens** 50 000 **Vyds** 214.72ha
Zonte's Footstep has been very successful since a group of long-standing friends, collectively with deep knowledge of every aspect of the wine business, decided it was time to do something together. Along the way, there has been some shuffling of the deck chairs, all achieved without any ill feelings by those who moved sideways or backwards. The major change has been a broadening of the regions (Langhorne Creek, McLaren Vale, the Barossa and Clare Valleys and elsewhere) from which the grapes are sourced. Even here, however, most of the vineyards supplying grapes are owned by members of the Zonte's Footstep partnership. The wine quality is as good as the prices are modest. Exports to all major markets.

𝟗𝟗𝟗𝟗𝟗 **Excalibur Adelaide Hills Sauvignon Blanc 2011** Pale straw-green; the highly
✪ aromatic bouquet has lots of snow pea and a flick of citrus, and the palate does not disappoint, the flavours precise, intense and long, adding a touch of grapefruit pith. Screwcap. 13% alc. **Rating** 94 **To** 2013 $18
Z-Force 2009 A blend of 85% shiraz, 15% petite sirah (durif) from McLaren Vale that is true to the blend, the petite sirah adding a major dimension to the intensity of the jet-black fruit flavours. An altogether strange but compelling wine, for you don't see the alcohol at any point. Cork. 15% alc. **Rating** 94 **To** 2020 $40

𝟗𝟗𝟗𝟗 **The Love Symbol Single Site Langhorne Creek Savignin Blanc 2011**
○ Rating 89 **To** 2014 $17
Sea Mist Single Site Langhorne Creek Verdelho 2011 Rating 88
To 2013 $18
Violet Beauregard Single Site Clare Valley Malbec 2010 Rating 88
To 2016 $22
Scarlet Ladybird Single Site Fleurieu Peninsula Rose 2011 Rating 87
To Now $18
Avalon Tree Single Site Langhorne Creek Cabernet 2010 Rating 87
To 2018 $22

Index

♀	**Cellar door sales**
♍	**Food:** lunch platters to à la carte restaurants
⊫	**Accommodation:** B&B cottages to luxury vineyard apartments
⚭	**Music events:** monthly jazz in the vineyard to spectacular yearly concerts